INDEX

This Edition Covers Mechanical Specifications and Service Procedures on 1966-72 Models

*For your convenience in locating this section, a black bar has been positioned beneath all odd page numbers.

GENERAL SERVICE INFORMATION SECTION—1*

CAR INFORMATION SECTION—2

MOTOR'S
AUTO REPAIR MANUAL

35th Edition
First Printing

Editor
Louis C. Forier, S.A.E.

Managing Editor
John F. Moran

Associate Editors
Michael V. Kelty • Larry Solnik

Editorial Assistants
Connie DiMartino • Theodore Chieffo

Published by
MOTOR

250 West 55th St., New York, N. Y. 10019

The Automotive Business Magazine

Printed in the U.S.A. © Copyright 1971 by The Hearst Corporation

ISBN 0-910992-03-7

TROUBLE SHOOTING

Index of Symptoms

Engine Troubles

STARTING A STALLED ENGINE

When an engine fails to start the chances are that 90 per cent of the cases will involve the ignition system and seldom the fuel system or other miscellaneous reasons. If a systematic procedure is followed the trouble can almost always be found without the use of special equipment.

To begin with, turn on the ignition switch and if the ammeter shows a slight discharge (or if the telltale lamp lights) it indicates that current is flowing. A glance at the gas gauge will indicate whether or not there is fuel in the tank.

Operate the starter and if the engine turns over freely, both the battery and starter are functioning properly. On the other hand, if the starter action is sluggish it may be due to a discharged or defective battery, loose, corroded or dirty battery terminals, mechanical failure in the starter, starter switch or starter drive. If the starter circuit is okay, skip this phase of the discussion and proceed to ignition.

Starter Circuit Checkout

To determine which part of the starter circuit is at fault, turn on the light switch and again operate the starter. Should the lights go out or become dim, the trouble is either in the battery, its connections or cables. A hydrometer test of the battery should indicate better than 1.250 specific gravity, while a voltmeter, placed across the positive and negative posts, should indicate about 12 volts. If either of these tests prove okay, clean and tighten the battery connections and cable terminals or replace any cable which seems doubtful.

If the lights remain bright when the starter is operated, the trouble is between the battery and the starter, or the starter switch is at fault, since it is evident that there is no electrical connection between these points. If these connections are clean and tight, it is safe to assume that the starter or starter switch is defective.

Neutral Safety Switch

If the ammeter shows a slight discharge (or if the telltale lamp lights) when the ignition is turned on, but the system goes dead when the starting circuit is closed, the neutral safety switch may be at fault. To check, bypass the switch with a suitable jumper. If the engine now starts, adjust or replace the switch.

CAUTION: With the safety switch bypassed, the car can be started in any gear. *Be sure the transmission is in neutral or park and the parking brake is applied.*

Primary Ignition Checkout

Let's assume that the battery and starter are doing their job, and that fuel is reaching the carburetor, but the car does not start, then the trouble must be somewhere in the ignition circuit. But first, before starting your diagnosis, it is advisable to give the whole system a visual inspection which might uncover obvious things such as broken or disconnected wires etc.

The best way to start tracking down ignition troubles is to begin with the primary circuit since this is where troubles show up most frequently. First remove the distributor cap and block the points open with a piece of cardboard, then turn on the ignition and with a test bulb or voltmeter check to see if there is current at the terminal on the distributor. If you do not get a reading at this point, the current is cut off somewhere in the connections leading back to the ignition switch or it may be that the condenser has an internal short to the ground. The latter possibility can be eliminated if you can restore current at the distributor terminal by disconnecting the condenser from the distributor plate so that its outside shell is not grounded. With the possibility of a bad condenser out of the way, work toward the ignition switch and test for current at each connection until you get to one where you get a reading. Between this connection and the distributor lies the trouble.

The foregoing steps in checking the primary circuit should include checking the ignition coil resistor for defects or loose connections. As this is done, bear in mind that while the starter cranks the engine, the resistor is by-passed by the starter switch on Ford and Delco-Remy systems (see Ignition Systems Chapter for details). This means that while the circuit through the resistor may be satisfactory, a broken connection or high resistance between the starter switch by-pass terminal and the coil would prevent starting. On the other hand, a satisfactory by-pass circuit might start the engine while the engine would stall immediately upon releasing the starter switch if there was a defect in the coil resistance circuit.

If, to begin with, the test equipment shows a current reading at the distributor terminal, it is safe to assume that the trouble is in the unit itself, most likely burned or dirty breaker points. A final positive test for defective breaker points can be made very simply by removing the cardboard from between the points, and positioning the distributor cam by turning the engine to where the points are closed. With the points closed there should be no current at the distributor terminal. If there is current, replace the points.

In an emergency, the points can be cleaned by using the sanded side of a match box, a knife blade, or the sharp edge of a screwdriver to scrape the scale from the contact faces. After cleaning the points, if a gauge is not available to set the gap, a quick adjustment can be made by using four layers of a piece of newspaper. The thickness of the paper is equivalent to about .020", which is the approximate gap setting for most distributors. Of course, at the earliest opportunity, a precise point adjustment should be made.

If the procedure outlined under "Primary Ignition Checkout" does not uncover the trouble then it will be necessary to continue the tests into the secondary ignition circuit.

Secondary Ignition Checkout

First of all, remove the wire from one of the spark plugs, turn on the ignition and operate the starter. While the engine is cranking, hold the terminal of the spark plug wire about ¼" away from the engine or spark plug base. If the spark is strong and jumps the gap, the trouble is confined to either the spark plugs or lack of fuel. Before going any further, wipe the outside of the plugs to remove any dirt or dampness which would create an easy path for the current to flow, then try to start the engine again. It it still fails to start, remove one of the spark plugs and if it is wet around the base, it indicates that the fuel system is okay, so it naturally follows that the spark plugs are at fault. Remove all the plugs, clean them and set the gaps. An emergency adjustment of spark plug gaps can be made by folding a piece of newspaper into 6 or 7 layers. When changing the gap, always bend the side (ground) electrode and never the center one as there is danger of breaking the insulation.

Fuel System Checkout

If the spark plug that was removed showed no indication of dampness on its base, check the fuel system. A quick check can be made by simply removing the carburetor air cleaner and looking down into the carburetor. Open and close the throttle manually and if fuel is present in the carburetor, the throttle will operate the accelerating pump, causing it to push gasoline through the pump jet. If it does, check the choke valve. If the engine is cold, the choke valve should be closed. If the choke won't close, the engine can be started by covering the carburetor throat while the engine is cranking, provided, of course, that fuel is reaching the carburetor.

Check the operation of the fuel pump by disconnecting the fuel lines from the pump to the carburetor. Crank the engine and if the pump is working, fuel will pulsate out of the line. If not, either the pump isn't working or the line from the tank to the pump is clogged. Before blaming the pump, however, disconnect the line at the inlet side of the pump which leads to the tank and, while a companion listens at the tank, blow through the line. If a gurgling sound is heard back in the tank, the line is open and the trouble is in the pump. Remove the sediment bowl, if so equipped and clean the screen, then replace the bowl and screen, being sure that you have an air-tight fit. If the pump still refuses to function, it should be removed and repaired.

The foregoing discussion will, in most cases, uncover the cause of why an engine won't start. However, if further diagnosis is necessary, the following list will undoubtedly provide the answer.

CLOSED CRANKCASE VENTILATION

If the control valve becomes clogged with carbon or other foreign matter, the ventilation system will not operate and a slight pressure will build up in the crankcase which may cause oil leakage at the rear main bearing or by the piston rings. And should the valve fail to seat it will be impossible to make the engine idle satisfactorily.

SERVICE NOTE: If idle speed is slow, unstable, rolling, frequent stalling, breather backflow and oily engine compartment the ventilator valve may be completely plugged, or the valve may be stuck in the open position. A valve stuck in the closed position is indicated by breather backflow at heavy throttle and oily engine compartment. If the valve is stuck in the intermediate position it will be indicated by rough, fast idle and stalling.

The ventilation valve assembly should be cleaned every six months or 6000 miles (whichever comes first) and more frequently in service such as extensive engine idling during cold weather.

When the valve assembly is removed for cleaning, place a finger over the open end of the ventilator hose or tube and have the engine started. If the ventilator hose or tube and carburetor passages are open and operating normally, a strong suction will be felt and there will be a large change in engine idle quality when the end of the hose is uncovered. If these conditions are not observed, the carburetor passages and/or ventilator hose are plugged and must be cleaned. The carburetor should be removed from the engine and the ventilation passages cleaned by dipping the lower part of the carburetor in the cleaner. A pipe cleaner can be used to aid in cleaning passages.

ENGINE WON'T START

IMPORTANT—Alternator equipped cars cannot be push-started when the battery is completely dead because, unlike a generator, there is no residual magnetism in the rotor.

If the engine fires when the ignition switch is turned on but quits when the switch is released to its running position, it indicates that the ignition coil resistor has lost its continuity or there is a bad connection at the resistor terminals.

Due to Open Primary Ignition Circuit

1. Burned or oxidized ignition points.
2. Ignition coil resistance unit burned out or open.
3. Starting switch ignition coil resistance by-pass circuit open.
4. Ignition points not closing.
5. Breaker arm binding on pivot post, preventing closing of points.
6. Breaker arm spring weak or broken.
7. Breaker arm distorted or bent.
8. Dirty ignition points.
9. Primary lead connection loose at distributor or coil.
10. Primary windings in coil broken.
11. Open ignition switch circuit.

Due to Grounded Primary Ignition Circuit

A grounded coil primary winding, a grounded ignition switch, or a grounded switch-to-coil primary lead will cause excessive current flow and will usually cause wires to burn.

1. Ignition points not opening or closing due to improper adjustment.
2. Ignition points not opening due to worn rubbing block on breaker arm.
3. Faulty bushing in breaker arm.
4. Cracked or faulty insulator at distributor primary terminal.
5. Grounded condenser.
6. Distributor-to-coil lead grounded.
7. Primary coil winding grounded.

Due to Faulty Secondary Ignition Circuit

1. Corroded spark plug cable terminals.
2. Chafed or cracked cable insulation.
3. Ignition coil weak or inoperative.
4. Moisture on ignition coil, terminals, distributor cover, spark plug porcelains, or in distributor.
5. Improper type of spark plugs.
6. Cracked distributor cap or a burned carbon track from distributor cap center terminal to housing.
7. Improper installation of spark plug cables (not correct for firing order).
8. Spark plugs damaged, dirty or wet,

porcelains cracked, or gaps improperly spaced.
9. Rotor contact spring bent or broken.
10. Distributor rotor grounded.
11. Distributor cap center terminal (inner) broken or missing.
12. Broken or burned out radio suppressor in distributor cap.

Due to Battery

1. Battery run down.
2. Terminals loose or badly corroded.
3. Improper ground.
4. Battery cables frayed or undersize.

Due to Starter Motor

1. Not operating properly.
2. Congealed engine oil due to use of too heavy a grade of oil or to the formation of sludge.
3. Starter gear binding in flywheel gear.
4. Defective starter switch.
5. Faulty neutral safety switch on cars with automatic transmission.

Due to Excessive Fuel Supply (Flooding)

The engine is said to be flooded with fuel when a quantity of liquid fuel collects in the intake manifold, and perhaps also in the cylinders. This condition gives a mixture that is much too rich to ignite.

If the carburetor has a provision for opening the choke valve when the throttle is fully open, crank the engine with the throttle open until engine starts. It will start as soon as the extra fuel is pumped out.

If the choke valve is not designed to open when the throttle is fully opened, tie or block the choke valve open and crank the engine until it starts.

Flooding may also occur on the road. If the carburetor supplies too rich a mixture at full throttle, the intake manifold may be flooded with liquid fuel, with the result that when the engine is stopped, heat evaporates the fuel and thus provides an over-rich incombustible mixture. The engine won't start until the rich mixture is pumped out by cranking.
1. Choke not operating property.
2. Automatic choke not properly set.
3. Carburetor unloaded linkage (if equipped) not properly set.
4. Float level set too high.
5. Dirty, worn or faulty needle valve and seat.
6. Float sticking or rubbing against side of fuel bowl.
7. Leak in float, allowing fuel to get inside.
8. Fuel pump pressure too great.

Due to Insufficient Fuel Supply

1. Carburetor inlet needle stuck in its seat, due to gum in fuel.
2. Float level too low.
3. Clogged inlet screen at carburetor.
4. Faulty fuel pump or one of insufficient capacity.
5. Fuel pump strainer clogged.
6. Faulty fuel pump bowl gasket.
7. Flexible line (if used) twisted, deteriorated or restricted.
8. Fuel line to tank clogged, kinked, restricted or leaking.
9. Vent in fuel tank filler cap clogged or restricted.
10. Worn fuel pump camshaft lobe.

HARD STARTING
When Engine is Hot

This condition is usually caused by an over-supply of fuel due to any of the items listed under *Engine Won't Start Due to Excessive Fuel Supply*. In rare cases, an ignition coil may lose its efficiency when it is hot and cause ignition failure.

When Engine is Cold

Many of the conditions enumerated under *Engine Won't Start* also may cause hard starting in cold weather. Of particular importance, however, are the following:
1. Choke setting too lean.
2. Fuel may have kerosene in it or water, or ice in bottom of tank.
3. Ice in fuel filter bowl.
4. Ice in fuel lines.
5. Engine is cranked too slowly or won't turn over because: (a) engine oil is too thick in sub-zero weather; (b) battery weak due to extremely low temperature.
6. Another possibility, although remote, is that the water pump is jammed with ice, which will interfere with cranking engine if fan belt is tight.

Due to Vapor Lock

The term vapor lock means the flow of fuel to the mixing chamber in the carburetor has been stopped (locked) by the formation of vaporized fuel pockets or bubbles caused by overheating the fuel by hot fuel pump, hot fuel lines or hot carburetor.

The more volatile the fuel the greater the tendency for it to vapor lock. Vapor lock is encouraged by high atmospheric temperature, hard driving, defective engine cooling and high altitude.

A mild case of vapor lock will cause missing and hard starting when engine is warm. Somewhat more severe vapor lock will stop the engine which cannot be started again until it has cooled off enough so that any vaporized fuel has condensed to a liquid.

SERVICE NOTE: Some cars equipped with air conditioning have a vapor bypass system. These cars have a special fuel filter which has a metering outlet in the top. Any vapor which forms is bled off and returned to the fuel tank through a separate line alongside the fuel supply line. This system greatly reduces the possibility of vapor lock. However, if vapor lock is suspected examine the bypass valve to see if it is functioning.

Due to Percolation

Percolation means simply that gasoline in the carburetor bowl is boiling over into the intake manifold. This condition is most apt to occur immediately after a hot engine is shut off. Most carburetors have a provision for relieving the vapor pressure of overheated fuel in the carburetor bowl by means of ports. If, however, percolation should take place, the engine may be started by allowing it to cool slightly and then holding the throttle wide open while cranking to clear the intake manifold of excess fuel.

After Long Storage

1. The more volatile components in the fuel have evaporated and those remaining are not sufficiently volatile to provide a combustible mixture.
2. Low or run-down battery.
3. Corrosion of engine parts may result in so much friction that starter cannot crank engine at proper speed, if at all.
4. Pistons, etc. may be struck fast by gummy oil.
5. Engine valves may stick open due to gummy deposits.
6. There is the possibility that any small part essential to the running of the engine may be struck due to gummy film or to corrosion.
7. Some of these troubles are most likely to occur in hot, humid climate and near salt water.

ENGINE STALLS

Many troubles which prevent smooth running at idle may cause stalling. The list includes almost everything that may cause hard starting or missing. Some of the more common cuases are:
1. Engine idle speed set too low.
2. Large air leaks in intake manifold such as a disconnected windshield wiper vacuum line.
3. Ignition points need attention
4. Engine valves leaking.
5. Vapor lock.
6. Over-supply of fuel (flooding).
7. Valves set too tight.

If carburetor is equipped with a fast idle cam, which increases engine speed when the choke is in operation during the warm-up period, the engine may stall if the fast idle device fails to open the throttle due to sticking or need for adjustment.

On some cars equipped with a fluid coupling or torque converter, if the throttle is closed quickly the engine stalls. To avoid this trouble, most cars have a device which retards the speed of the throttle closing; this is called a throttle return check or dashpot and is usually mounted on the carburetor. It consists of a piston or diaphragm and a spring-closed check valve. If the linkage is out of adjustment or the check valve leaks, the engine will stall.

If the engine quits smoothly when car is in operation, the trouble is often caused by sudden lack of fuel due to:
1. Fuel tank empty.
2. Vapor lock.
3. Flooding.
4. Water in fuel.
5. Frozen fuel line.

Carburetor Icing

The carburetor discharges liquid fuel into the air stream in the form of an atomized spray which evaporates readily. The heat required to evaporate the gasoline is drawn from the entering air, thereby lowering its temperature. The cooler air chills the interior of the carburetor and may cause the moisture in the air to condense into droplets.

Under certain conditions of atmospheric temperature and humidity, the liberated moisture actually collects and freezes on the chilled carburetor surfaces, especially on the throttle plate and surrounding throttle body. When the throttle is almost completely closed for idling, this ice tends to bridge the gap between the throttle plate and throttle body, thereby cutting off the air supply and causing the engine to stall. Opening the throttle for restarting breaks the ice bridge but does not eliminate the possibility of further stalling until the engine and carburetor has warmed up.

For carburetor icing to occur, the outside air must be cool enough so that the refrigerating effect of fuel evaporation in the carburetor will lower the temperatures of the throttle plate and body below both the dew point of moist air and the freezing point of water. The air must also contain sufficient moisture for appreciable condensation of water to occur when it is chilled in the carburetor.

Generally speaking, carburetor icing occurs when winter grade gasoline (more volatile than summer grade) is used and when the atmospheric temperature ranges from 30° to 50° F. at relative humidities in excess of 65%.

Carburetor icing problems can be reduced by the use of anti-icing additives, such as alcohols, in the fuel. Some fuel refiners use anti-stalling additives in their gasolines which have proved effective in combating carburetor icing.

Another form of carburetor icing has been observed in some engines during high-speed driving on cool, moist days. When certain cars are driven steadily at 60 to 80 mph, the large quantities of cool air passing through the carburetor may result in gradual ice formation within the carburetor's venturi. Since this ice restricts the venturi passage, the resultant increased vacuum in the venturi tends to increase the rate of fuel flow. The fuel-air mixture thus becomes excessively rich, causing loss of power and high fuel consumption.

ENGINE STARTS BUT WON'T DRIVE CAR

1. Broken part in the drive line anywhere from clutch to rear axle shaft.
2. No oil or not enough oil in fluid coupling or torque converter.
3. Some defect in automatic transmission causes binding or dragging of clutches or slipping bands.
4. Engine develops only enough power to run itself due to: (a) extremely lean or rich mixture; (b) excessive engine friction; (c) throttle does not open; (d) very dirty air cleaner; (e) clogged exhaust system.
5. Oil in fluid coupling or torque converter is semi-solid due to zero temperature. This trouble is unlikely if the recommended oil is used.

ENGINE MISFIRES

At All Speeds

1. Fouled spark plug or broken porcelain.
2. Faulty spark plug cables.
3. Low battery voltage.
4. Low generator voltage.
5. Burned or pitted ignition points.
6. Incorrect ignition point gap.
7. Faulty condenser or coil.
8. Weak spark or no spark in one or more cylinders.
9. Faulty distributor cap or rotor.

10. Primary circuit restricted or open intermittently.
11. Primary circuit detoured by short intermittently.
12. Secondary circuit restricted or open intermittently.
13. Secondary circuit detoured by short intermittently.
14. Blown cylinder head gasket between cylinders. This can be noted when missing occurs in two adjacent cylinders.
15. Sticking valves.
16. Hydraulic tappet holds valve open slightly.
17. Broken valve spring.
18. Leak at intake manifold gaskets.
19. Mixture too rich or too lean.

At High Speed

1. Hot spark plugs. Change to colder type but note that a hot plug may be due to loose installation or lack of a plug gasket (if gasket is called for).
2. Ignition point gap much too wide.
3. Breaker arm binding or sticking.
4. Breaker arm spring weak.
5. Sticking engine valves.
6. Valve springs too weak to close valves promptly.
7. Valve springs broken.
8. Valve springs shimmy.
9. Intermittent delivery of fuel to carburetor so that momentarily the mixture is too weak for combustion.
10. Mild vapor lock.
11. Weak spark.
12. Exhaust manifold clogged with carbon.
13. Exhaust manifold, muffler or tail pipe restricted.
14. Improper ignition timing.
15. Centrifugal advance not functioning properly.
16. Manifold heater valve held closed.
17. Dirty carburetor air cleaner.
18. Choke valve not completely open.
19. Carburetor throttle lever loose on shaft.
20. Improper fuel pump operation.
21. Preignition.
22. Incorrect valve timing.

At Low or Idle Speeds

1. Faulty spark plugs.
2. Spark plugs gaps too narrow.
3. Dirty or corroded secondary circuit connections or faulty ignition cables.
4. Cracked or faulty distributor cap. Radial contacts in cap burned or worn.
5. Dirty air cleaner.
6. Leaky valves.
7. Ignition point gap too narrow.
8. Faulty carburetion due to: (a) float level too high or too low; (b) float valve leaking; (c) incorrect or loose jets; (d) restricted or partially clogged idle air passage or jet; (e) air leak occurring between upper and lower carburetor body; (f) air leak occurring around carburetor throttle shaft.
9. Air leaks in intake manifold or carburetor resulting from: (a) loose manifold connections or leaks occurring in vacuum lines; (b) loose manifold nuts or capscrews; (c) broken or damaged intake manifold or carburetor gaskets; (d) cracked manifold; (e) warped or damaged manifold contacting surface.

10. Slight leaks occurring at fuel pump check valves.
11. Air leak occurring around intake valve stem because of excessive valve stem-to-guide clearance.

When Car is Accelerated

If the engine misses when car is accelerated but does not miss when idling the reason is that the spark plugs stop firing because of increased compression pressure caused by:
1. Weak spark.
2. Plug gaps too wide.
3. Plug fouled or damp.
4. Plug porcelain below par.
Also see *Flat Spot*.

LACK OF POWER OR HIGH SPEED PERFORMANCE

It should be noted that the altitude at which the car is operated has a decided effect on performance. A car adjusted for normal altitudes will lack performance at high altitudes, whereas a car which operates normally at high altitudes may have a lean carburetor adjustment and show signs of preignition when operated at sea level.

1. Ignition timing incorrect.
2. Centrifugal governor advance not operating properly.
3. Vacuum advance not operating properly.
4. Ignition points burned, pitted, sticking or bouncing (due to weak breaker arm spring).
5. Faulty spark plugs.
6. Faulty ignition cables.
7. Faulty ignition coil.
8. Faulty carburetion.
9. Lack of engine compression.
10. Preignition.
11. Inoperative manifold heater valve (stuck closed).
12. Restricted carburetor inlet resulting from dirty air cleaner or choke valve not fully open.
13. Carburetor throttle lever loose on shaft.
14. Throttle linkage not properly adjusted.
15. Carburetor throttle valve not completely open.
16. Carburetor accelerating pump not functioning properly.
17. Improper fuel pump operation.
18. Partially restricted exhaust pipe, muffler or tail pipe.
19. Clutch slippage.
20. Excessive rolling resistance resulting from (a) dragging brakes, (b) tight wheel bearings, (c) misalignment of power transmitting units, (d) misalignment of rear axle, (e) underinflated tires.
21. Incorrect rear axle gear ratio.
22. Oversize tires.
23. Incorrect valve timing.
24. Inaccurate speedometer (gives impression of lack of performance).

ROUGH IDLE

The term "rough idle" means that the engine does not run smoothly when idling. The most likely cause is an over-rich mixture but any defect which produces uneven explosions or missing will cause a rough idle. The most common causes are:

1. Dirty idle jets and passages.
2. Improper idle mixture.
3. Dirty air cleaner.
4. Improper float level.
5. Choke set too rich.
6. Air leak into intake manifold.
7. Clogged idle jets.
8. Improper ignition point gap.
9. Improper spark plug gap.
10. Weak spark.
11. Leaky engine valve.
12. Sticking valve or rocker arm.
13. Broken valve spring.
14. Insufficient tappet clearance.
15. Improper fuel pump pressure.
16. Sticking breaker arm.
17. Hydraulic tappet holds valve open.
18. Fuel volatility too high or too low.

SPARK, KNOCK, PING, DETONATION

All three expressions mean the same thing. It is a sharp metallic knock caused by vibration of the cylinder head and block. The vibration is due to split-second high-pressure waves resulting from almost instantaneous abnormal combustion instead of the slower normal combustion.

The ping may be mild or loud. A mild ping does no harm but a severe ping will reduce power. A very severe ping may shatter spark plugs, break valves or crack pistons.

Pinging is most likely to occur on open throttle at low or moderate engine speed. Pinging is encouraged by:

1. Overheated engine.
2. Low octane fuel.
3. Too high compression.
4. Spark advanced too far.
5. Hot mixture due to hot engine or hot weather.
6. Heavy carbon deposit which increases the compression pressure.

Tendency to ping increases with mixture temperature including high atmospheric temperature; intake manifold heater valve "on" when engine is warm; hot cooling water; hot interior engine surfaces due to sluggish water circulation or water jackets clogged with rust or dirt especially around exhaust valves. Some of these troubles may be confined to one or two cylinders.

If an engine pings objectionably because of too low octane fuel, retard the spark setting but first be sure that the cooling system is in good condition, the mixture not too lean and the combustion chambers free of carbon deposit.

PRE-IGNITION

Pre-ignition means that the mixture is set on fire before the spark occurs, being ignited by a red hot spot in the combustion chamber such as an incandescent particle of carbon; a thin piece of protruding metal; an overheated spark plug, or a bright red hot exhaust valve. The result is reduction of power and overheating accompanied by pinging. The bright red hot exhaust valve may be due to a leak, to lack of tappet clearance, to valve sticking, or a weak or broken spring.

Pre-ignition may not be noticed if not severe. Severe pre-ignition results in severe pinging. The most common cause of pre-ignition is a badly overheated engine.

When the engine won't stop when the ignition is shut off, the cause is often due to red hot carbon particles resting on heavy carbon deposit in a very hot engine.

ENGINE KICKBACK

If ignition is set too far advanced, spark may occur too early when engine is cranked. The first (and only) explosion runs the engine backward. A kickback may jam the starter or break the starter drive housing.

BACKFIRE

Backfiring is a subdued explosion in the intake manifold. Causes are:

1. Lean mixture (often due to dirt or water in fuel).
2. Engine cold and choke too lean.
3. Leaky or sticking intake valve or weak or broken intake valve spring.
4. Leakage of current across distributor cap may cause backfire by enabling spark to occur in a cylinder which is on its intake stroke. Two mixed-up spark plug wires may also cause this trouble.
5. Popping back is synonymous with backfire.

MUFFLER EXPLOSION

1. Late ignition timing.
2. Late valve timing.
3. Burnt exhaust valve(s).
4. Weak or broken exhaust valve spring(s).
5. Tight exhaust valve(s).
6. Intermittent open circuit in primary (ammeter needle swings further away from zero when generator is charging).
7. Intermittent short in primary (ammeter swings toward zero when generator is charging).
8. Short in coil or secondary coil wire.
9. If just a couple of explosions are heard and then no more for a time (even for days) the trouble may be due to a gradually failing condenser.

AFTER-BURNING

A subdued put-putting at the exhaust tail pipe may be due to leaky exhaust valves which permit the mixture to finish combustion in the muffler. If exhaust pipe or muffler is red hot, better let it cool, as there is some danger of setting the car on fire. Most likely to occur when mixture is lean.

FLAT SPOT

If an engine does not respond promptly when the throttle is open quickly it (or the carburetor) is said to have a flat spot. This is usually caused by any of the following:

1. Accelerator pump piston (or diaphragm) leaks.
2. Accelerator pump valves leak.
3. Accelerator pump stroke too short.
4. Accelerator pump passages restricted.
5. Fuel volatility too low or too high.
6. Float level too low.
7. Fuel pump pressure too low.
8. The anti-percolating valve (on some carburetors) may open too soon when throttle is closed. If so, carburetor may have flat spot next time throttle is opened when engine is hot.
9. Fuel too hot due to hot engine and hot weather (see Vapor Lock).
10. If carburetor has a metering pin operated by throttle linkage and also a vacuum piston linked to the throttle to give a rich mixture at part throttle and moderate engine speed, a flat spot will be noted if the device fails to function properly because of stuck piston, vacuum leakage or restricted vacuum passages.
11. If carburetor has vacuum piston which provides richer mixture at part throttle and moderate engine speed by opening an additional passage or jet within carburetor, a flat spot will occur if fuel valves fail to work, or fuel passages are restricted, or if piston does not function because it is sticking, vacuum leakage or restricted vacuum passages.
12. Late ignition timing.

ENGINE FAILS TO REACH OPERATING TEMPERATURE

1. Defective thermostat.
2. Thermostat stuck open.
3. Thermostat removed from vehicle (during flushing cooling system and not replaced).
4. Defective temperature sending unit or dash unit.

ENGINE CONTINUES TO RUN AFTER IGNITION IS TURNED OFF

This condition, known as "dieseling," "run on," or "after running," is caused by improper idle speed and/or high temperature. Idle speed and engine temperature are affected by:

Carburetor Adjustment: High idle speed will increase the tendency to diesel because of the inertia of the engine crankshaft and flywheel. Too low an idle speed, particularly with a lean mixture, will result in an increase in engine temperature, especially if the engine is allowed to idle for long periods of time.

Ignition Timing: Because advanced ignition timing causes a corresponding increase in idle speed and retarded timing reduces idle speed, ignition timing influences the tendency to diesel in the same manner as Carburetor Adjustment.

Fuel Mixture: Enriching the idle fuel mixture decreases the tendency to diesel by causing the engine to run cooler.

Fuel Content: High octane fuels tend to reduce dieseling. Increased fuel content of lead alkyl increases the tendency to diesel. Phosphates and nickel fuel additives help prevent dieseling.

Spark Plugs: Plugs of too high a heat range for the engine in question can cause dieseling.

Throttle Plates: If the throttle plates are not properly aligned in the carburetor bore, a resulting leanness in fuel mixture occurs, contributing to dieseling.

Electrical System: Normally, during dieseling, ignition is self-supplied by a "hot spot," self-igniting fuel, etc. However, there is a possibility of the vehicle's electrical system supplying the necessary ignition. When the ignition switch is turned off, a small amount of current can flow from the generator into the primary of the ignition coil through the generator tell-tale light. This is particularly true when the warning light bulb has been changed for one of increased wattage.

NOTE: "Run on" is more prevalent in an engine when the ignition is turned off before the engine is allowed to return to idle. Therefore, it can be reduced by letting the engine return to idle before shutting off the ignition. "Run on" incidence can be reduced on automatic transmission units by turning off the engine when in gear.

A certain amount of "run on" can be expected from any gasoline engine regardless of make, size or configuration. (Diesel engines operate on this principle.) However, if the above suggestions are correctly employed, "run on" will be reduced to an unnoticeable level.

ENGINE OVERHEATS: WATER COOLED

Water is used to cool the engine and air is used to cool the water. Anything which prevents this water-air system from working properly will cause overheating. Oil or grease in the water will reduce the ability of the water to absorb heat from the block and to transfer heat in the water to the radiator. There are seven basic causes of overheating:
1. Water does not cool engine.
2. Air does not cool water.
3. Slow combustion.
4. Pre-ignition.
5. Detonation.
6. Excessive friction in engine or elsewhere in power transmitting units.
7. Excessive back pressure in exhaust system.

Water Too Hot
1. Slipping fan belt.
2. Not enough water in system.
3. Carburetor mixture too lean.
4. Clogged exhaust system.
5. Late ignition timing.
6. Centrifugal advance fails to advance spark as engine speed increases because weights stick or because of sticking elsewhere in mechanism.
7. Pre-ignition.
8. Detonation.
9. Water circulation impeded by installation of wrong head gasket.
10. Cylinder head gasket installed incorrectly, blocking off water holes.
11. Leaky cylinder head gasket permits exhaust gas to enter water. The gas

bubbles interfere with the ability of the water to cool the engine.
12. Water circulation slowed down by rust, scale or dirt in water jackets.
13. Water distributing tube (when used) within cylinder block rusted out, dented or improperly installed so that not enough water reaches some cylinders, thus causing local overheating.
14. Local overheating at one cylinder (or more) due to heavy deposit of rust, scale or dirt in water jacket around cylinder or exhaust valve port.
15. Water circulation impeded by thermostat which fails to open fully or sticks closed.
16. Water temperature increased by thermostat which fails to open at correct temperature. Or the installation of a thermostat which opens at too high a temperature.
17. Any water hose which has rotted on inside, allowing loosened strips of rubber to impede water circulation.
18. The baffle in top tank may be bent in such a way as to interfere with free discharge of water from the hose.
19. Water passages in radiator are partially clogged with dirt, rust, corrosion or scale (mineral salts).
20. Exterior of radiator clogged with dirt, leaves or insects.
21. Rotting of water hose may weaken it so that pump suction causes it to collapse when engine is running fast, thus throttling the water flow.
22. If water pump seal leaks, air may be drawn into the water. Air bubbles in cooling water reduce the cooling ability of the water.
23. Water pump impeller loose on its shaft or impeller blades corroded.
24. Overheats due to alcohol type antifreeze during mild weather.

Water Leakage

Cylinder Head
1. Loose attaching bolts.
2. Dirty, corroded or burred surface prevents tight fit.
3. Warped surface does not fit tight against gasket.
4. Cracked due to freezing or excessive heat.
5. On overhead valve head, exhaust valve seats may be cracked, allowing water to leak into cylinders and crankcase.

Cylinder Block
1. Dirty, corroded or burred surface prevents tight fit.
2. Warped surface does not fit tight against gasket.
3. Cracked due to freezing or excessive heat.
4. If L-head design, excessive heat may crack exhaust valve seats, allowing water to leak into crankcase.
5. Block cracked due to use of cylinder head bolt which is too long.
6. Leaky expansion plugs or pipe plugs in water jacket.

Cylinder Head Gasket
1. Dirty, corroded or broken.
2. Loose because cylinder head bolts are loose.
3. Leaks because it cannot make tight contact between head and block.

Water Pump
1. Loose pump.
2. Faulty gasket.
3. Improper installation.
4. Warped pump body or dirty metal surfaces.
5. Hole or crack in pump body.
6. Worn seal.
7. Seal improperly installed.
8. Bent pump shaft.
9. Loose bearings or bushings or worn pump shaft.

Radiator
1. Leaks due to freezing or corrosion.
2. Strain due to improper attachment to car.
3. Fan striking radiator.
4. Drain plug or petcock leaks.
5. Radiator baffle bent so that water is directed into overflow pipe.
6. Clogged radiator causing water to pile up in upper tank which causes coolant to flow out overflow pipe.

Hose
1. Hose clamps loose.
2. Hose improperly installed.
3. Hose rotted through.

Heater: See that all heater connections are tight and that its radiator does not leak.

ENGINE OVERHEATS: AIR COOLED

These engines run at a higher operating temperature and depend on circulation of air across the cooling fins to keep temperature at a safe level. Overheating can be caused by:
1. Broken fan belt.
2. Seized blower bearing.
3. Jammed or misadjusted damper doors.
4. Defective damper door thermostats.
5. Engine cooling fins clogged with leaves, dirt, etc.
6. Oil cooler fins clogged.
7. Lean carburetor mixture.
8. Incorrect ignition timing.
9. Preignition.
10. Detonation.

ENGINE OIL LEAKAGE

NOTE: If engine is equipped with a positive crankcase bent valve, check the valve for proper operation before checking cause of leak. A clogged crankcase vent valve can build up pressure in the crankcase which will cause seals and gaskets to leak.

1. Oil pan drain plug loose or gasket missing.
2. Crack or hole in oil pan.
3. Oil pan gasket leaks due to: (a) loose screws; (b) damaged gasket; (c) improperly installed gasket; (d) bent oil pan flange.
4. Timing case cover gasket leaks due to: (a) loose screws; (b) damaged gasket; (c) improperly installed gasket; (d) bent cover flange; (e) leakage at engine support plate.
5. Front crankshaft oil seal leaks due to: (a) worn oil seal; (b) seal not properly installed; (c) rough surface on crankshaft, or fan pulley or

damper; (d) damper or pulley loose; (e) seal or cover not centered on crankshaft; (f) oil return passage to crankcase clogged up.

6. Rear main bearing oil seal leaks due to: (a) worn oil seal; (b) improper oil seal installation; (c) worn rear main bearing; (d) rough crankshaft.
7. Oil return passage to crankcase clogged.
8. Expansion plug in block at rear of camshaft leaks due to poor fit, careless installation, or corrosion.
9. Leakage at any external piping.
10. Plugs at ends of oil passages in cylinder block leak.
11. Oil filter leaks.
12. Leakage at distributor housing.
13. Valve cover leaks due to loose screws, defective gasket, improperly installed gasket or bent cover flange.
14. Rocker arm cover or push rod cover leaks because of loose screws, defective gasket, improper gasket installation or bent cover flange.
15. Pipe connections loose on oil gauge or oil filter lines.
16. Loose oil pump or faulty gasket (if pump is on outside of block).
17. Clogged breather and/or crankcase ventilating discharge pipe, permits increase in pressure within engine, thus causing oil to be forced out past any oil seals or gaskets.
18. If oil pressure relief valve is mounted on outside of block, leakage may occur if unit is loose or its gasket defective.

HIGH OIL CONSUMPTION

1. External oil leaks.
2. Leaky piston rings due to wear.
3. Leaky piston rings due to sticking caused by gummy deposit. Try to free up with suitable solvent poured in fuel tank. Blue smoke at tail pipe indicates badly leaking rings.
4. Worn pistons and cylinders.
5. Cylinder block distorted by tightening cylinder head bolts unevenly.
6. Excessive clearance between intake valve stems and guides allows oil mist to be sucked into cylinders.
7. Punctured vacuum pump diaphragm permits oil from crankcase to be sucked into intake manifold.
8. Worn main or rod bearings allow excessive leakage from bearings. Result is cylinder walls are flooded with oil.
9. Oil pressure too high due to faulty action of oil pressure relief valve, or clogged relief passage.
10. If pressure lubricated, loose piston pins may permit excessive leakage to cylinder walls.
11. Grade of oil used is too light. A poor quality oil may become far too thin when engine is hot. Hard driving on hot days will also consume more oil.
12. Clogged crankcase ventilator system.

OIL PRESSURE RELIEF VALVE LEAKS

1. Relief valve needs tighter adjustment.

2. Relief valve spring weak or broken.
3. Valve seat worn or distorted.
4. Plunger type valve face worn.
5. Plunger type valve stuck open.
6. Ball type valve damaged.
7. Pump discharge pipe or passages leak.

ENGINE OIL DILUTION

1. Oil contains foam caused by presence of water in oil. Water may be due to condensation within crankcase or to a leaky cylinder head gasket.
2. Extreme dilution of oil by fuel may add enough liquid to oil to mislead. In extreme cases, oil level may increase. Dilution is greatest when frequent stops are made in cold weather.

NO OIL PRESSURE

1. Oil pressure gauge defective.
2. Pipe to oil pressure gauge stopped up.
3. Not enough oil in crankcase.
4. Oil pump inoperative.
5. Oil pressure relief valve stuck open.
6. Oil passages on discharge side of pump stopped up.
7. Oil screen or passages on intake side of pump stopped up.

LOW OIL PRESSURE

1. Oil pressure gauge inaccurate.
2. Pipe to pressure gauge restricted.
3. Oil too thin due to dilution, poor quality, or too light a grade used.
4. Oil pressure relief valve adjustment too light.
5. Relief valve spring weak.
6. Oil pump gears worn.
7. Oil pump cover worn.
8. Oil pump body or cover loose.
9. Oil pump gasket damaged, improperly installed or too thick.
10. Air leak in oil intake pipe (if oil level is low).
11. Air leak in top of floating screen (if used).
12. Oil intake pipe or screen clogged with water, sludge, gummy oil, dirt or ice.
13. Oil leak in discharge pipe.
14. Loose connections in oil lines.
15. Worn main, rod or camshaft bearings.

HIGH OIL PRESSURE

1. Oil pressure gauge defective.
2. Oil too heavy.
3. Oil pressure relief valve adjustment too heavy.
4. Relief valve spring too stiff.
5. Oil pressure relief passage clogged.
6. Plunger type relief valve stuck by gummy oil or plunger is too tight a fit.
7. Main oil passages on pressure side of pump clogged.

ENGINE NOISES
Loose Main Bearing

A loose main bearing is indicated by a powerful but dull thud or knock when the engine is pulling. If all main bearings are loose a noticeable clatter will be audible.

The thud occurs regularly every other revolution. The knock can be confirmed by shorting spark plugs on cylinders adjacent to the bearing. Knock will disappear or be less when plugs are shorted. This test should be made at a fast idle equivalent to 15 mph in high gear. If bearing is not quite loose enough to produce a knock by itself, the bearing may knock if oil is too thin or if there is no oil at the bearing.

Loose Flywheel

A thud or click which is usually irregular. To test, idle the engine at about 20 mph and shut off the ignition. If thud is heard, the flywheel may be loose.

Loose Rod Bearing

A metallic knock which is usually loudest at about 30 mph with throttle closed. Knock can be reduced or even eliminated by shorting spark plug. If bearing is not loose enough to produce a knock by itself, the bearing may knock if oil is too thin or if there is no oil at the bearing.

Piston Pin

Piston pin, piston and connecting rod noises are difficult to tell apart.

A loose piston pin causes a sharp double knock which is usually heard when engine is idling. Severity of knock should increase when spark plug to this cylinder is short-circuited. However, on some engines the knock becomes more noticable at 25 to 35 mph on the road.

Piston pin rubs against cylinder wall, caused by lock screw being loose or snap ring broken.

Piston & Rings

1. Excessive clearance between pistons and cylinders (piston slap).
2. Out-of-round or tapered bores.
3. Top piston ring strikes ridge at top of cylinder bore.
4. Carbon deposit on top of piston strikes cylinder head.
5. Piston rubs against cylinder head gasket.
6. Broken piston ring.
7. Excessive side clearance of ring in groove.
8. Worn or broken piston ring lands.
9. Broken piston.

Valves

1. Valve click due to too much tappet clearance, hydraulic tappet not working properly, warped valve, sticking valve, binding rocker arm.
2. Insufficient oil to valve mechanism, especially overhead valves.
3. Worn or scored parts anywhere in valve mechanism.
4. Broken valve springs.
5. Weak valve springs.
6. Cocked valve springs.
7. Excessive tappet guide clearance.
8. Lower end of tappet scored, chipped, rough, worn or broken.
9. Very rough surface on cams.
10. Excessive valve stem-to-guide clearance.

11. Valve face not concentric with valve stem.
12. Valve seat face not concentric with valve stem.
13. Valve covers on overhead valve engines tightened excessively will amplify normal noise.

Hydraulic Lifters

The malfunctioning of a hydraulic valve lifter is amost always accompanied by a clicking or tapping noise. More or less hydraulic lifter noise may be expected when the engine is cold but if lifters are functioning properly the noise should disappear when the engine warms up.

If all or nearly all lifters are noisy, they may be stuck because of dirty or gummy oil.

If all lifters are noisy, oil pressure to them may be inadequate. Foaming oil may also cause this trouble. If oil foams there will be bubbles on the oil level dipstick. Foaming may be caused by water in the oil or by too high an oil level or by a very low oil level.

If the hydraulic plungers require an initial adjustment, they will be noisy if this adjustment is incorrect.

If one lifter is noisy the cause may be:
1. Plunger too tight in lifter body.
2. Weak or broken plunger spring.
3. Ball valve leaks.
4. Plunger worn.
5. Lock ring (if any) improperly installed or missing.
6. Lack of oil pressure to this plunger.

If ball valve leaks, clean plunger in special solvent such as acetone and reinstall. Too often, plungers are condemned as faulty when all they need is a thorough cleaning.

Gum and dirty oil are the most common causes of hydraulic valve lifter trouble. Engine oil must be free of dirt. Select a standard brand of engine oil and use no other. Mixing up one standard brand with another may cause gummy oil and sticking plungers. Do not use any special oils unless recommended by the car manufacturer and change oil filter or element as recommended intervals.

Timing Gears

1. Gears loose on hubs or shafts.

2. Gears misaligned.
3. Excessive gear backlash.
4. Eccentric gear, usually due to high key.
5. Teeth meshed too tight (new oversize gear).
6. Too much end play in camshaft or crankshaft.
7. Front crankshaft bearing clearance excessive.
8. Chipped tooth usually on camshaft gear.

Timing Chain

1. Chain loose due to wear.
2. Sprocket teeth worn.
3. Sprockets loose on hubs or shafts.
4. Sprockets misaligned.
5. Front camshaft bearing clearance excessive.
6. Front main bearing clearance excessive.
7. Loose vibration damper or drive pulley.

Loose Engine Mountings

Occasional thud with car in operation. Most likely to be noticed at the moment the throttle is opened or closed.

Excessive Crankshaft End Play

A rather sharp rap which occurs at idling speed but may be heard at higher speeds also. The noise should disappear when clutch is disengaged.

Water Pump

1. Water pump shaft pulley loose.
2. Impeller loose on shaft.
3. Too much end play in pump shaft.
4. Too much clearance between shaft and bearings.
5. Impeller blades rubbing against pump housing.
6. Impeller pin sheared off or impeller broken.
7. Rough bearing.
8. Pump seal too hard.

Fan Belt

1. Belt worn or burned.
2. Wrong belt. Does not fit pulley grooves properly.

3. Belt too tight. Squeaks.
4. Belt or pulley dirty or sticky with gummy oil.
5. Pulley bent, cracked or broken.
6. Belt pulleys misaligned.
7. Belt loose; squeaks when engine is accelerated.

Fan

1. Fan blades bent.
2. Fan blades loose on hub.
3. Fan out of balance when made.
4. Fan blades strike radiator.
5. Fan shaft end play excessive.
6. Fan shaft loose on its bearings.
7. Defective fan bearings.
8. Bearings need lubrication.

Engine Vibration

1. Unequal compression in cylinders.
2. Missing at high speed.
3. Unbalanced fan or loose fan blade.
4. Incorrect adjustment of engine mount or damaged mounts.
5. Loose engine mounts.
6. Engine support loose on frame or cylinder block.
7. Unbalanced or sprung crankshaft.
8. Excessive engine friction due to tight pistons, etc.
9. Defective vibration damper.

Fuel Pump Noise

Diagnosis of fuel pumps suspected as noisy requires that some form of sounding device be used. Judgment by ear alone is not sufficient, otherwise a fuel pump may be needlessly replaced in attempting to correct noise contributed by some other component. Use of a stethoscope, a long screwdriver, or a sounding rod is recommended to locate the area or component causing the noise. The sounding rod can easily be made from a length of copper tubing $\frac{1}{4}$ to $\frac{3}{8}$ inch in diameter.

If the noise has been isolated to the fuel pump, remove the pump and run the engine with the fuel remaining in the carburetor bowl. If the noise level does not change, the source of the noise is elsewhere and the original fuel pump should be reinstalled. On models using a fuel pump push rod, check for excessive wear and/or galling of the push rod.

Electrical Troubles

NOTE—Ignition troubles are included in the *Engine Troubles* section under the various operating difficulties these troubles could cause.

BATTERY REQUIRES FREQUENT RECHARGING

Insufficient Current Flow to Battery
1. Defective generator or alternator.

2. Incorrect voltage regulator setting.
3. Regulator contacts oxidized or burned.
4. Sulphated battery.
5. Corroded battery terminals.
6. Regulator not grounded.
7. Loose connections or grounds in lighting or ignition circuits.
8. Slipping fan belt.
9. Blown regulator fuse.
10. Wrong size generator drive pulley.

11. Shortened or open alternator rectifiers.
12. Grounded stator windings in alternator.

Excessive Starting Load Causing Abnormal Current Flow From Battery
1. Frequent use of starting motor.
2. Excessive use of starting motor due to difficulty in starting.
3. Faulty starting motor.
4. Excessive engine friction due to tight pistons, etc., or heavy engine oil.

Excessive Lighting Load

1. Car operation confined largely to night driving.
2. Tail and stop light wires reversed.
3. Stop light switch inoperative (closed at all times).
4. Unnecessary use of head lamps while parking.
5. Ground or short in lighting circuit.

Abnormal Accessory Load

1. Radio.
2. Heater.
3. Windshield defroster.
4. Cigar lighter.
5. Spotlights.

Internal Discharge of Battery

1. Plates badly sulphated.
2. Cell leak due to cracked jar or sealing compound.
3. Water level not maintained at proper height.
4. Plate separators ineffective.
5. Exterior of battery covered with corrosion and acid-soaked dirt which forms a path to ground for current.

Miscellaneous

Radio suppressor connected to generator or regulator field terminal.

STARTER WON'T ROTATE OR ROTATES SLOWLY

If lights become dim or go out when the starter switch is closed, the battery may be too weak to operate the starter. In this case, the engine may be started by pushing the car.

NOTE—Some cannot be started by pushing because these transmissions have no rear oil pump to drive the engine through the transmission. In such cases, a fully charged battery should be installed or a "jumper" circuit should be used from another charged battery.

Cars equipped with alternators cannot be push started if the battery is completely dead because alternators retain no residual magnetism.

Due to Starter Circuit

1. Low battery. Lights grow very dim or go out when starter switch is closed.
2. Connections loose, dirty, corroded or broken at battery terminals, starter switch terminal, battery ground strap.
3. Short circuit across starter terminal.

Due to Starter Switch

1. Starter pedal (if any) stuck.
2. Starter switch stuck.
3. Pedal linkage fails to close starter switch (older cars).
4. Defective solenoid.
5. Neutral safety switch on cars with automatic transmissions out of adjustment or defective.
6. Starter switch makes poor contact due to dirt, corrosion, bent parts, weak contact spring.

7. Starter switch fails to close circuit because of sticking or broken contact parts.

Due to Armature & Field Circuits

1. Armature windings burned out, shorted, grounded or open-circuited.
2. Short circuit in armature winding or brush pigtail lead.
3. Broken wire in armature winding or brush pigtail lead.
4. Loose, dirty or corroded connections in armature circuit, including ground.
5. Field coils burned out, shorted or grounded.
6. Broken wire in field winding or broken lead.
7. Loose, dirty or corroded connections in field circuit.

Due to Commutator & Brushes

1. Brush pigtail leads loose or broken.
2. Starter brushes cracked crosswise (prevents flow of current).
3. Arm type brush holder sticks.
4. Brush sticks in sliding brush holder.
5. Bent brush holder misaligns brush and causes poor contact.
6. Starter brushes badly worn.
7. Brush leads shorted or have loose, dirty, corroded or broken connections.
8. Poor brush contact due to weak or broken springs.
9. Brushes coated with oil.
10. High mica between commutator segments prevents brush contact.
11. Commutator bars loose and/or solder melted.
12. Commutator dirty, corroded or burned.

Due to Engine Resistance

1. Piston sticking to cylinders in overheated engine.
2. Pistons struck to cylinders because of gummy oil.
3. Pistons binding in cylinders because of corrosion after long lay-up.
4. Jammed generator armature.
5. Combustion chamber full of water.
6. Solid ice in water pump.
7. Broken part in engine causes jamming.
8. Excessive engine friction, due to cold weather and too heavy oil.

Due to Improper Engine Repairs

1. New rings too tight.
2. New pistons too tight.
3. Main or rod bearings too tight.
4. New camshaft bearings too tight.

Due to Armature Binding

1. Loose field poles.
2. Armature shaft frozen in bearings.
3. Loose end plates.
4. Windings thrown out of armature slots.
5. Armature locked magnetically to field poles because of loose bearings or worn or bent armature shaft.
6. Bendix spring retaining screws loose (jammed against housing).

7. Cracked or distorted drive housing.
8. Starter misaligned.
9. Starter jams because of burred teeth on drive pinion or flywheel gear.
10. Starter pinion (sliding gear type) jams because of incorrect endwise clearance.

STARTER SPINS BUT WON'T ENGAGE FLYWHEEL GEAR

Bendix Type

1. Bendix pinion stuck on shaft due to dirty or gummy shaft or bent shaft.
2. Bendix spring broken.
3. Bendix spring bolt broken.
4. Pinion housing cracked.
5. Drive key sheared.
6. Pinion teeth broken off.
7. Starter ring gear has several teeth missing.
8. Armature shaft broken.

Sliding Gear Type

1. Weak or broken meshing spring.
2. Fault in sliding gear linkage.
3. Fault in solenoid.
4. Over-running clutch worn out or lubricant caked or gummy.
5. Drive key sheared.
6. Pinion teeth broken off.
7. Flywheel ring gear has several teeth missing.
8. Armature shaft broken, dirty or dry.
9. Wrong starter pinion clearance.

STARTER PINION JAMMED INTO FLYWHEEL GEAR

1. Burred teeth on pinion or ring gear.
2. Misalignment of starter or armature shaft.
3. If engine kicks back when being started, Bendix pinion may jam. Loosen starter to free pinion.

STARTER PINION DISENGAGES SLOWLY

Bendix Type

The most probable cause is a dirty Bendix drive shaft. Or the pinion may bind on its shaft due to a bent shaft or too tight a fit between pinion and splines.

When a Bendix Folo-Thru starter drive stays in mesh too long it is probably due to a sticking release pin which is designed to be released by centrifugal force at a certain engine rpm. In such an instance the drive should be replaced.

Sliding Gear Type

1. Pinion binds on its shaft due to too tight a fit or due to bent or burred shaft.
2. Pinion shaft sticky or dirty.
3. Sliding gear operating linkage sticking or binding.
4. Solenoid does not operate properly.

STARTER PINION WON'T RELEASE

Bendix Folo-Thru Drive

Failure to disengage would most probably be caused by a stuck release pin which is designed to be released by centrifugal force at a given engine rpm. If such is the case, replace the drive unit.

Sliding Gear Type

If solenoid operated, the solenoid may be defective. If pedal operated, the shift linkage may be binding or sticking. May also be caused by a defective starting switch on cars with key-starter switch or by improper starter pinion clearance.

STARTER NOISE

1. Loose pole pieces rubbing against armature.
2. Gear noise due to defective teeth.
3. Flywheel ring gear untrue.
4. Starter drive housing loose on flywheel housing.
5. Starter loose on drive housing.
6. Commutator end plate loose.
7. Armature shaft bent.
8. Worn armature shaft, bearings or bushings.
9. Drive pinion shaft bent.
10. Worn drive pinion shaft, bearings or bushings.
11. Misalignment caused by dirt or burrs on mating surfaces.

GENERATOR DOES NOT CHARGE

1. Fan belt broken or slips badly.
2. Belt pulley slips on armature shaft.
3. Cutout relay fails to close.
4. Armature won't rotate because of seized bearing, etc.
5. External wiring from generator to starter switch terminal short-circuited or circuit is open because of detached wire or very dirty or corroded connection.
6. Voltage regulator inoperative.
7. Open circuit or short circuit in armature or field windings.
8. Brushes stuck.
9. Brushes coated with oil.
10. Brush lead connections dirty or disconnected.
11. Improperly seated brushes.
12. Weak brush springs.
13. Very dirty commutator.
14. Burned or corroded commutator.
15. Commutator bars short-circuited.
16. High mica on commutator.
17. Solder melted at commutator bar connections.

GENERATOR NOISE

1. Generator loose on engine.
2. Generator end plates loose.
3. Armature shaft bent.
4. Armature shaft worn.
5. Bushing or bearing worn or needs lubrication.
6. Armature shaft end play excessive.

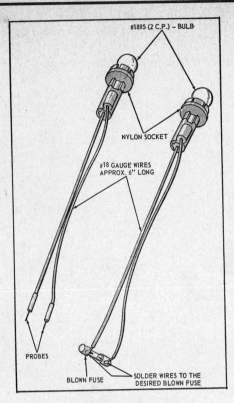

Test lamp for locating shorts

7. Generator pulley loose on its shaft.
8. Generator or pulley misaligned.
9. Bent, cracked or broken pulley.
10. Generator fan rubs on generator.

GENERATOR BRUSH NOISE

1. High mica between commutator bars.
2. Sprung armature shaft.
3. Rough, dirty or glazed commutator.
4. Worn or loose brushes.
5. Commutator out of round.
6. Brushes not seating properly.
7. Too little or too much brush spring tension.

ALTERNATORS

Alternator Fails to Charge

1. Drive belt loose.
2. Brushes sticking.
3. Open charging circuit.
4. Open in stator winding circuit.
5. Faulty soldered connections at output terminal stud.
6. Rectifiers open circuited.

Low Unsteady Charging Rate

1. Drive belt loose.
2. High resistance at battery terminal posts.
3. Loose connections.
4. Poor ground between engine and body ground wire.
5. Resistance in charging circuit.
6. Open stator windings.

Low Output

1. Grounded stator.
2. Shorted rectifier.
3. Voltage regulator faulty.

Excessive Charging Rate

1. Voltage regulator faulty.
2. Open circuited rectifier.

Noisy Alternator

1. Misaligned belt or pulley, or loose pulley.
2. Shorted rectifier.
3. Worn bearings.
4. Rotor shaft sprung.

Regulator Points Oxidized

1. Poor ground connections.
2. Improper voltage regulator air gap setting.
3. Shorted field in alternator.
4. Voltage regulator setting too high.

Burned Points or Coil Windings in Regulator

1. Voltage regulator setting too high.

Voltage Regulator Points Stuck

1. Poor ground connections between alternator and regulator.

LOCATING ELECTRICAL SHORTS WITH TEST LAMP

Due to the complexity of locating electrical short circuits where several circuits are protected by the same fuse, fabricate a test lamp from the material shown in the accompanying illustration. By substituting the test lamp for the blown fuse the short circuit can be isolated.

When the test lamp is inserted into the fuse panel, the bulb will light and continue to glow until the short circuit is removed. Determining which circuit is at fault can be accomplished by disconnecting the affected circuits one at a time until the test lamp goes out. Then trace the circuit to find the cause of the short (wire contacting sharp sheet metal edges, wire pinched between two metal objects, etc.).

For circuits that are not connected to the fuse panel but are protected by an in-line fuse cartridge, use a test lamp having two needle point probes in place of the blown fuse. Insert one probe through the insulation and into the wire on each side of the blown in-line fuse and follow the same testing procedure outlined above.

FUSIBLE LINKS

Some cars starting with 1965 models have fusible links located between the battery and the lower ends of the main supply wires. These links are the weakest point in the electrical supply system for the entire car and, as such, will act as a fuse for every wire harness in the car. Every electrical accessory is still protected by a fuse or circuit breaker, of course, but fusible links have been added to protect the wiring harnesses *before* the fuses.

In the past, if a wire became grounded in the portion between the battery and the fuse block, a long section of the wire would burn out, making replacement of a complete wiring harness necessary. Now, with the fusible links, a short or ground in any unfused wire will cause only a short link to burn out. Because of its location, possibility of a fire, such as was sometimes caused by a burned-out wiring harness, is very remote.

A fusible link is simply a short section of wire that is several sizes smaller in gauge than the wire in the circuit which it protects. If a short or ground occurs the fusible link will melt before the insulation is damaged elsewhere in the circuit. Replace burned-out fusible link as directed in the illustration.

LIGHTS FLICKER
Circuit Breaker Vibrates

When the circuit breaker vibrates and causes lights to flicker it indicates a short in one of the lighting circuits, which may be traced as follows:

1. Pull switch successively to each lighting position. If circuit breaker vibrates in all positions except "off" the trouble should be found in the tail lamp and license lamp circuit, or instrument, map light, or clock light circuits.
2. If circuit breaker vibrates in parking lamp position only, look for a short in the parking lamp circuit.
3. If circuit breaker vibrates in headlamp position only, inspect headlamp wiring circuit and lamp assemblies. If both filaments in headlamps burn at the same time, check dimmer switch.

LAMPS FAIL TO BURN

1. Burned out bulb.
2. An open circuit in wiring.
3. A defective switch.
4. Burned out fuse.

LIGHTS FLARE UP WHEN ENGINE IS SPEEDED UP

This condition is caused by high voltage in the electrical system due to one or more of the following:

1. Electrolyte in battery low or weak.
2. High resistance in circuit between generator and battery due to loose or dirty connections.
3. Poor ground between generator and engine.
4. Voltage regulator adjusted too high.
5. Voltage regulator inoperative.
6. Ground or short in generator field circuit.

STOP LIGHT TROUBLES

1. If only one stop light fails to burn, check lamp bulb, socket and wiring.
2. If both stop lights fail to burn also check stop light switch and fuse.
3. If stop light burns when brake pedal is released, check stop light switch, brake pedal clearance and for dragging brakes.

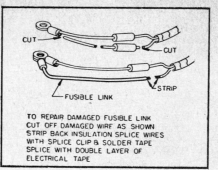

TO REPAIR DAMAGED FUSIBLE LINK
CUT OFF DAMAGED WIRE AS SHOWN
STRIP BACK INSULATION SPLICE WIRES
WITH SPLICE CLIP & SOLDER TAPE
SPLICE WITH DOUBLE LAYER OF
ELECTRICAL TAPE

Repairing fusible links

4. If compensating port in brake master cylinder is plugged by foreign material, or is covered by the piston primary cut when brake pedal is released, high pressure will be maintained in hydraulic system and stop light switch will remain closed.

TURN SIGNAL TROUBLES

1. If signals are inoperative on both turns, look for a blown fuse or a defective flasher.
2. If stop lights burn, the fuse and rear signal lamp bulbs are okay.
3. An inoperative right signal light may be caused by a burned out bulb at the right indicator or a right signal lamp. The opposite applies for an inoperative left signal light.
4. If bulbs are okay, look for an open circuit or defective switch.
5. If indicator light on dash burns steady when lever is placed in a turn position, check for burned out bulb in park or stop light. If park and stop light bulbs are okay, check for faulty flasher.
6. If indicator light on dash does not burn when lever is in a turn position, check for burned out bulb or a faulty flasher.
6. If indicator light on dash does not burn when lever is in a turn position, check for burned out bulb or a faulty flasher.
7. If switch fails to cancel after completion of turn, remove steering wheel and check for worn or broken mechanism.

ELECTRIC CLOCKS

If clock does not run, check for blown "clock" fuse. If fuse is blown check for short in wiring. If fuse is not blown check for open circuit.

With an electric clock, the most frequent cause of clock fuse blowing is low voltage at the clock which will prevent a complete wind and allow clock contacts to remain closed. This may be caused by any of the following: discharged battery, corrosion on contact surface of battery terminals, loose connections at battery terminals, at junction block, at fuse clips, or at terminal connection of clock. Therefore, if in reconnecting battery or clock it is noted that the clock is not ticking, always check for blown fuse, or examine the circuits at the points indicated above to determine and

correct the cause. See *Dash Gauge* chapter for Electric Clock data.

HAZARD WARNING FLASHER TROUBLES

To make a quick check of the system pull Hazard Warning switch to ON position. The rear turn signal bulbs should flash as well as the front turn signal bulbs, turn signal indicator bulbs and pilot bulb. All lights will burn continuously when the brake pedal is depressed; this is normal.

Pilot Bulb Fails to Flash

Check for burned out bulb and loose or defective ground wire. Replace bulb, repair ground wire or tighten ground wire screw. If this does not correct the condition, replace flasher switch and harness assembly. Then repeat quick check procedure.

All Bulbs Fail to Flash

1. Check for loose harness connections at Hazard Warning connectors and secure connectors if necessary.
2. Check for a burned out tail and stop light fuse and replace if necessary.
3. Check for a defective Hazard Warning flasher or switch. This may be done by removing the flasher and installing a known good flasher.
4. Pull switch to ON position. If flasher does not operate properly, replace flasher switch and harness assembly, installing old flasher. If system still does not operate properly, install new flasher along with new switch.

Some Bulbs Fail to Flash While Others are Operative

1. Turn ON ignition switch and turn OFF Hazard Warning switch.
2. Place turn signal lever first to right and then to left turn position. If turn signal circuits operate properly, the Hazard Warning switch and harness assembly should be replaced.
3. If the same bulbs fail to flash, the cause is most likely a burned-out bulb. In the case of turn signal indicator bulbs, a loose or defective ground wire can also cause this condition. Repair as necessary.

NOTE: If any turn signal bulb fails to flash when the turn signal circuit is actuated, the reduced current in the circuit will cause the remaining signals on the side of the car to burn steadily. If the Hazard Warning flasher is energized, however, all turn signal bulbs and indicator bulbs will flash except those that have a circuit defect. They will flash at a constant rate unless the battery is completely run down. This is because the Hazard Warning Flasher overrides the turn signal circuit flasher.

4. If the condition is still not resolved, disconnect the Hazard Warning connectors and again check the operation of the turn signal circuits. If the affected bulbs now flash, replace flasher switch and harness assembly.
5. If the condition is still not resolved, look for defects in the connectors to the affected bulb.
6. Repeat quick check test.

Clutch Troubles

CLUTCH DRAGS

Clutch drag means that when the clutch pedal is depressed fully the clutch disc is not completely released. In consequence it does not come to rest but continues to rotate, being dragged around by the rotation of the engine. Clutch dragging causes clashing of gears, especially when shifting from neutral to low or reverse.

1. Pedal cannot disengage clutch because of excessive free pedal travel. Pedal linkage should be adjusted so that the pedal shank is about 1" from the under side of the toe-board.
2. Worn clutch linkage.
3. Release levers need adjustment.
4. Clutch disc warped out of true.
5. High spots on clutch facing.
6. Broken or loose facings.
7. Loose rivet in facing.
8. Clutch disc hub binds on splined clutch shaft due to bent shaft, tight fit, burred splines or splines covered with gummy oil or dirt.
9. Clutch disc wobbles because of broken springs in hub.
10. Clutch disc hub out of true.
11. Clutch shaft bent.
12. Clutch shaft out of true because of worn bearings.
13. Transmission is not in alignment with flywheel housing.
14. Clutch pressure plate warped, thus throwing release levers out of adjustment.
15. Flange of clutch cover not in alignment with flywheel because of loose attaching screws, bent flange, dirt between flange and flywheel.
16. Grease on clutch facings.
17. Engine misaligned due to deteriorated or broken engine mounts.
18. Loose flywheel housing-to-engine attaching bolts.
19. Release fork pivot worn.

CLUTCH SLIPS

The clutch disc slips whenever the clutch pressure plate fails to hold it tight against the face of the flywheel. If clutch slippage is severe, the engine speed will rise above normal on full throttle in high gear. Slight but continuous slippage may go unnoticed until the clutch facings are ruined by excessive temperature caused by friction.

In a very high percentage of cases, clutch slippage is due to less than zero clearance between the shank of the pedal and the toe-board because of failure to have the pedal adjusted in time. The consequence is worn and burned clutch facings. Before the clutch starts slipping, the normal wear of the facings causes a gradual reduction in clutch pedal free play. When there is no free play of the pedal the clutch starts slipping.

Other causes of clutch slippage are:
1. Driving with foot resting on pedal.
2. Binding or sticking of pedal or its linkage.
3. Binding or sticking of clutch disc hub on clutch shaft.
4. Binding of release levers.
5. Release bearing sleeve sticks.
6. Weak or broken clutch pressure springs.
7. Worn clutch facings.
8. Facings covered with grease or oil.
9. Facings burned.
10. Release levers improperly adjusted.
11. Pressure plate sticks.

CLUTCH GRABS

A clutch is said to grab when it engages too abruptly. The usual causes are:
1. Loss of tension in cushioning plates in the rim of the steel clutch disc. These plates cause the clutch facings to bulge outward slightly. The resulting springy action of the facings aids in producing a smooth, gentle clutch engagement.
2. Use of wrong type of clutch facing.
3. Grease or oil on facings.
4. Clutch springs too stiff.
5. Momentary binding in clutch linkage while clutch is being engaged.
6. Exposed rivet heads due to excessively worn facings or loose rivets.

CLUTCH CHATTERS

If a clutch chatters while it is being engaged, the trouble is caused by rapid gripping and slipping. The usual causes are:
1. Somewhat sticky clutch friction surfaces due to engine or transmission oil leaking from defective seal.
2. Clutch friction surfaces damp or wet.
3. Weak clutch springs.
4. Slight binding in clutch linkage during engagement.
5. Slight binding of pressure plate during engagement.
6. Loose engine mounts.

CLUTCH PEDAL PULSATES

Clutch pedal pulsation has often been termed a nervous pedal. When a slight pressure is applied on the pedal, with the engine running, the pedal will vibrate or bounce with every revolution of the engine. As the pressure on the pedal is increased, the pulsation will cease.

1. Loose or improperly adjusted engine mounts.
2. Collar on clutch release sleeve does not run true due to a bent clutch

shaft, or the clutch shaft misaligned because of misalignment between crankshaft and transmission.
3. Clutch release levers not adjusted to uniform height.

CLUTCH RATTLES

This condition will occur when the engine is idling with transmission in neutral.
1. Excessive clearance at pressure plate driving lugs.
2. Anti-rattle springs or retractor springs on release levers (or release bearing) weak, broken or disconnected.
3. Looseness in clutch pedal operating linkage.
4. Loose flywheel.

NOISE WHEN PEDAL IS DEPRESSED

1. Clutch release bearing worn, dirty, damaged, broken or inadequately lubricated.
2. Clutch shaft bearing or bushing in crankshaft worn, damaged, broken or inadequately lubricated.
3. Clutch shaft rear bearing at front end of transmission, worn, dirty or lacks lubricant.

NOISE WHEN PEDAL IS RELEASED

1. Misalignment of transmission with engine causing slight wobble of clutch disc hub—noticeable with engine idling or at low road speed.
2. Disc hub loose fit on splined clutch shaft.
3. Disc damper springs weak or broken.
4. No pedal play.
5. Weak or broken pedal return spring.
6. Weak or broken release sleeve spring.
7. Clutch linkage sticks.
8. Clutch pedal sticks.
9. Clutch release sleeve sticks.
10. Clutch release fork binds.
11. Bad clutch release bearing.
12. Loose flywheel.

BEARING NOISE

Clutch Release Bearing:—With engine idling, there is a high-pitched rubbing noise when foot rests on clutch pedal.

Clutch Pilot Bearing:—Fairly high-pitched noise when clutch pedal is fully depressed with engine idling.

Three Speed Transmission Troubles

Fully Synchronized Transmission

Car Application Listed in Three Speed Manual Shift Transmission Chapter

STICKING IN GEAR

1. Clutch not releasing completely.
2. Low lubricant level.
3. Corroded transmission levers.
4. Tight main drive gear pilot bushing.
5. Defective synchronizer sleeve or blocking ring.

FORWARD GEARS CLASH

1. Clutch not releasing completely.
2. Weak or broken springs in synchronizer assembly.
3. Worn blocking rings and/or cone surfaces.
4. Broken blocking ring.

NOISY IN FORWARD SPEEDS

1. Insufficient or incorrect lubricant.
2. Transmission misaligned or loose.
3. Main drive gear or bearings worn or damaged.
4. Countergear bearings worn or damaged.
5. Synchronizers worn or damaged.

NOISY IN REVERSE

1. Reverse idler gear or shaft worn or broken.
2. Reverse gear worn or broken.

HARD SHIFTING

1. Improper clutch or adjustment.
2. Worn or damaged shift linkage.
3. Incorrect lubricant.
4. Synchronizers worn or broken.

JUMPING OUT OF GEAR

1. Misadjusted, worn or loose shift linkage.
2. Transmission loose or misaligned.
3. Worn pilot bearing.
4. Excessive end play in main drive gear.
5. Weak detent cam spring.
6. Detent cam notches worn.
7. Worn clutch teeth on main drive gear or synchronizer sleeve.
8. Worn or broken synchronizer.
9. Bent output shaft.

Three Speed Transmission Troubles

General Motors Transmission with Second Speed Gear Located at Rear of Mainshaft

Car Application Listed in Three Speed Manual Shift Transmission Chapter

SLIPS OUT OF HIGH AND/OR 2ND GEAR

1. Transmission mounting bolts loose.
2. Control rods interfere with engine mounts or clutch release lever.
3. Control linkage does not work freely.
4. Gear does not fully engage.
5. Damaged mainshaft pilot bearing.
6. Clutch gear bearing retainer broken or loose.
7. Dirt between transmission case and clutch housing (front mounted), or between transmission case and differential carrier (rear mounted).
8. Misalignment of transmission.
9. Worn or broken synchronizer assembly.
10. Weak springs in transmission cover.

SLIPS OUT OF LOW AND/OR REVERSE

1. First and/or reverse gears damaged from operating at part engagement.
2. Improperly mated splines on inside of first and reverse gear and/or external spline on 2nd and 3rd synchronizer sleeve.
3. Improperly adjusted linkage.
4. Weak springs in transmission cover.

NOISY IN ALL GEARS

1. Not enough lubricant.
2. Worn countergear bearings.
3. Worn or damaged clutch gear and countershaft drive gear.

4. Damaged clutch gear or mainshaft ball bearings.
5. Damaged speedometer gears.

NOISY IN HIGH GEAR

1. Damaged clutch gear bearing.
2. Damaged mainshaft bearing.
3. Damaged speedometer gears.

NOISY IN NEUTRAL WITH ENGINE RUNNING

1. Damaged clutch gear bearing.
2. Damaged mainshaft pilot bearing roller.

NOISY IN ALL REDUCTION GEARS

1. Not enough lubricant.
2. Worn or damaged clutch gear or countershaft drive gear.

NOISY IN SECOND ONLY

1. Damaged or worn 2nd speed gears.
2. Worn or damaged countergear rear bearings.

NOISY IN LOW AND REVERSE ONLY

1. Worn or damaged 1st and reverse sliding gear.

2. Damaged or worn low and reverse countergear.

NOISY IN REVERSE ONLY

1. Worn or damaged reverse idler.
2. Worn reverse idler bushings.
3. Damaged or worn reverse countergear.

EXCESSIVE BACKLASH IN SECOND ONLY

1. Second gear thrust washer worn.
2. Mainshaft rear bearing improperly installed in case.
3. Worn countergear rear bearing.

EXCESSIVE BACKLASH IN REDUCTION GEARS

1. Worn countergear bushings.
2. Excessive end play in countergear.

LEAKS LUBRICANT

1. Too much lube in transmission.
2. Loose or broken clutch gear bearing retainer.
3. Clutch gear bearing retainer damaged.
4. Cover loose or gasket damaged.
5. Operating shaft seal leaks.
6. Idler shaft expansion plugs loose.
7. Countershaft loose in case.
8. Lack of sealant on bolts.

Three Speed Transmission Troubles

All Transmissions with Low-Reverse Gear Located at Rear of Mainshaft

Car Application Listed in Three Speed Manual Shift Transmission Chapter

NOISES

When diagnosing transmission noise note the gear position in which the noise occurs. Noise present in all gear positions may be due to worn or damaged constant mesh gears or bearings. Noise present in only one gear can usually be traced to the particular gear involved. Other causes of noise are as follows:

1. Misalignment due to loose mounting bolts.
2. Clutch housing misalignment.
3. Dirt or metal chips in lubricant.
4. Not enough lube in transmission.
5. Improper lubricant.

HARD SHIFTING

1. Clutch linkage out of adjustment.
2. Linkage improperly adjusted.
3. Linkage binding due to bent, worn or broken parts.
4. Gearshift tube binding due to misaligned steering gear housing.
5. Improper lube in transmission.
6. Damaged synchronizer assembly.

JUMPS OUT OF GEAR

1. Improper shift procedure.
2. Linkage parts worn, bent, broken or out of adjustment.
3. Excessive end play caused by wear in shift forks, sliding gear fork grooves, thrust washers, mainshaft and countershaft bearings, or clutch pilot bushing.
4. Misalignment or excessive clearance between sliding gear and mainshaft.
5. Damaged synchronizer.
6. Weak springs in transmission cover.

LEAKAGE

1. Overfilled transmission or using a lube that foams or expands while car is in operation.
2. Loose gearshift housing capscrews.
3. Damaged gaskets.
4. Transmission vent plugged.
5. Extension housing rear seal leaks.

Corvair 4-Speed Trans. Troubles

SLIPS OUT OF GEAR

1. Transmission loose on differential carrier.
2. Control linkage binds or does not fully engage.
3. Damaged or missing mainshaft pilot bearings.
4. Clutch gear bearing retainer loose or broken.
5. Dirt between transmission case and differential carrier.
6. Worn or damaged synchronizer.
7. Weak detent spring (s).

NOISY IN ALL GEARS

1. Insufficient lubricant.
2. Worn countergear bearings.
3. Worn or damaged clutch gear and countergear.
4. Damaged clutch gear bearing or mainshaft rear bearing.

NOISY IN HIGH GEAR

1. Damaged clutch gear bearing.
2. Damaged mainshaft bearing.

NOISY IN NEUTRAL

1. Damaged clutch gear bearing.
2. Damaged mainshaft pilot roller bearings.

NOISY IN ALL REDUCTION GEARS

1. Insufficient lubricant.
2. Worn or damaged clutch gear or countergear.

NOISY IN 2nd ONLY

1. Damaged or worn 2nd speed gears.
2. Worn or damaged countergear bearings.

NOISY IN LOW & REVERSE

1. Worn or damaged low and reverse sliding gear.
2. Damaged or worn low and reverse countergear.

NOISY IN REVERSE ONLY

1. Worn or damaged reverse idler gear.
2. Worn reverse idler gear bushings.
3. Worn or damaged countergear reverse teeth.

EXCESSIVE BACKLASH IN ALL REDUCTION GEARS

1. Worn countergear bushings.
2. Excessive end play in countergear.

LEAKS LUBRICANT

1. Excessive amount of lubricant in transmission.
2. Loose or broken clutch gear bearing cover.
3. Clutch gear bearing retainer gasket damaged.
4. Cover loose or gasket damaged.
5. Shifter shall seal leaks.
6. Countershaft loose in case.

Four Speed Transmission Troubles

All Cars Other Than Corvair

NOISY IN ALL SPEEDS

1. Incorrect lubricant level.
2. Incorrect type lubricant.
3. Countergear bearings worn or damaged.
4. Countergear worn or damaged.
5. Clutch gear bearing worn or damaged.
6. Mainshaft bearing worn or damaged.
7. Clutch gear worn or damaged.
8. Transmission misaligned or loose.

NOISY IN 1st SPEED

1. First gear worn or damaged.
2. Countergear worn or damaged.
3. Countergear bearings worn or damaged.
4. Synchronizers worn or broken.
5. Countershaft worn or damaged.

NOISY IN 2nd SPEED

1. Second gear worn or damaged.
2. Countergear worn or damaged.
3. Countergear bearings worn or damaged.
4. Synchronizers worn or broken.
5. Countershaft worn or damaged.

NOISY IN 3rd SPEED

1. Third gear worn or damaged.
2. Countergear worn or damaged.
3. Countergear bearings worn or damaged.
4. Synchronizers worn or broken.
5. Countershaft worn or damaged.

NOISY IN 4th SPEED

1. Clutch shaft bearing worn or damaged.
2. Mainshaft bearing worn or damaged.
3. Synchronizers worn or broken.

NOISY IN REVERSE

1. Reverse idler gear or shaft worn or damaged.
2. Reverse sliding gear worn or damaged.
3. Shift linkage out of adjustment.
4. Shift linkage bent or damaged.
5. Shift linkage parts loose.
6. Shift levers, shafts or forks worn.

SHIFTS HARD

1. Clutch pedal free travel incorrect.
2. Clutch parts worn or damaged.
3. Shift linkage out of adjustment.
4. Shift linkage bent or damaged.
5. Shift linkage parts loose.
6. Shift levers, shafts or forks worn.
7. Lubricant type incorrect.
8. Lubricant level incorrect.

JUMPS OUT OF GEAR

1. Shift linkage out of adjustment.
2. Shift linkage bent or damaged.
3. Shift linkage parts loose.
4. Shift levers, shafts or forks worn.
5. Shift cover loose or gasket damaged.
6. Transmission misaligned or loose.
7. Synchronizers worn or broken.
8. Clutch gear bearing retainer broken.
9. Clutch gear bearing worn or damaged.
10. Clutch pilot bearing worn or broken.
11. Mainshaft and/or pilot worn or damaged.
12. Mainshaft bearing worn or damaged.

LEAKS LUBRICANT

1. Lubricant level incorrect.
2. Lubricant type incorrect.
3. Vent plugged.
4. Clutch gear bearing retainer or gasket loose.
5. Clutch gear bearing retainer broken.
6. Shift cover loose or gasket damaged.
7. Shifter shaft seals leaking.
8. Shift cover bolts not sealed.
9. Countershaft loose in case bore.

Overdrive Troubles

DIAGNOSIS

Figs. 1 to 3 illustrate the overdrive circuit diagrams in use. Since overdrive troubles may originate not only in the mechanical operation of the unit but also in the electrical circuit which controls that unit, always check the control system before disassembling the overdrive. If the trouble is not found after a thorough inspection of the control system, then the transmission and overdrive should be removed for examination. If the overdrive operation is unsatisfactory,

look for:

1. Blown fuse in governor-solenoid circuit.
2. Loose terminals on any of the connecting wires.
3. Incorrect terminal locations of connecting wires.
4. Circuits grounded by water, dirt or deformation.
5. Defective solenoid points.
6. Insufficient travel or unsatisfactory contacts in kickdown switch.
7. Excessive end play in governor shaft.
8. Improper adjustment of governor control springs.
9. Burned governor contact points.
10. Damage to governor cap and contacts.
11. Absence of rubber cover to exclude water and dirt.
12. Insufficient travel of shift rod (adjust control cable).

MECHANICAL TROUBLES

Overdrive Won't Drive Unless Locked Up Manually

1. Occasionally the unit may not drive the car forward in direct drive unless locked up by pulling the dash control. This may be caused by one or more broken rollers in the roller clutch, the remedy for which is to replace the entire set of rollers.
2. This condition may also be caused by sticking of the roller retainer upon the cam. This retainer must move freely to push the rollers into engaging position under the pressure of the two actuating springs.
3. Sometimes this condition is due to slight indentations, worn in the cam faces by the rollers spinning, remedied by replacing the cam.

Overdrive Does Not Engage or Lock-Up Does Not Release

1. Dash control improperly connected.
2. Transmission and overdrive improperly aligned.

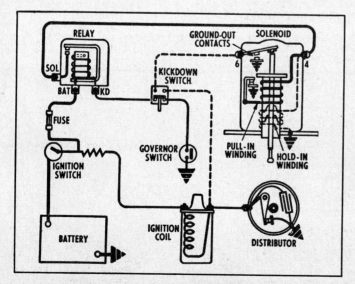

Fig. 1   Overdrive circuit diagram with relay

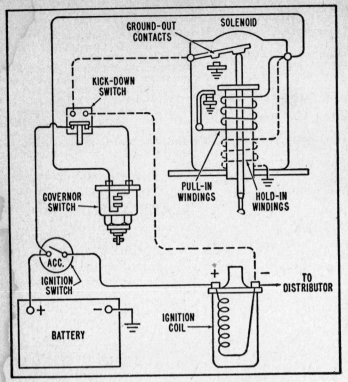

Fig. 2 Overdrive circuit diagram without relay. 1965-69

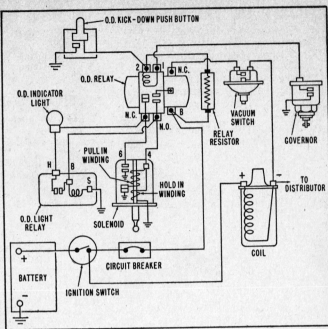

Fig. 3 Rambler twin stick overdrive circuit diagram. 1965

3. Kickdown switch improperly adjusted.
4. Improper installation of solenoid.
5. Improper positioning of blocker ring.
6. Broken or slipping governor drive pinion.

7. Too much end play in mainshaft.

Overdrive Engages with Severe Jolt or Noise

Insufficient blocker ring friction may cause the ring to lose its grip on the hub of the sun gear control plate.

Free-Wheels At Speeds Over 30 MPH

If cam roller retainer spring tension is weak the unit will free-wheel at all times.

Rear Axle Troubles

Noise When Pulling Straight Ahead

1. Not enough oil.
2. Wrong grade of oil.
3. Poor quality oil.
4. Ring gear and pinion have excessive backlash.
5. Ring gear and pinion worn.
6. Pinion shaft bearings worn or loose.
7. Pinion shaft end play excessive.
8. Ring gear and pinion misaligned because of bent axle housing or distorted differential case.
9. Ring gear warped.
10. Differential bearings worn or loose.
11. Ring gear rivets or screws loose.
12. Ring gear and pinion not matched set.

Noise When Coasting In Gear

Any axle noise which is heard when the engine is pulling the car is likely to be heard when coasting although not as loud as when pulling.

If ring gear and pinion are meshed too tight, the noise will be greater when decelerating. The noise will disappear when the engine is pulling unless the gears are very tight.

Excessive end play of pinion shaft due to loose pinion nut or incorrect adjustment.

Intermittent Noise

1. Warped ring gear.
2. Loose ring gear rivets or screws.
3. Ring gear improperly installed on differential case due to dirt or burrs between the two.

Knocks or Clicks

1. Flat spot on ring gear or pinion tooth, or tooth chipped, or particle of metal lodged on tooth.
2. Flat spot in bearing.
3. Loose axle shaft key.
4. Loose splined shafts.
5. Mis-matched differential case halves.

Noise On Turns

1. Differential pinions or side gears chipped, scuffed or teeth broken.
2. Differential pinions binding on pinion shaft.
3. Differential pinions or side gears loose due to worn bushings or shaft.

4. Excessive backlash between pinions and side gears.
5. Excessive axle shaft end play.
6. Contacting surfaces between side gear and differential case burred, scored or otherwise damaged.

Oil Leak At Axle Ends

1. Oil level too high.
2. Oil too light or poor quality.
3. Axle shaft oil seals worn.
4. Axle shaft bearing retainer loose.
5. Cracked rear axle housing.
6. Vent (if any) clogged.

Oil Leak At Pinion Shaft

1. Oil level too high.
2. Oil too light or poor quality.
3. Pinion oil seal worn.
4. Pinion oil seal retainer distorted, loose in housing or improperly installed.
5. Oil return passage in carrier housing restricted.
6. Universal joint companion flange hub rough, scored or out of round.
7. Universal joint companion flange loose on pinion shaft.

Drum Brake Troubles

One Brake Drags
1. Brake line restricted.
2. Improperly adjusted or worn wheel bearing.
3. Distorted or improperly adjusted brake shoe.
4. Faulty retracting spring.
5. Drum out of round.
6. Loose backing plate.
7. Faulty wheel cylinder.
8. Dirty brake fluid.
9. Air in hydraulic system.
10. Insufficient shoe-to-backing plate lubrication.

All Brakes Drag
1. Mechanical resistance at pedal or shoes; damaged linkage.
2. Brake line restricted.
3. Distorted or improperly adjusted brake shoes.
4. Dirty brake fluid.
5. Faulty master cylinder.
6. Sticking booster control valve.

Hard Pedal
1. Mechanical resistance at pedal or shoes; damaged linkage.
2. Brake line restricted.
3. Distorted or improperly adjusted brake shoes.
4. Linings glazed or worn.
5. Oil or grease in lining.

Spongy Pedal
1. Leaks or insufficient fluid.
2. Air in hydraulic system.

Car Pulls to One Side
1. Brake line restricted.
2. Improper tire pressure.
3. Improperly adjusted or worn wheel bearing.
4. Distorted or improperly adjusted brake shoes.
5. Faulty retracting spring.
6. Drum out of round.
7. Linings glazed or worn.
8. Oil or grease in lining.
9. Loose lining.
10. Faulty wheel cylinder.
11. Self-adjusters not operating.
12. Worn or binding front suspension parts.

One Wheel Locks
1. Distorted or improperly adjusted brake shoes.
2. Linings glazed or worn.
3. Oil or grease in lining.
4. Loose backing plate.
5. Faulty wheel cylinder.
6. Tire tread worn.

Brakes Chatter
1. Drum out of round.
2. Linings glazed or worn.
3. Oil or grease in lining.
4. Loose backing plate.
5. Loose lining.
6. Poor lining-to-drum contact.
7. Loose front suspension.

Excessive Pedal Travel
1. Leaks or insufficient fluid.
2. Distorted or improperly adjusted brake shoes.

3. Linings glazed or worn.
4. Faulty master cylinder.
5. Air in hydraulic system.
6. Self-adjusters not operating.
7. Cracked drum.

Pedal Gradually Goes to Floor
1. Leaks or insufficient fluid.
2. Faulty master cylinder.

Brakes Uneven
1. Improper tire pressure.
2. Oil or grease in lining.
3. Scored drum.
4. Dirty brake fluid.

Shoe Click Release
1. Self-adjusters not operating.
2. Insufficient shoe-to-backing plate lubrication.
3. "Threads" left by drum turning tool pull shoes sideways.

Noisy or Grabbing Brakes
1. Distorted or improperly adjusted brake shoes.
2. Linings glazed or worn.
3. Oil or grease in lining.
4. Scored drum.
5. Dirty on drum-lining surface.
6. Faulty wheel cylinder.
7. Sticking booster control valve.

Brakes Do Not Apply
1. Leaks or insufficient fluid.
2. Linings glazed or worn.
3. Oil or grease in lining.
4. Dirty brake fluid.
5. Faulty master cylinder.
6. Air in hydraulic system.

Front End & Steering Troubles

Hard Steering
1. Low or uneven tire pressure.
2. Steering gear or connections adjusted too tight.
3. Insufficient or incorrect lubricant used.
4. Excessive caster.
5. Suspension arms bent or twisted.
6. Front spring sagged.
7. Frame bent or broken.
8. Steering knuckle bent.
9. Kingpin galled or frozen in bushing.
10. Excessive steering shaft coupling misalignment.

Excessive Play or Looseness In Steering
1. Steering gear connections adjusted too loose or worn.
2. Steering knuckle bushings worn.
3. Front wheel bearings incorrectly adjusted or worn.
4. Worn ball joints.
5. Worn or loose worm steering shaft bearings.
6. Worn control arm bushings.

Rattle or Chuckle in Steering Gear
1. Insufficient or improper lubricant in steering gear.
2. Excessive backlash in steering gear.
3. Worn or loose worm steering shaft bearings.
4. Pitman arm loose on shaft.

Erratic Steering On Application of Brakes
1. Oil or brake fluid on lining.
2. Brakes improperly adjusted.
3. Front spring weak.
4. Low or uneven tire pressure.
5. Insufficient or uneven caster.
6. Steering knuckle bent.

Car Pulls to One Side
1. Low or uneven tire pressure.
2. Incorrected or uneven caster or camber.

3. Wheel bearings adjusted too tight.
4. Uneven front car height.
5. Toe-in incorrect.
6. Oil or brake fluid on brake lining.
7. Brakes incorrectly or unevenly adjusted.
8. Steering knuckle or knuckle support bent.
9. Frame bent or broken.
10. Shock absorbers inoperative.
11. Rear wheels not tracking with front wheels.
12. Rear axle shifted (spring U bolts loose or center bolt sheared).
13. Broken or weak rear springs.

Scuffed Tires
1. Tire improperly inflated.
2. Toe-in incorrect.
3. Excessive wheel or tire run-out.
4. Steering knuckle bushings worn.
5. Uneven camber.
6. Incorrect toe-out on turns.
7. Suspension arm bent or twisted.
8. Steering knuckle bent.
9. Excessive speed on turns.

Cupped Tires

1. Improper toe-in.
2. Tires improperly inflated.
3. Wheels, tires or brake drums out of balance.
4. Dragging brakes.
5. Worn steering knuckle bushings.
6. Wheel bearings incorrectly adjusted or worn.
7. Uneven camber.
8. Steering knuckle bent.
9. Excessive mileage without rotating tires.

Front Wheel Shimmy

1. Low or uneven tire pressure.
2. Wheels, tires or brake drums out of balance.
3. Excessive wheel or tire run-out.
4. Shock absorbers inoperative.
5. Steering connections incorrectly adjusted or worn.
6. Steering gear incorrectly adjusted.

7. Front wheel bearings incorrectly adjusted or worn.
8. Incorrect or uneven caster.
9. Steering knuckle bushings worn.
10. Toe-in incorrect.
11. Steering knuckle bent.
12. Eccentric or bulged tires.
13. Stabilizer inoperative.
14. Worn ball joints.
15. Worn control arm bushings.

Front Wheel Tramp

1. Wheels, tires or brake drums out of balance.
2. Wheel or tire not concentric.
3. Shock absorbers inoperative.
4. Stabilizer inoperative.

Car Wanders

1. Low or uneven tire pressure.
2. Steering gear or connections adjusted too loose or worn.
3. Steering gear or connections adjusted too tight.

4. Steering knuckle bushings worn.
5. Improper toe-in.
6. Incorrect or uneven caster or camber.
7. Steering knuckle bent.
8. Kingpin bent.
9. Rear axle shifted (spring U bolts loose or center bolt sheared).
10. Stabilizer inoperative.
11. Kingpins or bushings tight.
12. Bind in lower or upper control arm shaft.
13. Bind in rear spring shackles or dry rear springs.
14. Excessive backlash in steering gear.

Road Shocks

1. High air pressure in tires.
2. Steering gear or connections incorrectly adjusted.
3. Excessive caster.
4. Shock absorbers inoperative.
5. Front springs weak or sagged.
6. Wrong type or size of tires used.
7. Steering knuckle bent.

Power Top, Window & Seat Troubles

Top Will Not Operate

1. Mechanical interference due to luggage or other objects.
2. Hold down strap not removed.
3. Top not free from windshield header studs.
4. Electrical shorts or loose connections in control switch circuit.
5. Dirty control switch contacts.
6. Inoperative power unit motor.
7. Hydraulic fluid low.
8. Power unit pump inoperative.
9. Stoppage in fluid pipes.
10. Faulty hydraulic control valve.
11. Broken port plate in hydraulic pump.

Top Operates in One Direction Only

1. Mechanical interference due to luggage or other objects.
2. Hold down strap not removed.
3. Top not free from windshield header studs.
4. Electrical shorts or loose connections in control switch circuit.
5. Dirty control switch contact.
6. Improperly adjusted control rod.
7. Hydraulic power cylinder faulty.
8. Stoppage in fluid pipes.
9. Faulty hydraulic control valve.

Window Won't Operate from Main Switch Only

1. Broken wire between relay and remote switch.
2. Defective switch in master switch group.

3. Break in wire where it enters door opening.

Window Won't Operate from Main or Door Switch

1. Burned out motor or relay.
2. Defective circuit breaker.
3. Break in battery feed wire from starter solenoid to circuit breaker.

Window Operates In One Direction Only from Main or Door Switch

1. Defective relay.
2. Defective switch.
3. Broken ground wires.
4. Burned out motor.
5. Broken control wire.

Circuit Breaker in Door Clicks On and Off Continuously and Window Won't Operate

1. Control wire grounded.
2. Defective switch.
3. Relay points stuck.

Main Or Door Switch Operates Window In Wrong Direction

1. Lead wires are not connected to proper terminals.

Window Operates Sluggishly

1. Binding window regulator.
2. Broken wires or loose connections.

3. Worn motor brushes.

All Windows Do Not Operate

1. Circuit breaker open in control circuit.
2. Circuit breaker open in power circuit.

Seat Regulators Inoperative

1. Circuit breaker open in control circuit.
2. Circuit breaker open in power circuit.

One Seat Regulator Inoperative

1. Defective wiring between relay and circuit breaker.
2. Defective motor.
3. Defective wiring between switch and circuit breaker.
4. Defective relay.

Seat Regulator Operates in One Direction Only

1. Defective wiring between switch and relay that applies to direction of travel desired.
2. Defective toggle switch.

Seat Regulator Operates Sluggishly

1. Binding mechanism.
2. Defective wiring.
3. Loose connectors or poor ground.
4. Worn or dirty brushes in motor.

Windshield Wiper Troubles

GENERAL INSPECTION

Before deciding that a windshield wiper needs servicing it might be well to consider some of the external factors which affect their operation.

It must be remembered that windshield wipers will operate more slowly when they do their work on dry glass. This is specially true on cars with curved windshields. You will also find that wiper blades may chatter or fail to travel a complete arc on dry glass. It is therefore obvious that any testing of windshield wiper operation should be done after the windshield has been sprayed with water.

Windshield wipers that chatter or do not wipe the glass clean under normal operating conditions (wet windshield) may need only replacement of the wiper arms or blades instead of more extensive service. This can be determined by visual inspection and most replacements can be made simply without the aid of any special tools.

Uneven movement of the wiper arms with respect to one another is usually caused by cables, pivots or cranks that are out of adjustment in the windshield wiper transmission system.

ELECTRIC TYPE

All passenger car electric windshield wiper circuits, regardless of manufacturer, include a control switch, a small shunt wound motor, and the wiring connecting these units to the battery. A circuit breaker or fuse may be mounted as a separate unit or incorporated in the control switch itself. A worm gear on the motor armature shaft drives one or two gears mounted on crankshafts for wiper operation.

A parking switch is mounted on the motor and actuated by a cam on one of the cranks. The parking switch, connected to the battery through a control switch, keeps the motor in operation for a brief period after the control switch has been shut off, allowing the wiper blades to return to the parked position.

Both single and two speed motors are used, the latter incorporating one or several resistors in the field circuit. The resistors may be located either in the parking switch housing or in the control switch.

In the following text you will find a list of the conditions you are likely to encounter when faced with a repair job on electric wipers. By consulting these possibilities you will simplify the job of locating the source of trouble. But before going further a few words of caution are in order: After you have made your diagnosis and are ready to make repairs, disconnect the battery to avoid damage under the dash or possible personal injury from accidental shorts. Also, on models which use off-glass parking windshield wipers, never remove or disassemble the motor while in "park" position.

Wipers Won't Operate

1. Discharged battery.
2. Blown fuse or faulty circuit breaker.
3. No power to control switch.
4. Faulty control switch.
5. Faulty parking switch.
6. Binding pivots, cranks or linkages.
7. Poor connection at switch.
8. No ground at motor.
9. Faulty motor.

Wipers Won't Park

1. Incorrect adjustment of parking switch lever.
2. Open circuit in lead feeding parking switch.
3. Faulty parking switch.
4. Faulty control switch.
5. No ground at control switch (variable speed wipers).
6. Motor crank and parking switch improperly assembled.
7. Cams in linkage reversed or binding (variable speed wipers).

Wipers Operate Slowly

1. Discharged battery.
2. Binding pivots, cranks or linkages.
3. Faulty motor windings.
4. High resistance connections or wiring.
5. High resistance in control switch contacts.
6. No ground at control switch (variable speed wipers).
7. Faulty resistance unit (if only high speed in affected).
8. Dirty commutator or sticking brushes.
9. Worn or damaged motor.

Multiple Speed Wipers Operate Only at Single Speed

1. Short or open in motor wiring harness.
2. Incorrect connections at control switch.
3. Faulty control switch.
4. Faulty resistance unit.
5. No ground at control switch.
6. Open shunt field in motor.

VACUUM TYPE

For satisfactory windshield wiper operation, it is necessary to have an adequate supply of vacuum. On some cars the vacuum is made available by tapping directly into the intake manifold. With this type of arrangement it is considered normal for the wipers to slow down or stop entirely while going up a hill or during acceleration, since under those conditions the manifold vacuum would drop below the 8"-10" needed to operate the wipers. These conditions are almost completely eliminated on cars equipped with a vacuum booster pump. The purpose of this pump is to maintain enough vacuum to work the wipers under any driving condition.

Some of the conditions which prevent satisfactory windshield wiper operation are listed in the following text and may be used as a guide to help you locate the source of trouble. Always disconnect the battery when working under the dash.

Wipers Won't Operate

1. No vacuum supply to motor due to pinch, restriction or leak in the windshield wiper hose. A vacuum leak or a disconnected hose can easily be located because a hissing sound will be heard whenever the engine is running.
2. Faulty vacuum booster pump.
3. Wiper control switch inoperative or disconnected at motor.
4. Faulty wiper motor.
5. Frozen or binding pivots and linkages.
6. Linkages or cables improperly installed.

Wipers Operate Slowly

1. Low vacuum due to pinch or partial restriction in the wiper hose.
2. Loss of vacuum due to leaks at joints, fittings or in the wiper hose itself.
3. Faulty vacuum booster pump.
4. Faulty wiper motor.
5. Wiper control switch does not move operating valve on the motor to full "ON" position due to improper adjustment.
6. Air intake on motor (breather port) clogged.
7. Binding pivots, cranks, linkages or binding or frozen idler pulleys on cable tensioners.
8. Cables adjusted too tight.

Wipers Won't Park

1. Faulty parking valve on motor.
2. Wiper control switch out of adjustment.
3. Wiper arms not positioned properly on pivots.

PRESSURE WIPER

The windshield wiper is hydraulically operated. The hydraulic power for the motor is obtained from the power steering unit. Hydraulic fluid flows from the pump, through the steering gear to the wiper motor, and then to the fluid reservoir. During wiper operation, a part of the fluid is by-passed through the motor by a valve on the motor.

Checks and Adjustments: The only adjustment required is the control cable adjustment. To adjust, remove the seal plate mounting screws and position the plate and seal out of the way. Adjust the cable so that the control knob on instrument panel moves the valve control lever on motor from off to full on.

If the motor operates sluggishly, check the cable adjustment. If this is not the fault, check the hydraulic fluid pressure. If the power steering gear operates satisfactorily, it may be assumed that the fluid pressure is adequate. Check for binding wiper pivot shafts and arms. Repair or replace wiper motor and valves if necessary.

TUNE UP SERVICE

Tune up service has become increasingly important to the modern automotive engine with its vastly improved power and performance. With the higher compression ratios, improved fuel and electrical systems and especially the exhaust emission controls with their inherently critical settings, engines have become more sensitive to usage and operating conditions, which have a decided effect on power and performance. It is important, therefore, that this service to be performed on the engine every spring and fall or more often if conditions warrant.

In addition to the servicing of spark plugs, ignition points and condenser, a proper tune up includes a number of tests to check the condition of the engine and its related systems and uncover sources of future problems.

DIAGNOSIS & TESTING

Before a satisfactory tune up can be performed, the existing condition of the engine and its related systems must be determined. A tune up should not be attempted if tests indicate internal engine problems such as burnt valves, worn rings, blown head gasket, etc., until such conditions have been corrected.

Oscilloscope Test

Although oscilloscopes differ in many ways, they all display a light or "trace" on a screen which measures the voltage present at a given point and time. As the ignition system operates, its voltage creates a pattern on the screen. This pattern, when read in accordance with the manufacturers instructions for the particular unit, indicates the condition of the entire ignition system.

Compression Test

An engine cannot be tuned to develop maximum power and smooth performance unless the proper compression is obtained in each cylinder.

CAUTION: When cranking the engine for a compression test or any other reason, the coil high tension cable should be removed from the distributor cap and grounded to the engine block or the distributor primary grounded with jumper wire.

1. Remove any foreign matter from around spark plugs by blowing out plug area with compressed air. Then remove plugs.
2. Remove air cleaner and block throttle and choke in wide open position.
3. Insert compression gauge firmly in spark plug opening and crank engine through at least four compression strokes to obtain highest possible reading.
4. Test and record compression of each cylinder. Compression should read within the limits given in the *Tune Up Charts* in the car chapters. The

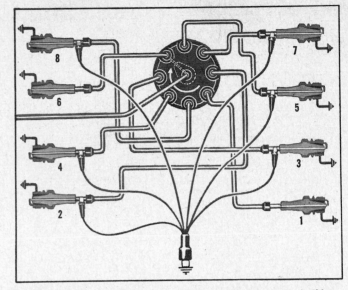

Fig. 1 Cylinder balance test connections. The firing order in this example is 1-8-4-3-6-5-7-2. Therefore, the cylinders to be tested together are 1-6, 8-5, 4-7, 3-2, using the grounding leads as shown

variation between the highest and lowest reading should not be more than 20 pounds.
5. If one or more cylinders read low, inject about a tablespoon of engine oil on top of pistons in the low reading cylinders. Crank engine several times and recheck compression.
6. If compression is now higher, it indicates worn piston rings. If compression does not improve, valves are sticking or seating poorly. If two adjacent cylinders show low compression and injecting oil does not improve the condition, the cause may be a head gasket leak between cylinders.

Cylinder Balance

It is sometimes difficult to locate a weak cylinder especially in an eight cylinder engine. A compression test, for example, will not locate a leaky intake manifold, a valve not opening properly due to a worn camshaft, or a defective spark plug.

With the cylinder balance test, the power output of one cylinder may be checked against another, using a set of grounding leads, Fig. 1. When the power of each cylinder is not equal, the engine will lose power and run roughly. The cylinder balance test is as follows:
1. Connect a tachometer and vacuum gauge.
2. Start engine and run it at a fast idle.
3. Gound large clip of grounding leads and connect individual leads to all spark plugs *except the pair being tested,* Fig. 1.
4. Divide the firing order in half and write down the first half over the second half. The cylinders to be tested together appear one over the other.

Firing Order	Pairs Tested
1-8-4-3-6-5-7-2	1-6, 8-5, 4-7, 3-2
1-2-7-8-4-5-6-3	1-4, 2-5, 7-6, 8-3
1-5-4-8-6-3-7-2	1-6, 5-3, 4-7, 8-2
1-5-4-2-6-3-7-8	1-6, 5-3, 4-7, 2-8
1-8-7-3-6-5-4-2	1-6, 8-5, 7-4, 3-2
1-3-7-2-6-5-4-8	1-6, 3-5, 7-4, 2-8
1-5-6-3-4-2-7-8	1-4, 5-2, 6-7, 3-8
1-6-5-4-3-2	1-4, 6-3, 5-2
1-5-3-6-2-4	1-6, 5-2, 3-4
1-4-5-2-3-6	1-2, 4-3, 5-6
1-3-4-2	1-4, 3-2
1-4-3-2	1-3, 4-2

5. Operate engine on each pair of cylinders in turn and note engine rpm and manifold vacuum for each pair. A variation of more than one inch of vacuum or 40 rpm between pairs of cylinders being tested indicates that the cylinders are off balance.
6. To isolate one weak cylinder, short out one bank of cylinders at a time. The bank giving the lower readings will include the weak cylinder.

Manifold Vacuum Test

NOTE: On some high performance engines, the camshaft provides such a great degree of valve overlap that vacuum at idle speed will be too low for an accurate test. For this reason, a vacuum test made on such units is of little value.

Manifold vacuum is affected by carburetor adjustment, valve timing, ignition timing, valve condition, cylinder compression, condition of positive crankcase ventilation system and leakage of manifold, carburetor, carburetor spacer or cylinder head gaskets.

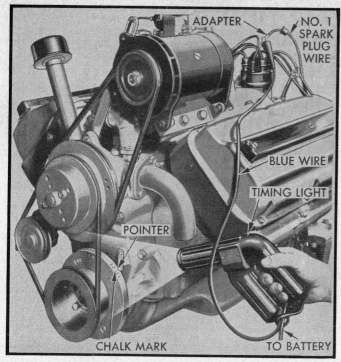

Fig. 2 Checking ignition timing with timing lights

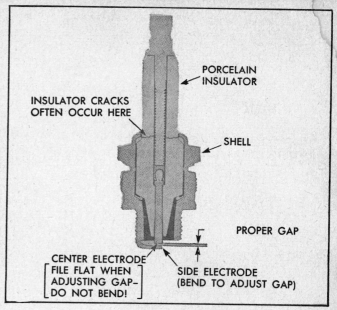

Fig. 3 Spark plug details

Because abnormal gauge readings may indicate that more than one of the above factors are at fault, use care in analyzing an abnormal reading. For example, if the vacuum is low, the correction of one item may increase the vacuum enough to indicate that the trouble has been corrected. It is important, therefore, that each cause of an abnormal reading be investigated and further tests conducted, where necessary, to arrive at the correct diagnosis of the trouble. To check manifold vacuum, proceed as follows:

1. Bring engine to operating temperature.
2. Connect an accurate vacuum gauge to the intake manifold.
3. Operate engine at recommended idle speed.
4. Check vacuum reading on gauge.

Test Conclusions

NORMAL READING: 18 inches or more. Allowance should be made for the effect of altitude on gauge reading.

LOW & STEADY: Loss of power in all cylinders possibly caused by late ignition or valve timing, or loss of compression.

VERY LOW: Intake manifold, carburetor spacer or head gasket leak.

NEEDLE FLUCTUATES STEADILY AS SPEED INCREASES: Partial or complete loss of power in one or more cylinders caused by a leaky head or manifold gasket, burnt valve, weak valve spring or a defect in the ignition system.

GRADUAL DROP IN READING AT IDLE SPEED: Excessive back pressure in exhaust system.

INTERMITTENT FLUCTUATION: Defect in ignition system or sticking valve.

SLOW FLUCTUATION OR DRIFTING OF

NEEDLE: Improper idle mixture, carburetor, carburetor spacer, intake manifold gasket leak or restricted crankcase ventilation system.

Cranking Voltage Test

The condition of the starting circuit can be checked by connecting a voltmeter across the battery posts, grounding the coil so the engine will not fire and cranking the engine. If, during cranking, the voltage reading drops below 9.6 volts, there is high resistance in the circuit.

Charging Circuit Test

The performance of the charging circuit should be checked during any tune-up. See specific unit section of this manual for test procedures.

Ignition Timing

The use of a timing light, Fig. 2, is recommended for checking and setting ignition timing. This setting is critical especially on units equipped with emission control systems.

NOTE: The timing light should be connected to the proper spark plug lead by the use of an adapter. The boots around the connections should not be pierced to connect the light as this can cause spark arcing and misfiring.

Lacking a timing light, the timing can be set with the engine stopped by using a jumper light. Be sure to use a light bulb that corresponds with the vehicle voltage.

1. Rotate engine until No. 1 cylinder is positioned at the specified timing mark.
2. Connect jumper light between distributor ignition terminal and ground.

3. Turn on ignition switch.
4. Loosen distributor and turn it in the direction of normal rotation until the points just close (light out). Then slowly turn the distributor in the opposite direction just to the exact point that the light goes on. Tighten distributor in this position.

Combustion Efficiency Test

This test checks the carburetor air/fuel mixture by measuring the amount of various chemicals present in the engine exhaust under different conditions. By following the manufacturer's instructions for the specific unit, the carburetor idle, intermediate, high speed and accelerator pump circuits can be checked for proper operation.

This test is especially important when working on engines equipped with exhaust emission controls because of the more critical mixture adjustments on such units.

SERVICE

Spark Plugs

1. Examine firing ends of plugs for evidence of oil fouling gas fouling, burned or overheated condition. *Oil fouling is usually identified by wet, sludgy deposits caused by excessive oil consumption. Gas fouling is identified by dry, black, fluffy deposits caused by incomplete combustion. Burned or overheated spark plugs are identified by white, burned or blistered insulator nose and badly burned electrodes. Improper fuel, insufficient cooling or improper ignition timing normally are the cause. Normal conditions are usually identified by white powdery deposits or rusty-brown to grayish-tan powdery deposits.*
2. Clean plugs with a suitable sand blast cleaner following the manufacturers instructions.

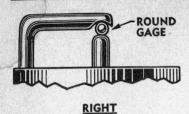

RIGHT

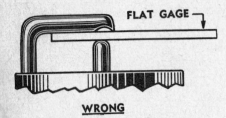

WRONG

Fig. 4   Correct and incorrect spark plug gauges

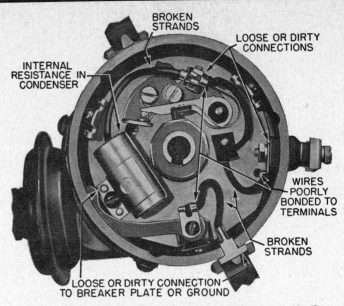

Fig. 5   What to look for when checking for high resistance in the primary circuit of the distributor. In addition to the points indicated, look for external circuit high resistance at ignition switch terminals, ammeter terminals, coil terminals and broken or poorly insulated wires in this circuit

3. Remove carbon and other deposits from threads with a stiff wire bruch.

NOTE: Do not use brush to clean electrodes as small pieces of wire can stick inside plug and later cause misfiring.

4. Dress electrodes with a small file to secure flat, parallel surfaces on both center and side electrodes, Fig. 3.
5. Use a round wire gauge to check the gap, Fig. 4, and adjust by bending the side (never center) electrode to the proper specifications as shown in the *Tune Up Charts* in the car chapters.
6. If gaskets are used, place new ones on plugs and torque plugs to specification.

IMPORTANT

Improper installation of spark plugs is one of the greatest single causes of unsatisfactory spark plug performance. Improper installation is the result of one or more of the following practices: 1) Installation of plugs with insufficient torque to fully seat the gasket; 2) excessive torque which changes gap settings; 3) installation of plugs on dirty gasket seal; 4) installation of plugs to corroded spark plug hole threads.

Failure to install plugs properly will cause them to operate at excessively high temperatures and result in reduced operating life under mild operation or complete destruction under severe operation where the intense heat cannot be dissipated rapidly enough.

Always remove carbon deposits in hole threads before installing plugs. When corrosion is present in threads, normal torque is not sufficient to compress the plug gasket (if used) and early failure from overheating will result.

Always use a new gasket (if required) and wipe seats in head clean. The gasket must be fully compressed on clean seats to complete heat transfer and provide a gas tight seal in the cylinder. For this reason as well as the necessity of maintaining correct plug gap, the use of correct torque is extremely important during installation.

Ignition System

1. Check to be sure all connections are clean and tight. Repair or replace any wires that are frayed, loose or damaged, Fig. 5. Replace brittle or damaged spark plug wires.
2. Remove distributor cap, clean and inspect for cracks, carbon tracks and burned or corroded terminals. Replace cap if necessary.
3. Clean rotor and inspect for damage or deterioration. Replace rotor if necessary.
4. Check distributor centrifugal advance mechanism (if used) by turning distributor rotor in direction of running rotation as far as possible, then release rotor to see if springs return it to its retarded position. If rotor does not return readily, the distributor must be disassembled and cause of trouble corrected.
5. Check to see that the vacuum spark control operates freely by turning the movable breaker plate (if used) or distributor housing in a direction opposite to that of running rotation to see if the spring returns it to the retarded position. Any stiffness in the operation of the spark control will affect ignition timing. Correct any interference or binding condition noted.
6. Examine distributor points and clean or replace if necessary. Points with an overall gray color and only slight roughness or pitting need not be replaced.
7. Dirty points should be cleaned with a clean point file. Use only a few strokes of the file. The file should not be used on other metals and should not be allowed to become dirty or greasy. *Never use emery cloth or sandpaper to clean points since particles will embed and cause arcing and rapid burning of points.* Do not attempt to remove all roughness nor dress the point surfaces down smooth. Merely remove scale or dirt.
8. Replace points that are badly burned or pitted. Where burned or badly pitted points are encountered, the ignition system and engine should be checked to determine the cause of the trouble so it can be eliminated. Unless the condition causing point burning is corrected, new points will provide no better service than the old points. See *Ignition* chapter for an analysis of point burning or pitting, and for proper installation of points & condenser.

Battery & Cables

Inspect for signs of corrosion on battery, cables and surrounding area, loose or broken carriers, cracked or bulged cases, dirt and acid, electrolyte leakage and low electrolyte level. Fill cells to proper level with distilled water or water passed through a "demineralizer."

The top of the battery should be clean and the battery hold-down bolts properly tightened.

For best results when cleaning batteries, wash first with a dilute ammonia or soda solution to neutralize any acid present and then flush off with clean water. Care must be taken to keep vent plugs tight so that the neutralizing solution does not enter the battery.

To insure good contact, the battery cables should be tight on the battery posts. Oil battery terminal felt washer. If the battery posts or cables terminals are corroded, the cables should be cleaned separately with a soda solution and a wire bruch.

If the battery has remained undercharged, check for a loose generator belt, defective generator, high resistance in charging circuit, oxidized voltage regulator contact points, or a low voltage setting.

If the battery has been using too much water, the voltage regulator setting is too high.

Fuel System

All fuel filters and the air cleaner element should be serviced during a tune up, including the sintered bronze "stone" used in some units.

Since carburetion is dependent in several ways on both compression and ignition, it should always be checked last when tuning an engine. Refer to the Carburetor Chapter for pertinent data on specific units.

IGNITION COILS & RESISTORS

IGNITION COILS

If poor ignition performance is obtained and the coil is suspected, it may be tested on the car or it may be removed for the test.

Ignition coils are often condemned when the trouble is actually in the ignition switch. A completely defective ignition switch will produce an open primary circuit, giving the same indications as if the coil were completely dead. A partly defective ignition switch will cause a weak spark.

By cutting the ignition switch out of the circuit, it can easily be determined whether the coil is defective or the fault lies in the ignition switch.

In the absence of any testing equipment a simple check of an ignition coil can be made as follows: Turn on ignition switch with breaker points closed. Remove the high tension cable from the center socket of the distributor cap and hold it ¼" to ⅜" away from a clean spot on the engine. If the coil and other units connected to it are in good condition a spark should jump from the wire to the engine as the points are opened. If not, use a jumper wire from the distributor terminal to the engine; if the primary is in good condition a spark will occur.

All ignition coils with metal containers can be tested for gounded windings by placing one test clip on a clean part of the metal container and touching the other clip to the primary and high tension terminals. If the lamp lights or tiny sparks appear at the points of contact, the windings are grounded and the coil should be replaced.

Coil Polarity

Most coils are marked positive and negative at the primary terminals. When installing or connecting a coil be sure to make the connections as shown in Fig. 1. A reversal of this polarity may affect the performance of the engine (or the radio).

If the coil is not marked as to its polarity, it can be checked by holding any high tension wire about ¼" away from its spark plug terminal with the engine running. Insert the point of a wooden lead pencil between the spark plug and the wire, Fig. 2. If the spark flares and has a slight orange tinge on the spark plug side of the pencil, polarity is correct. If the spark flares on the cable side, coil connections should be reversed.

IGNITION RESISTORS

The ignition coils used with 12-volt

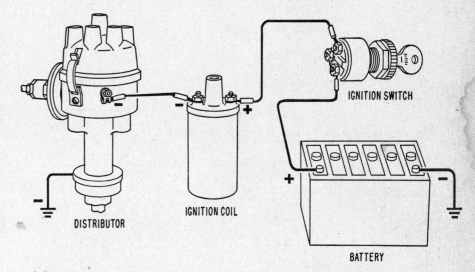

Fig. 1   Wiring connections for coil with negative grounded system

systems are specially designed 6-volt coils which operate with a resistor connected in series with the primary ignition circuit. The purpose of the resistor is to prolong the service life of the distributor breaker points.

Block Type Ballast Resistors

This type resistor came into existance with the introduction of the 12-volt battery. Its basic purpose is to allow full battery voltage to the ignition coil during engine starting, and to reduce battery voltage to the coil when the engine is running. The higher voltage during starts means easier starts. But sustained high voltage to the breaker points can cause point failure. The reduced voltage during engine operation increases breaker point life.

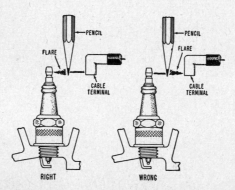

Fig. 2   Checking coil polarity

These resistors are normally very dependable. But if one fails, it can be one of the most difficult of all ignition malfunctions to diagnose. An open resistor means that no current reaches the coil and the engine cannot operate. It is possible for the resistance wire to warp or bend enough to touch the side of the case. When this happens, the engine may continue to run but the overall performance will be poor.

Resistors can change value. Any creeping change in resistance value of a ballast resistor is invariably an increase in resistance. This means that coil output to the spark plugs is reduced proportionately. If a ballast resistor is slowly increasing in value the engine could gradually deliver less and less horsepower, particularly under high load conditions. An unsuspecting mechanic could unsuccessfully try to get the engine back to where it will deliver acceptable power output by changing spark plugs, adjusting timing, etc. Replacement of the faulty resistor is the only cure in this case.

To check a ballast resistor, replace it with one of known good quality. Then road-test the vehicle for improved performance.

It is important to remember that new spark plugs can temporarily mask the need for resistor replacement because new plugs require less voltage to fire. This is why a new-plug tune-up may prove satisfactory for a time. But if the ballast resistor is faulty, eventually the engine will misfire under load.

IGNITION COILS & RESISTORS

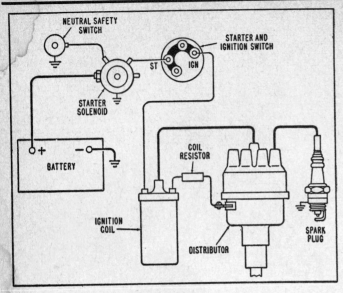

Fig. 3 Auto-Lite and Chrysler ignition circuit diagram with a temperature sensitive block-type resistor

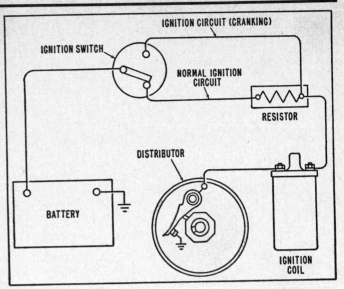

Fig. 4 Delco-Remy ignition circuit diagram with a constant temperature block-type resistor

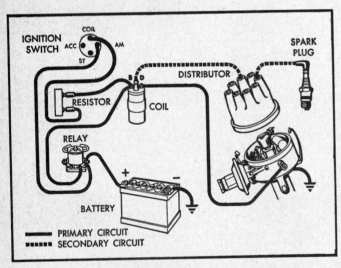

Fig. 5 Ford ignition circuit diagram with a constant temperature block-type resistor

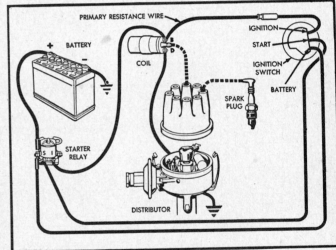

Fig. 6 Ford ignition circuit diagram with a resistance wire connected to a three-terminal ignition switch

In Auto-Lite, Prestolite and Chrysler systems the resistor consists of an ordinary resistance wire that is sensitive to temperature, Fig. 3. The wire has a lower resistance value when cold than when hot. When the ignition is first turned on, more current will flow through the primary windings of the coil for a very short time until the resistor heats up.

In Delco-Remy and Ford systems, Figs. 4 and 5, the resistor is of the constant temperature type; that is, it is not affected by temperature and its resistance is approximately the same when cold as when hot. However, a feature is employed which shorts out the resistor while the engine is being cranked by the starter and automatically puts the resistance back in the coil circuit as soon

as the starter switch is released. This is accomplished by by-passing the resistor through the starter solenoid. The solenoid has an additional terminal from which a wire runs directly to the coil.

On Delco-Remy systems, the resistor is by-passed by means of a "finger" inside the solenoid switch housing which is attached to the additional switch terminal.

On Ford systems, Fig. 6, the resistor is by-passed through a terminal on the starter relay which is connected directly to the positive terminal of the coil.

SERVICE NOTE: If the engine fires when the ignition switch is turned on but quits when the switch is released to its running position, it indicates that the resistor is defective and must be replaced.

Wire Type Resistors

The special resistance wires used with 12-volt systems are five to six feet long and contained in the regular wiring harness. The wire is made of stainless steel or special alloy, plastic-coated and covered with a glass braid. There is a relatively small temperature rise and the resistance wire is switched out of the circuit for starting and back in again for running.

These resistance wires, Figs. 6, 7, 8, are by-passed in the same manner as the ballast type described above.

SERVICE NOTE: If the engine fires when the ignition switch is turned on but quits when the switch is released to the "run" position, it indicates that the resistance wire has lost its continuity or

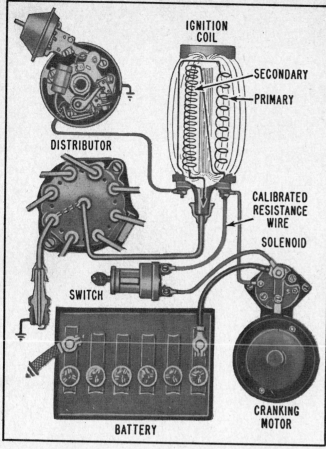

Fig. 7 Delco-Remy ignition circuit diagram with a resistance wire connected to a two-terminal ignition switch

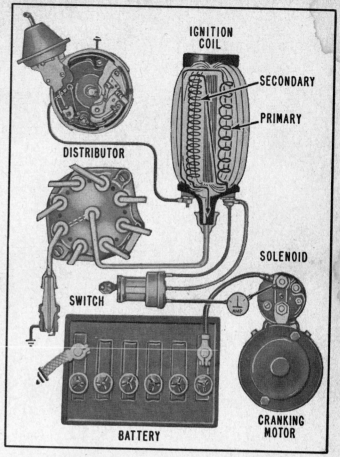

Fig. 8 Delco-Remy ignition circuit diagram with a resistance wire connected to a three-terminal ignition switch

there is a bad connection at the resistor terminals. If the wire is defective, it must be replaced, either by a ballast type resistor or a new length of resistance wire.

IMPORTANT: Do not attempt to operate the engine for an extended length of time with the resistor shorted out by means of a jumper wire as the breaker points will burn up in short order.

IGNITION COIL & RESISTOR SPECIFICATIONS

Year	Model	Coil Draw, Amps.		Coil Resistance, Ohms		Ignition Resistor Ohms @ 75°F.
		Engine Stopped	Engine Idling	Primary @ 75°F.	Secondary @ 75°F.	
BUICK—All Models						
1966–72	All	3.8	2.3	1.28–1.42	7200–9500	1.75–1.85
CADILLAC						
1966–68	All	2.4	1.25	1.81–1.95	7200–9500	1.30–1.35
1969–72	All	2.4	1.25	1.77–2.01	3000–20000	1.30–1.35

Continued

IGNITION COIL & RESISTOR SPECIFICATIONS—Continued

CHEVROLET, CHEVELLE, CHEVY II, CAMARO, VEGA

Year	Model	Coil Draw, Amps.		Coil Resistance, Ohms		Ignition Resistor Ohms @ 75°F.
		Engine Stopped	Engine Idling	Primary @ 75°F.	Secondary @ 75°F.	
1966-67	4 & 6 Cyl.	4.0	1.8	1.40-1.65	5400-7100	1.80
	V8 Std. Ign.	4.0	1.8	1.24-1.46	6500-9500	1.80
	Trans. Ign.	...	1.8	.38-.51	8200-12400	.43-.68
1968-72	4 & 6 Cyl.	4.0	1.8	1.41-1.63	3000-20000	1.80
	V8 Std. Ign.	4.0	1.8	1.77-2.05	3000-20000	1.35
	Trans. Ign.	4.0	1.8	.41-.51	3000-20000	.43-.68

CORVETTE

Year	Model	Engine Stopped	Engine Idling	Primary @ 75°F.	Secondary @ 75°F.	Ignition Resistor Ohms @ 75°F.
1966-67	Std. Ign.	4.0	1.8	1.24-1.46	6500-9500	1.80
	Trans. Ign.	...	1.8	.38-.51	8200-12400	.43-.68
1968-72	Std. Ign.	4.0	1.8	1.77-2.05	3000-20000	1.35
	Trans. Ign.	...	...	.41-.51	3000-20000	.43-.68

CORVAIR

Year	Model	Engine Stopped	Engine Idling	Primary @ 75°F.	Secondary @ 75°F.	Ignition Resistor Ohms @ 75°F.
1966-69	All	4.0	1.8	1.28-1.42	7200-9500	1.80

CHRYSLER, DODGE, PLYMOUTH, IMPERIAL—All Models

Year	Model	Coil Draw, Amps.		Coil Resistance, Ohms		Ignition Resistor Ohms @ 75°F.
		Engine Stopped	Engine Idling	Primary @ 75°F.	Secondary @ 75°F.	
1966-72	①	3.0	1.9	1.65-1.79	9400-11700	.50-.60
	②	3.0	1.9	1.41-1.55	9200-10600	.50-.60

① Chrysler, Auto-Lite and Prestolite coils. ② Essex coils.

FORD, MERCURY, LINCOLN, THUNDERBIRD—All Models

Year	Model	Engine Stopped	Engine Idling	Primary @ 75°F.	Secondary @ 75°F.	Ignition Resistor Ohms @ 75°F.
1966-72	Std. Ign.	4.5	2.5	1.40-1.54	7600-8800	1.30-1.40
1966-68	Trans. Ign.	4.0①	5.0	.262-.251	4900-5680	②

①—Engine cranking. ②—Emitter .31-.35 Collector .41-.45 Base 7.1-7.9

OLDSMOBILE—All Models

Year	Model	Engine Stopped	Engine Idling	Primary @ 75°F.	Secondary @ 75°F.	Ignition Resistor Ohms @ 75°F.
1966	6 Cyl.	6.0	1.35	1.45-1.63	6500-9500	1.85
	V8s	6.0	1.35	1.77-2.05	6500-9500	1.35
1967-70	Toronado	4.0	2.2	1.77-2.05	6500-9500	1.35
	Delmont	6.0	1.35	1.77-2.05	6500-9500	1.35
	6 Cyl.	4.0	1.8	1.45-1.63	6500-9500	1.85
	All Others	4.0	2.0	1.77-2.05	6500-9500	1.35
1971-72	6 Cyl.	...	...	1.45-1.63	6500-9500	1.85
	V8	...	...	1.77-2.05	6500-9500	1.35

IGNITION COIL & RESISTOR SPECIFICATIONS—Continued

Year	Model	Coil Draw, Amps.		Coil Resistance, Ohms		Ignition Resistor Ohms @ 75°F.
		Engine Stopped	Engine Idling	Primary @ 75°F.	Secondary @ 75°F.	

PONTIAC—All Models

Year	Model	Engine Stopped	Engine Idling	Primary @ 75°F.	Secondary @ 75°F.	Ignition Resistor
1966	6 Cyl.	3.5	2.8	1.45–1.63	5600–6900	1.80
	All V8s	3.4	2.1	1.81–2.01	7200–9500	1.32
1967	6 Cyl.	2.5	3.8	1.4–1.7	3000–20000	...
	Temp., F-Bird	3.4	2.1	1.7–2.0	3000–20000	...
	Pontiac	3.2–3.6	1.9–2.3	1.7–2.0	3000–20000	...
1968–69	Pontiac	3.2–3.6	1.9–2.3	1.7–2.0	3000–20000	...
	6 Cyl.	3.5	2.8	1.4–1.7	3000–20000	...
	Temp., F-Bird	3.4	2.1	1.7–2.0	3000–20000	...
1970	Six	3.4	2.1	1.4–1.7①	3000–20000	...
	V8	3.4	2.1	1.7–2.0	3000–20000	...
1971-72	Six	...	...	1.4–1.65	3000–20000	...
	V8	...	...	1.7–2.0	3000–20000	...

①—Firebird 1.4–1.65

RAMBLER—All Models

Year	Model	Engine Stopped	Engine Idling	Primary @ 75°F.	Secondary @ 75°F.	Ignition Resistor
1966	6 Cyl.	3.5	1.6	3.30–4.10	7200–9500	①
	V8s	3.5	1.6	1.77–2.05	6500–9500	1.30–1.40
1967	6 Cyl. ②	3.5	1.6	3.3–4.1	9400–11700	①
	6 Cyl. ③	3.5	1.6	3.9–4.2	9400–11700	①
	V8–290	3.5	1.6	1.75–2.05	6500–9500	1.30–1.40
	V8–343②	3.5	1.6	1.77–2.05	6500–9500	1.30–1.40
	V8–343③	3.5	1.6	1.65–1.79	9400–11700	1.30–1.40
1968	6 Cyl.	3.5	1.6	1.40–1.65	3000–20000	...
	V8②	3.5	1.6	1.77–2.05	6500–9500	...
	48③	3.5	1.6	1.65–1.79	9400–11700	...
1969–72	6 Cyl.	...	...	1.40–1.65	3000–20000	1.80
	V8②	...	...	1.77–2.05	3000–20000	1.35
	V8④	...	...	1.64–1.80	9300–11800	1.35

①—Resistor assembled inside of coil.　　③—Prestolite.
②—Delco-Remy.　　④—American Motors

VARIABLE SPEED FANS

The fan drive clutch, Fig. 1, is a fluid coupling containing silicone oil. Fan speed is regulated by the torque-carrying capacity of the silicone oil. The more silicone oil in the coupling the greater the fan speed, and the less silicone oil the slower the fan speed.

Two types of fan drive clutches are in use. On one, Fig. 2, a bi-metallic strip and control piston on the front of the fluid coupling regulates the amount of silicone oil entering the coupling. The bi-metallic strip bows outward with a decrease in surrounding temperature and allows a piston to move outward. The piston opens a valve regulating the flow of silicone oil into the coupling from a reserve chamber. The silicone oil is returned to the reserve chamber through a bleed hole when the valve is closed.

On the other type of fan drive clutch, Fig. 3, a heat-sensitive, bi-metal spring connected to an opening plate brings about a similar result. Both units cause the fan speed to increase with a rise in temperature and to decrease as the temperature goes down.

In some cases a Flex-Fan is used instead of a Fan Drive Clutch. Flexible blades vary the volume of air being drawn through the radiator, automatically increasing the pitch at low engine speeds.

Fig. 1 Typical variable-speed fan installed

Fan Drive Clutch Test

Run the engine at a fast idle speed (1000 rpm) until normal operating temperature is reached. This process can be speeded up by blocking off the front of the radiator with cardboard. Regardless of temperatures, the unit must be operated for at least five minutes immediately before being tested.

Stop the engine and, using a glove or a cloth to protect the hand, immediately check the effort required to turn the fan. If considerable effort is required, it can be assumed that the coupling is operating satisfactorily. If very little effort is required to turn the fan, it is an indication that the coupling is not operating properly and should be replaced.

Service Procedure

CAUTION: When it becomes necessary to remove a fan clutch of the silicone fluid type, Fig. 2, the assembly must be supported in the vertical (on car) position to prevent leaks of silicone fluid from the clutch mechanism. This loss of fluid will render the fan clutch inoperative.

The removal procedure for either type of fan clutch assembly is generally the same for all cars. Merely unfasten the unit from the water pump and remove the assembly from the car.

The type of unit shown in Fig. 2 may be partially disassembled for inspection and cleaning. Take off the capscrews that hold the assembly together and separate the fan from the drive clutch. Next remove the metal strip on the front by pushing one end of it toward the fan clutch body so it clears the retaining bracket. Then push the strip to the side so that its opposite end will spring out of place. Now remove the small control piston underneath it.

Check the piston for free movement of the coupling device. If the piston sticks, clean it with emery cloth. If the bi-metal strip is damaged, replace the entire unit. These strips are not interchangeable.

When reassembling, install the control piston so that the projection on the end of it will contact the metal strip. Then install the metal strip with any identification numerals or letters facing the clutch. After reassembly, clean the clutch drive with a cloth soaked in solvent. Avoid dipping the clutch assembly in any type of liquid. Install the assembly in the reverse order of removal.

The coil spring type of fan clutch cannot be disassembled, serviced or repaired. If it does not function properly it must be replaced with a new unit.

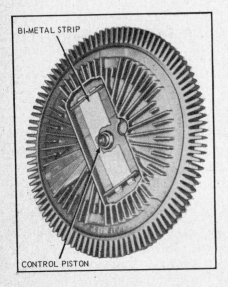

Fig. 2 Variable-speed fan with flat bi-metal thermostatic spring

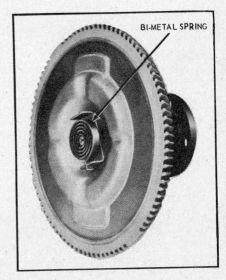

Fig. 3 Variable-speed fan with coiled bi-metal thermostatic spring

CONCEALED HEADLAMPS

BUICK RIVIERA
1966-67

When not is use, the headlights rotate 90 degrees to point straight up and grille panels on the headlight assemblies line up with the grille.

When the headlights are turned on, the circuit is closed to the electric motor which rotates the headlamp assemblies from the upward position to straight ahead. The headlamps can be kept in the forward position with the lights off by turning off the ignition before turning the lights off.

A relay is incorporated in the motor circuit to prevent any malfunction in the UP circuit from running down the battery. This relay opens the circuit to the motor whenever the ignition is turned off.

NOTE: In case of an electrical malfunction in the motor circuit, the lights can be rotated manually as follows:

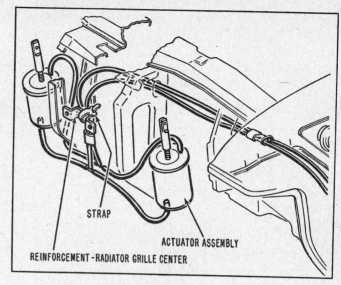

STRAP

ACTUATOR ASSEMBLY

REINFORCEMENT-RADIATOR GRILLE CENTER

Fig. 1   Headlight details. 1968-69 Buick Riviera

1. Raise hood and locate two set screws, one in each flexible cable. Loosen screws.
2. Rotate headlamps forward and tighten screws finger tight.

1968-69

These headlamps are vacuum controlled through a pair of vacuum actuators, one for each pair of headlamps, Fig. 1. Vacuum is taken at the intake manifold and vacuum storage tank and routed through the headlight switch to one side or the other of the actuator, depending on whether the lights are on or off.

When the lights are off, vacuum is supplied to the lower end of each actuator and the headlamp assemblies are rotated upward and held in this position by the actuators. When the lights are turned on, vacuum is supplied to the upper end of the actuators, causing the assemblies to rotate to the forward position as the electrical connection at the switch is closed to turn on the lights.

Also connected in the vacuum system is a vacuum relay. When the light switch is off, vacuum is applied to the diaphragm in the relay, moving the relay valve to connect the vacuum tank to the lower end of the actuators.

When the light switch is turned on, vacuum flow is cut off and normal air pressure acts on the relay to move the valve to connect the tank to the upper ends of the actuators. Thus, the headlights will remain in the forward position in case of a failure in the vacuum system.

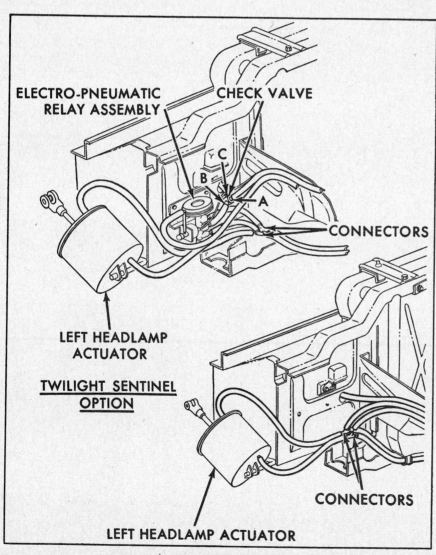

ELECTRO-PNEUMATIC RELAY ASSEMBLY

CHECK VALVE

C

B

A

CONNECTORS

LEFT HEADLAMP ACTUATOR

TWILIGHT SENTINEL OPTION

CONNECTORS

LEFT HEADLAMP ACTUATOR

Fig. 2   Headlight details. 1967-68 Cadillac Eldorado

CADILLAC ELDORADO
1967-68

This system consists of two headlight doors, two actuators, a vacuum storage tank and hoses, Fig. 2. A vacuum valve is integral with the headlight switch.

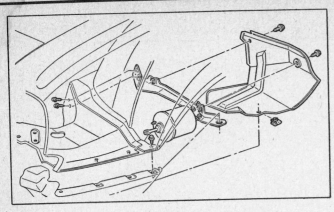

Fig. 3   Headlight details. 1968-69 Camaro

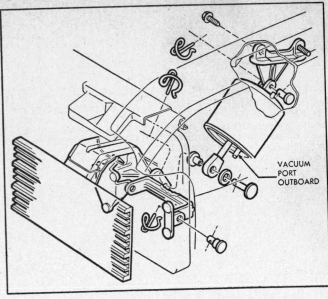

Fig. 4   Headlight details. 1968-69 Chevrolet

On cars without Twilight Sentinel, the vacuum valve has three hoses connected to it. The center hose is connected to the vacuum tank and is a constant source of vacuum to the vacuum valve. Each of the other two hoses connects one side of both vacuum actuators to the vacuum valve. When the headlights are turned on, vacuum is routed from the tank, through the valve, to the upper side of the actuators. The lower side of the actuators are vented to atmospheric pressure. This action provides a higher pressure on the lower side of the actuator, pushing the pistons in the actuators upward to open the doors. When the headlights are turned off, vacuum is routed to the lower side of the actuators and the upper side is vented to the atmosphere, causing the doors to close.

On cars equipped with Twilight Sentinel, a solenoid-operated valve is mounted on the left rear side of the radiator cradle.

This valve contains three ports:

1. When the left valve is vented to the atmosphere, the headlamp doors close.
2. When the upper valve is vented to the atmosphere, the doors open.
3. The right lower valve acts as a port of vacuum supply.

NOTE: On cars with Twilight Sentinel, two hoses are attached to the vacuum valve and the port nearest the headlight switch knob is plugged. This permits atmospheric pressure to seep into the system should the solenoid operated vacuum valve fail, allowing the doors to be opened by hand.

In each system there is a check valve that permits air flow from ports B and C to port A whenever the pressure at B and C is greater than at port A. When the pressure at A is greater, such as when the ignition switch is turned off, the valve closes. This permits a vacuum tight system with the ignition off and the headlamp doors may be operated through one or two cycles on the vacuum stored.

CAMARO RALLY SPORT
1967

In this system, the headlamps are fixed and sections of the grille cover them when the light switch is in the off posi-

tion. The grille sections, or doors, are opened by separate electric motors, one for each door, when the headlight switch is turned on. The motors are then shut off by limit switches when the doors reach the full open positions.

1968-69

The headlamps are fixed and sections of the grille cover them when not in use. Each grille section, or door, is controlled by a vacuum actuator located behind it and connected to the door mechanically, Fig. 3.

Vacuum from the vacuum storage tank is routed through a vacuum valve which is part of the headlight switch to the actuators to control the position of the doors.

A vacuum relay is also incorporated in the system so that the headlight doors will remain open in case of a failure in the vacuum system.

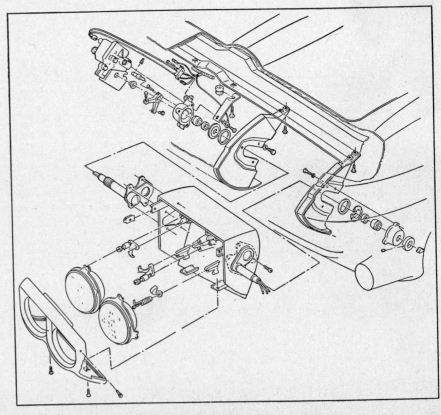

Fig. 5   Headlight details. 1966-67 Corvette

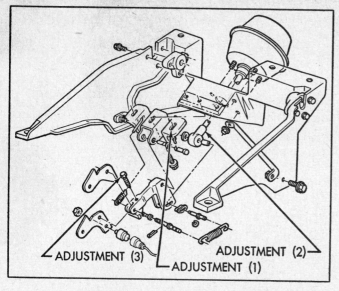

Fig. 6   Headlight details. 1968-71 Corvette

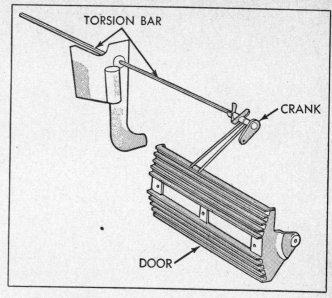

Fig. 7   Headlight details. 1968-71 Chrysler & Imperial (Typical)

CHEVROLET
1968-69

This system uses fixed headlights with moveable, vacuum actuator operated headlight covers, Fig. 4, similar to the 1968-69 Camaro system.

CORVETTE
1966-67

Headlamps are controlled by two reversible electric motors mounted under the front hood panel, Fig. 5. Each assembly operates independently and requires individual repairs and adjustment.

The headlamps and headlamp motors are controlled by two separate switches. The light switch is in the conventional place on the instrument panel while the headlamp motor switch is on the lower left edge of the panel. A warning light on the panel lights when the headlamps are switched on while in the closed position.

Two adjusting screws limit headlamp travel in each direction and are located on the arms of the shaft mounted stops.

1968-71

These units are vacuum operated through separate actuators for each headlamp assembly, Fig. 6. The operation is the same as that for the 1968-69 Camaro Rally Sport except that the Corvette uses moveable headlamp assemblies while the Camaro's lights are fixed. The vacuum actuators cause the headlamp "pods" to be raised up when in the on position and to be lowered flush with hood when turned off. Unlike the earlier Corvette system, the headlamps are lighted and brought into position by the same control switch. A vacuum valve on the headlamp switch routes vacuum to the proper side of the actuators according to the position of the light switch.

ALIGNMENT

1. "In-out", loosen screws fastening slotted bracket to underside of headlamp housing.
2. "Down", lamp cover top to opening; by turning hex head screw fastened to top of pivot link.
3. "Open," fully extended actuator with rod.
   a. Remove spring from actuator rod pin.
   b. Remove cotter pin from rod pin.
   c. Turn actuator rod until bushing hole aligns to forward end of slot in connecting link extended position, with engine idling for vacuum.
   d. Shut off engine, retract actuator rod and unscrew rod ½ turn to preload actuator rod in link.
4. "Up", (bezel to opening alignment). Loosen jam nut and turning bumper covered screw up or down to touch then up 1½ turns more. Micro switch on linkage must shut off warning lamp when lights are fully extended.

NOTE: The headlamp housing must be properly aligned before headlamps are aimed.

CHRYSLER 300 & IMPERIAL
1968-71

The headlamps in this system are stationary and the headlamp doors are operated by a single electric motor mounted on the hood lock vertical support, Fig. 7. The motor is connected to the doors through a torsion bar and crank assemblies. The motor has a worm gear drive and internal limit switches. A relay and circuit breaker assembly is mounted next to the temperature control lever in the instrument panel on 1968 units and the hand brake release bracket on 1969 models.

To manually open the headlamp doors, remove electrical connectors and, on 1968 units, remove torsion bar from crank assemblies and open doors. 1969-71 models have a hand wheel located on the lower end of the motor which will open the doors.

DODGE CHARGER
1966-67

These headlamps are rotated 180 degrees by separate electric motors when the headlight switch is turned on.

An indicator light on the instrument panel lights until the headlights are fully turned after the switch is turned on.

A separate toggle switch in the instrument panel can be used to override the system and leave the lights exposed but turned off.

1968-69

This system uses stationary headlamps and moveable headlamp doors. Each door is controlled by a separate vacuum actuator.

Vacuum is supplied from a vacuum tank to a vacuum control valve which is part of the ignition switch. When the headlamps are turned on, the vacuum valve routes vacuum through hoses to the proper side of the vacuum actuators to open the headlamp doors. Thus, as the electrical circuit to headlamps is closed by the light switch, the vacuum circuit to the doors is also completed. When the lights are turned off, the vacuum valve supplies vacuum to the other side of the actuators, closing the headlamp doors.

1970-71

See 1968-71 Chrysler 300 & Imperial.

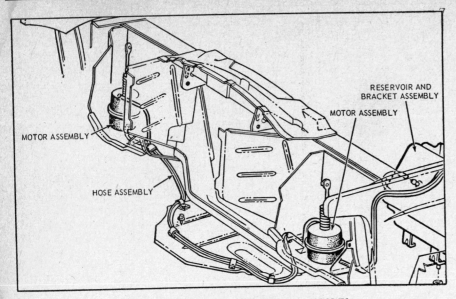

Fig. 8 Headlight details. 1967-68 Cougar, 1969-71 Lincoln Mk III, 1967-69 Thunderbird

COUGAR

1967-68

This system uses fixed headlamps with moveable headlamp covers, each controlled by a separate vacuum actuator, Fig. 8. When the headlights are turned on, current is also supplied to a solenoid valve which opens vacuum passages to the "open" sides of the vacuum actuators. As vacuum is supplied to one side of the actuators, the other side of each actuator is vented to atmospheric pressure. This action causes the necessary pressure on one side of the actuator piston to move the headlamp covers. In addition, the covers are equipped with over center springs to aid the action of the actuators. When the headlamps are turned off, the "close" side of each actuator is opened to vacuum and the "open" side is vented to the atmosphere.

1969-71

The headlamps are fixed and the headlight covers are opened and closed by a single vacuum actuator which is connected to them through a torsion bar, Fig. 9. Vacuum is supplied to one side of the actuator from a vacuum storage tank through the vacuum control valve mounted on the back of the headlamp switch. When the headlamps are turned on, the vacuum valve routes vacuum to the "open" side of the actuator and vents the "close" side to atmospheric pressure. The reverse applies when the lights are turned off.

The covers are equipped with over center springs which aid the actuators in holding the doors in position.

FORD & MERCURY

1968-71

See 1969-71 Cougar.

LINCOLN Mk III

1969-71

See 1967-68 Cougar.

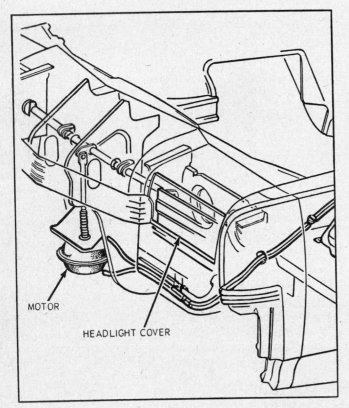

Fig. 9 Headlight details. 1969-71 Cougar, 1968-71 Ford & Mercury

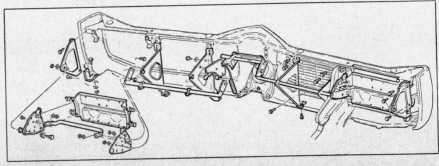

Fig. 12 Headlight details. 1967 Pontiac Grand Prix

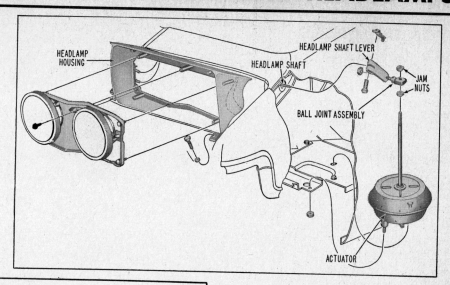

Fig. 10 Headlight details.
1966-67 Oldsmobile Toronado

THUNDERBIRD

1967-69

See 1967-68 Cougar.

OLDSMOBILE TORONADO

1966-67

This system uses headlamp "pods" which are raised when the lights are turned on and lowered flush with the hood when the lights are off. The headlamp pods are controlled by vacuum ac-

Fig. 11 Headlight details.
1968-69 Oldsmobile Toronado

tuators, one for each pod, Fig. 10. Vacuum is routed from a vacuum storage tank to the proper side of each actuator through a vacuum valve which is part of the headlamp switch so that when the headlamps are turned on, vacuum is also routed to the actuators and the headlamps are raised into position. When the headlights reach the full up position, they are held there by spring loaded lock assemblies. When the headlights are turned off, vacuum is directed to the locks, releasing them and the headlights are lowered by spring force. The 1967 system incorporates a check valve and a vacuum relay in the vacuum system.

1968-69

Headlamps are fixed and covers are moved by a single, centrally mounted vacuum actuator, Fig. 11. When the headlights are turned on, the vacuum valve on the light switch routes vacuum to the remote control valve which, in turn, routes it to the open side of the actuator and causes the headlamp covers to open. When the lights are turned off, vacuum is routed to the close side of the actuator.

A thermostatic vacuum switch is incorporated in the Outside Air Induction option so that if engine coolant temperature exceeds 220 degrees, vacuum is routed to the actuator and the headlamp covers open to provide more air flow to cool the engine.

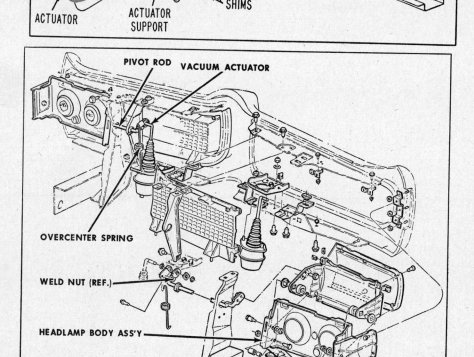

PLYMOUTH

1970-71

See 1968-71 Chrysler 300 & Imperial

Fig. 13 Headlight details. 1968
Pontiac Grand Prix, 1968-69 GTO

PONTIAC GRAND PRIX

1967

Headlamps are fixed and moveable headlamp covers are operated by a single, centrally mounted vacuum actuator, Fig. 12, which is in turn controlled by a vacuum valve which is part of the headlamp switch. The covers are held in either the open or closed position by overcenter springs.

1968

This system uses fixed headlamps and moveable, vacuum controlled headlamp covers, Fig. 13. Each cover is controlled by a separate vacuum actuator which receives vacuum from a vacuum tank through a vacuum valve attached to the light switch. The covers are held in either the open or closed position by overcenter springs.

PONTIAC GTO

1968-69

See 1968 Pontiac.

TROUBLE SHOOTING

Vacuum Type

Examine all hoses for splits, which occur most often around connections. Also, look for kinked or pinched hoses, a condition which often occurs when retaining clips are too tight, thus blocking off vacuum flow.

If inspection reveals that all the hoses are satisfactory, check each vacuum actuator by disconnecting the actuator hoses one at a time and hooking a vacuum gauge to the hose (s). With engine running, if the gauge indicates at least 14 inches of vacuum, the problem is either in the actuator, which must be replaced, or because of jammed covers or linkage.

If the gauge shows less than 14 inches of vacuum, check vacuum at the storage tank, distribution valve, check valve vacuum relay, if used, and at each hose connection.

Electrical Type

Connect a jumper wire directly from the battery to the motor (s). If the system operates, check the headlight or motor control switch. If the switch is eliminated as the cause of trouble, check the wiring; look for loose connections, broken wires or terminals.

If the system fails to operate with the jumper wire, remove the motor for repair or install a new or rebuilt unit.

AUTOMATIC LEVEL CONTROL

SUPERLIFT SYSTEM

This system, Fig. 1, combines the Superlift shock absorber option with an air compressor and a height control valve. When the Superlift option is used alone, the shocks are filled with (or deflated of) compressed air at any gas station through a fill valve. When used in this system, however, the air pressure is supplied by the compressor and the amount of pressure added or removed is controlled by a sensing valve.

The compressor, a two stage type requiring no lubrication, is designed to operate off engine vacuum to replenish air used from the reservoir which is part of the compressor. As the compressor cycles, the reservoir air pressure gradually increases, causing a back pressure on the secondary stage piston, until it equals the engine vacuum pull against the diaphragm and the unit stops operating until reservoir pressure drops again.

A pressure regulator is attached to the output side of the compressor to limit reservoir outlet pressure to 125 psi. The rear standing height is controlled by a valve which is mounted to the frame, and

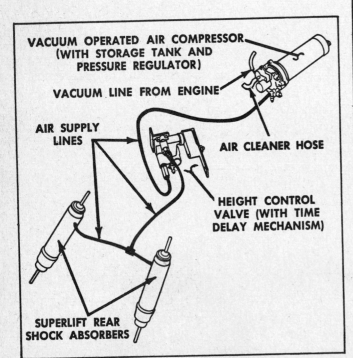

Fig. 1 Schematic diagram of Superlift Automatic Level Control System

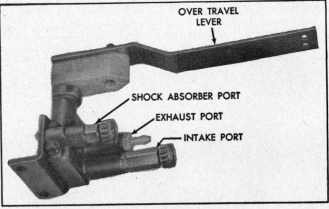

Fig. 2 Height control valve

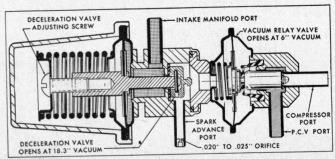

Fig. 3 Vacuum regulator valve in slow idle position

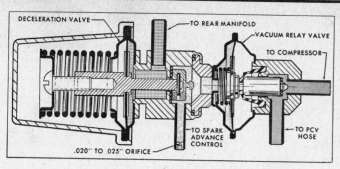

Fig. 4 Vacuum regulator valve in fast idle position

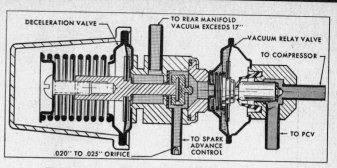

Fig. 5 Vacuum regulator valve in deceleration position

senses changes in vehicle loading through a link attached to the suspension upper control arm. Changes in the position of the link cause the control valve to either admit or exhaust air from the shocks to return the link to "neutral" position. A 4 to 18 second time delay mechanism inside the control valve prevents transfer of air during normal ride conditions. In this way the system only responds to actual changes in vehicle loading.

Some later systems incorporate a vacuum regulator valve which consists of a relay valve and a deceleration valve. The relay valve is connected to the compressor and the P.C.V. line by rubber hose. The spark advance port of the regulator is connected into the distributor advance vacuum line and the intake manifold port is tapped into the rear of the intake manifold.

When the engine is at slow idle, the compressor will not operate due to insufficient vacuum, Fig. 3. As engine speed increases to fast idle or cruising speed, the increased vacuum is applied through a .020-.025" orifice to the vacuum relay, overcoming valve spring tension and opening the relay valve. Vacuum from the P.C.V. line now acts upon the compressor and allows it to operate, Fig. 4.

During deceleration, vacuum at the rear of the intake manifold exceeds 17" and vacuum at the spark advance port is negligible. Manifold vacuum overcomes deceleration valve spring tension, opening the valve and permitting vacuum to overcome the relay valve spring and open the relay valve to admit P.C.V. vacuum and operate the compressor, Fig. 5.

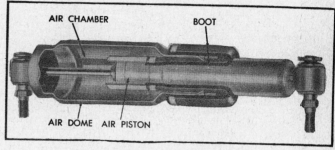

Fig. 6 Superlift shock absorber

The Superlift, Fig. 6, is essentially a conventional shock absorber enclosed in an air chamber. A pliable nylon reinforced boot seals the dust tube (air dome) to the reservoir tube (air piston). The unit will extend when inflated and retract when deflated by the control valve. An 8 to 15 psi air pressure is maintained in the unit to minimize boot friction. This is accomplished by a check valve in the exhaust fitting of the control valve.

TROUBLE SHOOTING GUIDE

Car Loaded, Will Not Rise

1. External damage or breakage.
2. Line leak.
3. Linkage to overtravel lever in wrong hole.
4. Control valve setting incorrect.
5. Defective component.

Car Loaded, Raises to Level, Then Leaks Down

1. Line leak.
2. Control valve exhaust leak.
3. Superlift leak.
4. Control valve leak.

Car Loaded, Raises Partially

1. Loan excessive (over 500 lbs at axle) on cars with special springs.
2. Control valve setting incorrect.
3. Low supply pressure.

Car Unloaded, Rides too High, Will Not Come Down

1. Control valve setting incorrect.

2. Improper springs.
3. External damage or breakage.
4. Linkage to overtravel in wrong hole.
5. Defective control valve.

Car Rises When Loaded but Leaks Down While Driving

1. Time delay mechanism not functioning properly.

CHECKS & ADJUSTMENTS

Quick Check of System

1. Record rear trim height of empty car (measure from center of rear bumper to ground).
2. Add weight equivalent to two-passenger load to rear of car. Car should begin to level in 4 to 15 seconds, and final position should be (plus or minus) $\frac{1}{2}$" of measured dimension.
3. Remove weight. After 4 to 18

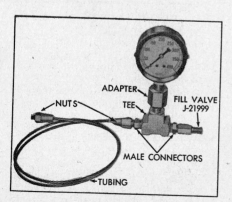

Fig. 7 Test gauge set (Kent-Moore No. J-22124)

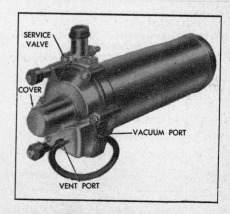

Fig. 8 Assembly leak test preparation

seconds car should begin to settle. Final unloaded position should be within approximately (plus or minus) ½" of the original measured dimension.

NOTE: To service the system it will be necessary to secure the gauge set shown in Fig. 7 or make one out of the materials illustrated.

Compressor Output Test

1. With all accessories off, run engine until engine settles to hot idle speed. Then turn off ignition.
2. Deflate system through service valve, then remove high pressure line at regulator adapter and connect test gauge.
3. Inflate reservoir to 70 psi through service valve.
4. Observe test gauge for evidence of compressor air leak.
5. If leaking, proceed to leak-test compressor reservoir and regulator. If not leaking, continue this test.
6. With engine running at hot idle speed, observe reservoir build-up for five minutes. Reservoir pressure should build up to a minimum of 90 psi.
7. If compressor fails to cycle, make sure vacuum and air intake lines are open and unobstructed before removing compressor for repair.
8. If build-up is too slow, repair compressor.
9. Satisfactory build-up indicates system problems to be in the control section. However, again observe the test gauge for evidence of an air leak and proceed accordingly.

Regulator Test & Adjustment General Motors

1. Performance test the regulator with a known good compressor on the car.
2. Deflate system through service valve, remove line at regulator and connect test gauge at regulator adapter.
3. Inflate reservoir through service valve to maximum pressure available. If less than 140 psi, start engine to build-up reservoir to this pressure.
4. Regulated pressure on test gauge should build up to 100-130 psi and hold steady within this range.
5. Recheck regulated pressure by momentarily depressing valve core on test gauge and observe gauge reading.
6. If regulated pressure exceeds 130 psi, replace regulator as a unit.

Control Valve Test

Exhaust—Superlifts Inflated

1. Disconnect control valve lever from link.
2. Hold lever down in exhaust position until Superlifts deflate or for a minimum of 15 seconds.
3. If Superlifts deflate, perform Intake Check.

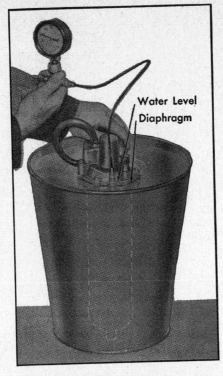

Fig. 9 Checking compressor, reservoir and regulator for leaks

Water Level Diaphragm

4. If Superlifts do not deflate, remove exhaust adapter from control valve and hold lever down as in Step 2. Replace adapter, O-ring and filter if this deflates Superlifts.
5. Replace control valve if none of the above steps solve problem.

Intake Check—Reservoir Pressure, 125 psi Minimum (Lincoln, 90 psi Min.)

1. Disconnect overtravel lever from link.
2. Hold lever up in intake position until Superlifts inflate or for a minimum of 15 seconds.
3. If Superlifts inflate and hold, proceed to Time Delay Test.
4. If Superlifts inflate and then leak down, perform leak test on lines and fittings and then on Superlifts and control valve. Repair or replace as required.

Time Delay Test, Lincoln

1. Disconnect overtravel lever from link.
2. Disconnect lines at Superlift and intake ports.
3. Connect test gauge to intake valve port and apply air pressure (95 lbs.).
4. Move overtravel lever down approximately one inch from neutral position then quickly move lever up two inches. Air should begin to escape from the Superlift port in 4 to 18 seconds. Repeat test.
5. Remove test gauge and plug intake port with fill valve (female end).
6. Connect test gauge to the Superlift port and apply air pressure (95 lbs.).
7. Repeat Step 4. If either test is not within specifications, valve is defective or there has been a loss of silicone fluid.

Time Delay Test, General Motors Reservoir Pressure 125 psi Minimum

1. Record rear trim height of empty car (measure from rear bumper to ground).
2. Add weight equivalent to two-passenger load to rear of car. Car should begin to level in 4 to 18 seconds and final position should be approximately (plus or minus) ½" of dimension measured above.
3. Remove weight. After 4 to 18 seconds, car should begin to settle. Final unloaded position should be (plus or minus) ½" of dimension measured above.
4. Replace valve if time delay is not within 4 to 18 seconds.

Trim Adjustment On Car

Trim adjustment should be performed with a full gas tank or the equivalent in load at rate of 6 lbs. per gallon.

Preparation

1. Raise car with rear axle supported.
2. Remove Superlift line at control valve, Fig. 2.
3. Connect a Fill Valve Assembly (see Fig. 7).
4. Inflate Superlifts to 8 to 18 psi. Jounce car to neutralize suspension.
5. Connect test gauge to Superlift adapter on control valve and attach air pressure source (80 to 110 psi).

Adjustment

1. Loosen overtravel lever adjusting nut.
2. Hold overtravel body down in exhaust position until air escapes from exhaust valve port.
3. Slowly move overtravel body and tighten nut at the point of minimum air bleed. With nut tight, a slight continuous air bleed should be noticeable.

Restore System

1. Remove test gauge and air pressure source from Superlift adapter.
2. Remove Fill Valve Assembly from Superlift line and reconnect line to control valve.
3. Lower car and inflate reservoir through service valve.

Leak Tests

Compressor, Reservoir & Regulator

1. Remove assembly intact.
2. Connect test gauge to regulator. Inflate reservoir through service valve to 80-100 psi.
3. Route an 8" rubber hose between vacuum and vent ports, Fig. 8.
4. Submerge in water, Fig. 9, and observe for air leaks at: a) Reservoir weld seam. b) Reservoir-to-compressor O-ring. c) Regulator-to-compressor O-ring. d) Regulator boot defective. e) Boot internal O-ring defective. f) Diaphragm between 1st and 2nd stage housing. g) Tightening thru bolts may correct leak. h) Cover gasket and retainer screw. A few bubbles here is not a leak. A

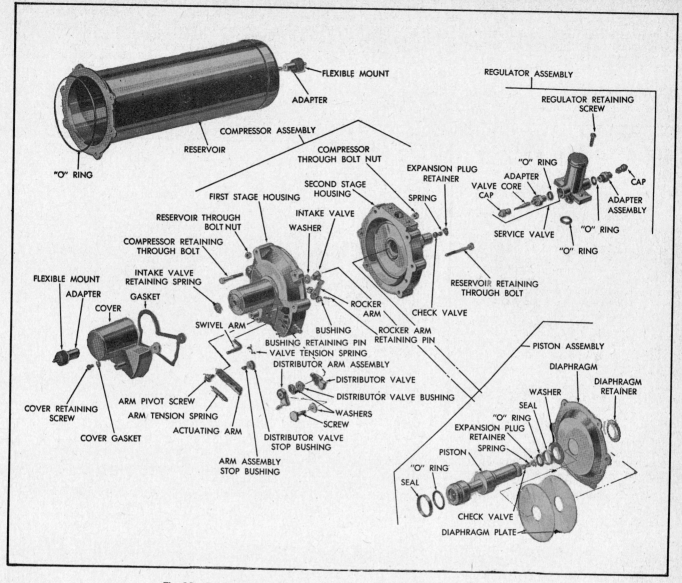

Fig. 10   Exploded view of General Motors compressor, reservoir and regulator

continuous stream indicates defective compressor check valves. i) Service valve. j) Test gauge connections.
5. Correct any leaks detected by either tightening screws or replacing parts.

Control Valve
1. Remove control valve from car.
2. Clean exterior of valve thoroughly.
3. Connect test gauge and air pressure source to intake adapter and open air pressure (80-110 psi).
4. Submerge unit in water. No air should escape if overtravel lever is in "neutral" position. If bubbles escape from Superlift port, replace control valve.
5. Shut off air pressure and detach test gauge from air intake port. Plug intake port with Fill Valve Assembly.
6. Connect test gauge to Superlift port and open air pressure.
7. With overtravel lever in "neutral"

position, no air should escape. If bubbles escape from exhaust port, replace control valve.
8. If air escapes around edge of cover plate, tighten screws or replace gasket.
9. Remove control valve from water. Actuate overtravel lever to expel any water from unit.
10. Shut off air pressure and remove line from Superlift port.

Lines and Fittings
1. Disconnect overtravel lever from link.
2. Hold lever up in intake position for maximum Superlift inflation and release.
3. Leak check all connections with a soap and water solution.

Superlifts
1. Disconnect lines and remove unit

from car.
2. Inflate individually to 50-60 psi, utilizing Fill Valve (see Fig. 7). Submerge in water and observe unit for leaks.
3. Install Superlifts.

COMPRESSOR SERVICE

Removal
1. Raise front end of car on hoist or jack stands.
2. For identification purpose, place a piece of tape on the air intake line attached to smooth end fitting on compressor, Fig. 8.
3. Remove air intake and vacuum hoses.
4. Unfasten compressor brackets from mounting points.

5. Remove compressor with brackets attached.
6. Deflate system, using service valve, and remove high pressure fitting at pressure regulator.
7. Remove brackets from compressor.

NOTE: The compressor is a precision-built mechanism, Fig. 10. If an overhaul is contemplated, all parts should be handled carefully. Take care to prevent entrance of dirt or foreign matter. Do not lubricate as unit is designed to run dry.

Installation

1. Attach brackets to compressor.
2. Install compressor to its mounting.
3. Attach air intake and vacuum hoses.
4. Secure air line to compressor pressure regulator.
5. Lower car.
6. Inflate reservoir to 140 psi through compressor service valve.
7. Be sure that vacuum and air intake lines are not rubbing against adjacent parts to prevent chafing.

AIR CYLINDER SYSTEM

This system, Fig. 1, consists of a vacuum-operated compressor, control valve, air cylinders and the connecting lines and fittings. In the event of accidental air loss, the conventional coil springs will support the vehicle.

The compressor is operated off engine vacuum and will supply a maximum pressure of 20 psi through the control valve to the air cylinders. The control valve is mounted on the cross member and senses rear riding height through a link attached to the rear suspension upper arm, Fig. 2.

The control valve is actuated by changes in the riding height, which moves the link, opening the proper valve to raise or lower the vehicle by adding or removing air from the air cylinders at the rear.

A dampening piston incorporated in the height control valve acts as a time delay within the valve to prevent rapid air transfer to and from the air cylinders under normal operation while the vehicle is in motion.

A check valve is also provided in the exhaust port of the height control valve to retain 2 to 4 psi residual pressure in the air cylinders when there is little or no load to prevent the coil springs from scuffing them.

The air cylinders are made of $\frac{1}{4}''$ thick butyl rubber and are encased in the rear coil springs.

CHECKING SYSTEM

Quick Check

1. Fill fuel tank or simulate the load at the rate of 6 lbs for each gallon of fuel, otherwise the vehicle should be empty.
2. Add a two-passenger load to the rear bumper or tailgate. Vehicle should lower when weight is added.
3. Start engine and observe rear of vehicle while maintaining load at rear bumper or tailgate.
4. If vehicle does not raise when engine is started or within two minutes, the system is not operating properly.
5. If the vehicle raises, remove the load and observe the rear of the vehicle. Air should then exhaust through the height control valve to lower the vehicle.

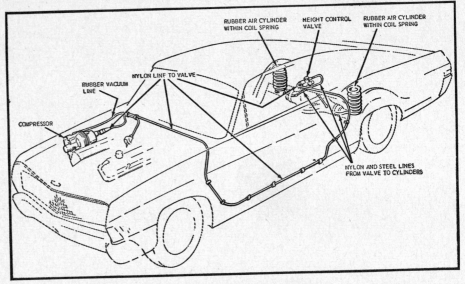

Fig. 1   Air cylinder leveling system

Compressor Output Check

1. Disconnect output line from compressor.
2. Connect pressure gauge to compressor.
3. Close one valve and open the other.
4. Start engine and note compressor output on gauge. If it is 12 to 20 psi, with a minimum engine vacuum of 15 inches, it can be considered normal.
5. Remove gauge and connect line.

Compressor-to-Control Valve Line Leak Check

1. Disconnect inlet fitting from height control valve.
2. Disconnect air inlet line from height control valve.
3. Connect pressure gauge to line.
4. Start engine and note pressure reading, which should be 12 to 20 psi.
5. Stop engine and observe reading on gauge. It should hold the maximum reading if line is not leaking.
6. Repair line as required to stop leak.

Trim Adjustment

1. Trim height is the distance between top of rear axle to bottom surface of frame side rail, Fig. 3. Raise vehicle on a hoist or jack that will support rear axle.

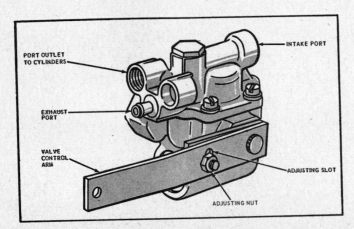

Fig. 2   Height control valve

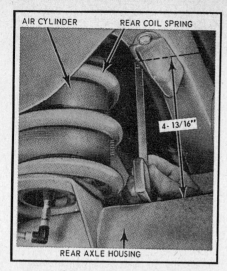

Fig. 3 Measuring trim adjustment. Ford and Mercury 4 13/16", 7 3/8" for Lincoln

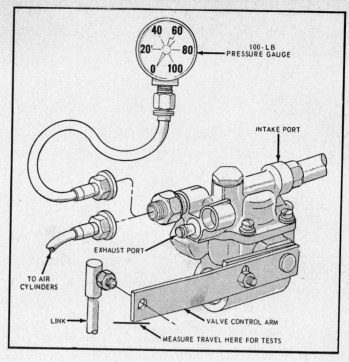

Fig. 4 Test gauge installation

2. Load rear of vehicle as required to obtain the specified trim height, Fig. 3.
3. Disconnect link from height control valve lever, Fig. 4.
4. Disconnect air line from inlet port of height control valve.
5. Connect test gauge to inlet port of height control valve.
6. Working from a 20 psi air source, hold height control valve lever in raised position for 60 seconds while inflating the system. Lower lever to the exhaust position. Hold lever in this position until air stops exhausting. This should leave approximately 2 to 4 psi in the air cylinders if the check valve is functioning properly.
7. Jounce vehicle to neutralize system.
8. Connect link to height control valve lever.
9. Readjust vehicle trim height to 4 13/16" if not at this dimension.
10. Loosen height control valve lever adjusting nut and allow it to neutralize itself. After the lever is neutralized, tighten adjusting nut.
11. Remove gauge and added weight from vehicle.
12. Connect air line to height control valve and check for leaks.

Control Valve Check

Exhaust Check, Air Cylinders Inflated

1. Disconnect link from height control valve lever.
2. Hold lever down (exhaust position) until air cylinders deflate, or for a minimum of 30 seconds. Release arm and allow it to return to neutral position.
3. If cylinders deflate perform a trim adjustment.
4. If cylinders do not deflate, disconnect air cylinder line at height control valve to make sure that there is no restriction in line.

5. Connect air cylinder line to control valve and link to lever.

Intake Check, Compressor at Engine Idle

1. Disconnect link from height control valve lever.
2. Hold lever up (intake position) until cylinders inflate or for a minimum of 60 seconds, then release lever and allow it to return to neutral position.
3. If cylinders inflate and hold perform a trim adjustment.
4. If cylinders inflate then leak down, perform a leak test on lines or fittings then check air cylinders.
5. If cylinders do not inflate, disconnect compressor output line at the height control valve and check it for restrictions.
6. If lines and fittings are satisfactory, check height control valve for leaks.
7. Connect link to control valve lever.

Time Delay Check

1. Disconnect link from control valve lever.
2. Disconnect both air lines from height control valve, Fig. 4.
3. Connect test gauge to intake port of control valve. Attach a 20 psi air source to gauge.
4. Move control valve lever downward approximately one inch from the neutral position. One inch distance is measured at end of lever.
5. Move lever upward two inches, at the same time start timing the number of seconds before air is expelled from air cylinder port. The time delay should be from 1 to 6 seconds. Repeat check to obtain an accurate reading. This operation is for air intake time only.

6. Connect air cylinder line to control valve outlet port.
7. Hold control valve lever in raised position and charge air cylinders with 15 to 20 psi air pressure from intake port of control valve.
8. Move lever to neutral position.
9. Move control valve lever upward approximately one inch from neutral position. One inch dimension is measured from end of lever. Quickly move lever downward two inches, at the same time start timing the number of seconds before air is expelled from exhaust port. The time delay should be from 1 to 6 seconds. Repeat check to obtain accurate reading.
10. If either delay is not within specifications, replace height control valve.

System Leak Test

1. Start engine and allow pressure to build up in system.
2. Apply a soap and water solution to all fittings and lines that are suspected to be leaking. If air bubbles appear at any fitting or section of line, make required repairs to eliminate the leak.

TROUBLE DIAGNOSIS

Vehicle Loaded, Will Not Raise

1. External damage or breakage.
2. Line or cylinder leak.
3. Pump inoperative or output inadequate.
4. Control valve setting incorrect.
5. Inadequate time delay.

Vehicle Loaded, Raises Partially

1. Load excessive (over 250 lbs) at axle.
2. Height control valve setting incorrect.
3. Low supply pressure.

Vehicle Unloaded, Rides too High, Won't Come Down

1. Control valve setting incorrect.
2. External damage or breakage.

3. Defective control valve.

Compressor Cycles Continuously

1. Line leak.
2. Air cylinder ruptured.
3. Inadequate time; may take five minutes to balance at idle.

Compressor Does Not Cycle

1. Vacuum hose off or leaking.
2. Pump internal failure.

3. Lines or hoses restricted.
4. Pump filter clogged.

Vehicle Loaded, Raises to Level and Then Leaks Down

1. Line leak.
2. Control valve exhaust leak.
3. Air cylinder leak.
4. Control valve exhaust leak.
5. If leak down while driving, check for control valve time delay less than one second.

ELECTRONIC IGNITION SYSTEMS

DELCO-REMY SYSTEMS

Two types of electronic controlled ignition systems have been developed by Delco-Remy, the Capacitor Discharge (CD) type, introduced in 1967, and the Transistor Controlled Type, used prior to 1967.

Both systems use an identical Magnetic Pulse Breakerless distributor. This unit, Fig. 1, resembles a conventional distributor. However, in the Magnetic Pulse unit, an iron timer core replaces the conventional breaker cam, Fig. 2. The timer core, which has equally spaced projections, one for each cylinder, rotates inside a magnetic pick-up assembly, which replaces the conventional breaker plate assembly.

The magnetic pick-up assembly consists of ceramic permanent magnet, a pole piece and a pick-up coil. The pole piece is metal plate having equally spaced internal teeth, one for each cylinder. The magnetic pick-up assembly is mounted over the main bearing on the distributor housing and is actuated by the vacuum advance unit. A conventional centrifugal advance is also used.

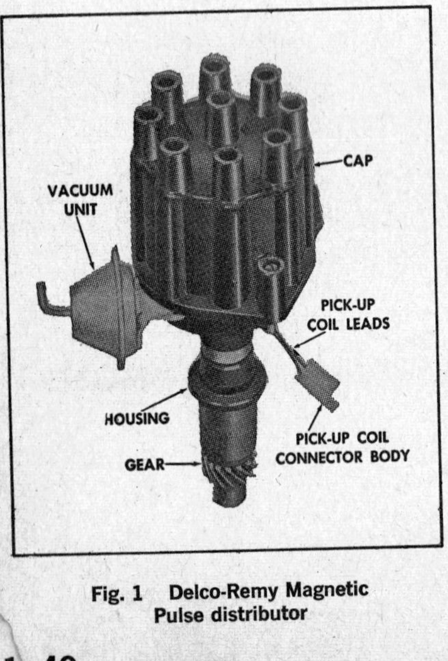

Ignition Pulse Amplifier

Transistor Controlled Type

This type amplifier, Fig. 3, consists primarily of transistors, resistors, diodes and condensers mounted on a printed circuit board. Since there are no moving parts, the control unit is a completely static assembly.

Fig. 4 shows a wiring diagram of the complete circuit. Note that there are two separate ballast resistors used. The resistor connected directly to the switch is by-passed during cranking, whereas the other is always in the circuit.

In order to fire the spark plugs, it is necessary to induce a high voltage in the ignition coil secondary winding by opening and closing the coil primary circuit. This is accomplished in the distributor by the timer core rotating through the magnetic field of the pole piece.

When the switch is closed, (engine not running) current comes from the battery, through the switch and ballast resistor to the amplifier unit. Current then flows to two transistors and three resistors, then to the coil primary winding and ballast resistor to ground, completing the circuit.

Capacitor Discharge Amplifier

This unit, Fig. 5, consists of transistors, diodes, resistors, a thyristor and a transformer. These are mounted on a printed circuit board to make the amplifier a solid state unit with no moving parts, with a capacity of delivering 30,000 volts.

The ignition coil primary is connected across a high voltage capacitor (condenser), which is charged to about 300 volts during the time the spark plugs are not firing. On impulse signal voltage from the distributor, the capacitor discharges this high voltage into the coil primary.

Due to the transformer action in the coil, the high voltage primary is increased many times to produce the high voltage secondary. Fig. 6 shows a typical circuit diagram.

Voltage is supplied to the transformer which operates through a rectifying bridge circuit of four diodes to keep the capacitor charged. A zener diode limits

this charge to 300 volts. This capacitor voltage is maintained at its maximum value during cranking even though battery voltage may be well below its normal 12 volts.

As the engine turns, the vanes on the rotating timer core in the distributor line up with the internal teeth on the pole piece. This establishes a magnetic path through the center of the pick-up coil. This voltage is amplified then applied at the gate of the thyristor, causing it to turn on. The charged capacitor then discharges through the thyristor and primary winding of the coil, inducing high voltage in the secondary winding to fire the spark plugs. This special ignition coil acts as a step up transformer to fire the spark plugs when the primary current *increases.*

This contrasts with the conventional ignition system in which the secondary voltage is induced when the distributor contacts open and the primary current *decreases.*

Trouble Shooting Procedure

Faulty engine performance usually will be evidenced by one of the following conditions: 1. Engine will not run at all.

Fig. 1 Delco-Remy Magnetic Pulse distributor

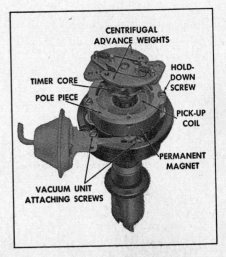

Fig. 2 Magnetic Pulse distributor components

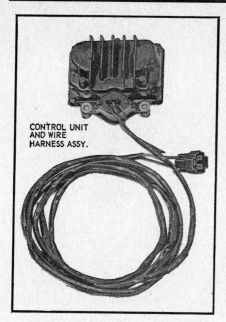

Fig. 3   Transistor controlled amplifier

2. Engine will start but not run. 3. Engine will miss or surge. *The special coil used in both systems cannot be tested on a conventional coil tester.*

Engine will not run at all

Hold one spark plug lead about ¼ inch from the engine block and crank the engine. If sparking occurs, the trouble most likely is not ignition. If sparking does not occur, check the ignition system. The wiring, distributor cap and rotor can be checked in the conventional manner. Only the coil requires a different procedure.

The special soil can be checked for primary and secondary winding continuity with an ohmmeter: With leads disconnected from coil, connect ohmmeter across primary terminals. If reading is infinite, winding is open. To check the secondary, connect ohmmeter to high voltage center tower and coil case. An infinite reading means coil secondary is open. *When checking secondary, use middle or high resistance range on ohmmeter.*

Checking Amplifier:

1. Temporarily connect a jumper lead from amplifier housing to a good ground.
2. If engine now will start and run, the amplifier is not properly grounded.
3. Detach positive and negative leads from coil. *Note carefully the color code so wires can be reconnected in the same manner.*
4. Connect a bulb between the two leads, Fig. 7.
5. Crank engine.
6. If bulb flickers on and off, amplifier is operating properly. In this case, recheck secondary system for the cause of "no run" condition.
7. If bulb does not flicker on and off, check distributor.

Distributor checks:

1. On CD system, be sure that the two distributor leads are connected to distributor connector body, Fig. 8.
2. With distributor connector disconnected from harness connector, connect an ohmmeter (1), Fig. 9, to the two terminals on distributor connector.
3. Connect a test stand vacuum source to the distributor and observe ohmmeter reading throughout vacuum range. (Distributor need not be removed from engine.)
4. Any reading outside the 550-750 ohm range indicates a defective pick-up coil in distributor.
5. Remove one ohmmeter (2) lead, Fig. 9, from connector body and connect to ground.
6. Observe ohmmeter reading throughout vacuum range.
7. Any reading less than infinite indicates a defective pick-up coil.
8. Reconnect harness connector to distributor connector.

Continuity checks-CD system

Carefully inspect all wiring connections to be sure that they are clean and tight.

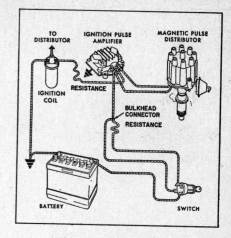

Fig. 4   Circuit diagram of transistor controlled system

If satisfactory, disconnect amplifier No. 3 and No. 4 leads, Fig. 8, from the two connectors, then proceed as follows:

1. Connect voltmeter from ground to No. 4 connector lead.
2. Turn switch to "Start" position.
3. If reading is zero, circuit is open between connector body and battery.
4. If reading is obtained, connect voltmeter from ground to No. 3 connector lead.
5. Turn switch to the run position.
6. If reading is zero, circuit is open between connector body and switch.
7. If reading is obtained, replace amplifier.

Engine will start but not run-CD System

If engine starts but then stops when switch is returned to the run position, proceed as follows:

1. Be sure that leads are properly connected to No. 3 lead connector body.
2. If satisfactory, connect a voltmeter from ground to the terminal con-

Fig. 5   Capacitor Discharge (CD) amplifier unit

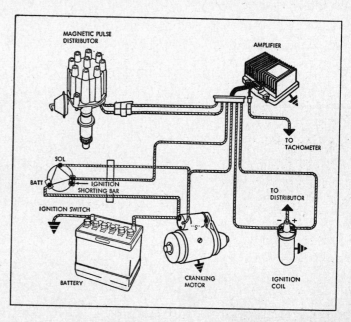

Fig. 6   CD ignition circuit (typical)

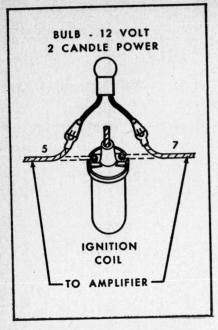

Fig. 7   Amplifier output test

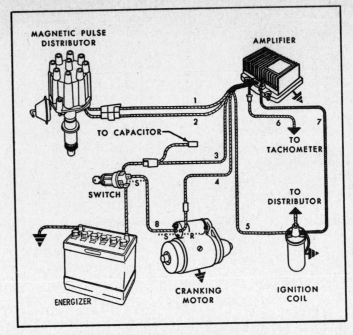

Fig. 8   Pictorial diagram of CD system

nector inside the connector.
3. Turn switch to run position.
4. If reading is zero, lead between connector and ignition switch is open.
5. If reading is obtained, replace amplifier.

Engine miss or surge:

The vehicle fuel system should be checked in the usual manner. If satisfactory, check the ignition system in the usual manner except the special coil which should be checked with a ohmmeter as described above.

A poorly ground amplifier can cause an engine miss or surge. If it is properly grounded and the plugs, wiring, cap and coil are satisfactory, the most likely cause for the miss or surge is a defective amplifier.

Distributor Service

Remove distributor in the usual manner, being sure to note position of rotor, then pull distributor up until rotor just stops turning and again note position of rotor. To insure correct timing of the distributor, it must be installed with the rotor correctly positioned as noted above.

If necessary to remove secondary wires from cap, mark position on cap tower for lead to No. 1 cylinder. This will aid in reinstallation of leads.

If the engine has been turned after the distributor was removed, it will be necessary to install a jumper wire and crank engine until the timing mark on vibration damper indexes with the proper mark on the engine front cover. If both valves of No. 1 cylinder are closed, the piston will be on top dead center of the firing stroke.

Fig. 10 shows an exploded view of the distributor.

No adjustments can be made on either system and no periodic maintenance is required.

FORD SYSTEMS

NOTE: Due to improvements in transistors, the transistor ignition system for 1966-67 requires fewer components and achieves greater system reliability. Units not required on the 1966-67 system that were used on past models are 1) toroid portion of amplifier, 2) cold start relay, 3) amplifier mounting plate and cover. The tach block, ballast resistor and amplifier are mounted as individual components.

The ignition coil primary in the transistor system is designed to draw a nor-

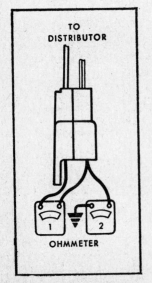

Fig. 9   Distributor test

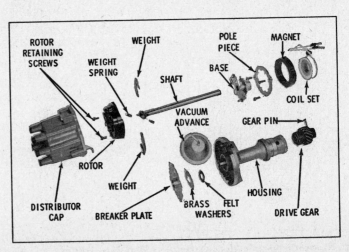

Fig. 10   Exploded view of Magnetic Pulse distributor

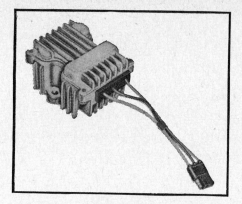

Fig. 11   Ford amplifier assembly

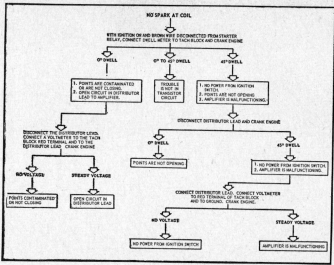

Fig. 12   Ford system test procedures for 1966-67 models

mal 12-ampere peak current, or approximately 5.5 amperes average current in order to provide high spark plug voltage at the higher engine speeds.

The transistor in the system acts as a switch or relay. It is similar in action to a horn relay except that it has no moving parts and thus acts with very little time lag. The transistor is connected between the battery and the coil and is used to make and break the coil primary circuit.

The distributor controls the transistor. The resistor connected between the distributor and transistor (in wiring harness) limits the transistor control current to 0.5 ampere. The low distributor point current eliminates pitting and gives long distributor point life.

The amplifier assembly, Fig. 11, is mounted under the instrument panel to protect the parts from engine heat.

A ceramic ballast resistor block and a tachometer connector block are mounted in the engine compartment.

A two-ampere fuse between the large terminal of the tachometer block and the coil primary circuit prevents the transistor from being damaged by the application of external devices other than normal testing equipment.

The tachometer block is used to connect a tachometer or other test equipment into the circuit.

CAUTION: Do not connect test equipment into the circuit in any other manner or readings may be inaccurate and damage may occur to the transistor or change its operating characteristics.

Prior to 1966 the system employed a cold start relay (discontinued in 1966). The contacts in this relay are normally closed and they are connected into the circuit only during the starting cycle. When the starter relay is closed, the cold start relay is actuated and opens its contacts. During starting, if the available voltage drops below 10.5 volts, the relay contacts close, by-passing the 0.33-ohm resistor in the ballast resistor block, thus applying full available voltage to the system.

Trouble Shooting

Ignition troubles are caused by a failure in the primary or secondary circuit, or incorrect ignition timing. To isolate the trouble, proceed as follows:

1. Remove high tension coil lead from distributor cap.
2. Disconnect brown wire from starter relay I terminal and red/blue wire from starter relay S terminal.
3. Turn on ignition switch.
4. While holding high tension lead approximately ¼" away from a good ground, crank engine, using an auxiliary starter switch between starter relay battery and S terminals.
5. If spark is good the trouble lies in the secondary circuit; if there is no spark or a weak spark the trouble is in the primary circuit.
6. Isolate the trouble by checking out the system as outlined in Fig. 12.

MOTOROLA SYSTEM

Factory installed on fleet models manufactured by Chrysler Corp., this transistor ignition system consists of a special ignition coil, ballast resistor, transistor amplifier and all necessary wiring to complete the installation. These parts are used in conjunction with the conventional ignition system components shown in Fig. 13.

Voltage Check

Fig. 14

1. With ignition on, engine not running, and distributor breaker points open, the voltmeter should read approximately 9.5 or more.
2. With ignition on, engine not running, and distributor breaker points closed, voltmeter should read approximately 3 to 5 volts.

NOTE: The above voltmeter readings represent average voltages and may vary from vehicle to vehicle. Some of the causes that contribute to these variations are: condition of battery, breaker points,

resistance in ignition switch or wiring.

With engine running, the engine rpm and distributor dwell settings will also affect these voltage readings. However, any marked deviation from the above voltmeter readings indicate a malfunction that should be corrected.

Ballast Resistor By-Pass Check

Fig. 15.

1. With ignition on, engine not running, and distributor breaker points open, voltmeter should read 0 volts.
2. With ignition on, engine not running, and distributor breaker points closed, voltmeter should read approximately 6 volts.
3. With engine on, and engine cranking, voltmeter should read approximately 1 volt or less. When the engine starts, voltmeter should read approximately 3 to 5 volts. Any marked deviation from the above voltmeter readings indicates a malfunction which should be corrected.

Trouble Check-out

Fig. 16—With ignition on, engine not running, distributor breaker points closed, and all accessories turned off, the voltmeter should not read more than 1.5 volts. A higher voltage reading indicates that one of the following conditions exist and must be corrected.

1. Excessive resistance in the circuit from the battery through the ignition switch to the ballast resistor. Check all wiring for incorrect installation or loose connections.
2. Excessive resistance in the circuit between battery and ballast resistor will cause hard starting, poor acceleration and sluggish engine performance.

Fig. 17—With ignition on, engine not running, distributor breaker points open, and all accessories turned off, the voltmeter should read 9.5 volts or more (battery voltage) on all three ballast resistor terminals. Any marked deviation from this voltmeter reading indicates one of the following conditions may exist and must be corrected.

1. If the correct battery voltage (9.5 volts) is present at terminal "A" of the ballast resistor, and there is no voltage at terminals "B" and "C", and the ballast resistor is cool, it indicates that the ballast resistor is defective and must be replaced.

2. If the voltage at terminal "C" is lower than the voltage at terminal "A", the cause may be one of the following:
   a) Defective wiring to distributor breaker points.
   b) Shorted transistor amplifier. Turn off ignition, disconnect the three-prong connector at amplifier. Turn ignition on. If volt-

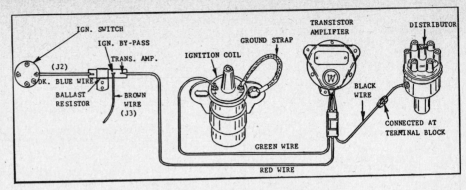

Fig. 13   Motorola transistor ignition system

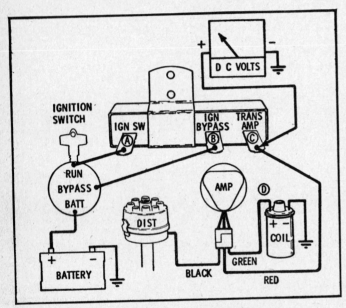

Fig. 14   Motorola voltage check hook-up

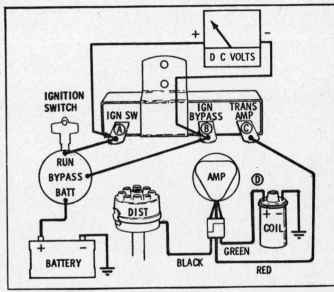

Fig. 15   Motorola ballast resistor by-pass check hook-up

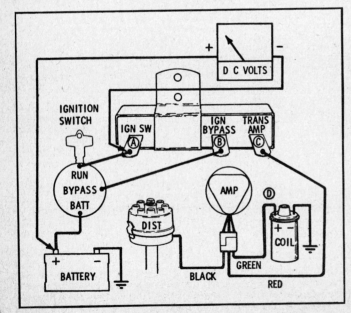

Fig. 16

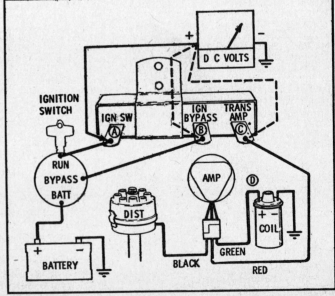

Fig. 17

age at terminal "C" is now the same as terminal "A", the transistor amplifier is defective and must be replaced.

c) If voltage at terminal "C" is still not the same as terminal "A", the installation may be incorrect. Check all wiring connections and be sure there are no other connections at the ballast resistor other than what is shown in Fig. 17.

d) With the amplifier unplugged, disconnect wiring connector from terminal "B" at ballast resistor. If voltage at terminal "C" is now the same as terminal "A", the ignition by-pass wiring is defec-

tive. If the voltage at terminal "C" is still lower than at terminal "A", the ballast resistor is defective and must be replaced.

Fig. 14—With ignition on, engine not running and distributor breaker points closed, the voltmeter should read approximately 3 to 5 volts. If the voltmeter reads 9.5 volts or more (battery voltage), the fault may be caused by one of the following conditions:

1. Distributor breaker points not closing or defective wiring to breaker points.
2. Defective transistor amplifier or ignition coil. Measure voltage at positive terminal of ignition coil (D.). If voltmeter reads 9.5 volts or more

(battery voltage), the ignition coil is improperly grounded or defective. If zero voltage is indicated at this point (D), the transistor amplifier is defective and must be replaced.

3. If the voltmeter reads zero volts at the transistor amplifier terminal (C) of the ballast resistor, and the ballast resistor is cool, the ballast resistor is defective and must be replaced.

NOTE: If all voltages read as specified in the check-out and trouble procedures, the ignition coil should be checked. This can be done by substituting a known good Motorola coil in the circuit.

IGNITION DISTRIBUTORS—Standard

CONTENTS

BREAKER CONTACT POINTS

Contact Analysis

The normal color of points should be a light gray. If the contact surfaces are black it is usually caused by oil vapor or grease from the cam. If they are blue, the cause is usually excessive heating due to improper alignment, high resistance or open condenser circuit.

If the contacts develop a crater or depression on one point and a high spot of metal on the other, the cause is an electrolytic action transferring metal from one contact to the other, Fig. 2, due to an unbalanced ignition system, which can sometimes be improved by a slight change in condenser capacity. If the mound is on the positive point, Fig. 3, install a condenser of greater capacity; if on the negative point, Fig. 4, use a condenser of lesser capacity.

One of the most common causes of point failure is the presence of oil or grease on the contact surfaces, usually from over-lubrication of the wick at the top of the cam or too much grease on the rubbing block of the breaker arm.

Breaker Point Gap

If points are set too close, arcing and

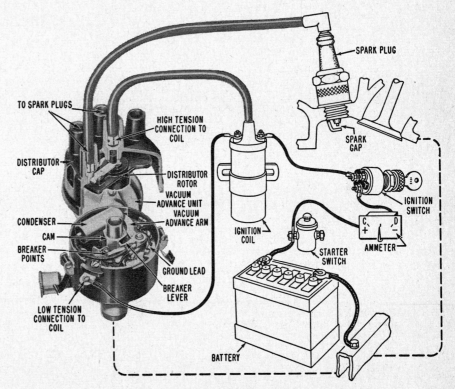

Fig. 1   Typical ignition system

burning will occur, causing hard starting and poor low speed performance. If points are set too wide, the cam angle or dwell will be too small to allow saturation of the coil at high engine speeds, resulting in weak spark.

Contact point opening has a direct bearing on cam angle or dwell which is the number of degrees that the breaker

cam rotates from the time the points close until they open again, Fig. 5. The cam angle or dwell increases as point opening is decreased and vice versa. If point gap is set with a feeler gauge, the cam angle or dwell should be checked either with a portable dwell meter or by installing the distributor in a distributor tester.

Fig. 2   Showing how metal from one contact transfers to the other

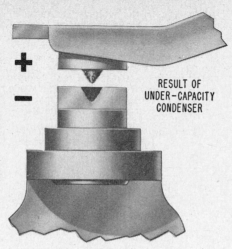

RESULT OF UNDER–CAPACITY CONDENSER

Fig. 3   Mound on positive point

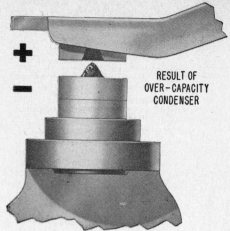

RESULT OF OVER–CAPACITY CONDENSER

Fig. 4   Mound on negative point

Breaker Arm Spring Tension

Breaker arm spring tension is important. If the tension is too great the arm will bounce, causing an interruption of the current in the coil and misfiring. If the spring tension is too little, the rubbing block will not follow the cam, causing a variation in cam dwell. The spring tension should always be set at the high limit as given in the *Distributor Specifications* chart in the car chapter, as it will be reduced as the rubbing block wears.

Hook a spring scale on the breaker arm and pull in a straight line as shown in Fig. 6. Take a reading as the points start to separate under the slow and steady pull of the scale. If the tension is not within specifications, loosen the screw that holds the end of the point spring and slide the end of the spring in or out as necessary. Tighten the screw and recheck the spring tension.

Breaker Point Alignment

Check alignment of points with points closed, Fig. 7. Align new points where necessary but do not attempt to align used points. Instead, replace used points where serious misalignment is observed. After aligning points, adjust point gap.

Adjusting Breaker Gap

Specifications for breaker gas, *as measured with a feeler gauge*, are listed in the *Tune Up Specifications* in the car chapters. However, if at all possible, this should be set on a distributor tester, with a dial indicator, Fig. 8, or by hooking up a portable dwell meter with the distributor cap and rotor removed and,

while cranking the engine, setting the dwell.

NOTE: When setting the dwell with the engine cranking, be sure to ground the coil secondary lead and do not operate the starter for sustained periods at a time.

This eliminates the possibility of an incorrect gap because of rough points, Fig. 9.

The advantage of a distributor testing machine is that it not only measures cam angle or dwell but it also uncovers irregularities between cam lobes, point bounce, alignment of rubbing block with cam, alignment of contacts and breaker arm spring tension.

Setting Prestolite & Chrysler Dual Points

The distributor used on some Chrysler Corp. cars contain two sets of points which permit additional current build-up in the primary winding of the coil, Fig. 10. Thus, maximum voltage is induced in the secondary winding.

The two sets of points are connected in parallel and are positioned in relation to the 8-lobe cam so as to provide a 7-degree overlap of points opening and closing. One set of points (circuit *maker* points) closes the primary circuit in the coil and the second set of points (circuit *breaker* points) opens the circuit, causing a spark at the plug. Immediately after the spark occurs, the circuit *maker* points are closed ahead of the circuit *breaker* points, thus providing a circuit to build-

up the primary winding. As the cam rotates further, the secondary points close and just before the secondary points open, the primary points open 7 degrees ahead.

Since the "make" and "break" points are timed to close and open at the exact instant necessary for efficient engine operation, adjustment of the points is an important factor in correct distributor operation.

Feeler Gauge or Dial Indicator Method—Rotate the distributor shaft until the breaker arm rubbing block of one set of points in on the high spot of the cam. Then, with a screwdriver blade in the triangular opening, close or open the points to the proper clearance by turning the screwdriver blade against the stationary point plate. Check the clearance with a clean wire gauge or dial indicator. Then turn the distributor shaft until the rubbing block of the second set of points is on the high spot of the cam and adjust the second set of points in the same manner.

Dwell Meter Method—If this method is used *block one set of points open* with a

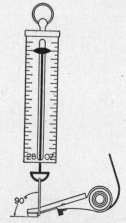

Fig. 6   Measuring breaker spring tension

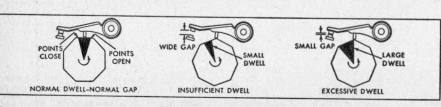

Fig. 5   Cam angle or dwell

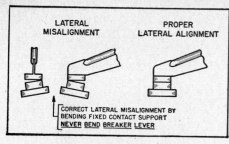

Fig. 7 Breaker point alignment

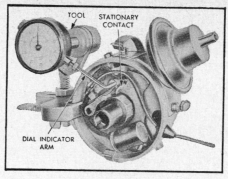

Fig. 8 Dial indicator for measuring breaker gap

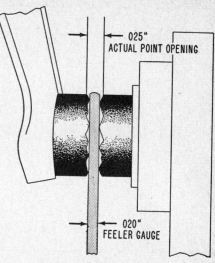

Fig. 9 Why flat feeler gauge will not provide accurate point spacing if points are rough

piece of wrapping paper or calling card. Then adjust the other set of points to the correct dwell angle. Now block open the first set of points and adjust the second set. After both sets of points have been adjusted, allow them to operate together while checking that their total dwell angle measures up to manufacturer's specifications.

Prestolite & Chrysler Single Point Set Adjustment

Adjustment of breaker gap is accomplished by loosening the lock screw in the stationary point and moving the adjusting screw as required to obtain the correct breaker gap.

Delco-Remy Internal Adjustment Breaker Points

A slot is provided in the contact point assembly which allows easy dwell angle or breaker point adjustment, Fig. 12.

Delco-Remy External Adjustment Breaker Points

With engine running at idle speed, the breaker gap is adjusted by first raising

the window provided in the cap and inserting a "hex" wrench into the adjusting screw, Fig. 13. Turn the adjusting screw clockwise until the engine begins to misfire. Then give the wrench one-half turn in the opposite direction which will provide the proper breaker gap. If a cam angle meter is to be used, turn the adjusting screw until the correct angle is obtained.

Holley Breaker Points

The breaker point set is attached to the movable breaker plate. A slot in the stationary point bracket allows for easy breaker point adjustment, Fig. 14.

CONDENSER

A condenser should not be condemned because the points are burned or oxidized. Oil vapor, or grease from the cam, or high resistance may be the cause of such a condition.

Condensers should be tested with a good condenser tester for leakage,

break-down, capacity, and resistance in series in the condenser circuit. Manufacturers of condenser testers furnish complete instructions as to their use.

CENTRIFUGAL ADVANCE

Except for Holley "full vacuum" type all other distributors utilize an automatic advance mechanism which functions by virtue of centrifugal weights. Some distributors employ both centrifugal and vacuum advance mechanisms while others make use of only the centrifugal mechanism.

When engine speed increases, the spark must be introduced in the cylinder earlier in the cycle in order that the fuel charge can be ignited as will have time to burn and deliver its power to the piston. To provide this spark advance based on engine speed, the centrifugal governor mechanism is used.

This mechanism, Fig. 15, consists of centrifugal advance weights which throw out against spring tension as the

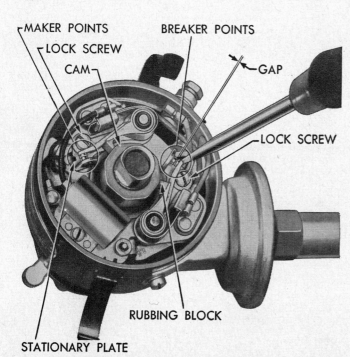

Fig. 10 Prestolite dual point distributor

Fig. 12 Breaker point setting. Delco-Remy internally adjusted points

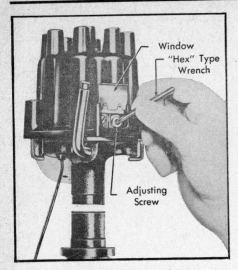

Fig. 13   Adjust breaker point gap through window in distributor cap

hinge pins and filling the pockets in the governor weights with grease. Do not use vaseline for this purpose as its melting point is comparatively low.

When installing new centrifugal governor assemblies, it is important that the spacer washers between the housing and shaft be installed correctly. If incorrectly installed, the governor assembly will be too high, causing it to rub against the bottom of the breaker plate.

On some distributors, both springs are alike, while on others there is one heavy and one light spring, as in Fig. 15. Another combination that may be found is an additional flat spring on the outside of the outer spring posts, Fig. 16. As the governor speed is increased, the flat springs are first pulled against the posts by the eyes of the coil springs to provide a rapid spark advance of a few degrees before the coil springs pull against the spring posts.

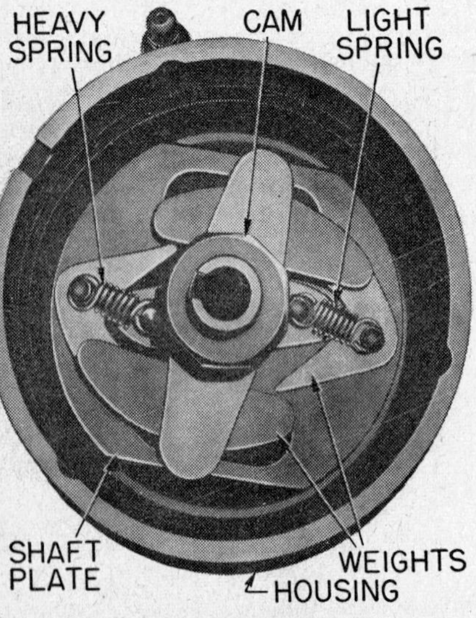

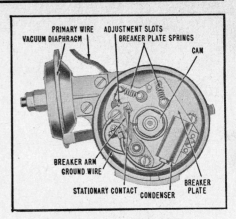

Fig. 14   Breaker plate details. Holley Loadamatic distributor. Note slot for adjusting breaker gap

engine speed increases. This movement imparts, through a toggle arrangement, rotational motion to the breaker cam or plate, depending on the model, causing it to rotate a number of degrees with respect to the distributor drive shaft. This causes the points to be opened and closed earlier in the cycle so the spark is delivered to the cylinder earlier.

In servicing the distributor, all weights should be removed from the hinge pins, cleaned and checked for excessive wear, either in the weights or pins, or the plate which is slotted for the movement of the pins on top of the governor weights. Replacement should be made if there is any appreciable wear in the slots, as any wear at this point would change the characteristic of the spark advance.

If these parts are in good condition, the hinge pins should be lubricated before being reassembled, by greasing the

VACUUM ADVANCE

Conventional Type

The vacuum advance unit consists of a spring loaded diaphragm, which is connected through linkage to the distributor breaker plate. The spring loaded side of the diaphragm is connected through a vacuum line to the carburetor or intake manifold. As vacuum increases, the diaphragm is drawn toward the source of vacuum, the diaphragm linkage is pulled with it and the breaker plate, attached to the linkage, is turned to advance the timing.

Exhaust Emission Control Types
Chrysler C.A.P.

The Chrysler vacuum advance units incorporate a vacuum advance control valve in the advance vacuum circuit to provide the necessary retard during closed throttle operation.

Chrysler C.A.S.

Some Chrysler C.A.S. engines have a solenoid incorporated in the distributor vacuum advance mechanism to retard the ignition timing when the throttle is closed. At closed throttle, electrical contacts on the carburetor throttle stop, with idle adjusting screw in the closed position, cause the distributor solenoid to energize. This retards the ignition timing to provide reduced exhaust emissions under hot idle conditions. Cold or part throttle starting is not penalized because the distributor solenoid is not energized unless the hot idle adjusting screw is against the throttle stop contact. Timing must be set at closed throttle to give accurate setting.

Ford Dual-Diaphragm

This unit consists of two independent diaphragms. The outer diaphragm uses carburetor vacuum to advance timing. The inner diaphragm uses intake manifold vacuum to provide additional retard during closed throttle operation.

Ford Single Diaphragm

This unit operates in the same manner as conventional units.

General Motors CCS

In this system, the advance is the ported type, that is the vacuum take-off is located above the throttle plate(s) so that during periods of closed throttle operation there is little or no vacuum reaching the advance unit and timing is retarded. As soon as the throttle is cracked, vacuum reaches the advance unit and timing is advanced.

NOTE: Some models of the Chevrolet V8-307 engine use the conventional type advance unit.

Prestolite IBP Distributors

Used on some late model Chrysler Corp. cars, this distributor uses a very different type vacuum spark advance. Unlike other systems which either rotate the breaker plate or the entire distributor when manifold vacuum is high, the IBP breaker plate is pivoted in such a way that the points swing in an arc about the cam when the vacuum advance unit is in operation. Thus, cam angle and breaker point gap change as high manifold vacuum advances the spark. For this reason cam angle should be checked with the vacuum line disconnected and the point gap checked or adjusted when the vacuum advance unit is in full retard position.

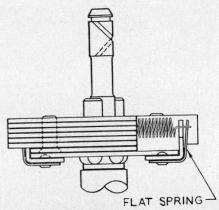

Fig. 16   Flat spring used on some governors to provide a rapid spark advance

Fig. 15   Top view of Delco-Remy distributor with breaker plate removed to show centrifugal governor mechanism

Distributor Service

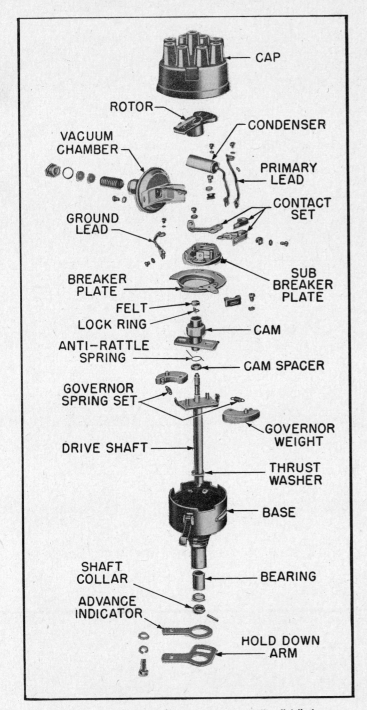

Fig. 17   Exploded view of typical Prestolite distributor

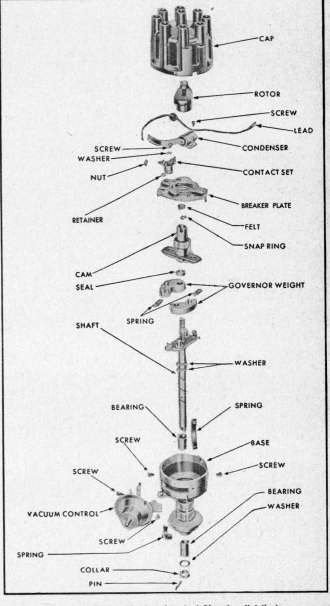

Fig. 18   Exploded view of typical Chrysler distributor

PRESTOLITE & CHRYSLER DISTRIBUTOR SERVICE

If the distributor has been disassembled, reassemble as follows, referring to Figs. 17 and 18 for guidance.

1. Check operation of centrifugal weights and weight springs for distortion. Lubricate governor weights.
2. Inspect all bearing surfaces and pivot pins for roughness, binding, or excessive looseness.
3. Install cam spacer (chamfered end down) on distributor shaft.
4. Slide cam and yoke on distributor shaft. Engage weight lugs with slots in yoke as shown in Fig. 19. Install cam retaining clip, being sure it is properly seated in distributor shaft groove.
5. Lubricate and install two concave washers for Prestolite distributors, or a single flat thrust washer for Chrysler distributors. Position washers on shaft and slide shaft into distributor body.
6. Position lower thrust washer and drive collar on lower end of shaft and install retainer pin.
7. Install oiler wick and oiler.
8. Install breaker plate assembly, align condenser lead, breaker point spring, primary lead and install attaching screw.

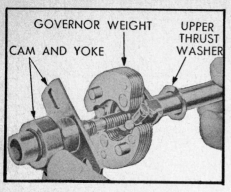

Fig. 19 Distributor shaft details

bled, refer to Fig. 20 for guidance when reassembling.

1. Place gasket on shaft housing.
2. Place felt washer around bushing in housing.
3. Install vacuum advance unit.
4. Install breaker plate in housing and spring retainer on upper bushing.
5. Install condenser.
6. Install breaker point set.
7. Install cam and weight base assembly on shaft. If lubrication in grooves at top of shaft was removed during disassembly, replace with Plastilube #2 or its equivalent.
8. Install shaft and cam weight assembly in housing.
9. Using a pin, install driven gear to shaft.
10. Install advance weights and springs.
11. Install cam lubricator.
12. Install rotor.
13. Check breaker arm spring tension and adjust breaker gap.

Internal Adjustment Type

If the distributor has been disassembled, refer to Fig. 21 when reassembling. Fig. 22 shows the details of the breaker plate and attaching parts.

1. Replace cam assembly to shaft. Lubricate top end of shaft with light engine oil prior to replacing.
2. Install weights on their pivot pins. Install weights, weight cover and stop plate.
3. Lubricate shaft and install in housing.
4. Install thrust washers and driven gear to shaft and secure with roll pins. Check to see that shaft turns freely. Install driven gear with mark on hub in line with rotor segment.
5. Install breaker plate.
6. Attach condenser and breaker point set in proper location with appropriate attaching screws, Fib. 22. Connect primary and condenser leads to

9. Install felt wick in top of cam.
10. Attach vacuum advance unit arm to breaker plate and install retainer. Install vacuum unit attaching screws and washers.
11. Test breaker arm spring tension and adjust breaker gap.
12. Lubricate felt pad in top of distributor cam with 3 to 5 drops of light engine oil and install rotor.

DELCO-REMY DISTRIBUTOR SERVICE

External Adjustment Type

If the distributor has been disassem-

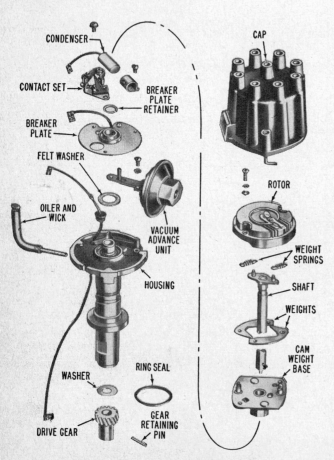

Fig. 20 Delco-Remy external adjustment distributor

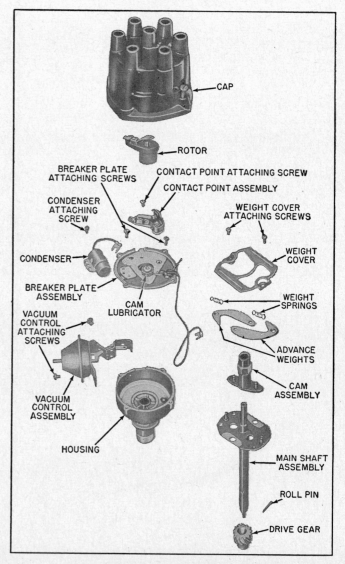

Fig. 21 Exploded view of typical Delco-Remy internal adjustment distributor

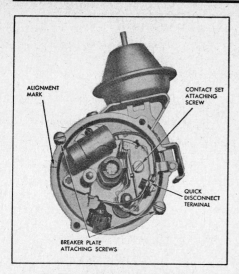

Fig. 22 Breaker plate installation. Delco-Remy internal adjustment distributor

breaker point set quick disconnect terminal. *Contact point set pilot must engage matching hole in breaker plate.*

7. Attach vacuum control assembly to distributor housing, using upper mounting holes.

8. Adjust breaker arm spring tension and breaker gap.
9. Install rotor.

HOLLEY DISTRIBUTORS

Ford Loadamatic Type

With these distributors, Figs. 23 and 24, engine speed and load requirements are satisfied by the action of the breaker plate which is controlled by a vacuum-actuated diaphragm working against the tension of two calibrated breaker plate springs. The breaker plate is free to rotate on the shaft bushing.

For distributors used with six-cylinder engines, the diaphragm moves the breaker plate in a counterclockwise direction to advance the spark, and the springs move the breaker plate in a clockwise direction to retard the spark. The degree of spark advance is determined by the strength of the vacuum acting on the diaphragm. For distributors used with eight-cylinder engines, spark is advanced by the diaphragm moving the breaker plate in a clockwise direction, and retarded by the springs moving the plate in a counterclockwise direction. Six-cylinder distributors rotate clockwise, eight-cylinder units counterclockwise.

For all eight-cylinder distributors, a vacuum-actuated spark control valve is attached to the carburetor throttle body

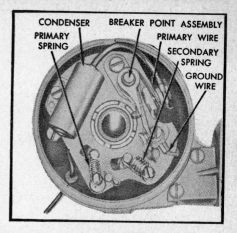

Fig. 23 Breaker plate installation. Holley Loadamatic distributor

to control manifold vacuum to the distributor and regulate spark advance.

Vacuum Advance, Adjust

The two breaker plate springs are precision set at the factory with special stroboscopic equipment. This equipment is available for adjustment purposes commercially. Shops having conventional distributor testers can include a mercury column to take care of the setting of these springs as the conventional vacuum

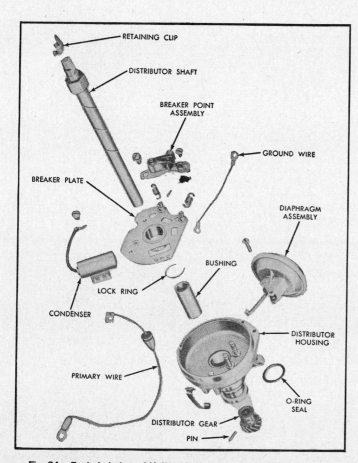

Fig. 24 Exploded view of Holley Loadamatic distributor

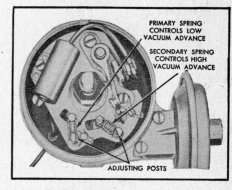

Fig. 25 Spark advance adjustment on Holley Loadamatic distributor

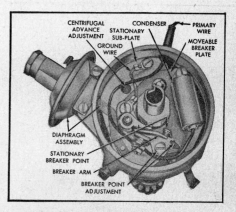

Fig. 26 Breaker plate installation. Holley dual advance distributor

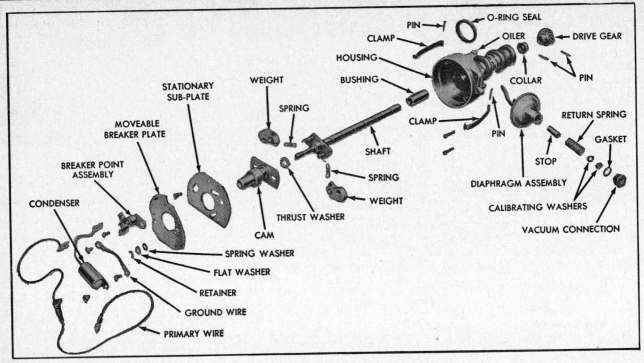

Fig. 27   Exploded view of Holley dual advance distributor

gauge will not provide the required accuracy.

The spring adjusting posts shown in Fig. 25 provide the means of adjusting the spark advance.

Distributor Service

If the distributor has been disassembled, refer to Fig. 24 for guidance on reassembly.

1. Pass primary wire assembly through opening in distributor, working from inside to outside of distributor housing. Pull wire through opening until locating stop is flush with inside of distributor. Install ground wire.
2. Position breaker plate in body and secure with lock ring.
3. Position breaker point set on breaker plate, Fig. 23. Be sure pivot pin enters hole in breaker plate.
4. Connect ground wire to breaker plate at end closest to adjustment slot. Install other screw and lock washer at opposite end of assembly.
5. Install condenser.
6. Install two return springs on adjustment and breaker plate post, Fig. 25. Make sure secondary spring is adjacent to vacuum chamber.
7. Install vacuum unit.
8. Insert top of vacuum rod through breaker plate. Attach rod with retainer.
9. Slide shaft into body, using care not to damage rubbing block on breaker points.
10. Press gear on shaft. If a new shaft is being installed, place a .028" feeler in position against distributor mounting flange, press gear on shaft until it bottoms against feeler gauge. Remove feeler gauge and secure with ⅛" pin after drilling hole in shaft.
11. Install distributor cap clamps. Lubricate cam with high temperature, non-fiber grease.
12. Adjust breaker arm spring tension, align and adjust breaker points, adjust vacuum advance and cam dwell.

Holley Dual Advance Distributor

This distributor, Figs. 26 and 27, is similar to conventional design in that both a centrifugal advance mechanism is provided to regulate ignition timing according to speed and a vacuum advance unit to regulate ignition timing according to load. However, unlike other make distributors, the centrifugal advance mechanism can be adjusted through a slot in the breaker plate.

Adjust centrifugal advance before adjusting vacuum advance. If the correct advance is not indicated when tested on a distributor machine, bend one spring bracket with a screwdriver through the hole in the breaker plate, Fig. 28. Bend bracket away from distributor shaft to decrease advance and toward shaft to increase advance. Identify bracket after adjustment is made. After an adjustment has been made to one spring, check the minimum advance point again. Then operate distributor at the specified rpm to give an advance just below maximum. If this advance is not up to specifications, bend the other spring bracket to give the

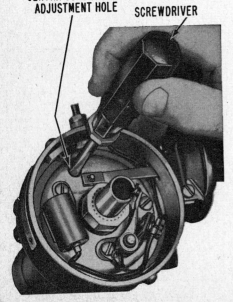

Fig. 28   Centrifugal advance adjustment

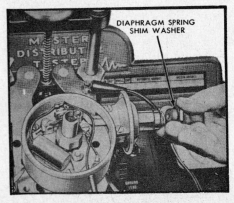

Fig. 29   Vacuum advance adjustment. Holley dual advance distributor

correct advance.

Vacuum advance can be adjusted by changing the calibrated washers between the vacuum chamber spring and nut, Fig. 29. The addition of one washer will decrease advance and the removal of a washer will increase advance.

Distributor Service

If the distributor has been disassembled, refer to Fig. 27 for guidance upon reassembly.

1. Oil shaft and slide it into distributor body.
2. Place collar in position on shaft and align holes in collar and shaft, then install a new pin.
3. Install distributor cap clamps.
4. Check shaft end play with feeler gauge placed between collar and base of distributor. If shaft end play is not within .024-.035", replace shaft and gear.

5. Fill grooves in weight pivot pin with ball bearing grease.
6. Position weights in distributor.
7. Install weight springs, being sure proper weight, spring and adjustment bracket are assembled together.
8. Install upper thrust washer.
9. Fill grooves in upper portion of distributor shaft with ball bearing grease.
10. Install cam assembly, being sure that slots in cam engage pins in weights.
11. Install cam retainer. Apply a light film of cam lubricant to cam lobes. Saturate wick with 10W engine oil. Install wick in cam.
12. Position stationary sub plate in distributor. Install one end of ground wire under plate retaining screw closest to diaphragm mounting flange.
13. Position movable breaker plate in distributor. Install spring washer on

pivot pin. Place flat washer on spring washer. Be sure protruding edges of spring washer are facing upward. Install retainer.
14. Install new breaker point assembly. Install ground wire on breaker point attaching screw furthest from point adjustment slot.
15. Install condenser.
16. Working from inside to outside of distributor housing, pass primary wire through opening in distributor. Pull wire through opening until locating stop is flush with inside of distributor.
17. Connect condenser wire and primary wire to breaker points.
18. Position diaphragm and hook its link over pin on breaker plate. Install diaphragm attaching screws. Secure link with retainer. Install oil seal.
19. Adjust breaker arm spring tension, align and adjust breaker points and check and adjust cam dwell, centrifugal and vacuum advance.

ALTERNATORS

CONTENTS

INTRODUCTION

Alternators are composed of the same functional parts as the conventional D.C. generator but they operate differently: The field is called a rotor and is the turning portion of the unit. A generating part, called a stator, is the stationary member, comparable to the armature in a D.C. generator. The regulator, similar to those used in a D.C. system, regulates the output of the alternator-rectifier system.

The power source of the system is the alternator. Current is transmitted from the field terminal of the regulator through a slip ring to the field coil and back to ground through another slip ring. The strength of the field regulates the output of the alternating current. This alternating current is then transmitted from the alternator to the rectifier where it is converted to direct current.

These alternators employ a three-phase

stator winding in which the phase windings are electrically 120 degrees apart. The rotor consists of a field coil encased between interleaved sections producing a magnetic field with alternate north and south poles. By rotating the rotor inside the stator the alternating current is induced in the stator windings. This alternating current is rectified (changed to D.C.) by silicon diodes and brought out to the output terminal of the alternator.

Diode Rectifiers

Six silicon diode rectifiers are used and act as electrical one-way-valves. Three of the diodes have ground polarity and are pressed or screwed into a heat sink which is grounded. The other three diodes (ungrounded) are pressed or screwed into and insulated from the end head; these diodes are connected to the alternator output terminal.

Since the diodes have a high resistance to the flow of current in one direction and a low resistance in the opposite direction, they may be connected in a manner which allows current to flow from the alternator to the battery in the low resistance direction. The high resistance in the opposite direction prevents the flow of current from the battery to the alternator. Because of this feature no circuit breaker is required between the alternator and battery.

SERVICE PRECAUTIONS

1. Be certain that battery polarity is correct when servicing units. Reversed battery polarity will damage rectifiers and regulators.

2. If booster battery is used for starting, be sure to use correct polarity in hook up.
3. When a fast charger is used to charge a vehicle battery, the vehicle battery cables should be disconnected *unless the fast charger is equipped with a special Alternator Protector*, in which case the vehicle battery cables need not be disconnected. Also the fast charger should never be used to start a vehicle as damage to rectifiers will result.
4. Lead connections to the grounded rectifiers (negative) on Prestolite and Chrysler units should never be soldered as the excessive heat may damage the rectifiers.
5. Unless the system includes a load relay or field relay, grounding the alternator output terminal will damage the alternator and/or circuits. This is true even when the system is not in operation since no circuit breaker is used and the battery is applied to the alternator output terminal at all times. The field or load relay acts as a circuit breaker in that it is controlled by the ignition switch.
6. When adjusting the voltage regulator, do not short the adjusting tool to the regulator base as the regulator may be damaged. The tool should be insulated by taping or by installing a plastic sleeve.
7. Before making any "on vehicle" tests of the alternator or regulator, the battery should be checked and the circuit inspected for faulty wiring or insulation, loose or corroded connections and poor ground circuits.

8. Check alternator belt tension to be sure the belt is tight enough to prevent slipping under load.
9. The ignition switch should be off and the battery ground cable disconnected before making any test connections to prevent damage to the system.
10. The vehicle battery must be fully charged or a fully charged battery may be installed for test purposes.

Chrysler Alternators

Three types of alternators are available on Chrysler Corp. cars; one with an electro-mechanical voltage regulator, Figs. C1 and C2, the insulated brush unit, Figs. C3 and C4 optional on some 1969 cars and the isolated field unit which is standard on 1970 cars, Figs. C5 and C6.

The difference between these units is in the area of the brushes. The electro-mechanical unit uses a ground brush, the insulated brush unit has a positive insulated brush with the system grounded through the regulator and the isolated field unit has two separate, insulated, field brushes.

Both the insulated brush and the isolated field units use a fully electronic voltage regulator which is a sealed, non-adjustable unit.

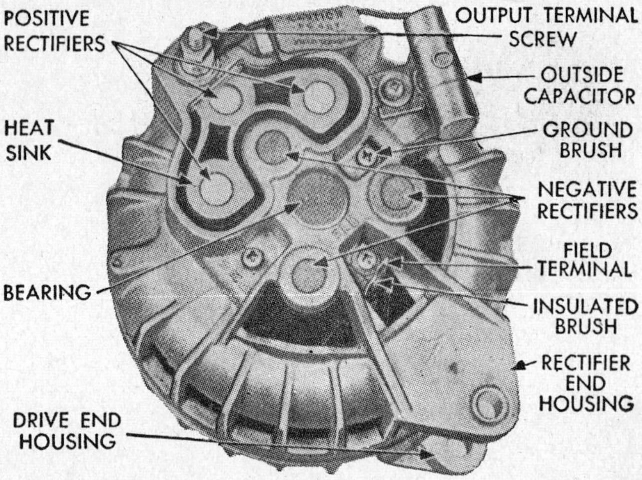

Fig. C1   Chrysler alternator, electro-mechanically regulated unit

TESTING SYSTEM ON VEHICLE

ELECTRO-MECHANICAL UNIT

Field Circuit Resistance Test

1. Referring to Fig. C7, disconnect ignition wire at coil side of ballast resistor and connect a test ammeter and voltmeter in the circuit as shown. All lights and accessories should be turned off.

2. Turn ignition switch on and turn voltmeter selector switch to the low voltage scale and read the meter. The voltage should not exceed .55 volt. A reading in excess of .55 volt indicates high resistance in field circuit between battery and voltage regulator field terminal.

3. If high resistance is indicated, move negative voltmeter lead to each connection along the circuit to the battery. A sudden drop in voltage indicates a loose or corroded connection between that point and the last point tested. To test the terminals for tightness, attempt to move the terminal while observing the voltmeter. Any movement of the meter pointer indicates looseness.

NOTE: *Excessive resistance in the regulator wiring circuit will cause fluctuation in the ammeter.*

4. Turn ignition switch off, disconnect test instrument and reconnect ignition primary wire at the coil side of the ballast resistor.

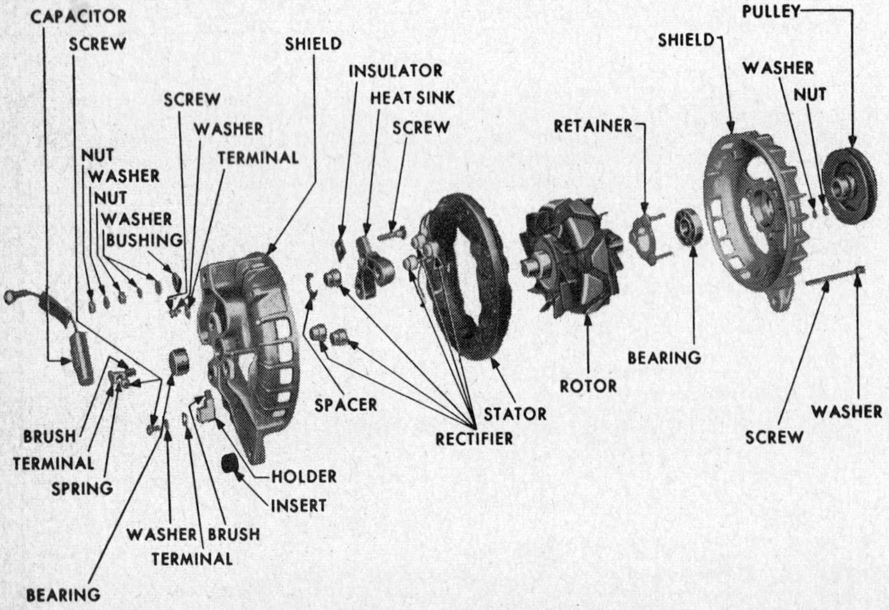

Charging Circuit Resistance Test

With battery in good condition and fully charged, first disconnect the battery ground cable to avoid accidental shorting of the charging or field circuit when making the test connections shown in Fig. C8.

1. With the test instruments connected as shown and with battery ground cable re-connected, start and operate engine at a speed to obtain 10 amperes flowing in the circuit.

2. The voltmeter should not exceed .3 volt. If a higher voltage drop is indicated, inspect, clean and tighten all connections in the charging circuit. A voltage drop test may be performed at each connection to locate the connection with excessive resistance.

3. Turn ignition switch off. Disconnect ground cable at battery to avoid accidental shorting of the charging

Fig. C2   Electro-mechanically regulated alternator disassembled

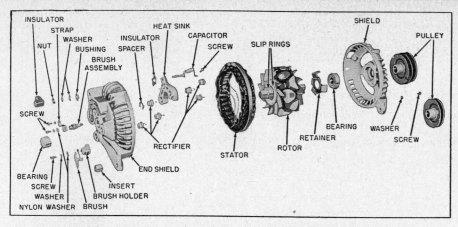

Fig. C3　Insulated brush alternator disassembled

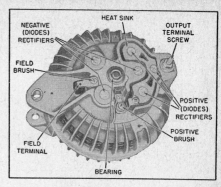

Fig. C4　Insulated brush alternator assembly

or field circuit when disconnecting the test instruments. Connect battery lead to alternator "BAT" terminal and tighten securely. Connect ignition lead to regulator ignition terminal and re-connect ground cable at battery.

Current Output Test

1. With test instruments connected in circuit as shown in Fig. C9, connect an engine tachometer.
2. Start and operate at 1250 rpm.
3. Adjust carbon pile rheostat to obtain a reading of 15 volts on the test voltmeter.
4. Observe reading on test ammeter.
5. If the output is slightly less (5 to 7 amperes) than the rated output of the alternator, it may be an indication of an open-circuited diode or other internal alternator problem.
6. If the output is considerably lower than the rated output of the alternator, it may be an indication of a short-circuited diode or other internal alternator problem. In either

case the alternator should be removed and tested.

NOTE: *Turn off the carbon pile rheostat immediately after observing reading on test ammeter.*

7. If the alternator current output tested satisfactorily, turn off the ignition switch and remove the jumper lead from the alternator field terminal and output terminal.

Voltage Regulator Test

UPPER CONTACT TEST

1. With engine at normal operating temperature and test instruments connected as shown in Fig. C10, start and operate the engine at 1250 rpm.
   Adjust carbon pile to obtain a 15 ampere output as indicated on test ammeter.

NOTE: *No current reading on the ammeter would indicate either a low regulator setting or a blown fuse wire inside the voltage regulator be-*

tween upper stationary contact and "IGN" terminal. Correct the cause and replace the fusible wire.

2. Operate engine at 1250 rpm and a 15 ampere load for 15 minutes to make sure entire regulator system is stabilized.
3. Measure temperature at regulator by holding a reliable thermometer $\frac{1}{4}$ inch from regulator cover.
4. Read test ammeter. With fully charged battery and 15 amperes flowing in circuit, voltmeter readings should be within specifications.
5. If regulator operates within specifications, proceed to the lower contact voltage test. If not, remove cover and adjust voltage setting as outlined under "Regulator Adjustments".

LOWER CONTACT VOLTAGE TEST

1. Increase engine speed to 2200 rpm. Vary carbon pile to decrease current load to 7 amperes output as registered on test ammeter. The voltage should *increase* and amperage *should* decrease.

NOTE: *There will be a slightly higher voltage at higher engine speeds above 2200 rpm. However, this increased voltage must not exceed the voltage specified by more than .7 volt at any temperature range.*

2. If the regulator setting is outside the specified limits, the regulator must be removed to remove the cover.
3. To adjust the voltage setting, bend the *regulator lower spring hanger*

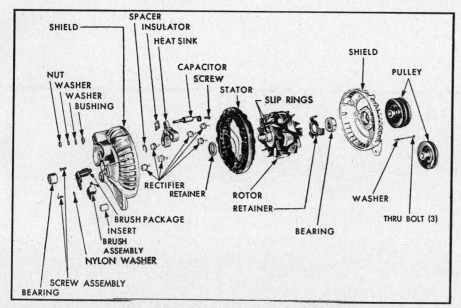

Fig. C5　Isolated field generator disassembled

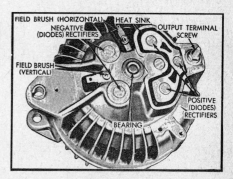

Fig. C6　Isolated field alternator assembly

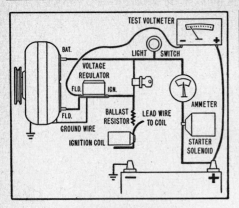

Fig. C7 Field resistance test, electro-mechanical regulator

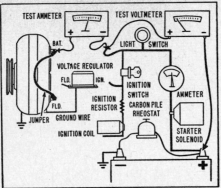

Fig. C8 Charging circuit resistance test, electro-mechanical regulator

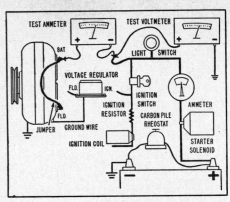

Fig. C9 Current output test, electro-mechanical regulator

down to increase voltage, or *up to* decrease voltage setting, Fig. C11. The regulator must be installed, correctly connected, and retested after each adjustment of the lower spring hanger.

NOTE: *If repeated readjustment is required, it is permissible to use a jumper wire to ground the regulator base to the fender splash shield for testing instead of reinstalling the regulator each time. However, it is important that the cover be reinstalled, the regulator connections correctly connected, and the regulator insulated to prevent grounding the regulator terminals or resistances. When testing, the regulator must be at the same attitude (or angle) as when installed on the vehicle.*

4. If the alternator and regulator tested satisfactorily, turn the ignition switch off. Disconnect battery ground cable, then the test instruments. Connect the leads to alternator and regulator. Finally reconnect battery ground cable.

Regulator Adjustments

If the regulator cannot be adjusted for voltage control, or if the regulator performance is erratic or malfunctions, it may be necessary to adjust the air gap and contact point gap.
1. Remove regulator from vehicle and

take off cover.
2. Insert a .048" wire gauge between regulator armature and core, next to stop pin on spring hanger side, Fig. C12.
3. Press down on armature (not contact spring) until it contacts wire gauge. Upper contacts should just open.

NOTE: *A battery and test light connected in series to the "IGN" and "FLD" terminals may be used to determine accurately the contact opening. When the contacts open, the test light will do dim.*

4. Insert a .052" wire gauge between armature and core, next to stop pin on spring hanger side.
5. Press down on armature until it contacts wire gauge. The contacts should remain closed and test light should remain bright.
6. If adjustment is required, adjust air gap by loosening the screw and moving the stationary contact bracket. Make sure air gap is measured with attaching screw fully tightened. Re-measure the gap as directed above.
7. Remove wire gauge. Measure lower contact gap with feeler gauge, which should be .012 to .016". Adjust lower contact gap by bending lower stationary contact bracket.
8. Install regulator cover and then

the regulator. Finally, make electrical adjustments as outlined above.

INSULATED BRUSH & ISOLATED FIELD ALTERNATORS

Charging Circuit Resistance Test

1. Disconnect battery ground cable. Disconnect "Batt" lead at the alternator.
2. Complete test connections as per Figs. C13 and C14.
3. Connect battery ground cable, start engine and operate at idle.
4. Adjust engine speed and carbon pile to obtain 20 amps in the circuit and check voltmeter reading. Reading should not exceed .7 volts. If a voltage drop is indicated, inspect, clean and tighten all connections in the circuit. A voltage drop test at each connection can be performed to isolate the trouble.

Current Output Test

1. Disconnect battery ground cable, complete test connections as per Figs. C15 and C16 and start engine and operate at idle. *Immediately after starting, reduce engine speed to idle.*
2. Adjust the carbon pile and engine speed in increments until a speed of 1250 rpm and 15 volts are obtained.

CAUTION: While increasing speed, do not allow voltage to exceed 16 volts.

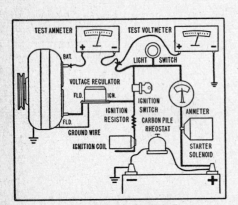

Fig. C10 Voltage regulator test, electro-mechanical regulator

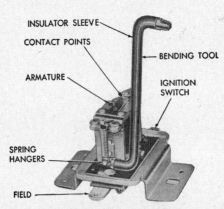

Fig. C11 Adjusting spring tension to obtain correct voltage, electro-mechanical units

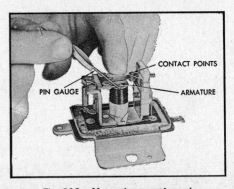

Fig. C12 Measuring armature air gap, electro-mechanical unit

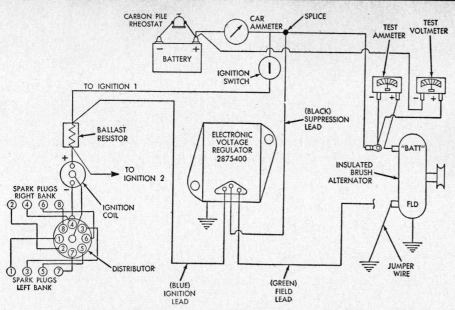

Fig. C13 Charging circuit resistance test, insulated brush units

age at the wiring harness terminal connected to the blue and green leads.

NOTE: Disconnect wiring harness from regulator when checking the leads.

7. Turn off ignition switch. If voltage is not present at either lead, the problem is in the vehicle wiring or alternator field circuit. *Use care to avoid bending the terminals with voltmeter probe.*

8. If Steps 4-7 tested satisfactorily, change voltage regulator and repeat Step 2. If voltage is slightly above limits, or is fluctuating, proceed as follows:

9. Check voltage regulator ground, check ground between vehicle body and engine.

10. Check ignition switch circuit between battery terminal of ignition switch and voltage regulator. If voltage is more than ½ volt above limits, replace the regulator.

BENCH TESTS

If the alternator performance does not meed current output specification limits, it will have to be disassembled for further tests and servicing.

To remove the alternator, disconnect the battery ground cable and the leads at the alternator. Then unfasten and remove the alternator from the vehicle.

Field Coil Draw

Electro-Mechanical Unit

1. Connect a test ammeter positive lead to the battery positive terminal of a fully charged battery.

2. Connect ammeter negative lead to the field terminal of the alternator.

3. Connect a jumper wire to negative terminal of battery, and ground it to the alternator end shield.

4. Slowly rotate alternator rotor by hand. Observe ammeter reading.

---

3. Check ammeter reading. Output current should be within specifications.

Voltage Regulator Test

NOTE: Battery must be fully charged for test to be accurate.

Insulated Brush Alternator

1. Make test connections as shown in Fig. C17.

2. Start and operate engine at 1250 rpm with all lights and accessories turned off.

3. As the engine starts, the instrument panel ammeter will deflect to the right. If it deflects less than ¼ scale, turn on high beams and heater blower. If deflection is greater than ¼ scale, turn on heater blower on high.

4. Voltage should be 13.8-14.4 if temperature at the regulator is 80 degrees F. and 13.3-14.0 at 140 degrees F.

5. If voltage is not correct, and the alternator is satisfactory, turn off ignition and disconnect regulator connector. Check for battery voltage at black and green leads. Turn on ignition without starting engine and check for battery voltage at blue lead. If voltage is not present at these connections, wiring is at fault.

6. Check regulator for good ground.

7. If regulator voltage is .5 volt away from specification, it must be replaced.

NOTE: The field circuit is grounded through the regulator. A good ground is established through the use of cup shaped washers on the regulator mounting screws which cut through body paint. These washers must be reinstalled whenever the regulator is removed.

Isolated Field Alternator

1. Complete test connections as per Fig. C18.

2. Start and operate engine at 1250 rpm with all lights and accessories turned off. Voltage should be 13.8-14.4 if temperature at the regulator is 80 degrees F. and 13.3-1.40 at 140 degrees F.

3. It is normal for the car ammeter to show an immediate charge then gradually return to normal position.

4. If voltage is below limits, check for good voltage regulator ground, and voltage drop between regulator cover and body on low voltage scale of voltmeter.

5. Turn off ignition switch and disconnect regulator connector.

6. Turn on ignition switch but do not start engine. Check for battery volt-

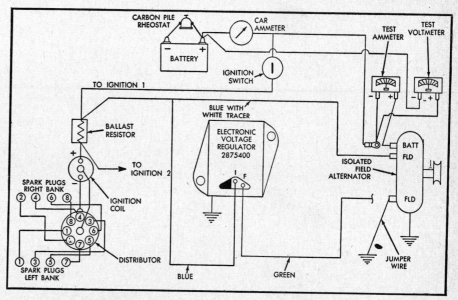

Fig. C14 Charging circuit resistance test, isolated field units

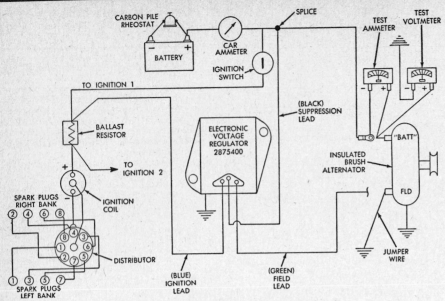

Fig. C15   Current output test, insulated brush unit

Isolated Field Alternator

1. Touch one probe of a 110 volt test lamp to one of the alternator field brush terminals and the other to the end shield. If lamp lights, rotor assembly or a field brush is grounded.
2. If lamp lights, remove field brush assemblies, remove through bolts and separate end shields.
3. Touch one test probe to a slip ring and the remaining probe to the end frame. If the lamp lights, rotor is grounded and must be replaced. If lamp does not light, cause is a grounded brush.

ALTERNATOR REPAIRS

Disassembly

To prevent possible damage to the brush assemblies, they should be removed before disassembling the alternator. The insulated (field) brush is mounted in a plastic holder which positions the brush against one of the slip rings. In the isolated field type alternator, both brushes are insulated and mounted in plastic holders. Disassembled views of all three types are shown in Figs. C2, C3 and C5.

1. Remove retained screw lockwasher, insulated washer and field terminal. Carefully lift plastic holder containing the spring and brush from the end housing.
2. On insulated brush units, remove the positive brush strap screw at the heat sink, the brush assembly screw, insulating nylon washer and lift out brush assembly. On isolated field units, remove both brush screws, insulating nylon washers and remove brush assemblies. On electro-mechanical units, remove the ground brush retaining screw and lift the clip, spring and brush from end shield.

The field coil draw should be 2.3 to 2.7 amperes at 12 volts.

Insulated Brush Alternator

1. Connect jumper wire between alternator "Batt" terminal and the positive terminal of a fully charged battery. Connect test ammeter positive lead to the alternator field terminal and negative lead to negative battery terminal.
2. Slowly rotate alternator rotor by hand and observe ammeter reading. Field coil draw should be 2.3 to 2.7 amperes at 12 volts.

A low rotor coil draw is an indication of a high resistance in the field coil circuit (brushes, slip rings or rotor coil). A higher rotor coil draw indicates a possible shorted rotor coil or a grounded rotor.

Isolated Field Alternator

1. Connect jumper wire between one alternator field terminal and the positive terminal of a fully charged battery.
2. Connect test ammeter positive lead to the other alternator field terminal and the ammeter negative lead to the negative battery terminal.
3. Slowly rotate alternator rotor by hand. Field coil draw should be 2.3-2.7 amps at 12 volts.
4. A low rotor coil draw is an indication of high resistance in the field coil circuit, (brushes, slip rings or rotor coil). A high rotor coil draw indicates shorted rotor coil or grounded rotor.

Testing Alternator Internal Field Circuit

Except Isolated Field Alternator

1. Remove ground brush (positive brush on insulated brush alternators). Touch one test prod from a

110 volt test lamp to the alternator insulated brush (field brush on insulated brush units) and the remaining test prod to the end shield. If rotor or insulated brush (field brush on insulated brush units) is not grounded, lamp will not light.
2. If lamp lights, remove insulated brush (field brush on insulated brush units) remove through bolts and separate end shields.
3. Touch one test prod to a slip ring and remaining prod to end shield. If lamp lights, rotor is grounded and must be replaced. If lamp does not brush (field brush on insulated brush units), the insulated brush is grounded.

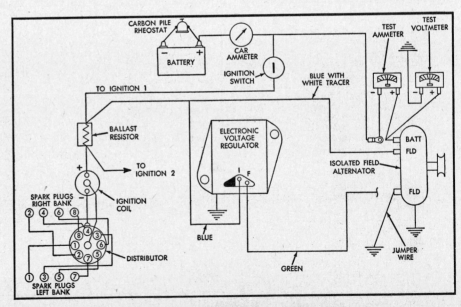

Fig. C16   Current output test, isolated field units

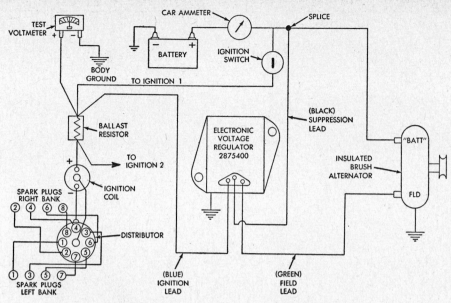

Fig. C17 Voltage regulator test, insulated brush unit

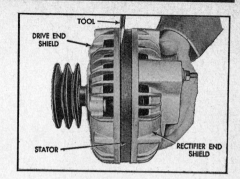

Fig. C19 Separating drive end shield from stator

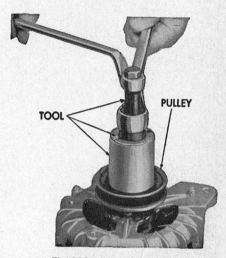

Fig. C20 Removing pulley

NOTE: The stator is laminated; do not burr it or the end shield.

3. Remove through bolts and pry between stator and drive end shield with a screwdriver. Carefully separate drive end shield, pulley and rotor from stator and diode rectifier shield, Fig. C19.
4. The pulley is an interference fit on the rotor shaft; therefore, a suitable puller must be used to remove it, Fig. C20.
5. Pry drive end bearing spring retainer from end shield with a screwdriver, Fig. C21.
6. Support end shield and tap rotor shaft with a plastic hammer to separate rotor from end shield.
7. The drive end ball bearing is an interference fit with the rotor shaft; therefore, a suitable puller must be used to remove it, Fig. C22.
8. Remove D.C. output terminal nuts and washers and remove terminal screw and inside capacitor (if equipped). *Note: The heat sink is also held in place by the terminal screw.*
9. Remove the insulator, Fig. C23.
10. The needle roller bearing in the rectifier end shield is a press fit. If it is necessary to remove the rectifier end frame needle bearing, protect the end shield by supporting the shield when pressing out the bearing as shown in Fig. C24.

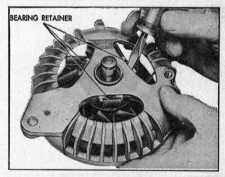

Fig. C21 Disengaging bearing retainer from end shield

Testing Diode Rectifiers

A special Rectifier Tester Tool C-3829 provides a quick, simple and accurate method to test the rectifiers without the necessity of disconnecting the soldered rectifier leads. This instrument is commercially available and full instructions for its use is provided. Lacking this tool, the rectifiers may be tested with a 12 volt battery and a test lamp having a No. 67 bulb. The procedure is as follows:

1. Separate the three stator leads at the "Y" connection, Fig. C25. *Cut the stator connections as close to the connector as possible because*

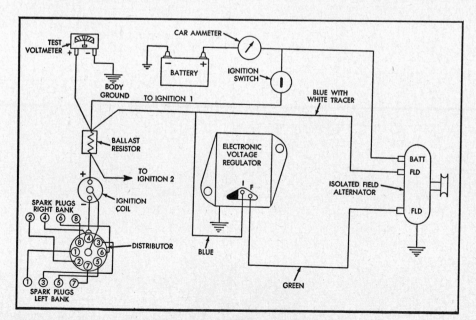

Fig. C18 Voltage regulator test, isolated field units

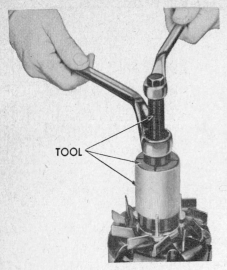

Fig. C22 Removing bearing
from rotor shaft

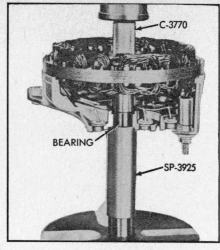

Fig. C24 Removing diode
end shield bearing

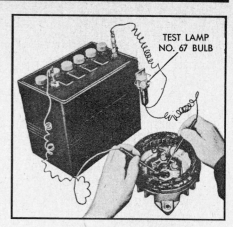

Fig. C26 Testing diodes with a test lamp

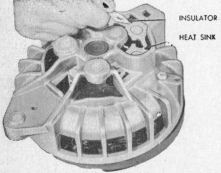

Fig. C23 Removing or installing
heat sink insulator

Fig. C25 Separating the
three stator leads

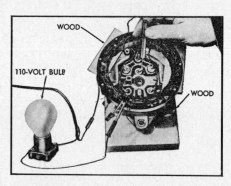

Fig. C27 Testing stator for grounds

If the lamp does not light in either
direction, the rectifier is open.

NOTE: *Possible cause of an open or
a blown rectifier is a faulty capacitor
or a battery that has been installed
on reverse polarity. If the battery
is installed properly and the rectifiers are open, test the capacitor
capacity, which should be .50 micro-
farad plus or minus 20%.*

they will have to be soldered together again. If they are cut too
short it may be difficult to get them
together again for soldering.

2. Connect one side of test lamp to
positive battery post and the other
side of the test lamp to a test probe.
Connect another test probe to the
negative battery post, Fig. C26.

3. Contact the outer case of the rectifier with one probe and the other

probe to the wire in the center of
the rectifier.

4. Reverse the probes, moving the
probe from the rectifier outer case
to the rectifier wire, and the probe
from the wire to the case.

5. If the lamp lights in one direction
but not in the other, the rectifier
is satisfactory. If lamp lights in both
directions, the rectifier is shorted.

Testing Stator

1. Unsolder rectifiers from stator

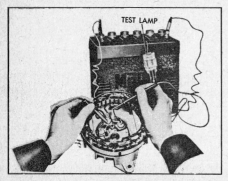

Fig. C28 Testing stator
windings for continuity

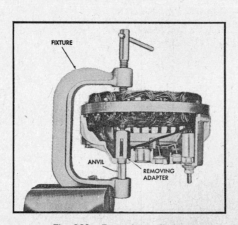

Fig. C29 Removing a diode

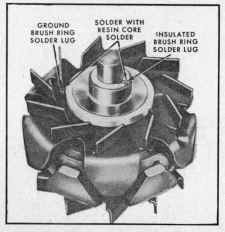

Fig. C30 Soldering points
with slip ring installed

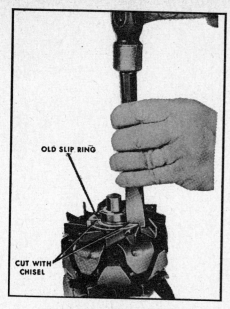

Fig. C31 Cutting old slip rings for removal

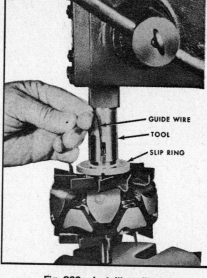

Fig. C33 Installing slip ring

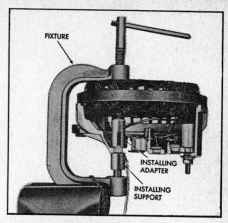

Fig. C35 Installing a diode

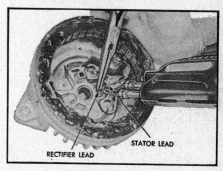

Fig. C36 Soldering diode and stator leads

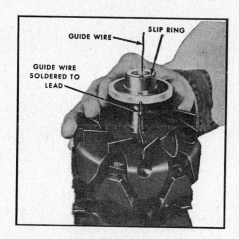

Fig. C32 Aligning slip ring with field wire and guide wire

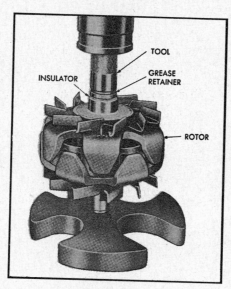

Fig. C34 Installing bearing grease retainer

leads.

2. Test stator for grounds using a 110 volt test lamp, Fig. C27. Use wood slats to insulate the stator from the rectifier shield.

3. Contact one prod of test lamp to the stator pole frame, and contact the other prod to each of the three stator leads. The lamp should not light. If the lamp lights, the stator windings are grounded.

4. To test the stator winding for continuity, connect one prod of the test lamp to all three stator leads at the "Y" connection. Contact each of the three stator leads (disconnected from diodes). The lamp should light when the prod contacts each of the three leads. If the lamp does not light, the stator winding is open, Fig. C28.

5. Install new stator if one tested is defective.

Removing Rectifiers

1. Three diodes are pressed into the heat sink and three in the end shield. When removing the diodes, it is necessary to support the end shield and/or heat sink to prevent damage to these castings.

2. Install the tools shown in Fig. C29, making sure bore of tool completely surrounds diode.

3. Carefully apply pressure to remove diode from end shield.

Replacing Slip Rings

1. Cut through rotor grease retainer with a chisel and remove retainer and insulator.

2. Unsolder field coil leads at solder lugs, Fig. C30.

3. Cut through copper of both slip rings at opposite points with a chisel, Fig. C31.

4. Break insulator and remove old ring.

5. Clean away dirt and particles of old slip ring from rotor.

6. Scrape ends of field coil lead wires clean for good electrical contact.

7. Scrape one end (about $3/16"$) of a piece of bare wire (about 18 gauge) three inches long to be used as a guide wire.

8. Tin the scraped area of the guide wire with resin core solder. Lap the tinned end of the wire over the field coil lead to the insulated ring and solder the two together.

9. Position new slip ring carefully over guide wire and rotor shaft so wire will lay in slip ring groove, Fig. C32. Groove in slip ring must be in line with insulated brush field lead to provide room for lead without damaging it.

10. Place installing tool over rotor shaft with guide wire protruding from slot in tool, Fig. C33.

11. Position rotor, slip ring and tool in arbor press, Fig. C33. Pull on guide wire, being careful to guide insulated field lead into slip ring groove. While guiding insulated field lead through groove, press slip ring on shaft. When slip ring is bottomed on rotor fan, end of field lead should be visible at solder lug, Fig. C30.

12. Unsolder guide wire from insulated brush slip ring lead. Press field lead into solder lug and solder to lug.

CAUTION: Be sure solder bead does

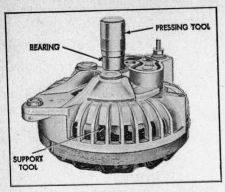

Fig. C37 Installing diode end shield bearing

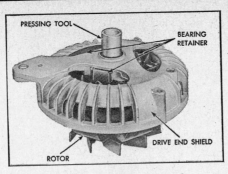

Fig. C38 Installing drive end shield and bearing

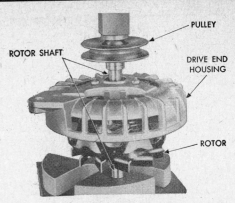

Fig. C39 Installing pulley

not protrude beyond surface of plastic material. Do not use acid core solder as a short may result and corrosion will definitely occur.

13. Coil ground brush field lead around solder lug and solder with resin core solder.
14. Test slip rings for ground with a 110 volt test lamp by touching one test lead prod to rotor pole shoe and remaining prod to slip rings. The lamp should not light. If lamp lights, slip rings are shorted to ground, possibly due to a grounded insulated field lead when installing slip ring.
15. If rotor is not grounded, lightly clean slip ring surfaces with No. 00 sandpaper and assemble to alternator.
16. Position grease retainer gasket and retainer on rotor shaft and press retainer on shaft, Fig. C34. Retainer is properly positioned when inner bore of installer tool bottoms on rotor shaft.

Alternator Assemble

1. Install diodes as shown in Fig. C35.

Do not use a hammer to start diode in its bore in end shield. Do not hammer or shock diode in any manner as this will fracture the thin

silicon wafer in the diode, causing complete diode failure.

2. Clean leads and mate stator lead with diode wire loop and bend loop snugly around stator lead to provide a good electrical and mechanical connection. Solder wires with resin core solder. Hold diode lead wire with pliers just below joint while soldering, Fig. C31. Pliers will absorb heat from soldering and protect diode.

NOTE: *After soldering, quickly cool soldered connection by touching a damp cloth against it. This will aid in forming a solid joint.*

3. Push stator leads down into slots in end shield and cement them to protect leads against possible interference with rotor fan. Test each diode to be sure it was not damaged during installation. (Cement is Mopar No. 2299314.)
4. Install diode end shield bearing, Fig. C37.
5. Press bearing onto rotor shaft, C38.
6. Press pulley on rotor shaft until it contacts bearing. *Do not exceed 6800 lbs.*
7. Make sure heat sink insulator is in place. Then install capacitor stud through heat sink and end shield.
8. Install insulating washers, lockwashers and lock nuts.

9. Make sure heat sink and insulator are in position and tighten lock nut.
10. Position stator on diode end shield.
11. Position rotor end shield on stator and diode end shield.
12. Align through bolt holes in stator, diode end shield and drive end shield.
13. Compress stator and both end shields by hand and install through bolts, washers and nuts.
14. Install insulated (field) brush in diode and shield. Place bronze terminal on plastic holder with tab of terminal in recess in holder.
15. Place nylon washer on bronze terminal and install lockwasher and attaching screws.
16. On insulated brush units, install positive brush, straps, nylon washer and attaching screws. *Nylon washer is assembled between strap and head of screw.* On all other units, install ground brush.
17. Rotate pulley slowly by hand to be sure rotor fans do not touch diodes, capacitor lead and stator connections.
18. Install alternator and adjust drive belt.
19. Connect leads to alternator.
20. Connect battery ground cable.
21. Start and operate engine and observe alternator operation.
22. If necessary, test current output and regulator voltage setting.

Delco-Remy "Delcotron" Alternator With External Regulator

TESTING SYSTEM IN VEHICLE

Current Output Test

1. Check and adjust belt tension if necessary.
2. Disconnect ground cable from battery.
3. Connect test ammeter between alternator "BAT" terminal and disconnected lead as shown in Fig. D5.

4. Connect tachometer from distributor terminal of coil to ground.
5. Reconnect battery ground cable and connect a voltmeter across battery.
6. Turn on all possible accessory load.
7. Apply parking brake firmly.
8. Start engine and adjust engine idle speed to the recommended setting (usually 500 rpm in Drive).
9. At this engine speed alternator output should be 5 amperes or more.
10. Shift transmission to Neutral. Then increase engine speed to 1500 rpm. Output should be 25 amperes or more.

11. Shut off engine and turn off all accessories.
12. If output is low in either of the above tests, try supplying the field directly to cause full alternator output. Unplug the connector from the alternator. Then connect a jumper wire from the alternator "F" terminal to the "BAT" terminal. Retest as described above. If the output is still low, the alternator is faulty and must be removed for bench tests and repairs.
13. If the output (using field jumper) is now satisfactory, the trouble is

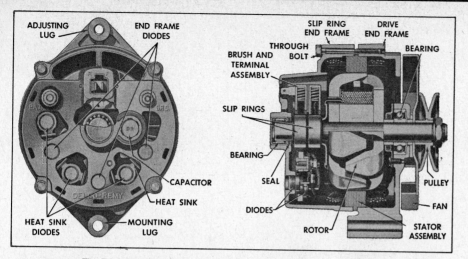

Fig. D1 Sectional end and side views of "Delcotron" alternator

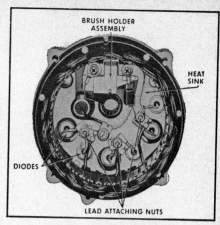

Fig. D2 Alternator internal lead connections

in the voltage regulator or wiring harness. Clean and test regulator, and check all wiring connections.

14. Remove field jumper and reinstall vehicle field connector.

Test & Adjust Regulator

1. Leave all test instruments in place, Fig. D5, but make sure field jumper is removed if one was used (see above).
2. Install a thermometer near the regulator.
3. Run engine at about 1500 rpm for 15 minutes. Make sure all electrical load except ignition is turned off.
4. Check ammeter reading. For an accurate voltage setting check, ammeter must read between 3 and 10 amperes. If ammeter reading is still high after 15 minutes, it may be necessary to substitute a fully charged battery.
5. Momentarily increase engine speed to 2000 rpm and read voltmeter and thermometer. See Fig. D6 to determine if upper voltage regulator setting is within limits for the existing temperature. If setting is within limits and battery condition

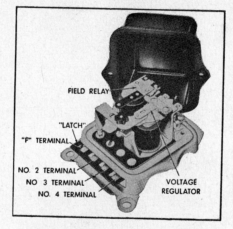

Fig. D3 Voltage regulator. The field relay is used only on vehicles having a charge indicator light instead of an ammeter

has been satisfactory, *voltage setting should not be disturbed.*

6. If voltage regulator setting is not within correct limits, make a note of the change required to place voltage in the middle of the specified range. Remove regulator cover, carefully lifting it straight up.

CAUTION: *If cover touches regulator unit, the resulting arc may ruin the regulator assembly.*

7. With cover off, voltage reading will change considerably. Starting with the changed voltage reading, increase or decrease voltage as required as shown in Fig. D7.

CAUTION: *Always make final adjustment by increasing spring tension to assure contact between screw head and spring support.*

8. After making an adjustment, replace cover carefully. Cycle the regulator by unplugging connector from alternator. Reinstall connector in alternator and recheck voltage setting of regulator.

Tailoring Voltage Regulator

It is important to remember that the voltage setting for one type of operating condition may not be satisfactory for a different type of operating condition. Vehicle under-hood temperatures, operating speeds, and night-time service all are factors which help determine the proper voltage setting. The proper setting is attained when the battery remains fully charged with a minimum use of water.

If no circuit defects are found, yet the battery remains undercharged, raise the setting by .3 volt, and then check for an improved battery condition over a service period of reasonable length. If the battery remains overcharged, lower the setting by .3 volt, and then check for an improved battery condition. However, never adjust the voltage setting out of the limits specified in Fig. D6.

ALTERNATOR SERVICE

Alternator Removal

1. Disconnect battery positive cable.
2. Remove two leads at alternator.
3. Loosen adjusting bolts and remove drive belt.
4. Remove alternator retaining bolts and take off alternator.

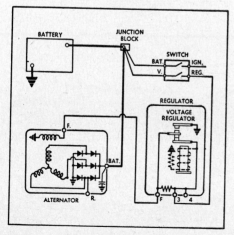

Fig. D4 Wiring diagram of the alternator charging circuit

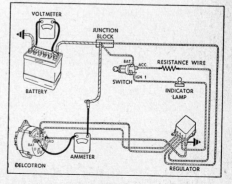

Fig. D5 Alternator test connections

DELCOTRON with External Regulator

Air Temperature at Regulator	85°	105°	125°	145°	165°
Voltage Setting	13.8–14.6	13.7–14.5	13.5–14.3	13.4–14.2	13.2–14.0

Fig. D6   Voltage regulator settings

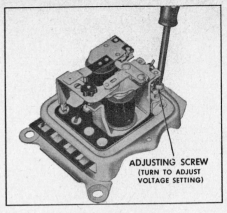

Fig. D7   Adjusting voltage regulator setting

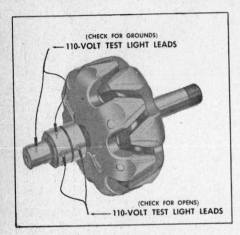

Fig. D8   Checking rotor for opens or grounds

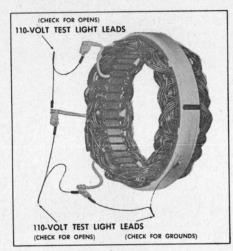

Fig. D9   Checking stator for opens or grounds

Alternator Disassembly

1. Remove pulley retaining nut by inserting a 5/16" Allen wrench into shaft to hold pulley while loosening nut. If an Allen wrench is not available, use a strap wrench around the pulley to hold it. Remove pulley.
2. Scribe a mark between the two halves of the alternator to help locate the parts in the same position during reassembly.
3. Remove four through bolts.
4. Separate the drive end frame and rotor assembly from the stator assembly by prying apart with a screwdriver at the stator slot. The fit between the two is not tight and the two can be separated easily. The separation is to be made between the stator and drive and frame.

CAUTION: *As the rotor and drive end frame is separated from the slip ring frame, the brushes will fall down onto the shaft and come in contact with the lubricant. Brushes which come in contact with the shaft should be cleaned immediately to avoid contamination by oil, or they will have to be replaced.*

Rotor Checks

1. To check for grounds, connect a 110 volt test lamp for either slip ring to the rotor shaft, Fig. D8. If the lamp lights the field winding is grounded.
2. To check for opens, connect the test lamp to each slip ring. If the lamp fails to light the winding is open.
3. The winding is checked for short

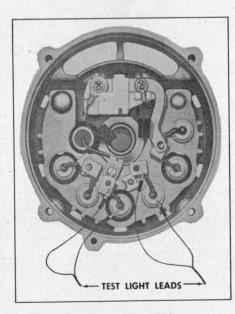

Fig. D10   Checking diodes for opens or shorts

circuits by connecting a battery and ammeter in series with the two slip rings. The field current at 12 volts and 80°F. should be between 1.9 and 2.3 amperes.

NOTE: *For vehicles with Delco-Remy transistorized ignition and transistor voltage regulator, the field current should be between 2.8 and 3.2 amperes.*

4. An ammeter reading above the values given indicates shorted windings, and the rotor assembly should be replaced.

Stator Checks

1. To check the stator windings, remove all three stator lead attaching nuts and separate the stator from the end frame.
2. The stator winding may be checked with a 110 volt test lamp. If the lamp lights when connected from any stator lead to the frame, the windings are grounded. If the lamp fails to light when successively connected between each pair of stator leads, the windings are open, Fig. D9.
3. A short circuit in the stator windings is difficult to locate without laboratory test equipment due to the low resistance of the windings. However, if all other electrical checks are normal and the alternator fails to supply rated output, shorted stator windings are indicated.

Diode Checks

1. Each diode should be checked electrically for a shorted or open condition using a test *lamp of not more than 12 volts*, Fig. D10.
2. With the stator disconnected, connect the test lamp leads across each diode, first in one direction and then in the other.
3. If the lamp lights in both checks, or fails to light in both checks, the diode is defective.
4. When checking a good diode, the lamp will light in only one of the two directions.

Diode Replacement

1. To remove a diode, place slip ring end frame in a vise with the remover equipment mounted as shown in Fig. D11. Tighten the vise to remove the defective diode.
2. To install a diode, place the new diode in the installer, Fig. D12. With the tools installed in the vise as shown, tighten the vise to install the new diode.

CAUTION: *Never attempt to remove or install a diode by striking it as the shock may damage the other diodes.*

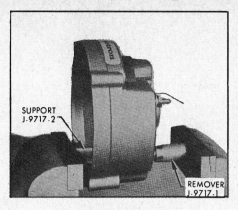

Fig. D11   Removing a diode

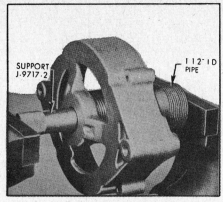

Fig. D13   Removing drive end frame bearing

Fig. D15   Removing slip ring end frame bearing

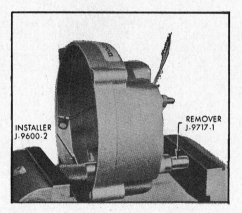

Fig. D12   Installing a diode

Fig. D14   Installing drive end frame bearing

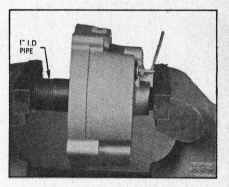

Fig. D16   Installing slip ring end frame bearing

Slip Ring Service

If the slip rings are dirty they may be cleaned with No. 400 silicon carbide paper and finish polished with crocus cloth. Spin the rotor in a lathe, or otherwise spin the rotor, and hold the polishing cloth against the slip rings until they are clean.

CAUTION: The rotor must be rotated in order that the slip rings will be cleaned evenly. Cleaning the slip rings by hand without spinning the rotor may result in flat spots on the slip rings, causing brush noise.

Slip rings that are rough or out-of-round should be trued in a lathe to .002" maximum runout as indicated on a dial gauge. Remove only enough material to make the rings smooth and round. Finish polish with crocus cloth and blow away all dust.

Bearing Replacement

1. The bearing in the drive end frame can be removed by detaching the retainer plate screws and then pressing the bearing from the end frame as shown in Fig. D13.
2. Press in new bearing with a tube or collar that just fits the outer race, Fig. D14. Install a new retainer plate if the felt seal in the existing plate is hardened or worn.
3. The bearing in the slip ring end frame can be removed by pressing with a tube or collar that just fits inside the end frame housing. Press

from the outside of the housing towards the inside as shown in Fig. D15.

4. To install the new bearing, place a flat plate over the bearing and press in from the outside towards the inside of the frame until the bearing is flush with the outside of the end frame. Support the inside of the frame with the pipe shown to prevent breakage of the end frame, Fig. D16.
5. Saturate the felt seal with S.A.E. 20 oil and reassemble the felt seal and steel retainer.

Brush Replacement

1. When the slip ring end frame assem-

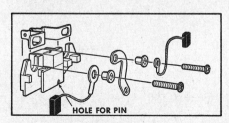

Fig. D17   Assembling brush holder and related parts

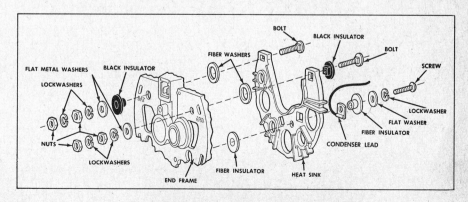

Fig. D18   Disassembled view of heat sink and related parts

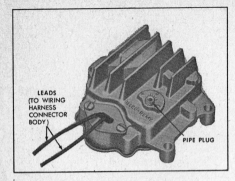

Fig. D19   Transistor regulator

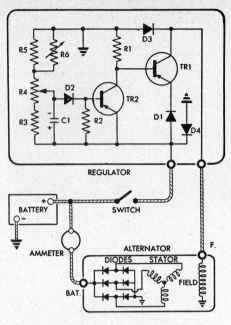

Fig. D20   Wiring diagram of transistor regulator in charging circuit

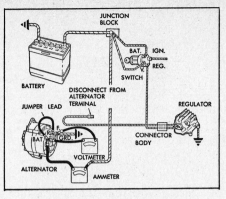

Fig. D21   Checking charging circuit for undercharged battery condition

bly is separated from the rotor and drive end frame, the brushes will fall down onto the shaft and come in contact with the lubricant. If the brushes are to be re-used, they must be thoroughly cleaned with a soft dry cloth immediately. Also, the shaft must be thoroughly cleaned before reassembly.

2. Inspect the brush springs for damage or corrosion. If there is any doubt as to the condition of the springs, they should be replaced.
3. To install new brushes, remove the brush holder assembly from the end frame by detaching the two screws.
4. Install the springs and brushes into the brush holder, and insert a straight wire or pin into the holes at the bottom of the holder to retain the brushes, Fig. D17.
5. Attach the brush holder assembly to the end frame, noting carefully the proper stack-up of the parts as shown. Allow the straight wire to protrude through the hole in the end frame.

Heat Sink Replacement

1. Remove the "BAT" and "GRD" terminals from the end frame and the screw attaching the condenser lead to the heat sink.
2. During reassembly, note carefully the proper stack-up of parts as shown in Fig. D18.

Alternator Reassembly

1. Reassembly is the reverse of disassembly. Refer to Fig. D2 for connection of internal leads.
2. When installing the pulley, secure the rotor in a vise only tight enough to permit tightening the shaft nut to a torque of 50-60 ft. lbs. If excessive pressure is applied to the rotor, the assembly may become distorted.
3. To install the slip ring end frame to the rotor and drive end frame, remove the tape over the bearing and shaft (if used for protection) upon disassembly, and make sure the shaft is perfectly clean.
4. Insert a straight wire as previously mentioned through the holes in the brush holder and end frame to retain the brushes in the holder. Then withdraw the wire after the alternator has been completely assembled. The brushes will then drop onto the slip rings.

TRANSISTOR REGULATOR

The transistor regulator, Fig. D19, is an assembly composed principally of transistors, diodes, resistors, a capacitor, and a thermistor to form a completely static unit containing no moving parts.

The transistor is an electrical devise which limits the alternator voltage to a preset value by controlling the alternator field current. The diodes, capacitor and resistors act together to aid the transistor in controlling the voltage, which is the only function that the regulator performs in the charging circuit. The thermistor provides a temperature-compensated voltage setting.

The voltage at which the alternator operates is determined by the regulator adjustment. The regulator voltage setting can be adjusted externally by removing a pipe plug in the cover, Fig. D19, and turning the adjusting arm inside the regulator. This procedure is explained later on, and permits regulator adjustments without removing the cover.

Operating Principles

A typical wiring diagram showing internal circuits is shown in Fig. D20. When the switch is closed, current flows through diode D1 and transistor TR1 in the regulator to the alternator "F" terminal, and then through the alternator field winding to ground.

When alternator voltage reaches a preset value, the other components of the regulator cause transistor TR1 alternately to "turn-off" and "turn-on" the alternator field current. The regulator thus operates automatically to limit the alternator voltage to a preset value.

Checking Circuit

1. Connect test ammeter and voltmeter in circuit as shown in Fig. D21, and connect a jumper wire from alternator "F" terminal to alternator "BAT" terminal.
2. Operate alternator at specified speed, turn on accessories as required to obtain specified voltage and observe output. For example, the alternator used with this regulator on 1963 Pontiac has a rated output of 52 amperes at 14 volts at a speed of 5000 rpm.
3. If current output is low, remove and check the alternator as outlined previously.

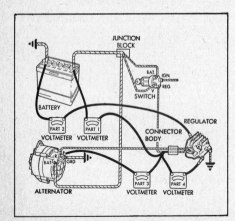

Fig. D22   Checking charging circuit for overcharged battery condition

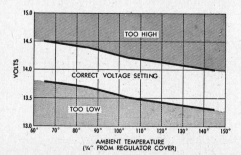

Fig. D23   Temperature correction chart

4. If the alternator failure was caused by a defective stator or diodes, the repaired alternator may be installed back on the vehicle and no further checks are needed.

5. If the alternator failure was caused by a defective field winding, the repaired alternator may be installed back on the vehicle and the following checks must be made to locate possible damage to regulator.

6. Referring to Fig. D21, remove jumper lead and reconnect wiring harness connector to alternator "F" terminal.

7. Turn on ignition switch but do not start engine.

8. Connect voltmeter positive lead to battery positive terminal and negative lead to regulator black lead connector body to make connection to regulator (Part 1, Fig. D22). Record voltage drop.

9. Connect voltmeter to negative terminal of battery and ground on regulator (Part 2, Fig. D22). Record voltage drop.

10. If addition of voltage readings is greater than .3 volt, check ignition switch for poor contacts and system wiring for high resistance. If voltage difference is less than .3 volt, proceed as follows, referring to Part 3, Fig. D22.

11. Connect voltmeter positive lead to regulator positive terminal and voltmeter negative lead to alternator "F" terminal. Slide voltmeter positive lead into regulator connector body (black lead terminal) to make connection. Record voltage.

12. If the voltage is .9 volt or less, replace regulator, as transistor is shorted. If voltage is 2.0 volts or greater, replace regulator as transistor is open. If voltage is between .9 and 2.0 volts, proceed as follows:

13. Operate engine at approximately 1500 rpm for 10 minutes with low beam headlights on. Referring to Part 4, Fig. D22, with engine running at 1500 rpm, record voltage reading from regulator positive terminal to ground by sliding voltmeter lead into regulator connector body black lead terminal to make connection.

14. Compare with Fig. D23. Ambient temperature is temperature of air measured 1/4" from regulator cover.

15. If voltage reading is within specifications, charging system is satisfactory but voltage setting may need to be changed to a different value to meet the requirements of driving conditions.

16. To do this, remove the pipe plug on regulator and insert a small screwdriver in adjustment slot. Turn counterclockwise for an undercharged battery one or two notches to increase setting.

17. For an overcharged battery, as evidenced by excessive water usage, turn clockwise one or two notches to decrease setting. For each notch moved, voltage setting will change by approximately .3 volt. Then check for an improved battery condition over a service period of reasonable length.

18. If voltage is not within specifications, check to see if the adjustment arm is in the center position. If the voltage reads out of specifications in the center position, replace the regulator.

1968 Delcotron Integral Charging System

DESCRIPTION

This unit, Fig. 1, is a self-contained charging system with miniaturized integrated circuitry which eliminates the traditional external regulator. The system voltage is controlled by an integrated regulator within the alternator, Fig. 2. In other words, there is no separate regulator mounting, no external wiring between regulator and alternator, no voltage adjustments for the life of the unit, and no periodic maintenance.

CHECKING REGULATOR

The procedure for testing and servicing the alternator proper is similar to the standard Delcotron. However, the integrated regulator may be checked for defects as follows:

1. Separate the stator from the end frame by removing the three stator lead attaching nuts, Fig. 2.

2. Remove numbers 3, 4 and 5 regulator lead clips from the studs.

3. Using the lowest range scale on an ohmmeter having a 1 1/2 volt cell, connect to one of the three disconnected regulator leads and to the alternator No. 1 terminal as shown in Fig. 3. Note ohmmeter reading.

4. Reverse ohmmeter lead connections and again note ohmmeter readings.

Fig. 1 External view of Delcotron Integral Charging System

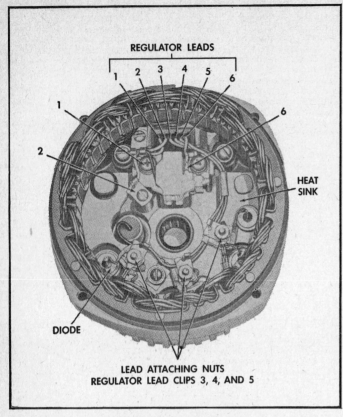

Fig. 2 Slip ring end frame and
regulator leads. ICS Delcotron

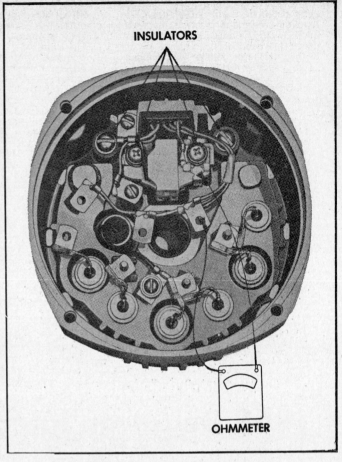

Fig. 3 Checking ICS Delcotron regulator

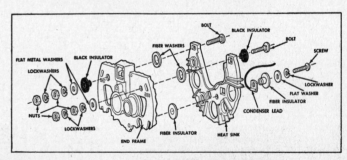

Fig. 4 Exploded view of heat sink.
Standard and ICS Delcotrons

5. If both readings are the same, the regulator is defective and must be replaced. The ohmmeter should give one high and one low reading. Check the other two regulator leads in the same manner.

REGULATOR, REPLACE

1. Detach the six regulator lead clips and two regulator heat sink attaching screws, sleeve insulators, and flat washer insulators, Fig. 2.
2. Remove regulator from heat sink by removing the regulator mounting screws. Carefully note stack-up of parts.
3. Attach negative brush connection to regulator heat sink.
4. Assemble regulator, noting carefully the proper stack-up of parts and being sure all electrical connectors at brush holder mounting screws are

located under the flat washer insulators. Also check brush lead positions to insure freedom of brush movement and absence of shorts or grounds.

NOTE: Except for attachment of regulator, stack-up of parts in heat sink assembly is the same in both the Integrated unit and the standard alternator, Fig. 4.

Delcotron Type SI Integral Charging System

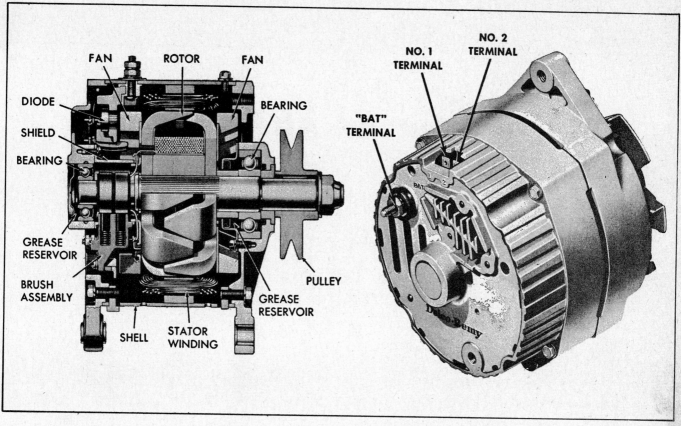

Fig. 1 Delcotron Type SI Integral Charging System

DESCRIPTION

This unit, Fig. 1, features a solid state regulator mounted inside the alternator slip ring end frame, Fig. 2, along with the brush holder assembly. All regulator components are enclosed in a solid mold with no need or provision for adjustment of the regulator. A rectifier bridge, containing six diodes and connected to the stator windings, changes A.C. voltage to D. C. voltage which is available at the output terminal. Generator field current is supplied through a diode trio which is also connected to the stator windings. The diodes and rectifiers are protected by a capacitor which is also mounted in the end frame.

No maintenance or adjustments of any kind are required on this unit.

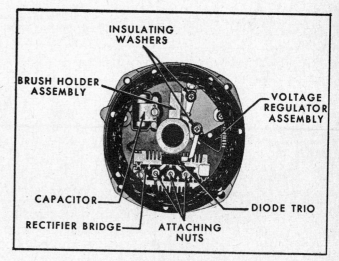

Fig. 2 Slip ring end frame. SI Delcotron

SYSTEM TESTS

Alternator

The procedures for testing the alternator proper are similar to the standard Delcotron.

Diode Trio

1. With diode unit removed, connect an ohmmeter to the single connector and to one of the three connectors.
2. Observe the reading. Reverse ohmmeter leads.
3. Reading should be high with one connection and low with the other. If both readings are the same, unit must be replaced.
4. Repeat between the single connector and each of the three connectors.

NOTE: There are two diode units differing in appearance. These are completely interchangeable.

The diode unit can be checked for a grounded brush lead while still installed in the end frame by connecting an ohmmeter from the brush lead clip to the end frame as in Setps 1 and 2 above. If both readings are zero, check for a grounded brush or brush lead.

Rectifer Bridge Test

1. Connect ohmmeter to the grounded heat sink and one of the three terminals.
2. Observe the reading then reverse leads.
3. Reading should be high with one connection and low with the other. If both readings are the same, unit must be replaced.

4. Repeat test for each of the other terminals.

Voltage Regulator/Brush Lead Test

Connect an ohmmeter from the brush lead clip to the end frame, note reading, then reverse connections. If both readings are zero, either the brush lead clip is grounded or the regulator is defective.

Ford Autolite Alternator

TESTING SYSTEM IN VEHICLE

Alternator Output Test

1. Make connections as shown in Fig. 2. Be sure that the Generator Field Control is in the "open" position at the start of the test.
2. Close the battery adapter switch. Start the engine, then open the battery adapter switch. *All electrical accessories, including door operated interior lights must be turned off.*
3. Carefully increase engine speed to a tachometer reading of 2900 rpm. *Do not exceed this speed.*
4. Adjust the Generator Field Control until the voltmeter reads exactly 15 volts. Observe the ammeter reading. Add 5 amperes to this reading to obtain total alternator output. The 5-ampere factor represents the field current and the ignition system current, and must be added to the am-

meter reading as these currents are not indicated on the ammeter. *Make this test in the shortest possible time and do not exceed 2900 rpm. If the battery was fully charged, it might not be possible to obtain maximum current output. If specified current is not obtained, make the following test before condemning the alternator.*

5. Turn the Generator Field Control to the "open" position. Rotate the tester control knob to the "load" position. Maintain 2900 rpm engine speed.
6. Adjust the Generator Field Control and the "load" control, maintaining a voltmeter reading of 15 volts maximum, until the Generator Field Control is at its maximum clockwise position.
7. Readjust the "load" control until the voltmeter reads exactly 15 volts. Observe the ammeter reading. Add 5 amperes to this reading to obtain total alternator output.
8. Stop the engine, return the Gener-

ator Field Control to the "open" position and disconnect the test equipment.

Test Analysis

1. An output of 2 to 5 amperes below specifications indicates and open diode rectifier. An output of approximately 10 amperes below specifications indicates a shorted diode rectifier. *An alternator with a shorted diode will usually whine, which will be noticeable at idling speed.*
2. A shorted *positive* diode may sometimes be accompanied by alternate flashing of the oil pressure and charge indicator lights when the ignition switch if off. The field relay contacts will also be closed and the battery will be discharging through the field to ground.
3. Under this condition, the instrument constant voltage regulator will receive power through the charge indicator light. The operating of the constant voltage through the charge

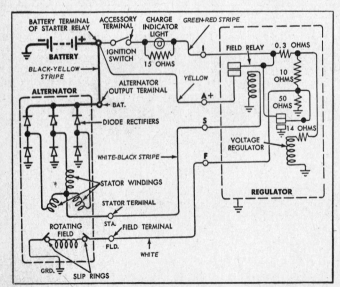

Fig. 1 Ford Autolite alternator wiring diagram with charge indicator light. Field wire is yellow on 1970 units and orange on 1971

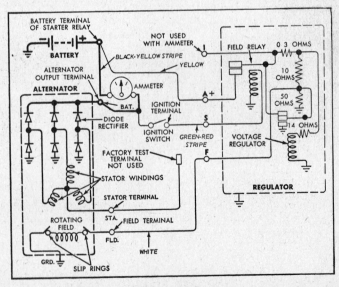

Fig. 1A Ford Autolite alternator wiring diagram with ammeter. Field wire is yellow on 1970 units and orange on 1971

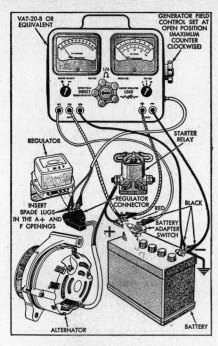

Fig. 2   Alternator output test

Make sure that the tip of the probe is sharp and that it penetrates the varnish at the diode terminal.

2. To test the negative diodes, make the connections shown in Fig. 4. Follow the same procedure as for positive diodes.

3. Good diodes will be indicated as on the meter in Figs. 3 and 4, that is, 2 amperes or more and readings alike within 2 scale divisions.

Field Open or Short Circuit Test

1. Make connections as shown in Fig. 5. The normal current draw, as indicated by the ammeter, should be as specified in the *Alternator and Regulator Specifications* chart in the car chapters.

2. If there is little or no current flow, the field has a high resistance or is open, or the brushes are not making proper contact with the slip rings.

3. A current flow considerably higher than that specified (usually 2.9 to 3.1 at 12 volts) indicates shorted or grounded turns.

4. If the test shows that the field is shorted, *and the field brush assembly is not at fault,* the entire rotor must be replaced.

Field Relay Supply Voltage Test

The regulator field relay will close only if the voltage supplied by the neutral terminal of the alternator is sufficient to operate the relay. The wiring from the alternator neutral terminal to the relay "S" terminal also must be intact. The following test will show that both sufficient voltage is available and that the wiring is in good condition.

1. Remove the connector plug from the regulator, remove the regulator, then reinstall the connector plug.

2. Connect the negative voltmeter lead to ground. Start the engine and operate it at 400 to 500 rpm.

3. Connect the positive voltmeter lead to a small screwdriver. Touch the screwdriver to the center rivet at the front of the regulator. *Use care to touch only the rivet or the rivet terminal so as not to short this point to ground or to the other nearby terminals.* The voltmeter should indicate at least 6 volts, and the relay contacts should be closed.

4. Low voltage at this point can be caused by a defective alternator or defective wiring.

REGULATOR TESTS

The following tests are to be made with the regulator in the vehicle. Be sure that the regulator is at "normal" operating temperature. This is equivalent to the temperature after 20 minutes of operation with a 10-ampere load.

Field Relay Test

1. Disconnect regulator terminal plug and remove the regulator cover.

2. Make connections shown in Fig. 6.

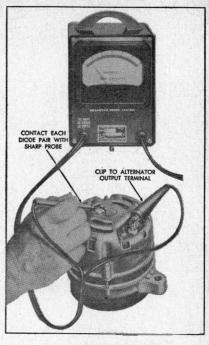

Fig. 3   Positive diode test

3. Slowly rotate field resistance control clockwise from the off position until the field relay contacts close.

4. Observe the voltmeter reading at the moment that the relay closes. This is the relay closing voltage.

5. If the relay closes immediately, even with the field resistance close to the "off" position, use a 6 volt battery for this test.

6. If the closing voltage is not within specifications, adjust the relay.

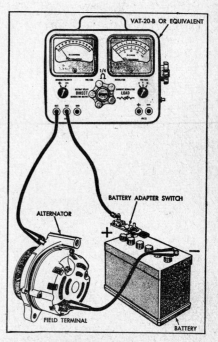

Fig. 5   Field open or short circuit test

indicator light causes the alternate flashing of the lights. When the regulator contacts close, the oil pressure light becomes dim and the charge indicator light becomes bright. When the contacts open the oil pressure light becomes bright and the charge indicator light becomes dim.

Diode Test

1. To test the positive diodes, make connections shown in Fig. 3. Connect the probe to each diode lead.

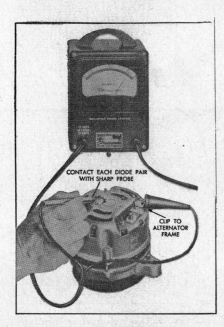

Fig. 4   Negative diode test

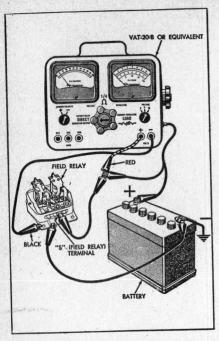

Fig. 6   Field relay test

1. Make test connections shown in Fig. 7.
2. Turn off all accessories, including door-operated dome lights.
3. Close battery adapter switch, start engine, then open adapter switch.
4. Attach the voltage regulation thermometer to regulator cover.
5. Operate engine at 2000 rpm for 5 minutes. Turn master control to "direct" position.
6. If the ammeter indicates more than 10 amperes, remove battery cables and charge the battery.
7. When battery is fully charged, and the voltage regulator has been temperature stabilized, rotate the master control to the "Voltage Reg." position, the ammeter should indicate less than 2 amperes.
8. Cycle the regulator as follows: Stop engine, close adapter switch, start engine, and open adapter switch.
9. Allow battery to normalize for a short time, then read the voltmeter.
10. Read the thermometer, and compare the voltmeter reading with the voltage given in Fig. 8.
11. If the regulated voltage is not within specifications, make a voltage limiter adjustment. *After each adjustment, be sure to cycle the regulator before each reading. Readings must be made with cover in place.*

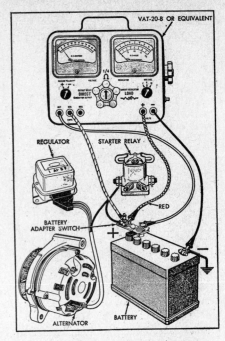

Fig. 7   Voltage limiter test

Voltage Limiter Test

For test purposes, the lower stage regulation is used (armature vibrating of the lower contact). Voltage limiter calibration test must be made with the regulator cover in place and the regulator at "normal" operating temperature (equivalent to temperature after 20 minutes of operation with a 10-ampere load).

Circuit Resistance Test

For the purpose of this test, the resistance values of the circuits have been converted to voltage drop readings for a current flow of 20 amperes.

Alternator to Battery Positive Terminal

1. Make connections shown in Fig. 9.
2. Turn off all lights and electrical accessories.
3. Close battery adapter switch, start engine, then open battery adapter switch.
4. Slowly increase engine speed until ammeter reads 20 amperes.
5. Voltage should be no greater than 0.3 volts.

Alternator to Battery Ground Terminal

1. Make connections shown in Fig. 10.
2. Close battery adapter switch, start engine and open battery adapter switch.
3. Slowly increase engine speed until ammeter reads 20 amperes.
4. Voltage indicated should be less than 0.1 volt.

REGULATOR ADJUSTMENTS

Erratic operation of the regulator, indicated by erratic movement of the voltmeter during a voltage limiter test, may be caused by dirty or pitted regulator contacts.

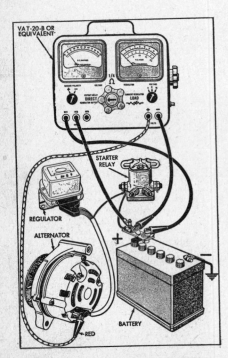

Fig. 9   Voltage drop test from alternator to battery positive terminal

Voltage Regulation Setting (Volts)	Ambient Air Temperature °F
14.3–15.1	50
14.1–14.9	75
13.9–14.7	100
13.8–14.6	125
13.6–14.4	150
13.5–14.3	175

Fig. 8   Voltage regulation versus ambient air temperature

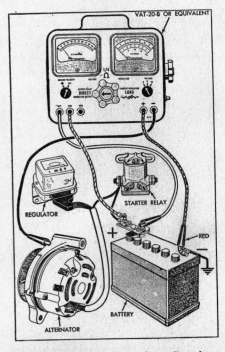

Fig. 10   Voltage drop test from alternator to negative battery terminal

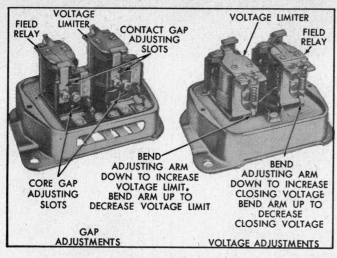

Fig. 11 Regular adjustments

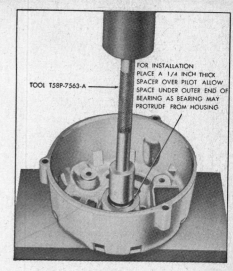

Fig. 14 Rear bearing removal

Use a very fine abrasive paper such as silicone carbide, 400 grade, to clean the contacts. Wear off the sharp edges of the abrasive by rubbing against another piece of abrasive paper. Fold the abrasive paper over and pull it through the contacts to clean them. Keep all oil or grease from contacting the points. *Do not use compressed air to clean the regulator. When adjusting the gap spacing, use only hospital clean feeler gauges.*

Regulator Bench Adjustments

The difference between the upper stage and lower stage regulation (0.3 volt), is determined by voltage limiter point and core gaps.

Adjust point gap first. Referring to Fig. 11, loosen the left side lock screw ¼ turn. Use a screwdriver blade in the

adjustment slot above the lock screw. Adjust the upper contact until there is .010 to .015" gap between lower contacts. Tighten lock screw and recheck the gap.

To adjust the core gap, loosen the center lock screw ¼ turn. Use a screwdriver blade in the slot under the lock screw. Adjust the core gap to .045 to .052" clearance between armature and core at edge of core closest to contact points. Tighten lock screw and recheck core gap.

Regulator Voltage Adjustments

Final adjustment of the regulator must be made with the regulator at operating temperature.

The field relay closing voltage is adjusted by bending the spring arm, Fig. 11. To increase the closing voltage, bend

the spring arm down. To decrease the closing voltage, bend the spring arm up.

The voltage limit is adjusted by bending the voltage limiter spring arm, Fig. 11. To increase the voltage bend the adjusting arm downward. To decrease the setting, bend the adjusting arm upward.

Before setting the voltage and before making a final voltage test, the alternator speed must be reduced to zero and the ignition switch opened momentarily to cycle the regulator.

ALTERNATOR REPAIRS

Disassembly, Fig. 12

1. Mark both end housings with a

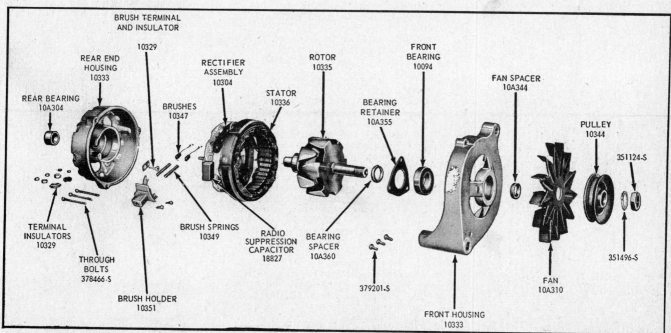

Fig. 12 Ford Autolite Alternator exploded

Fig. 13 Retracting alternator brushes

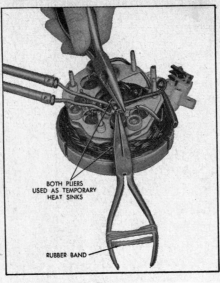

Fig. 15 Soldering diode leads

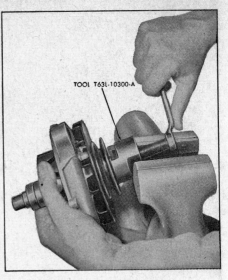

Fig. 16 Removing pulley

scribe mark for reassembly. Reach through a ventilation slot, raise both brushes off slip rings and install a short length of ⅛" rod or stiff wire through hole in rear end housing, Fig. 13, to hold brushes off slip rings.

2. Remove 3 housing through bolts and separate front housing and rotor from rear housing and stator. *Make certain that brushes do not contact the greasy rotor shaft.*

3. Remove nuts from rectifier-to-rear housing studs and remove rear housing. Remove two spacer sleeves from rectifier plate studs.

4. Press bearing from rear end housing, Fig. 14.

5. Remove terminal spacer block from studs and unsolder neutral wire from spacer block neutral terminal.

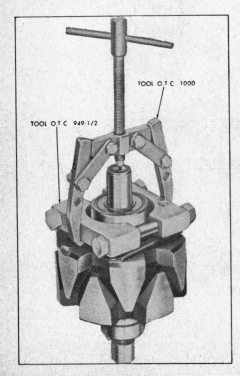

Fig. 17 Removing front bearing

6. If brushes are being replaced, straighten field brush, terminal blade locking tabs with a pair of pliers and remove terminal blade from terminal spacer block assembly. Remove brushes and holders.

7. If either diode plate is being replaced, carefully unsolder leads from diodes, Fig. 15. Use only a 100 watt soldering iron. Leave the soldering iron on contact with the diode terminals only long enough to remove the wires. Both pliers are used as temporary heat sinks in order to protect diodes. *Excessive heat can damage a good diode.*

8. Remove 3 insulated diode plate screws and insulators, and separate diode plates.

9. Remove drive pulley, Fig. 16.

10. Remove 3 screws that hold front bearing retainer and remove front housing.

11. If the bearing is being replaced, remove it as shown in Fig. 17. Remove bearing retainer and spacer. It will not be necessary to remove the stop ring unless it has been damaged.

Inspection

1. The rotor, stator, diodes and bearings are not to be cleaned with solvent. These parts are to be wiped off with a clean cloth. Cleaning solvent may cause damage to electrical parts or contaminate the bearing internal lubricant. Wash all other parts with solvent and dry them.

2. Rotate front bearing on drive shaft. Check for any scraping noise, looseness or roughness that would indicate that the bearing is excessively worn. As the bearing is being rotated, look for any lubricant leakage. If any of these conditions exist, replace the bearing.

3. Place the rear end bearing on the slip ring end of the shaft and rotate the bearing on the shaft. Make the same check for wear or damage as for the front bearing.

4. Check the housings for cracks. Check the front housing for stripped

threads in the mounting holes. Replace defective housings.

5. Pulleys that have been removed and installed several times may have to be replaced because of the increased bore diameter. A pulley is not suitable for reuse if more than ¼ of the shaft length will enter the pulley bore with light pressure. Replace any pulley that is bent out of shape. After installing the pulley, check for clearance between the fins and the alternator drive end housing.

6. Check all wire leads on both stator and rotor for loose soldered connections and for burned insulation. Resolder poor connections and replace parts that show burned insulation.

7. Check slip rings for damaged insulation. Check the slip rings for runout as shown in Fig. 18. If the slip rings are more than .0005" out of round, take a light cut (minimum diameter limit ½") from the face of the rings to true them up.

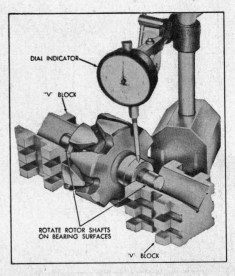

Fig. 18 Checking slip ring runout

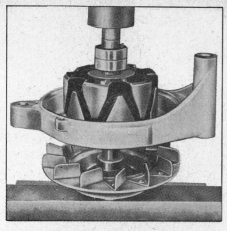

Fig. 19   Installing pulley

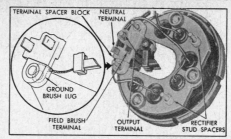

Fig. 20   Stator, heat sink and terminal spacer block assembly

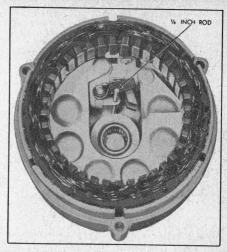

Fig. 21   Brushes retracted for assembly

If the slip rings are badly damaged, the entire rotor will have to be replaced as they are serviced only as a complete assembly.

8. Replace the terminal spacer block assembly if the neutral terminal is loose. Replace any parts that are burned or cracked. Replace brushes that are worn to less than .350" in length. Replace the brush spring if it has less than 7 to 12 ounces tension.

Assembly

1. If the stop ring on the drive shaft was broken, install a new stop ring. Push the new ring on the shaft and into the groove. *Do not open the ring with snap ring pliers.*
2. Position the front bearing spacer on the drive shaft against the stop ring, and position the bearing retainer on the shaft with the flat surface of the retainer outward.

3. Putting pressure on the inner race only, press the new bearing on the shaft until it contacts the spacer.
4. Place the front housing over the shaft with the bearing positioned in the front housing cavity. Install the bearing retainer mounting screws.
5. Press the pulley onto the shaft until the hub just touches the inner race of the front bearing, Fig. 19. *A new pulley must be installed if more than ¼ of the shaft length will enter the old pulley bore with light pressure.*
6. If a new diode plate is being installed, mount the two plates together so that they are insulated from each other, Fig. 20. Solder the wire leads to the diodes as shown in Fig. 15, using only a 100 watt iron. *Avoid excessive heat as this can result to damage to the diode.*
7. Insert the new field brush terminal blade into the slot in the terminal spacer block with the brush pigtail extending toward the brush holder pivots, Fig. 20.
8. Install brush holders and brush spring to terminal block, then position brushes in holders.
9. Solder the neutral wire to its terminal. Position terminal spacer block on rectifier plate mounting studs,

with the ground brush lug over the mounting stud farthest from the output terminal, Fig. 20.
10. Place spacers on rectifier mounting studs farthest from terminal block.
11. Install rear bearing so that its open end is flush with the inner surface of the housing boss, Fig. 14. Allow for space under the outer end of the bearing during installation.
12. Place rear end housing over rectifier plate and stator assembly and mount rectifier plates to housing.
13. Retract brushes and insert a short piece of ⅛" rod or stiff wire through hole in rear end housing to hold brushes in retracted position, Fig. 21.
14. Wipe clean the rear bearing surface of the rotor shaft.
15. Position rear housing and stator assembly over rotor and, after aligning marks made during disassembly, install housing through bolts. Remove brush retracting rod.

Ford Autolite Alternator With Integral Regulator

DESCRIPTION

Alternator

The alternator used with this unit is basically the same as the standard Ford Autolite unit. Modifications have been made in the brush holder assembly, rear end frame and the stator assembly to accommodate the integral regulator. Except for tests outlined here, refer to preceding chapter for service procedures.

Integral Regulator

The integral regulator, Fig. 1, consists of an integrated, solid state circuit, made up of transistors, diodes and resistors, all connected by aluminum conductors and fabricated within a ⅛" square silicon crystal. This is a one piece, non-adjustable unit which must be replaced if it malfunctions, or if it is not calibrated within specified limits of 13.5 to 15.3 volts between 50 and 125 degrees F.

SYSTEM TESTS

NOTE: Because the voltage sensing circuit is permanently connected across the charging system, resulting in a small but harmless current drain, a voltmeter cannot be connected in series with the battery for diagnosis. The integral regulator is not defective and should not be replaced because of leakage indicated by a voltmeter connected in series with the battery or regulator.

Voltage Regulator Test

1. Using a fully charged battery, turn off all lights and accessories. Be sure ignition switch is off and make test connections as shown in Fig. 2.
2. Open battery adapter switch. Ammeter should show zero amperes. A discharge (2 amperes) indicates a malfunction in the alternator field coil or the regulator. Refer to Field Circuit Tests. If ammeter shows zero, proceed as follows:
3. With transmission in neutral or park and parking brake applied, place tester master control at the 1/4 ohm resistor position.
4. Close battery adapter switch and start engine. Be sure all lights and accessories are off and open battery adapter switch.
5. Operate engine at approximately 2000 rpm for 5 minutes, and check voltage. If voltage is between 13.3 and 15.3 volts, the regulator is functioning satisfactorily. If voltage does not rise above battery voltage, check regulator supply voltage. If voltage exceeds 15.3 volts, perform field circuit tests.

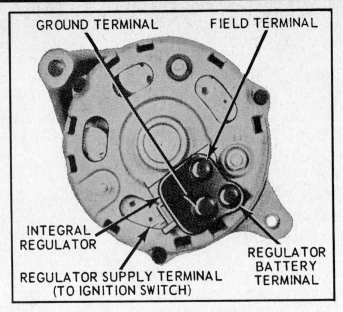

Fig. 1 Alternator with integral regulator

Supply Voltage Test

Check for voltage supply terminal of the alternator with a 12 volt test light or a voltmeter. If no voltage is indicated, the supply circuit is disconnected or broken. If voltage is present, perform Alternator Output Test.

Alternator Output Test Off Vehicle

When using test bench, refer to manufacturer's procedures and be sure to disconnect battery cable as the alternator output connector is always connected to the battery.

Alternator Output Test On Vehicle

NOTE: Under no circumstances should the regulator battery terminal be connected to the regulator field terminal. To do so will damage regulator.

1. With transmission in neutral or park and parking brake applied, make test connections as shown in Fig. 3.
2. Close battery adapter switch. Start engine and reopen adapter switch. Voltage reading must be maintained between 10 and 15 volts.
3. Increase engine speed to 2000 rpm.

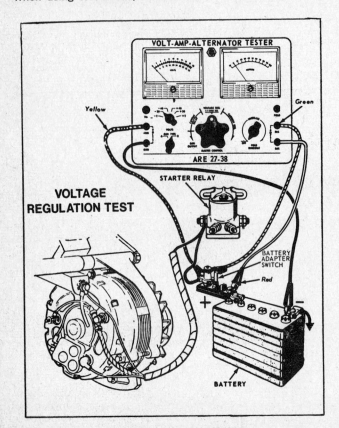

Fig. 2 Voltage regulator test

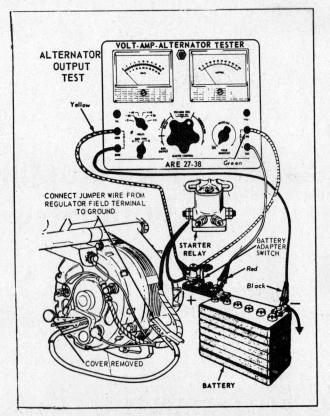

Fig. 3 Alternator output test

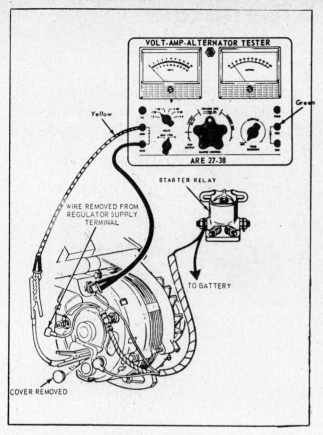

Fig. 4 Field voltmeter test

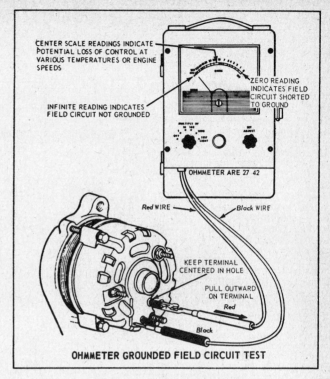

Fig. 5 Ohmmeter field circuit test

Turn off all lights and accessories.
4. Turn master control clockwise until voltmeter shows 15 volts. At 15 volts, ammeter should register 50 to 57 amperes. If alternator is working properly, regulator must be replaced.
5. Return engine speed to idle before releasing master control knob.
6. An alternator output of 2 to 8 amperes below minimum specification usually indicates an open diode rectifier. An alternator with a shorted diode will usually whine, most noticeably at idle speed.

Field Voltmeter Test

1. Turn off ignition switch and remove wire from regulator supply terminal.
2. Make test connections as shown in Fig. 4. Open battery adapter switch.

NOTE: if there was an ammeter drain that stopped when supply terminal was disconnected, an ignition switch or wiring problem is indicated. If discharge continues (2 or more amperes), proceed as follows:

3. Voltmeter should read 12 volts. If there is no voltage reading, the field circuit is open or grounded. Perform Alternator Field Ohmmeter Test. If ohmmeter tests show alternator field is okay, the regulator is shorted and must be replaced.
4. If voltmeter reading in Step 3 is

more than one volt but less than battery voltage, a partial ground in the alternator field circuit is indicated. Perform Field Ohmmeter Test to isolate trouble between alternator and regulator.

Fig. 6 Diode test

Field Ohmmeter Test

1. Disconnect battery ground cable and remove regulator from alternator.
2. Make ohmmeter connections as shown in Fig. 5.
3. If any of the conditions shown in Fig. 5 are found, remove and repair alternator. If alternator is okay, replace the regulator.

Diode Bench Test

1. Disassemble alternator and disconnect diode assembly from stator. Make test connections as shown in Fig. 6.
2. Touch one ohmmeter lead to diode plate and the other to each of the three stator lead terminals. Reverse probes and repeat test. Test the other set of diodes the same way.
3. All tests should show a low reading of approximately 60 ohms in one direction and an infinite reading with the probes reversed.

Open Stator Test

Connect ohmmeter probes between each pair of stator leads. If ohmmeter does not show equal readings between each pair of stator leads, the stator is open and must be replaced.

Grounded Stator Test

Connect ohmmeter probes between one of the stator leads and the stator core. If the ohmmeter shows any reading, stator is grounded and must be replaced.

Leece-Neville Alternators

SERIES 6000, 6200

These alternators, Fig. LN1, are the 40 and 50 ampere, three-phase type. The slip rings and brushes, which carry field current to the rotor coil, are enclosed for protection from abrasive dust yet are readily accessible for inspection and servicing. One brush is grounded to simplify the circuit.

The rectifier cells, or diodes, are mounted in the slip ring end housing and are internally connected to the stator windings. One end of each of the three stator windings, or phases, is connected to a positive and a negative diode. The other ends of the stator windings are connected together forming a "Y" type connection. The three negative and the three positive diodes are pressed (in sets) into two plates called "heat sinks". These multiple-purpose heat sinks serve as mountings for the diodes, as radiation plates for heat dissipation, and also as current conductors.

The two-element regulator used with these alternators consists of a voltage regulator and a load relay which is connected to the auxiliary terminal on the ignition switch, Fig. LN1. The load relay, controlled by the ignition switch, functions as a reverse current relay. When the ignition switch is turned on, the relay contacts close to energize the field coil in the alternator.

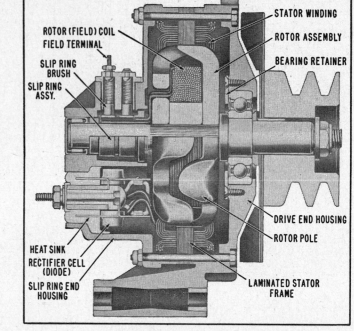

Fig. LN1   Sectional view of a Leece-Neville 6000 Series alternator

TESTING SYSTEM IN VEHICLE

Low or No Output

The field circuit must be closed in order to energize the rotor coil before the alternator can generate current.

A quick check of the field circuit can be made (with engine shut off) by turning on ignition switch and disconnecting the field terminal lead at the voltage regulator and then momentarily striking the FLD terminal with it.

If a medium spark is obtained, field circuit is closed. If spark is very light, a poor brush contact at the slip rings, or a poor connection, is indicated. If no spark is obtained, short or broken brushes, collapsed brush springs, poor or broken solder connections at the slip rings, or an open in the rotor coil, is indicated. A very heavy spark would indicate a short in the rotor coil. (Reconnect FLD terminal lead after making this check.)

If field circuit is found to be closed, alternator can be checked for output as follows:

With the engine at idle speed, remove the "F" lead from the alternator and attach a jumper wire from the "F" terminal to the "B" terminal. This jumper connection will take the regulator out of the circuit and allow the alternator to operate at full field strength.

If the alternator shows a high rate of charge when running with full field strength, the alternator is functioning and the problem lies with the regulator, system wiring or battery.

If the alternator shows a very low or no rate of charge when running with full field strength, the alternator will have to be removed from the engine and checked as outlined below if the system wiring and battery are good.

BENCH TESTS

1. Remove pulley, fan and spacer from shaft. Remove brushes. Remove through bolts holding unit together and remove drive end housing and rotor assembly.
2. To test the rotor without removing it from end housing, measure the resistance of the coil by placing the prods of an ohmmeter on the slip rings. If the meter reads from 3.8 to 4.2 ohms the rotor is good. If very little resistance is read, it would indicate a possible shorted coil circuit. Check for loose or broken wire at the slip rings. If no resistance is read, the coil is open. Should no loose or broken wires be detected at the slip rings, the short or open is within the rotor coils and the rotor is beyond repair.
3. If, upon removal of the brushes it is found that the brush springs are collapsed, the rotor has a shorted coil and should be replaced.
4. Check the slip ring brushes or springs. If the brushes or springs are cracked, broken or burned, they should be replaced. Brushes worn to a length less than $3/16$" are too short and must be replaced.
5. If the rotor checks good, the stator and rectifier sections should be tested. This can be accomplished without removing the stator and rectifier sections from the slip ring end housing.

Rectifier Tests On Units Having An "N" Terminal

Place the positive prod of an ohmmeter on the "N" terminal at the slip ring end housing and the negative prod on the "B" terminal. With the prods in this position, the meter will read approximately 4 to 5 ohms and indicate that this is the positive section rectifiers. With the prods reversed, the meter needle will read infinity (excessive resistance) which will indicate that the rectifiers are good. Color coding on bottom of rectifiers is red.

Place the negative prod of the ohmmeter on the "N" terminal and the positive prod on the "GRD" terminal. The ohmmeter will read approximately 4 to 5 ohms and indicate that this is the negative ground section. Reversing the position of the prods will make the meter read infinity. Color coding on bottom of rectifiers is black.

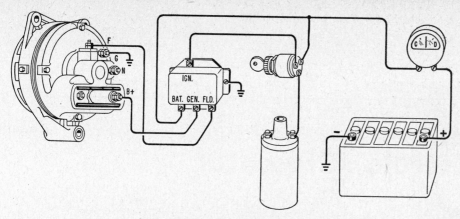

Fig. LN2   Leece-Neville alternator wiring diagram

Rectifier Tests On Units Without "N" Terminal

Since there is no "N" (neutral) terminal, it will be necessary to make the tests at the rectifier sections.

Place the negative prod of an ohmmeter on any one of the three lead connections between the stator and rectifier cells. Place the positive prod on the heat sink of the insulated section of rectifiers. The meter should read 4 to 5 ohms. Reverse the prod position and the meter should read infinity and indicate that this is the positive or grounded section of rectifiers.

Place the positive prod on any of the lead connections between stator and rectifier cells and the negative prod on the opposite heat sink. The meter should read 4 to 5 ohms. Reverse the prod positions and the meter will read infinity indicating that this is the negative rectifier section.

When making the above tests, if the meter readings do not fall in the category mentioned above, one or more of the rectifiers in the section are not operating properly and the section should be replaced. When replacing rectifiers, be certain that the correct section is grounded.

Alternate Rectifier Test

If an ohmmeter is not available a #57 bulb may be used to test the silicon rectifiers. This test is basically the same except that the bulb and battery replaces the ohmmeter.

If the bulb lights in one direction only the rectifiers are good.

If the bulb lights in both directions one or more of the cells in the section are shorted and the section found bad should be replaced.

If the bulb does not light in either direction one or more of the cells in the section are open and the section should be replaced.

Rectifier Section, Replace

To replace one or both rectifier sections, remove the nuts, etc. from the "B" terminal and the bolt holding the rectifier sections opposite the "B" terminal, and in the case of negative ground units,

the "N" terminal. Remove stator and rectifier section from slip ring housing and unsolder the stator leads from the rectifier section or sections to be replaced.

When resoldering the rectifier sections to the stator leads, care must be exercised to apply only enough heat to insure a good connection. Overheating may damage the rectifier cells.

Stator Ground Test

To ground test the stator it will be necessary to unsolder the AC stator leads from the rectifiers. Check each stator phase for grounds to the stator core. A 110 volt test lamp is used for this test. No circuit should be present.

Stator Winding Continuity Test

With the test lamp check the continuity of each of the three stator phases. Each phase should show a closed circuit.

ALTERNATOR REPAIRS

After the foregoing tests are completed and the part or parts found inoperative are replaced, the following inspection and cleaning of parts should be done.

Rotor

If the rotor has seen considerable service and the slip rings appear to be worn, they should be replaced. Check shaft threads. Press rotor from housing using an arbor press.

To disassemble rotor, unsolder both field coil leads from the slip rings and, using a small puller, carefully pull off the rings. In some cases it will be impossible to save the old slip rings due to the tight fit on the shaft.

To clean the rotor it may be washed with a brush dipped in a cleaning solvent or paint thinner. Rinse with another brush dipped in unleaded gasoline or kerosene and then wipe with a dry cloth or blow dry with compressed air. *Do not immerse complete rotor in the cleaning fluid.*

Stator

After visual inspection finds the stator free of broken or cracked insulation or other damage which would cause failure, the stator can be cleaned in the same manner described for the rotor.

Brushes, Bearings, Etc.

Replace worn or broken brushes, insulation washers, etc. and inspect all tapped holes for good threads. It is recommended that bearings be replaced at time of overhaul.

Remove bearing retainer screws and bearing retainer from drive end housing. Tap or press out bearing. With bearing removed, housing can be immersed in cleaning solvent or paint thinner for cleaning.

The slip ring end housing bearing needs no special tool for removal or replacement. It may be tapped or pressed out. However, a piece of fiber or similar material should be placed over the new bearing when installing to prevent damage.

Reassembly

The alternator should be assembled in the reverse order of disassembly. Care should be exercised not to damage the housing pilots and stator windings. When completely assembled, spin the rotor by hand for free rotation check.

Reinstall the alternator on the vehicle and run it "full field" as outlined under Alternator System Check.

REGULATOR, ADJUST
Load Relay

To check the load relay, connect leads from a 12 volt battery to the ground and ignition terminals on the regulator, with a variable resistor in series with one lead. Connect a voltmeter across the "IGN" and "GRD" terminals.

Start with all the resistance cut in and then gradually decrease it to allow the voltmeter reading to rise. The load relay should close at 5.8 to 6.2 volts.

To raise the closing voltage, increase the spring tension by bending the lower arm of the spring bracket. To lower the closing voltage decrease the spring tension.

Voltage Regulator

To check the voltage regulator remove the cover. Connect one voltmeter lead to the regulator "BAT" terminal and the other lead to the regulator or alternator ground. Then connect a pair of earphones of not less than 1,000 ohms resistance to the "FLD" and "GEN" regulator terminals to hear the operation of the regulator contacts. *After each of the three steps in the test, open the ignition switch to bring the alternator speed to zero.*

1. Raise alternator speed slowly and listen for the vibration indicating the start of regulation on the upper contacts. This should start within the range of 13.9 and 14.3 volts. To increase the voltage, bend the lower arm of the spring bracket down. To

lower the voltage, bend the arm up.
2. Slowly increase alternator speed past the start of regulation until the vibration ceases. Continue until the voltage reaches its maximum value, just before the lower set of contacts starts to vibrate. The maximum

should be 14.7 and is adjusted as outlined in Step 1.
3. Increase alternator speed slowly past maximum voltage until the regulator armature vibrates on the lower contacts. The operating voltage should be 13.9 to 14.3 volts. To

increase the voltage, increase the armature core gap; reduce the core gap to lower the voltage. The gap is adjusted by loosening the locking screw on the contact block to raise or lower the block.

Motorola Alternator

DESCRIPTION

The electrical circuit of the alternator, Fig. 1, uses 6 silicon diodes in a full wave rectifier circuit. Since the diodes will pass current from the alternator to the battery or load but not in the reverse direction, the alternator does not use a circuit breaker. Fig. 2 shows the charging circuit.

The entire DC output of the system passes through the "Isolation Diode". This diode is mounted in a separate aluminum heat sink and is replaced as an assembly. The isolation diode is not essential for rectification. It is used to:
1. Provide an automatic solid state switch for illuminating the charge-discharge indicator light.
2. Automatically connect the voltage regulator to the alternator and battery when the alternator is operating.
3. Eliminate electrical leakage over the alternator insulators so that maximum leakage is less than one milliampere when the car is not in use.

Voltage Regulator

The voltage regulator is an electrical

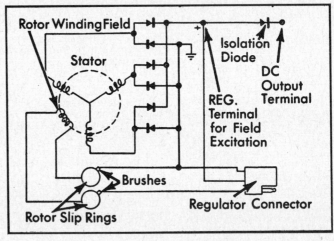

Fig. 1 Alternator circuit diagram

switching device sealed at the factory, requiring no adjustments. It senses the voltage appearing at the regulator ter-

minal of the alternator and supplies the necessary field current for maintaining the system voltage at the output terminal.

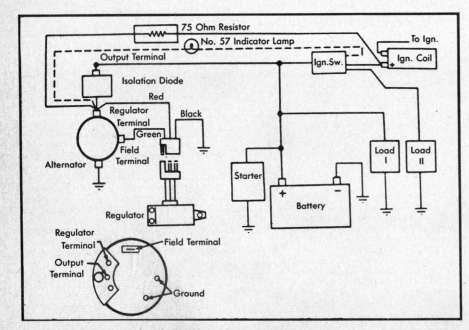

Fig. 2 Charging circuit diagram

TESTING SYSTEM IN VEHICLE

Alternator Output Test, Fig. 3

1. Close by-pass switch on battery post adapter, Fig. 4.
2. Start engine and adjust speed to 2000 rpm.
3. Open by-pass switch.
4. Rotate load control knob to the load

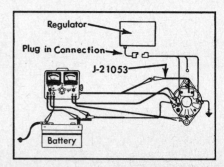

Fig. 3 Alternator output test connections

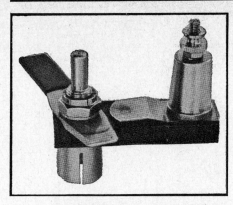

Fig. 4 Battery post adapter tool which provides a convenient method for connecting the ammeter leads of the volt-ammeter tester to the charging system

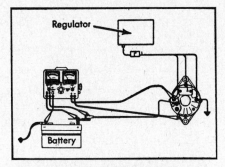

Fig. 5 Regulator terminal test connections

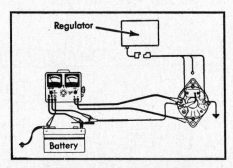

Fig. 6 Field current test connections

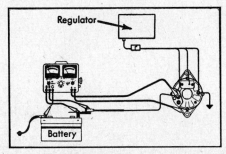

Fig. 7 Voltage regulator test connections

position and adjust until voltmeter reads approximately 6 volts.

5. Rotate alternator field control to direct position.
6. Adjust load control to obtain exactly 15 volts.
7. Observe ammeter; it should indicate maximum output of alternator with 25 amperes minimum. If no output is evident, observe voltmeter. *If there is over 12 volts at the regulator terminal and battery voltage is measured at the output terminal, the isolation diode is evidently open and should be replaced.*
8. Rotate alternator field control to open position.
9. Reduce engine speed to idle.
10. Rotate load control to direct position and stop engine.

Isolation Diode Test

If a commercial diode tester is used, follow the Test Equipment Manufacturer's instructions. If a commercial tester is not available, use a DC Test Lamp.

CAUTION: *Do not use a 120 volt test lamp as diodes will be damaged.*

1. Connect test lamp to output terminal and regulator terminal of isolation diode.
2. Reverse test probes.
3. The test lamp should light in one direction but should not light in the other direction.
4. If the test lamp lights in both directions the isolation diode is shorted.
5. If the test lamp does not light in either direction, isolation diode is open.

Rectifier Diode Tests

Any commercial in-circuit diode tester will suffice to make the test. Follow Test Equipment Manufacturer's instructions.

Check diodes individually after the diodes have been disconnected from the stator. A shorted stator coil or shorted insulating washers or sleeves on positive diodes would make diodes appear to be shorted.

A test lamp will not indicate an open condition unless all three diodes of either assembly are open. However, a shorted diode can be detected. This test is not 100% effective but can be used if so desired when an in-circuit diode tester is not available.

The test lamp should light in one direction but not in the other direction. If the test lamp lights in both directions, one or more of the diodes of the assembly being tested is shorted. If the test lamp does not light in either direction, *all three diodes in the assembly are open.* Check diodes individually after disassembly to ascertain findings.

NOTE: *A shorted stator coil would appear as a shorted negative diode. Also check stator for shorts after disassembly.*

Regulator Terminal Voltage Test, Fig. 5

1. Remove alternator field control leads.

0°-14.6-15.4	80°-14.0-14.8
20°-14.6-15.3	100°-13.8-14.6
40°-14.3-15.0	120°-13.7-14.5
60°-14.1-14.9	140°-13.6-14.4
160°-13.3-14.1	

Fig. 8 Voltages at various ambient temperatures under a 10 ampere load

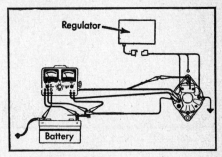

Fig. 9 Insulated circuit resistance test connections

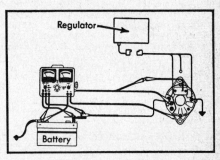

Fig. 10 Ground circuit resistance test connections

2. Remove field jumper leads.
3. Connect voltage regulator plug-in connector.
4. Connect slip-on field connector.
5. Turn on ignition switch.
6. Voltmeter indicates regulator terminal voltage which should be ½ to 2 volts.

NOTE: *If voltmeter indicates battery voltage of less than ½ volt, perform following steps to determine if voltage regulator is defective.*

7. Disconnect regulator plug-in connector.
8. Disconnect slip-on field connector and connect the field jumper lead to the alternator field terminal.
9. Connect field jumper clip to regulator terminal.
10. Voltmeter should now read 1 to 2 volts, which indicates voltage regulator is defective.

NOTE: *If results are other than specified, continue with Field Current Test. If field current is within specifications, test voltage regulator circuit.*

Field Current Test, Fig. 6

1. Disconnect voltage regulator plug-in connector.

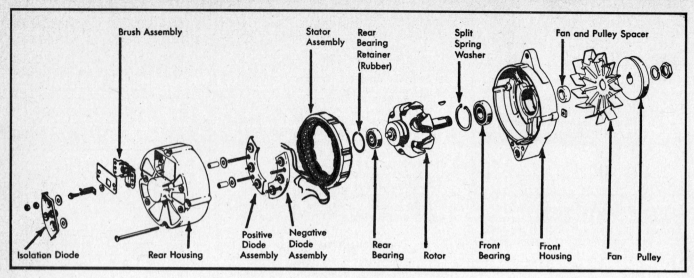

Fig. 11   Alternator disassembled

Labels: Brush Assembly, Stator Assembly, Rear Bearing Retainer (Rubber), Split Spring Washer, Fan and Pulley Spacer, Isolation Diode, Rear Housing, Positive Diode Assembly, Negative Diode Assembly, Rear Bearing, Rotor, Front Bearing, Front Housing, Fan, Pulley

2. Turn off ignition switch.
3. Disconnect slip-on field connector and connect the field jumper to the alternator field terminal.
4. Connect the clip of the field jumper lead to the alternator output terminal.
5. Ammeter now indicates field current draw which should be 2 to 2½ amperes.
6. Disconnect field jumper lead from output terminal.

Voltage Regulator Test, Fig. 7

1. Remove field jumper lead.
2. Connect voltage regulator plup-in connector.
3. Connect slip-on field connector.
4. Connect positive voltmeter lead to alternator output terminal.
5. Start engine and adjust speed to 1500 rpm.
6. Rotate load control knob to the ¼ ohm position.
7. Voltmeter indicates voltage regulator setting which should be 14 to 14.8 volts at 75 degrees ambient temperature (see Fig. 8).
8. Return load control knob to direct position.
9. Reduce engine speed and shut it off.

Insulated Circuit Resistance Test, Fig. 9

1. Disconnect voltage regulator plug-in connector.
2. Connect field control leads, one to the output terminal and one to the field jumper lead.
3. Connect the negative voltmeter lead to the battery end of the positive battery cable.
4. Close by-pass switch and start engine, then open by-pass switch.
5. Adjust engine speed to approximately 1500 rpm.
6. Rotate alternator field control slowly toward direct until ammeter indicates 10 amperes current flow.
7. Voltmeter now indicates the voltage drop in the alternator insulated circuit which should not exceed .3 volt.

Ground Circuit Resistance Test, Fig. 10

1. Connect negative voltmeter lead to

alternator housing.
2. Connect positive voltmeter lead to negative battery post.
3. With ammeter indicating 10 amperes, voltmeter should indicate not more than .05 voltage drop in the alternator ground circuit.
4. Rotate field control to open position. Reduce engine speed to idle and stop engine.

ALTERNATOR REPAIRS

Disassembly, Fig. 11

Brush Assembly

The brush assembly can be removed in most cases with the alternator on the vehicle. The spring clip is bent back so that the field terminal plug can be removed. Remove the two self-tapping

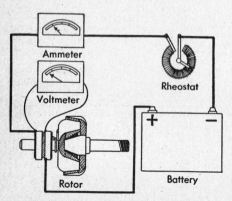

Fig. 12   Field coil test

Labels: Ammeter, Voltmeter, Rheostat, Rotor, Battery

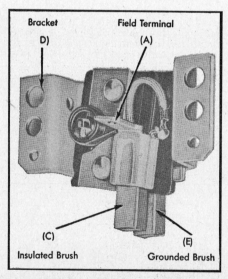

Fig. 13   Brush assembly test

Labels: Bracket (D), Field Terminal (A), (C) Insulated Brush, (E) Grounded Brush

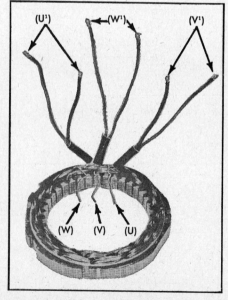

Fig. 14   Stator coil shorts and continuity tests

Labels: (U¹), (W¹), (V¹), (W), (V), (U)

screws, field plug retainer spring and cover. Pull brush assembly straight out far enough to clear locating pins, then lift brush assembly out. The complete brush assembly is available for replacement.

Isolation Diode

Remove the 2 lock nuts securing the isolation diode to the rear housing and slide it off the studs. The diode is replaced as an assembly.

Rear Housing

Remove the 4 through bolts and nuts. Carefully separate the rear housing and stator from the front housing by using 2 small screwdrivers and prying the stator from the front housing at 2 opposing slots where the "through bolts" are removed. Do not burr the stator core which would make assembly difficult.

Caution: *Do not insert screwdriver blade deeper than $1/16$" to avoid damaging stator winding.*

Stator and Diode Assembly

Do not unsolder stator-to-diode wire junction. Remove stator and diode as an assembly. Avoid bending stator wire at junction holding positive and negative diode assembly from housing.

Remove 4 lock nuts and insulating washers. The insulating washers and nylon sleeves are used to insulate the positive plate studs from the housing. With the 4 nuts removed, the stator can be separated from rear housing by hand.

Diode Replacement

In soldering and unsoldering leads from diodes, grasp the diode lead with pliers between the diode and stator lead to be removed. This will give better heat dissipation and protect the diode. Do not exert excessive stress on diode lead. *Make note of diode assembly to stator connections, and make sure replacement diode assembly connections are the same. The positive diode assembly has red markings, the negative black markings.*

ROTOR

The rotor should only require removal from the front housing if there is a defect in the field coil itself or in the front bearing. Front and rear bearings are permanently sealed, self-lubricating type. If the front housing must be removed from the rotor, use a two jaw puller to remove the pulley. The split spring washer must be loosened with snap ring pliers through the opening in the front housing. Remove the washer only after the housing is removed. The rotor and front bearing can be removed from the front housing by tapping the rotor shaft slightly.

NOTE: *Make certain that the split spring washer has been removed from its groove before attempting to remove the front housing from the bearing.*

Alternator Bench Tests

Field Coil Test

The rotor should be tested for grounds and for shorted turns in the winding. The ground test is made with test probes connected in series with a 110 volt test lamp. Place one test probe on the slip ring and the other probe on the rotor core. If the bulb lights the rotor is grounded.

To test for shorted turns, check rotor field current draw as shown in Fig. 12. Slowly reduce resistance of rheostat to zero. With full battery voltage applied to field coil, the field current should be 1.4 to 1.9 amperes. Excessive current draw indicates shorted turn in field winding.

Brush Insulation Test

Connect an ohmmeter or a test lamp to the field terminal and bracket. Resistance should be high (infinite) or test lamp should not light. If resistance is low or if test lamp lights, brush assembly is shorted and must be replaced.

Continuity Test

Connect an ohmmeter to field terminal and brush. Use an alligator clip to assure good contact to brush, test points "A" and "C" in Fig. 13.

CAUTION: *Do not chip brush.*

Resistance reading should be zero. Move brush and brush lead wire to make certain that brush lead wire connections are not intermittent. Resistance reading should not vary when brush and lead wire are being moved around. Connect ohmmeter to bracket and grounded brush, test points "E" and "D", Fig. 13. Resistance reading should be zero.

Stator In-Circuit Test

When making the in-circuit stator leakage test, some consideration must be given to the rectifier diodes that are connected to the stator winding. The negative diode assembly will conduct in one direction when properly polarized. A shorted diode in the negative diode assembly would make the stator appear to be shorted. For this reason, the rectifier diode plate assembly and stator must be checked individually after alternator has been disassembled if the problem is localized to the stator.

CAUTION: *Use a special diode continuity light or a DC test lamp. Do not use a 120 volt test lamp as diodes will be damaged.*

1. Connect the test lamp to a diode terminal of the negative assembly and ground terminal.
2. Reverse test probes. The lamp should light in one direction but not in the other.
3. If the test lamp does not light in either direction, this indicates that all three rectifiers in the negative diode assembly are open.
4. If the test lamp lights in both directions, the stator winding is shorted to stator or one of the negative diodes is shorted.
5. Check stator again when it is disassembled from diode assemblies.
6. With alternator disassembled, connect an ohmmeter or test lamp probes to one of the diode terminals and to stator.
7. Resistance reading should be infinite or test lamp should not light.
8. If resistance reading is not infinite or test lamp lights, high leakage or a short exists between stator winding and stator. In either case, stator should be replaced.

Stator Coil Shorts Test

1. This test checks for shorts between stator coil windings. The winding

junctions must be separated as shown in Fig. 14. An ohmmeter or test lamp may be used.

2. Connect one of the test probes to test point "U" and the other to test point "V" and then to test point "W". Resistance should be infinite or test lamp should not light.
3. Connect test probes to test V and W. Resistance should be infinite or test lamp should not light. In either test, if resistance reading is not infinite or test lamp lights, high leakage or a short exists between stator windings. Stator should be replaced.

Continuity Test

1. Measure resistance of each winding in stator between test points U and U1, V and V1, W and W1, Fig. 14. Resistance should be a fraction of an ohm (approximately .1 Ohm). An extremely accurate instrument would be necessary to ascertain shorted turns. Only an open condition can be detected with a commercial type ohmmeter.
2. If the alternator has been disassembled because of an electrical malfunction, replace stator only after all other components have been checked and found to be satisfactory.

Assemble Alternator

1. Clean bearing and inside of bearing hub of front housing. Support front housing and, using a suitable driver, apply sufficient pressure to outside race of bearing to seat bearing.
2. Insert split spring washer hub of front housing, seating washer into groove of hub.

NOTE: *Do nut use a screwdriver or any small object to compress washer that can slip off and damage bearing seal. Make certain that split spring washer has been installed prior to assembling front housing and rotor.*

3. Use sufficient pressure to seat front bearing against shoulder on rotor shaft. The bearing drive tool must fit the inner race of bearing.
4. Install fan and pulley.
5. Use a $7/16$" socket to fit inside race of rear bearing and apply sufficient pressure to drive bearing against shoulder of rotor shaft.
6. Assemble front and rear housings.
7. Make certain that rear bearing is properly seated in rear housing hub and that diode wires are properly dressed so that rotor will not contact diode wires.
8. Align stator slots with rear housing through bolt holes, then align front housing through bolt holes with respect to rear housing.

NOTE: *The position of the brush and belt adjusting screw boss must be in the same relative position to each other.*

9. Spin rotor to make certain that rotor is not contacting diode wires. Install bolts and tighten evenly.
10. Before mounting isolation diode, make certain that positive rectifier diode plate has been properly insulated from housing.
11. Install brush assembly, cover and field plug retainer spring.

Prestolite & American Motors Alternators

Alternator Output Test

1. Disconnect battery positive terminal.
2. Install battery post "knife switch" then complete test connections as per Fig. P1.
3. Close knife switch and start engine. Set engine speed at approximately 2000 rpm.
4. Open knife switch and adjust control knob clockwise to Load position until maximum ammeter reading is obtained. Add 5 amps to reading. Total reading should be the rated output of the alternator.

Regulator Test

1. Make test connections as per Fig. P1.
2. With engine speed at 2000 rpm, set control knob to 1/4 ohm position.
3. Read voltmeter. The reading should be not less than 13 volts and not more than 15 volts.

NOTE: Voltage readings vary due to underhood temperatures.

4. Return engine to idle, stop engine. Ammeter should read zero, indicating that isolation diode is functioning properly.
5. If a current draw exists, the isolation diode must be tested for leakage.

Isolation Diode Test

1. Close knife switch. Disconnect auxiliary or regulator lead from alternator.
2. Connect the positive voltmeter lead to the auxiliary or regulator terminal of the alternator and negative lead to the case of the alternator.
3. Set voltmeter to the 2 volt scale.
4. With regulator connected to the alternator and the ignition switch and all accessories off, measure voltage at the auxiliary or regulator terminal.
5. Voltage should not exceed .1 volt. Voltage in excess of .1 volt indicates that the isolation diode is leaking and must be replaced.

External Field Control Test

1. With the engine stopped and all test connections completed as per Fig. P1, disconnect field terminal from alternator and connect field rheostat as per Fig. P2.
2. With knife switch open, rotate rheostat to full clockwise (direct) position. Ammeter should read approximately minus 2 amps. If not, alternator brushes or rotor field windings are defective. Rotate rheostat back to full counterclockwise (open) position.
3. Close knife switch and set engine speed at 2000 rpm. Open knife switch.
4. Rotate rheostat control until al-

ternator specified output less 5 amps is obtained.
5. If output is low, alternator is defective. If output is satisfactory, regulator is at fault.

ALTERNATOR REPAIRS
Disassembly, Fig. P3

Brush Assembly

The brush assembly can be removed with the alternator on the car. Remove the two mounting screws and the cover. Tip the brush holder away from the alternator and remove. The brushes can be replaced by removing the retaining screws.

Rear Housing and Stator

The rear housing and stator must be removed as a unit. Mark housing and stator before disassembling to insure correct assembly.

Remove four retaining screws and tap lightly on stator and rear housing with a plastic mallet to separate from front drive housing.

Diode Replacement

To replace negative or positive rectifier diodes or the isolation diode, the stator leads must be unsoldered. When soldering or unsoldering any diodes, use a pair of pliers and a small piece of water soaked cotton for heat dissipation to protect the diode.

With stator removed, remove mounting nuts from "Aux" and "Output" terminals and remove the heat sink. Use a suitable press type tool to remove and install diodes, Fig. P4. Do not drive diodes in or out as damage will result.

Positive diodes are installed in the heat sink; negative diodes are installed in the rear housing.

With diodes correctly installed, resolder stator leads.

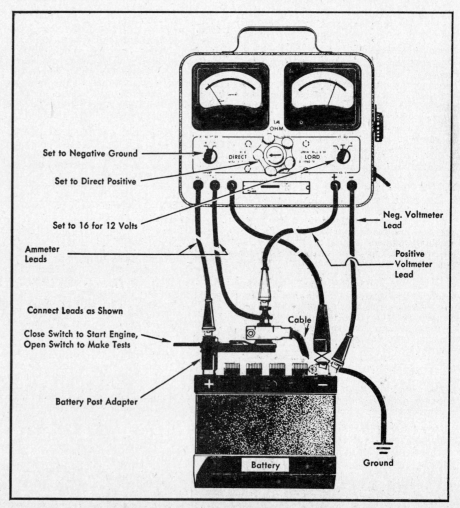

Set to Negative Ground
Set to Direct Positive
Set to 16 for 12 Volts
Ammeter Leads
Connect Leads as Shown
Close Switch to Start Engine, Open Switch to Make Tests
Battery Post Adapter
Neg. Voltmeter Lead
Positive Voltmeter Lead
Cable
Battery
Ground

Fig. P1   Charging circuit test connections

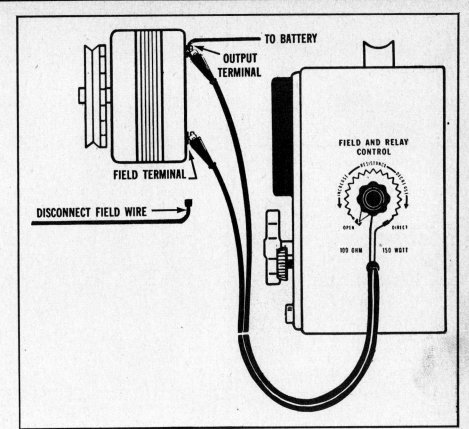

TO BATTERY

OUTPUT TERMINAL

FIELD TERMINAL

DISCONNECT FIELD WIRE

FIELD AND RELAY CONTROL

INCREASE — RESISTANCE — DECREASE

OPEN   DIRECT

100 OHM   150 WATT

Fig. P2   Alternator test with external field control

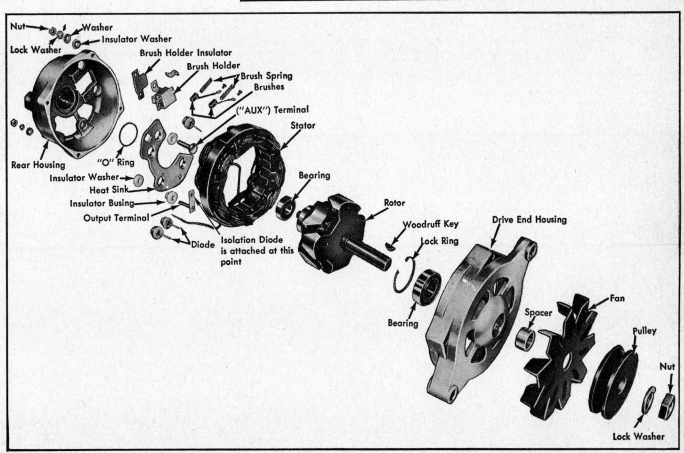

Nut
Washer
Insulator Washer
Lock Washer
Brush Holder Insulator
Brush Holder
Brush Spring
Brushes
("AUX") Terminal
Stator
Rear Housing
"O" Ring
Insulator Washer
Heat Sink
Insulator Busing
Output Terminal
Diode
Isolation Diode is attached at this point
Bearing
Rotor
Woodruff Key
Lock Ring
Drive End Housing
Bearing
Spacer
Fan
Pulley
Nut
Lock Washer

Fig. P3   Exploded view of Prestolite and American Motors alternator

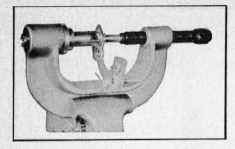

Fig. P4 Removing or installing diodes

Rotor Replacement

Remove retaining nut and, using a suitable puller, remove pulley. Remove fan, woodruff key and spacer. Remove rotor from front housing with puller, Fig. P5.

BENCH TESTS

Rotor

Test the rotor for grounds by touching one probe of a 110 volt test lamp to a slip ring and the other to the rotor core. If bulb lights the rotor winding is grounded.

To test for shorts, check rotor field current draw as shown in Fig. P6. Use rheostat to adjust the voltage to 10.0 volts. Field current should be 2.4-2.5 amps. Battery must be fully charged to carry out this test.

Excessive draw indicates a shorted field winding.

Stator

To test for an open winding use a number 57 bulb in series with a 12 volt battery and test probes. Touch one test probe to the connection of the three stator windings and the other to each stator lead that is connected to the di-

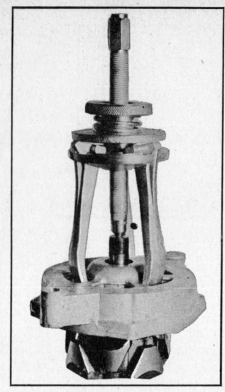

Fig. P5 Removing rotor from front end drive housing

odes. If the bulb fails to light, the winding is open.

Test for grounded winding with a 110 volt test lamp. For this test it is necessary to disconnect the diodes from the stator leads. Touch one lead to the stator core, the other to each of the three leads of the stator winding. If lamp lights, winding is grounded.

Shorted windings in the stator are dif-

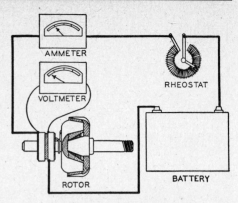

Fig. P6 Meter connections for testing rotor field current draw

ficult to detect, therefore, if rotor and diodes are not defective and the stator is not open or grounded, replace the stator.

Alternator, Assemble

1. Press front bearing into the front end drive housing, making sure the dust seal faces the rotor. Install bearing retainer stop ring.
2. Install spacer, fan and pulley. Install lockwasher and nut and tighten securely.
3. Install heat sink, negative diodes and stator. Solder all stator-to-diode connections that were previously disconnected.
4. Install rotor and front end drive housing to stator and rear housing.
5. Align marks made during disassembly on housings and install four retaining screws.
6. Install brush holder assembly and screws.
7. Check to be sure stator leads and brush holder assembly do not rub on the rotor and that the rotor turns freely when rotated by hand.

STARTING MOTORS

CONTENTS

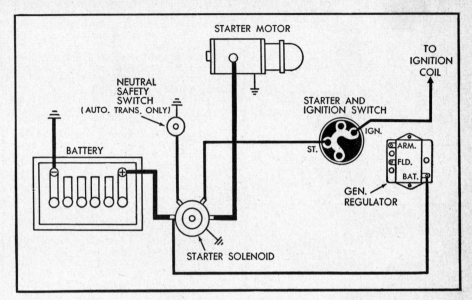

Fig. 1   Wiring diagram of a typical starting circuit

STARTER TROUBLE CHECK-OUT

When trouble develops in the starting motor circuit, and the starter cranks the engine slowly or not at all, several preliminary checks can be made to determine whether the trouble lies in the battery, in the starter, in the wiring between them, or elsewhere. Many conditions besides defects in the starter itself can result in poor cranking performance.

To make a quick check of the starter system, turn on the headlights. They should burn with normal brilliance. If they do not, the battery may be run down and it should be checked with a hydrometer.

If the battery is in a charged condition so that the lights burn brightly, operate the starting motor. Any one of three things will happen to the lights: (1) They will go out, (2) dim considerably or (3) stay bright without any cranking action taking place.

If Lights Go Out

If the lights go out as the starter switch is closed, it indicates that there is a poor connection between the battery and starting motor. This poor connection will most often be found at the battery terminals. Correction is made by removing the cable clamps from the terminals, cleaning the terminals and clamps, replacing the clamps and tightening them securely. A coating of corrosion inhibitor (vaseline will do) may be applied to the clamps and terminals to retard the formation of corrosion.

If Lights Dim

If the lights dim considerably as the starter switch is closed and the starter operates slowly or not at all, the battery may be run down, or there may be some mechanical condition in the engine or starting motor that is throwing a heavy burden on the starting motor. This imposes a high discharge rate on the battery which causes noticeable dimming of the lights.

Check the battery with a hydrometer. If it is charged, the trouble probably lies in either the engine or starting motor itself. In the engine, tight bearings or pistons or heavy oil place an added burden on the starting motor. Low temperatures also hamper starting motor performance since it thickens engine oil and makes the engine considerably harder to crank and start. Also, a battery is less efficient at low temperatures.

In the starting motor, a bent armature, loose pole shoe screws or worn bearings, any of which may allow the armature to drag, will reduce cranking performance and increase current draw.

In addition, more serious internal damage is sometimes found. Thrown armature windings or commutator bars, which sometimes occur on over-running clutch drive starting motors, are usually caused by excessive over-running after starting. This is the result of such conditions as the driver keeping the starting switch closed too long after the engine has started, the driver opening the throttle too wide in starting, or improper carburetor fast idle adjustment. Any of these subject the over-running clutch to extra strain so it tends to seize, spinning the armature at high speed with resulting armature damage.

Another cause may be engine backfire during cranking which may result, among other things, from ignition timing being too far advanced.

To avoid such failures, the driver should pause a few seconds after a false start to make sure the engine has come

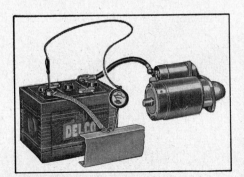

Fig. 2   Checking voltage drop between vehicle frame and grounded battery terminal post

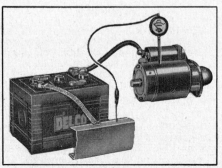

Fig. 3   Checking voltage drop between vehicle frame and starter field frame

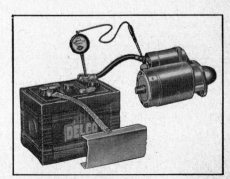

Fig. 4   Checking voltage drop between ungrounded battery terminal post and battery terminal on solenoid

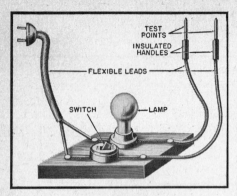

Fig. 5 A simple tester for use in making continuity and ground tests on armature and field windings

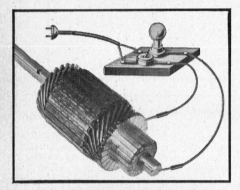

Fig. 6 Checking armature for grounds. If lamp lights armature is grounded and should be replaced

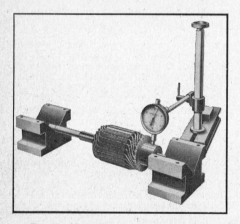

Fig. 7 Measuring commutator runout with dial indicator. Mount shaft in V blocks and rotate commutator. If runout exceeds .003″, commutator should be turned in a lathe to make it concentric

completely to rest before another start is attempted. In addition, the ignition timing should be reset if engine backfiring has caused the trouble.

Lights Stay Bright, No Cranking Action

This condition indicates an open circuit at some point, either in the starter itself, the starter switch or control circuit. The solenoid control circuit can be eliminated momentarily by placing a

heavy jumper lead across the solenoid main terminals to see if the starter will operate. This connects the starter directly to the battery and, if it operates, it indicates that the control circuit is not functioning normally. The wiring and control units must be checked to locate the trouble, Fig. 1.

If the starter does not operate with the jumper attached, it will probably have to be removed from the engine so it can be examined in detail.

Checking Circuit With Voltmeter

Excessive resistance in the circuit between the battery and starter will reduce cranking performance. The resistance can be checked by using a voltmeter to measure voltage drop in the circuits while the starter is operated. There are three checks to be made:

1. Voltage drop between car frame and grounded battery terminal post (not cable clamp), Fig. 2.
2. Voltage drop between car frame and starting motor field frame, Fig. 3.
3. Voltage drop between insulated battery terminal post and starting motor terminal stud (or the battery terminal stud of the solenoid), Fig. 4.

Each of these should show no more than one-tenth (0.1) volt drop when the starting motor is cranking the engine. Do not use the starter for more than 30 seconds at a time to avoid overheating it.

If excessive voltage drop is found in any of these circuits, make correction by disconnecting the cables, cleaning the connections carefully, and then reconnecting the cables firmly in place. A coating of vaseline on the battery cables and terminal clamps will retard corrosion.

NOTE—On some cars, extra long battery cables may be required due to the location of the battery and starter. This may result in somewhat higher voltage drop than the above recommended 0.1 volt. The only means of determining the normal voltage drop in such cases is to check several of these vehicles. Then when the voltage drop is well above the normal figure for all cars checked, abnormal resistance will be indicated and correction can be made as already explained.

STARTING MOTOR SERVICE

To obtain full performance data on a starting motor or to determine the cause of abnormal operation, the starting motor should be submitted to a no-load and torque test. These tests are best performed on a starter bench tester with the starter mounted on it.

From a practical standpoint, however, a simple torque test may be made quickly with the starter in the car. Make sure the battery is fully charged and that the starter circuit wires and terminals are in good condition. Then operate the starter to see if the engine turns over normally. If it does not, the torque developed is below standard and the

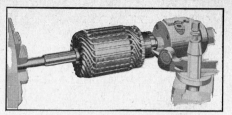

Fig. 8 Turning commutator in a lathe. Take light cuts until worn or bad spots are removed. Then remove burrs with No. 00 sandpaper

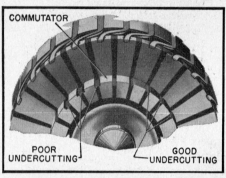

Fig. 9 Good undercutting should be .002″ wider than mica insulation, 1/64″ deep and exactly centered so that there are no burrs on the mica. Do not undercut molded commutators

Fig. 10 Checking armature for short circuit. As armature is rotated by hand, steel strip (hacksaw blade) will vibrate if short circuit exists

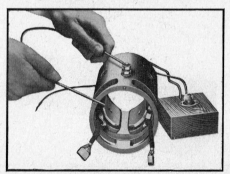

Fig. 11 Testing field coils for grounds. If a ground is present, lamp will light

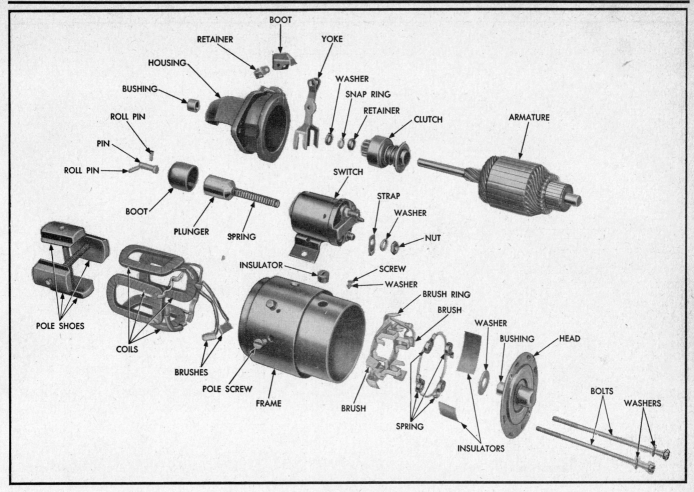

Fig. 12   Prestolite starter with over-running clutch drive

starter should be removed for further checking.

Remove the starter from the engine as outlined in the vehicle chapters, disassemble it as outlined further on and make the tests as suggested in Figs. 6 through 11.

PRESTOLITE STARTERS

Disassembling Overrunning Clutch Motor

1. Referring to Fig. 12, remove roll pin from shifting fork and solenoid coupling pin.
2. Remove solenoid.
3. Support solenoid coupling pin and drive out roll pin.
4. Remove solenoid rubber boot, plunger spring and coupling pin.
5. Remove thru bolts and take out commutator and cover, thrust washer and insulators.
6. Remove drive end housing, drive fork and armature from field frame.
7. Remove roll pin attaching shifting fork to pinion housing and remove retainer, dust cover and shifting fork.
8. Remove spacer and slide pinion gear toward commutator end of armature· then drive stop collar toward

pinion and remove lock ring.
9. Slide starter drive from armature.
10. Remove brush holder ring from field frame (3 screws).
11. Disconnect field lead wire at brush holder ring, disengage the brushes from the holders and carefully slide brush holder ring from field frame.

Overrunning Clutch

Place drive unit on shaft and, while holding armature, rotate pinion. The drive pinion should rotate smoothly in one direction (not necessarily easily), but should not rotate in the opposite direction. If drive unit does not function properly or pinion is worn or burred, replace drive unit.

CHRYSLER DIRECT DRIVE STARTER

This Chrysler built starting motor, Fig. 15, is a four coil assembly with an over-running clutch type drive and a solenoid shift-type switch mounted on the motor. The brush holders are riveted to a separate brush plate and are not serviced individually. Brush replacement can be made by removing the commutator bearing end head.

Disassembly

1. Remove through bolts and tap commutator end head from field frame.
2. Remove thrust washers from armature shaft.
3. Lift brush holder springs and remove brushes from holders.
4. Remove brush plate.
5. Disconnect field leads at solenoid connector.
6. Unfasten and remove solenoid and boot assembly.
7. Drive out over-running clutch shift fork pivot pin.
8. Remove drive end pinion housing and spacer washer.
9. Note position of shifter fork on starter and remove fork.
10. Slide over-running clutch pinion gear toward commutator end of armature. Drive stop retainer toward clutch pinion gear to expose snap ring and remove snap ring.
11. Slide clutch drive from armature shaft.
12. If necessary to replace the field coils, remove screw that holds ground brushes and raise brushes with the terminal and shunt wire up and away from field frame. Remove pole shoe screws and take out field coils.

Reassembly

1. Lubricate armature shaft and

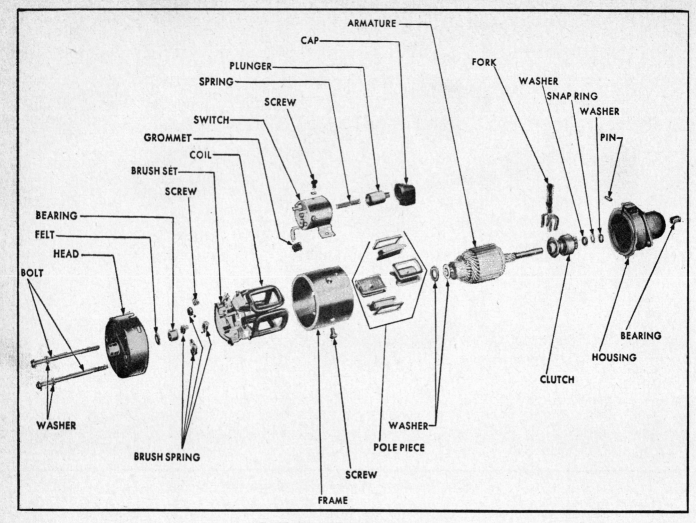

Fig. 15 Chrysler built direct drive starter

splines with SAE 10W or 30W rust preventive oil.

2. Install starter drive, stop collar (retainer), lock ring and spacer washer.
3. Install shifter fork over starter drive spring retainer washer with narrow leg of fork toward commutator. *If fork is not positioned properly, starter gear travel will be restricted, causing a lockup in the clutch mechanism.*
4. Install drive end (pinion) housing on armature shaft, indexing the shift fork with slot in drive end of housing.
5. Install shift fork pivot pin.
6. Install armature with clutch drive, shifter fork and pinion housing. Slide armature into field frame until pinion housing indexes with slot in field frame.
7. Install solenoid and boot assembly and tighten bolts securely.
8. Install ground brushes.
9. Connect field coil leads at solenoid connector.
10. Install brush holder ring, indexing tang of ring in hole of field frame.
11. Position brushes in brush holders. *Be*

sure field coil lead wires are properly enclosed behind brush holder ring and that they do not interfere with brush operation.
12. Install thrust washer on commutator end of armature shaft to obtain .010" minimum end play.
13. Install commutator end head.
14. Install through bolts and tighten securely.

Adjusting Pinion Clearance

1. Place starter in vise with soft jaws and tighten vise enough to hold starter. *Place a wedge or screwdriver between bottom of solenoid and starter frame to eliminate all deflection in solenoid when making pinion clearance check.*
2. Push in on solenoid plunger link, Fig. 16 (not fork lever) until plunger bottoms.
3. Measure clearance between end of pinion and pin stop with plunger seated and pinion pushed toward commutator end. Clearance should be 1/8". Adjust by loosening solenoid attaching screws and move solenoid

fore and aft as required.
4. Test starter operation for free running and install on engine.

CHRYSLER REDUCTION GEAR STARTER

This reduction gear starting motor, Fig. 17, has an armature-to-engine crankshaft ratio of 45 to 1; a 3½ to 1 reduction gear set is built into the motor assembly. The starter utilizes a solenoid shift. The housing of the solenoid is integral with the starter drive end housing.

Disassembly

1. Place gear housing of starter in a vise with soft jaws. *Use vise as a support fixture only; do not clamp.*
2. Remove through bolts and starter end head assembly.
3. Carefully pull armature up and out of gear housing, and starter frame and field assembly. Remove steel and fiber thrust washer. *The wire of the shunt field coil is soldered to the*

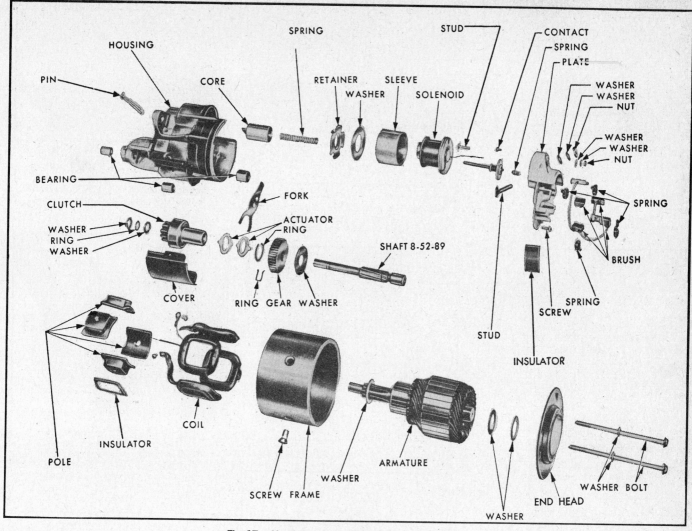

Fig. 17 Chrysler built reduction gear starting motor

brush terminal. One pair of brushes are connected to this terminal. The other pair of brushes is attached to the series field coils by means of a terminal screw. Carefully pull the frame and field assembly up just enough to expose the terminal screw and the solder connection of the shunt field at the brush terminal. Place two wood blocks between starter frame and gear housing, Fig. 18, to facilitate removal of terminal screw and unsoldering of shunt field wire at brush terminal.

4. Support brush terminal by placing a finger behind terminal and remove screw, Fig. 18.
5. Complete the disassembly procedure by referring to Figs. 19 through 33.

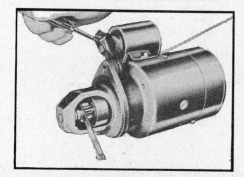

Fig. 16 Clearance between end of pinion and pin stop should be 1/8" with plunger seated and pinion pushed toward commutator end

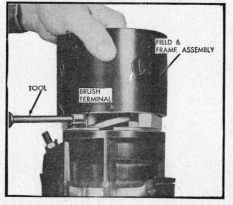

Fig. 18 Removing brush terminal screw

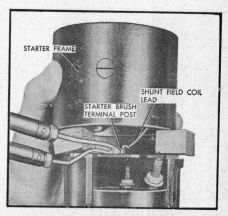

Fig. 19 Unsoldering shunt field coil lead from starter brush terminal

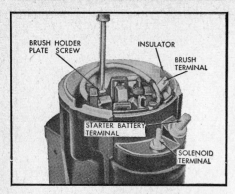

Fig. 20 Remove brush insulator which prevents contact between brush terminal and gear housing. Remove screw attaching brush holder plate to gear housing

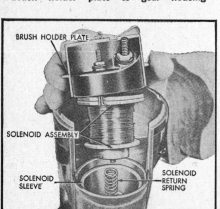

Fig. 21 Remove brush holder plate with brushes and solenoid as a unit

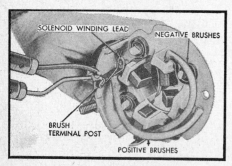

Fig. 22 Unsolder solenoid winding from brush terminal

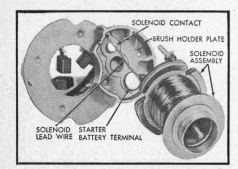

Fig. 23 Remove nut, steel washer and nylon washer from solenoid terminal. Separate brush holder plate from solenoid

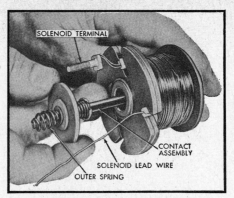

Fig. 24 Remove nut, steel washer and nylon washer from starter battery terminal. Remove terminal from holder plate. Then remove solenoid contact assembly

Fig. 25 Remove solenoid coil sleeve

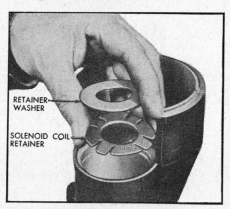

Fig. 26 Remove solenoid return spring (Fig. 21). Then remove solenoid coil retainer washer and retainer from solenoid housing

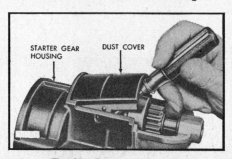

Fig. 27 Remove dust cover from gear housing

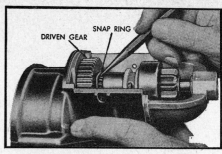

Fig. 28 Release snap ring that positions driven gear on pinion shaft. This ring is under tension and a cloth should be placed over ring to prevent it from springing away after removal

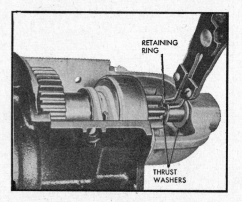

Fig. 29 Release retainer ring at front of pinion shaft. Do not spread ring any greater than the outside diameter of pinion shaft otherwise ring can be damaged

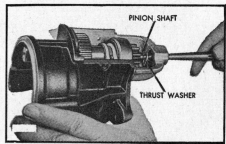

Fig. 30 Push pinion shaft toward rear of housing and remove snap ring and thrust washers

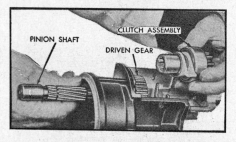

Fig. 31 Lift out clutch and pinion assembly with the two shifter fork nylon actuators

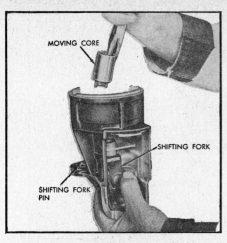

Fig. 32 Remove driven gear and friction washer. Then pull shift fork forward and remove solenoid moving core

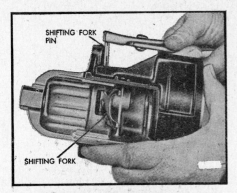

Fig. 33 Remove shift fork retainer pin and take out shift fork

Reassembly

The shifter fork consists of two spring steel plates assembled with two rivets, Fig. 34. There should be about 1/16" side movement to insure proper pinion gear engagement. Lubricate between plates sparingly with SAE 10 engine oil.

1. Position shift fork in drive housing and install fork retaining pin, Fig. 33. *One tip of pin should be straight, the other tip should be bent at a 15 degree angle away from housing. Fork and pin should operate freely after bending tip of pin.*
2. Install solenoid moving core and engage shifting fork, Fig. 32.
3. Enter pinion shaft in drive housing and install friction washer and driven gear.
4. Install clutch and pinion assembly, Fig. 31, thrust washer, retaining ring, and thrust washer.
5. Complete installation of pinion shaft, engaging fork with clutch actuators, Fig. 35. *Friction washer must be positioned on shoulder of splines of pinion shaft before driven gear is positioned.*
6. Install driven gear snap ring, Fig. 29. Install pinion shaft retaining ring, making sure ring fits tightly in shaft groove.

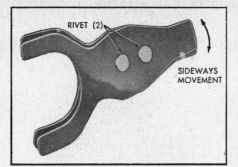

Fig. 34 Shifter fork assembly

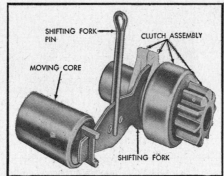

Fig. 35 Shifter fork and clutch arrangement

Fig. 36 Installing solenoid coil and sleeve

7. Install solenoid coil retainer, Fig. 26, with tangs down. *Space retainer in housing bore so that the four tangs rest on ridge in housing bore and not in the recesses.*
8. Install solenoid retainer washer.
9. Install solenoid return spring, Fig. 21. *Inspect condition of solenoid switch contacting washer. If top of washer is burned from arcing, disassemble switch and reverse washer.*
10. Install solenoid contact into solenoid, Fig. 24. Make sure contact spring is positioned in solenoid contact. *Inspect condition of contacts in brush holder plate. If contacts are badly burned, replace brush holder with brushes and contacts as an assembly.*

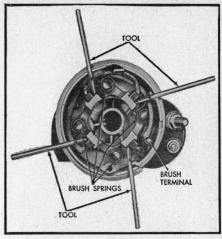

Fig. 37 Positioning of brushes with Tool Set C-3855

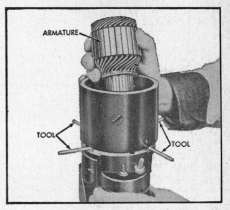

Fig. 38 Installing armature

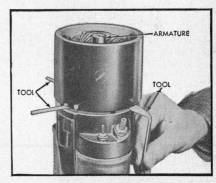

Fig. 39 Removing brush positioning tools

11. Enter solenoid lead wire through hole in brush holder, Fig. 23, and solenoid stud, insulating washer, flat washer and nut.
12. Solder solenoid lead wire to contact terminal, Fig. 22. Wrap wire securely around terminal and solder with a high temperature solder and resin flux.
13. Carefully enter solenoid coil and coil sleeve into bore of gear housing and position brush plate assembly into gear housing, Fig. 36. Align tongue

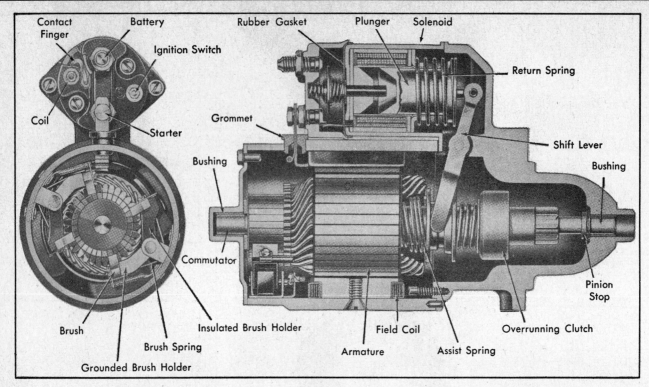

Fig. 40   Delco-Remy starter with enclosed shift lever

of ground terminal with notch in brush holder.

14. After brush holder is bottomed in housing, install attaching screw, Fig. 20. Tighten screw and install flat insulating washer and hold in place with friction tape.

15. Position brushes with tools shown in Fig. 37 or equivalent.

16. Position field frame to exact position and resolder field coil lead, Fig. 19.

17. Install brush terminal screw, Fig. 18.

18. Install armature thrust washer on brush holder plate and enter armature into field frame and gear housing, Fig. 38. Carefully engage splines of shaft with reduction gear.

19. Remove brush positioning tools, Fig. 39. Install fiber and steel thrust washers on armature shaft.

20. Position starter end head, install screws and tighten securely.

21. Install gear housing dust cover. *Make sure dimples on cover are securely engaged in holes provided in gear housing.* Test starter for free running and install on engine.

DELCO-REMY STARTERS

This type starting motor, Fig. 40, has the solenoid shift lever mechanism and the solenoid plunger enclosed in the drive housing, thus protecting them from exposure to road dirt, icing conditions and splash. They have an extruded field frame and an overrunning clutch type of drive. The overrunning clutch is operated by a solenoid switch mounted to a flange on the drive housing.

Solenoid

The solenoid is attached to the drive end housing by two screws. The angle of the nose of the plunger provides a greater bearing area between the plunger and core tube. A molded push rod, Fig. 41, is assembled in the contact assembly. A shoulder molded on the push rod and a cup that can easily be assembled to the rod and locked into position over two molded bosses holds the contact assembly in place.

To disassemble the cup from the push rod, push in on the metal cup and rotate 1/4 turn so the molded bosses on the rod are in line with openings in the cup; then slide the metal cup off the rod.

To assemble the metal cup on the rod, locate the parts on the rod as shown and align the large openings in the cup with the molded bosses on the rod; then push in on the cup and rotate it 1/4 turn so the small bosses on the rod fall into the keyways of the cup.

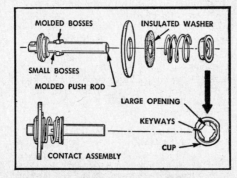

Fig. 41   Solenoid contact assembly

Solenoid Terminals

The terminals of the solenoid are assembled in a molded cover. Some solenoids have an additional small terminal which is identified with the letter "R". To this terminal is attached a small metal finger which makes contact with a disc inside the solenoid when it is energized. On the vehicle, this terminal is connected to the battery side of the ignition coil. The purpose of this is to short out the ignition resistor during cranking and thereby provide high ignition coil output for starting the engine.

Maintenance

Most motors of this type have graphite and oil impregnated bronze bearings which ordinarily require no added lubrication except at times of overhaul when a few drops of light engine oil should be placed on each bearing before reassembly.

Motors provided with hinge cap oilers should have 8-10 drops of light engine oil every 5000 miles, or every 300 hours of operation. Since the motor and brushes cannot be inspected without disassembling the unit, there is no service that can be performed with the unit assembled on the vehicle.

Free Speed Test

With the circuit connected as shown in Fig. 42, use a tachometer to measure armature revolutions per minute. Failure of the motor to perform to specifications may be due to tight or dry bearings, or high resistance connections.

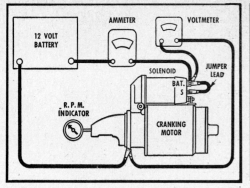

Fig. 42 Connections for checking free speed of motor

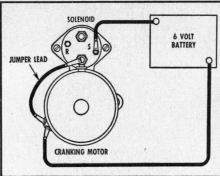

Fig. 43 Connections for checking pinion clearance

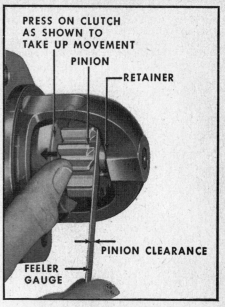

Fig. 44 Checking pinion clearance

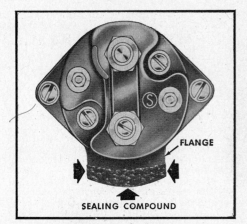

Fig. 45 Sealing solenoid housing to frame

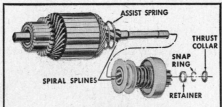

Fig. 46 View of armature and over-running clutch

Pinion Clearance

There is no provision for adjusting pinion clearance on this type motor. When the shift lever mechanism is correctly assembled, the pinion clearance should fall within the limits of .010 to .140". When the clearance is not within these limits, it may indicate excessive wear of the solenoid linkage or shift lever yoke buttons. Pinion clearance should be checked after the motor has been disassembled and reassembled. To check, make connections as shown in Fig. 43. **Caution:** *Do not connect the voltage source to the ignition coil terminal "R" of the solenoid. Do not use a 12-volt battery instead of the 6 volts specified as this will cause the motor to operate. As a further precaution to prevent motoring, connect a heavy jumper lead from the solenoid motor terminal to ground.*

After energizing the solenoid with the

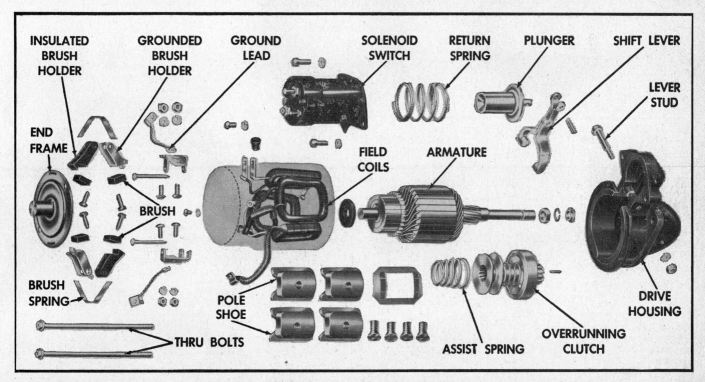

Fig. 47 Disassembled view of Delco-Remy starting motor

clutch shifted toward the pinion stop retainer, push the pinion back toward the commutator end as far as possible to take up any slack movement; then check the clearance with feeler gauge, Fig. 44.

Disassembling Motor

Normally the motor should be disassembled only so far as necessary to repair or replace defective parts.
1. Disconnect field coil connectors from solenoid "motor" terminal.
2. Remove thru bolts.
3. Remove commutator end frame and field frame assembly.
4. Remove armature assembly from drive housing. On some models it may be necessary to remove solenoid and shift lever assembly from the drive housing before removing the armature assembly. *Important: When solenoid is installed, apply sealing compound between field frame and solenoid flange, Fig. 45.*
5. Remove overrunning clutch from armature shaft as follows:
   a) Slide thrust collar off end of armature shaft, Fig. 46.
   b) Slide a standard 1/2" pipe coupling or other metal cylinder of suitable size onto shaft so end of coupling or cylinder butts against edge of retainer. Tap end of coupling with hammer, driving retainer toward armature and off snap ring.
   c) Remove snap ring from groove in shaft. If snap ring is too badly distorted during removal, use a new one when reassembling the clutch.
   d) Slide retainer, clutch and assist spring from armature shaft.

Reassembling Motor, Fig. 47

1. Lubricate drive end and splines of armature shaft with SAE 10 oil. *If heavier oil is used it may cause failure to mesh at low temperatures.*

2. Place "assist" spring on drive end of shaft next to armature, with small end against lamination stack.
3. Slide clutch assembly onto armature shaft with pinion outward.
4. Slide retainer onto shaft with cupped surface facing end of shaft.
5. Stand armature on end on wood surface with commutator down. Position snap ring on upper end of shaft and hold in place with a block of wood. Hit wood block with a hammer forcing snap ring over end of shaft. Slide snap ring into groove, squeezing it to ensure a good fit in groove.
6. Assemble thrust collar on shaft with shoulder next to snap ring.
7. Position retainer and thrust collar next to snap ring. With clutch pressed against assist spring, for clearance next to retainer, use two pairs of pliers at the same time (one pair on either side of shaft) to grip retainer and thrust collar. Then squeeze until snap ring is forced into retainer.
8. Place 4 or 5 drops of SAE 10 oil in drive housing bushing. Make sure thrust collar is in place against snap ring and retainer; then slide armature and clutch assembly into place in drive housing.
9. Attach solenoid and shift lever assembly to drive housing. Be sure lever buttons are located between sides of clutch collar.
10. Position field frame over armature, *applying sealing compound between frame and solenoid flange (Fig. 45).* Position frame against drive housing, using care to prevent damage to brushes.
11. Place 4 or 5 drops of SAE 10 oil in bushing in commutator end frame. Make sure leather brake washer is on armature shaft; then slide commutator end frame onto shaft.
12. Install thru bolts and tighten securely.
13. Reconnect filed coil connectors to solenoid "motor" terminal.

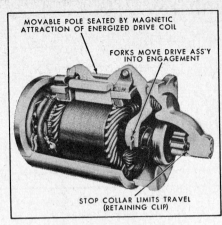

Fig. 49 Starter drive engaged

FORD AUTO-LITE STARTER WITH INTEGRAL POSITIVE ENGAGEMENT DRIVE

This type starting motor, Fig. 48, is a four pole, series parallel unit with a positive engagement drive built into the starter. The drive mechanism is engaged with the flywheel by lever action before the motor is energized.

When the ignition switch is turned on to the start position, the starter relay is energized and supplies current to the motor. The current flows through one field coil and a set of contact points to ground. The magnetic field given off by the field coil pulls the movable pole, which is part of the lever, downward to its seat. When the pole is pulled down, the lever moves the drive assembly into the engine flywheel, Fig. 49.

When the movable pole is seated, it functions as a normal field pole and opens the contact points. With the points open, current flows through the starter field coils, energizing the starter. At the same time, current also flows through a holding coil to hold the movable pole in its seated position.

When the ignition switch is released from the start position, the starter relay opens the circuit to the starting motor. This allows the return spring to force the lever back, disengaging the drive from the flywheel and returning the movable pole to its normal position, Fig. 50.

Disassembly

It may not be necessary to disassemble the starter completely to accomplish repair or replacement of certain parts. Thus, before disassembling the motor, remove the cover band and starter drive actuating lever cover. Examine brushes to make sure they are free in their holders. Replace brushes if defective or worn beyond their useful limit. Check the tension of each brush spring with a pull scale. Spring Tension should not be less than 45 ounces. If disassembly is necessary, proceed as follows:
1. Remove cover band and starter drive actuating lever cover.
2. Remove through bolts, starter drive

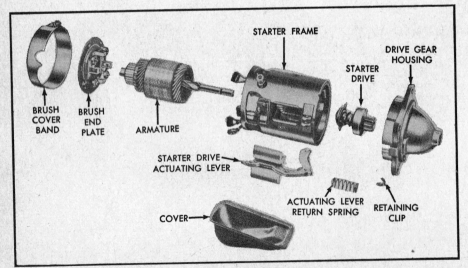

Fig. 48 Ford Auto-Lite starter with an integral positive engagement drive

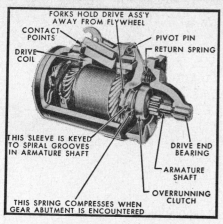

Fig. 50 Starter drive disengaged

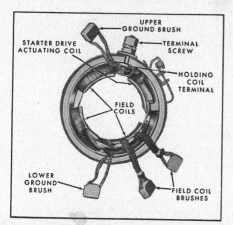

Fig. 51 Field coil assembly

gear housing, drive gear retaining clip cup and starter drive actuating lever return spring.

3. Remove pivot pin retaining starter gear actuating lever and remove lever and armature.

4. Remove and discard spring clip retaining starter drive gear to end of armature shaft, and remove starter drive gear.

5. Remove commutator brushes from brush holders and remove brush end plate.

6. Remove two screws retaining ground brushes to frame.

7. On the field coil that operates the drive gear actuating lever, bend tab up on field retainer and remove retainer.

8. Remove field coil retainer screws, Fig. 52. Unsolder field coil leads from terminal screw, and remove pole shoes and coils from frame.

9. Remove starter terminal nut and related parts. Remove any excess solder from terminal slot.

Reassembly

1. Install starter terminal, insulator, washers and retaining nut in frame, Fig. 51. Be sure to position slot in screw perpendicular to frame end surface.

2. Install field coils and pole pieces. As pole shoe screws are tightened, strike frame several sharp blows with a soft-faced hammer to seat and

SERVICE BULLETIN

Lincoln 1966 Starter Drive: The starter drive incorporates needle bearings at the drive end of the starter. When servicing this starter, precaution should be taken to avoid loss of needle bearings. If removal of the armature is required, a dummy shaft should be piloted into the drive end housing while removing the armature from the starter motor, Fig. 53. This dummy shaft should be left within the drive end housing to maintain needle bearing placement until the motor is repaired and the armature is back in position.

align pole shoes, then stake the screws.

3. Install solenoid coil retainer and bend tabs to retain tabs to frame.

4. Solder field coils and solenoid wire to starter terminal, using rosin core solder.

5. Check for continuity and grounds in the assembled coils.

6. Position solenoid coil ground terminal over ground screw hole nearest starter terminal.

7. Position ground brushes to starter frame and install retaining screws, Fig. 51.

8. Position starter brush end plate to frame with end plate boss in frame slot.

9. Install drive gear to armature shaft and install a new retaining spring clip.

10. Position fiber thrust washer on commutator end of armature shaft and install armature in frame.

11. Install starter drive actuating lever to frame and starter drive, and install pivot pin.

12. Position actuating lever return spring and drive gear housing to frame and install through bolts. Do not pinch brush leads between brush plate and frame.

13. Install brushes in holders, being sure to center brush springs on brushes.

14. Position drive gear actuating lever cover on starter and install brush cover band.

FORD AUTO-LITE SOLENOID ACTUATED STARTER

Description

The solenoid assembly, in this unit, is mounted to a flange on the starter drive housing which encloses the entire shift lever and solenoid plunger mechanism. The solenoid incorporates a pull-in winding and a hold-in winding.

Operation

As the solenoid is energized, it shifts the starting motor pinion into mesh with the engine flywheel ring gear.

At the same time, the solenoid contacts are closed and battery current flows to the motor, turning it and the engine.

After the engine starts, the starter drive is disengaged when the ignition switch is returned from the start position

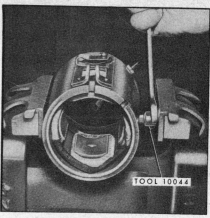

Fig. 52 Removing field coil pole shoe screws

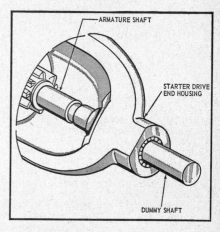

Fig. 53 Using dummy shaft to hold needle bearings in place while servicing 1966 Lincoln starter motor

to the run position and the solenoid spring pushes the shift lever back, disengaging the starter drive from the flywheel ring gear.

The starting motor is protected by an overrunning clutch built into the starter drive.

Disassembly, Fig. 54

1. Disconnect the copper strap from the starter terminal of the solenoid, remove the retaining screws and remove solenoid.

2. Loosen retaining screw and slide brush cover band back on frame.

3. Remove commutator brushes from holders. Hold each spring away from the brush with a hook while sliding brush from holder.

4. Remove through bolts and separate end plates and frame.

5. Remove solenoid plunger and shift fork assembly.

6. Remove armature and drive assembly from frame. Remove drive stop ring and slide drive assembly from shaft. Remove fiber thrust washer from commutator end of shaft.

7. Remove drive stop ring retainer from shaft.

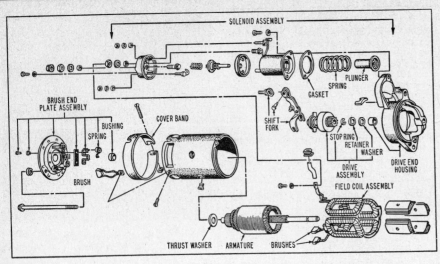

Fig. 54   Ford Auto-Lite solenoid actuated starter, exploded

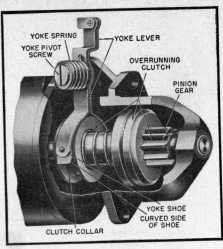

Fig. 55 Overrunning clutch drive. When assembling, make sure curved sides of yoke shoes are toward gear end of clutch. Reversed yoke shoes can cause improper meshing of pinion

Reassembly

1. Install drive assembly on shaft and install new stop ring.
2. Install solenoid plunger and shift fork.
3. Place new retainer in drive housing and install armature and drive in housing. Be sure shift lever tangs properly engage drive assembly.
4. Install fiber washer on commutator end of shaft and position frame to drive housing, being sure to index frame and drive housing correctly.
5. Install brush plate assembly being sure to index it properly, install through bolts and tighten to 55-75 in lbs.

6. Install brushes by pulling each spring away from holder with a hook to allow entry of the brush. Center the brush springs on the brushes. Press insulated brush leads away from all other components to prevent possible shorts.
7. Install rubber gasket and solenoid.
8. Connect copper strap to starter terminal of solenoid.
9. Position cover band and tighten retaining screw.
10. Connect starter to battery and check operation.

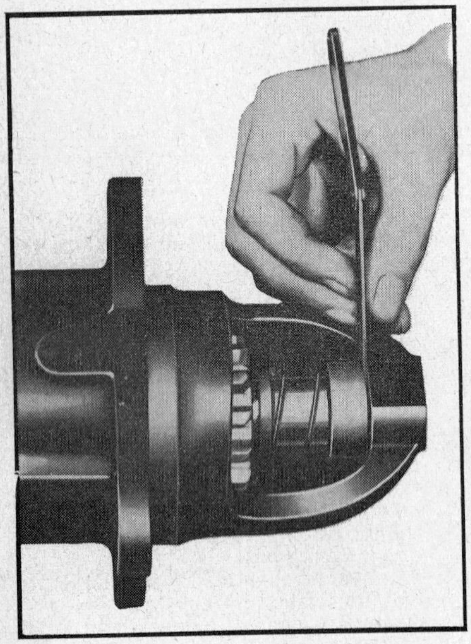

STARTER DRIVE TROUBLES

Starter drive troubles are easy to diagnose and they usually cannot be confused with ordinary starter difficulties. If the starter does not turn over at all or if it drags, look for trouble in the starter or electrical supply system. Concentrate on the starter drive or ring gear if the starter is noisy, if it turns but does not engage the engine, or if the starter won't disengage after the engine is started. After the starter is removed, the trouble can usually be located quickly.

Worn or chipped ring gear or starter pinion are the usual causes of noisy operation. Before replacing either or both of these parts try to find out what caused the damage. With the Bendix type drive, incomplete engagement of the pinion with the ring gear is a common cause of tooth damage. The wrong pinion clearance on starter drives of the overrunning clutch type leads to poor meshing of the pinion and ring gear and to rapid tooth wear.

A less common cause of noise with either type of drive is a bent starter armature shaft. When this shaft is bent, the pinion gear alternately binds and then only partly meshes with the ring gear. Most manufacturers specify a maximum of .003" radial run-out on the armature shaft.

When Clutch Drive Fails

The over-running clutch type drive seldom becomes so worn that it fails to engage since it is directly activated by a fork and lever, Fig. 55. The only thing that is likely to happen is that, once engaged, it will not turn the engine because the clutch itself is worn out. A much more frequent difficulty and one that rapidly wears ring gear and teeth is partial engagement. Proper meshing of the pinion is controlled by the end clearance between the pinion gear and the starter housing or pinion stop, if used.

The clearance is set with the starter off the car and with the drive in the engaged position. To check the clearance, supply current to the starter solenoid with the electrical connection between starter and solenoid removed. Supplying current to the solenoid but not the starter will prevent the starter from rotating during the test. Take out all slack by pushing lightly on the starter drive clutch housing while inserting a feeler gauge between pinion and housing or pinion stop, Fig. 56.

On late model cars, the solenoids are completely enclosed in the starter housing and the pinion clearance is not adjustable. If the clearance is not correct, the starter must be disassembled and checked for excessive wear of solenoid linkage, shift lever mechanism, or improper assembly of parts.

Fig. 56   Measuring overrunning clutch drive stop clearance. Do not compress anti-drift spring as this will give an incorrect clearance. If clearance is not present there is danger of the drive housing being broken as gear or collar slams back against it

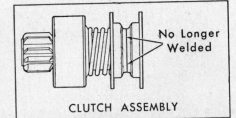

CLUTCH ASSEMBLY

Fig. 57   New design overrunning clutch collar

Failure of the over-running clutch drive to disengage is usually caused by binding between the armature shaft and the drive. If the drive, particularly the clutch, shows signs of overheating it indicates that it is not disengaging immediately after the engine starts. If the clutch is forced to over-run too long, it overheats and turns a bluish color. For the cause of the binding, look for rust or gum between the armature shaft and the drive, or for burred splines. Excess oil on the drive will lead to gumming, and inadequate air circulation in the flywheel housing will cause rust.

Over-running clutch drives cannot be overhauled in the field so they must be replaced. In cleaning, never soak them in a solvent because the solvent may enter the clutch and dissolve the sealed-in lubricant. Wipe them off lightly with kerosene and lubricate them sparingly with SAE 10 or 10W oil.

NOTE: Beginning in 1968 some Delco Remy starter drives used an overrunning clutch with a split collar. Side by side but not welded together as in previous models, Fig. 57. Do not mistake this split design as a defective collar.

When Bendix Drive Fails

When a Bendix type drive doesn't engage the cause usually is one of three things: either the drive spring is broken, one of the drive spring bolts has sheared off, or the screwshaft threads won't allow the pinion to travel toward the flywheel.

In the first two cases, remove the drive by unscrewing the set screw under the last coil of the drive spring and replace the broken parts. Gummed or rusty screwshaft threads are fairly common causes of Bendix drive failure and are easily cleaned with a little kerosene or steel wool, depending on the trouble. Here again, as in the case of over-running clutch drives, use light oil sparingly, and be sure the flywheel housing has adequate ventilation. There is usually a breather hole in the bottom of the flywheel housing which should be open.

The failure of a Bendix drive to disengage or to mesh properly is most often caused by gummed or rusty screwshaft threads. When this is not true, look for mechanical failure within the drive itself.

STARTING SWITCHES

MAGNETIC and SOLENOID SWITCHES are designed to perform mechanical jobs electromagnetically such as closing a heavy circuit or shifting the starter drive pinion with the engine flywheel ring gear for cranking. Switches of this type consist basically of contacts and a winding (or windings) around a hollow cylinder containing a movable core or plunger. When the winding (or windings) is energized by the battery through an external control circuit the plunger is pulled inward, producing the necessary mechanical movement.

MAGNETIC SWITCHES

Figs. 1 and 2 illustrate two typical Delco-Remy switches. The switch shown in Fig. 1 is not designed for disassembly and must be replaced if defective.

In the switch shown in Fig. 2 the terminals are assembled into a molded terminal ring which is held in place on the switch case by the cover and screws. Gaskets on both sides of the ring seals the contact compartment as a protection against moisture and dirt. The winding assembly is not removable from the case on this unit although the contact disk, plunger and plunger return spring can be removed after the cover is taken off.

Fig. 3 is a heavy duty magnetic switch. It is completely serviceable and easy to disassemble and assemble. To disassemble, remove the four terminal plate nuts and washers and take off the terminal plate assembly. The contact disk may be removed by taking off the castellated nut. It is necessary to remove the spring and washers on the plunger rod only when the plunger rod needs to be disassembled. To remove the plunger, unscrew the large metal cover, take out the cotter pin in the plunger shaft, re-

move spring retainer washer and spring, and withdraw the plunger. The winding and switch case is an integral assembly. The only parts that can be removed are the switch terminals. Before removing the switch terminals, the winding leads must be unsoldered from the terminal studs. Whenever the switch is disassembled, upon reassembly, locate the contact disk properly by turning the castellated nut on the disk in or out as required to obtain the dimension shown in Fig. 3 between the contact disk and edge of housing.

NOTE

On vehicles with overrunning clutch starting motors, a magnetic switch is normally used to shift the drive pinion into mesh and to close the starter circuit. There are two variations of three-terminal switches and also one type with four terminals. Any of these switches

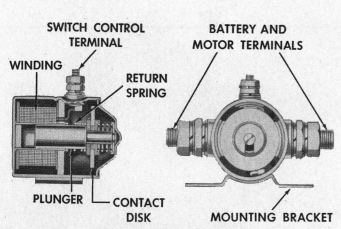

Fig. 1 End and sectional views of a typical magnetic switch

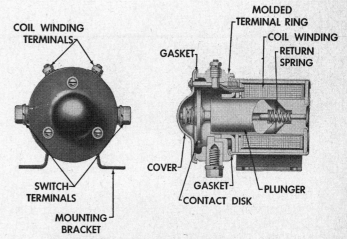

Fig. 2 End and sectional views of a sealed type magnetic switch which uses gaskets to seal the contact compartment

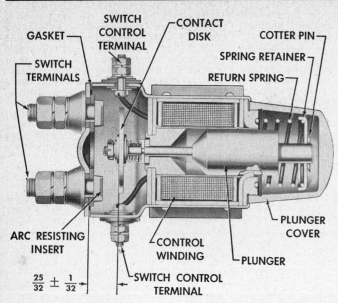

Fig. 3 Sectional view of heavy duty sealed type magnetic switch. To adjust the location of the contact disk turn the nut on the disk in or out as required to obtain the dimension shown

$\frac{25}{32} \pm \frac{1}{32}$

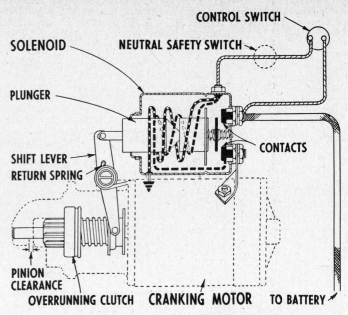

Fig. 6 Wiring circuit of a typical solenoid switch

may be manufactured with either a grounded or insulated base. When installing a switch that is not marked "grounded base" or "insulated base", it must be checked out as follows, using a battery and test lamp in series.

Three Terminal Switches

1. If the switch has a grounded base the test lamp will light when connected between the starter ("S") terminal or ignition ("I") terminal and switch mounting bracket.
2. If the switch has an insulated base the test lamp will light when connected between the "S" and "I" terminals and either one of the $\frac{5}{16}$ threaded studs.
3. If the test lamp fails to light when connected between the "S" and "I" terminals and any external part of the switch, disassemble the switch to determine whether the base is grounded or insulated.

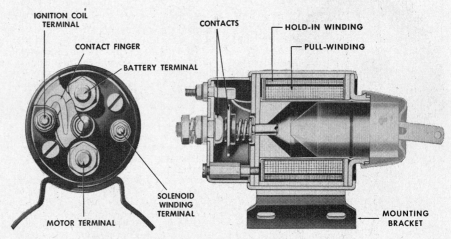

Fig. 4 End and sectional views of a typical solenoid switch

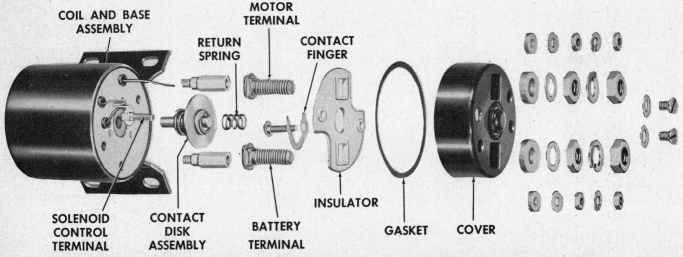

Fig. 5 Exploded view of solenoid switch shown in Fig. 4

Four Terminal Switches

1. If the switch has a grounded base the test lamp will light when connected between the "S" terminal and switch mounting bracket.
2. If the switch has an insulated base the test lamp will light when connected between the "S" and "I" terminals.
3. If the test lamp fails to light when connected between the "S" terminal and any other external part of the switch, disassemble the switch to determine whether it has an insulated or grounded base.

SOLENOID SWITCHES

The solenoid switch on a cranking motor not only closes the circuit between the battery and the cranking motor but also shifts the drive pinion into mesh with the engine flywheel ring gear. This is done by means of a linkage between the solenoid switch plunger and the shift lever on the cranking motor. Some linkages are adjustable while others are not (see *Starting Motors* chapter). The linkage is not adjustable on the type shown in Fig. 4 but adjustment of the entire assembly is made by moving the switch on the motor frame.

Fig. 4 shows two views of a solenoid switch used on vehicles with 12-volt systems. Like other solenoid switches, this type is energized by the battery through a separate starting switch. Note, however, that the switch includes an additional small terminal and contact finger. This terminal has no functional duty in relation to the switch, but is used to complete a special ignition circuit during the cranking cycle only. When the solenoid is in the cranking position, the finger touches the contact disk and provides a direct circuit between the battery and ignition coil.

Fig. 5 is an exploded view of the solenoid switch shown in Fig. 4. When reassembling the switch the contact finger should be adjusted to touch the contact disk before the disk makes contact with the main switch terminals. There should be $1/16''$ to $3/32''$ clearance between the contact disk and the main terminals when the finger touches.

Fig. 6 is a wiring circuit of a typical solenoid switch. There are two windings in the solenoid; a pull-in winding (shown as dashes) and a hold-in winding (shown dotted). Both windings are energized when the external control switch is closed. They produce a magnetic field which pulls the plunger in so that the drive pinion is shifted into mesh, and the main contacts in the solenoid switch are closed to connect the battery directly to the cranking motor. Closing the main switch contacts shorts out the pull-in winding since this winding is connected across the main contacts. The magnetism produced by the hold-in winding is sufficient to hold the plunger in, and shorting out the pull-in winding reduces drain on the battery. When the control switch is opened, it disconnects the hold-in winding from the battery. When the hold-in winding is disconnected from the battery, the shift lever spring withdraws the plunger from the solenoid, opening the solenoid switch contacts and at the same time withdrawing the drive pinion from mesh. Proper operation of the switch depends on maintaining a definite balance between the magnetic strength of the pull-in and hold-in windings.

This balance is established in the design by the size of the wire and the number of turns specified. *An open circuit in the hold-in winding or attempts to crank with a discharged battery will cause the switch to chatter.*

To disassemble the solenoid, remove nuts, washers and insulators from the switch terminal and battery terminal. Remove cover and take out the contact disk assembly.

When the solenoid has been removed from the starter motor for repair or replacement, the linkage must be adjusted to provide the correct pinion clearance or pinion travel when the solenoid is remounted on the motor. Some solenoids equipped with relays have an adjustable plunger stud, but others must be moved on the motor frame to adjust pinion travel.

DASH GAUGES

TESTING

Gauge failures are often caused by defective wiring or grounds. Therefore, the first step is locating trouble should be a thorough inspection of all wiring and terminals. If wiring is secured by clamps, check to see whether the insulation has been severed thereby grounding the wire. In the case of a fuel gauge installation, rust may cause failure by corrosion at the ground connection of the tank unit.

CONSTANT VOLTAGE TYPE

Voltage Regulator Test

Except American Motors
1. Turn on ignition switch.
2. Connect one lead of a test light or positive lead of a voltmeter to the feed terminal of one of the gauges without disconnecting wire.
3. If regulator is okay, voltage will oscillate.
4. If it does not, voltage regulator is defective or there is a short or ground between regulator and gauges.

CAUTION: Applying 12 volts to any part of the system except the regulator input terminal or grounding the regulator or system in any way except to connect test equipment may burn out one or more components. When replacing any part of the system, battery ground cable must be disconnected.

American Motors
1. Connect a 10 ohm resistor in series with each indicator wire.
2. Ground fuel and temperature gauge wires.
3. The fuel gauge should read Full to two needle widths above. The temperature gauge should read Hot to two needle widths above.

Dash Gauge Test

1. Turn off ignition switch.
2. Connect terminals of two series-connected flashlight batteries to the gauge terminals in question (fuel, oil or temperature).
3. The three volts of the batteries should cause the gauge to read approximately full scale.
4. If the gauge unit is inaccurate or does not indicate, replace it with a new unit.
5. If the gauge unit still is erratic in its operation, the sender unit or wire to the sender unit is defective.

Fuel Tank Gauge Test

1. Test the dash gauge as outlined above.
2. If dash gauge is satisfactory, remove flashlight batteries.
3. Then disconnect wire at tank unit and ground it momentarily to a

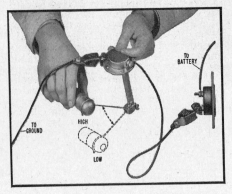

Fig. 1 Hook-up for testing dash gauge with a spare tank unit

clean, unpainted portion of the vehicle frame or body with *ignition switch on*.
4. If the dash gauge does not indicate, the wire is defective. Repair or replace the wire.
5. If grounding the new or repaired wire causes the gauge to indicate, the tank unit is faulty and should be replaced.

Oil & Temperature Sending Unit Tests

1. Test dash gauge as outlined above.
2. If dash gauge is satisfactory, remove flashlight batteries.
3. Then start engine and allow it to run to warm up to normal temperature.
4. If no reading is indicated on the gauge, check the sending unit-to-gauge wire by removing the wire from the sending unit and momentarily ground this wire to a clean, unpainted portion of the engine.
5. If the gauge still does not indicate, the wire is defective. Repair or replace the wire.
6. If grounding the new or repaired wire causes the dash gauge to indicate, the sending unit is faulty.

VARIABLE VOLTAGE TYPE

The procedure given herewith applies to AC, Auto-Lite and Stewart-Warner systems. The following are two methods of quickly checking the gauge system to determine which component (sender or receiver) of a given system is defective.

Grounded Wire Method

1. Turn on ignition switch.
2. Remove wire connected at sending unit in question (fuel, oil or temperature).
3. Momentarily ground wire by holding it against a clean, unpainted portion of engine, vehicle body or frame.
4. The gauge pointer should indicate a full scale reading within 30 seconds.

5. As soon as the full scale reading is indicated, discontinue grounding the wire.
6. If during the test the gauge does *not* indicate a full scale reading, either the lead wire from the gauge to the sending unit is severed or the gauge is defective.
7. If the gauge *does* indicate a full scale reading, the sending unit is defective and should be replaced.

Fuel Gauge Tank Unit Method

1. Use a spare gauge tank unit known to be correct.
2. To test whether the dash gauge in question (fuel, oil or temperature) is functioning, disconnect the wire at the gauge which leads to the sending unit.
3. Attach a wire lead from the dash gauge terminal to the terminal of the "test" tank gauge, Fig. 1.
4. Ground the test tank unit to an unpainted portion of the dash panel and move the float arm.
5. If the gauge operates correctly, the sending unit is defective and should be replaced.
6. If the gauge does not operate during this test, the dash gauge is defective and should be replaced.

AMMETERS

This instrument shows whether the battery is being charged by the generator or alternator or is being discharged by lights, radio, engine, etc. If a constant discharge is indicated on the ammeter, it is a signal that the battery is being run down. It is often a signal that the generator is out of order. Since both a charged battery and a working generator are very necessary—especially with vehicles equipped with many electricity-consuming devices such as heater, defroster, fog lights, radio, etc.—an inoperative ammeter should be given prompt attention.

The typical ammeter, Fig. 2, consists of a frame to which a permanent magnet is attached. The frame also supports an armature and pointer assembly.

When no current flows through the ammeter, the magnet holds the pointer armature so that the pointer stands at the center of the dial. When current passes in either direction through the ammeter, the resulting magnetic field attracts the armature away from the effect of the permanent magnet, thus giving a reading proportional to the strength of the current flowing.

Trouble Shooting

When the ammeter apparently fails to register correctly, there may be trouble in the wiring which connects the ammeter to the generator and battery or in the generator or battery themselves.

To check the connections, first tighten

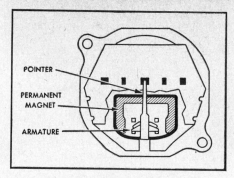

Fig. 2 Drawing of a typical automobile ammeter

the two terminal posts on the back of the ammeter. Then, following each wire from the ammeter, tighten all connections on the ignition switch, battery and generator. Chafed, burned or broken insulation can be found by following each ammeter wire from end to end.

All wires with chafed, burned or broken insulation should be repaired or replaced. After this is done, and all connections are tightened, connect the battery cable and turn on the ignition switch. The needle should point slightly to the discharge (−) side.

Start the engine and speed it up a little above idling speed. The needle should then move to the charge side (+), and its movement should be smooth.

If the pointer does not behave correctly, the ammeter itself is out of order and a new one should be installed.

GENERATOR INDICATOR LIGHT

A red generator or alternator "no charge" light is used on many cars in lieu of an ammeter. This light flashes on if the battery is discharging and the generator or alternator is not supplying current.

The light should glow when the ignition is turned on and before the engine is started. If the bulb does not light, either the bulb is burned out or the indicator light wiring has an open circuit. After the engine is started, the light should be out at all times with the alternator system. With the D.C. generator system, the light should also be out at all times with the engine running except in cases where the engine idling speed is set too low; however, when the engine is speeded up the light should go out.

If the light fails to go out when the engine is running, the drive belt may be loose or missing or the generator or alternator or voltage regulator may be defective.

Light Circuit With D.C. Generator

The light is usually connected between the armature terminal of the generator regulator and the necessary terminal on the ignition switch, Fig. 3. If the ignition switch is on and the cutout relay contacts are open, the light will flow, indicating that the gen-

erator is not electrically connected to the battery. As soon as the generator is speeded up, the cutout relay contacts close. This by-passes the indicator light and thus indicates that the battery is electrically connected to the generator.

Light Circuit With Alternator

A double contact voltage regulator together with a field relay is used on Delco-Remy and Ford alternators when used with the indicator light. The circuit is as follows:

With the ignition switch turned on (engine not running), current flow is through the ignition switch through the indicator light on the dash panel. From there it goes to a terminal of the regulator (marked "4" or "L" on Delco-Remy or "I" on Ford). The circuit continues through the lower contacts of the voltage regulator (held closed by a spring), out the "F" terminal of the regulator, in the "F" terminal of the alternator, through a brush and slip ring, through another brush and slip ring to ground.

After the engine is started, the voltage output of the alternator immediately closes the field relay. This causes battery voltage from the battery terminal of the regulator (marked "3" or "V" on Delco-Remy, "B" on Ford) to be present at the "4", "L" or "I" terminal. Since battery voltage is present on both sides of the indicator light, the light goes out.

If the generator light comes on with the engine running, the charging circuit should be tested as soon as possible to determine the cause of the trouble.

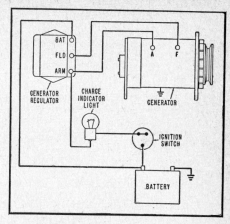

Fig. 3 Wiring diagram of a typical charge indicator light circuit

(The presence of sealing compound on the threads of the engine unit will cause a poor ground).

If the warning light remains lit with it normally should be out, replace the engine unit before proceeding further to determine the cause for a low pressure indication.

The warning light sometimes will light up or will flicker when the engine is idling, even though the oil pressure is adequate. However, the light should go out when the engine is speeded up. There is no cause for alarm in such cases; it simply means that the pressure switch is not calibrated precisely correct.

OIL PRESSURE INDICATOR LIGHT

Many cars utilize a warning light on the instrument panel in place of the conventional dash indicating gauge to warn the driver when the oil pressure is dangerously low. The warning light is wired in series with the ignition switch and the engine unit—which is an oil pressure switch.

The oil pressure switch contains a diaphragm and a set of contacts. When the ignition switch is turned on, the warning light circuit is energized and the circuit is completed through the closed contacts in the pressure switch. When the engine is started, build-up of oil pressure compresses the diaphragm, opening the contacts, thereby breaking the circuit and putting out the light.

Trouble Shooting

The oil pressure warning light should go on when the ignition is turned on. If it does not light, disconnect the wire from the engine unit and ground the wire to the frame or cylinder block. Then if the warning light still does not go on with the ignition switch on, replace the bulb.

If the warning light goes on when the wire is grounded to the frame or cylinder block, the engine unit should be checked for being loose or poorly grounded. If the unit is found to be tight and properly grounded, it should be removed and a new one installed.

TEMPERATURE INDICATOR LIGHTS

A temperature (bimetal) switch, located in cylinder head, controls the operation of a "Cold" temperature indicator light with a green lens and a "Hot" temperature indicator light with a red lens. When the cooling system water temperature is below approximately 110 defrees F., the temperature switch grounds the "Cold" indicator circuit and the green light goes on. When the green light goes out, the water temperature is high enough so that the heater can be turned on and be effective. *Note: The car should never be subjected to full throttle accelerations or high speeds until after the green light has gone out.*

If the engine cooling system is not functioning properly and the water temperature should reach a point where the engine approaches an overheated condition, the red light will be turned on by the temperature switch.

NOTE: *As a test circuit to check whether the red bulb is functioning properly, a wire which is connected to the ground terminal of the ignition switch is tapped into its circuit. When the ignition is in the "Start" (engine cranking) position, the ground terminal is grounded inside the switch and the red bulb will be lit. When the engine is started and the ignition switch is in the "On" position, the test circuit is opened and the bulb is then controlled by the temperature switch.*

Trouble Shooting

If the red light is not lit when the engine is being cranked, check for a burned out bulb, an open in the light circuit, or a defective ignition switch.

If the red light is lit when the engine is running, check the wiring between light and switch for a ground, temperature switch defective, or overheated cooling system.

If the "Cold" light is not lit when ignition is on and engine cold, check for a burned out bulb, an open in the light circuit, or a defective temperature switch.

If the "Cold" light stays on after normal engine warm-up period, check for a ground between light and switch, defective temperature switch, or a defective cooling thermostat.

SPEEDOMETERS

The following material covers only that service on speedometers which is feasible to perform by the average service man. Repairs on the units themselves are not included as they require special tools and extreme care when making repairs and adjustments and only an experienced speedometer mechanic should attempt such servicing.

The speedometer has two main parts —the indicating head and the speedometer drive cable. When the speedometer fails to indicate speed or mileage, the cable or housing is probably broken.

Speedometer Cable

Most cables are broken due to lack of lubrication or a sharp bend or kink in the housing.

A cable might break because the speedometer head mechanism binds. If such is the case, the speedometer head should be repaired or replaced before a new cable or housing is installed.

A "jumpy" pointer condition, together with a sort of scraping noise, is due, in most instances, to a dry or kinked speedometer cable. The kinked cable rubs on the housing and winds up, slowing down the pointer. The cable then unwinds and the pointer "jumps".

To check for kinks, remove the cable, lay it on a flat surface and twist one end with the fingers. If it turns over smoothly the cable is not kinked. But if part of the cable flops over as it is twisted, the cable is kinked and should be replaced.

Lubrication

The speedometer cable should be lubricated with special cable lubricant every 10,000 miles.

Fill the ferrule on the upper end of the housing with the cable lubricant. Insert the cable in the housing, starting at the upper end. Turn the cable around carefully while feeding it into the housing. Repeat filling the ferrule except for the last six inches of cable. Too much lubricant at this point may cause the lubricant to work into the indicating hand.

Installing Cable

During installation, if the cable sticks when inserted in the housing and will not go through, the housing is damaged inside or kinked. Be sure to check the housing from one end to the other. Straighten any sharp bends by relocating clamps or elbows. Replace housing if it is badly kinked or broken. Position the cable and housing so that they lead into the head as straight as possible.

Check the new cable for kinks before installing it. Use wide, sweeping, gradual curves where the cable comes out of the transmission and connects to the head so the cable will not be damaged during its installation.

If inspection indicates that the cable and housing are in good condition, yet pointer action is erratic, check the speedometer head for possible binding.

The speedometer drive pinion should also be checked. If the pinion is dry or its teeth are stripped, the speedometer may not register properly.

The transmission mainshaft nut must be tight or the speedometer drive gear may slip on the mainshaft and cause slow speed readings.

ELECTRIC CLOCKS

Regulation of electric clocks used on automobiles is accomplished automatically by merely resetting the time. If the clock is running fast, the action of turning the hands back to correct the time will automatically cause the clock to run slightly slower. If the clock is running slow, the action of turning the hands forward to correct the time will automatically cause the clock to run slightly faster (10 to 15 seconds a day).

Winding Clock When Connecting Battery or Clock Wiring

The clock requires special attention when reconnecting a battery that has been disconnected for any reason, a clock that has been disconnected, or when replacing a blown clock fuse. *It is very important that the initial wind be fully made.* The procedure is as follows:

1. Make sure that all other instruments and lights are turned off.
2. Connect positive cable to battery.
3. Before connecting the negative cable, press the terminal to its post on the battery. Immediately afterward strike the terminal against the battery post to see if there is a spark. If there is a spark, allow the clock to run down until it stops ticking, and repeat as above until there is no spark. Then immediately make the permanent connection before the clock can again run down. The clock will run down in approximately two minutes.
4. Reset clock after all connections have been made. *The foregoing procedure should also be followed when reconnecting the clock after it has been disconnected, or if it has stopped because of a blown fuse. Be sure to disconnect battery before installing a new fuse.*

Trouble Shooting

If clock does not run, check for blown "clock" fuse. If fuse is blown check for short in wiring. If fuse is not blown check for open circuit.

With an electric clock, the most frequent cause of clock fuse blowing is low voltage at the clock which will prevent a complete wind and allow clock contacts to remain closed. This may be caused by any of the following: discharged battery, corrosion on contact surface of battery terminals, loose connections at battery terminals, at junction block, at fuse clips, or at terminal connection of clock. Therefore, if in reconnecting battery or clock it is noted that the clock is not ticking, always check for blown fuse, or examine the circuits at the points indicated above to determine and correct the cause.

FIBER OPTIC MONITORING SYSTEM

Fiber optics are non-electric light conductors made up of coated strands which, when exposed to a light source at one end, will reflect the light through their entire length, thereby illuminating a monitoring lens on the instrument panel without the use of a bulb when the exterior lights are turned on.

FUEL PUMPS

NOTE: Fuel pump pressures are listed in Tune Up Charts in car chapters.

MECHANICAL FUEL PUMP FIG. 1

Operation

During the suction stroke, the rotation of the camshaft eccentric moves the pump rocker arm which in turn pulls the diaphragm up, causing fuel to be drawn in through the one-way inlet valve. This suction also closes the outlet valve. During the return stroke, the diaphragm is forced down by the diaphragm spring. The resulting fuel pressure opens the outlet valve and closes the inlet valve. Fuel is then forced out through the outlet valve to the carburetor.

Vacuum Section Operation

The vacuum section of combination pumps operates the windshield wipers at almost constant speed. The rotation of the camshaft eccentric in this type pump also operates the vacuum booster section by actuating the pump arm which pushes

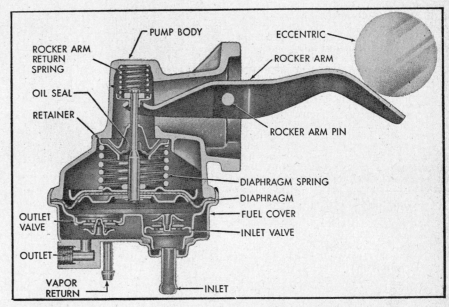

Fig. 1   Single action mechanical fuel pump. Typical

a link and bellows diaphragm downward, expelling the air in the vacuum chamber through its exhaust valve out into the intake manifold of the engine. On the return stroke of the pump arm, the diaphragm is moved upward, producing a suction in the vacuum chamber. This suction operates the vacuum section and draws air through the inlet passage from the windshield wiper.

Fuel Pump Performance

It is essential that the fuel pump deliver sufficient fuel to supply the requirements of the engine under all operating conditions and that it maintain sufficient pressure in the line between the pump and carburetor to keep the fuel from boiling and to prevent vapor lock.

Excessive fuel pump pressure holds the carburetor float needle valve off its seat, causing high gasoline level in the float chamber which in turn increases gasoline consumption.

The pump usually delivers a minimum of ten gallons of gasoline per hour at top engine speeds, under an operating pressure of from 2 to 6 psi. The highest operating pressure will be attained at idling speed and the lowest at top speed.

Fuel Pump Tests

The fuel pump can be tested on the car with a pressure gauge, a hose and a pint measuring can. With this equipment, it is possible to check the fuel pump to see if it is delivering the proper amount of gasoline at the correct pressure.

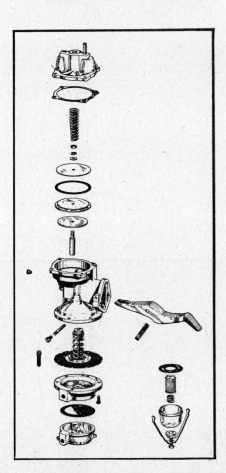

Fig. 2   American Motors double action (combination) pump. Exploded

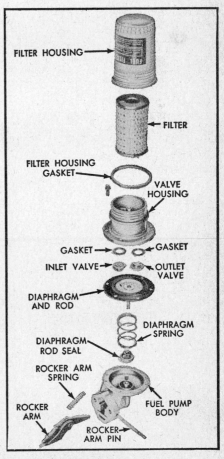

Fig. 3   Ford fuel pump with integral fuel filter. Exploded

FUEL PUMPS

Pressure Test

To make the pressure test, disconnect the fuel pipe at the carburetor inlet and attach the pressure gauge and hose between the carburetor inlet and the disconnected fuel pipe, Fig. 4. Take the pressure reading with the engine running. The pressure should be within the limits given in the *Tune Up* chart in each car chapter, depending on the pump model and the car on which it is installed. The pressure should remain constant or return very slowly to zero when the engine is stopped.

Capacity Test

To make this test, connect the hose so the pump will deliver gasoline into the pint measure held at carburetor level. Run the engine at idle speed and note the time it takes to fill the measure. On the average it should take from 20 to 30 seconds, depending on the pump tested.

When Pressure Is Low

Low pressure indicates extreme wear on one part, small wear on all parts, rup-

Fig. 4   Testing fuel pump pressure

tured diaphragm, dirty valve or gummy valve seat.

Wear in the pump usually occurs at the rocker arm pivot pin and on the contacting surfaces of the rocker arm and links. Due to the leverage design, wear at these points is multiplied five times in the movement of the diaphragm. It is apparent therefore, that very little wear will materially reduce the stroke of the diaphragm. The worn parts must be replaced for a satisfactory correction.

The diaphragm pull rod has an oil seal around it which prevents the hot oil vapors from the crankcase coming in contact with the diaphragm. If this seal is damaged, the oil vapors have a tendency to shorten the life of the diaphragm.

The first three conditions—extreme wear on one part, small wear on all parts, and ruptured diaphragm—are brought about by usage, while dirty and/or poor fuel is sually the cause of valve trouble.

When Pressure Is High

High pressure is caused by a tight diaphragm, fuel between diaphragm layers, diaphragm spring too strong, pump link frozen to rocker arm.

A tight diaphragm will stretch slightly on the down stroke. As the pump operates, the diaphragm will rebound on the

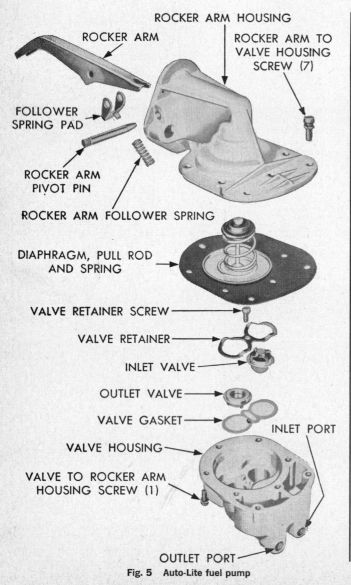

Fig. 5   Auto-Lite fuel pump

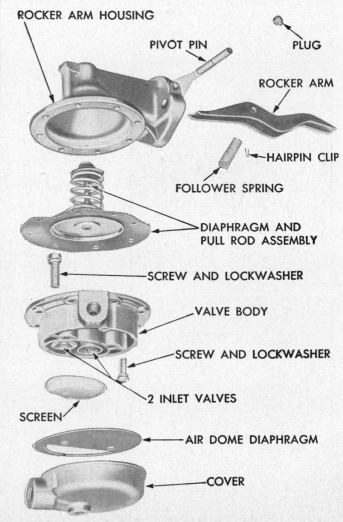

Fig. 6   Carter fuel pump

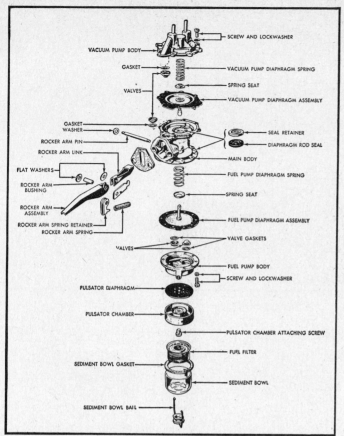

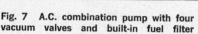

Fig. 7 A.C. combination pump with four vacuum valves and built-in fuel filter

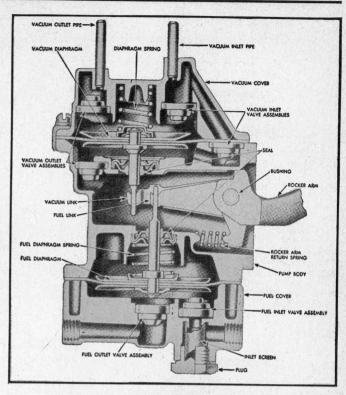

Fig. 8 A.C. combination pump with four vacuum valves

up stroke beyond its normal position, much as a stretched rubber band when it is suddenly released. This rebound will cause a higher than normal pressure in the pump chamber.

A loose diaphragm retainer nut or poor riveting on the diaphragm assembly may allow fuel to seep between the diaphragm layers. This will cause a bulge in the diaphragm and have the same effect as a diaphragm that is too tight.

A diaphragm spring that is too strong also causes a high pressure for the diaphragm will operate longer before pressure of the fuel on the diaphragm will overcome the diaphragm spring.

On a combination pump there are times when the operating parts may become badly corroded and the links freeze to the rocker arm. In this condition the pump operates continually, resulting in a very high pressure and a flooding carburetor.

The remedy for all these conditions is to remove the pump for replacement or repair, using a repair kit.

When Capacity Is Low

Low capacity is usually caused by an air leak in the intake pipe at these points: fuel pipe fitting at pump, bowl flange or diaphragm flange, fuel bowl. (It is assumed that the conditions of too little fuel have already been checked and the pump is the cause of the difficulty.)

An air leak at fuel pipe fittings indicates either poor installation of pump or a defective fitting. The fitting should be tightened or replaced.

A leak at the diaphragm flange may be caused by a warped cover casting, loose diaphragm cover screws or foreign material between cover casting and diaphragm.

A leak at the bowl flange of the cover casting can usually be corrected by the installation of an extra gasket. A warped top cover indicates that the pump must be replaced.

A chipped glass or bent metal bowl may cause a leak at the bowl flange as may a defective gasket or foreign material between gasket and bowl or cover casting. A chipped glass bowl must be replaced while a dented metal bowl can be straightened.

Vacuum Pump Troubles

To assist the manifold vacuum to operate the windshield wiper at a uniform rate under any engine load is the only function of the vacuum pump. Of course, "uniform rate" infers a wet windshield and not one covered with snow or ice. Failure to do the above indicates difficulty in either the vacuum system of the pump, windshield wiper motor, or tubes and connections.

Symptoms of trouble in the vacuum section show up in four ways: oil consumption, slow windshield wiper action, poor idle, noise.

In some cases it has been found that an engine which has given very good oil mileage suddenly appears to be using oil. Upon investigation, it will often be found that the vacuum booster has a ruptured diaphragm and is drawing oil fumes from the crankcase into the intake manifold. This can be checked by removing the cover of the vacuum section.

When the windshield wiper slows down excessively under engine load, it usually is an indication of a ruptured vacuum diaphragm or defective valve in the vacuum pump. This condition may not be discovered immediately as the windshield wipers may not be used for long intervals.

Oil will be evidenced in the cover casting recesses if the diaphragm is ruptured. The pump should be removed and the diaphragm replaced.

On some cars the engine will idle very poorly when the vacuum diaphragm is ruptured. This is true when the tube from the vacuum pump is connected to one end of the intake manifold. The air leak through the vacuum section will give those cylinders on the end a lean mixture which results in a miss or poor idle. In many cases, this leads one to believe the valves of the engine are sticking; but if they are ground, the miss or poor idle remains.

This condition can be checked by removing the vacuum pump tube at the manifold and plugging the hole. If the miss or rough idle disappears, the trouble is an air leak through the pump or tube connections. The pump should be removed and repaired or the connections tightened to eliminate this trouble.

Sometimes a combination pump will give off a peculiar grunting sound or idle. In come cases this can be remedied by stuffing curled horse hair into the pump breather.

Vacuum Pump Test

With a combination fuel and vacuum pump the windshield wiper should operate at 80 to 100 strokes per minute through all ranges of car speed and load. The windshield should be wet when the test is made, otherwise the action will be slow.

Checking With Vacuum Gauge

To check the vacuum section, disconnect both inlet and outlet tubes and attach a vacuum gauge to the inlet (side that goes to windshield wiper). It is assumed that the engine, windshield wiper motor and blade, and connecting tubing have been checked and are in satisfactory condition.

Read the vacuum gauge when the engine is running at 1000 rpm. It should read from 7 to 12 inches of vacuum on a normal pump. If the reading is less than 7, the pump should be removed and repaired or replaced. When making this test, the tube to the manifold should be plugged and the pump outlet should always be open or damage may result to the mechanism.

Checking Without Gauge

Disconnect the outlet tube (to manifold) from the pump and plug the end. Then operate the engine from an idle through slow acceleration to about 40 mph. If the wiper starts operating at about 15 mph and reaches full speed at about 40 mph, the vacuum section is okay. If it does not operate, it may be the windshield wiper motor. This can be checked by connecting the intake manifold directly to the windshield wiper tube. Then slowly accelerate the engine from idle to about 25 mph. The wiper should operate at full speed. If it does not it can be assumed that the wiper motor or tubing is defective.

Fuel Pump Service

NOTE: Many modern fuel pumps are sealed, non-serviceable units. These pumps cannot be repaired and must be replaced as units.

Illustrated are representative fuel pumps among the many models that have been produced. Before disassembling any pump, scribe a mark across the housings in such a manner that they may be reassembled with inlet and outlet fitting holes in correct location.

When disassembled, clean all parts (except diaphragms) in solvent and blow dry with compressed air. Examine the diaphragm for cracks, torn screws holes or ruptures. If deteriorated, install new diaphragm and pull rod assembly. Check the strainer screen and if found to be corroded or clogged, install a new screen. Check the rocker arm for wear or scoring on that portion that contacts the camshaft eccentric. If arm is scored or worn install a new one.

When reassembling a pump, do not use shellac or other adhesive on a diaphragm.

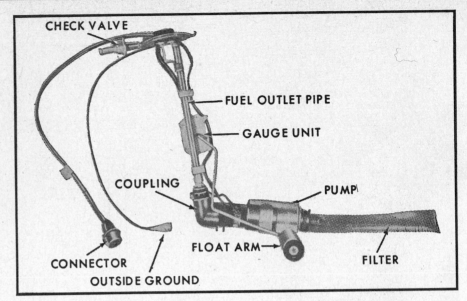

Fig. 9 Electric fuel pump and gauge tank unit assembly. 1969-71 Riviera

ELECTRIC FUEL PUMP
1969-70 Buick Riviera

These models have a turbine type electric pump located at the lower end of the fuel pick-up pipe in the bottom of the tank, Fig. 9. This pump is controlled by a switch located near the oil filter and hydraulically connected to the engine oil system so engine oil pressure controls the switch.

Operation

During cranking, current is taken from the starter solenoid and supplied to the pump as long as the starter is energized and oil pressure remains below 3 psi.

With the ignition switch in the run position and the engine oil pressure above 3 psi, current is supplied to the pump through another set of contacts in the control switch. If oil pressure drops below 3 psi with the ignition switch in the run position, the control switch opens the current, shutting off the pump.

Fuel Pump Test

1. Turn ignition switch on and be sure oil and generator lights are lit. If not, check fuse.
2. Make sure oil light goes out while cranking engine. If not, remove fuse from in-line holder just above master cylinder and replace with a new 4 amp ⅝" fuse.
3. Disconnect fuel hose from steel pipe and install pressure gauge. With engine idling, minimum pressure is 4½ psi.
4. Insert fuel hose in a suitable container. With engine idling, a pint measure should be filled in 30 seconds.
5. If pressure is low, check voltage at tank connector. If voltage is satisfactory and ground is clean and tight, pump is defective. If only fuel flow is low, check for kinked hoses or lines.
6. If no fuel flow, unplug connector from oil pressure switch and check for current at one of the parallel slots of connector.
7. If current is present at one of the slots, connect a jumper wire between the two slots and again check for flow.
8. If still no fuel flow, raise car and check fuel tank connector for current. If current is present and ground connection is clean and tight, disconnect fuel line at tank and check for fuel flow, check for kinked lines and hoses. If no fuel flow, remove pump.

1971-72 Vega

An electric fuel pump is located in the fuel tank and is an integral part of the tank unit assembly, which includes the fuel gauge metering unit. Since no repairs can be performed on the pump it must be replaced if found faulty.

Operation

The fuel pump is energized when the ignition switch is in the start position. After the engine starts, the pump receives current through the oil pressure switch as long as there is about 2 pounds of oil pressure. If, for any reason, the oil pressure drops below 2 pounds the contact is broken at the pressure switch and the pump is de-activated.

Fuel Pump Test

NOTE: Operating the pump for more than 30 seconds will seriously damage the motor unless submerged in gasoline.

The following checks should be made:
1. Check fuel flow.
2. Check for proper ground and voltage at the pump.
3. If there is no current at the tank, it will be necessary to check back to the source.
4. If there is fuel flow on the cranking cycle but not when the engine runs, jump the oil pressure switch. If this provides fuel flow, replace the switch.

CARBURETORS

INDEX

CARBURETION

Since carburetion is dependent in several ways on both compression and ignition, it should always be checked last when tuning an engine. See the car chapter for adjustments for the unit you are interested in.

Before adjusting the carburetor, consider the factors outlined below and which definitely affect engine performance.

Performance Complaints

Flooding, flat spots or other performance complaints are often caused by dirt, or water in the carburetor. To aid in diagnosing the complaint, the carburetor should be carefully removed from the engine without draining the fuel from the bowl. The contents of the fuel bowl can then be examined for contamination as the carburetor is disassembled. A magnet moved through the fuel in the bowl will pick up any iron oxide dust that may have caused needle valve leakage.

Check float setting carefully. Too high a level will cause flooding while too low a level will starve the engine.

Before installing carburetor, fill the bowl with clean fuel and operate the throttle by hand several times to visually check the discharge from pump jets.

Inspect gasketed surfaces between body and air horn. Small nicks or burrs should be smoothed down to eliminate air or fuel leakage. On carburetors having a vacuum piston, be especially particular when inspecting the top surface of the inner wall of the bowl around the vacuum piston passage. A poor seal at this location may contribute to a "cutting out" on turns complaint.

Dirty or Rusty Choke Housing

In cases where it is found that the interior of the choke housing is dirty, gummed or rusty while the carburetor itself is comparatively clean, look for a punctured or eroded manifold heat tube (if one is used).

Manifold Heat Control Valve

An engine equipped with a manifold heat control valve can operate with the valve stuck in either the open or closed position. Because of this, an inoperative valve is frequently overlooked at vehicle lubrication or tune-up.

A valve stuck in the "heat-off" position can result in slow warm up, deposits in combustion chamber, carburetor icing, flat spots during acceleration, low gas mileage and spark plug fouling.

A valve stuck in the "heat-on" position can result in power loss, engine knocking, sticking or burned valves and spark plug burning.

To prevent the possibility of a stuck valve, check and lubricate the valve each time the vehicle is lubricated or tuned-up. Check the operation of the valve manually. To lubricate the valve, place a few drops of penetrating oil on the valve shaft where it passes through the manifold. Then move the valve up and down a few times to work the oil in. *Do not use engine oil to lubricate the valve as it will leave a residue which hampers valve operation.*

Carburetor Flange

Check the flange for looseness on the manifold. If one of the flange nuts is loose as little as one-half turn, a sufficient amount of air will enter the intake manifold below the throttle plate to destroy engine idle and all engine performance.

If a tight fit cannot be obtained by tightening the nuts, install a new gasket but be sure that all the old gasket material has been removed.

Throttle Linkage

If the throttle linkage is adjusted so that the accelerator pedal will strike the floor board before the throttle plate is wide open, it will result in low top speed.

Fuel Lines

A restriction of the fuel line will result in an apparent vapor lock action or a definite cut-off of gasoline. This can generally be corrected by blowing out the line with compressed air. In some cases, it may be necessary to replace the line.

Fuel Pump

The pump should be tested to make sure that it will draw an adequate supply of fuel from the tank and deliver it to the carburetor under all conditions of operation. If the pump functions inefficiently, proper adjustment and operation of the carburetor is impossible because the fuel will not be maintained at the prescribed level in the idle passages and main discharge jet (or jets) of the carburetor under all operating conditions.

Fuel Tank

The fuel tank should not be overlooked as a possible source of trouble with carburetion. A shortage of fuel at the fuel pump or carburetor may be caused by pieces of filling station pump hose or other material obstructing the mouth of the feed pipe in the tank, or by a restriction of the air vents in the filler cap and neck.

An unusual amount of dirt, water or

CARBURETORS

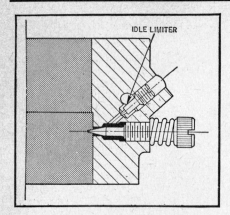

Internal idle mixture limiter

rich mixture during engine warm up.

Choke Thermostat

If necessary to adjust the choke more than two marks from the specified setting, either rich or lean, it indicates that the thermostat spring may be bent or has lost its tension.

Carter Float Settings

When replacing a solid float needle and seat with the new type resilient seat, the float setting should be reduced $1/32$" on AFB, WCFB, WGD and WCD carburetors.

Stromberg Carburetor Ball Checks

Whenever it becomes necessary to dismantle a carburetor be sure to account for the ball checks that may be found under pump plungers and compensating or power valves.

External idle mixture limiter

gum in the fuel filter indicates that the tank is contaminated with these substances, which should be cleaned out to prevent future failure of the pump or carburetor.

Intake Manifold Leaks

Leakage of air into the intake manifold at any point will affect carburetion and general engine performance. Air may leak into the manifold through the joints at the carburetor or cylinder head, cracks in the manifold, cracks or poor connections in the windshield wiper or windshield washer hose lines, or the connections of any accessories which may be connected to the manifold. All such joints should be tested for leaks.

To test the intake manifold for leaks, apply oil from an oil can along the gasket joints with the engine idling. An air leak is indicated when oil is drawn past the gaskets by the suction of the engine. Tighten the nuts or cap screws holding the manifold to the engine and retest for leaks. If tightening fails to stop the leaks, replace the manifold gaskets. If the new gaskets fail to stop the leaks, carefully inspect the manifold for cracks and test any suspicious area with oil.

Air Cleaner

An air cleaner with a dirty element, or with oil that is dirty, too heavy, or too high in the sump, will restrict the air flow through the carburetor and cause a rich mixture at high speeds. In such a condition the air cleaner likewise will not properly remove dirt from the air, and the dirt entering the engine will cause rapid formation of carbon, sticking valves, and wear of piston rings and cylinder bores.

Automatic Choke

The choke mechanism must be inspected and cleaned to make sure it is operating freely. Sluggish action or sticking of the choke will cause excessive fuel consumption, poor performance during warm-up, and possibly hard starting.

The choke thermostat should be set in accordance with the average air temperature as well as the volatility of the fuel being used. It is desirable to have the thermostat set as lean as operating conditions permit in order to avoid an over-

CARBURETOR IDLE ADJUST
Cars Without Exhaust Emission Controls

NOTE: The following text outlines the general procedure for idle and mixture settings on vehicles not equipped with Exhaust Emission Control devices. This, together with pertinent data given in the *Tune Up Charts* in the car chapters should suffice for these vehicles.

Turn the screw clockwise by hand until it just contacts its seal. Then turn it out one turn as an initial setting. Start the engine and run it until it reaches normal operating temperature, at which time the choke valve should be wide open with the idle speed screw resting on lowest step of fast idle cam. Slowly turn the idle mixture screw a little at a time until the engine shows a tendency to hesitate and stall. Then turn it to the left until the engine runs smoothly. Continue turning the screw to the left until the fuel mixture is rich and the engine starts to "lope" or "gallop". Finally turn the screw to the right until the engine runs evenly.

On two-barrel carburetors, there is an idle mixture screw for each barrel. On four-barrel carburetors there are also two idle mixture screws on the primary side of the carburetor. When idle ports are provided on the secondary side, they are non-adjustable or they are rendered non-functional by being blocked with gaskets.

When adjusting the idle mixture on two- and four-barrel carburetors, adjust one screw at a time until the engine runs smoothly as directed above. Then adjust the other screw in like manner.

After the idle mixture has been adjusted, it is recommended that a tachometer (engine speed indicator) be used to set the slow idle speed to the rpm indicated in the *Tune Up* table in the car chapter. If a tachometer is not available, adjust the idle speed screw until the engine runs smoothly without racing. If the

car has an automatic transmission place the shift lever in Drive range with hand brake off. Then very slowly increase engine speed until the car begins to creep, then back off slightly until creeping is eliminated.

Cars With Exhaust Emission Controls

There are two basic types of exhaust emission control systems—air injection type and engine modification type. With both types, the slow idle adjustment method, referred to as "Lean Roll" is to be used. This method insures proper idle, ignition timing and mixture settings for greatest possible exhaust emission reduction and proper engine operation. It should be noted here that smooth idle is extremely sensitive to vacuum leaks. If rough idle is noted, check for vacuum leaks at the carburetor, manifold, etc.

Carburetor Idle Limiters

Some carburetors are equipped with idle adjustment limiters which restrict the maximum idle richness of the air/fuel mixture and prevents overly rich adjustments. There are two types of idle limiters: internal and external (see illustrations). The internal needle limiter is located in the idle channel and is not visible externally. This limiter is set and sealed at the factory and, under no circumstances, during normal service or during overhaul, should the seal be removed and adjustments made to this needle.

The other type of idle limiter is an external idle limiter cap installed on the knurled head of the idle mixture adjusting screw. Any adjustment to the idle fuel mixture on carburetors with this type of limiter must be made within the range of the limiter cap.

Under no circumstances may the limiter cap, the stop boss or the power valve cover, which the limiter caps stop against, be mutilated or deformed in any way to render the limiter inoperative. A satisfactory idle is obtainable within the range of the limiter cap.

The addition of idle limiters does not eliminate the need for adjusting idle speed and mixture. All the limiters do is prevent overly rich mixtures, which increase the amount of hydro-carbons emitted into the atmosphere.

1. With engine at operating temperature, set parking brake and block drive

wheels.
2. Make sure choke valve is wide open.
3. On C.C.S. equipped vehicles, see that the air cleaner thermostatic valve is open.
4. On carburetors so equipped, hold hot idle compensator hole closed with eraser on pencil.
5. Turn air conditioner off or on according to directions given in *Tune Up Charts* in car chapters.
6. Set idle mixture screw(s) for maximum idle rpm.
7. Adjust speed screw (or idle stop solenoid screw on C.C.S.) to obtain the specified rpm in Drive or Neutral as specified.
8. Set ignition timing according to specifications with vacuum advance line disconnected and hole in manifold plugged.
9. Adjust mixture screw IN to obtain a 20 rpm drop (lean roll).
10. Adjust mixture screw OUT ¼ turn.
11. Repeat Steps 9 and 10 for second mixture screw (2 and 4 barrel carbs).
12. Readjust speed screw (or solenoid screw) if necessary to obtain specified rpm.
13. On C.C.S. with idle solenoid stop on carburetor, electrically disconnect solenoid and adjust carburetor idle speed screw to obtain 400 rpm in neutral; then reconnect wire to solenoid.

NOTE: Exact instructions for each C.C.S. equipped engine-transmission combination is given for this Lean Roll (low idle) speed method on a decal permanently affixed to the vicinity of the radiator support as well as in the *Tune Up Charts* in the car chapter of this manual.

Carter Carburetor Section

CARTER YF ADJUSTMENT SPECIFICATIONS

See Tune Up Chart in car chapter for hot idle speed.

Year	Carb. Model	Initial Idle Mixture Screw Setting	Float Level	Float Drop	Idle Vent Setting	Fast Idle Setting	Choke Unloader Setting	Vacuum Break Setting	Choke Setting
AMERICAN MOTORS									
1970	4767S	14.0 to 1①	29/64	1¼	.052	See Text	.300	—	Index
	4768S	14.0 to 1①	29/64	1¼	.052	See Text	.325	—	Index
	4769S	14.0 to 1①	29/64	1¼	.055	See Text	.300	—	Index
	4770S	14.0 to 1①	29/64	1¼	.055	See Text	.300	—	Index
	4978S	14.0 to 1①	29/64	1¼	.055	See Text	.300	—	1 Rich
1971	6038S	14.0 to 1①	29/64	1¼	—	See Text	.300	—	Index
	6093S	14.0 to 1①	29/64	1¼	—	See Text	.300	—	Index
	6094S	14.0 to 1①	29/64	1¼	—	See Text	.300	—	1 Rich
	6095S	14.0 to 1①	29/64	1¼	—	See Text	.300	—	Index
	6096S	14.0 to 1①	29/64	1¼	—	See Text	.300	—	1 Rich
1972	6199S	14.0 to 1①	29/64	1¼	—	See Text	.300	—	Index
	6200S	14.0 to 1①	29/64	1¼	—	See Text	.300	—	Index

①—Air/fuel ratio.

Year	Carb. Model	Initial Idle Mixture Screw Setting	Float Level	Float Drop	Idle Vent Setting	Fast Idle Setting	Choke Unloader Setting	Vacuum Break Setting	Choke Setting
CHEVROLET									
1966	3379SA	1½	½	1³⁄₁₆	.035	See Text	—	—	—
	3402SB	1½	½	1³⁄₁₆	.035	See Text	—	—	—
	4079S	1½	½	1³⁄₁₆	.035	See Text	.260	.320	See Text
	4080S	1½	½	1³⁄₁₆	.035	See Text	.260	.300	See Text
1967	4367S	1½	7⁄32	1³⁄₁₆	.065	See Text	.250	.240	See Text
	4368S, 78S	1½	7⁄32	1³⁄₁₆	.065	See Text	.250	.220	See Text
	4373S, 74S	1½	7⁄32	1³⁄₁₆	—	See Text	.250	—	—
	4377S, 87S	1½	7⁄32	1³⁄₁₆	.065	See Text	.250	.240	See Text

Year	Carb. Model	Initial Idle Mixture Screw Setting	Float Level	Float Drop	Idle Vent Setting	Fast Idle Setting	Choke Unloader Setting	Vacuum Break Setting	Choke Setting
FORD									
1967	C7ZF-A①	1½	7⁄32	—	—	.065	.250	—	1 Rich
1968	C8DF-A	1½	7⁄32	—	—	.035	.280	—	Index
	C8DF-B	1½	7⁄32	—	—	.046	.280	—	1 Lean
1969	C8AF-BF	13.9 to 1②	7⁄32	—	—	.035	.280	—	Index
	C8DF-G	13.6 to 1②	7⁄32	—	—	.046	.280	—	Index
	C8DF-H	13.9 to 1②	7⁄32	—	—	.040	.280	—	1 Lean

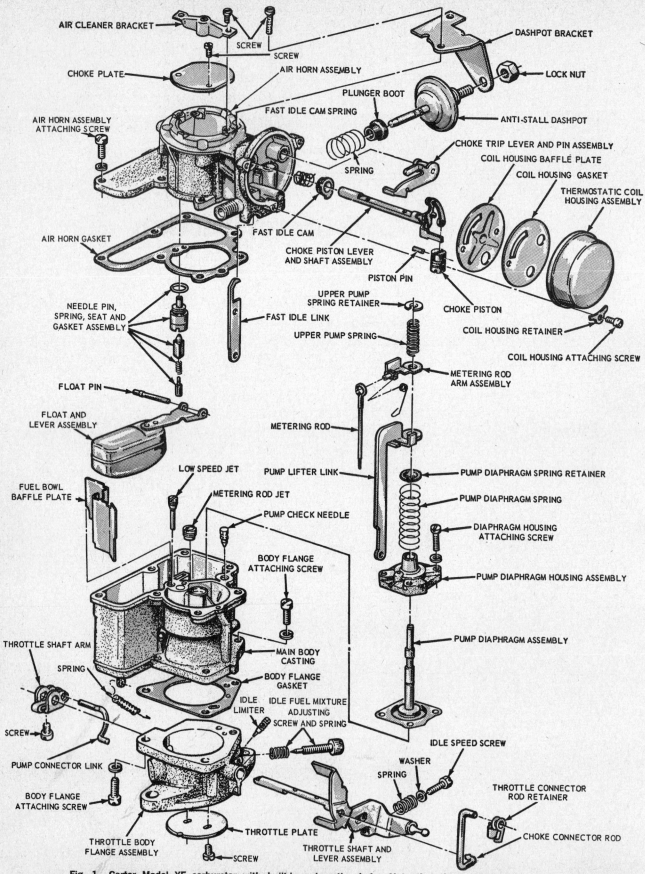

Fig. 1 Carter Model YF carburetor with built-in automatic choke. Note that this unit is provided with an idle limiter screw which is used to prevent an overly rich mixture on cars with exhaust emission control

CARTER YF ADJUSTMENT SPECIFICATIONS—Continued

See Tune Up Chart in car chapter for hot idle speed.

Year	Carb. Model	Initial Idle Mixture Screw Setting	Float Level	Float Drop	Idle Vent Setting	Fast Idle Setting	Choke Unloader Setting	Vacuum Break Setting	Choke Setting
FORD—Continued									
1970	D0AF-A	14.4 to 1②	3/8	—	—	.029	—	—	Index
	D0AF-B	14.4 to 1②	3/8	—	—	.025	—	—	1 Lean
	D0DF-L	14.4 to 1②	3/8	—	—	.036	—	—	Index
	D0DF-M	14.4 to 1②	3/8	—	—	.031	—	—	Index
	D0DF-N	14.4 to 1②	7/32	—	—	.035	—	—	Index
	D0DF-R	14.4 to 1②	7/32	—	—	.036	—	—	1 Rich
	D0DF-S	14.4 to 1②	7/32	—	—	.035	—	—	Index
	D0DF-T	14.4 to 1②	3/8	—	—	.031	—	—	Index
	D0DF-U	14.4 to 1②	7/32	—	—	.036	—	—	1 Rich
	D0DF-V	14.2 to 1②	3/8	—	—	.036	—	—	Index
1971	D1DF-EA	14.5 to 1②	3/8	—	—	.105	.250	—	Index
	D1DF-GA, HA	14.5 to 1②	3/8	—	—	.170	.250	—	Index
	D1DF-JA, LA	14.2 to 1②	3/8	—	—	.140	.250	—	Index
	D1DF-KA, MA	14.2 to 1②	3/8	—	—	.140	.250	—	Index
	D1DF-PA	14.5 to 1②	3/8	—	—	.190	.250	—	Index
	D1DF-RA	③	3/8	—	—	.220	.250	—	Index
1972	D2DF-AA	—	3/8	—	—	—	.170	—	Index
	D2DF-BA	—	3/8	—	—	—	.200	—	Index
	D2DF-CA	—	3/8	—	—	—	.200	—	Index
	D2DF-DA	—	3/8	—	—	—	.230	—	Index
	D2DF-EA	—	3/8	—	—	—	.230	—	Index
	D2AF-JA	—	3/8	—	—	—	.230	—	1 Lean

①—Identification tag marked "Autolite".　②—Air/fuel ratio.　③—Air/fuel ratio greater than 14.5 to 1.

OLDSMOBILE

1966–67	4072SA	1½	7/32	2¼	.060	See Text	¼	.215	See Text
	4367S	1½	7/32	2¼	.060	See Text	¼	.230	See Text

MODEL YF ADJUSTMENTS

The YF carburetor, Figs. 1 and 2, is a single-barrel, downdraft unit combining the fundamental features of other Carter carburetors. In addition, it features a diaphragm-type accelerating pump. It also has a diaphragm-operated metering rod, both vacuum and mechanically controlled.

The 1966 version of this carburetor, Fig. 2, with an automatic choke used in conjunction with a temperature sensing choke coil (mounted in a cast depression on the exhaust manifold) is used with Chevy II six-cylinder engines when the *Air Injection Reactor System* is used.

Float Adjustment

Fig. 3—Invert bowl cover and measure float level (distance between float and cover at free end of float). Adjust by bending lip of float (not float arm) that rests on needle.

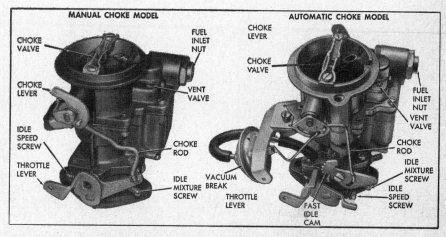

Fig. 2 YF carburetor exteriors. The automatic choke model has the choke coil mounted on the exhaust manifold of the engine

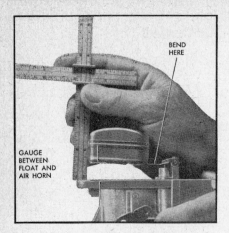

Fig. 3 YF float level adjustment

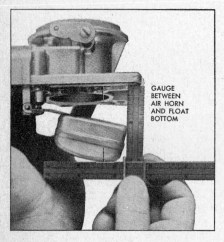

Fig. 4 YF float drop adjustment

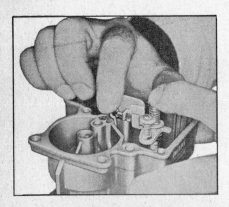

Fig. 5 YF metering rod adjustment

Hold cover in upright position (allowing float to hang down, Fig. 4), and measure float drop from cover to float at end opposite hinge. If the measurement does not correspond to the dimension listed in the *YF Specifications Chart*, adjust by bending stop tab on float arm.

Pump Adjustment

With throttle valve seated in bore of carburetor, press down on upper end of diaphragm shaft until it reaches its bottom position. The metering rod arm should now contact the pump lifter link at the outer end nearest the springs. Adjust by bending the pump connector link at its lower angle.

Metering Rod Adjustment

Fig. 5—With throttle valve seated in bore of carburetor, press down on upper end of diaphragm shaft until diaphragm bottoms in vacuum chamber. Metering rod should contact bottom of metering rod well, and metering rod arm should contact lifter link at the outer end nearest the springs and at supporting lug. Adjust by bending lip of metering rod arm to which metering rod is attached, up or down as required.

Idle Vent Adjustment

Fig. 6—This adjustment should be made after completing pump and metering rod adjustments. Install bowl cover and air horn assembly with gasket. With throttle

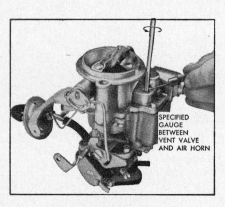

Fig. 6 YF idle vent adjustment

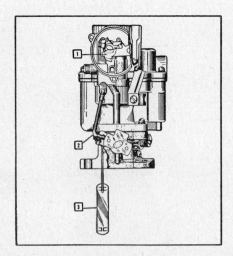

Fig. 7 YF fast idle adjustment for Fig. 1 carburetors. 1) Fast idle cam. 2) Bend at connector link. 3) Gauge

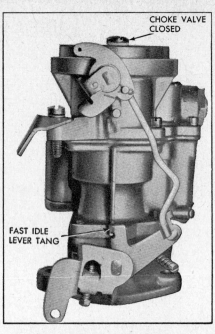

Fig. 8 YF choke rod adjustment (manual choke) for Fig. 2 carburetors

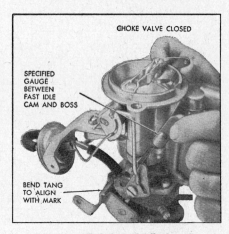

Fig. 9 YF choke rod adjustment (automatic choke) for Fig. 2 carburetors

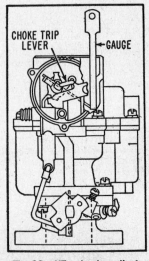

Fig. 10 YF unloader adjustment for Fig. 1 carburetors

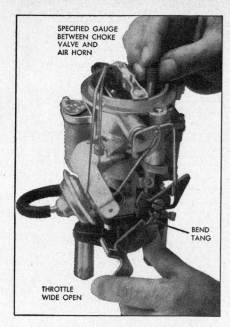

Fig. 11 YF unloader adjustment
for Fig. 2 carburetors

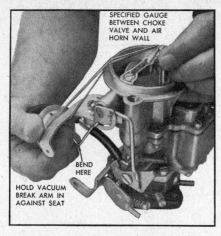

Fig. 12 YF vacuum break adjustment
for Fig. 2 carburetors

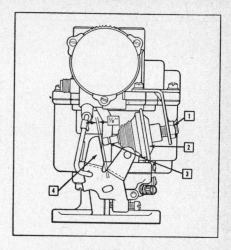

Fig. 13 YF dashpot adjustment
(Rambler). 1) Locknut. 2) Dashpot.
3) Dashpot stem. 4) Throttle lever

valve tightly closed in carburetor bore there should be the clearance listed in the *YF Specifications Chart* between idle vent valve and inside of bowl cover. Adjust idle vent screw as required.

Fast Idle Adjustment

Unit With Built-In Auto. Choke

Referring to Fig. 7, remove choke coil housing, gasket and baffle plate. Crack throttle valve (barely open) and hold choke valve firmly in closed position, then close throttle valve. This will allow the fast idle cam to revolve to the fast idle position.

With choke valve held tightly closed, and with slight tension on throttle lever, there should be the clearance listed in the *YF Specifications Chart* between the throttle valve and carburetor bore (side opposite idle port). Adjust by bending connector link as required.

With Manual Choke, Fig. 8

With choke valve in wide open position, tang on throttle lever should just contact stop boss on carburetor body. To adjust, bend rod at offset portion as required.

With Automatic Choke, Fig. 9

With choke valve fully closed, bend choke rod at offset to obtain a slight clearance (.015") between fast idle cam and boss on carburetor bowl.

With choke valve fully closed, index mark on fast idle cam must be at the mid-point of the fast idle tang on throttle lever. Bend fast idle tang up or down to adjust.

Choke Unloader Adjustment

With throttle valve held wide open and choke valve held toward closed position with a rubber band, there should be the clearance listed in the *YF Specifications Chart* between lower edge of choke valve and inner air horn wall.

On Fig. 1 carburetors, adjust by bending arm on choke trip lever, Fig. 10. On Fig. 2 carburetors adjust by bending unloader tang on throttle lever, Fig. 11.

Vacuum Break Adjustment

Fig. 12—With vacuum break arm held against its stop, and choke valve held toward closed position with a rubber band, bend vacuum break link to obtain the clearance listed in the *YF Specifications Chart* between lower edge of choke valve and air horn wall.

Automatic Choke Adjustment

For Fig. 1 Units

Loosen choke cover retaining screws and turn choke cover so that line or index mark on cover lines up with the specified mark listed in *YF Specifications Chart* on choke housing.

Choke Diaphragm Linkage

For Fig. 2 Units

With vacuum diaphragm bottomed, close choke valve as far as possible without forcing. Adjust choke diaphragm connector rod to give the clearance listed in the *YF Specifications Chart* between lower edge of choke valve and inner wall of air horn. Remove connector rod to prevent damage to diaphragm.

CARTER CARBURETORS

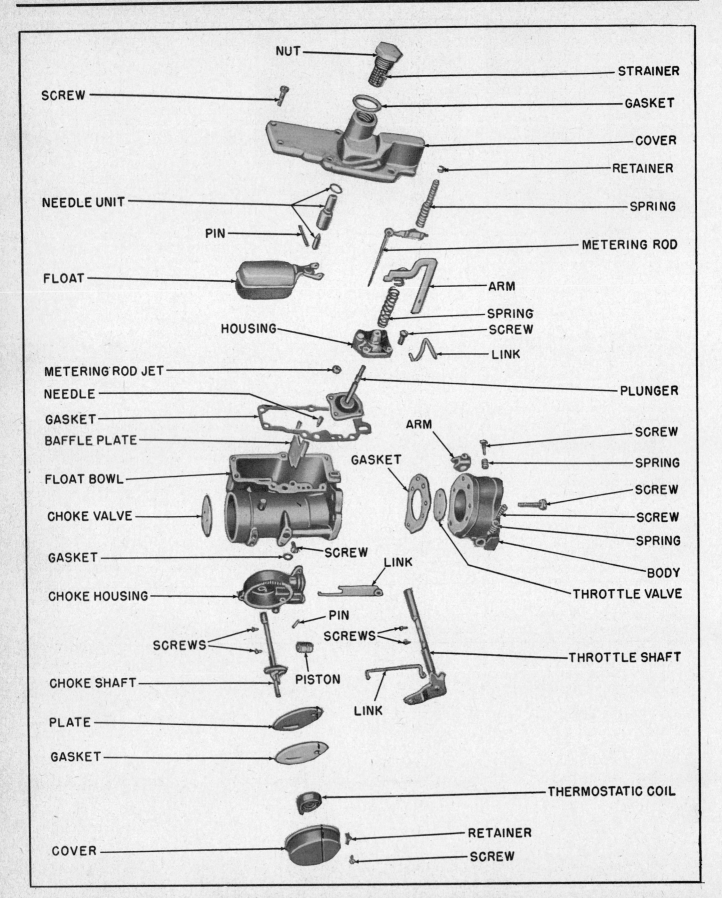

NUT

STRAINER

SCREW

GASKET

COVER

RETAINER

NEEDLE UNIT

SPRING

PIN

METERING ROD

FLOAT

ARM

SPRING

HOUSING

SCREW

LINK

METERING ROD JET

NEEDLE

PLUNGER

GASKET

ARM

BAFFLE PLATE

SCREW

GASKET

SPRING

FLOAT BOWL

SCREW

CHOKE VALVE

SCREW

SPRING

GASKET

SCREW

BODY

LINK

THROTTLE VALVE

CHOKE HOUSING

PIN

SCREWS

SCREWS

THROTTLE SHAFT

CHOKE SHAFT

PISTON

LINK

PLATE

GASKET

THERMOSTATIC COIL

COVER

RETAINER

SCREW

Fig. 1   Carter Model YH used with Corvair Turbocharged engines

CARTER YH ADJUSTMENT SPECIFICATIONS

See Tune Up Chart in car chapter for hot idle speed.

Year	Carb. Model	Idle Screw (Mixture) Turns Open	Float Level	Float Drop	Metering Rod	Pump	Fast Idle	Unloader	Automatic Choke	Dashpot
CORVAIR TURBOCHARGED										
1966	4141S-SA	¼–2	⅝	2⅜	See Text	See Text	.033	7/16	1 Lean	—

MODEL YH ADJUSTMENTS

The YH carburetor, Figs., 1 and 2, is comparable to the YF model except that the circuits are rearranged to operate in a horizontal or sidedraft position, and in conjunction with the Turbocharger on Corvair cars.

Float Adjustment

Figs. 3 and 4—With bowl cover inverted, distance between cover gasket surface and float (at center) should be as listed in the *YH Specifications Chart*. Adjust by bending float arm as required.

To adjust float drop, invert cover to upright position as shown, allowing float to hang down. Distance between cover gasket surface and bottom of free end of float should be as listed. Adjust by bending tang on hinge end.

Metering Rod Adjustment

Fig. 5—Insert gauge in place of metering rod. With throttle valve tightly closed, press down on diaphragm shaft until metering rod arm contacts lifter link at diaphragm stem. With diaphragm shaft held in this position, metering rod pin must rest lightly on metering rod gauge (T109-104). To adjust, bend metering rod arm.

Accelerating Pump

There is no adjustment provided. If acceleration is not satisfactory, examine diaphragm for wear or damage. Clean and blow out all passages. Replace all worn or damaged parts.

Fast Idle Adjustment

Fig. 6—With choke coil housing removed, have choke valve tightly closed and with fast idle link on high step of cam. Adjust choke connector rod to give the clearance listed in the *YH Specifications Chart* between edge of throttle valve and carburetor bore (side opposite idle port). To adjust, bend fast idle connector link at curvature.

Choke Unloader Adjustment

Hold throttle valve wide open and close choke valve. There should be the clearance listed in the *YH Specifications Chart* between lower edge of choke valve and inner wall of air horn. To adjust, bend choke shaft unloader tang, Fig. 6.

Automatic Choke Adjustment

Loosen choke coil housing retaining screws and rotate housing by hand to the setting listed in the *YH Specifications Chart*. Hold in position and tighten screws.

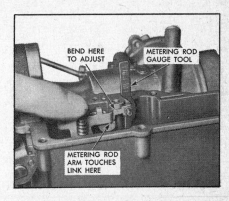

Fig. 5 YH metering rod adjustment

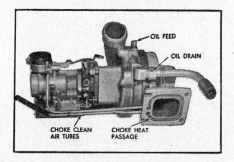

Fig. 2 YH carburetor exterior

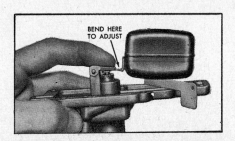

Fig. 3 YH float level adjustment

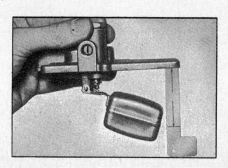

Fig. 4 YH float drop adjustment

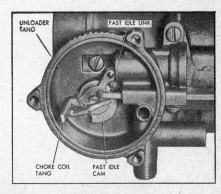

Fig. 6 YH fast idle adjustment

CARTER CARBURETORS

CARTER RBS ADJUSTMENT SPECIFICATIONS

See Tune Up Chart in car chapter for hot idle speed.

Year	Carb. Model	Idle Screw (Mixture) Turns Open	Float Level	Step-Up Rod	Pump & Bowl Vent	Fast Idle Linkage	Fast Idle Throttle Valve	Choke Unloader	Dashpot Setting	Choke Setting
AMERICAN MOTORS										
1966	3765S	¼-1¾	¹⁵⁄₃₂	—	¹⁄₁₆	See Text	.028	⅛	—	1 Rich
	3766S	¼-1¾	¹⁵⁄₃₂	—	¹⁄₁₆	See Text	.040	⅛	—	1 Rich
1966-67	3882S	¼-1¾	¹⁵⁄₃₂	—	¹⁄₁₆	See Text	.033	⅛	—	1 Rich
1968	4470S	1	⁹⁄₁₆	—	⁵⁄₆₄	See Text	.035	⅛	—	2 Rich
	4626S	½-1½	⁹⁄₁₆	—	⁵⁄₆₄	See Text	.035	⅛	—	2 Rich
1969	4631S	1	⁹⁄₁₆	—	⁵⁄₆₄	See Text	—	⅛	³⁄₃₂	Index
	4633S	1	⁹⁄₁₆	—	⁵⁄₆₄	See Text	—	³⁄₁₆	³⁄₃₂	Index
	4634S	1	⁹⁄₁₆	—	⁵⁄₆₄	See Text	—	³⁄₁₆	—	2 Rich
	4666S	1	⁹⁄₁₆	—	⁵⁄₆₄	See Text	—	⅛	—	2 Rich

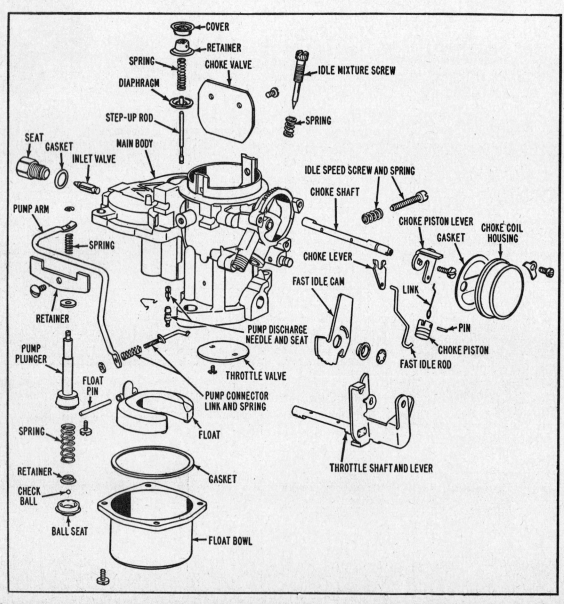

Fig. 1 Carter Model RBS single barrel carburetor

CARTER RBS ADJUSTMENT SPECIFICATIONS—Continued

See Tune Up Chart in car chapter for hot idle speed.

Year	Carb. Model	Idle Screw (Mixture) Turns Open	Float Level	Step-Up Rod	Pump & Bowl Vent	Fast Idle Linkage	Fast Idle Throttle Valve	Choke Unloader	Dashpot Setting	Choke Setting
FORD ENGINES										
1970	D0ZF-C	14.2 to 1①	9/16	—	—	See Text	.040	—	—	Index
	D0ZF-D	14.2 to 1①	9/16	—	—	See Text	.046	—	—	1 Rich
	D0ZF-F	14.2 to 1①	9/16	—	—	See Text	.046	—	—	1 Rich
1971	D1ZF-HA, LA	14.2 to 1①	9/16	—	—	See Text	—	.25	—	Index
	D1ZF-KA	14.2 to 1①	9/16	—	—	See Text	—	.25	—	1 Rich
	D1ZF-NA	14.2 to 1①	9/16	—	—	See Text	—	.25	—	1 Rich
1972	D2OF-LA	—	9/16	—	.400	See Text	—	.300	1/8	Index
	D2OF-MA	—	9/16	—	.400	See Text	—	.190	1/8	1 Rich
	D2OF-SA	—	9/16	—	.400	See Text	—	.190	1/8	1 Rich

①—Air/fuel ratio.

MODEL RBS ADJUSTMENTS

Fig. 2   RBS float level adjustment

Fig. 3   RBS pump adjustment

This carburetor, Fig. 1, incorporates a single aluminum casting with a pressed steel bowl. Adjustments are readily accessible and most calibration points are located in the single casting.

Fuel pickups are located near the centerline of the carburetor bore to gain the benefits of a concentric bowl carburetor, yet so located that engine heat being radiated through the bore are conducted through the casting but is not readily conducted to the fuel in the bowl.

Vapor vents allow rapid dissipation of the vapors to assure smooth idle and to minimize hard starting while the engine is hot. A diaphragm controlled step-up provides instantaneous response to engine demands.

The carburetor model number is stamped on the side of the flange near the throttle lever.

Float Level Adjustment

Fig. 2—With carburetor inverted, bowl and bowl gasket removed, and only weight of float pressing needle into its seat, measure vertical distance from casting to the small "bump" at outer ends of float. Gauge both ends of float. If the vertical distance is not as listed in the *RBS Specifications Chart*, adjustment can be made by removing float from casting, or by

holding lip end of float bracket securely with needle-nose pliers. However, be sure to hold float lip away from needle when adjusting. To adjust, bend bracket at its narrowest portion.

Pump & Bowl Vent Adjustment

Fig. 3—Back out throttle lever (idle speed) adjusting screw and hold choke valve wide open so throttle valve seats in carburetor bore. Turn pump adjusting nut to obtain the clearance listed in the *RBS Specifications Chart* between washer on pump plunger and bushing.

Fast Idle Linkage Adjustment

With choke valve tightly closed and choke connector rod in upper end of slot in cam, align cam index with center of fast idle tang. Adjust by bending choke connector rod at lower angle.

Fast Idle Throttle Valve Clearance Adjustment

With choke valve closed there should

be the clearance listed in the *RBS Specifications Chart* between edge of throttle valve and carburetor bore with center of fast idle tang on index mark. On all models, adjust by bending fast idle tang.

Choke Unloader Adjustment

With throttle valve wide open, there should be the clearance listed in the *RBS Specifications Chart* between top edge of choke valve and inner wall of air horn. To adjust, bend unloader arm on throttle lever.

Dashpot Adjustment

Rambler—With throttle valve tightly closed and diaphragm stem fully depressed, adjust dashpot to give the clearance listed in the *RBS Specifications Chart* between stem and throttle lever.

Automatic Choke Adjustment

Loosen retainer screws and turn choke cover so that line or index mark on cover lines up with the specified mark on choke housing (see *RBS Specifications Chart*).

CARTER BBS ADJUSTMENT SPECIFICATIONS

See Tune Up Chart In car chapter for hot idle speed.

Year	Carb. Model	Initial Idle Mixture Screw Turns Open	Float Level	Pump Travel Inch	Bowl Vent Drill Size	Choke Unloader Drill Size	Fast Idle Cam Position Drill Size	Choke Vacuum Kick Drill Size	Automatic Choke Setting
DODGE & PLYMOUTH									
1966	4099S	1–2	¼	—	.060	³⁄₁₆	48 Drill	22 Drill	2 Rich
	4100S	1–2	¼	—	.060	³⁄₁₆	48 Drill	35 Drill	2 Rich
	4101S	1–2	¼	—	.060	³⁄₁₆	48 Drill	22 Drill	2 Rich
	4102S	1–2	¼	—	.060	³⁄₁₆	48 Drill	28 Drill	2 Rich
	4103S	1–2	¼	—	.060	³⁄₁₆	48 Drill	22 Drill	2 Rich
	4104S	1–2	¼	—	.060	³⁄₁₆	48 Drill	35 Drill	2 Rich
	4105S	1–2	¼	—	.060	³⁄₁₆	48 Drill	22 Drill	2 Rich
	4106S	1–2	¼	—	.060	³⁄₁₆	48 Drill	28 Drill	2 Rich
1967	4286S	1–2	¼	—	.060	³⁄₁₆	48 Drill	20 Drill	2 Rich
	4287S	1–2	¼	—	.060	³⁄₁₆	48 Drill	41 Drill	2 Rich
	4302S	1–2	¼	—	.060	³⁄₁₆	48 Drill	20 Drill	2 Rich
	4303S	1–2	¼	—	.060	³⁄₁₆	48 Drill	28 Drill	2 Rich
1968	4414S	2	¼	—	.060	³⁄₁₆	48 Drill	20 Drill	2 Rich
	4415S	2½	¼	—	.060	³⁄₁₆	48 Drill	35 Drill	2 Rich
1969	4601S	1–2	¼	—	.060	³⁄₁₆	48 Drill	35 Drill	2 Rich
	4602S	1–2	¼	—	.060	³⁄₁₆	48 Drill	35 Drill	2 Rich
1970	4715S	14.0–14.4 to 1①	¼	—	¹⁄₃₂	³⁄₁₆	48 Drill	35 Drill	2 Rich
	4716S	14.0–14.4 to 1①	¼	—	¹⁄₃₂	³⁄₁₆	48 Drill	48 Drill	2 Rich
	4717S	14.0–14.4 to 1①	¼	—	¹⁷⁄₆₄	³⁄₁₆	48 Drill	35 Drill	2 Rich
	4718S	14.0–14.4 to 1①	¼	—	¹⁷⁄₆₄	³⁄₁₆	48 Drill	48 Drill	2 Rich
1971	4955S	14.0–14.4 to 1①	¼	—	¹⁷⁄₆₄	³⁄₁₆	48 Drill	35 Drill	2 Rich
	4956S	14.0–14.4 to 1①	¼	—	¹⁷⁄₆₄	³⁄₁₆	48 Drill	35 Drill	2 Rich

①—Air/fuel ratio.

MODEL BBS ADJUSTMENTS

Float Level Adjustment

Fig. 3—Invert main body so that weight of floats only is forcing needle against seat. If proper gauge is not available, measure from surface of fuel bowl to crown of each float at center. Float setting should be as listed in the *BBS Specificaions Chart*. If an adjustment is necessary, bend lip of float lever in or out until correct setting is obtained.

Bowl Vent Adjustment

Fig. 4

This adjustment automatically adjusts the accelerator pump as well. The procedure is as follows:

1. Back off idle speed adjusting screw. Open choke valve so that when throttle valve is closed the fast idle adjusting screw will not contact fast idle cam.
2. Be sure pump operating rod is in center hole in throttle lever and that bowl vent clip on pump stem is in center groove.
3. Close throttle valve tightly. It should be possible to insert a drill of the specified size between bowl vent and air horn.
4. If an adjustment is necessary, bend pump operating rod at the lower angle as required to obtain the cor-

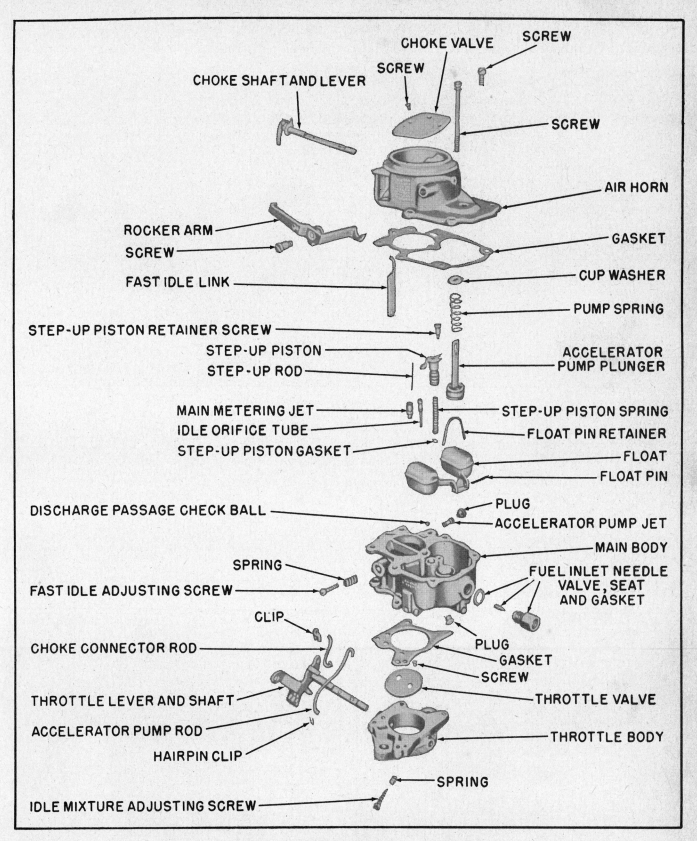

Fig. 1   Carter Model BBS single barrel carburetor. Exploded

CARTER CARBURETORS

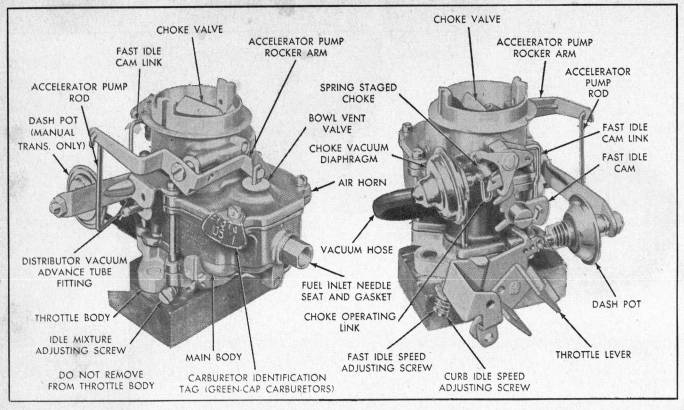

Fig. 2 Exterior of late model BBS carburetor used with C.A.P.

rect bowl vent opening.

NOTE: This is an important adjustment since too much lift at the bowl vent will result in considerable loss in low speed fuel economy. If the pump operating rod is moved to either the short or long stroke position, a corresponding change must be made in the location of the bowl vent clip, and the amount of lift of the bowl rechecked and adjusted.

Choke Unloader Adjustment

Fig. 5—Hold throttle valve in wide open position. Insert a drill of the specified size between upper edge of choke valve and inner wall of air horn. With a finger lightly pressing against choke valve, a slight drag should be felt as the drill is being withdrawn. If an adjustment is necessary, bend unloader tang on throttle lever as required.

Fast Idle Cam Position

Fig. 6

1. With fast idle speed adjusting screw contacting the second highest step on the fast idle cam, move choke valve toward closed position with light pressure on choke shaft lever.

2. Insert specified drill between choke valve and wall of air horn. If an adjustment is necessary, bend fast idle rod at upper angle until correct valve opening has been obtained.

Vacuum Kick Adjustment

Fig. 7

The choke diaphragm adjustment controls the fuel delivery while the engine is running. It positions the choke valve within the air horn by action of the linkage between the choke shaft and diaphragm. The diaphragm must be energized to measure the vacuum kick ad-

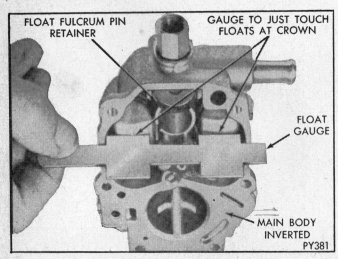

Fig. 3 Checking float level. BBS carburetors

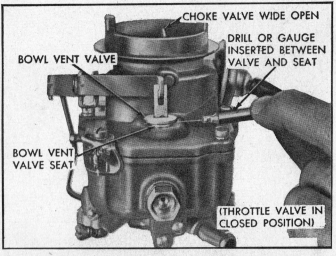

Fig. 4 Bowl vent adjustment. BBS carburetors

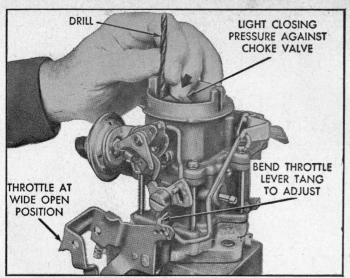

**Fig. 5 Checking choke unloader setting
(wide open kick). BBS carburetors**

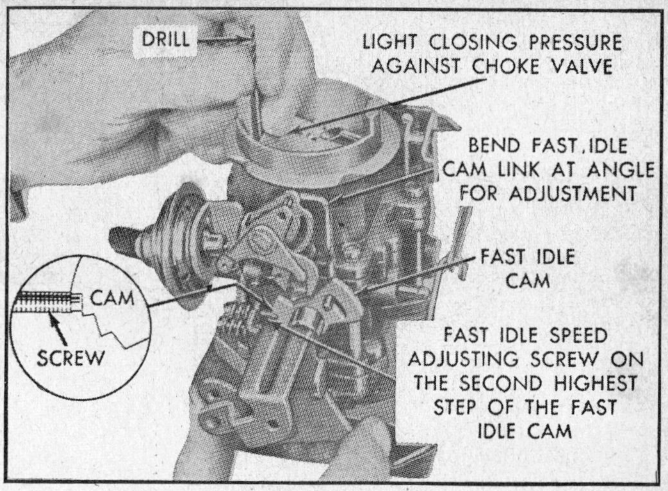

Fig. 6 Fast idle cam position. BBS carburetors

justment. Use a vacuum source, or vacuum supplied by another vehicle. Adjust as follows:

1. If adjustment is to be made with the engine running, back off the fast idle speed screw until choke can be closed to the kick position with engine at curb idle.

   NOTE: Number of screw turns required so that fast idle can be returned to original adjustment.

   If an auxiliary vacuum source is to be used, open throttle valve (engine not running) and move choke to closed position. Release throttle first, then release choke.

2. When using an auxiliary vacuum source, disconnect vacuum hose from carburetor and connect it to hose from vacuum supply with a small length of tube to act as a fitting. Removal of hose from diaphragm may require forces which change the system. Apply a vacuum of 10 inches or more of mercury.

3. Insert specified drill between choke valve and wall of air horn. Apply sufficient closing pressure on lever to which choke rod attaches to provide a minimum stroke valve opening without distortion of diaphragm link. Note that cylindrical stem of diaphragm will extend as internal spring is compressed. This spring must be fully compressed for proper measurement of vacuum kick adjustment.

4. An adjustment will be necessary if a slight drag is not obtained as drill is being removed. Shorten or lengthen diaphragm link to obtain correct choke opening. Length changes should be made carefully by bending (open or closing) the bend provided in the diaphragm link. Do not apply

twisting or bending force to diaphragm.

5. Reinstall vacuum hose on correct carburetor fitting. Return fast idle screw to its original location if disturbed as suggested in Step 1.

6. Check the adjustment as follows: With no vacuum applied to diaphragm, choke valve should move freely between open and closed positions. If movement is not free, examine linkage for misalignment or interferences caused by bending operation. Repeat adjustment if necessary to provide proper link operation.

Spring Staged Choke Adjustment
Fig. 8

The spring staged choke is a device incorporated in the choke mechanism that

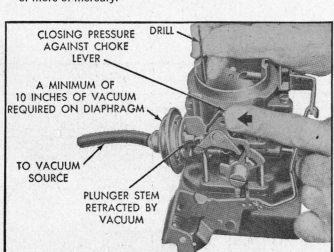

Fig. 7 Vacuum kick adjustment. BBS carburetors

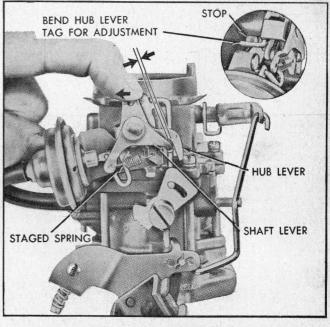

Fig. 8 Spring staged choke adjustment. BBS carburetors

limits the choke blade closing torque when cranking the engine at temperatures below zero. Thus the spring staging of the choke is a better match for the engine's starting mixture requirements at low temperatures.

To check the spring staged choke for correct operating clearance, proceed as follows:

1. Push on hub lever with finger at closed choke position. A small opening should exist between shaft and hub levers as indicated.
2. Using a drill or gauge, measure the opening which should be from .010 to .040".
3. If adjustment is necessary, bend hub lever tang until correct opening is obtained.

Choke Adjustment

Fig. 9—Loosen mounting post lock nut and turn mounting post with screwdriver until index mark on disc is positioned as listed in the *BBS Specifications Chart*. Hold in this position with screwdriver and tighten lock nut.

NOTE: Screwdriver may be held in a vise

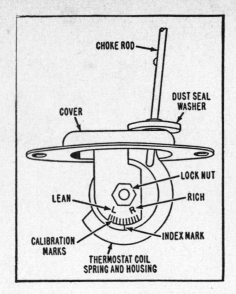

Fig. 9   BBS well-type choke setting

so that one hand may be used to support housing while tightening nut. After adjustment is completed and coil housing and rod and carburetor are installed on engine, lift cover disc and open and close choke valve manually to see if connector rod clears sides of hole in housing cover without binding. If rod does not clear housing cover without binding, replace with a new unit since connecting rod cannot be bent without affecting calibration.

Dashpot Adjustment

Clean Air Carburetors

The dashpot is used only on cars equipped with the Cleaner Air Package and manual transmission, Fig. 2.

To adjust the dashpot, have the curb idle speed and mixture properly adjusted, and install a tachometer. Position throttle lever so that actuating tab on lever is contacting stem of dashpot but not depressing it. The tachometer should read 2000 rpm if the setting is correct. If not correct, screw dashpot in or out as required, then tighten lock nut on dashpot against the bracket.

MODEL BBD ADJUSTMENTS

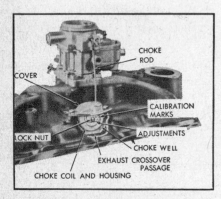

Fig. 2   Well-type automatic choke mounted on intake manifold

Fig. 1 is an exploded view of the BBD two barrel carburetor. The choke housing containing the thermostatic coil spring is located in a well at the exhaust crossover passage, Fig. 2.

The carburetor shown in Fig. 3 is a standard model when the vehicle is equipped with either a manual shift or automatic transmission. When used with C.A.P. (Cleaner Air Package) equipment, a dashpot (slow closing throttle device) is provided for vehicles with manual transmission only.

The carburetors illustrated in Fig. 4 are used on the larger V8 engines; the one on the right is a standard model while the one at the left is used with C.A.P. equipment. Note that the C.A.P. model incorporates a dashpot for use with manual shift transmissions only.

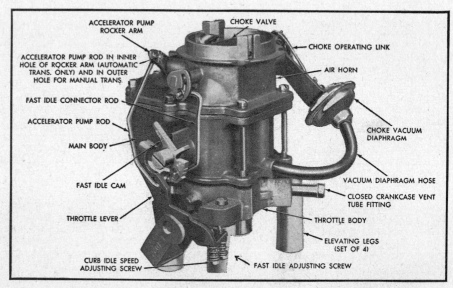

Fig. 3   Late model BBD carburetor used on the smaller V8 engines

Float Level Adjustment

Fig. 5—With carburetor body inverted so that weight of floats ONLY is forcing needle against its seat, use a T-scale or the tool shown, and check the float level from surface of fuel bowl to crown of each float at center.

If an adjustment is necessary, hold floats on bottom of bowl and bend float lip as required to give the specified dimension.

CAUTION: When bending the float lip, do not allow the lip to push against the needle as the synthetic rubber tip (if used) can be compressed sufficiently to cause a false setting which will affect correct level of fuel in bowl. After being compressed, the tip is very slow to recover its original shape.

Accelerating Pump

Except 1¼" Bore Units, Fig. 6

1. Back off idle adjusting screw. Open

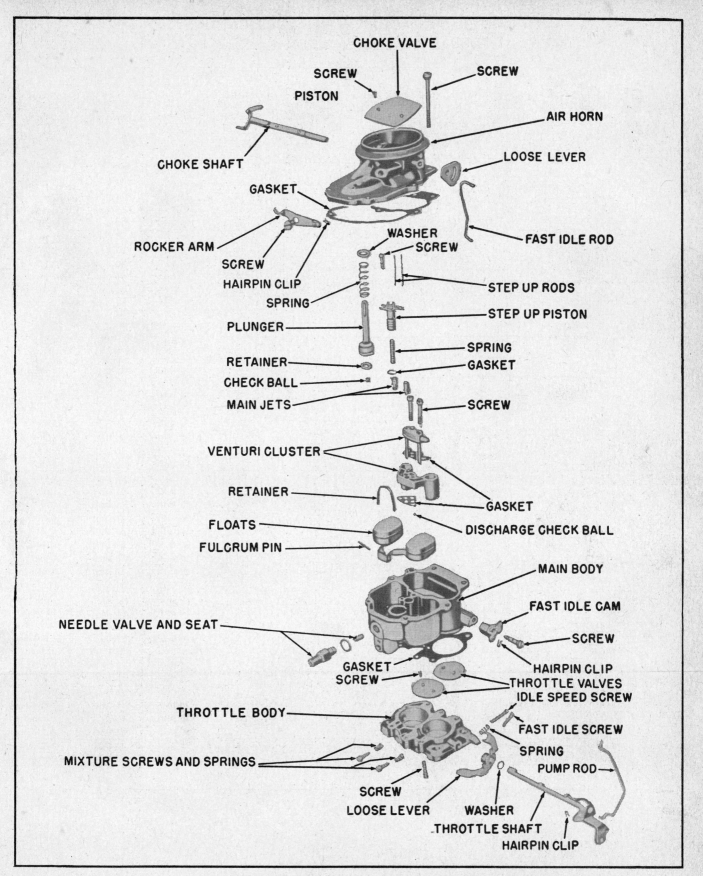

Fig. 1 Carter Model BBD two-barrel carburetor exploded

CARTER CARBURETORS

CARTER BBD ADJUSTMENT SPECIFICATIONS

See Tune Up Chart in car chapter for hot idle speed.

Year	Carb. Model	Initial Idle Mix. Screws Turns Open	Float Level	Pump Travel Inch	Bowl Vent Drill Size	Choke Unloader Drill Size	Choke Vacuum Kick Drill Size	Fast Idle Cam Position Drill Size	Automatic Choke Setting
CHRYSLER, DODGE & PLYMOUTH									
1966	4113S	1	1/4	—	.060	1/4	16 Drill	41 Drill	2 Rich
	4114S	1	1/4	—	.060	1/4	30 Drill	41 Drill	2 Rich
	4115S	2	1/4	—	—	1/4	16 Drill	41 Drill	On Index
	4116S	2	1/4	—	—	1/4	30 Drill	41 Drill	On Index
	4125S	1	5/16	1	1/16	1/4	15 Drill	30 Drill	2 Rich
	4126S	1	5/16	1	1/16	1/4	15 Drill	30 Drill	2 Rich
	4127S	1	5/16	1	1/16	1/4	26 Drill	30 Drill	2 Rich
	4128S	1	5/16	1	.050	1/4	26 Drill	30 Drill	2 Rich
1967	4113SA	1	1/4	—	.060	1/4	15 Drill	41 Drill	2 Rich
	4114SA	1	1/4	—	.060	1/4	1/8	41 Drill	2 Rich
	4115SA	2	1/4	—	—	1/4	15 Drill	41 Drill	On Index
	4116SA	2	1/4	—	—	1/4	1/8	41 Drill	On Index
	4296S	1 1/2	5/16	29/32	1/16	1/4	20 Drill	42 Drill	2 Rich
	4297S	1 1/2	5/16	29/32	1/16	1/4	42 Drill	42 Drill	2 Rich
	4306S	1 1/2	5/16	1	.050	1/4	20 Drill	42 Drill	2 Rich
	4307S	1 1/2	5/16	1	.050	1/4	30 Drill	42 Drill	2 Rich
	4463S	2	1/4	—	1/16	1/4	28 Drill	41 Drill	2 Rich
1968	441S	3	1/4	—	1/16	1/4	4 Drill	50 Drill	2 Rich
	4417S	3	1/4	—	1/16	1/4	41 Drill	50 Drill	2 Rich
	4420S	2 1/2	1/4	—	1/16	1/4	4 Drill	41 Drill	2 Rich
	4421S	2 1/2	1/4	—	1/16	1/4	28 Drill	41 Drill	2 Rich
	4422S	1 1/2	5/16	29/32	.050	1/4	1 Drill	30 Drill	2 Rich
	4423S	1 1/2	5/16	29/32	.050	1/4	16 Drill	30 Drill	2 Rich
	4578S	1 1/2	11/32	1	3/64	1/4	11/64	30 Drill	2 Rich
1969	4605S	2	1/4	—	1/16	1/4	20 Drill	41 Drill	On Index
	4606S	2	1/4	—	1/16	1/4	41 Drill	41 Drill	On Index
	4607S	1	1/4	—	1/16	1/4	20 Drill	41 Drill	On Index
	4608S	1	1/4	—	1/16	1/4	28 Drill	41 Drill	On Index
	4613S	1 1/2	5/16	1	1/16	1/4	20 Drill	30 Drill	2 Rich
	4614S	1 1/2	5/16	1	1/16	1/4	20 Drill	30 Drill	2 Rich
	4474S	1 1/2	5/16	1	1/16	1/4	20 Drill	30 Drill	2 Rich
1970	4721S	14.0–14.4 to 1①	1/4	—	1/32	1/4	20 Drill	41 Drill	On Index
	4722S	14.0–14.4 to 1①	1/4	—	1/32	1/4	20 Drill	41 Drill	On Index
	4723S	14.0–14.4 to 1①	1/4	—	15/64	1/4	20 Drill	41 Drill	On Index
	4724S	14.0–14.4 to 1①	1/4	—	15/64	1/4	20 Drill	41 Drill	On Index
	4725S	14.0–14.4 to 1①	11/32	—	1/32	1/4	20 Drill	28 Drill	2 Rich
	4726S	14.0–14.4 to 1①	11/32	—	1/32	1/4	28 Drill	28 Drill	2 Rich
	4727S	14.0–14.4 to.1①	11/32	—	5/32	1/4	20 Drill	28 Drill	2 Rich
	4728S	14.0–14.4 to 1①	11/32	—	5/32	1/4	28 Drill	28 Drill	2 Rich
	4894S	14.0–14.4 to 1①	5/16	—	1/32	1/4	28 Drill	28 Drill	2 Rich
	4895S	14.0–14.4 to 1①	1/4	—	1/32	1/4	20 Drill	41 Drill	On Index
1971	4957S	14.0–14.4 to 1①	1/4	—	—	1/4	20 Drill	41 Drill	On Index
	4958S	14.0–14.4 to 1①	1/4	—	—	1/4	20 Drill	41 Drill	On Index
	4961S	14.0–14.4 to 1①	5/16	—	3/16	1/4	20 Drill	20 Drill	2 Rich
	4962S	14.0–14.4 to 1①	5/16	—	3/16	1/4	28 Drill	20 Drill	2 Rich

①—Air/fuel ratio.

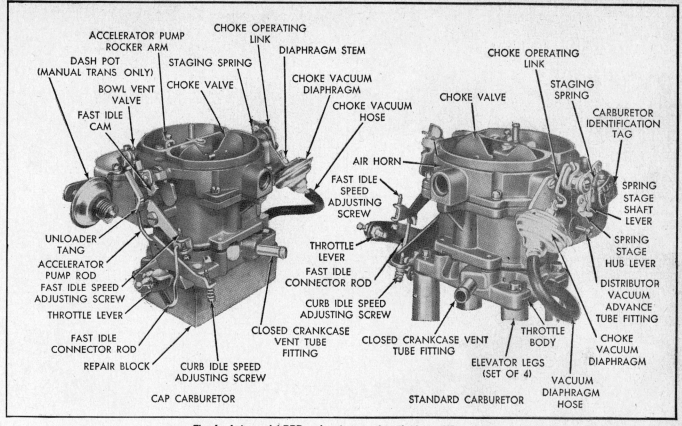

Fig. 4   Late model BBD carburetors used on the larger V8 engines

choke valve so that fast idle cam allows throttle valves to fully close. Be sure that pump connector rod is installed in center hole of throttle lever.

2. With throttle valves closed tightly, measure distance between top of air horn and end of pump plunger shaft. If the dimension is not as specified, bend pump connector rod at the angle on the rod until correct setting is obtained.

Accelerator Pump and Bowl Vent

$1\frac{1}{4}''$ Bore Units, Fig. 7

1. Back off idle speed adjusting screw. Open choke valve so that fast idle cam allows throttle valves to close completely.
2. Be sure pump operating rod is in medium stroke hole in throttle lever, and that bowl vent clip on pump stem is on center notch.
3. With throttle valves closed tightly, it should be just possible to insert the specified gauge or drill size between bowl vent and its seat.
4. If an adjustment is necessary, bend pump operating rod at the angle. On CAP carburetors, bend pump operating rod to give the height of pump plunger stem above bowl cover as specified in the table.

NOTE: This is an important adjustment, since too much lift at the bowl vent will result in considerable loss in low speed fuel economy.

Remember that if the pump operating rod is moved to either the short or long stroke position, a corresponding change must be made in the location of the bowl vent clip, and the amount of lift of the bowl vent rechecked.

Bowl Vent Adjustment

Models with Separate Pump Adjustment

With throttle valves closed tightly, it should be possible to insert a gauge or drill of the size listed between the bowl vent valve and air horn. If an adjustment is necessary, bend the short tang on the vent valve operating lever until the specified clearance has been obtained.

Choke Unloader Adjustment

Fig. 8—The choke unloader is a mechanical device to partially open the choke valve at wide open throttle. It is used to eliminate choke enrichment during engine cranking. Engines that have been flooded or stalled by excessive choke enrichment can be cleared by the use of the unloader. Adjust as follows:

1. Hold throttle valve in wide open position. Insert the specified drill size between upper edge of choke valve and inner wall of air horn.
2. With a finger lightly pressing against choke valve, a slight drag should be felt as the drill is being withdrawn.
3. If an adjustment is necessary, bend unloader tang on throttle lever until specified opening has been obtained.

Fast Idle Cam Position

Figs. 9 and 10

1. With fast idle adjusting screw con-

tacting second highest step on fast idle cam, move choke valve toward closed position with light pressure on choke shaft lever.

2. Insert the specified size drill between choke valve and air horn wall. An adjustment will be necessary if a slight drag is not obtained as drill is being removed.
3. If an adjustment is required, bend the fast idle connector rod at the angle on $1\frac{1}{4}''$ bore units, or, on other carburetors, bend stop on choke shaft.

Choke Vacuum Kick Adjustment

Figs. 11 and 12

The choke diaphragm adjustment controls the fuel delivery while the engine is running. It positions the choke valve within the air horn by action of the linkage between choke shaft and diaphragm. The diaphragm must be energized to measure the vacuum kick adjustment. Use either a distributor test machine with a vacuum source, or vacuum supplied by another vehicle.

1. If adjustment is to be made with engine running, disconnect fast idle linkage to allow choke to close to kick position with engine at curb idle. If an auxiliary vacuum source is to be used, open throttle valves (engine not running) and move choke to closed position. Release throttle first, then release choke.
2. When using an auxiliary vacuum source, disconnect vacuum hose from carburetor and connect it to hose from vacuum supply with a small

Fig. 5 Checking float level. BBD carburetors

FUEL INLET
NEEDLE VALVE,
SEAT AND
GASKET

FLOAT FULCRUM
PIN RETAINER

CROWN OF FLOATS

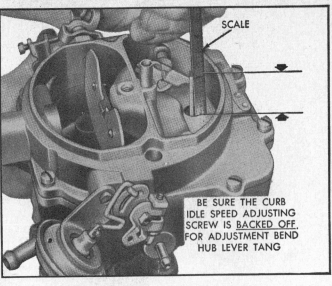

SCALE

BE SURE THE CURB
IDLE SPEED ADJUSTING
SCREW IS BACKED OFF.
FOR ADJUSTMENT BEND
HUB LEVER TANG

Fig. 6 Checking accelerator pump travel.
BBD except 1¼" bore carburetors

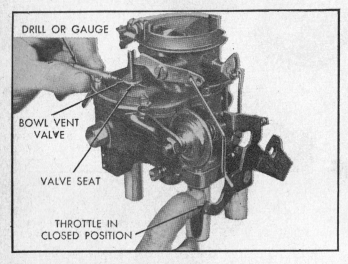

DRILL OR GAUGE

BOWL VENT
VALVE

VALVE SEAT

THROTTLE IN
CLOSED POSITION

Fig. 7 Checking bowl vent opening.
BBD 1¼" bore carburetors

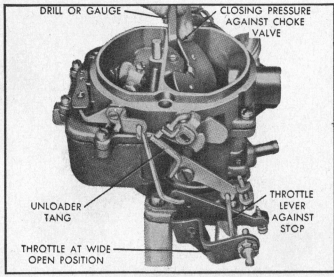

DRILL OR GAUGE

CLOSING PRESSURE
AGAINST CHOKE
VALVE

UNLOADER
TANG

THROTTLE
LEVER
AGAINST
STOP

THROTTLE AT WIDE
OPEN POSITION

Fig. 8 Choke unloader setting. BBD carburetors

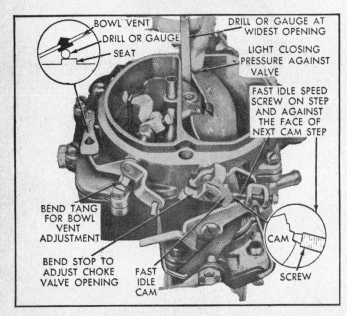

BOWL VENT
DRILL OR GAUGE
SEAT

DRILL OR GAUGE AT
WIDEST OPENING

LIGHT CLOSING
PRESSURE AGAINST
VALVE

FAST IDLE SPEED
SCREW ON STEP
AND AGAINST
THE FACE OF
NEXT CAM STEP

BEND TANG
FOR BOWL
VENT
ADJUSTMENT

BEND STOP TO
ADJUST CHOKE
VALVE OPENING

FAST
IDLE
CAM

CAM

SCREW

Fig. 10 Fast idle cam position adjustment.
BBD except 1¼" bore carburetors

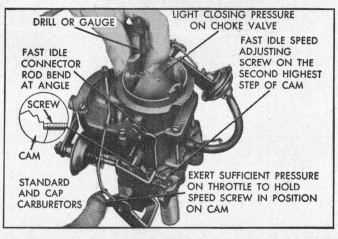

DRILL OR GAUGE

LIGHT CLOSING PRESSURE
ON CHOKE VALVE

FAST IDLE SPEED
ADJUSTING
SCREW ON THE
SECOND HIGHEST
STEP OF CAM

FAST IDLE
CONNECTOR
ROD BEND
AT ANGLE

SCREW

CAM

STANDARD
AND CAP
CARBURETORS

EXERT SUFFICIENT PRESSURE
ON THROTTLE TO HOLD
SPEED SCREW IN POSITION
ON CAM

Fig. 9 Fast idle cam position adjustment.
BBD 1¼" bore carburetors

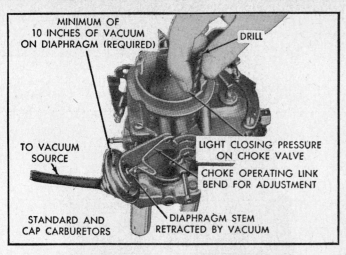

Fig. 11 Choke vacuum kick setting.
BBD 1¼" bore carburetors, 1966-71

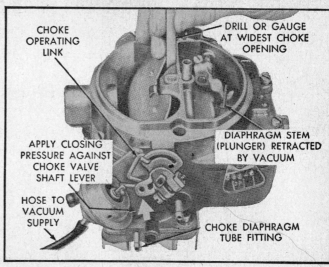

Fig. 12 Choke vacuum kick setting.
BBD except 1¼" bore carburetors, 1966-71

length of tube to act as a fitting. Removal of hose from diaphragm may require forces which damage the system. Apply a vacuum of 10 or more inches of mercury.

3. Insert the specified drill size between choke valve and wall of air horn. Apply sufficient closing pressure on lever to which choke rod attaches to provide a minimum choke valve opening without distortion of diaphragm link. Note that the cylindrical stem of diaphragm will extend as internal spring is compressed. This spring must be fully compressed for proper measurement of vacuum kick adjustment.

4. An adjustment will be necessary if a slight drag is not obtained as drill is being removed. Shorten or lengthen diaphragm link to obtain correct choke opening. Length changes should be made carefully by bending (opening or closing) the bend provided in the diaphragm link. *Do not apply twisting or bending force to diaphragm.*

5. Reinstall vacuum hose on correct carburetor fitting. Return fast idle linkage to its original condition if it has been disturbed as in Step 1.

6. Check as follows: With no vacuum applied to diaphragm, choke valve should move freely between open and closed positions. If movement

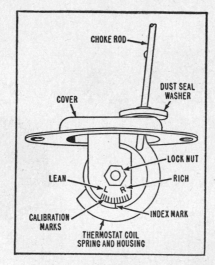

Fig. 13 BBD well-type choke setting

is not free, examine linkage for misalignment or interferences caused by bending operation. Repeat adjustment if necessary.

Well-Type Choke Setting

Fig. 13—Loosen mounting post lock nut and turn mounting post with screwdriver until index mark on disc is positioned as listed in the *BBD Specifications Chart.* Hold in this position with screwdriver and lock nut.

NOTE: Screwdriver may be held in vise so that one hand may be used to support housing while tightening nut. After adjustment is completed and coil housing, rod and carburetor are installed on engine, lift cover disc and open and close choke valve manually to see if connector rod clears sides of hole in housing cover without binding. If rod does not clear housing cover without binding, replace with a new unit since connecting rod cannot be bent without affecting calibration.

Dashpot Adjustment

Cleaner Air Carburetors

The dashpot is used only on vehicles with the Cleaner Air Package and manual shift transmission, Fig. 4.

To adjust the dashpot, have the curb idle speed and mixture properly adjusted, and install a tachometer. Position throttle lever so that actuating tab on lever is contacting stem of dashpot but not depressing it. Tachometer should read 2000 rpm if the setting is correct. If not correct, screw dashpot in or out as required, then tighten lock nut on dashpot against the bracket.

CARTER WCD ADJUSTMENT SPECIFICATIONS

See Tune Up Chart in car chapter for hot idle speed.

Year	Carb. Model	Idle Screw (Mixture) Turns Open	Float Level	Pump Setting	Metering Rod	Fast Idle Setting	Choke Unloader	Dashpot Setting	Automatic Choke
AMERICAN MOTORS									
1966–67	3888S	¼–1¾	①	See Text	See Text	.020	3/16	—	On Index
1966	4191S	¼–1¾	17/64	See Text	See Text	.015	3/16	—	2 Rich
1967	4365S	¼–1¾	7/32	See Text	See Text	—	3/16	—	2 Rich
1968	4410S	1	7/32	See Text	See Text	—	3/16	1/16–3/32	On Index
	4537S	1	7/32	See Text	See Text	—	3/16	1/16–3/32	On Index
1969	4667S	1½	7/32	See Text	See Text	—	3/16	7/64	On Index
	4668S	1½	7/32	See Text	See Text	—	3/16	7/64	On Index
1970	4816S	14.0 to 1②	7/32	See Text	See Text	.021	3/16	3/32	Index
	4817S	14.0 to 1②	7/32	See Text	See Text	.024	3/16	3/32	Index
	4950S	14.0 to 1②	7/32	See Text	See Text	.024	3/16	—	Index

①—With green inspection tag ¼", others ⅛".   ②—Air/fuel ratio.

MODEL WCD ADJUSTMENTS

The WCD carburetor, Fig. 1, is a two-barrel unit containing the five basic circuits. The carburetor uses a single needle valve even though two floats are provided. On some WCD units the two floats operate independently of each other so that the highest float always controls the fuel level. This is necessary when the carburetor is mounted with the centerline of the floats parallel to the centerline of the engine.

Float Adjustment

Lateral Adjustment—Referring to Fig. 2 and with bowl cover inverted and gasket removed, place float gauge directly under floats with notched portions of gauge fitted over edges of casting. Sides of float should barely touch vertical uprights of float gauge. Adjustment is made by bending arms of floats.

Vertical Adjustment—With float gauge in same position as shown, floats should just clear horizontal portion of gauge. The vertical distance between top center of float and machined surface of casting must be the dimension given in the *WCD Specifications Chart*. Adjust by bending float arms as required. Remove floats, install bowl cover gasket and reinstall floats.

Pump Adjustment

Fig. 3—Install pump connector link in outer hole (long stroke) of pump arm

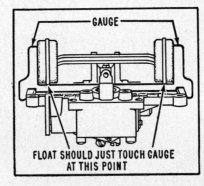

Fig. 2 WCD float level adjustment

with ends extending away from countershaft arm. Back out throttle lever set screw until throttle valves seat in carburetor bores. Be sure fast idle adjusting screw does not hold throttle open.

Hold straightedge across top of dust cover boss at pump arm. The flat on top of pump arm should be parallel to straightedge. Adjust by bending throttle connector rod to the upper angle.

Metering Rod Adjustment

This adjustment must be made after completing the pump adjustment. No metering rod gauges are necessary. Adjust as follows:

1. Back out throttle lever set screw to allow throttle valves to seat in bores of carburetor and loosen metering rod arm clamp screw.
2. With metering rod in place, press down on vacumeter link until metering rods bottom in carburetor body casting.
3. While holding rods in downward position and throttle valves seated, revolve metering rod arm until finger on arm contacts lip of vacumeter link. Hold in place and carefully tighten clamp screw.

Fast Idle Adjustment

Fig. 4—Loosen choke lever clamp screw on choke shaft. Insert a .010" feeler gauge between lip of fast idle cam and boss of flange casting. Hold choke valve tightly closed and take slack out of linkage by pressing choke lever towards closed position.

With choke valve tightly closed, tighten fast idle adjusting screw until there is the clearance listed in the *WCD Specifications Chart* between throttle valve and carburetor bore (side opposite idle port). Be sure fast idle adjusting screw is on high step of cam or index mark while making this adjustment.

Choke Unloader Adjustment

Fig. 5—With throttle valves wide open, there should be the clearance listed in the *WCD Specifications Chart* between

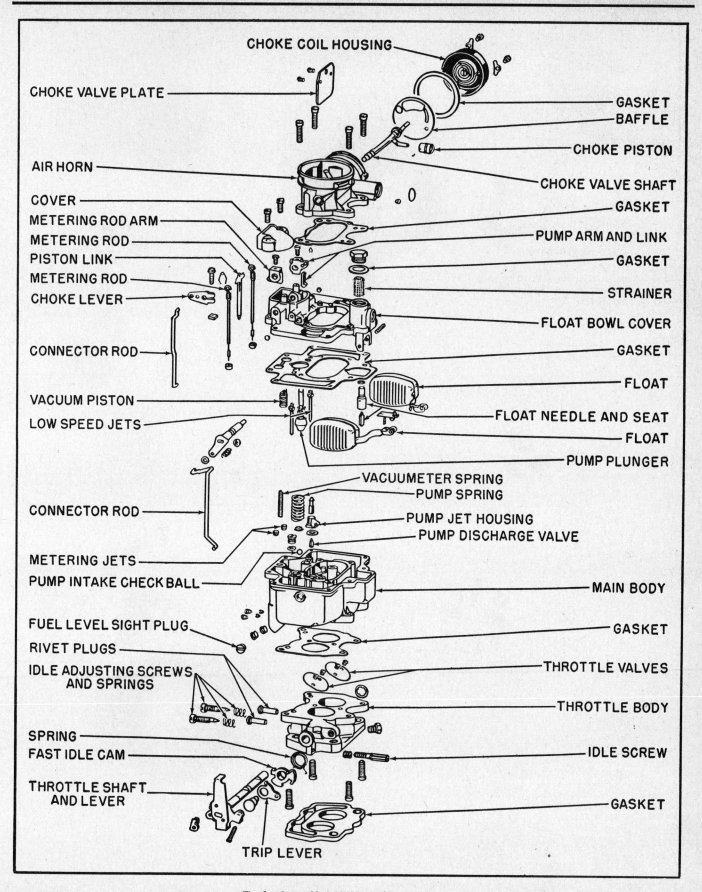

CHOKE COIL HOUSING

CHOKE VALVE PLATE

AIR HORN

COVER
METERING ROD ARM
METERING ROD
PISTON LINK
METERING ROD
CHOKE LEVER

CONNECTOR ROD

VACUUM PISTON
LOW SPEED JETS

CONNECTOR ROD

METERING JETS
PUMP INTAKE CHECK BALL

FUEL LEVEL SIGHT PLUG
RIVET PLUGS
IDLE ADJUSTING SCREWS
AND SPRINGS

SPRING
FAST IDLE CAM

THROTTLE SHAFT
AND LEVER

TRIP LEVER

GASKET
BAFFLE
CHOKE PISTON
CHOKE VALVE SHAFT
GASKET
PUMP ARM AND LINK
GASKET
STRAINER
FLOAT BOWL COVER
GASKET
FLOAT
FLOAT NEEDLE AND SEAT
FLOAT
PUMP PLUNGER

VACUUMETER SPRING
PUMP SPRING
PUMP JET HOUSING
PUMP DISCHARGE VALVE

MAIN BODY

GASKET

THROTTLE VALVES

THROTTLE BODY

IDLE SCREW

GASKET

Fig. 1   Carter Model WCD two-barrel carburetor

CARTER CARBURETORS

Fig. 3　WCD pump adjustment

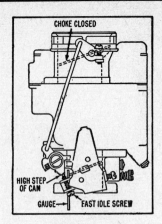

Fig. 4　WCD fast idle adjustment

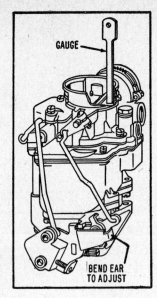

Fig. 5　WCD unloader adjustment

upper edge of choke valve and inner wall of air horn. Adjust by bending unloader lip (ear) on throttle shaft lever.

Dashpot Adjustment

Rambler—With throttle valves tightly closed and diaphragm stem fully depressed, adjust dashpot to give the clear-ance listed in the *WCD Specifications Chart* between dashpot stem and throttle lever.

Automatic Choke Adjustment

Loosen choke cover retaining screws and turn cover so that line or index mark on cover lines up with the specified mark on choke housing (see *WCD Specifica-tions Chart*).

CARTER AVS ADJUSTMENT SPECIFICATIONS

See Tune Up Chart in car chapter for hot idle speed.

Year	Carb. Model	Idle Screw (Mixture) Turns Open	Float Level	Float Drop	Pump Travel	Bowl Vent	Fast Idle Throttle Valve Clearance	Choke Unloader	Choke Vacuum Break	Secondary Throttle Lockout
CHEVROLET, CHEVELLE, CHEVY II										
1966	4027S-SA	1-2½	15/64	23/32	33/64	.065	.015	11/64	.120	.020
	4028S-SA	1-2½	15/64	23/32	33/64	.065	.015	11/64	.160	.020
CHRYSLER, DODGE, PLYMOUTH, IMPERIAL										
1968	4401S	1-2	5/16	23/32	7/16	1/8	.016	1/4	3/32	.020
	424S	1-2	7/32	23/32	7/16	1/8	.015	1/4	3/16	.020
	4425S	1-2	7/32	23/32	7/16	1/8	.012	1/4	5/64	.020
	4426S	1-2	5/16	23/32	7/16	1/8	.012	1/4	3/16	.020
	4428S	1-2	7/32	23/32	7/16	1/8	.014	1/4	3/16	.020
	4429S	1-2	7/32	23/32	7/16	1/8	.014	1/4	5/32	—
1969	4611S	1-2	7/32	1/2	7/16	1/8	50 Drill①	1/4	35 Drill	.020
	4612S	1-2	7/32	1/2	7/16	1/8	50 Drill①	1/4	50 Drill	.020
	4615S	1-2	5/16	1/2	7/16	1/8	50 Drill①	1/4	35 Drill	.020
	4616S	1-2	5/16	1/2	7/16	1/8	50 Drill①	1/4	50 Drill	.020
	4617S	1-2	7/32	1/2	7/16	1/8	50 Drill①	1/4	25 Drill	.020
	4618S	1-2	7/32	1/2	7/16	1/8	50 Drill①	1/4	35 Drill	.020
	4638S	1-2	5/16	1/2	7/16	1/8	50 Drill①	1/4	50 Drill	.020
	4639S	1-2	7/32	1/2	7/16	1/8	50 Drill①	1/4	50 Drill	.020
	4640S	1-2	7/32	1/2	7/16	1/8	50 Drill①	1/4	35 Drill	.020
	4682S	—	5/16	1/2	7/16	1/8	50 Drill①	1/4	50 Drill	.020
	4711S	1-2	5/16	1/2	7/16	1/8	50 Drill①	1/4	35 Drill	.020
1970	4732S	14.0-14.4 to 1②	5/16	23/32	7/16	—	50 Drill①	1/4	44 Drill	.020
	4734S	14.0-14.4 to 1②	5/16	23/32	7/16	—	50 Drill①	1/4	44 Drill	.020
	4736S	14.0-14.4 to 1②	5/16	23/32	7/16	—	50 Drill①	1/4	44 Drill	.020
	4737S	14.0-14.4 to 1②	7/32	23/32	7/16	—	50 Drill①	1/4	20 Drill	.020
	4738S	14.0-14.4 to 1②	7/32	23/32	7/16	—	50 Drill①	1/4	20 Drill	.020
	4739S	14.0-14.4 to 1②	7/32	23/32	7/16	—	50 Drill①	1/4	20 Drill	.020

CARTER AVS ADJUSTMENT SPECIFICATIONS—Continued

See Tune Up Chart in car chapter for hot idle speed.

Year	Carb. Model	Idle Screw (Mixture) Turns Open	Float Level	Float Drop	Pump Travel	Bowl Vent	Fast Idle Throttle Valve Clearance	Choke Unloader	Choke Vacuum Break	Secondary Throttle Lockout
CHRYSLER, DODGE, PLYMOUTH, IMPERIAL—Continued										
1970	4740S	14.0–14.4 to 1②	$\frac{7}{32}$	$\frac{23}{32}$	$\frac{7}{16}$	—	50 Drill①	$\frac{1}{4}$	20 Drill	.020
	4741S	14.0–14.4 to 1②	$\frac{7}{32}$	$\frac{23}{32}$	$\frac{7}{16}$	—	50 Drill①	$\frac{1}{4}$	20 Drill	.020
	4933S	14.0–14.4 to 1②	$\frac{7}{32}$	$\frac{23}{32}$	$\frac{7}{16}$	—	50 Drill①	$\frac{1}{4}$	35 Drill	.020
	4934S	14.0–14.4 to 1②	$\frac{7}{32}$	$\frac{23}{32}$	$\frac{7}{16}$	—	50 Drill①	$\frac{1}{4}$	50 Drill	.020
	4935S	14.0–14.4 to 1②	$\frac{7}{32}$	$\frac{23}{32}$	$\frac{7}{16}$	—	50 Drill①	$\frac{1}{4}$	50 Drill	.020
	4936S	14.0–14.4 to 1②	$\frac{7}{32}$	$\frac{23}{32}$	$\frac{7}{16}$	—	50 Drill①	$\frac{1}{4}$	35 Drill	.020
	4937S	14.0–14.4 to 1②	$\frac{7}{32}$	$\frac{23}{32}$	$\frac{7}{16}$	—	50 Drill①	$\frac{1}{4}$	50 Drill	.020
1971	4966S	14.0–14.4 to 1②	$\frac{7}{32}$	$\frac{1}{2}$	$\frac{7}{16}$	$\frac{3}{4}$	—	$\frac{1}{4}$	—	.020
	4967S	14.0–14.4 to 1②	$\frac{7}{32}$	$\frac{1}{2}$	$\frac{7}{16}$	$\frac{3}{4}$	—	$\frac{1}{4}$	—	.020
	4968S	14.0–14.4 to 1②	$\frac{7}{32}$	$\frac{1}{2}$	$\frac{7}{16}$	$\frac{3}{4}$	—	$\frac{1}{4}$	—	.020
	6125S	14.0–14.4 to 1②	$\frac{7}{32}$	$\frac{1}{2}$	$\frac{7}{16}$	$\frac{3}{4}$	—	$\frac{1}{4}$	—	.020

①—With fast idle adjusting screw contacting second highest speed step on fast idle cam the clearance between choke valve and wall of air horn should be as specified.

②—Air/fuel ratio.

MODEL AVS ADJUSTMENTS

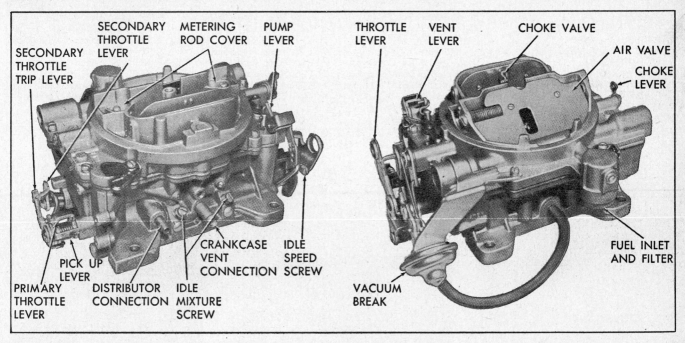

Fig. 1   Carter Model AVS four-barrel carburetor

The AVS carburetor, Figs. 1, 2, 3, is used in conjunction with a temperature sensing choke coil mounted on the intake manifold over the exhaust crossover passage. The AVS is similar to the more familiar AFB which employs a built-in automatic choke.

AVS means "Air Valve Secondary". The spring loaded air valve, located above the secondary fuel nozzles, gives smooth response whenever the secondary throttle valves are actuated.

The primary side of the carburetor uses venturi clusters for fine fuel control in the idle and economy ranges. The use

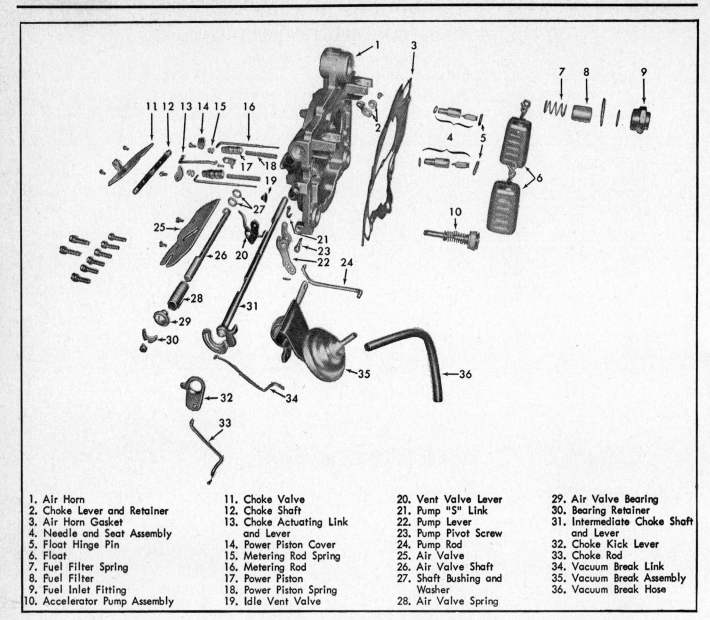

1. Air Horn
2. Choke Lever and Retainer
3. Air Horn Gasket
4. Needle and Seat Assembly
5. Float Hinge Pin
6. Float
7. Fuel Filter Spring
8. Fuel Filter
9. Fuel Inlet Fitting
10. Accelerator Pump Assembly
11. Choke Valve
12. Choke Shaft
13. Choke Actuating Link and Lever
14. Power Piston Cover
15. Metering Rod Spring
16. Metering Rod
17. Power Piston
18. Power Piston Spring
19. Idle Vent Valve
20. Vent Valve Lever
21. Pump "S" Link
22. Pump Lever
23. Pump Pivot Screw
24. Pump Rod
25. Air Valve
26. Air Valve Shaft
27. Shaft Bushing and Washer
28. Air Valve Spring
29. Air Valve Bearing
30. Bearing Retainer
31. Intermediate Choke Shaft and Lever
32. Choke Kick Lever
33. Choke Rod
34. Vacuum Break Link
35. Vacuum Break Assembly
36. Vacuum Break Hose

Fig. 2 AVS air horn parts exploded

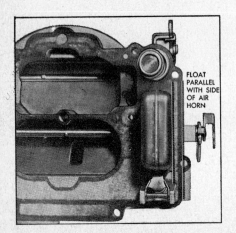

Fig. 4 AVS float alignment

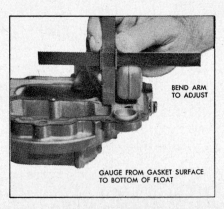

Fig. 5 AVS float level

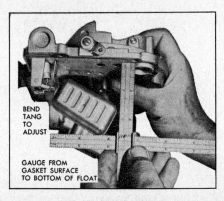

Fig. 6 AVS float drop

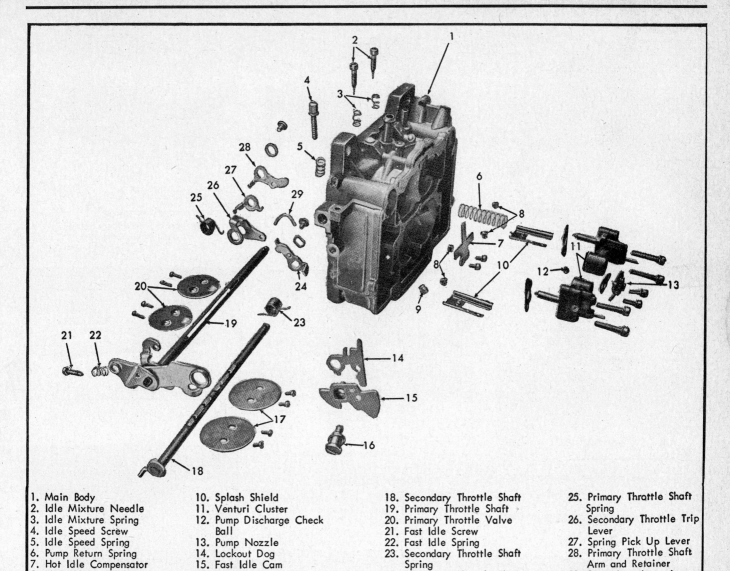

1. Main Body
2. Idle Mixture Needle
3. Idle Mixture Spring
4. Idle Speed Screw
5. Idle Speed Spring
6. Pump Return Spring
7. Hot Idle Compensator
8. Main Metering Jet
9. Pump Inlet Assembly
10. Splash Shield
11. Venturi Cluster
12. Pump Discharge Check Ball
13. Pump Nozzle
14. Lockout Dog
15. Fast Idle Cam
16. Pivot Screw
17. Secondary Throttle Valve
18. Secondary Throttle Shaft
19. Primary Throttle Shaft
20. Primary Throttle Valve
21. Fast Idle Screw
22. Fast Idle Spring
23. Secondary Throttle Shaft Spring
24. Secondary Throttle Shaft Dog Lever and Retainer
25. Primary Throttle Shaft Spring
26. Secondary Throttle Trip Lever
27. Spring Pick Up Lever
28. Primary Throttle Shaft Arm and Retainer
29. Secondary Actuating Link

Fig. 3   AVS main body parts exploded

of fuel nozzles pressed into the secondary side of the fuel bowl virtually eliminates secondary bore restriction, thus giving this carburetor high air capacity in the power ranges.

A hot idle compensator, consisting of a bi-metal strip, a valve and a mounting bracket, is located between the secondary bores to supply additional air to the idle mixture during prolonged hot idle periods.

Float Alignment

Fig. 4—Sides of floats should be parallel to edge of casting with minimum clearance between lever and air horn lugs without binding. To adjust, bend float lever.

Float Level Adjustment

Fig. 5—There should be the dimension

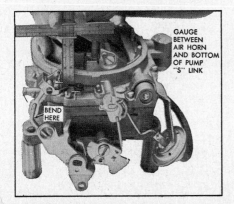

Fig. 7   AVS pump adjustment

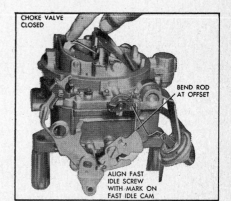

Fig. 8   AVS fast idle linkage adjustment

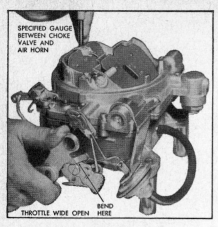

Fig. 9   AVS choke unloader adjustment

Fig. 12   AVS secondary
air valve adjustment

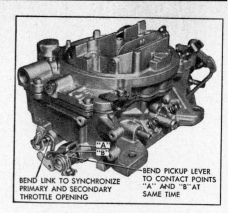

BEND LINK TO SYNCHRONIZE
PRIMARY AND SECONDARY
THROTTLE OPENING

BEND PICKUP LEVER
TO CONTACT POINTS
"A" AND "B" AT
SAME TIME

Fig. 14   AVS secondary throttle
opening adjustment

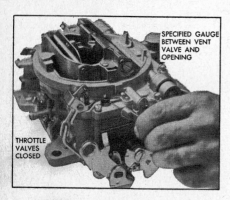

Fig. 10   AVS bowl vent adjustment

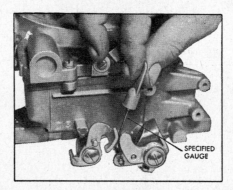

Fig. 13   AVS closing shoe adjustment

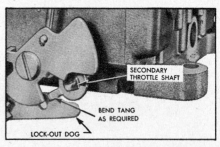

Fig. 15   AVS throttle lockout adjustment

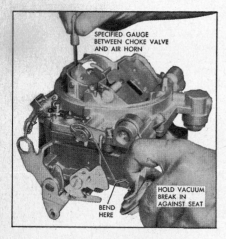

Fig. 11   AVS choke diaphragm
linkage adjustment

Pump Adjustment

Fig. 7—With throttle valves tightly closed there should be the dimension listed in the *AVS Specifications Chart* from top of bowl cover to top of pump plunger shaft with throttle connector rod in inner hole of pump arm. To adjust, bend throttle connector rod.

Fast Idle Linkage Adjustment

Fig. 8—With choke valve closed, index mark on cam should align with adjusting screw. To adjust, bend fast idle connector rod.

Fast Idle Throttle Valve Clearance

There should be the clearance listed in the *AVS Specifications Chart* between lower edge of throttle valve and carburetor bore with adjusting screw on index mark of cam.

Choke Unloader Adjustment

Fig. 9—With throttle valves wide open there should be the clearance listed in the *AVS Specifications Chart* between upper edge of choke valve and inner wall of air horn. To adjust, bend unloader lip on throttle lever.

Bowl Vent Adjustment

Fig. 10—With throttle valves seated there should be the clearance listed in the *AVS Specifications Chart* between heel of rubber grommet and its seat on bowl cover.

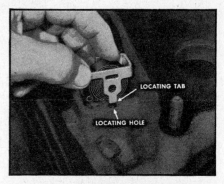

Fig. 16   AVS choke coil location
on intake manifold

To adjust, bend lip on vent arm. *If pump has been changed from standard setting, readjust vent arm.*

Choke Vacuum Break

Fig. 11—Holding vacuum break in against its stop and choke valve toward the closed position with a rubber band, bend vacuum break link at the offset to obtain specified clearance between upper edge of choke valve and air horn wall.

Secondary Air Valve Adjustment

Fig. 12

1. Release air valve retainer screw that locks air valve shaft nylon bushing. This releases air valve spring and air valve should now be wide open.
2. Check at this point that air valve and shaft are free to operate and not binding in any position.

listed in the *AVS Specifications Chart* between top of floats (at outer end) and air horn gasket. To adjust, bend float lever.

Float Drop Adjustment

Fig. 6—There should be the dimension listed in the *AVS Specifications Chart* between top of floats (at outer end) and air horn gasket. To adjust, bend stop tabs on float brackets.

3. To adjust, use a screwdriver in slot of air valve shaft bushing. Turn shaft bushing slowly in a counterclockwise direction until air valve spring contacts air valve. Then turn shaft bushing 2 1/4 turns more. This should bring the valve to its proper setting (plus or minus 1/4 turn). At this point, hold shaft bushing in place and tighten air valve retainer screw.

Closing Shoe Adjustment

Fig. 13—With primary and secondary throttle valves closed, bend secondary closing shoe to obtain .020″ clearance between positive closing shoes on primary and secondary throttle levers. To adjust, bend shoe on secondary lever.

Secondary Throttle Opening

Fig. 14—The pickup lever, located on the primary throttle shaft, has two points of contact with the loose lever on the primary shaft. Care should be taken that the pickup lever contacts the loose lever at both points at the same time. If they do not make this contact, bend pickup lever to obtain proper engagement.

The primary and secondary throttle valves must come to the wide open position at the same time. If the secondary throttle valve opening is not synchronized with that of the primary, bend the connecting link.

Secondary Throttle Lockout

Fig. 15—Crack throttle valves and manually open and close choke valve. Tang on secondary throttle lever should freely engage in notch of lockout dog. To adjust, bend tang on secondary throttle lever.

Automatic Choke Coil

The AVS carburetor must be removed to replace the remote choke actuating coil. After removing carburetor, pry shield off coil after which remove the coil and actuating rod.

When replacing, the locating tab on the choke coil should engage the locating hole in the intake manifold, Fig. 16. Install the choke rod in the coil. Leave the shield off. Carefully lower carburetor into place, but do not bolt it down.

Hold choke valve closed and push rod against stop on thermostat bracket. The bottom of rod should be even with bottom of hole in choke lever. If necessary, bend choke rod at the offset angle to change its length. The rod should enter the hole freely and squarely to prevent binding. Then remove carburetor, being careful not to change the adjustment.

Lower choke shield over the rod and install over coil. Move it along the manifold for best fit. Install carburetor. Check for freedom of action from full-open to full-closed. Warm up engine and observe operation.

CARTER AFB ADJUSTMENT SPECIFICATIONS

See Tune Up Chart in car chapters for hot idle speed.

Year	Carb. Model	Idle Screws (Mixture) Turns Open	Float Level	Float Drop	Pump Travel	Fast Idle Throttle Valve Clearance	Choke Unloader Setting	Secondary Throttle Lever Setting	Vacuum Choke Break Setting	Choke Piston Linkage Setting	Choke Setting
AMERICAN MOTORS											
1967	4216S	3/4–1 3/4	5/16	2	3/8	.018	9/32	.020	—	9/64	2 Rich
	4258S	3/4–1 3/4	5/16	2	3/8	.018	5/32	.020	—	3/32	1 Rich
	4352S	1–2	5/16	2	3/8	.018	9/64	.020	—	3/32	On Index
	4353S	1/2–1 1/2	5/16	2	3/8	.018	9/64	.020	—	3/32	2 Rich
	4354S	3/4–1 3/4	5/16	2	3/8	.018	9/32	.020	—	9/64	2 Rich
	4358S	1/2–1 1/2	5/16	2	3/8	.018	5/32	.020	—	3/32	On Index
1968	4467S	1	11/32	23/32	13/32	.014	5/32	.020	—	.088	2 Rich
	4468S	1	11/32	23/32	7/16	.018	5/32	.020	—	.120	1 Rich
	4469S	1	11/32	23/32	7/16	.018	5/32	.020	—	.110	2 Rich
	4583S	2–3	11/32	23/32	13/32	.020	5/32	.020	—	.110	2 Rich
	4584S	2–3	11/32	23/32	7/16	.020	5/32	.020	—	.096	1 Rich
	4585S	2–3	11/32	23/32	7/16	.024	5/32	.020	—	.096	1 Rich
	4622S	—	11/32	23/32	13/32	.014	5/32	.020	—	.088	2 Rich
	4623S	—	11/32	23/32	7/16	.018	5/32	.020	—	.120	1 Rich
	4624S	—	11/32	23/32	7/16	.018	5/32	.020	—	.110	2 Rich
1969	4660S	2	11/32	2	21/64	—	5/32	.020	—	5/64	2 Rich
	4661S	2	11/32	2	21/64	—	5/32	.020	—	1/8	On Index
	4662S	2	11/32	2	21/64	—	5/32	.020	—	7/64	On Index
	4663S	2	11/32	2	21/64	—	5/32	.020	—	1/8	On Index
	4664S	2	11/32	2	21/64	—	5/32	.020	—	7/64	On Index
	4665S	2	11/32	2	21/64	—	5/32	.020	—	1/8	On Index
BUICK											
1966	4053S	1/4–1 3/4	15/64	23/32	7/16	.033	7/32	.020	—	.109	On Index
	4054S	1/4–1 3/4	15/64	23/32	7/16	.029	7/32	.020	—	.109	On Index
	4055S	1/4–1 3/4	11/64	23/32	7/16	.033	5/32	.020	—	.095	1 Rich
	4056S	1/4–1 3/4	11/64	23/32	7/16	.026	5/32	.020	—	.082	On Index
	4059S	1/4–1 3/4	15/64	23/32	7/16	.033	7/32	.020	—	.102	On Index
	4060S	1/4–1 3/4	15/64	23/32	1/2②	.029	7/32	.020	—	.109	On Index

continued

CARTER AFB ADJUSTMENT SPECIFICATIONS—Continued

See Tune Up Chart in car chapters for hot idle speeds.

Year	Carb. Model	Idle Screws (Mixture) Turns Open	Float Level	Float Drop	Pump Travel	Fast Idle Throttle Valve Clearance	Choke Unloader Setting	Secondary Throttle Lever Setting	Vacuum Choke Break Setting	Choke Piston Linkage Setting	Choke Setting
BUICK—Continued											
1966	4061S	¼-1¾	11/64	23/32	7/16	.033	5/32	.020	—	.088	1 Rich
	4179S	¼-1¾	15/64	23/32	½②	.029	7/32	.020	—	.135	On Index
	4180S	¼-1¾	15/64	23/32	½②	.033	7/32	.020	—	.128	On Index
	4181S	¼-1¾	15/64	23/32	½②	.033	7/32	.020	—	.109	On Index
1967	4331S	1	1 13/32	¾	7/16③	.033	.160	.020	—	.090	1 Rich
	4332S	1	1 13/32	¾	7/16③	.026	.160	.020	—	.090	Index
	4344S	1	1 13/32	¾	17/32④	.033	.160	.020	—	.090	2 Rich

①—With solid seat 7/32″, resilient seat 3/16″. ②—Throttle connector rod in inner hole. ③—Center Hole. ④—Top Hole.

Year	Carb. Model	Idle Screws (Mixture) Turns Open	Float Level	Float Drop	Pump Travel	Fast Idle Throttle Valve Clearance	Choke Unloader Setting	Secondary Throttle Lever Setting	Vacuum Choke Break Setting	Choke Piston Linkage Setting	Choke Setting
CADILLAC											
1966	4168S	1-2¾	②	15/16	31/64	.020	5/16	.020	—	Flush	On Index
	4169S	1-2¾	②	15/16	31/64	.020	5/16	.020	—	Flush	On Index
	4170S	2½-4	②	15/16	31/64	.020	5/16	.020	—	Flush	1 Rich
	4171S	2½-4	②	15/16	31/64	.020	5/16	.020	—	Flush	1 Rich

①—Solid seat 3/8″, resilient seat 21/64″. ②—Solid seat 3/8″, resilient seat 11/32″.

Year	Carb. Model	Idle Screws (Mixture) Turns Open	Float Level	Float Drop	Pump Travel	Fast Idle Throttle Valve Clearance	Choke Unloader Setting	Secondary Throttle Lever Setting	Vacuum Choke Break Setting	Choke Piston Linkage Setting	Choke Setting
CHRYSLER, IMPERIAL, DODGE, PLYMOUTH											
1966	4119S	¼-2¾	②	23/32	7/16	.013	7/32	.020	1/8	—	2 Rich
	4120S	¼-2¾	②	23/32	7/16	.020	7/32	.020	3/32	—	2 Rich
	4121S	¼-2¾①	②	23/32	7/16	.018	7/32	.020	1/8	—	On Index
	4122S	2¼-3¼①	②	23/32	7/16	.018	7/32	.020	1/8	—	On Index
	4130S	1¼-2¾	②	23/32	7/16	.020	3/8	.020	1/8	—	2 Rich
	4131S	¼-2¾	②	23/32	7/16	.025	3/8	.020	7/64	—	2 Rich
	4132S	1½-2½	②	23/32	7/16	.018	5/16	.020	5/64	—	On Index
	4133S	2½-3½①	②	23/32	7/16	.018	5/16	.020	5/64	—	On Index
	4136S	1½-2½①	②	23/32	7/16	.018	5/16	.020	5/64	—	On Index
	4137S	2½-3½①	②	23/32	7/16	.018	5/16	.020	5/64	—	On Index
1966-67	4139S	¼-2¾	③	23/32	7/16	—	—	.020	—	—	—
1966	4140S	¼-2¾	②	23/32	7/16	.030	¼	.020	—	—	1 Rich
1967	4294S	1-2	7/32	¾	7/16	—	7/32	.020	—	—	2 Rich
	4295S	1-2	7/32	¾	7/16	—	7/32	.020	—	—	2 Rich
	4298S	1-2	7/32	¾	7/16	—	3/8	.020	—	—	2 Rich
	4299S	1-2	7/32	¾	7/16	—	3/8	.020	—	—	2 Rich
	4304S	1-2	5/16	¾	7/16	—	7/32	.020	—	—	On Index
	4305S	1-2	5/16	¾	7/16	—	7/32	.020	—	—	On Index
	4309S	1-2	5/16	¾	7/16	—	5/16	.020	—	—	On Index
	4310S	1-2	5/16	¾	7/16	—	5/16	.020	—	—	On Index
	4311S	1-2	5/16	¾	7/16	—	5/16	.020	—	—	On Index
	4312S	1-2	5/16	¾	7/16	—	5/16	.020	—	—	On Index
	4324S	1-2	5/16	¾	7/16	—	—	.020	—	—	—
	4325S	1-2	7/32	¾	7/16	—	¼	.020	—	—	1 Rich
	4326S	1-2	7/32	¾	7/16	—	3/8	.020	—	—	On Index
	4327S	1-2	7/32	¾	7/16	—	3/8	.020	—	—	On Index
	4328S	1-2	5/16	¾	7/16	—	3/8	.020	—	—	On Index
	4329S	1-2	5/16	¾	7/16	—	3/8	.020	—	—	On Index
	4343S	1-2	7/32	¾	7/16	—	3/8	.020	—	—	1 Rich

continued

CARTER AFB ADJUSTMENT SPECIFICATIONS—Continued

See Tune Up Chart in car chapters for hot idle speeds.

Year	Carb. Model	Idle Screws (Mixture) Turns Open	Float Level	Float Drop	Pump Travel	Fast Idle Throttle Valve Clearance	Choke Unloader Setting	Secondary Throttle Lever Setting	Vacuum Choke Break Setting	Choke Piston Linkage Setting	Choke Setting
CHRYSLER, IMPERIAL, DODGE, PLYMOUTH—Continued											
1968	4430S	—	19/64	23/32	7/16	—	—	17/64	—	—	—
	4431S	3	7/32	23/32	7/16	.013	1/4	17/64	—	3/32	2 Rich
	4432S	3½	7/32	23/32	7/16	.013	1/4	17/64	—	7/64	2 Rich
1969	4619S	—	7/32	3/4	7/32	—	—	17/64	—	—	—
	4620S	1–2	7/32	3/4	7/16	50 Drill④	1/4	17/64	—	39 Drill	2 Rich
	4621S	1–2	7/32	3/4	7/16	50 Drill④	1/4	17/64	—	39 Drill	2 Rich
1970	4742S	14.0–14.4 to 1⑤	19/64	23/32	7/16	—	—	17/64	—	—	—
	4745S	14.0–14.4 to 1⑤	7/32	23/32	7/16	50 Drill④	1/4	17/64	—	54 Drill	2 Rich
	4746S	14.0–14.4 to 1⑤	7/32	23/32	7/16	50 Drill④	1/4	17/64	—	39 Drill	2 Rich
1971	4969S	14.0–14.4 to 1⑤	7/32	3/4	31/64	—	—	17/64	—	—	—
	4970S	14.0–14.4 to 1⑤	7/32	3/4	31/64	50 Drill④	—	17/64	—	—	—
	4971S	14.0–14.4 to 1⑤	7/32	3/4	31/64	50 Drill④	—	17/64	—	—	—

①—When adjusting idle mixture screw, do not turn screw more than 1/16 turn at a time. Idle screw is not removable and the screw locks approximately a maximum of 2¾ turns open on 4121, 3¼ turns on 4122, 2½ turns on 4132 and 4136, 3½ turns on 4133 and 4137.
②—Solid seat 7/32", resilient seat 3/16".
③—Solid seat 19/64", resilient seat 17/64".
④—With fast idle speed adjusting screw contacting second highest speed step on fast idle cam the clearance between choke valve and wall of air horn should be as specified.
⑤—Air/fuel ratio.

Year	Carb. Model	Idle Screws (Mixture) Turns Open	Float Level	Float Drop	Pump Travel	Fast Idle Throttle Valve Clearance	Choke Unloader Setting	Secondary Throttle Lever Setting	Vacuum Choke Break Setting	Choke Piston Linkage Setting	Choke Setting
LINCOLN											
1966	4147S	½–1½	②	23/32	15/32	.026	1/8	.020	—	7/64	1 Rich
	4148S	½–1½	②	23/32	15/32	.026	1/8	.020	—	7/64	1 Rich
	4204S	1/4–1¾	②	23/32	15/32	.026	1/8	.020	—	7/64	1 Rich
	4205S	1/4–1¾	②	23/32	15/32	.026	1/8	.020	—	7/64	1 Rich
1967	C7VF-A③	½–1½	3/16	23/32	①	.026	1/8	.020	—	7/64	1 Rich
	C7VF-B③	½–1½	3/16	23/32	①	.026	1/8	.020	—	7/64	1 Rich
	C7VF-C③	½–1½	3/16	23/32	①	.026	1/8	.020	—	7/64	1 Rich
	C7VF-D③	½–1½	3/16	23/32	①	.026	1/8	.020	—	7/64	1 Rich
1968	C8VF-E③	1	3/16	23/32	①	.026	1/8	.020	—	7/64	1 Lean

①—Place connector rod in inner hole.
②—Solid seat 3/16", resilient seat 5/32".
③—Identification tag on carburetor bowl is marked "Autolite".

Year	Carb. Model	Idle Screws (Mixture) Turns Open	Float Level	Float Drop	Pump Travel	Fast Idle Throttle Valve Clearance	Choke Unloader Setting	Secondary Throttle Lever Setting	Vacuum Choke Break Setting	Choke Piston Linkage Setting	Choke Setting
PONTIAC											
1966	4030S	¾–2½	1/4	23/32	35/64	.027	5/32	.020	—	Flush	1 Rich
	4031S	¾–2½	5/16	23/32	35/64	.027	5/32	.020	—	Flush	1 Rich
	4033S	½–2¼	5/16	23/32	35/64	.027	5/32	.020	—	Flush	1 Rich
	4034S	½–2¼	5/16	23/32	35/64	.031	5/32	.020	—	Flush	1 Rich
	4035S	½–2¼	3/8	23/32	35/64	.027	5/32	.020	—	Flush	1 Rich
	4036S	½–2¼	1/4	23/32	35/64	.031	5/32	.020	—	Flush	1 Rich
	4037S	½–2¼	5/16	23/32	35/64	.031	5/32	.020	—	Flush	1 Rich
	4041S	¾–2½	5/16	23/32	35/64	.027	5/32	.020	—	Flush	1 Rich

continued

CARTER CARBURETORS

CARTER AFB ADJUSTMENT SPECIFICATIONS—Continued

See Tune Up Chart in car chapters for hot idle speeds.

Year	Carb. Model	Idle Screws (Mixture) Turns Open	Float Level	Float Drop	Pump Travel	Fast Idle Throttle Valve Clearance	Choke Unloader Setting	Secondary Throttle Lever Setting	Vacuum Choke Break Setting	Choke Piston Linkage Setting	Choke Setting
PONTIAC—Continued											
1967	4242S	½–3	5/16	23/32	3/8	.031	5/32	.020	—	Flush	1 Rich
	4243S	½–3	3/8	23/32	3/8	.027	5/32	.020	—	Flush	1 Rich
	4244S	1–2½	¼	23/32	3/8	.031	5/32	.020	—	Flush	1 Rich
	4245S	1–2½	5/16	23/32	3/8	.027	5/32	.020	—	Flush	1 Rich
	4246S	½–3	5/16	23/32	3/8	.031	5/32	.020	—	Flush	1 Rich
	4248S	2–3½	5/16	23/32	3/8	.031	5/32	.020	—	Flush	1 Rich

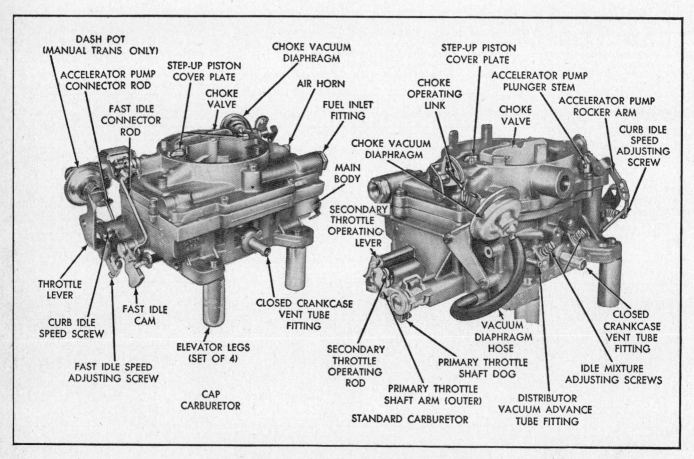

Fig. 2   AFB exterior views (Chrysler). The unit at left is used with C.A.P. equipment, the one at right is a standard unit

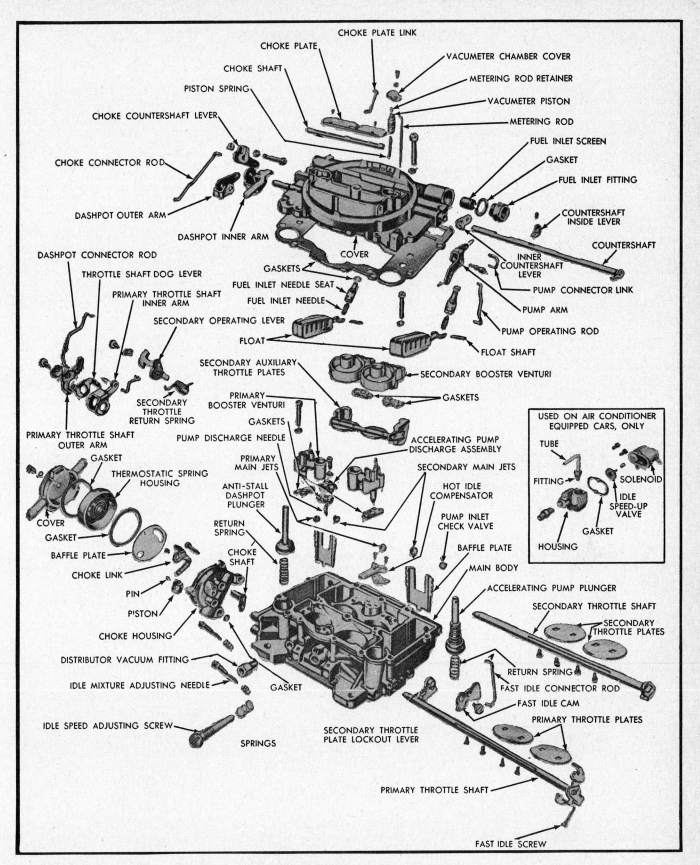

Fig. 1   Carter Model AFB four-barrel carburetor

MODEL AFB ADJUSTMENTS

The AFB carburetor, Figs. 1 and 2, contains many features, some of which are the locations of the step-up rods and pistons. The step-up rods, pistons and springs are accessible for service without removing the air horn or the carburetor from the engine. The venturi assemblies (primary and secondary) are replaceable and contain many of the calibration points for both the high and low speed systems. One fuel bowl feeds both the primary and secondary nozzles on the right side while the other fuel bowl takes care of the primary and secondary nozzles on the left side. This provides excellent performance in cornering, quick stops and acceleration.

All the major castings of the carburetor are aluminum, with the throttle body integral with the main body. This allows an overall height reduction in the carburetor. The section containing the accelerating pump is termed the primary side of the carburetor; the rear section is the secondary.

Float Alignment

Fig. 3—Sight down side of float to determine if it is parallel to the outer edge of the air horn casting. To adjust, bend float lever by applying just enough pressure to make the adjustment. Apply the pressure on the end of the float with the fingers while supporting the float lever with the thumb.

After aligning the float, remove as much clearance as possible between arms of float lever and lugs on air horn by bending the float lever. Arms of float lever should be as parallel to the inner surfaces of the lugs on the air horn as possible. Floats must operate freely without excess clearance on its hinge pin.

Float Level Adjustment

Fig. 4—With air horn inverted, bowl cover gasket in place and needle seated, clearance between top of float (at outer end) and air horn gasket should be as listed in the *AFB Specifications Chart*. To adjust, bend float arm. Adjust both floats and recheck float alignment.

Float Drop Adjustment

Fig. 5—With bowl cover held in upright position, measure between outer end of each float, the distance between top of floats and bowl cover gasket should be as listed in the *AFB Specifications Chart*. To adjust, bend tabs on float brackets.

Pump Adjustment

Fig. 6—Back out idle speed screw until throttle valves seat in carburetor bores. With throttle connector rod in center hole (medium stroke) of pump arm, distance from top of bowl cover to top of pump plunger shaft should be as listed in the *AFB Specifications Chart*. Adjust by bending throttle connector rod at its offset angle.

NOTE: Some models require the throttle connector rod to be placed in either the inner hole (long stroke) or outer hole (short stroke). In such cases the chart will indicate the proper hole connection.

Fast Idle Linkage Adjustment

Fig. 7—With choke valve tightly closed and lug on outer choke shaft lever contacting stop on inner choke shaft lever, align center of fast idle screw with index mark on cam. To adjust, bend fast idle connector rod. On some models it may be necessary to bend stop lug on fast idle cam.

Fast Idle Throttle Valve Clearance

Fig. 8—With choke valve tightly closed, tighten fast idle adjusting screw on index mark on cam until the clearance between throttle valve and carburetor bore (side opposite idle port) is as listed in the *AFB Specifications Chart*.

Choke Unloader Adjustment

Fig. 9—With throttle wide open, clearance between upper edge of choke valve and inner wall of air horn should be as listed in the *AFB Specifications Chart*. To adjust, bend unloader lip on throttle shaft lever.

Secondary Throttle Lever Adjustment

Figs. 10 and 11—Block choke valve wide open. Secondary throttle valves should just start to open when primary throttle valves are opened to the clearance listed in the *AFB Specifications Chart* between lower edge of throttle valve and carburetor bore (side opposite idle port). To adjust, bend throttle operating rod, Fig. 10.

Primary and secondary throttle valves should reach wide open position at the same time.

With primary and secondary throttle valves tightly closed, there should be the clearance listed in the *AFB Specifications Chart* between the positive closing shoes and primary and secondary throttle levers. To adjust, bend shoe on secondary lever.

Secondary Throttle Lockout

Fig. 12—Crack throttle valves and manually open and close choke valve. Tang on secondary throttle lever should freely engage in notch of lockout dog. To adjust, bend tang on secondary throttle lever.

On Cadillac models, with lockout dog held tight against stop on flange casting and secondary throttle valves partially open, there should be .026″ clearance between tang on secondary throttle lever and lockout arm. To adjust, bend arm at slot of lockout dog. Fast idle cam may be removed to facilitate gauging and adjusting.

On Lincoln units, with choke valve closed, adjust tang on secondary throttle lever to give .070″ opening of secondary valves (high side of valves adjacent to

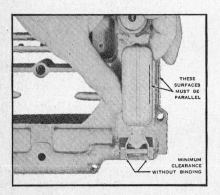

Fig. 3 AFB float alignment

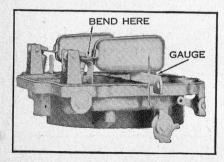

Fig. 4 AFB float level adjustment

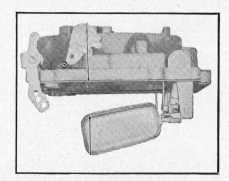

Fig. 5 AFB float drop adjustment

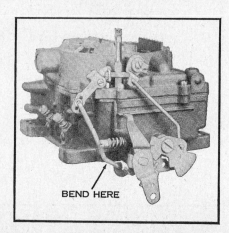

Fig. 6 AFB pump adjustment

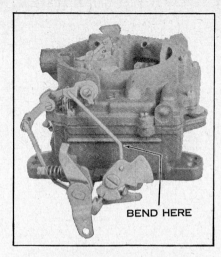

Fig. 7 AFB fast idle linkage adjustment

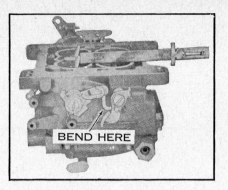

Fig. 10 AFB secondary throttle lever adjustment

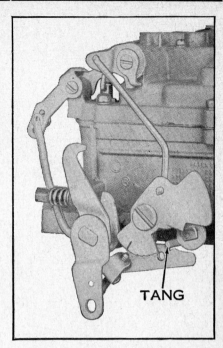

Fig. 12 AFB secondary lockout adjustment

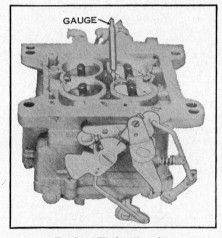

Fig. 8 AFB throttle valve clearance adjustment

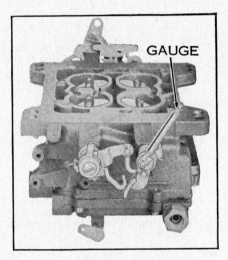

Fig. 11 AFB gauging clearance between positive closing shoes on primary and secondary throttle valves

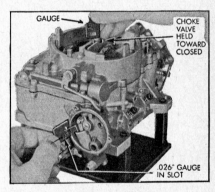

Fig. 13 AFB choke piston clearance

throttle lever) when primary valves are wide open.

Choke Piston Lever Adjustment

All Cadillac and Pontiac

Choke piston should be flush with top of piston housing with choke valve closed. Choke valve should be held closed by applying pressure to piston lever in piston housing. To adjust, bend choke connector rod.

Choke Piston Linkage Adjustment

Fig. 13—Except Cadillac and Pontiac

Bend a .026" wire gauge at a 90-degree angle approximately $\frac{1}{8}$" from its end. Open choke valve and insert the wire gauge so that bent portion is between top of slot in choke piston cylinder and bottom of slot in piston.

Hold wire gauge in position and close choke valve by pressing on piston lever in choke housing until resistance is felt. There should now be the clearance listed in the *AFB Specifications Chart* between top of choke valve and air horn wall. To adjust, bend choke connector link.

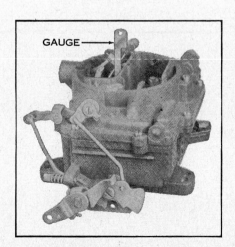

Fig. 9 AFB choke unloader adjustment

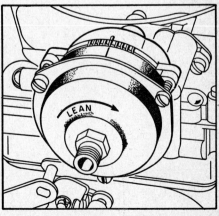

Fig. 14 AFB choke setting (built-in type)

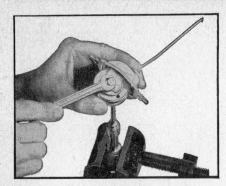

Fig. 15   AFB well-type choke
setting (Chrysler line)

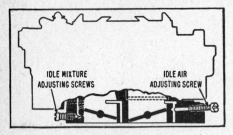

Fig. 16   AFB slow idle
air adjusting screw

Automatic Choke Setting

Built-In Type, Fig. 14

Loosen retaining screws and turn choke cover so that index mark or line on cover lines up with specified mark on choke housing listed in the *AFB Specifications*.

Well-Type Choke

Loosen mounting post lock nut and turn mounting post with screwdriver until

---

index mark on disc is positioned as listed in the *AFB Specifications Chart*. Hold in this position with a screwdriver and tighten lock nut, Fig. 15.

After adjustment is completed and coil housing and carburetor are installed on engine, lift cover disc and open and close choke valve manually to see if connector rod clears sides of hole in housing cover without binding. If binding exists, replace with a new unit since the connector rod cannot be bent without affecting calibration.

Dashpot Adjustment

Chrysler Line with C.A.P.

Use only on cars with manual transmission, make the dashpot adjustment after the fast idle setting. Then with the fast idle screw on highest step of cam, adjust dashpot for a clearance of .052" between dashpot stem and lever. Tighten lock nut.

Lincoln

There should be ⅛" clearance between top of bowl cover to top of plunger shaft with primary throttle valves tightly closed. To adjust, bend flat portion of dashpot lever. Check to be sure lever does not contact bowl cover screw.

Vacuum "Choke Break" Setting

Chrysler Line Only

With vacuum diaphragm plate (not stem) bottomed, close choke valve as far as possible without forcing. Then adjust connector rod to give the clearance listed in the *AFB Specifications Chart* between top edge of choke valve and inner wall of air horn. Remove connector rod to adjust to prevent damage to diaphragm.

Idle Air Adjustment

Fig. 16—Used on most Cadillac and Pon-

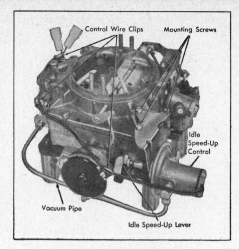

Fig. 18   AFB idle speed-up device used
on Cadillac air-conditioned cars

tiac carburetors and on some Chrysler and Lincoln units, the idle air adjustment screw is employed in lieu of the familiar throttle speed screw.

With engine at normal operating temperature, turn the air adjustment screw outward to increase engine speed, which will also lean the mixture supplied to the manifold. This must be compensated for by adjusting the idle mixture screws.

A/C Fast Idle Device

Cadillac with Air Conditioner, Fig. 18

This adjustment must be made with carburetor installed, engine at normal operating temperature and slow idle speed properly adjusted. With shift lever in neutral and A/C turned on, engine should idle at 900-950 rpm. To adjust, hold diaphragm shaft and adjust screw to get the desired rpm.

CARTER TQ ADJUSTMENT SPECIFICATIONS

See Tune Up Chart in car chapters for hot idle speeds.

Year	Carb. Model	Air/Fuel Ratio	Float Setting	Secondary Throttle Linkage	Secondary Air Valve Opening	Secondary Air Valve Spring	Pump Travel	Choke Control Lever (On Car)	Choke Unloader	Choke Setting
1971	4972S	14.2 to 1	1	11/32	31/64	1¼ Turn	31/64	541/64	11 Drill	2 Rich
	4973S	14.2 to 1	1	11/32	31/64	1¼ Turn	31/64	541/64	11 Drill	2 Rich

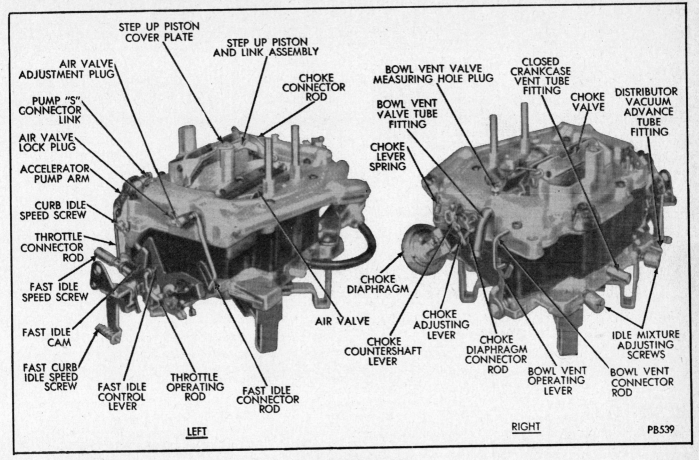

Fig. 1 TQ exterior views

MODEL TQ ADJUSTMENTS

The TQ (Thermo-Quad) carburetor, Figs. 1 and 2, is unique in design in that it has a black main body or fuel bowl of molded phenolic resin. This acts as an effective heat insulator. Fuel is kept cooler by about 20 degrees Fahrenheit than in carburetors of all metal design. Another reason for the lower operating temperatures is its suspended design metering system. All calibration points with the exception of the idle adjusting screws, are in the upper aluminum casting or air horn and are in effect suspended in cavities in the plastic main body.

Float Setting

Fig. 3—With bowl cover inverted, gasket installed and floats resting on seated needle, the dimension of each float from bowl cover gasket to bottom side of float should be as shown in *TQ Specifications Chart*.

Secondary Throttle Linkage

Fig. 4—Block choke valve in wide open position and invert carburetor. Slowly open the primary throttle valves until it is possible to measure between lower edge of primary valve and its bore. When dimension is as shown in *TQ Specifications Chart*, the secondary valves should just start to open. If necessary to adjust, bend rod until correct dimension is obtained.

Secondary Air Valve Opening

1. With air valve in closed position, the opening along air valve at its long side must be at its maximum and parallel with air horn gasket surface.
2. With air valve wide open, the opening of the air valve at the short side and air horn must be as shown in *TQ Specifications Chart*. The corner of air valve is notched for adjustment. Bend the corner with a pair of pliers to give proper opening.

Secondary Air Valve Spring Tension

Fig. 6—Loosen air valve lock plug and allow air valve to position itself wide open. With a long screwdriver that will enter center of tool C-4152 positioned on air valve adjustment plug, turn plug counterclockwise until air valve contacts stop lightly, then turn additional turn as specified in *TQ Specifications Chart*. Hold plug with screwdriver and tighten lock plug securely with tool C-4152.

Accelerator Pump Stroke

Fig. 7—Move choke valve wide open to release fast idle cam. Back off idle speed adjusting screw until throttle valves are seated in bores. Be sure throttle connector rod is in center hole of pump arm. Close throttle valve tightly and measure distance between top of bowl cover and end of plunger shaft. Dimension should be as shown in *TQ Specifications Chart*. Bend throttle connector rod at lower angle to adjust.

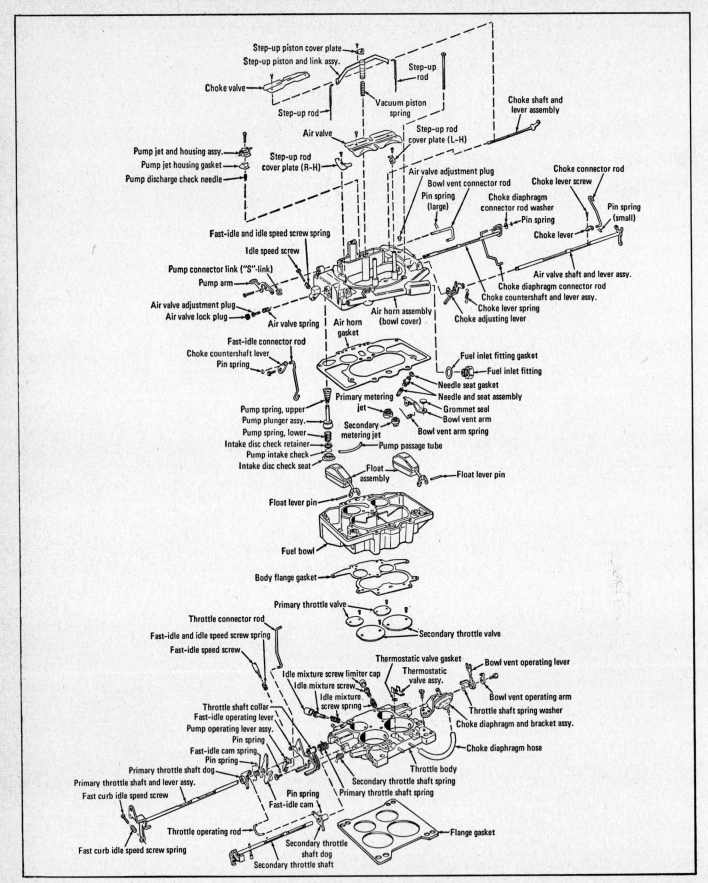

Fig. 2 Carter TQ model exploded view

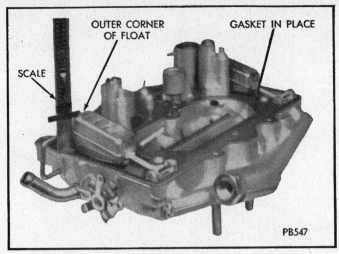

Fig. 3   TQ float setting

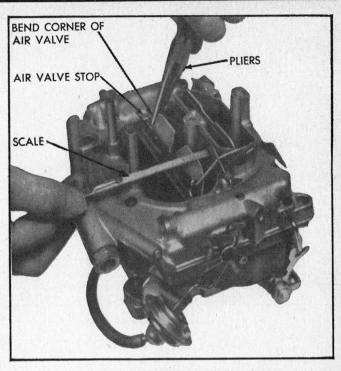

Fig. 5   TQ secondary air valve opening

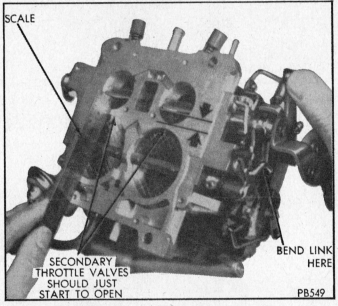

Fig. 4   TQ secondary throttle adjustment

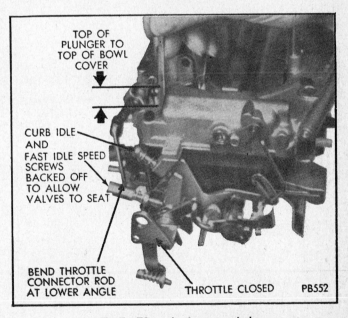

Fig. 7   TQ accelerator pump stroke

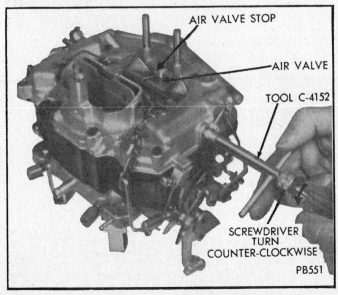

Fig. 6   TQ secondary air valve spring tension

Choke Control Lever

Fig. 8—Remove choke assembly, stainless steel cup and gasket. Close choke by pushing on choke lever with throttle partly open. Measure verticle distance from top of rod hole in control lever down to clean choke pad surface. Dimension should be as shown in *TQ Specifications Chart*. To adjust, bend link connecting two choke shafts.

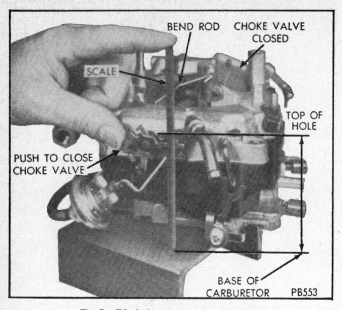

Fig. 8   TQ choke control lever adjustment

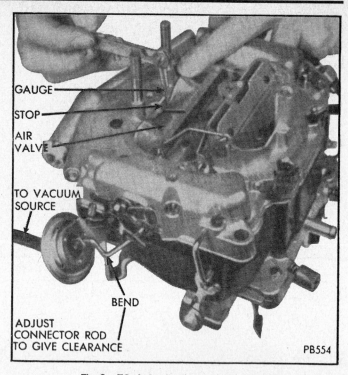

Fig. 9   TQ choke diaphragm connector rod

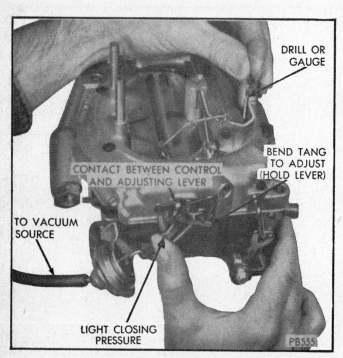

Fig. 10   TQ vacuum kick adjustment

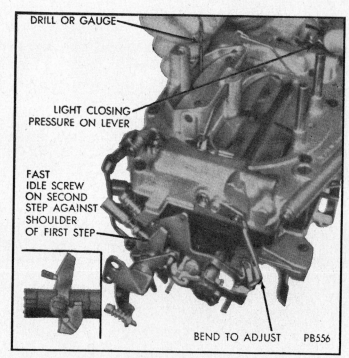

Fig. 11   TQ fast idle cam & linkage adjustment

Choke Diaphragm Connector Rod

Fig. 9—Apply a vacuum of 10 or more inches of Mercury to diaphragm to fully depress diaphragm stem. An auxiliary source like a distributor test machine can be used for this purpose. With air valve closed, adjust connector rod to give .040" clearance between air valve and stop.

Vacuum Kick Adjustment

Fig. 10—With engine running, back off fast idle speed screw until choke can be closed to kick position at idle. Note number of screw turns so fast idle can be turned back to original adjustment. Insert a #35 drill between long side (lower edge) of choke valve and the air horn wall. Apply

sufficient pressure on choke control lever to provide a minimum choke valve opening. The spring connecting the control lever to the adjustment lever must be fully extended for proper adjustment. Bend tang as shown to change contact with end of diaphragm rod. Do not adjust diaphragm rod. A slight drag should be felt as drill is being removed.

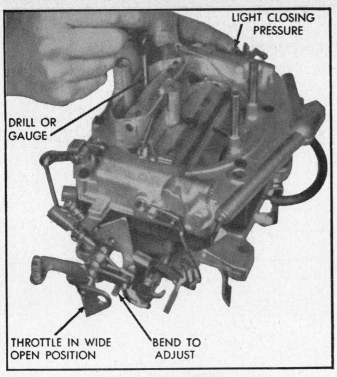

LIGHT CLOSING PRESSURE

DRILL OR GAUGE

THROTTLE IN WIDE OPEN POSITION

BEND TO ADJUST

Fig. 12 TQ choke unloader adjustment

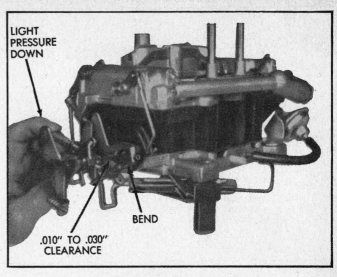

LIGHT PRESSURE DOWN

BEND

.010" TO .030" CLEARANCE

Fig. 13 TQ secondary throttle lockout

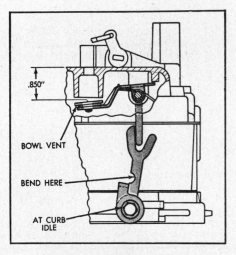

.850"

BOWL VENT

BEND HERE

AT CURB IDLE

Fig. 14 TQ bowl vent valve adjustment

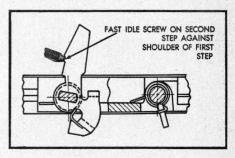

FAST IDLE SCREW ON SECOND STEP AGAINST SHOULDER OF FIRST STEP

Fig. 15 TQ fast idle speed cam position

Fast Idle Cam & Linkage

Fig. 11—With fast idle screw on second step of cam against shoulder of first step, adjust fast idle connector rod to obtain .110" opening between air horn wall and edge of choke valve (long side of valve nearest lever).

Choke Unloader Adjustment

Fig. 12—Hold throttle valves in wide open position and insert specified drill between long side (lower edge) of choke valve and inner wall of air horn. With finger lightly pressing against choke valve control lever, a slight drag should be felt as drill is withdrawn. Bend tang on fast idle control lever to adjust.

Secondary Throttle Lockout

Fig. 13—Move choke control lever to open choke position. Measure clearance between lockout lever and stop. Bend tang on fast idle control lever to adjust.

Bowl Vent Valve Adjustment

Fig. 14—Remove bowl vent valve checking hole plug in bowl cover. With throttle valves at curb idle, insert a narrow ruler down through hole. Allow ruler to rest lightly on top of valve. Reading should be as shown. Bend bowl vent operating lever at notch to adjust. Install a new plug.

Fast Idle Speed Cam

Fig. 15—With engine off and transmission in Park or Neutral, open throttle slightly. Close choke valve until fast idle screw can be positioned on second step of cam against shoulder of first step. Start engine and adjust screw to secure 1800 rpm. With throttle solenoid disconnected speed should drop to 900 rpm.

AUTOLITE MODEL 1V CARB. ADJUSTMENT SPECIFICATIONS

See Tune Up Chart in car chapters for hot idle speeds.

Year	Carb. Model (9510)	Idle Screws (Mixture) Turns Open	Float Setting	Pump Stroke	Fast Idle Speed	Choke Pulldown	Dechoke Clearance	Choke Link Position	Choke Setting
1971	711-BDA	③	①	.085	1700	.120	.210	Outer Hole	Index
	711-BDB	②	①	.070	1700	.075	.210	Outer Hole	Index
1972	721F-KFA	—	①	.070	—	.075	—	—	Index

① —With body in vertical position, set at 1.16–1.20.
    With body horizontal set at 1.35–1.37 (see Fig. 2).
② —Air/fuel ratio 13.4 to 13.9 to 1.

MODEL 1V ADJUSTMENTS

Fuel & Float Level Adjust

Fig. 2—With carburetor upper body held in vertical position, measure distance between upper body gasket and bottom of float (left view in illustration). Bend tab to adjust.

Turn upper body to horizontal position and measure distance from bottom of float to gasket (right view in illustration). Bend tab to adjust.

Choke Plate Pull-Down

Fig. 3—Remove air cleaner, thermostatic spring and water housing. Depress vacuum piston until vacuum bleed port is

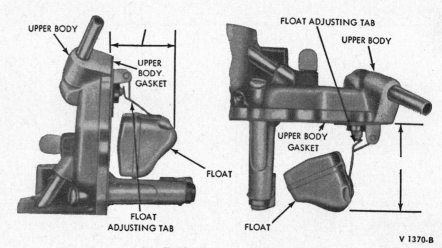

Fig. 2   Fuel and float level setting

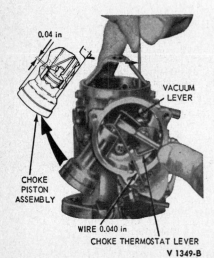

Fig. 3   Choke plate pull-down clearance

revealed and insert a piece of wire .040" thick, suitably bent, into this port. Raise piston to trap wire. With wire and piston held in this position, close the choke plate until its movement is stopped through the linkage. Partially open throttle for fast idle tab to clear cam. Bottom of choke plate should now be as specified from carburetor body. If necessary, bend extension of choke thermostat lever to adjust.

Dechoke Adjustment

Fig. 4—Open throttle fully and hold it against stop. Check clearance between bottom of choke plate and carburetor body. Adjust if necessary, by bending the projection on the fast idle cam.

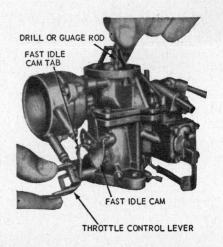

Fig. 4   De-choke adjustment

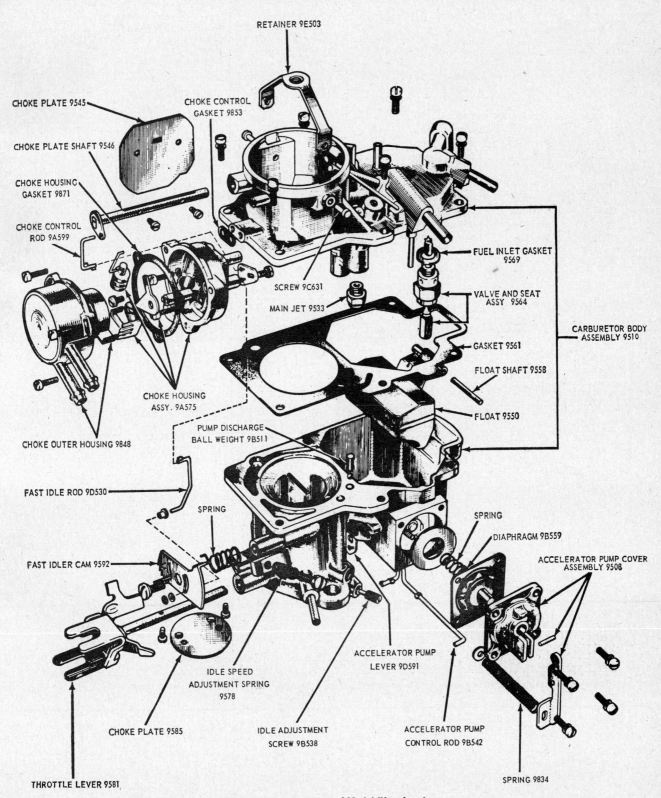

RETAINER 9E503

CHOKE PLATE 9545

CHOKE CONTROL GASKET 9853

CHOKE PLATE SHAFT 9546

CHOKE HOUSING GASKET 9871

CHOKE CONTROL ROD 9A599

FUEL INLET GASKET 9569

SCREW 9C631

VALVE AND SEAT ASSY 9564

MAIN JET 9533

CARBURETOR BODY ASSEMBLY 9510

GASKET 9561

FLOAT SHAFT 9558

CHOKE HOUSING ASSY. 9A575

FLOAT 9550

PUMP DISCHARGE BALL WEIGHT 9B511

CHOKE OUTER HOUSING 9848

FAST IDLE ROD 9D530

SPRING

SPRING

DIAPHRAGM 9B559

ACCELERATOR PUMP COVER ASSEMBLY 9508

FAST IDLER CAM 9592

IDLE SPEED ADJUSTMENT SPRING 9578

ACCELERATOR PUMP LEVER 9D591

CHOKE PLATE 9585

IDLE ADJUSTMENT SCREW 9B538

ACCELERATOR PUMP CONTROL ROD 9B542

THROTTLE LEVER 9581

SPRING 9834

Fig. 1   Exploded view of Model IV carburetor

AUTOLITE 1100-1V CARB. ADJUSTMENT SPECIFICATIONS

See Tune Up Chart in car chapters for hot idle speeds.

Year	Carb. Model (Code 9510)	Idle Screw (Mixture) Turns Open	Float Setting (Dry)	Pump Setting	Dashpot Setting	Fast Idle Cam Linkage Clearance	Fast Idle Speed	Manual Choke Plate Clearance	Automatic Choke Plate Clearance	Dechoke Clearance ①	Automatic Choke Setting
1966	C5DF-C	1-1½	1.090	.190	—	—	1300	—	.120	1/16	1 Lean
	C5DF-L	1-1½	1.090	.190	—	—	1400	—	.100	1/16	2 Lean
	C5DF-M	1-1½	1.090	.190	3½	—	1500	—	.150	1/16	At Index
	C5OF-AC	1-1½	1.090	.190	—	—	1400	—	.140	1/16	1 Lean
	C5OF-Y	1-1½	1.090	.190	—	—	1400	—	.140	1/16	1 Lean
	C5OF-Z	1-1½	1.090	.190	3½	—	1500	—	.150	1/16	At Index
	C6AF-M	1-1½	1.093	.210	—	.020	1500	—	.200	1/16	At Index
	C6AF-N	1-1½	1.093	.210	3½	.020	1600	—	.150	1/16	At Index
	C6AF-R	1-1½	1.093	.210	—	.020	1500	—	.200	1/16	At Index
	C6AF-S	1-1½	1.093	.210	3½	.020	1600	—	.200	1/16	At Index
	C6AF-V	1-1½	1.093	.210	—	.020	1500	—	.200	1/16	At Index
	C6AF-Y	1-1½	1.093	.210	3½	.020	1600	—	.200	1/16	At Index
	C6DF-D	1-1½	1.090	.190	3½	—	1500	—	.150	1/16	At Index
	C6DF-G	1-1½	1.090	.190	3½	—	1500	—	.150	1/16	At Index
1967	C6AF-R	1-1½	1.093	.210	—	.020	1500	—	.200	1/16	At Index
	C6DF-R	1-1½	1 3/32	.190	3½	—	1500	—	.150	1/16	Index
	C6DF-S	1-1½	1 3/32	.190	—	—	1300	—	.110	1/16	2 Lean
	C6AF-AK	1-1½	1 3/32	.210	6	—	1500	—	.180	1/16	Index
	C6AF-BL	1-1½	1 3/32	.210	6	—	1600	—	.180	1/16	Index
	C6AF-BM	1-1½	1 3/32	.210	6	—	1600	—	.125	1/16	2 Rich
	C6OF-AB	1-1½	1 3/32	.190	—	—	1300	—	.140	1/16	1 Lean
	C6OF-AC	1-1½	1 3/32	.190	3½	—	1500	—	.150	1/16	Index
	C6OF-AD	1-1½	1 3/32	.190	—	—	1300	—	.140	1/16	1 Lean
	C6TF-F	1-1½	1.020	.190	—	—	—	—	.375	—	—
	C6TF-G	1-1½	1.020	.190	—	—	—	—	.375	—	—
	C6UF-AF	1-1½	1 3/32	.210	—	—	—	—	.375	—	—
	C6UF-V	1-1½	1 3/32	.210	—	—	—	—	.375	—	—
	C7AF-AA	1-1½	1 3/32	.210	2	—	1500	—	.200	1/16	Index
	C7AF-AB	1-1½	1 3/32	.210	2	—	1600	—	.200	1/16	1 Lean
	C7DF-J	1-1½	1 3/32	.190	2	—	1400	—	.110	1/16	2 Lean
	C7DF-K	1-1½	1 3/32	.190	2	—	1500	—	.150	1/16	Index
	C7OF-N	1-1½	1 3/32	.190	2	—	1400	—	.110	1/16	2 Lean
	C7OF-R	1-1½	1 3/32	.190	2	—	1500	—	.150	1/16	Index
	C7TF-K	1-1½	1 1/16	.190	2	—	—	—	.375	—	—
	C7UF-A, B	1-1½	1 3/32	.190	2	—	—	—	.375	—	—
	C7UF-C, D	1-1½	1 1/32	.210	2	—	—	—	.375	—	—
	C5UF-L, M	1-1½	1 3/32	.190	—	—	—	—	.375	—	—
1968–69	C8AF-E④	13.9 to 1②	1 3/32	.190	.080	—	1600	—	.280	15/64	3 Lean
	C8OF-A③	1-1½	1 3/32	.190	.080	—	1400	—	.234	15/64	2 Lean
	C8OF-B④	14.5 to 1②	1 3/32	.190	.100	—	1500	—	.234	15/64	1 Lean
1969	C9DF-B	14.0 to 1②	1 3/32	.150	3	—	1400	—	.150	1/4	3 Lean
	C9OF-A	13.5 to 1②	1 3/32	.190	.080	—	1600	—	.200	.160	3 Lean
	C9OF-B	14.0 to 1②	1 3/32	.190	.080	—	1400	—	.200	.160	1 Lean
	C9OF-J	14.0 to 1②	1 3/32	.190	—	—	1400	—	.200	.160	1 Lean
	C9OF-K	13.5 to 1②	1 3/32	.190	—	—	1600	—	.200	.160	3 Lean

①—Minimum clearance between choke plate and air horn with throttle plates wide open
②—Air/fuel ratio.
③—Thermactor system.
④—Imco system.

MODEL 1100-1V ADJUSTMENTS

Figs. 1 and 2 illustrate exterior views of the two types of one-barrel carburetors while Figs. 3 and 4 illustrate the units exploded. Fig. 1 carburetor is available only with an automatic choke whereas Fig. 2 unit may be had with or without an automatic choke.

As shown, both types consist of two main assemblies, the upper body (air horn) and the lower (throttle) body. The upper body contains the metering components which include the main and idle fuel systems with power valve, float chamber vent and fuel inlet system. The lower body contains the fuel bowl, accelerating pump, idle mixture adjusting screw (needle) and spark valve.

On 1100 models a built-in hydraulic dashpot is incorporated in the lower body as shown. However, the 1101 model differs in that it has an externally mounted

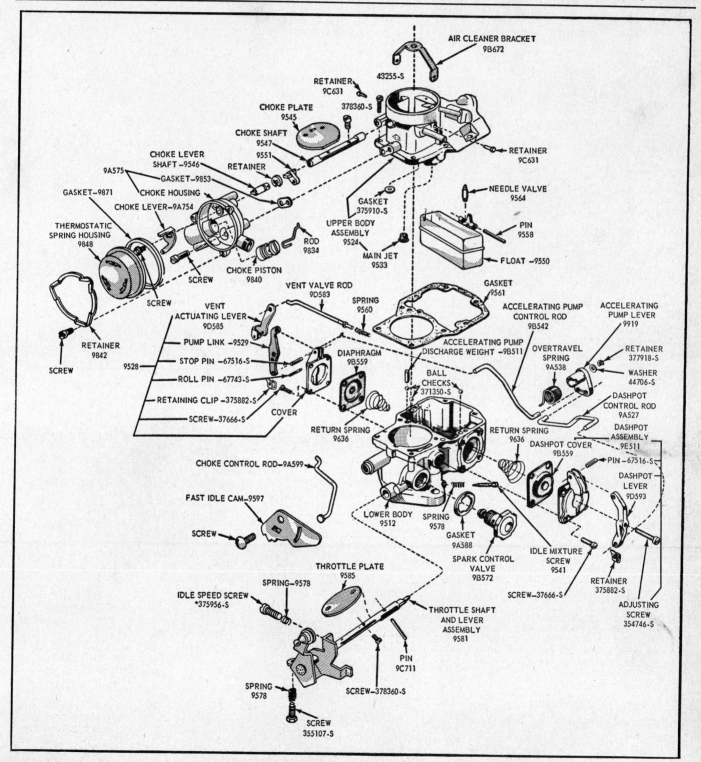

Fig. 3 Exploded view of Autolite 1100 carburetor shown in Fig. 1

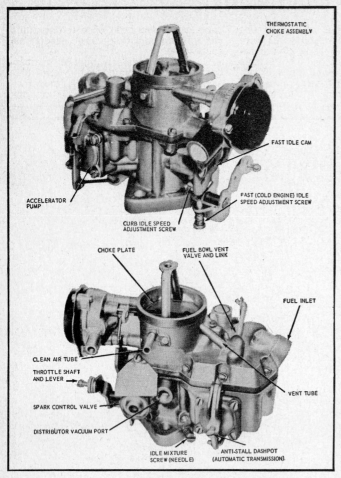

Fig. 1 Autolite 1100 carburetor with automatic choke mounted on air horn

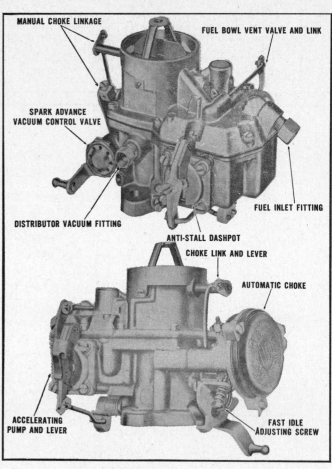

Fig. 2 Autolite 1100 carburetor with automatic choke mounted on throttle body

dashpot fastened to a bracket on the upper body.

Float Level Adjustment

Fig. 5—With air horn inverted and gasket removed, measure distance from gasket surface of air horn to top of float. If the dimension is not as listed in the *Ford Specifications Chart*, bend float arm tab as required to obtain the specified dimension.

Vent Valve Adjustment

Fig. 6—With throttle valve fully closed, groove on vent valve rod should be even with open end of vent. To adjust, bend arm on vent valve rod actuating lever (where it contacts pump lever) to align groove with edge of bore.

Pump Adjustment

Position throttle and choke valve linkage so that throttle valve will be completely closed. Hold throttle valve closed and place a gauge of the thickness listed in the *Ford Specifications Chart* between roll pin and cover surface, Fig. 7. Bend

pump actuating rod to obtain specified clearance between cover and roll pin in pump lever.

Acceleration requirements in various climates are satisfied by controlling the amount of fuel discharged from the pump. The pump stroke is controlled by changing the location of the roll pin in the lever stop hole, Fig. 8.

For operation in temperatures of 50 degrees and below, place the roll pin in the hole marked "HI". For best performance and fuel economy at normal temperatures and high altitudes (5000 ft.) place roll pin in hole marked "LO".

Fig. 5 Float level adjustment

REFER TO SPECIFICATION

BEND TAB ON FLOAT ARM TO OBTAIN CORRECT FLOAT HEIGHT

Dashpot Adjustment

Fig. 9—With throttle valve fully closed, turn dashpot adjusting screw outward until it clears dashpot plunger. Turn adjusting screw inward until it just contacts dashpot plunger, then continue turning inward the number of turns listed in the *Ford Specifications Chart* against the dashpot plunger.

Manual Choke (Pull-Down) Adjustment

Fig. 10—This adjustment refers to Fig. 2 carburetor only. Place choke linkage in full-choke position. Then insert a gauge or drill of a size listed in the *Ford Specifications Chart* between choke valve and inner wall of air horn. While maintaining full-choke position, adjust choke pull-down nut so it just contacts swivel on cam lever.

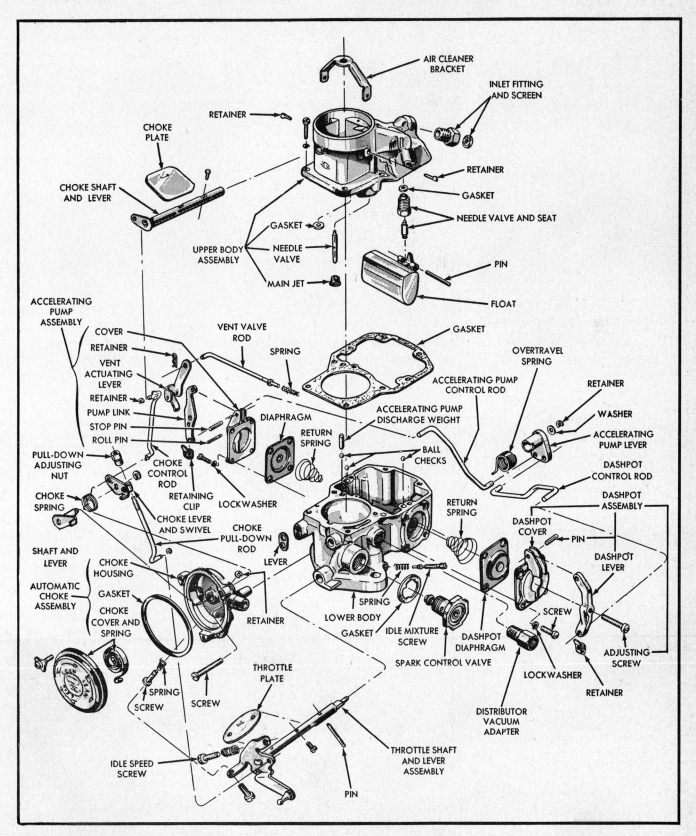

Fig. 4 Exploded view of Autolite 1100 carburetor shown in Fig. 2

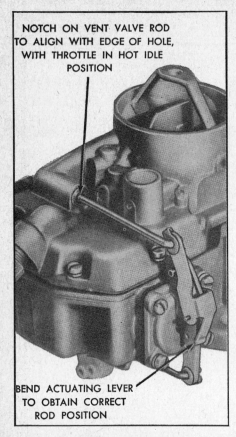

NOTCH ON VENT VALVE ROD TO ALIGN WITH EDGE OF HOLE, WITH THROTTLE IN HOT IDLE POSITION

BEND ACTUATING LEVER TO OBTAIN CORRECT ROD POSITION

Fig. 6 Vent valve adjustment

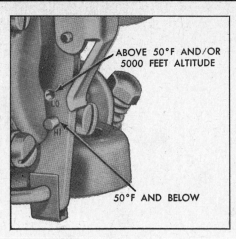

ABOVE 50°F AND/OR 5000 FEET ALTITUDE

50°F AND BELOW

Fig. 8 Accelerator pump lever adjustment

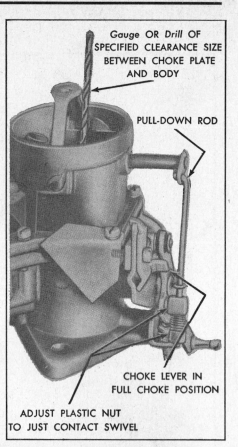

Gauge OR Drill OF SPECIFIED CLEARANCE SIZE BETWEEN CHOKE PLATE AND BODY

PULL-DOWN ROD

CHOKE LEVER IN FULL CHOKE POSITION

ADJUST PLASTIC NUT TO JUST CONTACT SWIVEL

Fig. 10 Manual choke adjustment (Fig. 2 unit)

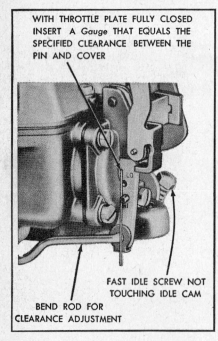

WITH THROTTLE PLATE FULLY CLOSED INSERT A Gauge THAT EQUALS THE SPECIFIED CLEARANCE BETWEEN THE PIN AND COVER

FAST IDLE SCREW NOT TOUCHING IDLE CAM

BEND ROD FOR CLEARANCE ADJUSTMENT

Fig. 7 Accelerator pump adjustment

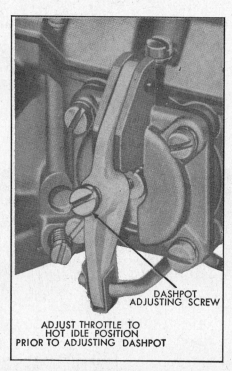

DASHPOT ADJUSTING SCREW

ADJUST THROTTLE TO HOT IDLE POSITION PRIOR TO ADJUSTING DASHPOT

Fig. 9 Anti-stall dashpot adjustment

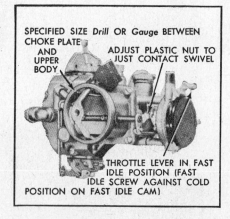

SPECIFIED SIZE Drill OR Gauge BETWEEN CHOKE PLATE AND UPPER BODY

ADJUST PLASTIC NUT TO JUST CONTACT SWIVEL

THROTTLE LEVER IN FAST IDLE POSITION (FAST IDLE SCREW AGAINST COLD POSITION ON FAST IDLE CAM)

Fig. 12 Automatic choke linkage adjustment (Fig. 2 unit)

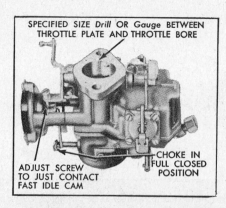

SPECIFIED SIZE Drill OR Gauge BETWEEN THROTTLE PLATE AND THROTTLE BORE

ADJUST SCREW TO JUST CONTACT FAST IDLE CAM

CHOKE IN FULL CLOSED POSITION

Fig. 11 Automatic choke fast idle adjustment (Fig. 2 unit)

carburetor only. Insert a gauge or drill of the size listed in the *Ford Specifications Chart* between throttle valve and carburetor bore. Close choke valve and turn fast idle adjusting screw inward until it just contacts fast idle cam.

Automatic Choke Fast Idle Adjustment

Fig. 11—This adjustment refers to Fig. 2

Automatic Choke Linkage (Pull-Down) Adjustment

Fig. 12—This adjustment refers to Fig. 2

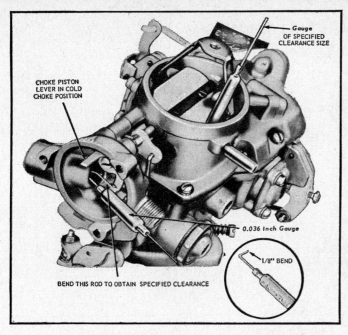

Fig. 13   Choke plate clearance adjustment (Fig. 1 unit)

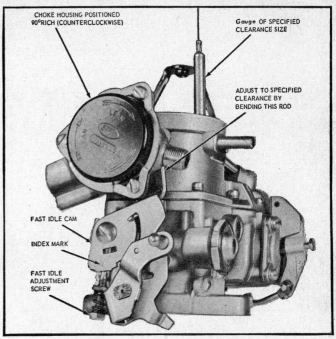

Fig. 14   Fast idle cam linkage adjustment (Fig. 1 unit)

carburetor only. The fast idle adjustment must be made before making this adjustment because the position of the pull-down rod is one of the determining factors affecting throttle-to-choke opening relationship.

Place a drill or gauge of a size listed in the *Ford Specifications Chart* between choke valve and inner wall of air horn. Close choke valve on gauge or drill and hold it securely. Close throttle until fast idle screw touches fast idle cam. Adjust plastic nut to just contact swivel on choke lever.

Choke Plate Clearance & Fast Idle Linkage

Figs. 13 and 14—These adjustments refer to Fig. 1 carburetor only.
1. Remove air cleaner and choke thermostatic spring housing from carburetor.
2. Bend a .036" wire gauge as shown in inset, Fig. 13.
3. Block throttle about half open so that fast idle cam does not contact fast idle adjusting screw.
4. Insert bent end of gauge between lower end of piston slot and upper edge of right-hand slot in choke housing, Fig. 13, and pull choke piston lever counterclockwise until gauge is snug in piston slot.
5. Hold gauge in place by exerting light pressure on choke piston lever.

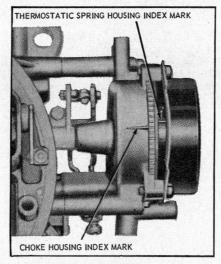

Fig. 15   Automatic choke setting

6. Gradually bend rod (link) between choke piston and piston lever until choke plate opens just wide enough to allow gauge or drill of the specified size between front of choke plate and air horn, Fig. 13 (see *Ford Specifications Chart*).
7. Install thermostatic spring housing

and gasket on choke housing and secure with clamp and screws.
8. Rotate spring housing counterclockwise (rich direction) to align center index mark on choke housing with index mark on spring housing; then rotate spring housing 90 degrees counterclockwise.
9. Position fast idle adjusting screw on index mark on fast idle cam, Fig. 14.
10. Adjust fast idle cam linkage to specification by bending choke control rod, Fig. 14, to provide the specified clearance between front of choke plate and air horn. Bend rod inward to decrease (outward to increase) clearance. Make certain fast idle screw remains on index mark of fast idle cam during adjustment procedure.
11. Set thermostatic spring housing to specified mark listed in the *Ford Specifications Chart*.

NOTE: If the foregoing adjustments were made with the carburetor installed on the engine, adjust engine idle speed and mixture, fast idle speed and dashpot as outlined above.

Automatic Choke Setting

Fig. 15—Loosen retaining screws and set thermostatic spring housing to the mark specified in the *Ford Specifications Chart* and tighten retaining screws.

AUTOLITE 1940-1V CARB. SPECIFICATIONS

See Tune Up Chart in car chapters for hot idle speeds.

Carb. Model	Float Setting (Dry)	Pump Setting	Fast Idle Cam	Vacuum Kick	Choke Unloader	Automatic Choke Adjustment	Dashpot Setting	Fast Idle Speed
DOPF-A	①	②	5/64	3/16	5/32	Index	—	2100
DOPF-C	①	②	5/64	3/16	5/32	Index	—	2100
DOPF-D	①	②	5/64	3/16	5/32	Index	3/32	2100
DOPF-E	①	②	③	—	④	—	—	—
DOPF-F	①	②	③	—	④	—	—	—
DOPF-G	①	②	③	—	④	—	3/32	—
DOPF-H	①	②	③	—	④	—	3/32	—
DOPF-J	①	②	③	—	④	—	3/32	—
DOPF-K	①	②	1/16	5/32	1/8	Index	3/32	2100
DOPF-L	①	②	1/16	5/32	1/8	Index	3/32	—
DOPF-M	①	②	—	—	—	—	3/32	—
DOPF-N	①	②	—	—	—	—	3/32	—
DOPF-R	①	②	—	—	—	—	3/32	—
DOPF-T	①	②	—	—	—	—	3/32	—

①—Toe in float, flush with gasket surface of main body.

②—27/32" from centerline of pump link hole in pump rod to edge of 5/16" boss on main body.

③—No vacuum, second step.

④—At wide open throttle.

MODEL 1940-1V ADJUSTMENTS

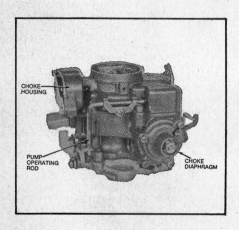

Fig. 1A 1940-1V carburetor with automatic choke

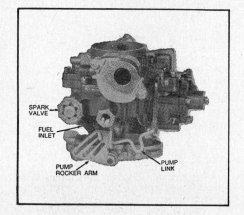

Fig. 2A 1940-1V carburetor with manual choke

The model 1940-1V, Figs. 1A, 2A, 3A, is a concentric unit, that is, the fuel bowl completely surrounds the venturi, and is available with either manual or automatic choke.

Principal sub-assemblies include a bowl cover, carburetor body and throttle body. A thick gasket between the throttle body and carburetor body retards heat transfer to the fuel to resist percolation.

In addition to the usual circuits, this unit incorporates a spark valve. This is a diaphragm operated, spring loaded valves in the main body connected to the throttle bore port. When the spark valve closes off the port, spark advance vacuum is decreased, retarding the ignition timing.

Float Level Adjustment

Fig. 4A—Install float assembly in float shaft cradle. Insert retaining spring and while holding with fingers, invert the bowl. A straight edge placed across the surface of the bowl should just touch the toes of the float. If necessary, bend the float tang to obtain this adjustment.

Pump Adjustment

Fig. 5A—With throttle in the curb idle position, the distance from the vacuum passage casting to the center of the hole in the pump operating rod should be as listed in specifications.

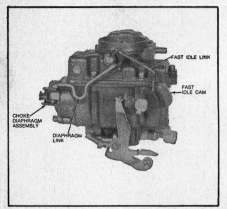

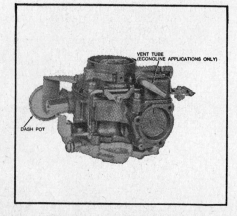

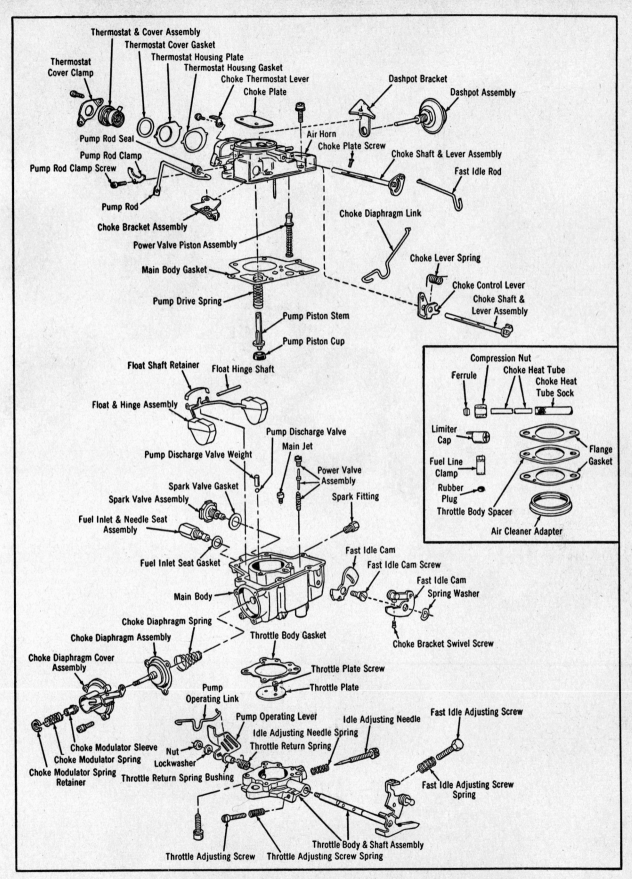

Fig. 3A   1940-1V carburetor. Exploded

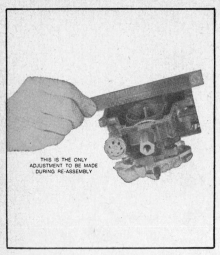

Fig. 4A   Checking float setting

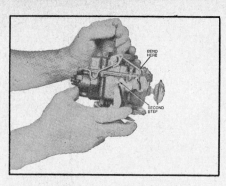

Fig. 6A   Fast idle cam adjustment

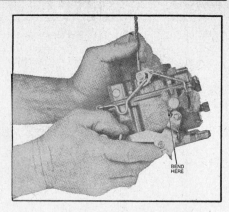

Fig. 9A   Unloader adjustment. Type B tang

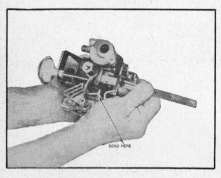

Fig. 5A   Pump piston stroke adjustment

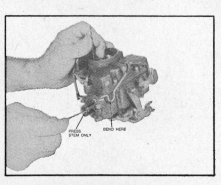

Fig. 7A   Vacuum kick adjustment

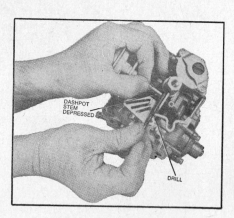

Fig. 10A   Dashpot adjustment

Fast Idle Cam

Fig. 6A—With throttle lever contacting the second highest speed step on the fast idle cam, move the choke valve toward closed position with light pressure on choke shaft lever.

Insert specified drill between choke valve and wall of air horn. Adjust by bending fast idle connector rod.

Vacuum Kick

Fig. 7A—Depress diaphragm with a small drift. Insert specified drill between choke valve and wall of air horn while holding pressure on choke lever. Note that the diaphragm extends as spring is compressed. Spring must be fully compressed for proper measurement.

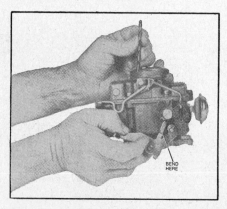

Fig. 8A   Unloader adjustment. Type A tang

Choke Unloader

Figs. 8A, 9A—With throttle valve in wide open throttle position, insert specified drill between upper edge of choke valve and inner wall of air horn. With finger lightly pressing against shaft lever, a slight drag should be felt as drill is withdrawn. Bend unloader tang on throttle if necessary.

Dashpot

Fig. 10A—With curb idle speed properly adjusted and the engine at idle, depress the dashpot. Insert specified drill between end of stem and tang.

AUTOLITE 2100, 6200-2V CARB. ADJUSTMENT SPECIFICATIONS

See Tune Up Chart in car chapters for hot idle speeds.

Year	Carb. Model (Code 9510) ①	Idle Screws (Mixture) Turns Open	Float Level (Dry)	Fuel Level (Wet)	Pump Setting Hole No.	Choke Plate Clearance (Pull-Down)	Fast Idle Cam Linkage Clearance	Fast Idle Speed (Hot Engine)	Dechoke Clearance ②	Dashpot Setting	Choke Setting
AMERICAN MOTORS											
1968	8HM2	1–1½	⅜	¾	④	.125	.120	1600	—	—	Index
	8HA2	1–1½	⅜	¾	④	.140	.120	1600	—	.095	Index
	8ZA2	1–1½	⅜	¾	④	.140	.120	1600	—	.095	Index
1969	9HM2	2	½	13/16	④	.125	.120	1600	.080	.140	Index
	9HA2	2	½	13/16	④	.140	.120	1600	.080	.140	Index
	9ZA2	2	½	13/16	④	.140	.120	1600	.080	.140	Index
1970	0DA2	14.0 to 1③	⅜	13/16	④	.300	.170	1600	.200	⅛	2 Rich
	0DM2	14.0 to 1③	⅜	13/16	④	.260	.170	1600	.200	⅛	Index
	0RA2	14.0 to 1③	⅜	13/16	④	.350	.170	1600	.200	⅛	1 Rich
1971	1DA2	14.0 to 1③	⅜	13/16	④	.190	.170	1600	.200	⅛	2 Rich
	1DM2	13.5 to 1③	⅜	13/16	④	.190	.170	1600	.200	⅛	1 Rich
	1RA2	14.0 to 1③	⅜	13/16	④	.190	.170	1600	.200	⅛	2 Rich
1972	2DA2	14.0 to 1③	⅜	¾	No. 3	.130	.120	1600	.200	9/64	2 Rich
	2DM2	13.5 to 1③	⅜	¾	No. 3	.140	.130	1600	.200	7/64	1 Rich
	2RA2	14.0 to 1③	⅜	¾	No. 3	.130	.120	1600	.200	—	2 Rich
FORD AND MERCURY											
1966	C6AF-A	1–1½	.491	.875	④	.140	.150	1400	1/16	—	At Index
	C6AF-AA	1–1½	.371	.750	④	.120	.110	1600	1/16	—	2 Rich
	C6AF-AH	1–1½	.431	.810	④	.200	.160	1500	1/16	—	At Index
	C6AF-B	1–1½	.491	.875	④	.120	.110	1600	1/16	.060–.090	2 Rich
	C6AF-C	1–1½	.491	.880	④	.200	.160	1400	1/16	—	At Index
	C6AF-Z	1–1½	.371	.750	④	.140	.130	1400	1/16	—	At Index
	C6DF-A	1–1½	.491	.875	④	.140	.150	1400	1/16	—	At Index
	C6DF-B	1–1½	.491	.875	④	.120	.110	1600	1/16	.060–.090	2 Rich
	C6DF-E	1–1½	.371	.750	④	.140	.130	1400	1/16	—	At Index
	C6DF-F	1–1½	.371	.750	④	.120	.110	1600	1/16	.060–.090	2 Rich
	C6MF-A	1–1½	.491	.880	④	.180	.160	1400	1/16	.060–.090	At Index
	C6MF-D	1–1½	.431	.810	④	.180	.160	1500	1/16	—	At Index
	C6OF-B	1–1½	.491	.880	④	.200	.160	1300	1/16	—	At Index
	C6OF-C	1–1½	.491	.880	④	.180	.160	1400	1/16	.060–.090	At Index
	C6OF-K	1–1½	.431	.810	④	.200	.160	1300	1/16	—	At Index
	C6OF-L	1–1½	.431	.810	④	.180	.160	1500	1/16	.060–.090	At Index
	C6TF-BG	1–1½	.450	29/32	④	.250	—	—	—	—	—
	C6TF-BH	1–1½	.450	29/32	④	.250	—	—	—	—	—
1967	C7AF-N	1–1½	.484	.875	④	.140	.130	1400	1/16	—	Index
	C7AF-R	1–1½	.484	.875	④	.120	.110	1600	1/16	—	2 Rich
	C7AF-S	1–1½	.531	.905	④	.120	.110	1400	1/16	.130	Index
	C7AF-T	1–1½	.531	.905	④	.120	.110	1600	1/16	.130	2 Rich
	C7AF-U	1–1½	.484	.875	④	.200	.160	1300	1/16	—	Index
	C7AF-V	1–1½	.375	.750	④	.180	.150	1400	1/16	—	2 Rich
	C7AF-Y	1–1½	.531	.905	④	.200	.170	1300	1/16	.095	Index
	C7AF-Z	1–1½	.531	.905	④	.180	.150	1500	1/16	.095	Index

Continued

FORD AUTOLITE CARBURETORS

AUTOLITE 2100, 6200-2V CARB. ADJUSTMENT SPECIFICATIONS—Continued

See Tune Up Chart in car chapters for hot idle speeds.

Year	Carb. Model (Code 9510) ①	Idle Screws (Mixture) Turns Open	Float Level (Dry)	Fuel Level (Wet)	Pump Setting Hole No.	Choke Plate Clearance (Pull-Down)	Fast Idle Cam Linkage Clearance	Fast Idle Speed (Hot Engine)	Dechoke Clearance ②	Dashpot Setting	Choke Setting
1967	C7DF-AJ	1–1½	17/32	29/32	④	.120	.110	1400	.060	—	2 Rich
	C7DF-AL	1–1½	3/8	3/4	④	.120	.110	1600	.060	1/8	2 Rich
	C7DF-E	1–1½	.375	.750	④	.120	.110	1400	1/16	—	Index
	C7DF-F	1–1½	.531	.905	④	.120	.110	1600	1/16	.075	2 Rich
	C7DF-G	1–1½	.531	.905	④	.120	.110	1400	1/16	.125	Index
	C7DF-H	1–1½	.531	.905	④	.120	.110	1600	1/16	.125	2 Rich
	C7DF-R	1–1½	3/8	3/4	④	.120	.110	1600	.060	1/8	2 Rich
	C7DF-S	1–1½	17/32	29/32	④	.120	.110	1400	.060	—	2 Rich
	C7OF-J	1–1½	.484	.875	④	.200	.160	1300	1/16	—	Index
	C7OF-K	1–1½	.375	.750	④	.180	.150	1400	1/16	—	2 Rich
	C7OF-L	1–1½	.531	.905	④	.200	.170	1300	1/16	.095	Index
	C7OF-M	1–1½	.531	.905	④	.180	.150	1500	1/16	.095	Index
	C7TF-C	1–1½	.531	.905	④	.250	—	1400	—	—	—
	C7TF-D	1–1½	.531	.905	④	.250	—	1400	—	.125	—
1968	C8AF-AK	1–1½	3/8	3/4	④	.120	.110	1200	.060	—	Index
	C8AF-L	1–1½	3/8	3/4	④	.140	.120	1400	.060	.125	1 Lean
	C8AF-M	1–1½	31/64	7/8	④	.210	.170	1300	.060	—	Index
	C8AF-AN	1–1½	31/64	7/8	④	.120	.100	1500	.060	.125	Index
	C8AF-N	1–1½	31/64	7/8	④	.120	.100	1500	.060	.125	Index
	C8OF-K, U	—	31/64	7/8	④	.120	.100	1500	.060	1/8	Index
	C8ZF-G		3/8	3/4	④	.140	.120	1400	.060	1/8	1 Lean
1968–69	C8AF-BD	14.0 to 1③	3/8	3/4	④	.130	.110	1400	.060	1/8	2 Rich
1969	C9AF-A	13.8 to 1③	3/8	3/4	④	.120	.110	1600	.060	1/8	Index
	C9AF-B	14.0 to 1③	31/64	7/8	④	.210	.170	1300	.060	1/8	1 Rich
	C9AF-C	14.4 to 1③	31/64	7/8	④	.130	.100	1500	.060	1/8	2 Rich
	C9OF-C	14.0 to 1③	31/64	7/8	④	.120	.100	1600	.060	—	2 Rich
	C9ZF-A	14.0 to 1③	9/16	15/16	④	.150	.130	1300	.060	7/64	1 Rich
	C9ZF-B	14.0 to 1③	31/64	7/8	④	.120	.100	1600	.060	—	2 Rich
	C9ZF-G	13.8 to 1③	3/8	3/4	④	.120	.110	1600	.060	1/8	Index
	C9MF-A	14.4 to 1③	31/64	7/8	④	.150	.120	1500	.060	1/8	2 Rich
1970	D0AF-C	12.0 to 1③	7/16	13/16	④	.150	.130	1400	.060	—	1 Rich
	D0AF-D	12.5 to 1③	7/16	13/16	④	.150	.130	1500	.060	1/8	1 Rich
	D0AF-E	12.0 to 1③	7/16	13/16	④	.230	.190	1300	.060	—	2 Lean
	D0AF-F	12.5 to 1③	7/16	13/16	④	.200	.170	1600	.060	1/8	2 Lean
	D0AF-G	—	7/16	13/16	④	.210	.170	1400	.060	1/8	1 Rich
	D0AF-J	12.2 to 1③	7/16	13/16	④	.200	.160	1400	.060	1/8	—
	D0AF-T	12.2 to 1③	7/16	13/16	④	.200	.160	1400	.060	—	—
	D0AF-U	12.5 to 1③	7/16	13/16	④	.150	.130	1500	.060	—	1 Rich
	D0AF-V	12.5 to 1③	7/16	13/16	④	.200	.170	1600	—	—	2 Lean
	D0AF-Y	13.3 to 1③	7/16	13/16	④	.210	.170	1400	.060	—	1 Rich
	D0AF-Z	13.3 to 1③	7/16	13/16	④	.200	.160	1500	.060	1/8	—
	D0AF-AA	13.3 to 1③	7/16	13/16	④	.200	.160	1500	.060	—	—
	D0AF-AU	—	7/16	13/16	④	.200	.170	1600	.060	—	2 Lean
	D0AF-AV	—	7/16	13/16	④	.200	.170	1600	.060	1/8	2 Lean
	D0OF-K	12.0 to 1③	7/16	13/16	④	.220	.190	1500	—	—	Index
	D0OF-L	12.5 to 1③	7/16	13/16	④	.190	.130	1500	—	1/8	1 Rich
	D0OF-M	12.5 to 1③	7/16	13/16	④	.190	.130	1500	—	—	1 Rich
	D0OF-T	—	7/16	13/16	④	.190	.160	1500	.060	1/8	1 Rich
	D0OF-U	—	7/16	13/16	④	.220	.190	1500	.060	—	Index
	D0OF-V	—	7/16	13/16	④	.190	.160	1500	.060	—	1 Rich

FORD AND MERCURY—Continued

Continued

AUTOLITE 2100, 6200-2V CARB. ADJUSTMENT SPECIFICATIONS—Continued

See Tune Up Chart in car chapters for hot idle speeds.

Year	Carb. Model (Code 9510) ①	Idle Screws (Mixture) Turns Open	Float Level (Dry)	Fuel Level (Wet)	Pump Setting Hole No.	Choke Plate Clearance (Pull-Down)	Fast Idle Cam Linkage Clearance	Fast Idle Speed (Hot Engine)	Dechoke Clearance ②	Dashpot Setting	Choke Setting
FORD AND MERCURY—Continued

1971	D1AF-DA	⑤	7/16	13/16	④	.150	.130	1500	.060	—	Index
	D1AF-FA	⑤	7/16	13/16	④	.220	.190	1300	.060	—	1 Rich
	D1AF-JA	⑤	7/16	13/16	④	.190	.130	1600	.060	1/8	1 Rich
	D1AF-KA	⑤	7/16	13/16	④	.190	.130	1600	.060	—	Index
	D1MF-FA	⑤	7/16	13/16	④	.200	.160	1400	.060	1/8	1 Rich
	D1MF-JA	⑤	7/16	13/16	④	.190	.160	1500	.060	1/8	1 Rich
	D1MF-KA	⑤	7/16	13/16	④	.190	.160	1500	.060	1/8	1 Rich
	D1OF-ABA	⑤	7/16	13/16	④	.170	.150	1400	.060	—	1 Rich
	D1OF-PA	⑤	7/16	13/16	④	.230	.190	1500	.060	—	Index
	D1OF-RA	⑤	7/16	13/16	④	.200	.170	1500	.060	—	1 Rich
	D1OF-YA	⑤	7/16	13/16	④	.200	.170	1500	.060	—	1 Rich
	D1OF-ZA	⑤	7/16	13/16	④	.230	.190	1500	.060	—	Index
	D1YF-DA	⑤	7/16	13/16	④	.200	.160	1500	.060	—	Index
	D1ZF-AA	⑤	7/16	13/16	④	.150	.130	1500	.060	—	Index
	D1ZF-SA	⑤	7/16	13/16	④	.200	.170	1500	.060	—	1 Rich
	D1ZF-UA	⑤	7/16	13/16	④	.200	.170	1500	.060	—	1 Rich
1972	D2AF-FB	—	7/16	13/16	—	.140	—	—	—	1/8	Index
	D2AF-GB	—	7/16	13/16	—	.140	—	—	—	1/8	Index
	D2AF-HA	—	7/16	13/16	—	.140	—	—	—	1/8	1 Rich
	D2GF-AA	—	7/16	13/16	—	.150	—	—	—	1/8	1 Rich
	D2GF-BA	—	7/16	13/16	—	.150	—	—	—	1/8	1 Rich
	D2MF-FB	—	7/16	13/16	—	.180	—	—	—	—	1 Rich
	D2OF-KA	—	7/16	13/16	—	.140	—	—	—	1/8	1 Rich
	D2OF-UB	—	7/16	13/16	—	.190	—	—	—	—	⑥
	D2WF-CA	—	7/16	13/16	—	.190	—	—	—	—	⑥
	D2ZF-FA	—	7/16	13/16	—	.150	—	—	—	1/8	1 Rich
	D2ZF-LA	—	7/16	13/16	—	.140	—	—	—	1/8	1 Rich

①—Stamped on left side of fuel bowl or on tag attached to bowl cover.
②—Minimum clearance between choke plate and air horn wall with throttle plates wide open.
③—Air/fuel ratio.
④—With link in inboard hole in pump lever, place overtravel lever in the longest stroke hole for extremely cold weather, intermediate stroke hole for moderate weather, and short stroke hole for extremely warm weather.
⑤—Air/fuel ratio greater than 14.5 to 1.
⑥—California 1 Rich; all others 2 Rich.

FORD AUTOLITE CARBURETORS

AUTOLITE 4100-4V ADJUSTMENT SPECIFICATIONS

See Tune Up Chart in car chapters for hot idle speeds.

Year	Carb. Model (Code 9510) ①	Idle Screws (Mixture) Turns Open	Float Level (Dry)	Fuel Level (Wet)	Pump Setting (Hole No.)	Choke Plate Clearance (Pull-Down)	Fast Idle Cam Linkage Clearance	Fast Idle Speed (Hot Engine)	Secondary Throttle Plate Clearance ②	Dechoke Clearance ③	Dashpot Setting	Choke Setting
1966	C6AF-AB	1–1½	⑥	⑦	④	.160	.130	1300	—	1/16	—	2 Rich
	C6AF-AC	1–1½	⑥	⑦	④	.140	.120	1500	—	1/16	—	1 Rich
	C6AF-AF	1–1½	⑧	⑨	④	.160	.130	1300	—	1/16	—	At Index
	C6AF-AG	1–1½	⑧	⑨	④	.140	.120	1500	—	1/16	—	1 Rich
	C6AF-AJ	1–1½	⑥	⑦	④	.120	.120	1500	—	1/16	—	1 Rich
	C6AF-E	1–1½	⑧	⑨	④	.160	.130	1200	1 Turn	1/16	—	2 Rich
	C6AF-F	1–1½	⑧	⑨	④	.140	.120	1300	1 Turn	1/16	.060–.090	1 Rich
	C6AF-K	1–1½	⑧	⑨	④	.140	.120	1300	1 Turn	1/16	.060–.090	1 Rich
	C6AF-L	1–1½	.531	.910	④	.140	.120	1500	1 Turn	1/16	.060–.090	At Index
	C6OF-D	1–1½	⑧	⑨	④	.160	.130	1200	1 Turn	1/16	—	2 Rich
	C6OF-E	1–1½	⑧	⑨	④	.140	.120	1300	1 Turn	1/16	.060–.090	1 Rich
	C6OF-H	1–1½	⑥	⑦	④	.160	.130	1300	1 Turn	1/16	—	2 Rich
	C6OF-J	1–1½	⑥	⑦	④	.140	.120	1500	1 Turn	1/16	.060–.090	1 Rich
	C6ZF-A	1–1½	.531	.910	④	.110	.120	1400	1 Turn	1/16	—	2 Rich
	C6ZF-B	1–1½	⑩	⑪	④	.120	.100	1600	1 Turn	1/16	.060–.090	2 Rich
	C6ZF-C	1–1½	⑥	⑫	④	.230	—	—	1 Turn	—	—	—
	C6ZF-D	1–1½	⑥	⑦	④	.120	.120	1400	1 Turn	1/16	—	2 Rich
	C6ZF-E	1–1½	⑥	⑦	④	.120	.100	1600	1 Turn	1/16	.060–.090	2 Rich
1969	C8AF-AE	14.1 to 1⑤	⑬	⑭	④	.140	.120	1350	—	.060	7/64	2 Rich

①—Stamped on left side of primary bowl cover or tag attached to blow cover.
②—Additional turns in after screw contacts lever.
③—Minimum clearance between choke plate and air horn with primary throttle plates wide open.
④—With link in inboard hole in pump lever, place overtravel lever in longest stroke hole for extremely cold weather, intermediate stroke holes for moderate weather, and short stroke hole for extremely warm weather.
⑤—Air/fuel ratio.

⑥—Primary floats .491″, secondary .621″.
⑦—Primary floats .880″, secondary 1.00″.
⑧—Primary floats .531″, secondary .681″.
⑨—Primary floats .910″, secondary 1.06″.
⑩—Primary floats .571″, secondary .531″.
⑪—Primary floats, .940″, secondary .910″.
⑫—Primary floats .875″ secondary 1.00″.
⑬—Primary floats 17/32″, secondary 1 1/16″.
⑭—Primary floats 29/32″, secondary 1 1/16″.

2100, 6200-2V & 4100-4V ADJUSTMENTS

Autolite 2100, 6200-2V, Fig. 16

These carburetors have two main bodies—the air horn and throttle body. The air horn assembly, which serves as a cover for the throttle body, contains the choke plate and vents for the fuel bowl. The throttle plate, accelerating pump, power valve and fuel bowl are in the throttle body. The choke housing is attached to the throttle body.

The two bodies each contain a main and booster venturi, main fuel discharge, accelerating pump discharge, idle fuel discharge, and a throttle plate. An antistall dashpot is attached to the carburetor when the vehicle is equipped with an automatic transmission.

Autolite 4100-4V

In these carburetors, Fig. 19, the choke plate magnet has been eliminated but an automatic choke clean air pick-up tube has been added. A rubber hose and steel tube connects the clean air pick-up tube to the automatic choke heat chamber in the right-hand exhaust manifold.

Float Level Adjustment

2100, 6200, 4100, Fig. 20—This is a preliminary adjustment; the final adjustment

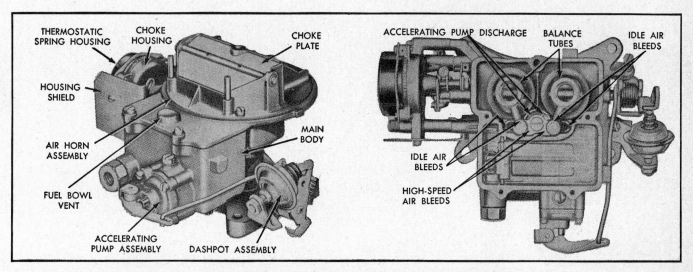

Fig. 16 Autolite 2100, 6200 carburetor—¾ front and top views

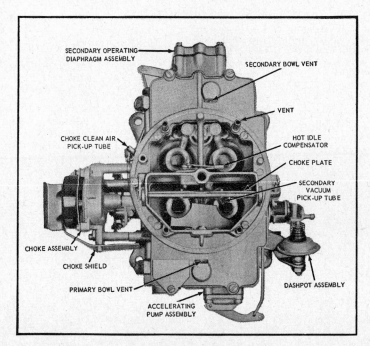

Fig. 17 Autolite 4100 carburetor showing hot idle compensator and choke clean air pick-up tube

must be made after the carburetor is mounted on the engine.

With air horn removed, float raised and fuel inlet needle seated, measure distance between top surface of throttle body and top surface of float. Take measurement near center of float at a point ⅛" from free end of float.

If a cardboard float gauge is used, place the gauge in the corner of the enlarged end section of the fuel bowl as shown. The gauge should touch the float near the end but not on the end radius.

Depress the float tab to seat the fuel inlet needle. The float height is measured from the gasket surface of the throttle body with gasket removed. If the float height is not as listed in the *Ford Specifications Chart*, bend tab on float as required to achieve the desired setting.

Fuel Level Adjustment

Fig. 21—With vehicle on a level surface, operate engine until normal temperature is reached, then stop engine and check fuel level as follows:

1. Remove carburetor air cleaner.
2. Remove air horn retaining screws and carburetor identification tag.
3. Temporarily leave air horn and

FORD AUTOLITE CARBURETORS

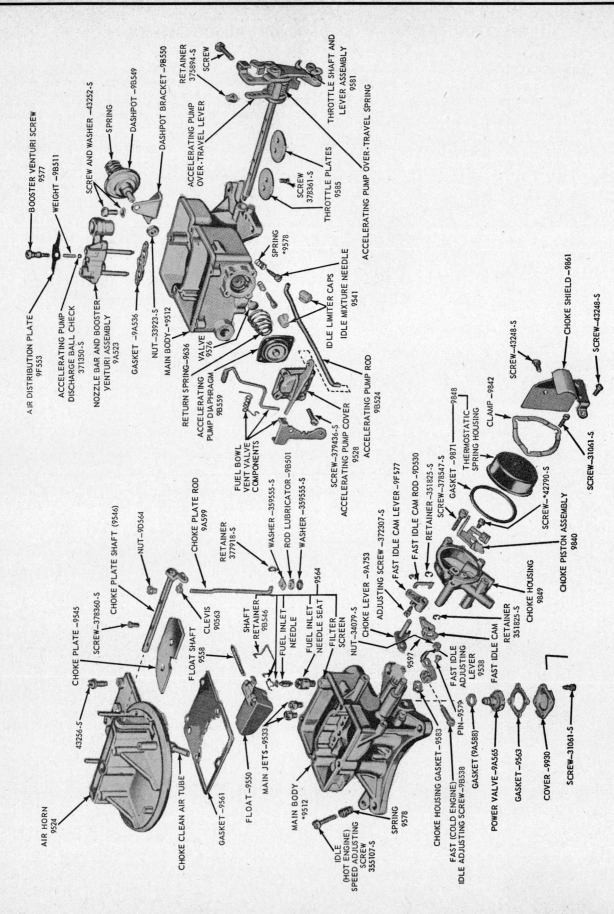

Fig. 18 Exploded view of a typical Autolite 2100, 6200 two-barrel carburetor. Note that this unit is provided with the idle limiter caps which are used to prevent an overly rich mixture adjustment on cars with exhaust emission control

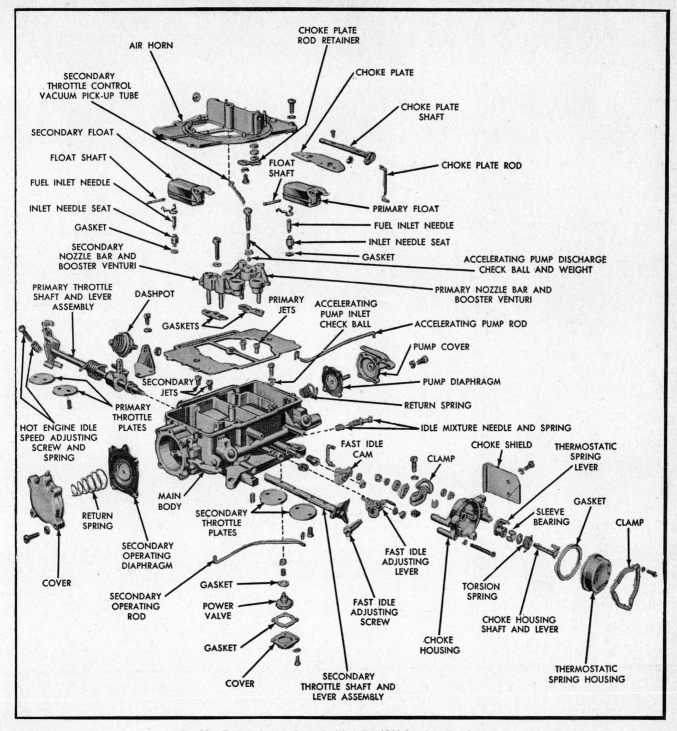

Fig. 19   Exploded view of a typical Autolite 4100 four-barrel carburetor

gasket in position on throttle body and start engine.

4. Allow engine to idle for several minutes, then rotate air horn and remove air horn gasket to gain access to float or floats.

5. While engine is idling, use a standard depth gauge to measure vertical distance from top machined surface of throttle body to level of fuel in bowl. The measurement must be made at least ¼″ away from any vertical surface to assure an accurate reading.

6. If the fuel level is not as listed in the *Ford Specifications Chart*, stop the engine to avoid any fire hazard due to fuel spray when float setting is disturbed.

7. To adjust fuel level, bend float tab (contacting fuel inlet needle) upward in relation to original position to raise the fuel level, and downward to lower it.

8. Each time an adjustment is made to the float tab to alter the fuel level, the engine must be started and permitted to idle for at least three minutes to stabilize the fuel level. Check fuel level after each adjustment until the specified level is achieved.

9. Assemble carburetor with a new air horn gasket. Then adjust idle speed and mixture, and anti-stall dashpot, if so equipped.

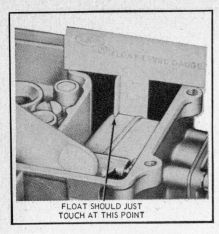

Fig. 20 Float level adjustment. 2100, 4100

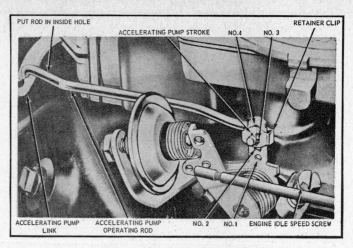

PUT ROD IN INSIDE HOLE | ACCELERATING PUMP STROKE | NO.4 | NO. 3 | RETAINER CLIP

ACCELERATING PUMP LINK | ACCELERATING PUMP OPERATING ROD | NO. 2 | NO.1 | ENGINE IDLE SPEED SCREW

Fig. 22 Pump stroke and idle speed adjusting points. 2100, 6200, 4100

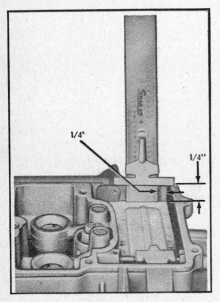

1/4" 1/4"

Fig. 21 Fuel level adjustment. 2100, 6200, 4100

Accelerating Pump Adjustment

Fig. 22—The primary throttle shaft lever (overtravel lever) has 4 holes and the accelerating pump link has 2 holes to control the pump stroke for various atmospheric temperatures and operating condition of the engine.

The pump operating rod should be in the hole specified in the *Ford Specifications Chart* in the overtravel lever and the inboard hole (closest to pump plunger) in the pump link.

1. To release rod from retainer clip, press tab end of clip toward rod. Then, at the same time, press rod away from clip until it is disengaged.
2. Position clip over specified hole in overtravel lever. Press ends of clip together and insert operating rod through clip and lever. Release clip to engage rod.

Secondary Throttle Plate

Fig. 23, 4-Barrel Units

Hold secondary throttle plate closed. Turn secondary throttle shaft lever adjusting screw out (counterclockwise) until the secondary throttle plates stick in throttle bores. Turn screw in (clockwise) until it just contacts secondary lever. Then turn it the additional number of turns listed in the *Ford Specifications Chart*.

Choke Plate Clearance & Fast Idle Cam Linkage

1. Bend a .036″ pin gauge as shown in inset of Fig. 24.
2. Block throttle about half-way open so that fast idle cam does not contact fast idle adjustment screw.
3. Insert bent edge of gauge between lower edge of piston slot and upper edge of right-hand slot in choke housing as shown.
4. Pull choke countershaft lever counterclockwise until gauge is snug in piston slot.
5. Hold gauge in place by exerting light pressure on countershaft lever, and adjust choke plate clevis adjusting nut to obtain the clearance listed in the *Ford Specifications Chart* between front of choke plate and air horn, Fig. 24.
6. Install choke thermostatic spring housing.
7. Rotate spring housing counterclockwise to align center index mark on choke housing with index mark on spring housing. Then rotate spring housing an additional 90 degrees counterclockwise, Fig. 25, and tighten spring housing retaining screws.
8. Position fast idle adjusting screw on index mark on fast idle cam, Fig. 25.
9. Check clearance between front of choke plate and air horn as shown.
10. If clearance is not as listed in the

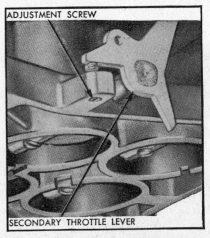

ADJUSTMENT SCREW

SECONDARY THROTTLE LEVER

Fig. 23 Secondary throttle plate adjustment. 4100

Ford Specification Chart, turn fast idle cam lever adjusting screw inward to increase (outward to decrease) clearance. Make certain fast idle screw remains on index mark of fast idle cam during adjustment.

11. Set thermostatic choke housing to specified position as listed in the *Ford Specifications Chart* and tighten retaining screws, Fig. 26.

Automatic Choke Valve Tension

Turn thermostatic spring cover against spring tension until index mark on cover is aligned with mark specified in the *Ford Specifications Chart* on choke housing, Fig. 26.

Anti-Stall Dashpot Adjustment

Fig. 27—With engine idle speed and mix-

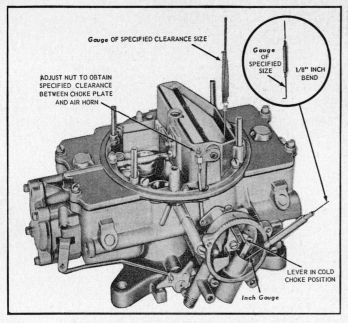

Fig. 24 Vacuum piston type choke plate clearance adjustment. 2100, 6200, 4100

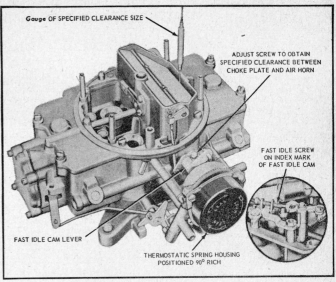

Fig. 25 Vacuum piston type choke fast idle cam linkage adjustment. 2100, 6200, 4100

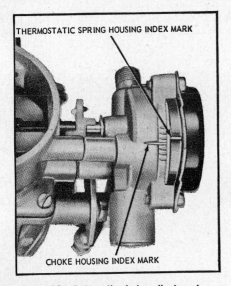

Fig. 26 Automatic choke adjustment. 2100, 6200, 4100

ture properly adjusted and with engine at normal operating temperature, loosen dashpot lock nut. Hold throttle in closed position and depress plunger with screwdriver as shown. Check clearance between throttle lever and plunger tip. If clearance is not as listed in the *Ford Specifications Chart*, turn dashpot in its bracket as required to obtain the desired clearance. Tighten lock nut.

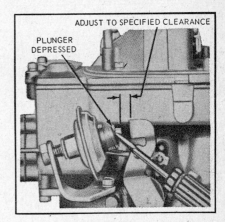

Fig. 27 Anti-stall dashpot adjustment. 2100, 6200, 4100

AUTOLITE 4300-4V ADJUSTMENT SPECIFICATIONS

See Tune Up Chart in car chapters for hot idle speeds.

Year	Carb. Model (Code 9510) ①	Idle Screws (Mixture) Turns Open	Float Level (Dry)	Pump Setting (Hole No.)	Choke Plate Clearance (Pull-Down)	Fast Idle Cam Linkage Setting	Fast Idle Speed (Hot Engine)	Secondary Throttle Plate Clearance	Dechoke Clearance	Dashpot Setting	Choke Setting
AMERICAN MOTORS											
1970	OWA4	13.5 to 1②	13/16	Center	.170	.190	1600	—	.300	1/8	2 Rich
	OWM4	13.5 to 1②	13/16	Center	.190	.200	1600	—	.300	1/16	2 Rich
1971	ITA4	14.0 to 1②	13/16	Center	.190	.200	1600	—	.300	1/8	Index
	ITM4	13.5 to 1②	13/16	Center	.170	.190	1600	—	.300	1/16	Index
1972	2RA4	14.0 to 1②	13/16	Center	.190	.190	1600	—	.300	9/64	1 Rich
	2TA4	14.0 to 1②	13/16	Center	.190	.190	1600	—	.300	9/64	1 Rich
	2TM4	13.5 to 1②	13/16	Center	.190	.190	1600	—	.300	9/64	1 Rich

①—Tag attached to bowl cover.
②—Air/fuel ratio.

Year	Carb. Model (Code 9510) ①	Idle Screws (Mixture) Turns Open	Float Level (Dry)	Pump Setting (Hole No.)	Choke Plate Clearance (Pull-Down)	Fast Idle Cam Linkage Setting	Fast Idle Speed (Hot Engine)	Secondary Throttle Plate Clearance	Dechoke Clearance	Dashpot Setting	Choke Setting
FORD AND MERCURY ENGINES											
1966	C6AF-BU	1-1½	25/32	#2	.120	.090	1200	7/16	1/16	—	Index
1967	C7AF-F	1-1½	25/32	#2	.200	.100	1400	7/16	1/16	—	Index
	C7AF-L	1-1½	25/32	#2	.210	.100	1300	7/16	1/16	1/8	Index
	C7AF-M	1-1½	25/32	#2	.200	.100	1500	7/16	1/16	1/8	Index
	C7AF-AC	1-1½	25/32	#1	.200②	.100②	1200	7/16	1/16	—	Index
	C7AF-AD	1-1½	25/32	#2	.110	.090	1200	7/16	1/16	—	Index
	C7AF-AE	1-1½	25/32	#2	.210②	.100②	1200	7/16	1/16	—	Index
	C7AF-AF	1-1½	25/32	#2	.120	.090	1200	7/16	1/16	—	Index
	C7AF-AG	1-1½	25/32	#1	.200	.100	1300	7/16	1/16	1/8	Index
	C7AF-AH	1½	25/32	#3	.100	.080	1200	7/16	1/16	—	Index
	C7AF-BH	1½	25/32	#3	.100	.080	1200	7/16	1/16	—	Index
	C AF-AV	1½	25/32	#2	.120	.090	1200	7/16	1/16	—	Index
	C7AF-BJ	1½	25/32	#2	.100	.080	—	7/16	1/16	—	Index
	C7AF-AY	1½	25/32	#2	.120	.090	1500	7/16	1/16	—	Index
1968	C8AF-A	1-1½	25/32	#3	.300	.100	1300	—	—	.093	③④
	C8AF-B	1-1½	25/32	#3	.300	.100	1400	—	—	.093	③④
	C8SF-E	—	25/32	#2	.230	.160	1500	—	.300	3/32	1 Rich
	C8VF-F	—	25/32	#1	.230	.160	1500	—	.300	3/32	1 Rich
	C8VF-H	—	25/32	#2	.230	.160	1300	—	.300	3/32	1 Rich
	C8ZF-C	—	13/16	#2	.120	.090	1900	—	.300	.100	—
	C8ZF-D	—	13/16	#1	.140	.100	2100	—	.300	.100	—
1969	C8SF-H	14.3 to 1⑤	25/32	#2	.230	.160	1300	—	.300	3/32	1 Rich
	C8VF-J	14.3 to 1⑤	25/32	#2	.230	.160	1300	—	.300	3/32	1 Rich
	C9AF-G	14.0 to 1⑤	25/32	#2	.270	.220	1200	—	.300	3/32	Index
	C9AF-R	14.3 to 1⑤	25/32	#2	.230	.160	1300	—	.300	—	1 Rich
	C9OF-D	14.3 to 1⑤	13/16	#2	.160	.100	1400	—	.300	—	1 Lean
	C9OF-E	14.8 to 1⑤	13/16	#3	.250	.230	1400	—	.300	—	1 Lean
	C9ZF-C	14.0 to 1⑤	13/16	#2	.170	.130	1250	—	.300	3/32	2 Lean
	C9ZF-D	14.3 to 1⑤	13/16	#2	.160	.100	1400	—	.300	—	1 Lean
	C9ZF-E	14.0 to 1⑤	13/16	#3	.230	.210	1300	—	.300	1/8	Index
	C9ZF-F	14.8 to 1⑤	13/16	#3	.250	.230	1400	—	.300	—	1 Lean
1970	DOAF-K	14.3 to 1⑤	49/64	#2	.220	.170	1300	—	.300	.070	Index
	DOAF-L	12.6 to 1⑤	49/64	#2	.250	.220	1400	—	.300	.070	Index
	DOAF-M	14.3 to 1⑤	1.00	#3	.160	.120	1600	—	.300	.080	2 Rich
	DOAF-R	14.3 to 1⑤	1.00	#3	.160	.120	1600	—	.300	—	2 Rich
	DOAF-AD	14.3 to 1⑤	1.00	#3	.160	.120	1600	—	.300	.080	2 Rich
	DOAF-AJ	14.3 to 1⑤	1.00	#3	.160	.120	1600	—	.300	.080	2 Rich
	DOAF-AE	14.3 to 1⑤	1.00	#3	.160	.120	1600	—	.300	—	2 Rich
	DOAF-AK	14.3 to 1⑤	1.00	#3	.160	.120	1600	—	.300	—	2 Rich
	DOAF-AB	12.6 to 1⑤	25/32	#2	.250	.220	1400	—	.300	.070	Index
	DOAF-AL	12.6 to 1⑤	49/64	#2	.250	.220	1400	—	.300	.070	Index

Continued

AUTOLITE 4300-4V ADJUSTMENT SPECIFICATIONS—Continued

See Tune Up Chart in car chapters for hot idle speeds.

Year	Carb. Model (Code 9510) ①	Idle Screws (Mixture) Turns Open	Float Level (Dry)	Pump Setting (Hole No.)	Choke Plate Clearance (Pull-Down)	Fast Idle Cam Linkage Setting	Fast Idle Speed (Hot Engine)	Secondary Throttle Plate Clearance	Dechoke Clearance	Dashpot Setting	Choke Setting
1970	D0AF-AG	12.8 to 1⑤	49/64	#2	.220	.170	1300	—	.300	.070	Index
	D0AF-AM	12.8 to 1⑤	49/64	#2	.220	.170	1300	—	.300	.070	Index
	D0AF-AN	—	49/64	#2	.225	.170	1350	—	.300	.070	Index
	D0OF-B	—	13/16	#2	.180	.160	1250	—	.300	—	Index
	D0OF-C	—	13/16	#2	.200	.180	1400	—	.300	.080	Index
	D0OF-D	—	13/16	#2	.180	.160	1250	—	.300	—	Index
	D0OF-H	—	13/16	#2	.200	.180	1400	—	.300	—	Index
	D0OF-Y	12.2 to 1⑤	13/16	#2	.180	.160	1250	—	.300	—	Index
	D0OF-Z	13.1 to 1⑤	13/16	#2	.180	.160	1250	—	.300	—	Index
	D0OF-AA	12.2 to 1⑤	13/16	#2	.200	.180	1400	—	.300	—	Index
	D0OF-AB	13.1 to 1⑤	13/16	#2	.180	.160	1250	—	.300	—	Index
	D0OF-AC	12.2 to 1⑤	13/16	#2	.200	.180	1400	—	.300	.080	Index
	D0OF-AD	12.2 to 1⑤	13/16	#2	.200	.180	1400	—	.300	—	Index
	D0OF-AE	—	13/16	#2	.180	.160	1250	—	.300	—	Index
	D0SF-A	12.8 to 1⑤	25/32	#2	.220	.170	1300	—	.300	.070	Index
	D0SF-D	12.8 to 1⑤	25/32	#2	.220	.170	1300	—	.300	.070	Index
	D0SF-E	12.8 to 1⑤	25/32	#2	.220	.170	1300	—	.300	.070	Index
	D0VF-A, C	12.0 to 1⑤	25/32	#2	.230	.170	1250	—	.300	.100	1 Rich
1971	D1AF-MA	⑥	49/64	#2	.220	—	1350	—	—	1/16	Index
	D1OF-AAA	⑥	13/16	#2	.200	.180	1400	—	—	—	Index
	D1OF-EA	14.3 to 1⑤	13/16	#2	.180	.160	1250	—	—	—	Index
	D1SF-AA	⑥	49/64	#2	.220	—	1350	—	—	1/16	Index
	D1VF-AA	14.2 to 1⑤	49/64	#2	.220	.170	1250	—	—	.100	1 Rich
	D1ZF-FA	—	13/16	#3	.220	.220	1200	—	—	—	1 Lean
	D1ZF-GA	—	13/16	#3	.200	.200	1200	—	—	—	Index
1972	D2AF-AA	—	49/64	#1	.220	—	—	—	—	—	2 Rich
	D2AF-LA	—	49/64	#1	.220	—	—	—	—	—	2 Rich
	D2SF-AA	—	49/64	#1	.220	—	—	—	—	—	2 Rich
	D2SF-BA	—	49/64	#1	.220	—	—	—	—	—	2 Rich
	D2VF-AA	—	49/64	#1	.230	—	—	—	—	—	Index
	D2VF-BA	—	49/64	#1	.230	—	—	—	—	—	Index
	D2ZF-AA	—	13/16	#1	.200	—	—	—	—	—	Index
	D2ZF-BB	—	13/16	#1	.200	—	—	—	—	—	Index
	D2ZF-DA	—	13/16	#1	.200	—	—	—	—	—	Index
	D2ZF-GA	—	13/16	#1	.200	—	—	—	—	—	Index

FORD AND MERCURY ENGINES—Continued

①—Tag attached to bowl cover.
②—Front.
③—8-390 with Imco 2 Rich, with Thermactor 1 rich.
④—8-428 with Imco Index, with Thermactor 1 rich.
⑤—Air/fuel ratio.
⑥—Air/fuel ratio greater than 14.5 to 1.

MODEL 4300-4V ADJUSTMENTS

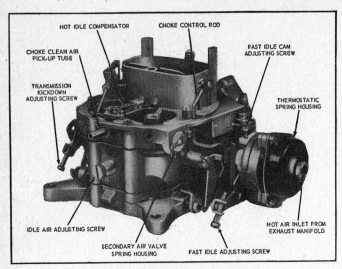

Fig. 32   Right rear view of Autolite 4300-4V carburetor

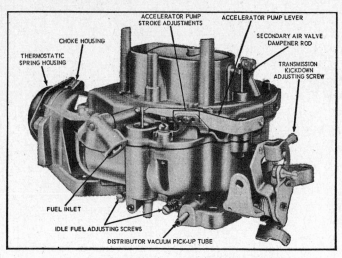

Fig. 33   Left front view of Autolite Model 4300-4V carburetor

The model 4300, Figs. 32, 33 and 34, is a four barrel, three piece, separately cast design consisting of air horn, main body and mounting flange. A cast-in center fuel inlet has provision for a supplementary fuel inlet system. The fuel bowl is vented by an internal balance vent and a mechanical atmospheric vent operates during idle. An idle air by-pass system is designed to provide a consistent idle and a hot idle compensator is used to help stability.

The main (primary) fuel system has booster-type venturii cast integral with the air horn, and the main venturii are cast integral with the main body. The secondary throttle plates are mechanically operated from the primary linkage. Air valve plates are located above the main venturii and an integral hydraulic dashpot dampens sudden movement of the air valve plates to help prevent plate flutter and erratic engine operation.

A single fuel bowl supplies both the primary and secondary fuel systems. Pontoon-type floats are used to help stabilize fuel level during cornering and hill-climbing. The accelerator pump is of the piston type. It is located in the fuel bowl for more positive displacement and a safeguard against external leaks.

Float Setting

Fig. 35

1. Adjust gauge to specified height.
2. Insert gauge into air horn outboard holes as shown.
3. Check clearance and alignment of float pontoons to gauge. Both pontoons should just touch gauge for proper setting. Align pontoons if necessary by slightly twisting pontoons.
4. If it is necessary to adjust float clearance, bend primary needle tab downward to raise float and upward

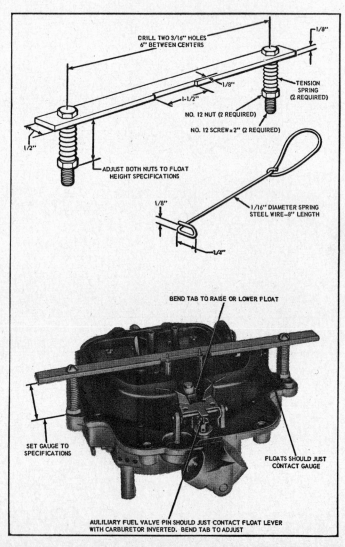

Fig. 35   Float and auxiliary fuel valve setting

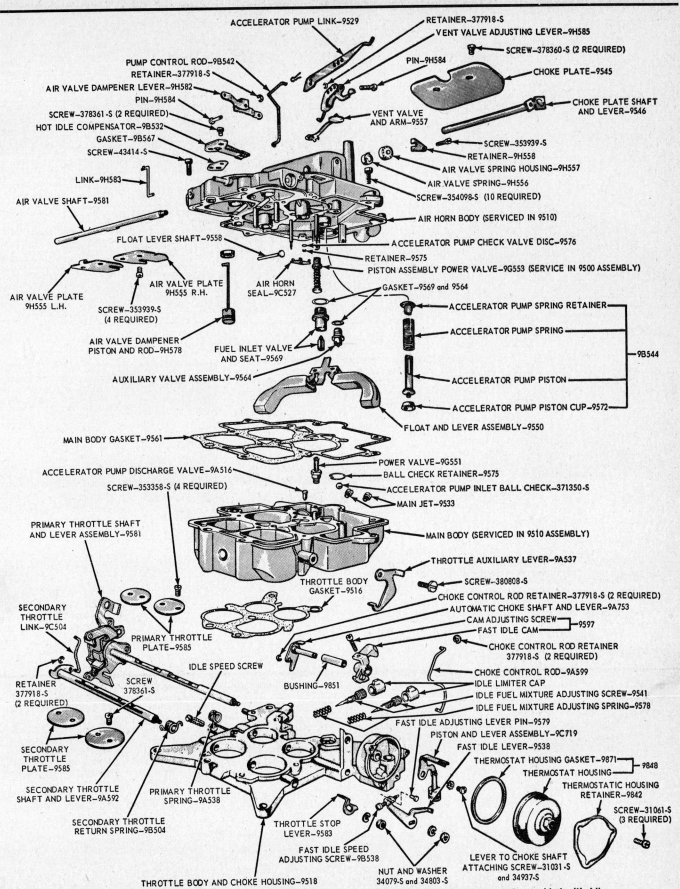

ACCELERATOR PUMP LINK-9529
RETAINER-377918-S
VENT VALVE ADJUSTING LEVER-9H585
SCREW-378360-S (2 REQUIRED)
PIN-9H584
CHOKE PLATE-9545
PUMP CONTROL ROD-9B542
RETAINER-377918-S
AIR VALVE DAMPENER LEVER-9H582
PIN-9H584
SCREW-378361-S (2 REQUIRED)
HOT IDLE COMPENSATOR-9B532
GASKET-9B567
SCREW-43414-S
CHOKE PLATE SHAFT AND LEVER-9546
VENT VALVE AND ARM-9557
SCREW-353939-S
RETAINER-9H558
AIR VALVE SPRING HOUSING-9H557
AIR VALVE SPRING-9H556
SCREW-354098-S (10 REQUIRED)
AIR HORN BODY (SERVICED IN 9510)
LINK-9H583
AIR VALVE SHAFT-9581
FLOAT LEVER SHAFT-9558
ACCELERATOR PUMP CHECK VALVE DISC-9576
RETAINER-9575
PISTON ASSEMBLY POWER VALVE-9G553 (SERVICE IN 9500 ASSEMBLY)
AIR VALVE PLATE 9H555 R.H.
AIR HORN SEAL-9C527
GASKET-9569 and 9564
AIR VALVE PLATE 9H555 L.H.
SCREW-353939-S (4 REQUIRED)
AIR VALVE DAMPENER PISTON AND ROD-9H578
FUEL INLET VALVE AND SEAT-9569
AUXILIARY VALVE ASSEMBLY-9564
ACCELERATOR PUMP SPRING RETAINER
ACCELERATOR PUMP SPRING
ACCELERATOR PUMP PISTON
ACCELERATOR PUMP PISTON CUP-9572
9B544
FLOAT AND LEVER ASSEMBLY-9550
MAIN BODY GASKET-9561
ACCELERATOR PUMP DISCHARGE VALVE-9A516
SCREW-353358-S (4 REQUIRED)
POWER VALVE-9G551
BALL CHECK RETAINER-9575
ACCELERATOR PUMP INLET BALL CHECK-371350-S
MAIN JET-9533
PRIMARY THROTTLE SHAFT AND LEVER ASSEMBLY-9581
MAIN BODY (SERVICED IN 9510 ASSEMBLY)
PRIMARY THROTTLE PLATE-9585
THROTTLE BODY GASKET-9516
THROTTLE AUXILIARY LEVER-9A537
SCREW-380808-S
CHOKE CONTROL ROD RETAINER-377918-S (2 REQUIRED)
AUTOMATIC CHOKE SHAFT AND LEVER-9A753
CAM ADJUSTING SCREW
FAST IDLE CAM
9597
SECONDARY THROTTLE LINK-9C504
CHOKE CONTROL ROD RETAINER 377918-S (2 REQUIRED)
CHOKE CONTROL ROD-9A599
IDLE LIMITER CAP
IDLE FUEL MIXTURE ADJUSTING SCREW-9541
IDLE FUEL MIXTURE ADJUSTING SPRING-9578
IDLE SPEED SCREW
BUSHING-9851
RETAINER 377918-S (2 REQUIRED)
SCREW 378361-S
FAST IDLE ADJUSTING LEVER PIN-9579
PISTON AND LEVER ASSEMBLY-9C719
FAST IDLE LEVER-9538
THERMOSTAT HOUSING GASKET-9871
THERMOSTAT HOUSING
9848
SECONDARY THROTTLE PLATE-9585
THERMOSTATIC HOUSING RETAINER-9842
SCREW-31061-S (3 REQUIRED)
SECONDARY THROTTLE SHAFT AND LEVER-9A592
PRIMARY THROTTLE SPRING-9A538
SECONDARY THROTTLE RETURN SPRING-9B504
THROTTLE STOP LEVER-9583
FAST IDLE SPEED ADJUSTING SCREW-9B538
NUT AND WASHER 34079-S and 34803-S
LEVER TO CHOKE SHAFT ATTACHING SCREW-31031-S and 34937-S
THROTTLE BODY AND CHOKE HOUSING-9518

Fig. 34 Exploded view of a typical Autolite 4300 four-barrel carburetor. Note that this unit is provided with idle limiter caps which are used to prevent an overly rich mixture on cars with exhaust emission control

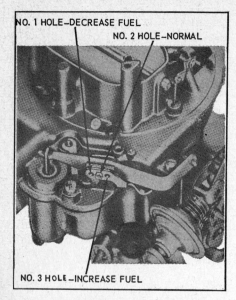

Fig. 36 Accelerator pump stroke adjustment

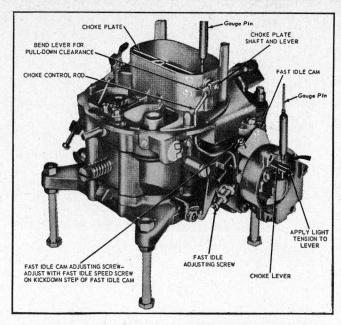

Fig. 39 Choke plate pulldown and fast idle cam adjustment

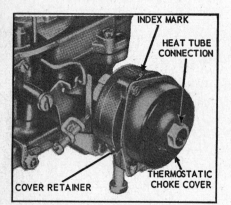

Fig. 37 Automatic choke setting

2. Final adjustments are made on the car with engine running and engine temperature normalized. Install a tachometer and check hot idle speed.
3. Turn idle air adjusting screw clockwise to decrease engine speed and counterclockwise to increase engine speed.
4. Turn one idle fuel adjusting screw, Fig. 33, clockwise until engine rpm begins to drop, then turn screw counterclockwise ¼ turn. Repeat for other idle fuel screw.
5. Slightly rotate idle adjusting screws as required for smoothest idle quality. The screws should be within ⅛ turn of each other.

Accelerator Pump Stroke
Fig. 36

The accelerator pump stroke has been calibrated to inject a pre-determined quantity of fuel into the air stream with the pump pivot pin in the center (No. 2) hole. The amount of fuel injected into the air stream may be altered by inserting the pivot pin into the left (No. 1) hole to decrease the fuel quantity, or to the right (No. 3) hole to increase the fuel quantity. If necessary to alter the setting, proceed as follows:
1. Remove pump rod from pump arm.
2. Remove pump pivot pin.
3. Insert pivot pin into desired hole. *Holes in fuel bowl vent lever, main body casting and pump lever must be in line.*
4. Install pivot pin retainer. Position pump rod end into pump arm and install retainer.
5. Adjust vent valve clearance as outlined further on.

Automatic Choke Setting
Fig. 37
1. If carburetor is installed on engine, loosen choke heat tube nut.
2. Loosen choke cover retaining screws.
3. Rotate choke cover clockwise to re-

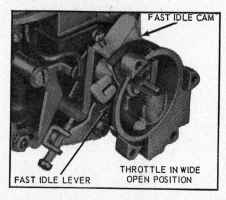

Fig. 38 Dechoke clearance setting

duce choking action or counterclockwise to increase choking action.
4. Tighten choke cover screws and choke heat tube nut.

Dechoke Clearance
Fig. 38
1. Open and hold throttle plate to wide open position.
2. Rotate choke plate toward closed position until pawl on fast idle speed lever contacts fast idle cam.
3. Check clearance between upper edge of choke plate and air horn wall.
4. Adjust clearance to specifications by bending pawl on fast idle speed lever forward to increase (backward to decrease) clearance.

Choke Plate Pulldown and Fast Idle Cam
Fig. 39
1. Remove choke cover.
2. Bend a .036" wire gauge at a 90° angle, approximately ⅛" from the end.
3. Insert bent edge of gauge between piston slot and upper edge of right

to lower float.

NOTE: To raise float, insert open end of bending tool to *right* side of float lever tab and between needle and float hinge. Raise float lever off needle and bend tab downward.
To lower float, insert open end of bending tool to *left* side of float lever tab, between needle and float hinge. Support float lever and bend tab upward.

Auxiliary Valve Setting
Fig. 35
1. Adjust float gauge to specified auxiliary valve setting.
2. Insert gauge in outboard holes in air horn.
3. Invert air horn and allow floats to rest on gauge. Valve pin should just contact tab on float lever.
4. If necessary to bend tab for proper contact, use bending tool to bend tab up or down as required.

Idle Speed Adjustment
1. Referring to Fig. 32, turn idle air by-pass screw clockwise until it lightly seats, then turn screw counterclockwise 3½ turns.

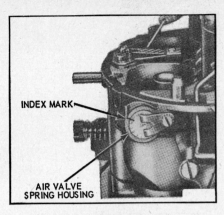

Fig. 40 Secondary air valve spring adjustment

hand slot in choke housing.

4. Rotate automatic choke lever counterclockwise until gauge is snug in piston slot. Exert light pressure on choke lever to hold gauge in place.
5. Using a gauge pin, check pulldown clearance between lower edge of choke plate and air horn wall.
6. Adjust pulldown clearance to specifications by bending adjusting arm on choke shaft lever. Bend downward to increase (upward to decrease) clearance.
7. Remove gauge and install choke cover loosely so it can rotate. Be sure thermostatic spring end is en-

gaged in choke lever slot.

8. Rotate choke cover to 90° rich.
9. Position fast idle adjusting screw end to kickdown step on fast idle cam and hold in this position.
10. Using a gauge pin, check fast idle cam clearance between lower ege of choke plate and air horn wall.
11. Adjust fast idle cam clearance to specifications by turning adjusting screw clockwise to increase (counterclockwise to decrease) clearance.
12. Install choke cover and rotate it to specified setting, then tighten cover.

Secondary Air Valve Spring

Fig. 40

The secondary air valve spring and housing are adjusted to apply a pre-determined load on the secondary air valve shaft. If the spring housing has been moved or maladjusted, adjust the spring tension as follows:

1. Loosen housing screw and let housing rotate to no-load position.
2. With air valves closed, scribe an index mark on air horn casting and nylon spring housing.
3. Rotate spring housing counterclockwise 140 degrees (7 knobs on spring housing).
4. Position retainer and tighten screw.

NOTE: If secondary air valve spring requires replacement, make sure open end of spring hook is facing to left of bottom of housing cavity in air horn.

Fig. 41 Fuel bowl vent valve adjustment

Fuel Bowl External Vent Valve

Fig. 41

1. Set throttle plates in closed position.
2. Check clearance between vent valve and valve seat.
3. If clearance is not as specified, bend end of vent valve lever downward to decrease (upward to increase).

AUTOLITE/WEBER 5200 ADJUSTMENT SPECIFICATIONS

See Tune Up Chart in car chapters for hot idle speeds.

Year	Carb. Model (9510) ①	Idle Screws (Mixture) Turns Open	Float Level	Pump Setting (Hole)	Choke Pulldown	Dechoke Clearance	Fast Idle Speed	Fast Idle Cam Clearance	Dashpot Setting	Choke Setting
1971	D12F-AA	—	.420	Lower	.236	.256	1800	.010	—	Index
	D12F-BA	—	.420	Lower	.236	.256	1600	.010	—	Index
	D12F-CA	—	.420	Lower	.236	.256	1800	.010	—	Index
	D12F-DA	—	.420	Lower	.236	.256	1800	.010	—	1 Rich
	D12F-EA	—	.420	Lower	.236	.256	1600	.010	—	1 Rich
	D12F-FA	—	.420	Lower	.236	.256	1800	.010	—	1 Rich
1972	D22F-AB	—	.420	#3	.236	—	—	—	—	1 Lean
	D22F-BB	—	.420	#2	.236	—	—	—	—	1 Lean
	D22F-CB	—	.420	#3	.236	—	—	—	—	1 Lean
	D22F-DB	—	.420	#2	.236	—	—	—	—	1 Lean
	D22F-EA	—	.420	#3	.236	—	—	—	—	Index
	D22F-GA	—	.420	#3	.236	—	—	—	—	Index

①—Tag attached to carburetor

MODEL 5200 ADJUSTMENTS

This carburetor is a two stage, two venturi carburetor, Fig. 1. The primary stage or venturi is smaller than the secondary venturi. The secondary is operated by mechanical linkage.

The primary stage includes a curb idle system, accelerator pump system, idle transfer system, main metering system and power enrichment system.

The secondary stage includes a transfer system, main metering system, and power system. Both the primary and secondary systems draw fuel from a common fuel bowl.

Dry Float Setting

Fig. 2—With bowl cover held in inverted position, measure distance between edge of float and bowl cover. Adjust by bending proper float tang.

Dechoke Clearance

Fig. 3—Hold throttle lever in wide open position and take slack out of choke linkage by applying finger pressure to top edge of choke plate. Measure clearance between lower edge of choke plate and air horn wall. Adjust by bending tab on fast idle lever where it touches air horn wall. Remove slack from choke linkage by applying finger pressure to top edge of choke plate. To adjust, remove plug from diaphragm and turn adjusting screw as required.

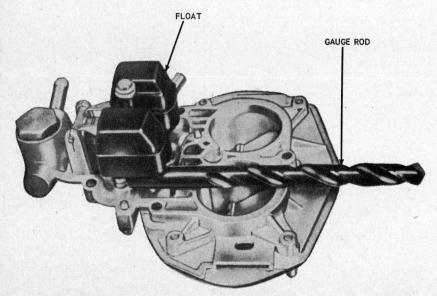

Fig. 2 Dry float setting

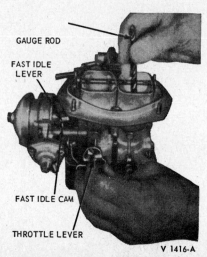

Fig. 3 De-choke adjustment

V 1416-A

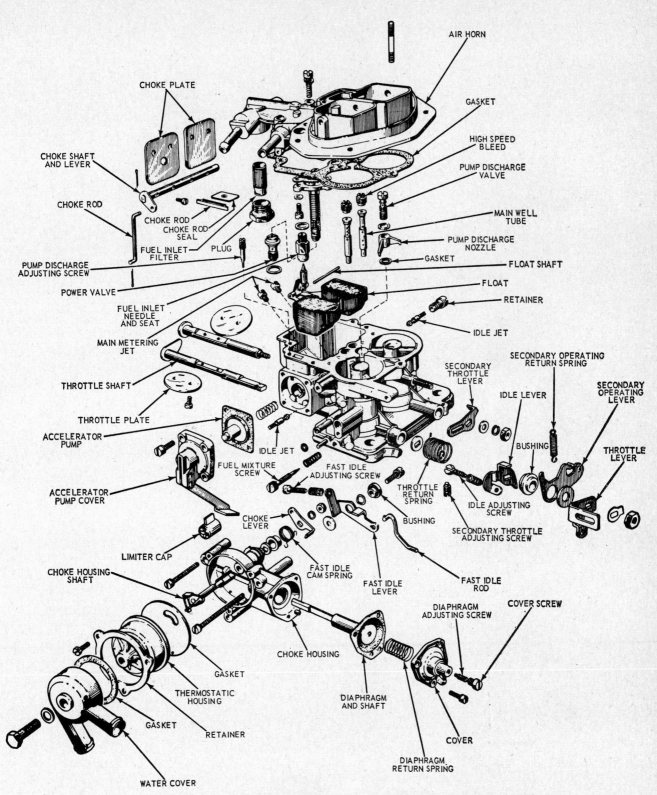

Fig. 1 Exploded view of Autolite/Weber 5200 carburetor. All bolts and screws are Metric thread.
Early production Metric heads; later production U.S. heads

Choke Plate Vacuum Pull-Down

Fig. 4—Remove three screws and ring retaining choke spring cover and pull the water cover and choke spring cover out of way. Push diaphragm stem back against its stop. Place proper gauge between lower edge of choke plate and fast idle cam.

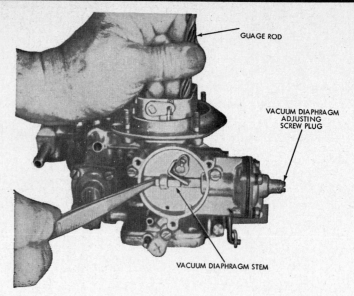

Fig. 4 Choke plate pull-down

Holley Carburetor Section

HOLLEY ONE & TWO BARREL CARB. ADJUSTMENT SPECIFICATIONS

See Tune Up Chart in car chapter for hot idle speeds.

Year	Carb. Part No.[1]	Carb. Model	Idle Screw (Mixture) Turns Open	Float Level (Dry)	Fuel Level (Wet)	Pump Setting	Bowl Vent Clearance	Fast Idle Bench	Fast Idle On Car	Choke Unloader Clearance	Anti-Stall Dashpot Clearance	Choke Setting
AMERICAN MOTORS												
1966	R-3250-1A	1931	3/4-1 1/4	5/16	—	[2]	1/16	—	1600[7]	15/64	3/32	On Index
	R-3251A	1931	3/4-1 1/4	5/16	—	[2]	1/16	—	1500[7]	15/64	—	1 Lean
	R-3292A	1931	3/4-1 1/4	5/16	—	[2]	1/16	—	1600[7]	15/64	3/32	On Index
	R-3304A	2209	1-1 1/2	11/32	1/2	[2]	5/64	—	1800[12]	3/16	5/32	On Index
	R-3305A	2209	1-1 1/2	11/32	1/2	[2]	5/64	—	1800[12]	3/16	—	On Index
	R-3388A	2209	1-1 1/2	11/32	1/2	[3]	5/64	—	1800[12]	3/16	5/32	On Index
	R-3438A	1931	3/4-1 1/4	5/16	—	[2]	1/16	—	1600[7]	15/64	—	1 Rich
1967	R-3253	1931	1 1/2-3 1/2	5/16	—	[2]	1/16	—	1400[7]	15/64	—	1 Lean
	R-3307-1	2209	1-1 1/2	11/32	1/2	[2]	5/64	—	1650[7]	3/16	5/32	1 Lean
	R-3308-1	2209	1-1 1/2	11/32	1/2	[2]	5/64	—	1650[7]	3/16	—	1 Lean
	R-3483-1	2209	1-1 1/2	11/32	1/2	[2]	5/64	—	1600[7]	3/16	5/32	1 Lean
	R-3484-1	2209	1-1 1/2	11/32	1/2	[3]	5/64	—	1400[7]	3/16	3/16	1 Rich
	R-3704	1931	1-1 1/2	5/16	—	[2]	1/16	—	1400[7]	15/64	3/32	On Index
	R-3705	1931	1-1 1/2	5/16	—	[2]	1/16	—	1400[7]	15/64	—	On Index
	R-3706	1931	3/4-1 1/2	5/16	—	[2]	1/16	—	1550[7]	15/64	3/32	1 Rich
	R-3707	1931	1 1/2-3 1/2	5/16	—	[2]	1/16	—	1600[7]	15/64	3/32	On Index
	R-3708	1931	1-1 1/2	5/16	—	[2]	1/16	—	1400[7]	15/64	—	1 Rich
	R-3709	1931	3/4-1 1/2	5/16	—	[2]	1/16	—	1400[7]	15/64	—	1 Rich
	R-3978	1931	1/2-1 1/2	5/16	—	[2]	1/16	—	1550[11]	15/64	—	1 Rich
1968	3966A	1931	1	5/16	—	[2]	1/16	—	1600[7]	15/64	—	1 Rich
	3967A	1931	1	5/16	—	[2]	1/16	—	1600[7]	15/64	—	1 Rich
	3968A	1931	1	5/16	—	[2]	1/16	—	1600[7]	15/64	3/32	1 Rich
	4102A	1931	1	5/16	—	[2]	1/16	—	1600[7]	15/64	—	1 Rich
1969	4294A	1931	1	5/16	—	[2]	1/16	—	1600[7]	15/64	—	1 Rich
CHEVROLET ENGINES												
1967	R3659-A	2300	—	.350	—	[3]	—	—	—	—	—	—
	R3660-A	2300	1 1/2	.350	.015	[3]	—	.025	2200	.275	—	[6]
	R3888-A	2300	1 1/2	.350	.015	[3]	—	.025	2200	.275	—	[6]
1968–70	R4055-A	2300	1 1/2	.350	.015	[3]	.085	.025	2200	.250	—	[6]
	R4056-A	2300	1 1/2	.350	.015	[3]	.085	.025	2200	.250	—	[6]
	R3659-A	2300	—	.350	—	[3]	—	—	—	—	—	—
CHRYSLER ENGINES												
1966	R-3271A	1920	2	See Text	27/32	[6]	—	—	700[9]	[8]	—	2 Rich
	R-3272A	1920	2	See Text	27/32	[6]	—	—	700[9]	[8]	—	2 Rich
	R-3273A	1920	2	See Text	27/32	[6]	—	—	1550[1]	[8]	—	2 Rich
	R-3274A	1920	2	See Text	27/32	[6]	—	—	1550[1]	[8]	—	2 Rich
	R-3275A	1920	2	See Text	27/32	[6]	—	—	700[9]	[8]	—	2 Rich
	R-3276A	1920	2	See Text	27/32	[6]	—	—	700[9]	[8]	—	2 Rich
	R-3277A	1920	2	See Text	27/32	[6]	—	—	1550[1]	[8]	—	2 Rich
	R-3278A	1920	2	See Text	27/32	[6]	—	—	1550[1]	[8]	—	2 Rich
	R-3279A	1920	2	See Text	27/32	[6]	—	—	700[9]	[8]	—	2 Rich
	R-3280A	1920	2	See Text	27/32	[6]	—	—	700[9]	[8]	—	2 Rich
	R-3281A	1920	2	See Text	27/32	[6]	—	—	1550[1]	[8]	—	2 Rich
	R-3282A	1920	2	See Text	27/32	[6]	—	—	1550[1]	[8]	—	2 Rich

Continued

HOLLEY ONE & TWO BARREL CARB. ADJUSTMENT SPECIFICATIONS—Continued

See Tune Up Chart in car chapter for hot idle speeds.

Year	Carb. Part No.[1]	Carb. Model	Idle Screw (Mixture) Turns Open	Float Level (Dry)	Fuel Level (Wet)	Pump Setting	Bowl Vent Clearance	Fast Idle Bench	Fast Idle On Car	Choke Unloader Clearance	Anti-Stall Dashpot Clearance	Choke Setting
CHRYSLER ENGINES—Continued												
1967	R-3275-1A	1920	2	See Text	27/32	[6]	—	—	700[9]	[8]	—	2 Rich
	R-3276-1A	1920	2	See Text	27/32	[6]	3/32	—	700[9]	[8]	—	2 Rich
	R-3279-1A	1920	2	See Text	27/32	[6]	3/32	—	700[9]	[8]	—	2 Rich
	R-3280-1A	1920	2	See Text	27/32	[6]	3/32	—	700[9]	[8]	—	2 Rich
	R-3671-A	1920	2	See Text	27/32	[6]	3/32	—	1550[11]	[8]	—	—
	R-3672-A	1920	2	See Text	27/32	[6]	3/32	—	1550[11]	[8]	—	2 Rich
	R-3673-A	1920	2	See Text	27/32	[6]	3/32	—	1550[11]	[8]	—	2 Rich
	R-3674-A	1920	2	See Text	27/32	[6]	3/32	—	1550[11]	[8]	—	—
1968	R-3919-A	1920	2	See Text	27/32	[6]	3/32	—	1400[11]	[8]	—	2 Rich
	R-3920-A	1920	2	See Text	27/32	[6]	3/32	—	1600[11]	[8]	—	2 Rich
	R-3921-A	1920	2	See Text	27/32	[6]	3/32	—	1400[11]	[8]	—	2 Rich
	R-3922-A	1920	2	See Text	27/32	[6]	3/32	—	1600[11]	[8]	—	—
	R-3924-A	1920	2	See Text	27/32	[6]	3/32	—	1400[11]	[8]	—	—
1969	R-4161-A	1920	14.2 to 1[18]	See Text	27/32	[6]	3/32	—	1600[11]	9/32[15]	—	2 Rich
	R-4162-A	1920	14.2 to 1[18]	See Text	27/32	[6]	3/32	—	1800[11]	9/32[15]	—	2 Rich
	R-4163-A	1920	14.2 to 1[18]	See Text	27/32	[6]	3/32	—	1600[11]	9/32[15]	—	2 Rich
	R-4164-A	1920	14.2 to 1[18]	See Text	27/32	[6]	3/32	—	1800[11]	9/32[15]	—	2 Rich
	R-4165-A	1920	14.2 to 1[18]	See Text	27/32	[6]	3/32	—	1700[11]	9/32[15]	—	—
	R-4391-A	2300	14.2 to 1[18]	9/16	[3]	.015	.080–.125	.059	2200	5/32	—	See Text
	R-4392A	2300	14.2 to 1[18]	9/16	[3]	.015	.080–.125	.059	1800	5/32	—	See Text
	R-4393A	2300	14.2 to 1[18]	3/4	[3]	—	—	—	—	—	—	—
	R-4394A	2300	14.2 to 1[18]	3/4	[3]	—	—	—	—	—	—	—
1970	R-4351A	1920	14.2 to 1[18]	See Text	27/32	[6]	3/32	—	1600[11]	—	—	2 Rich
	R-4352A	1920	14.2 to 1[18]	See Text	27/32	[6]	3/32	—	1800[11]	—	—	2 Rich
	R-4353A	1920	14.2 to 1[18]	See Text	27/32	[6]	3/32	—	1600[11]	—	—	2 Rich
	R-4354A	1920	14.2 to 1[18]	See Text	27/32	[6]	3/32	—	1800[11]	—	—	2 Rich
	R-4355A	1920	14.2 to 1[18]	See Text	27/32	[6]	3/32	—	1700[11]	—	—	2 Rich
	R-4363A	1920	14.2 to 1[18]	See Text	27/32	[6]	3/32	—	1700[11]	—	—	2 Rich
	R-4371A	2210	14.2 to 1[18]	.200	—	—	5/64	—	1700[11]	—	—	2 Rich
	R-4175AF	2300	14.2 to 1[18]	[17]	[3]	—	—	—	—	—	—	—
	R-4144A	2300	14.2 to 1[18]	[17]	[3]	.015	.101	.059	1800	—	—	2 Rich
	R-4365AR	2300	14.2 to 1[18]	[17]	[3]	—	—	—	—	—	—	—
	R-4374A	2300	14.2 to 1[18]	[17]	[3]	.015	.101	.059	2200	—	—	2 Rich
	R-4375A	2300	14.2 to 1[18]	[17]	[3]	.015	.101	.059	2200	—	—	2 Rich
	R-4376A	2300	14.2 to 1[18]	[17]	[3]	.015	.101	.059	1800	—	—	2 Rich
	R-4382A	2300	14.2 to 1[18]	[17]	[3]	—	—	—	—	—	—	—
	R-4383A	2300	14.2 to 1[18]	[17]	[3]	—	—	—	—	—	—	—
1971	R-4655A	1920	14.2 to 1[18]	See Text	27/32	—	1/32	.063	1600	9/32	—	2 Rich
	R-4656A	1920	14.2 to 1[18]	See Text	27/32	—	1/32	.063	1900	9/32	—	2 Rich
	R-4659A	1920	14.2 to 1[18]	See Text	27/32	—	1/32	.063	1800	9/32	—	2 Rich
	R-6363A	1920	14.2 to 1[18]	See Text	27/32	—	1/64	.063	2000	9/32	—	2 Rich
	R-6364A	1920	14.2 to 1[18]	See Text	27/32	—	1/64	.063	1900	9/32	—	2 Rich
	R-4373A	2210	14.2 to 1[18]	.200	—	9/16	5/64	.110	1700	11/64	—	2 Rich
	R-4665A	2210	14.2 to 1[18]	.200	—	9/16	.015	.110	1800	1/4	—	2 Rich
	R-4666A	2210	14.2 to 1[18]	.200	—	9/16	.015	.110	1800	1/4	—	2 Rich
	R-4669A	2300	14.2 to 1[18]	[17]	[3]	.015	.101	.059	1800	5/32	—	2 Rich
	R-4670A	2300	14.2 to 1[18]	[17]	[3]	.015	.101	.059	1800	5/32	—	2 Rich
	R-4671A	2300	14.2 to 1[18]	[17]	[3]	—	—	—	—	—	—	—
	R-4672A	2300	14.2 to 1[18]	[17]	[3]	—	—	—	—	—	—	—
	R-4789A	2300	14.2 to 1[18]	[17]	[3]	—	—	—	—	—	—	—

Continued

HOLLEY ONE & TWO BARREL CARB. ADJUSTMENT SPECIFICATIONS—Continued

See Tune Up Chart in car chapter for hot idle speeds.

Year	Carb. Part No.①	Carb. Model	Idle Screw (Mixture) Turns Open	Float Level (Dry)	Fuel Level (Wet)	Pump Setting	Bowl Vent Clearance	Fast Idle		Choke Unloader Clearance	Anti-Stall Dashpot Clearance	Choke Setting
								Bench	On Car			
CHRYSLER ENGINES—Continued												
1971	R-4790A	2300	14.2 to 1⑱	⑰	③	—	—	—	—	—	—	On Index
	R-4791A	2300	14.2 to 1⑱	⑰	③	.015	.101	.059	2600	5/32	—	On Index
	R-4792A	2300	14.2 to 1⑱	⑰	③	.015	.101	.059	2800	5/32	—	On Index

①—Located on tag attached to carburetor or on casting.
②—Seasonal setting holes in lever; long stroke for cold weather, short stroke for warm weather.
③—At lower edge of sight plug opening.
⑥—Seasonal setting; use center hole for moderate weather, long stroke hole for cold weather, and short stroke hole for warm weather.
⑦—Engine hot and screw on second step of cam.
⑧—See "Fast idle index adjustment" in text.
⑨—Engine hot and screw on lowest step of cam.
⑩—With headlights on A-C operating (if equipped); engine hot and screw on lowest step of cam.

⑪—Engine hot and screw on highest step of cam.
⑫—Engine hot and screw on second highest step of cam.
⑬—Lever touching screw; then tighten screw ¼ turn.
⑭—Between throttle valve and carburetor bore.
⑮—With fast idle speed adjusting screw contacting second highest step on fast idle cam there should be 1/16" clearance between choke valve and wall of air horn. When this adjustment is correct the choke unloader clearance should be as specified in the chart.
⑯—Top of rod should be even with bottom of hole.
⑰—Center float in bowl with bowl inverted.
⑱—Air/fuel ratio.

HOLLY ONE & TWO BARREL CARBURETOR ADJUSTMENTS

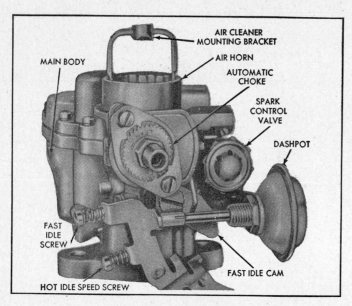

Fig. 1   Holley Model 1909 single-barrel carburetor

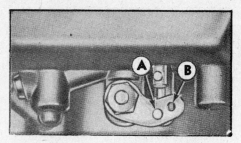

Fig. 4   Accelerating pump setting
on 1909 carburetor

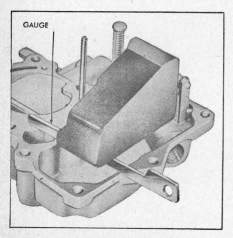

Fig. 3   Checking float level
on 1909 carburetor

Fig. 6   Anti-stall dashpot setting
on 1909 carburetor

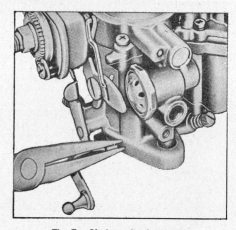

Fig. 5   Choke unloader setting
on 1909 carburetor

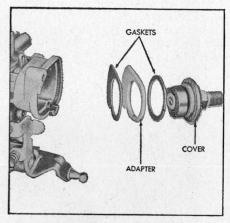

Fig. 7   Automatic choke setting
on 1909 carburetor

MODEL 1909

This carburetor, Figs. 1 and 2, consists of an aluminum die cast carburetor body and a zinc air horn assembly.

Float Level Setting

Fig. 3—Adjust float lever at a point 1/4" from end of float so gauge shown will just fit between float and air horn when float needle is seated. To decrease float level bend float tab with needle nose pliers. To avoid damage to float and needle tip, never decrease float level by pressing down on float. If checking gauge is not available, measure float level as shown with needle valve seated. If the level is not as listed in the Holley Specifications Chart, adjust as required.

Accelerating Pump Stroke

Fig. 4—Two holes are provided in the throttle lever for seasonal setting of the pump link. Use the hole marked "B" for cold weather operation, and the hole marked "A" for moderate and warm weather operation.

Choke Unloader Setting

Fig. 5—With throttle lever held in wide open position, clearance between choke plate and inner air horn wall should be as listed in the Holley Specifications Chart. Adjust by bending unloader lever portion of throttle shaft lever as shown.

Anti-Stall Dashpot Setting

Fig. 6—Loosen dashpot lock nut and screw dashpot away from throttle oper-

ating lever. Hold throttle closed. Bottom plunger with a screwdriver, then turn dashpot toward throttle lever until the clearance listed in the Holley Specifications Chart exists between lever and tip of plunger.

Automatic Choke Setting

Fig. 7—Loosen retaining screws, pull out choke cover and then mesh teeth on cover with teeth on adapter to the specified point on the adapter, as listed in the

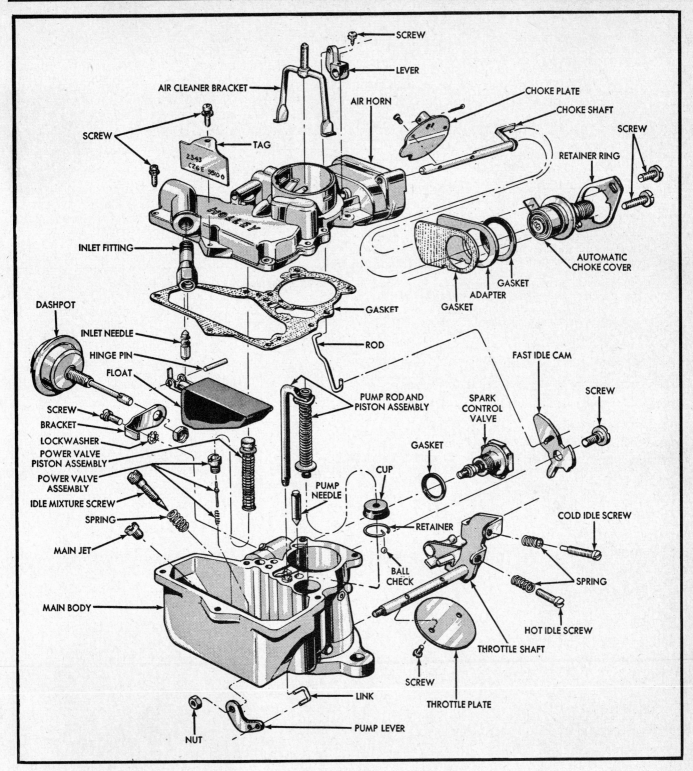

Fig. 2 Exploded view of Holley 1909 carburetor

Holley Specifications Chart. When assembling, tab on thermostatic spring must be positioned so that spring pressure closes choke plate.

MODEL 1920

On these units, Figs. 8 and 9, the choke valve located in the carburetor bore is connected to a well type choke.

Some models are equipped with a spring-staged choke, shown in Fig. 15, which is a device incorporated in the choke mechanism that limits the choke valve closing torque when cranking the engine at temperatures below zero. The spring-staging of the choke is suited for starting mixture requirements at both low and moderate temperatures.

The accelerator pump is a diaphragm, spring driven type operated by a lever connected to the throttle shaft.

A two stage power valve mounted in the metering body and actuated by manifold vacuum delivers additional fuel for full power and high speed operation.

Float Level Setting

Fig. 10—With carburetor inverted, slide float gauge into position and test setting on "touch" leg of gauge. Float should just touch gauge. Reverse gauge and test "no touch" leg. Float should just clear gauge. To adjust, bend float tab which touches head of fuel inlet needle, using needle nose pliers.

NOTE: Do not allow float tab to contact float needle head during the adjustment procedure as the rubber tip of the needle can be compressed, giving a false reading.

Checking Fuel Level

Fig. 11—With engine running and vehicle on a level floor, measure fuel level through the economizer diaphragm opening. Use a 6″ scale with a depth gauge, measure distance from machined surface of the opening to the exact fuel surface. If the level is not as listed in the *Holley Specifications Chart*, adjust the float level as outlined above.

Float Bowl Vent Valve Setting

Fig. 12—With throttle valve closed, bowl

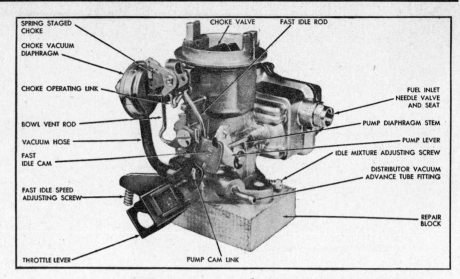

Fig. 8   Holley Model 1920 single-barrel carburetor

vent should be adjusted so that the shank of a drill of the size listed in the *Holley Specifications Chart* can be inserted between valve and surface of carburetor body. Adjust by bending bowl vent operating lever up or down as required. Be sure vent rod does not bind in the guide after adjusting.

Fast Idle Index & Choke Unloader

Fig. 13—Open throttle valve and hold choke valve fully closed. Now close throttle valve. Index mark on fast idle cam should split center of fast idle adjusting screw. Adjust by bending fast

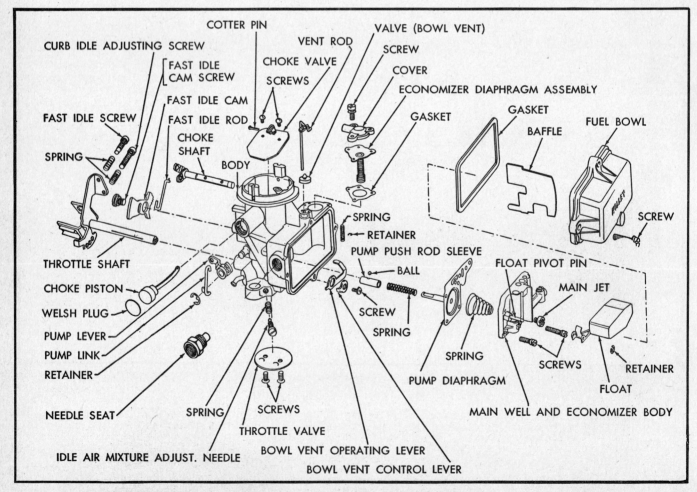

Fig. 9   Exploded view of Holley 1920 carburetor

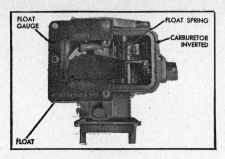

Fig. 10   Measuring float level
on 1920 carburetor

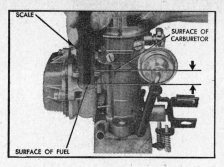

Fig. 11   Measuring fuel level
on 1920 carburetor

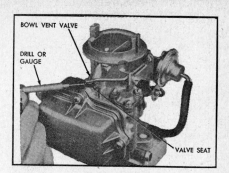

Fig. 12   Measuring bowl vent opening
on 1920 carburetor

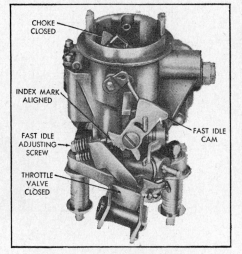

Fig. 13   Fast idle index and choke
unloader setting on 1920 carburetor

idle connector rod. This adjustment also positions the choke unloader mechanism.

Well-Type Automatic Choke

Fig. 14—To function properly, it is important that all parts be clean and move freely. Other than an occasional cleaning, the choke requires no attention. However, it is important that the choke control unit work freely in the well and at the choke shaft. Move the choke rod up and down to check for free movement on the pivot. If the unit binds, a new choke unit should be installed.

This type choke is serviced only as a unit. Do not attempt to repair or change the setting.

When installing the choke unit, be certain that the coil housing does not contact the sides of the well in the exhaust manifold. Any contact at this point will affect choke operation. Do not lubricate any parts of the choke or the control unit. This causes an accumulation of dirt which will result in binding of the mechanism.

Spring Staged Choke Adjustment

To test the adjustment on carburetors equipped with the feature, press against the choke lever firmly, Fig. 15. Measure clearance between hub lever and shaft lever. If the clearance is not within .010" and .025", bend fast idle rod slightly until normal clearance is obtained. The cam

position and unloader setting resulting from such bending of the choke link are satisfactory.

MODEL 1931

This carburetor, Figs. 16 and 17, features a one-piece main body and throttle body casting together with a large capacity fuel bowl. The fuel inlet and float assembly, located in the center of the fuel bowl cover, maintains a stable fuel level for best performance on turns. The large capacity fuel bowl is designed to handle efficiently vapor loaded fuels and fuel vapors.

The automatic choke is mounted in a heat sink on the exhaust manifold and is connected to the carburetor by a choke rod.

Float Adjustment

Figs. 18, 19, 20—Invert carburetor fuel bowl cover and check float setting at both ends, Fig. 18. If float adjustment is necessary the float may be lowered by pulling on the center of the float, Fig. 19. The float may be raised by pushing on the center of the float, Fig. 20.

CAUTION: During float adjustment do not allow the float tab to contact the fuel inlet needle as the resilient tip of the

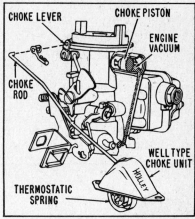

Fig. 14   Well-type automatic choke
used with 1920 carburetor

needle can be damaged or compressed, resulting in an improper float setting and a leaky needle and seat.

If the proper gauge is not available, measure the distance between the roof of the float cover and top of float. If the setting is not as listed in the *Holley Specifications Chart*, adjust as required.

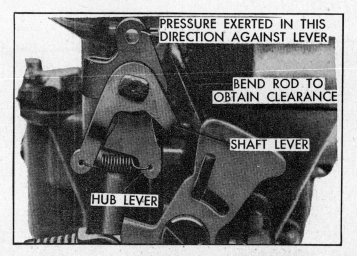

Fig. 15   Spring-staged choke adjustment on 1920 carburetor

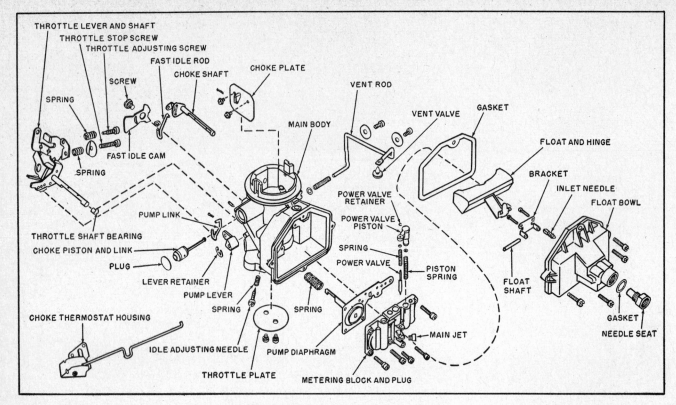

Fig. 17 Exploded view of Holley 1931 carburetor

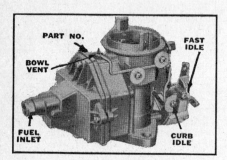

Fig. 16 Holley Model 1931
single-barrel carburetor

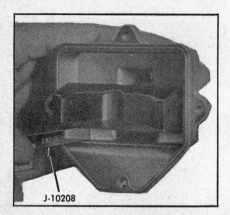

Fig. 18 Checking float level
on 1931 carburetor

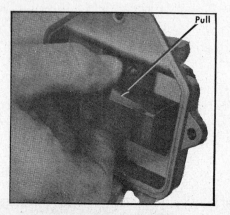

Fig. 19 Lowering float by pulling it
out on 1931 carburetor

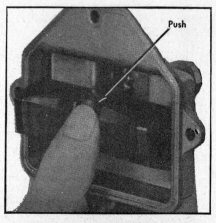

Fig. 20 Raising float by pushing it
in on 1931 carburetor

Bowl Vent Setting

Fig. 21—With throttle set at curb idle, clearance between vent valve and seat should be as listed in the *Holley Specifications Chart*. If an adjustment is necessary, bend vent rod at the horizontal portion above the fuel bowl. Check operation of vent rod for binding.

Accelerator Pump Setting

The accelerator link is set in the middle hole in the throttle lever for normal driving conditions. In the event a richer pump discharge is required, place the pump link in the outer hole of the throttle lever. For a leaner pump discharge, place the pump link in the inner hole of the throttle lever.

Fast Idle Adjustment

With the fast idle screw resting on second step of fast idle cam, and engine at normal operating temperature, the fast idle rpm should be as listed in the *Holley Specifications Chart*. Turning the fast idle screw in clockwise increases (counterclockwise decreases) speed.

Choke Unloader Setting

Fig. 22—With throttle valve held in wide open position and choke plate rotated toward closed position, the distance between top edge of choke plate and flat portion of air horn should be as listed in the *Holley Specifications Chart*. Adjust by bending tab on throttle lever.

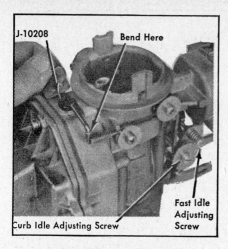

Fig. 21 Bowl vent adjustment
on 1931 carburetor

Fig. 22 Choke unloader adjustment
on 1931 carburetor

Fig. 28 Choke unloader adjustment
on 2209 carburetor

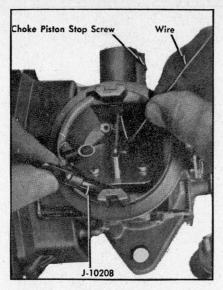

Fig. 23 Choke piston stop adjustment
on 1931 carburetor

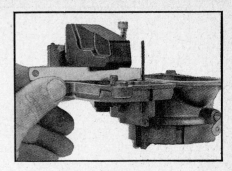

Fig. 26 Float adjustment
on 2209 carburetor

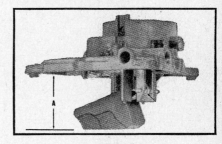

Fig. 27 Float drop adjustment
on 2209 carburetor

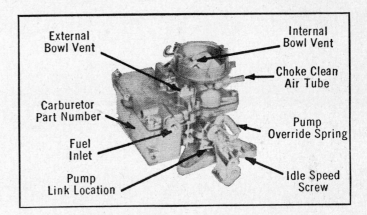

Fig. 24 Holley Model 2209 two-barrel carburetor

Choke Piston Stop Adjustment

Fig. 23—Hold choke piston against stop screw with a wire inserted in slot above choke piston link. Rotate choke plate toward closed position until link is firm. The distance between top edge of choke plate and flat portion of air horn should be $3/16$". Adjust by turning piston stop screw in or out as required.

Automatic Choke Setting

The adjustment is made by loosening choke cover screws and rotating cover in the desired direction as indicated by an arrow on the cover. The choke should be set to the mark specified in the *Holley Specifications Chart* for all normal driving. Never set the choke more than two graduations in either direction of the specified setting.

MODEL 2209

This carburetor, Figs. 24 and 25, fea-

Fig. 29 Automatic choke setting
on 2209 carburetor

tures a large capacity side inlet fuel bowl with a separate throttle body. The large capacity fuel bowl is designed to handle

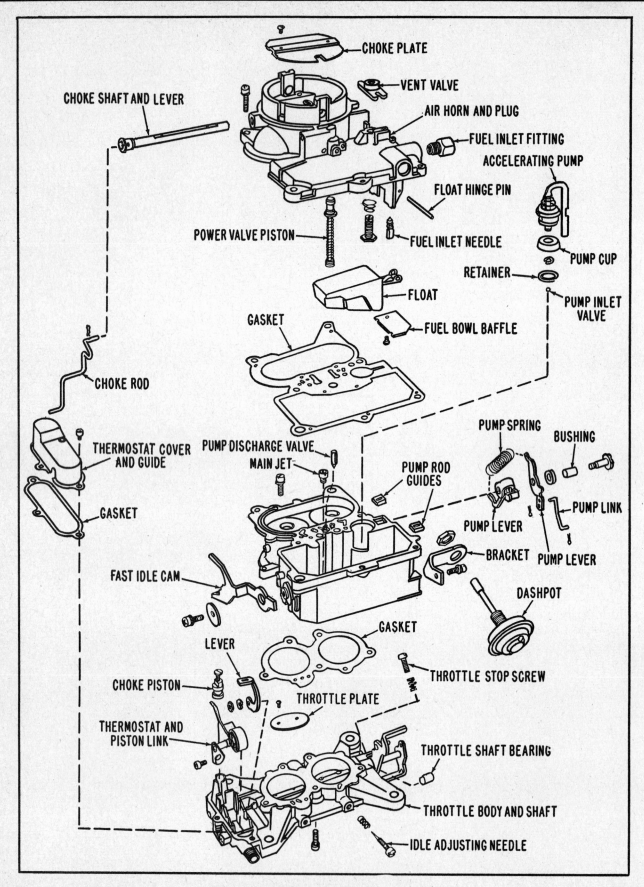

Fig. 25 Exploded view of Holley 2209 carburetor

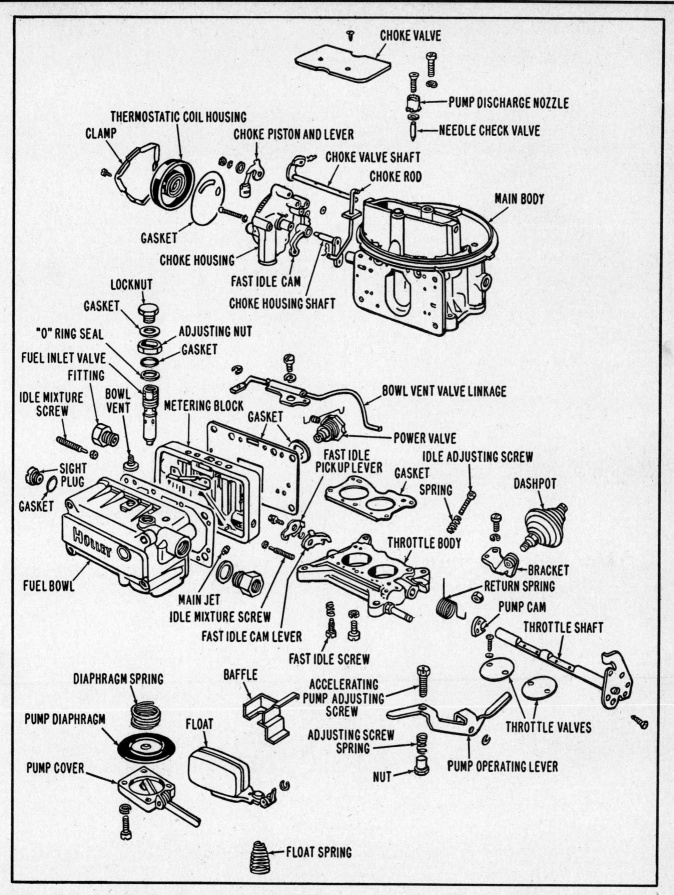

Fig. 32 Exploded view of Holley 2300 carburetor. Typical except secondary units on three-carb setup

Fig. 30　Fast idle setting on 2209 carburetor

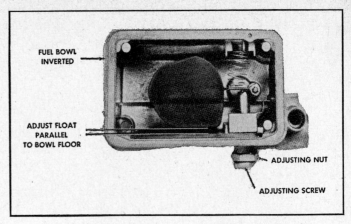

FUEL BOWL INVERTED

ADJUST FLOAT PARALLEL TO BOWL FLOOR

ADJUSTING NUT

ADJUSTING SCREW

Fig. 33　Float adjustment on 2300 carburetor

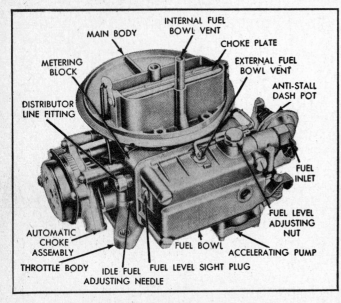

MAIN BODY

INTERNAL FUEL BOWL VENT

CHOKE PLATE

EXTERNAL FUEL BOWL VENT

METERING BLOCK

ANTI-STALL DASH POT

DISTRIBUTOR LINE FITTING

FUEL INLET

FUEL LEVEL ADJUSTING NUT

AUTOMATIC CHOKE ASSEMBLY

FUEL BOWL

ACCELERATING PUMP

THROTTLE BODY

IDLE FUEL ADJUSTING NEEDLE

FUEL LEVEL SIGHT PLUG

Fig. 31　Holley Model 2300 two-barrel carburetor

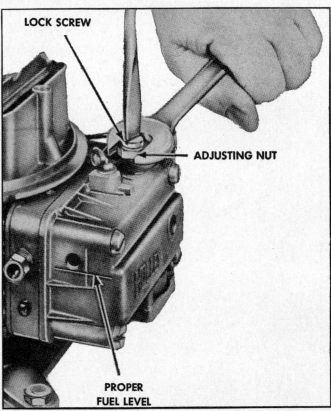

LOCK SCREW

ADJUSTING NUT

PROPER FUEL LEVEL

Fig. 34　Fuel level adjustment on 2300 carburetor

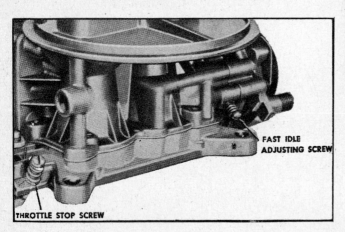

FAST IDLE ADJUSTING SCREW

THROTTLE STOP SCREW

Fig. 35　Fast idle adjustment on 2300 carburetor

efficiently vapor loaded fuels and fuel vapors. The separate throttle body and gasket creates a thermal barrier which reduces heat transfer to the fuel. The automatic choke is part of the throttle body and is connected to the choke plate by a choke rod.

Float Level Setting

Fig. 26—Check float setting with float dry and air horn inverted. Measure distance between float and air horn. If dimension is not as listed in the *Holley Specifications Chart*, adjust by bending float tab as required.

Checking Float Drop

Fig. 27—With air horn held upright, bottom surface of float should be parallel with air horn as shown. Adjust by bending float drop tab.

Choke Unloader Setting

Fig. 28—With throttle held in wide open position, there should be the clearance listed in the *Holley Specifications Chart* between top edge of choke plate and air horn wall as shown. Adjust by bending tab on fast idle cam.

Choke Adjustment

Fig. 29—Set automatic choke on index mark for all normal driving. If for some

Fig. 36   Automatic choke setting on 2300 carburetor, carburetor mounted unit

Fig. 38   Carburetor adjustments on 2300 carburetor

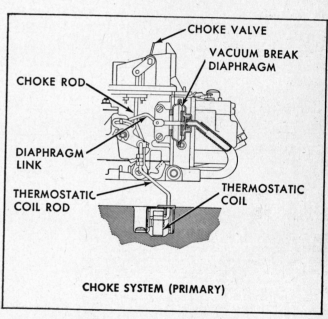

Fig. 37   Well type choke. 2300 carburetor

reason a richer or leaner mixture is desired during warm-up period, the choke can be reset by rotating choke thermostat shaft clockwise for a richer (counterclockwise for leaner) mixture. Never set the choke more than 2 graduations in either direction from the specified mark listed in the *Holley Specifications Chart.*

Fast Idle Adjustment

Fig. 30—With throttle stopped on high step of fast idle cam, the fast idle speed should be as listed in the *Holley Specifications Chart* with engine at normal temperature. Adjust by bending tab on throttle lever as shown.

Accelerator Pump Adjustment

The accelerating pump operating link is set in the inner hole of the pump lever for all normal driving conditions. If a leaner pump discharge is required, set the link in the outer hole.

Anti-Stall Dashpot Setting

With the throttle set at curb idle, there should be the clearance listed in the *Holley Specifications Chart* between dashpot stem and tab on throttle lever. Loosen lock nut and position dashpot to obtain this clearance. Tighten nut against bracket and recheck clearance.

MODEL 2300

This carburetor, Figs. 31 and 32, is a two-barrel unit but can be considered as two carburetors built side by side into one unit, utilizing the same fuel inlet and air inlet. Each barrel has its own venturi, idle system, main metering system, booster venturi and throttle plate.

Earlier models use a carburetor-mounted choke, Fig. 36, while later units use a well type, Fig. 37.

On Chevrolet and Chrysler Corp. three carburetor applications, the center or primary, carburetor is a standard unit while the outboard, or secondary, units do not include choke, power enrichment, accelerator pump, idle and spark advance circuits. Because of this, the metering bodies of the secondary units are much smaller than the standard 2300 and are inside the float bowl assembly rather than between the float bowl and main body.

The secondary carburetor throttles are opened by vacuum and closed mechanically.

The only adjustments required on secondary carburetors are the float level and wet fuel level. All other adjustments are made on the primary unit.

Float Adjustment

Fig. 33—With fuel bowl inverted so that float arm rests on fuel inlet needle holding it closed, set the float crease line parallel with the horizontal crease line of the fuel bowl. The adjustment is made by turning the fuel inlet needle and seat assembly adjusting nut as shown. The adjustment must be rechecked with the carburetor on the engine for proper wet fuel level as outlined below.

HOLLEY CARBURETORS

Wet Fuel Level

Fig. 34—With car on a level floor and engine idling, remove sight plug from fuel bowl. Fuel level should be in line with threads at bottom of sight plug hole. To adjust, loosen lock screw and turn adjusting nut as required to reise or lower fuel level.

Fast Idle Setting

Fig. 35—This adjustment with the carburetor off the car is made by turning the fast idle screw to obtain the clearance listed in the *Holley Specifications Chart* between throttle valve and carburetor bore on side opposite idle port with fast idle screw resting on high step of fast idle cam.

Automatic Choke Setting

Figs. 36, 37—On units equipped with carburetor-mounted choke, rotate thermostat cover to setting listed in the *Holley Specifications Chart*. On Chevrolet three-carburetor setups, bend the choke rod or thermostatic coil rod to match specification. On Chrysler three-carburetor setups, bend choke rod so that with choke valve closed, the top of hole in control lever is 3⁴⁹/₆₄" above choke well assembly with the carburetor on the engine.

NOTE: Improper bending of the rod will result in binding.

Vacuum Break Setting, Well Type

Holding choke closed and diaphragm fully in, either by hand or by applying sufficient vacuum to it, measure dimension between choke valve lower edge and main body. Bend rod to adjust.

Choke Unloader Setting

The choke unloader dimension listed in the *Holley Specifications Chart* is measured from the top edge of choke plate to forward top edge of air horn wall with throttle plates wide open. To adjust, bend tab on throttle shaft lever where it contacts fast idle cam.

Accelerator Pump Setting

Fig. 38—The pump screw should be in the No. 1 position on the throttle lever for all normal driving conditions. For extreme cold weather operation the No. 2 position can be used to provide maximum pump discharge.

The pump override spring is adjusted with throttle plates fully open and pump lever in compressed position. With screw just touching pump lever, tighten screw ¼ turn. To insure positive pump action, there must be no lag in the pump linkage. The slightest movement of the throttle lever from curb idle must actuage the pump lever. To remove any lag in this linkage, lengthen the pump override spring screw.

Bowl Vent Adjustment

Fig. 38—The bowl vent opening should be as listed in the *Holley Specifications Chart* and is adjusted by bending the operating lever as required.

HOLLEY 4150 & 4160 CARB. ADJUSTMENT SPECIFICATIONS

See Tune Up Chart in car chapters for hot idle speeds.

Year	Carb. Part No. ①	Float Level (Dry)	Fuel Level (Wet)	Pump Lever Clearance	Choke Setting	Choke Unloader Clearance	Bowl Vent Clearance	Fast Idle Bench	Fast Idle On Car	Choke Vacuum Break	Dashpot Setting
AMERICAN MOTORS											
1966	3201	See Text	④	.015	1 Lean	³⁄₁₆	¹⁄₁₆	.025	2000	—	—
	3202	See Text	④	.015	1 Lean	³⁄₁₆	¹⁄₁₆	.025	2000	—	³⁄₃₂
CHEVROLET ENGINES											
1966	R3123-A	②	④	.015	See Text	.260	.065	.035	2200	.170	—
	R3139-1A	②	④	.015	See Text	.260	.065	.035	2000	.170	—
	R3140-1A	②	④	.015	See Text	.260	.065	.035	2000	.170	—
	R3230-A	②	④	.015	See Text	.260	.065	.035	2000	.170	—
	R3245-A	②	④	.015	See Text	.260	.065	.025	2200	.180	—
	R3246-A	③	④	.015	See Text	.350	.065	.025	2200	.350	—
	R3247-A	③	④	.015	See Text	.350	.065	.025	2200	.350	—
	R3312-A	②	④	.015	See Text	.260	.065	.025	2200	.180	—
	R3327-A	②	④	.015	See Text	.260	.065	.035	2000	.180	—
	R3328-A	②	④	.015	See Text	.260	.065	.035	2000	.180	—
	R3367-A	②	④	.015	See Text	.260	.065	.035	2200	.170	—
	R3370-A	②	④	.015	See Text	.260	.065	.035	2000	.180	—
	R3416-A	③	④	.015	See Text	.260	.065	.035	2200	.170	—
	R3419-A	②	④	.015	See Text	.260	.065	.035	2000	.170	—
	R3420-A	②	④	.015	See Text	.260	.065	.035	2000	.170	—
	R3433-A	②	④	.015	See Text	.260	.065	.035	2000	.180	—
1967	R3418-A	③	④	.015	See Text	.350	.065	.025	2200	.350	—
	R3806-A	②	④	.015	See Text	.265	.065	.025	2200	.190	—
	R3807-A	②	④	.015	See Text	.265	.065	.025	2200	.190	—
	R3810-A	②	④	.015	See Text	.265	.065	.035	2200	.190	—
	R3811-A	②	④	.015	See Text	.265	.065	.035	2200	.175	—
	R3814-A	②	④	.015	See Text	.265	.065	.035	2000	.175	—
	R3815-A	③	④	.015	See Text	.265	.065	.035	2200	.175	—

Continued

HOLLEY 4150 & 4160 CARB. ADJUSTMENT SPECIFICATIONS—Continued

See Tune Up Chart in car chapters for hot idle speeds.

Year	Carb. Part No. ①	Float Level (Dry)	Fuel Level (Wet)	Pump Lever Clearance	Choke Setting	Choke Unloader Clearance	Bowl Vent Clearance	Fast Idle		Choke Vacuum Break	Dashpot Setting
								Bench	On Car		
CHEVROLET ENGINES—Continued											
1967	R3836-A	②	④	.015	See Text	.265	.065	.035	2200	.175	—
	R3837-A	②	④	.015	See Text	.265	.065	.035	2200	.175	—
	R3838-A	②	④	.015	See Text	.265	.065	.035	2200	.175	—
	R3839-A	②	④	.015	See Text	.265	.065	.035	2200	.175	—
1968	R4053-A	⑩	④	.015	See Text	.350	.065	.025	2200	.300	—
	R4054-A	⑩	④	.015	See Text	.350	.065	.025	2200	.300	—
1969–70	R4053-A	⑩	④	.015	⑬	.350	—	.025	2200	.300	—
	R4296-A	⑩	④	.015	⑬	.350	—	.025	2200	.350	—
	R4346	⑩	④	.015	⑬	.350	—	.025	2200	.300	—
	R4492-A	⑩	④	.015	⑬	.350	—	.025	2200	.350	—
	R4557-A	⑩	④	.015	⑬	.350	—	.025	2200	.350	—
1971	R4800-A	⑯	④	.015	1.320⑰	.350	—	.025	2200	.350	—
	R4801-A	⑯	④	.015	1.320⑰	.350	—	.025	2200	.350	—
	R4802-A	⑯	④	.015	1.320⑰	.350	—	.025	2200	.350	—
	R4803-A	⑯	④	.015	1.320⑰	.350	—	.025	2200	.350	—
1972	R6238-A	⑯	④	.015	1.320⑰	.350	—	.025	2350	.350	—
	R6239-A	⑯	④	.015	1.320⑰	.350	—	.025	2350	.350	—
CHRYSLER, IMPERIAL, DODGE, PLYMOUTH											
1967	R-3575-A	⑦	⑨	.015	—	5/32	3/32	53 Drill	700⑧	—	—
	R-3667-A	⑦	⑨	.015	—	5/32	3/32	53 Drill	700⑧	—	—
1968	R-3918-A	⑪	⑨	.015	See Text	5/32	50 Drill	46 Drill	1400⑭	—	—
1969	R-4166-A	⑪	⑨	.015	See Text	5/32	5/64	46 Drill	1400⑧	—	—
	R-4440-A	⑪	⑨	.015	See Text	5/32	5/64	46 Drill	1500⑭	—	—
1970–71	R4360-A	⑪	⑨	.015	2 Rich	25 Drill	72 Drill	53 Drill	1600	46 Drill	—
	R4366-A	⑪	⑨	.015	2 Rich	25 Drill	5/64	53 Drill	1600	46 Drill	—
1971	R4668-A	⑪	⑨	.015	2 Rich	25 Drill	.015	53 Drill	1700	46 Drill	—
	R4735-A	⑪	⑨	.015	2 Rich	25 Drill	.015	53 Drill	1700	46 Drill	—
	R6191-A	⑪	⑨	.015	2 Rich	25 Drill	.015	53 Drill	1800	18 Drill	—
	R6193-A	⑪	⑨	.015	2 Rich	25 Drill	.015	53 Drill	1800	18 Drill	—
FORD ENGINES											
1966–67	C5AF-BC	See Text	④	⑥	—	—	—	—	—	—	—
	C5AF-BD	See Text	④	⑤	3 Lean	—	—	—	—	—	—
1966	C6OF-M	See Text	④	.015	Index	—	.080	—	1200	—	—
	C6OF-N	See Text	④	.015	Index	—	.080	—	1300	—	.075
1967	C7OF-A	See Text	④	—	3 Rich	—	—	—	2100	—	—
	C7OF-B	See Text	④	—	3 Rich	—	—	—	2100	—	—
	C7OF-C	See Text	④	—	2 Rich	—	—	—	2100	—	—
	C7OF-D	See Text	④	—	2 Rich	—	—	—	2100	—	—
	C5AF-BV	See Text	④	—	Index	—	—	—	—	—	—

Continued

HOLLEY CARBURETORS

HOLLEY 4150 & 4160 CARB. ADJUSTMENT SPECIFICATIONS—Continued
See Tune Up Chart in car chapters for hot idle speeds.

Year	Carb. Part No. ①	Float Level (Dry)	Fuel Level (Wet)	Pump Lever Clearance	Choke Setting	Choke Unloader Clearance	Bowl Vent Clearance	Fast Idle Bench	Fast Idle On Car	Choke Vacuum Break	Dashpot Setting
FORD ENGINES—Continued											
1968	C8OF-AA	See Text	④	—	Index	—	—	—	1350	—	—
	C8OF-AB	See Text	④	—	Index	—	—	—	1550	—	.100
	C8OF-C	See Text	④	No. 1⑮	3 Rich	.300	—	—	1900	—	.100
	C8OF-D	See Text	④	No. 2⑮	3 Rich	.300	—	—	2100	—	.100
	C8AF-AD	See Text	④	No. 2⑮	—	.300	—	—	2100	—	.100
1969	C9AF-M	See Text	④	No. 2⑯	2 Rich	—	.060–.090	.060	1350⑫	—	.100
	C9AF-N	See Text	④	No. 2⑮	1 Rich	—	.060–.090	.080	1550⑫	—	.100
	C9OF-H	See Text	④	No. 2⑯	1 Rich	—	.060–.090	.080	1550⑫	—	—
1970	D0OF-N	See Text	④	—	2 Rich	—	—	—	2200	—	—
	D0OF-R	See Text	④	—	2 Rich	—	—	—	2400	—	—
	D0OF-S	See Text	④	—	—	—	—	—	1900	—	.140
	D0ZF-AA	See Text	④	.015	—	—	—	—	2100	—	.200
	D0ZF-AB	See Text	④	.015	—	—	—	—	1900	—	—
	D0ZF-AC	See Text	④	.015	—	—	—	—	2100	—	—
	D0ZF-AD	See Text	④	.015	—	—	—	—	—	—	—
	D0ZF-Z	See Text	④	—	—	—	—	—	2100	—	⅛
1971	D1ZF-VA	See Text	④	.015	—	—	—	—	2400	—	—
	D1ZF-XA	See Text	④	.015	2 Rich	1⁹⁄₆₄	—	—	2400	—	—
	D1ZF-YA	See Text	④	.015	2 Rich	1⁹⁄₆₄	—	—	2200	—	⁷⁄₆₄

①—Located ont ag attached to carburetor, on casting or on choke plate flange.
②—Primary .170", secondary .300".
③—Primary .350", secondary .450".
④—Use sight plug hole in fuel bowl as outlined in text.
⑤—Seasonal setting in pump lever holes; long stroke for cold weather, short stroke for moderate weather.
⑥—With lever touching screw, then tighten ¼ turn more.
⑦—Primary ⁷⁄₆₄", secondary ¹⁵⁄₆₄".
⑧—No. 5 Step on cam.
⑨—Primary ⁹⁄₁₆", secondary ¹³⁄₁₆".
⑩—Primary .350", secondary .500".
⑪—Primary ¹⁵⁄₆₄", secondary ¹⁷⁄₆₄".
⑫—On top step of cam.
⑬—Top of rod even with bottom of hole.
⑭—No. 2 Step on cam.
⑮—Hole setting.
⑯—Float centered in bowl.
⑰—Bottom of throttle body to center of hole in operating lever.

MODELS 4150, 4160 ADJUSTMENTS

These carburetors, Figs. 39 and 40, are four barrel units whose primary sides contain all the basic systems that make up a complete carburetor. The secondary sides of these units contain a fuel transfer and by-pass system which operates when a greater quantity of fuel-air mixture is required.

As shown in Fig. 39, some late model 4150 units have a central fuel inlet whereas other 4150 and 4160 units have a side inlet.

As shown in Figs. 39 and 41, fuel inlet systems vary slightly between models. In some units, the floats are hinged in the center while in others they are hinged at the float end.

Dry Float Setting

Except Fig. 41 Units—Invert fuel bowl. Loosen lock screw enough to allow adjusting nut to rotate. Turn adjusting nut to proper setting:

On Ford and Rambler units, adjust float parallel to bowl floor, Fig. 42.

On Chevrolet & Chrysler units, whether the float is hinged at the center or the end, set level to obtain specified dimension between float and bowl with bowl inverted, Fig. 42.

For Fig. 41 Units Only—Referring to Fig. 50, adjust float so that its center is an equal distance from top and bottom of fuel bowl with fuel bowl inverted. After carburetor is installed on engine, check and adjust fuel level.

Fuel Level Adjustment

Fig. 44—With car on a level floor and engine idling, fuel level should be at the level with the threads on the bottom of the sight plug hole (plus or minus 1/16″). To adjust, loosen lock screw and turn adjusting nut as required.

Secondary Throttle Plate Adjustment

Late Model Units—Referring to Fig. 45, back the secondary throttle stop screw out until secondary throttle plates are closed in the bores. Turn screw in (clockwise) until it touches stop on secondary throttle lever; then turn it in an additional 1/2 turn.

Accelerating Pump Adjustment

Late Model Units—Using a feeler gauge and with primary throttle plates in wide open position, there should be the clearance listed in the *Holley Specifications Chart* between pump operating lever adjusting screw and pump arm when pump arm is fully depressed manually, Fig. 46. Turn adjusting screw in to increase (out to decrease) clearance. One-half turn of adjusting screw is equal to .015″.

To satisfy acceleration requirements in various climates, the pump discharge can be adjusted, Fig. 46. The bottom hole

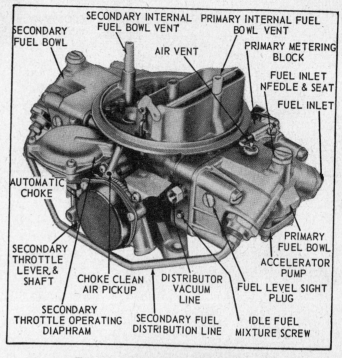

Fig. 41 Holley 4150 carburetor featuring an external fuel distributor tube connecting primary and secondary fuel inlets. These units also feature a choke clean air pick-up tube

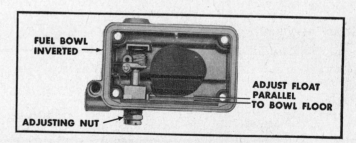

Fig. 42 Float adjustments except Fig. 41 type Ford units. On Chevrolet and Chrysler, adjust to specified dimension

(No. 2) in the cam provides a maximum pump discharge for extreme cold weather and the top hole (No. 1) provides the minimum pump discharge for warm weather operation.

Late Model Units—Referring to Fig. 47, the pump cam screw should be in the No. 1 position on the throttle lever for all normal operating conditions. For extreme cold weather the No. 2 position can be used to provide maximum pump discharge.

With throttle plates held in wide open position, there should be the clearance listed in the *Holley Specifications Chart* between the pump diaphragm actuating lever and the lower portion of the pump

override spring screw.

This adjustment *must* be rechecked with the throttle plates closed to make certain that there is no lag between throttle linkage and pump lever. The slightest movement of the throttle lever must correspondingly actuate the pump lever. Should there be any lag, a stumble or flat spot will result. To eliminate the lag, lengthen the adjusting screw.

Bowl Vent Valve Adjustment

Fig. 48—The fuel bowl vent valve clearance must be adjusted whenever the accelerator pump lever and/or pump stroke

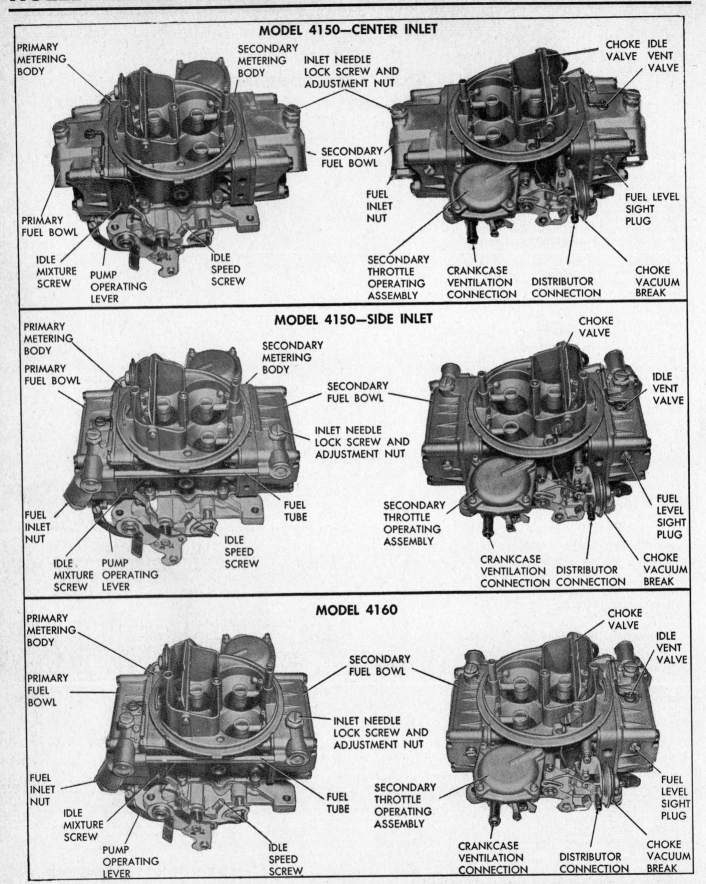

Fig. 39   Holley Models 4150 and 4160 late model four-barrel carburetors

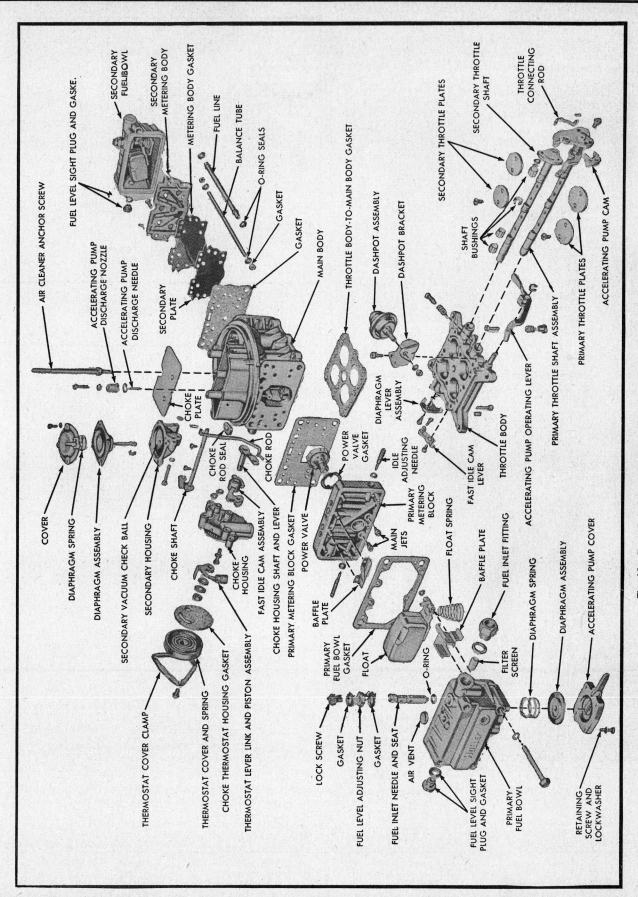

Fig. 40 Exploded view of a typical 4150 and 4160 carburetor

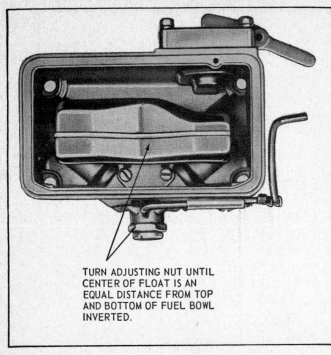

TURN ADJUSTING NUT UNTIL CENTER OF FLOAT IS AN EQUAL DISTANCE FROM TOP AND BOTTOM OF FUEL BOWL INVERTED.

Fig. 43   Float adjustment on Fig. 41 type Ford units

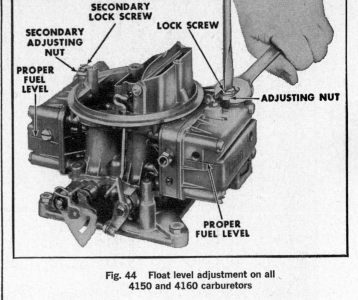

SECONDARY LOCK SCREW

SECONDARY ADJUSTING NUT

LOCK SCREW

PROPER FUEL LEVEL

ADJUSTING NUT

PROPER FUEL LEVEL

Fig. 44   Float level adjustment on all 4150 and 4160 carburetors

SECONDARY THROTTLE STOP SCREW

SECONDARY THROTTLE DIAPHRAM OPERATING LEVER

Fig. 45   Secondary throttle plate adjustment on Fig. 48 type carburetors

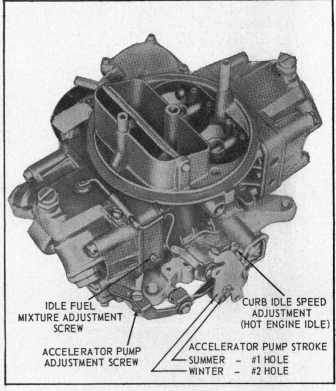

IDLE FUEL MIXTURE ADJUSTMENT SCREW

CURB IDLE SPEED ADJUSTMENT (HOT ENGINE IDLE)

ACCELERATOR PUMP ADJUSTMENT SCREW

ACCELERATOR PUMP STROKE
SUMMER - #1 HOLE
WINTER - #2 HOLE

Fig. 46   Carburetor adjustment points on late type carburetors

adjustments have been changed. A change in the pump adjustments will affect the fuel bowl vent valve clearance.

With engine temperature stabilized and engine operating at curb idle speed, check clearance between bottom of vent valve and top of fuel bowl at vent opening. If clearance is not as listed in the *Holley Specifications Chart*, bend vent rod as required.

Fast Idle Speed

Units With Built-in Choke—With hot idle

speed properly adjusted, set fast idle speed with transmission in neutral, engine at normal operating temperature, tachometer attached, headlamps turned on, and air conditioner operating (if so equipped). Referring to Fig. 49, align kickdown step of fast idle cam with the adjusting screw, and turn adjusting screw to obtain the specified rpm listed in the *Holley Specifications Chart*.

Units With Well Type Choke—With fast idle lever on high step of cam and choke valve wide open (engine warm) set fast idle to give the rpm listed in *Holley Specifications Chart*. Adjust fast idle screw on 4150 units or bend fast idle lever on 4160 units.

Fast Idle Cam Setting

Units With Well Type Choke—The fast

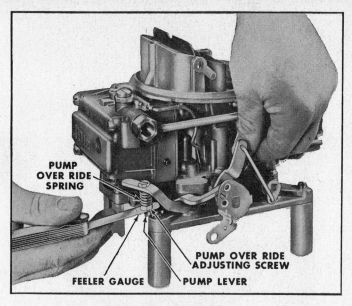

Fig. 47 Pump adjustment on Fig. 46 type carburetors

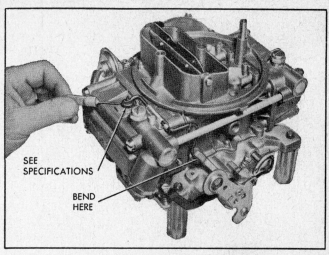

Fig. 48 Bowl vent valve clearance adjustment on 4150 and 4160 carburetors

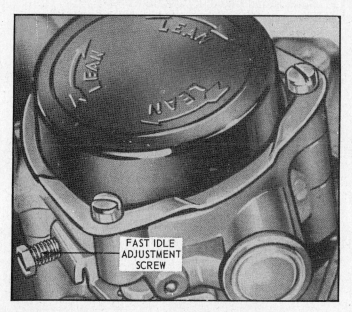

Fig. 49 Fast idle adjustment. Units with built-in choke

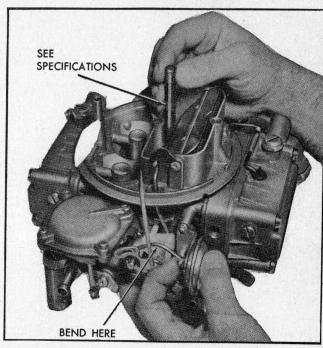

Fig. 50 Vacuum break adjustment. Well type choke

idle setting with the carburetor off the car is made by turning the fast idle adjusting screw to obtain the clearance listed in the *Holley Specifications Chart* between throttle valve and carburetor bore (idle port side) with fast idle screw on high step of cam.

Vacuum Break Adjustment

Fig. 50—On models so equipped, hold choke valve closed with a rubber band. Hold vacuum break in against its stop. Measure distance between lower edge of choke valve and wall of air horn. If the clearance is not as listed in the *Holley Specifications Chart*, bend vacuum break link to adjust.

Choke Unloader Adjustment

Fig. 51—Hold throttle lever wide open with a rubber band. Hold choke valve toward closed position toward unloader tang of throttle shaft. Then measure opening between lower edge of choke valve and air horn wall. If the opening is not as listed in the *Holley Specifications Chart*, bend choke rod at offset angle.

Built-in Choke Setting

Fig. 52—Loosen retaining screws and turn choke cover so that index mark or line on choke cover lines up with specified mark on choke housing. See *Holley Specifications Chart*.

Well Type Choke Adjustment

With throttle half open and choke valve closed, bend the choke rod to obtain specified clearance for Chevrolet units. On Chrysler units, follow same procedure so that the top of the choke rod hole in the control lever is $1^{23}/_{32}$" above the bottom of the carburetor base.

Air/Fuel Ratio

On Chrysler units, adjust air/fuel ratio to 14.2 to 1. On Ford applications, adjust

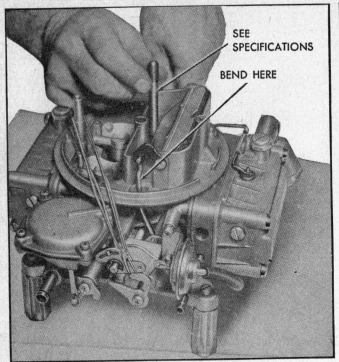

SEE
SPECIFICATIONS

BEND HERE

Fig. 51   Choke unloader adjustment. Well type choke

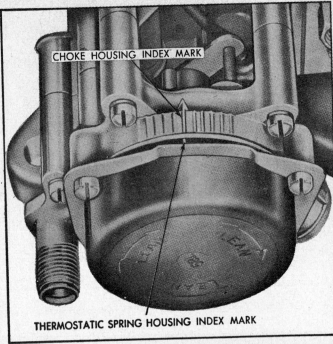

CHOKE HOUSING INDEX MARK

THERMOSTATIC SPRING HOUSING INDEX MARK

Fig. 52   Built-in Automatic choke adjustment

as follows:
1969 units; 14.1 to 1
1970 units;
   DOZF-Z, 13.5 to 1
   DOZF-AA, DOZF-AC, 13.8 to 1
   DOZF-AB, DOZF-AD, 14.3 to 1
   DOOF-S, 14.2 to 1
1971 units:
   Greater than 14.5 to 1

Rochester Carburetor Section

ROCHESTER BV CARBURETOR ADJUSTMENT SPECIFICATIONS

See Tune Up Chart in car chapter for hot idle speeds.

Year	Carburetor Part No. ①	Carb. Model	Float Level	Float Drop	Vacuum Break	Automatic Choke	Choke Rod	Choke Unloader	Idle Vent
CHEVROLET ENGINES									
1966–67	7025000	BV	1⁹⁄₃₂	1¾	.140	—	.090	.350	.050
1966	7025003	BV	1⁹⁄₃₂	1¾	.160	—	.100	.350	.050
1966–67	7025105	BV	1⁹⁄₃₂	1¾	.160	—	.100	.350	.050
	7025108	BV	1⁹⁄₃₂	1¾	.140	—	.090	.350	.050
1966–67	7026027	BV	1⁹⁄₃₂	1¾	.160	—	.100	.350	.050
	7026028	BV	1⁹⁄₃₂	1¾	.140	—	.090	.350	.050
1967	7022503	BV	1⁹⁄₃₂	1¾	.160	—	.100	.350	.050
	7025000	BV	1⁹⁄₃₂	1¾	.140	—	.090	.350	.050
	7025105	BV	1⁹⁄₃₂	1¾	.160	—	.100	.350	.050
	7025108	BV	1⁹⁄₃₂	1¾	.140	—	.090	.350	.050
	7026027	BV	1⁹⁄₃₂	1¾	.160	—	.100	.350	.050
	7026028	BV	1⁹⁄₃₂	1¾	.140	—	.090	.350	.050
OLDSMOBILE INTERMEDIATE MODELS									
1966–67	7026027	BV	1⁹⁄₃₂	1⅞	.140	On Index	.075	.300	.050
	7026028	BV	1⁹⁄₃₂	1⅞	.160	On Index	.075	.300	.050
1967	7016627	BV	1⁹⁄₃₂	1¾	.160	—	.100	.350	.050
	7016628	BV	1⁹⁄₃₂	1¾	.140	—	.090	.350	.050
PONTIAC INTERMEDIATE MODELS									
1966–67	7026167	BV	1⁹⁄₃₂	1⅞	.170	—	.060	.230	.040
	7026168	BV	1⁹⁄₃₂	1⅞	.150	—	.060	.230	.040
1966	7026169	BV	1⁹⁄₃₂	1⅞	.150	—	.060	.230	.040
1966–67	7036167	BV	1⁹⁄₃₂	1⅞	.170	—	.060	.230	.040
1966–67	7036168	BV	1⁹⁄₃₂	1⅞	.150	—	.060	.230	.040
1967	7027167	BV	1⁵⁄₁₆	1⅞	.170	—	.060	.230	.040
	7027168	BV	1⁵⁄₁₆	1⅞	.160	—	.060	.230	.040
	7037167	BV	1⁵⁄₁₆	1⅞	.170	—	.060	.230	.040
	7037168	BV	1⁵⁄₁₆	1⅞	.160	—	.060	.230	.040
1968	7028168	BV	1⁹⁄₃₂	1¾	.160	—	.080	.230	.050

①—Located on tag attached to or stamped on carburetor.

MODEL BV ADJUSTMENTS

The Model BV unit, Fig. 1, uses a fully automatic choke. However, instead of the conventional choke piston and housing, a vacuum operated diaphragm plunger is used. The thermostatic coil is mounted on the exhaust manifold instead of the choke housing and is connected to the carburetor choke shaft by connecting linkage.

Design features included in all three carburetors include the following:

A concentric type float bowl is used which allows fuel in the float bowl to completely surround the main carburetor bore and venturi. The concentric float bowl design plus the centrally located main fuel discharge nozzle prevents fuel spill-over during abnormal car maneuvers such as sharp turns, quick starts and stops.

The main assembly is a detachable unit which contains the metering parts of the carburetor. It is attached to the air horn and is easily removed for inspection and service. It is suspended in the fuel in the float chamber which insulates it from heat which may be transmitted from the engine directly to the bottom of the float bowl. This type design helps maintain more accurate fuel metering because less fuel vapors enter the main metering parts of the assembly during hot engine operation.

Float Level Adjustment

Fig. 2—With air horn inverted and gasket in place, check height of each float as shown. Bend tang that contacts needle seat until each pontoon is set to the dimension specified in the *Rochester Specifications Chart*. Align floats to avoid interference in bowl.

NOTE: On models using a spring-loaded needle and seat assembly, place a .030" shim between head of float needle pin and float arm. With float arm resting freely on shim, check float height with

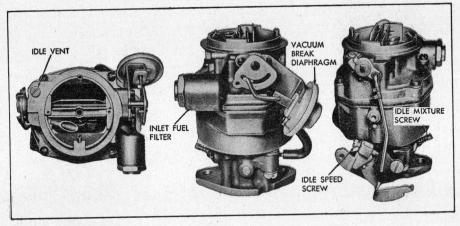

Fig. 1 Rochester Model BV single-barrel carburetor

gauge. Bend float arms until each pontoon is set to the specified dimension. After adjustment, remove shim from between float needle and float arm.

Float Drop Adjustment

Fig. 3—With air horn assembly held upright and floats suspended freely, carefully bend float tang at rear of float arm so that bottom of float pontoon is set as specified in the *Rochester Specifications Chart*.

Vacuum Break Adjustment

Model BV, Fig. 4—To assure correct initial choke valve opening, push vacuum break diaphragm plunger in until seated, making sure choke valve is closed so that connecting rod is at end of slot. In this position, adjust rod so that the specified gauge size listed in the *Rochester Specifications Chart* will fit between lower edge

of choke valve and inner wall of air horn. To adjust, bend connecting rod at point indicated.

Choke Rod Adjustment

Fig. 5—With idle screw on second step and against high step of fast idle cam, bend choke rod to obtain the specified dimension between lower edge of choke valve and air horn wall (see *Rochester Specifications Chart*).

Choke Unloader Adjustment

Fig. 6—Bend unloader tang on throttle lever as necessary to obtain specified clearance listed in the *Rochester Specifications Chart* between lower edge of choke valve and air horn wall with throttle valve wide open.

Idle Vent Adjustment

Model BV, Fig. 7—With idle rpm set to

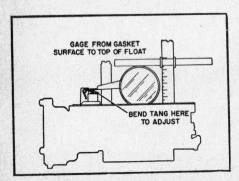

Fig. 2 Float level adjustment for BV carburetors

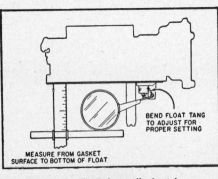

Fig. 3 Float drop adjustment for BV carburetors

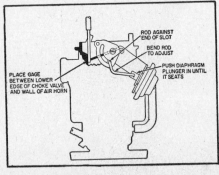

Fig. 4 Vacuum break adjustment for BV carburetors

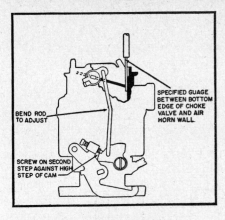

Fig. 5 Choke rod setting for BV carburetors

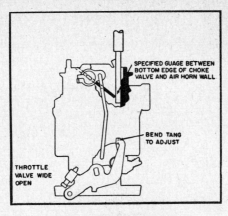

Fig. 6 Choke unloader setting for BV carburetors

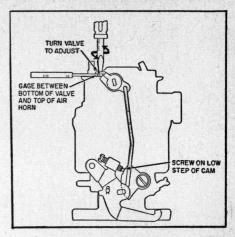

Fig. 7 Idle vent adjustment for BV carburetors

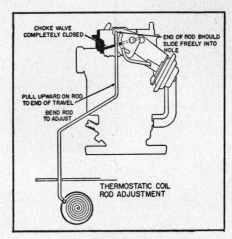

Fig. 8 Thermostatic coil rod adjustment for BV carburetors

the specification listed in the *Tune Up Chart* in the car chapter, and screw on low step of cam, idle vent should be open as specified in the *Rochester Specifications Chart*. Adjust by turning valve on top of air horn as required to obtain the desired setting.

Thermostatic Coil Rod Adjustment

Model BV, Fig. 8—Disconnect thermostat rod from upper end of choke lever. Pull upward on rod to end of its travel. Holding choke valve closed, bottom of rod should be even with top of hole in choke shaft lever. Bend rod to adjust.

ROCHESTER CARBURETORS

ROCHESTER HV CARB. ADJUSTMENT SPECIFICATIONS

See Tune Up Chart in car chapter for hot idle speeds.

Year	Carburetor Part No. ①	Float Level	Float Drop	Idle Vent	Vacuum Break	Choke Rod	Choke Unloader	Fast Idle	Secondary Lockout Lever Stop
CORVAIR									
1966	7025226	1 1/16	1 13/16	.015	.190	.190	.325	—	.060
	7025227	1 1/16	1 13/16	.015	.190	.190	.325	—	.060
	7026023	1 1/16	1 13/16	.015	.190	.190	.325	—	—
	7026024	1 1/16	1 13/16	.015	.190	.190	.325	—	—
	7026026	1 1/16	1 13/16	.015	.190	.190	.325	—	—
1966–67	7036014	1 1/16	1 13/16	.015	.190	.190	.325	—	—
	7036015	1 1/16	1 13/16	.015	.190	.190	.325	—	—
	7036023	1 1/16	1 13/16	.015	.190	.190	.325	—	—
	7036024	1 1/16	1 13/16	.015	.190	.190	.325	—	—
1966–69	7027026	1 1/16	1 13/16	—	—	—	—	—	.060
1968	7028004	1 1/16	1 9/16	.015	.190	.190	.500	—	—
1968–69	7028005	1 1/16	1 13/16	.015	.190	.190	.500	—	—

①—Located on tag attached to or stamped on carburetor.

MODEL HV ADJUSTMENTS

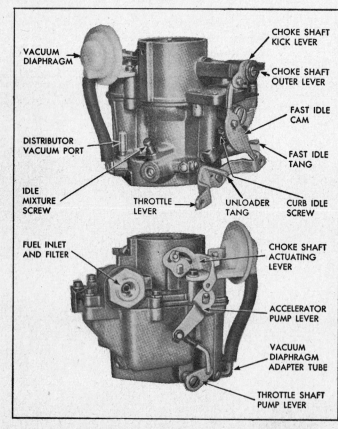

Fig. 1   Rochester Model HV single-barrel carburetor

The automatic choke mechanism consists of a thermostatic coil mounted to the lower side of the cylinder head and linked directly to the choke valve shaft; a vacuum diaphragm is provided on the air horn.

Float Level Adjustment

Fig. 2—With air horn inverted and gasket in place, check height of each float. Bend tang that contacts needle until each pontoon is set to the specified dimension listed in the *Rochester Specifications Chart.* Float pontoons should be parallel with air horn surface when set correctly. Align floats to prevent interference in bowl.

Float Drop Adjustment

Fig. 3—With air horn assembly held upright and floats suspended freely, measure dimension from air horn gasket to bottom of float pontoon at the toe. Adjust to dimension listed in the *Rochester Specifications Chart* by bending the tang that contacts seat at rear of float arm.

Pump Rod Adjustment

Fig. 4—Back out idle stop screw until throttle valves are completely closed in bore. Bend pump rod as shown until index line on upper pump lever just aligns with sharp edge on air horn casting.

NOTE: On Powerglide applications using

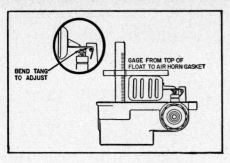

Fig. 2   Float level adjustment for HV carburetors

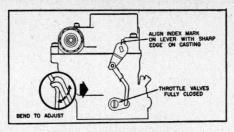

Fig. 4   Pump rod adjustment for HV carburetors

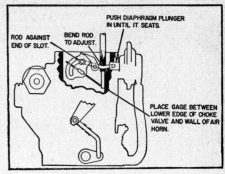

Fig. 6   Vacuum break diaphragm adjustment for HV carburetors

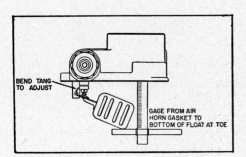

Fig. 3   Float drop adjustment for HV carburetors

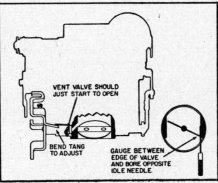

Fig 5   Idle vent valve adjustment for HV carburetors

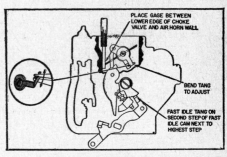

Fig. 7   Choke rod adjustment for HV carburetors

a two-hole lower pump lever, setting should be made with pump rod placed in outer hole. After setting is made, pump rod should be moved to inner hole on lever for proper operation.

Idle Vent Valve Adjustment

Model HV, Fig. 5—To adjust, bend tang on throttle lever so that when vent valve just starts to open, the proper gauge size will just go between throttle valve and bore directly opposite the idle needle (see *Rochester Specifications Chart*). *Do not bend spring arm on vent valve as distortion may result.*

Vacuum Break Diaphragm Adjustment

Model HV, Fig. 6—To adjust, push diaphragm plunger in until seated. Then close choke valve to a point where connecting rod is to end of slot in choke lever. With choke valve in this position, specified gauge size should fit between lower edge of choke valve and inner air horn wall as shown (see *Rochester Specifications Chart*). To adjust, bend connecting rod at point shown.

Choke Rod Adjustment

Model HV, Fig. 7—To adjust, place fast idle tang on second step of fast idle cam next to highest step. Close choke valve so that trip lever on choke shaft just contacts choke tang on lever and collar.

Specified gauge size listed in *Rochester Specifications Chart* should just fit between lower edge of choke valve and inner wall of air horn. To adjust, bend tang on trip lever up or down as required.

Choke Unloader Adjustment

Fig. 8—With throttle valve wide open (accelerator pedal pressed to floor), the specified gauge size listed in the *Rochester Specifications Chart* should just fit between lower edge of choke valve and inner air horn wall. To adjust, bend unloader tang on throttle lever.

Fast Idle Adjustment

Model HV, Fig. 9—To check this adjustment, place fast idle tang on second step of fast idle cam next to highest step. With idle speed screw set to normal idle position (approximately $\frac{3}{4}$ turn in from closed throttle valve), measure clearance between idle stop screw and edge of throttle lever. To adjust, bend fast idle

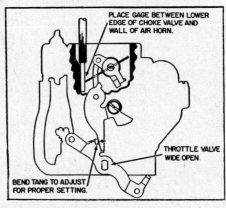

Fig. 8   Choke unloader adjustment for HV carburetors

tang up or down as required (see *Rochester Specifications Chart*).

Synchronizing Carburetors

Models with Four Carburetors

1. Synchronize primary carburetors, leaving choke rods disconnected.
2. With primary choke valve in full open position and a .160″ gauge between secondary carburetor lockout lever and lockout tang on throttle lever, bend secondary carburetor trip lever so it just contacts carburetor choke lever, Fig. 10. Repeat operation on other secondary carburetor.
3. Hold choke valves closed and actuate accelerator cross shaft (to set fast idle cams). Pull choke rod upward to end of travel and adjust rod until bottom of rod is even with top of hole in choke lever. Connect choke rod and repeat operation on remaining choke.
4. Disconnect left and right secondary carburetor actuating rods. Then hold carburetor cross shaft so primary carburetors are in full open position.
5. With choke valves closed (secondary throttles locked out) adjust secondary carburetor actuating rod so actuating spring is fully compressed and clevis will just enter hole in cross shaft lever. Then back off adjustment a minimum of 2 and a maximum of 3 turns. Repeat operation on other actuating rod.
6. Connect both secondary actuating rods and, with choke valves held wide open, slowly rotate carburetor cross shaft to the full throttle position, checking that all carburetors reach full throttle simultaneously.

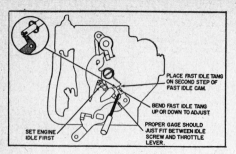

Fig. 9 Fast idle adjustment for HV carburetors

7. With choke valves held closed, rotate carburetor cross shaft to full throttle position and check primary carburetors for full throttle position; check that secondary carburetors are locked out and that secondary actuating springs are fully compressed.

Secondary Lockout Adjustment

Fig. 11—With throttle closed and edge of throttle lever lockout tang flush with

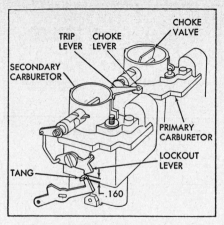

Fig. 10 Secondary linkage adjustment (4 carb. installation)

lockout lever, bend throttle lever tang to obtain specified clearance listed in the *Rochester Specifications Chart* between notch in lockout lever and throttle lever tang.

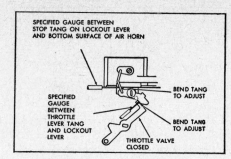

Fig. 11 Secondary lockout adjustment (4 carb. installation)

With throttle lever in locked-out position, bend stop tang on lockout lever to obtain specified clearance between stop tang and bottom surface of air horn.

NOTE: The primary carburetor choke mechanism operates the lockout mechanism on the secondary carburetor. Therefore, final adjustment must be made with the carburetor installed on the engine.

ROCHESTER 2G, 2GC, 2GV CARBURETOR ADJUSTMENT SPECIFICATIONS

See Tune Up Chart in car chapters for hot idle speeds.

★Located on tag attached to or stamped on carburetor.

Year	Carb. Part No. ★	Float Level	Float Drop	Pump Rod	Idle Vent	Intermediate Choke Rod	Vacuum Break	Automatic Choke	Choke Rod	Choke Unloader	Fast Idle Speed
BUICK											
1966	7026046	$\frac{1}{2}$	$1\frac{27}{32}$	$1\frac{5}{32}$	—	—	—	On Index	.055	.140	—
	7026047	$\frac{1}{2}$	$1\frac{27}{32}$	$1\frac{11}{32}$	—	—	—	On Index	.055	.140	—
	7026144	$\frac{1}{2}$	$1\frac{27}{32}$	$1\frac{5}{32}$	—	—	—	On Index	.055	.140	—
	7026145	$\frac{1}{2}$	$1\frac{27}{32}$	$1\frac{11}{32}$	—	—	—	On Index	.055	.140	—
	7026146	$\frac{15}{32}$	$1\frac{9}{16}$	$1\frac{5}{32}$	$1\frac{1}{16}$	—	—	On Index	.055	.140	—
	7026147	$\frac{15}{32}$	$1\frac{9}{16}$	$1\frac{11}{32}$	—	—	—	On Index	.055	.140	—
	7036046	$\frac{1}{2}$	$1\frac{27}{32}$	$1\frac{5}{32}$	$1\frac{1}{16}$	—	—	On Index	.055	.140	—
	7036048	$\frac{1}{2}$	$1\frac{27}{32}$	$1\frac{11}{32}$	$1\frac{1}{16}$	—	—	On Index	.055	.140	—
	7036144	$\frac{1}{2}$	$1\frac{27}{32}$	$1\frac{1}{16}$	$\frac{31}{32}$	—	—	On Index	.055	.140	—
1967	7027040	$\frac{1}{2}$	$1\frac{9}{32}$	$1\frac{1}{16}$	$\frac{31}{32}$	—	—	On Index	.055	.140	—
	7027041	$\frac{1}{2}$	$1\frac{9}{32}$	$1\frac{1}{16}$	$\frac{31}{32}$	—	—	On Index	.055	.140	—
	7027042	$\frac{1}{2}$	$1\frac{9}{32}$	$1\frac{5}{32}$	$\frac{31}{32}$	—	—	On Index	.055	.140	—
	7027044	$\frac{15}{32}$	$1\frac{9}{16}$	$1\frac{5}{32}$	$\frac{31}{32}$	—	—	On Index	.055	.140	—
	7027045	$\frac{15}{32}$	$1\frac{9}{16}$	$1\frac{5}{32}$	$\frac{31}{32}$	—	—	On Index	.055	.140	—
	7027046	$\frac{15}{32}$	$1\frac{9}{16}$	$1\frac{5}{32}$	$\frac{31}{32}$	—	—	On Index	.055	.140	—
	7027049	$\frac{15}{32}$	$1\frac{9}{16}$	$1\frac{5}{32}$	$\frac{31}{32}$	—	—	On Index	.055	.140	—
1968	7028140	$\frac{15}{32}$	$1\frac{9}{32}$	$1\frac{11}{32}$	.025③	—	.120	①	.050	.140	—
	7028141	$\frac{15}{32}$	$1\frac{9}{32}$	$1\frac{11}{32}$	.025③	—	.120	①	.050	.140	—
1969	7029140	$\frac{15}{32}$	$1\frac{7}{32}$	$1\frac{11}{32}$	.020③	—	.110	③	.055	.140	—
	7029141	$\frac{15}{32}$	$1\frac{7}{32}$	$1\frac{11}{32}$	.020③	—	.110	③	.055	.140	—
1970	7040142	$\frac{15}{32}$	$1\frac{7}{32}$	$1\frac{13}{32}$	—	—	.150	③	.080	.180	—
	7040143	$\frac{15}{32}$	$1\frac{7}{32}$	$1\frac{15}{32}$	—	—	.190	③	.100	.200	—
	7040446	$\frac{15}{32}$	$1\frac{7}{32}$	$1\frac{13}{32}$	—	—	.150	③	.080	.180	—

Continued

ROCHESTER 2G, 2GC, 2GV CARBURETOR ADJUSTMENT SPECIFICATIONS—Continued

See Tune Up Chart in car chapters for hot idle speeds.
★Located on tag attached to or stamped on carburetor.

Year	Carb. Part No. ★	Float Level	Float Drop	Pump Rod	Idle Vent	Intermediate Choke Rod	Vacuum Break	Automatic Choke	Choke Rod	Choke Unloader	Fast Idle Speed
BUICK—Continued											
1971	7040143	15/32	1 7/8	1 15/32	—	—	.160④	—	.080	.180	—
	7041142	15/32	1 7/8	1 15/32	—	—	.150④	—	.080	.180	—
	7041442	15/32	1 7/8	1 15/32	—	—	.150④	—	.080	.180	—
1972	7042142	15/32	1 7/8	1 15/32	—	—	.150④	—	.080	.180	—
	7042143	15/32	1 7/8	1 15/32	—	—	.160④	—	.080	.180	—
	7042842	15/32	1 7/8	1 15/32	—	—	.150④	—	.080	.180	—

①—Rod is installed in lower of two lever holes.
②—At slow idle RPM vent valve should be open to specified dimension.
③—Holes in lever are marked "ALT" or "STD". Install in proper hole.
④—Secondary adjustment .140".

CHEVROLET ENGINES

Year	Carb. Part No. ★	Float Level	Float Drop	Pump Rod	Idle Vent	Intermediate Choke Rod	Vacuum Break	Automatic Choke	Choke Rod	Choke Unloader	Fast Idle Speed
1966	7024101	3/4①	1 3/4	1 1/8	1	—	.120	—	.060	.200	—
	7024110	3/4①	1 3/4	1 1/8	1	—	.090	—	.060	.200	—
	7024112	3/4①	1 3/4	1 1/8	1	—	.090	—	.060	.200	—
	7025103	3/4①	1 3/4	1 1/8	1	—	.120	—	.060	.200	—
	7036101	3/4①	1 3/4	1 1/8	1	—	.130	—	.060	.200	—
	7036103	3/4①	1 3/4	1 1/8	1	—	.130	—	.060	.200	—
	7036110	3/4①	1 3/4	1 1/8	1	—	.120	—	.060	.200	—
	7036112	3/4①	1 3/4	1 1/8	1	—	.120	—	.060	.200	—
	7036146	15/32②	1 9/16	1 5/32	1 1/16	—	—	On Index	.055	.140	—
	7036248	15/32②	1 9/16	1 5/32	1 1/16	—	—	On Index	.055	.140	—
1967	7027101	3/4②	1 3/4	1 1/8	1	—	.120	—	.060	.215	—
	7027103	3/4②	1 3/4	1 1/8	1	—	.120	—	.060	.215	—
	7027110	3/4②	1 3/4	1 1/8	1	—	.110	—	.060	.215	—
	7027112	3/4②	1 3/4	1 1/8	1	—	.110	—	.060	.215	—
	7037101	3/4②	1 3/4	1 1/8	1	—	.130	—	.060	.215	—
	7037103	3/4②	1 3/4	1 1/8	1	—	.130	—	.060	.215	—
	7037110	3/4②	1 3/4	1 1/8	1	—	.110	—	.060	.215	—
	7037112	3/4②	1 3/4	1 1/8	1	—	.110	—	.060	.215	—
	7027114	3/4②	1 3/4	1 1/8	1	—	.110	—	.060	.200	—
	7027116	3/4②	1 3/4	1 1/8	1	—	.110	—	.060	.200	—
	7037034	15/32②	1 9/16	1 5/32	31/32	—	—	On Index	.055	.140	—
1968	7028110	3/4②	1 3/4	1 1/8	.025③	—	.100	—	.060	.200	—
	7028101	3/4②	1 3/4	1 1/8	.025③	—	.100	—	.060	.200	—
	7028112	3/4②	1 3/4	1 1/8	.025③	—	.100	—	.060	.200	—
	7028103	3/4②	1 3/4	1 1/8	.025③	—	.100	—	.060	.200	—
1969	7029101	27/32②	1 3/4	1 1/8	.020	—	.100	—	.060	.215	—
	7029102	3/4②	1 3/8	1 13/32	.020	—	.215	—	.085	.275	—
	7029103	27/32②	1 3/4	1 1/8	.020	—	.100	—	.060	.215	—
	7029104	3/4②	1 3/8	1 13/32	.020	—	.215	—	.085	.275	—
	7029110	27/32②	1 3/4	1 1/8	.020	—	.100	—	.060	.215	—
	7029112	27/32②	1 3/4	1 1/8	.020	—	.100	—	.060	.215	—
	7029113	3/4②	1 3/8	1 13/32	.020	—	.200	—	.085	.275	—
	7029114	3/4②	1 3/8	1 13/32	.020	—	.200	—	.085	.275	—
	7029115	3/4②	1 3/8	1 13/32	.020	—	.200	—	.085	.275	—
	7029116	3/4②	1 3/8	1 13/32	.020	—	.200	—	.085	.275	—
	7029117	3/4②	1 3/4	1 13/32	.020	—	.215	—	.085	.275	—
	7029118	3/4②	1 3/4	1 13/32	.020	—	.215	—	.085	.275	—
	7029119	5/8②	1 3/4	1 13/32	.020	—	.215	—	.085	.275	—
	7029120	5/8②	1 3/4	1 13/32	.020	—	.215	—	.085	.275	—
	7029127	3/4②	1 3/8	1 13/32	.020	—	.215	—	.085	.275	—
	7029129	3/4②	1 3/8	1 13/32	.020	—	.215	—	.085	.275	—

ROCHESTER CARBURETORS

ROCHESTER 2G, 2GC, 2GV CARBURETOR ADJUSTMENT SPECIFICATIONS—Continued

See Tune Up Chart in car chapters for hot idle speeds.

★Located on tag attached to or stamped on carburetor.

Year	Carb. Part No. ★	Float Level	Float Drop	Pump Rod	Idle Vent	Intermediate Choke Rod	Vacuum Break	Automatic Choke	Choke Rod	Choke Unloader	Fast Idle Speed
CHEVROLET ENGINES—Continued											
1970	7040101	27/32②	1 3/4	1 3/8	.025	—	.130	—	.060	.160	—
	7040103	27/32②	1 3/4	1 3/8	.025	—	.130	—	.060	.160	—
	7040110	27/32②	1 3/4	1 3/8	.025	—	.100	—	.060	.215	—
	7040112	27/32②	1 3/4	1 3/8	.025	—	.100	—	.060	.215	—
	7040113	23/32②	1 3/8	1 17/32	.025	—	.215	—	.085	.275	—
	7040114	23/32②	1 3/8	1 17/32	.025	—	.200	—	.085	.325	—
	7040115	23/32②	1 3/8	1 17/32	.025	—	.215	—	.085	.275	—
	7040116	23/32②	1 3/8	1 17/32	.025	—	.200	—	.085	.325	—
	7040117	23/32②	1 3/8	1 17/32	.025	—	.215	—	.085	.325	—
	7040118	23/32②	1 3/8	1 17/32	.025	—	.215	—	.085	.325	—
	7040119	23/32②	1 3/8	1 17/32	.025	—	.215	—	.085	.325	—
	7040120	23/32②	1 3/8	1 17/32	.235	—	.215	—	.085	.325	—
1971	7041101	27/32②	1 3/4	1 5/16	—	—	.110	—	.075	.215	—
	7041102	25/32②	1 3/8	1 17/32	—	—	.170	—	.100	.325	—
	7041110	27/32②	1 3/4	1 5/16	—	—	.080	—	.040	.215	—
	7041113	23/32②	1 3/8	1 17/32	—	—	.180	—	.100	.325	—
	7041114	25/32②	1 3/8	1 17/32	—	—	.170	—	.100	.325	—
	7041117	23/32②	1 3/8	1 17/32	—	—	.170	—	.100	.325	—
	7041118	23/32②	1 3/8	1 17/32	—	—	.170	—	.100	.325	—
	7041127	23/32②	1 3/8	1 17/32	—	—	.180	—	.100	.325	—
	7041137	23/32②	1 3/8	1 17/32	—	—	.180	—	.100	.325	—
	7041181	21/32②	1 7/8	1 3/8	—	—	.120	—	.080	.180	—
	7041182	21/32②	1 7/8	1 3/8	—	—	.120	—	.080	.180	—
1972	7042100	25/32	1 31/32	1 5/16	—	—	.080	—	.040	.215	—
	7042101	25/32	1 31/32	1 5/16	—	—	.110	—	.075	.215	—
	7042106	19/32	1 7/8	1 1/16	—	—	.085	—	.060	.215	—
	7042107	19/32	1 7/8	1 1/16	—	—	.100	—	.080	.215	—
	7042111	23/32	1 9/32	1 1/2	—	—	.180	—	.100	.325	—
	7042112	23/32	1 9/32	1 1/2	—	—	.170	—	.100	.325	—
	7042113	23/32	1 9/32	1 1/2	—	⊥	.180	—	.100	.325	—
	7042114	23/32	1 9/32	1 1/2	—	—	.170	—	.100	.325	—
	7042118	23/32	1 9/32	1 1/2	—	—	.190	—	.100	.325	—
	7042820	25/32	1 31/32	1 5/16	—	—	.080	—	.040	.215	—
	7042821	25/32	1 31/32	1 5/16	—	—	.110	—	.075	.215	—
	7042826	19/32	1 7/8	1 1/16	—	—	.085	—	.060	.215	2800
	7042827	19/32	1 7/8	1 1/16	—	—	.100	—	.080	.215	2400
	7042831	23/32	1 9/32	1 1/2	—	—	.180	—	.100	.325	—
	7042832	23/32	1 9/32	1 1/2	—	—	.170	—	.100	.325	—
	7042833	23/32	1 9/32	1 1/2	—	—	.180	—	.100	.325	—
	7042834	23/32	1 9/32	1 1/2	—	—	.170	—	.100	.325	—
	7042838	23/32	1 9/32	1 1/2	—	—	.190	—	.100	.325	—

①—Gauge from toe of float to air horn gasket. ②—Gauge from lip at toe of float to air horn gasket.

③—At slow idle RPM vent valve should be opened to specified dimension.

DODGE AND PLYMOUTH

Year	Carb. Part No. ★	Float Level	Float Drop	Pump Rod	Idle Vent	Intermediate Choke Rod	Vacuum Break	Automatic Choke	Choke Rod	Choke Unloader	Fast Idle Speed
1971	7041180	21/32	1 3/4	1 5/64	—	—	41 Drill	—	—	29 Drill	1800

ROCHESTER 2G, 2GC, 2GV CARBURETOR ADJUSTMENT SPECIFICATIONS—Continued

See Tune Up Chart in car chapters for hot idle speeds.

★Located on tag attached to or stamped on carburetor.

Year	Carb. Part No. ★	Float Level	Float Drop	Pump Rod	Idle Vent	Intermediate Choke Rod	Vacuum Break	Automatic Choke	Choke Rod	Choke Unloader	Fast Idle Speed
OLDSMOBILE											
1966	7026052	3/4	1 7/8	1 7/16	1 11/32	Flush	—	On Index	.150	.160	900③
	7026053	19/32	1 7/8	1 7/16	1 11/32	—	Flush	On Index	.150	.160	900③
	7026054	3/4	1 7/8	1 7/16	1 11/32	Flush	—	1 Lean	.150	.160	900③
	7026055	3/4	1 3/4	27/32	—	—	—	—	—	—	—
	7026056	5/8	1 3/4	1 11/32	1 9/32	—	.260	—	.100	.160	—
	7026057	3/4	1 3/4	27/32	—	—	—	—	—	—	—
	7026058	3/4	1 7/8	1 7/16	1 11/32	Flush	—	On Index	.150	.160	900③
	7026059	3/4	1 7/8	1 7/16	1 11/32	Flush	—	On Index	.150	.160	900③
	7036052	3/4	1 7/8	1 7/16	1 11/32	Flush	—	On Index	.150	.160	900③
	7036053	19/32	1 7/8	1 7/16	1 3/8	—	Flush	On Index	.150	.160	900③
	7036058	3/4	1 7/8	1 7/16	1 11/32	Flush	—	On Index	.150	.160	900③
	7036152	3/4	1 7/8	1 7/16	1 11/32	Flush	—	1 Lean	.150	.160	900③
	7036159	3/4	1 7/8	1 7/16	1 11/32	Flush	—	On Index	.150	.160	900③
1967	7027033	19/32	1 3/8	1 7/16	1 5/16	—	Flush	On Index	.150	.160	—
	7027035	19/32	1 3/8	1 7/16	1 5/16	—	1st Groove	On Index	.150	.160	—
	7027133	19/32	1 3/8	1 7/16	1 5/16	—	1st Groove	On Index	.150	.160	—
	7027136	19/32	1 3/8	1 7/16	1 5/16	—	1st Groove	On Index	.150	.160	—
	7027139	9/16	1 3/8	1 7/16	1 5/16	—	Flush	On Index	.150	.160	—
	7037050	19/32	1 3/8	1 7/16	1 5/16	—	1st Groove	On Index	.150	.160	—
	7037051	19/32	1 3/8	1 7/16	1 5/16	—	1st Groove	On Index	.150	.160	—
	7037052	19/32	1 3/8	1 7/16	1 5/16	—	1st Groove	On Index	.150	.160	—
	7037053	19/32	1 3/8	1 7/16	1 5/16	—	1st Groove	On Index	.150	.160	—
	7037054	19/32	1 3/8	1 7/16	1 5/16	—	Flush	On Index	.150	.160	—
	7037055	19/32	1 3/8	1 7/16	1 5/16	—	Flush	On Index	.150	.160	—
	7037056	1/2	1 3/8	1 7/16	1 5/16	—	Flush	On Index	.150	.160	—
	7037057	1/2	1 3/8	1 7/16	1 5/16	—	Flush	On Index	.150	.160	—
	7037058	19/32	1 3/8	1 7/16	1 5/16	—	Flush	1 Lean	.150	.160	—
1968	7028154	9/16	1 3/8	1 7/16	.025②	—	1st Groove	On Index	.150	.160	—
	7028155	9/16	1 3/8	1 7/16	.025②	—	Flush	1 Lean	.150	.160	900③
	7028156	9/16	1 3/8	1 7/16	.025②	—	1st Groove	On Index	.150	.160	900③
	7028157	9/16	1 3/8	1 7/16	.025②	—	1st Groove	On Index	.150	.160	900③
	7028158	9/16	1 3/8	1 7/16	.025②	—	Flush	On Index	.150	.160	900③
	7028159	9/16	1 3/8	1 7/16	.025②	—	Flush	1 Lean	.150	.160	900②
1969	7029155	9/16	1 3/8	1 7/16	.025②	—	.180	1 Lean	.140	.170	900③
	7029156	9/16	1 3/8	1 7/16	.025②	—	.180	On Index	.140	.170	900③
	7029158	9/16	1 3/8	1 7/16	.025②	—	.180	On Index	.140	.170	900③
	7029159	9/16	1 3/8	1 7/16	.025②	—	.180	On Index	.140	.170	900③
1970	7040154	9/16	1 3/8	1 11/32	—	—	.160	On Index	.140	.170	900③
	7040155	9/16	1 3/8	1 11/32	—	—	.160	1 Lean	.140	.170	900③
	7040156	9/16	1 3/8	1 11/32	—	—	.160	On Index	.140	.170	900③
	7040158	9/16	1 3/8	1 11/32	—	—	.160	On Index	.140	.170	900③
	7040159	9/16	1 3/8	1 11/32	—	—	.160	On Index	.140	.170	900③
1971	7041155	9/16	1 3/8	1 11/32	—	—	.200	1 Lean	.140	.170	1000③
	7041156	9/16	1 3/8	1 11/32	—	—	.200	On Index	.140	.170	1000③
	7041159	9/16	1 3/8	1 11/32	—	—	.215	On Index	.140	.170	1000③
1972	7042155	9/16	1 3/8	1 11/32	—	—	.200	1 Lean	.160	.170	1000③
	7042156	9/16	1 3/8	1 11/32	—	—	.200	On Index	.160	.170	1000③

②—At slow idle RPM vent valve should open to specified dimension. ③—On low step of cam.

ROCHESTER 2G, 2GC, 2GV CARBURETOR ADJUSTMENT SPECIFICATIONS—Continued

See Tune Up Chart in car chapters for hot idle speeds.

★Located on tag attached to or stamped on carburetor.

Year	Carb. Part No. ★	Float Level	Float Drop	Pump Rod	Idle Vent	Intermediate Choke Rod	Vacuum Break	Automatic Choke	Choke Rod	Choke Unloader	Fast Idle Speed
PONTIAC											
1966	7024078	21/32	1 3/4	27/32	—		—	—	—	—	—
	7024079	21/32	1 3/4	27/32	—		—	—	—	—	—
	7024178	21/32	1 3/4	27/32	—		—	—	—	—	—
	7024179	21/32	1 3/4	27/32	—		—	—	—	—	—
	7025078	21/32	1 3/4	27/32	—		—	—	—	—	—
	7025079	21/32	1 3/4	27/32	—		—	—	—	—	—
	7025178	21/32	1 3/4	27/32	—		—	—	—	—	—
	7025179	21/32	1 3/4	27/32	—		—	—	—	—	—
	7026074	19/32	1 3/4	1 11/32	1 9/32		.160	—	.095	.160	—
	7026075	19/32	1 3/4	1 11/32	1 9/32		.230	—	.095	.160	—
	7036175	19/32	1 3/4	1 11/32	1 9/32		.230	—	.095	.160	—
1967	7027060	9/16	1 9/16	1 11/32	1 9/16	Flush	—	Index	.085	.160	2800
	7027061	9/16	1 9/16	1 11/32	1 9/32	Flush	—	Index	.085	.160	2800
	7027062	9/16	1 9/16	1 11/32	1 9/32	Flush	—	Index	.085	.160	2800
	7027066	9/16	1 9/16	1 11/32	1 9/32	Flush	—	Index	.085	.160	2500
	7027071	9/16	1 9/16	1 11/32	1 9/32	Flush	—	Index	.085	.160	2500
	7037061	9/16	1 9/16	1 11/32	1 9/32	Flush	—	Index	.085	.160	2500
	7037062	9/16	1 9/16	1 11/32	1 9/32	Flush	—	Index	.085	.160	2500
	7037066	9/16	1 9/16	1 11/32	1 9/32	Flush	—	Index	.085	.160	2500
	7037071	9/16	1 9/16	1 11/32	1 9/32	Flush	—	Index	.085	.160	2500
	7037162	9/16	1 9/16	1 11/32	1 9/32	Flush	—	Index	.085	.160	2500
1968	7028060	9/16	1 3/4	1 11/32	—		.150	—	.085	.180	—
	7028062	9/16	1 3/4	1 11/32	—		.150	—	.085	.180	—
	7028066	9/16	1 3/4	1 11/32	—		.170	—	.085	.180	—
	7028071	9/16	1 3/4	1 11/32	—		.160	—	.085	.180	—
1969	7028066	9/16	1 3/4	1 11/32	—		.170	①	.085	.180	—
	7028071	9/16	1 3/4	1 11/32	—		.160	①	.085	.180	—
	7029060	9/16	1 3/4	1 11/32	—		.150	①	.085	.180	—
	7029062	9/16	1 3/4	1 11/32	—		.150	①	.085	.180	—
1970	7040060	11/16	1 3/4	1 11/32	—		.180	①	.085	.180	—
	7040062	9/16	1 3/4	1 11/32	—		.150	①	.085	.180	—
	7040064	11/16	1 3/4	1 11/32	—		.150	①	.085	.180	—
	7040066	11/16	1 3/4	1 11/32	—		.170	①	.085	.180	—
	7040071	9/16	1 3/4	1 11/32	—		.160	①	.085	.180	—
	7040072	9/16	1 3/4	1 11/32	—		.150	①	.085	.180	—
	7040460	11/16	1 3/4	1 11/32	—		.150	①	.085	.180	—
	7040461	11/16	1 3/4	1 11/32	—		.150	①	.085	.180	—
	7040462	9/16	1 3/4	1 11/32	—		.150	①	.085	.180	—
	7040463	9/16	1 3/4	1 11/32	—		.150	①	.085	.180	—
	7040466	11/16	1 3/4	1 11/32	—		.170	①	.085	.180	—
	7040471	9/16	1 3/4	1 11/32	—		.160	①	.085	.180	—
1971	7041060	11/16	1 3/4	1 11/32	—		.125	①	.085	.180	—
	7041061	11/16	1 3/4	1 11/32	—		.125	①	.085	.180	—
	7041062	9/16	1 3/4	1 11/32	—		.105	①	.085	.180	—
	7041063	9/16	1 3/4	1 11/32	—		.105	①	.085	.180	—
	7041064	11/16	1 3/4	1 11/32	—		.130	①	.085	.180	—
	7041070	11/16	1 3/4	1 11/32	—		.125	①	.085	.180	—

Continued

ROCHESTER 2G, 2GC, 2GV CARBURETOR ADJUSTMENT SPECIFICATIONS—Continued

See Tune Up Chart in car chapters for hot idle speeds.

★Located on tag attached to or stamped on carburetor.

Year	Carb. Part No. ★	Float Level	Float Drop	Pump Rod	Idle Vent	Intermediate Choke Rod	Vacuum Break	Automatic Choke	Choke Rod	Choke Unloader	Fast Idle Speed
PONTIAC—Continued											
1971	7041072	9/16	1¾	1¹¹/₃₂	—	—	.105	①	.085	.180	—
	7041074	11/16	1¾	1¹¹/₃₂	—	—	.130	①	.085	.180	—
	7041171	9/16	1¾	1¹¹/₃₂	—	—	.140	①	.085	.180	—
1972	7042060	5/8	1⁹/₃₂	1¹¹/₃₂	—	—	.122	①	.085	.180	—
	7042061	5/8	1⁹/₃₂	1¹¹/₃₂	—	—	.122	①	.085	.180	—
	7042062	9/16	1⁹/₃₂	1¹¹/₃₂	—	—	.105	①	.085	.180	—
	7042064	5/8	1⁹/₃₂	1¹¹/₃₂	—	—	.150	①	.085	.180	—
	7042100	25/32	1³¹/₃₂	1⁵/₁₆	—	—	.080	①	.040	.215	—
	7042101	25/32	1³¹/₃₂	1⁵/₁₆	—	—	.100	①	.075	.215	—

①—With choke valve closed, pull upward on choke rod to the limit of its travel.   The end of rod should fit the gauge notch on the choke lever.

2G, 2GC, 2GV ADJUSTMENTS

Model 2G carburetor is equipped with a manually-operated choke valve. Its major applications are on trucks and marine engines where an automatic choke is not an absolute necessity. However, on multiple carburetor applications, such as the "Tri-Power" set-up used on some Pontiacs where three carburetors are used, the two end carburetors are 2G models, the center one being equipped with an automatic choke. Models 2GC and 2GV use an automatic choke.

There are four different types of automatic choke systems used on these units; 1) The carburetor mounted thermostatic coil; 2) the well type, Fig. 4; 3) the split linkage type, Fig. 5 and the hot water system, Fig. 6.

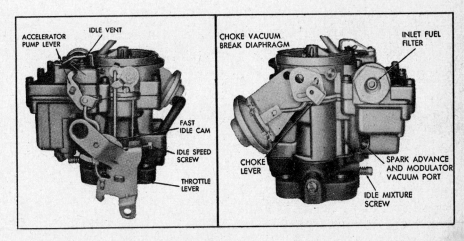

Fig. 1   Rochester Model 2GV two-barrel carburetor

Float Level Adjustment

Fig. 7—Adjust float level as directed for the type of float shown in the specification listed in the *Rochester Specifications Chart.*

Float Drop Adjustment

Fig. 8—Adjust float drop as directed for the type of float shown in the specification listed in the *Rochester Specifications Chart.*

Pump Rod Adjustment

Fig. 9—Back out idle stop screw and completely close throttle valves in bore. Place proper size gauge listed in the *Rochester Specifications Chart* on top of air horn ring. Bend pump rod at lower angle to obtain specified dimension to top of pump rod.

Idle Vent Adjustment

Fig. 10—Open throttle until vent valve just closes. Place proper size gauge on top of air horn ring. Dimension to top of pump rod should be as specified in the *Rochester Specifications Chart.* Adjust by bending tang on pump lever.

Intermediate Choke Rod Adjustment

Choke Mounted on Throttle Body, Fig. 11 —Remove thermostat cover and coil as-

sembly and inside baffle plate. Hold choke valve completely closed and bend intermediate choke rod as necessary to that end of choke piston is as specified in the *Rochester Specifications Chart* with end of choke piston bore.

Split Linkage Choke, Fig. 12—Remove thermostat cover and coil assembly and inside baffle plate. Open throttle valves and hold choke valve completely closed by pushing upward on intermediate choke lever. Adjust intermediate choke rod as necessary by bending so that choke piston is in the location shown in the illustration.

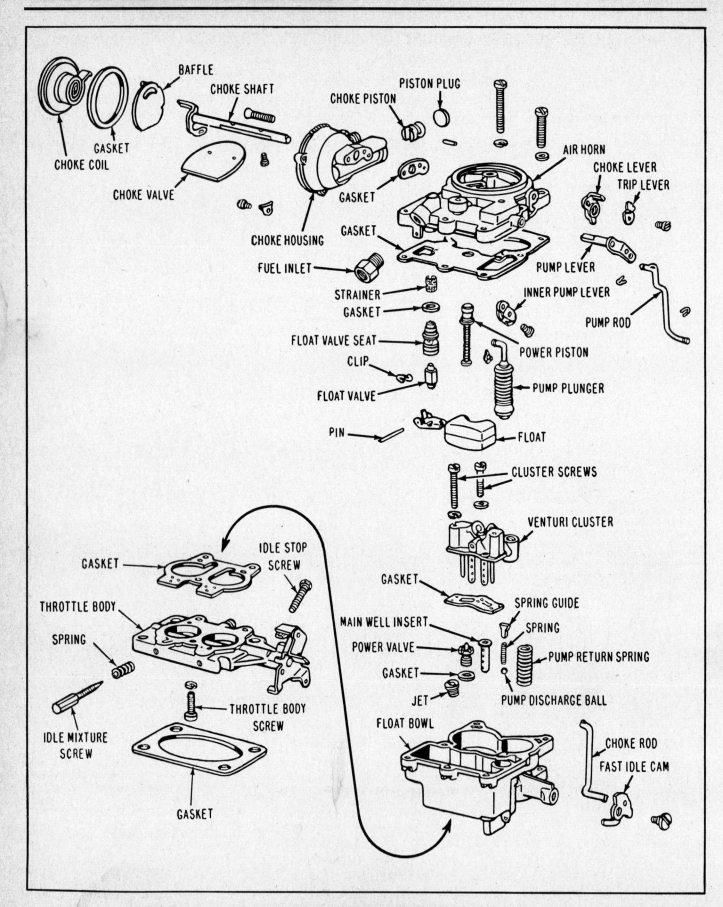

Fig. 2 Exploded view of Rochester two-barrel carburetor

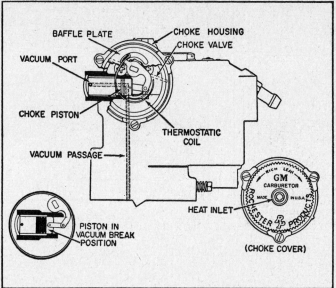

Fig. 3 Carburetor mounted automatic choke

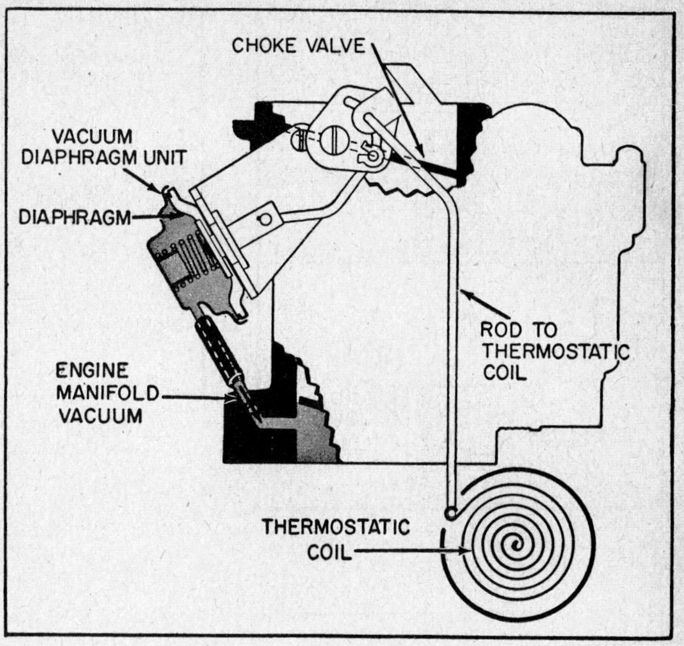

Fig. 4 Well-type choke. 2GV models

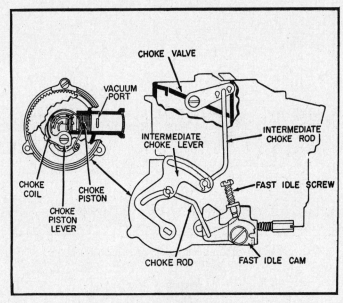

Fig. 5 Split linkage type automatic choke

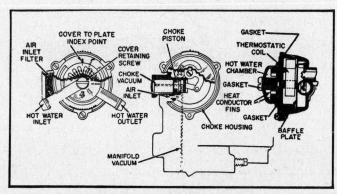

Fig. 6 Hot water choke system

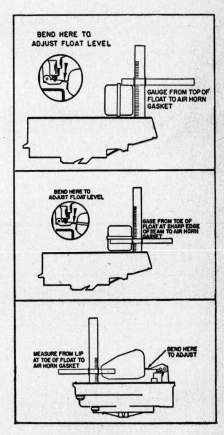

Fig. 7 Float level adjustment.
Rochester 2G, 2GC, 2GV

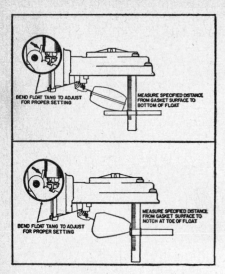

Fig. 8   Float drop adjustment.
Rochester 2G, 2GC, 2GV

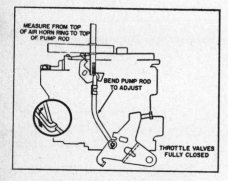

Fig. 9   Pump rod adjustment
for 2G, 2GC, 2GV carburetors

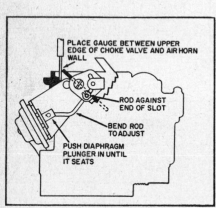

Fig. 13   Vacuum break adjustment
for 2GV carburetors

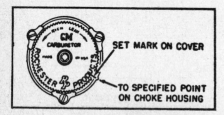

Fig. 14   Automatic choke adjustment
for 2GC carburetors

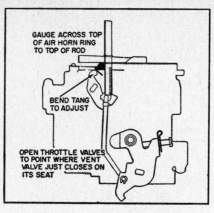

Fig. 10   Idle vent adjustment
for 2G, 2GC, 2GV carburetors

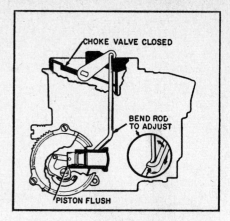

Fig. 11   Intermediate choke rod adjustment
for 2GC chokes mounted on throttle body

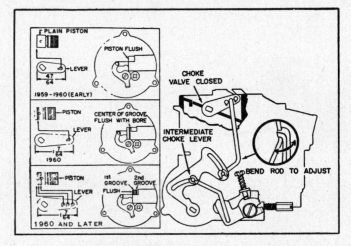

Fig. 12   Intermediate choke rod adjustment for 2GC
carburetors having split linkage chokes

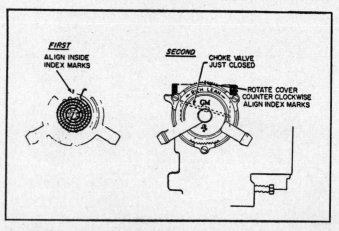

Fig. 15   Hot water choke coil adjustment
on some 2GC carburetors

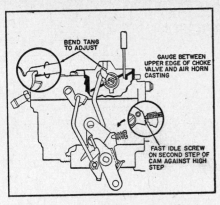

Fig. 16 Choke rod adjustment for models without split linkage

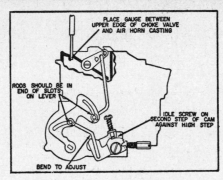

Fig. 17 Choke rod adjustment for 2GC split linkage type chokes

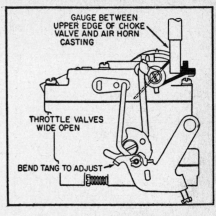

Fig. 18 Choke unloader adjustment for 2GC, 2GV carburetors

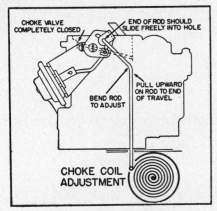

Fig. 19 Thermostatic coil rod adjustment for 2GV carburetors

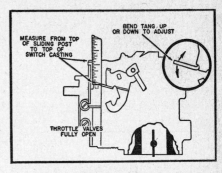

Fig. 20 Vacuum switch adjustment for some 2GC carburetors

Vacuum Break Adjustment

Model 2GV, Fig. 13—Push vacuum break diaphragm plunger in until it is seated and make sure choke valve is closed so that connecting rod is at end of slot in choke shaft lever. In this position, adjust rod by bending so that specified gauge will fit between upper edge of choke valve and inner wall of air horn (see *Rochester Specifications Chart*). Adjust by bending connecting rod at point shown.

Automatic Choke Setting

Carburetor Mounted Choke, Fig. 14—Loosen three retaining screws and rotate choke cover against coil tension until index mark is in line with specified point on choke housing (see *Rochester Specifications Chart*).
Hot Water Choke Coil, Fig. 15—There are two adjustments necessary to provide proper choke indexing. The inner choke cover containing the thermostatic coil must be indexed with the outer cover. This indexing can be accomplished by aligning the scribe mark on the inner cover with the index point on the outer cover as shown. The complete choke cover assembly which has a scribe mark on the outside which must be aligned with the proper index point on the choke housing.

Choke Rod Adjustment

Exc. Split Linkage Type, Fig. 16—It is important to position both slow idle and fast idle screws as follows before making choke rod adjustment.

1. On models using a single idle stop screw, turn stop screw in until it just contacts bottom step of fast idle cam. Then turn screw in one full turn farther.
2. On models using both a slow idle and a fast idle screw, turn slow idle stop screw in until it just contacts stop. Then turn this screw in one full turn from this point. Next turn the fast idle screw in until it touches bottom step of fast idle cam.
3. On all models, place idle screw on second step of fast idle cam against shoulder of high step. While holding screw in this position, check clearance between upper edge of choke valve and air horn wall as shown. Adjust to specified dimension by bending tang on choke lever and collar assembly (see *Rochester Specifications Chart*).

Split Linkage Choke, Fig. 17—Position slow idle and fast idle screws as outlined in Steps 1 and 2 above. Then place fast idle screw on second stop of fast idle cam next to high step as shown. Make sure intermediate choke rod and choke rod are in ends of slots in intermediate choke lever by pushing upward on lever. Bend choke rod until specified gauge size will just fit between upper edge of choke valve and inner wall of air horn (see *Rochester Specifications Chart*).

Choke Unloader Adjustment

Fig. 18—With throttle valves held wide open, the choke valve should be open just enough to admit the specified gauge between upper edge of choke valve and air horn wall (see *Rochester Specifications Chart*). To adjust, bend tang on throttle lever.

Thermostatic Coil Rod Adjustment

Model 2GV, Fig. 19—Disconnect upper end of thermostatic coil rod from choke lever. Hold choke valve completely closed and pull upward on coil rod to the limit of its travel. Bottom of rod should be even with top of hole in choke shaft lever. Adjust by bending coil rod.

Vacuum Switch Adjustment

Fig. 20—With throttle wide open measure distance from top of post to top of switch. This distance should be $1\frac{3}{32}$". If adjustment is required, loosen switch attaching screws and move switch up or down to correct.

Be careful not to bend or bump lever after adjustment has been made. Open and close throttle to be sure that arm on pump lever does not bind post on switch.

ROCHESTER CARBURETORS

ROCHESTER 4GC FLOAT ADJUSTMENT SPECIFICATIONS

Year	Carburetor Part No. [1]	Float Level		Float Toe		Float Drop		Vacuum Assist Spring
		Primary	Secondary	Primary	Secondary	Primary	Secondary	
BUICK								
1966	7026040	1 7/16	1 7/16	—	—	1 1/16	1 1/16	—
CADILLAC								
1966	7026030	1 7/16	1 3/8	5/8	3/8	1 1/2	1 1/16	1 1/16
	7026031	1 7/16	1 3/8	5/8	3/8	1 1/2	1 1/16	1 1/16
CHEVROLET ENGINES								
1966	7025126	1 17/32	1 19/32	—	—	2 1/4	2 1/4	—
	7025127	1 17/32	1 19/32	—	—	2 1/4	2 1/4	—
	7025128	1 17/32	1 19/32	—	—	2 1/4	2 1/4	—
	7036118	1 17/32	1 19/32	—	—	2 1/4	2 1/4	—
	7036119	1 17/32	1 19/32	—	—	2 1/4	2 1/4	—
	7036120	1 17/32	1 19/32	—	—	2 1/4	2 1/4	—
	7036121	1 17/32	1 19/32	—	—	2 1/4	2 1/4	—

[1]—Located on tag attached to or stamped on carburetor.

ROCHESTER 4GC ADJUSTMENT SPECIFICATIONS (Except Float Data)

See Tune Up Chart in car chapters for hot idle speeds.

Year	Carb. Part No.[1]	Pump Rod	Idle Vent	Intermediate Choke Rod	Auto. Choke	Choke Rod	Fast Idle Speed	Choke Unloader	Anti-Stall Dashpot	Secondary	
										Lockout	Contour
BUICK											
1966	7026040	1 [2]	—	.030 Out	Index	.060	650 [3]	.120	—	.015	.030
CADILLAC											
1966	7026030	13/16 [5]	—	Flush	Index	.040	1700	.130	—	.020	.020
	7026031	13/16 [5]	—	Flush	Index	.040	1700	.130	—	.020	.020
CHEVROLET ENGINES											
1966	7025126	1 1/16 [2]	31/32	Flush	Index	.055	—	.250	—	.015	.015
	7025127	1 1/16 [4]	31/32	Flush	Index	.055	—	.250	—	.015	.015
	7025128	1 1/16 [2]	31/32	Flush	Index	.055	—	.250	—	.015	.015
	7036118	1 1/16 [2]	31/32	Flush	Index	.055	—	.250	—	.015	.015
	7036119	1 1/16 [2]	31/32	Flush	Index	.055	—	.250	—	.015	.015
	7036120	1 1/16 [2]	31/32	Flush	Index	.055	—	.250	—	.015	.015
	7036121	1 1/16 [2]	31/32	Flush	Index	.055	—	.250	—	.015	.015

[1]—Located on tag attached to or stamped on carburetor.
[2]—In center hole.
[3]—On low step of cam.
[4]—In inner hole.
[5]—In outer hole.

4GC ADJUSTMENTS

The carburetor, Figs. 1 and 2, is divided into a primary and secondary side. The primary side covers the forward half of the unit and is essentially a complete two-bore carburetor containing float, idle, main metering, accelerator pump, power and choke systems.

The secondary side is a supplementary two-bore carburetor that feeds extra air and fuel to the engine when needed for power requirements. This section contains only a float system, main metering system and, on some applications, a fixed idle system. It also has a set of throttle valves and separate auxiliary valves that are located in the bores above the throttle valves.

Both high and low float bowl designs are used in these carburetors. The type used is dependent upon engine demands and underhood clearance. Both round and "D" shaped float pontoons are used in the high float bowl. A smaller wedge-shaped float is used in the low bowl design.

Float assist springs are used on some high bowl and all low bowl applications. Their purpose is to assist the floats in holding the float needle valve closed, especially where fuel pressures are encountered.

Fig. 3 shows an idle compensator valve used on some standard and air-conditioned models. A thermostatic valve mounted on the secondary side of the float bowl between secondary venturi, allows additional air to enter the primary bores under extreme "hot idle" conditions.

Some 4GC models use an idle air by-pass system, Fig. 4. The purpose of this system is to allow the primary throttle valves to be completely closed during curb idle operation. The design prevents carbon and gum formations which may form around the throttle valves from disrupting engine idle speed.

There are three designs of automatic choke systems used on 4GC carburetors: 1) the conventional system mounted on the carburetor; 2) the split linkage system, and 3) the hot water system. All three of these systems are illustrated and described briefly in the Rochester two-barrel carburetor section of this chapter.

Float Level Adjustment

Fig. 5—With air horn inverted and gasket in place, gauge from gasket surface to top of each float next to seam. Adjust to specified dimension by bending float arms at junction point near needle and seat (see *Rochester Specifications Chart*).

Float Toe Adjustment

Fig. 6—With air horn inverted and gasket in place, measure distance from gasket to center of dimple of each float

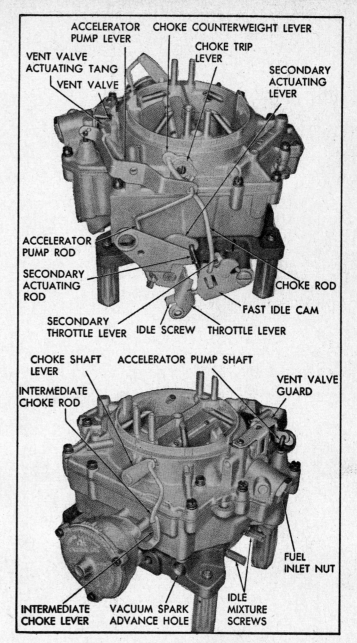

Fig. 1   Rochester 4GC "Low Silhouette" four-barrel carburetor

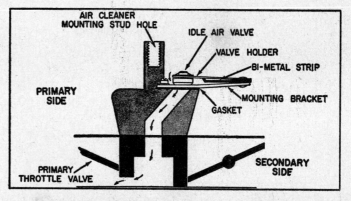

Fig. 3   Hot idle compensator on some 4GC carburetors

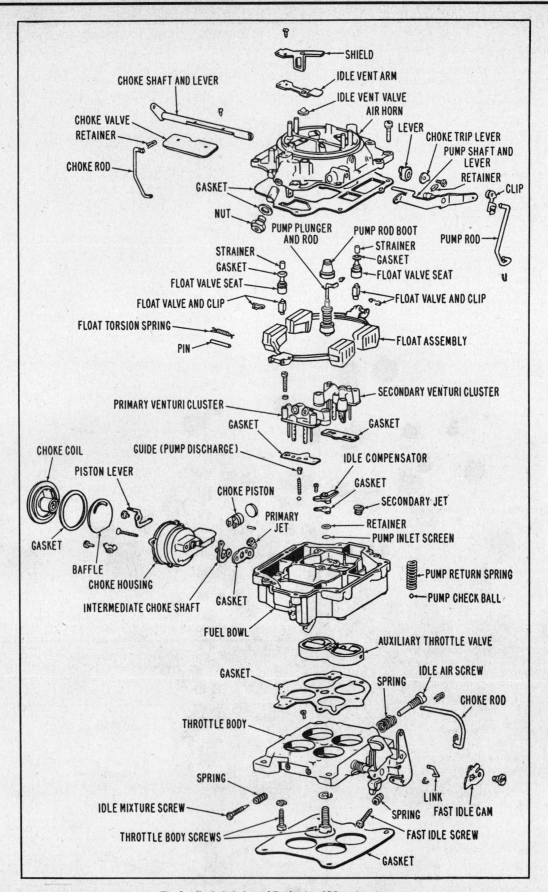

Fig. 2 Exploded view of Rochester 4GC carburetor

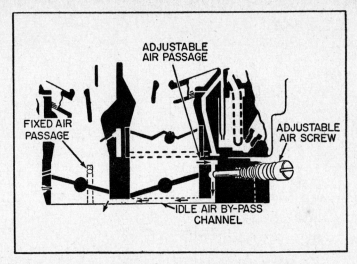

Fig. 4   Idle air by-pass system on some 4GC carburetors

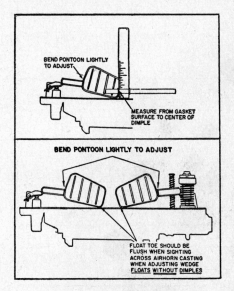

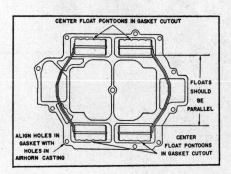

Fig. 6   Float toe adjustment
on 4GC carburetors

Fig. 7   Float alignment
on 4GC carburetors

at toe (small end). Adjust to specified dimension by bending toe of each float up or down as required (see *Rochester Specifications Chart*).

NOTE: Wedge type floats that do not have dimples in sides of floats should

be adjusted so lower tip of float toe is flush with air horn casting when sighting across air horn casting as shown in lower view, Fig. 6.

Float Alignment

Fig. 7—Align screw holes in air horn gasket with screw holes in air horn. Then make sure floats are centered in the cutout section of gasket and sides of float pontoons are parallel with adjacent edges of gasket. Bend float arms as necessary to adjust.

Float Drop Adjustment

Fig. 8—With air horn upright and level, gasket in place and floats hanging freely, measure distance on each float from gasket surface to center of dimple, or bottom of scribe line (wedge floats). Measure to lower edge of toe for wedge floats without dimple. Measure to lowest point on "D" or round pontoon floats. Adjust to specified dimension by bending tang that contacts seat or spring (see *Rochester Specifications Chart*).

Vacuum Assist Spring Adjustment

Fig. 9—With air horn held upright and level, hold power piston in full up position (with thumb). Jounce pontoon lightly to make sure cup retainer on vacuum assist spring is not binding on power piston stem. Measure distance from gasket to center of dimple on float pontoon at toe. To adjust, bend tang at center of float arms (see *Rochester Specifications Chart*). Always hold power piston In "up" position.

Pump Rod Adjustment

Fig. 10—Install pump rod in hole specified for model being serviced. Back out slow idle screw until throttle valves are completely closed. Place proper size gauge on top of air horn next to pump plunger. With throttle valves closed and lower edge of gauge resting on top of air horn, distance from top of air horn to bottom of pump plunger shaft should be as specified in the *Rochester Specifications Chart*. Bend pump rod to adjust.

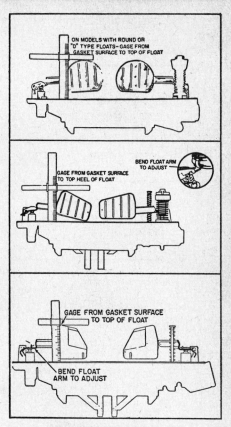

Fig. 5   Float level adjustment
on 4GC carburetors

NOTE: After adjusting pump rod to the specified dimension, the rod can be moved to the inboard hole (where used) for richer pump discharge or to the outboard hole (where used) for leaner pump discharge.

Idle Vent Adjustment

Fig. 11—After making pump adjustment, open throttle valves enough to obtain the specified measurement from air horn to bottom of pump plunger shaft. At this point the idle vent should just close. To adjust, bend tang on pump lever as shown.

On older models, adjust by bending tang that contacts face of valve under pump lever.

Intermediate Choke Rod Adjustment

Fig. 12—This applies only to models with the choke mounted on throttle body or bowl. Holding choke valve closed, bend intermediate choke rod as necessary so that end of choke piston is flush with end of choke piston sleeve.

Intermediate Choke Adjustment

Fig. 13—Place fast idle screw on high step of fast idle cam and raise intermediate choke lever to its full up position. Be sure all lash is removed from rods in slots. The choke piston should be flush with end of choke piston bore. Bend intermediate choke rod to position the choke piston correctly.

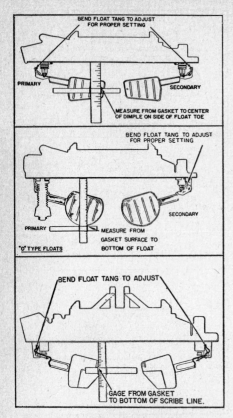

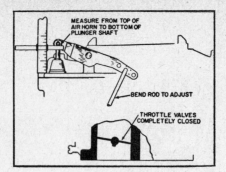

Fig. 10   Pump rod adjustment on 4GC carburetors

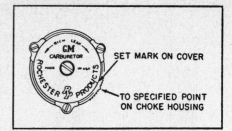

Fig. 14   Automatic choke adjustment on 4GC carburetors

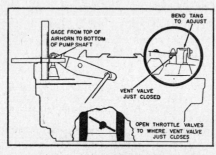

Fig. 11   Idle vent adjustment on 4GC carburetors

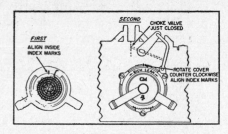

Fig. 15   Hot water choke coil adjustment on some 4GC carburetors

Fig. 8   Float drop adjustment on 4GC carburetors

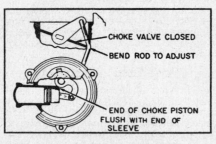

Fig. 12   Intermediate choke rod adjustment on some 4GC carburetors

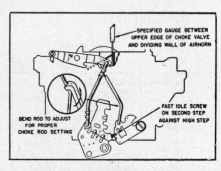

Fig. 16   Choke rod adjustment for chokes mounted on air horn. 4GC carburetors

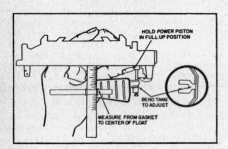

Fig. 9   Vacuum assist spring adjustment on 4GC carburetors

Automatic Choke Adjustment

Fig. 14—Loosen three retaining screws and rotate choke cover against coil tension until index mark on cover is aligned with specified mark on housing (see *Rochester Specifications Chart*).

Hot Water Choke Coil Adjustment

Fig. 15—There are two adjustments necessary to provide proper choke indexing. The inner choke cover containing the thermostatic coil must be indexed with the outer cover. This indexing can be accomplished by aligning the scribe mark on the inner cover with the index point on the outer cover as shown. The complete choke cover assembly has a scribe mark on the outside which must be aligned with the proper indexing point on the choke housing (see *Rochester Specifications Chart*).

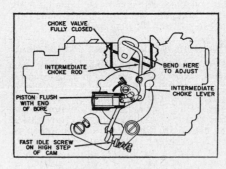

Fig. 13   Intermediate choke adjustment on some 4GC carburetors

Choke Rod Adjustment

Models With Air Horn Mounted Chokes, Fig. 16—It is important to position both slow idle and fast idle before making the choke rod adjustment.
1. On models having a single idle screw, turn stop screw in until it contacts bottom step of fast idle cam. Then turn screw in one full turn.
2. On models using a separate fast idle

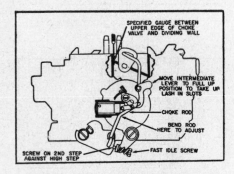

Fig. 17   Choke rod adjustment for chokes mounted on throttle body. 4GC carburetors

screw, turn slow idle stop screw in until it touches the stop, then turn screw in one additional turn. Turn fast idle screw in until it touches bottom step of fast idle cam.
3. After positioning slow and fast idle screws, position idle screw on second step of fast idle cam against shoulder of high step. Then check clearance between upper edge of choke valve and air horn wall (see *Roches-*

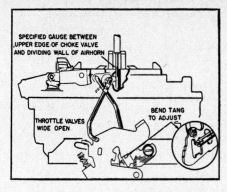

Fig. 18   Choke unloader adjustment on 4GC carburetors

Fig. 19   Secondary lockout adjustment on 4GC carburetors

ter *Specifications Chart*). To adjust, bend choke rod as required.

Models With Intermediate Choke Rod, Fig. 17—Position slow and fast idle screws as outlined above. Then position fast idle screw on second step of fast idle cam and raise intermediate choke lever to the full open position. Be sure

intermediate rod and choke rod are at the upper limit of travel in the slots. Adjust choke rod by bending to obtain the specified clearance between choke valve and the dividing wall of air horn (see *Rochester Specifications Chart*).

Choke Unloader Adjustment

Fig. 18—Fully open primary throttle valves While holding lever in this position, check for specified clearance between upper edge of choke valve and air horn wall (see *Rochester Specifications Chart*). To adjust, bend unloader tang on fast idle cam.

On a few models, this adjustment is made by bending unloader tang on pump lever.

Secondary Lockout Adjustment

Fig. 19—With choke valve fully closed, bend lockout lever as shown to obtain specified clearance between the cam and widest surface of lockout lever (see *Rochester Specifications Chart*).

Secondary Contour Adjustment

Fig. 20—With choke valve wide open, bend lockout lever to obtain specified clearance between the cam and narrowest surface of lockout lever at point shown *(see Rochester Specifications Chart)*.

Vacuum Break Adjustment

Fig. 21—Push diaphragm plunger in un-

Fig. 20   Secondary contour adjustment on 4GC carburetors

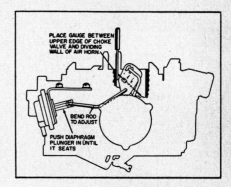

Fig. 21   Vacuum break adjustment on some 4GC carburetors

til it seats. While holding plunger seated, close choke valve to the point where vacuum diaphragm connecting rod is in end of plunger. At this point, a .060" gauge should just fit between upper edge of choke valve and the dividing wall of air horn. To adjust for proper clearance, bend rod.

ROCHESTER QUADRAJET 4MC & 4MV ADJUSTMENT SPECIFICATIONS

See Tune Up Chart in car chapters for hot idle speeds.

Year	Carb. Model	Float Level	Pump Rod Hole	Pump Rod Adj.	Idle Vent	Air Valve	Fast Idle (Bench)	Choke Rod	Vacuum Break	Air Valve Dashpot	Choke Unloader	Air Valve Lockout	Secondary Metering Rods	Air-Valve Valve Spring Wind-Up
BUICK														
1966	7026240	1/4	Inner	9/32	3/8	1³/₁₆	2 Turns	.140①	.230	1³/₁₆	.325	.030	5³/₆₄	5/8
	7026242	1/4	Inner	9/32	3/8	1³/₁₆	2 Turns	.140①	.230	1³/₁₆	.325	.030	5³/₆₄	5/8
	7036240	1/4	Inner	9/32	3/8	1³/₁₆	2 Turns	.140①	.230	1³/₁₆	.325	.030	5³/₆₄	5/8
	7036242	1/4	Inner	9/32	3/8	1³/₁₆	2 Turns	.140①	.230	1³/₁₆	.325	.030	5³/₆₄	5/8
1967	7027140	9/32	Inner	9/32	7/16	—	2 Turns	.130	.200	.030	.325	.045	5³/₆₄	1/2
	7027141	9/32	Outer	13/32	7/16	—	2 Turns	.130	.200	.030	.325	.045	5³/₆₄	1/2
	7027146	7/32	Outer	9/32	1/2	—	2 Turns	.130	.200	.030	.325	.045	5³/₆₄	1/2
	7027147	7/32	Outer	13/32	1/2	—	2 Turns	.130	.200	.030	.325	.045	5³/₆₄	1/2
	7027148	7/32	Inner	9/32	3/8	—	2 Turns	.130	.215	.030	.325	.015	5³/₆₄	1/2
	7027149	7/32	Inner	9/32	3/8	—	2 Turns	.130	.215	.030	.325	.015	5³/₆₄	1/2
	7027240	9/32	Inner	9/32	7/16	—	2 Turns	.130	.200	.030	.325	.045	5³/₆₄	1/2
	7027241	9/32	Outer	13/32	7/16	—	2 Turns	.130	.200	.030	.325	.045	5³/₆₄	1/2
	7027244	1/4	Outer	13/32	1/2	—	2 Turns	.130	.200	.030	.325	.045	5³/₆₄	1/2
	7027246	1/4	Inner	9/32	3/8	—	2 Turns	.120	.215	.030	.325		5³/₆₄	1/2
	7027248	5/16	Inner	9/32	7/16	—	2 Turns	.120	.200	.030	.325	.045	5³/₆₄	1/2

Continued

ROCHESTER CARBURETORS

ROCHESTER QUADRAJET 4MC & 4MV ADJUSTMENT SPECIFICATIONS—Continued

See Tune Up Chart in car chapters for hot idle speeds.

Year	Carb. Model	Float Level	Pump Rod Hole	Pump Rod Adj.	Idle Vent	Air Valve	Fast Idle (Bench)	Choke Rod	Vacuum Break	Air Valve Dash-pot	Choke Unloader	Air Valve Lockout	Secondary Metering Rods	Air-Valve Valve Spring Wind-Up
BUICK—Continued														
1968	7028240	[2]	[3]	[4]	½	—	2 Turns	.130	.200	.030	.325	.045	53/64	½
	7028242	3/8	Inner	9/32	½	—	2 Turns	.130	.180	.030	.325	.045	53/64	½
	7028243	7/16	Outer	11/32	½	—	2 Turns	.140	.215	.030	.325	—	53/64	½
	7028244	5/16	Outer	13/32	½	—	2 Turns	.130	.200	.030	.325	.045	53/64	½
	7028245	5/16	Outer	13/32	½	—	2 Turns	.130	.215	.030	.325	—	53/64	½
	7028248	9/32	Outer	13/32	½	—	2 Turns	.130	.180	.030	.325	.045	53/64	½
1969	7029240	3/8	Outer	13/32	½	—	—	.130	.180	.030	.325	.045	53/64	½
	7029241	5/16	Outer	13/32	½	—	—	.130	.180	.030	.325	.045	53/64	½
	7029242	3/8	Outer	13/32	½	—	—	.130	.180	.030	.325	.045	53/64	½
	7029243	3/8	Outer	13/32	½	—	—	.140	.215	.030	.325	.015	53/64	½
	7029244	5/16	Outer	13/32	½	—	—	.130	.190	.030	.325	.045	53/64	½
	7029245	5/16	Outer	13/32	½	—	—	.130	.215	.030	.325	.015	53/64	½
1970	7040240	3/8	Inner	9/32	—	—	—	.130	.180	.030	.335	—	53/64	½
	7040243	3/8	Inner	9/32	—	—	—	.130	.215	.030	.335	—	53/64	½
	7040244	5/16	Outer	13/32	—	—	—	.130	.170	.030	.335	.045	53/64	½
	7040245	5/16	Outer	13/32	—	—	—	.130	.215	.030	.335	—	53/64	½
	7040246	5/16	Inner	9/32	—	—	—	.130	.200	.030	.335	—	53/64	½
	7040247	3/8	Inner	9/32	—	—	—	.130	.160	.030	.325	—	53/64	½
1971	7041242	3/8	Inner	1/4	—	—	—	.130	.200[5]	.030	.335	—	53/64	½
	7041243	13/32	Inner	1/4	—	—	—	.130	.215[6]	.030	.335	—	53/64	½
	7041245	15/32	Inner	9/32	—	—	—	.130	.170[7]	.030	.335	—	53/64	½
	7041540	3/8	Inner	1/4	—	—	—	.130	.180[5]	.030	.335	—	53/64	½
	7041544	15/32	Inner	9/32	—	—	—	.130	.170[7]	.030	.335	—	53/64	½
1972	7042240	3/8	Inner	1/4	—	—	—	.130	.180[5]	.030	.335	.015	53/64	½
	7042242	3/8	Inner	1/4	—	—	—	.130	.200[5]	.030	.335	.015	53/64	½
	7042243	13/32	Inner	1/4	—	—	—	.130	.215[6]	.030	.335	.015	53/64	½
	7042244	15/32	Inner	9/32	—	—	—	.130	.170[7]	.030	.335	.015	53/64	½
	7042245	15/32	Inner	9/32	—	—	—	.130	.170[7]	.030	.335	.015	53/64	½
	7042940	3/8	Inner	1/4	—	—	—	.130	.180[5]	.030	.335	.015	53/64	½
	7042942	3/8	Inner	1/4	—	—	—	.130	.200[5]	.030	.335	.015	53/64	½
	7042944	15/32	Inner	9/32	—	—	—	.130	.170[7]	.030	.335	.015	53/64	½

[1]—4MC carburetor; set choke thermostat cover on index mark.   [2]—Early 3/8"; late 7/16".   [3]—Early, inner; late, outer.
[4]—Early 9/32"; late 13/32".   [5]—Secondary adjustment .160".   [6]—Secondary adjustment .195".   [7]—Secondary adjustment .150".

CADILLAC

Year	Carb. Model	Float Level	Pump Rod Hole	Pump Rod Adj.	Idle Vent	Air Valve	Fast Idle (Bench)	Choke Rod	Vacuum Break	Air Valve Dash-pot	Choke Unloader	Air Valve Lockout	Secondary Metering Rods	Air-Valve Valve Spring Wind-Up
1967	7027230	1/4	Outer	11/16	—	—	1 Turn	.090	.180	.030	.300	.015	55/64	1/4
	7027231	1/4	Outer	11/16	—	—	1 Turn	.090	.180	.030	.300	.015	55/64	1/4
	7027233	1/4	Outer	11/16	—	—	1 Turn	.090	.180	.030	.300	.015	55/64	1/4
	7027234	1/4	Outer	11/16	—	—	1 Turn	.090	.180	.030	.300	.015	55/64	1/4
	7027235	1/4	Outer	11/16	—	—	1 Turn	.090	.180	.030	.300	.015	55/64	1/4
	7037230	1/4	Outer	11/32	—	—	1 Turn	.090	.180	.030	.300	.015	55/64	1/4
	7037231	1/4	Outer	11/32	—	—	1 Turn	.090	.180	.030	.300	.015	55/64	1/4
	7037234	1/4	Outer	11/32	—	—	1 Turn	.090	.180	.030	.300	.015	55/64	1/4
	7037235	1/4	Outer	11/32	—	—	1 Turn	.090	.180	.030	.300	.015	55/64	1/4
1968	7028230	1/4	Outer	11/32	—	—	1½ Turns	.090	.180	.030	.300	.030	55/64	½
	7028231	1/4	Outer	11/32	—	—	1½ Turns	.090	.180	.030	.300	.030	55/64	½
	7028234	11/32	Outer	11/32	—	—	1½ Turns	.090	.180	.030	.300	.030	55/64	7/16
	7028235	11/32	Outer	11/32	—	—	1½ Turns	.090	.180	.030	.300	.030	55/64	7/16
	7028236	1/4	Outer	11/32	—	—	1½ Turns	.090	.215	.030	.300	.030	55/64	½
	7028237	1/4	Outer	11/32	—	—	1½ Turns	.090	.215	.030	.300	.030	55/64	½
	7028238	11/32	Outer	11/32	—	—	1½ Turns	.090	.215	.030	.300	.030	55/64	7/16
	7028239	11/32	Outer	11/32	—	—	1½ Turns	.090	.215	.030	.300	.030	55/64	7/16

Continued

ROCHESTER QUADRAJET 4MC & 4MV ADJUSTMENT SPECIFICATIONS—Continued

See Tune Up Chart in car chapters for hot idle speeds.

Year	Carb. Model	Float Level	Pump Rod Hole	Pump Rod Adj.	Idle Vent	Air Valve	Fast Idle (Bench)	Choke Rod	Vacuum Break	Air Valve Dashpot	Choke Unloader	Air Valve Lockout	Secondary Metering Rods	Air-Valve Valve Spring Wind-Up
CADILLAC—Continued														
1969	7029230	1/4	Outer	11/32	—	—	1 1/2 Turns	.090	.230	.030	.300	.015	27/32	1/2
	7029231	1/4	Outer	11/32	—	—	1 1/2 Turns	.090	.230	.030	.300	.015	27/32	1/2
1970	7047030	1/4	Outer	11/32	—	—	1 1/2 Turns	.090	.230	.030	.300	.015	27/32	1/2
1971	7041766	1/4	Outer	11/32	—	—	1 1/2 Turns	.090	.300	.030	.310	.015	.840	1/2
	7041777	23/64	Outer	11/32	—	—	1 1/2 Turns	.090	.300	.030	.310	.015	.840	1/2
1972	7047231	15/64	Outer	11/32	—	—	1 1/2 Turns	.090	.110	—	.312	.015	.840	1/2
	7047232	23/64	Outer	11/32	—	—	1 1/2 Turns	.090	.110	—	.312	.015	.840	1/2
CHEVROLET ENGINES														
1966	7026200	1/4	Inner	9/32	3/8	1 1/4	2 Turns	.100	.160	—	.300	.015	27/32	1
	7026201	1/4	Inner	9/32	3/8	1 1/4	2 Turns	.100	.245	—	.300	—	27/32	1
	7026202	1/4	Inner	9/32	3/8	1 1/8	2 Turns	.110	.150	—	.245	.015	53/64	1
	7026203	1/4	Inner	9/32	3/8	1 1/8	2 Turns	.110	.200	—	.300	—	53/64	1
	7026204	1/4	Inner	9/32	3/8	1 1/4	2 Turns	.100	.160	—	.300	.015	27/32	1
	7026205	1/4	Inner	9/32	3/8	1 1/4	2 Turns	.100	.245	—	.300	—	27/32	1
	7026210	1/4	Inner	9/32	3/8	1 1/8	2 Turns	.110	.150	—	.245	.015	53/64	1
	7036200	1/4	Inner	9/32	3/8	1 1/4	2 Turns	.100	.160	—	.300	.015	27/32	1
	7036201	1/4	Inner	9/32	3/8	1 1/4	2 Turns	.100	.245	—	.300	—	27/32	1
	7036202	1/4	Inner	9/32	3/8	1 1/8	2 Turns	.110	.150	—	.245	.015	53/64	1
	7036203	1/4	Inner	9/32	3/8	1 1/8	2 Turns	.110	.200	—	.300	—	53/64	1
	7036204	1/4	Inner	9/32	3/8	1 1/4	2 Turns	.100	.160	—	.300	.015	27/32	1
	7036205	1/4	Inner	9/32	3/8	1 1/4	2 Turns	.100	.245	—	.300	—	27/32	1
	7036210	1/4	Inner	9/32	3/8	1 1/8	2 Turns	.110	.150	—	.245	.015	53/64	1
1967	7027200	9/32	—	9/32	3/8	—	2 Turns	.100	.160	.015	.180	.015	27/32	7/8
	7027201	9/32	—	9/32	3/8	—	2 Turns	.100	.245	.015	.180	—	27/32	7/8
	7027202	9/32	—	9/32	3/8	—	2 Turns	.100	.160	.015	.180	.015	27/32	7/8
	7027203	9/32	—	9/32	3/8	—	2 Turns	.100	.200	.015	.180	—	27/32	7/8
	7027210	3/16	Inner	9/32	3/8	—	2 Turns	.100	.160	.015	.180	.015	27/32	7/8
	7027211	3/16	Inner	9/32	3/8	—	2 Turns	.100	.245	.015	.180	—	27/32	7/8
	7027212	9/32	Inner	9/32	3/8	—	2 Turns	.110	.160	.015	.180	.015	27/32	7/8
	7027213	9/32	Inner	9/32	3/8	—	2 Turns	.100	.200	.015	.180	—	27/32	7/8
	7027216	3/16	Inner	9/32	3/8	—	2 Turns	.100	.160	.015	.180	.015	27/32	7/8
	7027218	9/32	Inner	9/32	3/8	—	2 Turns	.110	.160	.015	.180	—	27/32	7/8
	7037200	9/32	—	9/32	3/8	—	2 Turns	.100	.160	.015	.180	.015	27/32	7/8
	7037201	9/32	—	9/32	3/8	—	2 Turns	.100	.245	.015	.180	—	27/32	7/8
	7037202	9/32	—	9/32	3/8	—	2 Turns	.110	.160	.015	.180	.015	27/32	7/8
	7037203	9/32	—	9/32	3/8	—	2 Turns	.110	.230	.015	.180	—	27/32	7/8
	7037210	3/16	Inner	9/32	3/8	—	2 Turns	.100	.160	.015	.180	.015	27/32	7/8
	7037211	3/16	Inner	9/32	3/8	—	2 Turns	.100	.245	.015	.180	—	27/32	7/8
	7037212	9/32	Inner	9/32	3/8	—	2 Turns	.110	.160	.015	.180	.015	27/32	7/8
	7037213	9/32	Inner	9/32	3/8	—	2 Turns	.110	.230	.015	.180	—	27/32	7/8
	7037216	—	—	—	—	—	—	—	—	—	—	—	—	—
	7037218	—	—	—	—	—	—	—	—	—	—	—	—	—
1968	7028212	1/4	Inner	9/32	3/8	—	2 Turns	.100	.180	.015	.260	.010	27/32	3/8
	7028213	1/4	Inner	9/32	3/8	—	2 Turns	.100	.245	.015	.300	.010	27/32	3/8
	7028229	1/4	Inner	9/32	3/8	—	2 Turns	.100	.245	.015	.300	.010	27/32	7/8
	7028208	1/4	Inner	9/32	3/8	—	2 Turns	.100	.180	.015	.260	.010	27/32	3/8
	7028207	1/4	Inner	9/32	3/8	—	2 Turns	.100	.245	.015	.300	.010	27/32	3/8
	7028219	1/4	Inner	9/32	3/8	—	2 Turns	.100	.245	.015	.300	.010	27/32	7/8
	7028218	3/16	Inner	9/32	3/8	—	2 Turns	.100	.160	.015	.300	.010	27/32	7/8
	7028217	3/16	Inner	9/32	3/8	—	2 Turns	.100	.245	.015	.300	.010	27/32	7/8

Continued

ROCHESTER QUADRAJET 4MC & 4MV ADJUSTMENT SPECIFICATIONS—Continued

See Tune Up Chart in car chapters for hot idle speeds.

Year	Carb. Model	Float Level	Pump Rod Hole	Pump Rod Adj.	Idle Vent	Air Valve	Fast Idle (Bench)	Choke Rod	Vacuum Break	Air Valve Dash-pot	Choke Unloader	Air Valve Lockout	Secondary Metering Rods	Air-Valve Valve Spring Wind-Up
CHEVROLET ENGINES—Continued														
1968	7028210	3/16	Inner	9/32	3/8	—	2 Turns	.100	.160	.015	.300	.010	27/32	7/8
	7028211	3/16	Inner	9/32	3/8	—	2 Turns	.100	.245	.015	.300	.010	27/32	7/8
	7028216	3/16	Inner	9/32	3/8	—	2 Turns	.100	.160	.015	.300	.010	27/32	7/8
	7028209	3/16	Inner	9/32	3/8	—	2 Turns	.100	.245	.015	.300	.010	27/32	7/8
1969	7029202	7/32	Inner	5/16	3/8	—	2 Turns	.100	.180	.015	.450	.015	—	7/16
	7029203	7/32	Inner	5/16	3/8	—	2 Turns	.100	.245	.015	.450	.015	—	7/16
	7029204	1/4	Inner	5/16	3/8	—	2 Turns	.100	.180	.015	.450	.015	—	13/16
	7029207	3/16	Inner	5/16	3/8	—	2 Turns	.100	.245	.015	.450	.015	—	13/16
	7029215	1/4	Inner	5/16	3/8	—	2 Turns	.100	.245	.015	.450	.015	—	13/16
1970	7040200	1/4	Inner	5/16	—	—	2 Turns	.100	.245	.020	.450	—	—	13/16
	7040201	1/4	Inner	5/16	—	—	2 Turns	.100	.275	.020	.450	—	—	13/16
	7040202	1/4	Inner	5/16	—	—	2 Turns	.100	.245	.020	.450	—	—	7/16
	7040203	1/4	Inner	5/16	—	—	2 Turns	.100	.275	.020	.450	—	—	7/16
	7040204	1/4	Inner	5/16	—	—	2 Turns	.100	.245	.020	.450	—	—	13/16
	7040205	1/4	Inner	5/16	—	—	2 Turns	.100	.275	.020	.450	—	—	13/16
	7040207	1/4	Inner	5/16	—	—	2 Turns	.100	.275	.015	.450	—	—	13/16
	7040500	1/4	—	5/16	—	—	2 Turns	.100	.245	.020	.450	—	—	13/16
	7040501	1/4	—	5/16	—	—	2 Turns	.100	.275	.020	.450	—	—	13/16
	7040502	1/4	—	5/16	—	—	2 Turns	.100	.275	.020	.450	—	—	7/16
	7040503	1/4	—	5/16	—	—	2 Turns	.100	.275	.020	.450	—	—	7/16
	7040505	1/4	—	5/16	—	—	2 Turns	.100	.275	.020	.450	—	—	13/16
	7040507	3/16	—	5/16	—	—	2 Turns	.100	.275	.020	.450	—	—	13/16
	7040509	1/4	—	5/16	—	—	2 Turns	.100	.275	.020	.450	—	—	13/16
	7040511	1/4	—	5/16	—	—	2 Turns	.100	.245	.020	.450	—	—	7/16
1971	7041200	1/4	—	—	—	—	—	.100	.260	.020	—	—	—	—
	7041201	1/4	—	—	—	—	—	.100	.275	.020	—	—	—	—
	7041202	1/4	—	—	—	—	—	.100	.260	.020	—	—	—	—
	7041203	1/4	—	—	—	—	—	.100	.275	.020	—	—	—	—
	7041204	1/4	—	—	—	—	—	.100	.260	.020	—	—	—	—
	7041205	1/4	—	—	—	—	—	.100	.275	.020	—	—	—	—
	7041212	1/4	—	—	—	—	—	.100	.260	.020	—	—	—	—
	7041213	1/4	—	—	—	—	—	.100	.275	.020	—	—	—	—
1972	7042202	1/4	—	3/8	—	—	—	.100	.215	.020	.450	—	—	—
	7042203	1/4	—	3/8	—	—	—	.100	.215	.020	.450	—	—	—
	7042215	1/4	—	3/8	—	—	—	.100	.250	.020	.450	—	—	—
	7042216	1/4	—	3/8	—	—	—	.100	.215	.020	.450	—	—	—
	7042217	1/4	—	3/8	—	—	—	.100	.250	.020	.450	—	—	—
	7042220	1/4	—	3/8	—	—	—	.100	.250	.020	.450	—	—	—
	7042902	1/4	—	3/8	—	—	—	.100	.215	.020	.450	—	—	—
	7042903	1/4	—	3/8	—	—	—	.100	.215	.020	.450	—	—	—

FORD ENGINES

Year	Carb. Model	Float Level	Pump Rod Hole	Pump Rod Adj.	Idle Vent	Air Valve	Fast Idle (Bench)	Choke Rod	Vacuum Break	Air Valve Dash-pot	Choke Unloader	Air Valve Lockout	Secondary Metering Rods	Air-Valve Valve Spring Wind-Up
1970–71	D0OF-A	11/32	Outer	5/16	—	—	2 Turns	.130	.140	.030	.300	.015	—	—
	D0OF-B	11/32	Outer	5/16	—	—	2 Turns	.166	.190	.030	.300	.015	—	—
	D0OF-E	11/32	Outer	5/16	—	—	2 Turns	.166	.190	.030	.300	.015	—	—
	D0OF-F	11/32	Outer	5/16	—	—	2 Turns	.130	.140	.030	.300	.015	—	—

ROCHESTER QUADRAJET 4MC & 4MV ADJUSTMENT SPECIFICATIONS—Continued
See Tune Up Chart in car chapters for hot idle speeds.

Year	Carb. Model	Float Level	Pump Rod Hole	Pump Rod Adj.	Idle Vent	Air Valve	Fast Idle (Bench)	Choke Rod	Vacuum Break	Air Valve Dash-pot	Choke Unloader	Air Valve Lockout	Secondary Metering Rods	Air-Valve Valve Spring Wind-Up
OLDSMOBILE														
1966	7026250	11/32	Inner	9/32	3/8	1 1/8	2 Turns	.120	.190	—	.300	.015	7/8	3/4
	7026254	11/32	Inner	9/32	3/8	1 1/8	2 Turns	.130	.200	—	.300	.015	7/8	1/2
	7026255	11/32	Inner	9/32	3/8	1 1/8	2 Turns	.130	.200	—	.300	.015	7/8	5/8
	7026256	11/32	Inner	9/32	3/8	1 1/8	2 Turns	.120	.190	—	.300	.015	7/8	3/4
	7036250	11/32	Inner	9/32	3/8	1 1/8	2 Turns	.120	.190	—	.300	.015	7/8	3/4
	7036254	11/32	Inner	9/32	3/8	1 1/8	2 Turns	.130	.200	—	.300	.015	7/8	1/2
1967	7027032	1/4	Inner	5/16	3/8	—	2 Turns	.140	.200	.030	.325	.020	7/8	3/4
	7027036	1/4	Inner	5/16	3/8	—	2 Turns	.140	.200	.030	.325	.020	7/8	1/2
	7027130	1/4	Inner	5/16	3/8	—	2 Turns	.140	.200	.030	.325	.020	7/8	3/4
	7027131	1/4	Inner	5/16	3/8	—	2 Turns	.140	.200	.030	.325	.020	7/8	3/4
	7027132	1/4	Inner	5/16	3/8	—	2 Turns	.140	.200	.030	.325	.020	7/8	3/4
	7027135	1/4	Inner	5/16	3/8	—	2 Turns	.140	.200	.030	.325	.020	7/8	1/2
	7027153	1/4	Inner	5/16	3/8	—	2 Turns	.140	.200	.030	.325	.020	7/8	1/2
	7027156	1/4	Inner	5/16	3/8	—	2 Turns	.140	.200	.030	.325	.020	7/8	3/4
	7027157	1/4	Inner	5/16	3/8	—	2 Turns	.140	.200	.030	.325	.020	7/8	3/4
1968	7028250	1/4	—	5/16	—	—	—	.140	.180	.030	.200	.020	—	1/2
	7028251	1/4	—	5/16	—	—	—	.140	.180	.030	.200	.020	—	3/4
	7028252	1/4	—	5/16	—	—	—	.140	.180	.030	.200	.020	—	3/4
1969	7029250	1/4	Inner	5/16	—	—	—	.140	—	.030	.200	.020	—	1/2
	7029251	1/4	Inner	5/16	—	—	—	.140	—	.030	.200	.020	—	3/4
	7029252	1/4	Inner	5/16	—	—	—	.140	—	.030	.200	.020	—	3/4
	7029253	1/4	Outer	3/8	—	—	—	.120	—	.050	.200	.020	—	3/4
	7029254	1/4	Inner	5/16	—	—	—	.140	—	.030	.200	.020	—	3/4
	7029255	1/4	Inner	5/16	—	—	—	.090	—	.050	.200	.020	—	3/4
1970	7040250	1/4	Inner	3/8	—	—	—	.120	.200	.030	.200	.020	—	1/2
	7040251	1/4	Inner	3/8	—	—	—	.120	.200	.030	.200	.020	—	3/4
	7040252	1/4	Inner	3/8	—	—	—	.120	.200	.030	.200	.020	—	3/4
	7040253	1/4	Inner	3/8	—	—	—	.120	.275	.030	.200	.020	—	3/4
	7040255	1/4	Inner	3/8	—	—	—	.120	.325	.030	.200	.020	—	3/4
	7040256	1/4	Inner	3/8	—	—	—	.120	.325	.030	.200	.020	—	3/4
	7040257	1/4	Inner	3/8	—	—	—	.120	.200	.030	.200	.020	—	3/4
	7040258	1/4	Inner	3/8	—	—	—	.120	.200	.030	.200	.020	—	3/4
1971	7041250	1/4	Inner	3/8	—	—	—	.120	.200	.050	.200	.035	—	1/2
	7041251	1/4	Inner	3/8	—	—	—	.120	.200	.050	.200	.035	—	3/4
	7041252	1/4	Inner	3/8	—	—	—	.120	.200	.050	.200	.035	—	3/4
	7041253	1/4	Inner	3/8	—	—	—	.120	.200	.050	.200	.035	—	3/4
	7041257	1/4	Inner	3/8	—	—	—	.120	.200	.050	.200	.035	—	3/4
1972	7042250	1/4	Inner	3/8	—	—	—	.120	.230	.050	.200	.035	—	1/2
	7042251	1/4	Inner	3/8	—	—	—	.120	.215	.050	.200	.035	—	3/4
	7042252	1/4	Inner	3/8	—	—	—	.120	.215	.050	.200	.035	—	3/4
	7042953	1/4	Inner	3/8	—	—	—	.120	.275	.050	.200	.035	—	3/4
PONTIAC														
1966	7026260	7/32	Inner	9/32	3/8	1 1/8	2 Turns	.090	.140	.030	.300	.015	53/64	1/4
	7026261	7/32	Inner	9/32	3/8	1 1/8	2 Turns	.090	.140	.030	.300	.015	53/64	1/2
1967	7027260	7/32	Inner	9/32	3/8	—	2 Turns	.085	.245	.030	.325	.020	53/64	1/2
	7027261	7/32	Inner	9/32	3/8	—	2 Turns	.085	.245	.030	.325	.020	53/64	1/2
	7027262	3/16	Inner	9/32	3/8	—	2 Turns	.040	.160	.030	.325	.020	53/64	1/2
	7027263	3/16	Inner	9/32	3/8	—	2 Turns	.090	.230	.030	.325	.020	53/64	1/2
	7027268	3/16	Inner	9/32	3/8	—	2 Turns	.085	.245	.030	.325	.020	53/64	1/2
	7027269	3/16	Inner	9/32	3/8	—	2 Turns	.085	.245	.030	.325	.020	53/64	1/2

Continued

ROCHESTER CARBURETORS

ROCHESTER QUADRAJET 4MC & 4MV ADJUSTMENT SPECIFICATIONS—Continued

See Tune Up Chart in car chapters for hot idle speeds.

Year	Carb. Model	Float Level	Pump Rod Hole	Pump Rod Adj.	Idle Vent	Air Valve	Fast Idle (Bench)	Choke Rod	Vacuum Break	Air Valve Dash-pot	Choke Unloader	Air Valve Lockout	Secondary Metering Rods	Air-Valve Valve Spring Wind-Up
PONTIAC—Continued														
1967	7027272	3/16	Inner	9/32	3/8	—	2 Turns	.085	.060	.030	.325	.020	53/64	1/2
	7027273	3/16	Inner	9/32	3/8	—	2 Turns	.090	.230	.030	.325	.020	53/64	1/2
	7037260	7/32	Inner	9/32	3/8	—	2 Turns	.085	.245	.030	.325	.020	53/64	1/2
	7037261	7/32	Inner	9/32	3/8	—	2 Turns	.085	.245	.030	.325	.020	53/64	1/2
	7037262	3/16	Inner	9/32	3/8	—	2 Turns	.040	.160	.030	.325	.020	53/64	1/2
	7037263	3/16	Inner	9/32	3/8	—	2 Turns	.090	.230	.030	.325	.020	53/64	1/2
	7037268	3/16	Inner	9/32	3/8	—	2 Turns	.085	.245	.030	.325	.020	53/64	1/2
	7037269	3/16	Inner	9/32	3/8	—	2 Turns	.085	.245	.030	.325	.020	53/64	1/2
	7037271	3/16	Inner	9/32	3/8	—	2 Turns	.085	.060	.030	.325	.020	53/64	1/2
	7037272	3/16	Inner	9/32	3/8	—	2 Turns	.085	.060	.030	.325	.020	53/64	1/2
	7037273	3/16	Inner	9/32	3/8	—	2 Turns	.090	.230	.030	.325	.020	53/64	1/2
	7037276	3/16	Inner	9/32	3/8	—	2 Turns	.085	.060	.030	.320	.020	53/64	1/2
1968	7028260	5/16	Inner	9/32	3/8	—	2 Turns	.085	.245	.030	.300	.015	53/64	1/2
	7028261	5/16	Inner	9/32	3/8	—	2 Turns	.085	.245	.030	.300	.015	53/64	1/2
	7028262	1/4	Inner	9/32	3/8	—	2 Turns	.100	.230	.030	.300	.015	53/64	1/2
	7028263	1/4	Inner	9/32	3/8	—	2 Turns	.100	.245	.030	.300	.015	53/64	1/2
	7028264	1/4	Inner	9/32	3/8	—	2 Turns	.100	.230	.030	.300	.015	53/64	1/2
	7028265	1/4	Inner	9/32	3/8	—	2 Turns	.100	.245	.030	.300	.015	53/64	1/2
	7028266	1/4	Inner	9/32	3/8	—	2 Turns	.100	.230	.030	.300	.015	53/64	1/2
	7028267	1/4	Inner	9/32	3/8	—	2 Turns	.100	.245	.030	.300	.015	53/64	1/2
	7028268	1/4	Inner	9/32	3/8	—	2 Turns	.100	.230	.030	.300	.015	53/64	1/2
	7028269	1/4	Inner	9/32	3/8	—	2 Turns	.100	.245	.030	.300	.015	53/64	1/2
	7028271	1/4	Inner	9/32	3/8	—	2 Turns	.100	.245	.030	.300	.015	53/64	1/2
	7028274	1/4	Inner	9/32	3/8	—	2 Turns	.100	.230	.030	.300	.015	53/64	1/2
	7028275	1/4	Inner	9/32	3/8	—	2 Turns	.100	.245	.030	.300	.015	53/64	1/2
	7028276	1/4	Inner	9/32	3/8	—	2 Turns	.100	.230	.030	.300	.015	53/64	1/2
	7028277	1/4	Inner	9/32	3/8	—	2 Turns	.100	.245	.030	.300	.015	53/64	1/2
1969	7028270	1/4	Inner	9/32	3/8	—	3 Turns	.100	.245	.030	.300	.015	53/64	1/2
	7028273	1/4	Inner	9/32	3/8	—	3 Turns	.100	.245	.030	.300	.015	53/64	1/2
	7029260	3/16	Inner	9/32	3/8	—	3 Turns	.100	.150	.030	.300	.015	53/64	1/2
	7029261	3/16	Inner	9/32	3/8	—	3 Turns	.100	.180	.030	.300	.015	53/64	1/2
	7029262	9/32	Inner	9/32	3/8	—	3 Turns	.100	.245	.030	.300	.015	53/64	1/2
	7029263	9/32	Inner	9/32	3/8	—	3 Turns	.100	.245	.030	.300	.015	53/64	1/2
	7029268	9/32	Inner	9/32	3/8	—	3 Turns	.100	.245	.030	.300	.015	53/64	1/2
	7029270	9/32	Inner	1/4	3/8	—	3 Turns	.100	.245	.030	.300	.015	53/64	1/2
	7029273	9/32	Inner	1/4	3/8	—	3 Turns	.100	.245	.030	.300	.015	53/64	1/2
1970	7040262	9/32	—	—	—	—	—	.100	.400	.025	—	.015	—	—
	7040263	9/32	—	—	—	—	—	.100	.400	.025	—	.015	—	—
	7040264	9/32	—	—	—	—	—	.100	.400	.025	—	.015	—	—
	7040267	9/32	—	—	—	—	—	.100	.400	.025	—	.015	—	—
	7040268	9/32	—	—	—	—	—	.100	.400	.025	—	.015	—	—
	7040270	9/32	—	—	—	—	—	.100	.245	.025	—	.015	—	—
	7040273	9/32	—	—	—	—	—	.100	.245	.025	—	.015	—	—
	7040274	9/32	—	—	—	—	—	.100	.400	.025	—	.015	—	—
	7040562	9/32	—	—	—	—	—	.100	.400	.025	—	.015	—	—
	7040563	9/32	—	—	—	—	—	.100	.400	.025	—	.015	—	—
	7040564	9/32	—	—	—	—	—	.100	.400	.025	—	.015	—	—
	7040567	9/32	—	—	—	—	—	.100	.400	.025	—	.015	—	—
	7040568	9/32	—	—	—	—	—	.100	.400	.025	—	.015	—	—
	7040570	9/32	—	—	—	—	—	.100	.245	.025	—	.015	—	—
	7040573	9/32	—	—	—	—	—	.100	.245	.025	—	.015	—	—

Continued

ROCHESTER QUADRAJET 4MC & 4MV ADJUSTMENT SPECIFICATIONS—Continued

See Tune Up Chart in car chapters for hot idle speeds.

Year	Carb. Model	Float Level	Pump Rod		Idle Vent	Air Valve	Fast Idle (Bench)	Choke Rod	Vacuum Break	Air Valve Dash-pot	Choke Unloader	Air Valve Lockout	Secondary Metering Rods	Air-Valve Valve Spring Wind-Up
			Hole	Adj.										
PONTIAC—Continued														
1971	7041262	9/32	—	—	—	—	—	.100	.240	.025	—	.015	—	—
	7041263	9/32	—	—	—	—	—	.100	.240	.025	—	.015	—	—
	7041262	9/32	—	—	—	—	—	.100	.240	.025	—	.015	—	—
	7041267	9/32	—	—	—	—	—	.100	.370	.025	—	.015	—	—
	7041268	9/32	—	—	—	—	—	.100	.430	.025	—	.015	—	—
	7041270	9/32	—	—	—	—	—	.100	.430	.025	—	.015	—	—
	7041271	9/32	—	—	—	—	—	.100	.240	.025	—	.015	—	—
	7041273	9/32	—	—	—	—	—	.100	.370	.025	—	.015	—	—
1972	7042262	1/4	—	13/32	—	—	—	.100	.290	.025	.310	.015	—	—
	7042263	1/4	—	13/32	—	—	—	.100	.290	.025	.310	.015	—	—
	7042264	1/4	—	13/32	—	—	—	.100	.290	.025	.310	.015	—	—
	7042270	1/4	—	7/16	—	—	—	.100	.290	.025	.310	.015	—	—
	7042273	1/4	—	7/16	—	—	—	.100	.290	.025	.310	.015	—	—

QUADRAJET 4MV, 4MC ADJUSTMENTS

The Quadrajet unit, Figs. 1, 2, has two stages in operation. The primary (fuel inlet) side has small bores with a triple venturi equipped with plain tube nozzles. The triple venturi feature, plus the smaller primary bores, give a more stable and finer fuel control in the idle and economy ranges of operation. Fuel metering in the primary side is accomplished with tapered metering rods positioned by a manifold vacuum responsive piston.

The secondary side has two very large bores which have greatly increased air capacity to meet all engine demands. The air valve principle is used in the secondary side for metering control and supplements fuel flow from the primary bores. Using the air valve principle, fuel is metered in direct proportion to the air passing through the secondary bores.

The fuel reservoir is centrally located to avoid problems of fuel slosh causing engine turn cut-out and delayed fuel flow to the carburetor bores. The float system uses a single float pontoon for ease of service. The float needle valve is pressure balanced to overcome problems encountered with high fuel pump pressures and to permit use of a small float to control fuel "shut-off" through the large fuel inlet needle seat. It has a synthetic tip which gives added insurance against flooding problems casued by dirt.

The primary side of the carburetor has six systems of operation: float, idle, main metering, power, pump and choke. The secondary side has one metering system which supplements the primary main metering system and receives fuel from a common float chamber.

Model 4MV Choke System

Fig. 3—The choke system consists of a choke valve located in the primary air horn bore, a vacuum diaphragm unit, fast idle cam, connecting linkage, air valve lockout lever and a thermostatic coil. Some applications may use a split choke pick-up spring or a vacuum break modulating spring. The thermostatic coil is located in the engine manifold and is connected to the intermediate choke shaft and lever assembly. Choke operation is controlled by a combination of engine intake manifold vacuum, the offset choke valve, temperature and throttle position.

Model 4MC Choke System

Fig. 4—The choke consists of a choke valve located in the primary air horn bore, a choke housing and vacuum diaphragm assembly, fast idle cam, connecting linkage, air valve lockout lever, and thermostatic coil. Choke operation is controlled by a combination of intake manifold vacuum, the offset choke valve, temperature, and throttle position.

Air Valve Operation

Fig. 5—When the engine reaches a point where the primary bores cannot meet engine air and fuel demands, the primary throttle lever, through connecting linkage to the secondary throttle shaft lever, begins to open the secondary throttle valves. As air flow through the secondary bores creates a low pressure (vacuum) beneath the air valve, atmospheric pressure on top of the air valve forces the air valve open against spring tension. This allows the required air for increased engine speed to flow past the air valve.

Air Valve Dashpot Operation

Fig. 6—The secondary air valve has an attached piston assembly which acts as a damper to prevent oscillation of the valve due to engine pulsations. The damper piston operates in a well that is filled with fuel from the float bowl. The motion of the piston is retarded by fuel which must by-pass the piston when it moves up in the fuel well. The piston is attached loosely to a plunger rod. The rod has a rubber seal which retains the damper piston to the plunger rod and also acts as a valve. The purpose of the valve is to seat on the piston when the air valve opens and the piston rod moves upward. This closes off the area through the center of the piston and slows down the air valve opening to prevent secondary discharge nozzle lag.

ADJUSTMENTS
Float Level Adjustment

Fig. 7—With adjustable T-scale, measure from top of float bowl gasket surface

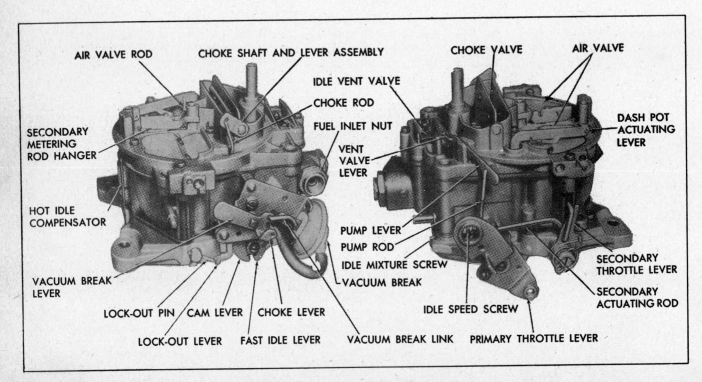

Fig. 1   Rochester Quadrajet Model 4MV carburetor

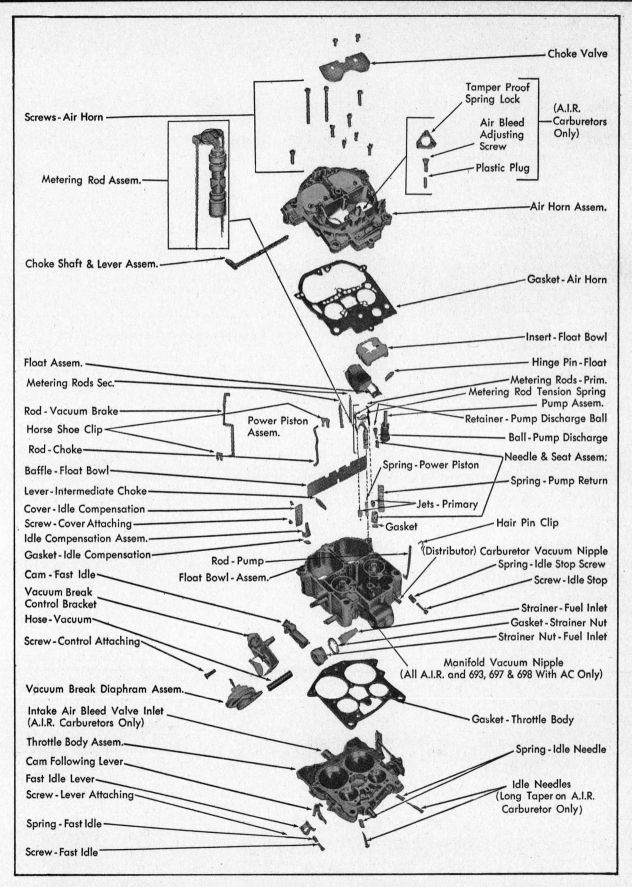

Fig. 2   Rochester 4MV Quadrajet carburetor. Typical

(gasket removed) to top of float at toe (locate gauging point 3/16" back from toe). Adjust as directed in the illustration to the dimension listed in the *Rochester Specifications Chart*. Make sure retaining pin is held firmly in place and tang of float is seated on float needle.

Pump Rod Adjustment

Fig. 8—With throttle valves completely closed and pump rod in specified hole in pump lever, measure from top of choke valve wall (next to vent stack) to top of pump stem. Dimension should be as listed in the *Rochester Specifications Chart*. To adjust, bend pump lever as required.

Idle Vent Adjustment

Fig. 9—After pump rod adjustment has been made, open primary throttle valve to a point where the idle vent just closes. With T-scale, measure distance from top of choke valve wall (next to vent stack) to top of pump plunger stem. If dimension is not as specified in the *Rochester Specifications Chart*, bend wire tang on pump lever.

Air Valve Adjustment

Fig. 10—With air valve wide open and valve against stop tang, distance between upper inside edge of air valve and back of choke valve wall (at torsion spring end) should be as specified in the *Rochester Specifications Chart*. To adjust, bend stop tang on dashpot lever.

Fast Idle Adjustment

Fig. 11—With primary throttle valves completely closed, and the cam follower over the high step of the fast idle cam, turn fast idle screw 3 turns (2 on 1967) after screw makes contact on lever.

Choke Rod Adjustment

Fig. 12—With the fast idle adjustment made, and cam follower on second step of fast idle cam and against the high step, rotate choke valve toward closed position by pushing down on vacuum break lever (Model 4MV) or thermostatic coil tang (Model 4MC). Dimension between lower edge of choke valve (at choke lever end) should be as specified in the *Rochester Specifications Chart*. Adjust by bending choke rod.

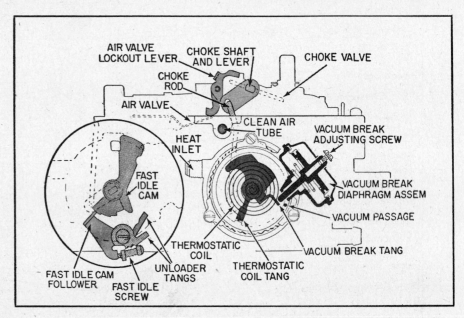

Fig. 3   Rochester Model 4MV choke system

Fig. 4   Rochester Model 4MC choke system

Vacuum Break Adjustment

1967-71 4MV, Fig. 13

With vacuum break diaphragm stem against its seat and choke valve held toward the closed position, the dimension between lower edge of choke valve and air horn, at choke lever end, should be as specified. To adjust, bend vacuum break tang.

1966 Except Buick, Fig. 14

With choke spring pick-up located in specified notch, hold choke valve toward closed position, using a rubber band on vacuum break lever. Hold vacuum break diaphragm stem against its seat so vacuum link is at end of slot. Dimension between lower edge of choke valve and air horn should be as specified. Adjust by bending vacuum link.

1966 4MC Buick, Fig. 15

With choke valve closed, and choke rod in bottom of slot in upper choke lever, align thermostatic pick-up tang directly over index tab on inside of choke housing. After tang is aligned, adjust vacuum break tang to the specified dimension between tang and vacuum break pin.

With vacuum break diaphragm seated and tang against vacuum break pin, the dimension between wall and lower edge of choke valve should be as specified. Make sure choke rod is in bottom of slot in choke lever when gauging. Turn screw on vacuum break cover to adjust. Install baffle and thermostat cover, adjusting cover to specified mark.

Air Valve Dashpot Adjustment

Fig. 16—With vacuum break diaphragm seated, there must be the specified clearance between dashpot rod and end of slot in air valve lever. To adjust, bend rod at air valve end.

Split Choke Spring Adjustment

Fig. 17—With split choke spring in specified notch, (see automatic choke specifications) open choke valve by pushing upward on vacuum break lever to end of travel making sure choke rod is in upper end of slot in choke lever. Dimension between end of torsion spring and tang should be as specified in the *Rochester Specifications Chart*. Bend tang to adjust.

Choke Unloader Adjustment

1966-71, Figs. 18 and 19

With choke valve held closed by means of a rubber bank on vacuum break lever, open throttle valves fully. With valves in this position, dimension between lower edge of choke valve and air horn wall should be as specified. To adjust, bend tang on fast idle lever.

Air Valve Lockout Adjustment

1967-71 Models, Fig. 20

With choke valve wide open, apply sufficient force to thermostat tang to move the choke rod to the *top of the slot* in the choke lever. If necessary, bend the upper end of the valve lockout lever to obtain the specified opening between the lockout tang and front edge of air valve.

1966 Oldsmobile, Fig. 21

A—*Opening Clearance:* With cam follower positioned against rise to lowest step of fast idle cam, apply a light force to vacuum break lever in the direction of closed choke and rotate choke valve to

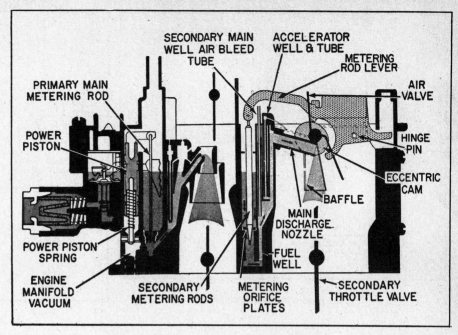

Fig. 5 Diagram of Quadrajet power system

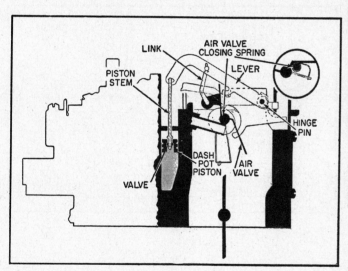

Fig. 6 Quadrajet air valve dashpot

its wide open stop by applying force to the UP side of the choke valve. Move air valves to open position. Bend upper end of air valve lockout lever, if necessary, to give the specified opening between lockout tang and front edge of choke valve.

B—*Lockout Clearance:* With cam follower positioned against the rise to the lowest effective step of the fast idle cam, apply a light force to the vacuum break lever in the direction of closed choke. Rotate choke valve in closed direction by applying a light force to the UP side of the choke valve so that the choke link is at the upper end of the slot in the choke lever. Air valves must be locked closed. If any adjustment is necessary, the opening clearance must be rechecked.

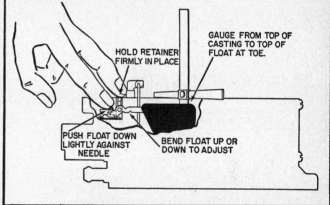

Fig. 7 Quadrajet float level adjustment

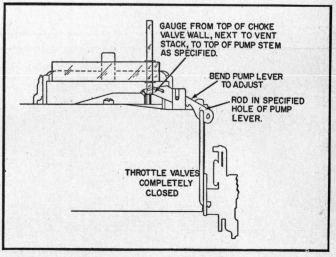

Fig. 8 Quadrajet pump rod adjustment

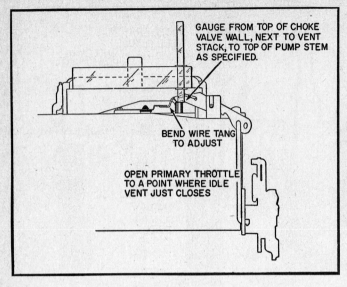

Fig. 9   Quadrajet idle vent adjustment

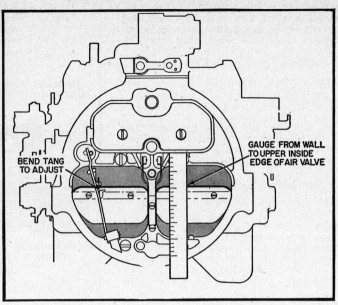

Fig. 10   Quadrajet air valve adjustment

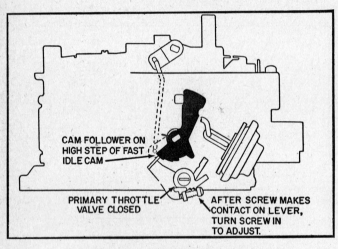

Fig. 11   Quadrajet fast idle adjustment

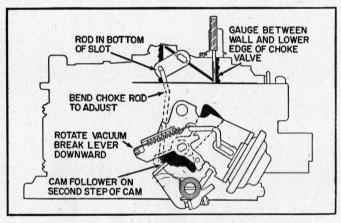

Fig. 12   Quadrajet choke rod adjustment

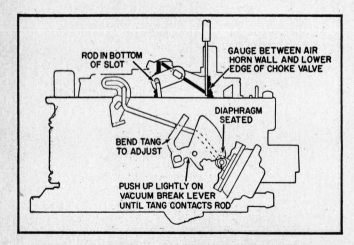

Fig. 13   Quadrajet vacuum break adjustment. 1967-71

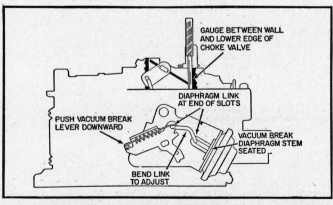

Fig. 14   Quadrajet vacuum break adjustment.
1966 Chevrolet, Olds and Pontiac

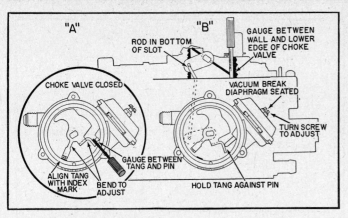

Fig. 15   Quadrajet vacuum break adjustment. 1966 Buick

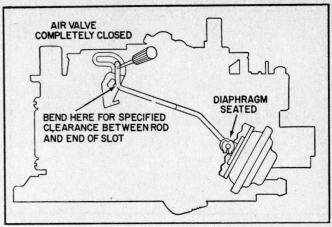

Fig. 16   Quadrajet air valve dashpot adjustment

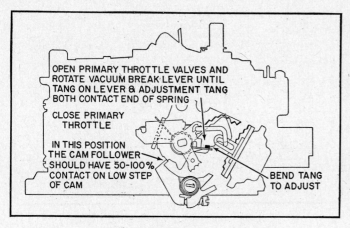

Fig. 17   Quadrajet split choke adjustment

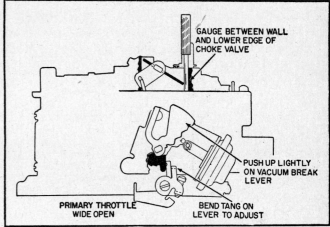

Fig. 18   Quadrajet unloader adjustment. 1967-71

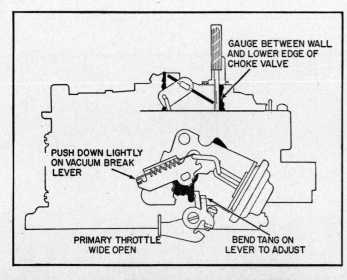

Fig. 19   Quadrajet unloader adjustment. 1966

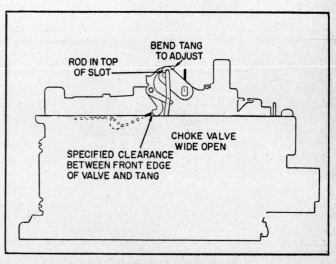

Fig. 20   Quadrajet air valve lockout adjustment. 1967-71

ROCHESTER CARBURETORS

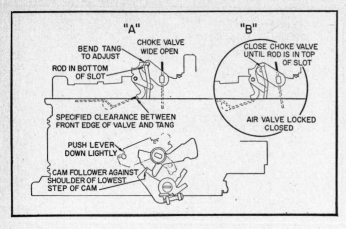

Fig. 21   Quadrajet air valve lockout adjustment. 1966 Olds

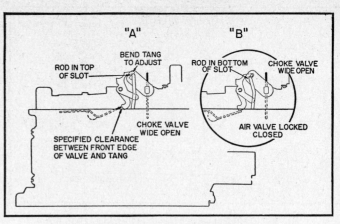

Fig. 22   Quadrajet air valve lockout adjustment. 1966 Buick, Chevrolet and Pontiac

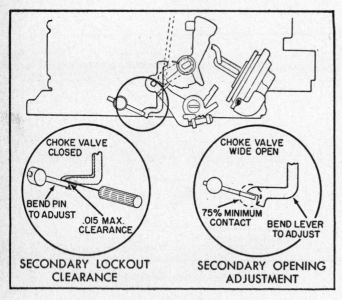

Fig. 23   Quadrajet secondary lockout clearance and secondary opening adjustment

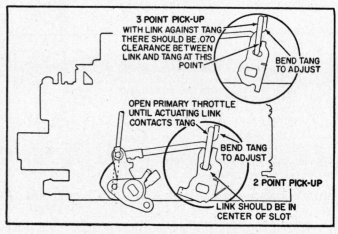

Fig. 24   Quadrajet secondary throttle valves opening adjustment. 1967-71

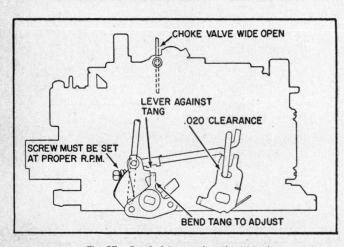

Fig. 25   Quadrajet secondary throttle valves closing adjustment. 1967-71

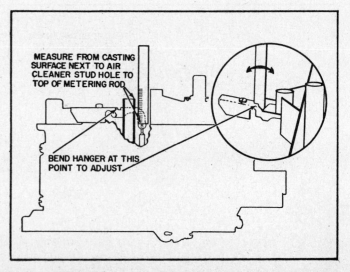

Fig. 26   Quadrajet secondary metering rod adjustment

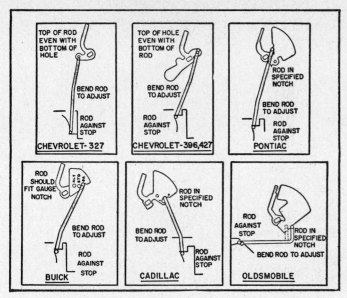

Fig. 29 Choke coil adjustments. 1967-68 all and 1969-71 Buick

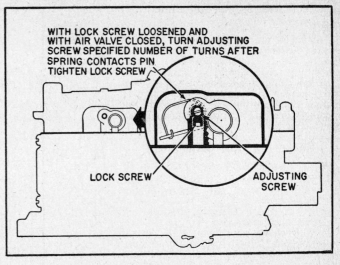

Fig. 27 Quadrajet air valve spring adjustment

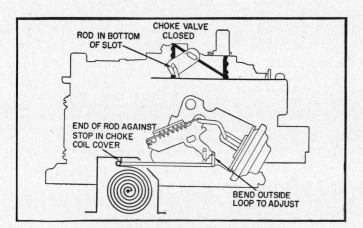

Fig. 30 Quadrajet choke coil rod adjustments. 1966 Olds

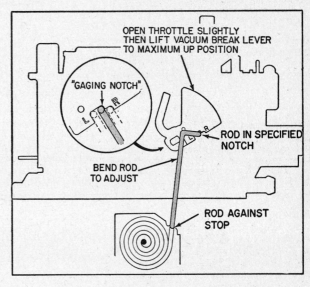

Fig. 28 Choke coil adjustment. 1969-71 Cadillac

1966 Buick, Chevrolet, Pontiac, Fig. 22

A—Opening Clearance: With choke valve wide open, apply sufficient force to thermostat tang to move choke rod *to top of slot* in choke lever. Move air valve in open direction. Bend upper end of air valve lockout lever, if necessary, to give the specified opening between lockout tang and front edge of air valve.

B—Lockout: With all other adjustments made, open choke valve fully by applying force to the UP side of choke valve. Making sure choke rod is in *bottom of slot* in choke lever, the air valve lockout tang must hold air valve closed.

Secondary Lockout Clearance

Fig. 23—With choke valve and both primary and secondary throttle valves fully closed, the lockout lever should not contact lockout pin. Clearance must not exceed .015". Bend lockout pin to adjust.

Secondary Opening Adjustment

Fig. 23—Holding choke valve and primary throttle valves in wide open position and secondary throttle valves closed, the lockout pin should have a minimum of 75% contact on lockout lever. To adjust, bend lockout lever.

1967-71 Secondary Throttle Valves, Adjust

Throttle Opening, Fig. 24

With a two-point pickup, open primary throttle valves until actuating link contacts tang on secondary lever. With valves in this position, bottom of link should be in center slot of secondary lever.

With a three-point pickup, there should be .070" clearance between link and tang as indicated. If necessary to adjust, bend tang on secondary lever.

Throttle Closing, Fig. 25

Set curb idle screw to recommended rpm (listed in *Tune-Up Specifications* table in car chapters), making sure cam follower is not resting on fast idle cam. There should be .020" clearance between actuating link and front of slot in secondary lever when tang of actuating lever on primary shaft is against pin. If necessary to adjust, bend tang on primary actuating lever.

Secondary Metering Rod Adjustment

Fig. 26

Measure from top of metering rod to top of air horn casting next to air cleaner stud hole. Dimension should be as specified. To adjust, bend metering rod hanger at point shown. *Make sure both rods are adjusted to the same dimension.*

ROCHESTER CARBURETORS

Air Valve Spring Adjustment

Fig. 27

To adjust the air valve spring wind-up, loosen Allen head lockscrew and turn adjusting screw counterclockwise to remove all spring tension. With air valve closed, turn adjusting screw clockwise the specified number of turns after the torsion spring contacts pin on shaft. Hold adjusting screw in this position and tighten lock screw.

Choke Coil Rod Adjustment

1969-71 Cadillac and Ford, Fig. 28

1. Remove choke coil assmebly to disengage choke rod from vacuum break lever.
2. Reinstall coil assembly but do not install rod into lever.
3. With choke valve completely closed, fast idle cam in cold start position, and vacuum break lever in maximum upward position, pull choke rod upward to end of travel. Upper end of rod should be positioned in gauging notch, Fig. 28. Bend choke rod to adjust and reassemble coil assembly, rod and lever.

1969-71 Chevrolet, Oldsmobile and Pontiac

With fast idle adjusted and cam follower on second step and against high step of cam, close choke and check dimension between lower edge of choke valve and inner wall of main body. Bend choke rod to adjust.

1967-68 All and 1969-71 Buick, Fig. 29

With choke valve completely closed and choke rod in bottom of choke lever slot, pull or push choke coil rod to end of travel. Rod should be positioned as shown. Bend choke coil rod to adjust.

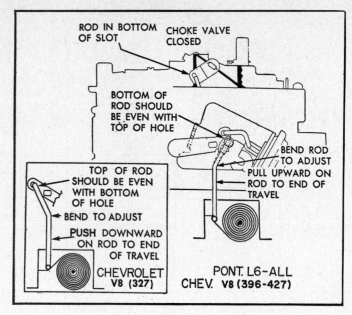

Fig. 31 Quadrajet choke coil rod adjustments. 1966 Chevrolet and Pontiac

Oldsmobile 1966, Fig. 30

With choke valve completely closed and choke rod in bottom of choke lever slot, pull forward on choke coil rod until rod is against stop on choke coil cover. Bend outer loop on rod to specified position. Connect choke coil rod to vacuum break lever and secure with clip.

Chevrolet & Pontiac, 1966, Fig. 31

With choke valve completely closed and choke rod in bottom of choke lever slot, pull upward or push downward on choke coil rod to end of travel. Thermostat rod position should be as specified in illustration. To adjust, bend choke coil rod, connect rod to vacuum break lever and secure with clip.

ROCHESTER MONOJET M, MV ADJUSTMENT SPECIFICATIONS

See Tune Up Chart in car chapters for hot idle speeds.

Year	Carb. Part No. ①	Initial Idle Mix Screw Turns Open ①	Float Level	Metering Rod	Idle Vent	Fast Idle Off Car	Choke Rod	Vacuum Break	Unloader	Fast Idle R.P.M.
BUICK										
1968	7028014	1½-2	⁹⁄₃₂	.100	.050	②	.180	.245	.350	②
	7028047	1½-2	⁵⁄₁₆	.140	.020	②	.190	.275	.325	②
1969	7029014	2	¼	.070	.050	—	.170	.245	.350	620④
	7029047	2	⁹⁄₃₂	.140	.020	—	.190	.275	.350	720④
1970	7040014	2	¼	.070	.050	—	.170	.245	.350	650④
	7040015	2	¼	.140	.050	—	.200	.275	.350	900④
	7040017	—	¼	.070	—	.100	.190	.230	.350	900④
1971	7041014	—	¼	.080	.050	—	.160	.225	.500	500④
	7041017	—	¼	.080	.050	—	.180	.225	.350	550④
CHEVROLET ENGINES										
1968	7028008	1½-2	⁹⁄₃₂	.080	.050	1½③	.150	—	—	2400⑤
	7028009	1½-2	⁹⁄₃₂	.080	.050	1½③	.150	—	—	2400⑤
	7028014	1½-2	⁹⁄₃₂	.120	.050	1½③	.150	.245	.350	2400⑤
	7028015	1½-2	⁹⁄₃₂	.130	.050	1½③	.150	.275	.350	2400⑤
	7028017	1½-2	⁹⁄₃₂	.130	.050	1½③	.150	.275	.350	2400⑤

Continued

ROCHESTER MONOJET M, MV ADJUSTMENT SPECIFICATIONS—Continued

See Tune Up Chart in car chapters for hot idle speeds.

Year	Carb. Part No. ①	Initial Idle Mix Screw Turns Open ①	Float Level	Metering Rod	Idle Vent	Fast Idle Off Car	Choke Rod	Vacuum Break	Unloader	Fast Idle R.P.M.
CHEVROLET ENGINES—Continued										
1969	7029008	3	¼	.080	.050	.100	.150	—	—	2400⑤
	7029014	3	¼	.070	.050	.100	.170	.245	.350	2400⑤
	7029015	3	¼	.090	.050	.100	.200	.275	.350	2400⑤
	7029017	3	¼	.090	.050	.100	.200	.275	.350	2400⑤
1970	7040008	—	¼	.080	—	.100	.200	—	—	2400⑤
	7040014	—	¼	.070	—	.110	.170	.200	.350	2400⑤
	7040017	—	¼	.090	—	.100	.190	.160	.350	2400⑤
1971	7041014	—	¼	.080	—	.100	.160	.200	.350	—
	7041017	—	¼	.080	—	.100	.180	.230	.350	—
	7041023	—	1⁄16	—	—	.110	.120	.200	.350	—
	7041024	—	1⁄16	—	—	.110	.080	.140	.350	—
1972	7042014	—	¼	.080	—	—	.125	.190	.500	2400
	7042017	—	¼	.078	—	—	.125	.190	.500	2400
	7042023	—	⅛	—	—	.110	.130	.200	.350	2400
	7042024	—	1⁄16	—	—	.110	.070	.200	.350	2800
	7042984	—	¼	.078	—	—	.150	.225	.500	2400
	7042987	—	¼	.076	—	—	.150	.225	.500	2400
	7042993	—	⅛	—	—	.110	.130	.120	.350	2400
	7042994	—	1⁄16	—	—	.110	.070	.120	.350	2800
OLDSMOBILE										
1968	7028014	1½–2	9⁄32	.120	.050	—	.180	.245	.350	650④
	7028057	1½–2	11⁄32	.120	.050	—	.190	.275	.350	650④
1969	7029014	—	¼	.070	.050	—	.170	.245	.350	750④
	7029057	—	5⁄16	.120	.030	—	.180	.260	.350	750④
1970	7040014	—	¼	.070	—	—	.170	.200	.350	900④
	7040017	—	¼	.070	—	—	.190	.225	.350	750④
1971	7041014	—	¼	.070	—	—	.160	.200	.350	900④
	7041019	—	¼	.070	—	—	.180	.225	.350	750④
PONTIAC										
1968	7028067	1½–2	5⁄16	.085	.040	.090	.200	.300	.245	2400⑤
	7028075	1½–2	5⁄16	.085	.040	—	.200	.290	.245	2400⑤
	7028065	1½–2	5⁄16	.075	.040	.090	.200	.300	.245	2400⑤
1969	7029165	5	9⁄32	.085	.040	.120	.200	.275	.450	2400⑤
	7029166	5	9⁄32	.085	.040	.130	.180	.260	.450	2800⑤
	7029167	5	9⁄32	.085	.040	.120	.200	.275	.450	2600⑤
	7029168	5	9⁄32	.085	.040	.130	.180	.260	.450	2800⑤
1970	7040014	—	¼	.100	—	—	.170	.200	.350	—
	7040017	—	¼	.100	—	—	.190	.230	.350	—
1971	7041014	—	¼	.080	—	—	.160	.200	.350	—
	7041017	—	¼	.078	—	—	.180	.225	.350	—
1972	7042014	—	¼	.080	—	—	.160	.200	.500	2400
	7042017	—	¼	.080	—	—	.180	.230	.500	2400
	7042984	—	¼	.080	—	—	.160	.200	.500	2400
	7042987	—	¼	.080	—	—	.180	.230	.500	2400

①—On tag attached to carburetor.
②—20 RPM above slow idle speed.
③—Turns in from slow idle position.
④—On low step of cam.
⑤—On high step of cam.

ROCHESTER CARBURETORS

MONOJET M & MV ADJUSTMENTS

The Monojet carburetor is a single-bore downdraft unit with a triple venturi coupled with a refined metering system which results in a unit having superior fuel mixture control and performance.

A plain tube nozzle is used in conjuction with the multiple venturi. Fuel flow through the main metering system is controlled by a mechanically and vacuum operated variable orifice jet. This consists of a specially tapered rod which operates in the fixed orifice main metering jet and is connected directly by linkage to the main throttle shaft. A vacuum-operated enrichment system is used in conjunction with the main metering system to provide good performance during moderate to heavy accelerations.

A separate and adjustable idle system is used in conjunction with the main metering system to meet fuel mixture requirements during engine idle and low speed operation. The off-idle discharge port is of a vertical slot design which gives good transition between curb idle and main metering system operation.

The idle system incorporates a hot idle compensator on some models where necessary to maintain smooth engine idle during periods of extreme hot engine operation.

The main metering system has an adjustable flow feature which enables production to control the fuel mixture more accurately then attained heretofore.

The Monojet carburetor is designed so that a manual or automatic choke system can be used. The conventional choke valve is located in the air horn bore. On automatic choke models, the vacuum diaphragm unit is an integral part of the air horn. The automatic choke coil is manifold mounted and connects to the choke valve shaft by connecting linkage.

The choke system has a new feature to give added enrichment during cold start. This feature greatly reduces starting time and yet allows the use of low torque thermostatic coils for increased economy.

The carburetor has internally balanced venting through a vent hole in the air horn. An external idle vent valve is used on some models where necessary for improved hot engine idle and starting.

Float Level Adjustment
Fig. 2
1. Hold float retaining pin firmly in place and float arm against top of float needle by pushing downward on float arm at point between needle seat and hinge pin as shown.
2. With adjustable T-scale, measure distance from top of float at toe to float bowl gasket surface (gasket removed). Measurement should be made at a point $1/16''$ in from end of flat surface at float toe (not on radius).
3. Bend float pontoon up or down at float arm junction to adjust.

Metering Rod Adjustment
Fig. 3
1. Remove metering rod by holding throttle valve wide open. Push down-

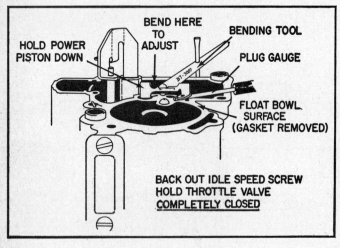

Fig. 3   Monojet metering rod adjustment

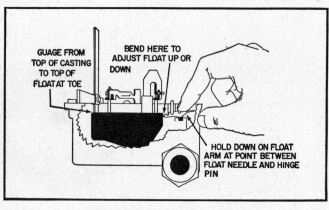

Fig. 2   Monojet float level adjustment

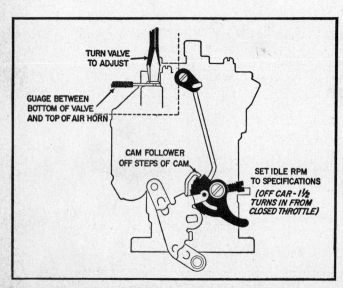

Fig. 4   Monojet idle vent adjustment

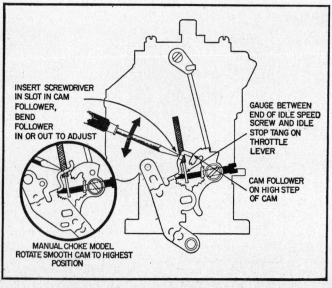

Fig. 5   Monojet fast idle adjustment (off car)

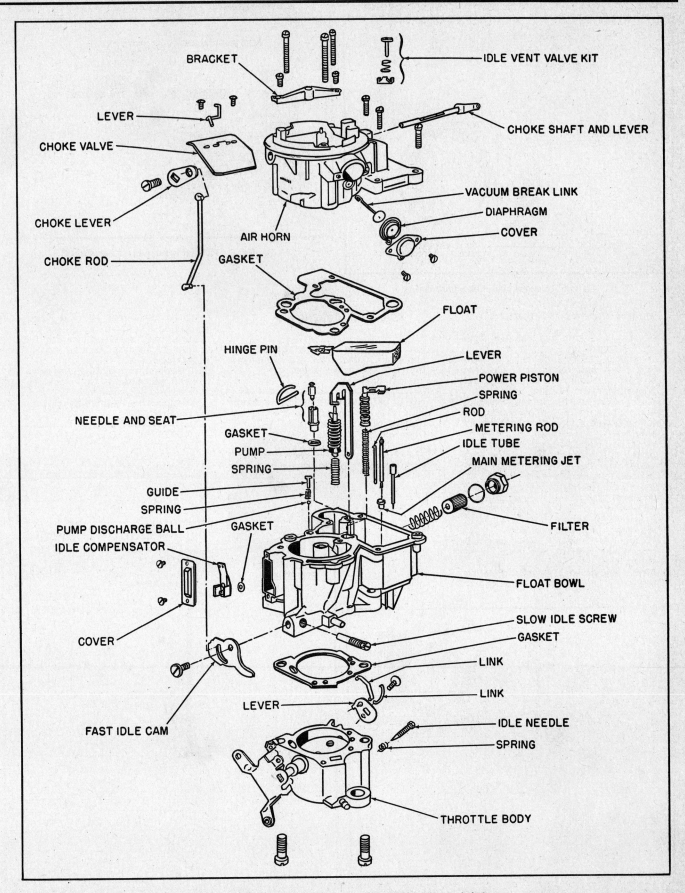

Fig. 1 Monojet Model MV carburetor. Model M has manual choke

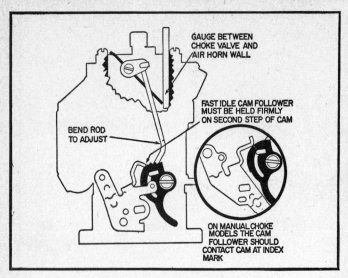

Fig. 6 Monojet choke rod adjustment

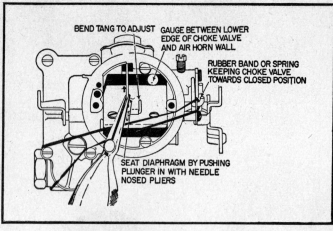

Fig. 7 Monojet vacuum break adjustment

ward on metering rod against spring tension, then slide metering rod out of slot in holder and remove from main metering jet.

2. To check adjustment, back out slow idle screw and rotate fast idle cam so that fast idle cam follower is not contacting steps on cam.

3. With throttle valve completely closed, apply pressure to top of power piston and hold piston down against its stop.

4. While holding downward pressure on power piston, swing metering rod holder over flat surface of bowl casting next to carburetor bore.

5. Use specified size drill and insert between bowl casting sealing bead and lower surface of metering rod holder. Drill should have a slide fit between both surfaces as shown.

6. To adjust, carefully bend metering rod holder up or down at point shown.

7. After adjustment, install metering rod.

Idle Vent Adjustment

Fig. 4

1. Set engine idle rpm to specification and hold choke valve wide open so that fast idle cam follower is not hitting fast idle cam.

NOTE: Initial idle setting can be made with the carburetor off the car by turning idle speed screw in 1½ turns from closed throttle valve position. Recheck setting on the car as follows:

2. With throttle stop screw held against idle stop screw, the idle vent valve should be open as specified. To measure, insert specified size drill between top of air horn casting and bottom surface of vent valve.

3. To adjust, turn slotted vent valve head with a screwdriver clockwise (inward) to decrease clearance and counterclockwise to increase clearance as required.

NOTE: On models provided with the idle stop solenoid, make sure solenoid is activated when checking and adjusting vent valve.

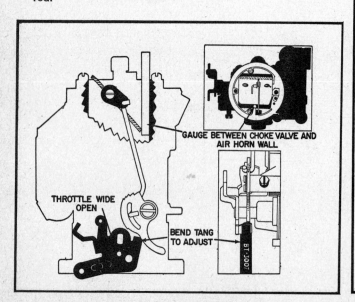

Fig. 8 Monojet unloader adjustment

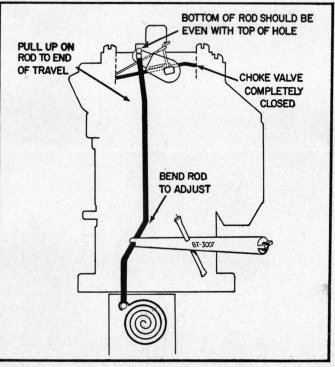

Fig. 9 Monojet choke coil adjustment

Fast Idle Adjustment

Automatic Choke Models, Fig. 5

1. Set normal engine idle speed.
2. Place fast idle cam follower tang on highest step of cam.
3. With tang held against cam, check clearance between end of slow idle speed screw and idle stop tang on throttle lever. It should be as specified.
4. To adjust, insert screwdriver in slot provided in fast idle cam follower tang and bend inwards (towards cam) or outward to obtain specified dimension.

Manual Choke Models

Use same procedure as above except in Step 2 rotate fast idle cam clockwise to its farthest up position.

Choke Rod Adjustment

Automatic Choke Models, Fig. 6

1. With fast idle adjustment made, place fast idle cam follower on second step of fast idle cam and hold firmly against the rise to the high step.
2. Rotate choke towards direction of closed choke by applying force to choke coil lever.
3. Bend choke rod at point shown to give specified opening between lower edge of choke valve (at center of valve) and inside air horn wall.

Manual Choke Models

Use same procedure as above except in Step 1. As there are no steps on the manual choke cam, the index line on side of cam should be lined up with contact point of fast idle cam follower tang.

Vacuum Break Adjustment

Fig. 7

1. Open throttle valve so that cam follower on throttle lever will clear highest step on fast idle cam.
2. Rotate choke valve to closed position. If thermostatic coil is warm, hold choke valve closed with rubber band or spring attached between choke shaft lever and stationary part of carburetor.
3. Grasp vacuum break plunger rod with needle nose pliers and push straight inward until diaphragm seats.
4. With specified drill size, measure clearance between lower edge of choke valve and inside air horn wall at center of valve as shown.
5. Bend end of vacuum break lever at point shown to adjust.

Unloader Adjustment

Fig. 8

1. Hold choke valve in closed position by applying a light force to choke coil lever.
2. Rotate throttle lever to wide open throttle valve position.
3. Bend unloader tang on throttle lever to obtain specified dimension between lower edge of choke valve (at center) and air horn wall.

Choke Coil Adjustment

Fig. 9

1. Hold choke valve closed.
2. Pull upward on coil rod to end of travel.
3. Bottom of rod end which slides into hole in choke lever should be even with top of hole. *On Pontiac applications rod should be adjusted to fit in notch in top of choke lever.*
4. Bend choke coil rod at point shown to adjust.
5. Connect coil rod to choke lever and install retaining clip.

Fast Idle Adjustment

1. With carburetor installed on vehicle, warm up engine.
2. Place fast idle cam follower on specified step of fast idle cam.
3. With cam follower held against specified stop, insert screwdriver in adjustment slot and bend tang towards or away from cam to obtain specified rpm.

Stromberg Carburetor Section

STROMBERG CARBURETOR ADJUSTMENT SPECIFICATIONS

See Tune Up Chart in car chapters for hot idle speeds.

Year	Carb. Model	Initial Idle Mixture Screws Turns Open	Float Level Inch	Fast Idle R.P.M.	Fast Idle Cam Position		Vacuum Kick	Choke Unloader	Pump Travel Inch	Bowl Vent	Choke Setting
					Idle Screw Turns In	Clearance					
CHRYSLER, DODGE & PLYMOUTH											
1966	3-258	1 1/4	7/32	700	—	#28 Drill	G Drill	5/16	—	.060	2 Rich
	3-259	1 1/4	7/32	700	—	#28 Drill	D Drill	5/16	—	.060	2 Rich
	3-260	1/2	7/32	1450	—	#28 Drill	G Drill	5/16	—	.050	On Index
	3-261	1/2	7/32	1600	—	#28 Drill	D Drill	5/16	—	.050	On Index
	3-262	1 1/2	5/32	700	—	#38 Drill	#28 Drill	15/64	7/16	.040	2 Rich
	3-263	1 1/2	5/32	1300	—	#38 Drill	#22 Drill	15/64	7/16	.020	On Index
1967	3-272	1 1/4	7/32	700	—	#20 Drill	A Drill	5/16	—	.060	2 Rich
	3-273	1 1/4	7/32	700	—	#20 Drill	#4 Drill	5/16	—	.060	2 Rich
	3-274	1 1/2	7/32	1400	—	#20 Drill	A Drill	5/16	—	.050	On Index
	3-275	1 1/2	7/32	1400	—	#20 Drill	#4 Drill	5/16	—	.050	On Index
	3-276	1 1/2	5/32	700	—	#42 Drill	#42 Drill	15/64	7/16	.040	2 Rich

STROMBERG ADJUSTMENTS

MODELS WA & WW

These carburetors, Figs. 1 and 2, are fundamentally the same, the WA model being a one-barrel unit whereas the WW model is a two-barrel carburetor.

Both models consist of two main assemblies, namely the air horn and the main body. The air horn serves as a fuel bowl cover and includes parts of the idle system, choke system, accelerating and power systems. The main body includes the fuel inlet, fuel bowl, fuel metering systems and throttle mechanism. Exploded views of these carburetors are shown in Figs. 3 and 4.

Float Level Adjustment

Figs. 5 and 6

1. Install float with fulcrum pin and retaining spring in main body.
2. Install needle, seat and gasket in body and tighten securely.
3. Invert main body so that weight of float *only* is forcing needle against seat.
4. Using the tool shown or a T-scale, check float level from surface of bowl with gasket removed to top of float at center.
5. If an adjustment is necessary, hold float on bottom of bowl, then bend float lip toward or away from needle. Recheck setting again, then repeat lip bending operation if required.

CAUTION: When bending float lip, do not allow lip to push against the needle as the synthetic rubber tip (if equipped) can be compressed sufficiently to cause a false setting which will affect correct level of fuel in bowl. After lip is compressed the tip is very slow to recover its original shape. It is important that float lip be perpendicular to the needle or slant not more than 10 deg. away from the needle when float is set correctly.

Fast Idle Cam Setting

Figs. 7 and 8

1. With fast idle speed adjusting screw on second highest step of fast idle cam, move choke valve toward closed position with light pressure on choke shaft lever.
2. Insert specified gauge or drill size between choke valve and air horn wall. An adjustment will be necessary if a slight drag is not obtained as drill or gauge is being removed.
3. To adjust, bend stop on choke shaft as required ($1\frac{1}{2}$" units); on $1\frac{1}{4}$" units, bend fast idle rod at the angle.

Vacuum Kick Adjustment

Figs. 9 and 10

The choke diaphragm adjustment controls fuel delivery while the engine is running. It positions the choke valve within the air horn by action of the linkage between the choke shaft and diaphragm. The diaphragm must be energized to measure the vacuum kick adjustment. Use either a distributor test machine with a vacuum source or vacuum supplied by another vehicle. Adjust as follows:

1. If adjustment is to be made with engine running, disconnect fast idle linkage to allow choke to close to kick position with engine at curb idle. If an auxiliary vacuum source is to be used, open throttle valves (engine not running) and move choke to close position. Release throttle first, then release choke.
2. When using an auxiliary vacuum source, disconnect vacuum hose from carburetor and connect it to a hose from vacuum supply with a small length of tube to act as a fitting. Removal of hose from diaphragm may require forces which damage the system. Apply a vacuum of 10 or more inches of mercury.
3. Insert specified drill between choke valve and air horn wall. Apply sufficient closing pressure on lever to which choke rod attaches to provide a minimum choke valve opening without distortion of diaphragm link. Note that link must deflect a wire spring before it reaches end of travel within lever slot. Link must travel to end of slot for proper measurement of kick adjustment.
4. An adjustment will be necessary if a slight drag is not obtained as drill is being removed. Shorten or lengthen diaphragm link to obtain correct

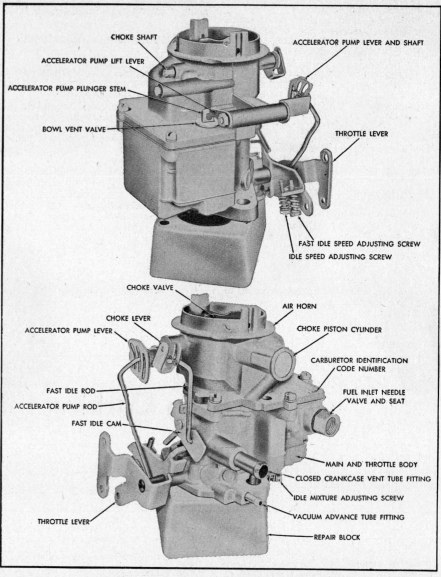

Fig. 1 Stromberg Model WA single-barrel carburetor

CHOKE SHAFT
ACCELERATOR PUMP LEVER AND SHAFT
ACCELERATOR PUMP LIFT LEVER
ACCELERATOR PUMP PLUNGER STEM
BOWL VENT VALVE
THROTTLE LEVER
FAST IDLE SPEED ADJUSTING SCREW
IDLE SPEED ADJUSTING SCREW
CHOKE VALVE
CHOKE LEVER
AIR HORN
ACCELERATOR PUMP LEVER
CHOKE PISTON CYLINDER
CARBURETOR IDENTIFICATION CODE NUMBER
FAST IDLE ROD
ACCELERATOR PUMP ROD
FUEL INLET NEEDLE VALVE AND SEAT
FAST IDLE CAM
MAIN AND THROTTLE BODY
CLOSED CRANKCASE VENT TUBE FITTING
IDLE MIXTURE ADJUSTING SCREW
VACUUM ADVANCE TUBE FITTING
THROTTLE LEVER
REPAIR BLOCK

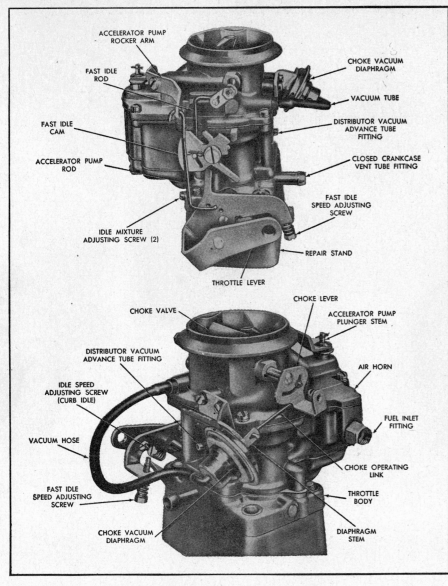

Fig. 2 Stromberg Model WW two-barrel carburetor

choke opening. Length changes should be made carefully by bending (open or closing) the bend provided in diaphragm link. *Do not apply twisting or bending force to diaphragm.*

5. Reinstall vacuum hose on correct carburetor fitting. Return fast idle linkage to its original condition if it was disturbed as in Step 1.

6. Make following check: With no vacuum applied to diaphragm, choke valve should move freely between open and closed positions. If movement is not free, examine linkage for misalignment or interferences caused by the bending operation. Repeat adjustment if necessary to provide proper link operation.

Choke Unloader Adjustment

Figs. 11 and 12

The choke unloader is a mechanical device to partially open the choke valve at wide open throttle. It is used to eliminate choke enrichment during engine cranking. Engines that have been flooded or stalled by excessive choke enrichment can be cleared by use of the unloader. Adjust as follows:

1. With throttle valve held in wide open position, insert the specified drill size between upper edge of choke valve and air horn wall.

2. With finger lightly pressing against choke valve, a slight drag should be felt as drill is being withdrawn.

3. If an adjustment is necessary, bend unloader tang on throttle lever until correct opening has been obtained.

Accelerator Pump Adjustment

1½" Carburetors, Fig. 13

1. With throttle valves closed, measure pump travel from fully closed to fully open throttle.

2. If the dimension is not as specified, bend pump rod as shown until correct travel is obtained.

Bowl Vent Adjustment

1½" Carburetors, Fig. 14

This setting is made after the pump setting. Adjust as follows:

1. With throttle valves at curb idle, there should be the specified clearance between bowl vent valve and air horn when measured at center of vent valve and seat with a gauge or drill shank.

2. If an adjustment is necessary, bend bowl vent lever as required. *Any adjustment to the accelerator pump means that the bowl vent must be readjusted.*

Bowl Vent & Pump Adjustment

1¼" Carburetors, Fig. 15

When assembling the pump to the air horn, note that the horseshoe clip (which opens the bowl vent) can be placed in any one of three positioning notches. These notches correspond to the long, medium and short pump stroke holes in the throttle lever. Normally the bowl vent clip on the pump stem will be in the middle notch and the pump rod in the medium stroke hole. The proper procedure is to adjust the amount of bowl vent opening instead of measuring and setting the height of the pump plunger. Adjust as follows:

1. Back off idle speed adjusting screw. Open choke valve so that when throttle valves are closed, the fast idle adjusting screw will not contact fast idle cam.

2. Be sure pump rod is in medium stroke hole in throttle lever and that bowl vent clip on pump stem is in center notch.

3. Close throttle valves tightly. It should be just possible to insert the specified gauge or drill between bowl vent and vent seat.

4. If an adjustment is necessary, bend pump rod at lower angle as required to obtain correct bowl vent opening.

NOTE: This is an important adjustment since too much lift at bowl vent will result in considerable loss in low speed fuel economy. Remember that if the pump rod is moved to either the short or long stroke position a corresponding change must be made in the location of the bowl vent clip, and the amount of lift of the bowl vent rechecked and adjusted. The pump travel is automatically taken care of when the bowl vent is properly adjusted.

Automatic Choke Setting

Well-Type Choke, Chrysler Engines, Fig. 16—The choke control, mounted in the intake manifold well, is accurately adjusted when originally assembled. Under normal service operations, it is recommended not to change the setting or to disassemble the components for servicing. However, if the setting has been disturbed, loosen the locknut "A" and

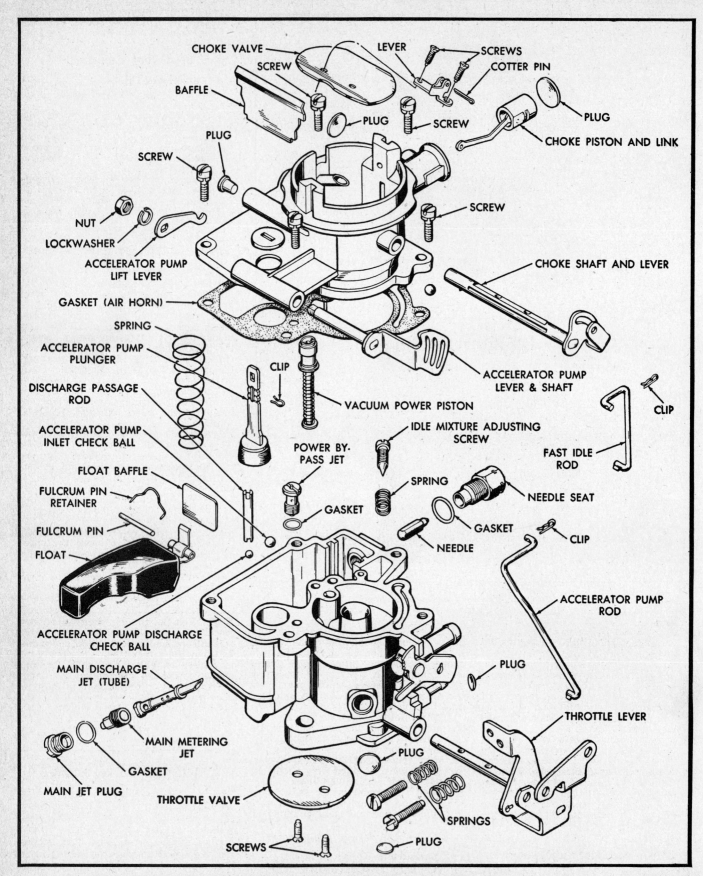

CHOKE VALVE · LEVER · SCREWS · COTTER PIN · SCREW · BAFFLE · PLUG · SCREW · PLUG · CHOKE PISTON AND LINK · SCREW · PLUG · NUT · LOCKWASHER · ACCELERATOR PUMP LIFT LEVER · SCREW · CHOKE SHAFT AND LEVER · GASKET (AIR HORN) · SPRING · ACCELERATOR PUMP PLUNGER · CLIP · ACCELERATOR PUMP LEVER & SHAFT · CLIP · DISCHARGE PASSAGE ROD · VACUUM POWER PISTON · IDLE MIXTURE ADJUSTING SCREW · FAST IDLE ROD · ACCELERATOR PUMP INLET CHECK BALL · POWER BY-PASS JET · SPRING · NEEDLE SEAT · FLOAT BAFFLE · GASKET · GASKET · CLIP · FULCRUM PIN RETAINER · NEEDLE · FULCRUM PIN · FLOAT · ACCELERATOR PUMP ROD · ACCELERATOR PUMP DISCHARGE CHECK BALL · PLUG · MAIN DISCHARGE JET (TUBE) · THROTTLE LEVER · MAIN METERING JET · GASKET · PLUG · MAIN JET PLUG · THROTTLE VALVE · PLUG · SPRINGS · SCREWS · PLUG

Fig. 3   Exploded view of Stromberg WA single-barrel carburetor

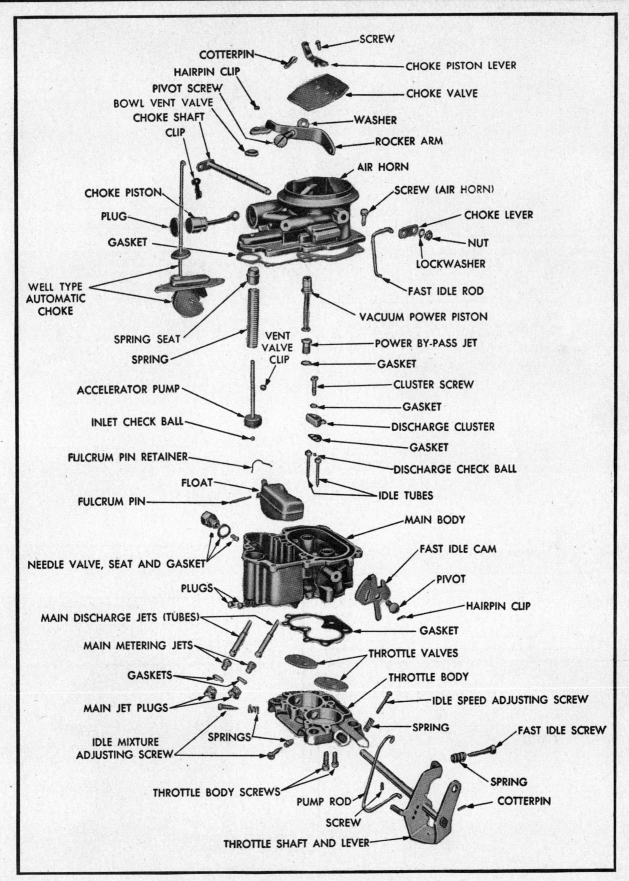

Fig. 4 Exploded view of Stromberg WW two-barrel carburetor

The following labels appear in the exploded view:

- SCREW
- COTTERPIN
- CHOKE PISTON LEVER
- HAIRPIN CLIP
- CHOKE VALVE
- PIVOT SCREW
- BOWL VENT VALVE
- CHOKE SHAFT
- CLIP
- WASHER
- ROCKER ARM
- AIR HORN
- CHOKE PISTON
- SCREW (AIR HORN)
- PLUG
- CHOKE LEVER
- GASKET
- NUT
- LOCKWASHER
- WELL TYPE AUTOMATIC CHOKE
- FAST IDLE ROD
- VACUUM POWER PISTON
- SPRING SEAT
- VENT VALVE CLIP
- POWER BY-PASS JET
- SPRING
- GASKET
- ACCELERATOR PUMP
- CLUSTER SCREW
- GASKET
- INLET CHECK BALL
- DISCHARGE CLUSTER
- FULCRUM PIN RETAINER
- GASKET
- DISCHARGE CHECK BALL
- FLOAT
- IDLE TUBES
- FULCRUM PIN
- MAIN BODY
- NEEDLE VALVE, SEAT AND GASKET
- FAST IDLE CAM
- PIVOT
- PLUGS
- HAIRPIN CLIP
- MAIN DISCHARGE JETS (TUBES)
- GASKET
- MAIN METERING JETS
- THROTTLE VALVES
- GASKETS
- THROTTLE BODY
- MAIN JET PLUGS
- IDLE SPEED ADJUSTING SCREW
- SPRING
- IDLE MIXTURE ADJUSTING SCREW
- SPRINGS
- FAST IDLE SCREW
- THROTTLE BODY SCREWS
- SPRING
- PUMP ROD
- COTTERPIN
- SCREW
- THROTTLE SHAFT AND LEVER

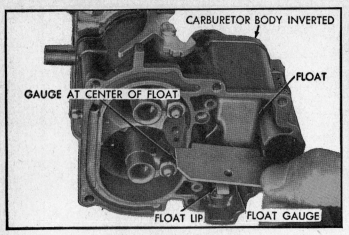

Fig. 5   Checking float level on Stromberg 1¼″ units

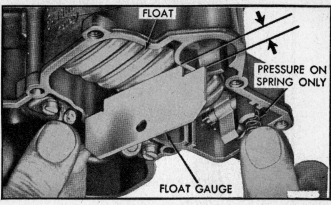

Fig. 6   Checking float level on Stromberg 1½″ units

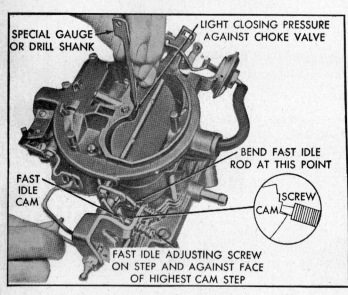

Fig. 8   Fast idle cam position.
Stromberg 1½″ units

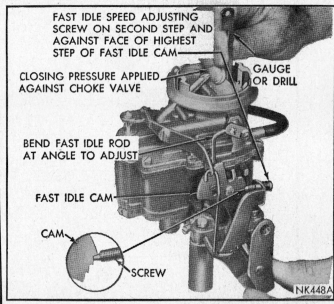

Fig. 7   Fast idle position.
Stromberg 1¼″ units

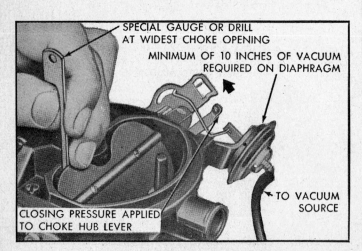

Fig. 10   Vacuum kick adjustment.
Stromberg 1½″ units

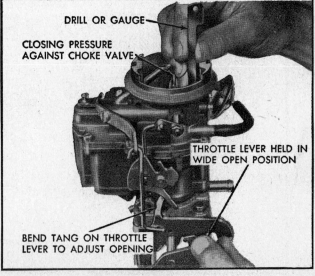

Fig. 11   Choke unloader adjustment.
Stromberg 1¼″ units

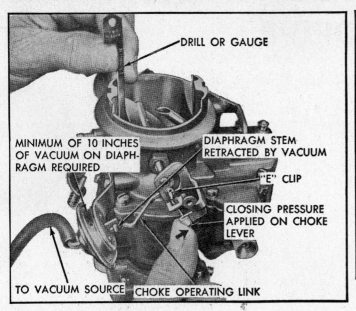

Fig. 9   Vacuum kick adjustment.
Stromberg 1¼″ units

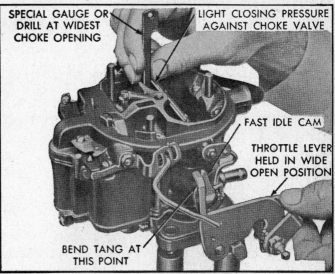

Fig. 12   Choke unloader adjustment
Stromberg 1½″ units

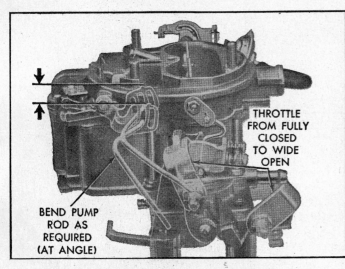

Fig. 13   Accelerator pump adjustment.
Stromberg 1½″ units

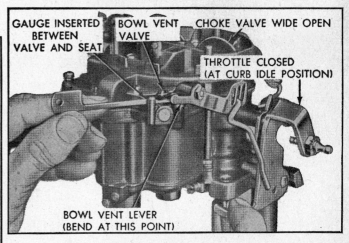

Fig. 14   Bowl vent adjustment. Stromberg 1½″ units

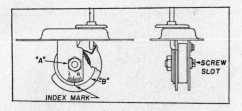

Fig. 16   Well-type automatic choke
on Chrysler engines

turn part with a screwdriver until index mark on disc "B" coincides with mark listed in the *Stromberg Specifications Chart.* Hold in correct position with screwdriver while tightening locknut. When installed, lift cover disc to see that rod has clearance when choke is opened and closed. If there is any binding in the rod, replace the choke assembly.

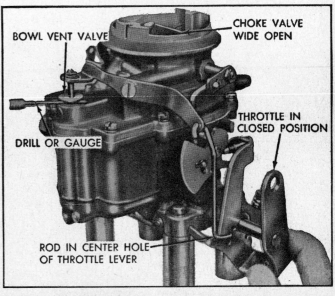

Fig. 15   Bowl vent adjustment. Stromberg 1¼″ units

OVERDRIVE

See Trouble Shooting Chapter For Diagnosis Procedure On These Units

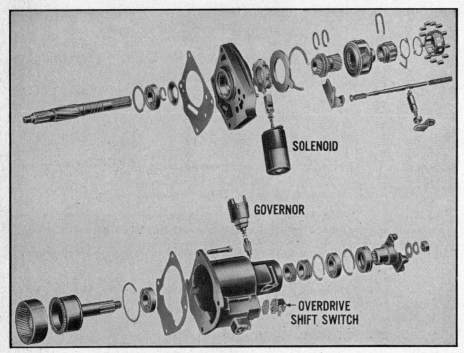

Fig. 2 Second version of full-electric overdrive with centrifugal governor. This unit is similar to the first version except the design of the second version is more compact. Some models do not use the shift (lockout) switch

Overdrive units are essentially automatic two-speed planetary transmissions attached to the rear of conventional three-speed transmissions. As shown in Fig. 1, the heart of the over-drive is the planetary unit consisting of sun gear, planetary pinions and internal (ring) gear. In overdrive, the pinions are connected to the mainshaft, and revolve around the sun gear which holds against rotation. The internal gear, connected to the tailshaft, is thus forced to rotate at a speed greater than the mainshaft. The engagement of the gearset is controlled by coupling the internal gear to the tail shaft, or holding the sun gear stationary, or by a combination of the two methods.

By following the procedure shown pictorially in Figs. 3 through 12, no difficulty should be experienced in servicing these units.

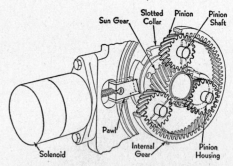

Fig. 1 Through the planetary unit shown, the overdrive provides a higher gear ratio, and when in operation, engine speed is approximately 30 per cent slower than when operating in conventional high gear

Fig. 3 Remove companion flange and governor. Also lockout switch if so equipped

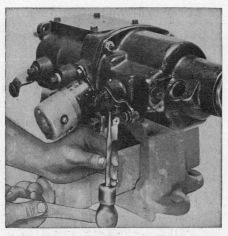

Fig. 4 After driving out locating pin, pull shift shaft as far as possible to disengage operating cam from shift rail. Remove overdrive housing. Tap end of shaft to prevent its coming off with housing and spilling free wheel rollers. Parts inside housing may then be removed.

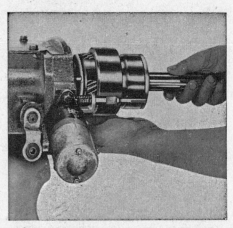

Fig. 5 Hold the adapter plate to the transmission case with one screw and remove the overdrive shaft, catching the free wheel rollers as shown. Removing snap ring permits ring gear to be taken off shaft.

Fig. 6   Remove retaining clip and take off free wheel unit and pinion cage

Fig. 7   Separate pinion cage from free wheel unit by removing retaining clip

Fig. 8   Remove overdrive sun gear and shift rail

Fig. 9   Remove attaching screws, rotate solenoid 1/4 turn and take off

Fig. 10   After releasing snap ring from adapter plate, remove sun gear cover plate, blocker and solenoid pawl

Fig. 11   At this point, if repairs are to be made on the transmission, remove the mainshaft, adapter plate, gears and synchronizer as a unit

Fig. 12   Reverse the order of disassembly to assemble the unit. After inserting the pawl with the notched side up as shown, install blocker assembly and cover plate, being sure blocker ring and pawl are properly positioned. Then install large snap ring in adapter plate

THREE SPEED MANUAL SHIFT TRANSMISSIONS

See Car Chapters for procedures on removing the transmission and adjusting the gearshift linkage

APPLICATION INDEX

Type One

DISASSEMBLE TRANS.

1. Remove transmission cover and shift levers.
2. Remove front retainer and gasket and front bearing snap rings.
3. Align notch in clutch shaft with 3rd speed gear and use suitable puller to remove clutch shaft using care not to lose rollers.
4. Remove front bearing with puller.
5. Remove extension case and remove snap rings that retain speedometer drive gear.
6. Remove speedometer gear using care not to lose drive ball.
7. Remove rear bearing snap rings and remove rear bearing with a puller.
8. Move mainshaft to side and remove shift forks.
9. Place front synchronizer in 2nd speed position and remove mainshaft by tilting front of shaft up and lifting through top of case, Fig. 3.
10. Use a punch to remove roll pins from shift shafts and push shafts into case. Detent assembly may now be removed from case.
11. Using a brass drift drive reverse idler gear shaft out of rear of case and remove idler gear. Do not lose rollers.
12. To retain rollers in countershaft gear, use a dummy shaft to drive countershaft out of rear of case.
13. After disassembling mainshaft carefully inspect all bearings and gear.

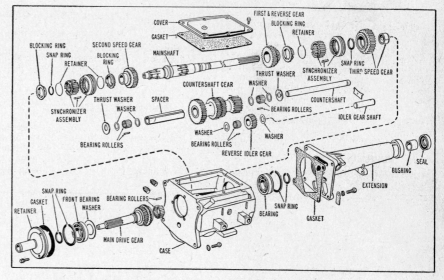

Fig. 1   Type 1 fully synchronized transmission exploded

Fig. 3   Removing mainshaft

REASSEMBLE TRANS.

Mainshaft Assemble

1. Place low speed and rear synchronizer on mainshaft and install rear synchronizer snap ring.

NOTE: Snap rings are available in select thicknesses. Clearance between first gear and collar on mainshaft must be .003-.012".

2. Place 2nd speed gear and 2nd & 3rd synchronizer on shaft and install snap ring.

NOTE: Snap rings are available in select thicknesses. Clearance between

Fig. 2   Removing clutch shaft with puller

Fig. 4   Installing mainshaft with Pilot End Support J-22994

THREE SPEED TRANSMISSIONS

2nd speed gear and color on main-shaft must be .003-.010".

3. Slide reverse speed gear on main-shaft and set assembly aside to be installed later.

Countergear

1. Coat bore at each end of counter gear with grease to hold rollers in place.
2. Install dummy shaft in countergear and install spacer, washers and rollers.
3. Place countergear in transmission case and position thrust washers at each end so tabs align with slots in case.
4. Use a plastic mallet to install countershaft.

Reverse Idler Gear

1. Coat bore of idler gear with grease to retain rollers.

2. Install idler gear in case and position thrust washers.
3. Use plastic mallet to install idler gear shaft.

Shifter Shafts

1. Partially install shifter shafts in transmission case.
2. Align detent assembly with shifter shafts and case stud.
3. Push shift detent assembly and shift shafts into place and install roll pins.

Mainshaft Installation

1. Place front synchronizer in 2nd speed position and place mainshaft in case.
2. Move mainshaft to side and install shift forks by pulling detent lever up and placing forks in the shifting assembly.

3. Position mainshaft assembly in center of case and install Pilot End Support J-22994, Fig. 4.
4. Place rear bearing on mainshaft and drive bearing into position and install snap ring.
5. Install speedometer gear and snap ring.

Final Assembly

1. Install rollers in clutch shaft using grease to retain them.
2. Slide clutch shaft into position through front of case.
3. Install front bearing, snap rings, gasket and retainer.
4. Replace seal if necessary and install extension housing, shift levers and case cover.
5. Fill transmission with lubricant and check operation.

Type Two

This transmission, Fig. 1, is a conventional synchromesh transmission except for the use of concentric input and output shafts and its mounting on the differential carrier. Because of its attachment to the differential carrier, the mainshaft is hollow to permit passage of the clutch shaft to the clutch gear at the front of the transmission. The clutch gear drives a countergear and the remaining power flow sequence is identical to the conventional three speed transmission. All drive gears have helical teeth and all forward gears are synchronized. A spring-loaded dampener plate (anti-rattle) on the countergear loads the clutch gear to eliminate torsional rattle.

Disassembly

1. Remove side cover and shift forks.
2. Remove clutch gear bearing cover.
3. Remove clutch gear bearing snap ring.
4. Use a brass drift and tap clutch gear bearing out of case bore, tapping through side cover opening.
5. Remove reverse idler gear retainer "E" ring and rear bearing retainer strap and bolt.
6. Remove rear bearing retainer, mainshaft, pilot bearings, and clutch gear as an assembly through rear of case. Move synchronizer sleeves forward as necessary to allow clearance between mainshaft and countergear assemblies.
7. Using a long drift through clutch gear bearing case bore, drive out reverse idler shaft and its woodruff key. Remove reverse idler gear and tanged thrust washer.
8. Using a suitable arbor, drive countershaft and its woodruff key out rear of case. Remove countergear, roller

bearings and tanged thrust washers through rear case bore.
9. If necessary, remove two screws attaching shift finger to selector shaft and remove shaft out front of case. The shaft seal may now be pryed from case and replaced if necessary.

Disassemble Mainshaft

1. Remove 2-3 sliding clutch hub snap ring from mainshaft and remove clutch assembly, 2nd speed blocker ring and 2nd speed gear from front of mainshaft.
2. Remove mainshaft rear bearing snap ring.
3. Support reverse gear in a press and press on rear of mainshaft to remove reverse gear, thrust washer, spring washer, rear bearing and bearing retainer assembly.

Synchronizers

1. Clutch hubs and sliding sleeves are a selected assembly and should be kept together as originally assembled but the keys are two springs may be replaced if worn or broken. Mark hub and sleeve so they can be matched on reassembly.
2. When assembling, place three keys and two springs in position (one on each side of hub) so all three keys are engaged by both springs. The tanged end of each synchronizer spring should be installed into different key cavities on either side. Slide the sleeve into the hub, aligning the marks made before disassembly.

NOTE: A groove around the outside of the synchronizer hub identifies the end

that must be opposite the fork slot in the sleeve when assembled. This groove indicates the end of the hub with a .07" greater recess depth.

Assemble Mainshaft

1. Referring to Fig. 2, turn front of mainshaft upward and install 2nd speed gear with clutching teeth upward; rear face of gear will butt against flange on mainshaft.
2. Install blocking ring with clutching teeth downward over synchronizing surface of 2nd speed gear.
3. Install 2-3 synchronizer assembly with fork slot downward; press it onto splines on mainshaft until it bottoms out. Be sure notches of blocker ring align with synchronizer keys.
4. Install synchronizer hub-to-main-shaft snap ring.
5. Turn rear of mainshaft upward and install 1st speed gear with clutching teeth upward; front face of gear will butt against flange on mainshaft.
6. Install blocker ring with clutching teeth downward over synchronizing surface of 1st speed gear.
7. Install 1st-reverse synchronizer with fork slot downward, pressing it onto splines of mainshaft. Be sure notches of blocker ring align with synchronizer keys.
8. Install synchronizer hub-to-mainshaft snap ring.
9. Install reverse gear with clutching teeth downward. Install reverse gear thrust washer (steel), and reverse spring washer.
10. Using snap ring pliers, expand rear bearing retainer snap ring and assemble rear bearing into retainer so

1—252

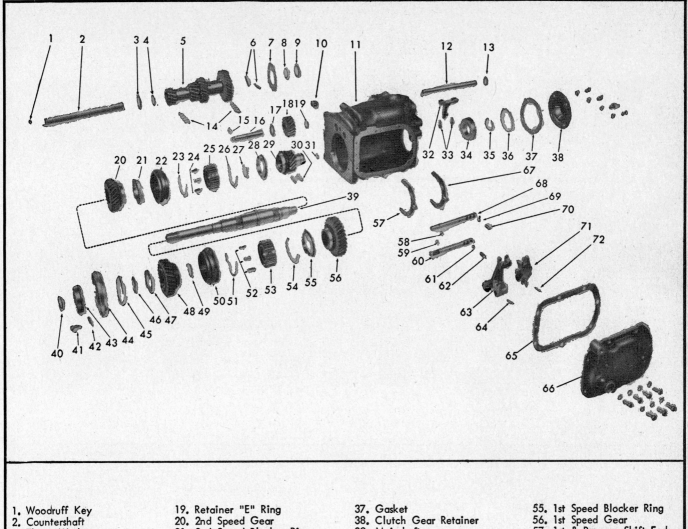

Fig. 1   Type 2 Corvair transmission

1. Woodruff Key	19. Retainer "E" Ring	37. Gasket	55. 1st Speed Blocker Ring
2. Countershaft	20. 2nd Speed Gear	38. Clutch Gear Retainer	56. 1st Speed Gear
3. Thrust Washer	21. 2nd Speed Blocker Ring	39. Mainshaft	57. 1st & Reverse Shift Fork
4. Needle Washer	22. 2-3 Synchronizer Sleeve	40. Snap Ring—Bearing to Shaft	58. Interlock Ball
5. Countergear	23. Synchronizer Key Retainer	41. Retainer Bolt	59. Interlock Ball
6. Spring—N.S.S.	24. Synchronizer Keys	42. Retainer Strap	60. 1st & Reverse Shift Rail
7. Anti-Rattle Plate—N.S.S.	25. Synchronizer Hub	43. Mainshaft Rear Bearing	61. Detent Ball
8. Needle Washer	26. Synchronizer Key Retainer	44. Bearing Retainer	62. Detent Spring
9. Thrust Washer	27. Snap Ring	45. Snap Ring—Bearing to Retainer	63. 1st & Reverse Shifter Head
10. Filler Plug	28. 3rd Speed Blocker Ring	46. Spring Washer	64. Roll Pin
11. Case	29. Clutch Gear	47. Thrust Washer	65. Gasket
12. Shift Selector Shaft	30. Pilot Bearings	48. Reverse Gear	66. Side Cover
13. Seal	31. Snap Ring	49. Snap Ring	67. 2nd & 3rd Shift Fork
14. Needle Bearings	32. Shifter Finger	50. 1st & Reverse Synch. Sleeve	68. 2nd & 3rd Shift Rail
15. Woodruff Key	33. Screws & L. Washers	51. Synchronizer Key Retainer	69. Detent Ball
16. Reverse Idler Shaft	34. Clutch Gear Bearing	52. Synchronizer Keys	70. Detent Spring
17. Thrust Washer (Tanged)	35. Snap Ring—Bearing to Gear	53. Synchronizer Hub	71. 2nd & 3rd Shifter Head
18. Reverse Idler Gear	36. Snap Ring—Bearing to Case	54. Synchronizer Key Retainer	72. Roll Pin

snap ring groove is toward chamfered edge of retainer. Be sure to seat retainer snap ring into bearing groove.

11. Press rear bearing and retainer assembly onto rear of mainshaft so that chamfered retainer edge is toward gears.

12. Install rear bearing-to-mainshaft snap ring.

Assemble Transmission

1. Load countergear with 27 rollers and a thrust washer at each end, Fig. 3. Use heavy grease to hold them in place.

2. Place countergear through rear of case with a tanged thrust washer (tang away from gear) at each end and install countershaft and woodruff key

from rear of case. *Be sure countershaft picks up both thrust washers and that tangs are aligned with their notches in case.*

3. Install reverse idler gear thrust washer, gear and shaft with woodruff key from rear of case. Be sure thrust washer is between gear and rear of case with its tang toward notch is case. *Do not install idler*

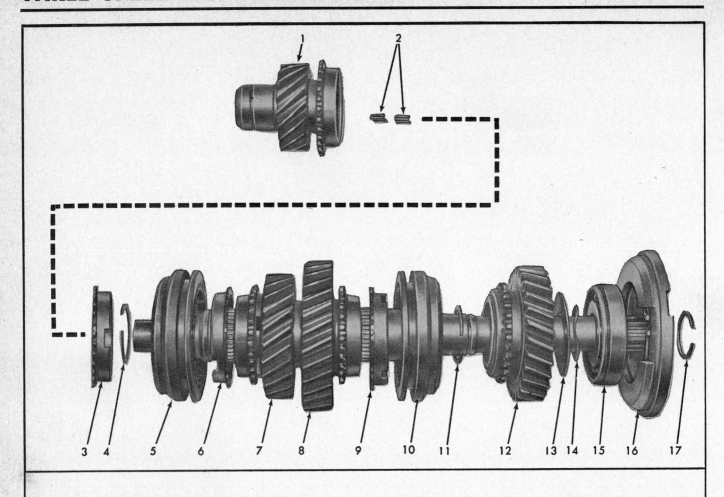

1. Clutch Gear
2. Mainshaft Pilot Bearings (76)
3. 3rd Speed Blocker Ring
4. Snap Ring
5. 2-3 Synchronizer Assembly
6. 2nd Speed Blocker Ring
7. 2nd Speed Gear
8. 1st Speed Gear
9. 1st Speed Blocker Ring
10. 1st Speed Synchronizer Assembly
11. Snap Ring
12. Reverse Gear
13. Reverse Gear Thrust Washer
14. Spring Washer
15. Rear Bearing
16. Rear Bearing Retainer & Snap Ring
17. Snap Ring

Fig. 2 Clutch gear and mainshaft assembled loosely to show location of parts

shaft "E" ring at this time.

4. Load two rows of mainshaft pilot bearings (74) into clutch gear cavity and assemble 3rd speed blocker ring onto clutch gear clutching surface

Fig. 3 Loading bearings into countergear

with its teeth toward gear.

5. Place clutch gear, pilot bearings and 3rd speed blocker ring assembly over front of mainshaft. *Do not assemble bearing to gear at this time. Be sure notches in blocker ring align with keys in the 2-3 synchronizer assembly.*

6. From rear of case, assemble clutch gear and mainshaft assembly into case and install rear bearing retainer strap and bolt to case, Fig. 4.

7. Install front bearing outer snap ring to bearing and position bearing over hub of clutch gear and into front case bore.

8. Install snap ring to clutch gear hub, and bearing retainer and gasket to case. *Retainer oil hole should be at bottom.*

9. Install reverse idler gear retainer "E" ring to shaft. Be sure thrust washer tang engages notch in case.

10. Install selector shaft and shift finger so the 90-deg. finger projection is facing clutch gear end of transmission.

11. Shift synchronizer sleeves to neutral positions and install cover, gasket and fork assembly to case. *Be sure forks align with their synchronizer sleeve grooves and selector finger with shifter heads.*

Fig. 4 Rear bearing, retainer and strap

Type Three

DISASSEMBLE TRANS.
Case Components

1. Remove side cover assembly, gasket and shift forks.
2. Remove clutch gear retainer and gasket.
3. Remove clutch gear bearing to stem snap ring, then slide bearing off over clutch gear stem. The clutch gear bearing is a slip fit on the gear and into the case bore.
4. Remove rear extension to case bolts.
5. Rotate extension to left until groove in extension housing flange lines up with the reverse idler shaft. Drive reverse idler shaft out of gear and case, Fig. 2.
6. Remove entire clutch gear, mainshaft and extension assembly through case rear opening. Remove reverse idler gear from case.

Mainshaft Disassembly

1. Remove clutch gear from mainshaft, Fig. 3.
2. Expand extension snap ring and tap end of mainshaft to remove extension, Fig. 4.
3. Depress speedometer gear retaining clip and slide gear from mainshaft.
4. Remove rear bearing snap ring, support Reverse gear and press on rear of mainshaft to remove Reverse gear, thrust washer and rear bearing.
5. Remove 1st and Reverse sliding clutch hub snap ring from mainshaft.
6. Support 1st gear and press on rear of mainshaft to remove the clutch assembly, blocker ring and 1st gear.
7. Remove 2nd and 3rd speed sliding clutch hub snap ring.
8. Support 2nd gear and press on front of mainshaft to remove clutch assembly, 2nd speed blocker ring and 2nd speed gear.

Synchronizer Clutch Keys & Springs

NOTE: Clutch hubs and sleeves are a selected assembly and should be kept together as originally assembled, but the keys and springs may be replaced separately.

Before disassembling synchronizers, mark hub and sleeve so they can be matched upon reassembly.

Place the keys and springs in position so all three keys are engaged by both springs. The tanged end of each spring should be installed into different key cavities on either side. Slide sleeve onto hub, aligning marks made before disassembly.

NOTE: A groove around the outside of the hub identifies the end that must be opposite the fork slot in the sleeve.

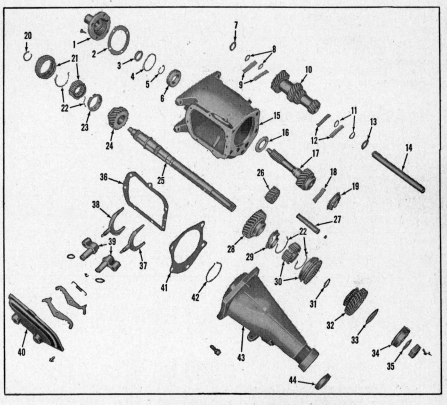

Fig. 1 Type three fully synchronized transmission. Exploded view

1. Bearing Retainer	16. Slinger	31. Snap Ring
2. Gasket	17. Clutch Gear	32. Reverse Gear
3. Oil Seal	18. Roller Bearings	33. Thrust Washer
4. Snap Ring	19. Blocking Ring	34. Bearing
5. Snap Ring	20. Snap Ring	35. Snap Ring
6. Bearing	21. Synchronizer	36. Gasket
7. Thrust Washer	22. Spring	37. Shift Fork
8. Thrust Washer	23. Blocking Ring	38. Shift Fork
9. Roller Bearings	24. 2nd Speed Gear	39. Shifter Shaft
10. Counter Gear	25. Mainshaft	40. Cover
11. Thrust Washer	26. Reverse Idler Gear	41. Gasket
12. Roller Bearings	27. Idler Gear Shaft	42. Snap Ring
13. Thrust Washer	28. 1st Speed Gear	43. Extension
14. Counter Shaft	29. Blocking Ring	44. Oil Seal
15. Case	30. Synchronizer	

Mainshaft Reassemble

With front of mainshaft up:

1. Install 2nd speed gear with clutching teeth upward; the rear face of the gear will butt against the shoulder on the shaft.
2. Install blocker ring with teeth downward over gear. All three blocker rings used in this unit are identical.
3. Install 2nd and 3rd synchronizer assembly with fork slot downward and press onto splines until it bottoms.

Install snap ring.

NOTE: Be sure the notches of the blocker ring align with the keys of the synchronizer assembly.

With rear of mainshaft up:

4. Install 1st speed gear with clutching teeth upward. Install a blocker ring with teeth downward over synchronizer surface of the gear.
5. Install 1st and Reverse synchronizer assembly with fork slot up.

NOTE: Be sure the notches of the

THREE SPEED TRANSMISSIONS

blocker ring align with the keys of the synchronizer assembly and that both synchronizer sleeves face the front of the mainshaft.

6. Install snap ring.
7. Install Reverse gear with clutching teeth downward. Install steel thrust washer.
8. Press rear bearing onto mainshaft with snap ring slot downward. Install snap ring.
9. Install speedometer drive gear and retaining clip.

REASSEMBLE TRANS.

1. Load a double row of roller bearings and a thrust washer at each end of the countergear. Use heavy grease to hold them in place.
2. Place countergear through case rear opening with tanged thrust washer (tang away from gear) at each end and install countergear shaft and woodruff key from rear of case.

NOTE: Be sure countershaft picks

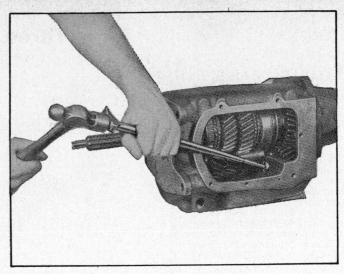

Fig. 2   Removing reverse idler shaft

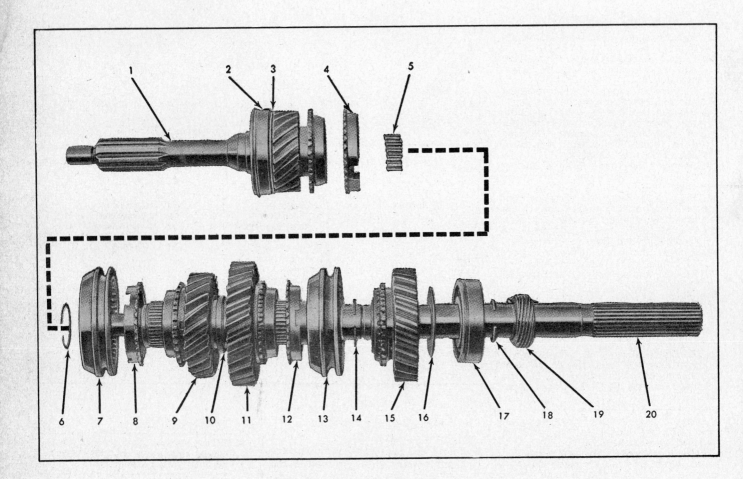

1. Clutch Gear	6. Snap Ring	11. 1st Speed Gear	16. Reverse Gear Thrust Washer
2. Clutch Gear Bearing	7. 2-3 Synchronizer Assembly	12. 1st Speed Blocker Ring	17. Rear Bearing
3. Oil Slinger	8. 2nd Speed Blocker Ring	13. 1st Speed Synchronizer Assembly	18. Snap Ring
4. 3rd Speed Blocker Ring	9. 2nd Speed Gear	14. Snap Ring	19. Speedo Drive Gear
5. Mainshaft Pilot Bearings (16)	10. Shoulder (Part of Mainshaft)	15. Reverse Gear	20. Mainshaft

Fig. 3   Mainshaft assembly

up both thrust washers and that the tangs are aligned with their notches in the case.

3. Position reverse idler gear in case but do not install shaft.
4. Install mainshaft assembly into rear extension housing.
5. Load roller bearings into clutch gear bore, install blocker ring onto clutch gear and install clutch gear assembly onto mainshaft.

NOTE: Be sure notches in blocker ring align with keys in synchronizer assembly.

6. Using new gasket, install the mainshaft assembly through the rear of the case. Be sure the clutch gear engages the teeth of the countergear anti-lash plate and that the oil slinger is in place on the clutch gear.
7. Rotate extension housing and install reverse idler shaft and woodruff key. Install extension bolts.
8. Install front bearing on clutch gear stem, install snap ring and bearing retainer.
9. With synchronizers in Neutral, install cover assembly. Be sure forks align with their synchronizer sleeve grooves.

Fig. 4 Removing extension housing snap ring

Type Four

DISASSEMBLE TRANS.
Case Components

1. Shift transmission into 2nd gear for shift fork clearance and remove side cover and shifter assembly, Fig. 1.
2. Remove front bearing retainer.
3. Tap drive pinion forward with brass drift as far as possible to provide clearance for mainshaft removal, Fig. 2.
4. Rotate cut away part of second gear next to countergear for mainshaft removal clearance. Shift 2-3 synchronizer sleeve forward.
5. Remove speedometer gear.
6. Remove rear extension housing.

7. Using dummy shaft, push reverse idler shaft and key out of case.
8. Remove idler gear with dummy shaft in place to retain rollers. Remove thrust washers.
9. Remove mainshaft through rear case opening, Fig. 3.
10. Using dummy shaft to retain rollers, tap countershaft out rear of case and lower countergear to bottom of case to permit removal of drive pinion.
11. Remove snap ring from pinion bearing outer race, drive pinion into case and remove through rear case opening, Fig. 4.
12. Remove countergear through rear case opening.

Mainshaft, Disassemble

1. Remove 2-3 synchronizer clutch gear retaining ring from front of mainshaft.
2. Slide 2-3 synchronizer and 2nd gear stop ring off of shaft. Remove 2nd gear.
3. Spread snap ring in mainshaft bearing retainer and slide retainer off bearing race, Fig. 5.
4. Remove snap ring securing bearing to mainshaft.
5. Support front side of the reverse gear in press and press bearing off shaft. When bearing clears shaft, do not allow parts to drop through.
6. Remove 1st-Reverse synchronizer retaining ring and remove synchronizer assembly from mainshaft, Fig. 6.

7. Remove 1st gear and stop ring.
8. Reverse procedure to assemble mainshaft.

Mainshaft, Reassemble

1. Slide 1st gear and stop ring onto mainshaft and against flange, Fig. 7.
2. Slide 1st-Reverse synchronizer over mainshaft, indexing hub slots to stop ring lugs.
3. Install clutch gear snap ring on mainshaft.
4. Install reverse gear and mainshaft bearing, support inner race of bearing and press shaft through to shoulder. Be sure snap ring groove on outer race is forward. Install bearing retaining ring on mainshaft.

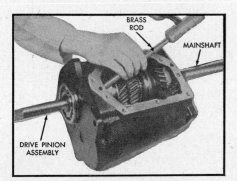

Fig. 2 Tapping drive pinion forward for mainshaft clearance

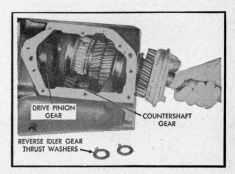

Fig. 3 Removing mainshaft assembly

THREE SPEED TRANSMISSIONS

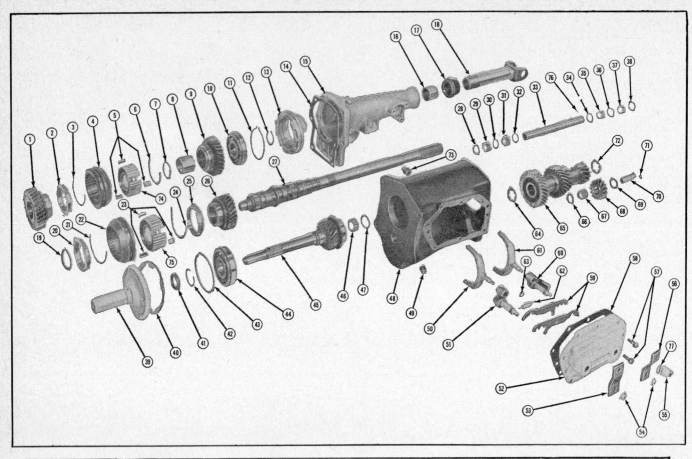

1. Gear, First	14. Gasket	27. Shaft, Output	40. Gasket	53. Lever	66. Washer
2. Ring	15. Extension	28. Washer	41. Seal	54. Nut Locking	67. Roller
3. Spring	16. Bushing	29. Roller	42. Snap Ring	55. Switch	68. Gear, Idler
4. Sleeve	17. Seal	30. Washer	43. Snap Ring	56. Lever	69. Washer
5. Struts (3)	18. Yoke	31. Roller	44. Bearing	57. Bolt	70. Shaft
6. Spring	19. Snap Ring	32. Washer	45. Pinion, Drive	58. Gasket	71. Key
7. Snap Ring	20. Ring	33. Countershaft	46. Roller	59. Lever, Interlock	72. Washer
8. Bushing	21. Spring	34. Washer	47. Snap Ring	60. Lever	73. Plug, Filler
9. Gear, Reverse	22. Sleeve	35. Roller	48. Case	61. Fork	74. Gear, Clutch
10. Bearing	23. Struts (3)	36. Washer	49. Plug, Drain	62. Spring	75. Gear, Clutch
11. Snap Ring	24. Spring	37. Roller	50. Lever	63. Snap Ring	76. Key
12. Snap Ring	25. Ring	38. Washer	51. Lever	64. Washer	77. Gasket
13. Retainer	26. Gear, Second	39. Retainer	52. Housing	65. Gear, Countershaft	

Fig. 1   Type 4 fully synchronized three speed transmission

5. Spread snap ring in mainshaft bearing retainer and slide retainer over bearing. Be sure snap ring seats in groove.
6. Referring to Fig. 1, install 2nd gear,

stop ring and 2nd-3rd gear synchronizer. Install snap ring.

Transmission, Assemble

1. Using dummy shaft to hold rollers in place and heavy grease to hold thrust washers, carefully place countergear assembly in bottom of case. *Do not finish installation until drive pinion is installed.*
2. Load rollers and retaining ring in drive pinion bore and install drive pinion through rear case opening and into case bore. Install large snap ring on bearing and install front bearing retainer.
3. Align countergear with its shaft bore and install countershaft through gear, driving dummy shaft out as countershaft is installed. Install countershaft key.
4. Carefully tap drive pinion forward to provide mainshaft installation clearance.

5. With 2-3 synchronizer sleeve fully forward and cut out on 2nd gear turned so it is toward countershaft, insert mainshaft assembly through rear case opening.

NOTE: If installation is correct, the

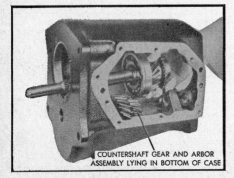

COUNTERSHAFT GEAR AND ARBOR ASSEMBLY LYING IN BOTTOM OF CASE

Fig. 4   Removing drive pinion

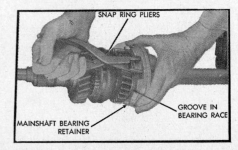

SNAP RING PLIERS

GROOVE IN BEARING RACE

MAINSHAFT BEARING RETAINER

Fig. 5   Removing mainshaft bearing retainer

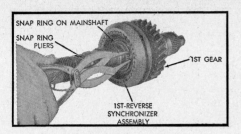

Fig. 6   Removing 1st-Reverse synchronizer snap ring

bearing retainer will bottom in the case without force. If not, check for strut, roller or stop ring is out of position.

6. Using dummy shaft to hold rollers, install reverse idler in case and install idler shaft and key.

7. Install rear extension housing, speedometer gear and with transmission shifted in 2nd gear, install cover and shifter assembly.

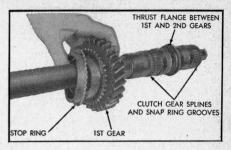

Fig. 7   First gear installation

Types Five & Six

NOTE

These transmissions, Figs. 1 and 2, are quite similar, the chief difference being the cut of the mainshaft splines and the double set of counter gear needle bearings used in the heavy duty unit, Fig. 1. Note that in Fig. 2 there are only one set of needle bearings at each end of the counter gear. The procedure which follows apply to both units unless otherwise indicated.

DISASSEMBLE TRANS.

1. Pull flange from rear of mainshaft.
2. Slide extension housing off mainshaft.
3. Remove transmission cover.

Main Drive Gear

1. Remove drive gear bearing retainer.
2. On H.D. models, Fig. 1, when removing drive gear from transmission, slide front synchronizer inner stop ring from short splines on gear as assembly is being removed from case.
3. On S.D. models, Fig. 2, grasp drive gear shaft and pull assembly out of case. *Be careful not to bind inner synchronizer ring on drive gear clutch teeth.*
4. Remove bearing rollers from drive gear pocket, using a hook or flat blade.

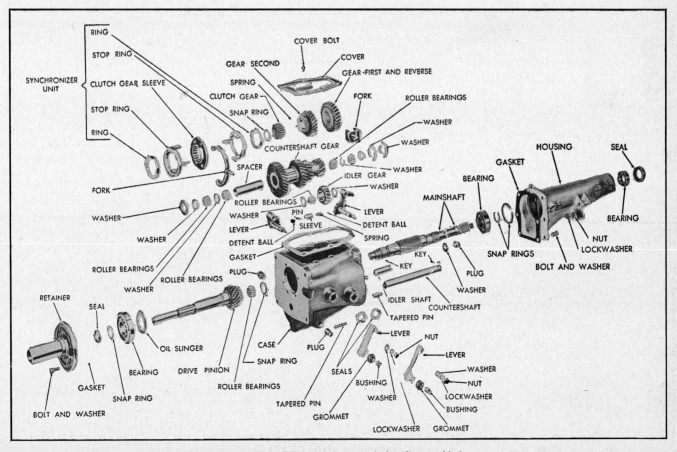

Fig. 1   Type 5 heavy duty transmission disassembled

THREE SPEED TRANSMISSIONS

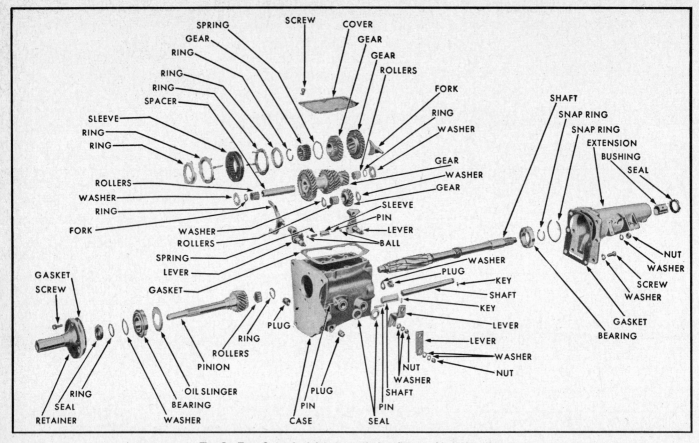

Fig. 2   Type 6 standard duty transmission disassembled. Note that low-reverse mainshaft gear shift fork groove goes to the front

Counter Gear

1. Use a suitable bearing loading tool to drive countershaft toward rear of case until key can be removed from countershaft. Then drive countershaft all the way out, keeping loading tool tight against end of countershaft to keep needle bearings in place.

Mainshaft

1. With transmission in reverse, remove outer center bearing snap ring, using a hook or flat blade, then partially remove mainshaft.
2. Cock mainshaft, then remove clutch sleeve, outer synchronizer rings, front inner ring and 2-3 shift fork, Figs. 3 and 4.

3. Remove clutch gear snap ring. Slide clutch gear off end of mainshaft.
4. Slide 2nd speed gear, stop ring and synchronizer spring off mainshaft.
5. Remove low-reverse sliding gear and shift fork as mainshaft is withdrawn from case.
6. Lift counter gear assembly from case.

Reverse Idler Gear

1. Drive reverse idler shaft towards rear and out of case. Remove key from end of shaft.
2. Lift out idler gear, thrust washers and needle bearings from case.

Gearshift Mechanism

HEAVY DUTY UNIT, Fig. 5

1. Remove both lever shaft seals.
2. Drive tapered lock pins from lever shafts, driving from bottom toward top of transmission.
3. Remove lever shafts from transmission, being careful not to lose spring-loaded detent balls.
4. Remove interlock sleeve, spring, pin and balls.

STANDARD DUTY UNIT, Fig. 6

1. Remove operating levers from shafts.
2. Drive out tapered pin from either of two lever shafts, then withdraw shaft from inside of case. The detent balls are spring-loaded; as the shaft is

being withdrawn, ball will drop to bottom of case.
3. Remove interlock sleeve, spring, pin and both balls from case. Then drive out remaining tapered pin and slide shaft out of transmission.
4. Drive out shaft seals and discard.

REASSEMBLE TRANS.

Gearshift Mechanism

1. Center two new seals over holes in case, then drive both seals into case.
2. Slide low-reverse shaft into rear boss of case, through seal and into position. Lock with tapered pin.

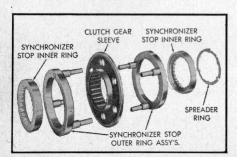

Fig. 3   Type 5 synchronizer unit

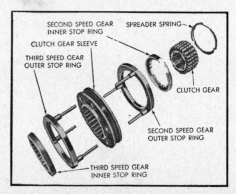

Fig. 4   Type 6 synchronizer unit

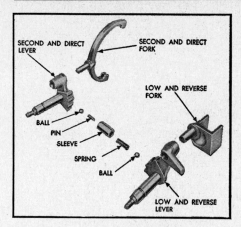

Fig. 5   Type 5 gearshift mechanism

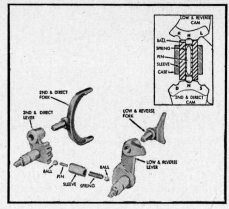

Fig. 6   Type 6 gearshift mechanism

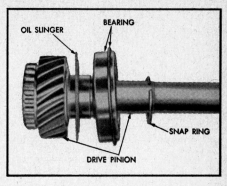

Fig. 7   Main drive gear components

Turn lever until center (neutral) detent is in line with interlock bores. Use sealer on pins.

3. Slide interlock sleeve in its bore, followed by one interlock ball. Install interlock spring and pin.

4. Place remaining interlock ball on top of spring. Depress interlock ball and at the same time install 2-3 lever into fully seated position with center (neutral) detent aligned with detent ball. Secure shaft with tapered pin.

Counter Gear

1. Slide bearing spacer over bearing loading tool. Coat bore of gear with lubricant. Then slide tool and spacer into gear bore.

2. Lubricate needle bearings and install half the total of bearings at each end of gear around loading tool (Type 6 transmission uses a total of 88 bearings, Type 7 uses 44 total).

3. Install bearing retainer rings at each end of gear. Apply grease to hold bearings in place.

4. Thrust washers are available in two sizes, marked A and B. Make a selection to obtain .004-.012" total end play of counter gear.

5. Install thrust washers at each end of assembly and over loading tool, using grease to hold washers in place.

6. Install counter gear assembly in case, making sure tabs on thrust washers slide into grooves in case.

Reverse Idler Gear

1. Coat bore of gear with grease and slide a suitable bearing loading too into bore.

2. Lubricate 22 needle bearings and install around loading tool.

3. Install new thrust washer at each end of gear and over loading tool using grease to hold washers in place.

4. With bevelled ends of gear teeth forward, slide gear down into position in case.

5. Install gear shift in its opening at rear of case.

6. Install key in shaft, and position shaft with keyway.

7. Raise idler gear slightly to align with shaft, then drive shaft into case through thrust washer and gear until

end of shaft is about 1/64" below surface of case.

Mainshaft

1. If new bearing is to be installed, press it on mainshaft and install snap ring.

2. Install low-reverse fork with offset to rear. Engage fork in low-reverse sliding gear. Position in case by shifting into reverse.

3. Slide mainshaft into case and through low-reverse gear.

4. Install 2-3 shift fork with offset toward rear.

5. Install 2nd speed gear and spreader spring on mainshaft.

NOTE: *Synchronizer float should be .050" to .090" when measured between end of synchronizer outer ring pin and opposite synchronizer outer ring. This measurement must be made 180 degrees apart with equal gap on both pin ends for float determination. To be acceptable, the gauge should be a snug fit between pins and outer rings. In cases where float dimension is over .090", synchronizer shims (part no. 2464724) should be installed to reduce float to .090" or less. This shim is to be installed on the 2nd speed gear before the energizing spring is installed. In cases where float is below .050", material should be removed from ends of all six synchronizer pins, using a magnetic grinder or other suitable equipment.*

6. Install 2nd gear inner stop ring and outer stop ring assembly. Engage synchronizer clutch sleeve with 2-3 shift fork.

7. Slide clutch gear over end of mainshaft and down against 2nd speed gear. Select a snap ring of the correct thickness and install. This snap ring eliminates end play and must be a snug fit.

8. Measure clearance between clutch gear and 2nd speed gear. Limits are .002-.011". If clearance is in excess of .011", "gear jump-out" may result.

9. Position mainshaft further in case by tapping on outer bearing race until bearing bottoms. Install a snap ring of the correct thickness in case.

Main Drive Gear

1. Slide oil slinger (if removed) over shaft and down against gear, Fig. 7.

2. Slide bearing over shaft with snap ring groove away from gear end. Seat bearing on shaft with a press. Be *sure slinger does not hang up in snap ring groove during pressing operation.*

3. Install keyed washer. Then secure bearing and washer with the correct thickness snap ring. Four snap rings are available to eliminate end play. If large snap ring around bearing was removed, install at this time.

4. Install rollers in drive gear pocket using grease to hold them in place, and retain with lock ring (14 rollers used with Fig. 2 unit, 15 with Fig. 1 unit).

5. Install 3rd gear outer stop ring and inner stop ring. Guide drive gear through front of case and engage inner stop ring with clutch teeth. Then seat bearing. Bearing is fully seated when snap ring is in full contact with case.

6. Install new seal in drive gear bearing retainer. Slide bearing retainer (less gasket) down against case.

7. Hold retainer against case and measure clearance between case and retainer, using a feeler gauge. Select a gasket .003" to .004" thicker than the clearance to eliminate all end play in bearing.

8. Install gasket selected and reinstall bearing retainer. Install attaching bolts and tighten to 23 ft-lbs. torque.

9. Install the countershaft, driving the bearing loading tool forward and out of counter gear until key can be inserted in shaft. Continue to drive shaft into case until about 1/64" below surface of case.

Extension Housing & Cover

1. Slide extension housing over mainshaft and down against case, at the same time guiding mainshaft into oil sea. Torque attaching bolts to 50 ft-lbs.

2. Install companion flange and torque nut to 175 ft-lbs.

3. Install cover with new gasket and torque attaching bolts to 12 ft-lbs.

Type Seven

DISASSEMBLE TRANS.

1. Remove transmission cover, Fig. 1.
2. Remove extension housing. To prevent mainshaft from following housing (with resultant loss of needle bearings) tap end of mainshaft while withdrawing housing.
3. Remove front bearing retainer.
4. Remove filler plug from right side of case. Then working through plug opening, drive roll pin out of case and countershaft with small punch, Fig. 2.
5. Hold counter gear with a hook and, with a dummy shaft, push countershaft out rear of case until counter gear can be lowered to bottom of case, Fig. 3.
6. Pull main drive gear forward until gear contacts case, then remove large snap ring.

NOTE: *It is necessary to move gear forward to provide clearance when removing mainshaft assembly. This applies to transmissions used with*

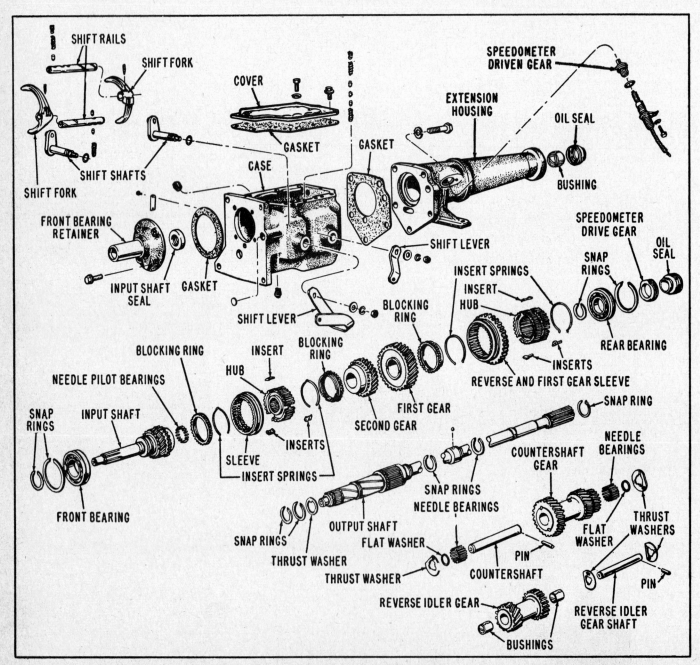

Fig. 1   Type 7 transmission disassembled

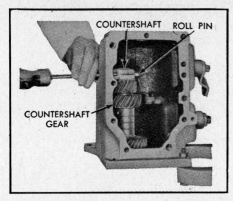

Fig. 2 Removing countershaft roll pin

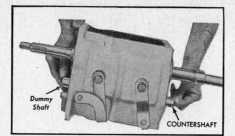

Fig. 3 Removing countershaft

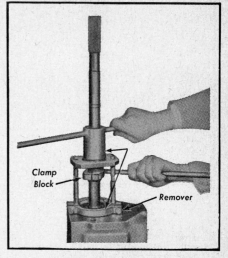

Fig. 4 Removing mainshaft bearing

V8-352 and 390 engines. On all other models, the drive gear is removed from front of case.

7. Remove snap ring and slide speedometer drive gear off mainshaft. Remove lock ball from shaft.
8. Remove snap ring and remove mainshaft rear bearing from shaft and case, Fig. 4.
9. Place both shift levers in neutral (central) position.
10. Remove a set screw that retains detent springs and plugs in case. Remove one spring and plug. Fig. 5.
11. Remove low-reverse set screw and slide shift rail out through rear of case.
12. Rotate low-reverse shift fork upward and lift it from case.
13. Remove 2-3 set screw and rotate 2-3 shift rail 90 degrees with pliers.

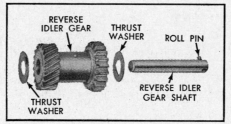

Fig. 6 Reverse idler gear disassembled

14. Lift interlock plug from case with a magnet rod.
15. Tap inner end of 2-3 shift rail to remove expansion plug from front of case. Remove shift rail.
16. Remove 2-3 detent plug and spring from detent bore.
17. Rotate 2-3 shift fork upward and lift from case.
18. Lift mainshaft assembly out through top of case.

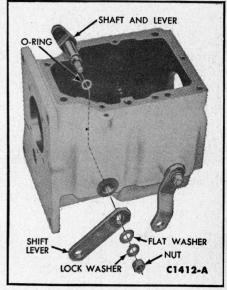

Fig. 8 Shift lever and related parts

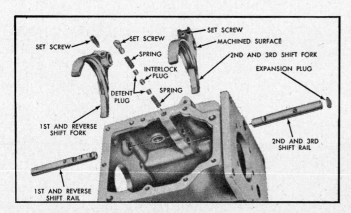

Fig. 5 Shift rails and forks disassembled

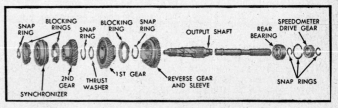

Fig. 9 Mainshaft disassembled

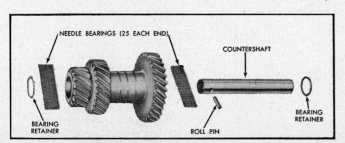

Fig. 7 Counter gear disassembled

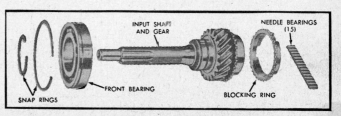

Fig. 10 Main drive gear disassembled

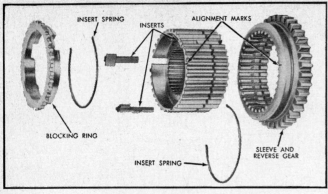

Fig. 11   Low-reverse synchronizer disassembled

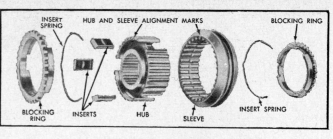

Fig. 12   Second-high synchronizer disassembled

19. On transmissions used with V8-352 and 390 engines, push main drive gear into case until bearing is free of bore; then lift gear and bearing out through top of case.
20. Working through front bearing opening, drive reverse idler gear shaft out through rear of case with a drift, Fig. 6.
21. Lift reverse idler gear and two thrust washers from case.
22. Lift counter gear and thrust washers from case, Fig. 7. Be careful not to allow dummy shaft and needle bearings to fall out of gear.
23. Remove countershaft-to-case retaining pin and any needle bearings that may have fallen into case.
24. Unfasten and lift shift levers off shafts. Slide each lever and shaft out of case. Discard O-ring seal from each shaft, Fig. 8.
25. Remove snap ring from front end of mainshaft and remove synchronizers, gears and related parts, Fig. 9.
26. If main drive gear is to be disassembled, refer to Fig. 10.

REASSEMBLE TRANS.

Counter Gear

1. Coat bore at each end of counter gear with grease.
2. Hold appropriate dummy shaft in gear and install 25 needle bearings and a retainer washer in each end of gear, Fig. 7.
3. Install counter gear, thrust washers and countershaft in case.
4. Place transmission case in vertical position and check end play with a feeler gauge as shown in Fig. 13. If end play exceeds .018″, replace thrust washers as required to obtain .004-.018″ end play.
5. Once end play has been established, remove countershaft with dummy shaft.
6. Allow counter gear assembly to remain in case.

Reverse Idler Gear

1. Install idler gear, thrust washers and shaft in case.
2. Make sure that thrust washer with flat side is at the web end, and that

the spur gear is toward the rear of case, Fig. 6.
3. Check reverse idler gear end play in same manner and to the same clearance as the counter gear. If end play is within limits of .004-.018″ leave gear in case.

Low-Reverse Synchronizer

1. Install an insert spring, Fig. 11, in groove of low-reverse synchronizer hub. Make sure spring covers all insert grooves.
2. Start hub in sleeve, making sure that alignment marks are properly indexed.
3. Position three inserts in hub, making sure that small end is over spring and that shoulder is on inside of hub.
4. Slide sleeve and reverse gear onto hub until detent is engaged.
5. Install other insert spring in front of hub to hold inserts against hub.

Second-Third Synchronizer

1. Install one insert spring, Fig. 12, into a groove of synchronizer hub, making sure that all three insert slots are fully covered.
2. With alignment marks on hub and sleeve aligned, start hub into sleeve.
3. Place three inserts on top of retaining spring and push assembly together.

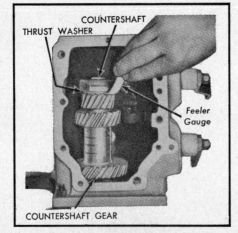

Fig. 13   Checking counter gear end play

4. Install remaining insert spring so that spring ends cover same slots as do other spring. Do not stagger springs.
5. Place a synchronizer blocking ring in each end of sleeve.

Main Drive Line

1. Lubricate mainshaft splines and machined surfaces with transmission lube.
2. Slide low-reverse synchronizer, Fig. 9, onto mainshaft with teeth end of gear facing toward rear of shaft. Secure in place with snap ring.
3. Coat tapered machined surface of low gear with grease. Place blocking ring on greased surface.
4. Slide low gear onto mainshaft with blocking ring toward rear of shaft. Rotate gear as necessary to engage the three notches in blocking ring with synchronizer inserts. Secure low gear with thrust washer and snap ring.
5. Coat tapered machined surface of 2nd gear with grease and slide blocking ring onto it. Slide 2nd gear with blocking ring and 2-3 synchronizer onto mainshaft. Tapered machined surface of 2nd gear must be toward front of shaft. Make sure that notches in blocking ring engage synchronizer inserts. Secure synchronizer with snap ring.
6. Install new O-ring on each of two shift lever shafts, Fig. 8. Lubricate shafts with transmission lube and install them in case. Secure each lever on its shaft with a flat washer, lock washer and nut.
7. Coat bore of main drive gear shaft with thick coat of grease. Install 15 needle bearings in gear pocket, Fig. 10.
8. Position drive gear assembly into case.
9. Place a detent spring and plug in case, Fig. 5. Place 2-3 shift fork in synchronizer groove. Rotate fork into position and install 2-3 shift rail. It will be necessary to depress detent plug to enter rail in bore. Move rail inward until detent plug engages center (neutral) notch. Secure fork to shaft with set screw.
10. Install interlock plug in case. If 2-3 shift rail is in neutral position, top of interlock will be slightly lower than surface of low-reverse shift rail bore.
11. Place low-reverse shift fork in groove of synchronoizer. Rotate fork into position and install low-reverse shift rail. Move rail inward until center (neutral) notch is aligned with detent bore. Secure fork to shaft with set screw.

12. Install remaining detent plug and spring. Secure spring with slotted head set screw. Turn set screw in until head is flush with case.
13. Install new expansion plug in case.
14. Install large snap ring on drive bearing. Work drive gear into case and onto mainshaft until snap ring is seated against case. Make sure that needle bearings do not fall out of place and that notches in blocking ring engage inserts in synchronizer.

NOTE: *The foregoing applies only to transmissions used with V8-352 and 390 engines. On all other models, the drive gear is installed through front of case with bearing in place on shaft.*

15. Position new front bearing retainer gasket on case. Place bearing retainer on case, making sure oil return groove is at the bottom. Install and tighten attaching screws to 19-25 ft-lbs.
16. Install large snap ring on mainshaft rear bearing. Place bearing on mainshaft with snap ring end toward rear of shaft. Press bearing into place and secure with snap ring.
17. Hold speedometer drive gear lock ball in detent and slide gear into place. Secure gear with snap ring.

Final Assembly

1. Place transmission in vertical position. Working through drain hole in bottom of case, align bore of counter gear and thrust washers with bore of case, using a screwdriver.
2. Working through rear of case, push dummy shaft out with countershaft. Before countershaft is completely inserted, make sure the hole that accommodates roll pin is aligned with hole in case.
3. Working through lubricant filler hole, install roll pin (Fig. 2) in case and countershaft.
4. Install filler and drain plugs, making sure magnetic plug is installed in bottom of case.
5. Install extension housing with new gasket and torque attaching cap screws to 42-50 ft-lbs.
6. Place transmission in gear, pour lubricant over entire gear train while rotating input and output shafts.
7. Install cover with new gasket and torque attaching screws to 14-19 ft-lbs. Coat gasket and cover screws with sealer.

Type Eight

DISASSEMBLE TRANS.

1. Referring to Fig. 1, remove cover.
2. Remove extension housing. *To prevent mainshaft from following housing (with resultant loss of needle bearings) tap end of mainshaft while withdrawing extension housing.*
3. Remove speedometer drive gear snap ring, gear and drive ball from mainshaft.
4. Remove idler gear shaft and countershaft retainer. If necessary tap front ends of both shafts to free retainer.
5. Using a suitable bearing loading tool, drive countershaft rearward out of gear and case. Then carefully lower counter gear to bottom of case, Fig. 2.
6. After removing main drive gear bearing retainer, remove drive gear and front synchronizer blocking ring from case, Fig. 3.
7. Remove synchronizer retaining snap ring from mainshaft. Then, while holding synchronizer together, pull mainshaft out of case. Lift synchronizer, gears and shift forks from case. *For reference on reassembly, note which end of synchronizer hub faces forward.*
8. Drive reverse idler shaft out of case and lift out idler gear, shaft and counter gear.
9. Remove shift levers.
10. From underside of case, drive out tapered pins, Fig. 4. Using a plastic hammer, drive 2-3 shift cam and shaft toward outside of case and separate balls and springs from plunger. Push out cam and shaft assemblies and remove plunger.
11. If necessary, shift lever oil seals may be removed with a slide hammer type hooked tool.
12. Remove snap ring and press main drive gear out of bearing and oil slinger.
13. Remove snap ring and press bearing from mainshaft.

REASSEMBLE TRANS.

1. Press main drive gear bearing and oil slinger on shaft, securing with snap ring.
2. Press mainshaft bearing on shaft and secure with snap ring.
3. Insert spacer and dummy shaft, Fig. 2, into counter gear. Position one flat washer at each end of spacer. Apply grease to needle bearings and assemble them around dummy shaft at each end of gear. Apply grease to other two flat washers and thrust washers and assemble at each end of

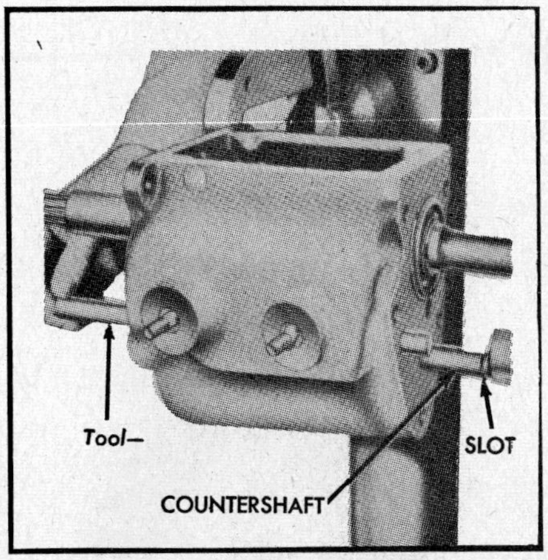

Fig. 2 Countershaft removal and installation

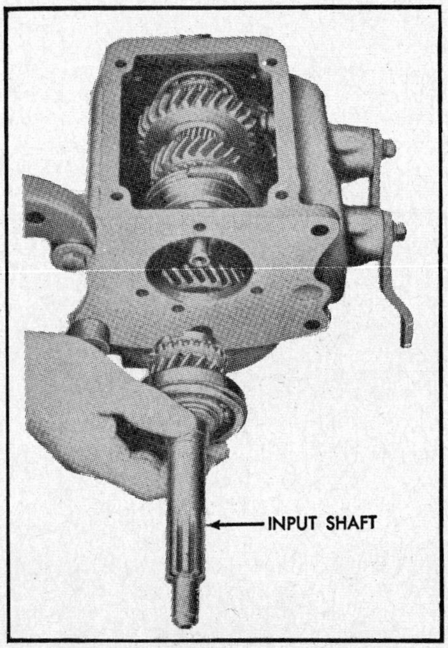

Fig. 3 Removing main drive gear

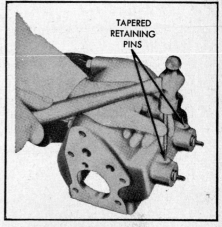

Fig. 4 Removing shift shaft retaining pins. Note that pins are driven out from the bottom

THREE SPEED TRANSMISSIONS

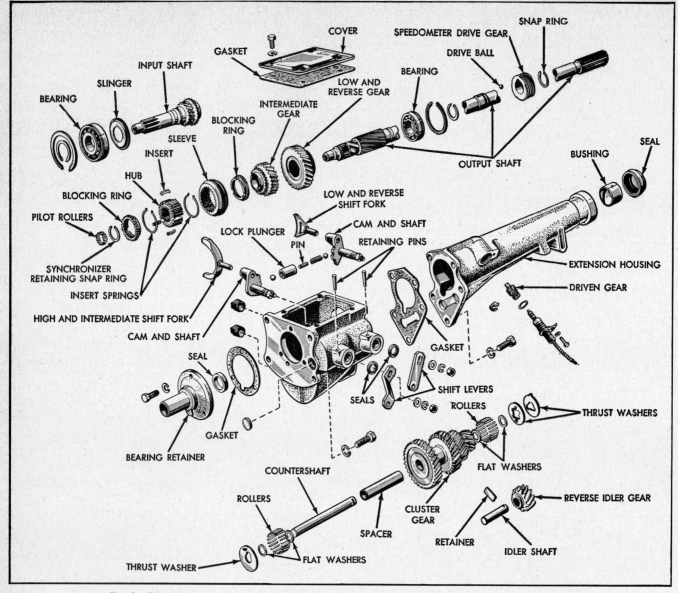

Fig. 1 Type 8 transmission. Note that longer end of synchronizer hub goes to the front. CAUTION: On some models the shift fork groove for low-reverse sliding gear goes to rear as shown; on other models fork goes to front. Check position after cover is removed

counter gear. Note position of tangs on thrust washers, Fig. 1.

4. Position counter gear assembly in bottom of case with larger gear toward front.

5. Install low-reverse shift cam through case opening. Assemble spacer and spring in plunger. Hold plunger in position and install 2-3 cam and shaft in case opening, allowing balls to register in cam detents.

6. Align cam and shaft grooves with openings in shaft bosses, and install retaining pins, Fig. 4. Check cam action; bent pins may restrict movement.

7. Position reverse idle gear, and insert shaft (from rear) through case just far enough to hold gear.

8. After assembling three inserts in synchronizer hub and securing them with two spring retainers, insert hub into 2-3 synchronizer sleeve. Install one block ring in rear side of hub.

Coat blocking rings with grease.

9. Using a coating of grease, assemble needle bearings in drive gear pocket and install front synchronizer blocking ring on drive gear shaft.

10. Install shift forks in shift lever shafts with large fork in 2-3 shaft. Web of low-reverse fork must be to rear of shaft center.

11. Start mainshaft through rear of case. Place low-reverse gear on shaft, followed by 2nd speed gear. Tilt mainshaft enough to allow rear shift fork to engage sliding gear groove.

12. *With longer hub forward*, slide synchronizer onto mainshaft and engage synchronizer sleeve in 2-3 shift fork.

13. Install synchronizer hub and snap ring.

14. Position main drive gear and front synchronizer blocking ring.

15. Place a new gasket on drive gear bearing retainer. If shaft oil seal was removed from retainer, install a new

seal. Install bearing retainer, using sealer on bolts. Line up oil drain groove in retainer with oil hole in case.

16. Raise counter gear assembly and align dummy shaft with countershaft opening in case. Start countershaft into case from rear, and carefully drive shaft into position.

17. Install idler gear shaft and retainer.

18. Secure speedometer drive gear and ball with snap ring.

19. Using a new gasket, install extension housing.

20. Start new seal over each cam and shaft and drive in seals.

21. Fill transmission to proper level with lubricant. Then, using a new gasket and sealer on bolts, install transmission cover.

NOTE: *Cover gasket vent holes must be toward rear and cover vent hole must be toward front.*

Type Nine

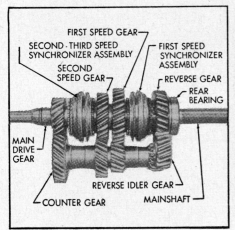

Fig. 1   Type 9 Saginaw three speed transmission

Fig. 2   Removing reverse idler "E" ring

Fig. 3   Removing rear bearing retainer after spreading snap ring as shown

Disassemble

1. Drain lubricant.
2. Remove side cover and gasket.
3. Remove front bearing retainer.
4. Remove clutch gear bearing-to-stem snap ring then slide bearing off over clutch gear stem. The clutch gear bearing is a slip fit on the gear and into the case bore.
5. Remove extension-to-case bolts.
6. Remove reverse idler shaft-to-gear "E" ring, Fig. 2.
7. Remove clutch gear, mainshaft and extension assembly together through rear case opening.
8. Expand snap ring and remove rear bearing retainer and mainshaft from extension, Fig. 3.
9. Drive countershaft and woodruff key out through the rear of the case. Remove countergear and bearings.
10. Use a long drift and drive reverse

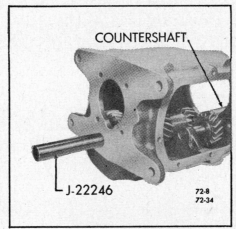

Fig. 4   Removing counter shaft, using aligning arbor to hold needle bearings in place

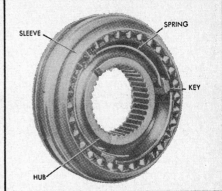

Fig. 6   Synchronizer assembly

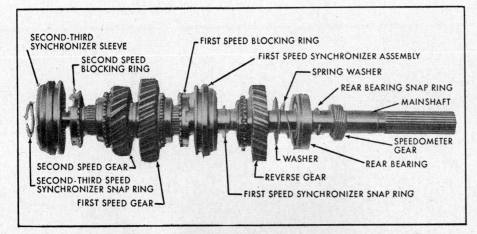

Fig. 5   Mainshaft and related parts assembled loosely to show location of parts

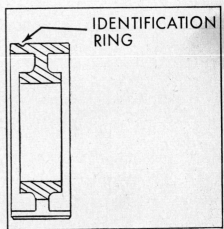

Fig. 7   Identification chamfer around synchronizer hub

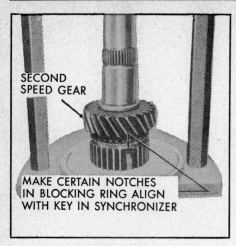

Fig. 8 Installing second speed gear

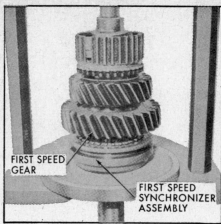

Fig. 9 Installing first speed gear

Fig. 10 Anti-rattle gear is riveted to countergear

idler shaft and key through rear of case.

11. Remove reverse idler gear tanged thrust washer.

Disassemble Mainshaft

1. Remove clutch gear, roller bearings and blocking ring from mainshaft. Referring to Fig. 5, remove 2-3 synchronizer sleeve.
2. Remove speedometer gear.
3. Remove rear bearing snap ring, and press off rear bearing, spring washer, thrust washer and Reverse gear.
4. Remove 1st and Reverse sliding clutch hub snap ring and clutch assembly, 1st speed blocker ring and gear.

Synchronizers

NOTE: The synchronizer hubs and sliding sleeves are a selected assembly and should be kept together as originally assembled. The keys and springs may be replaced if worn or broken.

1. Mark hub and sleeve so they can be reassembled in same position.
2. Remove sleeve from synchronizer hub.
3. Remove keys and springs from hub.
4. Place three keys and two springs in position (one on each side of hub) so all three keys are engaged by both springs, Fig. 6. The tanged end of each synchronizer spring should be installed in different key cavities on either side of hub. Slide sleeve onto hub, aligning marks made before disassembly.

NOTE: A chamfer or groove around the outside of synchronizer hub identifies the end that must be opposite the fork slot in the sleeve, Fig. 7.

Assemble Mainshaft

With front of mainshaft up:
1. Install second speed gear with clutching teeth upward.

2. Install blocking ring with clutching teeth downward. All blocking rings in this unit are identical.
3. Press 2-3 synchronizer onto mainshaft, Fig. 8. *Be sure notches in blocking ring align with keys in synchronizer.*

With rear of mainshaft up:
4. Install first speed gear with clutching teeth upward.
5. Install blocking ring on gear with teeth downward.
6. Press first and reverse synchronizer onto mainshaft. *Be sure notches in blocking ring align with keys in synchronizer.* Install snap ring.

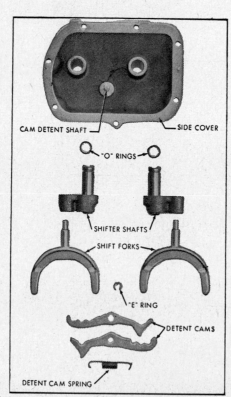

Fig. 11 Disassembled view of side cover

7. Install reverse gear, thrust washer, spring washer, rear bearing and bearing snap ring.
8. Install speedometer gear.

Assemble Transmission

1. Install countergear-to-case thrust washers. Install countergear into case from rear. Make certain wooruff key is in place. Note that anti rattle gear is riveted to countergear in four places and is not serviced separately, Fig. 10.
2. Install reverse idler gear tanged steel thrust washer. Install idler gear, shaft and woodruff key. *Reverse idler gear snap ring will be installed after installation of mainshaft.*
3. Install rear bearing retainer. Spread snap ring in retainer to allow snap ring to drop around rear bearing. Press on end of mainshaft until snap ring engages groove in rear bearing.
4. Install 14 needle rollers in main drive gear pocket, using grease to hold them in place. Assemble third speed blocking ring on main drive gear. Pilot main drive gear and blocking ring over front of mainshaft. Make certain notches in blocking ring align with keys in 2-3 synchronizer.
5. Install rear bearing retainer-to-case gasket, using heavy grease to hold gasket in place.
6. Install rear bearing retainer and mainshaft assembly into case. Torque bearing retainer-to-case bolts to 35-55 ft-lbs. torque.
7. Install bearing on main drive gear. Outer snap ring groove must be toward front of gear. Install snap ring.
8. Install front bearing retainer and gasket.
9. Install reverse idler gear "E" ring.
10. If repairs are required to the side cover, refer to Fig. 11.
11. Install side cover gasket. Place transmission gears in neutral and install side cover. Install attaching bolts and tighten evenly to avoid cover distortion.

Type Ten

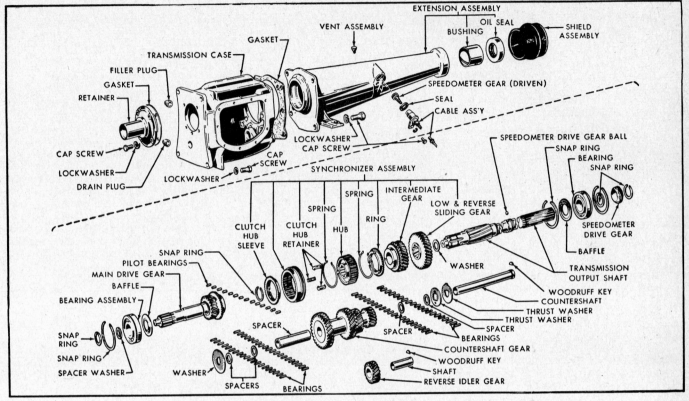

Fig. 1   Type 10 transmission disassembled. Note that shift fork groove on low-reverse gear goes toward front of case

DISASSEMBLE TRANS.

1. Remove gearshift housing.
2. Remove drive gear bearing retainer, Fig. 1. Remove snap ring and washer from drive gear shaft.
3. Unfasten and pull extension housing to the rear. Pull drive gear shaft forward.
4. Slide synchronizer sleeve forward. Tilt case and mainshaft so that mainshaft gears clear counter gear and remove mainshaft and extension housing as a unit.
5. Remove main drive gear through cover opening and remove rollers from drive gear pocket.
6. Using a suitable bearing loading tool, Fig. 2, remove countershaft. As front end of shaft clears rear of case, counter gear will drop to bottom of case. Take counter gear out of case.
7. Drive out idler gear shaft.

8. Remove snap ring and slide synchronizer and gears from mainshaft.
9. Remove mainshaft rear bearing snap ring and remove mainshaft from extension housing.
10. Remove speedometer drive gear snap ring, gear and driving ball from mainshaft.
11. If gearshift housing requires service,

Fig. 2   Countershaft removal

refer to Fig. 3. Install new seals on reassembly.

REASSEMBLE TRANS.

1. Install speedometer drive gear front snap ring. Position gear and ball, holding them in place with lubricant. Install retaining snap ring.
2. Tap mainshaft into extension housing and install snap ring that holds shaft in housing.
3. Coat mainshaft with transmission lube and position low-reverse gear (shift fork groove to front) on shaft. Place 2nd gear on shaft with synchronizer teeth and taper to the front.
4. Assemble synchronizer by placing spring at each end of hub, with ends of springs between same two inserts. Position inserts in hub grooves and slide sleeve (with shift fork groove to rear) onto hub.
5. Slide synchronizer with shoulder of

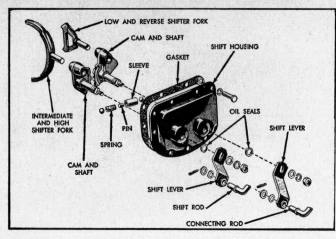

Fig. 3   Gearshift housing disassembled

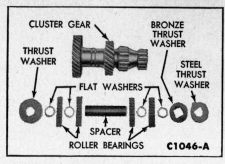

Fig. 4   Counter gear disassembled

hub forward onto shaft and install snap ring. Use a snap ring that will provide .003-.012″ clearance between rear side of ring and synchronizer hub when hub is forced as far back as possible.

6. Assemble counter gear as suggested by Fig. 4, using dummy shaft in gear to hold bearings and thrust washer in place.

7. Coat front thrust washer with grease and place it in front of case with washer tab in its slot.

8. Coat countershaft rear inner thrust washer with grease and place in counter gear pocket.

9. Position counter gear assembly in case. Start countershaft in case, center gear and thrust washers and continue to slide shaft into gear. Before rear end of shaft enters case, place key in shaft slot, making sure key lines up with keyway in case. Drive shaft rest of the way until it is flush with or slightly inside machined surface of case.

10. Install reverse idler gear with large shoulder to rear and install gear shaft.

11. Install pilot rollers in drive gear pocket and install drive gear into case.

12. Install bearing retainer, using new gasket. Line up oil drain hole in retainer with oil hole in case. Secure retainer with attaching bolts.

13. Install extension housing (with new gasket) and mainshaft into case. Secure extension housing with attaching bolts.

14. Install gear shift housing.

Type Eleven

DISASSEMBLE TRANS.

1. After draining transmission and overdrive, remove solenoid retaining screw and rotate solenoid about ¼ turn to remove it.

2. Remove governor and transmission cover.

3. With a sharp punch, pierce snap ring hole cover and remove cover, Fig. 2.

4. Remove overdrive housing-to-transmission case bolts and overdrive control shaft pin.

5. Pull overdrive control lever and shaft out as far as possible. Spread snap ring that retains overdrive output shaft bearing and remove overdrive housing, Fig. 2. It may be necessary to tap output shaft to free bearing from housing.

6. Remove overdrive output shaft. Catch any free wheel unit rollers that drop out. Remove rest of rollers.

7. Remove snap ring and take off speedometer gear and drive ball.

8. Remove free wheel unit retainers. Then remove clutch, planet carrier, sun gear and shaft rail.

9. Remove snap ring from adapter and remove plate and trough, balk ring gear and pawl.

10. Remove input shaft bearing retainer.

11. Rotate overdrive adapter to expose countershaft lock and remove lock.

12. With a drift, drive countershaft toward rear until it just clears hole at front of case. Support countershaft gear with a hook, then push countershaft out of rear with a special mandrel or a spare countershaft cut to the length of the countershaft gear to hold the roller bearings and thrust washers in place, Fig. 3.

13. Lower countershaft gear assembly to bottom of case to provide clearance for removal of input shaft and bearing. Tap input shaft and bearing out of front of case.

14. Remove shift lever shaft retaining pins, Fig. 4.

15. Pull low-reverse shift lever out as far as it will go, then remove low-reverse fork.

16. Remove output shaft and overdrive adapter, Fig. 5.

17. Remove snap ring at front of transmission output shaft, then strip shaft of gears.

18. While holding washers and bearing retainer tool at small end of countershaft gear, lift gear assembly from case.

19. Drive reverse idler gear shaft out of rear of case and remove idler gear from case.

20. Remove lock plunger, spring, pin and detent balls from case, Fig. 6.

Synchronizer Repairs

1. Disassemble synchronizer, Fig. 1, by

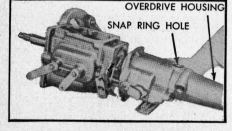

Fig. 2   Removing overdrive housing

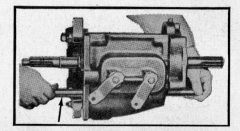

Fig. 3   Removing countershaft

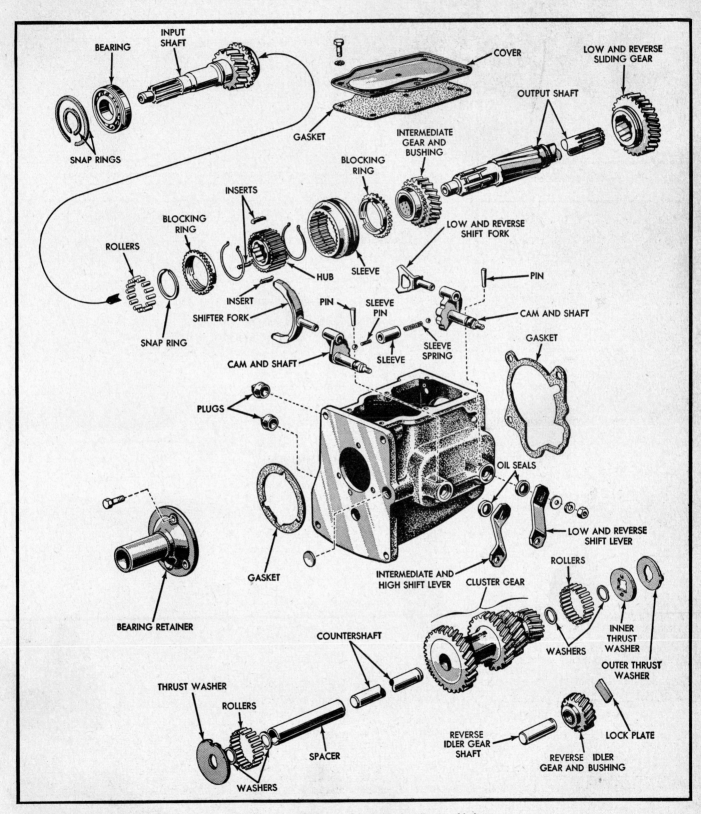

Fig. 1 Type 11 overdrive transmission disassembled

Fig. 4 Removing shift lever retaining pin

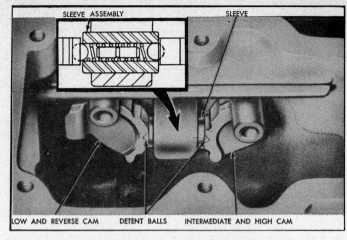

Fig. 6
Cams and
detent balls
installed

LOW AND REVERSE CAM   DETENT BALLS   INTERMEDIATE AND HIGH CAM

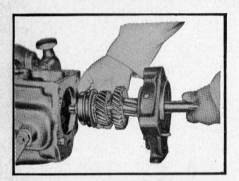

Fig. 5 Removing output shaft
and overdrive adapter

sliding 2-3 sleeve off hub. Remove three inserts and two springs from hub.

2. Assemble synchronizer unit by installing the two springs on hub and placing three inserts in hub. Hook one spring end in an insert as shown in Fig. 7.

3. After lining up etched marks on sleeve and hub splines, slide sleeve into place on hub.

Cam & Shaft Seals

1. Remove levers from shafts and cams.
2. Remove cams and shafts, detent balls, pin, spring and sleeve from case.
3. Remove seals with suitable puller.
4. Install new seals with suitable driver.
5. Install 2-3 shift fork and shaft in case.
6. Insert a detent ball, sleeve, spring and pin in bore of case. Move cam and shaft so that detent ball seats in neutral (center) notch.
7. Install low-reverse cam and shaft, then install levers on shafts with nuts and lockwashers.
8. Install detent ball in sleeve at low-reverse end. Then push low-reverse cam toward detent ball far enough to hold ball in place in neutral notch. Ball must seat in notch in cam.
9. Install shift lever shaft retaining pins, Fig. 4.
10. In order to assure positive shifting and eliminate the possibility of engaging more than one set of gears at the same time, the clearance be-

tween ramp of one cam and sleeve must be checked.

Countershaft Rollers

1. Remove thrust washers from end of countershaft.
2. Remove dummy shaft, retainer washers, rollers and spacer from gear.
3. Position spacer and dummy shaft in gear.
4. Place a retainer washer in each end of gear.
5. Coat bore in each end of gear with grease. Hold dummy shaft in gear and install roller bearings and retainer washer in each end of gear.
6. Apply grease to two remaining retainer washers and to the contact surface of thrust washers. Install retainer washers and thrust washers on each end of gear.

Assemble Trans.

Use new gaskets and gasket sealer during assembly. To provide initial lubrication, apply a thin coating of grease on all parts before installation.

1. Place countergear with dummy shaft and roller bearings in case.
2. With case in vertical position, align countershaft gear bore and thrust washers with bores in case and install countershaft.
3. With case in horizontal position, check countergear end play with a feeler gauge. End play should be .004-.018". If not within these limits, replace thrust washers.
4. After establishing correct end play, install dummy shaft in countershaft gear and allow gear to remain in bottom of case.
5. Install reverse idler gear in case with chamfered teeth ends toward front.
6. Drive reverse idler shaft in case with locking notch aligned with countershaft hole.
7. Install low-reverse sliding gear on mainshaft with shifter fork groove toward front.
8. Install intermediate gear on mainshaft with clutch teeth toward front.
9. Place a blocking ring on intermediate gear and install synchronizer on mainshaft with hub thrust surface toward rear, Fig. 1. Rotate intermediate gear as necessary to line up notches in blocker ring with synchronizer in-

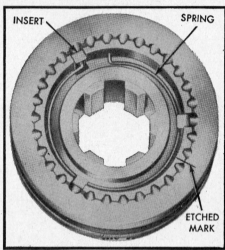

Fig. 7 Synchronizer

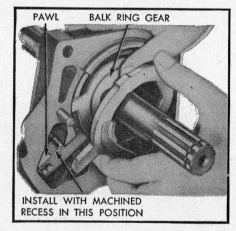

Fig. 8 Installing balk ring gear and pawl

serts. Install snap ring that retains synchronizer.

10. Install shift forks in cams inside case. The offset in low-reverse fork goes toward front.
11. Install new solenoid seal in overdrive adapter.
12. Place a new gasket on adapter, using gasket sealer to hold it in place.
13. Install overdrive adapter and transmission output shaft assembly in transmission.

14. Engage shift forks with 2-3 synchronizer sleeve and with low-reverse sliding gear.
15. Seat overdrive adapter squarely against transmission case and secure with a capscrew.
16. Insert pilot roller bearings in input shaft and retain with grease.
17. Place a blocking ring on input shaft gear.
18. Tap input shaft and bearing into case, and at the same time line up slots in blocking ring with synchronizer inserts.
19. Place a new gasket on input shaft bearing retainer, holding it in place with gasket sealer.
20. Install input shaft bearing retainer in case.
21. Invert transmission and remove capscrew from overdrive adapter. Pull adapter out about ¼" and rotate it to expose countershaft hole.
22. Work countershaft gear into normal position by rotating input and output shafts.
23. Push countershaft into case from rear.
24. Align slots in countershaft with slot in reverse idler shaft and install lock plate.
25. Rotate adapter to its normal position and set it squarely against transmission case. Check blocking rings to make sure slots are aligned with synchronizer inserts.
26. With input shaft pointing down, place

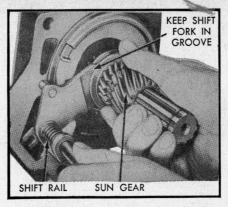

KEEP SHIFT FORK IN GROOVE

SHIFT RAIL   SUN GEAR

Fig. 9 Installing sun gear and shift rail

balk ring gear and pawl in adapter, Fig. 8.
27. Place plate and trough in adapter and install snap ring.
28. Install sun gear and shift rail, Fig. 9.
29. Install planet carrier and clutch cam, and retainers.
30. Install 12 clutch rollers and hold them in position with a rubber band.
31. Rotate roller cage counterclockwise (from rear) until rollers are off cam surfaces (rubber band will hold them there).
32. Slide overdrive output shaft over clutch rollers (rubber band will not

affect overdrive operation).
33. Align shift rail spring with holes in overdrive housing.
34. Place a new gasket on overdrive adapter and hold it in place with gasket sealer.
35. Install overdrive housing over output shaft and shift rail. Secure housing to transmission case with four bolts.
36. Engage overdrive shaft lever by pushing it inward. Lever is correctly engaged when a spring load is apparent as lever is pushed forward.
37. Install retaining pin in overdrive housing to hold control shaft in place.
38. Thread governor into overdrive housing.
39. Rotate solenoid ¼ turn from normal position so that half ball on solenoid stem can engage pawl. Install solenoid screws.

NOTE: If solenoid stem is properly engaged, solenoid cannot be removed from overdrive in its normal position. Any attempt to pull it out will merely compress the engaging spring in solenoid.

40. Install transmission cover with new gasket.
41. Install drain plugs in transmission case and overdrive housing.
42. Check gear operation in all positions.

Type Twelve

DISASSEMBLE TRANS.
Case Components

1. Remove side cover and shift forks.
2. Unfasten attaching screws and rotate extension housing clockwise to expose reverse idler gear shaft.
3. Drive reverse idler shaft and its woodruff key out through rear of case, Fig. 2.
4. Rotate extension housing counterclockwise to expose countershaft and use a brass drift at front of shaft to drive shaft and its woodruff key out rear of case, Fig. 3.

5. With countergear dropped to bottom of case remove entire mainshaft and extension assembly through rear of case, Fig. 4. Remove mainshaft pilot roller bearings from clutch gear.
6. Expand snap ring in extension and remove extension from rear bearing and mainshaft by tapping on end of mainshaft, Fig. 5.
7. Remove clutch gear bearing retainer, bearing snap ring and washer from mainshaft, Fig. 6.
8. Drive clutch gear through its bearing into case, Fig. 7, and remove bearing by tapping out from inside of case.

9. Remove countergear assembly from case.

Mainshaft Disassembly

1. Remove snap ring and strip front of mainshaft, Fig. 8.
2. Remove rear bearing snap ring, Fig. 9.
3. Support reverse gear with press plates and press on rear of mainshaft to remove reverse gear, rear bearing, special washer, snap ring and speedometer drive gear from rear of mainshaft.

CAUTION: When pressing rear bearing be sure special washer is clear of snap

Fig. 2 Removing reverse idler shaft

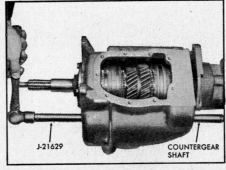

J-21629   COUNTERGEAR SHAFT

Fig. 3 Removing countershaft

Fig. 4 Removing mainshaft and extension from case

THREE SPEED TRANSMISSIONS

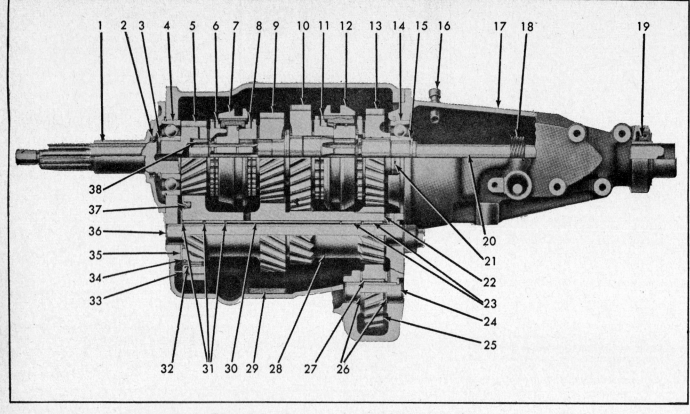

Fig. 1   Type 12 three speed fully synchronized transmission

1. Bearing Retainer
2. Lip Oil Seal
3. Snap Ring and Special Washer
4. Clutch Gear Bearing
5. Clutch Gear
6. 3rd Speed Blocker Ring
7. 2-3 Sliding Clutch Sleeve
8. 2nd Speed Blocker Ring
9. Second Speed Gear
10. First Speed Gear

11. 1st Speed Blocker Ring
12. 1st and Reverse Sliding Clutch Sleeve
13. Reverse Gear
14. Mainshaft Rear Bearing
15. Snap Ring and Special Washer
16. Vent
17. Extension
18. Speedo Drive Gear
19. Extension Oil Seal

20. Mainshaft
21. Extension to Bearing Retainer Ring
22. Countergear Thrust Washer
23. Roller Bearings
24. Reverse Idler Shaft
25. Reverse Idler Gear
26. Thrust Washer
27. Roller Bearings
28. Countergear
29. Magnet

30. Tube Spacer
31. Washers
32. Roll Pin
33. Dampener Plate
34. Spiral-Lox Retainer
35. Countergear Thrust Washer
36. Countergear Shaft
37. Dampener Spring
38. Mainshaft Pilot Bearings

---

ring groove. Also, be careful to center gear, bearing, washer and snap ring on mainshaft before attempting to press off speedometer drive gear.

4. Remove low-reverse sliding clutch hub snap ring from mainshaft, Fig. 10, and remove clutch assembly, blocker ring and low gear from mainshaft.

11. Place keys in position and, holding them in place, slide sleeve onto hub, aligning marks made previously.

Synchronizer Clutch Keys & Springs

NOTE: The clutch hubs and sliding sleeves are a selected assembly and should be kept together as originally assembled. However, the two keys and springs may be replaced if worn or broken.

1. If relation of hub and sleeve are not already marked, mark for assembly purposes.
2. Push hub from sliding sleeve. Keys will fall free and springs may easily be removed.
3. Place two springs in position (one on each side of hub) so all three keys are engaged by both springs, Fig.

Fig. 5   Extension-to-rear bearing snap ring

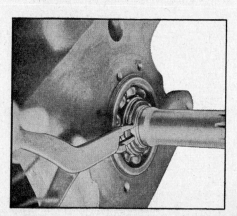

Fig. 6   Clutch gear bearing-to-gear snap ring

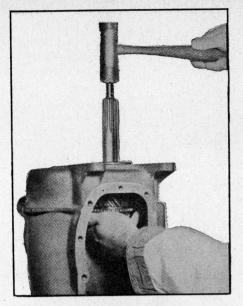

Fig. 7 Removing clutch gear from bearing end of case

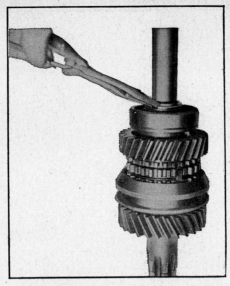

Fig. 9 Rear bearing-to-mainshaft snap ring

Fig. 10 First-reverse clutch hub snap ring

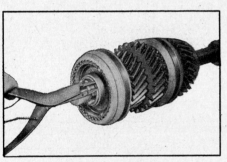

Fig. 8 2nd-3rd clutch hub snap ring

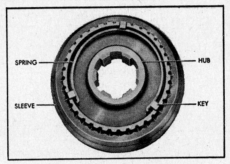

SPRING — HUB
SLEEVE — KEY

Fig. 11 2nd-3rd synchronizer clutch

Fig. 14 Loading countershaft bearings

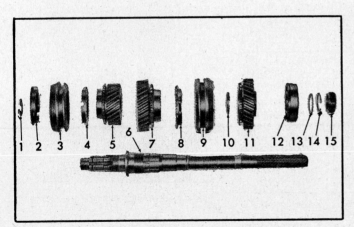

Fig. 12 Mainshaft disassembled

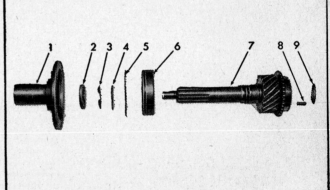

Fig. 13 Clutch gear components

1. Snap Ring
2. 3rd Speed Blocker Ring
3. 2-3 Clutch Assembly
4. 2nd Speed Blocker Ring
5. 2nd Speed Gear
6. Mainshaft
7. 1st Speed Gear
8. 1st Speed Blocker Ring

9. 1st Reverse Clutch Assembly
10. Snap Ring
11. Reverse Gear
12. Rear Bearing
13. Special Washer
14. Snap Ring
15. Speedo Drive Gear

1. Retainer
2. Lip Seal
3. Snap Ring
4. Special Washer
5. Snap Ring

6. Clutch Gear Bearing
7. Clutch Gear
8. Mainshaft Pilot Bearings
9. Bearing Spacer

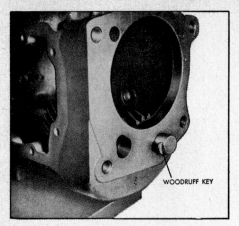

Fig. 15   Installing countershaft

Fig. 16   Checking countergear end play

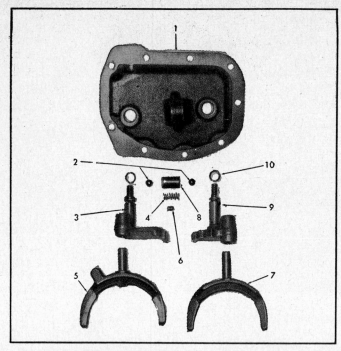

Fig. 19   Side cover disassembled

1. Side Cover
2. Poppet
3. 1st and Reverse Shifter Lever and Shaft
4. Poppet Spring
5. 1st and Reverse Shifter Fork
6. Interlock Pin
7. 2nd and 3rd Shifting Fork
8. Interlock Sleeve
9. 2nd and 3rd Shifter Lever and Shaft
10. "O" Ring Seal

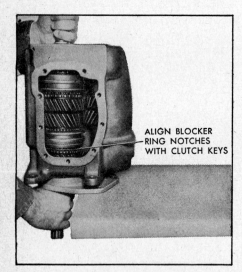

Fig. 17   Installing mainshaft assembly

Mainshaft Reassemble

1. Referring to Fig. 12, install 1st gear on rear of mainshaft with gear clutching teeth to rear.
2. Install 1st gear blocking ring over 1st gear tapered cone end area with clutch key notches toward rear.
3. Install 1st-reverse sliding clutch as-

sembly over rear of mainshaft, being careful to engage three keys with notches of blocker ring. Properly installed, straightest side of clutch hub and taper of sliding sleeve should both be toward rear of mainshaft (see Fig. 1).

4. Install snap ring in front of 1st-reverse clutch hub, Fig. 10.

NOTE: Snap ring is available in three thicknesses. Use thikest sanp ring that will assemble with all parts stacked tight endwise.

5. Install reverse gear over mainshaft with gear clutch teeth toward front.
6. Press rear bearing on mainshaft with its outer race snap ring groove closest to reverse gear.
7. Install rear bearing special washer and snap ring to mainshaft, Fig. 9.

NOTE: This snap ring is available in six thicknesses. Use thickest snap ring that will assemble with all parts stacked tight endwise.

8. Press speedometer drive gear on rear of mainshaft until centered on shaft boss.
9. Install 2nd speed gear over front of mainshaft with gear clutch teeth toward front.
10. Install blocker ring over 2nd gear tapered cone end with clutch key notches toward front.

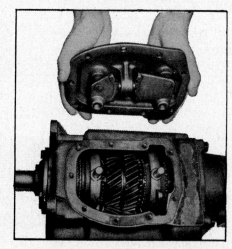

Fig. 18   Installing side cover assembly

11. Install 2-3 sliding clutch assembly over front of mainshaft, engaging clutch keys with notches of 2nd gear blocker ring. Properly installed the straightest side of clutch hub should be toward rear and clutch sliding sleeve taper should be toward front of mainshaft (see Fig. 1).
12. Install 2-3 clutch hub snap ring to mainshaft, Fig. 8.

NOTE: This snap ring is available in four

thicknesses. Use thickest snap ring that will assemble with all parts stacked tight endwise.

ASSEMBLE TRANS.
Case Components

1. Insert tube spacer and a double row of roller bearings and bearing retainer washers at each end of countergear, using grease to hold them in place, Fig. 14.
2. Place countergear assembly through case rear opening along with a tanged thrust washer (tang away from gear) at each end (large washer at front). Install countershaft and woodruff key from rear of case, Fig. 15.

CAUTION: Be sure countershaft picks up both thrust washers and that washer tangs are aligned with their notches in case.

3. Attach a dial indicator as shown in Fig. 16 and check end play of countergear. If end play is greater than .025″ new thrust washers must be installed.
4. Use grease to hold 25 reverse idler gear roller bearings in position and place gear and bearings along with a thrust washer on each end into position inside case so that bevelled edge of gear teeth face toward front of case.
5. Load pilot bearing rollers and spacer into clutch gear with grease to hold them in place and position gear in case. *Do not install clutch gear bearing at this time.*
6. Stand case on end with clutch gear shaft through hole in bench or stand,

and place 3rd gear blocker ring over clutch gear.

7. Install mainshaft assembly through rear of case, picking up spacer, pilot bearings and 3rd gear blocker rings, Fig. 17.
8. Install reverse idler gear shaft and woodruff key. *Be sure shaft picks up both thrust washers during installation.*
9. Install extension gasket on rear of case and, using snap ring pliers, expand snap ring, Fig. 5, and install extension over mainshaft and rear bearing. Be sure snap ring has started over bearing, then install and tighten extension case bolts. *Use graphite sealer on the two lower bolts.*
10. Tap on front of clutch gear shaft to force rear bearing snap ring to seat in its groove.

NOTE: This snap ring is available in five thicknesses. Use thickest snap ring that will assemble with all parts stacked tight endwise.

11. Install snap ring in outer race of clutch gear bearing. If snap ring groove is partially inside case opening, tap on inside bearing outer race with a long drift used through side cover opening.

NOTE: If mainshaft does not turn freely, check clutch sliding sleeves for neutral positions and that blocker rings are free on their gear cone surfaces.

12. Install gaskets and clutch gear bearing retainer and lip seal with oil drain passages at bottom and tighten. *Use graphite sealer on threads of retainer bolts.*

NOTE: Install two retainer-to-case gaskets (one .010″ and .015″) to replace the one .025″ production gasket removed.

13. Install shift forks to clutch sleeve grooves with 1st-reverse fork "hump" toward bottom of case, Fig. 18.
14. Install side cover and gasket. *The two rear side cover-to-case bolts have special oil sealing splines and must be used at these two "through" hole locations.*

SIDE COVER
Disassemble

1. Referring to Fig. 19, remove shift forks from shift levers.
2. Remove outer shift levers and lightly tap shift lever shafts from assembly.
3. Remove two steel balls, poppet spring, interlock pin and sleeve from cover.
4. Remove O-ring seals from shafts.

Reassemble

1. Install new O-ring seals on shafts.
2. Install low-reverse shaft and plate to cover.
3. Place shift shaft and plate in neutral (middle detent) and install interlock sleeve, ball, spring and interlock pin.
4. Install remaining ball and then install 2-3 shift shaft and plate.
5. Check clearance between end of interlock sleeve and cams when one plate is in neutral and the other is shifted into gear position. Clearance should be .002″ to .008″. Sleeves are available in four sizes to give the proper clearance.
6. Install outer shift levers. Install forks to levers with 1st-reverse fork "hump" toward bottom.

Type 13

DISASSEMBLE TRANS.

1. Refer to Fig. 1 and proceed as follows: Remove TCS and backup lamp switches and shift lever boot.
2. Remove cotter pins from each end of shift control rod, Fig. 2. Remove washers and control rod.
3. Remove serrated pin retaining selector lever to the boss on rear extension, Fig. 3.
4. Remove retaining rings, wave washer and selector ring from selector ring from selector shaft.

NOTE: Slide selector lever and shift idler lever shaft from intermediate shift lever assembly while simultaneously removing selector ring. Selector lever will just slip off selector ring.

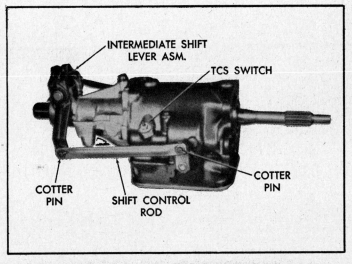

Fig. 2 Cotter pins securing shift control rod

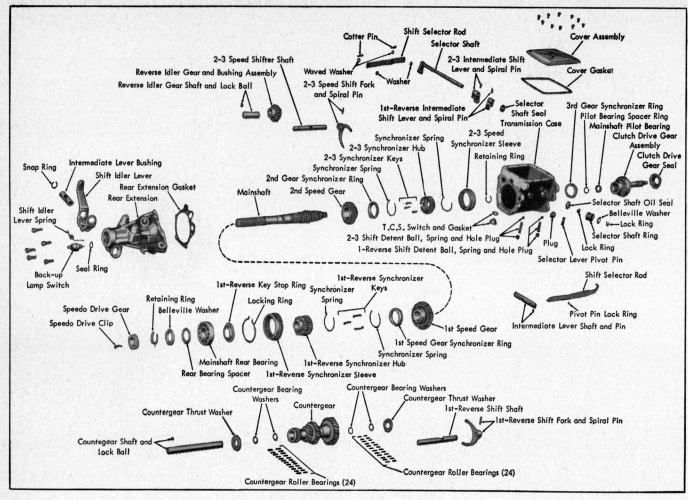

Fig. 1   Exploded view of Type 13 transmission

5. Remove transmission case cover and invert transmission to drain oil.
6. Remove rear extension bolts and rotate extension until countergear shaft is exposed, Fig. 4.
7. From front of transmission and using tool J-23562, remove countergear shaft. Be sure that lock ball is not lost, Fig. 5. With special tool inserted lift countergear from case and remove thrust washers.
8. Using a 1/8" pin punch to remove lock pins, engage second gear to prevent 2-3 fork pin binding against case. Drive out lock pins from both shifter forks.

NOTE: Before driving shifter shafts, place transmission in 3rd gear and make sure 2nd-3rd intermediate lever engages shifter shaft. This allows selector shaft and intermediate levers to pivot as shifter shaft is driven from case.

9. Insert a long narrow drift through bolt hole at rear of case and drive 2nd-3rd shifter shaft out front of case, Fig. 6. Remove fork from case.
10. Using a suitable drift, drive 1st-Reverse shifter shaft out front of case, Fig. 7 and remove fork.

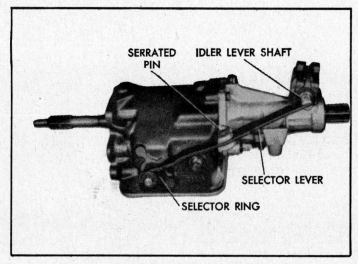

Fig. 3   Pin securing selector lever

11. Remove selector shaft intermediate lever lock pins, Fig. 8, and remove shaft and levers from case.
12. Remove snap ring from rear bearing retainer groove and slide rear extension from mainshaft assembly, Fig. 9.
13. Remove clutch drive gear from case. Position 1st-Reverse sliding gear to rear of hub shaft and remove main-

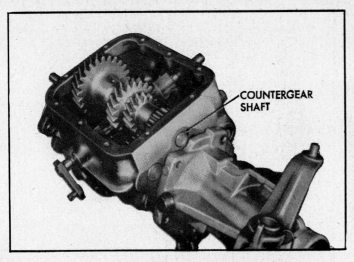

Fig. 4   Countergear shaft exposed for removal

Fig. 5   Removing countergear shaft

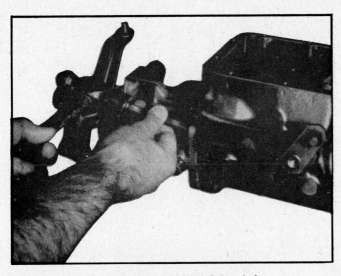

Fig. 6   Removing 2nd-3rd shifter shaft

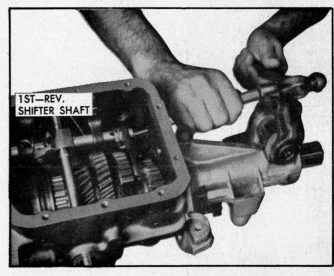

Fig. 7   Removing 1st-Reverse shifter shaft

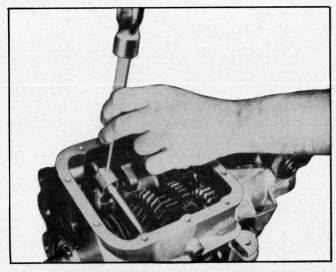

Fig. 8   Removing selector shaft intermediate lever pins

Fig. 9   Releasing rear extension retainer ring

Fig. 10   Removing mainshaft assembly

Fig. 11   Removing reverse idler gear shaft

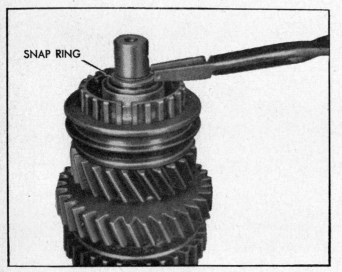

Fig. 12   Removing snap ring in front of clutch hub

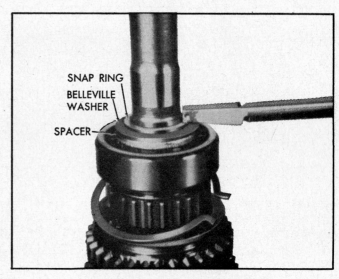

Fig. 13   Removing rear bearing snap ring

shaft assembly, Fig. 10. Remove lock pins and detent balls from bottom of case.

14. Insert a punch into shaft rail detent holes and drive out hole plugs and springs.

15. Using tool J-22923, remove reverse idler shaft and gear from case, Fig. 11.

Mainshaft Disassembly

1. Remove snap ring in front of clutch hub, Fig. 12.

NOTE: The synchronizer hubs and sliding sleeves are a selected assembly and should be kept together as originally assembled.

2. Depress retaining clamp and slide speedo drive gear from shaft.

3. Remove snap ring, belleville washer and spacer from shaft, Fig. 13.

4. Support 1st gear and press main-shaft until bearing and synchronizers are free on shaft, Fig. 14. Remove all loose parts.

5. Support 2nd speed gear and press shaft from 2nd-3rd synchronizer and 2nd speed gear, Fig. 15.

Drive Gear Bearing

1. Remove snap ring retaining bearing on shaft.

2. Support outer race of bearing and press drive gear from bearing.

3. Position new bearing on shaft with slinger toward gear and press onto shaft using tool J-5390 or other suitable piece of pipe.

4. Install snap ring on shaft behind bearing, Fig. 16.

Mainshaft Assembly

IMPORTANT: The snychronizer hubs and sliding sleeves are a selected assembly and should be kept together as originally assembled, but the keys and springs may be replaced if worn or broken.

1. From front of mainshaft install 2nd speed gear onto mainshaft. Gear must turn freely on shaft.

2. Install 2nd-3rd speed synchronizer ring onto 2nd speed gear cone.

3. Install front and rear synchronizer key springs into 2nd-3rd synchronizer hub so that hooked spring ends rest in the same slot and raised ends are against the blocker rings.

4. Install sliding sleeve and keys on clutch hub.

NOTE: Arrow on keys must point to front of shaft.

5. Press 2nd-3rd synchronizer hub onto mainshaft, Fig. 17. Secure with snap ring.

6. Install both clutch key springs into 1st-Reverse synchronizer hub so that hooked ends of both springs rest in same hub slot and raised spring ends

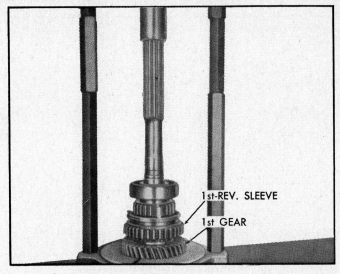

Fig. 14   Removing rear bearing from mainshaft

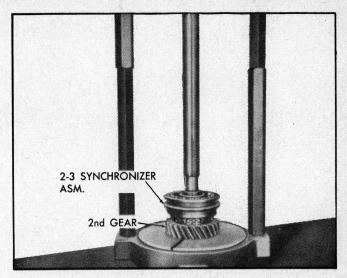

Fig. 15   Removing 2nd-3rd clutch hub from mainshaft

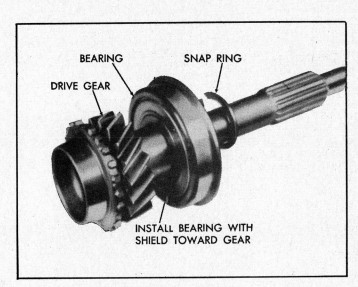

Fig. 16   Drive gear assembly

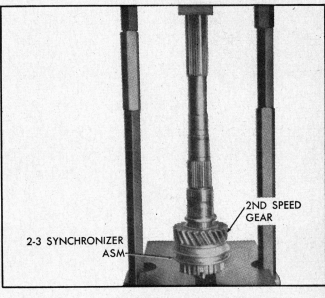

Fig. 17   Pressing 2nd-3rd synchronizer on mainshaft

are positioned to each other and to-wards the blocker rings, Fig. 18.

7. Assemble sliding gear and keys on hub assembly with longer key flat and fork groove on gear toward rear of shaft.

8. From rear of shaft slide 1st speed gear onto shaft. Gear must turn freely on shaft, Fig. 19.

9. Place 1st-Reverse speed synchronizer ring onto 1st speed gear cone.

10. Slide 1st-Reverse synchronizer assembly onto mainshaft. Slide stop ring, rear extension retaining ring and rear bearing onto shaft. Support rear bearing inner race and press components together.

CAUTION: Align slots in synchronizer rings with keys.

11. Place spacer and belleville washer on mainshaft and secure with snap ring.

12. Position speedo gear retaining clip on shaft and install speedo gear.

13. Place mainshaft assembly into rear extension up to its stop and secure with retaining ring.

ASSEMBLE TRANS.

1. Install new gasket onto rear extension and slide mainshaft assembly into case. Install one or two retainer bolts to keep extension from rotating.

2. From the front, slide lock ring and pilot roller bearing assembly onto mainshaft.

3. Install blocker ring on clutch drive gear and install gear into case up to snap ring stop.

4. Insert 1st-Reverse speed shifter shaft at front of case with notches down, pushing it through the shifter fork, positioning fork shoulder toward front of case. Drive lock pin in place allowing it to protrude $1/16$ to $5/64''$ above fork.

5. Insert 2nd-3rd speed shifter shaft from front of case, with notches down, pushing it through the shifter fork shoulder toward front. Install lock pin allowing it to protrude $1/16$ to $5/64''$ above fork.

6. Insert selector shaft in case, push through 2nd-3rd speed intermediate lever and through 1st-Reverse lever. Install lock pins allowing to protrude $1/16$ to $5/64''$ above lever.

7. Insert both lock balls and thrust springs into bores in case and drive in plugs.

8. Remove rear extension bolts, pull back on extension and rotate extension until bore for reverse idler is exposed.

9. Place lock ball into shaft and from rear of case install shaft into gear. Drive shaft into place.

10. Using tool J-23562 install a spacer, row of roller bearings (24) and a spacer at each end of countergear.

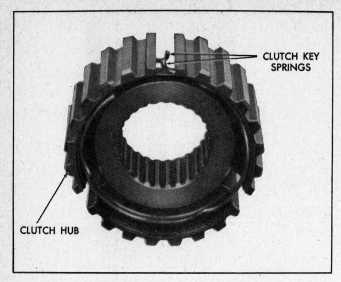

Fig. 18   Both clutch key springs installed

CLUTCH KEY SPRINGS

CLUTCH HUB

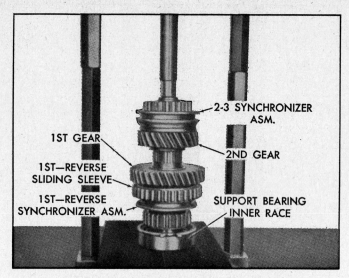

Fig. 19   Pressing mainshaft components together

2-3 SYNCHRONIZER ASM.

1ST GEAR

2ND GEAR

1ST—REVERSE SLIDING SLEEVE

1ST—REVERSE SYNCHRONIZER ASM.

SUPPORT BEARING INNER RACE

Use heavy grease to hold them in place.
11. Coat thrust washer with ball and roller bearing grease and stick to case.

NOTE: Lugs of thrust washers must fit into case slots.

12. Turn case extension until countergear shaft bore is exposed.

13. Place lock ball into shaft and from rear of case insert shaft so that thrust washer is held in position. Hold opposite thrust washer in position by using a short drift.
14. Insert countergear into case.
15. Insert shaft into countergear pushing out special tool. Align lock ball with groove in case and tap shaft into case.
16. Align rear bearing retainer and in-

stall retaining bolts.
17. Install case cover gasket, cover and screws.
18. Install gearshift linkages in reverse sequence to removal.

NOTE: Start idler lever shaft into shift control simultaneously when installing selector ring.

FOUR SPEED MANUAL SHIFT TRANSMISSIONS

See Car Chapters for Linkage Adjustments and Removal Procedures

APPLICATION INDEX

Type One Warner T-10

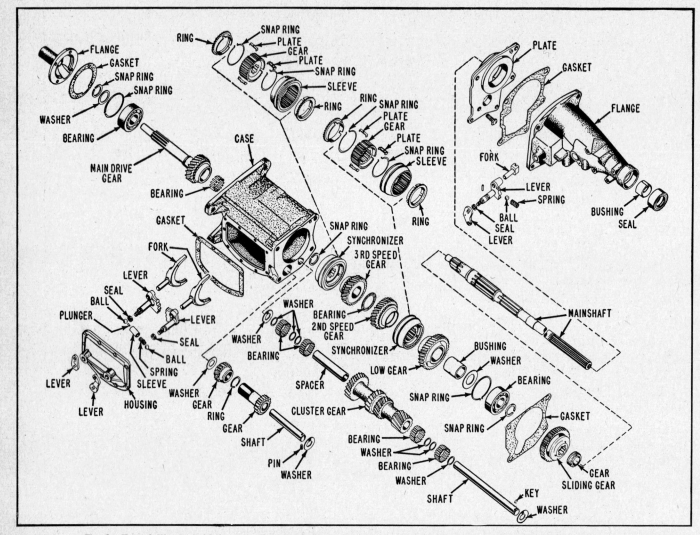

Fig. 1 Type 1 Warner T-10 four speed transmission. Some units do not have the mainshaft low gear bushing shown.

Side Cover, Remove

1. Disconnect control rods from levers.
2. Remove cover assembly from transmission and allow oil to drain.
3. Remove outer shift lever nuts and lockwashers and pull levers from shaft.
4. Carefully push shifter shafts into cover, allowing detent balls to fall free, then remove both shifter shafts.
5. Remove interlock sleeve, pin and poppet spring.

Side Cover, Install

1. Install interlock sleeve and one shifter shaft. Place detent ball into sleeve followed by poppet spring and interlock pin.
2. Start second shifter shaft into position and place second detent ball on poppet spring. Compress ball and spring with screwdriver and push shifter shaft fully in.
3. With transmission in neutral and shifter forks and levers in place, lower side cover into place. Install attaching bolts, using sealer on bolts to prevent leakage. Tighten bolts evenly.

Disassemble Transmission

1. Remove side cover as outlined above.
2. Remove front bearing retainer.
3. Drive lock pin from botton side of reverse shifter lever boss, Fig. 3, and pull shifter out about 1/8". This disengages reverse shift fork from reverse gear.
4. Unfasten extension housing from rear bearing retainer (adapter). Tap extension with soft hammer in rearward direction to start. When reverse idler shaft is out as far as it will go, move extension to left so reverse fork clears reverse gear, and remove extension and gasket.
5. Remove speedometer drive gear with a suitable puller.
6. The rear reverse idler gear, tanged thrust washer and reverse gear may now be removed, Figs. 4 and 5.
7. Remove self-locking bolts attaching rear bearing retainer (adapter) to transmission case. Then carefully remove entire mainshaft assembly.
8. Lift front reverse ider gear and thrust washer from case, Fig. 6.

Fig. 3   Removing reverse shifter lock pin

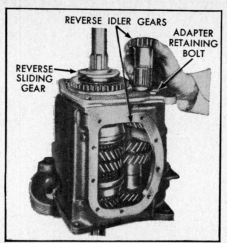

REVERSE IDLER GEARS

ADAPTER RETAINING BOLT

REVERSE SLIDING GEAR

Fig. 5   Reverse gear rear idler removal

Fig. 7   Removing main drive gear snap ring

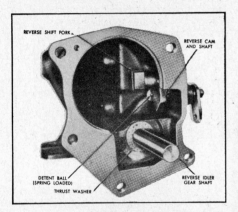

REVERSE SHIFT FORK

REVERSE CAM AND SHAFT

DETENT BALL (SPRING LOADED)

THRUST WASHER

REVERSE IDLER GEAR SHAFT

Fig. 4   Reverse idler shaft and reverse shifter

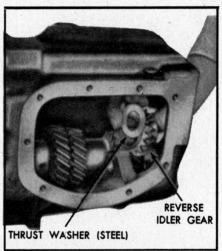

THRUST WASHER (STEEL)

REVERSE IDLER GEAR

Fig. 6   Reverse gear front idler removal

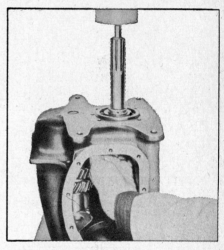

Fig. 8   Removing main drive gear from front bearing

9. Unload bearing rollers from main drive gear and remove 4th speed synchronizing ring.
10. Remove main drive gear snap ring, Fig. 7, and remove spacer washer.
11. With soft hammer, tap main drive gear down from front bearing, Fig. 8.
12. From inside case, tap out front bearing and snap ring.
13. From front of case, tap out countershaft, Fig. 9, using a dummy shaft as shown. Remove countergear and both tanged thrust washers.
14. Remove dummy shaft, all 80 rollers and six spacers from countergear.
15. Remove mainshaft front snap ring, Fig. 10, and slide 3-4 speed synchronizer, 3rd speed gear and synchronizing ring, 2-3 speed gear thrust washer (needle roller bearing), 2nd speed gear and synchronizing ring from front of mainshaft.
16. Spread rear bearing snap ring and press mainshaft out of retainer, Fig. 11.
17. Remove mainshaft rear snap ring. Support 1-2 speed synchronizer assembly Fig. 12, and press on rear of mainshaft to remove shaft from remaining parts on shaft.

Cleaning & Inspection

1. Wash transmission case inside and out with cleaning solvent and inspect for cracks. Inspect front face of case for

burrs and, if present, dress them off with a fine cut mill file.
2. Wash front and rear bearings in cleaning solvent. Blow out bearings with compressed air. *Do not allow bearings to spin; turn them slowly by hand. Spinning bearings will damage race and balls.*
3. Make sure bearings are clean, then lubricate them with light engine oil and check them for roughness. Roughness may be determined by turning outer race by hand.
4. All main drive gear and countergear bearing rollers should be inspected closely and replaced if they show wear. Inspect countershaft and replace if necessary. Replace all worn spacers.
5. Inspect all gears and first speed gear bushing (or sleeve) and, if necessary, replace all that are worn or damaged.

Synchronizers

Clutch hubs and sliding sleeves are a selected assembly and should be kept together as originally assembled, but the

three keys and two springs may be replaced if worn or broken.
Push hub from sliding sleeve. Keys will fall free and springs may be easily removed. To assemble, place the two springs in position (one on each side of hub) so tanged end of each spring falls into same keyway in hub. Place keys in position and, holding them in place, slide hub into sleeve.

Assemble Mainshaft

1. From rear of mainshaft, assemble 1-2 speed synchronizer to mainshaft with sleeve taper toward rear. Press 1st gear bushing on shaft, Fig. 13.
2. Install 1st gear synchronizing ring so that notches in ring correspond to keys in hub, Fig. 14.
3. Install 1st gear with hub toward front, and 1st gear thrust washer. Make certain that grooves in washer are facing 1st gear.
4. Press on rear bearing with snap ring groove toward front of transmission.
5. Choose correct selective fit snap ring and install it in groove in mainshaft behind rear bearing. *Always*

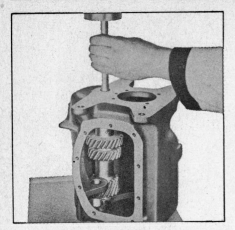

Fig. 9   Removing countershaft

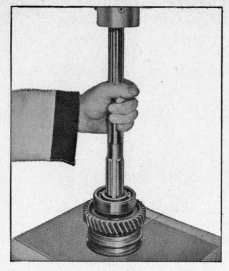

Fig. 12   Removing mainshaft from rear bearing and synchronizer

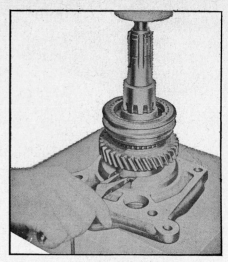

Fig. 15   Installing rear bearing retainer

Fig. 10   Removing mainshaft front snap ring

Fig. 13   Installing first speed gear bushing

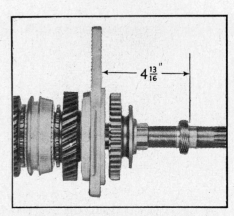

Fig. 16   Installing speedometer drive gear. Note: On Ford and Mercury units, take measurement from rear end of shaft to rear face of speedometer gear; Ford 9¼", Mercury 8⅞"

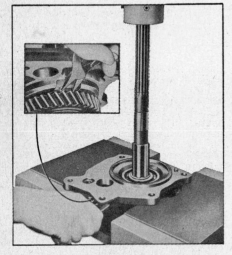

Fig. 11   Removing mainshaft from rear bearing retainer

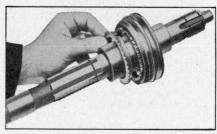

Fig. 14   Installing synchronizer ring

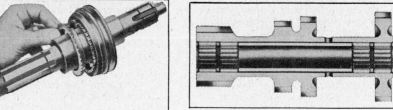

Fig. 17   Cross section of countergear assembly

use new snap ring and do not expand it further than necessary for assembly.

6. From front of mainshaft, install 2nd gear synchronizing ring so notches in ring correspond to keys in hub.

7. Install 2nd gear with hub of gear to-ward back of transmission. Install 2-3 speed gear thrust washer (needle roller bearing).

8. Install 3rd gear with hub to front of transmission, and 3rd gear synchronizing ring with notches to front of transmission.

9. Install 3-4 synchronizer with sleeve taper toward front, making sure keys in hub correspond to notches with 3rd gear synchronizing ring.

10. Install snap ring in groove in mainshaft in front of 3-4 synchronizer. *With the correct size snap ring, 3rd speed gear will have .010-.015" end play with 3-4 synchronizer hub for-ward against snap ring.*

11. Install rear bearing retainer, Fig. 15. Spread selective fit snap ring in plate to allow snap ring to drop around rear

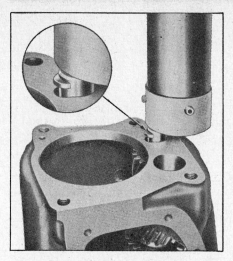

Fig. 18   Installing countershaft

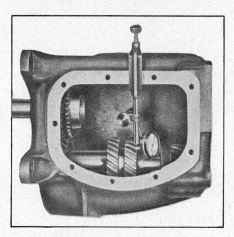

Fig. 19   Checking countershaft end play

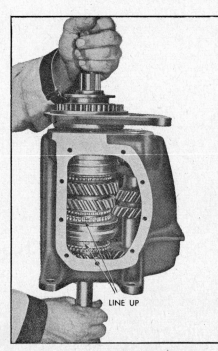

Fig. 20   Installing mainshaft assembly

LINE UP

bearing and press end of mainshaft until snap ring engages groove in rear bearing (use largest size snap ring that will fit into groove).

12. Install reverse gear with shift collar to rear.

13. Press speedometer drive gear onto mainshaft. Position speedometer gear as shown in Fig. 16 for all units except those used on Ford and Mercury. *On Ford and Mercury units, take measurement from rear end of shaft to rear face of speedometer gear; Ford 9¼", Mercury 8⅞".*

Assemble Countergear

1. Install roller spacer in countergear.
2. Using heavy grease to retain rollers, install 20 rollers in either end of countergear, two spacers, 20 more rollers, then one spacer, Fig. 17.
3. Assemble rollers and spacers in the same manner in other end of countergear. Then insert dummy shaft in countergear to retain rollers.

Assemble Transmission

1. Rest case on its side with side cover opening toward you. Place countergear tanged thrust washers in place, retaining them with heavy grease, making sure that tangs are resting in notches in case.
2. Place countergear assembly in bottom of case, making sure that tanged thrust washers are not knocked out of place.
3. Press bearing onto main drive gear with snap ring groove to front.
4. Install spacer washer and selective fit snap ring in groove on gear stem.
5. Install main drive gear assembly through side cover opening and into position in transmission front bore. Tap lightly into place with a soft hammer, if necessary. Place snap ring in groove in front bearing.
6. With transmission resting on its front face, move countergear into mesh with main drive gear, making sure thrust washers remain in place. Install key in end of countershaft and, from front of case, tap or press shaft, Fig. 18, until end of shaft is flush with rear of case and dummy shaft is displaced.
7. Attach dial indicator as shown in Fig. 19 and check end play of countergear. End play must not be more than .025".
8. Install 14 rollers into main drive gear, using heavy grease to hold them in place. Place gasket in position on front face of rear bearing retainer, using heavy grease to hold it in position.
9. Install 4th gear synchronizing ring on main drive gear with clutch key notches toward rear of case.
10. Position reverse idler gear thrust washer (untanged) on machined face of ear cast in case for reverse idler shaft. Position front reverse idler gear on top of thrust washer, with hub facing toward rear of case.
11. Lower mainshaft assembly into case, making certain that notches on 4th

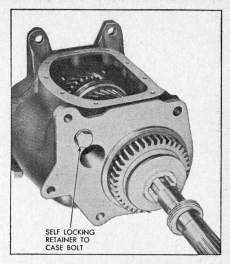

SELF LOCKING RETAINER TO CASE BOLT

Fig. 21   Self-locking bearing retainer-to-case bolt

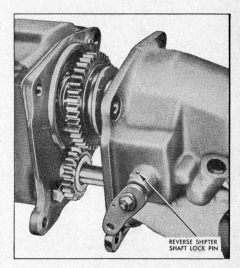

REVERSE SHIFTER SHAFT LOCK PIN

Fig. 22   Installing extension housing on transmission case

USE SEALER

Fig. 23   Sealing lower right attaching bolt

gear synchronizing ring correspond to keys in synchronizer, Fig. 20.

12. Install self-locking bolt attaching rear bearing retainer to case, Fig. 21.
13. From rear of case, insert rear reverse idler gear, engaging splines with portion of gear within case.

14. Using heavy grease, place gasket into position on rear face of rear bearing retainer.

15. Install remaining tanged thrust washer into place on reverse idler shaft, being sure tang on washer is in notch in idler thrust face of extension.

16. Place two synchronizers in neutral position. *If locking-up of gears is encountered, a small amount of petrolatum may be applied to the 1st speed gear synchronizing ring, enabling it to turn freely on 1st speed gear hub.*

17. Pull reverse shifter shaft to left side of extension and rotate shaft to bring reverse shift fork to extreme forward position in extension. Line up front and rear reverse idler gears, making sure front thrust washer is in place.

18. Start extension into case. Fig. 22, by carefully inserting reverse idler shaft through reverse idler gears. Slowly push it on shifter shaft until shift fork engages reverse gear shift collar. When fork engages, rotate shifter shaft to move reverse gear rearward, permitting extension to slide onto transmission case.

19. Install extension and retainer to case attaching bolts, and extension to retainer attaching bolts. Use suitable sealer on the bolt indicated in Fig. 23.

20. Adjust reverse shifter shaft so that groove in shaft lines up with hole in boss and drive in lock pin from top of boss, Fig. 22.

21. Install main drive gear bearing retainer and gasket, being sure oil well lines up with oil outlet hole.

22. Install shift fork in each synchronizer sleeve. With both synchronizers in neutral, install side cover with gasket. Use suitable sealer when installing lower right cover bolt.

23. Install shifter levers, lock washers and nuts.

Type Two

Disassemble Transmission

1. Disconnect the three shift rods from shift levers. Reverse shift lever nut must be loosened to free reverse rod.

2. Remove selector assembly from extension housing.

3. Unhook retainer that secures clutch release lever to retainer bracket, Fig. 2-2.

4. Detach clutch housing from transmission.

5. Remove cover from transmission.

6. Remove main drive gear bearing retainer.

7. Remove extension housing and rear bearing retainer.

8. Drive countershaft out from front of case toward rear until it just clears front wall of case. Then using a dummy shaft, Fig. 2-3, push countershaft out until tool and countergear drop out of position.

9. Remove mainshaft assembly, Fig. 2-4.

10. Remove main drive gear and bearing from front of case, Fig. 2-5.

11. Lift countergear assembly out through cover opening.

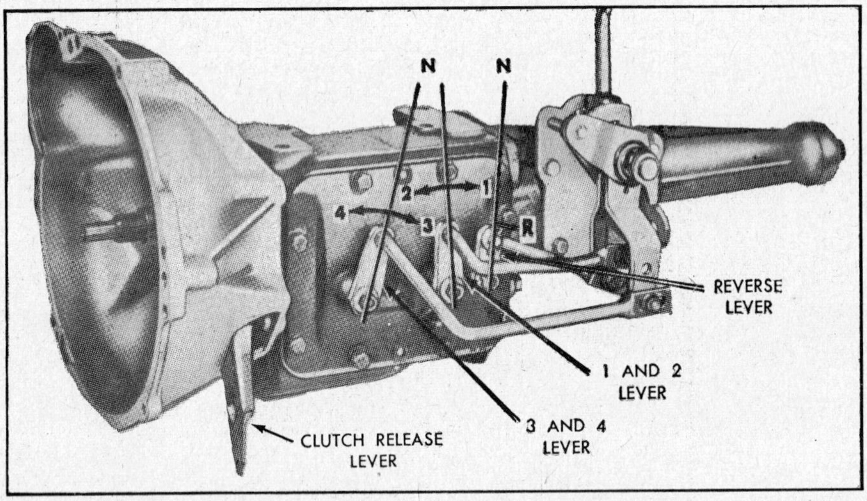

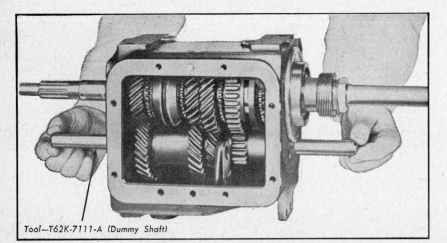

Fig. 2-1   Type Two transmission and clutch housing

12. Install a $5/16$-24 bolt into rear end of reverse idler gear shaft and pull out shaft. Remove idler gear.

13. Remove nut from mainshaft and strip shaft of all parts, Fig. 2-6.

14. If necessary, disassemble, inspect and reassemble shift selector and gearshift housing assemblies, replacing all worn or damaged parts. Refer to Figs. 2-7, 2-8, 2-9.

15. Clean and air-dry all parts except bearings. Rotate bearings in solvent until all lube is removed. Then hold bearing to keep it from rotating and dry with compressed air. After inspection, lubricate bearing with transmission lube and protect from dirt until ready for use.

Synchronizers

1. When assembling synchronizers, Fig. 2-10, place long inserts into slots in 1-2 synchronizer hub and slide combination sleeve and reverse gear over it with the etch marks on hub and sleeve aligned.

2. Snap insert springs in place. The tab on each spring must set into the underside of an insert.

3. Position short inserts into slots in 3-4 synchronizer hub and slide sleeve over it with etch marks aligned. In-

Tool—T62K-7111-A (Dummy Shaft)

Fig. 2-3   Countershaft removal and installation

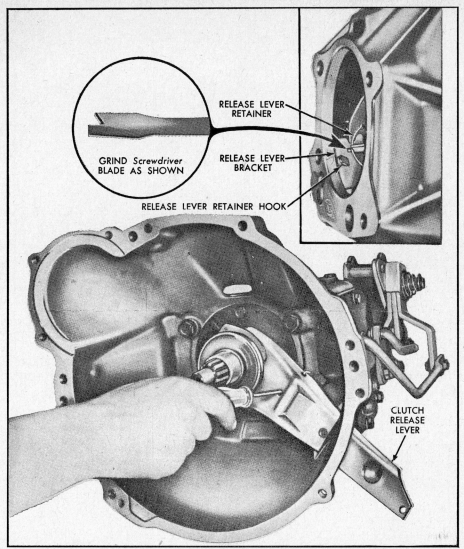

Fig. 2-2 Clutch release lever retainer attachment and disengagement

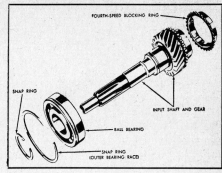

Fig. 2-5 Main drive gear and bearing

stall insert springs in same manner as with 1-2 synchronizer.

Assemble Mainshaft

1. Assemble mainshaft and related parts in the sequence shown in Fig. 2-6, and observe the following precautions:

2. Be sure 2nd speed blocking ring is not cocked on gear and that the three index slots align with the synchronizer inserts.

3. Assemble mainshaft ball bearing into recess in bearing adapter. Position adapter and bearing onto rear of mainshaft with adapter forward. Hold 1st gear and sleeve (bushing) forward and place assembly in a press with the tool (or equivalent) shown in Fig. 2-11 resting against rear of bearing inner race. Press into place until bearing is seated firmly against 1st gear bushing.

4. When installing the speedometer drive gear and related parts, be

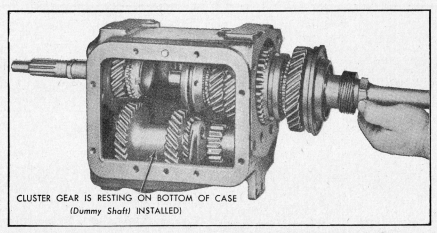

Fig. 2-4 Mainshaft removal and installation

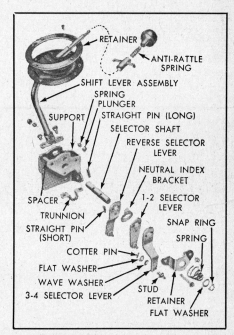

Fig. 2-7 Shift selector components

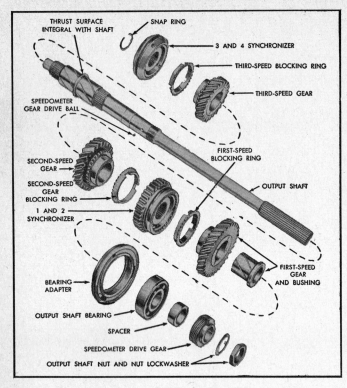

THRUST SURFACE INTEGRAL WITH SHAFT
SNAP RING
3 AND 4 SYNCHRONIZER
THIRD-SPEED BLOCKING RING
THIRD-SPEED GEAR
SPEEDOMETER GEAR DRIVE BALL
FIRST-SPEED BLOCKING RING
SECOND-SPEED GEAR
SECOND-SPEED GEAR BLOCKING RING
OUTPUT SHAFT
1 AND 2 SYNCHRONIZER
BEARING ADAPTER
FIRST-SPEED GEAR AND BUSHING
OUTPUT SHAFT BEARING
SPACER
SPEEDOMETER DRIVE GEAR
OUTPUT SHAFT NUT AND NUT LOCKWASHER

Fig. 2-6 Mainshaft components

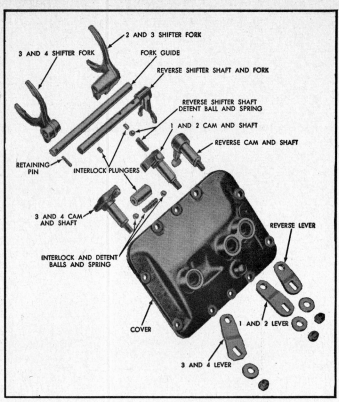

3 AND 4 SHIFTER FORK
2 AND 3 SHIFTER FORK
FORK GUIDE
REVERSE SHIFTER SHAFT AND FORK
REVERSE SHIFTER SHAFT DETENT BALL AND SPRING
1 AND 2 CAM AND SHAFT
REVERSE CAM AND SHAFT
RETAINING PIN
INTERLOCK PLUNGERS
3 AND 4 CAM AND SHAFT
REVERSE LEVER
INTERLOCK AND DETENT BALLS AND SPRING
1 AND 2 LEVER
COVER
3 AND 4 LEVER

Fig. 2-8 Gearshift housing details

sure to install the driving ball into recess in gear and mainshaft, Fig. 2-6.

Assemble Transmission

1. Place dummy shaft into countergear. Then starting on either end, Fig. 2-12, drop a steel washer over tool and into

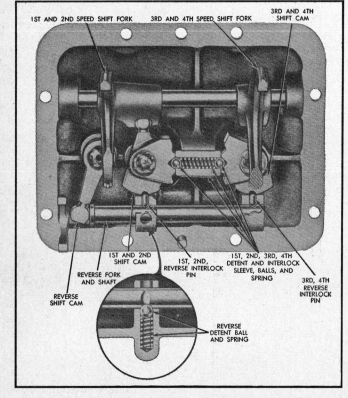

1ST AND 2ND SPEED SHIFT FORK
3RD AND 4TH SPEED SHIFT FORK
3RD AND 4TH SHIFT CAM
1ST AND 2ND SHIFT CAM
REVERSE FORK AND SHAFT
1ST, 2ND, REVERSE INTERLOCK PIN
1ST, 2ND, 3RD, 4TH DETENT AND INTERLOCK SLEEVE, BALLS, AND SPRING
3RD, 4TH REVERSE INTERLOCK PIN
REVERSE SHIFT CAM
REVERSE DETENT BALL AND SPRING

Fig. 2-9 Transmission shift mechanism details

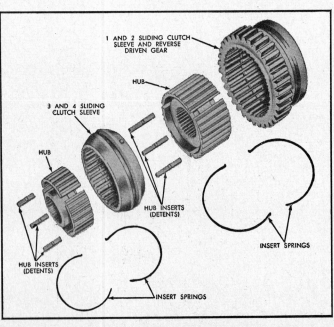

1 AND 2 SLIDING CLUTCH SLEEVE AND REVERSE DRIVEN GEAR
HUB
3 AND 4 SLIDING CLUTCH SLEEVE
HUB
HUB INSERTS (DETENTS)
INSERT SPRINGS
HUB INSERTS (DETENTS)
INSERT SPRINGS

Fig. 2-10 Synchronizer details

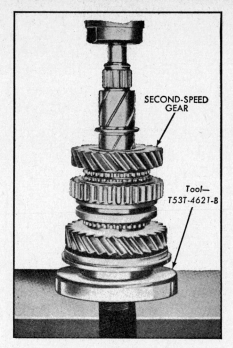

Fig. 2-11 Mainshaft bearing installation

gear. Coat each needle bearing with grease and install 22 of them into gear. Lay another steel washer on ends of needle bearings and the proper (greased) thrust washer or washer as shown.

2. Repeat foregoing operation for other end of gear. Do not lose bearings and spacer in the initially assembled end when inverting the gear to assemble opposite end.

3. Install countergear assembly in case with the two thrust washers at the front. Allow gear and dummy shaft assembly to rest in bottom of case until main drive gear and mainshaft assemblies are installed.

4. Assemble main drive gear as suggested by Figs. 2-5 and 2-13. Then, using grease to hold them in place install 17 roller bearings in bore of main drive gear.

5. Stick the extension housing gasket to rear of transmission case with a non-drying sealer.

6. Install main drive gear into front case bore. Place 4th gear blocking ring onto rear end of main drive gear with clutch teeth forward.

7. Enter mainshaft assembly through rear of case and guide the shaft front pilot into the main drive gear bore. Be sure 4th gear blocking ring slots index with slots on synchronizer.

8. Raise countergear assembly and insert countershaft through the rear. Shaft should push through, easily displacing tool, until front of case is contacted, Fig. 2-3.

9. Position flat on rear end of countershaft in horizontal plane so it will align with slot in extension housing. Tap shaft into place.

10. Install reverse idler gear with fork groove toward rear and with idler shaft flat horizontal and parallel with countershaft flat.

11. Install extension housing. Align dowel in housing with hole in rear bearing adapter, Fig. 2-14. Be sure housing is sealed squarely on case, bearing and adapter before tightening bolts. If

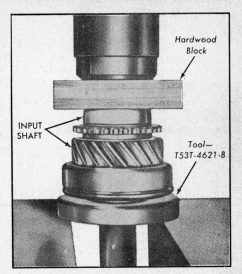

Fig. 2-13 Installation of main drive gear bearing

two long and two shorter bolts are used, install the two long bolts in the upper right and lower left holes.

12. Install new bearing retainer gasket, using sealer. Install bearing retainer with drain slot facing downward. Seal and tighten bolts.

13. Place 1-2 and 3-4 synchronizers in neutral and reverse idler gear into reverse (forward) position. Set shift housing into reverse. Install new shift housing gasket on case, using sealer. Install shift housing, using sealer on bolts and tighten.

14. Install clutch housing. Use sealer on retaining bolts.

15. Install clutch release bearing onto clutch release lever. Position release lever through housing from inside housing and clip lever retainer onto its hook, Fig. 2-2.

16. Install shift selector assembly on

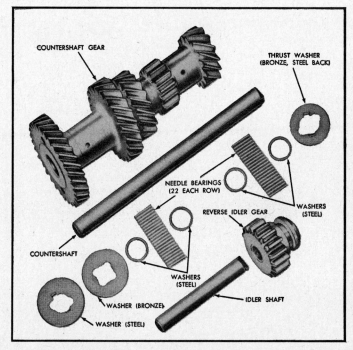

Fig. 2-12 Countergear and idler gear assemblies

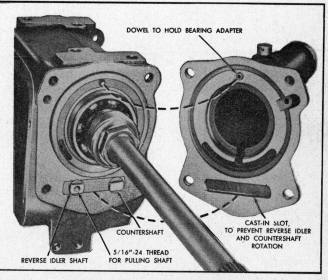

Fig. 2-14 Extension housing installation

17. Install shift rods to cam levers and secure them with spring washers and cotter pins or clips. Tighten reverse cam lever nut.

18. Loosely assembly shift rods to linkage levers. Insert a ¼" drill or rod through three linkage levers and into the support. Move levers until gauge

rod will enter all three alignment holes and tighten lock nuts.

19. Assemble shield over shift selector assembly.

Type Three Corvair

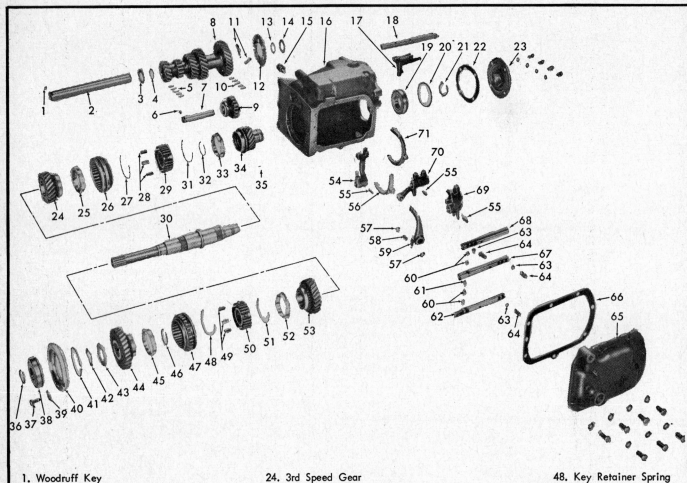

1. Woodruff Key
2. Countershaft
3. Thrust Washer
4. Bearing Washer
5. Needle Bearings
6. Woodruff Key
7. Reverse Idler Shaft
8. Countergear
9. Reverse Idler Gear
10. Needle Bearings
11. Spring
12. Anti-Rattle Plate
13. Bearing Washer
14. Thrust Washer
15. Filler Plug
16. Case
17. Shift Finger
18. Selector Shaft
19. Clutch Gear Bearing
20. Snap Ring—Bearing to Case
21. Snap Ring—Bearing to Gear
22. Gasket
23. Bearing Retainer

24. 3rd Speed Gear
25. 3rd Speed Blocker Ring
26. 3-4 Synchronizer Sleeve
27. Key Retainer Spring
28. Clutch Keys
29. 3-4 Synchronizer Hub
30. Mainshaft
31. Key Retainer Spring
32. Snap Ring—Hub to Shaft
33. 4th Speed Blocker Ring
34. Clutch Gear
35. Pilot Bearings
36. Snap Ring—Bearing to Shaft
37. Bearing Retainer Strap Bolt
38. Rear Bearing
39. Bearing Retainer Strap
40. Bearing Retainer
41. Snap Ring—Bearing to Retainer
42. Spring Washer
43. Thrust Washer
44. 1st Speed Gear
45. 1st Speed Blocker Ring
46. Snap Ring—Hub to Shaft
47. 1-2 Synch. Sleeve & Reverse Gear

48. Key Retainer Spring
49. Clutch Keys
50. 1-2 Synchronizer Hub
51. Key Retainer Spring
52. 2nd Speed Blocker Ring
53. 2nd Speed Gear
54. Reverse Shifter Head
55. Roll Pin
56. 1-2 Shift Fork
57. "E" Ring
58. Pin
59. Reverse Shift Fork
60. Interlock Balls
61. Interlock Pin
62. Reverse Shifter Shaft
63. Detent Ball
64. Detent Spring
65. Side Cover
66. Gasket
67. 3-4 Shifter Shaft
68. 1-2 Shifter Shaft
69. 3-4 Shifter Head
70. 1-2 Shifter Head
71. 3-4 Shift Fork

Fig. 1 Type 3 Corvair four speed transmission

A great deal of similarity and interchangeability exists between this transmission, Fig. 1, and the Type 14 Corvair three-speed transmission shown before. Therefore, the following material deals only with the differences in service between the 3 and 4 speed units. Other 4 speed service procedures are similar to the 3 speed unit and are not repeated here.

Mainshaft Assembly

Assembly procedures described for the Type 14 Corvair 3 speed transmission also apply to this transmission. However, the synchronizer assembly at the front of the mainshaft is used for the 3rd and 4th rather than the 2-3 shift. The synchronizer assembly at the rear of the mainshaft is used for the 1st and 2nd rather than the 1st and reverse shifts. Gear teeth cut in the 1st and 2nd synchronizer sleeve distinguish it from the 3rd and 4th synchronizer sleeve.

All parts except the gears and the 1st and 2nd synchronizer sleeve in this 4 speed transmission mainshaft assembly are also used in the Type 14 Corvair 3 speed mainshaft assembly. However, starting from the front, gears on the mainshaft are 3rd, 2nd and 1st rather than 2nd, 1st and reverse. A fourth blocker ring is used between the 1-2 synchronizer assembly and 1st gear on the 4 speed transmission.

Reverse Idler Gear Parts

There is a sliding reverse idler gear and shaft retained by a woodruff key. Elimination of the thrust washer between the gear and case, and removal of the snap ring groove to allow movement of the reverse idler gear, distinguishes this shaft from the 3 speed transmission reverse idler shaft. Otherwise service procedures are the same as for the 3 speed transmission.

Type Four Muncie

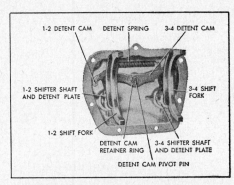

Fig. 4-2   Transmission side cover

SIDE COVER, REPLACE

1. Referring to Fig. 4-2 disconnect control rods from levers.
2. Shift transmisson into 2nd speed before removing cover by moving 1-2 shifter lever into forward detent position.
3. Remove cover from case.
4. Reverse procedure to install the cover, being sure first to shift the transmission into 2nd gear. Make sure shift forks are aligned with their respective grooves in synchronizer sliding sleeves.

DISASSEMBLE TRANSMISSION

1. Remove side cover.
2. Remove front bearing retainer.
3. Shift transmission into two gears at once to keep mainshaft from turning, then remove retainer nut from main drive gear.
4. With gears in neutral, drive lock pin from reverse shifter lever boss and pull shifter shaft out about 1/8". This disengages reverse shift fork from reverse gear.
5. Unfasten extension case from main case. Tap extension case rearward

with a soft hammer to start. When reverse idler shaft is out as far as it will go, move extension to left so reverse fork clears reverse gear. Then remove extension and gasket.
6. Now remove rear reverse idler gear, shaft and plate thrust washer.
7. Use a suitable puller to remove speedometer gear from mainshaft, after which remove reverse gear.
8. Slide 3-4 synchronizer clutch sleeve to 4th gear position before trying to remove mainshaft assembly from case.
9. Remove rear bearing retainer and mainshaft assembly from case by tapping retainer with soft hammer.
10. Unload bearing rollers from main drive gear and remove 4th gear synchronizer blocking ring.
11. Lift front half of reverse idler gear and its tanged washer from case.
12. Press main drive gear down into case and remove. From inside of case, tap out front bearing and snap ring.
13. From front of case, press out countershaft. Then remove countergear and both tanged washers.
14. Remove mainshaft front snap ring and strip mainshaft of loose parts.
15. Spread rear bearing retainer snap ring and press mainshaft out of retainer.

NOTE: Early models of this transmission use a snap ring behind the 1-2 synchronizer hub to retain the hub in position while later units have a sleeve within the 1st speed gear. This sleeve acts as a spacer between the rear bearing and 1-2 synchronizer hub.

16. Remove mainshaft rear snap ring. Support 1st gear in a press and press against rear of shaft to remove it from rear bearing, 1st gear thrust washer, 1st gear and synchronizing ring.
17. Remove 1-2 synchronizer snap ring and remove 1-2 synchronizer unit, 2nd gear synchronizer ring and 2nd gear from shaft, Fig. 4-3.

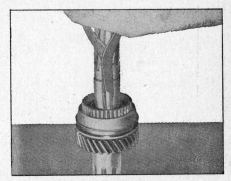

Fig. 4-3   Removing 1-2 synchronizer clutch snap ring

UNIT REPAIRS
Reverse Idler

Because of the high degree of accuracy to which the reverse idler gear bushings are machined, the bushings are not serviced separately. Check bushings for excessive wear by using a narrow feeler gauge between shaft and bushing. Proper clearance is from .003 to .005".

Reverse Shifter Shaft & Seal

1. With extension case removed as outlined previously, remove shift fork.
2. Drive shifter shaft into case extension, allowing ball detent to drop into case. Remove shaft and ball detent spring.
3. Place ball detent spring into its hole and, from inside extension, install shifter shaft fully into its opening until detent plate is butted against inside of extension housing.
4. Place detent ball on spring, Fig. 4-4, and, holding ball down with thumb or a suitable tool, push shifter shaft back in, away from case until it is directly over ball and turn until ball drops into detent on shaft detent plate.
5. Install shift fork.

NOTE: Do not drive shifter shaft lock pin into place until extension has been

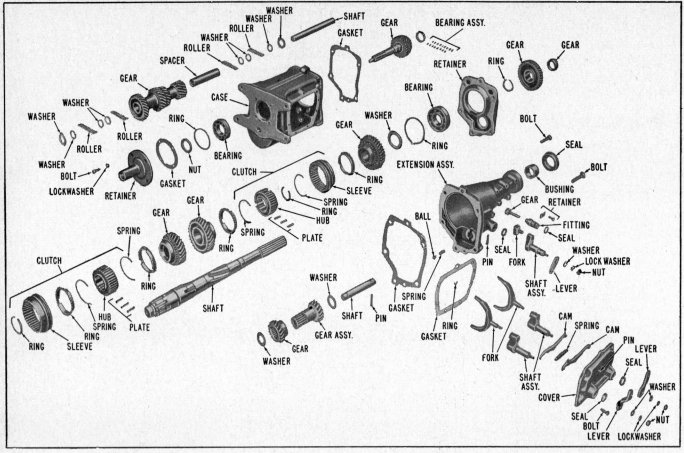

Fig. 4-1 Muncie four speed transmission. Early models use a snap ring (illustrated) behind the 1-2 synchronizer hub to retain the hub in position. Later units have a spacer sleeve within the 1st speed gear, (not illustrated)

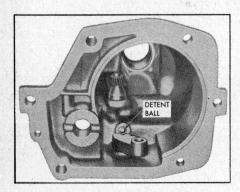

Fig. 4-4 Installing reverse shifter shaft and detent ball

installed on transmission case.

Extension Oil Seal or Bushing

If bushing in rear of extension requires replacement, remove oil seal and drive bushing into case extension. Drive new bushing in from the rear. Coat I.D. of bushing with transmission lubricant, then install new oil seal.

Clutch Keys & Springs

NOTE: The clutch hubs and sliding sleeves are a selected assembly and should be kept together as originally assembled. However, the three keys and two springs may be replaced if worn or broken.

1. To replace, push hub from sliding sleeve. Keys will fall free and springs easily removed.
2. Place the two springs in position (one on each side of hub) so all three keys are engaged by both springs. Place keys in position and, holding them in place, slide hub into sleeve.

Assemble Mainshaft

1. From rear of mainshaft, assemble 2nd gear with hub of gear toward rear of shaft.
2. Install 1-2 synchronizer clutch, with clutch sleeve taper to rear, together with a blocker ring on each side so their keyways line up with clutch keys, Fig. 4-5. On early units, install 1-2 synchronizer retainer snap ring (smaller of the two). On later units, install 1st gear spacer sleeve.
3. Install 1st gear (hub toward front) and 1st gear thrust washer.

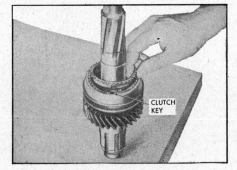

Fig. 4-5 Installing synchronizer ring

4. Press rear bearing on mainshaft, Fig. 4-6, being sure to seat bearing firmly.
5. Choose correct selective fit snap ring and install it in groove of mainshaft behind rear bearing. (Snap rings of .084″, .087″, .090″, .093″, .096″ are available.) With proper snap ring, maximum distance between ring and rear face of bearing will be from zero to .005″.
6. Install 3rd gear (hub to front) and 3rd gear synchronizing ring (notches to front).

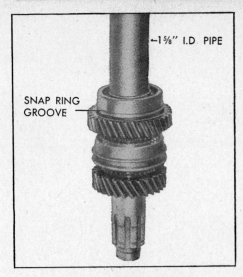

Fig. 4-6 Installing mainshaft rear bearing

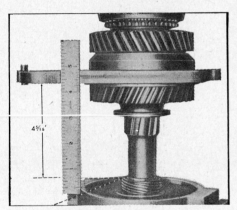

Fig. 4-7 Installing speedometer drive gear

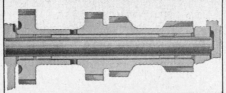

Fig. 4-8 Sectional view of countergear assembly

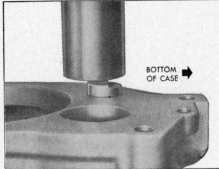

Fig. 4-9 Installing countershaft

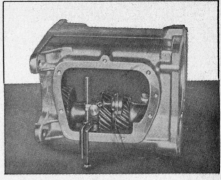

Fig. 4-10 Checking countergear end play

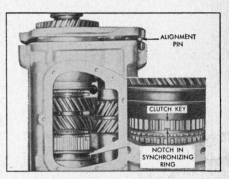

Fig. 4-11 Installing mainshaft assembly

7. Install 3-4 clutch assembly with both sleeve taper and hub toward front, making sure keys in hub correspond to notches in 3rd gear synchronizing ring.
8. Install snap ring in mainshaft groove in front of 3-4 synchronizer clutch with ends of snap ring seated behind spline teeth.
9. Install rear bearing retainer. Spread snap ring in plate to allow ring to drop around rear bearing and press on end of mainshaft until snap ring engages groove in rear bearing.
10. Install reverse gear with shift collar to rear.
11. Press speedometer drive gear on mainshaft to distance shown in Fig. 4-7.

Assemble Countergear

1. Install roller spacer in countergear.
2. Using heavy grease to retain rollers, install 20 rollers in either end of countergear, two .050" spacers, 20 more rollers, then one .050" spacer. Make same installation at other end of countergear, Fig. 4-8.

ASSEMBLE TRANS.

1. With transmission case on its side, put countergear tanged thrust washers in place, retaining them with heavy grease, and making sure tangs are resting in notches in case.
2. Set countergear in bottom of case.
3. Position transmission so it is resting on its front face.
4. Lubricate and insert countershaft through rear of case. Turn countershaft so flat on end of shaft is horizontal and facing bottom of case.
5. Align countergear with shaft in rear and hole in front of case. Press countershaft into case until flat on shaft is flush with rear of case, Fig. 4-9. Be sure thrust washers remain in place.
6. Attach a dial indicator as shown in Fig. 4-10 and check end play of countergear. If end play is greater than .025", new thrust washers must be installed.
7. Install 17 roller bearings in main drive gear, using heavy grease to hold bearings and cage in place.
8. Install main drive gear and pilot bearings through side cover opening and into transmission front bore.
9. Place gasket in position of front face of rear bearing retainer.
10. Install 4th gear synchronizing ring on main drive gear with notches toward rear.
11. Position tanged reverse idler gear thrust washer on machined face of ear cast in case for reverse idler shaft and hold with heavy grease. Position front reverse idler gear next to thrust washer, with hub facing toward rear.

NOTE: Before attempting to install mainshaft assembly in case, slide 3-4 synchronizer clutch sleeve forward into 4th speed detent position.

12. Lower mainshaft into case making certain notches in 4th speed synchronizing ring correspond to keys in clutch, Fig. 4-11.
13. Tap rear bearing into position.
14. Insert rear reverse idler gear.
15. Install remaining flat thrust washer on reverse idler shaft. If new idler shaft in being used, drive out roll pin and press it into new shaft.
16. Install reverse idler shaft, making sure to pick up rear tanged thrust washer. *Roll pin should be in a vertical position.*
17. Pull reverse shifter shaft to left side of extension and rotate shaft to bring reverse shift fork forward in extension (reverse detent position). Start extension onto transmission case, while slowly pushing in on shifter shaft to engage shift fork with reverse gear shift collar. Then pilot reverse idler shaft into extension housing, permitting extension to slide into transmission case.
18. Install extension attaching bolts. Torque upper three bolts to 15-25-ft-lbs, and lower three bolts to 25-35 ft-lbs.
19. Push or pull reverse shifter shaft to line up holes and drive in lock pin. Then install shifter lever.
20. Press bearing onto main drive gear (snap ring groove to front) and into case until several main drive gear retaining nut threads are exposed.
21. Lock transmission by shifting into two gears. Install main drive gear retaining nut. Be sure bearing fully seats against shoulder of gear. Torque nut to 40 ft-lbs and lock it in place by staking securely into shaft hole with center punch.

22. Install main drive gear bearing retainer, using sealer on bolts. Torque to 15-20 ft-lbs.
23. Shift 3-4 sliding sleeve into neutral and 1-2 sliding sleeve into 2nd gear position. Shift side cover 3-4 shift lever into neutral and 1-2 shift lever into 2nd gear.
24. Install side cover with gasket. Torque attaching bolts evenly to avoid cover distortion and torque to 15-20 ft-lbs.

Type Five Chrysler

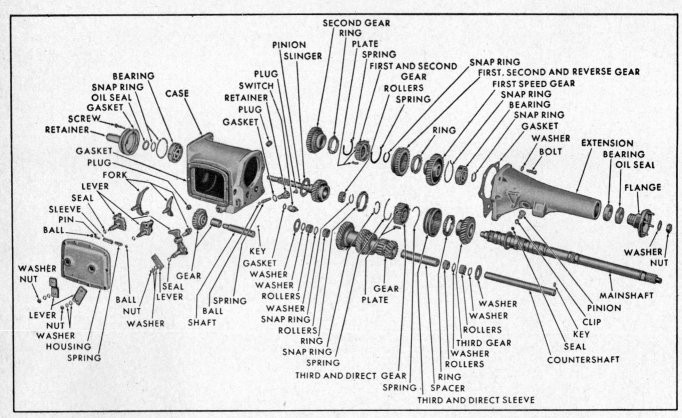

Fig. 5-1   Type Eive Chrysler four-speed transmission. NOTE: The drive pinion bearing oil slinger shown has been eliminated with the release of new drive pinions which do not use an oil slinger

DISASSEMBLE TRANS.

1. On early models, disconnect shift control rods from shift levers, shift transmission into two gears at once to prevent mainshaft from turning and remove flange from end of mainshaft.
2. All units, unfasten shift housing and with all levers in neutral position, Fig. 5-2, pull housing out and away from case. Work shift forks out of synchronizer sleeves and remove from case.
3. Remove main drive gear bearing retainer.
4. Unbolt extension housing from transmission case.

5. Slide 3-4 synchronizer slightly forward and slide mainshaft and extension housing out of case, Fig. 5-3.

Disassemble Mainshaft

1. Remove snap ring in front of 3-4 synchronizer and slide off synchronizer.
2. Slide off 3rd gear and stop ring.
3. While holding center bearing snap ring compressed, Fig. 5-4, pull mainshaft assembly and bearing out of extension housing.
4. Remove mainshaft rear bearing snap ring, insert steel plates on front side of 1st speed gear, and press gear and rear bearing from mainshaft. Remove 1st gear stop ring.

5. Remove snap ring and slide 1-2 synchronizer clutch unit from mainshaft.

NOTE: Fig. 5-6 shows mainshaft bearing surfaces. Inspect these surfaces for any condition that would warrant the use of a new mainshaft. Fig. 5-7 shows details of reverse gearing and related parts.

6. With a feeler gauge, Fig. 5-8, measure countergear end play by inserting gauge between thrust washer and gear. Measurement should not exceed .0155″ to .028″. If greater than specified, new thrust washers should be used upon reassembly.
7. Remove reverse lever detent parts.

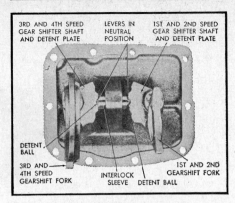

Fig. 5-2 Shift housing assembly

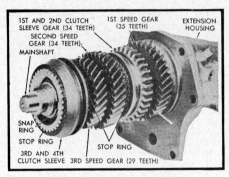

Fig. 5-3 Mainshaft assembly

8. Press or drive reverse slider gear shaft (from front to rear) far enough out of case to remove slider gear. Remove key from shaft and shaft from case, Fig. 5-9.
9. Push reverse lever shaft into case and remove as shown in Fig. 5-10. Lift out detent ball from bottom of case, and remove shift fork from shaft and detent plate.
10. Using a suitable arbor, drive countershaft out of case, allowing cluster gear to rest in bottom of case to permit removal of main drive gear.
11. Remove snap ring and remove main drive gear by driving it into case. Remove snap ring and press bearing from main drive gear.
12. Lift cluster gear from case.

REASSEMBLE TRANS.
Countergear

1. Using heavy grease, coat inside of gear bore at each end, then center bearing spacer. Insert arbor through gear and spacer.
2. Grease needle rollers and, at each end of gear, install 19 rollers, followed by a spacer ring, 19 more rollers and a spacer ring.
3. Coat thrust washers with grease and install them over arbor with tang side toward case boss.
4. Install countergear into case, Fig. 5-11. Allow assembly to rest in bottom of case until after main drive gear is installed.

Mainshaft

1. Slide 2nd gear over mainshaft, synchronizer cone toward rear, and into position against shoulder on shaft, Fig. 5-5.
2. Slide 1-2 clutch sleeve gear including 2nd gear stop ring over mainshaft with shift fork slot toward front, and down into position against 2nd gear. Be sure stop ring is indexed with shift plates and install snap ring.
3. Slide low gear stop ring over shaft and down into position and index with shift plates.
4. Slide 1st gear synchronizer (synchronizer cone toward clutch gear sleeve just installed) over mainshaft and down against clutch sleeve gear.
5. Install mainshaft bearing retainer ring followed by mainshaft bearing. Drive or press bearing down into position and secure with snap ring.
6. On earlier units, install extension housing bearing.
7. Install partially assembled mainshaft into extension housing far enough to engage retaining ring in slot in extension housing. Compress retaining ring and at same time rest mainshaft in extension housing (see Fig. 5-4). Be sure retaining ring is seated all around slot.
8. Slide 3rd gear on shaft, synchronizer cone toward front, followed by 3rd gear stop ring.
9. Install 3-4 synchronizer clutch assembly with shift fork slot toward rear. Be sure to index rear stop ring with clutch gear shift plates (see Fig. 5-4). Install snap ring.

Service Bulletin

Quiets Gear Rattle: A gear rattle, or neutral noise, having automatic transmission

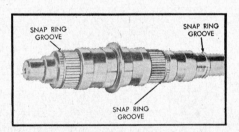

Fig. 5-6 Mainshaft bearing surfaces

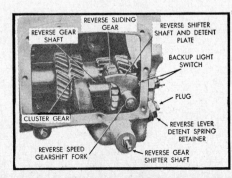

Fig. 5-7 Reverse gearing and countergear

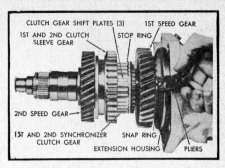

Fig. 5-4 Compressing center bearing snap ring so mainshaft can be pulled from bearing housing

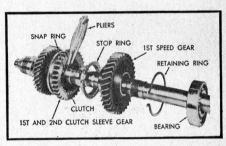

Fig. 5-5 Removing clutch gear snap ring

fluid in the case can be quieted by changing the lubricant. Drain the automatic transmission fluid and replace it with SAE-140 multipurpose gear lube. If the SAE-140 causes hard or stiff shifting during cold weather operation, change to SAE-80 or 90. This will lessen the effort required for shifting.

10. Using heavy grease, position front stop ring over clutch gear, indexing ring slots with shift plates.

CAUTION: It is very important that indexing of all stop rings and positioning of gears and clutches on mainshaft be correct, or the mating of the extension housing to the case will not be possible without damage.

Main Drive Gear & Countershaft

1. Slide oil slinger (if used) over shaft, then press bearing onto shaft. Be sure outer snap ring groove is toward front. Seat bearing fully against shoulder of gear.
2. Install new inner snap ring into groove to retain bearing.
3. Install gear and bearing into case and position in front bore. Tap lightly into place. Install outer snap ring in bearing groove.
4. Start countershaft in its bore at rear of case. Raise countergear to mesh with main drive gear. Be sure thrust washer tangs are aligned with slots in case.
5. Drive or press countershaft into gear. Install woodruff key. Continue to press shaft into case until end of shaft is flush with rear face of case.

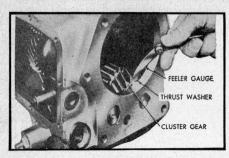

Fig. 5-8 Measuring countergear end play

Fig. 5-9 Removing reverse slider gear

6. Measure countergear end play (see Fig. 5-8). If end play is greater than .028" install new thrust washers.

Reverse Gearing

1. Install reverse shaft detent and spring. Install spring retainer gasket and retainer (see Fig. 5-7).
2. Position reverse slider gear shaft in end of case and drive it far enough

to position slider gear on protruding end of shaft with shift slot toward rear (see Fig. 5-9). At same time engage slot with reverse shift fork.

3. Drive reverse gear shaft into case far enough to permit installation of woodruff key. Drive shaft flush with end of case.

Mainshaft & Extension Housing

1. Grease both sides of extension housing gasket and stick it on case.
2. Center reverse slider gear on its shaft, then insert mainshaft into case. Be sure 3-4 speed stop ring is indexed with shifter plates.
3. Move 3-4 speed clutch sleeve slightly toward front and at same time align front of mainshaft with main drive gear. Push in on extension housing and bottom against case and housing.
4. Install bolts and tighten securely.
5. Move reverse slider gear ahead to neutral position and install shift housing.

Service Bulletin

Cures Hard Shifting: Hard shifting can result if there is a binding of the shifter shafts in the case or in the cover. This happens when moisture enters between the shaft and bore and causes a build-up of corrosion.

To restore normal shifting, remove the external shift levers from the transmission, leaving the levers attached to the shift rods. It is not necessary to drain oil from the unit.

Place a ¾" diameter hole saw over the shifting shaft protruding from the case and cut a ⅛" deep counterbore in the case. After blowing out the cuttings, apply to the shaft a penetrating oil that will not dam-

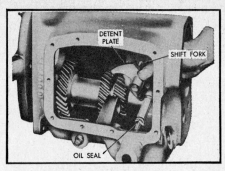

Fig. 5-10 Removing reverse shift fork and lever

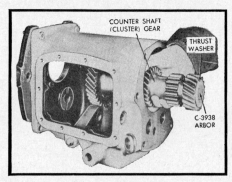

5-11 Installing countergear

age the "O" ring, and work the shaft until it is free. Now apply a liberal amount of multi-purpose grease to the shaft and counterbore, and then insert an "O" ring, available for the purpose, in the counterbore.

Type Six Ford

DISASSEMBLE TRANS.

1. Remove shift linkage and control bracket.
2. Remove transmission cover.
3. Remove extension housing.
4. Remove input shaft bearing retainer.
5. Support countergear with a wire hook. Then working from front of case, push countershaft out rear of case and lower countergear to bottom of case.
6. Place 1-2 shift lever and reverse shift lever in neutral. Place 3-4 shift lever in 3rd speed position.
7. Remove bolt that retains 3-4 shift rail detent spring and plug in left side of case, Fig. 6-2. Remove spring and plug with a magnet.
8. Remove detent mechanism set screw from top of case and take out detent spring and plug with a magnet.
9. Remove attaching screw from 3-4 speed shift fork. Tap on inner end of shift rail to unseat expansion plug from front of case. Then withdraw 3-4 shift rail from front of case. Do not lose interlock pin from shift rail.
10. Remove attaching screw from 1-2 shift fork. Slide 1-2 shift rail out of rear of case.
11. Remove interlock plug and detent plug from top of case with a magnet.
12. On early models, remove snap ring securing speedometer drive gear to output shaft. Slide gear off shaft and remove speedometer drive gear ball. On later units, depress tang on retaining clip and remove gear.
13. Remove snap ring that secures output shaft bearing to shaft and use a suitable puller to remove bearing.
14. Remove input shaft and bearing and blocking ring from front of case.
15. Move output shaft to right side of case to provide clearance for shift forks. Rotate forks as shown in Fig. 6-3 and lift them from case.
16. Support 1st gear to prevent it from sliding off shaft, then lift output shaft assembly from case, Fig. 6-4.
17. Remove reverse gear shift fork at-

taching screw. Rotate reverse shift rail 90 deg. as shown in Fig. 6-5. Slide shift rail out rear of case and lift fork from case.
18. Remove reverse detent plug and spring from case with a magnet.
19. Remove reverse idler gear shaft from case, Fig. 6-6.
20. Lift reverse idler gear and thrust washers from case.
21. Lift countergear and thrust washers from case.

Disassemble Output Shaft

1. Remove snap ring from front of output shaft. Slide 3-4 synchronizer blocking ring and 3rd gear off shaft, Fig. 6-7.
2. Remove next snap ring and 2nd gear thrust washer. Slide 2nd gear and blocking ring from shaft.
3. Remove next snap ring, thrust washer, 1st speed gear and blocking ring from rear of shaft. On later models, the 1-2 synchronizer hub is a press fit. On these units, use an arbor press to remove hub. On earlier models, slide hub off output shaft.

UNIT REPAIRS
Cam & Shaft Seals

1. Referring to Fig. 6-8, remove three shift levers.
2. Remove three cams and shafts from inside of case.
3. Remove O-ring from each cam and shaft.
4. Dip new O-rings in gear lubricant and install them on cam and shafts.
5. Slide each cam and shaft into its respective bore in case.
6. Secure each shift lever.

Input Shaft Bearing

1. Referring to Fig. 6-9, remove snap ring that secures bearing to shaft.
2. Press input shaft gear out of bearing.
3. Press new bearing onto shaft and secure bearing with snap ring.

Synchronizers

1. Referring to Fig. 6-10, push synchronizer hub from each sleeve.
2. Separate inserts and springs from hubs. Do not mix parts from one synchronizer to another.

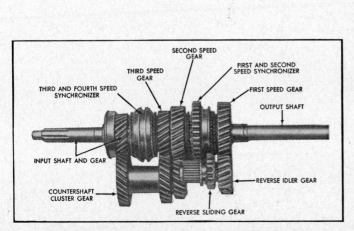

Fig. 6-1   Type Six Ford four speed transmission

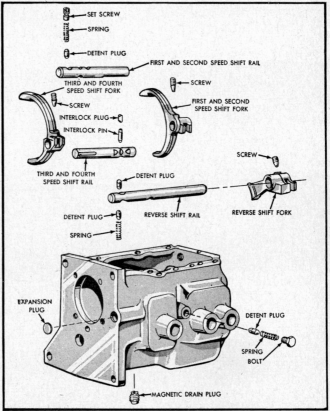

Fig. 6-2   Shift rails and forks disassembled

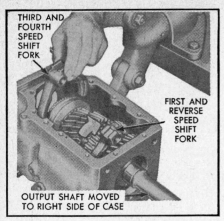

Fig. 6-3 Removing shift forks from case

Fig. 6-4 Removing output shaft assembly

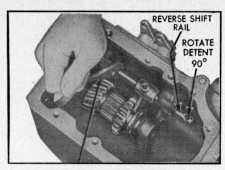

Fig. 6-5 Rotating reverse shift rail

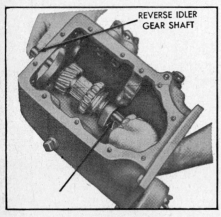

Fig. 6-6 Removing reverse idler gear shaft

3. Position hub in sleeve, being sure that alignment marks are properly indexed.
4. Place three inserts into hub. Install insert springs, making sure that irregular surface (hump) is seated in one of inserts. Do not stagger springs.

Countergear

1. Referring to Fig. 6-11, and with unit disassembled, coat bore in each end of countergear with grease.
2. Hold a suitable dummy shaft in gear and insert 21 rollers and a retainer washer in each end of gear.

Reverse Idler Gear

1. With unit disassembled, Fig. 6-12, coat bore at each end of gear with grease.
2. Hold a suitable dummy shaft in gear and insert 22 rollers and retainer washer at each end of gear.
3. Install sliding gear on reverse idler gear, making sure that shift fork groove is toward front.

REASSEMBLE TRANS.
Countergear

1. Coat countergear thrust surfaces in case with a film of grease and posi-

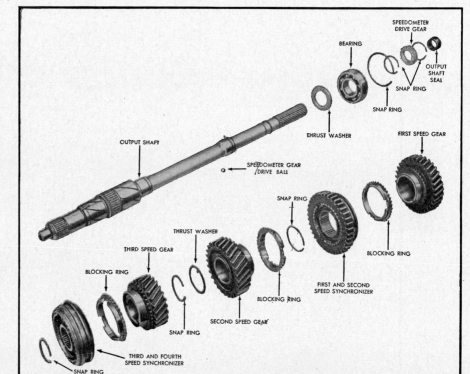

Fig. 6-7 Output shaft disassembled

tion a thrust washer at each end of case.
2. Place assembled countergear in case.
3. With case in a vertical position, align gear bore and thrust washers with bores in case and install countershaft.
4. With case in horizontal position, check countergear end play with a feeler gauge. If not within limits of .004" to .018", install new thrust washers.
5. After establishing correct end play, install dummy shaft in countergear and allow gear to remain in bottom of case.

Reverse Gearing

1. Coat gear thrust surfaces in case with a film of grease and position two

thrust washers in place, Fig. 6-12.
2. Position idler gear, sliding gear, dummy shaft and roller bearings in place, making sure that shift fork groove in sliding gear is toward front of case.
3. Align gear bore and thrust washers with case bores and install reverse idler shaft.
4. Measure reverse idler gear end play with feeler gauge. If not within the limits of .004" to .018", install new thrust washers.
5. Position reverse gear shift rail detent spring and plug in case. Hold reverse shift fork in place on sliding gear and install shift rail from rear of case. Secure fork to rail with set screw.

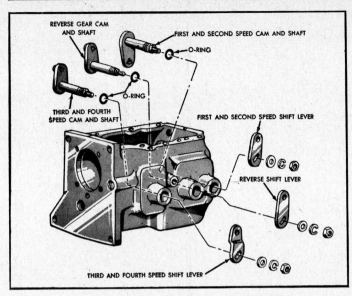

Fig. 6-8 Cam and shafts and levers disassembled

Fig. 6-9 Input shaft gear disassembled

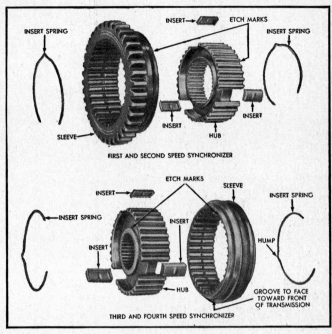

Fig. 6-10 Synchronizers disassembled

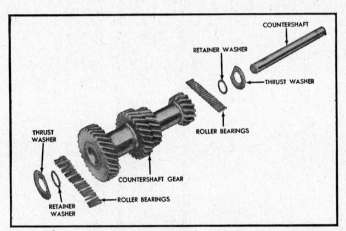

Fig. 6-11 Countergear disassembled

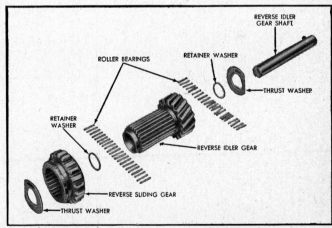

Fig. 6-12 Reverse idler gear disassembled

Output Shaft

1. Referring to Fig. 6-7, install 1-2 synchronizer on shaft.
2. Slide 2nd gear onto front of shaft with synchronizer coned surface facing to rear.
3. Install 2nd gear thrust washer and snap ring.
4. Slide 3rd gear on shaft with synchronizer coned surface to front.
5. Coat coned surface of 3rd gear with grease and place blocking ring on gear.
6. Slide 3-4 synchronizer onto shaft making sure inserts in synchronizer engage notches in blocking ring. Install snap ring on front of shaft.
7. Coat coned surface of 2nd gear with grease and place blocking ring on gear.
8. Slide 1-2 synchronizer on rear of shaft, making sure that inserts engage notches in blocking ring and that shift fork groove is toward rear.
9. Coat coned surface of 1st gear with grease and place blocking ring on it.
10. Slide 1st gear onto rear of shaft,

making sure notches in blocking ring engage synchronizer inserts.
11. Install thrust washer on rear of shaft and lower output shaft assembly into case, Fig. 6-4.

Shift Rails & Forks

1. Referring to Fig. 6-2, position 1-2 shift fork and 3-4 shift fork in place on their respective gears and rotate them in place.

2. Place detent plug in its bore and place reverse shift rail into neutral position.
3. Coat 3-4 shift rail interlock pin with grease and plate it in shift rail.
4. Align 3-4 shift fork with shift rail bores and slide rail into place, making sure three detents are facing outside of case.
5. Place front synchronizer into 3rd gear position and install set screw in 3-4 shift fork. Move synchronizer

to neutral position. Install 3-4 rail detent plug, spring and bolt in left side of case. Place interlock plug (tapered ends) in detent bore.

6. Align 1-2 shift fork with case bores and slide shift rail into place. Secure fork with set screw. Install detent plug and spring in detent bore. Thread set screw into case until its head is flush with case.

Final Assembly

1. Coat input gear bore with just enough grease to hold roller bearings in place,

then install 15 roller bearings.

2. Install input gear in case, making sure output shaft pilot enters roller bearings in input gear.

3. Stick a new gasket on input shaft bearing retainer. Dip attaching bolts in sealing compound and install and tighten.

4. Install output shaft bearing and secure with snap ring.

5. On early units, place speedometer gear ball in output shaft, slide gear into place and secure with snap ring.

On later units, slip gear onto shaft and secure with retaining clip.

6. With transmission in vertical position, align countergear bore and thrust washers with bore in case and install countershaft.

7. Use a new gasket and secure extension housing to case. Use sealing compound on attaching screws.

8. Pour specified gear lube over entire gear train while rotating output shaft. Then install cover and shift linkage and adjust as outlined in the car chapters.

Type 7 Saginaw

DISASSEMBLE TRANSMISSION

1. Remove side cover assembly and shift forks.

2. Remove clutch gear bearing retainer.

3. Remove clutch gear bearing to gear stem snap ring, then remove bearing by pulling clutch gear outward until a screwdriver can be inserted between large snap ring and case to complete removal, Fig. 7-2. Do not remove clutch gear. The bearing is a slip fit on the gear and into the case bore.

4. Remove extension to case bolts and remove clutch gear, mainshaft and extension assembly through rear case opening. Remove clutch gear and blocker ring from mainshaft.

5. Expand extension housing to rear mainshaft bearing snap ring and remove extension, Fig. 7-3.

6. Using a dummy shaft, drive countershaft and woodruff key out through

rear of case, Fig. 7-4. Dummy shaft will hold roller bearings in position within countergear bore. Remove countergear.

7. Remove reverse idler gear stop ring and, using a long drift, drive idler shaft and woodruff key out through rear of case.

Disassemble Mainshaft

1. Remove snap ring and press 3-4 syn-

chronizer clutch assembly, 3rd speed blocker ring and 3rd gear off mainshaft, Fig. 7-5.

2. Depress speedometer gear retaining clip and remove gear.

3. Remove rear bearing to mainshaft snap ring, support 1st gear with press plates and press on rear of mainshaft to remove 1st speed gear, thrust washer, spring washer and rear bearing, Fig. 7-6.

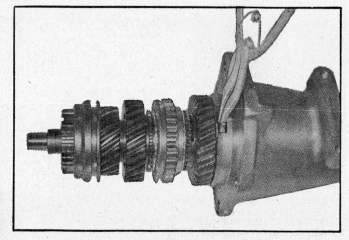

Fig. 7-3 Removing extension

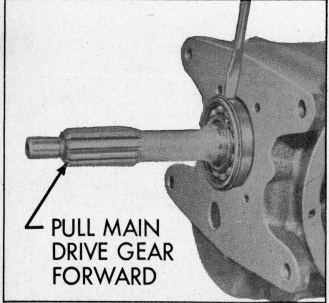

Fig. 7-2 Removing clutch gear bearing

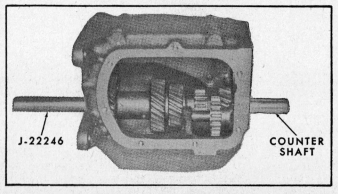

Fig. 7-4 Removing countershaft

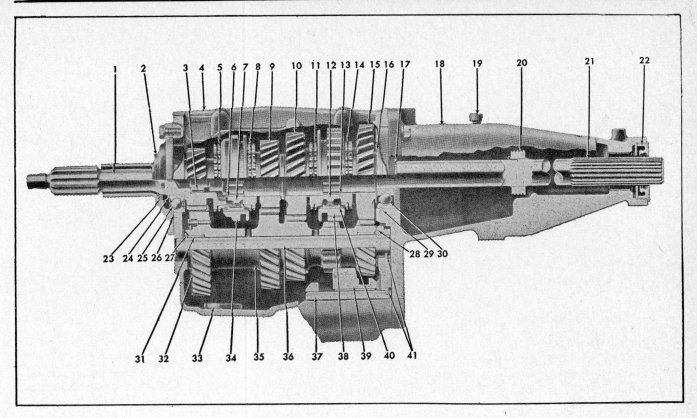

1. Clutch Gear
2. Bearing Retainer
3. Pilot Bearings
4. Case
5. 4th Speed Blocker Ring
6. 4-3 Synch. Snap Ring
7. 4-3 Synch. Hub
8. 3rd Speed Blocker Ring
9. 3rd Speed Gear
10. 2nd Speed Gear
11. 2nd Speed Blocker Ring
12. 1-2 Speed Synch. Hub

13. 1-2 Speed Synch. Snap Ring
14. 1st Speed Blocker Ring
15. First Gear
16. Reverse Gear Thrust and Spring Washers
17. Snap Ring-Bearing to Mainshaft
18. Extension
19. Vent
20. Speedometer Drive Gear and Clip
21. Mainshaft
22. Rear Oil Seal

23. Retainer Oil Seal
24. Snap Ring-Bearing to Gear
25. Clutch Gear Bearing
26. Snap Ring-Bearing to Case
27. Thrust Washer-Front
28. Thrust Washer-Rear
29. Snap Ring-Bearing to Extension
30. Rear Bearing
31. Countergear Roller Bearings

32. Anti-Lash Plate Assembly
33. Magnet
34. 4-3 Synch. Sleeve
35. Countergear Assembly
36. Counter Shaft
37. Reverse Idler Shaft
38. 1-2 Speed Synch. Sleeve and Reverse Gear
39. Reverse Idler Gear (Sliding
40. Clutch Key
41. Woodruff Key

Fig. 7-1 Type seven Saginaw transmission

4. Remove 1-2 sliding clutch hub snap ring, support 2nd speed gear and press clutch assembly, 2nd speed blocker ring and gear from mainshaft, Fig. 7-7.

Clutch Keys & Springs

NOTE: The clutch hubs and sleeves are a selected assembly and should be kept together as originally assembled, but the keys and springs may be replaced separately.

1. Mark hub and sleeve so they can be matched upon reassembly.
2. Push hub from sliding sleeve and remove keys and springs.
3. Install the three keys and two springs so all three keys are engaged by both springs. The tanged end of each spring should be installed into different key cavities on either side. Slide sleeve onto hub, aligning marks made before disassembly.

NOTE: A groove around the outside of the hub identifies the end that must be opposite the fork slot in the sleeve when assembled. This groove indicates the end of the hub with a .070" greater recess depth.

Assemble Mainshaft

With front of mainshaft up:
1. Install 3rd speed gear with clutching teeth upward.
2. Install blocker ring with clutching teeth downward over cone of gear. All blocker rings in this unit are identical.
3. Install 3-4 synchronizer assembly with fork slot downward and press it onto mainshaft until it bottoms. *Be sure the notches of the blocker ring align with the keys of the synchronizer assembly.*
4. Install synchronizer hub to mainshaft snap ring. Both synchronizer snap rings are identical.

With rear of mainshaft upward:
5. Install 2nd speed gear with clutching teeth upward.
6. Install a blocker ring with clutching teeth downward over cone of gear.
7. Press 1-2 synchronizer assembly onto mainshaft with fork slot downward. *Be sure notches in blocker ring align with keys of synchronizer assembly.*
8. Install synchronizer hub snap ring.
9. Install a blocker ring with notches downward so they align with the synchronizer keys.
10. Install 1st gear with clutching teeth downward. Install 1st gear thrust washer and spring washer.
11. Press rear bearing onto mainshaft. Install snap ring.
12. Install speedometer drive gear and clip.

ASSEMBLE TRANS.

1. Load a row of roller bearings and a

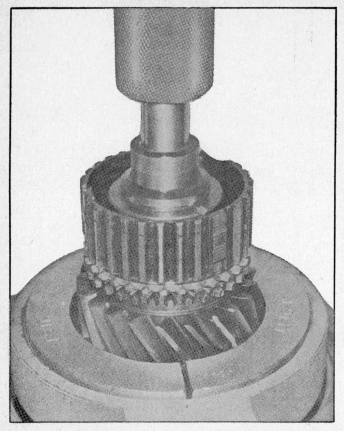

Fig. 7-5   Removing 3-4 synchronizer assembly

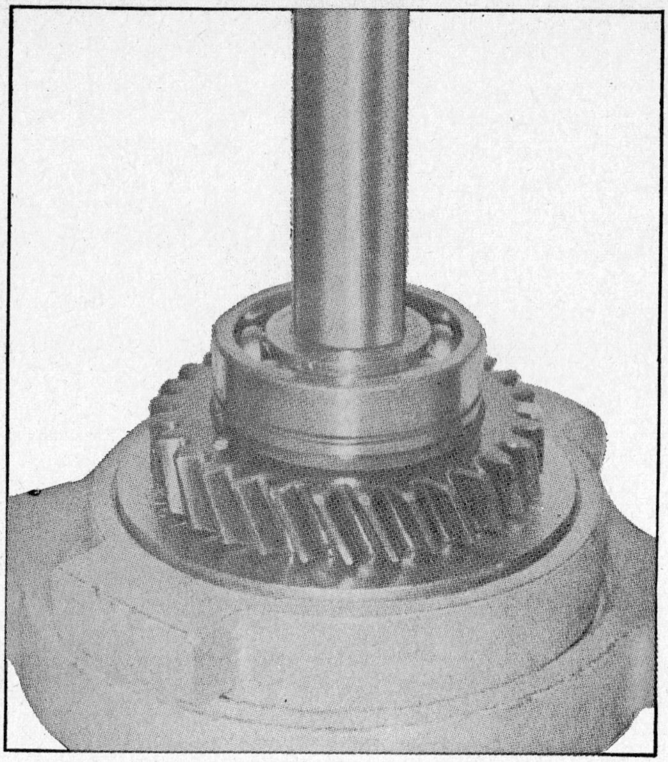

Fig. 7-6   Removing 1st gear and rear bearing

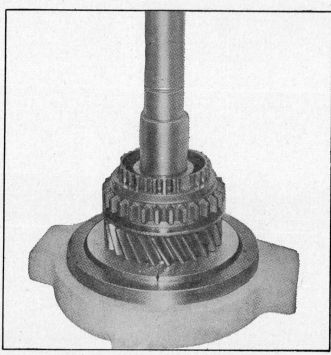

Fig. 7-7   Removing 1-2 synchronizer and 2nd speed gear

thrust washer at each end of the countergear. Use heavy grease to hold them in place.

2. Install countergear through case rear opening with a tanged thrust washer at each end and install countershaft and woodruff key from rear of case. *Be sure countershaft picks up both thrust washers and that the tangs are aligned with their notches in the case.*

3. Install reverse idler gear, shaft and woodruff key from rear of case.

4. Expand extension housing snap ring and assemble extension housing over mainshaft.

5. Load roller bearings into clutch gear bore, using heavy grease to hold them in place, place blocker ring on gear cone with teeth toward gear, and install gear and ring onto mainshaft. Do not install clutch gear bearing at this time. *Be sure notches in blocker ring align with synchronizer keys.*

6. Using new gasket, install mainshaft and extension assembly through rear opening in case. Use sealing cement on bottom bolt.

7. Install large outer snap ring on clutch gear bearing and install bearing onto gear and into case bore. Install gear stem snap ring and bearing retainer.

NOTE: The retainer oil hole should be at the bottom.

8. With transmission in neutral, install cover assembly. *Be sure the shift forks are properly aligned in their grooves in the synchronizer sleeves before attempting to tighten cover bolts.*

Type 8

DISASSEMBLE TRANS.

1. Remove TCS and backup lamp switches from case and extension, Fig. 1.
2. Remove cotter pins securing ends of shift control rod and remove rod, Fig. 2.
3. Remove serrated bolt retaining selector lever to boss on rear extension, Fig. 3.
4. Remove lock nut and selector ring.

NOTE: Slide lever and gearshift intermediate shaft from gearshift bracket while simultaneously removing selector ring. Selector lever will just slip off selector ring.

5. Remove snap ring from intermediate shift lever bushing and using a suitable brass drift, drive bushing from lever assembly.
6. Remove transmission case cover and discard gasket.
7. Remove detent cap, spring and ball, Fig. 4.
8. Invert transmission to drain oil.
9. Remove rear extension retaining bolts and rotate extension to expose countergear shaft, Fig. 5.
10. From front of transmission, using tool J-22911, drive out shaft. Be sure lock ball, Fig. 6, is not lost. With tool J-22911 inserted, take countergear out of case and remove thrust washers from case.
11. Drive out reverse intermediate shift lever pivot pin and remove intermediate lever, Fig. 7.

NOTE: Slide reverse shaft to rear of case so scallop in selector shaft will clear reverse shaft.

12. Shift transmission to neutral and push in on selector shaft. Turn selector shaft so lock pins are in vertical position. First drive lock pin out of 3rd-4th speed intermediate lever cam and then out of 1st-2nd speed lever cam, Fig. 8. Remove selector shaft.
13. With screwdriver, pry out selector shaft seal rings on transmission case.
14. Pull out both lock ball plugs using tool J-21715 with slide hammer J-7004, Fig. 9. Remove thrust springs and balls.
15. With transmission in 1st gear drive lock pins out of shifter forks and selector levers, Fig. 10. Remove 1st-2nd

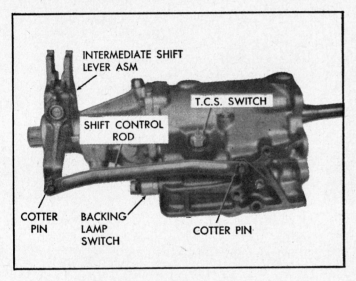

Fig. 2   Cotter pins securing shift control rod

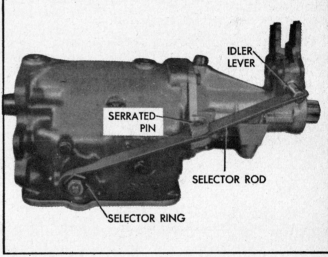

Fig. 3   Serrated pin location

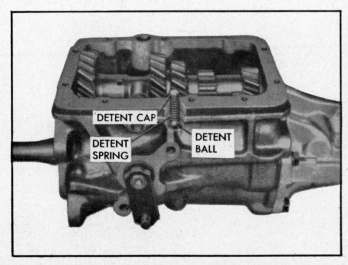

Fig. 4   Reverse detent cap, spring and ball

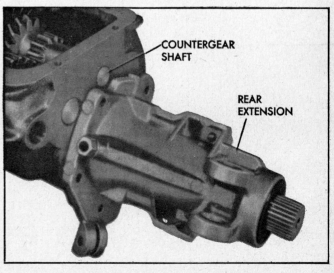

Fig. 5   Countergear shaft exposed for removal

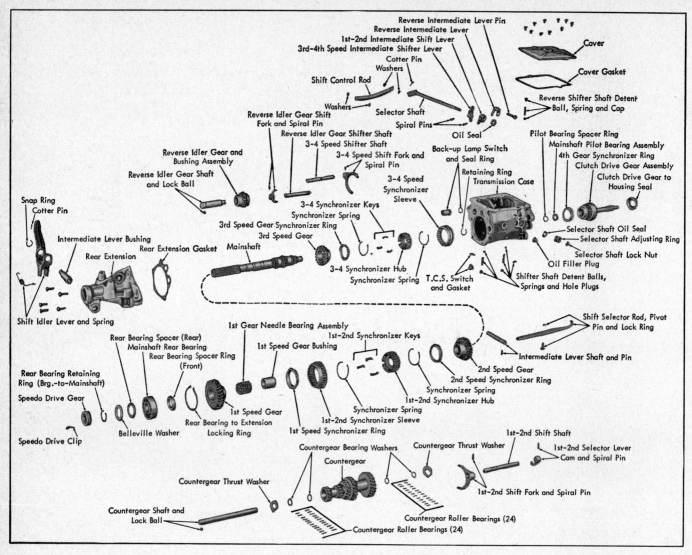

Fig. 1   Exploded view of Type 8 transmission

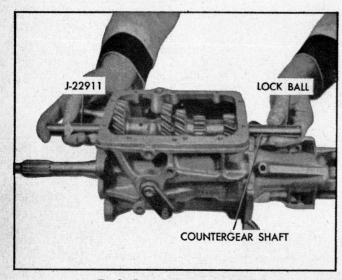

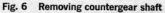

Fig. 6   Removing countergear shaft

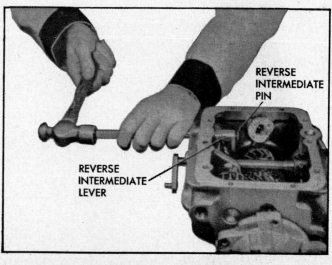

Fig. 7   Removing reverse intermediate lever pin

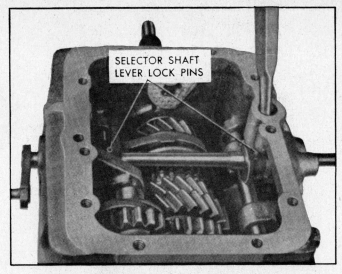

Fig. 8   Removing lock pins from selector shaft levers

Fig. 9   Removing detent ball lock plugs

Fig. 10   Position of lock pins

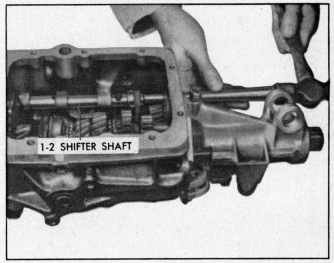

Fig. 11   Removing 1st-2nd shifter shaft

lever pin first.

16. From rear of transmission, drive out 1st-2nd shifter shaft using a brass drift, Fig. 11. Remove fork from sliding sleeve.
17. Tap 3rd-4th shifter shaft rearward until fork may be removed from shaft. Then drive out 3rd-4th shifter shaft through front of case.
18. Remove clutch drive gear from case.
19. Carefully slide rear extension and mainshaft assembly from case.
20. With tool J-22923 push out reverse idler gear shaft from front towards rear. Be sure lock ball is not lost, Fig. 12. Remove gear and shaft from case.
21. Using a brass drift and from the front of the transmission, drive out reverse shifter shaft. Remove shifter fork from case.

Mainshaft Disassemble

1. Remove snap ring from rear bearing

retainer groove and remove mainshaft assembly from bearing retainer, Fig. 13.
2. Depress retaining clamp and slide speedo drive gear from shaft.
3. Remove loose parts such as needle bearing, spacer ring and synchronizer ring. The sliding sleeve, keys and front clutch key spring may also be removed.

NOTE: The snychronizer hubs and sliding sleeves are a selected assembly and should be kept together as originally assembled.

4. Remove snap ring in front of synchronizer hub, Fig. 14.
5. Remove snap ring, belleville washer and spacer from shaft, Fig. 15.
6. Support 2nd gear and press mainshaft until bearing and synchronizers are free on shaft. Remove all loose parts, Fig. 16.
7. Remove 3rd speed synchronizer hub

snap ring. Support 3rd speed gear and press shaft from synchronizer assembly and 3rd speed gear, Fig. 17.

Mainshaft Assemble

1. From front of mainshaft install 3rd speed gear. Gear must turn freely on mainshaft.
2. Install 3rd speed synchronizer ring onto 3rd speed gear.
3. Install rear clutch key spring into 3rd-4th speed synchronizer hub so that hooked spring end rests in one of the slots and raised end is toward blocker ring.
4. Press 3rd-4th speed synchronizer hub on mainshaft.
5. Secure 3rd-4th speed synchronizer hub with snap ring, Fig. 19.
6. From rear of mainshaft slide 2nd speed gear onto mainshaft. Gear must turn freely on mainshaft.
7. Place 2nd speed synchronizer ring onto to 2nd speed gear cone.

Fig. 12   Removing reverse idler gear shaft

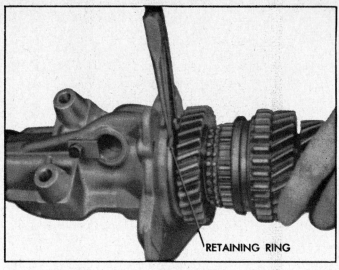

Fig. 13   Removing snap ring from rear extension

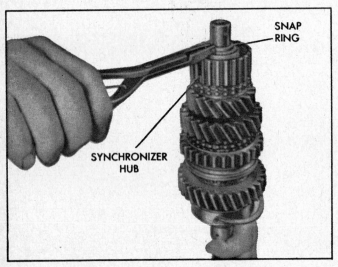

Fig. 14   Removing snap ring in front of synchronizer hub

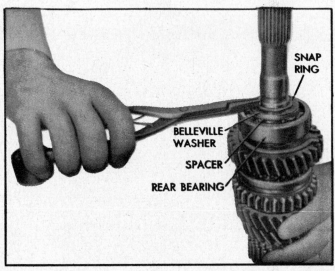

Fig. 15   Removing rear bearing snap ring

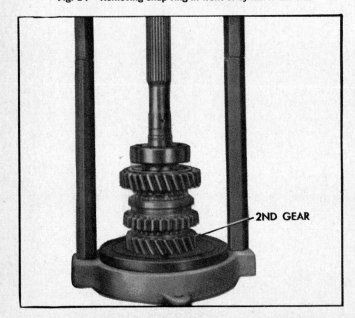

Fig. 16   Removing components from mainshaft

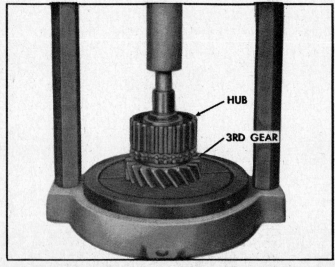

Fig. 17   Removing 3rd speed synchronizer hub

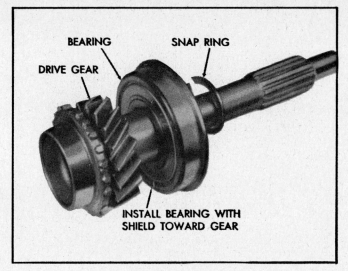

Fig. 18   Drive gear assembly

Fig. 19   Securing 3rd-4th synchronizer hub on mainshaft

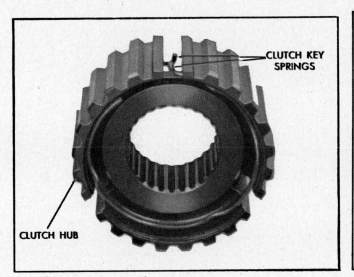

Fig. 20   Both synchronizer key springs installed

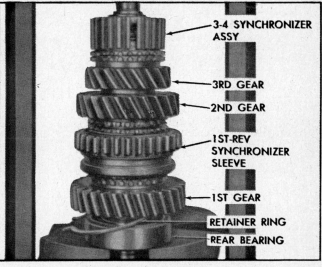

Fig. 21   Pressing mainshaft components

8. Install both synchronizer key springs into 1st-2nd synchronizer hub so that hooks of both springs rest in the same hub slot and other spring ends are positioned opposite to each other and toward blocker rings, Fig. 20. Install sliding gear and keys on hub.

9. Slide 1st-2nd speed synchronizer hub, needle bearing and inner sleeve onto mainshaft. Slide spacer, rear extension retaining ring and rear bearing onto shaft. Support rear bearing inner race and press components together, Fig. 21.

CAUTION: Align slots in synchronizer rings with synchronizer keys.

10. Place spacer and belleville washer on mainshaft and secure with snap ring.

NOTE: Concave side of belleville washer should face toward bearing.

11. Position speedo gear retaining clip on shaft and install gear.

12. Place mainshaft assembly into rear bearing retainer up to its stop. Secure with snap ring, Fig. 22.

13. Assemble 3rd-4th speed synchronizer on hub with raised end of key springs toward blocker ring.

NOTE: Arrow on keys point towards shifter fork groove (front of shaft).

ASSEMBLE TRANS.

1. With sealer, install new gasket onto rear extension.
2. Slide mainshaft assembly into case.
3. From front, slide spacer ring and needle bearing onto mainshaft.

NOTE: Coat needle bearing with ball and roller bearing grease.

4. Install synchronizer blocker ring on clutch drive gear and install gear into

transmission case up to snap ring stop.

5. Insert 1st-2nd shifter shaft at front of case with notches down, pushing it first through "L" shaped selector dog. Dog should be positioned as shown in Fig. 23.

Then push 1st-2nd selector shaft through shifter fork, positioning shoulder toward front of case. Drive lock pins in place allowing them to protrude $1/16$ to $5/64''$ above fork. Install selector dog pin first.

6. Insert 3rd-4th shifter shaft from front of case with notches down, pushing it through 3rd-4th shifter fork, positioning shouldering toward front, Fig. 24. Install lock pin allowing it to protrude $1/16$ to $5/64''$ above fork.

7. Install reverse shifter shaft from rear of case, with notches up, pushing it through reverse shifter fork, Fig. 24. Install lock pin.

NOTE: Position shoulder of shift fork

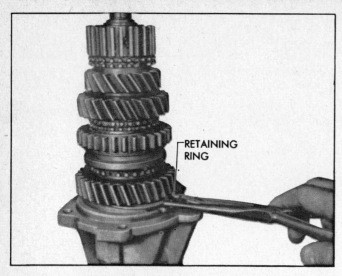

Fig. 22   Installing rear bearing retainer ring

Fig. 23   1st-2nd shifter shaft installed

toward front of case.

8. Insert selector shaft in case, push through 3rd-4th speed intermediate lever, then through 1st-2nd speed intermediate lever. Install lock pins.

NOTE: Place transmission in neutral and rotate selector shaft to engage levers with shifter shafts.

9. Engage reverse speed intermediate lever with 3rd-4th speed intermediate lever and install pivot pin. Reverse speed intermediate lever end play on pin should be .004—.012″.
10. Insert both lock balls and thrust springs into bores in transmission case and drive in plugs.
11. Turn extension case until bore for reverse idler shaft is exposed.
12. Place lock ball into shaft and from rear of case install shaft into gear.
13. Simultaneously position reverse idler gear and reverse shifter fork.

NOTE: Shifter fork groove of reverse idler gear and shoulder of shifter fork should be toward front of mainshaft.

14. Using tool J-22911, install a spacer, a roll of roller bearings (24) and a spacer at each end of countergear. Use heavy grease to hold them in place.
15. Coat thrust washers with ball and roller bearing grease and stick to case.

NOTE: Lugs of thrust washers must

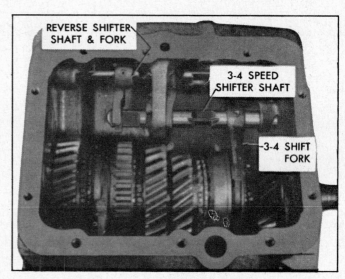

Fig. 24   3rd-4th shifter shaft installed

fit into case slots.

16. Turn case extension until countergear shaft bore is exposed.
17. Place lock ball into shaft and from rear of transmission insert shaft so thrust washer is held in position. Hold opposite thrust washer in position by using a short drift.
18. Insert countergear into case.
19. Insert shaft into countergear and push

out special tool J-22911. Align lock ball with groove in case and drive shaft into case.
20. Align rear bearing retainer and torque bolts to case.
21. Install lock ball and thrust spring and spring cap into top transmission bore.
22. Install case cover gasket, cover and bolts.
23. Install gearshift linkage in reverse order of removal.

Type 9

This section covers the English built unit which can be identified by having only 4 top cover bolts. The next section covers the German built unit which has 10 top cover bolts of 10 mm metric size.

DISASSEMBLE TRANS.

1. Remove clutch release bearing and lever from clutch housing.
2. Remove clutch housing to transmission bolts and remove housing.
3. Mount transmission in suitable holding fixture and remove top cover bolts.
4. Using a suitable tool, pry blanking plug from extension housing.
5. Remove meshlock plunger set screw, spring and detent ball from side of case.
6. Using suitable punch, remove roll pin securing shift boss to rail. Be sure the pin can be punched through clear of any output shaft components. It may be necessary to position the synchronizer hub on the output shaft to suit.
7. Withdraw shift rail rearward, taking care not to let the shift boss and C-cam drop into case.
8. To remove shift forks, move 1st-2nd and 3rd-4th synchronizer hubs to their foremost position towards input shaft bearing.
9. Remove spring pin securing 3rd-4th shift fork to relay lever and remove fork.
10. Remove bolts securing extension housing to case.
11. Using a plastic faced mallet, tap the extension housing slightly rearward until it is possible to rotate it so countershaft aligns with cutaway in extension housing flange.
12. Tap countershaft rearward using a drift until it is just clear of front of case. Push countershaft out using a dummy countershaft. The countershaft gear will drop to bottom of case.
13. Remove extension housing and output shaft assembly. It is necessary to push 3rd-4th synchronizer sleeve forward to provide clearance between synchronizer and countershaft gear.

NOTE: Do not move synchronizer sleeve beyond 4th gear position or synchronizer inserts will fall out.

14. Unfasten bearing retainer from front of case and pry the oil seal from the retainer.
15. Remove needle bearing from recess in end of input shaft gear.
16. Remove outer snap ring from around input shaft bearing. Using a suitable drift, tap the outer race inward evenly until bearing is free of case. Lift assembly out of transmission.
17. Remove countershaft gear and two thrust washers from case. In both ends of gear there are 20 needle rollers retained by a washer on each side of each set. Remove the rollers, washers and dummy shaft.
18. Withdraw reverse idler shaft, Fig. 3. Should these tools not be available, locate a nut, flat washer and a sleeve

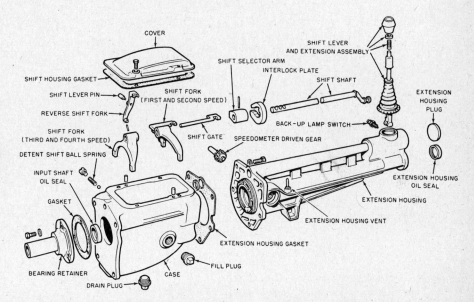

Fig. 1   Type 9 transmission case and related parts

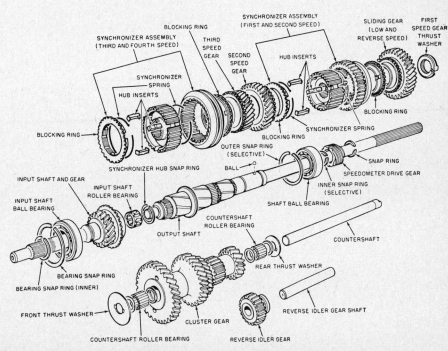

Fig. 2   Type 9 transmission internal parts

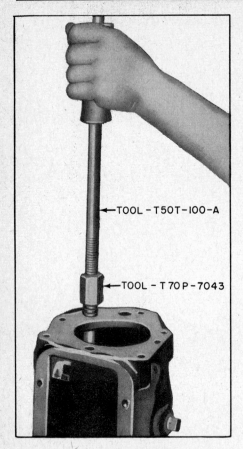

Fig. 3   Removing reverse idler shaft

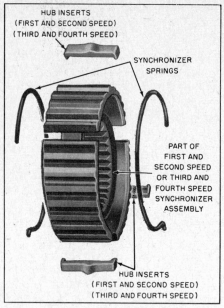

Fig. 4   Synchronizer spring rotation

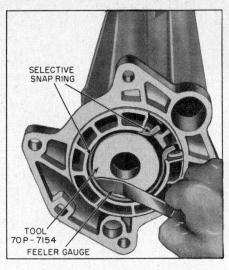

Fig. 5   Determining snap ring thickness

Part Number	Identifi-cation	Thickness
DORY-7030-A	Yellow	0.0726—0.0736
DORY-7030-B	Red	0.0715—0.0725
DORY-7030-C	Blue	0.0703—0.0713
DORY-7030-D	Violet	0.0691—0.0701
DORY-7030-E	Green	0.0679—0.0689
DORY-7030-F	Magenta	0.0677—0.0667
DORY-7030-G	Plain	0.0665—0.0655

Fig. 6   Output shaft bearing snap ring thickness chart

on a ⁵/₁₆" 24UNF threaded bolt. Screw bolt into reverse idler shaft and tighten nut to withdraw shaft.
19. Slide reverse relay lever from fulcrum pin on case. Do not remove pin.

3rd-4th Synchronizer

1. Lift 4th gear blocking ring from front of 3rd-4th synchronizer.
2. Remove snap ring at forward end of output shaft and discard it. Press output shaft out of 3rd-4th synchronizer and 3rd gear while supporting the shaft so it will not drop.
3. Prior to disassembly of synchronizer scribe alignment marks on sleeve and hub so they may be assembled in original positions. Disassemble synchronizer by pulling sleeve off hub and withdrawing inserts and springs.
4. To assemble, reverse procedure and refer to Fig. 4 for proper positioning of synchronizer springs.

1st-2nd Synchronizer

1. Remove snap ring securing output shaft bearing to extension housing. Tap output shaft out of extension using a plastic faced mallet. Remove snap ring retaining speedo gear to output shaft and pull off gear being careful not to lose the drive ball from the shaft. Remove snap ring retaining output shaft bearing.
2. Press low and reverse sliding gear, spacer, snap ring and output shaft bearing from the output shaft.

3. Remove snap ring securing 1st-2nd synchronizer to output shaft.
4. Press 2nd gear and 1st-2nd synchronizer assembly complete with blocking rings off the output shaft.
5. Prior to disassembly of synchronizer, scribe alignment marks on sleeve and hub so they may assembled in original positions. Disassemble unit by pulling sleeve off hub and withdrawing the inserts and springs.
6. To assemble, reverse the procedure and refer to Fig. 4 for proper positioning of synchronizer springs.

Output Shaft

1. When installing output shaft assembly into extension, place master spacer tool T70P-7154 in output shaft bearing bore of extension, Fig. 5.
2. Determine thickness of the snap ring required to remove all end play from the master gauge as follows:
   a. Measure width of shaft bearing outer race with micrometer. The difference in thickness between master gauge and bearing outer race will determine thickness of selective ring to be used.
   b. If bearing race thickness is more than that stamped on master gauge, the snap ring thickness must be decreased by that closest to available ring, Fig. 6.
   c. If the thickness is less, the snap ring thickness must be increased.
3. Position the selected snap ring and the bearing on the output shaft.
4. Position tool T71P-4621B on the shaft, then place assembly into press. Press the bearing into place, Fig. 7, and secure with the thickest snap ring that will fit the groove in the output shaft.
5. Locate drive ball in output shaft detent and push speedo gear onto shaft so it just clears the snap ring groove in the shaft. Install a new snap ring to shaft to retain the gear.
6. Heat the front end of the extension

housing, using a suitable hot plate or by placing in hot water. This will expand the extension housing so that the shaft can easily be installed.

NOTE: Do not use a welding torch.

7. Secure the output shaft bearing in the extension housing with the snap ring selected previously.

Input Shaft and Gear

1. Remove snap ring from input shaft and discard snap ring.
2. The bearing should not be removed unless it is noisey, rough, spalled or cracked. Position input shaft bearing, Fig. 8, and press bearing off shaft.
3. To assemble, press bearing on input shaft. The bearing must be placed on the shaft with the ring groove facing away from the gear. The tool used to replace the bearing insures that all the load is taken through the bearing inner race so the bearing will not be damaged in the pressing operation.
4. Install the thickest snap ring to secure the bearing to the shaft.

ASSEMBLE TRANS.

1. Slide reverse relay lever onto fulcrum pin on case.

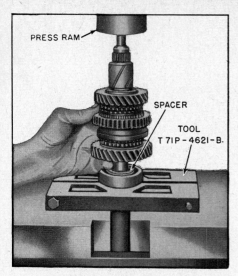

Fig. 7   Installing output shaft bearing

2. Lubricate idler shaft and push it into case. Install reverse idler gear on shaft and locate reverse relay lever in groove in reverse idler gear.
3. Tap reverse idler shaft into position with copper mallet.
4. Slide dummy countershaft into countershaft gear. Install a retainer washer over dummy shaft and push it into the gear bore. Grease needle rollers and assemble 20 into the recess; install 2nd retaining washer and repeat procedure at other end of gear.
5. Grease thrust washers and locate them so their tab side seats into recess in case.
6. Position countershaft gear in bottom of case, taking care not to displace washers.
7. Assemble input shaft and gear into transmission. Using a copper drift on the bearing outer race, tap it into place until the snap ring groove appears on the outside of the case. Take care that the dog teeth on the input shaft gear are not damaged by the countershaft gear.

NOTE: The bearing is an interference fit in the case, it is important that the outer race is tapped. Do not tap on input shaft gear as the bearing will be damaged.

8. Install snap ring to periphery of the bearing.
9. Lubricate input shaft needle bearing and position it in recess of input shaft gear.
10. Place a new oil seal on input shaft retainer and install so lips of seal face transmission. Drive seal into retainer until it bottoms.
11. Lubricate front bearing retainer seal and the seal journal area on input shaft. Place a new gasket on retainer. Fabricate a plastic sleeve and slide it over input shaft splines to prevent damage to seal lip. Be sure that oil groove in retainer is in line with oil passage in case and that gasket does not cover this passage. Coat attaching screws with suitable sealer and install them. Remove plastic sleeve. Apply a light film of grease to release bearing surface on bearing retainer.
12. Prior to installing output shaft and extension assembly, lubricate input shaft gear cone and position 4th gear blocking ring on input shaft gear cone.
13. If necessary, install a new seal in shaft rail aperture in rear of case and use a standard socket to drive in the seal.
14. Thread cord or suitable plastic covered wire under countershaft gear at each end to facilitate lifting into position later.
15. Install new gasket on extension using a sealer.
16. Slide extension and output shaft assembly into position after pulling the 3rd-4th synchronizer sleeve forward to clear countershaft gear.

NOTE: Do not move sleeve beyond 4th gear position as synchronizer inserts will drop out. Be sure 4th gear blocking ring locates correctly.

17. Align cutaway on extension housing with countershaft opening in rear face of transmission.
18. Carefully, with string or wire attached previously, lift countershaft gear into mesh with output shaft and input shaft gears. Take care that thrust in case at each end of gear are not displaced.
19. Check that countershaft gear bore aligns with apertures of countershaft. Push dummy shaft out of gear by inserting countershaft from rear. Finally, tap countershaft into position with suitable mallet. Be sure that lug on rear of countershaft is positioned horizontally so it will install into recess

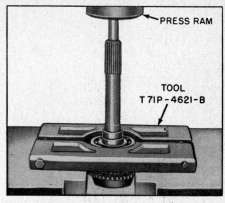

Fig. 8   Removing input shaft bearing

on extension housing flange. The front of the countershaft must be flush with front face of transmission case after installation.
20. Rotate extension so bolts align and push extension fully home onto the transmission. Secure housing to case using sealer on bolts.
21. Replace shift forks on relay lever and secure the 3rd and 4th fork to lever with new roll pin.
22. Position assembled shift forks on their synchronizer sleeves and move the synchronizer hubs into neutral position so that shift fork extension arms locate beneath the reverse idler shift arm mounted on side of case.
23. Grease shift rail oil seal in rear of case and slide the rail through the extension housing. Position the shift boss and the C-cam so that the cam locates the cutouts in the shift fork extension arms. Pass the rail through the boss and forks until the spring pin holes in the boss and rail align. Take care not to damage the shift rail seal.
24. Assemble detent ball and spring to their bore and install set screw using sealer.
25. Install roll pin to retain shift boss to shift rail.
26. Apply sealer to blanking plug and tap it into extension housing behind shift rail.
27. Using a new gasket and sealer, install top cover.
28. Remove transmission from holding fixture, install clutch housing, release lever and bearing. Refill with oil to proper level.

Type 10

This section covers the German built unit which can be identified by having 10 top cover bolts. The previous section covers the English built unit which has only 4 top cover bolts.

DISASSEMBLE TRANS.

1. Remove clutch release bearing, lever and clutch housing.
2. Remove top cover bolts with 10mm wrench and drain lubricant.
3. Remove threaded plug, spring and shift rail detent plunger from case, Fig. 1.
4. Drive access plug from rear of case, Fig. 2, and drive the interlock plate retaining pin from case, Fig. 3. Lift interlock plate from case.
5. Remove roll pin from selector lever arm, Fig. 2.
6. Tap front end of shaft rail to displace plug at rear of extension housing.
7. Withdraw shift rail from extension and case, Fig. 4.
8. Lift selector arm and shift fork from case.
9. Remove extension housing bolts and tap extension housing with plastic mallet to loosen it from case so it may be rotated.
10. Rotate extension to align countershaft with cutaway in extension flange. Using a brass drift, drive countershaft rearward until it just clears front of case. Install a dummy shaft in the case and gear until the countershaft gear can be lowered to bottom of case, then remove the countershaft.
11. Lift extension housing and mainshaft from case as an assembly, Fig. 5.
12. Remove 10mm input shaft attaching bolts and remove the input shaft and bearing retainer from case as an assembly.
13. Remove reverse idler gear shaft from rear of case, Fig. 6. Remove reverse idler gear.
14. Remove bearing retaining washers, Fig. 7, bearing (19 each end),

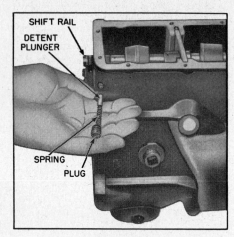

Fig. 1 Shift rail detent plunger

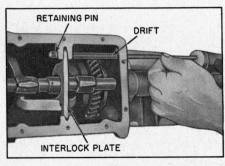

Fig. 3 Removing interlock plate retaining pin

dummy shaft and the spacer from countershaft gear.
15. Remove bearing retainer and pilot bearing from input shaft gear.

NOTE: Do not remove the ball bearing from input shaft unless replacement is necessary. If so, remove snap ring from input shaft, Fig. 8, and press the shaft out of the bearing, Fig. 9.

16. Pry input shaft seal out of bearing retainer, Fig. 8.
17. Lift 4th gear blocker ring, Fig. 10, from front of output shaft.
18. Remove snap ring from forward end of output shaft and discard it.
19. Position tool T69P-4621A behind 3rd speed gear. Place output shaft and extension assembly in a press and press output shaft out of 3rd-4th synchronizer and the 3rd gear while supporting the extension housing and output shaft to prevent it from dropping.
20. Remove snap ring and washer, then slide 2nd gear and blocker ring off output shaft and discard snap ring.
21. Disassemble synchronizer assembly by pulling sleeve off hub and removing inserts and springs.
22. Remove snap ring that retains output shaft bearing in extension housing.
23. Tap output shaft assembly out of extension with a plastic hammer.
24. Position tool T69P-4621A behind 1st gear, then place assembly in press as shown in Fig. 11.
25. The 1st-2nd speed synchronizer and hub are serviced only as an assembly and no attempt should be made to separate the hub from the shaft. The

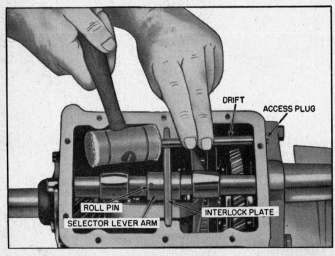

Fig. 2 Removing interlock plate access plug

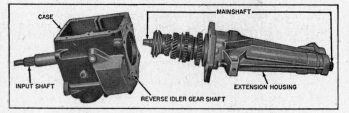

Fig. 4 Removing or installing shift rail

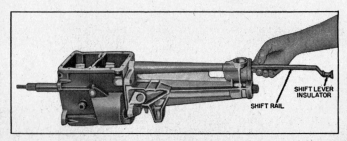

Fig. 5 Removing or installing extension and mainshaft

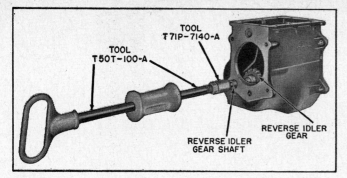

Fig. 6 Removing reverse idler gear shaft

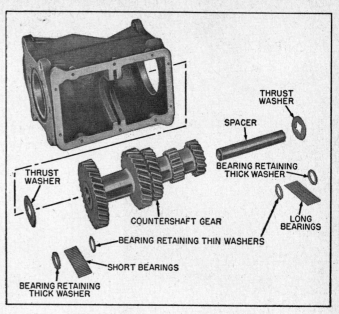

Fig. 7 Countershaft gear disassembled

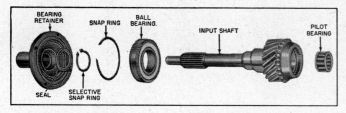

Fig. 8 Input shaft disassembled

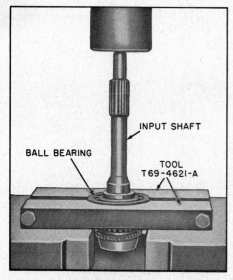

Fig. 9 Removing input shaft bearing

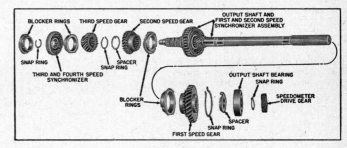

Fig. 10 Output shaft disassembled

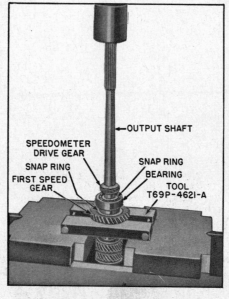

Fig. 11 Removing 1st gear, spacer, output shaft bearing, snap rings and speedo gear from output shaft

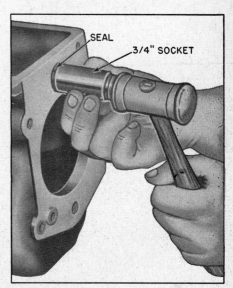

Fig. 12 Installing shift rail seal

sleeve, springs and inserts may be removed from the hub.

26. Drive shift rail bushing from rear of extension with a $^{9}/_{16}"$ socket and extension. Do not remove bushing if serviceable.

27. Pry shift rail seal from rear of transmission case.

28. Remove remaining shift linkage from case.

ASSEMBLE TRANS.

1. Seat new shift rail seal in rear of case, Fig. 12.

2. If shift rail bushing was removed, drive a new one into place with a $^{9}/_{16}"$ socket and extension.

3. If 1st-2nd synchronizer was disassem-

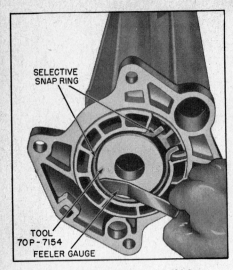

Fig. 13 Determining snap ring thickness

Part No.	Thickness	Identification
D1FZ-7030-A	0.0679-	Color Coded—Copper
D1FZ-7030-B	0.0689-	Letter—W
D1FZ-7030-C	0.0699-	Letter—V
D1FZ-7030-D	0.0709-	Letter—U
D1FZ-7030-E	0.0719-	None
D1FZ-7030-F	0.0728-	Color Coded—Blue
D1FZ-7030-G	0.0738-	Color Coded—Black
D1FZ-7030-H	0.0748-	Color Coded—Brown

Fig. 14 Output shaft bearing snap ring thickness chart

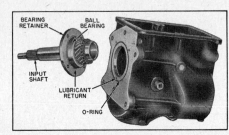

Fig. 16 Installing input shaft gear

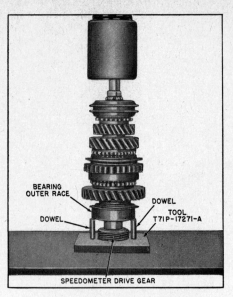

Fig. 15 Installing speedo drive gear

bled, slide the sleeve over the hub making sure the shift fork groove is toward front of shaft. The sleeve and hub are select fit and must be reassembled with etch marks in same location. Locate an insert in each of three slots cut in the hub. Install insert spring inside the sleeve beneath the inserts. The tab on end of spring must locate in the section of an insert. Fit the other spring to the opposite face of the synchronizer unit, being sure the spring tab locates in the same insert as the spring just installed and is in the same rotational direction. Looking down at the synchronizer, the tab end of one spring should be in line with the tab of the spring on the opposite side.

NOTE: Oil all parts at time of assembly.

4. Assemble a blocker ring on the 1st gear side of the 1st-2nd synchronizer. Apply grease to the cone surface of the 1st gear. Slide 1st gear onto output shaft so that cone surface engages blocker ring.
5. Position spacer on shaft making certain the large diameter is toward rear of staff.
6. Place master spacer tool T70P-7154 in the output shaft bearing bore of the extension, Fig. 13. Determine thickness of snap ring required to remove all end play from master gauge. Then measure width of the output shaft bearing outer race with a micrometer. The difference in thickness between the master gauge and the bearing outer race will determine thickness of selective snap ring. If the bearing race thickness is more than that stamped on the master gauge, the snap ring thickness must be decreased to the closest available ring, Fig. 14. If the thickness is less, the snap ring thickness must be increased.
7. Position selected snap ring and the bearing on the output shaft. Position tool T69P-4621A on the shaft, then place assembly in a press and press bearing into place. Secure bearing with

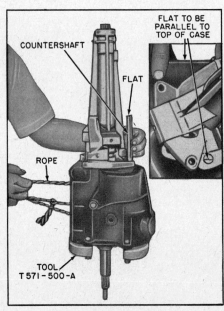

Fig. 17 Installing countershaft

thickest snap ring that will fit the groove in the output shaft.

8. Slide the synchronizer sleeve over the hub and locate an insert in each of the three slots cut into sleeve. The sleeve and hub are select fit and must be reassembled with etch marks in same relative location.
9. Install an insert spring inside the synchronizer sleeve beneath the inserts. The tab on the end of the spring must locate in the U section of an insert. Fit the other spring to the opposite face of the synchronizer unit, being sure that the spring tab locates in the

same insert as the spring just installed and is in the same rotational direction. Looking down at the unit, the tab end of one spring should be in line with the tab of the spring on the opposite side.

10. Position the 2nd gear and blocker ring on output shaft so that dog teeth face rearward. Install washer and snap ring. Position 3rd gear on output shaft so dog teeth face forward. Apply grease to cones of the gears and assemble the blocker ring on the 3rd gear cone.
11. Position the 3rd-4th synchronizer on output shaft with the hub boss facing forward.
12. Position tool T69P-4621A so that it butts against the boss on the synchronizer hub.
13. Place entire unit, extension end up, in a press and push the synchronizer unit onto the output shaft as far as possible.
14. Retain the 3rd-4th synchronizer to output shaft with snap ring. Pull up on the synchronizer assembly so the snap ring is tight in its groove.
15. Prior to assembling output shaft and extension housing into the case, apply lubricant to the cone of the gear and place the 4th gear blocker ring on the input shaft gear cone.
16. Press the speedo gear onto the shaft with tools shown in Fig. 15, until dowels just contact bearing outer race.

NOTE: The dowels must contact the bearing outer race to properly locate the speedo gear on the shaft.

17. Coat the bearing bore of the extension housing with lubricant and install the output shaft in the housing. It may be necessary to tap the shaft with a plastic hammer while holding the two synchronizer sleeves firmly to prevent sleeve separation from the hubs. Secure it to the extension with the selective snap ring that was previously installed.
18. Press bearing on input shaft with

snap ring groove toward front of shaft. Secure bearing to shaft with thickest selective snap ring.

19. Slide spacer and dummy shaft into countershaft gear. Position a thin bearing retaining washer, one each end of dummy shaft. Coat the 38 bearings with lubricant and load the 19 long bearings in the small end of the gear and the 19 short bearings in the large end of the gear. Fit a thick retaining washer over each end of dummy shaft. Coat each thrust washer with lubricant and position one on each end of the dummy shaft. Make sure the tabs are in the same relative position so they may engage the slots in the case when the gear is lowered into place. Loop a piece of rope or wire around each end of the gear. Carefully install the countershaft gear with rope through rear end of case and lower the gear into place being careful not to distrub thrust washers and making sure that the tabs engage slots in case.

20. Apply lubricant to reverse idler gear shaft. If selector lever relay was removed, position it on the pivot pin. Secure lever on pin with spring clip. Hold gear in the lever with long hub toward rear of case. Slide reverse idler gear shaft into place and seat the shaft in the case with a copper hammer.

21. Install a new seal in input shaft bearing retainer.
22. Assemble input shaft to case using a new retainer O ring, Fig. 16. If necessary, tap outer race of bearing with copper hammer evenly until outer snap ring is seated against case.

NOTE: Do not tap on input shaft as this may damage the races/or bearings.

23. Carefully slide 3rd-4th speed synchronizer sleeve into 4th speed position (forward to provide clearance).
24. Position new gasket on extension housing.
25. Lubricate input shaft pilot bearing and install in shaft. Slide extension housing and output shaft into place being careful not to disturb 3rd-4th synchronizer.
26. Align cutaway in extension housing flange with countershaft bore in rear or case.
27. Lift countershaft gear into place with cord or wire, then slip countershaft into place making sure both thrust washers are in place. Make sure that the flat on the countershaft is toward top of case and in horizontal position, Fig. 17. Then tap it into case with brass hammer until front of shaft is flush with case.
28. Place shift forks in synchronizers sleeves. Position interlock lever and

install new retaining pin. Lubricate shift rail oil seal and slide shift rail through extension housing, transmission case and the 1st and 2nd speed shift fork. Position selector arm on the rail, then slide the rail through the 3rd and 4th speed shift fork, then through the front of case until center detent is aligned with the detent plunger bore. Install new retaining pin in selector arm.

29. Install detent plunger, spring and plug with sealer.
30. Install new access plug in rear of case.
31. Rotate extension to align bolt holes, then install bolts loosely. Before tightening bolts make sure shift rail slides freely in bore.
32. Position new oil seal in input shaft retainer so tension spring and lip face the case. Drive seal into position.
33. Position new O ring in groove in face of case. Install input shaft bearing retainer to case. Be sure that oil passage in case is in line with oil groove in retainer, Fig. 16. Apply sealer to bolts and attach to case.
34. Reinstall clutch release bearing.
35. Apply sealer to new extension housing plug and install it.
36. Install top cover with vent toward rear. Make sure that sealer is applied to bolt over detent plunger bore.

AUTOMATIC TRANSMISSIONS

NOTE:—This chapter deals only with maintenance, adjustments and "in car" repairs. For major service work, Motor's Automatic Transmission Manual is available. Current edition is an 891 page volume that includes 281 pages of oil circuit diagrams mostly in full color.

INDEX

NOTE: For 1972 linkage adjustment information, see car chapters.

HOW TO PUSH AND TOW AUTOMATIC DRIVE CARS—Inside Back Cover

TURBO HYDRA-MATIC 400 &
SUPER TURBINE 400

TRANSMISSION IDENTIFICATION

An identification plate is attached to the transmission. The plate indicates year of production, code letters, and serial number.

BUICK	CODE
1966 V8-401	BR
V8-425 Wildcat, Riviera G.S.	BS
V8-425 Exc. Above	BT
V8-340 LeSabre	BU
1967 V8-430 Wildcat, Electra, Riviera	BT
V8-400 G. S. 400	BA
V8-430 Sport Wagon 400	BW
V8-340 LeSabre 400	BU
1968 V8-430 Wildcat, Electra, Riviera	BT
V8-400 G. S. 400	BA
V8-400 Sport Wagon 400	BW
V8-350 LeSabre	BU
1969 V8-350 LeSabre	BU
V8-400 Sportwagon	BW
V8-400 G. S. 400	BA, BB
V8-430 Wildcat, Electra	BC
V8-430 Riviera	BT
1970 V8-455 G.S. 455	BA
V8-455 G.S. 455 Stage 1	BB
V8-455 Riviera	BT
V8-455 All Others	BC
1971 V8-455 G.S. 455	BA
V8-455 G.S. 455 Stage 1	BB, OW
V8-455 Riviera	BT
V8-455 All Others	BC

CADILLAC	CODE
1966-67 75 Sedan & Limousine	AC
Commercial Chassis	AB
All Others	AA
1968-69 75 and Commercial Chassis	AB
All Others	AA
1970-71 All Models	AA

CHEVROLET	CODE
1966 V8-396	CA
V8-427	CB
1967-68 V8-396	CA
V8-427	CB
V8-396 Chevelle & Camaro	CC
V8-327	CD
V8-396 High Perf.	CE
V8-396	CH
V8-327 Corvette	CK
V8-327 Corvette	CL
1969 V8-350 Chevrolet	CA
V8-396 Chevrolet	CA
V8-427, 390 H.P.	CB
V8-396, 325 H.P.	CC
V8-350, 250 H.P. Chevrolet	CD
V8-327, 235 H.P. Chevrolet	CD

CHEVROLET—Continued	CODE
V8-396, 350 H.P. Chevelle, Camaro, Nova	CE
V8-427, 335 H.P.	CF
V8-396, 265 H.P. Chevrolet	CG
V8-427, 390 H.P. Chevrolet	CH
V8-350, 300 H.P. Corvette	CK
V8-427, 400 H.P. Corvette	CL
V8-427, 335 H.P. Chevrolet	CQ
V8-427, 425 H.P. Chevrolet	CY①
V8-427, 430 H.P. Corvette	CY①
V8-427, 435 H.P. Corvette	CY①
V8-396, 375 H.P. Chevelle, Camaro, Nova	CY①
1970 V8-400 Chevrolet	CA
V8-454 Chevrolet	CB
V8-400 Chevelle, Monte Carlo	CD
V8-400 Camaro, Chevrolet, Nova	CF
V8-454 Police	CG
V8-350 Corvette	CK
V8-454 Camaro, Chevelle, Nova	CR
V8-454 Chevelle, Monte Carlo, Corvette	CS
V8-400 Camaro, Chevelle, Nova	CW
V8-454 Camaro, Chevelle, Corvette	CY

① High shift point.

OLDSMOBILE	CODE
1966 Standard Unit	OB
Ultra Hi Perf. Engine	OD
Jetstar 88	OF
Heavy Duty Unit	OE
1967 Vista Cruiser	OA
Senior Models 2 & 4 Bar. Carbs.	OB
Senior Models with Low Comp. Eng.	OC
Starfire Engine	OD
Heavy Duty Transmission	OE
Delmont 88	OF
F-85 with V8-400 and 4 Bar. Carb.	OG
F-85 with V8-400 and 2 Bar. Carb.	OH
1968 V8-350 Vista-Cruiser	OA
V8-455 4 barrel carb.	OB
V8-455 2 barrel carb.	OC
V8-350 Delmont	OF
V8-400 4 barrel carb. F-85, Cutlass, 4-4-2	OG
V8-400 2 barrel carb. 4-4-2	OH
V8-455 4 barrel carb. Heavy Duty, Police	OL
V8-400 Vista-Cruiser	OP
1969 V8-350 Vista-Cruiser	OA
V8-350 Delta 88 W/Cruise Control	OA
V8-455 4 barrel carb. "98"	OB
V8-455 2 barrel carb. Delta	OC

OLDSMOBILE—Continued	CODE
V8-350 Delta 88	OF
V8-400 4-4-2 Exc. Ram Air	OG
V8-455 4 bar. carb. "98", Delta	OK
V8-400 4 barrel carb. Vista-Cruiser	OP
V8-455 Heavy Duty, Police	OL
V8-455 2 barrel carb. Delta	OR
V8-400 4-4-2 Ram Air	OW
1970 V8-350 Exc. Below	OF
V8-350 W/Cruise Control	OA
V8-455 2 bar. carb. Exc. Below	OC
V8-455 Delta 88, 4 bar. carb.	OB
V8-455 2 bar. carb. Cruise Control	OR
V8-455 Cutlass Exc. SX	OD
V8-455 Cutlass, 442 SX Exc. Ram Air	OG
V8-455 Senior models W/Cruise Control & 4 bar. carb.	OK
V8-455 Vista-Cruiser	OK
V8-455 Police	OL
V8-455 442 Ram Air	OW
1971 V8-455 Supreme 4 Bar. Carb.	OD
V8-455 4-4-2	OG
V8-455 4-4-2 W/Air Induction	OW
V8-455 Vista Cruiser	OA
V8-455 Vista Cruiser 2 Bar. Carb.	OR
V8-455 Vista Cruiser 4 Bar. Carb.	OK
V8-455 Senior Models 2 Bar. Carb.	OR
V8-455 Senior Models Dual Exhaust	OK
V8-455 Delta 88 Single Exhaust	OR

PONTIAC	CODE
1966 With 3 Carburetors	PA
With V8-389	PB
With V8-421	PC
Heavy Duty Unit	PH
V8-421 Except 2+2	PG
1967 V8-400 2 Bar. Carb.	PB
V8-428 4 Bar. Carb.	PC
V8-400 4 Bar. Carb.	PD
V8-400 4 Bar. Carb. (GP)	PG
V8-400 for Heavy Duty	PH
GTO V8-400 4 Bar. Carb.	PS
GTO V8-400 2 Bar. Carb.	PT
1968 V8-428 with Single Exhaust	PA
V8-400 with 2 Barrel Carburetor	PB
V8-428 with 4 Bar. Carb. and High Perf.	PC
V8-400 with 4 Bar. Carb. (Grand Prix)	PG
V8-400, 428 Heavy Duty	PH
V8-400 Ram Air (GTO, Firebird)	PQ
V8-400 with 2 Bar. Carb. (GTO)	PT
V8-400 with 4 Bar. Carb. (GTO, Firebird)	PX

Continued

TRANSMISSION IDENTIFICATION—CONTINUED

PONTIAC—Continued	CODE
V8-400 with 4 Bar. Carb. (Firebird with A/C)	PY
1969 V8-350 2 Barrel carb. (Tempest, Firebird)	PV
V8-350 H.O. (Tempest, Firebird)	PS
V8-400 2 barrel carb.	PB
V8-400 2 barrel carb. (GTO, Grand Prix)	PT
V8-400 4 barrel carb. (Grand Prix)	PW
V8-400 4 barrel carb. (GTO, Firebird)	PX
V8-400 Ram Air (GTO, Firebird)	PQ
V8-428 H.O.	PC
V8-428 Bonneville	PH
V8-428 H.O. (Grand Prix)	PR
1970 V8-400 (Pontiac)	PB

PONTIAC—Continued	CODE
V8-400 Ram Air (GTO)	PD
V8-400 (Tempest, Grand Prix)	PT
V8-400 4 bar. carb. (Grand Prix)	PW
V8-400 2 bar. carb. (Firebird)	PF
V8-400 Sports Option	PX
V8-400 Ram Air, HO	PQ
V8-455 Exc. HO (Pontiac)	PA
V8-455 HO (Pontiac)	PC
V8-455 Heavy Duty (Pontiac)	PH
V8-455 HO (Tempest, Grand Prix)	PR
1971 V8-455 (Pontiac)	PA
V8-400 (Pontiac)	PB
V8-455 4 Bar. Carb., W/Dual Exh. (Pontiac)	PC
V8-400 (Pontiac)	PD

PONTIAC—Continued	CODE
V8-455 (Pontiac)	PF
V8-400 2 Bar. Carb. (Police & H.D.)	PH
V8-455 4 Bar. Carb. (Police & H.D.)	PH
V8-455 H.O. (LeMans, GTO, Firebird)	PQ
V8-455 4 Bar. Carb. (LeMans, GTO, Firebird)	PR
V8-400 2 Bar. Carb. (LeMans, GTO, Firebird)	PT
V8-455 4 Bar. Carb. (LeMans, GTO, Firebird, Grand Prix)	PW
V8-400 4 Bar. Carb. (LeMans, GTO, Firebird, Grand Prix)	PX
V8-400 4 Bar. Carb. (LeMans, GTO, Firebird)	PY

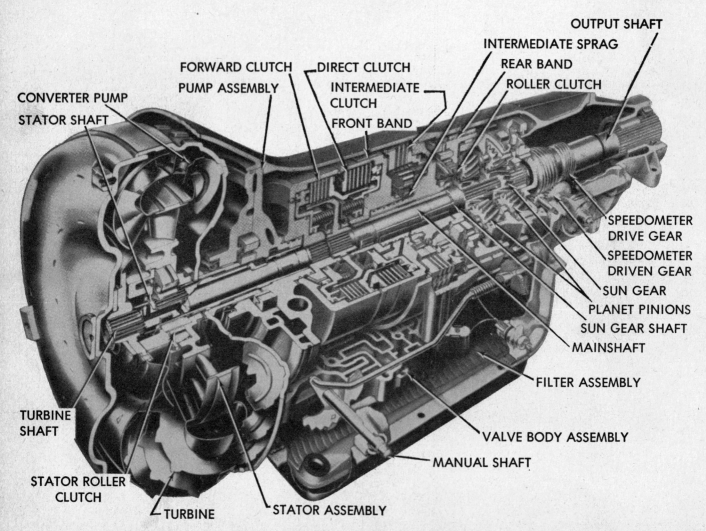

Fig. 1   Cutaway view of transmission assembly

GENERAL DESCRIPTION

This transmission, Fig. 1, is a fully automatic unit consisting primarily of a three-element hydraulic torque converter and a compound planetary gear set. Three multiple-disc clutches, two one-way clutches, and two bands provide the friction elements required to obtain the desired functions of the planetary gear set.

NOTE: On early units, the two one-way clutches mentioned above consist of an intermediate sprag and a low sprag. In late 1965 a roller clutch was substituted for the low sprag.

The torque converter, the multiple-disc clutches and the one-way clutches couple the engine to the planetary gears through oil pressure, providing three forward speeds and reverse. The torque converter, when required, supplements the gears by multiplying engine torque.

Torque Converter

The torque converter is of welded construction and is serviced as an assembly. The unit is made up of two vaned sections, or halves, that face each other in an oil-filled housing. The pump half of the converter is connected to the engine and the turbine half is connected to the transmission.

When the engine makes the converter pump revolve, it sends oil against the turbine, making it revolve also. The oil then returns in a circular flow back to the converter pump, continuing this flow as long as the engine is running.

Stator

The converter also has a smaller vaned section, called a stator, that funnels the oil back to the converter pump through smaller openings, at increased speed. The speeded up oil directs additional force to the engine-driven converter pump, thereby multiplying engine torque. In other words, without the stator, the unit is nothing more than a fluid coupling.

The stator assembly in some transmissions is a variable pitch unit. The stator blades are operated at either of two positions: maximum or high angle, and minimum or low angle.

Maximum or high angle means greater redirection of the oil and increased engine speed, and torque multiplication for maximum performance. At engine idle, it reduces the converter's efficiency, reducing "creep". Minimum or low angle results in a more efficient converter for cruising operation.

External Controls

The external control connections to the transmission are:
1. Manual linkage to select the desired operating range.
2. Engine vacuum to operate the vacuum modulator unit.
3. An electrical signal to operate an electric detent solenoid.
4. A stator solenoid (to 1967) to "switch the pitch" or stator angle. *This device is used only with transmissions having a variable pitch stator.*

Vacuum Modulator

A vacuum modulator is used to sense engine torque input to the transmission automatically. The vacuum modulator transmits this signal to the pressure regulator, which controls line pressure, so that all torque requirements of the transmission are met and proper shift spacing is obtained at all throttle openings.

Detent Solenoid

The detent solenoid is activated by an electric switch at the carburetor. When the throttle is opened sufficiently to close this switch, the solenoid in the transmission is activated, causing a downshift at speeds below 70 mph. At lower speeds, downshifts will occur at lesser throttle openings without use of the electric switch.

Stator Solenoid

Used only with 1966-67 transmissions having the variable pitch stator, the solenoid is activated in several ways:

On 1966-67 Buick and Oldsmobile, the solenoid is activated by a signal from a switch on the carburetor linkage at idle speed which changes the stator blade angle from low to high. It is also energized at 40° and over of carburetor opening (48° on Buick) by a switch on the throttle linkage to change the blade angle from low to high.

On 1966-67 Cadillac, the stator solenoid is activated by a signal from a switch at the carburetor or by the brake light switch. The brake light switch changes the blade angle from low to high whenever the brake pedal is applied. The switch at the carburetor changes the angle from low to high above 40° throttle opening.

TROUBLE SHOOTING GUIDE

Oil Pressure High or Low

1. Vacuum line or fittings clogged or leaking.
2. Vacuum modulator.
3. Modulator valve.
4. Pressure regulator.
5. Oil pump.
6. Governor.

No Drive In Drive Range

1. Low oil lever (check for leaks).
2. Manual control linkage not adjusted properly.
3. Low oil pressure. Check for blocked strainer, defective pressure regulator, pump assembly or pump drive gear. See that tangs have not been damaged by converter.
4. Check control valve assembly to see if manual valve has been disconnected from manual lever pin.
5. Forward clutch may be struck or damaged. Check pump feed circuits to forward clutch including clutch drum ball check.
6. Sprag or roller clutch assembled incorrectly.

1 - 2 Shift At Full Throttle Only

1. Detent switch may be sticking or defective.
2. Detent solenoid may be stuck open, loose or have leaking gasket.
3. Control valve assembly may be leaking, damaged or incorrectly installed.

1st Speed Only - No 1 - 2 Shift

1. Governor valve may be sticking.
2. Driven gear in governor assembly loose, worn or damaged.
3. The 1-2 shift valve in control valve assembly stuck closed. Check governor feed channels for blocks, leaks, and position. Also check control valve body gaskets for leaks and damage.
4. Intermediate clutch plug in case may be leaking or blown out.
5. Check for porosity between channels and for blocked governor feed channels in case.
6. Check intermediate clutch for proper operation.

No 2 - 3 Shift - 1st & 2nd Only

1. Detent solenoid may be stuck open.
2. Detent switch may not be properly adjusted.
3. Control valve assembly may be stuck, leaking, damaged, or incorrectly installed.
4. Check direct clutch case center support for broken, leaking or missing oil rings.
5. Check clutch piston seals and piston ball check in clutch assembly.

Moves Forward In Neutral

1. Manual control linkage improperly adjusted.
2. Forward clutch does not release.

No Drive In Reverse or Slips In Reverse

1. Check oil level.
2. Manual control linkage improperly adjusted.
3. Vacuum modulator assembly may be defective.
4. Vacuum modulator valve sticking.
5. Strainer may be restricted or leaking at intake.
6. Regulator or boost valve in pump assembly may be sticking.
7. Control valve assembly may be stuck, leaking or damaged.
8. Rear servo and accumulator may have damaged or missing servo piston seal ring.
9. Reverse band burned out or damaged. Determine that apply pin or anchor pins engage properly.
10. Direct clutch may be damaged or may have stuck ball check in piston.
11. Forward clutch does not release.
12. Low-reverse ball check missing from case.

Slips In All Ranges & On Starts

1. Check oil level.
2. Vacuum modulator defective.
3. Modulator valve sticking.
4. Strainer assembly plugged or leaking at neck.

5. Pump assembly regulator or boost valve sticking.
6. Leaks from damaged gaskets or cross leaks from porosity of case.
7. Forward and direct clutches burned.

Slips 1 - 2 Shift

1. Incorrect oil level.
2. Vacuum modulator valve sticking.
3. Vacuum modulator defective.
4. Pump pressure regulator valve defective.
5. Porosity between channels in case.
6. Control valve assembly.
7. Pump-to-case gasket may be mispositioned.
8. Intermediate clutch plug in case may be missing or leaking excessively.
9. Intermediate clutch piston seal missing or damaged.
10. Intermediate clutch plates burned.
11. Front or rear accumulator oil ring may be damaged.

Slips 2 - 3 Shift

1. Items 1 through 6 under Slips 1-2 Shift will also cause 2-3 shift slips.
2. Direct clutch plates burned.
3. Oil seal rings on direct clutch may be damaged permitting excessive leaking between tower and bushing.

Rough 1 - 2 Shift

1. Modulator valve sticking.
2. Modulator assembly defective.
3. Pump pressure regulator or boost valve stuck or inoperative.
4. Control valve assembly loosened from case, damaged or mounted with wrong gaskets.
5. Intermediate clutch ball missing or not sealing.
6. Porosity between channels in case.
7. Rear servo accumulator assembly may have oil rings damaged, stuck piston, broken or missing spring or damaged bore.

Rough 2 - 3 Shift

1. Items 1, 2 and 3 under Rough 1-2 Shift will also cause rough 2-3 shift.
2. Front servo accumulator spring broken or missing. Accumulator piston may be sticking.

No Engine Braking in Second Speed

1. Front servo or accumulator oil rings may be leaking.
2. Front band may be broken or burned out.
3. Front bank not engaged on anchor pin and/or servo pin.

No Engine Braking In Low Range

1. Low-reverse check ball may be missing from control valve assembly.
2. Rear servo may have damaged oil seal ring, bore or piston; leaking, apply pressure.
3. Rear band broken, burned out or not engaged on anchor pins or servo pin.

No Part Throttle Downshifts

1. Vacuum modulator assembly.

2. Modulator valve.
3. Regulator valve train.
4. Control valve assembly has stuck 3-2 valve or broken spring.

No Detent Downshifts

1. Detent switch needs fuse, connections tightened or adjustment.
2. Detent solenoid may be inoperative.
3. Detent valve train in control valve assembly malfunctioning.

Low or High Shift Points

1. Oil pressure. Check vacuum modulator assembly, vacuum line connections, modulator valve, and pressure regulator valve train.
2. Governor may have sticking valve or feed holes that are leaking, plugged or damaged.
3. Detent solenoid may be stuck open or loose.
4. Control valve assembly. Check detent, 3-2, and 1-2 shift valve trains, and check spacer plate gaskets for positioning.
5. Check case for porosity, missing or leaking intermediate plug.

Won't Hold In Park

1. Manual control linkage improperly adjusted.
2. Internal linkage defective; check for chamfer on actuator rod sleeve.
3. Parking pawl broken or inoperative.

Excessive Creep At Idle

NOTE: Transmissions have the variable pitch stator.

1. High idle speed.
2. Stator switch inoperative or defective.
3. Stator solenoid defective.
4. Pump may have stator valve train stuck.
5. Pump lead wires disconnected or grounded out.
6. Pump feed circuit to stator may be restricted or blocked.
7. Converter out check valve may be broken or stuck.
8. Turbine shaft may have defective oil seal ring.
9. Stator orifice plug in case may be blocked.
10. Converter assembly defective.

Poor Performance - ¾ Throttle

NOTE: Transmissions having the variable pitch stator.

1. Stator and detent switch inoperative.
2. Items 3 through 10 above will also cause poor performance at ¾ throttle.

Noisy Transmission

1. Pump noises caused by high or low oil level.
2. Cavitation due to plugged strainer, porosity in intake circuit or water in oil.
3. Pump gears may be damaged.
4. Gear noise in low gear of Drive Range-transmission grounded to body.
5. Defective planetary gear set.

6. Clutch noises during application can be worn or burned clutch plates.

Forward Clutch Plates Burned

1. Check ball in clutch housing damaged, stuck or missing.
2. Clutch piston cracked, seals damaged or missing.
3. Low line pressure.
4. Manual valve mispositioned.
5. Restricted oil feed to forward clutch.
6. Pump cover oil seal rings missing, broken or undersize; ring groove oversize.
7. Case valve body face not flat or porosity between channels.
8. Manual valve bent and center land not properly ground.

Intermediate Clutch Plates Burned

1. Constant bleed orifice in center support missing.
2. Rear accumulator piston oil ring damaged or missing.
3. 1-2 accumulator valve stuck in control valve assembly.
4. Intermediate clutch piston seal damaged or missing.
5. Center support bolt loose.
6. Low line pressure.
7. Intermediate clutch plug in case missing.
8. Case valve body face not flat or porosity between channels.
9. Manual valve bent and center land not ground properly.

Direct Clutch Plates Burned

1. Restricted orifice in vacuum line to modulator.
2. Check ball in direct clutch piston damaged, stuck or missing.
3. Defective modulator bellows.
4. Center support bolt loose.
5. Center support oil rings or grooves damaged or missing.
6. Clutch piston seals damaged or missing.
7. Front and rear servo pistons and seals damaged.
8. Manual valve bent and center land not cleaned up.
9. Case valve body face not flat or porosity between channels.
10. Intermediate sprag clutch installed backwards.
11. 3-2 valve, 3-2 spring or 3-2 spacer pin installed in wrong location in 3-2 valve bore.

MAINTENANCE
Checking & Adding Fluid

Fluid level should be checked at every engine oil change. The full ("F") and "ADD" marks on the transmission dipstick are one pint apart and determine the correct fluid level at normal operating temperature (170°F.). *Careful attention to transmission oil temperature is necessary as proper fluid level at low operating temperatures will be below the "ADD" mark on the dipstick. Proper fluid level at higher operating temperatures will rise above the "F" mark.*

Fluid level must always be checked with

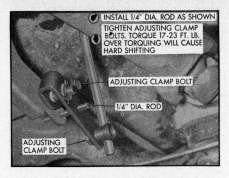

Fig. 2 Manual linkage adjustment. Buick Wildcat and Riviera 1966-68

the car on a level surface, and with the engine running to make certain the converter is full. To determine proper fluid level, proceed as follows:

1. Operate engine at a fast idle for about 1½ minutes with selector lever in park ("P") position.
2. Reduce engine speed to slow idle and check fluid level.
3. With engine running, add fluid as required to bring it to the proper level.

CAUTION: *Do not overfill as foaming might occur when the fluid heats up. If fluid level is too low, especially when cold, complete loss of drive may result after quick stops. Extremely low fluid level will result in damage to transmission.*

Draining Bottom Pan Only

1. Disconnect filler tube at bottom pan and allow fluid to drain. Remove and discard filler tube O-ring.
2. Use a new O-ring on filler tube and install tube on pan.
3. Lower car and add three quarts of transmission fluid through filler tube when replacing intake pipe and strainer assembly. When just draining bottom pan, add only two quarts.
4. Operate engine at a fast idle for about 1½ minutes with selector lever in park ("P") position.
5. Reduce engine speed to slow idle and check fluid level. Then add fluid as required to bring it to the proper level.

Adding Fluid to Fill Dry Transmission and Converter

1. Add seven quarts of fluid through filler tube.
2. Operate engine at a fast idle for about 1½ minutes with selector lever in park ("P") position.
3. Reduce engine speed to slow idle and add three more quarts of fluid.
4. Check fluid level and add as required to bring it to the proper level.

IMPORTANT: Beginning with 1969 General Motors units are equipped with anti-theft systems which lock not only the steering column but the transmission linkage as well. It is essential that this "back drive"

linkage also be adjusted when any adjustment to the manual shift linkage is made. This adjustment must be precise as any inaccuracies may result in unit operation without controls in full detent which, in turn, will cause reduced oil pressure and subsequent failure of the transmission.

BACK DRIVE LINKAGE, ADJUST

Adjust back drive at trunnion so that:
1. Transmission is in full detent in each selector position.
2. With key in Run position and transmission in Reverse, key cannot be removed and steering wheel is not locked.
3. With key in Lock position and transmission in Park, key can be removed and steering wheel is locked.

MANUAL LINKAGE, ADJUST

Buick 1966

Wildcat (console)
1. Place selector lever in Park and loosen adjusting clamp bolt.
2. Place transmission in Park.
3. Adjust as directed in Fig. 2.

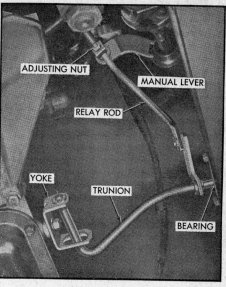

Fig. 3 Manual linkage adjustment. Cadillac

All Other Models
1. Place selector lever in Park and loosen adjusting strap bolt.
2. Place transmission in Park.
3. Tighten swivel clamp bolt at transmission to 17-23 ft-lbs.

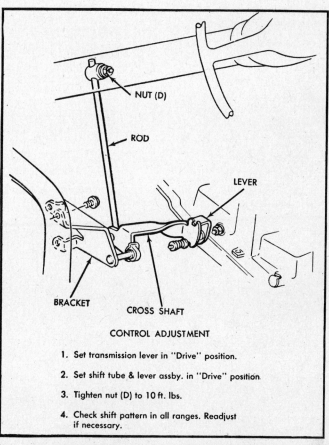

CONTROL ADJUSTMENT

1. Set transmission lever in "Drive" position.

2. Set shift tube & lever assby. in "Drive" position.

3. Tighten nut (D) to 10 ft. lbs.

4. Check shift pattern in all ranges. Readjust if necessary.

Fig. 4 Manual linkage adjustment. Chevrolet 1966-68 column shift

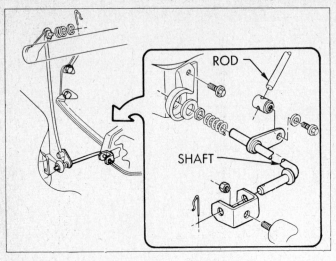

Fig. 5   Manual linkage adjustment. 1969-71 Chevrolet column shift

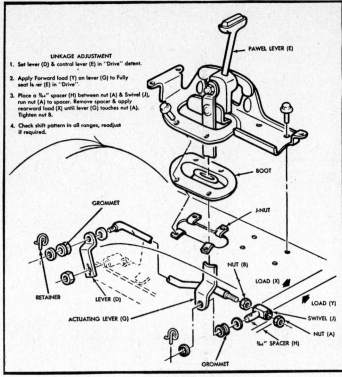

LINKAGE ADJUSTMENT

1. Set lever (D) & control lever (E) in "Drive" detent.
2. Apply Forward load (Y) on lever (G) to Fully seat lever (E) in "Drive".
3. Place a ³⁄₃₂" spacer (H) between nut (A) & Swivel (J), run nut (A) to spacer. Remove spacer & apply rearward load (X) until lever (G) touches nut (A). Tighten nut B.
4. Check shift pattern in all ranges, readjust if required.

Fig. 6   Manual linkage adjustment. Chevrolet 1966-67 console shift

1967-70 Buick Column Shift

1. Loosen shift rod adjusting clamp.
2. Place selector lever against Drive stop.
3. Place transmission in Drive.
4. Tighten clamp bolt to 17-23 ft-lbs.

1967-70 Buick Console Shift

1967 All, 1968 Wildcat & Riviera
1. Place selector lever in Park.
2. Loosen adjusting clamp bolt.
3. Place transmission in Park.
4. Adjust as directed in Fig. 2.

1968 Special
1. Loosen trunnion bolt.
2. Set selector lever against Drive stop.
3. Place transmission in Drive.
4. Tighten trunnion bolt to 6-9 ft-lbs.

1969-70 All
1. Set transmission shift lever in Drive.
2. Loosen trunnion bolt.
3. Set shift bar assembly in Drive position.
4. Tighten trunnion bolt.
5. Set selector lever in park and set back drive adjustment as described previously.

1971 All
1. Loosen trunnion bolt.
2. Set selector lever against Neutral stop.
3. Place transmission in Neutral.
4. Tighten trunnion bolt to 6-9 ft. lbs.
5. Set selector lever in Park and set back drive adjustment as described previously

1971 Buick Column Shift

1. Loosen shift rod adjusting clamp bolts.
2. Place selector lever against Neutral stop.
3. Place transmission in Neutral.
4. Tighten clamp bolt to 17-23 ft. lbs.

1966-71 Cadillac

1. Referring to Fig. 3 loosen nut on steering column manual lever-to-relay rod clamp.
2. Pull relay rod up to position transmission shift valve in PARK; then push rod down to third (neutral) step.
3. Position selector lever in neutral.
4. Tighten clamp nut. Selector lever should enter all positions and indicator pointer should index correctly.

Chevrolet 1966-67 All, 1968-71 Column Shift

When properly adjusted, the following conditions must be met for manual operation of the shift lever, Figs. 4, 5 and 6.
1. From reverse to drive position travel the transmission detent feel must be noted and related to indicated position on dial.
2. When in drive and reverse positions, pull lever rearward (toward steering wheel) and then release. It must drop back into position with no restrictions.

Chevy Nova 1970 Floor Shift

Refer to Fig. 7, and proceed as follows:
1. Loosely assemble nuts (A) and (B) on lower rod (C).
2. Set transmission lever (D) in Drive.
3. Set control pawl rod (E) in the Neutral or Drive notch of detent (F).
4. Apply load in direction of arrow (Y) on actuating lever (G) until pawl rod comes in contact with detent at con-tact point (Z).
5. Place a .094" spacer (H) between nut (A) and swivel (J), run nut (A) until it touches spacer. Tighten nut (B) against swivel and lock swivel between nuts (A) and (B).
6. Place transmission and shift lever in Park.
7. Install column rod (K) to column lever and cross shaft (L).

NOTE: With shift lever in Park the ignition key must move freely to Lock position.

Chevy Nova 1971 Floor Shift

Refer to Fig. 8 and proceed as follows:
1. Loosely assemble nuts (B) and (C) on rod (E).
2. Set transmission lever (F) in Drive position.
3. Set pawl rod (K) in the Neutral or Drive notch of detent.
4. Apply load in direction of arrow (Y) on actuating lever (D) until pawl rod (K) comes in contact with detent at contact point (Z).
5. Place a .094" spacer between nut (B) and swivel, run nut (B) until it touches spacer. Remove the spacer and tighten nut (C) against swivel and lock swivel between nuts (B) and (C).
6. Set transmission lever (F) in Park position and turn ignition switch to Lock.
7. Install rod (G) to idler lever (J) and transmission lever (F).
8. Install rod (A) to shift lever and idler

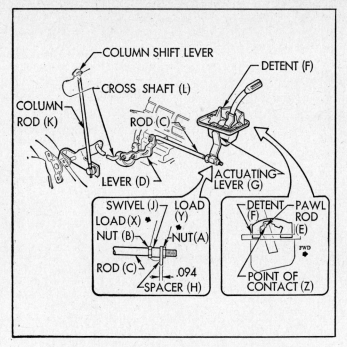

Fig. 7   Manual linkage adjustment. 1970 Nova floor shift

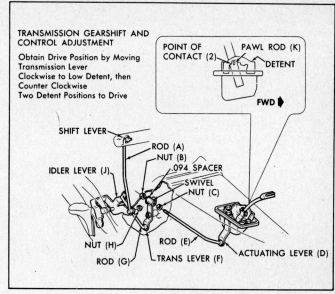

Fig. 8   Manual linkage adjustment. 1971 Nova floor shift

lever (J).

NOTE: Loosely attach clamp to idler lever.

9. Remove column lash by rotating shift lever in a downward direction and secure with attaching nut (H).

Camaro, Chevelle and Chevrolet 1970-71 Floor Shift

1. Place shift lever in Drive position, Fig. 9.
2. Raise vehicle. Disconnect cable from transmission lever. Manually place transmission lever in Drive position.
3. Measure distance from rearward face of attachment bracket to center of cable attachment pin. This dimension should be 5½". If not, adjust pin to obtain this dimension.
4. Install cable to transmission lever, lower vehicle and check for proper operation.

Camaro, Chevelle and Chevrolet 1968-69 Floor Shift

1. Place shift handle in Drive.
2. Raise vehicle. Disconnect cable from transmission lever, Fig. 10. Place transmission in Drive range. Check dimension A and adjust by loosening stud nut and moving stud to obtain proper setting. Reinstall cable and lock clip.
3. Lower vehicle and remove shift quadrant cover. Raise quadrant plate, disconnect bulbs and remove plate. Remove cable clip and disengage cable from shift lever.
4. Insert a .07" gauge between pawl and detent as shown in view A. Check dimension B. Adjust by loosening bolt A and moving lever to obtain proper adjustment. Tighten bolt.

5. Adjust cable end until it freely enters pin. Install clip.

NOTE: If lift on handle button does not clear detents or detents can be cleared without lifting handle, pawl engagement can be adjusted by raising or lowering of the detent plate after loosening bolt B. If such an adjustment is made, repeat step 4.

Corvette 1968-71

1. Place selector lever in Drive. Fig. 11.
2. Place transmission control lever in Drive position by moving lever counterclockwise to low detent, then clockwise two positions for Drive.
3. Install cable and secure with retain-

6. Remove gauge. Check operation.
7. Reinstall shift plate and cover.

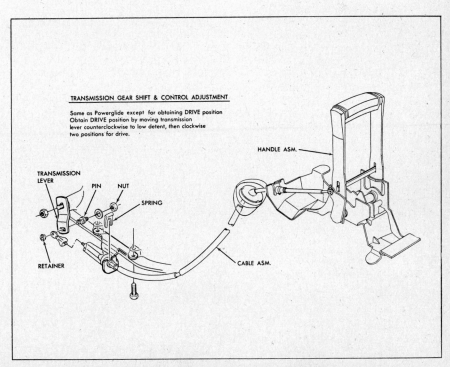

Fig. 9   Console shift linkage. 1970-71 Camaro, Chevelle and Chevrolet

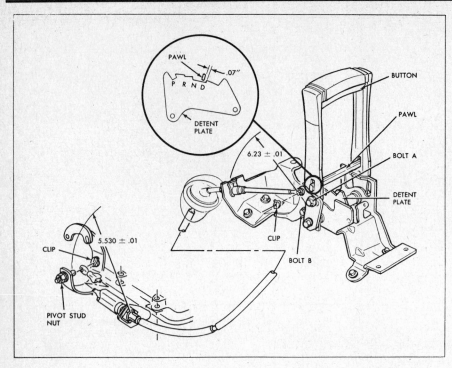

Fig. 10   Console shift linkage adjustment. 1968-69 Camaro, Chevelle and Chevrolet

ing clip and cotter pin.

Oldsmobile

Column Shift, 1966-71

1. Use enough washers to obtain zero clearance at upper shift lever and shift rod.
2. Set outer shift lever in "D".
3. Loosen swivel bolt.
4. Push up on shift rod until selector lever is against the "D" position stop in upper steering column.
5. Tighten swivel bolt to 20 ft-lbs.
6. Check neutral switch adjustment.

Console Shift, 1966

1. Place selector lever in "D".
2. Disconnect manual rod from transmission manual lever.
3. Place transmission manual lever in "D" detent position.
4. Loosen lock nut on manual rod.
5. With selector lever held against its stop in "D" position and transmission manual lever in "D" detent position, adjust manual rod until it enters transmission manual lever.
6. Shorten manual rod three turns and check adjustment.

Console Shift, 1967-71

1. Place shift lever in Park.

2. Set transmission outer shift lever in Park position.
3. Set pin to just enter hole in shift cable.
4. Tighten nut and check through all detent positions and recheck adjustment.

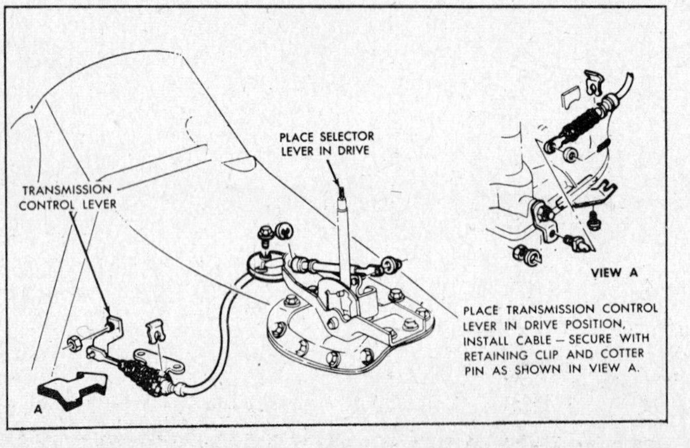

Pontiac

Column Shift, 1969-71

1. Loosen screw on adjusting swivel clamp.
2. Set transmission selector lever in Park detent.
3. Set upper gearshift lever in Park position and lock ignition.
4. Push up on gearshift control rod to take up clearance in steering column lock mechanism and tighten screw on adjusting swivel clamp to 20 ft. lbs.

Column Shift, 1967-68

1. Loosen nut on adjusting swivel clamp.
2. Set transmission shift lever in Drive position.
3. Set shift lever in Drive position.
4. Tighten swivel clamp nut to 9 ft-lbs for all 1967 units, 20 ft-lbs for 1968 Pontiac and GTO and 30 ft-lbs for 1968 Firebird.

Console Shift, 1966-68

1. Disconnect cable at transmission.
2. With transmission lever in Park, adjust pin in lever to permit smooth shifting through all detents.
3. Torque selector pin nut to 30 ft-lbs, set the gearshift lever in Park position and connect shift cable to pin.

Console Shift, 1969-71

1. Disconnect shift cable from transmission.
2. Adjust back drive linkage as outlined at the front of this section.
3. After adjusting back drive, unlock ignition and set transmission and gear selector in Neutral position.
4. Install cable and tighten nut to 30 ft-lbs.

Column Shift, 1966

1. Loosen nut on adjusting swivel clamp.
2. Set transmission selector lever in park detent.
3. Set shift lever in park position.
4. Tighten nut on adjusting swivel.

THROTTLE LINKAGE, ADJUST

Buick

1968-70 Special and 1971 All

This unit is equipped with a flexible cable type linkage which is not adjustable.

1968-70 Except Special

1. Remove air cleaner. Make sure that linkage is free in all positions and

Fig. 11   Shift linkage adjustment. 1968-71 Corvette

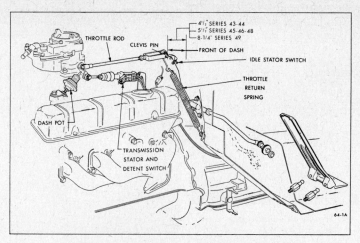

Fig. 12   Throttle linkage adjustment. 1966-67 All 1968-70 except Special

that nothing interferes with the linkage. Hold choke open and make sure that return spring fully closes throttle, even through throttle is released very slowly.

2. With throttle linkage in hot curb idle position, measurement from throttle rod pin horizontally to dash, Fig. 12, must be as follows:

   1968 Ser. 45, 46, 48000 . . . 6½"
   1968 Ser. 4900 . . . . 6¼"
   1969-70 Ser. 45, 46, 48000 .5⅞"
   1969 Ser. 49000 . . . . 8¼"
   1970 Ser. 49000 . . . . 6⅛"

3. Operate linkage to open carburetor and make sure that carburetor wide open stop is contacting.
4. As a final check, have a helper depress accelerator pedal and check to make sure wide open stop contacts at carburetor.

1966-67 All

1. Remove air cleaner.
2. Make sure linkage is free in all positions.
3. Hold choke open and make sure that return spring fully closes throttle, though throttle is released very slowly.
4. Adjust engine idle speed and mixture.
5. With throttle linkage at hot idle position, measurement from throttle rod clevis pin to dash must be as shown in Fig. 12.
6. If measurement is off, shorten or lengthen operating rod as required.
7. Operate linkage to open carburetor and make sure carburetor wide open stop is contacting. If carburetor does not reach wide open position and nothing is interfering with throttle linkage, transmission stator and detent switch must be adjusted as outlined below.

Cadillac

1971

Although a cable is used in place of the rod, procedures to adjust remain basically the same as previous models.

1966-70

1. Remove air cleaner. Check linkage for free movement in all positions, and check to see that return spring fully closes the throttle.
2. Remove cotter pin that holds end of throttle rod in relay lever and remove washers and rod from lever.
3. If equipped with Cruise Control, detach linkage at Cruise Control power unit end.
4. While a helper presses accelerator pedal to the floor, hold carburetor throttle lever in full throttle (wide open) position. Make sure choke valve is wide open.
5. Turn throttle rod end in either direction as necessary to allow free entry into bushing on relay lever Fig. 13.
6. With accelerator pedal released, reinstall washer on throttle rod and install rod into bushing in relay lever.
7. Install other washer and then the cotter pin.
8. With accelerator pedal pressed again to floor mat, recheck throttle for wide open position.
9. Install Cruise Control linkage (if equipped) and adjust if necessary.

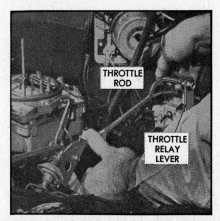

Fig. 13   Throttle linkage adjustment. Cadillac 1966-70

Chevrolet, Chevelle & Camaro

1970-71

The throttle control system is of the cable type and therefore requires no adjustment.

1966-69

NOTE: Chevelle throttle, control is cable operated and not adjustable.

1. Disconnect throttle rod swivel at carburetor throttle lever.
2. Hold carburetor throttle in wide open position, push throttle rod rearward (to position accelerator pedal at the floor mat) and adjust swivel to just enter hole in throttle lever.
3. Connect swivel to throttle lever and install accelerator return spring.

Corvette

1968-71

1. Loosen cable clamp bolt and hold accelerator pedal to the floor.
2. Move carburetor throttle to wide open position.
3. Tighten cable clamp bolt to 45 in lbs.

Oldsmobile

1970-71

The throttle control system is cable operated and therefore has no adjustment.

Carburetor Rod, 1968-69

1. With slow idle adjusted and adjusting screw off fast idle cam, disconnect swivel on carburetor rod from auxiliary bellcrank.
2. Push upper lever of auxiliary bellcrank towards cowl until it hits its stop.
3. Pull carburetor rod towards firewall until throttle is wide open.
4. Adjust swivel until swivel pin enters the "2" notch for 2 bbl. carburetor or the "4" notch for 4 bbl. carburetor.
5. Reconnect carburetor rod to auxiliary bellcrank.

Carburetor Rod, 1966-67

With slow idle properly adjusted and carburetor in slow idle position, engine shut off, transmission stator must be in high angle position (test lamp on). To adjust, lengthen carburetor rod until test lamp just goes off. Shorten rod two more complete turns and tighten lock nut.

Accelerator Pedal Height

When slow idle and carburetor rod properly adjusted adjust accelerator rod so the distance from pedal lever to floor carpet is 5¹⁄₁₆".

Pontiac

1967-69 Intermediates; 1970-71 All

The throttle control system is cable operated and requires no adjustment.

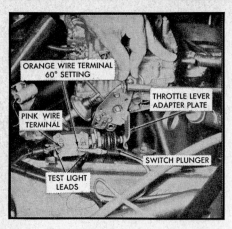

Fig. 14   Downshift switch adjustment.
Cadillac 1966

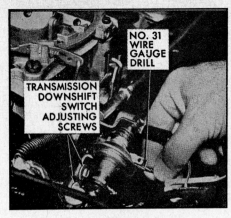

Fig. 15   Downshift adjustment.
Cadillac 1967-69

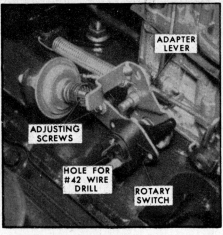

Fig. 16   Detent switch adjustment.
1970-71 Cadillac

1969 Full Size Models

With accelerator rod and throttle return spring disconnected, insert ¼" diameter gauge pin through hole in mounting bracket and through holes in throttle control lever. Holding carburetor lever extension at full throttle, adjust rod to line up with carburetor extension stud plus three additional turns toward front of car (counterclockwise). Attach rod, remove gauge pin and connect return spring.

1967-68

With carburetor set at hot idle position, line up throttle rod socket with attaching ball stud on carburetor extension lever, turn rod counterclockwise five turns and snap into place.

1966

1. Check accelerator pedal height.
2. If necessary, adjust linkage to obtain 4¹¹/₁₆" between accelerator pedal and floor pan with carburetor set at hot idle speed.
3. Depress accelerator pedal to floor and check to see that carburetor throttle valves are wide open.

GTO, Firebird & 1969 Grand Prix

1967-71

Throttle is cable operated and requires no adjustment. A reference dimension of 1⁹/₁₆" between the bottom of the accelerator pedal and the floor pan is used only to check for bent bracket assemblies.

STATOR & DETENT (DOWNSHIFT) SWITCHES
Buick

Detent Switch, 1971

1. Install cable through throttle lever hole and install retainer (nylon) being sure it is seated.
2. Position retainer on upper end of cable.
3. With turbo throttle cable connected to car-

buretor and throttle lever, fully depress accelerator pedal to adjust retainer.

Detent Switch, 1968-70

With plunger bottomed in switch, fully depress accelerator pedal and tighten lock screw to 16 ft lbs.

Idle Stator Switch, 1966-67

1. Referring to Fig. 12, adjust switch with throttle at closed position and return spring attached.
2. With attaching screws loose, rotate switch until the switch stop screw bottoms against case.
3. Hold screw in this position and tighten attaching screws.

Stator & Detent Switch, 1966-67

1. With carburetor throttle wide open and switch plunger bottomed, adjust link until it will slip over carburetor lever pin.
2. Then screw link into plunger 1½ turns.
3. Install washer and retainer.

Cadillac

1970-71

1. Remove air cleaner.
2. Make certain carburetor is adjusted to specification and that linkage is at low speed idle setting.
3. Loosen two mounting screws and insert a #42 drill through calibrating hole below lower wire terminal extending through to carburetor side of switch, Fig. 16. Adjust position of switch so that lever just touches the carburetor adapter plate arm.
4. Tighten mounting screws and remove drill.
5. Install air cleaner.

1967-69

1. Remove carburetor air cleaner.
2. Make sure that low idle speed is properly adjusted.
3. If downshift switch is properly adjusted, a ⅛" drill or rod can be inserted through calibrating hole be-

low wire terminal extending through carburetor side of switch, Fig. 15.

NOTE: With this adjustment the stator should break contact 5½° to 7½° from closed hot idle throttle and make contact at 40° throttle. The downshift should make contact above 60° throttle.

4. If adjustment is necessary, loosen the two ⁷/₁₆" switch mounting screws and position switch for proper alignment as in Step 3.
5. With switch positioned, tighten mounting screws and remove drill or rod from calibrating hole through switch.

1966

1. Remove carburetor air cleaner.
2. Referring to Fig. 14, disconnect throttle rod from throttle plate and attach spring to fast idle cam to hold choke open. This will facilitate movement of throttle plate when adjusting switch.
3. Disconnect leads from terminals under switch. Note color code of leads.
4. Connect a test lamp to switch terminals.
5. Loosen front and rear locking nuts that hold switch on mounting bracket.

NOTE: A gauge for adjusting the switch can be made out of an 8" length of ⅛" rod. Bend one end of the rod at a right angle ¾" from end. Insert angled end of gauge rod between machined boss on carburetor base and wide open throttle stop tang on throttle plate as shown and hold stop tang against rod. This will set primary throttle opening at about 60 degrees, the setting at which switch must energize.

CAUTION: Make certain gauge rod is properly located, otherwise setting of primary throttle opening will be incorrect.

6. Continue to hold stop tang against gauge rod and move switch fore and aft until cam surface on throttle

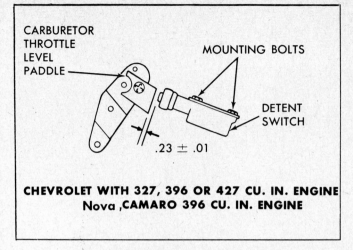

Fig. 17 Detent switch adjustment. Camaro and Chevrolet except V8-307

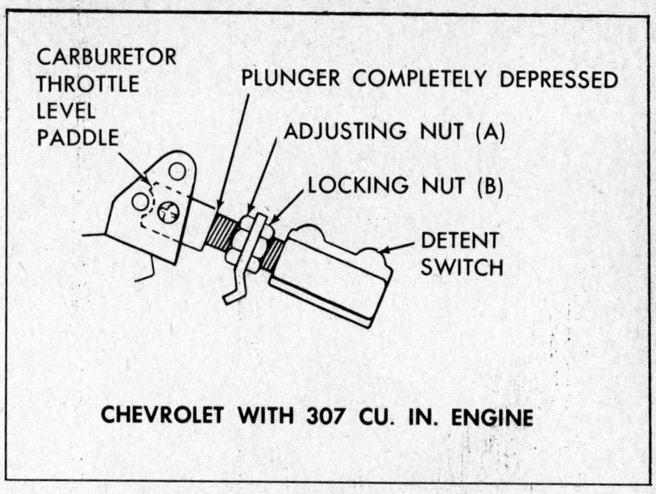

Fig. 18 Detent switch adjustment. Chevrolet V8-307

plate depresses switch plunger sufficiently to close circuit and light test lamp.
7. Tighten locknuts securely to prevent loss of adjustment.
8. Recheck adjustment by moving throttle plate stop tang back and forth against gauge rod to make certain switch energizes at proper setting.

NOTE: *Make certain switch plunger does not impede wide open throttle. If carburetor will not reach wide open throttle, reposition switch mounting bracket and readjust switch.*

9. Remove test lamp and connect electrical leads. Connect throttle rod and return spring to throttle plate. Install air cleaner.

Camaro, Chevrolet and Nova

1970-71
1. Refer to Fig. 17 and loosen mounting bolts.
2. With choke in open position, move accelerator to wide open throttle position. Depress detent switch plunger till it bottoms in switch. Move switch towards throttle lever paddle until there is only .23″ between lever paddle and plunger.

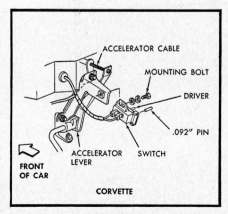

Fig. 19 Detent switch adjustment. Corvette

3. Tighten mounting bolts.

Chevrolet (Except V8-307) & Camaro

1966-69
1. Loosen mounting bolts.
2. With automatic choke and accelerator linkage in wide open position, depress detent switch plunger until it bottoms in switch. Move switch toward throttle lever paddle to obtain a clearance of .23″ between lever paddle and plunger, Fig. 17.
3. Tighten mounting bolts.

Chevrolet V8-307

1968-69
1. Loosen adjusting nut, Fig. 18.
2. With automatic choke in wide open position, turn adjusting nut to bring switch forward until plunger is completely depressed and threaded barrel of switch contacts throttle lever paddle.
3. Tighten lock nut.

Chevelle and Corvette

1967-71
1. Pull detent switch driver rearward until the hole in the switch body aligns with the hole in the driver. Insert a .092″ pin through the aligned holes to a depth of .10″ to hold driver in position, Figs. 19 and 20.
2. Loosen mounting bolt.
3. With accelerator pedal in wide open position, move switch forward until driver contacts accelerator lever.
4. Tighten mounting bolt and remove pin

Oldsmobile

1968-71
1. Push plunger of switch forward until flush with switch housing.
2. Push accelerator pedal to wide open position to set switch.
3. Energizing of switch can be checked with a test light.

1966-67
1. With slow idle, carburetor rod and

accelerator pedal height properly adjusted, disconnect carburetor rod and rotate until it hits stop.
2. Connect carburetor rod (without moving lever) to wide open throttle position.
3. Depress throttle through detent and release.

Pontiac, GTO

1967-71
After installing switch, fully bottom plunger to insure proper setting then fully depress accelerator pedal, Figs. 21 and 22.

1966
Using adjusting nuts, position detent switch at carburetor so that when throttle is in wide open position, detent circuit is closed.

Firebird

1967-71
1. Loosen lock nut. Switch is mounted at carburetor and should not be confused with the idle stop solenoid.
2. With automatic choke in wide open position, adjust switch so that when throttle is in wide open position, detent circuit is closed.

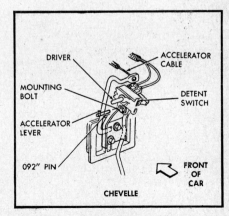

Fig. 20 Detent switch adjustment 1967-71 Chevelle

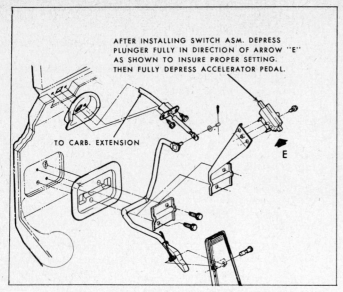

Fig. 21   Detent switch adjustment. GTO 1967-69

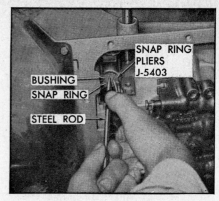

Fig. 23   Removing and installing Pressure regulator valve

IN CAR REPAIRS

Services outlined in this section can be performed without removing the transmission from the vehicle.

Pressure Regulator Valve

1. Remove bottom pan and strainer.
2. Using a screwdriver or steel rod, compress regulator boost valve bushing against pressure regulator spring, Fig. 23.

CAUTION: Pressure regulator spring is under extreme pressure and will force valve bushing out of bore when snap ring is removed if valve bushing is not held securely.

3. Continue to exert pressure on valve bushing and remove snap ring. Gradually release pressure on valve bushing until spring force is exhausted.
4. Carefully remove regulator boost valve bushing and valve, and pressure regulator spring. Be careful not to drop parts as they will fall out if they are not held.
5. Remove pressure regulator valve and spring retainer. Remove spacers if present.
6. Reverse procedure to install.

Control Valve Body

1. Remove bottom pan and strainer.
2. Remove control valve body attaching screws and detent roller spring assembly. *Do not remove solenoid attaching screws.*
3. Remove control valve body and governor pipes. If care is used in removing control valve body, the six check balls will stay in place above spacer plate.
4. Remove governor pipes and manual valve from control valve body.
5. Reverse procedure to install.

Governor

1. Remove governor cover and discard gasket.

2. Withdraw governor from case.
3. Reverse procedure to install, using a new gasket.

Modulator & Modulator Valve

1. Remove modulator attaching screw and retainer.
2. Remove modulator assembly from case and discard O-ring seal.
3. Remove modulator valve from case.
4. Reverse procedure to install, using a new O-ring seal.

Parking Linkage

1. Remove bottom pan and oil strainer.

2. Unthread jam nut holding detent lever to manual shaft.
3. Remove manual shaft retaining pin from case.
4. Remove manual shaft and jam nut from case.
5. Remove O-ring seal from manual shaft.
6. Remove parking actuator rod and detent lever assembly.
7. Remove parking pawl bracket, pawl return spring and pawl shaft retainer.
8. Remove parking pawl shaft, O-ring seal and parking pawl.
9. Reverse procedure to install, using new seals and gasket.

Rear Seal

1. Remove propeller shaft.
2. Pry out seal with screwdriver.

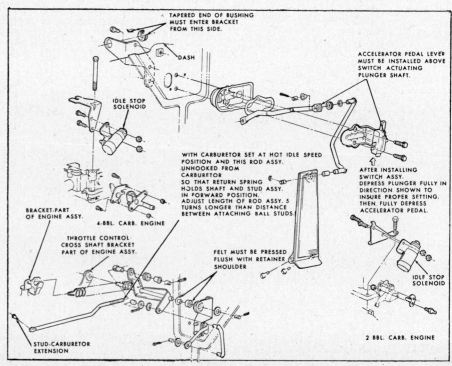

Fig. 22   Detent switch adjustment. Pontiac 1967-71

3. Install new seal with a suitable seal driver.
4. Install propeller shaft.

TRANSMISSION, REPLACE
Buick, 1966-71

1. Raise and support front and rear of car.
2. Disconnect front exhaust crossover pipe if necessary. Remove propeller shaft.
3. Place suitable jack under transmission.
4. Remove vacuum line from vacuum modulator.
5. Separate cooler lines from transmission.
6. Remove transmission crossmember.
7. Disconnect detent and stator electrical connectors from transmission. Starting with 1968, stator wire is not used.
8. Disconnect speedometer cable.
9. Disconnect shift linkage from transmission.
10. Remove transmission filler pipe.
11. Support engine at oil pan.
12. Remove flywheel cover pan.
13. Mark flywheel and converter pump for reassembly in same position, then remove three converter pump-to-flywheel bolts.
14. Remove transmission-to-engine bolts.
15. Move transmission rearward to provide clearance between converter pump and crankshaft. Install a suitable holding tool to secure converter. Then lower and remove transmission.
16. Reverse above procedure to install.

Cadillac 1966-71

1. Disconnect negative battery cable.
2. Raise car on hoist or place on jack stands.
3. Disconnect relay rod from trunnion lever and wire relay rod up out of the way to prevent damage while removing transmission.
4. Remove two screws and bearing from frame side rail.
5. Disconnect trunnion from manual yoke on left side of transmission.
6. Remove speedometer drive cable and disconnect detent and stator wires.

NOTE: 1968-71 units are not equipped with variable pitch stator therefore have no stator wires.

7. Remove transmission filler tube bracket screw from right exhaust manifold.
8. Remove filler tube from transmission case and plug hole in case.
9. Disconnect oil cooler pipes at transmission. Cap pipes and plug connector holes in transmission. Position cooler pipes out of the way.
10. Disconnect vacuum pipe hose from vacuum modulator and position pipe out of the way.
11. Remove resonator support bracket from extension housing.
12. Remove propeller shaft.
13. Unfasten and remove two starter motor brackets and slide starter forward.
14. Remove lower flywheel housing cover and two engine-to-transmission struts.

15. Remove three converter-to-flex plate screws.

NOTE: This is done by inserting a heavy screwdriver in open slot under one of weld nuts on converter, and rotating converter and flex plate until bolts can be reached for removal. Do not pry on flex plate ring gear to rotate converter as flex plate might be damaged.

16. Support rear of engine.
17. Position jack under transmission and raise it just enough to take load off rear engine support.
18. Remove two rear engine mount-to-extension housing screws.
19. Remove rear engine support (4 bolts).
20. Remove six transmission case-to-engine screws. It may be necessary to lower engine and transmission slightly to gain access to upper screws.
21. Move transmission toward rear, disengaging case from locating dowels on engine. Install a holding clamp on front of case and lower transmission from car.

CAUTION: Converter holding clamp must be used when removing transmission otherwise converter can fall out when transmission is removed.

22. Remove holding clamp and converter from transmission, using care not to drop it as it weighs about 50 pounds.
23. Reverse removal procedure to install transmission assembly.

Chevrolet Line 1970-71

Before raising car, disconnect negative battery cable and release the parking brake.
1. Place car on a hoist and remove propeller shaft.
2. Disconnect speedometer cable, electrical lead to case connector, vacuum modulator line and cooler lines.
3. Disconnect shift control linkage.
4. Support transmission with suitable jack.
5. Disconnect rear mount from frame crossmember.
6. Remove two bolts at each end of frame crossmember (plus through bolt at inside of frame and parking brake pulley on Corvette). Remove crossmember.
7. Remove converter underpan.
8. Remove converter to flywheel bolts.
9. On Chevrolet and Chevelle, loosen exhaust pipe to manifold bolts about ¼″.
10. Lower transmission until jack is barely supporting it.
11. Remove transmission to engine mounting bolts and remove oil filler tube.
12. Raise transmission to its normal position, support engine with jack and slide transmission rearward from engine and lower it away from car.

NOTE: Use converter holding tool when lowering transmission or keep rear of transmission lower than front so as not to lose converter.

13. Reverse removal procedure to install transmission.

Chevrolet Line 1968-69

1. Raise car on hoist.
2. On Camaro models, disconnect parking brake cables, and left exhaust pipe from manifold. Remove underbody reinforcement (convertible models only).
3. On Corvette only, remove both exhaust pipes.
4. Remove propeller shaft.
5. Disconnect speedometer cable, electrical leads, vacuum line and oil cooler pipes.
6. Disconnect shift control linkage.
7. Support transmission with suitable jack.
8. Disconnect rear mount from frame crossmember, remove two bolts at each end of crossmember. Remove crossmember.

NOTE: On Corvette models, through bolt at inside of frame and parking brake pulley must also be removed before removing crossmember.

9. Remove converter under pan.
10. Remove converter to flywheel bolts.
11. On Chevrolet and Chevelle, loosen exhaust pipe to manifold bolts to drop pipes approximately ¼″.
12. Lower transmission until jack is barely supporting it, remove engine to transmission bolts, leaving one lower bolt installed. Remove oil filler tube.
13. Raise transmission to its normal position, support engine with jack, remove last attaching bolt and slide transmission rearward and lower it away from vehicle.

CAUTION: Converter holding clamp must be used when removing transmission otherwise converter can fall out when transmission is removed.

14. Remove holding clamp and converter from transmission, using care as it weighs about 50 pounds.
15. Reverse removal procedure to install transmission.

Chevrolet Line 1967

1. Disconnect battery ground cable and release parking brake.
2. Raise vehicle and remove propeller shaft.
3. Disconnect speedometer cable, electrical lead, vacuum line, and oil cooler pipes at transmission.
4. Disconnect shift control linkage from transmission.
5. Remove converter underpan, and remove converter-to-flywheel bolts.
6. Position jack under transmission.
7. Remove transmission mount bolts.
8. Remove rear crossmember.
9. Loosen exhaust pipes at exhaust manifolds.
10. Lower transmission until jack is barely supporting it. Remove six transmission mounting bolts.
11. Remove transmission. It may be necessary to tilt transmission, rear portion down, on some models to remove it from the vehicle.

NOTE: When installing the transmission, it may be necessary on some models to tilt it, rear portion down, when it is being raised to its installation position. With the transmission in its proper position, loosely install four lower attaching bolts. If there is adequate space between transmission case and the vehicle's underbody, install two upper bolts. If there is not, raise transmission until it bottoms on underbody and install two upper bolts from the top.

Chevrolet Line 1966

1. Disconnect battery and release parking brake.
2. Remove propeller shaft.
3. Disconnect speedometer cable, electrical lead to case connector, vacuum line at modulator, and oil cooler pipes.
4. Disconnect shift control linkage.
5. Support transmission with a jack.
6. Disconnect rear mount from frame crossmember.
7. Remove crossmember (2 bolts each side).
8. Remove oil cooler lines, vacuum modulator line, speedometer cable, and detent solenoid connector wire at transmission.
9. Remove converter dust shield, and converter-to-flex plate bolts.
10. Loosen exhaust pipe-to-manifold bolts about ¼", and lower transmission until jack is barely supporting it.

11. Remove transmission-to-engine mount bolts, and remove oil filler tube at transmission.
12. Raise transmission to its normal position, support engine with a jack and slide transmission rearward from engine and lower it away from vehicle. *Keep rear of transmission lower than front so as not to lose converter.*
13. Reverse above procedure to install.

Oldsmobile 1966-71

1. Remove flywheel cover and torque converter attaching bolts.
2. Mark flywheel and converter so they can be installed in same position.
3. Support engine at rear.
4. Disconnect solenoid wires and manual shift linkage at side of transmission.
5. Disconnect oil cooler lines, vacuum modulator line and oil filler pipe.
6. Disconnect parking brake cable.
7. Before removing propeller shaft, scribe marks on drive shaft and companion flange for correct assembly.
8. Disconnect exhaust pipe bracket at rear of crossmember.
9. Support transmission, then remove crossmember.
10. Unfasten transmission from engine.
11. Move transmission away from engine, then, before removing transmission, fasten a suitable piece of strap

iron to housing to prevent converter from falling out as transmission is removed.

Pontiac 1966-71

1. Disconnect battery and release parking brake. Then raise car.
2. Remove propeller shaft.
3. Disconnect speedometer cable, electrical lead to case connector, vacuum line at modulator, and oil cooler pipes.
4. Disconnect shift control linkage.
5. Support transmission with jack.
6. Disconnect rear mount from transmission and crossmember.
7. Remove crossmember (2 bolts at each end).
8. Remove converter dust shield.
9. Remove converter-to-flex plate bolts.
10. Loosen exhaust pipe to manifold about ¼", and lower transmission until jack is barely supporting it.
11. Remove transmission-to-engine mount bolts.
12. Raise transmission to its normal position, slide it rearward and lower it away from vehicle.

NOTE: When lowering transmission, keep rear of unit lower than front so as not to drop converter.

13. Reverse procedure to install.

GM FRONT WHEEL DRIVE
TURBO HYDRA-MATIC

TRANSMISSION IDENTIFICATION

CADILLAC ELDORADO

1967-71 . . . . .AJ

OLDSMOBILE TORONADO

1966-71 With Std. Engine. . . . . .OJ

1968-70 With High Perf. Eng. . . . . .OM

DESCRIPTION

This transmission is a fully automatic unit used for front wheel drive applications, Fig. 1. It consists primarily of a three-element hydraulic torque converter, dual sprocket and chain link assembly, compound planetary gear set, three multiple disc clutches, a sprag clutch, a roller clutch, two band assemblies, and a hydraulic control system.

Torque Converter

The torque converter consists of a pump or driving member, a turbine or driven member and a stator or reaction member.

The stator is mounted on a one-way roller clutch which allows it to overrun when not used as a reaction member. The stator on 1968-71 units is a fixed type while earlier units use a variable pitch type. In the variable pitch type, the stator blades are operated at either of two positions, maximum, or high angle or minimum or low angle.

The torque converter couples the engine to the planetary gear set through the use of a drive sprocket, a chain link assembly, and a driven sprocket. Clockwise engine torque turns the drive sprocket clockwise. This, in turn, drives the driven sprocket in a clockwise direction. This in effect is a reverse in the direction of engine torque due to the side mounting of the gear unit.

Planetary Gear Set

The gear set provides three forward ratios and reverse. The approximate gear ratios are: First $2\frac{1}{2}$ to 1, second $1\frac{1}{2}$ to 1, third 1.1 to 1, reverse 2.1 to 1. Second and third are also multiplied by a lesser degree.

Converter stall ratio, first gear ($2\frac{1}{2}$ x 2) equals 5 to 1. Converter stall ratio, reverse (2.1 x 2) equals 4.2 to 1.

External Controls

External control connections to the transmission are: a) Engine vacuum, b) 12-volt electrical signals, c) manual linkage control.

Engine vacuum is used to operate the vacuum modulator assembly. The vacuum modulator automatically senses any change in torque input to the transmission that the driver induces through a change in accelerator position.

On all models an electrical signal is used to operate an electrical solenoid. The solenoid is activated by a switch at the carburetor. When the throttle is opened sufficiently to close this switch, the solenoid in the transmission is activated, causing a downshift at speeds below approximately 70 mph. At lower speeds, downshifts will occur at lesser speeds without use of the switch.

On 1966-67 models, a stator solenoid is also activated by an electrical switch on the carburetor. The stator is activated at small throttle openings to reduce creep, and at larger throttle openings and high speeds to increase engine output.

TROUBLE SHOOTING GUIDE

NOTE: In many of the following diagnosis procedures, it is recommended that air pressure be applied to help in determining if the seal, rings or pistons are stuck, missing or damaged. Therefore, when air is applied, listen carefully for escaping air and piston action as air is applied to a particular area.

No Drive In "D" Range

1. Low oil level. Check for external leaks or vacuum modulator diaphragm leaking.
2. Manual linkage maladjusted. Correct alignment in manual lever shift quadrant.
3. Low oil pressure.
4. Oil strainer O-ring seal missing or damaged, neck weld leaking, strainer blocked.
5. Oil pump pressure regulator stuck or inoperative. Pump drive gear tangs damaged by converter.
6. Case porosity in intake bore.
7. Control valve. Manual valve disconnected from manual lever pin. (Other shift lever positions would also be affected.)
8. Forward clutch does not apply. Piston cracked; seals missing or damaged. These defects can be checked by removing the valve body and applying air pressure to the drive cavity in the case valve body face. Missing, damaged or worn oil rings on driven support housing can also be checked in this manner at the same time because they can also cause the forward clutch not to apply. Clutch plates burned.
9. Roller clutch inoperative. Rollers worn, damaged springs, or damaged races. May be checked by placing selector lever in "L" range.

No Drive In "R" or Slips In Reverse

1. Low oil level.
2. Manual linkage.
3. Oil pressure. Vacuum modulator defective, modulator valve sticking.
4. Restricted strainer, leak at intake pipe or O-ring seal. Pressure regulator or boost valve sticking.

5. Control valve body gaskets leaking or damaged (other malfunctions may also be indicated). Low-reverse check ball missing from case (this will cause no overrun braking in low range). The 2-3 valve train stuck open (this will also cause 1-3 upshifts in drive range). Reverse feed passage not drilled; also check case passages. Apply air to reverse passage in case valve body face.
6. Rear servo and accumulator. Servo piston seal ring broken or missing. Apply air pressure to drilled hole in intermediate clutch passage of case valve body face to check for piston operation and excessive leakage. Band apply pin too short (this may also cause no overrun braking or slip in overrun braking in low range).
7. Rear band burned, loose lining, apply pin or anchor pin not engaged; band broken.
8. Direct clutch outer seal damaged or missing. Clutch plates burned (may be caused by stuck ball check in piston).
9. Forward clutch does not release (will also cause drive in neutral range).

Drive In Neutral

1. Manual linkage maladjusted.
2. Forward clutch does not release (this condition will also cause no reverse).

1st Speed Only—No 1-2 Upshift

1. Governor valve sticking; driven gear loose, damaged or worn. If driven gear shows signs of wear or damage, check output flange drive gear for nicks or rough finish.
2. Control valve. The 1-2 shift valve train stuck closed. Dirt, chips or damaged valve in 1-2 shift valve train. Governor feed channels blocked or leaking; pipes out of position. Valve body gaskets leaking or damaged. Case porosity between oil channels. Governor feed passage blocked.
3. Intermediate clutch. Case center support oil rings missing, broken or defective. Clutch piston seals missing, improperly assembled, cut or damaged. Apply air to intermediate clutch passage located in case valve body face to check for these defects.

1-2 Shift Obtained Only At Full Throttle

1. Detent switch sticking or defective.
2. Detent solenoid loose, gasket leaking, sticks open, electrical wire pinched between cover and casting.
3. Control valve body gasket leaking or damaged. Detent valve train stuck.

1st & 2nd Speeds Only No 2-3 Shift

1. Detent solenoid stuck open (the 2-3

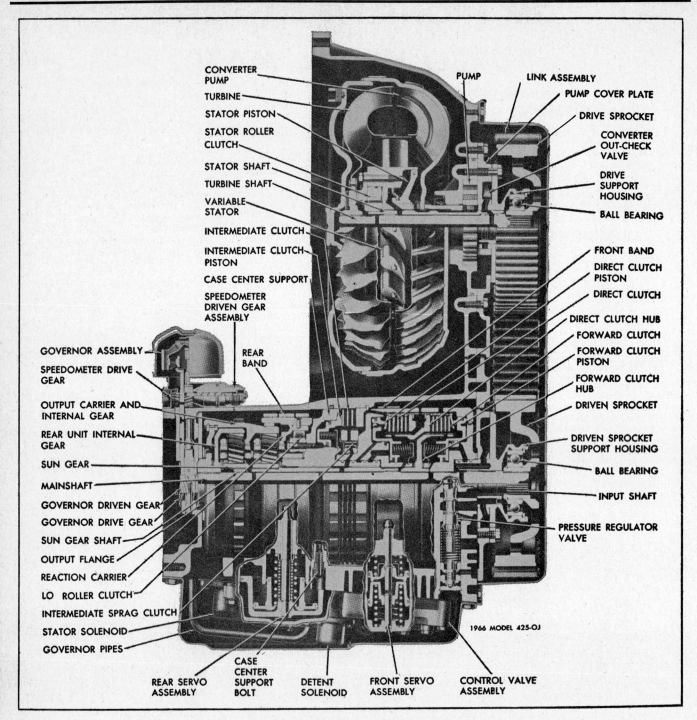

CONVERTER PUMP
TURBINE
STATOR PISTON
STATOR ROLLER CLUTCH
STATOR SHAFT
TURBINE SHAFT
VARIABLE STATOR
INTERMEDIATE CLUTCH
INTERMEDIATE CLUTCH PISTON
CASE CENTER SUPPORT
SPEEDOMETER DRIVEN GEAR ASSEMBLY

PUMP
LINK ASSEMBLY
PUMP COVER PLATE
DRIVE SPROCKET
CONVERTER OUT-CHECK VALVE
DRIVE SUPPORT HOUSING
BALL BEARING

FRONT BAND
DIRECT CLUTCH PISTON
DIRECT CLUTCH
DIRECT CLUTCH HUB
FORWARD CLUTCH
FORWARD CLUTCH PISTON
FORWARD CLUTCH HUB
DRIVEN SPROCKET
DRIVEN SPROCKET SUPPORT HOUSING
BALL BEARING
INPUT SHAFT
PRESSURE REGULATOR VALVE

GOVERNOR ASSEMBLY
SPEEDOMETER DRIVE GEAR
OUTPUT CARRIER AND INTERNAL GEAR
REAR UNIT INTERNAL GEAR
SUN GEAR
MAINSHAFT
GOVERNOR DRIVEN GEAR
GOVERNOR DRIVE GEAR
SUN GEAR SHAFT
OUTPUT FLANGE
REACTION CARRIER
LO ROLLER CLUTCH
INTERMEDIATE SPRAG CLUTCH
STATOR SOLENOID
GOVERNOR PIPES

REAR BAND

REAR SERVO ASSEMBLY
CASE CENTER SUPPORT BOLT
DETENT SOLENOID
FRONT SERVO ASSEMBLY
CONTROL VALVE ASSEMBLY

1966 MODEL 425-OJ

Fig. 1   General Motors Front Wheel Drive Turbo Hydra-Matic

shift would occur at very high speeds) may be diagnosed as no 2-3 shift.
2. Detent switch sticking or defective.
3. Control valve body. The 2-3 valve train stuck with dirt or foreign material. Valve body gaskets leaking or damaged.
4. Direct clutch. Case center support oil rings missing or broken. Clutch piston seals missing, improperly assembled, cut or damaged; piston ball check stuck or missing. Apply air to

direct clutch passage in case valve body face to check these conditions.

Slips In All Ranges

1. Oil level incorrect.
2. Low oil pressure. Vacuum modulator defective or valve sticking. Oil strainer plugged or leaks at neck; O-ring (case to strainer) missing or damaged. Pressure regulator or boost valve sticking.

3. Case cross channel leaks; porosity.
4. Forward, intermediate and direct clutches slipping. Clutch plates burned. Always look for a primary defect that would cause clutch plates to burn. (Missing feed holes, seals and oil rings, etc., are primary defects).
5. Roller clutch rollers worn; springs or cage damaged, and worn or damaged races (operates normally in low and reverse ranges).

Slips 1 - 2 Shift

1. Oil level incorrect.
2. Low oil pressure. Look for defective vacuum modulator or valve sticking. Pump pressure regulator valve stuck.
3. Front servo accumulator piston cracked or porous, oil ring damaged or missing.
4. Control valve. The 1-2 accumulator valve train (may cause a slip-bump shift). Porous valve body or case valve body face.
5. Rear servo accumulator oil ring missing or damaged; case bore damaged; piston cracked or damaged.
6. Case porous between oil passages.
7. Intermediate clutch lip seals missing, cut or damaged. Apply air pressure to intermediate clutch passage in case valve body face to check. Clutch plates burned. Case center support leaks in feed circuits (oil rings damaged or grooves damaged) or excessive leak between tower and bushing.

Rough 1 - 2 Shift

1. Oil pressure. Check vacuum modulator for loose fittings, restrictions in line; defective vacuum modulator. Modulator valve stuck. Pressure regulator boost valve stuck.
2. Control valve. 1-2 accumulator valve train; valve body-to-case bolts loose; gaskets inverted, off location, or damaged.
3. Case. Intermediate clutch passage check ball missing or not seating. Case porous between channels.
4. Rear servo accumulator piston stuck. Apply air pressure to 1-2 accumulator passage in case valve body face (you should hear the servo piston move). Broken or missing spring; bore scored or damaged.

Slips 2 - 3 Shift

1. Oil level high or low.
2. Low oil pressure. Modulator defective or valve sticking. Pump pressure regulator valve or boost valve sticking.
3. Control valve. Accumulator piston pin leak at valve body end.
4. Direct clutch piston seals leaking. Case center support oil seal rings damaged or excessive leak between tower and bushing. Apply air to direct clutch passage in case valve body face. If air comes out intermediate passage, center support is defective.

Rough 2 - 3 Shift

1. Oil pressure high. Vacuum modulator defective or valve sticking. Pump pressure regulator valve or boost valve stuck or inoperative.
2. Front servo accumulator spring missing or broken; accumulator piston stuck.

Shifts Occur at too High or too Low Car Speed

1. Oil pressure. Vacuum modulator defective or valve sticking. Leak in vacuum line (engine to transmission).

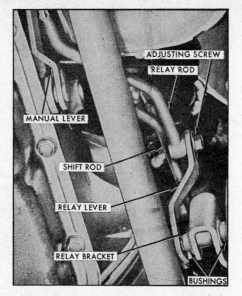

Fig. 2 Manual control linkage adjustment. Cadillac Eldorado

Vacuum modulator line fitting on carburetor blocked. Pump pressure regulator valve or boost valve train stuck.
2. Governor valve stuck or sticking. Feed holes restricted or leaking; pipes damaged or mispositioned.
3. Detent solenoid stuck open or loose on valve body (will cause late shifts).
4. Control valve. Detent valve train sticking; 3-2 valve train sticking; 1-2 shift valve stuck; 1-2 detent valve sticking open (will probably cause early 2-3 shift).
5. Spacer plate gaskets inverted or mispositioned; orifice holes missing or blocked; check balls missing or mislocated.
6. Case porous in channels or foreign material blocking channels.

No Detent Downshift

1. Detent switch mispositioned or electrical connections loose.
2. Solenoid defective or electrical connections loose.
3. Control valve detent valve train stuck.

No Engine Braking—Super Range 2nd Speed

1. Front servo or accumulator piston rings broken or missing. Case or valve body bores worn oversize, causing excessive leakage.
2. Front band worn or burned (check for cause); band end lugs broken or damaged; band lugs not engaged on anchor pins or servo apply pin (check for cause).

No Engine Braking—Low Range 1st Speed

1. Control valve low-reverse check ball missing from case.
2. Rear servo oil ring damaged or missing; piston damaged or porous, causing a leak in apply pressure.

3. Rear band lining worn or burned (check for cause); band end lugs broken; band ends not engaged on anchor pin or servo apply pin. These items will also cause slip in reverse or no reverse.

Will Not Hold Car In Park Position

1. Manual linkage maladjusted (external).
2. Parking brake lever and actuator rod assembly defective (check for proper actuator spring action). Parking pawl broken or inoperative.

Poor Performance or Rough Idle

1. Stator switch defective or maladjusted.
2. Stator solenoid defective or wire ground to solenoid housing; electrical connection loose; stator valve train stuck (located in valve body); oil feed circuit to stator restricted or blocked (check feed hole in stator shaft); converter-out check valve broken or missing (reed valve located in cover plate under drive support housing).
3. Turbine shaft converter return passage not drilled; oil seal rings broken, worn or missing.
4. Case porous in feed circuit channels or foreign material blocking feed circuit.
5. Converter assembly defective.

Transmission Noise

1. Pump noise. Oil level high or low; water in oil, driving gear assembled upside down; driving or driven gear teeth damaged.
2. Gear noise (1st gear drive range). Check planetary pinions for tooth damage. Check sun gear and front and rear internal gears for tooth finish or damage.
3. Clutch noise during application. Check clutch plates.
4. Sprocket and chain link assembly. Chain link too long (sounds similar to popcorn popping). There will be a rough burr along teeth of drive sprocket if chain link is too long; replace chain link and drive sprocket. Drive or driven sprocket teeth damaged. Engine mounts worn or damaged.

Burned Forward Clutch Plates

1. Check ball in clutch housing damaged, stuck or missing.
2. Clutch piston cracked, seals damaged or missing.
3. Low line pressure.
4. Manual valve mispositioned.
5. Restricted oil feed to forward clutch.
6. Pump cover oil seal rings missing, broken or undersize or ring groove oversize.
7. Case valve body face not flat or porosity between channels.
8. Manual valve bent and center land not ground properly.

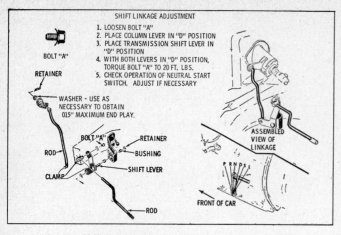

Fig. 3   Shift linkage adjustment. Toronado column shift

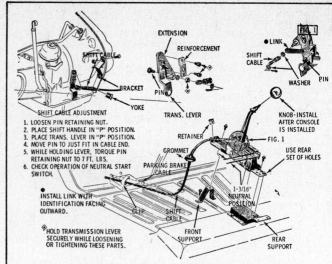

Fig. 4   Shift linkage adjustment. Toronado console shift

Burned Intermediate Clutch Plates

1. Rear accumulator piston oil ring damaged or missing.
2. 1-2 accumulator valve stuck in control valve assembly.
3. Intermediate clutch piston seals damaged or missing.
4. Center support bolt loose.
5. Low line pressure.
6. Intermediate clutch plug in case missing.
7. Case valve body face not flat or porosity between channels.
8. Manual valve bent and center land not ground properly.

Burned Direct Clutch Plates

1. Restricted orifice in vacuum line to modulator.
2. Check ball in direct clutch piston damaged, stuck or missing.
3. Defective modulator bellows.
4. Center support bolt loose.
5. Center support oil rings or grooves damaged or missing.
6. Clutch piston seals damaged or missing.
7. Front and rear servo pistons and seals damaged.
8. Manual valve bent and center land not cleaned up.
9. Case valve body face not flat or porosity between channels.
10. Intermediate sprag clutch installed backwards.

MAINTENANCE
Adding Oil

The fluid level should be checked at every engine oil change interval, and should be changed at 24,000 mile intervals. The fluid level should be checked with the selector lever in PARK position, engine running at idle speed and car on a level surface. The oil indicator and filler tube are located under the hood at the left front corner of the engine. *The filler tube comes out from the final drive housing but it is for the transmission.*

NOTE: If any work is performed on the transmission, it will require the following amounts of oil to bring the oil to the correct level:

1. Pan removed 5½ qts.
2. Drive cover sprocket housing ½ qt.
3. Converter changed 3½ qts.
4. Total overhaul (total capacity) 13 qts.

Changing Oil

When changing transmission oil, first add 4 quarts, start the engine, and add oil to bring the fluid level to the FULL mark on the dipstick. Use only the recommended automatic transmission oil.

MANUAL LINKAGE, ADJUST
Cadillac Eldorado

1. Referring to Fig. 2, loosen adjusting screw on relay bracket.
2. Pull relay rod up to position transmission shift valve in Park, then push rod down to the third (Neutral) step. Make sure rod is centered in this detent position.
3. Position selector lever in Neutral against quadrant stop in steering column.
4. Tighten relay rod adjusting screw, making sure shift lever is held against Neutral stop while this operation is being performed.

Olds Toronado

Make the adjustment as directed in Figs. 3 and 4.

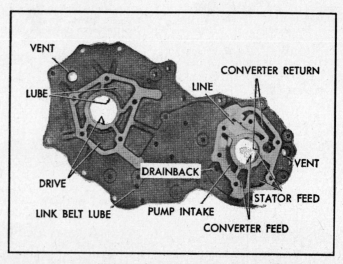

Fig. 5   Location of check balls

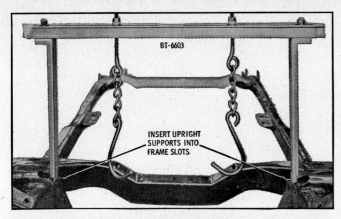

Fig. 6   Installing support bar. Olds Toronado

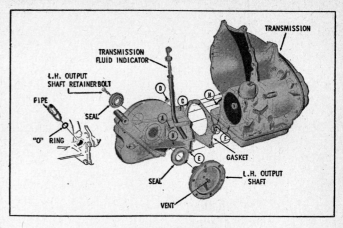

Fig. 7   Transmission attachment

DOWNSHIFT SWITCH, ADJUST

Cadillac Eldorado

1. Remove carburetor air cleaner.
2. Make sure that carburetor is properly adjusted and that throttle linkage is at low speed idle setting.
3. If the downshift switch is properly adjusted, a #31 (wire gauge size) drill can be inserted in the calibrating hole below lower wire terminal extending through to carburetor side of switch.
4. If adjustment is necessary, loosen the two switch mounting screws and position the switch for proper alignment.
5. With switch positioned, tighten mounting screws, remove drill gauge and install air cleaner.

Olds Toronado

1. With slow idle and carburetor rod properly adjusted, engine off, proceed as follows:
2. Disconnect carburetor rod and move switch lever towards closed throttle position until lever hits stop.
3. Connect carburetor rod without moving switch lever to wide open throttle position.
4. Push accelerator pedal to wide open throttle through the detent. This

moves the internal switch contacts to the proper position.

NOTE: Trailer Hauling Switch (Y-73 option) is bronze colored. When checking the special throttle switches with a test lamp, the test lamp *should light* only when the throttle valves are at idle or at wide open throttle position. The test lamp *will not light* at the 40° throttle opening as it does when checking a regular switch.

IN CAR REPAIRS

Operations Not Requiring Transmission Removal

1. Oil cooler fitting replacement or adjustment.
2. Governor assembly service.
3. Vacuum modulator, bushing and valve service.
4. Speedometer drive gear service.
5. Cruise Control service.
6. Oil level check.
7. Oil pressure check with oil pressure gauge.

Units That Can Be Serviced After Oil Pan Removal

1. Oil pan and pan-to-case gasket.
2. Pressure regulator valve assembly.
3. Valve body assembly.
4. Rear servo and accumulator assembly.
5. Front servo and accumulator assembly.
6. Governor pipes.
7. Detent solenoid.
8. Stator solenoid.
9. Solenoid connector.
10. Manual linkage.
11. Parking linkage.
12. Valve body-to-case spacers and gaskets.
13. Check balls for proper location (7 balls), Fig. 5.
14. Detent roller and spring assembly.

TRANS., REPLACE

1966-71 Olds Toronado

Removal
1. Disconnect battery.

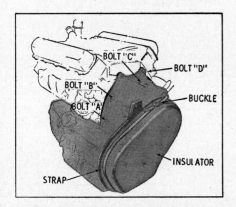

Fig. 8   Transmission to engine attachment

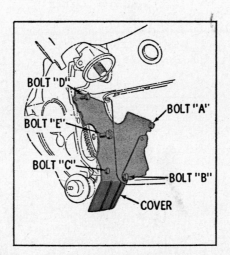

Fig. 9   Converter attachment

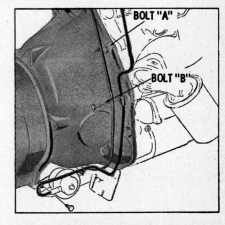

Fig. 10   Transmission to engine attachment

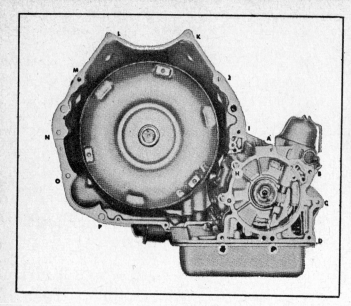

Fig. 11   Transmission attaching bolt
locations. Cadillac Eldorado

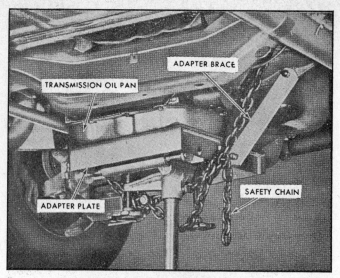

Fig. 12   Positioning transmission jack to
transmission. Cadillac Eldorado

2. Disconnect oil cooler lines at transmission and speedometer cable at governor. On 1969-71 models, remove governor and cover opening to prevent entry of dirt.
3. Install a suitable engine support bar, such as shown in Fig. 6.
4. Remove nut D and bolts A, B and C, Fig. 7.
5. Remove bolts A, B, C, D, Fig. 8.
6. Remove flywheel cover plate bolt, A, Fig. 10.
7. Hoist car and remove starter.
8. Remove bolts B, C and D from flywheel cover plate, Fig. 9.
9. Remove flywheel to converter bolt E, Fig. 9. Rotate flywheel until bolts are removed.
10. Disconnect vacuum modulator line and stator wiring.
11. Install transmission lift.
12. Remove shift linkage.
13. Remove bolts E, F, G and nut H, Fig. 7.
14. Remove bolts A and B, Fig. 10.
15. Remove two upper engine mount bracket-to-transmission bolts.
16. Remove four bracket-to-engine mount bolts.
17. Slide transmission rearward and down.
18. Attach converter holding strap to housing to prevent converter from falling out when transmission is being removed.
19. After transmission is removed from vehicle, the link assembly cover insulator can be removed or installed.

Installation

When installing the transmission the engine mount bracket must be positioned loosely on the link assembly cover until the transmission is in place. Then reverse removal procedure and torque bolts to ft-lb values as follows:
Engine to converter housing 25
Engine bracket to transmission 55
Engine bracket to rubber mount 55
Oil cooler lines to transmission 25

Final drive to transmission 25

1967-71 Cadillac Eldorado

Removal—Figs. 11 and 12
1. Disconnect ground cable at battery.
2. Remove hood on 1967 models.
3. Remove transmission dipstick.
4. Remove filler tube.
5. Remove bolts at locations A, B and C, securing final drive case to transmission.
6. Disconnect speedometer cable at governor.
7. Disconnect oil cooler pipes at transmission and at radiator. Cap pipes and plug connector holes in transmission and radiator.
8. Remove bolt securing cooler pipe bracket to final drive bracket and position pipes away from governor.
9. Remove nut at location H, securing final drive case to transmission.
10. Remove bolts at locations I, J, K and L, securing transmission to engine and adapter plate.
11. Remove upper left bolt securing rear engine mount bracket to transmission.
12. Remove ground strap from cowl.
13. Remove upper left nut securing converter cover plate to transmission.

NOTE: Use a 7/16″ universal socket and extension and reach underneath left exhaust manifold. Removal of this screw can be facilitated by having a helper under the car, verbally guiding socket onto nut.

14. Position cable (with looped ends) under engine intake manifold and hook looped ends to chain fall. Take up slack in chain fall and cable, putting engine mounts under tension.
15. Position safety chain over top of transmission.
16. Raise car and place on jack stands,

adjusting chain fall as required.
17. Disconnect leads from starter motor.
18. Remove bolt at location O, securing starter motor to transmission case and remove ground strap from bolt.
19. Remove bolt at location P and remove starter.
20. Remove three remaining screws securing converter cover plate to transmission and remove cover plate.
21. Position transmission jack.
22. Disconnect electrical connector from transmission connector.
23. Remove pipe from vacuum modulator.
24. Secure transmission to transmission jack adapter plate with safety chain.
25. Remove three flex plate-to-converter attaching bolts.

NOTE: This can be done by installing a 9/16-18 bolt and washer into end of crankshaft at vibration damper, after removing cork plug, and rotating converter and flex plate until bolts are accessible for removal. Do not pry on flex plate ring gear to rotate flex plate and converter as flex plate may be damaged.

26. Remove bolts at locations M and N securing transmission to engine and adapter plate.
27. On left side of transmission, separate relay rod from manual yoke.
28. Remove bolts at locations D, E and F, and nut at location G, securing final drive to transmission.

NOTE: Position drain pan under point where transmission and final drive meet as approximately 1½ quarts of transmission fluid will be lost when transmission and final drive are separated.

29. Remove five bolts and washers securing rear of acromat (cushion) to front cross bar and frame horns

and allow acromat to hang free.

30. Through access holes in bottom of front cross bar, remove left bolt and loosen right bolt securing front engine mount to front cross bar. Turn wheels all the way to the left to provide maximum clearance.

31. Have a helper, using a large pry bar, shift engine forward, while you use a small pry bar to help separate transmission from engine and final drive. *Select pry points with care to avoid damaging any components.*

32. After initial separation has been made, allow transmission oil to drain at final drive junction.

33. Remove two bolts on right side securing rear engine mount bracket to transmission.

34. Through access hole in bottom of transmission support bar, remove two bolts, one each side, securing rear mounts to transmission support bar, and position mounts and bracket rearward to underbody.

35. While a helper pries and holds engine forward, move transmission rearward to disengage transmission case from dowels on engine adapter and to disengage final drive from studs on transmission case. Top of transmission should be tilted slightly rearward.

36. Slowly lower transmission, making certain top of transmission case clears flex plate ring gear and splined input shaft of final drive, until converter is approximately half-way exposed from flex plate.

37. Install a suitable clamp to transmission case at location N to avoid possibility of converter becoming disengaged when transmission is removed.

38. Lower transmission from car.

CAUTION: Rear engine mount bracket will follow transmission out of car; to avoid damage or injury, remove bracket as soon as there is sufficient clearance.

39. Remove and discard final drive gasket and clean mounting surface of final drive.

Installation

1. Position transmission, on jack, under car.

2. Install new gasket on final drive, after first soaking gasket with transmission fluid.

3. Position rear engine mount bracket on top of transmission support bar against underbody.

4. Raise transmission in place until converter is approximately half-way covered by flex plate, then remove converter holding clamp.

5. While a helper assists in holding engine forward with pry bar, continue raising transmission, making certain top of transmission case clears splined input shaft of final drive, and position to engine.

6. Position transmission to engine and final drive by aligning following points in the order listed, while a helper assists:
   a. Studs on transmission case to mounting holes in final drive.
   b. Guide holes in transmission case to dowels on adapter.
   c. Internal flange on final drive to transmission.

NOTE: As engagement of splined final drive input shaft to transmission is hidden, extreme care must be taken to avoid damaging transmission and final drive.

To facilitate engagement of final drive splines, rotate one front wheel while a helper holds the other. When alignment is complete and proper, gap between final drive case and transmission should not exceed $\frac{1}{4}''$.

7. Loosely install bolts ($\frac{3}{8}$ x $1\frac{1}{4}$) at locations D and F attaching transmission to final drive and bolt ($\frac{3}{8}$ x $2\frac{1}{2}$) at location N attaching transmission to engine adapter, alternately tightening bolts to avoid cocking transmission. *Do not torque bolts at this time.*

8. Working in engine compartment, loosely install bolt ($\frac{3}{8}$ x $1\frac{3}{8}$) at location J attaching transmission to adapter. *Do not torque bolt at this time.*

9. Install bolt ($\frac{3}{8}$ x $1\frac{3}{8}$) at location M attaching transmission to adapter plate. *Do not torque bolt at this time.*

10. Position rear engine mount bracket to transmission and loosely install three bolts securing bracket to transmission. *Upper left bolt is installed from engine compartment.*

11. Position rear engine mounts and bracket to transmission support bar and loosely install bolts through access holes in bottom of bar, attaching mounts to bar.

12. Reposition engine as necessary and install left bolt securing front engine mount to front cross bar. Tighten both front mount bolts to 90 ft-lbs.

13. Remove transmission jack.

14. Torque rear engine mounts to transmission support bar bolts to 55 ft-lbs. Torque rear engine mounts to transmission bolts (2 on right side) to 55 ft-lbs. Torque transmission to adapter to engine bolts (located N) to 30 ft-lbs. Torque transmission to adapter bolts (location M) to 30 ft-lbs.

15. Rotate converter until two of the three weld nuts on converter line up with two of the three bolt holes in flex plate. Position converter so that weld nuts are flush with flex plate, making certain converter is not cocked and that pilot in center of converter is properly seated in crankshaft.

16. Install two flex plate-to-converter attaching bolts through accessible holes in flex plate and tighten to 28 ft-lbs. *Bolts must be tightened at this time to assure proper alignment of converter.*

17. Rotate flex plate and converter by rotating bolt previously installed in forward end of crankshaft until third bolt hole is accessible. Install bolt in this hole and tighten to 28 ft-lbs. Remove bolt from crankshaft and install cork plug.

18. Install hose on vacuum modulator.

19. Install electrical connector to transmission connector.

20. Position converter cover plate to transmission case and install two lower and one upper right bolts securing cover plate to transmission, tightening to 5 ft-lbs.

21. Position starter to transmission case and install bolt at location P.

22. Position ground strap to transmission and install bolt securing ground strap and starter to transmission at location O. Tighten bolts at locations O and P to 25 ft-lbs.

23. Install leads on starter motor.

24. Install bolts at locations C and E and nut at location G, securing transmission to final drive.

25. Torque bolts at locations C through F to 25 ft-lbs.

26. Position acromat (cushion) to front cross bar and frame horns and install five bolts and washers.

27. Connect relay rod to manual yoke with cotter pin.

28. Check operation of manual linkage and adjust.

29. Remove chain fall or engine support tool.

30. Install bolts at locations A and B and nut at location H, securing transmission to final drive. Tighten bolts to 25 ft-lbs.

31. Install upper left bolt securing converter cover plate to transmission in the manner described for removing it in Step 13.

32. Install bolts at locations I, J, K and L, securing transmission to engine and adapter. Torque to 25 ft-lbs.

33. Tighten brass cooler pipe connectors at case to 28 ft-lbs. Clean ends of cooler pipes with solvent, connect pipes to transmission and tighten fittings to 28 ft-lbs.

34. Connect cooler pipes to radiator and tighten fittings to 40 ft-lbs.

35. Install cooler pipe clamp.

36. Install speedometer cable to governor.

37. Install new O-ring seal on transmission oil filler tube through hole in final drive case. Fasten filler tube bracket to exhaust manifold.

38. Install body ground strap to firewall.

39. Connect battery cable, fill transmission with fluid and install hood if previously removed.

TURBO HYDRA-MATIC "350"

TRANSMISSION IDENTIFICATION

A production day and shift built number, transmission model and model year are stamped on the 1-2 accumulator cover, which is located on the middle lower right side of the transmission case.

BUICK	CODE
1969 Except Sportwagon	JH
Sportwagon	JJ
1970 6-250	JE
8-350 2 bar. carb. Exc. LeSabre	JH
8-350 4 bar. carb. Exc. LeSabre	JR
8-350 2 bar. carb. LeSabre	JJ
8-350 4 bar. carb. LeSabre	JS
1971 6-250	JE
V8-350 Exc. Below	LA
V8-350 Gran Sport	MA
V8-350 LeSabre	KL

CHEVROLET	
1969-70	B, X, Y

OLDSMOBILE	
1969 F-85 V8-350 2 bar. carb.	JG
F-85 V8-350 4 bar. carb.	JL

OLDSMOBILE—Cont'd	CODE
1970 6-250	JE
8-350 2 bar. carb.	JG
8-350 4 bar. carb. Exc. below	JL
8-350 Ram Air	JO
8-350 Vista Cruiser	JM
1971 6-250	JE
V8-350 Exc. Below	LA
V8-350 Delta 88	LL

PONTIAC	
1969 Tempest 6-250 1 bar. carb.	JA
Firebird 6-250 1 bar. carb.	JB
Tempest 6-250 4 bar. carb.	JC
Firebird 6-250 4 bar. carb.	JD
Tempest & Firebird V8-350 2 bar. carb.	JF
1970 Tempest 6-250	JE
Tempest 8-350	JF
Catalina 8-350	JU

PONTIAC—Cont'd	CODE
1971 6-250	JE
V8-350 Exc. Below	MA
V8-350 Catalina	ML

DESCRIPTION

The Turbo Hydra-Matic 350, Fig. 1, is a fully automatic three speed transmission consisting of a three element torque converter and a compound planetary gear set. Four multiple-disc clutches, two roller clutches and a band provide the friction elements required to obtain the desired function of the planetary gear set.

The friction elements couple the engine to the planetary gears through oil pres-

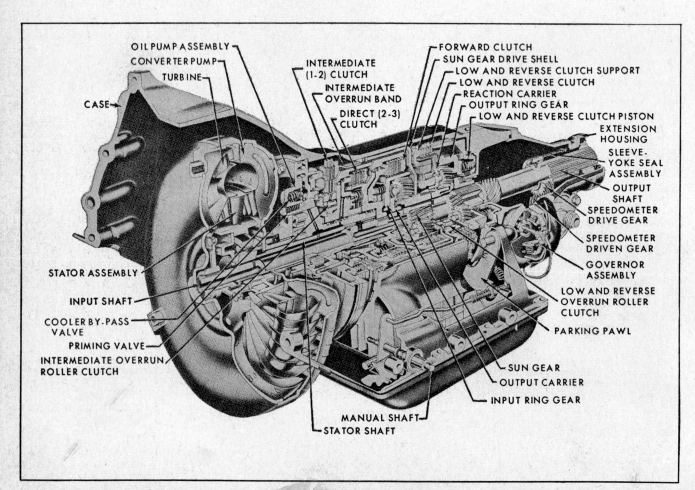

Fig. 1 Cutaway view of Turbo Hydra-Matic 350 transmission

sure, providing three forward speeds and one reverse.

The three element torque converter is of welded construction and is serviced as an assembly. The unit consists of a pump or driving member, a turbine or driven member and a stator assembly. When required, the torque converter supplements the gears by multiplying engine torque.

TROUBLE SHOOTING GUIDE

No Drive In Drive Range

1. Low oil level (check for leaks).
2. Manual control linkage improperly adjusted.
3. Low oil pressure due to blocked strainer, defective pressure regulator, pump assembly or pump drive gear. See that tangs have not been damaged by converter. Check case for porosity in intake bore.
4. Check control valve assembly to be sure manual valve has not been disconnected from inner lever.
5. Forward clutch may be stuck or damaged. Check pump feed circuits to forward clutch, including clutch drum ball check.
6. Roller clutch assembly broken or damaged.

Oil Pressure High or Low

High Pressure:
1. Vacuum line or fittings leaking.
2. Vacuum modulator.
3. Modulator valve.
4. Pressure regulator.
5. Oil pump.

Low Pressure:
1. Vacuum line or fittings obstructed.
2. Vacuum modulator.
3. Modulator valve.
4. Pressure regulator.
5. Governor.
6. Oil pump.

1 - 2 Shift At Full Throttle Only

1. Detent valve may be sticking or linkage may be misadjusted.
2. Vacuum line or fittings leaking.
3. Control valve body gaskets leaking, damaged or incorrectly installed. Detent valve train or 1-2 valve stuck.
4. Check case for porosity.

First Speed Only, No 1 - 2 Shift

1. Governor valve may be sticking.
2. Driven gear in governor assembly loose, worn or damaged. If driven gear shows damage, check output shaft drive gear for nicks or rough finish.
3. Control valve governor feed channel blocked or gaskets leaking. 1-2 shift valve train stuck closed.
4. Check case for blocked governor feed channels or for scored governor bore which will allow cross pressure leak. Check case for porosity.
5. Intermediate clutch or seals damaged.
6. Intermediate roller clutch damaged.

1st & 2nd Only, No 2 - 3 Shift

1. Control valve 2-3 shift train stuck. Valve body gaskets leaking, damaged or improperly installed.
2. Pump hub-to-direct clutch oil seal rings broken or missing.
3. Direct clutch piston seals damaged. Piston ball check stuck or missing.

Moves Forward In Neutral

1. Manual linkage misadjusted.
2. Forward clutch not releasing.

No Drive In Reverse or Slips In Reverse

1. Low oil level.
2. Manual linkage misadjusted.
3. Modulator valve stuck.
4. Modulator and reverse boost valve stuck.
5. Pump hub-to-direct clutch oil seal rings broken or missing.
6. Direct clutch piston seal cut or missing.
7. Low and reverse clutch piston seal cut or missing.
8. Number 1 check ball missing.
9. Control valve body gaskets leaking or damaged.
10. 2-3 valve train stuck in upshifted position.
11. 1-2 valve train stuck in upshifted position.
12. Intermediate servo piston or pin stuck so intermediate overrun band is applied.
13. Low and reverse clutch piston out or seal damaged.
14. Direct clutch plates burned — may be caused by stuck ball check in piston.
15. Forward clutch not releasing.

Slips In All Ranges

1. Low oil level.
2. Vacuum modulator valve defective or sticking.
3. Filter assembly plugged or leaking.
4. Pressure regulator valve stuck.
5. Pump to case gasket damaged.
6. Check case for cross leaks or porosity.
7. Forward clutch slipping.

Slips 1 - 2 Shift

1. Low oil level.
2. Vacuum modulator assembly defective.
3. Modulator valve sticking.
4. Pump pressure regulator valve defective.
5. 2-3 accumulator oil ring damaged or missing. 1-2 accumulator oil ring damaged or missing. Case bore damaged.
6. Pump to case gasket mispositioned or damaged.
7. Check for case porosity.
8. Intermediate clutch piston seals damaged. Clutch plates burned.

Rough 1 - 2 Shift

1. Vacuum modulator, check for loose fittings, restrictions in line or defective modulator assembly.
2. Modulator valve stuck.
3. Valve body regulator or boost valve stuck.

4. Pump to case gasket mispositioned or damaged.
5. Check case for porosity.
6. Check 1-2 accumulator assembly for damaged oil rings, stuck piston, broken or missing spring, or damaged case bore.

Slips 2 - 3 Shift

1. Low oil level.
2. Modulator valve or vacuum modulator assembly defective.
3. Pump pressure regulator valve or boost valve; pump to case gasket mispositioned.
4. Check case for porosity.
5. Direct clutch piston seals or ball check leaking.

Rough 2 - 3 Shift

1. High oil pressure. Vacuum leak, modulator valve sticking or pressure regulator or boost valve inoperative.
2. 2-3 accumulator piston stuck, spring broken or missing.

No Engine Braking In Second Speed

1. Intermediate servo or 2-3 accumulator oil rings or bores leaking or accumulator piston stuck.
2. Intermediate overrun band burned or broken.
3. Low oil pressure: Pressure regulator and/or boost valve stuck.

No Engine Braking In 1st Speed

1. Manual low control valve assembly stuck.
2. Low oil pressure: Pressure regulator and/or boost valve stuck.
3. Low and reverse clutch piston inner seal damaged.

No Part Throttle Downshift

1. Oil pressure: Vacuum modulator assembly, modulator valve or pressure regulator valve train malfunctioning.
2. Detent valve and linkage sticking, disconnected or broken.
3. 2-3 shift valve stuck.

No Detent Downshifts

1. 2-3 valve stuck.
2. Detent valve and linkage sticking, disconnected or broken.

Low or High Shift Points

1. Oil pressure: Check engine vacuum at transmission end of modulator pipe.
2. Vacuum modulator assembly vacuum line connections at engine and transmission, modulator valve, pressure regulator valve train.
3. Check governor for sticking valve, restricted or leaking feed holes, damaged pipes or plugged feed line.
4. Detent valve stuck open.
5. 1-2 or 2-3 valve train sticking.
6. Check case for porosity.

Won't Hold In Park

1. Manual linkage misadjusted.
2. Parking brake lever and actuator assembly defective.
3. Parking pawl broken or inoperative.

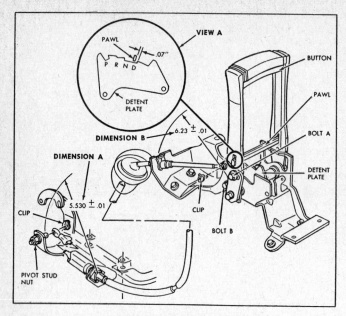

Fig. 2 Manual linkage adjustments. Camaro, Chevelle & Chevrolet console shift

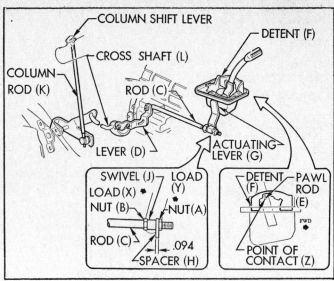

Fig. 3 Manual linkage adjustments. Nova console shift

Burned Forward Clutch Plates

1. Check ball in clutch drum damaged, stuck or missing.
2. Clutch piston cracked, seals damaged or missing.
3. Low line pressure.
4. Pump cover oil seal rings missing, broken or undersize; ring groove oversize.
5. Transmission case valve body face not flat or porosity between channels.

Burned Intermediate Clutch Plates

1. Intermediate clutch piston seals damaged or missing.
2. Low line pressure.
3. Transmission case valve body face not flat or porosity between channels.

Burned Direct Clutch Plates

1. Restricted orifice in vacuum line to modulator.
2. Check ball in clutch drum damaged, stuck or missing.
3. Defective modulator.
4. Clutch piston cracked, seals damaged or missing.
5. Transmission case valve body face not flat or porosity between channels.

MAINTENANCE

Fluid should be checked every 6,000 miles with engine idling, selector lever in neutral position, parking brake set and transmission at operating temperature. Use only General Motors Dexron transmission fluid when adding oil. Do not overfill.

Every 24,000 miles, remove drain plug in transmission oil pan and drain transmission oil sump. Add 1½ quarts after

replacing plug, check fluid and add enough fluid to bring level to the Full mark.

MANUAL LINKAGE, ADJUST

Buick

Console Shift

1. Loosen trunnion bolt.
2. Set selector lever against Drive stop.
3. Place transmission in Drive.
4. Tighten trunnion bolt to 6-9 ft-lbs.
5. Set selector lever in Park and set Back Drive Adjustment as outlined below.

Column Shift, 1969-70

1. Loosen adjusting clamp bolt.
2. Place selector lever against Drive stop.
3. Place transmission in Drive.
4. Tighten clamp bolt to 17-23 ft. lbs.

Column Shift, 1971

1. Loosen adjusting clamp bolt.
2. Place selector lever against Neutral stop.
3. Place transmission in Neutral.
4. Tighten clamp bolt to 17-23 ft. lbs.

Chevrolet

Camaro, Chevelle & Chevrolet Console Shift

1. Place shift lever in Drive.
2. Raise vehicle, disconnect cable from transmission lever and manually place transmission lever in Drive. Measure distance from rearward face of attachment bracket to center of cable attachment stud. This dimension should be 5.5". If not, loosen stud nut and move stud accordingly. Rein-

stall stud nut and adjust end of cable so that it fits freely on stud. Reinstall clip.
3. Lower vehicle and remove shift quadrant cover. Raise quadrant plate, disconnect bulbs and remove plate. Remove cable clip and disengage cable from shift lever.
4. Insert a .07" gauge between pawl and detent, Fig. 2. Measure distance from forward face of shifter bracket and center of cable pin. This dimension should be 6.25". If not, loosen bolt A and move lever until dimension is obtained. Retighten bolt and adjust cable end until it freely enters pin. Install clip. Pawl engagement can be adjusted by raising or lowering the detent plate after loosening bolt B. If such an adjustment is made, step 4 must be repeated.
5. Remove gauge and check operation.
6. Reinstall shift plate and cover.
7. Set selector lever in Park and adjust Back Drive as outlined below.

Nova Console Shift

1. Loosen assembly nuts A and B, Fig. 3 on lower rod.
2. Set transmission lever in Drive.
3. Set pawl rod in the Neutral or Drive notch of detent.
4. Apply load in direction of arrow on actuating lever until pawl rod comes in contact with detent.
5. Place a .094" spacer between nut and swivel and run nut up until it touches spacer. Tighten lock nuts.
6. Place transmission and shift lever in Park position.
7. Install column rod to column lever and cross shaft.
8. Set selector lever in Park and adjust Back Drive as outlined below.

Column Shift

1. Place selector lever in Drive as determined by the transmission detent.

2. Loosen adjustment swivel at cross shaft and rotate transmission lever so it contacts the Drive stop in the steering column.
3. Tighten swivel and recheck adjustment.
4. Readjust indicator needle if necessary to agree with the transmission detent positions.
5. Readjust neutral safety switch if necessary.
6. Set selector lever in Park and adjust Bakc Drive as outlined below.

Oldsmobile

Console Shift

1. Loosen shift rod clamp screw and pin in transmission manual lever. Place shift handle and transmission manual lever in Park position.
2. With rod held lightly against Park stop, tighten screw in clamp at lower end of shift rod.
3. Move pin to give "free pin" fit in manual lever and tighten.

Column Shift

1. With shift rod clamp and screw loosely assembled to shift rod, set transmission outer lever in Drive. Check to see that steering column lever is in Drive and tighten clamp on shift rod.

Pontiac Firebird & Tempest

Console Shift

1. Place shift handle in Park and transmission manual lever in Park.
2. With rod held lightly against Park stop, tighten screw in clamp at lower end of rod.
3. Adjust pin in selector lever to freely enter the end of the shift cable and tighten pin nut.

Column Shift

With shift rod clamp and screw loosely

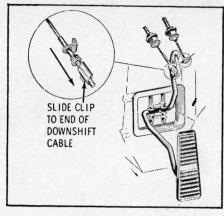

Fig. 4   Detent cable clip. Buick Oldsmobile & Pontiac

(caption in figure: SLIDE CLIP TO END OF DOWNSHIFT CABLE)

assembled to shift rod, set transmission outer lever in Park position. Check to see that steering column lever is in Park position and tighten clamp on shift rod.

BACK DRIVE, ADJUST

1. Disconnect lower rod at transmission lever.
2. Move transmission lever to Park position.
3. Place transmission selector lever in Park position.
4. Attach lower rod to transmission lever and check for proper operation.

NOTE: Any inaccuracies in the above adjustments may result in premature failure of the transmission due to operation without the controls in full detent. Such operation results in reduced oil pressure and in turn partial engagement of the affected clutches.

THROTTLE LINKAGE, ADJUST

Buick Special

Buick Special throttle linkage is of the cable type and no provision is made for adjustment.

Chevrolet

Camaro, Chevelle & Nova

These models use cable controls and require no adjustment.

Chevrolet (Rod Type)

1. Disconnect throttle rod swivel at throttle lever on carburetor.
2. Hold carburetor throttle in wide open position, push throttle rod rearward to place accelerator pedal at the floor mat and adjust swivel to just enter hole in throttle lever.
3. Connect swivel to throttle lever and install accelerator return spring.

Corvette

1. Loosen throttle cable clamp bolt.
2. Hold accelerator pedal to floor against stop.
3. Move carburetor throttle lever to wide open position and tighten throttle cable clamp bolt to 45 in-lbs.

Oldsmobile

Cable Type

Cable type controls require no adjustment.

Carburetor Rod

1. With slow idle adjusted, engine off, choke open and fast idle off, disconnect swivel on carburetor rod from bellcrank.
2. Push upper lever of auxiliary bell crank towards firewall until it hits stop.
3. Pull carburetor rod towards firewall until throttle is wide open.
4. Adjust swivel until pin just enters hole in bellcrank.
5. Reconnect carburetor rod to auxiliary bellcrank.

Firebird & Tempest

The throttle control system is of the cable type with no adjustment provided. A reference dimension of 1⁹⁄₁₆" between the bottom of the accelerator pedal roller and floor pan should be used to check for bent bracket assemblies.

DETENT CABLE, ADJUST

Buick, Oldsmobile & Pontiac

The detent cable is adjusted from inside the driver's compartment as follows:

1. With engine off, throttle closed and fast idle off, position retainer clip against the insert on the detent cable, Fig. 4.
2. Grasp throttle pedal lever adjacent to the detent cable and pull the carburetor cable to the wide open position. By following this procedure, the detent cable will be adjusted properly.

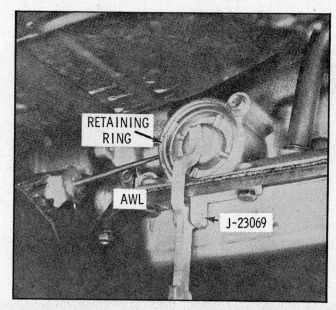

Fig. 5   Intermediate clutch accumulator piston removal

(labels in figure: RETAINING RING, AWL, J-23069)

Chevrolet

On Chevrolet units, the detent cable is adjusted at the carburetor.
1. Remove air cleaner.
2. Loosen detent cable screw.
3. With choke off and accelerator linkage properly adjusted, position carburetor lever in the wide open throttle position.
4. Pull detent cable rearward until wide open throttle stop in transmission is felt.

NOTE: Cable must be pulled through detent position to reach wide open throttle stop in transmission.

5. Tighten detent cable screw and check linkage for proper operation.

IN CAR REPAIRS
Valve Body Assembly

1. Remove oil pan and strainer.
2. Remove retaining pin to disconnect downshift actuating lever bracket, remove valve body attaching bolts and detent roller and spring assembly.
3. Remove valve body assembly while disconnecting manual control valve link from range selector inner lever.

CAUTION: Do not drop valve.

4. Remove manual valve and link from valve body assembly.
5. Reverse procedure to install.

Governor

1. Where necessary, remove shift linkage and transmission to crossmember bolts.
2. Raise transmission with jack and remove crossmember. Lower transmission enough to remove governor.
3. Remove governor cover retainer and cover.
4. Remove governor.

Intermediate Clutch Accumulator Piston Assembly

1. Remove two oil pan bolts adjacent to accumulator piston cover, install compressor on oil pan lip and retain with these two bolts, Fig. 5.
2. Compress intermediate clutch accumulator piston cover and remove retaining ring piston cover and O ring from case.
3. Remove spring and intermediate clutch accumulator piston.

Vacuum Modulator & Modulator Valve Assembly

1. Disconnect vacuum hose from modulator stem and remove vacuum modulator screw and retainer.
2. Remove modulator and its O ring.
3. Remove modulator valve from case.

Extension Housing Oil Seal

1. Remove propeller shaft.
2. Pry out lip seal with screwdriver or small chisel.

Manual Shaft, Range Selector Inner Lever & Parking Linkage Assemblies

1. Remove oil pan and strainer.
2. Remove manual shaft to case retainer and unthread jam nut holding range selector inner level to manual shaft.
3. Remove jam nut and remove manual shaft from range selector inner lever and case. *Do not remove manual shaft lip seal unless replacement is required.*
4. Disconnect parking pawl actuating rod from range selector inner lever and remove bolt from case.
5. Remove bolts and parking lock bracket.
6. Remove pawl disengaging spring.
7. If necessary to replace pawl or shaft, clean up bore in case and remove shaft retaining plug, shaft and pawl.

TRANSMISSION, REPLACE
BUICK
1969-71

1. Raise car and remove propeller shaft. If necessary, disconnect exhaust crossover pipe.
2. Place suitable jack under transmission and fasten transmission securely to jack.
3. Remove vacuum line from vacuum modulator.
4. Loosen cooler line nuts and separate cooler lines from transmission.
5. Remove detent cable from accelerator lever assembly. *Do not bend cable.* Remove plastic guide from bracket and slide cable out through slot.
6. Remove detent cable from detent valve link.
7. Remove crossmember.
8. Disconnect speedometer cable, shift linkage and filler pipe. Remove filler pipe.
9. Support engine at oil pan.
10. Remove transmission flywheel cover pan.
11. Mark flywheel and converter for reassembly and remove three flywheel to converter bolts.
12. Be sure transmission is supported by transmission jack and remove transmission case to engine block bolts.
13. Move transmission rearward to provide clearance between converter and crankshaft. Install converter holding tool, lower transmission and remove.

CHEVROLET
1969-71

1. Disconnect negative battery cable and raise car.
2. On Camaro only, disconnect parking brake cables, remove underbody re-

inforcement plate (convertible). Disconnect left exhaust pipe from manifold.
3. Remove propeller shaft, disconnect speedometer cable, detent cable, modulator vacuum line and oil cooler pipes.
4. Disconnect shift linkage.
5. Support transmission with suitable jack and remove crossmember.
6. Remove converter under pan.
7. Remove converter to flywheel bolts.
8. On Chevrolet and Chevelle, loosen exhaust pipe to manifold bolts approximately $1/4''$. Lower transmission until jack is barely supporting it.

NOTE: On V8 engines, care must be taken no to lower the rear of the transmission too far as the distributor housing may be forced against firewall causing damage to the distributor.

9. Remove transmission to engine mounting bolts and remove oil filler tube at transmission.
10. Raise transmission to its normal position, support engine with jack and slide transmission rearward from engine and lower it away from vehicle.
11. Reverse procedure to install.

OLDSMOBILE
1969-71

1. From inside the car, slide clip to the end of the detent cable.
2. Remove transmission oil level dipstick.
3. Raise car and remove detent cable from link. Plug hole.
4. Disconnect oil cooler lines at transmission.
5. Remove flywheel cover pan and mark converter and flywheel for reassembly. Remove three flywheel to converter bolts.
6. Disconnect vacuum modulator line. Remove speedometer clip and driven gear. Plug hole.
7. Disconnect shift linkage.
8. Remove propeller shaft.
9. Support transmission with a suitable jack and remove crossmember.
10. Lower transmission slightly and remove transmission to engine bolts.
11. Remove oil level indicator tube and clip holding detent cable to tube.
12. Lower transmission being careful not to damage cooler lines, detent cable, modulator line and shift linkage.
13. Reverse procedure to install.

PONTIAC
1969-71

1. Disconnect battery ground cable and release parking brake.
2. Raise car and remove propeller shaft.
3. Disconnect speedometer cable, vacu-

um hose at modulator, detent cable at transmission and shift linkage.

NOTE. When removing detent cable, be careful not to bend it.

4. Support transmission with a suitable jack and remove crossmember.
5. On Firebird L6, remove driveline damper.
6. Remove converter dust pan, mark flywheel and converter for reassembly and remove flywheel to converter bolts. Make sure converter hub is free of converter.
7. Disconnect transmission filler pipe at engine and remove pipe from transmission.
8. Lower transmission and engine to gain access to cooler line fitting nuts and disconnect cooler lines. On some models it may be necessary to loosen the exhaust system.
9. With transmission in lowered position, remove the transmission to engine bolts.
10. Raise transmission to its normal position, support engine and slide transmission rearward and lower it away from car.

NOTE: When lowering transmission, keep rear of transmission lower than the front so as not to lose the converter.

11. Reverse procedure to install.

CORVAIR POWERGLIDE

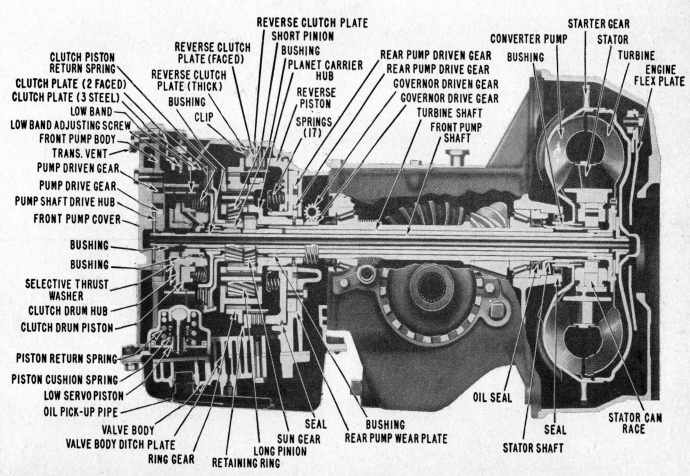

Fig. 1   Corvair Powerglide

TRANSMISSION IDENTIFICATION

All transmissions carry the unit number B-706-D. This number is stamped on the oil pan at the shallow end.

DESCRIPTION

As shown in Fig. 1, the transmission is integrated with the differential carrier to form a transaxle. As a result, the converter is remote from the main transmission assembly, being separated by the differential carrier. Two shafts run axially through the hollow pinion shaft; one from the converter cover hub to the front pump and the other from the turbine to the input sun gear to transmit converter torque to the transmission gear box.

Construction

This transmission, Fig. 1, consists of an air-cooled, three-element torque converter driving a two-speed planetary gear set. The selector lever has four positions providing Drive, Neutral, Low and Reverse. No Park Range is provided.

The torque converter is attached through a flex plate to the engine crankshaft. From the converter the transmission input shaft goes through the hollow hypoid pinion and transmission output shafts.

Inside the transmission the compound planetary gear set is employed to provide a 1.82 reduction for Low and Reverse. A double-wrap band provides the reaction for Low, and a multiple plate clutch connects the input and output for Direct Drive. A multiple plate clutch supplies the reaction for Reverse operation.

The torque converter features an all welded cover to facilitate air cooling and provide a positive seal. Maximum torque multiplication is 2.6 to 1.

Special provision is made to drive the transmission front pump. A special shaft is splined to the converter front cover and runs through the hollow input shaft to the transmission front pump. The front pump shaft also serves as the bearing support for the input shaft under the drive clutch.

Drive Range performance features a smooth upshift from the 1.82 to 1 geared reduction to Direct Drive. The shift speed is determined by the combined influence of an engine vacuum modulator, output shaft driven governor and accelerator linkage controlled throttle valve.

TROUBLE SHOOTING

Oil Forced Out Filler Tube

1. Oil level too high causing planet carrier to run in oil and cause foam.
2. Oil pickup pipe split or not sealed, allowing air in system.

No Drive In Any Position

1. Low oil level.
2. Clogged oil suction pipe screen.
3. Broken or disconnected manual valve cable.

4. Defective pressure regulator valve.
5. Front pump defective.
6. Rear pump check valve, check valve poppet, or rear pump priming ball not seating. Both must occur for possible malfunction.
7. Defective line pressure limit valve.
8. Front pump shaft disengaged at either converter or pump gear.
9. Front pump priming ball not seating.

Erratic Operation or Slippage (Light to Medium Throttle)

1. Low oil level.
2. Clogged pickup pipe screen.
3. Improper bank adjustment.
4. Band facing worn.
5. Low band apply linkage disengaged or broken.
6. Servo piston apply passage blocked.
7. Servo piston ring broken or missing.
8. Converter stator not holding (rare).

Engine Speed Flares on Upshift

1. Low oil level.
2. Improper band adjustment.
3. Clogged oil suction screen.
4. High clutch partially applied (blocked feed orifice).
5. High clutch plates worn.
6. High clutch seals leak.
7. High clutch piston hung up.
8. High clutch relief ball not seating.
9. Vacuum modulator hose plugged.
10. Vacuum modulator defective.

Will Not Upshift

1. Maladjusted manual valve lever.
2. Throttle valve stuck or maladjusted.
3. No rear pump output caused by stuck priming valve, sheared pin or defective pump.
4. Defective governor.
5. Stuck low-drive valve.

Harsh Upshifts

1. Throttle valve linkage improperly adjusted.
2. Vacuum modulator hose broken or disconnected.
3. Vacuum modulator diaphragm leaks.
4. Vacuum modulator valve stuck.
5. Hydraulic modulator valve stuck.
6. Improper low band adjustment.

Harsh Closed Throttle Downshifts

1. High engine idle speed.
2. Improper low band adjustment.
3. Vacuum modulator hose disconnected or broken.
4. Vacuum modulator diaphragm ruptured.
5. Vacuum modulator valve stuck.
6. Sticking valves in valve body (pressure regulator or hydraulic modulator valves).

Creeps In Neutral

1. Manual linkage improperly adjusted.
2. High clutch or low bank not released.

No Drive In Reverse

1. Manual valve linkage improperly adjusted (cable).
2. Reverse clutch piston stuck.

3. Reverse clutch plates worn out.
4. Reverse clutch leaking excessively.
5. Blocked reverse clutch apply orifice.

Improper Shift Points

1. Throttle valve linkage improperly adjusted.
2. Incorrectly adjusted TV valve.
3. Governor defective.
4. Rear pump priming valve stuck.

Unable to Push Start

1. Rear pump drive gear not engaged with drive pins on planet carrier hub.
2. Drive pin sheared off or missing.
3. Rear pump priming ball not seating.
4. Rear pump defective.

MAINTENANCE
Adding Oil

Oil level should be checked every 1000 miles. Oil should be added only when the level is near the "ADD" mark on the dipstick with oil at normal operating temperature. The oil level dipstick is located in the right front of the engine compartment. *The difference in oil level between "FULL" and "ADD" is one pint.*

To check oil level accurately, the engine should be idled with the transmission oil at normal operating temperature and the control lever in Neutral position. Oil level should be maintained no higher than the "FULL" mark on the dipstick. Do not overfill as foaming and aerating of the oil will result because the planetary unit will be running in oil, causing improper application of the bank or clutches.

Draining and Refilling

SERVICE NOTE: Periodic draining of the oil pan on all transmissions every 12,000 miles under normal operation and more frequently under extreme service usage is now recommended. It is realized that only a portion of the fluid can be drained at the oil pan. However, the addition of even this volume of fresh fluid will replenish the additives in the remaining fluid to increase transmission durability.

To drain the oil, loosen the filler tube attaching nut in the oil pan and allow the oil to drain. When drained, tighten filler tube nut and add 3 quarts of approved transmission fluid to the transmission.

Set the parking brake and operate the transmission through all ranges. Then with engine idling, selector lever in neutral and transmission at operating temperature, recheck the fluid level and add fluid as necessary to bring the level up to the "Full" mark on the dipstick. Do not overfill as damage to the transmission can result.

Refilling After Repairs

To refill the transmission, tighten the filler tube nut and add 4 pints of transmission fluid, using a suitable filler tube and funnel. Start engine and allow it to idle in Neutral for 3 to 5 minutes to warm the transmission fluid. Then add oil as required to bring the level to the "FULL" mark on the dipstick. Assuming that the converter was not drained

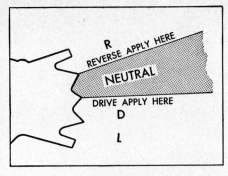

Fig. 2   Shift linkage check diagram

(since it is welded) and allowing for nominal spillage or draindown, approximately 3 quarts are required for a refill.

MANUAL LINKAGE
Check Operation

If improper shift linkage adjustment is suspected, a check can be made quickly without any disassembly as follows:
1. Start engine and allow to run for 2 to 3 minutes to warm up the transmission fluid.
2. With engine at normal idle speed, very slowly move range selector lever up from "N" to "R" and note by feel the point at which the reverse clutch applies. Properly adjusted, the reverse clutch should apply at the peak of the tooth separating Neutral and Reverse detents, Fig. 2.
3. Make the same check as in Step 2 while moving the selector lever from "N" toward "D". Properly adjusted, the low band should apply as the selector lever follower is felt to be at the tooth peak separating Neutral from Drive and full Drive detent.
4. Unless the shifts are obtained at the points illustrated, the shift linkage should be adjusted with Gauge J-8365, Fig. 3.

Adjustment

1. Drain oil and remove oil pan.
2. Place selector lever in "D".
3. Insert Gauge J-8365 into manual valve bore as shown in Fig. 3 with tab of gauge upward so it engages to forward port of valve body as shown in inset.
4. With gauge in place, push forward on manual valve levers. Properly adjusted, the gauge will be held in place horizontally without being supported.
5. If readjustment is required, loosen lock screw and push manual valve levers forward so that gauge is held in this attitude. Recheck adjustment as in Step 4.
6. When satisfactory adjustment is obtained, install oil pan and filler tube; then refill transmission with oil as described above.

THROTTLE LINKAGE
1966-69

NOTE: Accelerator linkage should be ad-

justed to get simultaneous full throttle position at the accelerator pedal, the linkage idler lever and the carburetor throttle lever. The pedal downward travel stop (at idler lever at transmission) is adjustable to furnish a pedal angle comfortable to the driver.

1. To adjust, disconnect accelerator pull rod swivel from rear idler lever.
2. Disconnect carburetor pull-back spring. Remove carburetor cross shaft actuating rod swivel from cross shaft.
3. Pull carburetor cross shaft actuating rod rearward until rear idler lever hits stop on its bracket. Rotate carburetor cross shaft to move L.H. primary carburetor into wide open throttle position (thru detent on Powerglide).
4. With carburetor cross shaft and its actuating rod held in the foregoing positions, align actuating rod swivel until it freely engages its mating hole in cross shaft lever. Remove swivel and back it off five full turns and replace it in lever hole.
5. Connect pull-back spring.
6. Depress pedal to within 1⅛" of floor carpet and block pedal in this position. *This pedal setting is measured from the underside of the rubber flange at the top of the pedal.*
7. Rotate rear idler lever into wide open throttle position and reconnect accelerator pull rod after adjusting rod swivel so it freely engages its mating hole in idler lever.
8. Remove pedal block and check complete accelerator control linkage adjustment by depressing pedal and inspecting carburetor throttle valve to to sure it is at wide open position.

LOW BAND, ADJUST

As no periodic adjustment of the low band is recommended, access to the adjusting screw has been provided from inside the vehicle via the parcel compartment area behind the rear seat.

To gain access to the low band, remove the parcel shelf and the plug covering the access hole in the floor pan.

Adjustment of the low band requires an improvised tubular hex ¾" socket approximately 4½ to 6" long. Probably the simplest way to fabricate this tool would be to weld two ¾" tubular stamped steel spark plug wrenches together.

To adjust, loosen the lock nut and tighten the adjusting screw to 35 to 45 inch lbs., then back off 4 complete turns exactly. While holding the adjusting screw stationary by means of the socket, inserted through the improvised wrench, tighten the lock nut securely.

CONTROL CABLE, REPLACE
1966-69

Removal
1. Remove instrument cluster.
2. Disconnect control cable from range selector.

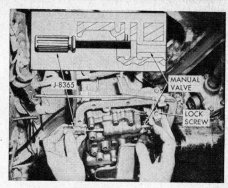

Fig. 3   Adjusting manual valve linkage

3. Remove tunnel covers.
4. At front of vehicle remove cable from dash clip, Fig. 4, and from beneath parking brake pulley shaft.
5. Remove cable from three body harness clips in tunnel.
6. Remove grommet plate at rear of tunnel, free cable sheath from plate, and remove clip in underbody kick-up area.
7. Disconnect throttle rods from TV lever on transmission.
8. Complete cable removal by rotating transmission TV lever its full limit to free cable ball from inner manual valve lever slot in transmission and withdraw cable. Bow cable towards center line of vehicle to guide cable through hole in engine front support.

Installation
1. With tunnel covers removed, lay cable out beneath car in its correct relationship.
2. Insert front of cable up into passenger compartment. Cable must then be routed under parking brake cable and then over brake pipe to prevent brake cable riding against shift cable and establishing a sawing action.
3. After cable routing is satisfactory, connect shift cable to range selector.
4. Shift range selector to Drive position, then route cable through upper dash clip and close clip. Continue routing cable through underbody opening and under parking brake pulley shaft at base of toe pan. Be sure rubber protector is installed on cable sheath.
5. Secure cable with two clips provided in tunnel area. Bow cable towards center line of vehicle to guide cable through hole in engine front support.
6. Install O-ring seal on cable, Fig. 5, applying lubriplate lightly on seal.
7. With throttle rods disconnected from TV lever on transmission, rotate TV lever its full limit counter-clockwise and insert cable ball into slot of manual valve lever.
8. Fully seat O-ring seal and secure installation by installing cap screw and lock washer.
9. Correctness of installation is easily checked. Once fully tightened, exert a slight hand pressure in counter-clockwise direction and check that the hole in the notched arm of the TV lever is below the transmission

CORVAIR POWERGLIDE

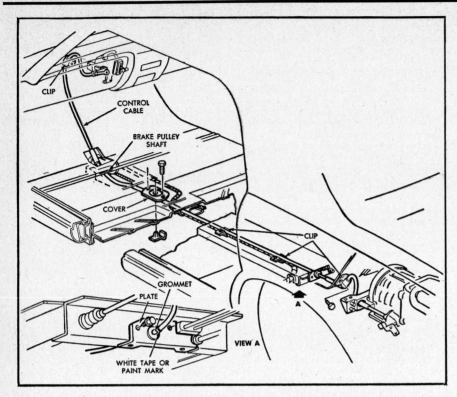

Fig. 4   Shift control cable routing. 1966-69

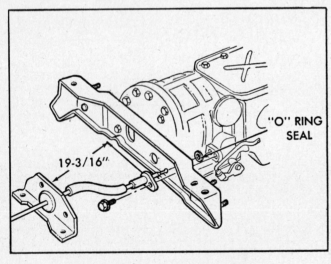

Fig. 5   Cable-to-case installation. 1966-69

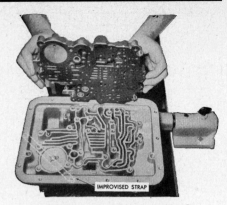

Fig. 6   Removing valve body

smoky exhaust and continually low transmission oil level. No repairs are possible on the modulator; replace with new unit.

When installing, center the gasket in place with vaseline and hold it centered during installation to prevent an external oil leak.

GOVERNOR

Governor is accessible from beneath the vehicle and is mounted on the left side of the transmission. To remove, unscrew lock screw and pull the unit out of the transmission.

VALVE BODY & LOW SERVO

Removal

1. Drain oil pan and disconnect throttle valve rods from TV lever on transmission.
2. Remove oil pan and oil pick-up pipe.
3. Make an improvised sheet metal strap, Fig. 6, and loosely install with one pan bolt.
4. Remove bolts securing valve body to transmission, tap valve body lightly with a soft hammer to loosen from its dowels in transmission case, then carefully lower the valve body about $1/16''$, rotate improvised strap into place so it spans the servo piston hub and secure strap with pan bolt. This eliminates possibility of servo piston slipping down out of its bore and the loss of low band engagement with its apply components.
5. To remove the low servo piston, pull downward on the hub of the piston shaft with a screwdriver. *Do not remove piston in vehicle unless low band screw is first tightened fully.*

Low Servo Piston Repairs

Disassemble the servo piston by removing the hairpin clip. Remove ring from piston and install it in low servo bore to measure the ring gap which should be .002″ to .012″.

oil pan rail. If hole is above pan rail, cable installation is faulty and must be re-checked.
10. Install cable rear grommet, Fig. 4, in grommet plate, then install grommet plate in rear of tunnel and pull cable through grommet until white tape or paint mark is visible outside grommet.
11. Install clip on cable in rear kick-up area.
12. Check shift linkage for proper operation.

VACUUM MODULATOR

The vacuum modulator is mounted on the right side of the transmission and can be serviced from beneath the vehicle. Disconnect the vacuum hose and unscrew the modulator from the transmission with channel lock pliers or a thin one-inch wrench.

The vacuum modulator can be checked with a vacuum source for leakage. However, leakage normally results in transmission oil pull-over and results in oil

Assemble ring to piston and measure clearance between ring and one wall of piston groove which should be .0005" to .005".

Installation

1. Install low servo piston and return spring in transmission bore and engage notch in piston shaft with low band apply strut, loosening low band screw slightly to permit piston ring to seat in case bore.
2. Install valve body in transmission while simultaneously loosening low band screw until it is possible to index valve body on dowels in case. If manual valve is installed, index it with a manual valve lever in case; then secure valve body with 20 bolts to a torque of 9-11 ft. lbs.
3. Install O-ring in valve body and install oil pick-up pipe and secure with screw.
4. Complete installation and adjust low band as outlined previously.

POWER TRAIN, REPLACE

1. Remove shrouds and shields as required.
2. Back car into place so that rear bumper is under a chain hoist.
3. Use holes provided to attach a chain to bumper.
4. Raise car with hoist and install jack stands.
5. Disconnect all necessary wires, hoses, pipes, linkage, etc.
6. Loosen (do not remove) bolts attaching engine to mounts.
7. Lower car so that engine rests absolutely flat on two 6 x 6 inch blocks.
8. Reach under car and remove loosened bolts from mounts.
9. Raise car body to clear engine.
10. Slide power train out under car.
11. Reverse procedure to install.

BUICK SUPER TURBINE 300
OLDS JETAWAY, 1966-69
PONTIAC TWO SPEED, 1966-69

TRANSMISSION IDENTIFICATION

The transmissions can be identified by either the metal tag or the stamping on the low servo cover. For 1966-69 the data is stamped on the low servo cover. The identification data includes the year of production, code letters or numbers followed by the transmission serial number. The model application is as follows:

BUICK	CODE
1966-67 V6-225 engine	LJ
V8-300 except Sportwagon	MJ
V8-340 Sportwagon	MR
V8-340 except Sportwagon	ML
V8-400 Skylark Gran Sports	NK
1968-69 All Sportwagons	MH
All V8-350 engines except Sportwagons	ME
All models with 6-250 engine	LC

OLDSMOBILE INTERMEDIATE MODELS

1966 F-85 with V6 engine	LC
F-85 with V8-330 and two barrel carburetor	ML
F-85 with V8-330 and four barrel carburetor	MK
V8-400 and four barrel carburetor	NJ
Jetstar 88 with V8-330 engine	MT
1967 F-85 with V6 engine	LC
Others with two-barrel carburetor	ML
Others with four-barrel carburetor	MK
Delmont 88	MT
1968 All models with 6-250 engine	LC
Cutlass with V8-350 engine	MM
Delmont 88 with V8-350 engine	MT

1969 6-250	LC
V8-350 Except Delta "88"	MM
V8-350 Delta "88"	MS
V8-350 Delta "88" w/Cruise Control	MU

PONTIAC INTERMEDIATE MODELS

1966 L-6 engine with one barrel carburetor	LA
L-6 engine with four barrel carburetor	LB
V8 with two barrel carburetor	MA
V8 with four barrel carburetor	MB
V8 G.T.O.	NA
V8 with A/C and A.I.R.	MC
1967 L-6 with 1 barrel carburetor	LA
L-6 with 4 barrel carburetor	LB
L-6 with 1 barrel carburetor and A/C	LD
V8-326 with 2 barrel carburetor	MA
V8-326 with 4 barrel carburetor	MB
V8-326 with A/C and A.I.R.	MC
1968 6-250 engine with 1 barrel carburetor	LA
6-250 engine with 4 barrel carburetor	LB
6-250 engine with 1 barrel carburetor and A/C	LD
6-250 engine with 1 barrel carburetor, Firebird	LF
6-250 engine with 4 barrel carburetor, Firebird	LG
V8-350 with 2 barrel carburetor	MA
V8-350 with 4 barrel carburetor	MB
V8-350 with 2 barrel carburetor and A/C	MC
1969 Six w/1 bar. carb.—Tempest	LA
Six w/1 bar. carb. & air cond.—Tempest	LD
Six w/1 bar. carb.—Firebird	LF
Six w/1 bar. carb. & air cond.—Firebird	LH
V8-350 w/2 bar. carb.	MA
V8-350 w/2 bar. carb. & air cond.	MC

DESCRIPTION

This transmission, Fig. 1, is a combination torque converter and two-speed planetary geared unit. Torque multiplication is obtained hydraulically through the converter and mechanically through the compound planetary gear set. The gear set, in combination with the torque converter, provides a high starting ratio for acceleration from a stop, up steep grades, etc. The torque converter provides torque multiplication for performance and exceptionally smooth operation. It functions as a fluid coupling at normal road load conditions and at higher speeds.

Torque Converter

The torque converter is connected to the engine flywheel and serves as a hydraulic coupling through which engine torque is transmitted to the input shaft. The converter steps up or multiplies engine torque whenever operating conditions demand greater torque than the engine alone can supply.

Converter Pump

The function of the converter pump is to convert engine torque into an energy transmitting a flow of oil to drive the converter turbine into which the oil is projected. The converter pump operates as a centrifugal pump, picking up oil at its center and discharging the oil at its rim. However, the converter is shaped to discharge the oil parallel to its axis in the form of a spinning hollow cylinder.

Variable Pitch Stator

Used on 1966-67 Buick and V8 Oldsmobile, this type stator is located between the converter pump and converter turbine, and is supported by the stator shaft. The stator is equipped with an overrunning clutch. When the clutch is held stationary, it changes the direction of oil flow from the turbine to the proper angle for smooth entrance into the converter pump. As the turbine approaches pump speed, the direction of oil flow changes until the stator no longer opposes pump rotation. The stator then free wheels so that it will not interfere with the flow of oil between turbine and converter pump. For normal operation in Drive Range the stator blades are set at low angle. For increased acceleration and performance, torque is obtained by setting the stator blades at high angle.

Fixed Stator

Used on Tempest, Firebird and some Oldsmobiles and all 1968-69 units, the performance of the fixed stator is the same as the variable pitch type except that the stator remains at a pre-set angle.

Converter Turbine

The function of the converter turbine is to absorb energy from the oil projected

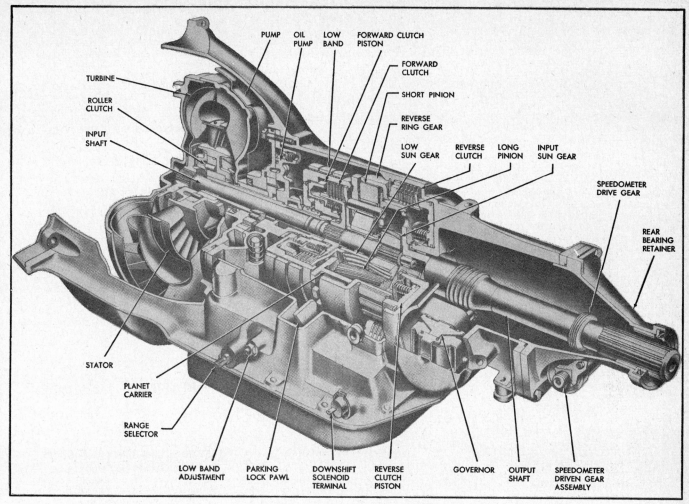

Fig. 1 Cutaway view of transmission

into it by the converter pump and convert the energy into torque and transmit that torque to the input shaft.

External Controls

Vacuum Modulator

The vacuum modulator is used to sense automatically any change in the torque input to the transmission. The vacuum modulator transmits this signal to the pressure regulator, which controls line pressure, so that all torque requirements of the transmission are met and smooth shifts are obtained at all throttle openings.

Stator Control Solenoid

Used only on Oldsmobile V8's and Buick up to and including 1967, with the variable pitch stator, the stator control solenoid is activated by a signal from the idle stator switch on the throttle linkage which changes the blade angle from low to high. The stator and detent switch is also energized at 3/4 throttle openings to change the stator blades from low to high angle.

Detent Solenoid

The detent solenoid is activated by the detent switch in the throttle linkage.

When the throttle is fully open, the switch is closed, activating the detent solenoid and causing the transmission to downshift at speeds below approximately 60 mph.

Oil Pump

A positive displacement internal-external gear type oil pump is used to supply oil to fill the converter, for engagement of forward and reverse clutches, for application and release of the low band and to provide oil for lubrication and heat transfer.

Planetary Gear Set

The planetary gear set consists of an input sun gear, low sun gear, long and short pinions, a reverse ring gear and a planet carrier.

The input sun gear is splined to the input shaft. The low sun gear, which is part of the forward clutch assembly, may revolve freely until the low band or high clutch is applied.

The input sun gear is in mesh with three long pinions and the long pinions are in mesh with three short pinions. The

short pinions are in mesh with the low sun gear and reverse ring gear.

The input sun gear and short pinions always rotate in the same direction. Application of either the low band or the reverse clutch determines whether the output shaft rotates forward or backward.

Forward Clutch

The forward clutch assembly consists of a drum, piston, cushion ring, springs, piston seals, and a clutch pack. These parts are retained inside the drum by the low sun gear and the flange assembly and retainer ring.

When oil pressure is applied to the piston, the clutch plates are pressed together, connecting the clutch drum to the input shaft through the clutch hub. Engagement of the clutch causes the low sun gear to rotate with the input shaft.

Low Band

The low band is a double-wrap steel band faced with a bonded lining which surrounds the forward clutch drum. The band is hydraulically applied by the low servo piston, and released by spring pressure.

Reverse Clutch

The reverse clutch consists of a piston, cushion ring, inner and outer seal, coil springs, clutch pack, and reaction plate. These parts are retained inside the case by a retaining snap ring.

When oil pressure is applied to the piston, the clutch plates are pressed together, holding the reverse ring gear stationary. This engagement of the clutch causes reverse rotation of the output shaft.

Governor

The governor is located to the rear of the transmission case on the left side and is driven off the output shaft. The purpose of the governor is to generate a speed sensitive modulating oil pressure that increases up to a point with output shaft or car speed.

Valve Body

The valve body assembly is bolted to the bottom of the transmission case and is accessible for service by removing the oil pan. The valve body assembly consists of manual valve, shift valve, modulator limit valve, and high speed downshift timing valve.

TROUBLE SHOOTING GUIDE

Oil Forced Out Of Filler Tube

1. Oil level too high; foaming caused by planet carrier running in oil.
2. Water in oil.
3. Leak in pump suction circuits.

Oil Leaks

1. Check extension oil seal.
2. Check outer shift lever oil seal.
3. Check speedometer driven gear fitting.
4. Check oil cooler pipe connections.
5. Check vacuum modulator assembly and case.

No Drive In Any Position

1. Low oil level.
2. Clogged oil strainer screen or suction pipe loose.
3. Defective pressure regulator valve.
4. Front pump defective.
5. Input shaft broken.

Erratic Operation and Slippage Light to Medium Throttle

1. Low oil level.
2. Clogged oil strainer screen.
3. Servo piston seal leaking.
4. Band facing worn.
5. Low band apply struts disengaged or broken.
6. Vacuum modulator.

Engine Speed Flares On Upshifts

1. Low oil level.
2. Improper band adjustment.

3. Clogged oil strainer screen.
4. Forward clutch not fully engaging.
5. Forward clutch plates worn.
6. Forward clutch piston hanging up.
7. Forward clutch drum relief ball not sealing.
8. Vacuum modulator.

Upshifts Harsh

1. Vacuum modulator line broken or disconnected.
2. Vacuum modulator diaphragm leaks.
3. Vacuum modulator valve stuck.

Closed Throttle (Coast) Downshift Harsh

1. High engine idle speed.
2. Improper low band adjustment.
3. Downshift timing valve malfunction.
4. High main line pressure. Check the following: a) vacuum modulator line broken or disconnected, b) modulator diaphragm ruptured, c) sticking pressure regulator coast valve, pressure regulator valve or vacuum modulator valve.

Car Creeps Excessively In Drive

1. Idle speed too high.
2. Closed throttle stator switch improperly adjusted (where used).

Car Creeps In Neutral

1. Forward clutch not released.
2. Low band not released.

No Drive In Reverse

1. Reverse clutch piston stuck.
2. Reverse clutch plates worn out.
3. Reverse clutch seal leaking excessively.
4. Blocked reverse clutch apply orifice.

MAINTENANCE

Checking Oil Level

The transmission oil level should be checked every 6000 miles. Oil should be added only when the level is near the ADD mark on the dipstick with oil at normal operating temperature.

NOTE: *The difference in oil level between FULL and ADD is one pint.*

To check oil level accurately, the car should be level, the engine should be idled with the transmission oil at normal temperature, and the control lever in Park position.

It is important that the oil level be maintained no higher than the FULL mark. *Do not overfill,* for when the oil level is at the full mark on the dipstick, it is just slightly below the planetary gear unit. If oil is added which brings the level above the full mark, the planetary unit will run in the oil foaming and aerating the oil. This will cause malfunctioning of the transmission assembly due to improper application of the band or clutches and excessive temperature.

If the transmission is found to be consistently low on oil, a thorough inspection should be made to find and correct all

external oil leaks. All mating surfaces, such as the oil pan rail, filler tube, governor and modulator should be carefully examined for signs of leakage. The modulator must also be checked to insure that the diaphragm has not ruptured as this would allow transmission oil to be drawn into the intake manifold of the engine. Usually, the exhaust will be excessively smoky if the diaphragm ruptures, due to transmission oil being drawn into the combustion chambers of the engine.

Draining & Refilling

Draining the transmission oil at 24,000 mile intervals is recommended. Drain the oil by removing the oil pan (no drain plug is provided). Clean oil strainer.

To refill the transmission, replace the oil pan, using a new gasket, and add five (5) pints of transmission fluid, using filler tube and funnel. Start and allow engine to idle in Park position three to five minutes to warm the oil, then check oil level and add as required to bring the level to the Full mark. Assuming that the converter has not been drained (since it is welded) and allowing for normal spillage or drain-down, approximately six pints will be required for refill.

MANUAL LINKAGE, ADJUST

Buick

1967-69 Column Shift & Back Drive
1. Loosen swivel clamp bolt.
2. Place selector lever against Drive stop.
3. Place transmission lever in Drive detent (2nd from rear).
4. Torque swivel clamp bolt to 17-23 ft-lbs.

1967-69 Console Shift & Back Drive
1. Loosen shift rod adjusting clamp bolt (to '67) or trunnion nut (1968).
2. Place selector lever against Drive stop.
3. Place transmission in Drive detent (2nd from rear).
4. Tighten adjusting clamp bolt to 17-23 ft-lbs or trunnion nut to 6-9 ft-lbs.
5. On 1969 models adjust back drive: Place transmssion in Park push back drive rod up until column lever hits stop, hold lightly and tighten clamp.

1966 Buick Special Column Shift
1. Place selector lever in Drive.
2. Loosen swivel clamp bolt.
3. Place transmission in Drive detent (2nd from rear).
4. Tighten swivel clamp bolt to 17-23 ft-lbs.

1966 Le Sabre Column Shift
1. Place selector lever in Park.
2. Loosen adjusting clamp bolt.
3. Set transmission lever in Park.
4. Tighten swivel clamp bolt to 17-23 ft-lbs.

1966 Console Shift
1. Place selector lever in Park.

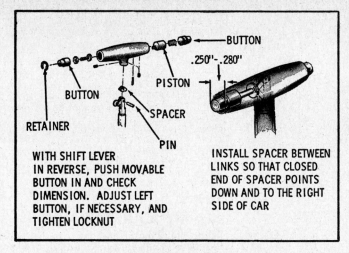

WITH SHIFT LEVER IN REVERSE, PUSH MOVABLE BUTTON IN AND CHECK DIMENSION. ADJUST LEFT BUTTON, IF NECESSARY, AND TIGHTEN LOCKNUT

INSTALL SPACER BETWEEN LINKS SO THAT CLOSED END OF SPACER POINTS DOWN AND TO THE RIGHT SIDE OF CAR

Fig. 1   Console shift lever. Oldsmobile 1966

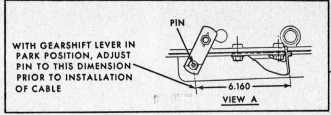

WITH GEARSHIFT LEVER IN PARK POSITION, ADJUST PIN TO THIS DIMENSION PRIOR TO INSTALLATION OF CABLE

Fig. 2   Console shift adjustment. Pontiac Tempest & Firebird 1967. Dimension for 1968-69 is 7.260

2. Loosen shift rod adjusting clamp bolt.
3. Place transmission lever in Park.
4. Tighten adjusting clamp bolt to 17-23 ft-lbs.

Oldsmobile

1969 Console Shift & Back Drive
1. Place shift handle in Park position, transmission in Park position and ignition key in lock.
2. Loosen shift rod clamp and pull shift rod lightly against lock stop. Tighten shift rod clamp.
3. Move shift cable pin to obtain a free pin fit in transmission lever and tighten nut.
4. Check to be sure that with key in Run position and transmission in Reverse, key cannot be removed and steering wheel is not locked. With key in Lock position and transmission in Park, be sure that key can be removed and steering wheel is locked.

1967-69 Column Shift & Back Drive
1. Set transmission shift lever in Drive.
2. Loosen swivel bolt.
3. Hold upper shift lever against Drive stop in upper steering column. Tighten swivel bolt.
4. On 1969, check to be sure that with key in Run position, and transmission in Reverse, key cannot be removed and steering wheel is not locked. With key in Lock position and transmission in Park, be sure that key can be removed and steering wheel is locked.

1967-68 Console Shift
1. Place shift lever in Park.
2. Set transmission outer shift lever in Park.
3. Set pin to just enter hole in shift cable.
4. Tighten nut and check adjustment.

1966 Column Shift
1. Set transmission outer shift lever in Drive detent.
2. Loosen swivel nut.
3. Hold manual rod up against Drive position stop.

4. Be sure outer shift lever is in Drive position detent, then tighten swivel nut.

1966 Console Shift
Adjust as directed in Fig. 1.

NOTE: The shift indicator can be adjusted by removing the snap-on cover and loosening the set screw. Position indicator properly and tighten set screw.

Pontiac Tempest & Firebird

1969 Column Shift & Back Drive
1. Loosen adjusting swivel clamp.
2. Set transmission in Park position.
3. Set upper gearshift lever in Park position and lock ignition.
4. Push up on gearshift control rod to take up clearance in steering column lock mechanism and tighten swivel clamp to 20 ft-lbs. on Tempest and 30 ft-lbs. on Firebird.

1968-69 Console Shift & Back Drive
1. Disconnect shift cable from transmission range selector lever pin.
2. Set console gearshift lever in Park. On 1969, lock ignition.
3. Rotate transmission range selector lever clockwise to Park position and adjust pin on selector to 7.260", Fig. 2.
4. Torque pin nut to 30 ft-lbs. and connect shift cable to pin.

Column Shift, 1968
1. Loosen screw (nut on Firebird) on adjusting swivel clamp.
2. Set transmission selector lever in Drive. Obtain Drive position by rotating transmission lever clockwise to Park position, then counterclockwise three positions to Drive position.
3. Set upper gearshift lever against Drive stop.
4. Tighten screw on swivel clamp to 20 ft-lbs (Tempest) or tighten nut on swivel clamp to 30 ft-lbs. (Firebird).

1967 Column Shift
1. Set transmission lever in Drive.
2. Set selector lever in Drive.
3. Tighten screw on adjusting swivel clamp.

1966 Column Shift
1. Set transmission lever in Park.
2. Set selector lever in Park.
3. Tighten clamp on adjusting swivel.

1966-67 Console Shift
With shift lever in Park position, adjust pin to the dimension shown, Fig. 2, prior to installation of cable.

THROTTLE LINKAGE
Buick 1968-69

Intermediate Models
The flexible cable type linkage is used and is not adjustable.

Le Sabre
Follow procedure outlined for 1967 models except that dimension from throttle rod pin to dash should be 6⅛" on 1968 and 5⅞" on 1969.

Buick 1966-67
1. Remove air cleaner.
2. Make sure linkage is free in all positions.
3. Hold choke open and make sure that return spring fully closes throttle, even though throttle is released very slowly.
4. Adjust engine idle speed and mixture.
5. With throttle linkage at hot idle position, measurement from throttle rod clevis pin to dash must be 4½", (5½" on Le Sabre), Fig. 3.
6. If measurement is off, shorten or lenghen operating rod as required.
7. Operate linkage to open carburetor and make sure carburetor wide open stop is contacting. If carburetor does not reach wide open position and nothing is interfering with throttle linkage, transmission stator and detent switch must be adjusted as outlined below.

Oldsmobile

1969 Models
These units use cable type accelerator

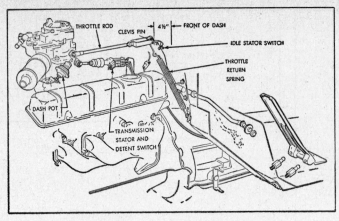

Fig. 3 Throttle linkage adjustment. Buick 1966-67. On LeSabre models, dimension is 5½"

controls and no provision is made for adjustment.

Carburetor Rod 1968 V8

1. With slow idle adjusted and adjusting screw off fast idle cam, disconnect swivel on carburetor rod from bellcrank.
2. Push upper lever of bellcrank towards cowl until it hits stop.
3. Pull carburetor rod toward firewall until throttle is wide open, then adjust swivel until swivel pin just enters the "2" notch for 2 barrel carburetor or the "4" notch for 4 barrel carburetor.
4. Reconnect carburetor rod.

1968 6-250 Engine

The throttle on the 6-250 engine is cable operated and requires no adjustment.

Carburetor Rod, 1966-67

With slow idle properly adjusted and carburetor in slow idle position, engine shut off, transmission stator must be in high angle position with test lamp on. (Stator with 6-250 engine has fixed angle.) To adjust, lengthen carburetor rod until test lamp goes off. Slowly shorten rod until test lamp just comes on. Then shorten rod two more complete turns and tighten lock nut.

Accelerator Pedal, 1966

With slow idle and carburetor rod properly adjusted, adjust accelerator rod so the distance from accelerator pedal lever to floor carpet on Jetstar 88 is 5¹/₁₆". For F-85 models, distance is 4¹¹/₁₆".

Pontiac Tempest & Firebird

1966-69

Throttle linkage adjustments cannot be made. A reference dimension of 1⁹/₁₆" between the bottom of the accelerator pedal roller and floor pan can be used only as a check for bent bracket assemblies.

DOWNSHIFT SWITCH
Buick, Olds, Pontiac 1968-69

The downshift switch is in the throttle linkage. To adjust, depress the switch plunger fully to insure proper setting, then depress the accelerator pedal fully.

STATOR & DETENT SWITCHES, ADJUST
Buick

Idle Stator Switch, 1966-67

1. Referring to Fig. 3, adjust switch with throttle at closed position and return spring attached.
2. With attaching screws loose, rotate switch until the switch stop screw bottoms against case.
3. Hold screw in this position and tighten attaching screws.

Stator & Detent Switch, 1966-67

1. With carburetor throttle wide open and switch plunger bottomed, adjust link until it will slip over carburetor lever pin.
2. Then screw link into plunger 1½ turns.
3. Install washer and retainer.

Oldsmobile

Throttle Switch, 1966-67

Disconnect carburetor rod and rotate switch lever forward until it hits stop. Connect carburetor rod without moving switch lever to wide open throttle position. Depress accelerator pedal through detent and release.

NOTE: Trailer Hauling Switch (Y-73 option) is bronze colored. When checking this switch with a test lamp, the test lamp should light only when the throttle valves

are at closed or wide open position. The test lamp will NOT light at the 40° throttle opening as it does when checking a regular switch.

Pontiac Tempest

Throttle Downshift Switch

If a forced downshift cannot be obtained it may be caused by an improperly set downshift switch. To re-set the switch, push the plunger all the way forward toward the firewall. Now, when the accelerator is fully depressed, the switch will automatically adjust itself to the linkage travel.

IN CAR REPAIRS

The following operations can be performed without removing the transmission from the car.
1. Oil pan and strainer.
2. Rear bearing retainer.
3. Vacuum modulator.
4. Valve body.
5. Governor.
6. Low servo.
7. Selector and parking mechanism.
8. Pressure regulator valve.

LOW BAND, ADJUST

The low band adjusting screw is located on the left side of the transmission adjacent to the range selector lever. Adjustment is made as follows:

Remove protective cap, loosen lock nut and tighten adjusting screw 35 to 45 inch pounds with a torque wrench. Then back off *exactly four full turns*. While holding adjusting screw stationary, tighten lock nut securely and replace cap.

TRANSMISSION, REPLACE
Buick

1. Raise and support front and rear of car.
2. Disconnect front exhaust crossover pipe if necessary.
3. Remove propeller shaft.
4. Support transmission with suitable jack.
5. Remove line from vacuum modulator.
6. Separate cooler lines from transmission.
7. Remove cross member.
8. Disconnect speedometer cable.
9. Where necessary, disconnect detent solenoid wire.
10. Disconnect shift linkage from transmission.
11. Remove oil filler pipe.
12. Support engine at oil pan.
13. Remove flywheel cover pan.
14. Mark flywheel and converter for reassembly in same position and remove flywheel to converter bolts.
15. Unfasten transmission from engine.
16. Move transmisson rearward to provide clearance between converter pump and crankshaft.
17. Install holding tool to retain converter, then lower transmission from car.
18. Reverse procedure to install.

Oldsmobile

1. Remove transmission oil filler pipe. Hoist car.
2. Disconnect control wires at transmission, and manual rod from transmission lever.
3. Remove propeller shaft.
4. Remove flywheel dust cover.
5. Support engine with a suitable jack or support bar.
6. Remove transmission cross support bar. *On models with dual exhaust, it may be necessary to disconnect the left hand exhaust pipe at exhaust manifold to provide clearance.*
7. Disconnect and cap oil cooler lines.
8. Disconnect speedometer cable (or speed adapter if so equipped) from speedometer driven gear.
9. Remove three flywheel-to-converter attaching bolts. Mark flywheel and converter so they can be assembled in the same relationship.
10. Support transmission with a suitable lift and remove transmission-to-flywheel housing bolts. *It may be necessary to lower engine slightly to permit removal of the upper bolts.*
11. Carefully move transmission rearward and out of car.
12. Reverse removal procedure to install the unit and adjust the shift linkage as outlined below.

Pontiac Tempest & Firebird

1. Disconnect speedometer cable and remove speedometer driven gear to allow oil to drain during removal procedure.
2. Remove propeller shaft.
3. Disconnect vacuum line and downshift switch lead.
4. Disconnect shift linkage from outer shift lever.
5. Support transmission and remove frame crossmember.
6. Remove flywheel housing bottom cover.
7. After removing flywheel-to-converter bolts, make sure converter hub is free of crankshaft.
8. Lower transmission and engine assembly to gain access to cooler line fittings (V8 only). Disconnect cooler lines, using a crowfoot adapter and a suitable extension. *On some cars it may be necessary to loosen exhaust system.*
9. With transmission in lowered position, remove case-to-engine bolts.
10. Move transmission down and to the rear and install a suitable strap across the converter housing to hold the converter in position until transmission is to be disassembled.
11. Reverse removal procedure to install the unit and adjust shift linkage.

CHEVROLET TORQUE DRIVE

GENERAL DESCRIPTION

The "Torque-Drive" transmission is basically a modified Powerglide consisting of a torque converter and a two-speed planetary gear set. As the automatic shifting provisions have been removed the transmission can only be shifted manually.

The selector lever positions are PARK-R-N-Hi-1st. 1st speed should be used for speeds up to 20 mph but never exceeding 55 mph. When in Hi position, do not downshift to 1st at speeds above 55 mph.

LUBRICATION & MAINTENANCE

Lubrication, maintenance and service information as it is covered in the Aluminum Case Powerglide section of this manual will also apply to the "Torque-Drive" with the exception of the following operation.

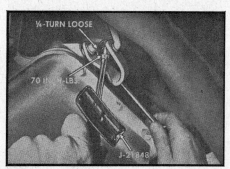

Fig. 1   Low band adjustment (in vehicle)

LOW BAND, ADJUST

Band adjustment should be performed at the first transmission oil change and sooner if slipping is evident.

1. With the selector in Neutral, back off the locknut ¼ turn. Tighten the adjusting screw to 70 in. lbs., Fig. 1.
2. Next, back off the adjusting screw exactly four turns if the band has more than 6,000 miles on it, or three turns if the band has less than 6,000 miles of use.

CAUTION: Be sure to hold the locknut at ¼ turn loose during the adjusting procedure. Then tighten locknut. The amount of back off is not an approximate figure; it must be exact.

CHEVROLET POWERGLIDE
PONTIAC TWO SPEED, 1970-71

TRANSMISSION IDENTIFICATION

On 1966-71 models the unit number is located on the right rear vertical surface of oil pan. There is no particular code with which a transmission may be identified. Therefore, when ordering parts use the transmission serial number. This unit is also used on 1970-71 Pontiac cars.

DESCRIPTION

This Powerglide is essentially a torque converter coupled to a two-speed transmission, Fig. 1. The gear portion of the transmission is a two-speed compound planetary gear set, permitting a gear reduction of 1.82 to 1 on the light duty version and 1.76 to 1 on the heavy duty version. The shift from low gear to direct drive is automatic, and the vehicle speed at which the shifts occur is determined by the interaction of a governor driven by the output shaft and a throttle valve controlled by the accelerator pedal. Thus, the transmission starts with both the torque converter and the gear box multiplying torque. As vehicle speed increases, the gear box section upshifts to direct drive, leaving only the torque converter for any speed-torque changes required. The torque mutliplication ability of the converter multiplied by the planetary gear reduction allows an overall torque multiplication of approximately 4.55 to 1.

Earlier units include a rear oil pump. All 1967 and later units omit the rear pump.

TROUBLE SHOOTING
Oil Forced Out Of Filler Tube

1. Oil level too high; aeration and foaming caused by planet carrier running in oil.
2. Water in oil.
3. Leak in pump suction circuits.

Oil Leaks

1. Transmission case and extension: extension oil seal, shifter shaft oil seal, speedometer driven gear fitting, pressure taps, oil cooler pipe connections, vacuum modulator and case, transmission oil pan gasket.
2. A very smoky exhaust indicates a ruptured vacuum modulator diaphragm.
3. Converter cover pan; front pump attaching bolts, pump seal ring, pump oil seal, plugged oil drain in front pump, prosity in transmission case.

No Drive In Any Position

1. Low oil level.
2. Clogged oil suction screen.
3. Defective pressure regulator valve.
4. Front pump defective.
5. Input shaft broken.
6. Front pump priming valve stuck.

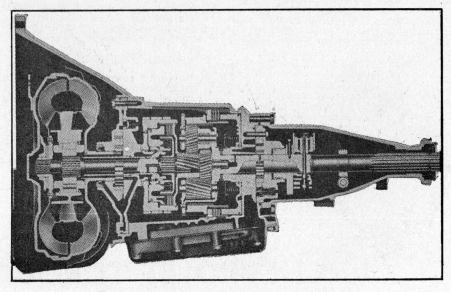

Fig. 1   Sectional view of Powerglide with aluminum case

Erratic Operation and Slippage— Light to Medium Throttle

1. Low oil level.
2. Clogged oil suction screen.
3. Improper band adjustment.
4. Band facing worn.
5. Low band apply linkage disengaged or broken.
6. Servo apply passage blocked.
7. Servo piston ring broken or leaking.
8. Converter stator not holding (rare).

Engine Speed Flares On Upshift

1. Low oil level.
2. Improper band adjustment.
3. Clogged oil suction screen.
4. High clutch partially applied—blocked feed orifice.
5. High clutch plates worn.
6. High clutch seals leak.
7. High clutch piston hung up.
8. High clutch drum relief ball not sealing.
9. Vacuum modulator line plugged.
10. Vacuum modulator defective.

Will Not Upshift

1. Maladjusted manual valve lever.
2. Throttle valve stuck or maladjusted.
3. No rear oil pump output caused by stuck priming valve, sheared drive pin or defective pump.
4. Defective governor.
5. Stuck low-drive valve.

Harsh Upshifts

1. Throttle valve linkage improperly adjusted.
2. Vacuum modulator line broken or disconnected.
3. Vacuum modulator diaphragm leaks.

4. Vacuum modulator valve stuck.
5. Hydraulic modulator valve stuck.
6. Improper low band adjustment.

Harsh Closed Throttle (Coast) Downshifts

1. High engine idle speed.
2. Improper band adjustment.
3. Vacuum modulator line broken or disconnected.
4. Modulator diaphragm ruptured.
5. Sticking hydraulic modulator valve, pressure regulator valve or vacuum modulator valve.
6. Downshift timing valve malfunction.

No Downshift (Direct-to-Low) Accelerator Floored

1. Throttle control linkage improperly adjusted.
2. Sticking shifter valve or throttle and detent valve.

Car Creeps In Neutral

1. Manual control linkage improperly adjusted.
2. High clutch or low band not released.

No Drive In Reverse

1. Manual control linkage improperly adjusted.
2. Reverse clutch piston stuck.
3. Reverse clutch plates worn out.
4. Reverse clutch leaking excessively.
5. Blocked reverse clutch apply orifice.

Improper Shift Points

1. Throttle valve linkage improperly adjusted.

2. Incorrectly adjusted throttle velve.
3. Defective governor.
4. Rear pump priming valve stuck.

Unable To Push Start, 1966

1. Rear pump drive gear not engaged with drive pin on output shaft.
2. Drive pin sheared off or missing.
3. Rear pump priming valve not sealing.
4. Rear pump defective.

Burned Clutch Plates

1. Band adjusting screw backed off more than specified.
2. Improper order of clutch plate assembly.
3. Extended operation with low oil level.
4. Stuck relief ball in clutch drum.
5. Abnormally high speed upshift, probably due to:
   a. Improper governor action.
   b. Transmission operated at high speed in manual "Low".

MAINTENANCE
Oil Level

The transmission oil level should be checked every 1000 miles. Oil should be added only when the level is near the "Add" mark on the dipstick with oil hot or at operating temperature.

In order to check oil level accurately, the engine should be idled with the transmission oil hot and the control lever in neutral "N" position.

It is important that the oil level be maintained no higher than the "Full" mark on the oil level gauge. *Do not overfill for when the oil level is at the full mark on the dipstick, it is just slightly below the planetary gear unit. If additional oil is added, bringing the level above the full mark, the planetary unit will run in the oil, foaming and aerating the oil. This aerated oil carried through the various oil pressure passages may cause malfunction of the transmission assembly, resulting in cavitation noise in the converter and improper band or clutch application.*

Changing Oil

Periodic draining of the oil pan when equipped with a drain plug is recommended every 12,000 miles under normal operating conditions and more frequently under extreme service usage. It is realized that only a portion of the total transmission fluid can be drained at the oil pan. However, the addition of even this volume of fresh fluid will replenish the additives in the remaining fluid sufficiently to increase transmission durability.

After draining the oil pan, pour two quarts of applied transmission fluid into the transmission. Then set the parking brake and operate the transmission through all ranges. With engine idling, transmission selector lever in neutral, and transmission at operating temperature, recheck the fluid level and add fluid as

necessary to bring the level to the "Full" mark on the dipstick. Do not overfill as damage to the transmission can result.

Units Without Drain Plug:

When the transmission is to be removed for repairs, drain and refill as follows:

To drain the transmission, carefully loosen the oil pan bolts. Position a receptacle to catch the draining oil. If the transmission is to be removed for repairs, the draining operation may be performed after removal, if desired.

To refill the transmission, remove the dipstick from the filler tube and refill the transmission with approved fluid. The engine should then be run at a fast idle speed with the transmission in neutral until the oil warms up. Then add oil as required to raise the fluid level on the dipstick to the "Full" mark. Refill capacity is $1\frac{1}{2}$ quarts.

MANUAL LINKAGE, ADJUST

CAUTION: Shift linkage adjustment must be accurately made. Any inaccuracies may result in premature failure of the transmission due to operation without controls in full detent. Such operation results in reduced oil pressure and in turn partial engagement of the affected clutches. Partial engagement of the clutches with sufficient pressure to cause apparent normal operation of the vehicle will result in failure of the clutches or other internal parts after only a few miles of operation.

1970-71 Pontiac Column Shift

1. Place steering column selector lever in Park position and lock ignition.
2. Loosen screw on adjusting swivel clamp at shaft and lever assembly.
3. Make sure transmission range selector lever is in Park detent.
4. Push up on gearshift control rod to take up clearance in steering lock mechanism and tighten screw on adjusting swivel clamp to 20 ft. lbs.
5. Unlock ignition, readjust indicator needle if necessary to agree with transmission detent positions.

1971 Pontiac Console Shift

1. Place console gearshift lever in Park position and lock ignition.
2. Disconnect shift cable from transmission range selector lever by removing nut from pin.
3. Loosen screw on adjusting swivel at the shaft lever assembly.
4. Make sure transmission range selector lever is in Park position.
5. Push up on gearshift control rod to take up clearance in steering column lock mechanism and tighten screw on adjusting swivel to 20 ft. lbs.
6. Unlock ignition and rotate transmission range selector lever counterclockwise by two detent positions.
7. Set the console gearshift lever in Neu-

tral range and move it forward against its stop in Neutral.
8. Assemble the shift cable and pin to the transmission range selector lever, allowing the cable to position its pin in the slot of the selector lever and then install and tighten the nut to 20 ft. lbs.

1967-71 Chevrolet Column Shift

1. Shift tube and lever assembly must be free in mast jacket.
2. To check for proper adjustment, lift selector lever toward steering wheel. Allow selector lever to be positioned in D by transmission detent.

NOTE: Do NOT use the indicator pointer as a reference to position the selected lever. When performing linkage adjustment, pointer is adjusted last.

3. Release selector lever. Lever should be inhibited from engaging low range unless the lever is lifted.
4. Lift selector lever towards steering wheel and allow lever to be positioned in N by the transmission detent.
5. Release selector lever. Lever should now be inhibited from engaging reverse range unless lever is lifted.

NOTE: A properly adjusted linkage will prevent the selector lever from moving from beyond both the neutral detent and the drive detent unless the lever is lifted to pass over the mechanical stop in the steering column.

6. If an adjustment is required, place the selector lever in D as determined by the transmission detent (see Steps 2 and 3).
7. Loosen adjusting swivel at cross shaft and rotate the transmission lever so that it contacts the drive stop in the steering column.
8. Tighten swivel and recheck adjustment.
9. Readjust indicator needle if required.
10. On 1969-71 models, adjust back drive linkage as outlined below.

1968-71 Floor Shift

Camaro, Chevelle and Chevrolet

1. Place shift handle in Drive.
2. Raise vehicle. Disconnect cable from transmission lever, Fig. 2. Place transmission in Drive range. Check dimension A and adjust by loosening stud nut and moving stud to obtain proper setting. Reinstall cable and lock clip.
3. Lower vehicle and remove shift quadrant cover. Raise quadrant plate, disconnect bulbs and remove plate. Remove cable clip and disengage cable from shift lever.
4. Insert a .07" gauge between pawl and detent as shown in view A. Check dimension B. Adjust by loosening bolt A and moving lever to obtain proper adjustment. Tighten bolt.
5. Adjust cable end until it freely

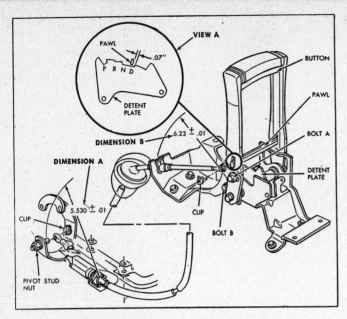

Fig. 2   Floor shift linkage adjustment. 1968-71 Camaro, Chevelle & Chevrolet

enters pin. Install clip.

NOTE: If lift on handle button does not clear detents or detents can be cleared without lifting handle, pawl engagement can be adjusted by raising or lowering of the detent plate after loosening bolt B. If such an adjustment is made repeat step 4.

6. Remove gauge. Check operation.
7. Reinstall shift plate and voer.
8. On 1969-71 models, adjust back drive linkage as outlined below.

Chevy II

1. Place shift handle in Drive position.
2. Loosen swivel lock nuts and place transmission lever in Drive.
3. Tighten lock nuts.
4. On 1969-71 models, adjust back drive linkage as outlined below.

1966 Column Shift

1. Tube and lever must be free in mast jacket.
2. Assemble swivel and related parts loosely.
3. Set transmission lever in DRIVE position. Obtain drive position by moving lever counter-clockwise to LOW detent, then clockwise one detent to drive position.
4. Place tube and lever assembly in reverse position and then bring lever down to insert rod in swivel and retainer.
5. Set tube and lever assembly in drive position and tighten swivel nut.

CAUTION: Any inaccuracies in the foregoing adjustment may result in premature failure of the transmission due to operation without controls in full detent.

1966-67 Floor Shift

1. Place shift handle in Drive position.

2. Loosen swivel lock nuts and place transmission in Drive.
3. Tighten lock nuts.

BACK DRIVE LINKAGE, ADJUST

1. Disconnect lower rod at transmission

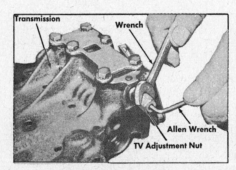

Fig. 3   Adjusting throttle pressure (on bench)

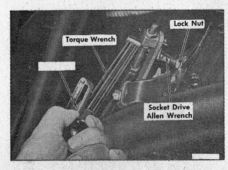

Fig. 4   Adjusting low band (in vehicle)

lever.
2. Move transmission selector lever fully clockwise to Park position.
3. Place steering column lever in Park position.
4. Attach lower rod to transmission and check operation.

CAUTION: Any inaccuracies in the above adjustment may result in premature failure of the transmission due to operation without controls in full detent.

THROTTLE LINKAGE, ADJUST

Chevrolet 4 & 6 Cyl. Engines

With accelerator pedal depressed, bellcrank must be at wide open throttle position.

Dash lever must be $1/64$-$1/16$" off lever stop and transmission lever must be against transmission internal stop.

With accelerator lever in wide open position and transmission lever against stop, adjust swivel to accelerator control lever.

Chevrolet & Pontiac V8

1. Remove air cleaner.
2. Disconnect accelerator linkage at carburetor.
3. Disconnect accelerator return and TV rod return springs.
4. With right hand, pull TV upper rod forward until transmission is through detent. With left hand, open carburetor to wide open throttle position. Carburetor must reach wide open throttle position at the same time the ball stud contacts the end of slot in upper TV rod.
5. Adjust swivel on end of upper TV rod to obtain setting described in step 4. Allowable tolerance is about $1/32$".
6. Connect and adjust accelerator linkage.
7. Check for throttle linkage freedom.

Pontiac 6 Cyl. Engine

1. Remove air cleaner.
2. Disconnect TV control rod swivel and clip from carburetor lever and TV return spring from flywheel housing.
3. With right hand, push TV control rod rearward until transmission TV lever is against internal stop of transmission.
4. With left hand, hold carburetor lever in wide open throttle position.
5. Adjust TV control rod swivel so that swivel pin freely enters hole in carburetor lever.
6. Secure swivel and control rod to carburetor lever with clip, connect return spring and check for linkage freeness. Install air cleaner.

THROTTLE VALVE, ADJUST

No provision is made for checking TV

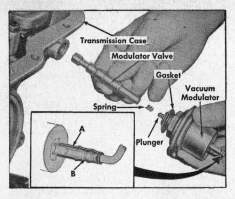

Fig. 5 Vacuum modulator, gasket and valve

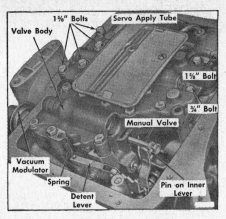

Fig. 7 Control valve assembly installed

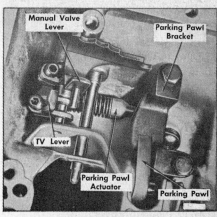

Fig. 8 Inner control levers, parking pawl and bracket

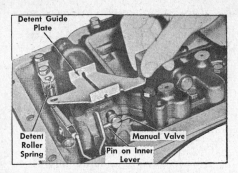

Fig. 6 Detent guide plate installation

remove rear mount bolts from crossmember and move transmission slightly toward passenger side of vehicle.

Loosen adjusting screw locknut ¾ turn and hold in this position with a wrench, Fig. 4.

Using a suitable inch-pound torque wrench as whown, adjust band to 70 inch-lbs and back off four complete turns for a band that has been in operation for 6000 miles or more, or three turns for one in use less than 6000 miles.

CAUTION: Be sure to hold the locknut at ¼ turn loose during the adjusting procedure. Then tighten locknut. The amount of back off is not an approximate figure; it must be exact.

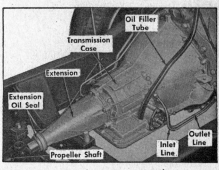

Fig. 9 Exterior of transmission

pressures. However, if operation of the transmission is such that some adjustment of the throttle valve is indicated, pressures may be raised or lowered by adjusting the position of the jam nut on the throttle valve assembly, Fig. 3.

To raise TV pressure 3 psi, back off the jam nut one full turn. This increases the dimension from the jam nut to the TV valve stop. Conversely, tightening the jam nut one full turn lowers TV pressure 3 psi.

A difference of 3 psi in TV pressure will cause a change of approximately 2 to 3 mph in the wide open throttle upshift point. Smaller pressure adjustments can be made by partial turns of the jam nut. The end of the TV adjusting screw has an allen head so the screw may be held stationary while the jam nut is moved. *Use care when making this adjustment since no pressure tap is provided to check TV pressure.*

LOW BAND, ADJUST

Low band adjustment should be performed at 12,000 mile intervals, or sooner if operating performance indicates low band slippage.

1. Raise vehicle and place selector lever in Neutral.
2. Remove protective cap from transmission adjusting screw.

NOTE: On Corvette models it may be necessary to drop the left exhaust pipe for clearance. On Chevelle models, to gain clearance between underbody and transmission, it may be necessary to

VACUUM MODULATOR VALVE

1. To remove, disconnect line from vacuum modulator, Fig. 5.
2. Unscrew vacuum modulator from oil pan.
3. Remove vacuum modulator, gasket and valve.
4. Reverse removal procedure to install.

LOW SERVO

1. Remove servo cover and gasket (3 screws).
2. Remove cover oil seal, servo piston and return spring.
3. Reverse removal procedure to install.

CONTROL VALVE BODY

1. To remove control valve, remove vacuum modulator valve as outlined above.
2. Remove oil pan and gasket.
3. Remove two bolts attaching detent guide plate to valve body and transmission case. Remove guide plate and range selector detent roller spring, Fig. 6.
4. Remove remaining control valve bolts, Fig. 7.
5. Carefully remove valve body and gas-

ket, disengaging servo apply tube from transmission case as valve body is removed.
6. Reverse removal procedure to install valve body, being sure range selector detent lever is in position shown in Fig. 7 and that pin on parking lock and range selector inner lever is engaged in slot in manual valve.

PARKING PAWL

After removing the control valve assembly as outlined above, remove the parking pawl, bracket and inner control levers. To make the installation, proceed as follows:

1. Install parking lock pawl and shaft. Install a new "E" ring on shaft.
2. Install parking lock pawl pull-back spring over its boss to rear of pawl. Short leg of spring should locate in hole in parking pawl, Fig. 8.
3. Install parking lock pawl reaction bracket (2 bolts). Fit actuator assembly between parking lock pawl and bracket.
4. Insert outer shift lever into case, making sure to pick up inner shift lever and parking lock assembly. Tighten Allen head nut.
5. Insert outer TV lever and shaft special washer and O-ring seal into case and pick up inner TV lever. Tighten Allen head nut.
6. Install selector lever detent roller.
7. Install valve body as directed above.

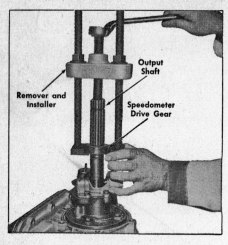

Fig. 10   Removing speedometer drive gear

EXTENSION HOUSING SEAL

1. Referring to Fig. 9, disconnect propeller shaft from transmission.
2. Use a suitable puller to remove extension rear oil seal.
3. With a suitable installer, drive new seal into bore of extension. Sealing cement should be used at outer diameter of seal to prevent leakage. Wipe off excess cement. Reconnect propeller shaft.

EXTENSION BUSHING

1. Remove extension oil seal as outlined above. Then, using a suitable remover too, pull bushing from rear of extension.
2. Place new bushing in pilot end of a suitable installer and drive bushing into bore of extension. Install rear oil seal.

SPEEDOMETER DRIVE GEAR

1. Disconnect speedometer drive cable fitting. Remove cap screw and retainer clip holding driven gear in extension and remove gear.
2. Reverse removal procedure to install.

EXTENSION CASE

1. Disconnect propeller shaft from transmission output shaft.
2. Disconnect speedometer cable fitting.
3. Install transmission lift to support transmission and engine.
4. Unfasten extension from support crossmember (2 studs).
5. Unfasten extension from transmission case (5 bolts.)

NOTE: *Remove any shims found between extension and crossmember.*

Tie shims together as it is vital that exactly the same number of shims be used when the extension is reinstalled as these shims affect the drive line angle.

6. Reverse removal procedure to install.

SPEEDOMETER DRIVE GEAR

1. Remove extension case as outlined above. Remove speedometer drive gear from output shaft, Fig. 10.
2. Using a suitable installer, install gear on output shaft and replace extension case.

GOVERNOR

1. Remove extension case and speedometer drive gear as outlined above.
2. Remove "C" clip from governor shaft on weight side of governor.
3. Remove shaft and governor valve from opposite side of governor. Remove two Belleville springs, Fig. 11.
4. Loosen governor drive screw and lift governor from output shaft.
5. Reverse removal procedure to install governor. However, be sure concave side of Belleville springs are against transmission output shaft.

REAR OIL PUMP TO '66

1. Remove extension case, speedometer drive gear and governor as outlined above.
2. Unfasten pump from case.
3. Remove pump body, drain back baffle, seal ring and drive and driven gears.

NOTE: *When drive gear is removed, drive pin may fall out when output shaft is horizontal and hole in shaft is at bottom.*

4. Remove drive pin and pump wear plate.
5. Reverse removal procedure to install.

TRANSMISSION, REPLACE
1966-71

1. Disconnect oil cooler lines (external cooled models), vacuum modulator line and speedometer drive cable fitting at transmission. Tie lines out of the way.
2. Disconnect manual and TV rods from transmission.
3. Disconnect propeller shaft from transmission.
4. Attach transmission jack on transmission.
5. Disconnect engine rear mount on transmission extension, then disconnect transmission support crossmem-

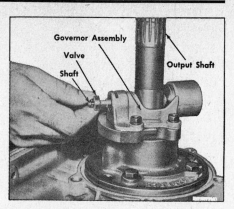

Fig. 11   Removing governor valve and shaft

ber and slide rearward. Remove crossmember on 1967-69 Camaro.
6. Remove converter underpan. Scribe flywheel-converter relationship for reassembly, then remove flywheel-to-converter bolts.

NOTE: The "light" side of the converter is denoted by a "blue" stripe painted across the ends of the converter cover and housing. This marking should be aligned as closely as possible with the "white" stripe painted on the engine side of the flywheel outer rim (heavy side of engine) to maintain balance during assembly.

7. Support engine at oil pan rail with a jack or other suitable brace capable of supporting engine when transmission is removed.
8. Lower rear of transmission slightly so that upper transmission housing-to-engine attaching bolts can be reached, using a universal socket and a long extension. Remove upper bolts.

CAUTION: On V8 engines, care must be taken not to lower rear of transmission to far as the distributor housing may be forced against the dash, causing damage to the distributor. It is best to have an assistant observe clearance of all upper engine components while transmission rear end is being lowered.

9. Remove remainder of transmission-to-engine bolts.
10. Remove transmission by moving it slightly to the rear and downward, then remove from under vehicle.

NOTE: Observe converter when moving transmission rearward. If it does not move with the transmission, pry it free of flywheel before proceeding.

CAUTION: Keep front of transmission upward to prevent converter from falling out. Install a suitable holding strap or length of strong wire across the housing to keep the converter in place.

11. Reverse procedure to install.

CHRYSLER TORQUEFLITE

IDENTIFICATION

Transmission identification markings shown in the following application chart are cast in raised letters and numerals on the lower left side of the ball housing. NOTE: There are sufficient variations within each of the main categories listed below to make it necessary to service them by serial number—a stamped 7-digit number appearing on the oil pan side rail.

1968-71 6-170, 6-198, 6-225 engines....................A-904-G	V8-383, V8-426, V8-440 engines.................A-727-B
V8-273 engine..............................A-904-A	1966-67 6-170, 6-225 engines....................A-904-G
V8-318 engine..............................A-904-LA	V8-273 engine...........................A-904-LA
6-225 police and taxi.....................A-727-RG	V8-318 engine...........................A-727-A
V8-318, V8-340; V8-360 engines.............A-727-A	V8-361, 383, 413, 426, 440....................A-727-B

DESCRIPTION

These transmissions, Figs. 1 and 2, combine a torque converter with a fully automatic three speed gear system. The converter housing and transmission case are an integral aluminum casting. The transmission consists of two multiple disc clutches, an overrunning (one-way) clutch, two servos and bands and two planetary gear sets to provide three forward speeds and reverse.

The common sun gear of the planetary gear sets is connected to the front clutch by a driving shell that is splined to the sun gear and to the front clutch retainer.

On 1965 and earlier models the hydraulic system consists of a front and rear pump and a single valve body that contains all of the valves except the governor valve.

On 1966 and later models the hydraulic system consists of a single oil pump and a valve body that contains all the valves except the governor valve.

Venting of the transmission is accomplished by a drilled passage through the upper part of the front pump housing.

The torque converter is attached to the engine crankshaft through a flexible driving plate. The converter is cooled by circulating the transmission fluid through an oil-to-water type cooler located in the radiator lower tank. The converter is a sealed assembly that cannot be disassembled.

TROUBLE SHOOTING GUIDE

Harsh Engagement In D-1-2-R

1. Engine idle speed too high.

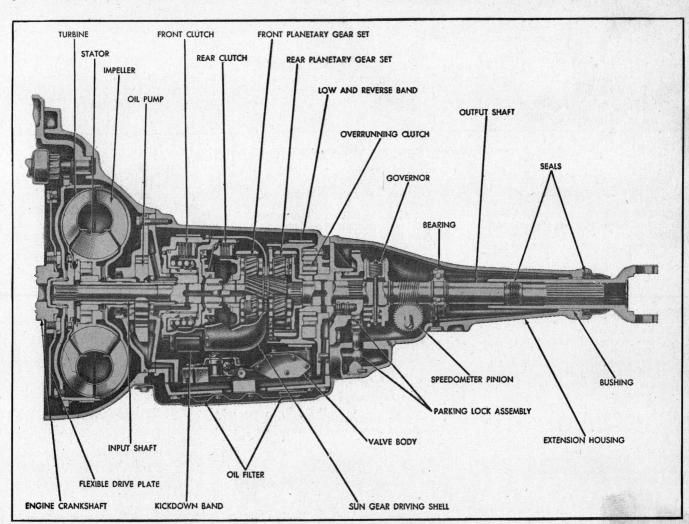

Fig. 1   Series 904 Torqueflite transmission used on 1966-71. Earlier models have a rear pump

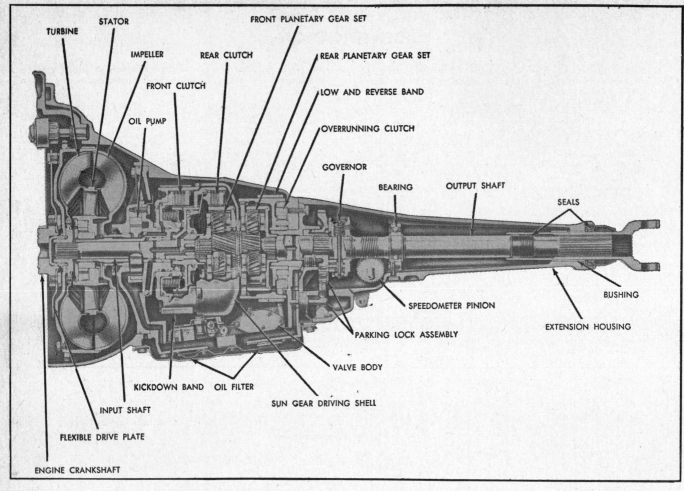

Fig. 2 Series 727 Torqueflite transmission used on 1966-71. Earlier models have a rear pump

2. Hydraulic pressures too high or too low.
3. Low-reverse band out of adjustment.
4. Accumulator sticking, broken rings or spring.
5. Low-reverse servo, band or linkage malfunction.
6. Worn or faulty front and/or rear clutch.
7. Valve body malfunction or leakage.

Delayed Engagement In D-1-2-R

1. Low fluid level.
2. Incorrect manual linkage adjustment.
3. Oil filter clogged.
4. Hydraulic pressures too high or low.
5. Valve body malfunction or leakage.
6. Accumulator sticking, broken rings or spring.
7. Clutches or servos sticking or not operating.
8. Faulty front oil pump.
9. Worn or faulty front and/or rear clutch.
10. Worn or broken input shaft and/or reaction shaft support seal rings.
11. Aerated fluid.

Runaway or Harsh Upshift and 3 - 2 Kickdown

1. Low fluid level.

2. Incorrect throttle linkage adjustment.
3. Hydraulic pressures too high or low.
4. Kickdown band out of adjustment.
5. Valve body malfunction or leakage.
6. Governor malfunction.
7. Accumulator sticking, broken rings or spring.
8. Clutches or servos sticking or not operating.
9. Kickdown servo, band or linkage malfunction.
10. Worn or faulty front clutch.
11. Worn or broken input shaft and/or reaction shaft support seal rings.

No Upshift

1. Low fluid level.
2. Incorrect throttle linkage adjustment.
3. Kickdown band out of adjustment.
4. Hydraulic pressures too high or low.
5. Governor sticking.
6. Valve body malfunction or leakage.
7. Accumulator sticking, broken rings or spring.
8. Clutches or servos sticking or not operating.
9. Faulty oil pump.
10. Kickdown servo, band or linkage malfunction.
11. Worn or faulty front clutch.

12. Worn or broken input shaft and/or reaction shaft support seal rings.

No Kickdown or Normal Downshift

1. Incorrect throttle linkage adjustment.
2. Incorrect gearshift linkage adjustment.
3. Kickdown band out of adjustment.
4. Hydraulic pressure too high or low.
5. Governor sticking.
6. Valve body malfunction or leakage.
7. Accumulator sticking, broken rings or spring.
8. Clutches or servos sticking or not operating.
9. Kickdown servo, band or linkage malfunction.
10. Overrunning clutch not holding.

Erratic Shifts

1. Low fluid level.
2. Aerated fluid.
3. Incorrect throttle linkage adjustment.
4. Incorrect gearshift control linkage adjustment.
5. Hydraulic pressures too high or low.
6. Governor sticking.
7. Oil filter clogged.
8. Valve body malfunction or leakage.
9. Clutches or servos sticking or not operating.

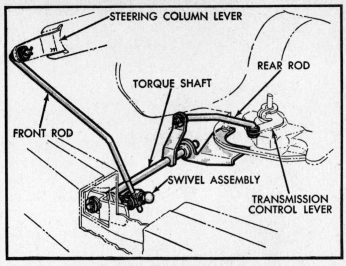

Fig. 3   Column gearshift linkage. 1970-71 Dart & Valiant. 1970 Coronet, Charger, Belvedere & Satellite, 1966-69 Chrysler Dodge & Plymouth, 1967-69 Imperial

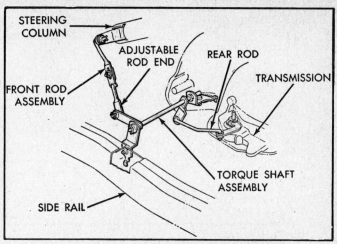

Fig. 4   Column gearshift linkage. 1970-71 Chrysler, Imperial, Fury, Monaco & Polara

10. Faulty oil pump.
11. Worn or broken input shaft and/or reaction shaft support rings.

Slips In Forward Drive Positions

1. Low oil level.
2. Aerated fluid.
3. Incorrect throttle linkage adjustment.
4. Incorrect gearshift control linkage adjustment.
5. Hydraulic pressures too low.
6. Valve body malfunction or leakage.
7. Accumulator sticking, broken rings or springs.
8. Clutches or servos sticking or not operating.
9. Worn or faulty front and/or rear clutch.
10. Overrunning clutch not holding.
11. Worn or broken input shaft and/or reaction shaft support seal rings.

Slips In Reverse Only

1. Low fluid level.
2. Aerated fluid.
3. Incorrect gearshift control linkage adjustment.
4. Hydraulic pressures too high or low.
5. Low-reverse band out of adjustment.
6. Valve body malfunction or leakage.
7. Front clutch or rear servo sticking or not operating.
8. Low-reverse servo, band or linkage malfunction.
9. Faulty oil pump.

Slips In All Positions

1. Low fluid level.
2. Hydraulic pressures too low.
3. Valve body malfunction or leakage.
4. Faulty oil pump.
5. Clutches or servos sticking or not operating.

6. Worn or broken input shaft and/or reaction shaft support seal rings.

No Drive In Any Position

1. Low fluid level.
2. Hydraulic pressures too low.
3. Oil filter clogged.
4. Valve body malfunction or leakage.
5. Faulty oil pump.
6. Clutches or servos sticking or not operating.

No Drive In Forward Drive Positions

1. Hydraulic pressures too low.
2. Valve body malfunction or leakage.
3. Accumulator sticking, broken rings or spring.
4. Clutches or servos, sticking or not operating.
5. Worn or faulty rear clutch.
6. Overrunning clutch not holding.
7. Worn or broken input shaft and/or reaction shaft support seal rings.

No Drive In Reverse

1. Incorrect gearshift control linkage adjustment.
2. Hydraulic pressures too low.
3. Low-reverse band out of adjustment.
4. Valve body malfunction or leakage.
5. Front clutch or rear servo sticking or not operating.
6. Low-reverse servo, band or linkage malfunction.
7. Worn or faulty front clutch.

Drives In Neutral

1. Incorrect gearshift control linkage adjustment.
2. Incorrect control cable adjustment.
3. Valve body malfunction or leakage.
4. Rear clutch inoperative.

Drags or Locks

1. Kickdown band out of adjustment.
2. Low-reverse band out of adjustment.
3. Kickdown and/or low-reverse servo, band or linkage malfunction.
4. Front and/or rear clutch faulty.
5. Planetary gear sets broken or seized.
6. Overrunning clutch worn, broken or seized.

Grating, Scraping or Growling Noise

1. Kickdown band out of adjustment.
2. Low-reverse band out of adjustment.
3. Output shaft bearing and/or bushing damaged.
4. Governor support binding or broken seal rings.
5. Oil pump scored or binding.
6. Front and/or rear clutch faulty.
7. Planetary gear sets broken or seized.
8. Overrunning clutch worn, broken or seized.

Buzzing Noise

1. Low fluid level.
2. Pump sucking air.
3. Valve body malfunction.
4. Overrunning clutch inner race damaged.

Hard to Fill, Oil Flows Out Filler Tube

1. High fluid level.
2. Breather clogged.
3. Oil filter clogged.
4. Aerated fluid.

Transmission Overheats

1. Low fluid level.
2. Kickdown band adjustment too tight.
3. Low-reverse band adjustment too tight.
4. Faulty cooling system.
5. Cracked or restricted oil cooler line or fitting.
6. Faulty oil pump.

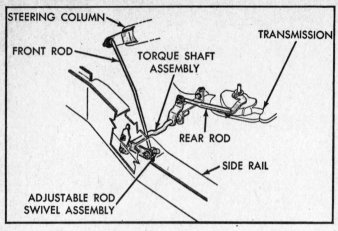

Fig. 5   Column gearshift linkage. 1970-71 Barracuda & Challenger.
1971 Coronet, Charger & Satellite

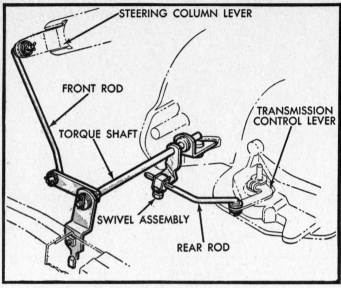

Fig. 6   Column gearshift linkage. 1966 Imperial

7. Insufficient clutch plate clearance in front and/or rear clutches.

Starter Will Not Energize in Neutral or Park

1. Incorrect gearshift control linkage adjustment.
2. Faulty or incorrectly adjusted neutral starting switch.
3. Broken lead to neutral switch.

MAINTENANCE
Service Note

It has been found that an occasional "no-drive" condition, generally occurring after making the first stop when a car is cold can be caused by incorrect transmission oil level. In cases where this condition is encountered, it is essential that the transmission oil level be checked and corrected.

If the no-drive condition still exists with the correct oil level, the push button cable adjustment should be checked.

After the above corrections have been made, if the no-drive condition still exists, it is suggested that the transmission be removed and the front pump disassembled for inspection before attempting any further repairs. Inspect the pump inner rotor and front support for wear, especially where the pinion rubs the support. The clearance specified for the front pump rotors and the face of the housing is .001" to .0025". If this clearance is increased in any way, such as wear, out-of-flatness, foreign objects between housing and support, the clearance will increase and the front pump will not be able to maintain capacity.

Adding Oil

To check the oil level, apply the parking brake and operate the engine at idle speed. Depress each push button momentarily, ending with the "N" button pushed in. Then add oil as necessary to bring the oil to the prescribed level.

Changing Oil

Oil should be changed every 32,000 miles. Police cars, taxicabs and cars that frequently tow trailers, operate in hot weather or operate continuously with abnormal loads should have more frequent periodic maintenance. Transmission should not be idled in gear for long periods.

1. Remove drain plug (if equipped) from transmission oil pan and allow oil to drain.

NOTE: *If the oil pan does not have a drain plug, loosen pan bolts and tap pan with a soft mallet to break it loose, permitting fluid to drain.*

---

2. Remove flywheel access plate, remove torque converter drain plug and allow to drain. Replace drain plug.
3. Remove transmission oil pan, clean intake screen and pan, and reinstall.
4. Install initial amount of approved automatic transmission fluid through filler tube (five quarts on Series 904 units; eight quarts on Series 727 units.
5. Start engine and add approximately one quart while engine is idling.
6. Allow engine to idle for about two minutes. Then with parking brake applied, depress each push button momentarily, ending with the "N" button pushed in.
7. Add oil as necessary to bring to proper level (see service note under "Maingenance" at front of this chapter).

BANDS, ADJUST
Kickdown Band

The kickdown band adjusting screw is located on the left side of the transmission case near the throttle lever shaft.
1. Loosen lock nut and back off approximately five turns. Check adjusting

screw for free turning in transmission case.
2. Using an inch-pound torque wrench, tighten the band adjusting screw to a reading of 72 inch lbs.
3. Back off adjusting screw 2 turns with the following exceptions:
6-170 engine ....$2\frac{5}{8}$ turns
V8-426, 1968-71 ......$1\frac{1}{2}$ turns
V8-440 3 carbs. 1971 ..$1\frac{1}{2}$ turns
V8-440 dual exhaust, 1971 ....2 turns
All other 1971 with A-727 model trans ....$2\frac{1}{2}$ turns
Hold adjusting screw in this position and tighten locknut.

Low and Reverse Band

1. Raise vehicle, drain transmission and remove oil pan.
2. Loosen adjusting screw lock nut and back off nut approximately five turns. Check adjusting screw for free turning in the lever.
3. Using an inch-pound torque wrench, tighten band adjusting screw to a reading of 72 inch lbs.
4. On Series 904 units, back off adjusting screw 34 turns (4 turns for 318 engine). Hold adjusting screw in this position and tighten lock nut to 20 ft-lbs.
5. On Series 727 units, back off adjusting screw two turns. Hold adjusting screw in this position and tighten lock nut to 35 ft-lbs.
6. Install oil pan and filler transmission.

GEARSHIFT CONTROL LINKAGE, ADJUST
1966-71

1. Referring to Figs. 3 to 8, place selector lever in Park and loosen control rod swivel clamp screw a few turns.

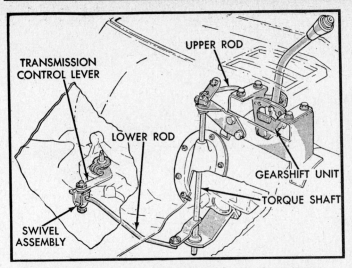

Fig. 7 Torqueflite Console gearshift linkage. 1971 Dart & Valiant. 1966-69 except 1966-68 Dart and Valiant

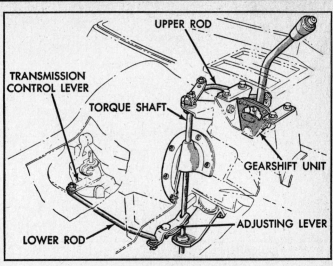

Fig. 8 Console gearshift linkage. 1966-68 Dart and Valiant

2. Move transmission control lever all the way to rear (in Park detent).
3. With both levers still in Park position, hold selector down against park gate and tighten swivel clamp screw securely.

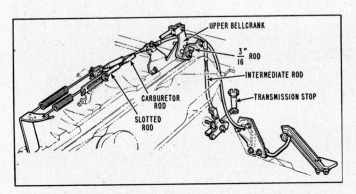

Fig. 9 Throttle linkage adjustment. All 1966 V8-383 (2 barrel carb.) and V8-440. On 1966 V8-383 with 4 barrel carburetor, the throttle linkage rod should be located 180° opposite to position shown in bellcrank. 1966 Polara, Monaco, 880, Fury

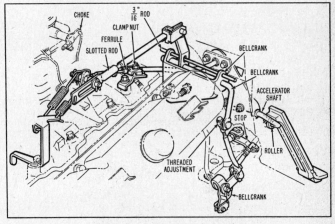

Fig. 11 Throttle linkage. 1966 Coronet, Belvedere, Satellite with V8-273 engine

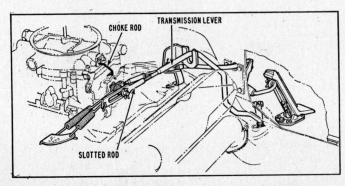

Fig. 10 Throttle linkage adjustment. 1966 Imperial

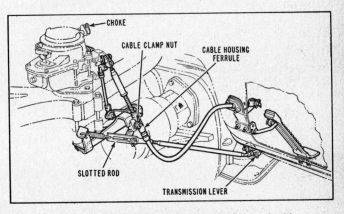

Fig. 12 Throttle linkage. 1966 Dodge and Plymouth with six-cylinder engine (except Dart and Valiant)

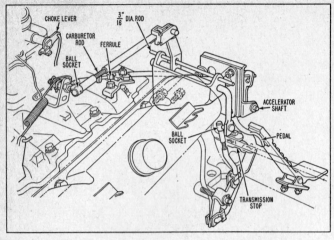

Fig. 13   1966 Dart and Valiant with V8-273 engine

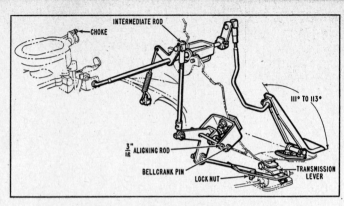

Fig. 14   Throttle linkage. 1966 Dart and Valiant with six-cylinder engine

THROTTLE LINKAGE, ADJUST

1966 Chrysler

1. Referring to Fig. 9, disconnect slotted rod from carburetor lever pin.
2. Disconnect transmission intermediate rod ball socket from upper bellcrank.
3. Disconnect or block open choke valve fully. Open throttle slightly to release fast idle cam, then return carburetor to curb idle.
4. With a 3/16" rod placed in holes provided in upper engine-mounted bellcrank, adjust length of intermediate rod by means of threaded adjustment at upper end. Ball socket must line up with ball end of rod held upward against transmission stop.
5. Assemble ball socket to ball end and remove 3/16" rod.
6. Hold carburetor rod forward against transmission stop and adjust its length by means of the threaded adjustment so that rear end of slot in adjusting link just contacts carburetor lever pin.
7. Lenghten carburetor rod two full turns by turning slotted link.
8. Assemble slotted link to carburetor.
9. Loosen cable clamp nut and adjust position of housing ferrule in clamp to remove all slack from cable with carburetor at curb idle. Then back off ferrule 1/4" and tighten clamp nut.

1966 Imperial

1. Referring to Fig. 10, disconnect slotted rod from carburetor lever pin.
2. Disconnect or block choke valve fully open. Open throttle slightly to release fast idle cam, then return carburetor to curb idle.
3. Hold transmission lever forward against its stop and adjust length of transmission rod by means of threaded adjustment at upper end. Rear end

of rod should contact carburetor lever pin without exerting any forward force.
4. Lengthen rod by one full turn.
5. Assemble slotted rod to lever pin and connect linkage return spring.
6. To check transmission linkage for freedom of operation, move slotted link to full forward position, then allow it to return slowly, making sure it returns to full forward position.
7. Adjust position of cable housing ferrule in the clamp to remove all slack in cable with carburetor at curb idle. Then back off ferrule 1/4" and tighten clamp nut.

1966 Polara, Monaco, 880, Fury

1. Referring to Fig. 9, disconnect return spring and slotted rod from carburetor lever pin. Disconnect intermediate rod ball socket from upper bellcrank.
2. Disconnect choke at carburetor or block choke valve in full open position.
3. With a 3/16" diameter drill rod placed in holes provided in upper engine mounted bellcrank and lever, adjust length of intermediate transmission rod by means of threaded adjustment at upper end. The ball socket must line up with ball end of rod held upward against transmission stop.
4. Assemble ball socket to ball end and remove 3/16" gauge rod.
5. Hold carburetor rod forward against transmission stop and adjust its length by means of threaded adjustment so that rear end of slot in adjusting link just contacts carburetor lever pin.
6. Lengthen carburetor rod two full turns by turning slotted link.
7. Assemble slotted link to carburetor.
8. Adjust cable housing ferrule so that all slack is removed from cable with carburetor at curb idle. Then back off ferrule 1/4" and tighten nut.

Figs. 11, 12, 13

1. Disconnect return spring and slotted transmission rod from carburetor lever pin.
2. Disconnect choke at carburetor or block choke valve in full open position
3. Open throttle slightly to release fast idle cam, then return carburetor to curb idle.
4. Hold transmission lever forward against its stop and adjust length of transmission rod by means of threaded adjustment at upper end. Rear end of slot should contact carburetor lever pin without exerting any forward force.
5. Lengthen rod by one full turn.
6. After reconnecting linkage, check it for freedom of operation by moving slotted adjuster link to full rearward position. Then allow it to return slowly, making sure it returns to full forward position.
7. Adjust cable housing ferrule so that all slack is removed from cable with carburetor at curb idle. Then back off ferrule 1/4" and tighten clamp nut.

Fig. 14

1. Disconnect transmission intermediate rod ball socket from bellcrank ball end.
2. Disconnect choke at carburetor or block choke valve in full open position. Open throttle slightly to release fast idle cam, then return throttle to curb idle.
3. Loosen lock nut in transmission rod. Insert a 3/16" rod in holes provided in transmission rod bellcrank bracket and lever assembly.
4. Move transmission lever forward against the stop and tighten lock nut.
5. Disconnect top end of accelerator pedal rod. Adjust length of this rod to provide a pedal angle of 111 to 113 degrees as shown. To increase pedal angle, increase length of rod by means of screw adjustment. Reinstall top end of rod.
6. Remove 3/16" rod. Adjust length of transmission bellcrank-to-torque shaft rod by means of screw adjust-

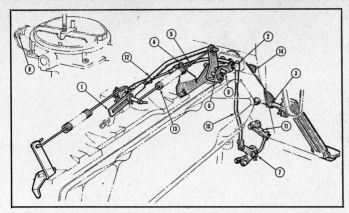

Fig. 15 Throttle linkage adjustment. All 1967-69 models with 383 and 440 engines. Also 1967 Charger and 1968-69 Monaco and Polara with 318 engine and Fury with 318 engine

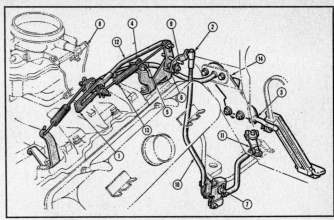

Fig. 16 Throttle linkage adjustment. 1967-68 Coronet and Belvedere with 273 and 318 engines. Also 1968 Fury with 318 engine

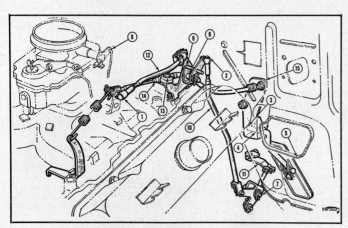

Fig. 17 Throttle linkage adjustment. 1967 Dart and Valiant with 273 engine

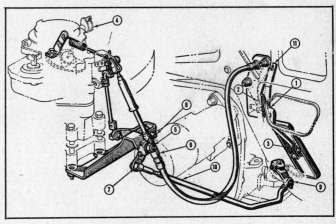

Fig. 18 Throttle linkage adjustment. 1967 Dart and Valiant with 6-cylinder engine

ment at top end. The correct rod length allows ball socket to line up with ball end when rod is held upward against transmission stop.

7. Install ball socket on torque shaft lever ball. Connect choke.

1967-71 Adjustments

NOTE: Before proceeding with the adjustment, disconnect the choke rod at the carburetor or block the choke valve wide open. Open the throttle slightly to release the fast idle cam, then return carburetor to the hot idle position.

Hold or fasten the transmission lever firmly forward against the stop while performing the adjustment to insure a proper adjustment.

Models Indicated in Figs. 15 and 16

1. With a $3/16''$ diameter rod (9) placed in the holes provided in the upper bellcrank (6) and lever, adjust length of intermediate transmission rod (10) by means of threaded adjustment (2) at upper end. The ball socket must line up with the ball end with a slight downward effort on rod.

2. Assemble ball socket to ball end and

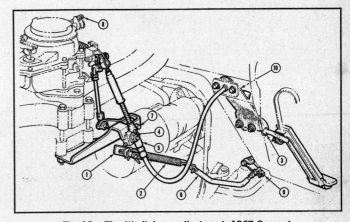

Fig. 19 Throttle linkage adjustment. 1967 Coronet, Belvedere and Fury with 6-cylinder engine

remove $3/16''$ gauging rod from upper bellcrank and lever.

3. Disconnect return spring (13), then adjust length of carburetor rod (12) by pushing rearward on rod with slight effort and turning threaded adjustment (1). Rear end of slot should contact carburetor lever pin without exerting any forward force when slotted

adjuster link (1) is in its normal operating position against lever pin nut.

4. Assemble slotted adjustment (1) to carburetor lever pin and install washer and retaining pin. Connect transmission linkage return spring (13).

5. Release transmission lever, then check linkage for freedom of operation. Move

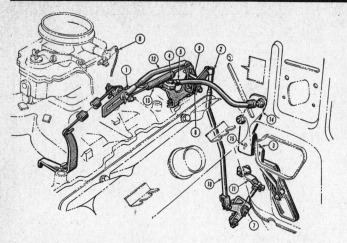

Fig. 20 Throttle linkage adjustment. 1968-69 Dart Valiant and Barracuda with 273, 318 or 340 engine. 1970-71 V8 with 3 section rod

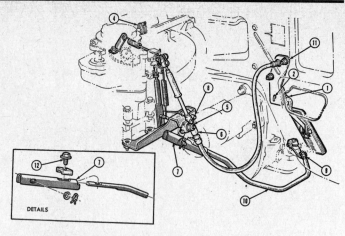

Fig. 21 Throttle linkage adjustment. 1968-71 models with 6-cylinder engine

slotted adjuster link (1) to full rearward position, then allow it to return slowly, making sure it returns to full forward position.

6. Loosen cable clamp nut (4) and adjust position of cable housing ferrule (5) in clamp so that all slack is removed from cable with carburetor at hot idle position. To remove slack from cable, move ferrule in clamp in a direction away from carburetor lever.

7. Back off ferrule ¼" which provides enough free play between front edge of accelerator shaft lever and dash bracket. Tighten clamp nut to 45 inch-lbs.

8. Connect choke rod or remove blocking fixture.

Models Indicated in Fig. 17

1. With a ³⁄₁₆" diameter rod (9) placed in holes provided in upper bellcrank (6) and lever, adjust length of intermediate transmission rod (10) by means of threaded adjustment at upper end. Ball socket (2) must line up with ball end with a slight downward effort on rod.

2. Assemble ball socket to ball end and remove the ³⁄₁₆" gauging rod from upper bellcrank (6) and lever.

3. Adjust length of carburetor rod (12) by pushing rearward on rod with a slight effort and turning threaded adjustment (1) so that ball socket lines up with ball end on carburetor lever.

4. Assemble ball socket to ball end and release transmission lever.

5. Loosen cable clamp not (13) and adjust position of cable housing ferrule (14) in clamp so that all slack is removed from cable with carburetor at hot idle position. To remove slack from cable, move ferrule in clamp in a direction AWAY from carburetor lever.

6. Back off ferrule ¼" which provides the free play necessary between front edge of accelerator shaft lever and dash bracket. Tighten clamp nut to 45 inch-lbs.

7. Connect choke rod or remove blocking fixture.

Models Indicated in Fig. 18

1. Adjust length of transmission rod (10) by pushing rearward on rod with a slight effort and turning threaded adjustment (7). Ball socket (7) must line up directly with ball end.

2. Assemble ball socket to ball end, then release transmission lever.

3. When carburetor throttle is opened, transmission lever (9) should begin its travel at the same time with no vertical movement of lever or vertical movement of rod (10) in lever.

4. Loosen cable clamp nut (5) and adjust position of cable housing ferrule in the clamp so that all slack is removed from cable with carburetor at hot idle position. To remove slack from cable, move ferrule in clamp in a direction AWAY from carburetor lever.

5. Back off ferrule ¼" which will provide enough free play between dash-mounted accelerator lever and bracket. Tighten clamp nut to 45 inch-lbs.

6. Connect choke rod or remove blocking fixture.

Models Indicated in Fig. 19

1. Adjust length of carburetor rod (6) by pushing rearward on rod with a slight effort and turning threaded adjustment (1). Rear end of slot should contact carburetor lever pin without exerting any forward force on pin when slotted adjuster link (1) is in its normal operating position against lever pin nut.

2. Assemble slotted adjuster link (1) to carburetor lever pin and install washer and retainer pin. Connect transmission linkage return spring (2).

3. Release transmission lever, then check linkage for freedom of operation. Move slotted adjuster link (1) to full rearward position, then allow it to return slowly, making sure it returns to its full forward position.

4. Loosen cable clamp nut (4) and adjust position of ferrule (5) in clamp so that all slack is removed from

cable with carburetor at hot idle position. To remove slack from cable, move ferrule in the clamp in a direction AWAY from carburetor lever.

5. Back off ferrule ¼" which provides ¼" cable slack at idle. Tighten clamp nut to 45 inch-lbs.

6. Connect choke rod or remove blocking fixture.

Models Indicated in Fig. 20

1. With a ³⁄₁₆" diameter rod (9) placed in the holes provided in upper bellcrank and lever, adjust length of intermediate transmission rod (10) by means of threaded adjustment at upper end. The ball socket (2) must line up with the ball end with a slight downward effort on rod.

2. Assemble ball socket (2) to ball end and remove ³⁄₁₆" rod (9) from upper bellcrank and lever.

3. Disconnect return spring (13), then adjust length of carburetor rod (12) by pushing rearward on rod with a slight effort and turning the threaded adjuster (1). The rear end of slot should contact carburetor lever pin without exerting any forward force on pin when slotted adjuster link (1) is in its normal operating position against lever pin nut.

4. Assemble slotted adjustment (1) to carburetor lever pin and install washer and retaining pin. Assemble transmission linkage return spring (13) in place.

5. Release transmission lever and check linkage for freedom of operation. Move slotted adjuster link (1) to full rearward position and allow it to return slowly, making sure it returns to full forward position.

6. Loosen cable clamp nut (4), adjust position of cable housing ferrule (5) in the clamp so all slack is removed from cable with carburetor at curb idle. To remove slack, move ferrule (5) in the clamp in direction away from carburetor lever.

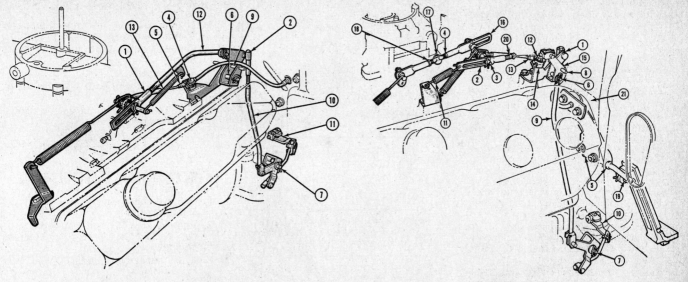

Fig. 22 Throttle linkage adjustment. 1968-69 Dart and Barracuda with 383 engine

Fig. 23 Throttle linkage adjustment. 1968-71 models with 426 engine

7. Back off ferrule (5) ¼″. This provides ¼″ free play between front edge of accelerator shaft lever and dash bracket. Tighten cable clamp nut (4) to 45 inch lbs.
8. Connect choke (8) rod or remove blocking fixture.

Models Indicated in Fig. 21
1. Adjust length of transmission rod by loosening slotted link lock nut (12). Pull forward on slotted adjuster link (7) so it contacts carburetor lever pin.
2. Tighten transmission rod adjustment lock nut (12) to 95 inch lbs. Check transmission linkage for freedom of operation by moving slotted adjuster link to full rearward position and allow it to return slowly, making sure it returns to full forward position.
3. When carburetor throttle is opened, the transmission lever (9) should begin its travel at the same time with no vertical movement of lever or vertical movement of rod (10) in the lever.
4. Loosen cable clamp nut (5), adjust position of housing ferrule (6) in the clamp so all slack is removed from cable with carburetor at curb idle. To remove slack, move ferrule (6) in the clamp in direction away from carburetor lever.
5. Back off ferrule (6) ¼″. This provides ¼″ free play between dash mounted accelerator lever and the bracket. Tighten cable clamp nut to 45 inch lbs.
6. Connect choke rod (4) or remove blocking fixture.

Models Indicated in Fig. 22
1. With a ¾″ diameter rod (9) placed in the holes provided in upper bellcrank and lever, adjust length of transmission rod (10) by means of threaded adjustment at upper end. The ball socket (2) must line up with the ball

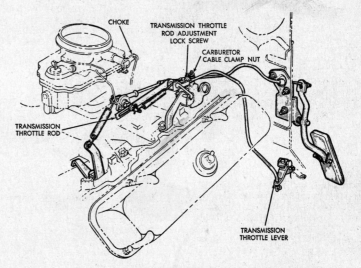

Fig. 24 Throttle linkage adjustment. 1970-71 V8 models with single section throttle rod

end with a slight downward effort on rod.
2. Assemble ball socket (2) to ball end and remove ³⁄₁₆″ rod (9) from upper bellcrank and lever.
3. Disconnect return spring (13), washer and retainer pin (14), then adjust length of carburetor rod (12) by pushing rearward on rod with a slight effort and turning the threaded adjustment (1). The rear end of slot should contact carburetor lever pin without exerting any forward force on pin when slotted adjuster link (1) is in its normal operating position against lever pin nut.
4. Assemble slotted adjustment (1) to carburetor lever pin and install washer and retainer pin (14). Assemble transmission linkage return spring (13).

5. Release transmission lever and check linkage for freedom of operation by moving slotted adjuster link (1) to full rearward position, then allow it to return slowly, making sure it returns to the full forward position.
6. Loosen cable clamp nut (4), adjust position of cable housing ferrule (5) in the clamp so that all slack is removed from the cable with carburetor at curb idle. To remove slack, move the ferrule (5) in the clamp in direction away from carburetor lever.
7. Back off ferrule (5) ¼″. This provides ¼″ free play between front edge of the accelerator shaft lever and the dash bracket. Tighten cable clamp nut (4) to .45 inch lbs.
8. Connect choke rod or remove blocking fixture.

Models Indicated in Fig. 23

1. With a 3/16" diameter rod (8) placed in holes provided in upper bellcrank and lever (15), adjust length of transmission rod (9) by means of threaded adjuster at upper end. The ball socket must line up with the ball end with a slight downward effort on rod.
2. Assemble ball socket to ball end and remove 3/16" rod (8) from upper bellcrank and lever (15).
3. Disconnect return spring (11), adjust length of rod (20) by pushing rearward on rod with a slight effort and turning threaded adjuster link (2). The rear end of slot should contact carburetor lever stud without exerting any forward force on the stud when slotted adjuster link is in its normal operating position.
4. Assemble slotted adjuster link (2) to carburetor lever stud and install washer and retainer pin. Assemble linkage return spring (11) in place.
5. Release transmission lever and check linkage for freedom of operation by moving slotted adjuster link (2) to full rearward position, then allow it to return slowly to the full forward position against the stud.
6. Loosen cable clamp nut (12), adjust position of cable housing ferrule (13) in the clamp (14) so all slack is removed from cable with rear carburetor at curb idle. To remove slack from cable, move ferrule (13) in clamp (14) in direction away from carburetor lever.
7. Back off ferrule (13) 1/4". This provides 1/4" free play between front edge of accelerator shaft lever and dash bracket. Tighten clamp (14) to 45 inch lbs.
8. Route cable so it does not interfere with carburetor rod (20) or upper bellcrank (15) throughout full throttle linkage travel.
9. Attach carburetor rod assembly (4) between carburetors with slotted rod end (16) attached to outboard side of inboard lever on rear carburetor. With rear carburetor at wide open throttle, adjust length of connector rod (4) so that front carburetor is also at wide open throttle. To lengthen this rod (4) turn adjusting stud (17) clockwise as viewed from front of engine. Tighten lock nut (18).
10. Remove choke valve blocking fixture.

Models Indicated in Fig. 24

1. Disconnect choke at carburetor or block choke valve fully open. Open throttle slightly to release fast idle cam and return carburetor to curb idle position.
2. Loosen transmission throttle rod adjustment lock screw.
3. Hold transmission forward against its stop while adjusting transmission linkage. (On engines with solenoid idle stops, the solenoid plunger must also be in its fully extended position).
4. Adjust the transmission rod by pulling forward on the slotted link with a slight effort so that the rear edge of the slot is against the carburetor lever pin. Tighten transmission rod adjusting lock screw.

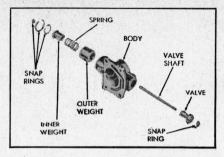

Fig. 25   Governor disassembled

NOTE: The slotted link and transmission lever must be held forward while the locking screw is being tightened.

5. To check transmission linkage freedom of operation, move slotted link to the full rearward position, then allow it to return slowly, making sure it returns to the full forward position.
6. Loosen carburetor cable clamp nut. Adjust position of cable housing ferrule in the clamp so that all slack is removed from cable with carburetor at curb idle. To remove slack from cable, move ferrule in the clamp in direction away from carburetor lever.
7. Back off ferrule 1/4". This provides 1/4" free play. Tighten cable clamp nut to 45 inch lbs.
8. Connect choke or remove blocking fixture.

PARKING PAWL, REPLACE

Extension Housing In Car

1. Remove parking lock cable adapter cover from bottom of extension housing.
2. Remove plug from extension housing, slide out shaft to remove parking lock lever, shim and cable adapter. Replace cable adapter spring if it is distorted.
3. Slide bushing sleeve out of housing to remove the parking pawl and spring.

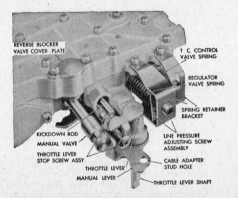

Fig. 26   Valve body external parts

OUTPUT SHAFT OIL SEAL

1. To remove seal, disconnect propeller shaft at transmission.
2. Remove transmission flange or brake drum.
3. Remove seal.
4. Install new seal with lip side facing in.
5. Install transmission flange and tighten nut to proper torque.
6. Connect propeller shaft.

EXTENSION HOUSING

1. Remove speedometer drive pinion and sleeve assembly.
2. Remove transmission flange or parking brake drum and cable (if so equipped).
3. Drain about two quarts of fluid from transmission.
4. On models with parking lock lever, loosen parking brake cable clamp bolt where cable enters the housing cover. Remove housing cover lower plug. Insert screwdriver through hole, then, while exerting pressure against projecting portion of cable lock spring, withdraw brake cable.
5. Remove bolts securing extension housing insulator to crossmember.
6. With a suitable jack, raise transmission slightly to clear crossmember.
7. Remove crossmember. If parking brake cable to rear wheels interferes with removal, first disconnect cable and housing.
8. Unfasten and remove extension housing from transmission.
9. If necessary, the extension housing bushing may be replaced at this time. However, when installing the new bushing, make sure the oil hole in the bushing lines up with the slot in the housing.

NOTE: *On 6 Cyl. it is necessary to burnish bushing for proper fit.*

10. Install the extension housing in the reverse order of its removal.

GOVERNOR

1. To remove the governor, take off the extension housing.
2. Using a screwdriver, carefully pry the snap ring from the weight end of the governor valve shaft, Fig. 25. Slide the valve and shaft out of governor housing.
3. Remove large snap ring from weight end of governor housing, and lift out weight assembly.
4. Remove snap ring from inside governor weight and remove inner weight and spring from outer weight.
5. Remove snap ring from behind governor housing, then slide governor housing and parking brake sprag assembly off input shaft. If necessary, separate governor housing from sprag (4 screws).

6. The primary cause of governor operating failure is due to a sticking governor valve or weights. Rough surfaces may be removed with crocus cloth. Thoroughly clean all parts and check for free movement before assembly.
7. Reverse above operations to assemble and install governor.

VALVE BODY

1. To remove valve body and accumulator piston, drain transmission fluid and remove oil pan.
2. Loosen clamp bolt and lift throttle lever, washer and seal off transmission throttle lever shaft, Fig. 26.
3. Shift manual control into "L" position to expose the nut securing the cable adapter to the manual lever. Remove nut and disengage cable adapter from lever.
4. Place drain pan under transmission; then remove ten hex-head valve body-to-transmisson case bolts.
5. Lower valve body down out of transmission, being careful not to cock throttle lever shaft in case hole or lose the accumulator spring.
6. Withdraw accumulator piston from transmission case. Inspect piston for scoring, and check rings for wear or breakage.

TRANSMISSION, REPLACE
1966-71

CAUTION: The transmission and converter must be removed as an assembly, otherwise, the converter drive plate, front pump bushing and oil seal will be damaged. The drive plate will not support the load; therefore, none of the weight of the transmission should be allowed to rest on the plate during removal.

1. Disconnect high tension wire from distributor cap or coil.
2. Place selector lever in Park.
3. Remove cover plate from in front of converter to provide access to converter drain plug and mounting bolts.
4. Using a remote control starter switch, rotate engine to bring drain plug to "6 o'clock" position. Then drain converter and transmission.
5. Mark converter and drive plate to aid in reassembly.
6. Rotate engine to locate two converter-to-drive plate bolts at 5" and 7 clock" positions. Remove the two bolts, rotate engine and remove other two bolts.

CAUTION: Do not rotate converter or drive plate by prying with a screwdriver or similar tool as the drive plate might become distorted. Also, the starter should never be engaged if the drive plate is not attached to the converter with at least one bolt or if the transmission case-to-engine bolts have been loosened.

7. Disconnect battery ground cable.
8. Remove starting motor.
9. Disconnect wire from neutral starting switch.
10. On all models, disconnect gearshift rod from transmission lever. Remove gearshift torque shaft from transmission housing and left side rail. On Console shift, remove two bolts securing torque shaft lower bracket to extension housing. Swing bracket out of the way for transmission removal. Disconnect gearshift rod from transmission lever. On earlier models, remove gearshift control cable-to-transmission adjusting wheel lock screw. Pull cable out of case as far as possible, backing off adjusting wheel a few turns if necessary.
11. Insert a small screwdriver above and slightly to the right of the control cable. Disengage cable adapter lock spring by pushing screwdriver handle to the right while pulling outward on cable.
12. Disconnect throttle rod from lever on transmission.
13. Disconnect oil cooler lines at transmission and remove oil filler tube.
14. Remove speedometer pinion and sleeve from transmission.
15. Loosen transmission parking lock cable clamp bolt. Remove housing cover lower plug. Insert screwdriver through hole, then gently exert pressure against projecting portion of cable lock spring and withdraw lock cable.
16. On all cars disconnect propeller shaft at rear universal joint and carefully pull shaft out of extension housing.
17. Remove two bolts securing extension housing to crossmember insulator.
18. Install engine support fixture and raise engine slightly.
19. Unfasten and remove crossmember.
20. Support transmission with a jack.
21. Attach a small "C" clap to edge of bell housing to hold converter in place during removal of transmission.
22. Remove converter housing retaining bolts. Work transmission rearward off engine dowels and disengage converter housing to hold converter in place during removal of transmission.
23. Lower transmission jack and remove converter and transmission as a unit.
24. To remove converter, release "C clamp and slide converter out of transmission.
25. Reverse procedure to install.

C4 SEMI-AUTOMATC

TRANSMISSION IDENTIFICATION

Maverick	Code
1970	PEG-A
1971	PEG-A1

GENERAL DESCRIPTION

This unit is essentially the same as the C4 Cruise-O-Matic except that the automatic shifting provisions have been removed.

The major differences between this unit and the C4 are the control valve body and the manual linkage. The manual linkage adjustment procedures are the same as the C4, however, the shift selector position of "Hi" on this unit is the equivalent of "D" on the C4.

For service procedures on this unit, refer to the C4 Dual Range chapter.

C4 DUAL RANGE AUTOMATIC

TRANSMISSION IDENTIFICATION

Each transmission may be identified by the tag attached to the low-reverse servo cover bolt. The tag includes the model prefix and suffix, a service identification number and a build date code. The service identification number indicates changes to service details which affect interchangeability when the transmission model is not changed. For interpretation of this number the Ford Master Parts Catalog should be consulted.

YEAR	CAR MODEL	TRANS. MODEL	ENGINE MODEL
1966	Comet[3]	PCS-W	6-200
	Comet[4]	PCS-AA	V8-289
	Comet[3]	PCW-AN	V8-289
	Comet[4]	PCW-AR	V8-289
	Fairlane[3]	PCS-W	6-200
	Fairlane[4]	PCS-AA	6-200
	Fairlane[3]	PCW-AN	V8-289
	Fairlane[4]	PCW-AR	V8-289
	Fairlane[4]	PCW-AY	6-200
	Fairlane[6]	PCW-AZ	V8-289
	Falcon	PCS-V	6-170
	Falcon	PCS-W	6-200
	Falcon	PCW-AN	V8-289
	Ford	PCV-E	6-240
	Ford[3]	PCW-AW	V8-289
	Ford[4]	PCW-AV	V8-289
	Ford[6]	PDA-D	6-240
	Ford[7]	PDA-D	V8-289
	Mustang	PCS-Y	6-200
	Mustang	PCW-AS	V8-289
1967	Comet[4]	PEE-B	V8-289
	Comet[4]	PEE-J	V8-289
	Cougar	PEE-C	V8-289
	Fairlane[3]	PEB-F	6-200
	Fairlane[3]	PEE-J	V8-289
	Fairlane[3]	PEE-A	V8-289
	Fairlane[3]	PEB-E	6-200
	Fairlane[4]	PEE-B	V8-289
	Fairlane[7]	PEE-D	6-200
	Fairlane[7]	PEE-E	V8-289
	Falcon	PEB-A	6-170
	Falcon	PEB-H	V8-289
	Falcon	PEB-C	6-200
	Ford[3]	PEA-A	6-240
	Ford[3]	PEA-B	V8-289
	Ford[3]	PEA-C	V8-289
	Mustang	PEE-C	V8-289
	Mustang	PEB-B	6-200
1968	Cougar[4]	PEE-N	V8-302
	Cougar[4]	PEE-S	V8-302
	Fairlane[4]	PEB-E1	6-200
	Fairlane[3]	PEB-F2	6-200
	Fairlane[4]	PEE-M	V8-302
	Fairlane[3]	PEE-V	V8-302
	Falcon[3]	PEB-A2	6-170
	Falcon[3]	PEB-C2	6-200
	Falcon[3]	PEE-H2	V8-289
	Falcon[3]	PEE-R	V8-302
	Ford[3]	PHA-B	V8-302
	Ford[3]	PHB-A	V8-390
	Ford[3]	PFA-B-1	V8-390
	Ford[7]	PFA-D-1	6-240
	Ford[7]	PFA-F	V8-302
	Montego[4]	PEB-E1	6-200
	Montego[3]	PEB-F2	6-200
	Montego[4]	PEE-M	V8-302
	Montego[4]	PEE-U	V8-302
	Montego[4]	PEE-R	V8-302
	Montego[3]	PEE-V	V8-302
	Mustang[4]	PEB-B1	6-200
	Mustang[4]	PEE-S	V8-302
1969	Fairlane[3]	PEE-V	V8-302
	Fairlane[3]	PEE-M	V8-302
	Fairlane[3]	PEE-AE	6-250
	Fairlane[4]	PEE-AF	6-250
	Falcon[3]	PEB-C2	6-170, 200
	Falcon[3]	PEE-V	V8-302
	Ford[3]	PEA-A2	6-240
	Ford[3]	PEA-M1	V8-302
	Ford[4]	PEA-N1	V8-302
	Montego[4]	PEE-M	V8-302
	Montego[3]	PEE-V	V8-302
	Montego[3]	PEE-AE	6-250
	Montego[4]	PEE-AF	6-250
	Mustang[4]	PEB-B2	6-200
	Mustang[4]	PEE-AC	V8-302
	Mustang[4]	PEE-AD	6-250
1970	Cougar	PEE-AC2	V8-302
	Fairlane[4]	PEE-M1	V8-302
	Fairlane[3]	PEE-V1	V8-302
	Fairlane	PEE-AC1	V8-302
	Fairlane	PEE-AD1	6-250
	Fairlane[3]	PEE-AE1	6-250
	Fairlane[4]	PEE-AF1	6-250
	Fairlane[3]	PEF-D	V8-351
	Fairlane[4]	PEF-E	V8-351
	Falcon	PEE-M1	V8-302
	Falcon	PEE-V2	V8-302
	Falcon	PEE-AC1	V8-302
	Falcon	PEE-AD1	6-250
	Falcon	PEE-AE1	6-250
	Falcon	PEE-AF1	6-250
	Falcon	PEB	6-200
	Ford	PEA-M2	6 & V8-302
	Ford	PEA-N2	V8-302
	Ford	PEA-A3	6-240
	Ford[3]	PEF-A	V8-351
	Ford[4]	PEF-B	V8-351
	Maverick	PEB-D	6-170, 200
	Maverick	PEB-D1	6-170, 200
	Maverick	PEE-AK	6-250
	Montego[4]	PEE-M1	V8-302
	Montego[3]	PEE-V1	V8-302
	Montego[3]	PEE-AE1	6-250
	Montego[4]	PEE-AF1	6-250
	Montego[3]	PEF-D	V8-351
	Montego[4]	PEF-E	V8-351
	Mustang	PEE-AC1	V8-302
	Mustang	PEE-AD1	6-250
	Mustang	PEB-B3	6-200
1971	Comet[3]	PEB-D2	6-200
	Comet[4]	PEB-H	6-200
	Comet[3]	PEE-AK1	6-250
	Comet[4]	PEE-AM	6-250
	Comet[3]	PEE-AH1	V8-302
	Comet[4]	PEE-AL	V8-302
	Fairlane[3]	PEE-AE2	6-250
	Fairlane[4]	PEE-AF2	6-250
	Fairlane[3]	PEE-M2	V8-302
	Fairlane[4]	PEE-V2	V8-302
	Fairlane[3]	PEF-D1	V8-351
	Fairlane[4]	PEF-E1	V8-351
	Ford	PEA-M3	6-240
	Ford[3]	PEA-M3	V8-302
	Ford[4]	PEA-N3	V8-302
	Ford[3]	PEF-A1	V8-351
	Ford[4]	PEF-B1	V8-351
	Montego[3]	PEE-AE2	6-250
	Montego[4]	PEE-AF2	6-250
	Montego[4]	PEE-M2	V8-302
	Montego[4]	PEE-V2	V8-302
	Montego[3]	PEF-D1	V8-351
	Montego[4]	PEF-E1	V8-351
	Maverick[3]	PEB-D2	6-200
	Maverick[4]	PEB-H	6-200
	Maverick[3]	PEE-AK1	6-250
	Maverick[4]	PEE-AM	6-250
	Mustang	PEE-AD2	6-250
	Mustang	PEE-AC2	V8-302
	Pinto	PEJ-B	4-122

[1]—Two-barrel carburetor. [3]—Column shift.
[2]—Four-barrel carburetor. [4]—Floor shift.
[5]—High performance engine.
[6]—Taxi.
[7]—Police, or Fleet.

DESCRIPTION

Starting with 1967 the unit is basically the same as the 1966 C4 unit except that the main control assembly has been revised to incorporate a manually selected first and second gear range. The transmission features a drive range that provides for fully automatic upshifts and downshifts, and manually selected low and second gears.

As shown in Fig. 1 the transmission consists essentially of a torque converter, a compound planetary gear train, two multiple disc clutches, a one-way clutch and a hydraulic control system.

For all normal driving the selector lever is moved to the green dot under "Drive" on the selector quadrant on the steering column or on the floor console. As the throttle is advanced from the idle position, the transmission will upshift automatically to intermediate gear and then to high.

The driver can force downshift the transmission from high to intermediate at speeds up to 65 mph. A detent on the downshift linkage warns the driver when the carburetor is wide open. Accelerator pedal depression through the detent will bring in the downshift.

With the throttle closed the transmis-

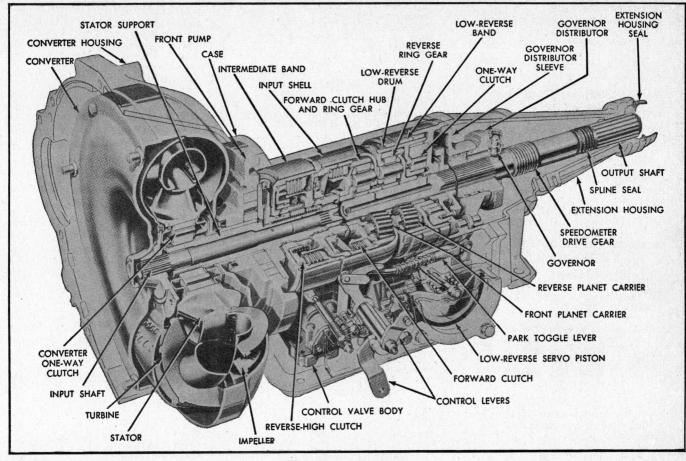

Fig. 1 C4 Dual Range Automatic

sion will downshift automatically as the car speed drops to about 10 mph. With the throttle open at any position up to the detent, the downshifts will come in automatically at speeds above 10 mph and in proportion to throttle opening. This prevents engine lugging on steep hill climbing, for example.

When the selector lever is moved to "L" with the transmission in high, the transmission will downshift to intermediate or to low depending on the road speed. At speed above 25 mph, the downshift will be from high to intermediate. At speeds below 25 mph, the downshift will be from high to low. With the selector lever in the "L" position the transmission cannot upshift.

TROUBLE SHOOTING GUIDE

Rough Initial Engagement In D1 or D2

1. Engine idle speed.
2. Vacuum diaphragm unit or tubes restricted, leaking or maladjusted.
3. Check control pressure.
4. Pressure regulator.
5. Valve body.
6. Forward clutch.

1-2 or 2-3 Shift Points Erratic

1. Check fluid level.
2. Vacuum diaphragm unit or tubes restricted, leaking or maladjusted.
3. Intermediate servo.
4. Manual linkage adjustment.
5. Governor.
6. Check control pressure.
7. Valve body.
8. Make air pressure check.

Rough 1-2 Upshifts

1. Vacuum diaphragm unit or tubes restricted, leaking or maladjusted.
2. Intermediate servo.
3. Intermediate band.
4. Check control pressure.
5. Valve body.
6. Pressure regulator.

Rough 2-3 Upshifts

1. Vacuum diaphragm unit or tubes restricted, leaking or maladjusted.
2. Intermediate servo.
3. Check control pressure.
4. Pressure regulator.
5. Intermediate band.
6. Valve body.
7. Make air pressure check.
8. Reverse-high clutch.
9. Reverse-high clutch piston air bleed valve.

Dragged Out 1-2 Shift

1. Check fluid level.
2. Vacuum diaphragm unit or tubes restricted, leaking or maladjusted.
3. Intermediate servo.
4. Check control pressure.
5. Intermediate band.
6. Valve body.
7. Pressure regulator.
8. Make air pressure check.
9. Leakage in hydraulic system.

Engine Overspeeds on 2-3 Shift

1. Manual linkage.
2. Check fluid level.
3. Vacuum diaphragm unit or tubes restricted, leaking or maladjusted.
4. Reverse servo.
5. Check control pressure.
6. Valve body.
7. Pressure regulator.
8. Intermediate band.
9. Reverse-high clutch.
10. Reverse-high clutch piston air bleed valve.

No 1-2 or 2-3 Shift

1. Manual linkage.
2. Downshift linkage, including inner lever position.
3. Vacuum diaphragm unit or tubes restricted, leaking or maladjusted.
4. Governor.

5. Check control pressure.
6. Valve body.
7. Intermediate band.
8. Intermediate servo.
9. Reverse-high clutch.
10. Reverse-high clutch piston air bleed valve.

No 3-1 Shift in D1 or 3-2 Shift in D2

1. Governor.
2. Valve body.

No Forced Downshifts

1. Downshift linkage, including inner lever position.
2. Valve body.
3. Vacuum diaphragm unit or tubes restricted, leaking or maladjusted.

Runaway Engine on Forced 3-2 Downshift

1. Check control pressure.
2. Intermediate servo.
3. Intermediate band.
4. Pressure regulator.
5. Valve body.
6. Vacuum diaphragm unit or tubes restricted, leaking or maladjusted.
7. Leakage in hydraulic system.

Rough 3-2 or 3-1 Shift at Closed Throttle

1. Engine idle speed.
2. Vacuum diaphragm unit or tubes restricted, leaking or maladjusted.
3. Intermediate servo.
4. Valve body.
5. Pressure regulator.

Shifts 1-3 in D1 and D2

1. Intermediate band.
2. Intermediate servo.
3. Vacuum diaphragm unit or tubes restricted, leaking or maladjusted.
4. Valve body.
5. Governor.
6. Make air pressure check.

No Engine Braking In 1st Gear —Manual Low

1. Manual linkage.
2. Reverse band.
3. Reverse servo.
4. Valve body.
5. Governor.
6. Make air pressure check.

Slips or Chatters in 1st Gear—D1

1. Check fluid level.
2. Vacuum diaphragm unit or tubes restricted, leaking or maladjusted.
3. Check control pressure.
4. Pressure regulator.
5. Valve body.
6. Forward clutch.
7. Leakage in hydraulic system.
8. Planetary one-way clutch.

Slips or Chatters in 2nd Gear

1. Check fluid level.
2. Vacuum diaphragm unit or tubes restricted, leaking or maladjusted.
3. Intermediate servo.
4. Intermediate band.

5. Check control pressure.
6. Pressure regulator.
7. Valve body.
8. Make air pressure check.
9. Forward clutch.
10. Leakage in hydraulic system.

Slips or Chatters in R

1. Check fluid level.
2. Vacuum diaphragm unit or tubes restricted, leaking or maladjusted.
3. Reverse band.
4. Check control pressure.
5. Reverse servo.
6. Pressure regulator.
7. Valve body.
8. Make air pressure check.
9. Reverse-high clutch.
10. Leakage in hydraulic system.
11. Reverse-high piston air bleed valve.

No Drive In D1 Only

1. Check fluid level.
2. Manual linkage.
3. Check control pressure.
4. Valve body.
5. Make air pressure check.
6. Planetary one-way clutch.

No Drive In D2 Only

1. Check fluid level.
2. Manual linkage.
3. Check control pressure.
4. Intermediate servo.
5. Valve body.
6. Make air pressure check.
7. Leakage in hydraulic system.
8. Planetary one-way clutch.

No Drive in L Only

1. Check fluid level.
2. Manual linkage.
3. Check control pressure.
4. Valve body.
5. Reverse servo.
6. Make air pressure check.
7. Leakage in hydraulic system.
8. Planetary one-way clutch.

No Drive in R Only

1. Check fluid level.
2. Manual linkage.
3. Reverse band.
4. Check control pressure.
5. Reverse servo.
6. Valve body.
7. Make air pressure check.
8. Reverse-high clutch.
9. Leakage in hydraulic system.
10. Reverse-high clutch piston air bleed valve.

No Drive in Any Selector Position

1. Check fluid level.
2. Manual linkage.
3. Check control pressure.
4. Pressure regulator.
5. Valve body.
6. Make air pressure check.
7. Leakage in hydraulic system.
8. Front pump.

Lockup in D1 Only

1. Reverse-high clutch.
2. Parking linkage.
3. Leakage in hydraulic system.

Lockup in D2 Only

1. Reverse band.
2. Reverse servo.
3. Reverse-high clutch.
4. Parking linkage.
5. Leakage in hydraulic system.
6. Planetary one-way clutch.

Lockup in L Only

1. Intermediate band.
2. Intermediate servo.
3. Reverse-high clutch.
4. Parking linkage.
5. Leakage in hydraulic system.

Lockup in R Only

1. Intermediate band.
2. Intermediate servo.
3. Forward clutch
4. Parking linkage.
5. Leakage in hydraulic system.

Parking Lock Binds or Won't Hold

1. Manual linkage.
2. Parking linkage.

Maximum Speed Too Low, Poor Acceleration

1. Engine performance.
2. Brakes bind.
3. Converter one-way clutch.

Noisy in N or P

1. Check fluid level.
2. Pressure regulator.
3. Front pump.
4. Planetary assembly.

Noisy in All Gears

1. Check fluid level.
2. Pressure regulator.
3. Planetary assembly.
4. Forward clutch.
5. Front pump.
6. Planetary one-way clutch.

Car Moves Forward in N

1. Manual linkage.
2. Forward clutch.

MAINTENANCE
Checking Oil Level

1. Make sure car is standing level.
2. Firmly apply parking brake.
3. If transmission fluid is at normal operating temperature, run engine at normal idle speed. If transmission fluid is cold, run engine at a fast idle until fluid reaches normal operating temperature. Then reduce engine speed to slow idle.
4. Shift selector lever through all positions, then place the lever in reverse.
5. With engine idling, remove dipstick and check fluid level. It should be at the full dot to ⅜" above the full dot. This ⅜" position above the center of the full dot is halfway between the letter "F" and "T" of the word transmission on the dipstick.
6. Add fluid as required to bring the fluid to the proper level.

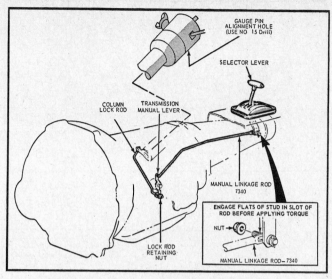

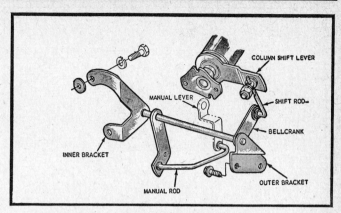

Fg. 4   Manual linkage. 1966-68 Ford column shift

Fig. 2   Manual linkage, floorshift. Typical.
Column lock rod is used beginning 1970

Drain & Refill

NOTE: *Normal maintenance and lubrication requirements do not necessitate periodic fluid changes. If a major failure has occurred in the transmission, it will have to be removed for service. At this time the converter must be thoroughly flushed to remove any foreign matter.*

When filling a dry transmission and converter, install five quarts of fluid. Start engine, shift the selector lever through all ranges and place it at R position. Check fluid level and add enough to raise the level in the transmission to the "F" (full) mark on the dipstick.

When a partial drain and refill is required due to front band adjustment or minor repair, proceed as follows:

1. Loosen and remove all but two oil pan bolts and drop one edge of the pan to drain the oil.
2. Remove and clean pan and screen.
3. Place a new gasket on pan and install pan and screen.
4. Add three quarts of fluid to transmission.
5. Run engine at idle speed for about two minutes.
6. Check oil level and add oil as necessary.
7. Run engine at a fast idle until it reaches normal operating temperature.
8. Shift selector lever through all ranges and then place it in P position.
9. Add fluid as required to bring the level to the full mark.

MANUAL LINKAGE, ADJUST

1967-71

Floor Shift

1. Place transmission selector lever in

D position.
2. Raise car and loosen shift rod retaining nut, Fig. 2.
3. Move transmission manual lever to D position (fourth detent position from rear of transmission).
4. Tighten attaching nut to 10-20 ft. lbs.

NOTE: After adjusting manual linkage on 1970-71 floor shift models, adjust lock rod as follows:

1. Raise car and loosen rod retaining nut, Fig. 2.
2. Lower car and place shift lever in D position.
3. Align hole in steering column socket casting with column alignment mark and insert a .180″ diameter gauge pin. Column casting must not rotate with pin in place.
4. Raise car and torque lock rod nut to 10-20 ft. lbs.

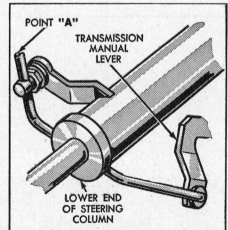

Fig. 3   Manual linkage. 1966-67 column shift (except Ford)

Column Shift

1. Place selector lever in D position (HI on Maverick with semi-automatic).
2. Loosen shift rod adjusting nut at point A, Figs. 4, 5, 6, 7, 8.
3. Shift manual lever at transmission to D or HI position. (Third from rear).
4. Tighten adjusting nut to 10-20 ft. lbs.

1966 Except Ford

Floor Shift

1. Referring to Fig. 2, position selector lever in D-1 (large dot) position.
2. Raise car and loosen manual control lever rod retaining nut.
3. Move manual lever to D-1 position (2nd detent from back of transmission). The last detent position is manual low.
4. With selector lever and manual lever in D-1 position, tighten retaining nut.
5. Check operation in all positions.

Column Shift

1. With engine stopped, loosen clamp at shift lever at point "A" so that shift rod is free to slide in the clamp, Fig. 3.
2. Place transmission selector lever into the D1 (large dot) position.
3. Shift manual lever at transmission into D1 detent position (second from rear).
4. Tighten clamp on shift rod at point "A".
5. Check pointer alignment and transmission operation for all ranges.

1966 Ford

1. Place selector lever in the D1 (circle) position tight against D stop.
2. Loosen nut at column shift lever enough to permit lever to slide on shift rod, Fig. 4.
3. Shift manual lever at transmission into D1 detent position (second from rear).

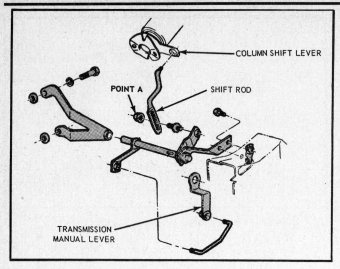

Fig. 5   Manual linkage. 1969-71 Ford column shift

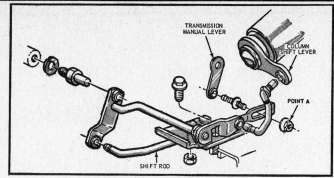

Fig. 6   Manual linkage. 1968-70 Fairlane, Falcon
& Montego column shift

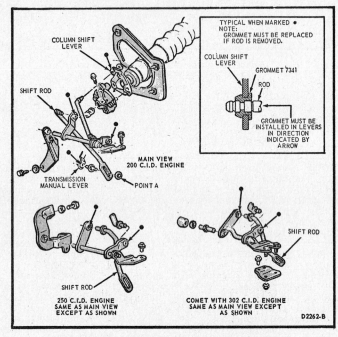

Fig. 7   Manual linkage. 1970-71 Maverick and Comet
column shift

4. Make sure that selector lever has not moved from the D1 stop, then tighten nut at column shift lever.
5. Check pointer alignment and transmission operation for all selector lever positions.

THROTTLE & DOWNSHIFT LINKAGE, ADJUST

1. Apply parking brake and place selector lever in "N".
2. Run engine at normal idle speed.
3. Connect tachometer to engine.
4. Adjust engine idle speed to specified rpm with selector lever in either Drive position.

NOTE: The carburetor throttle lever must be against the hot idle speed adjusting screw at the specified idle speed.

5. Proceed with the adjustments as outlined below.

1968-71 Comet, Fairlane, Falcon, Montego & Mustang & 1969-71 Cougar

NOTE: On Fairlane and Montego V8 units, throttle bellcrank must be adjusted first. Disconnect carburetor rod and accelerator connecting link from bellcrank and stabilizer rod from stabilizer. Insert a $\frac{1}{4}$" diameter pin through the stabilizer and bracket and adjust the rods so their trunnions freely enter holes. Secure rods and remove pins.

1. On units with rod controlled throttle only, with engine off, check accel-

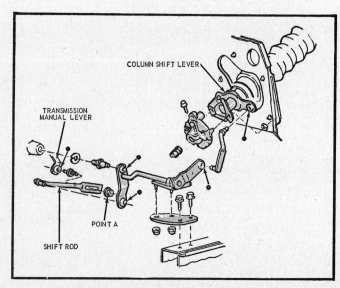

Fig. 8   Manual linkage. 1971 Torino & Montego
column shift

erator pedal for a height of 4½"
Figs. 9, 10, 11 and 12. Adjust accelerator connecting link to correct.
This step is not required on units
with cable controlled throttles.

2. Disconnect downshift control cable
from accelerator shaft lever.

3. With carburetor choke in the off position, depress the accelerator and block
it in the wide open position.

4. Rotate the downshift lever counterclockwise to place it against internal
stop.

5. Except 1969 Mustang V8 and all 1970-
71: With the lever held in this position
and all slack removed from the cable,
adjust the trunnion so that it will slide
into the lever. Turn it one additional
turn to increase length of cable then
secure it to the lever with retaining
clip.

6. On 1969 Mustang V8 and all 1970-71,
turn adjustment screws on carburetor
kick down lever to within .040" to
.080" gap of contacting pick up surface of carburetor throttle lever.

1969-71 Ford

On all engines, the conduit covering
the cable at the carburetor end must be
evenly nestled between the clamp and
the accelerator shaft bracket. Due to the
fixed clamping of the cable conduit, accelerator pedal height adjustment is not required.

1. Disconnect the downshift lever return
spring.

2. Hold throttle in wide open position
and hold downshift rod against the
through detent stop.

3. Adjust the downshift screw to provide .050"-.070" clearance between
the screw and the throttle shaft
lever. On 6-240, tighten the lock nut
to maintain the screw position. End
play adjustments is not required.

4. Connect downshift lever return spring.

Mustang 1966-67

1. Referring to Fig. 9, and with engine
idling speed properly adjusted, stop
engine and check for proper accelerator pedal height of 3⅞".

2. On six cylinder engines, disconnect
carburetor rod and adjust length of
rod to bring pedal height within specifications. On V8 engines, disconnect
carburetor rod at point "C" and adjust
length of rod as required.

3. To adjust kickdown linkage on six
cylinder engines, disconnect kickdown
cable return spring at transmission,
carburetor return spring at manifold,
and kickdown cable at point "A". Position kickdown lever in downshift
position (carburetor wide open). Hold
kickdown lever on transmission against
the stop in a counter-clockwise direction (kickdown position). Adjust trun-

nion at "A" on kickdown cable so it
aligns with hole in kickdown lever and
install attaching clip. Install return
springs.

4. On V8s, disconnect kickdown return
spring at bellcrank, carburetor return
spring and kickdown lever rod at
point "B". Hold carburetor rod in wide
open position. Step in rod should
place bellcrank in downshift position.
Hold kickdown lever in downward position. Adjust lever trunnion at point
"B" so it aligns with hole in bellcrank. Install trunnion and retaining
clip. Release levers and install carburetor rod and bellcrank return springs.

1966-67 Comet 6, Fairlane 6 & Falcon 6 & V8

1. Referring to Figs. 10 and 11, with
engine shut off, check accelerator
pedal for a height of 4½", measured
as shown. If necessary, adjust con-
nectiing link at point "A".

2. Disconnect downshift control cable at
point "B" from accelerator shaft lever.

3. With carburetor choke in off position,
depress accelerator pedal to floor.
Block pedal to hold it in wide open
position.

4. Rotate downshift lever "C" counterclockwise to place it against the internal stop.

5. With lever held in this position, and
all slack removed from cable, adjust
trunnion so that it will slide into accelerator shaft lever. Turn it one additional turn clockwise and secure it
with clip.

6. Remove block to release linkage.

1966-67 Comet & Fairlane V8-289

1. Referring to Fig. 12, disconnect bell-
crank-to-carburetor rod at point "C"
and accelerator connecting link from
throttle shaft at point "B".

2. Disconnect stabilizer rod from stabilizer at point "A".

3. Insert a ¼" diameter pin through
stabilizer and bracket.

4. Adjust length of stabilizer rod so
that trunnion enters stabilizer freely.
Secure with clip.

5. Secure carburetor-to-bellcrank rod with
clip at point "C".

6. Adjust length of accelerator connecting link to obtain a pedal height of 4
to 4½" as shown. Connect link to
accelerator shaft with clip after proper
pedal height has been established.

7. With engine off, disconnect downshift
control cable at point "D" from accelerator shaft lever.

8. Rotate downshift lever "E" clockwise
to place it against the internal stop.

9. With lever held in this position, and
all slack removed from cable, adjust

trunnion so that it will slide into downshift lever. Turn it one additional turn
clockwise and secure with clip.

1966-68 Ford

1. Apply parking brake and place selector
lever at N.

2. With engine idling at normal operating temperature, connect a tachometer.

3. Adjust idle speed to specified rpm
with transmission selector lever at
D1 (large dot) or D2 (circle) drive
position.

4. With carburetor throttle lever against
hot idle adjusting screw, loosen accelerator cable clamp.

5. With accelerator pedal to floor and
throttle lever held in wide open position, slide cable conduit to rear (to
left on 6 cylinder engines) to remove
slack from cable.

6. Connect downshift lever return
springs, Figs. 14 and 15.

7. Hold throttle lever at wide open position and depress downshift rod to
the "through detent stop". Set downshift lever (at carburetor) adjusting
screw against throttle lever.

8. Connect both return springs to their
levers.

BANDS, ADJUST

NOTE: The intermediate and low-reverse
bands from 1967 are basically the same
as 1966 except that the adjusting screw
locknut must be discarded and a new one
installed each time a band is adjusted.

Intermediate Band

1. Loosen lock nut several turns.

2. With tool shown in Fig. 15, tighten
adjusting screw until tool handle
clicks. This tool is a pre-set torque
wrench which clicks and overruns
when the torque on the adjusting
screw reaches 10 ft-lbs.

3. Back off adjusting screw exactly 1¾
turns.

4. Hold adjusting screw from turning
and tighten lock nut.

Low-Reverse Band

1. Loosen lock nut several turns.

2. Tighten adjusting screw until tool
handle clicks, Fig. 16. Tool shown is
a pre-set torque wrench which clicks
and overruns when the torque on the
adjusting screw reaches 10 ft-lbs.

3. Back off adjusting screw exactly 3
full turns.

4. Hold adjusting screw from turning
and tighten lock nut.

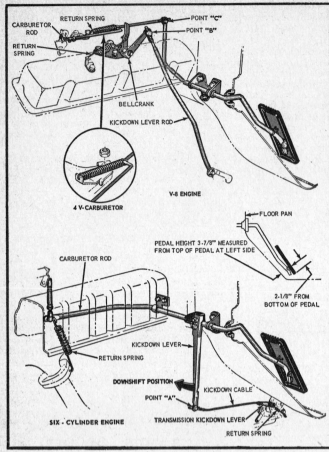

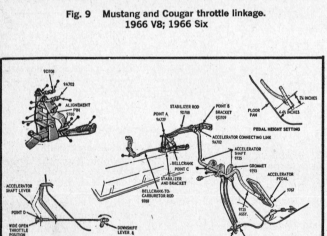

Fig. 9 Mustang and Cougar throttle linkage. 1966 V8; 1966 Six

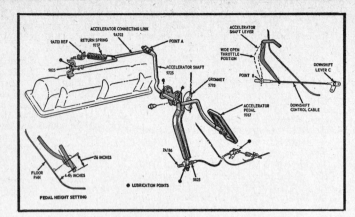

Fig. 10 Throttle linkage. 1966-69 Falcon with V8; 1967-68 Mustang and Cougar V8

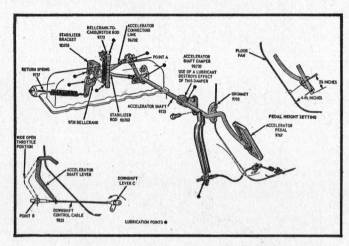

Fig. 11 Throttle linkage. 1966-68 Comet, Fairlane, 1968 Montego, 1967-68 Mustang 6 & 1966-69 Falcon 6

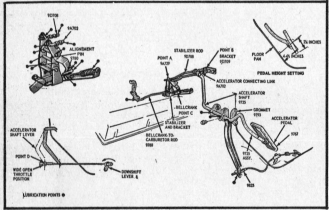

Fig. 12 Throttle linkage. 1966-69 Comet and Fairlane V8

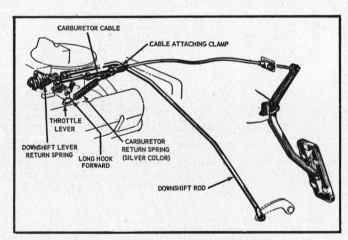

Fig. 13 Throttle linkage. 1966-69 Ford V8

"IN CAR" REPAIRS

The following operations may be performed without removing the transmission from the vehicle.

1. Oil pan remove and replace.
2. Valve body replacement.
3. Intermediate servo repair.
4. Low-reverse servo piston replace.
5. Extension housing bushing and rear seal.
6. Extension housing and governor replace.

TRANSMISSION, REPLACE
1966-71

1. On 1966 Ford, disconnect neutral safety switch wires in engine compartment.
2. Raise car and remove converter cover at low front side of converter housing.
3. Drain converter.
4. Remove propeller shaft.
5. Remove vacuum line hose from transmission vacuum unit. Disconnect vacuum line from clip.
6. Remove two extension housing to crossmember bolts.
7. Remove speedometer cable from ex-

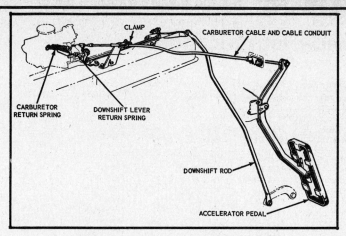

CLAMP

CARBURETOR CABLE AND CABLE CONDUIT

CARBURETOR RETURN SPRING

DOWNSHIFT LEVER RETURN SPRING

DOWNSHIFT ROD

ACCELERATOR PEDAL

Fig. 14   Throttle linkage. 1966-70 Ford 6

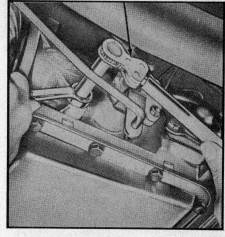

Fig. 15   Intermediate band adjustment

tension housing.

8. Disconnect exhaust pipe from manifold.
9. Remove parking brake cable from equalizer lever.
10. On Ford units, remove fluid filler tube from the oil pan and drain the transmission. On intermediate units, loosen transmission oil pan bolts and drain oil at one corner of pan. Tighten bolts.
11. Disconnect cooler lines from the transmission.
12. Remove the manual and kick down linkage rods from transmission shift levers.
13. Where necessary, disconnect the neutral start switch wires.
14. Remove starter.
15. On intermediate models, remove fluid filler tube.
16. Remove four converter-to-flywheel nuts.
17. Support transmission with jack.
18. Remove crossmember.
19. Remove converter housing-to-engine bolts.
20. Lower transmission and remove from car.

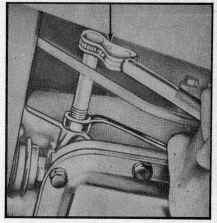

Fig. 16   Low-reverse band adjustment

C6 DUAL RANGE AUTOMATIC

TRANSMISSION IDENTIFICATION

An identification tag attached to the servo cover bolt, includes the model prefix and suffix.

YEAR	CAR MODEL	TRANS. MODEL	ENGINE MODEL
1966	Comet(1)	PDD-J	V8-390(3)
	Comet(2)	PDD-P	V8-390(3)
	Comet(1)	PDD-E	V8-390(4)
	Comet(2)	PDD-R	V8-390(4)
	Fairlane same as Comet.		
	Ford(1)	PDD-B	V8-390(3)
	Ford(2)	PDD-W	V8-390(3)
	Ford(1)	PDD-C	V8-390(4)
	Ford(2)	PDD-K	V8-390(4)
	Ford(1)	PDD-H	V8-428
	Ford(2)	PDD-N	V8-428
	Lincoln	PDE-A	V8-462
	Mercury(5)	PDD-D	V8-410
	Mercury(6)	PDD-L	V8-410
	Mercury(7)	PDD-U	V8-410
	Mercury(8)	PDD-T	V8-410
	Mercury(1)	PDD-H	V8-428
	Mercury(2)	PDD-N	V8-428
	Thunderbird	PDD-S	V8-390
	Thunderbird	PDD-F	V8-428
1967	Comet(1)	PGA-B	V8-390(3)
	Comet(2)	PGA-C	V8-390(3)
	Comet(2)	PGA-M	V8-390(4)
	Cougar	PGA-P	V8-390
	Fairlane(1)	PGA-B	V8-390(3)
	Fairlane(2)	PGA-C	V8-390(3)
	Fairlane(1)	PGA-F	V8-390(4)
	Fairlane(2)	PGA-G	V8-390(4)
	Fairlane(1)	PGA-R	V8-390(4)
	Fairlane(2)	PGA-M	V8-390(4)
	Ford(1)	PGA-A	V8-390(4)
	Ford(2)	PGA-L	V8-390(4)
	Ford(1)	PGB-F	V8-428
	Ford(9)	PGB-G	V8-390
	Ford(9)	PGB-H	V8-428
	Ford(1)	PGA-H	V8-390(4)
	Ford(2)	PGA-J	V8-390(4)
	Ford(1)	PGB-A	V8-428
	Ford(2)	PGB-B	V8-428
	Lincoln	PGC-A	V8-462
	Mercury(1)	PGA-A	V8-390(4)
	Mercury(7)	PGA-H	V8-410
	Mercury(6)	PGB-A	V8-410
	Mercury(1)	PGB-A	V8-428
	Mercury(2)	PGB-B	V8-428
	Mercury(9)	PGB-F	V8-428
	Mercury(1)	PGB-G	V8-390(3)
	Mercury(8)	PGB-G	V8-410
	Mercury(1)	PGB-H	V8-410
	Mercury(5)	PGB-H	V8-428
	Mustang	PGA-P	V8-390
	Thunderbird	PGA-K	V8-390
	Thunderbird	PGB-C	V8-428
1968	Cougar(2)	PGA-S	V8-390
	Cougar(1)	PGB-W	V8-427
	Cougar(2)	PGA-P2	V8-390(4)
	Fairlane(1)	PGA-B3	V8-390(3)
	Fairlane(5)	PGA-C2	V8-390(3)
	Fairlane(2)	PGA-M2	V8-390(4)
	Fairlane(1)	PGA-R2	V8-390(4)
	Fairlane(1)	PGB-Y	V8-427(4)
	Fairlane(2)	PGB-2	V8-427(4)
	Ford(1)	PGA-A-2	V8-390(3)
	Ford(9)	PGB-G-1	V8-390
	Ford(2)	PGA-L-2	V8-390(3)
	Ford(1)	PGA-H-2	V8-390
	Ford(2)	PGA-J-2	V8-390(4)
	Ford(1)	PGB-A-2	V8-428
	Ford(9)	PGB-H-1	V8-428

YEAR	CAR MODEL	TRANS. MODEL	ENGINE MODEL
	Ford(2)	PGB-B-2	V8-428(4)
	Ford(9)	PGB-F-1	V8-428(4)
	Ford(1)	PGB-AA	V8-427(4)
	Ford(2)	PGB-AB	V8-427(4)
	Lincoln	PGC-A3	V8-462
	Lincoln	PGC-B	V8-460
	Mercury(1)	PGA-A-2	V8-390(4)
	Mercury(9)	PGB-G-1	V8-390
	Mercury(1)	PGA-H-2	V8-390
	Mercury(1)	PGB-A-2	V8-428
	Mercury(1)	PGB-H-1	V8-428
	Mercury(9)	PGB-F-1	V8-428(4)
	Montego(1)	PGA-B3	V8-390(3)
	Montego(2)	PGA-C2	V8-390(3)
	Montego(2)	PGA-M2	V8-390(4)
	Montego(1)	PGA-R2	V8-390(4)
	Montego(1)	PGB-Y	V8-427(4)
	Montego(2)	PGB-2	V8-427(4)
	Mustang(2)	PGA-P2	V8-390(4)
	Thunderbird	PGB-C, C1, C2	V8-428
	Thunderbird	PGA-K1, K2	V8-390
1969	Cougar(2)	PGA-AE	V8-390(3)
	Cougar(2)	PGB-AF-1	V8-428(4)
	Fairlane(1)	PGA-AC	V8-390(4)
	Fairlane(2)	PGA-AD	V8-390(4)
	Fairlane(2)	PGB-AG	V8-428(4)
	Fairlane(2)	PGB-AH	V8-428(4)
	Ford(1)	PGA-A3	V8-390(4)
	Ford(2)	PGA-J3	V8-390(4)
	Ford(1)	PGA-Z	V8-429(3)
	Ford(1)	PGA-AA	V8-429(4)
	Ford(1)	PGB-F2	V8-428(4)
	Ford(1)	PBG-G2	V8-390
	Ford(1)	PGB-H2	V8-428(4)
	Ford(1)	PGB-AD	V8-429(4)
	Ford(2)	PGB-AE	V8-429(4)
	Lincoln	PGC-B	V8-460
	Mark III	PGC-C1	V8-460
	Mercury(1)	PGA-A3	V8-390(3)
	Mercury(1)	PGA-J3	V8-390(3)
	Mercury(1)	PGA-Z	V8-429(3)
	Mercury(2)	PGA-AA	V8-429(4)
	Mercury(1)	PGB-F2	V8-428(4)
	Mercury(1)	PGB-G2	V8-390
	Mercury(1)	PGB-H2	V8-428(4)
	Mercury(1)	PGB-AD	V8-429(4)
	Mercury(2)	PGB-AE	V8-429(4)
	Montego(1)	PGA-AC	V8-390(4)
	Montego(2)	PGA-AD	V8-390(4)
	Montego(1)	PGB-AG	V8-428(4)
	Montego	PGB-AH	V8-428(4)
	Mustang(2)	PGA-AE	V8-390(3)
	Mustang(2)	PGB-AF-1	V8-428(4)
	Thunderbird	PGB-J1	V8-429(4)
1970	Cougar	PGB-AF2	V8-428
	Fairlane(1)	PJB-A	V8-429
	Fairlane(1)	PJB-B	V8-429
	Fairlane(1)	PJB-J	V8-429
	Fairlane(1)	PJC-A	V8-429
	Fairlane(2)	PJC-B	V8-429
	Fairlane(1)	PJC-E	V8-429
	Fairlane(2)	PJC-F	V8-429
	Ford(1)	PGA-A4	V8-390
	Ford(2)	PGA-J4	V8-390
	Ford(1)	PGB-F3	V8-428
	Ford(1)	PGB-G3	V8-390

YEAR	CAR MODEL	TRANS. MODEL	ENGINE MODEL
	Ford(1)(3)	PJA-A	V8-429
	Ford(2)(3)	PJA-B	V8-429
	Ford(1)(4)	PJB-C	V8-429
	Ford(2)(4)	PJB-D	V8-429
	Ford(1)(4)	PJB-F	V8-429
	Lincoln	PJD-CF	V8-460
	Mark III	PJD-BE	V8-460
	Mercury(1)	PGA-A4	V8-390
	Mercury(2)	PGA-J4	V8-390
	Mercury(1)	PGB-F3	V8-428
	Mercury(1)	PGB-G3	V8-390
	Mercury(1)(3)	PJA-A	V8-429
	Mercury(2)(3)	PJA-B	V8-429
	Mercury(1)(4)	PJB-D	V8-429
	Mercury(2)(4)	PJB-F	V8-429
	Montego(1)	PJB-A	V8-429
	Montego(2)	PJB-B	V8-429
	Montego(1)	PJB-J	V8-429
	Montego(1)	PJC-A	V8-429
	Montego(2)	PJC-B	V8-429
	Montego(1)	PJC-E	V8-429
	Montego(2)	PJC-F	V8-429
	Mustang	PGB-AF2	V8-428
	Thunderbird	PJB-GH	V8-429
1971	Cougar	PGA-AH	V8-351
	Cougar	PJC-G	V8-429
	Fairlane(1)	PGA-AF	V8-351
	Fairlane(1)	PGA-AG	V8-351
	Fairlane(1)	PJC-A	V8-429
	Fairlane(2)	PJC-B	V8-429
	Ford(1)	PGA-A4	V8-390
	Ford(2)	PGA-J4	V8-390
	Ford(1)(9)	PGB-G3	V8-390
	Ford(1)(3)	PJA-A	V8-429
	Ford(2)(3)	PJA-B	V8-429
	Ford(1)(3)	PJA-C	V8-400
	Ford(2)	PJA-D	V8-400
	Ford(1)(4)	PJB-C	V8-429
	Ford(2)(4)	PJB-D	V8-429
	Ford(1)(4)	PJB-F	V8-429
	Ford(1)(9)	PJB-K	V8-400
	Ford(9)	PJC-HI	V8-429
	Lincoln	PJD-F	V8-460
	Mark III	PJD-E	V8-460
	Mercury(1)(3)	PJA-A	V8-429
	Mercury	PJA-C	V8-400
	Mercury(1)(4)	PJB-C	V8-429
	Mercury(1)(9)	PJB-F	V8-429
	Mercury(1)(9)	PJB-K	V8-400
	Mercury(1)(9)	PJC-HI	V8-429
	Montego(1)	PGA-AF	V8-351
	Montego(2)	PGA-AG	V8-351
	Montego(1)	PJC-A	V8-429
	Montego(2)	PJC-B	V8-429
	Mustang	PGA-AH	V8-351
	Mustang	PJC-G	V8-429
	Thunderbird	PJB-H	V8-429

(1)—Column shift.
(2)—Floor shift.
(3)—Two barrel carburetor.
(4)—Four barrel carburetor.
(5)—Column shift, dual exhaust.
(6)—Floor shift, dual exhaust.
(7)—Floor shift, single exhaust.
(8)—Column shift, single exhaust.
(9)—Police or Fleet.

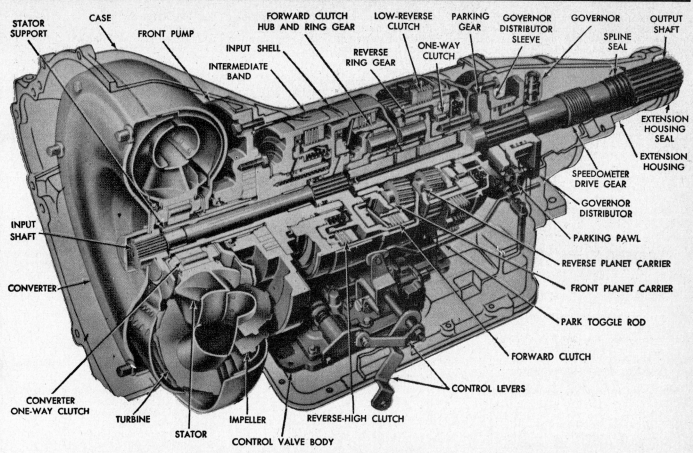

Fig. 1   Sectional view of C6 transmission

DESCRIPTION

As shown in Fig. 1, the transmission consists essentially of a torque converter, a compound planetary gear train controlled by one band, three disc clutches and a one-way clutch, and a hydraulic control system.

The transmission is made so that in the first design (1966) the shifting is fully automatic from the "D" position. In the later design (some Comets and Fairlanes in 1966 and in all models from 1967) a system of manual and automatic shifting is provided.

Fully Automatic Type, 1966

The shift selector has six positions: Park, Reverse, Neutral, D2 (small dot), D1 (large dot), and manual low.

In the normal driving range (D1), the car starts in low gear, with automatic upshifts to second and high as road speed increases. With the throttle closed, the transmission downshifts from high to low in D1 at about 10 mph.

D2 range provides a second gear start and upshift to high. The coasting or closed throttle downshift to second gear occurs at about 10 mph.

Manual low (L) range is designed primarily for engine braking. Starting in this position, the car is in low gear and there is no upshift. If the transmission is in

high gear in D2 or D1 and the driver moves the selector lever to L, a downshift to second occurs, and the transmission stays in second down to 10 mph. Then it downshifts to low.

Automatic & Manual Shifting 1966-71

This unit has a shift pattern which is indicated on the selector as P-R-N-D-2-1. This refers respectively to Park, Reverse, Neutral, Full Automatic, Second Gear (manual), Low Gear (manual).

In this unit an overriding control is provided which enables the driver to exercise his own judgement with regard to the gear ratios to be selected and an understanding of what is possible greatly enhances the pleasure to be derived from driving the car. No automatic mechanism has the power of anticipation, but the driver can see ahead and has the means for over-riding the automatic mechanism.

Automatic Shift

In "D" position the shift sequence is fully automatic in that the transmission starts in low gear and upshifts through second gear to third or high gear.

Manual Shifting

The shift to 2 or 1 is done manually by shifting the lever from neutral to either position. In "1" position, the transmisson

starts in 1st (low gear) and is retained. In "2" position it starts in 2nd gear and remains in 2nd gear, regardless of road speed.

Manual Shift To "1"

Manual shifting from "D" to "1" can also be accomplished any time. Here the transmission immediately shifts to second and remains in second until the predetermined governor control speed allows it to shift down to low gear where it remains. The governor speed control at this point eliminates the possibility of a direct down shift to low gear until the road speed is reduced.

Shift Lever Controls

A shift lever button control is used to shift from neutral to reverse or park, also when shifting from "D" to "2" or "1" position. However, the button control function is not required when shifting from neutral to "D", or to shift forward from "1" to "2" position.

Parking Pawl

The transmission gear train is in neutral in both P and N positions. There is no pressure to any clutch and only the transmission input shaft turns. In park, a pawl engages a parking gear which is splined to the transmission output shaft, Fig. 1, to lock the rear wheels to the transmission main case.

A neutral start switch, mounted on the transmission and operated by the selector linkage, completes the engine cranking circuit in P and N only so that the engine cannot be started in any drive gear.

Forced Downshifts

Forced downshifts (kickdown shifts) from high to second gear are possible at speeds as high as 65 mph in D1 or D2. In D1 it is possible to force a downshift to 1st gear up to 30 mph.

The carburetor is at full throttle before the accelerator is floored. Up to full throttle, a "torque demand" downshift to 2nd is possible up to 40 mph. "Kickdown" shifts require depressing the accelerator to the floor to actuate the downshift valve in the transmission.

TROUBLE SHOOTING GUIDE

No Drive In Forward Speeds

1. Manual linkage adjustment.
2. Check control pressure.
3. Valve body.
4. Make air pressure check.
5. Forward clutch.
6. Leakage in hydraulic system.

Rough Initial Engagement in D, D1, D2 or 2

1. Engine idle speed too high.
2. Vacuum diaphragm unit or tubes restricted, leaking or maladjusted.
3. Check control pressure.
4. Valve body.
5. Forward clutch.

1-2 or 2-3 Shift Points Incorrect or Erratic

1. Check fluid level.
2. Vacuum diaphragm unit or tubes restricted, leaking or maladjusted.
3. Downshift linkage, including inner lever position.
4. Manual linkage adjustment.
5. Governor defective.
6. Check control pressure.
7. Valve body.
8. Make air pressure check.

Rough 1-2 Upshifts

1. Vacuum diaphragm unit or tubes restricted, leaking or maladjusted.
2. Intermediate servo.
3. Intermediate band
4. Check control pressure.
5. Valve body.

Rough 2-3 Shifts

1. Vacuum diaphragm or tubes restricted leaking or maladjusted.
2. Intermediate servo.
3. Check control pressure.
4. Intermediate band.
5. Valve body.
6. Make air pressure check.
7. Reverse-high clutch.
8. Reverse-high clutch piston air bleed valve.

Dragged Out 1-2 Shift

1. Check fluid level.

2. Vacuum diaphragm unit or tubes restricted, leaking or maladjusted.
3. Intermediate servo.
4. Check control pressure.
5. Intermediate band.
6. Valve body.
7. Make air pressure check.
8. Leakage in hydraulic system.

Engine Overspeeds on 2-3 Shift

1. Manual linkage adjustment.
2. Check fluid level.
3. Vacuum diaphragm unit or tubes restricted, leaking or maladjusted.
4. Intermediate servo.
5. Check control pressure.
6. Valve body.
7. Intermediate band.
8. Reverse-high clutch.
9. Reverse-high clutch piston air bleed valve.

No 1-2 or 2-3 Shift

1. Manual linkage adjustment.
2. Downshift linkage including inner lever position.
3. Vacuum diaphragm unit or tubes restricted, leaking or malajusted.
4. Governor.
5. Check control pressure.
6. Valve body.
7. Intermediate band.
8. Intermediate servo.
9. Reverse-high clutch.
10. Leakage in hydraulic system.

No 3-1 Shift In D1, 2 or 3-2 Shift In D2 or D

1. Governor.
2. Valve body.

No Forced Downshifts

1. Downshift linkage, including inner lever position.
2. Check control pressure.
3. Valve body.

Runaway Engine on Forced 3-2 Shift

1. Check control pressure.
2. Intermediate servo.
3. Intermediate band.
4. Valve body.
5. Vacuum diaphragm unit or tubes restricted, leaking or maladjusted.
6. Leakage in hydraulic system.

Rough 3-2 Shift or 3-1 Shift at Closed Throttle

1. Engine idle speed.
2. Vacuum diaphragm unit or tubes restricted, leaking or maladjusted.
3. Intermediate servo.
4. Check control pressure.
5. Valve body.

Shifts 1-3 in D, D1, 2, D2

1. Intermediate band.
2. Intermediate servo.
3. Valve body.
4. Governor.
5. Make air pressure check.

No Engine Braking in 1st Gear—Manual Low Range

1. Manual linkage adjustment.
2. Low-reverse clutch.

3. Valve body.
4. Governor.
5. Make air pressure check.
6. Leakage in hydraulic system.

Creeps Excessively

1. Engine idle speed too high.

Slips or Chatters In 1st Gear, D1

1. Check fluid level.
2. Vacuum diaphragm unit or tubes restricted, leaking or maladjusted.
3. Check control peessure.
4. Valve body.
5. Forward clutch.
6. Leakage in hydraulic system.
7. Planetary one-way clutch.

Slips or Chatters In 2nd Gear

1. Check fluid level.
2. Vacuum diaphragm unit or tubes restricted, leaking or maladjusted.
3. Intermediate servo.
4. Intermediate band.
5. Check control pressure.
6. Valve body.
7. Make air pressure check.
8. Forward clutch.
9. Leakage in hydraulic system.

Slips or Chatters In Reverse

1. Check fluid level.
2. Vacuum diaphragm unit or tubes restricted, leaking or maladjusted.
3. Manual linkage adjustment.
4. Low-reverse clutch.
5. Check control pressure.
6. Valve body.
7. Make air pressure check.
8. Reverse-high clutch.
9. Leakage in hydraulic system.
10. Reverse-high clutch piston air bleed valve.

No Drive In D1 or 2

1. Manual linkage adjustment.
2. Check control pressure.
3. Valve body.
4. Planetary one-way clutch.

No Drive In D, D2

1. Check fluid level.
2. Manual linkage adjustment.
3. Check control pressure.
4. Intermediate servo.
5. Valve body.
6. Make air pressure check.
7. Leakage in hydraulic system.

No Drive In L or 1

1. Check fluid level.
2. Check control pressure.
3. Valve body.
4. Make air pressure check.
5. Leakage in hydraulic system.

No Drive In R Only

1. Check fluid level.
2. Manual linkage adjustment.
3. Low-reverse clutch.
4. Check control pressure.
5. Valve body.
6. Make air pressure check.
7. Reverse-high clutch.
8. Leakage in hydraulic system.
9. Reverse-high clutch piston air bleed valve.

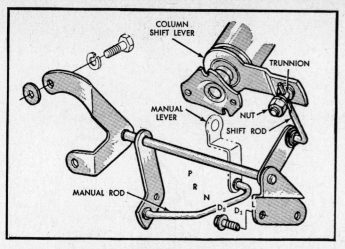

Fig. 2   Column shift linkage. 1966-68

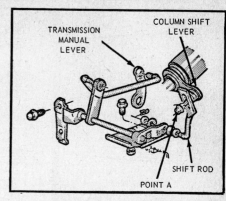

Fig. 3   Column shift linkage.
1968 Fairlane & Montego

No Drive In Any Selector Position

1. Check fluid level.
2. Manual linkage adjustment.
3. Check control pressure.
4. Valve body.
5. Make air pressure check.
6. Leakage in hydraulic system.
7. Front pump.

Lockup In D1 or 2

1. Valve body.
2. Parking linkage.
3. Leakage in hydraulic system.

Lockup In D2 or D

1. Low-reverse clutch.
2. Valve body.
3. Reverse-high clutch.
4. Parking linkage.
5. Leakage in hydraulic system.
6. Planetary one-way clutch.

Lockup In L or 1

1. Valve body.

2. Parking linkage.
3. Leakage in hydraulic system.

Lockup In R Only

1. Valve body.
2. Forward clutch.
3. Parking linkage.
4. Leakage in hydraulic system.

Parking Lock Binds or Does Not Hold

1. Manual linkage adjustment.
2. Parking linkage.

Transmission Overheats

1. Oil cooler and connections.
2. Valve body.
3. Vacuum diaphragm unit or tubes restricted, leaking or maladjusted.
4. Check control pressure.
5. Converter one-way clutch.
6. Converter pressure check valves.

Maximum Speed Too Low, Poor Acceleration

1. Engine performance.
2. Car brakes.
3. Forward clutch.

Transmission Noisy In N and P

1. Check fluid level.
2. Valve body.
3. Front pump.

Noisy In 1st, 2nd, 3rd or Reverse

1. Check fluid level.
2. Valve body.
3. Planetary assembly.
4. Forward clutch.
5. Reverse-high clutch.
6. Planetary one-way clutch.

Car Moves Forward In N

1. Manual linkage adjustment.
2. Forward clutch.

Fluid Leak

1. Check fluid level.
2. Converter drain plugs.
3. Oil pan gasket, filler tube or seal.
4. Oil cooler and connections.
5. Manual or downshift lever shaft seal.
6. ⅛" pipe plugs in case.
7. Extension housing-to-case gasket.
8. Extension housing rear oil seal.

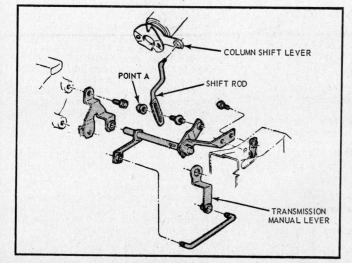

Fig. 4   Column shift linkage. 1969-71 Ford & Mercury

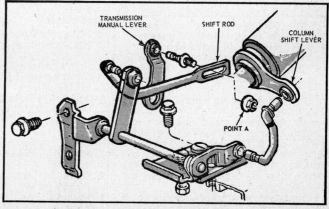

Fig. 5   Column shift linkage. 1969 Fairlane & Montego

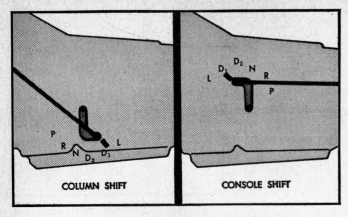

Fig. 6 Manual valve lever positions for 1966 fully automatic transmission

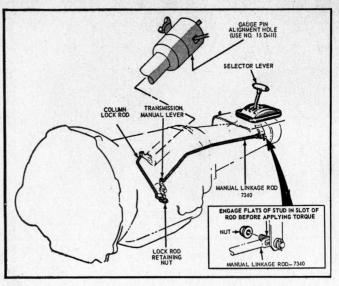

Fig. 7 Manual linkage, floor shift. Typical. Column lock rod is used beginning 1970 models

9. Speedometer driven gear adapter seal.
10. Vacuum diaphragm unit or tubes.
11. Intermediate servo.
12. Engine rear oil seal.

MAINTENANCE
Checking Oil Level

1. Make sure care is on a level floor.
2. Apply parking brake firmly.
3. Run engine at normal idle speed. If transmission fluid is cold, run engine at a fast idle until fluid reaches normal operating temperature. When fluid is warm, slow engine to normal idle speed.
4. Shift selector lever through all positions, then place lever at "P". Do not shut down engine during fluid level checks.
5. Clean all dirt from dipstick cap before removing dipstick from filler tube.
6. Pull dipstick out of tube, wipe it clean and push it all the way back in tube.
7. Pull dipstick out of tube again and check fluid level. If necessary, add enough fluid to raise the level to the "F" mark on dipstick. Do not overfill.

Drain & Refill

NOTE: The Ford Motor Company recommends the use of an automatic transmission fluid with Qaulification No. M2C-33D (on container) instead of the conventional Type A fluid. The recommended fluid is said to have a greater coefficient of friction and greater ability to handle maximum engine torques without band or clutch slippage.

Normal maintenance and lubrication requirements do not necessitate periodic fluid changes. If a major failure has occured in the transmission, it will have to be removed for service. At this time the converter must be thoroughly flushed to remove any foreign matter.

1. To drain the fluid, loosen pan attaching bolts and allow fluid to drain.

2. After fluid has drained to the level of the pan flange, remove pan bolts working from rear and both sides of pan to allow it to drop and drain slowly.
3. When fluid has stopped draining, remove and clean pan and screen. Discard pan gasket.
4. Using a new gasket, install pan.
5. Add 3 quarts of recommended fluid to transmission through filler tube.
6. Run engine at idle speed for 2 minutes, and then run it at a fast idle until it reaches normal operating temperature.
7. Shift selector lever through all positions, place it at "P" and check fluid level.
8. If necessary, add enough fluid to transmission to bring it to the "F" mark on the dipstick.

MANUAL LINKAGE, ADJUST
1967-71

Column Shift

1. Place selector lever in D position.
2. Loosen shift rod adjusting nut, point A in Figs. 3, 4, 5.
3. Shift transmission manual lever to D, third detent from rear of transmission.
4. Make sure selector lever has not moved from D position then tighten adjusting nut to 10-20 ft. lbs.

Floor Shift

1. Place transmission selector lever in D position.
2. Raise car and loosen shift rod retaining nut, Fig. 7.
3. Move transmission manual lever to D position, third detent from rear of transmission.

4. Tighten retaining nut to 10-20 ft. lbs.

NOTE: Beginning on 1970 models, after adjusting manual linkage, adjust lock rod as follows:

1. Raise car and loosen lock rod retaining nut, Fig. 7.
2. Lower car and place shift lever in D position.
3. Align hole steering column socket casting with column alignment mark and insert a .180" diameter gauge rod. Column casting must not rotate with rod in place.
4. Raise car and torque lock rod nut to 10-20 ft. lbs.

1966

Column Shift

1. Move the selector to D1.
2. Loosen the nut on the shift rod trunnion, Fig. 2, to permit the column shift lever to slide on the rod.
3. Shift the manual lever on the transmission to D1, Fig. 6.
4. Check that the selector lever is against the gate stop in D1, then tighten the nut on the trunnion.
5. Check the other positions and for starting in park and neutral. If necessary, adjust the neutral start switch.

Console Shift

1. Move the selector to D1.
2. Loosen the nut, Fig. 7, that holds the manual lever control rod to the shift lever link.
3. Move the manual-shift lever on the transmission to the D1 position, Fig. 6.
4. Tighten the nut while the selector and shift lever are both in D1.
5. Check the other selector positions, and for starting in neutral and park. If necessary, adjust the neutral start switch.

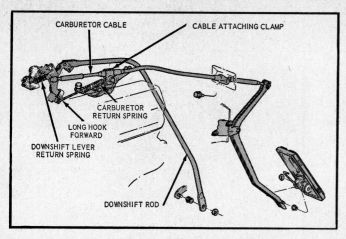

Fig. 8   Ford and Mercury throttle linkage

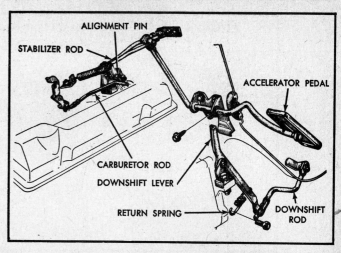

Fig. 9   Comet and Fairlane throttle linkage

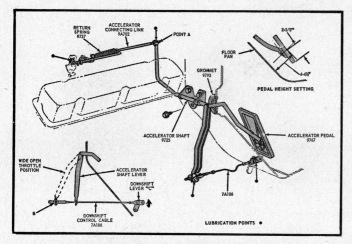

Fig. 10   Throttle linkage. 1966-68 Mustang & Cougar

THROTTLE & DOWNSHIFT LINKAGE

Adjusting the throttle linkage is important to be certain the throttle and kickdown systems are properly adjusted. The kickdown system should come in when the accelerator is pressed through detent, and not before detent.

1969-71 Ford & Mercury & 1970-71 Lincoln

On all engines, the conduit covering the cable at the carburetor end must be evenly nestled between the clamp and the accelerator shaft bracket. Due to the fixed clamping of the cable conduit, accelerator pedal height adjustment is not required.

1. Disconnect downshift lever return spring.
2. Hold throttle in wide open position and hold downshift rod against the through detent stop.
3. Adjust the downshift screw to provide .050"-.070" clearance between the screw and the throttle shaft lever.
4. Connect downshift lever return spring.

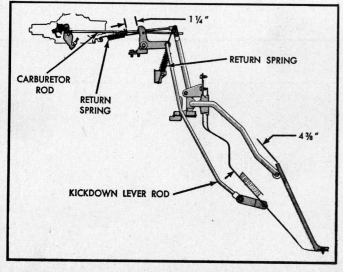

Fig. 11   Thunderbird throttle linkage. 1966

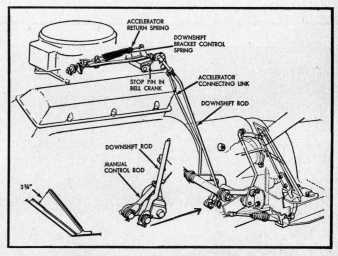

Fig. 12   Lincoln throttle linkage

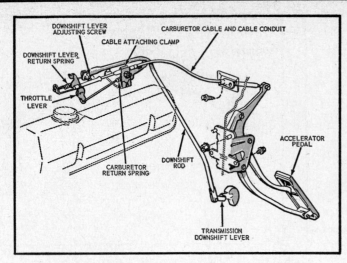

Fig. 13 Thunderbird throttle linkage. 1967-69 (Typical)

1967-68 Ford & Mercury

1. Loosen accelerator cable attaching clamp, Fig. 8.
2. Open choke plate and position throttle lever against the hot idle adjusting screw.
3. Slide the cable conduit to the rear until the cable end fitting at the accelerator pedal bottoms at the end of the cable stroke. While holding the cable in the fully bottomed position, tighten the cable conduit attaching clamp. Following this adjustment, the throttle must remain in contact with the hot idle speed adjusting screw. If the hot idle speed is changed, the cable must be readjusted.
4. Disconnect the downshift lever return spring.
5. Hold the throttle lever at the wide open throttle position and depress the downshift rod through detent to the stop. Set the downshift lever adjusting screw against the throttle lever at the carburetor.
6. Connect the downshift lever return spring.

1966 Ford & Mercury

1. Disconnect the throttle return springs,

Fig. 8.
2. Loosen the conduit clamp on the carburetor control cable.
3. Push the accelerator pedal all the way to the floor and secure it.
4. Pull on the cable conduit until the throttle shaft lever is right against the wide-open stop. Tighten the clamp in this position.
5. Push down on the downshift rod until the lever on the transmission is against its internal stop. Hold the rod down and turn the downshift lever adjusting screw to take up *all* the clearance at the carburetor throttle shaft lever.
6. Lock the adjusting screw and release the accelerator pedal. Then connect the return springs.

1966-68 Comet, Fairlane & Montego

1. Disconnect the carburetor rod and the accelerator rod, Fig. 9.
2. Disconnect the stabilizer rod from the bell crank lever.
3. Insert a ¼-inch diameter pin through the bell crank and bracket.
4. Adjust the length of the stabilizer rod so that the trunnion enters the bell

crank freely, with the alignment pin in place. Secure the stabilizer rod with the retaining clip.
5. Secure the carburetor rod to the bell crank with the attaching clip.
6. Adjust the length of the accelerator rod to obtain an accelerator pedal height of 4-4½ inches measured from the pedal to the toe pan. Connect the accelerator rod to the accelerator shaft with the retaining clip after the proper accelerator pedal height has been established. Remove the alignment pin.
7. With the engine off, disconnect the downshift rod trunnion from the lever.
8. With the carburetor choke in the off position, depress the accelerator pedal to the floor. Block the pedal to hold it in the wide-open position.
9. Rotate the downshift lever on the transmission in a counterclockwise direction to place it against the internal stop.
10. Adjust the trunnion so that it enters the downshift lever freely.
11. Turn the trunnion one additional turn counterclockwise to lengthen the rod. Secure it to the lever with the retaining clip.
12. Release the accelerator pedal.

1969-71 Mustang & Cougar & 1970-71 Fairlane & Montego

Because the throttle is cable operated, the transmission kickdown is the only adjustment required.

1. Disconnect the throttle and downshift return springs.
2. Hold the carburetor throttle lever in the wide open position against the stop.
3. Hold the transmission in full downshift position against the internal stop.
4. Turn adjustment screw on the carburetor kickdown lever to within .040"-.080" gap of contacting pickup surface of carburetor throttle lever.
5. Release the transmission and carburetor to the normal free position.
6. Install the throttle and downshift return springs.

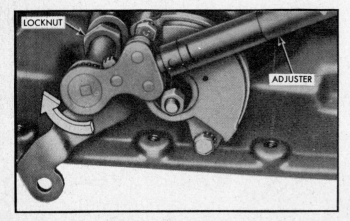

Fig. 14 Band adjustment

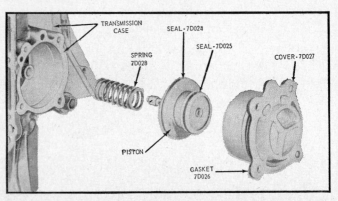

Fig. 15 Intermediate servo disassembled

1969 Fairlane & Montego
1966-68 Mustang & Cougar

1. With engine off, check and adjust accelerator pedal for a height of 4½", Fig. 10. Adjust connecting link at point "A" to obtain correct dimension.
2. Disconnect the downshift control cable or rod at point "B".
3. With the carburetor choke in the off position, depress the accelerator pedal to the floor and block it in the wide open position.
4. Rotate the downshift lever counterclockwise to place it against the internal stop.
5. With the lever held in this position and, if cable is used, all slack is removed from the cable, adjust the trunnion so that it will slide into the accelerator shaft lever. Turn it one additional turn clockwise then secure it to the lever with the retaining clip.
6. Remove the clock and release the accelerator linkage.

1969-71 Mark III, Thunderbird

The conduit covering the accelerator cable at the carburetor end must be evenly nestled between the clamp and the accelerator shaft bracket. Accelerator pedal height adjustment is not required.

1. Disconnect the downshift lever return spring.
2. With the throttle in the wide open position, hold the downshift rod against the through detent stop.
3. Adjust the downshift screw to provide .050"-.070" clearance between the screw and the throttle shaft lever. End play adjustment is not required.
4. Connect the downshift return spring.

1967-68 Thunderbird

1. Remove air cleaner and disconnect downshift lever spring, Fig. 13.
2. With carburetor throttle lever held in wide open position and downshift rod held down against the through detent stop, adjust the downshift lever adjusting screw against the throttle shaft lever tab. On 1968 models, back off adjusting screw two full turns.
3. Replace the downshift lever spring.
4. Adjust engine idle speed to specifications then loosen the accelerator cable conduit attaching clamp and disconnect the accelerator control cable at the throttle lever.
5. Open choke plate and pull throttle lever rearward to wide open position. While holding choke plate open, release throttle lever.
6. Slide accelerator control cable rearward until the cable ball stud is positioned approximately ⅛" forward of the carburetor throttle lever ball stud.
7. With the accelerator cable in the rearward position, tighten the cable conduit attaching clamp.
8. Connect the accelerator cable to the carburetor throttle lever ball stud and install air cleaner.

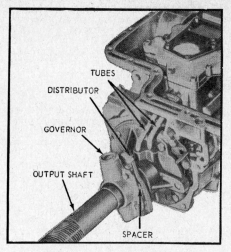

Fig. 16   Governor installed

1966 Thunderbird

1. Be certain the idle is correct in D1 or D2 and that the carburetor throttle lever is against the idle adjusting screw.
2. If the carburetor has an anti-stall dashpot, adjust the clearance. With the anti-stall dashpot plunger bottomed, the clearance with the throttle lever must be 0.060 to 0.090 inch.
3. Check that the fast idle cam is on the *hot* position.
4. Adjust the accelerator pedal height to specification at the carburetor connecting link, Fig. 11.
5. Position the speed nut on the downshift lever rod 1¼ inches from the forward face of the bushing in the downshift lever.

1966-69 Lincoln

1. With engine stopped, measure distance from top of accelerator pedal to carpet, Fig. 12. The 3¾" requirement is nominal only. Further adjustment (at accelerator connecting link) after a road test if the kickdown operation is not functioning.
2. Depress accelerator pedal and check for detent feel and kickdown action of the bellcrank.
3. Disconnect downshift rod from bellcrank. Make sure movable outer bracket on bellcrank is up against stop pin on inner mounting bracket on bellcrank.
4. Pull upward and hold downshift rod against transmission internal stop. Adjust length of rod until hole in rod is aligned with ball stud on bellcrank.
5. Lengthen downshift rod one turn and position it on ball stud. Slide spring clip over end of rod. Tighten lock nut.
6. Be sure bellcrank outer bracket remains against stop pin. If it is not against pin, lengthen downshift rod one additional turn. If the downshift rod is adjusted too long the transmission will not upshift because the downshift valve is open to line pressure.

BAND ADJUSTMENT

NOTE: The intermediate band adjustment for 1967-71 is basically the same as 1966 with the exception of the adjusting screw lock nut. The lock nut must be discarded and a new one installed each time the band is adjusted.

1. Loosen the locknut on the adjusting screw several turns, Fig. 14.
2. Torque the screw to 10 ft-lbs, or until the adjuster wrench overruns.
3. Back the screw off exactly 1½ turns.
4. Hold the adjustment and torque the locknut to the 35-45 ft-lbs.

OIL PAN & CONTROL VALVE

Removal

1. Raise car on hoist or jack stands.
2. Loosen and remove all but two oil pan bolts from front of case and drop rear edge of pan to drain fluid. Remove and clean pan and screen.
3. Unfasten and remove valve body.

Installation

1. Position valve body to case, making sure that selector and downshift levers are engaged, then install and torque attaching bolts to specifications.
2. Using a new pan gasket, secure pan to case and torque bolts to specifications.
3. Lower car and fill transmission to the correct level with specified fluid.

INTERMEDIATE SERVO

Removal

1. Raise car and remove engine rear support-to-extension housing bolts.
2. Raise transmission high enough to relieve weight from support.
3. Remove support (1 bolt).
4. Lower transmission.
5. Place drain pan beneath servo.
6. Remove servo cover-to-case bolts.
7. Loosen band adjusting screw locknut.
8. Remove servo cover, piston, spring and gasket from case, screwing band adjusting screw inward as piston is removed. *This insures that there will be enough tension on the band to keep the struts properly engaged in the band end notches while the piston is removed.*

Replacing Seal, Fig. 15

1. Apply air pressure to port in servo cover to remove piston and stem.
2. Remove seals from piston.
3. Remove seal from cover.
4. Dip new seals in transmission fluid.
5. Install seals in piston and cover.
6. Dip piston in transmission fluid and install in cover.

Installation

1. Position new gasket on servo cover and spring on piston stem.

2. Insert piston stem in case. Secure cover with bolts, taking care to back off band adjusting screw while tightening cover bolts. Make sure that vent tube retaining clip is in place.
3. Raise transmission high enough to install engine rear support. Secure support to extension housing. Lower transmission as required to install support-to-crossmember bolt.
4. Remove jack and adjust band.
5. Lower car and replenish fluid as required.

EXTENSION HOUSING & GOVERNOR

Removal

1. Raise car and drain transmission.
2. Disconnect parking brake cable at equalizer.
3. Remove torque plate.
4. Disconnect drive shaft from rear axle flange and remove from transmission.
5. Disconnect speedometer cable from extension housing.
6. Remove two nuts that secure engine rear mount to crossmember.
7. Raise transmission with a jack just high enough to relieve weight from crossmember. Remove crossmember.
8. Remove engine rear support.

9. Lower transmission to permit access to extension housing bolts. Remove bolts and slide housing off output shaft.
10. Disconnect governor from distributor (4 bolts) and slide governor off output shaft.

Installation, Fig. 16

1. Secure governor to distributor flange.
2. Position new gasket on transmission.
3. Secure extension housing to case.
4. Secure engine rear support to case.
5. Install crossmember.
6. Lower transmission and remove jack. Then install and torque engine rear support-to-extension housing bolts.
7. Install speedometer cable, connect parking brake cable to equalizer and install drive shaft.
8. Install torque plate to floor pan.
9. Replenish transmission fluid.

TRANSMISSION, REPLACE

NOTE: On models with the neutral safety switch wire harness connected at the dash panel, disconnect the harness before raising the vehicle.

1. Raise vehicle and drain transmission and converter.

2. Remove drive shaft and starter.
3. Remove four converter to flywheel attaching bolts.
4. Disconnect parking brake front cable from equalizer.
5. Disconnect speedometer cable and transmission linkage.

NOTE: On Lincoln and Thunderbird, remove shift rod bellcrank bracket and allow it to hang free.

6. Where necessary, disconnect muffler inlet pipes from exhaust manifold.

NOTE: On Mustang and Cougar, disconnect the entire exhaust system and allow it to hang on the rear axle.

7. Support the transmission with a suitable jack, remove parking brake rear cables from the equalizer and remove the crossmember.
8. Lower transmission and remove oil cooler lines, vacuum line and transmission oil filler tube.
9. Secure the transmission to the jack with the chain, remove the converter housing to cylinder block bolts and carefully move the transmission away from the engine, at the same time lowering it to clear the underside of the vehicle.
10. Reverse procedure to install.

CRUISEOMATIC, MERCOMATIC
WITH CAST IRON CASE
TRANSMISSION IDENTIFICATION

The identification tag is attached to the left side of the transmission case on all 1966 and 1967-68 MX units. On 1967-68 FMX and FX and all 1969-71 units, the tag is attached under the oil pan by a pan-to-case bolt.

YEAR	ENGINE MODEL	TRANS. MODEL

FAIRLANE & MONTEGO MODELS

YEAR	ENGINE MODEL	TRANS. MODEL
1969	8-351⑥⑦	PHB-C
	8-351⑥③	PHB-D
	8-351⑤⑦	PHB-F
	8-351⑥③	PHB-G
1970	8-351⑦	PHB-R
	8-351③	PHB-S

FORD MODELS

YEAR	ENGINE MODEL	TRANS. MODEL
1966	8-289④	⑦PCT-J3
	8-289	⑦PCT-K
	8-352	⑦PCD-Z
	8-352	⑦PCD-AB

YEAR	ENGINE MODEL	TRANS. MODEL
	8-352	③PCD-AA
	8-352	③PCD-AC
	8-390	⑦PCE-BK
	8-390	⑦PCE-BR
	8-390	③PCE-BL
	8-390	③PCE-BS
1967	8-390	⑥PFA-B
	6-240	PFA-D
	8-289	PFA-E
	8-289	PHA-A
1968	8-302	PHA-B
	8-302	PFA-F
	6-240	PFA-D-1
	8-390	PHB-A
	8-390	PFA-B-1
1969	6-240⑦	PHD-A
	8-302⑦	PHD-B
	8-390⑦	PHB-A
1970	6-240	PHD-A1
	8-302	PHD-B1
	8-351⑦	PHB-L1
	8-351③	PHB-V
1971	6-240	PHD-A1, A2
	8-302	PHD-B1, B2
	8-351⑦	PHB-L1, L2
	8-351③	PHB-V, V1

MERCURY MODELS

YEAR	ENGINE MODEL	TRANS. MODEL
1966	8-390⑥	⑦PCE-AK
	8-390⑥	③PCE-BL
	8-410①	⑦PDD-T
	8-410①	③PDD-U
	8-410, 428②	⑦PDD-D-H
	8-410, 428②	③PDD-H-N
1967	8-390	⑥PFA-B
1971	8-351	PHB-L1, L2

MUSTANG & COUGAR MODELS

YEAR	ENGINE MODEL	TRANS. MODEL
1969	8-351⑥③	PHB-E
	8-351⑤③	PHB-H
1970	8-351⑥	PHB-E1
	8-351⑤	PHB-P
1971	8-351⑥	PHB-E2, E3

THUNDERBIRD MODELS

YEAR	ENGINE MODEL	TRANS. MODEL
1966	8-390	PCE-BJ
	8-390	PCE-BT

①—Single exhaust.
②—Dual exhaust.
③—With floor shift.
④—Dual range unit.
⑤—With 4 barrel carburetor.
⑥—With 2 barrel carburetor.
⑦—With column shift.

DESCRIPTION
Dual Range Operation to 1966

D1 Range

This range is used for a high degree of maneuverability in traffic. It features maximum performance and flexibility by incorporating a low gear start. For fast acceleration, press the accelerator pedal as far as it will go and the transmission will downshift into low gear at speeds below approximately 30 mph.

To obtain maximum acceleration from a standstill, press the accelerator pedal to the floor and the car will move forward in low gear under wide open throttle. With the accelerator all the way to the floor, the transmission will shift from low to intermediate gear at approximately 50 mph and then into high gear at approximately 75 mph.

D2 Range

Most normal city and highway driving can be accomplished by using the position marked "D2". This range is economically desirable when on long trips, driving in open country, or in light city traffic. Simply position the selector at "D2" and push down on the accelerator for a smooth getaway. To go faster, press the accelerator down further.

For faster acceleration at speeds below approximately 70 mph, press the accelerator down as far as it will go and the transmission will automatically downshift to intermediate gear. For maximum acceleration from a standstill, position the selector at "D1" and then press accelerator to the floor. The selector can be alternated from "D2" and "D1" positions as desired.

Dual Range Operation From 1967

This transmission features a drive range that provides for fully automatic upshifts and downshifts, and manually selected low and second gears. The six selector lever positions provided are P (park), R (reverse), N (neutral), D (automatic drive range), 2 (second gear hold) and 1 (low gear hold).

D is a fully automatic range providing for a first gear start with automatic upshifts to second and high gear occurring at appropriate intervals, similar to operation in D1 in the 1966 transmission.

Second gear (2) is a manually selected second gear hold. When the selector lever is moved to 2, the transmission will engage and remain in second gear, regardless of throttle opening or road speed.

Low gear (1) is similar to manual low range in the 1966 transmission.

D—Drive

The normal automatic driving range is indicated by D. In this range the car starts off in first gear and gives the best combination of automatic gear shifts to provide for economy and full power starts. As the accelerator is depressed and the car picks up speed, automatic shifts to second and high gears will occur. The transmission will automatically downshift as speed decreases. Forced downshifts in

CRUISEOMATIC & MERCOMATIC

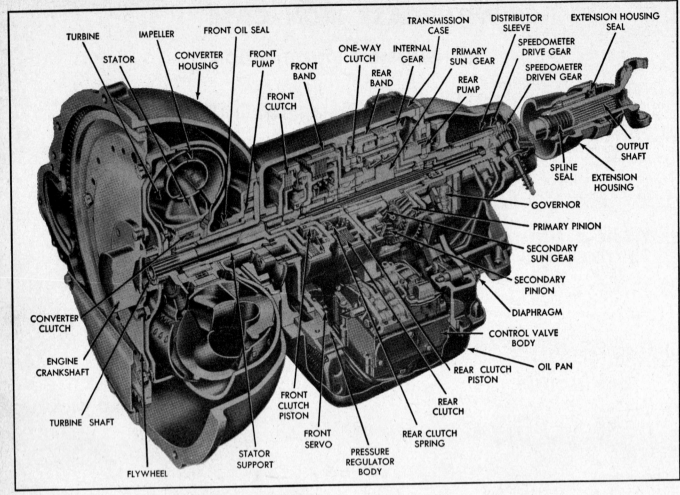

Fig. 1 Cruiseomatic and Mercomatic three speed dual range unit with cast iron case

D are made by pressing the accelerator pedal all the way to the floor.

2—Second Gear Hold

When the car is started and the shift lever is moved to 2, the car will start off and remain in second gear, regardless of throttle opening or road speed. This range is especially useful for starting the car on icy pavements or other slippery surfaces. Similarly, when engine braking is required and the shift lever is moved from D to 2, the transmission will engage and remain in second gear.

Selector lever position 2 is not a cruising range in the usual sense of the term. While the transmission is capable of limited cruising in second gear, maximum fuel economy and best all-around performance are realized in D range.

1—Low Gear Hold

This range is identical in operation to manual low range on the 1966 transmission except that when the shift lever is moved to 1 to provide engine braking, the automatic shift from second to low gear will occur between 22 and 39 mph (exact shift point will vary with axle ratio and tire size).

TROUBLE SHOOTING GUIDE

Rough Initial Engagement

1. Idle speed.
2. Vacuum unit or tubes.
3. Front band.
4. Check control pressure.
5. Pressure regulator.
6. Valve body.

Shift Points High, Low or Erratic

1. Fluid level.
2. Vacuum unit or tubes.
3. Manual linkage.
4. Governor.
5. Check control pressure.
6. Valve body.
7. Downshift linkage.

Rough 2-3 Shift

1. Manual linkage.
2. Front band.
3. Vacuum unit or tubes.
4. Pressure regulator.
5. Valve body.
6. Front servo.

Engine Overspeeds, 2-3 Shift

1. Vacuum unit or tubes.
2. Front band.
3. Valve body.
4. Pessure regulator.

No 1-2 or 2-3 Shifts

1. Governor.
2. Valve body.
3. Manual linkage.
4. Rear clutch.
5. Front band.
6. Front servo.
7. Leakage in hydraulic system.
8. Pressure regulator.

No Forced Downshifts

1. Downshift linkage.
2. Check control pressure.
3. Valve body.

Rough 3-2 or 3-1 Shifts

1. Engine idle speed.
2. Vacuum unit or tubes.
3. Valve body.

Slips or Chatters in 2nd

1. Fluid level.

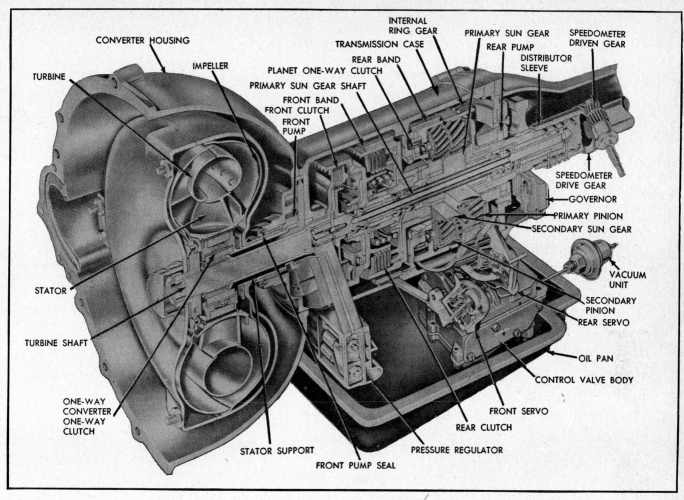

Fig. 2   Lincoln Turbo-Drive three speed dual range transmission with cast iron case

2. Vacuum unit or tubes.
3. Front band.
4. Check control pressure.
5. Pressure regulator.
6. Valve body.
7. Front servo.
8. Front clutch.
9. Leakage in hydraulic system.

Slips or Chatters in 1st

1. Fluid level.
2. Vacuum unit or tubes.
3. Check control pressure.
4. Pressure regulator.
5. Valve body.
6. Front clutch.
7. Leakage in hydraulic system.
8. Fluid distributor sleeve in output shaft.
9. Planetary one-way clutch.

Slips or Chatters in Reverse

1. Fluid level.
2. Rear band.
3. Check control pressure.
4. Pressure regulator.
5. Valve body.
6. Rear servo.
7. Rear clutch.
8. Vacuum unit or tubes.
9. Leakage in hydraulic system.

10. Fluid distributor sleeve in output shaft.

No Drive in D or D2

1. Valve body.
2. Make air pressure check.
3. Manual linkage.
4. Front clutch.
5. Leak in hydraulic system.
6. Fluid distributor sleeve in output shaft.

No Drive in D1

1. Manual linkage.
2. Valve body.
3. Planetary one-way clutch.

No Drive in L

1. Manual linkage.
2. Front clutch.
3. Valve body.
4. Make air pressure check.
5. Leak in hydraulic system.
6. Fluid distributor sleeve in output shaft.

No Drive in R

1. Rear band.
2. Rear servo.

3. Valve body.
4. Make air pressure check.
5. Rear clutch.
6. Leak in hydraulic system.
7. Fluid distributor sleeve in output shaft.

No Drive in Any Range

1. Fluid level.
2. Manual linkage.
3. Check control pressure.
4. Pressure regulator.
5. Valve body.
6. Make air pressure check.
7. Leak in hydraulic system.

Lockup in D or D1

1. Manual linkage.
2. Rear servo.
3. Front servo.
4. Rear clutch.
5. Parking linkage.
6. Leak in hydraulic system.

Lockup in D2

1. Manual linkage.
2. Rear band.
3. Rear servo.
4. Rear clutch.
5. Parking linkage.

6. Leak in hydraulic system.
7. Planetary one-way clutch.

Lockup in R

1. Front band.
2. Front servo.
3. Front clutch.
4. Parking lnkage.
5. Leak in hydraulic system.

Lockup in L

1. Front band.
2. Pressure regulator.
3. Valve body.
4. Rear clutch.
5. Parking linkage.
6. Leak in hydraulic system.

Parking Lock Binds or Won't Hold

1. Manual linkage.
2. Parking linkage.

Unable to Push Start

1. Fluid level.
2. Manual linkage.
3. Pressure regulator.
4. Valve body.
5. Rear pump.
6. Leak in hydraulic system.

Transmission Overheats

1. Oil cooler and connections.
2. Pressure regulator.
3. Converter one-way clutch.

Engine Runaway on Forced Downshift

1. Front band.
2. Pressure regulator.
3. Valve body.
4. Front servo.
5. Vacuum unit or tubes.
6. Leak in hydraulic system.

Maximum Speed Below Normal, Acceleration Poor

1. Converter one-way clutch.

No 3-1 Downshift

1. Engine idle speed.
2. Vacuum unit or tubes.
3. Valve body.

Noise in Neutral

1. Pressure regulator.
2. Front clutch.
3. Front pump.

Noise in 1-2-3 or R

1. Pressure regulator.
2. Planetary assembly.
3. Front clutch.
4. Rear clutch.
5. Front pump.

Noise in Reverse

1. Pressure regulator.
2. Front pump.

Noise on Coast in Neutral

1. Rear pump.

MAINTENANCE
Adding Fluid

The fluid level in the transmission should be checked at 1000-mile intervals. Make sure that the car is standing level, and firmly apply the parking brake.

Run the engine at normal idle speed. If the transmission fluid is cold, run the engine at fast idle speed until the fluid reaches normal operating temperature. When the fluid is warm, slow the engine down to normal idle speed, shift the transmission through all ranges and then place the lever or button at P.

Clean all dirt from the transmission fluid dipstick cap before removing the dipstick from the filler tube. Pull the dipstick out of the tube, wipe it clean and push it all the way back into the tube.

Pull the dipstick out again and check the fluid level. If necessary, add enough Automatic Transmission Fluid to the transmission to raise the fluid level to the F (full mark) on the dipstick.

Changing Fluid

The transmission fluid should be changed at 24,000-mile intervals. The procedure for changing fluid is as follows:

1. Remove cover from lower front side of converter housing.
2. Remove one of the converter drain plugs. Then rotate the converter 180 deg. and remove the other plug. *Do not attempt to turn the converter with a wrench on the converter stud nuts as there is danger of stripping threads as well as skinning your knuckles on the bell housing.*
3. When all fluid has drained, remove and clean the oil pan and screen.
4. Using a new pan gasket, install screen and pan.
5. Connect filler tube to oil pan and tighten fitting securely.
6. Install both converter drain plugs.
7. Install converter housing cover.
8. Install 5 quarts of Automatic Transmission Fluid.
9. Run engine at idle speed for about 2 minutes; then add the additional quantity of oil required for the particular transmission being serviced.
10. Run engine at a fast idle until it reaches normal operating temperature.
11. Shift the transmission through all positions; then place it at P and check fluid level. If necessary, add enough fluid to bring the level to the F mark on the dipstick.

MANUAL LINKAGE, ADJUST

Cougar, Fairlane, Ford, Mercury, Montego & Mustang

Floor Shift 1967-71

1. Place selector lever in D.
2. Raise vehicle and loosen manual shift rod retaining nut.
3. Move transmission manual lever to D position (fourth detent position from back of transmission).
4. Torque nut to 10-20 ft-lbs.

NOTE: After adjusting the manual linkage, the steering column lock rod starting with 1970 models, is adjusted as follows:
1. Raise vehicle and loosen lock rod retaining nut.
2. Lower vehicle and place selector lever in D position tight against the D stop.
3. Align the hole in the steering column socket casting with the column alignment mark and insert a .180" diameter gauge pin. The column casting must not rotate with gauge pin in position.
4. Raise vehicle and torque lock rod retaining nut to 10-20 ft. lbs.
5. Lower vehicle. Remove gauge pin and check linkage for proper operation.

Column Shift, 1967-71

1. Place selector lever in D.
2. Loosen nut on column shift lever to permit this lever to slide on shift rod.
3. Shift manual lever on transmission into D position.
4. Tighten nut to secure shift rod to lever.

Column Shift, 1966

1. Place selector lever in D or D1.
2. Loosen nut on column shift lever to permit this lever to slide on shift rod.
3. Shift manual lever at transmission into D or D1 position (2nd from rear).
4. Tighten nut to secure shift rod to shift lever.

Floor Shift, 1966

1. Move shift lever to D1 position.
2. Raise car and loosen manual linkage retaining nut and move transmission manual lever to D1 position (2nd from rear).
3. With selector and manual levers in D1 position, tighten rod lock nut.

1966 Thunderbird

1. With engine stopped, loosen nut at lower end of manual shift rod on transmission shift lever.
2. With steering column in straight ahead (locked in place) position, move manual selector lever so that pointer is down against steering column stop in D1 (large green dot) position.
3. Move shift lever on transmission to D1 position (2nd detent from bottom) and tighten nut on shift rod and shift lever.

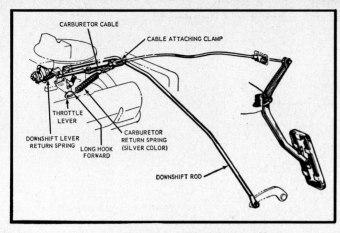

Fig. 3   Throttle linkage. 1966-71 Ford and Mercury

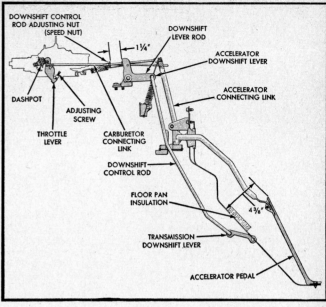

Fig. 4   Throttle linkage. 1966 Thunderbird

THROTTLE LINKAGE, ADJUST

1969-71 Ford & Mercury

The conduit covering the cable at the carburetor end must be evenly nestled between the clamp and the accelerator shaft bracket. Due to the fixed clamping of the cable conduit, accelerator pedal height adjustment is not required.

1. Disconnect the downshift lever return spring.
2. Hold the throttle in the wide open position and hold the downshift rod against the through detent stop.
3. Adjust the downshift screw to provide .050"-.070" clearance between the screw and the throttle shaft lever. On 6-240, tighten the lock nut to maintain the screw position. End play adjustment is not required.
4. Connect downshift lever return spring.

1969 Fairlane & Montego

1. With engine off, check accelerator pedal for a height of 4½". Adjust accelerator connecting link to correct.
2. Disconnect downshift control cable from accelerator shaft lever.
3. With carburetor choke in the off position, depress the accelerator and block it in the wide open position.
4. Rotate the downshift lever counter clockwise to place it against the internal stop.
5. With the lever in this position and all slack removed from the cable, adjust the trunnion so that it will slide into the lever. Turn it one additional turn to increase length of cable then secure it to the lever with retaining clip.

1970 Fairlane & Montego 1969-70 Mustang & Cougar

Because the throttle on these models is cable operated, transmission kickdown is the only adjustment required.
1. Disconnect throttle and downshift re-

turn springs and disconnect downshift control cable from accelerator shaft lever.
2. With carburetor choke in the off position, depress the accelerator and block it in the wide open position.
3. Rotate the downshift lever counter-clockwise to place it against the internal stop.
4. Turn adjustment screws on carburetor kickdown lever to within .040" to .080" gap of contacting pick up surface of carb. throttle lever.

1971 Cougar, Fairlane, Montego & Mustang

1. Hold transmission in full downshift against stop.
2. Hold carburetor throttle lever in wide open throttle against stop.
3. Turn the adjustment screw on the kickdown lever until a gap of .040-.080 " exists between the carburetor lever and the adjusting screw.
4. Release the transmission and carburetor to the normal free position.
5. Install throttle return spring.

1966-68 Ford & Mercury

1. Connect tachometer to engine and adjust engine slow idle speed with selector lever in either D1 or D2 position.
2. Stop engine and disconnect carburetor return spring from throttle lever, Fig. 3.
3. Loosen accelerator cable clamp.
4. With accelerator pedal to floor and throttle lever held in its wide open position, slide cable conduit to rear to remove slack from cable. Tighten cable clamp.
5. Disconnect downshift lever return spring. Hold throttle lever at wide open position and depress downshift rod to the "through detent stop."

6. Set downshift lever at carburetor adjusting screw against throttle lever.
7. Connect both return springs.

1966 Thunderbird

1. Connect a tachometer to engine and, after engine has been warmed up to operating temperature, adjust hot idle speed with selector lever in either D1 or D2 position.
2. Stop engine and adjust accelerator pedal height by disconnecting the carburetor connecting link from carburetor connecting link from carburetor and turning as required to obtain the proper height, Fig. 4.
3. Position speed nut on downshift lever rod 1¼" from forward face of bushing in downshift lever as shown.

BAND ADJUSTMENTS

The front and rear bands of the transmission should be adjusted at 15,000 mile intervals or as operation of the transmission dictates.

Front Band

1967-71 All Models

1. Drain fluid from transmission, remove and clean oil pan and screen.
2. Loosen front servo adjusting screw locknut.
3. Pull back on actuating rod and insert a ¼ inch spacer between adjusting screw and servo piston stem, Fig. 5.
4. Tighten adjusting screw to 10 inch-lbs torque. Remove spacer and tighten adjusting screw an additional ¾ turn. Hold adjusting screw stationary and tighten locknut securely.
5. Install oil pan with new gasket and add fluid to transmission.

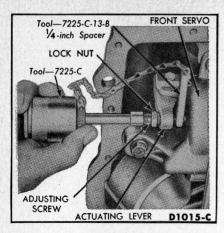

Fig. 5 Front band adjustment. Ford, Mercury and Thunderbird

1966 Ford, Mercury, Thunderbird

The tool shown in Fig. 5 is especially made for this adjustment. However, by using a piece of $\frac{1}{4}$" thick metal block and an ordinary end or box wrench a satisfactory adjustment can be made.

With the transmission oil pan removed, back off the adjusting screw lock nut and screw far enough to permit the $\frac{1}{4}$" block to be inserted between the servo piston rod and adjusting screw. Turn adjusting screw in until it contacts the $\frac{1}{4}$" block. Then tighten the adjusting screw a little more (equivalent to 10 inch-lbs) and back off one full turn. *Severe damage to the transmission may result if the adjusting screw is not backed off exactly one full turn.*

Rear Band

NOTE: On late 1969 and on all 1970-71 models, there is no access hole in the floor pan to adjust the rear band. With the use of special tools this band can be adjusted externally as follows, Figs. 8, 9:

1. Loosen rear bank adjusting screw lock-nut. A special tool is required to gain access in limited space.
2. Tighten adjusting screw until special tool clicks. It is preset to overrun when torque reaches 10 ft. lbs.
3. Back off adjusting screw $1\frac{1}{2}$ turns.
   NOTE: Severe damage may result if the adjusting screw is not backed off exactly $1\frac{1}{2}$ turns.
4. Hold adjusting screw stationary and tighten locknut securely.

1969 Fairlane, Montego, Mustang & Cougar

1. Drain transmission and remove oil pan and filter.
2. Loosen rear servo adjusting screw lock nut.
3. Pull the adjusting screw end of the actuating lever away from the servo body spacer tool between servo accumulator piston and the adjusting

screw, Fig. 7.

NOTE: Be sure that flat surfaces of the tool are positioned squarely between the adjusting screw and the accumulator piston. The tool must not touch the servo piston and the tool handle must not touch the servo piston spring retainer.

4. Using a torque wrench with an Allen head socket, tighten the adjusting screw to 24 in-lbs.
5. Back off the adjusting screw $1\frac{1}{2}$ turns. Hold the adjusting screw and tighten the lock nut securely. Remove spacer tool.
6. Replace oil filter and pan and fill transmission.

1966-68 All Models & 1969 Ford

The tool shown in Fig. 6 is especially made for this adjustment. However, a satisfactory adjustment may be made by using a conventional torque wrench. Loosen the lock nut and tighten the adjusting screw to a torque of 10 ft-lbs. Then back off the screw exactly $1\frac{1}{2}$ turns and tighten lock nut. *Severe damage may result to the transmission if the adjusting screw is not backed off exactly $1\frac{1}{2}$ turns.*

OIL PRESSURE REGULATOR

Remove oil pan and screen. Maintain constant pressure on spring retainer to prevent damage to springs and remove retainer from bosses on oil pressure regulator body. Remove springs and pilots. Remove the three pipes. Unfasten and remove the oil pressure regulator from the transmission case.

CONTROL VALVE

To remove the assembly, loosen the

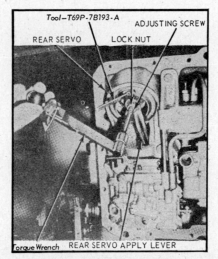

Fig. 7 Adjusting rear band. 1969 Fairlane, Montego, Mustang & Cougar

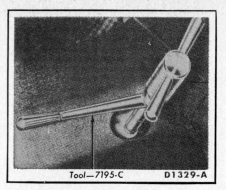

Fig. 6 Rear band adjustment. 1966-68 All and 1969 Ford

adjustment on the front and rear bands 5 or 6 turns. Loosen front servo attaching screws. Remove cap screws and washers which attach control valve to case. Align throttle and manual levers to permit removal of control valve. Disengage front servo tubes from control valve and lift valve assembly from case.

FRONT & REAR SERVOS

To remove the front servo, remove the cap screw which holds it to the case. Hold the actuating lever strut with one hand and lift the servo from the case.

To remove the rear servo, take out the attaching cap screws. Then hold the anchor strut and lift the servo from the case.

EXTENSION HOUSING SEAL

After removing the drive shaft and telescopic shield, the seal may be pulled out of the extension housing.

Before installing the new seal, inspect the sealing surface of the universal joint yoke for scores. If scores are evident, replace the yoke. Inspect the counterbore in the housing for burrs. Polish all burrs with crocus cloth.

To install the new seal, position it in the bore of the extension housing with the felt side of the seal to the rear. The seal may be driven into the housing with a special tool designed for the purpose.

OIL DISTRIBUTOR
With Bolted Distributor & Sleeve

After removing the extension case remove the spacer from the transmission output shaft and slide the distributor toward the rear of the transmission. Note that the tube spacer is located in the center tube.

Remove the three tubes and spacer from the distributor. Remove the screws which attach the distributor to the sleeve and separate these parts.

Inspect the distributor and sleeve for burrs on the mating surfaces and obstructed fluid passages. Check the fit of

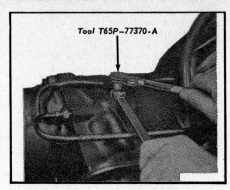

Fig. 8 Rear band adjustment. 1970-71 Ford, Fairlane and Montego

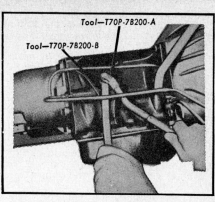

Fig. 9 Rear band adjustment. 1970-71 Cougar & Mustang

the tubes in the distributor. Inspect the distributor sleeve for wear and scores in the sleeve bore.

To assemble, align the distributor and sleeve and install the cap screws. Install the tubes in the distributor with the spacer installed on the center tube.

With One Piece Distributor & Sleeve

After removing the extension housing, remove the distributor drive gear snap ring. Remove distributor gear, taking care not to lose the gear drive ball. Remove distributor sleeve and pipes from the transmission. Inspect the 4 seal rings on the output shaft for wear or breakage, and replace if necessary. Inspect the distributor sleeve for wear and the tubes for proper alignment and fit into the distributor sleeve.

With tubes installed in the distributor sleeve, install distributor on output shaft (chamfer forward) sliding the distributor over the seal rings and at the same time guiding tubes into the case. Install speedometer drive ball and gear and install snap ring.

GOVERNOR

Remove the governor inspection cover from the extension housing. Rotate the drive shaft to bring the governor body in line with the inspection hole. Remove the two screws which attach the governor body to the counterweight, and remove the body.

Remove the valve from the new governor body. Lubricate the valve with automatic transmission fluid. Install the valve in the body, making sure the valve moves freely in the bore. Install the body in the counterweight making sure the fluid passages in the counterweight and body are aligned.

PARKING PAWL, REPLACE

Transmission In Car

1. Remove oil pan and screen, pressure regulator and control valve. Discon-

nect speedometer cable.
2. Completely tighten rear band to prevent movement of planetary assembly and dislocation of thrust washers on transmission shaft. Disconnect drive shaft from transmission.
3. Remove extension housing-to-case bolts and move extension housing rearward far enough to permit removal of snap ring which retains speedometer gear.
4. Slide oil delivery sleeve back far enough so that oil distributor tubes clear transmission case. *NOTE: On models with bolted on oil delivery tubes, the tubes may be removed without sliding sleeve back.*
5. Rotate rear oil pump housing until parking pawl pin in case is exposed.

NOTE: *Care should be taken to avoid damaging gaskets as they will have to be re-used.*

6. Disconnect link (parking pawl torsion rod) located between detent lever and torsion lever.
7. Remove hairpin clip retaining torsion lever and remove from shaft.
8. Tap toggle lever pin toward rear of transmission to remove plug and pin; then remove parking pawl pin by working pawl back and forth.
9. Remove toggle lever and parking pawl from transmission and replace any damaged parts.
10. Reverse the above procedure to reassemble.

TRANSMISSION, REPLACE
1969-71 Cougar, Fairlane, Montego & Mustang

1. On Mustang and Cougar, disconnect the neutral switch wires from the harness connector and retaining clip. Raise car and remove converter cover. Drain transmission.
2. Remove one of the converter drain plugs, rotate the converter 180 degrees and remove the other plug. *Do not attempt to turn the converter with a wrench on the converter stud nuts.*
3. Remove four flywheel-to-converter nuts, reinstall converter drain plugs and converter housing front plate to hold converter when transmission is removed.
4. Remove starter.
5. On Mustang and Cougar, disconnect the complete exhaust system and allow it to hang on the rear axle.
6. Disconnect oil cooler lines, speedometer cable, vacuum hose and manual downshift linkage. On column shift units, remove selector rod from manual lever.
7. Support transmission with suitable jack and remove crossmember.
8. Lower transmission and remove filler tube and dipstick.
9. Remove converter housing-to-engine bolts. Move transmission and jack rearward and lower away from vehicle.
10. Reverse procedure to install.

Ford & Mercury
Closed Cars & Wagons

The transmission can be disconnected from the converter and removed from the car, leaving the converter in place.
1. Disconnect hose from vacuum diaphragm unit. Disconnect oil filler tube from oil pan and rain fluid.
2. Remove drive shaft.
3. Disconnect oil cooler lines from transmission. Remove vent tube.
4. Disconnect manual and downshift linkage at transmission.
5. Disconnect speedometer cable.
6. Remove two engine rear support-to-transmission bolts.
7. Place jack under transmission and raise it slightly to take weight off crossmember.
8. Unfasten and remove crossmember. With jack in position, remove four transmission-to-converter housing bolts.
9. Support engine. Tilt rear of transmission slightly upward, and with jack, move transmission toward rear until it is clear of turbine shaft. Lower assembly and remove from car.

Soft Top Convertibles

The frame construction of these models will not permit the transmission to be moved rearward enough to clear the turbine shaft from the converter. For this reason the transmission and converter must be removed as a unit as follows:
1. Drive car on hoist but do not raise it. Remove two upper bolts that attach converter housing to engine.
2. Raise car and remove converter lower cover.
3. Remove one converter drain plug. Rotate converter 180 degrees and remove other drain plug. Drain oil. Replace plugs. If desired, converter may be drained after unit has been removed from car.
4. Disconnect oil filler tube from oil pan. Disconnect vacuum hose from vacuum diaphragm.
5. Remove flywheel-to-converter nuts. Install converter housing front plate to hold converter in place when transmission is removed.

6. Remove starter.
7. Disconnect oil cooler lines from transmission. Remove transmission vent tube.
8. Disconnect manual and downshift linkage from transmission.
9. Disconnect speedometer cable and remove drive shaft.
10. On some cars it may be necessary to drop exhaust system to allow converter to clear exhaust pipe.
11. Support transmission. Remove engine rear support-to-transmission bolts and raise transmission slightly to take weight off crossmember. Remove crossmember and support rear of engine.
12. Remove remaining converter housing-to-engine bolts and remove transmission.

13. Reverse removal procedure to install the assembly.

1966 Thunderbird

1. Drain fluid from oil pan and converter.
2. Remove drive shaft.
3. Disconnect pitman arm from steering idler arm.
4. Remove one bolt on each exhaust pipe-to-chassis bracket (toward rear of chassis).
5. Disconnect exhaust pipes from manifolds.
6. Disconnect transmission oil cooler lines.
7. Disconnect shift rods from transmission.
8. Remove diaphragm unit tube.

9. Disconnect speedometer cable.
10. Remove two engine rear support-to-transmission bolts.
11. Position jack under transmission and raise it slightly to take weight off crossmember.
12. Remove two transmission rear support bracket-to-chassis bolts. Remove support and parking brake cables from equalizer. Allow support and equalizer to hang down from front cable.
13. With transmission supported, unfasten transmission from converter housing.
14. Tilt rear of transmission slightly upward and move assembly toward rear until clear of converter housing. Lower and remove from car.
15. Reverse procedure to install.

AMERICAN MOTORS AUTOMATIC

1966-71

TRANSMISSION IDENTIFICATION

An identification plate is attached to the left side of the transmission case. Included on the plate is the transmission model and the serial number of the unit.

DESCRIPTION

Two basic types of this transmission are used, cast iron and aluminum case. Model application is as follows:

Cast Iron:

1966-71 V8 exc. V8-290 w/2 barrel carb and V8-304.

Aluminum Case:

1966-71 Six, V8-290 w/2 barrel carb. and V8-304.

While valve body and control location vary, gear units and power flow are essentially the same.

These transmissions combine a three-element torque converter and a hydraulically-controlled three speed and reverse planetary gear train. The drive is always through the torque converter and one of the planetary gear ranges.

The torque converter consists of an impeller (pump), a turbine and stator. All these parts operate in a fluid-filled housing which is sealed. The torque converter cannot be serviced and must be replaced as a unit in case of a malfunction.

The planetary gear train in all units transmits power from the torque converter turbine shaft to the transmission output shaft. Hydraulic clutches and servo-operated bands drive or hold certain gears to provide the various output ratios.

Single range transmissions of this type start in 2nd gear and shift to direct drive. However, single range transmissions using a one-way clutch in the pinion carrier start in 1st gear when the selector lever is in D position. In dual range transmissions, when shifted into the D1 position, the transmission starts in 1st, shifts into 2nd and then into direct drive. When the selector lever is placed in the D2 position the transmission starts in 2nd and shifts into direct drive.

When maximum acceleration is desired in order to pass a slow moving vehicle or to ascend a steep grade, the transmission may be downshifted from 3rd to 2nd by pushing the accelerator to the floor. If pressure is released on the pedal the transmission will automatically upshift to high.

Low range is used for going up very steep grades or driving in deep mud, sand or snow. This position is also used for descending steep grades in order to take advantage of engine braking. There is no automatic upshift in the L position regardless of car speed or throttle position. The selector lever may be moved from low to drive at any car speed and the transmission will then accomplish all the automatic upshifts.

Rambler Command Shift

Used on 1966-71 cars with floor shift, this arrangement permits manual shifting through all speed ranges. In short, whichever range the shift lever is placed in, the transmission will remain in that range until a manual shift is made to another range.

Initial start is made by placing the lever in range "1". It is then moved to range "2", then to "D" as the driver wishes.

TROUBLE SHOOTING GUIDE

Harsh Engagement

1. Front clutch seized or plates distorted.
2. Rear clutch seized or plates distorted.

Delayed Forward Engagement

1. Sealing rings missing or broken.
2. Front clutch piston check valve leaks.

Delayed Reverse Engagement

1. Sealing rings missing or broken.

No Engagement

1. Sealing rings missing or broken.
2. Broken input shaft.
3. Front pump drive tangs or converter hub broken.
4. Front pump worn.
5. Defective converter.

No Forward D-1

1. Sealing rings missing or broken.
2. Front clutch slipping, worn plates or faulty parts.
3. One-way (sprag) clutch slipping or incorrectly installed.
4. Front clutch piston check valve leaks.

No Forward D-2

1. Sealing rings missing or broken.
2. Front clutch slipping, worn plates or faulty parts.
3. Front clutch piston check valve leaks.

No Reverse

1. Sealing rings missing or broken.
2. Rear clutch slipping, worn or faulty parts.
3. Rear band worn or broken.

No Neutral

1. Front clutch seized or distorted plates.

No 1-2 Upshift

1. Sealing rings missing or broken.
2. Output shaft plug missing (6 cyl.).

No 2-3 Upshift

1. Sealing rings missing or broken.
2. Rear clutch slipping, worn or faulty parts.
3. Rear clutch piston ball check leaks.
4. Output shaft plug missing (6 cyl.).

Shift Points Too High

1. Sealing rings missing or broken.

Shift Points Too Low

1. Sealing rings missing or broken.

1-2 Delayed Followed Close By 2-3 Shift

1. Sealing rings missing or broken.
2. Front clutch slipping, worn plates or faulty parts.
3. Front band worn or broken.

2-3 Slips

1. Sealing rings missing or broken.
2. Rear clutch slipping, worn or faulty parts.
3. Front band worn or broken.
4. Rear clutch piston ball check leaks.

Harsh 1-2 Shift

1. Front clutch slipping, worn plates or faulty parts.

Harsh 2-3 Shift

1. Rear clutch seized or plates distorted.

1-2 Ties Up

1. Rear clutch seized or plates distorted.
2. One-way (sprag) clutch seized.

No 2-1 in D-1

1. One-way (sprag) clutch slipping or incorrectly installed.
2. Output shaft plug missing (6 cyl.).

No 2-1 in L Range

1. Rear band worn or broken.
2. Output shaft plug missing (6 cyl.).

No 3-2 Shift

1. Front band worn or broken.
2. Output shaft plug missing (6 cyl.).

Shift Points Too High or Too Low

1. Sealing rings missing or broken.

2-1 Slips

1. Front clutch slipping, worn plates or faulty parts.
2. Front pump drive tangs or converter hub broken.
3. Front clutch piston check valve leaks.

3-2 Slips

1. Sealing rings missing or broken.
2. Rear clutch slipping, worn or faulty parts.
3. Front band worn or broken.
4. Rear clutch piston ball check leaks.

Harsh 2-1 Shift

1. Sealing rings missing or broken.
2. Front clutch slipping, worn plates or faulty parts.
3. One-way (sprag) clutch slipping or incorrectly installed.

Harsh 3-2 Shift

1. Rear clutch slipping, worn or faulty parts.
2. Rear clutch seized or plates distorted.

Slips or Chatters in Reverse

1. Sealing rings missing or broken.
2. Front clutch seized or plates distorted.
3. Rear clutch slipping, worn or faulty parts.
4. Rear band worn or broken.
5. Rear clutch piston ball check leaks.

Reverse Tie Up

1. Sealing rings missing or broken.
2. Front clutch seized or plates distorted.

Low Idle Pressure

1. Sealing rings missing or broken.
2. Front pump worn.

Low Stall Pressure

1. Sealing rings missing or broken.
2. Front pump worn.
3. Output shaft plug missing (6 cyl.).

Stall Speed Too Low

1. Converter.

Stall Speed Too High D-1

1. Broken output shaft.
2. Broken gears.
3. Sealing rings missing or broken.
4. Front clutch slipping, worn plates or faulty parts.

5. One-way (sprag) clutch slipping or incorrectly installed.
6. Broken input shaft.
7. Converter.
8. Front clutch piston check valve leaks.

Reverse Stall Speed Too High

1. Broken output shaft.
2. Broken gears.
3. Rear band worn or broken.
4. Rear clutch slipping, worn or faulty parts.
5. Broken input shaft.
6. Converter.

Poor Acceleration

1. Output shaft plug missing (6 cyl.).
2. Converter.

Noisy in Neutral

1. Rear clutch seized or plates distorted.
2. Front pump.
3. Front clutch hub thrust washer missing (detectable in N, P, R only).
4. Converter.

Noisy in Park

1. Front pump.
2. Front clutch hub thrust washer missing (detectable in N, P, R only).
3. Converter.

Noisy in All Gears

1. Front pump.
2. Planetary assembly.
3. Converter.

Noisy in 1st & 2nd Gears Only

1. Front pump.
2. Planetary assembly.
3. Forward sun gear thrust washer missing.

Park Brake Does Not Hold

1. Parking linkage.

Oil Out Breather

1. Sealing rings missing or broken.
2. Breather baffle missing.

Oil Out Fill Tube

1. Sealing rings missing or broken.
2. Breather baffle missing.

Ties Up in L or D-1, 1st Gear

1. Rear clutch seized or plates distorted.
2. Sealing rings missing or broken.

Ties Up in D-1 or D-2, 2nd & 3rd Gears

1. Rear clutch seized or plates distorted.
2. Sealing rings missing or broken.
3. One-way (sprag) clutch seized.

Chatters - D-1, D-2 or Low

1. Sealing rings missing or broken.

2. Front clutch slipping, worn plates or faulty parts.
3. Front clutch piston check valve leaks.

MAINTENANCE

The fluid level in the transmission should be checked at 1000-mile intervals. Make sure that the car is standing on a level floor, and firmly apply the parking brake.

Run the engine at normal idle speed. If the transmission fluid is cold, run the engine at a fast idle speed until the fluid reaches normal operating temperature. When the fluid is warm, slow the engine to normal idle speed, shift the transmission through all ranges and then place the lever or button at "P."

Clean all dirt from the transmission fluid dipstick cap before removing the dipstick from the filler tube. Pull the dipstick out of the tube, wipe it clean and push it all the way back into the tube.

Pull the dipstick out again and check the fluid level. If necessary, add enough automatic transmission fluid to the transmission to raise the level to the "F" or "Full" mark on the dipstick.

Changing Fluid

The transmission fluid should be changed at 24,000-mile intervals. The procedure is as follows:

1. Turn converter until one drain plug is visible through the converter bell housing opening.
2. Remove the converter drain plug. Then rotate the converter 180 degrees and remove the other plug.

NOTE—*Do not attempt to turn the converter with a wrench on the converter stud nuts as there is danger of stripping threads as well as skinning your knuckles on the bell housing.*

3. As the oil is draining out of the converter, remove the transmission oil pan drain plug and allow oil to drain from transmission. If no drain plug is provided, remove oil filler tube.
4. When all oil is drained, remove and clean oil pan and screen. Then, using a new oil pan gasket, install oil pan and screen.
5. Install oil pan drain plug or connect filler tube and tighten securely. Then install both converter drain plugs.
6. Install converter housing cover.
7. Install 5 quarts of approved automatic transmission fluid.
8. Run engine at idle speed for about 2 minutes; then add the additional quantity of oil required for the particular transmission being serviced.
9. Run engine at a fast idle speed until it reaches normal operating temperature.
10. Shift transmission through all ranges; then place it in "P" and check fluid level. If necessary, add enough fluid to bring the level up to the "F" or "Full" mark on the dipstick.

MANUAL LINKAGE, ADJUST

1966-71 Column Shift

1. Turn ignition off. Then place selector lever in "N" position.
2. Disconnect manual lever from transmission outer lever. Move transmission outer lever to extreme rear notch or low range position. Move lever forward 3 notches to "N" (neutral) position.
3. Hold selector lever linkage against neutral stop.
4. On 1966 six-cylinder and all 1967-71 models, adjust linkage for a free fit in transmission outer lever and connect linkage.
5. On 1966 V8s, adjust linkage for a free fit. Then shorten linkage three full turns and connect to transmission outer lever.

1966-71 Console Shift

1. Place selector lever in "N."
2. Disconnect linkage rod from shift lever.
3. Move transmission outer lever to extreme forward notch (1 range position). Move lever to rear 3 notches to neutral position.
4. Adjust linkage for a free pin fit and connect linkage.
5. On 1970-71 models, place selector lever in Park position and lock steer-

Fig. 1   Adjusting front servo band

ing column. It may be necessary to move lower column lever upward until it is locked. Tighten first lower then upper trunnion nuts while holding trunnion centered in the column lever.

THROTTLE LINKAGE, ADJUST

With carburetor throttle valve in hot idle position, disconnect throttle cable at lever on carburetor throttle control shaft. Pull throttle cable toward carburetor and adjust clevis to obtain a free pin fit in the throttle shaft lever hole. Then lengthen clevis by two full turns.

FRONT BAND

Aluminum Case

Remove transmission oil pan. Loosen locknut on front servo adjusting screw and insert a .250" metal block between end of adjusting screw and servo piston rod, Fig. 1.

With metal block in place, tighten adjusting screw to a torque of 10 inch-pounds and tighten locknut to 23 ft-lbs torque. If a special adapter is used, torque adjusting screw to 9 inch-pounds.

Cast Iron Case

Adjusting Tool J-5880-01 should be used to make the adjustment. Tighten the adjusting, screw until the tool over-rides, then tighten locknut to 23 ft-lbs torque and remove gauge block.

NOTE: Beginning with 1969 models the front servo adjusting screw is a left hand thread.

REAR BAND, ADJUST

NOTE: To gain access to the rear band adjusting screw, it may be necessary to remove the crossmember bolts and lower the transmission on some models.

Aluminum Case

Loosen locknut and tighten adjusting screw to a torque of 10 ft-lbs. Then back off the adjusting screw $\frac{3}{4}$ turn and tighten locknut to 28 ft-lbs. torque.

Cast Iron Case

Loosen locknut and tighten adjusting screw to 10 ft-lbs torque. Then back off the adjusting screw $1\frac{1}{4}$ turns and tighten locknut.

OIL PRESSURE REGULATOR

Remove oil pan and screen. Maintain constant pressure on spring retainer to prevent damage to springs and remove retainer from bosses on oil pressure regulator body. Remove springs and pilots. Remove the three pipes. Unfasten and remove the oil pressure regulator from the transmission case.

CONTROL VALVE

To remove the assembly, loosen the adjustment on the front and rear bands 5 to 6 turns. Lossen front servo attaching screws. Remove cap screws and washers which attach control valve to case. Align throttle and manual levers to permit removal of control valve. Disengage front servo tubes from control valve and lift valve assembly from case.

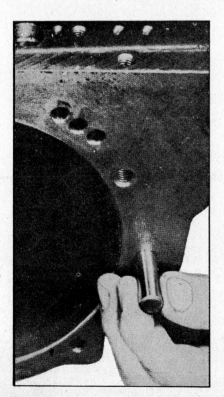

Fig. 2   Removing parking pawl shaft

Fig. 3   Removing toggle lever

FRONT & REAR SERVOS

To remove the front servo, remove the cap screw which holds it to the case. Hold the actuating lever strut with one hand and lift the servo from the case.

To remove the rear servo, take out the attaching cap screws. Then hold the anchor strut and lift the servo from the case.

EXTENSION HOUSING SEAL

Remove propeller shaft or torque tube and propeller shaft from transmission. Pull seal out of extension housing.

Before installing the new seal, inspect the sealing surface of the universal joint yoke for scores. If scores are evident, replace the yoke. Inspect the counterbore in the housing for burrs. Polish all burrs with crocus cloth.

To install the new seal, position it in the bore of the extension housing with the felt side of the seal to the rear. The seal may be driven into the housing with a special tool designed for the purpose.

OIL DISTRIBUTOR

NOTE: On 1966 Six, oil distribution is handled through the rear pump body, and oil distributor sleeve is therefore not used.

With Bolted Distributor & Sleeve

After removing the extension case remove the spacer from the transmission output shaft and slide the distributor toward the rear of the transmission. Note that the tube spacer is located in the center tube.

Remove the three tubes and spacer from the distributor. Remove the screws which attach the distributor to the sleeve and separate these parts.

Inspect the distributor and sleeve for burrs on the mating surfaces and obstructed fluid passages. Check the fit of the tubes in the distributor. Inspect the distributor sleeve for wear and scores in the sleeve bore.

To assemble, align the distributor and sleeve and install the cap screws. Install the tubes in the distributor with the spacer installed on the center tube.

With One Piece Distributor & Sleeve

After removing the extension housing, remove the distributor drive gear snap ring. Remove distributor gear, taking care not to lose the gear drive ball. Remove distributor sleeve and pipes from the transmission. Inspect the 4 seal rings on the output shaft for wear or breakage, and replace if necessary, Inspect the distributor sleeve for wear and the tubes for proper alignment and fit into the distributor sleeve.

With tubes installed in the distributor sleeve, install distributor on output shaft

(chamfer forward) sliding the distributor over the seal rings and at the same time guiding tubes into the case. Install speedometer drive ball and gear and install snap ring.

GOVERNOR

Remove the governor inspection cover from the extension housing, Rotate the drive shaft to bring the governor body in line with the inspection hole. Remove the two screws which attach the governor body to the counterweight, and remove the body.

Remove the valve from the new governor body. Lubricate the valve with automatic transmission fluid. Install valve in the body, making sure the valve moves freely in the bore. Install the body in the counterweight. Be sure the fluid passages in the counterweight and body are aligned.

PARKING PAWL, REPLACE

Transmission In Car

Aluminum Case

1. Support engine at rear.
2. Support torque tube with jack.
3. Remove speedometer cable and remove exhaust pipe clamp from lower bracket.
4. Unfasten and remove rear crossmember over exhaust pipe by pulling down on exhaust pipe.
5. Remove oil pan and control valve.
6. Remove parking brake toggle roll pin and remove toggle pin.
7. Unfasten rear extension housing from torque tube adapter and rotate housing clockwise until governor inspection plate is almost level to the bottom. The parking brake anchor pin will then clear extension housing.
8. Remove parking brake anchor pin with a magnet or remove pin from inside of case with needle nose pliers.
9. Remove parking brake toggle link and pawl assembly.
10. Reverse procedure to install.

Cast Iron Case

1. Remove oil pan and screen, pressure regulator and control valve. Disconnect speedometer cable.
2. Completely tighten rear band to prevent movement of planetary assembly and dislocation of thrust washers on the transmission shaft. Disconnect drive shaft or drive shaft and torque tube from the transmission.
3. Remove extension housing-to-case bolts and move housing rearward far enough to permit removal of snap ring which retains speedometer gear.
4. Slide oil delivery sleeve back just far enough so that the oil distributor tubes clear the transmission case.
5. Rotate oil pump housing until parking pawl pin in case is exposed.
6. Disconnect link (parking pawl torsion rod) located between detent

lever and torsion lever assembly.
7. Remove hair pin clip retaining torsion lever assembly and remove from shaft.
8. Tap toggle lever pin toward rear of transmission to remove plug and pin, then remove parking pawl pin by working pawl back and forth, Fig. 2.
9. Remove toggle lever and parking pawl assembly from transmission and replace any damaged parts, Fig. 3.
10. Reverse above procedure for reassembly.

TRANSMISSION, REPLACE

1967-71

1. Disconnect battery.
2. Raise car and support with car stands. *Car weight must be on rear springs, therefore, place stands under rear axle tubes.*

NOTE: Before removing the rear crossmember on Javelin and AMX with power steering, it is necessary to open the hood to avoid damage to the hood from the power steering pump wing nut.

3. Disconnect the following:
4. Oil filler tube and drain transmission.
5. Selector linkage at transmission outer manual lever.
6. Speedometer cable at transmission.
7. Vacuum hose and solenoid wire.
8. Exhaust pipe and remove pipe bracket from converter housing.
9. Position transmission hoist under transmission.
10. On American, remove body crossmember tie plate on Convertibles.
11. On models other than American, disconnect rear support crossmember from body side sill brackets and transmission.
12. With 199, 232, 258 engines, remove converter housing lower cover.
13. Remove converter access cover (in spacer plate on 290 engine) on V8.
14. Mark converter and drive plate to assure original location upon assembly.
15. Remove converter-to-drive plate capscrews (6-cyl.) stud nuts on V8s.
16. Remove starter mounting bolts and converter housing-to-cylinder block bolts.
17. Push converter housing and converter to rear a sufficient distance to clear crankshaft.

NOTE: Rear of engine tends to raise when transmission weight is removed and may bind the converter in the crankshaft pilot bushing. Blocking the engine up at the front will assist separating converter from crankshaft.

18. Maintain pressure against converter housing and lower assembly until converter housing is clear of engine. Then disconnect propeller shaft and remove transmission from vehicle.
19. Reverse procedure to install.

1966 Rambler

1. Disconnect battery.
2. Disconnect throttle valve control cable at throttle linkage bracket on engine.
3. Raise car and support with floor stands. *Car weight must be on rear springs; therefore, support rear of car with stands placed under rear axle tubes.*
4. Disconnect oil filler tube and drain transmission.
5. Disconnect selector linkage at transmission outer manual lever.
6. Disconnect speedometer cable at transmission.
7. Disconnect exhaust pipe from manifold and remove exhaust pipe bracket from converter housing.
8. Position transmission hoist with a suitable cradle under transmission.
9. Disconnect rear support crossmember from body side sill brackets and transmission. Remove body crossmember tie plate on Convertibles.
10. Lower transmission and rear of engine for access to upper converter housing-to-engine bolts.
11. Remove converter housing lower cover.
12. Mark converter and drive plate to assure original location upon reassembly.
13. Remove converter-to-drive plate capscrews.
14. Remove starter mounting bolts and converter housing-to-engine bolts.
15. Push converter housing and converter rearward a sufficient distance to clear crankshaft.

NOTE: Rear of engine tends to raise when transmission weight is removed and may bind converter in crankshaft pilot bushing. Blocking the engine up at the front will assist separating converter from crankshaft.

---

16. Maintain pressure against converter housing and lower transmission, converter housing and converter as an assembly until it is clear of engine.
17. Disconnect transmission from propeller shaft and torque tube.

VOLKSWAGEN AUTOMATIC

GENERAL DESCRIPTION

This transmission, Fig. 1, is a three speed, fully automatic unit consisting primarily of a three element torque converter and a planetary gear set. Two multiple disc clutches, one one way clutch and two brake bands provide the frictional elements required to obtain the desired functions of the planetary gear set.

The torque converter and the frictional elements couple the engine to the planetary gears through oil pressure, providing three forward speeds and one reverse. The torque converter, when required, supplements the gears by multiplying engine torque.

Selector Quadrant

The six positions are as follows:

"P" Park: Locks transmission by means of a small pawl which engages a gear on the output shaft of the transmission. Park must only be engaged when the vehicle is stationary and the handbrake is applied.

"R" Reverse: Must only be selected when the vehicle is stationary and the engine is idling.

"O" or "N" Neutral: Disengages the engine from the output shaft. The engine cannot be started unless the selector lever is in this position.

"3": This position is used for all normal driving conditions. The three forward gears are shifted up or down automatically.

"2": Transmission shifts as high as second speed but will not shift into third.

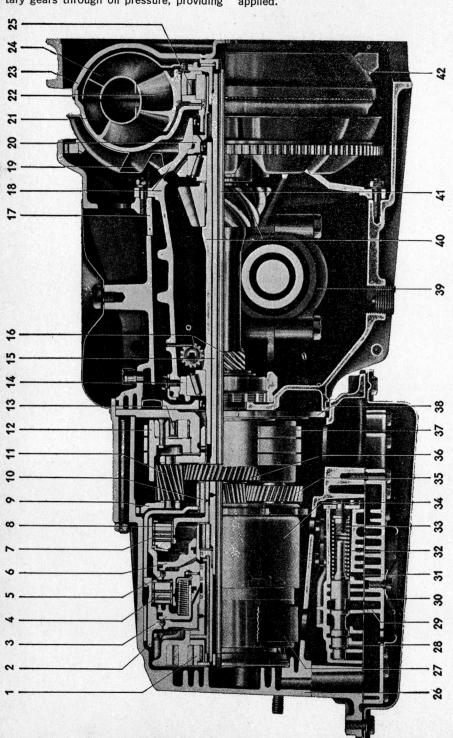

1 - Oil pump
2 - Clutch drum
3 - Piston for direct and reverse clutch
4 - Direct and reverse clutch
5 - Forward clutch drum with ball valve
6 - Piston for forward clutch
7 - Forward clutch
8 - Forward clutch hub
9 - Planetary gear carrier
10 - Small sun gear
11 - Small planet pinion
12 - Annulus or ring gear
13 - 1st gear one-way clutch
14 - Adjusting ring for pinion bearing
15 - Turbine shaft
16 - Governor drive
17 - Final drive housing
18 - Differential carrier
19 - Cooling fins
20 - Torque converter support tube
21 - Impeller
22 - Stator
23 - Converter housing
24 - Turbine
25 - One-way clutch
26 - Transmission case
27 - 2nd gear brake band
28 - Control valve
29 - Transfer plate
30 - Oil strainer
31 - Separator plate
32 - Valve body
33 - Spring for valve
34 - Driving shell
35 - Large planet pinion
36 - Large sun gear
37 - 1st and reverse brake band
38 - Bearing flange
39 - Bearing cap for differential
40 - Pinion with shaft
41 - Impeller shaft
42 - Connecting lug

Fig. 1   Volkswagen 1600 automatic transmission

This position must only be selected when the vehicle speed is below 60 mph and this speed should not be exceeded in this range.

"1": The transmission remains in first gear so that full use can be made of the engine braking when descending steep hills. This position must only be selected when vehicle speed is below 37 mph.

HYDRAULIC SYSTEM

The transmission is controlled automatically by the hydraulic system. Hydraulic pressure is supplied by the transmission oil pump which is engine driven. A pressure relief valve for reverse gear prevents the oil pressure from becoming too high. A further pressure relief valve for the forward gears is located in the transmission case.

Oil Pump

The oil pump is of the gear type and is driven by the engine via the converter housing, drive plate and pump shaft. The pump draws oil from the oil pan through a strainer and pumps it to the valve body.

Governor

The governor supplies an oil pressure signal which is dependent on vehicle speed and is routed to the control valve to regulate shift points. The governor consists of a driving shaft with a square end, oil passages and a flange. Mounted on the flange is an aluminum housing which contains the valve, centrifugal weight and springs. The governor is driven from the drive pinion so it only turns when the vehicle is moving.

Primary Throttle Pressure Valve (Vacuum Modulator)

Regulates a control pressure according to engine intake manifold vacuum. This pressure assists in the regulating of the main oil pressure and shift points according to engine operating conditions.

The valve is pushed against the oil pressure and a spring by means of a plunger and a spring loaded diaphragm. The tension of the diaphragm spring is adjustable and when a new vacuum unit is fitted it must be adjusted to suit the individual transmission.

Accumulator

Provides gradual application of the 2nd gear band when changing from 1st to 2nd. It consists of a cylinder with a freely floating piston which has a spring beneath it and can be supplied with oil from both sides.

At the beginning of the 1-2 shift, main oil pressure on the top of the piston holds it down against the spring. When the shift valve has moved, a restricted flow of oil is applied to the bottom of the piston which then moves slowly upwards, assisted by the spring. The pressure on the bottom of the piston then increases gradually and restrains the braking force of the 2nd gear band to the same extent that the spring tension is relieved.

Valve Body Assembly

This system of valves, located in the

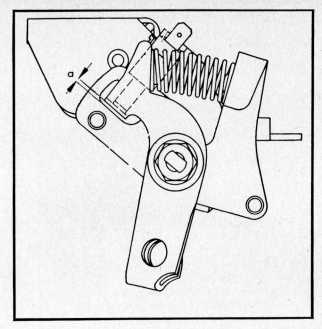

Fig. 2 Detent switch adjustment

oil pan, controls oil pressure and routing to the various units to control the operation of the unit.

TROUBLE SHOOTING GUIDE

No Drive In Any Range

1. Low oil level.
2. Oil pump or drive defective.
3. Shafts or planet gear set broken.
4. Drive plate broken.

No Drive In Any Forward Range

1. Forward clutch defective.

No Drive With Lever In 1 or Reverse

1. 1st and reverse band or servo faulty.

No Drive In 1st Gear With Lever In 3 Position

1. 1st gear one-way clutch in annulus gear defective.

No Drive In 2nd Gear With Lever In 2 or 3 Position

1. 2nd gear band or servo faulty.

No Drive In 3rd or Reverse

1. Direct and reverse clutch faulty.

No Upshift Out of 1st Gear

1. Governor drive defective.
2. Governor valve sticking.

Power Transmission Erratic

1. Low oil level.
2. Selector lever incorrectly adjusted.

Delayed Engagement, Engine Races

1. Oil level incorrect.

2. Friction linings burnt or worn.
3. Oil pressure wrong due to incorrect adjustment of vacuum unit.
4. Incorrect oil pressure due to internal leakage.

Shifts Occur When Speed Is Too Low

1. Defective governor.
2. Defective valve body.
3. Misadjusted vacuum unit.
4. Leakage in transmission.

Shifts Occur When Speed Is Too High

1. Vacuum unit or hose leaking.
2. Defective valve body.
3. Defective governor.
4. Misadjusted vacuum unit.
5. Leakage in transmission.

No Upshift To 3rd

1. Incorrect governor pressure.
2. Defective valve body.
3. Direct and reverse clutch defective.

Harsh Engagement When Lever Is Shifted Into Gear

1. Idle speed too high.
2. Vacuum hose leaking.

Vehicle Creeps

1. Idle speed too high.

No Kickdown

1. Incorrect throttle linkage and switch adjustment.
2. Electrical fault in kickdown circuit.
3. Valve body defective or dirty.

Poor Acceleration; Low Maximum Speed

1. Faulty converter.
2. Bands or clutches slipping.
3. Low oil level.

VOLKSWAGEN AUTOMATIC

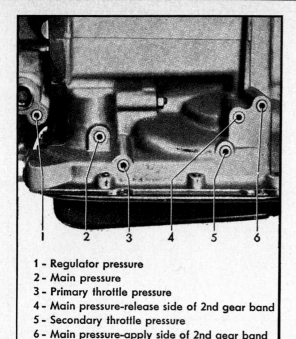

1 - Regulator pressure
2 - Main pressure
3 - Primary throttle pressure
4 - Main pressure-release side of 2nd gear band
5 - Secondary throttle pressure
6 - Main pressure-apply side of 2nd gear band

Fig. 3   Pressure test points

Poor Acceleration; Screeching Noise When Moving Off

1. Converter or one-way clutch faulty.

Oil Consumption Without External Leakage

1. Vacuum unit leaking.
2. Oil seals on pinion or governor shaft faulty (oil getting into final drive housing).

Parking Lock Not Working

1. Incorrect selector lever adjustment.
2. Operating linkage broken.

MANUAL LINKAGE, ADJUST

1. Place selector lever in Park position.
2. Push cable into clamp.

3. Push transmission lever fully to the rear, turn wheels slightly until parking lock engages then tighten nut on clamp, being careful to keep lever pushed to the rear.

THROTTLE LINKAGE, ADJUST

1. Block accelerator pedal in wide open position.
2. With adjusting nut, tighten the accelerator cable until the moving lever contacts the stop on the three arm lever against spring pressure.
3. Lock cable adjusting nut in this position.

DETENT SWITCH, ADJUST

1. Turn on ignition switch. Connect test lamp to the switch terminal for the transmission lead.
2. Allow accelerator pedal to return from kickdown position and adjust until there is a clearance of .020"-.040" at the stop for the moving lever, (a in Fig. 2).

VACUUM UNIT, ADJUST

1. Disconnect and plug vacuum line at unit.
2. Connect pressure gauge to primary throttle pressure test point, Fig. 3.
3. Run engine at idle speed and check pressure reading.
4. Adjust pressure with Allen head screw in vacuum unit to obtain proper pressure reading.

TRANSMISSION, REPLACE

1. Disconnect battery ground cable and remove air cleaner.
2. Disconnect wires from generator, ignition coil and oil pressure switch.
3. Disconnect accelerator cable, fuel line and heater cables and hoses. Remove carburetor pre-heating hose.
4. Remove dipstick, rubber boot and loosen clips on cooling air bellows and pull bellows off.
5. Disconnect half shafts.
6. Disconnect shift control cable and body ground strap.
7. Loosen screws in front transmission mount and remove two upper screws.
8. Support transmission with a suitable jack, remove mounting bolts and lower engine and transmission as a unit.
9. Disconnect converter from flywheel, detent switch cable and vacuum hoses from transmission and separate transmission/final drive from engine. Separate transmission from final drive.
10. Reverse procedure to install, taking care to align engine unit properly during installation.

UNIVERSAL JOINTS

SERVICE NOTES

Before disassembling any universal joint, examine the assembly carefully and note the position of the grease fitting (if used). Also, be sure to mark the yokes with relation to the propeller shaft so they may be reassembled in the same relative position. Failure to observe these precautions may produce rough car operation which results in rapid wear and failure of parts, and place an unbalanced load on transmission, engine and real axle.

When universal joints are disassembled for lubrication or inspection, and the old parts are to be reinstalled, special care must be exercised to avoid damage to universal joint spider or cross and bearing cups.

NOTE: Some late model cars use an injected nylon retainer on the universal joint bearings. When service is necessary, pressing the bearings out will sheer the nylon retainer. Replacement with the conventional steel snap ring type is then necessary.

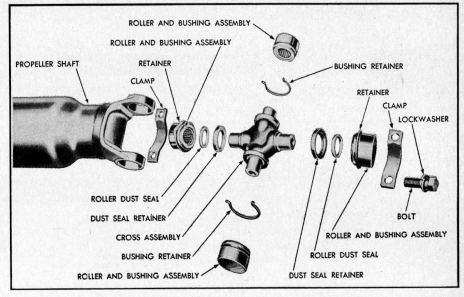

Fig. 1 Cross and roller type universal joint. Chrysler-built cars

CROSS & ROLLER TYPE

Figs. 1, 2 and 3 illustrate typical examples of universal joints of this type. They all operate on the same principle and similar service and replacement procedures may be applied to all.

Disassembly

1. Remove snap rings (or retainer plates) that retain bearings in yoke and drive shaft.
2. Place U-joint in a vise.
3. Select a wrench socket with an outside diameter slightly smaller than the U-joint bearings. Select another wrench socket with an inside diameter slightly larger than the U-joint bearings.
4. Place the sockets at opposite bearings in the yoke so that the smaller socket becomes a bearing pusher and the larger socket becomes a bearing receiver when the vise jaws come together, Fig. 4. Close vise jaws until both bearings are free of yoke and remove bearings from the cross or spider.
5. If bearings will not come all the way out, close vise until bearing in receiver socket protrudes from yoke as much as possible without using excessive force. Then remove from vise and place that portion of bearing which protrudes from yoke between vise jaws. Tighten vise to hold bearing and drive yoke off with a soft hammer.
6. To remove opposite bearing from yoke, replace in vise with pusher socket on exposed cross journal with receiver socket over bearing cup. Then tighten vise jaws to press bearing back through yoke into receiving socket.
7. Remove yoke from drive shaft and again place protruding portion of bearing between vise jaws. Then tighten vise to hold bearing while driving yoke off bearing with soft hammer.
8. Turn spider or cross ¼ turn and use the same procedure to press bearings out of drive shaft.

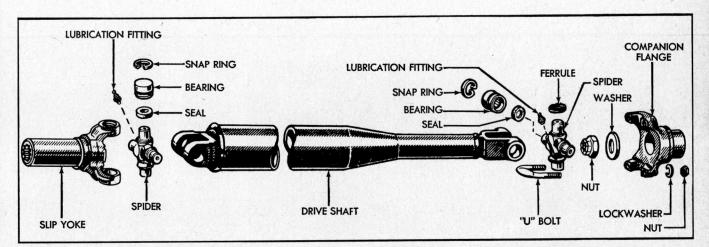

Fig. 2 Cross and roller universal joints and propeller shaft. Ford-built cars

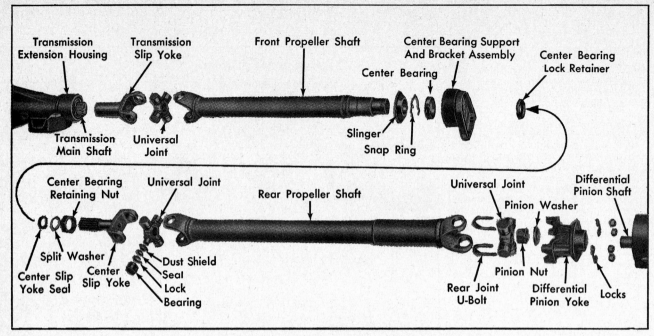

Fig. 3 Example of a two-piece propeller shaft with three cross and roller universal joints and center bearing support assembly. Cadillac

Reassembly

1. If old parts are to be reassembled, pack bearing cups with universal joint grease. *Do not fill cups completely or use excessive amounts as over-lubrication may damage seals during reassembly.* Use new seals.
2. If new parts are being installed, check new bearings for adequate grease before assembling.
3. With the pusher (smaller) socket, press one bearing part way into drive shaft. Position spider into the partially installed bearing. Place second bearing into drive shaft. Fasten drive shaft in vise so that bearings are in contact with faces of vise jaws,

Fig. 5. *Some spiders are provided with locating lugs which must face toward drive shaft when installed,* Fig. 6.

4. Press bearings all the way into position and install snap rings or retainer plates.
5. Install bearings in yoke in same manner. When installation is completed, check U-joint for binding or roughness If free movement is impeded, correct the condition before installation in vehicle.

BALL & TRUNNION TYPE
Disassembly

1. Referring to Fig. 7, straighten tabs and remove grease cover and gasket.
2. Push body back and remove thrust button, spring, ball, rollers and thrust washer from each end of pin.

3. Remove clamps and loosen dust cover. Remove and save breather located between shaft and cover.
4. Clean and examine trunnion and raceways in body for roughness and wear. If either part is to be replaced. press out pin. Care must be exercised to support end of drive shaft properly to avoid damage during pressing operation.

Reassembly

When the trunnion pin and body have not been removed, a new boot may be installed and the U-joint may be repacked. Coat all parts with universal joint grease and, without using tools, stretch boot over pin and work it through body into position on the shaft. Lubricate and complete boot installation as directed further on.

1. To assemble the U-joint, place boot clamps, boot and U-joint body on drive shaft.

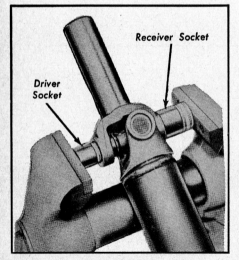

Fig. 4 Removing bearings from yoke using small and large wrench sockets as pusher and receiver tools, respectively

Fig. 5 Installing bearings into drive shaft yoke

Fig. 6 Some units have locating lugs which must face propeller shaft when installed

2. Press pin through end of propeller shaft so that pin is exactly centered.
3. Assemble parts on pin in the order shown in Fig. 7, then position U-joint body over pin assembly.
4. Position boot on propeller shaft, with breather parallel to shaft. Install and tighten clamp.
5. Place boot on U-joint body and install clamp.
6. Lubricate U-joint with two ounces of fibrous U-joint grease applied evenly in both raceways, one half in back of the trunnion pin and one half between pin and cover.
7. Install grease cover and gasket on body with tabs at grooves in body. Bend tabs to tighten in place.

CONSTANT VELOCITY TYPE

This type of U-joint, Fig. 8, is composed of two conventional cross and roller joints connected with a special link yoke. Because the two joint angles are the same, even though the usual U-joint fluctuation is present within the unit, the acceleration of the front joint (within the yoke) is always neutralized by the deceleration of the rear joint (within the yoke) and vice versa. The end result is the front and rear propeller shafts always turn at a constant velocity.

General Motors

For ease of handling and to prevent damage to the constant velocity U-joints, the front and rear propeller shafts must be separated at the slip joint before any service is attempted.

Disassemble Slip Joint

1. Pry lockwasher from flats on bearing locknut.
2. Loosen locknut until free of threads and slide locknut and seal against constant velocity joint.
3. Slide rear propeller shaft from front propeller shaft, making sure that index spring wire in splines is not lost.

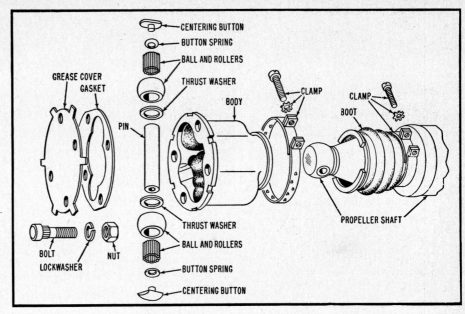

Fig. 7 Ball and trunnion type universal joint. Chrysler-built cars

Disassemble Constant Velocity U-Joint

1. Make yokes before disassembly to be sure reassembly is made in same relative position of components.
2. Disassemble rear section of constant velocity U-joint first as follows:
3. Remove snap rings from bearings using a punch.
4. Place rear propeller shaft yoke in a vise. Shaft must be supported horizontally and link yoke must be free to move vertically, Fig. 9.
5. Using a pipe coupling or a wrench socket with the inside diameter slightly larger than outside diameter of bearing, Fig. 9, drive link yoke downward until about a 1/4" of bearing projects from yoke. *Do not attempt to drive yoke down farther than ball socket will allow easily.*

6. Rotate shaft 180 degrees and repeat Steps 3, 4 and 5.
7. Clamp 1/4" projecting portion of either bearing in vise and remove bearing by driving link yoke upward. Remove other bearing in same manner, Fig. 10.
8. Separate spider, shaft yoke and shaft from link yoke.
9. To remove bearings from shaft yoke, clamp spider in vise with its jaws bearing against ends of spider journals. Yoke must be free to move vertically between jaws of vise.
10. Using the same bearing remover tool as in Step 5, apply force on shaft yoke around bearing. Drive yoke downward until bearing is free of yoke.

Reassemble Constant Velocity U-Joint—

All yokes must be carefully assembled using the marks made before disassembly for reference. Assemble front section of constant velocity joint first.

1. Position spider inside splined yoke. Install bearings by pressing between vise jaws. Make sure that spider journals enter bearings squarely to avoid damage, Fig. 11.

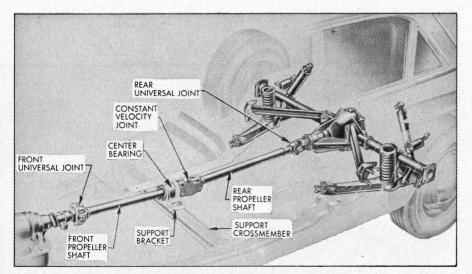

Fig. 8 Two piece propeller shaft with constant velocity universal joint. General Motors

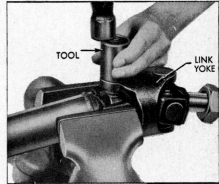

Fig. 9 Driving bearing from link yoke

Fig. 10 Removing bearing

DRIVE LINK YOKE UPWARD

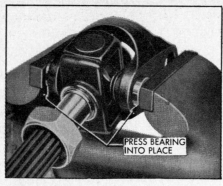

Fig. 11 Installing bearings

PRESS BEARING INTO PLACE

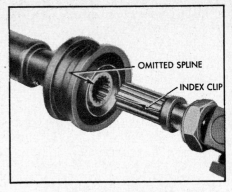

Fig. 12 Aligning index spring with missing internal spline on propeller shaft

OMITTED SPLINE

INDEX CLIP

2. Fully install bearings and install snap rings.
3. Position splined yoke and spider inside link yoke and install bearings into link yoke in same manner as for splined yoke.
4. Position spider inside rear propeller shaft yoke and install bearings.
5. Lubricate ball and socket with a high grade of extreme pressure grease.
6. Position spider of rear propeller shaft assembly in link yoke.
7. Engage socket with ball of splined yoke assembly. *Make sure that all reference marks are properly aligned.*
8. Install bearings into link yoke in same manner as above while holding spring loaded ball and socket assembly together to make sure that spider journals enter bearings squarely.

Reassemble Slip Joint

1. Make sure locknut, seal and split washer are in place on smooth part of spline shaft. Also make sure that index spring wire is in place in splines and that spacer washer and large lockwasher are in place on rear end of front propeller shaft.

2. Align index spring with missing internal spline in rear end of propeller shaft and slide slip joint together, Fig. 12.
3. Install locknut and tighten securely. Bend in rim of lockwasher to engage flat of locknut firmly.

Lincoln & American Motors

This type, Figs. 13 and 14, is similar in construction to the GM type shown in Fig. 8 except that no center bearing support is used. Also, the transmission mainshaft extension serves the same purpose as the front propeller shaft on GM cars.

Disassemble Constant Velocity U-Joint

1. Mark position of spiders, center yoke and centering socket yoke as related to yoke that is welded to the drive shaft tube. Also, note the position of the grease fittings as they must be assembled in the same position to provide proper clearance.
2. Remove grease fittings. Apply pressure on centering socket yoke and remove one bearing cup. Remove opposite bearing cup in same manner.

3. Remove snap rings which retain bearing cups in front of center yoke. As a remover tool, use a wrench socket or a piece of pipe with an outside diameter slightly smaller than the bearing cup. As a receiver tool, use a wrench socket or a piece of pipe with an inside diameter slightly larger than the bearing cup. Clamp center yoke in vise with driver and receiver tools in place as shown in Fig. 15.
4. Close vise to press bearing cup about $\frac{3}{8}''$ out of center yoke and into receiver tool. *The bearing cup cannot be pressed out more than this without causing damage.*
5. Tightly clamp exposed bearing cup in vise and drive yoke from cup, using a brass drift.
6. Remove opposite bearing from center yoke, using above procedure.
7. Pull centering socket yoke assembly off entering stud. Remove rubber seal from centering ball stud.
8. Remove snap rings from rear of center yoke and drive shaft yoke. Start disassembly by pressing bearing cups from drive shaft yoke, being careful to stop pressing operation when inside of center yoke almost contacts slinger ring at front of drive shaft yoke. Pressing bearing beyond this point will distort the ring, Fig. 16.
9. Removing remaining bearing cups from center yoke.

Reassembly

1. Position spider in drive shaft yoke. Make sure that grease fitting will be in same position as originally installed. Press in bearing cups and seals and install snap rings.
2. Position center yoke over spider ends, making sure that reference marks made before disassembly are properly aligned. Press bearing cups into center yoke and install snap rings.
3. Install new seal on centering ball stud and positon centering socket yoke on the stud.
4. Place front spider, with grease fitting properly positioned, in center yoke. Press bearing cups into center yoke and install remaining bearing cups and seals.

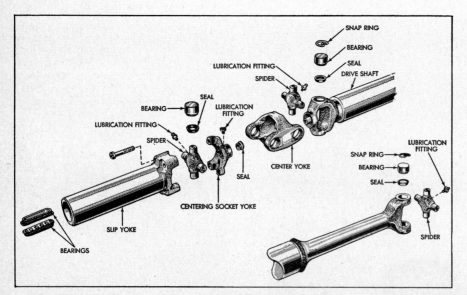

SNAP RING
BEARING
SEAL
DRIVE SHAFT
LUBRICATION FITTING
SPIDER
SEAL
BEARING
LUBRICATION FITTING
LUBRICATION FITTING
SPIDER
CENTER YOKE
SNAP RING
BEARING
SEAL
LUBRICATION FITTING
SEAL
CENTERING SOCKET YOKE
SPIDER
SLIP YOKE
BEARINGS

Fig. 13 Constant velocity universal joint used on Lincoln

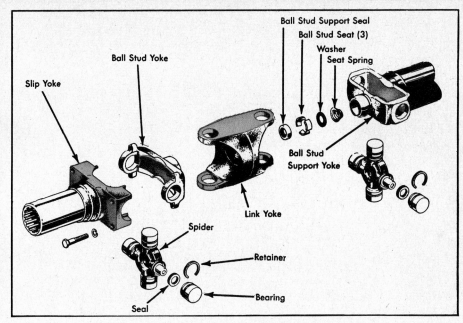

Fig. 14 American Motors constant velocity universal joint

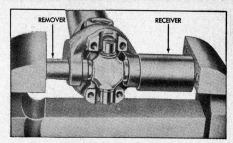

Fig. 15 Partially removing bearing cup from center yoke

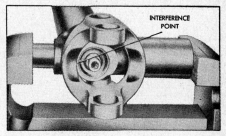

Fig. 16 Bearing cup removal and interference

HYDRAULIC BRAKE SYSTEM

For Brake Adjustments, see Car Chapters

SINGLE MASTER CYLINDER SYSTEM

Depressing the brake pedal moves the master cylinder push rod and piston, forcing hydraulic fluid out through a check valve, Fig. 1. This fluid flows through the hydraulic lines into the wheel cylinders, forcing the wheel cylinder pistons outward from the center of the cylinder and expanding the brake shoes and linings against the brake drums.

When the brake pedal is quickly released, the master cylinder piston returns to the released position faster than fluid returns from the lines. Holes in the piston head allow fluid to pass from the rear to the front of the piston head, past the primary cup to fill the space.

At the same time (when the pedal is released) the brake shoe return springs force the wheel cylinder pistons to return toward the center of the wheel cylinder (released position). Fluid forced out of the wheel cylinders by this action returns to the master cylinder by overcoming the pressure of the master cylinder piston spring which holds the check valve closed. As this fluid returns, the excess portion will return to the reservoir through the compensating port which is uncovered when the master cylinder piston is in the released position. The piston spring will close the check valve when the pressure in the lines is reduced to 8 to 12 lbs, maintaining a slight pressure in the lines at all times. The purpose of this

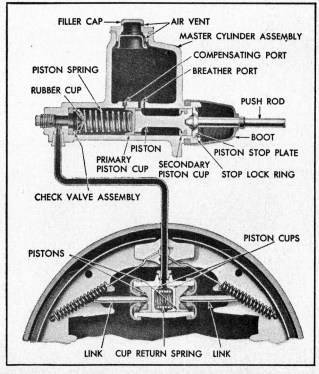

Fig. 1 Schematic diagram of a typical hydraulic brake system

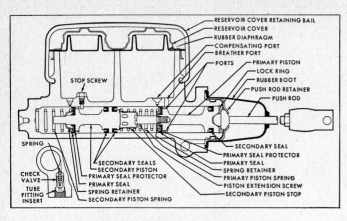

Fig. 2   Delco-Moraine dual master cylinder
used with drum brakes (typical)

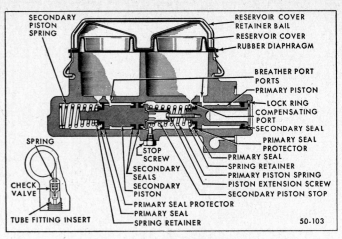

Fig. 3   Bendix dual master cylinder
used with drum brakes (typical)

pressure is to keep the wheel cylinder cups from leaking fluid and to reduce the possibility of air entering the system.

DUAL MASTER CYLINDER SYSTEM

When the brake pedal is depressed, both the primary (front brake) and the secondary (rear brake) master cylinder pistons are moved simultaneously to exert hydraulic fluid pressure on their respective independent hydraulic system. The fluid displacement of the two master cylinders is proportioned to fulfill the requirements of each of the two independent hydraulic brake systems, Figs. 2 and 3.

If a failure of a rear (secondary) brake system should occur, initial brake pedal movement causes the unrestricted secondary piston to bottom in the master cylinder bore. Primary piston movement displaces hydraulic fluid in the primary section of the dual master cylinder to actuate the front brake system.

Should the front (primary) brake system fail, initial brake pedal movement causes the unrestricted primary piston to bottom out against the secondary piston. Continued downward movement of the brake pedal moves the secondary piston to displace hydraulic fluid in the rear brake system to actuate the rear brakes.

The increased pedal travel and the increased pedal effort required to compensate for the loss of the failed portion of the brake system provides a warning that a partial brake system failure has occurred When the ignition switch is turned on, a brake warning light on the instrument panel provides a visual indication that one of the dual brake systems has become inoperative.

Should a failure of either the front or rear brake hydraulic system occur, the hydraulic fluid pressure differential resulting from pressure loss of the failed brake system forces the valve toward the low pressure area to light the brake warning lamp.

Brake Warning Light Switches

There are three basic types of brake warning light switches as shown in Figs. 5, 6 and 7, and usually they form a common electrical circuit with the brake warning light.

When a pressure differential occurs between the front and rear brake systems, the valves will shuttle toward the side with the low pressure.

As shown in Fig. 5, movement of the differential valve forces the switch

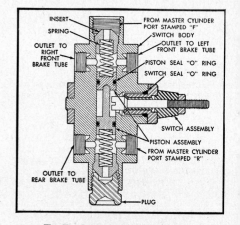

Fig. 7   Pressure differential valve
and brake warning light switch

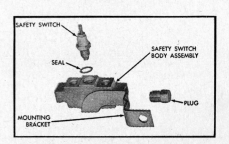

Fig. 8   Typical pressure valve and brake warning light switch. These switches are usually mounted on the left frame side rail

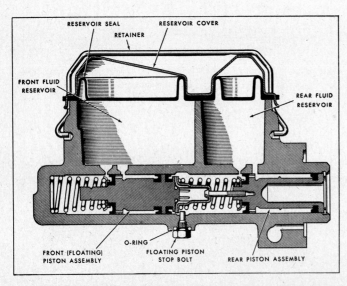

Fig. 4   Bendix dual master cylinder
used with disc brakes (typical)

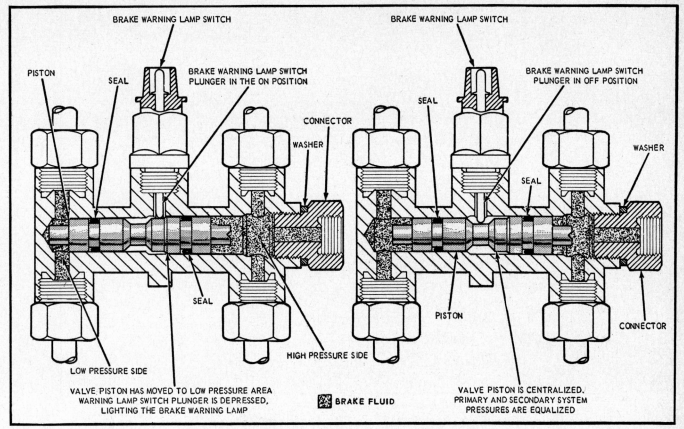

Fig. 5 Pressure differential valve and brake warning light switch

plunger upward over the tapered shoulder of the valve to close the switch contacts and light the dual brake warning lamp, signaling a brake system failure.

In Fig. 6 the valve assembly consists of two valves in a common bore that are spring loaded toward the centered position. The spring-loaded switch contact plunger rests on top of the valves in the centered position (right view). When a pressure differential occurs between the front and rear brake systems, the valves will shuttle toward the side with the low pressure. The spring-loaded switch plunger is "triggered" and the ground circuit for the warning light is completed, lighting the lamp (left view).

In Fig. 7, as pressure falls in one system, the other system's normal pressure forces the piston to the inoperative side, contacting the switch terminal, causing the warning light on the instrument panel to glow.

Testing Warning Light System

If the parking brake light is connected into the service brake warning light system, the brake warning light will flash only when the parking brake is applied with the ignition turned ON. The same light will also glow should one of the two service brake systems fail when the brake pedal is applied.

To test the system, turn the ignition ON and apply the parking brake. If the lamp fails to light, inspect for a burned out bulb, disconnected socket, a broken or disconnected wire at the switch.

Fig. 8 is an exterior view of one of these switches. They are usually mounted on the left frame side rail or on the brake pedal bracket.

To test the brake warning system, raise the car and open a wheel bleeder valve while a helper depresses the brake pedal and observes the warning light on the instrument panel. If the bulb fails to light, inspect for a burned out bulb, disconnected socket, or a broken or disconnected wire at the switch. If the bulb is not burned out, and the wire continuity is

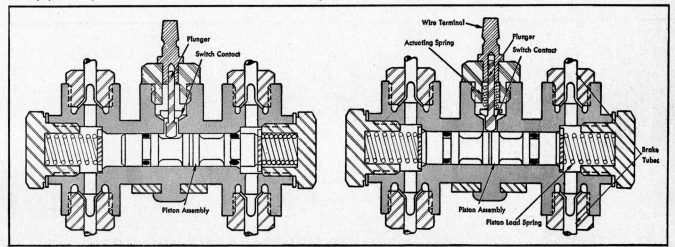

Fig. 6 Pressure differential valve and brake warning light switch

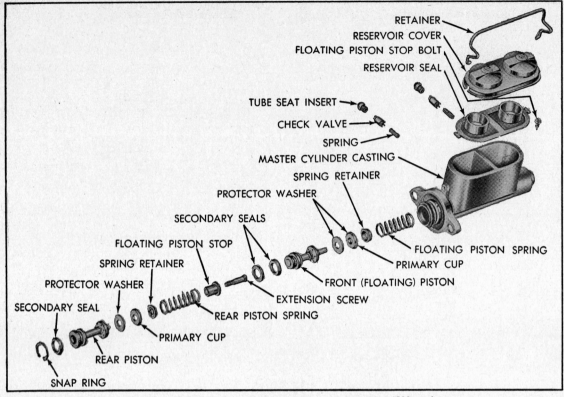

RETAINER
RESERVOIR COVER
FLOATING PISTON STOP BOLT
RESERVOIR SEAL

TUBE SEAT INSERT
CHECK VALVE
SPRING
MASTER CYLINDER CASTING
SPRING RETAINER
PROTECTOR WASHER
SECONDARY SEALS
FLOATING PISTON STOP
SPRING RETAINER
PROTECTOR WASHER
SECONDARY SEAL
SNAP RING
REAR PISTON
PRIMARY CUP
REAR PISTON SPRING
EXTENSION SCREW
FRONT (FLOATING) PISTON
PRIMARY CUP
FLOATING PISTON SPRING

Fig. 9   Delco-Moraine dual master cylinder disassembled (GM cars)

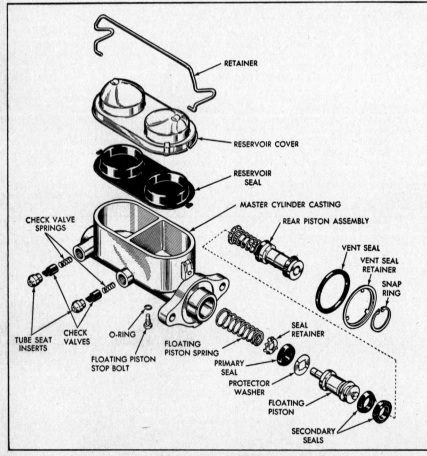

RETAINER
RESERVOIR COVER
RESERVOIR SEAL
MASTER CYLINDER CASTING
REAR PISTON ASSEMBLY
VENT SEAL
VENT SEAL RETAINER
SNAP RING
CHECK VALVE SPRINGS
SEAL RETAINER
TUBE SEAT INSERTS
CHECK VALVES
O-RING
FLOATING PISTON STOP BOLT
FLOATING PISTON SPRING
PRIMARY SEAL
PROTECTOR WASHER
FLOATING PISTON
SECONDARY SEALS

Fig. 10   Bendix dual master cylinder disassembled used
with drum brakes (GM and American Motors)

proven, replace the brake warning switch.

Master Cylinder Service

Figs. 9-14 show an array of dual and single master cylinders. With cylinder removed from vehicle, and from brake booster if so equipped, remove the covers and disassemble the unit as suggested by the illustration of the unit being serviced.

When disassembled, wash all parts in alcohol *only*. Use an air hose to blow out all passages, orifices and valve holes. Air dry and place parts on clean paper or lint-free cloth. Inspect master cylinder bore for scoring, rust, pitting or etching. Any of these conditions will require replacement of the housing. Inspect master cylinder pistons for scoring, pitting or distortion. Replace piston if any of these conditions exist.

If either master cylinder housing or piston is replaced, clean new parts with alcohol and blow out all passages with air hose.

Examine reservoirs for foreign matter and check all passages for restrictions. If there is any suspicion of contamination or evidence of corrosion, completely flush hydraulic system as outlined below.

When overhauling a master cylinder, use all parts contained in repair kit. Before starting reassembly, dip all cups, seals, pistons, springs, check valves and retainers in alcohol and place in a clean pan or on clean paper. *Wash hands with soap and water only to prevent contamination of rubber parts from oil, kerosene or gasoline.* During assembly, dip all parts in clean, heavy duty brake fluid.

Inspect through side outlet of dual master cylinder housing to make certain

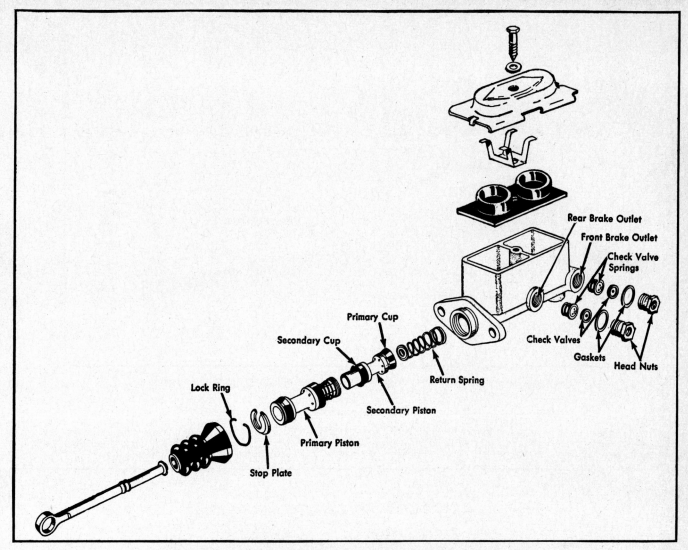

Fig. 12 Wagner dual master cylinder disassembled (Rambler American)

cup lips do not hand up on edge of hole or turn back, which would result in faulty operation. A piece of $3/16''$ rod with an end rounded off will be helpful in guiding cups past hole.

BLEEDING BRAKES

NOTE: Chrysler Corp. recommends only pressure bleeding for all 1967-71 models. Late 1968, all 1969-71 Lincoln Continental and 1970-71 Ford, Mercury, Mark III and Thunderbird with disc brakes must be bled with a pressure bleeder.

The bleeding operation itself is fairly well standardized. First step in all cases is cleaning the dirt from the filler cap before removing it from the master cylinder. This should be done thoroughly.

Pressure bleeding is fastest because the master cylinder doesn't have to be refilled several times, and the job can be done by one man. To prevent air from the pressure tank getting into the lines, do not shake the tank while air is being added to the tank or after it has been pressurized. Set the tank in the required loca-

tion, bring the air hose to the tank, and do not move it during the bleeding operation. The tank should be kept at least one-third full.

NOTE: On late 1968 and all 1969-71 Lincoln Continental and 1970-71 Ford, Mercury, Mark III, and Thunderbird, the metering valve release rod must be pulled outward and held a minimum of $1/16''$ while bleeding the primary brake system. On all prior models, the valve must be pushed inward while bleeding the system.

If air does get into the fluid, releasing the pressure will cause the bubbles to increase in size, rise to the top of the fluid, and escape. Pressure should not be greater than about 35 lb. per sq. in.

When bleeding without pressure, open the bleed valve three-quarters of a turn, depress the pedal a full stroke, then allow the pedal to return slowly to its released position. Some makers suggest that after the pedal has been depressed to the end of its stroke, the bleeder valve should be closed before the start of the return stroke. On cars with power brakes, first reduce the vacuum in the power unit to zero by

pumping the brake pedal several times with the engine off before starting to bleed the system.

Pressure bleeding, of course, eliminates the need for pedal pumping. Chrysler Corp. suggests that, when pressure is used, the bleeder valve should be opened and closed intermittently at about four-second intervals. This gives a whirling action to the fluid in the wheel cylinder, and helps expel the air.

At one time, some car makers recommended that a clean container be used for the drained fluid, so that the fluid could be reused. All now agree that drained fluid should be discarded. Care should be taken not to spill brake fluid, since this can damage the finish of the car.

Flushing is essential if there is water, mineral oil or other contaminants in the lines, and whenever new parts are installed in the hydraulic system. Fluid contamination is usually indicated by swollen and deteriorated cups and other rubber parts.

Wheel cylinders on disc brakes are equipped with bleeder valves, and are bled in the same manner as wheel cylinders for drum brakes.

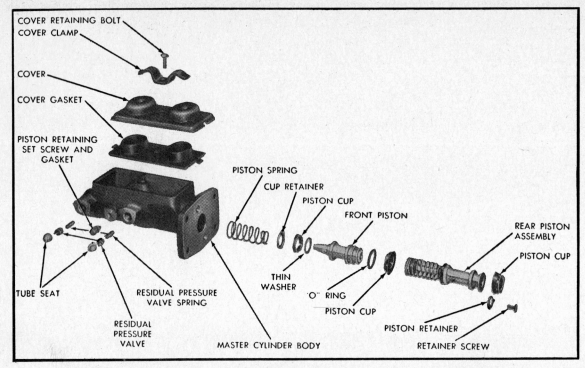

Fig. 11 Bendix dual master cylinder disassembled used with drum brakes (Chrysler line)

Bleeding is necessary on all four wheels if air has entered the system because of low fluid level, or the line or lines have been disconnected. If a line is disconnected at any one wheel cylinder, that cylinder only need be bled. Of course, on brake reline jobs, bleeding is advisable to remove any air or contaminants.

Master cylinders equipped with bleeder valves should be bled first before the wheel cylinders are bled. In all cases where a master cylinder has been overhauled, it must be bled. Where there is no bleeder valve, this can be done by leaving the line (or lines) loose, actuating the brake pedal to expel the air and then tightening the line (or lines).

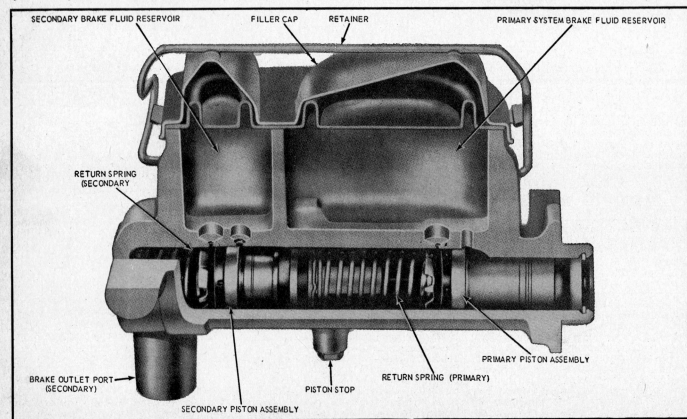

Fig. 13 Cutaway view of Bendix dual master cylinder used with disc brakes (typical)

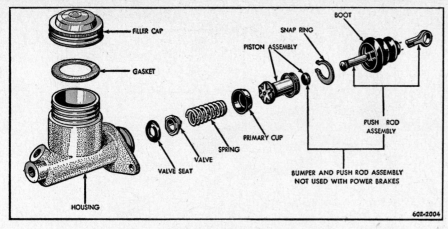

Fig. 14   Typical single brake master cylinder

NOTE: After overhauling a dual master cylinder used in conjunction with disc brakes, it is advisable to bleed the cylinder before installing it on the car. The reason for this recommendation is that air may be trapped between the master cylinder pistons because there is only one residual pressure valve (check valve) used in these units.

The recommended precedure for Chrysler Line cars is as follows:
1. Clamp master cylinder in a vise and attach the special Bleeding Tubes (Tool No. C-4029) Fig. 16. *Be sure that the residual pressure valve is on the end of the tube in the large capacity reservoir as shown. This keeps the brake fluid from being syphoned out of the reservoir while bleeding.*
2. Fill both reservoirs with approved brake fluid.
3. Using a wooden stick or dowel (cars with power brakes) depress push rod slowly and allow the pistons to return under pressure of the springs. Do this several times until all air bubbles are expelled.
4. Remove bleeding tubes from cylinder and install cover and gasket.
5. Install master cylinder on car and bleed wheel cylinders, preferably with a pressure bleeder.

Alternate Method
1. Support assembly in a vise and fill both reservoirs with brake fluid.
2. Loosely install a plug in each outlet port of the cylinder. Depress push rod several times until air bubbles cease to appear in the brake fluid.
3. Tighten plugs and attempt to depress the piston. Piston travel should be restricted after all air is expelled.
4. Install master cylinder on car and bleed wheel cylinders, preferably with a pressure bleeder.

Testing Dual Master Cylinders

Be sure that the master cylinder compensates in both ports. This can be done by applying the brake pedal lightly (engine running with power brakes), and observing for brake fluid squirting up in the reservoirs. This may only occur in the front chamber. To determine if the rear compensating port is open, pump up the brakes rapidly and hold the pedal down. Have an observer watch the fluid in the rear reservoir while the pedal is raised. A disturbance in the fluid indicates that the compensating port is open.

Wheel Bleeding Sequence

Difference of opinion as to whether the longest or shortest line should be bled first still exists. To be safe, use the sequence given below, recommended by the car manufacturers.

Chrysler Corp. cars	RR-LR-RF-LF
Ford Company cars	RR-LR-RF-LF
General Motors cars:	
All except Chevrolet	LF-RF-LR-RR
Chevrolet Division	LR-RR-LF-RF
American Motors	RR-LR-RF-LF

Dual Master Cylinder Bleeding Notes

Ford Motor Co. Cars

After the normal bleeding operation has been completed, note that the brake warning light will be ON because the pressure differential valve has moved off center, and must be returned to the central position. To do this, loosen the valve's inlet tube on the side opposite the wheel cylinder that was bled last. Apply the brake pedal slowly until the warning light goes out, and tighten fitting. Replace any fluid that has leaked out during the operation.

NOTE: 1970-71 cars use a self-centering valve. After any bleeding operation, turn ignition switch to ACC or ON position and depress brake pedal. Valve will center itself.

General Motors Cars

On cars with combined drum and disc brakes, the spring-loaded end of the pressure differential valve must be held in its open position while bleeding. This is done by depressing and holding in the plunger in the end of the valve either by hand or by taping. If pressure bleeding equipment is used, pressure must be below 30 psi.

Corvette

On Corvette models with disc brakes on all four wheels, there are two bleeder valves on each rear wheel disc brake. Remove the rear wheels to bleed. A single valve is used on front disc brakes.

American Motors

Before bleeding brakes, disconnect the switch terminal wire and remove nylon switch terminal, contact plunger actuating spring, and nylon plunger with contact.

In the event the valve has "triggered", the valve centering spring pressure may hold the switch plunger. If this happens, apply a slight amount of brake pedal pressure while releasing the plunger from the valve body.

After the bleeding operation, assemble the plunger spring and install valve with contact down. Install the nylon terminal and connect warning light wire to valve terminal. In the event brake fluid leaks from the center terminal body opening when the terminal is removed, replace the valve assembly.

Chrysler Corp.

Some Chrysler built cars with disc brakes are equipped with front disc

---

Fig. 15   Disassembled view of typical wheel cylinder

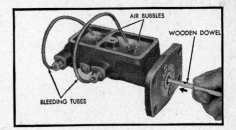

Fig. 16   Bleeding master cylinder used in conjunction with disc brakes

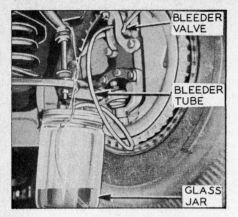

Fig. 17   Bleeding wheel cylinder

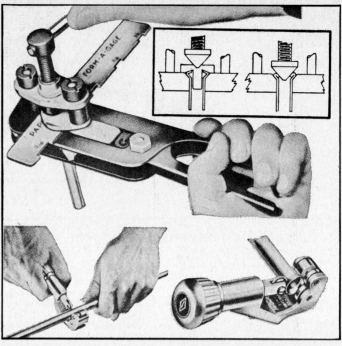

Fig. 18   Flaring hydraulic brake tubing

brake pressure metering valve which is located on the left frame rail directly under the battery.

The purpose of the metering valve is to provide a better match of the front disc brakes with the rear drum brakes, resulting in improved braking balance *in light pedal applications*.

Gravity bleed and pedal methods are not affected by the presence of the metering valve. However, pressure bleeding is influenced by the metering valve.

Bleed pressure, which is normally about 35 psi, is high enough to cause the metering valve to close, which stops the flow of fluid to the front brakes. However, the valve can be held open manually by depressing the pressure release plunger (located at the bottom of the valve) in its uppermost position by hand or secured with masking tape while bleeding the brakes.

CAUTION: Under no conditions should a rigid clamp, wedge or block be used to secure the plunger as this can cause an internal failure in the valve. It should be noted that the pressure release plunger of the valve is already in its uppermost position when there is no pressure present.

WHEEL CYLINDERS

1. Remove wheel, drum and brake shoes.
2. Disconnect hydraulic line at wheel cylinder. *Do not pull metal line away from cylinder as the cylinder connection will bend metal line and make installation difficult. Line will separate from cylinder when cylinder is moved away from brake backing plate.*
3. Remove screws holding cylinder to brake plate and remove cylinder.

Overhaul

1. Referring to Fig. 15 as a guide, remove boots, pistons, springs and cups from cylinder.
2. Place all parts, except cylinder casting in alcohol. Wipe cylinder walls with alcohol.
3. Examine cylinder bore. A scored bore may be honed providing the diameter is not increased more than .005". Replace worn or damaged parts from the repair kit.

4. Before assembling, wash hands with soap and water only as oil, kerosene or gasoline will contaminate rubber parts.
5. Lubricate cylinder wall and rubber cups with brake fluid.
6. Install springs, cups, pistons and boots in housing.
7. Wipe end of hydraulic line to remove any foreign matter.
8. Place hydraulic cylinder in position. Enter tubing into cylinder and start connecting fitting.
9. Secure cylinder to backing plate and then complete tightening of tubing fitting.
10. Install brake shoes, drum and wheel.
11. Bleed system as outlined previously, and adjust brakes.

FLUSHING HYDRAULIC SYSTEM

It may sometime become necessary to flush out the system due to the presence of mineral oil, kerosene, gasoline, etc., which will cause swelling of rubber piston cups and valves so they become inoperative. The procedure is as follows:

1. Attach bleeder tube and open bleeder valve at left front wheel, Fig. 17.
2. Flush out system thoroughly with clean denatured alcohol, pumping the fluid from the master cylinder reservoir and out of the wheel cylinder bleeder valve.
3. Repeat Steps 1 and 2 at remaining wheel cylinders. To ensure thorough flushing, about 1/2 pint of alcohol should be bled through each wheel cylinder.
4. Replace all rubber parts in master and wheel cylinders. Thoroughly clean cylinders and pistons in alcohol before installing new parts.
5. After installing parts, fill system

with recommended brake fluid and flush system of cleaning solution and then bleed brakes. In doing this, pump brake fluid from wheel cylinder bleeder valves until clear fluid flows from bleeder tube and then, if necessary, continue until no air bubbles emerge from bleeder tube.

HYDRAULIC TUBING

Steel tubing is used to conduct hydraulic pressure to the brakes. All fittings, tubing and hose should be inspected for rusted, damaged or defective flared seats. The tubing is equipped with a double flare or inverted seat to insure more positive seating in the fitting. To repair or reflare tubing, proceed as follows:

1. Using the tool shown in Fig. 18 or its equivalent, cut off the damaged seat or damaged tubing.
2. Ream out any burrs or rough edges showing on inside edges of tubing. This will make the ends of the tubing square and insure better seating of the flared end. *Before flaring tubing, place a compression nut on tubing.*
3. Open handles of flaring tool and rotate jaws of tool until mating jaws of tubing size are centered in the area between vertical posts.
4. Slowly close handles with tubing inserted in jaws but do not apply heavy pressure to handle as this will lock tubing in place.
5. Referring to Fig. 18, place gauge on edge over end of tubing and push tubing through jaws until end of tubing contacts recessed notch of gauge matching size of tubing.
6. Squeeze handles of flaring tool and lock tubing in place.
7. Place proper size plug of gauge down in end of tubing. Swing compression

disc over gauge and center tapered flaring screw in recess in disc.

8. Lubricate taper of flaring or screw and screw in until plug gauge has seated in jaws of flaring tool. This

action has started to invert the extended end of tubing.

9. Remove gauge and apply lubricant to tapered end of flaring screw and continue to screw down until tool is firmly

seated in tubing.

10. Remove tubing from flaring tool and inspect the seat. If seat is cracked, cut off cracked end and repeat flaring operation.

DISC BRAKES

CONTENTS

TROUBLE SHOOTING

Excessive Pedal Travel

1. Shoe and lining knock back after violent cornering or rough road travel.
2. Piston and shoe and lining assembly not properly seated or positioned.
3. Air leak or insufficient fluid in system or caliper.
4. Loose wheel bearing adjustment.
5. Damaged or worn caliper piston seal.
6. Improper booster push rod adjustment.
7. Shoe out of flat more than .005".
8. Rear brake automatic adjusters inoperative.
9. Improperly ground rear brake shoe and lining assemblies.

Brake Roughness or Chatter; Pedal Pumping

1. Excessive lateral run-out of rotor.
2. Rotor excessively out of parallel.

Excessive Pedal Effort

1. Frozen or seized pistons.
2. Brake fluid, oil or grease on linings.
3. Shoe and lining worn below specifications.
4. Proportioning valve malfunction.
5. Booster inoperative.
6. Leaking booster vacuum check valve.

Pull, Uneven or Grabbing Brakes

1. Frozen or seized pistons.
2. Brake fluid, oil or grease on linings.
3. Caliper out of alignment with rotor.
4. Loose caliper attachment.
5. Unequalized front tire pressure.
6. Incorrect front end alignment.
7. Lining protruding beyond end of shoe.

Brake Rattle

1. Excessive clearance between shoe and caliper or between shoe and splash shield.
2. Shoe hold-down clips missing or improperly positioned.

Heavy Brake Drag

1. Frozen or seized pistons.
2. Operator riding brake pedal.
3. Incomplete brake pedal return due to linkage interference.
4. Faulty booster check valve holding pressure in hydraulic system.
5. Residual pressure in front brake hydraulic system.

Caliper Brake Fluid Leak

1. Damaged or worn caliper piston seal.
2. Scores in cylinder bore.
3. Corrosion build-up in cylinder bore or on piston surface.
4. Metal clip in seal groove.

No Braking Effect When Pedal is Depressed

1. Piston and shoe and lining assembly not properly seated or positioned.
2. Air leak or insufficient fluid in system or caliper.
3. Damaged or worn caliper piston seal.
4. Bleeder screw open.
5. Air in hydraulic system or improper bleeding.

Rear Brakes Locking On Application

On brake systems equipped with a proportioning or rear pressure regulator valve, should the valve malfunction rear brakes may receive excess pressure, resulting in wheel lock-up.

SERVICE PRECAUTIONS

Brake Lines & Linings

Remove one of the front wheels and inspect the brake disc, caliper and linings. (The wheel bearings should be inspected at this time and repacked if necessary).

Do not get any oil or grease on the linings. If the linings are worn to within .030" of the surface of the shoe, replace both sets of shoe and lining assemblies. It is recommended that both front wheel sets be replaced whenever a respective shoe and lining is worn or damaged. Inspect and, if necessary, replace rear brake linings also.

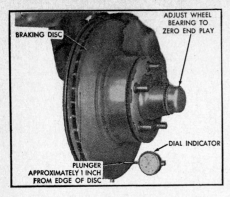

Fig. 1   Checking brake disc for runout

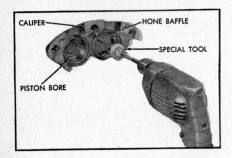

Fig. 2   Honing caliper piston bore

If the caliper is cracked or fluid leakage through the casting is evident, it must be replaced as a unit.

Shoe & Lining Wear

If visual inspection does not adequately determine the condition of the lining, a physical check will be necessary.

To check the amount of lining wear, remove a wheel from the car, the caliper from the steering knuckle, and the shoe and lining assemblies. Three thickness measurements should be taken (with a micrometer) across the middle section of the shoe and lining; one reading at each side and one reading in the center.

When a shoe and lining assembly has worn to a thickness of .180", it should be replaced. If shoes do not require replacement, reinstall them in their original inner and outer positions.

Brake Roughness

The most common cause of brake chatter on disc brakes is a variation in thickness of the disc. If roughness or vibration is encountered during highway operation or if pedal pumping is experienced at low speeds, the disc may have excessive thickness variation. To check for this condition, measure the disc at 12 points with a micrometer at a radius approximately one inch from edge of disc. If thickness measurements vary by more than .0005", the disc should be replaced with a new one.

Excessive lateral runout of braking disc may cause a "knocking back" of the pistons, possibly creating increased pedal travel and vibration when brakes are applied.

Before checking the runout, wheel bearings should be adjusted. The readjustment

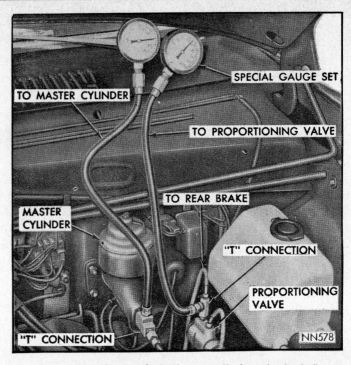

Fig. 3   Gauge hook-up for testing proportioning valve (typical)

is very important and will be required at the completion of the test to prevent bearing failure. Be sure to make the adjustment according to the recommendations given under *Front Wheel Bearings, Adjust* in the car chapters.

Brake Disc Service

Servicing of disc brakes is extremely critical due to the close tolerances required in machining the brake disc to insure proper brake operation. In manufacturing brake discs, tolerances of the rubbing surfaces for flatness is .001" and usually for parallelism .0005". Lateral runout of the faces should not exceed .004 to .005" in most cases although the limit on Ford Company cars in only .002".

The maintenance of these close controls of the shape of the rubbing surfaces is necessary to prevent brake roughness. In addition, the surface finish must be non-directional and maintained at a micro inch finish. This close control of the rubbing surface finish is necessary to avoid pulls and erratic performance and promote long lining life and equal lining wear of both left and right brakes.

In light of the foregoing remarks, refinishing of the rubbing surfaces should not be attempted unless precision equipment, capable of measuring in micro inches (millionths of an inch) is available. This equipment is expensive (about $300.00) and it is safer and less expensive to install a new disc when the runout exceeds the specifications mentioned above.

To check runout of a disc, mount a dial indicator on a convenient part (steering knuckle, tie rod, disc brake caliper housing) so that the plunger of the dial indicator contacts the disc at a point one inch from the outer edge, Fig. 1. If the total indicated runout exceeds specifica-

tions, install a new disc.

General Precautions

1. Grease or any other foreign material must be kept off the caliper, surfaces of the disc and external surfaces of the hub, during service procedures. Handling the brake disc and caliper should be done in a way to avoid deformation of the disc and nicking or scratching brake linings.
2. If inspection reveals rubber piston seals are worn or damaged, they should be replaced immediately.
3. During removal and installation of a wheel assembly, exercise care so as not to interfere with or damage the caliper splash shield, the bleeder screw or the transfer tube.
4. Front wheel bearings should be adjusted to specifications.
5. Be sure vehicle is centered on hoist before servicing any of the front end components to avoid bending or damaging the disc splash shield on full right or left wheel turns.
6. Before the vehicle is moved after any brake service work, be sure to obtain a firm brake pedal.
7. The assembly bolts of the two caliper housings should not be disturbed unless the caliper requires service.

Inspection of Caliper

Should it become necessary to remove the caliper for installation of new parts, clean all parts in alcohol, wipe dry using lint-free cloths. Using an air hose, blow out drilled passages and bores. Check dust boots for punctures or tears. If punctures or tears are evident, new boots should be installed upon reassembly.

Inspect piston bores in both housings for scoring or pitting. Bores that show light scratches or corrosion can usually

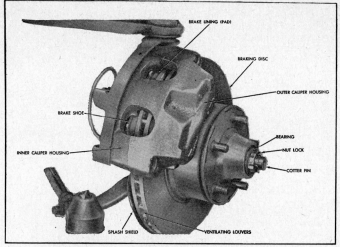

Fig. 4 Bendix opposed piston disc brake

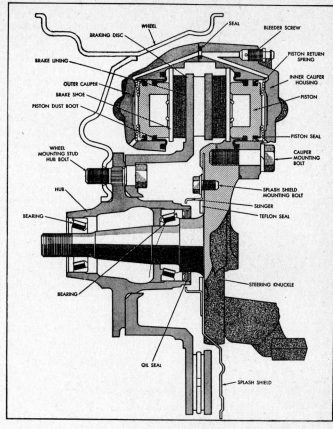

Fig. 5 Sectional view of Bendix opposed piston disc brake

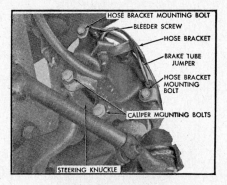

Fig. 6 Caliper mounting

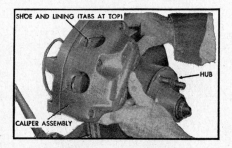

Fig. 7 Removing or installing caliper

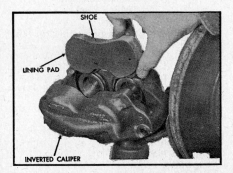

Fig. 8 Removing or installing brake shoe and lining

be cleaned with crocus cloth. However, bores that have deep scratches or scoring may be honed, provided the diameter of the bore is not increased more than .002". If the bore does not clean up within this specification, a new caliper housing should be installed (black stains on the bore walls are caused by piston seals and will do no harm).

When using a hone, Fig. 2, be sure to install the hone baffle before honing bore. The baffle is used to protect the hone stones from damage. Use extreme care in cleaning the caliper after honing. Remove all dust and grit by flushing the caliper with alcohol. Wipe dry with clean lint-less cloth and then clean a second time in the same manner.

Bleeding Disc Brakes

NOTE: Chrysler Corp. recommends only pressure bleeding for all 1967-70 models. Late 1968, and 1969-70 Lincoln Continental and 1970 Ford, Mercury, Mark III and Thunderbird with disc brakes must be bled with a pressure bleeder.

The disc brake hydraulic system can be bled manually or with pressure bleeding equipment (except as noted above). On vehicles with disc brakes the brake pedal will require more pumping and frequent checking of fluid level in master cylinder during bleeding operation.

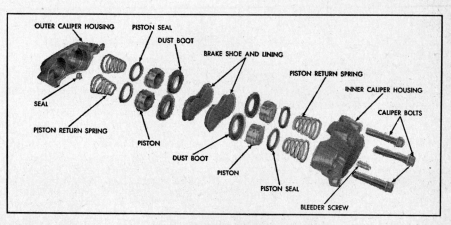

Fig. 9 Exploded view of caliper assembly

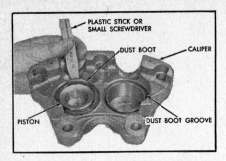

Fig. 10   Removing piston dust boot

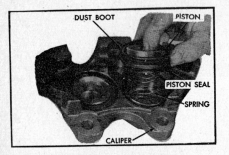

Fig. 11   Removing piston boot, seal and return spring

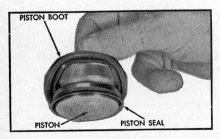

Fig. 12   Removing or installing piston boot

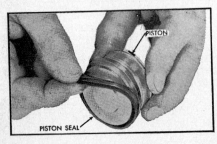

Fig. 13   Removing or installing piston seal

Never use brake fluid that has been drained from hydraulic system when bleeding the brakes. Be sure the disc brake pistons are returned to their normal positions and that the shoe and lining assemblies are properly seated. Before driving the vehicle, check brake operation to be sure that a firm pedal has been obtained.

Proportioning Valve

The proportioning valve (when used),

Fig. 3, provides balanced braking action between front and rear brakes under a wide range of braking conditions. The valve regulates the hydraulic pressure applied to the rear wheel cylinders, thus limiting rear braking action when high pressures are required at the front brakes. In this manner, premature rear wheel skid is prevented.

Testing Proportioning Valve

When a premature rear wheel slide is obtained on a brake application, it usually is an indication that the fluid pressure to the rear wheels is above the 50% reduction ratio for the rear line pressure and that a malfunction has occured within the proportioning valve.

To test the valve, install gauge set shown in Fig. 3 in brake line between master cylinder and proportioning valve, and at output end of proportioning valve and brake line as shown. Be sure all joints are fluid tight.

Have a helper exert pressure on brake pedal (holding pressure). Obtain a reading on master cylinder output of approximately 800 psi. While pressure is being held as above, reading on valve outlet should be 530-570 psi. If the pressure readings do not meet these specifications, the valve should be removed and a new valve installed.

BENDIX OPPOSED PISTONS

The front wheel disc brake, Fig. 4, consists of a fixed caliper (inner and outer housing), two friction pads (brake lining) molded to steel shoes, four pistons, piston return springs, piston seals and dust boots. The brake disc is made from high grade cast iron and has a series of air vent louvers to provide for cooling of the disc. The splash shield that is bolted to the spindle is used to prevent road contaminants from contacting the inboard side of the disc and lining surfaces, Fig. 5. The wheel itself provides for the outboard surface of the disc.

The brake disc is mounted on the front wheel hub by five bolts, and is straddled by the caliper which is attached to the steering knuckle by two bolts. Inserted between the pistons and the disc are the shoe and lining assemblies, which are held in position by parallel machined abutments within the caliper.

Brake Shoe Removal

1. Remove wheel assemblies.
2. Remove caliper-to-steering knuckle bolts, Fig. 6.
3. Remove caliper from disc by sliding it up and away from disc, Fig. 7.
4. Remove brake shoes and lining assemblies one at a time through bottom opening, Fig. 8.

Brake Shoe Installation

1. Referring to Fig. 8, slide shoe and lining assemblies into position in caliper, one at a time, with curved portion (with tabs) entering first and metal shoe against open ends of pistons. Using fingers, spread linings

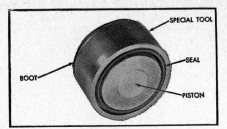

Fig. 14   Piston and seal installing tool

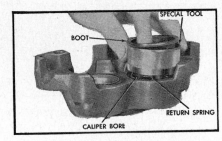

Fig. 15   Installing piston, seal and dust boot

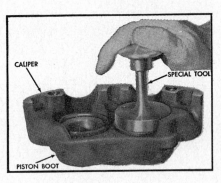

Fig. 16   Installing piston dust boot in caliper groove

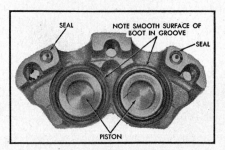

Fig. 17   Pistons and boots installed in caliper

apart until pistons are seated in their bores.
2. Slide caliper down into position over brake disc and align mounting holes. As caliper is being lowered, be sure that lining slides easily along brake disc.
3. Install caliper mounting bolts and torque to 85-90 ft-lbs.
4. Make sure disc rotates freely and with minimum drag.
5. Install wheel assembly.

CAUTION: Road test vehicle and make several heavy 40 mph stops to wear off any foreign material on the brakes and

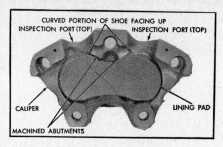

Fig. 18 Shoes and linings correctly positioned in caliper

to seat the linings. The vehicle may pull to one side if this is not done.

Removing Caliper

1. Remove wheels.
2. Disconnect brake line at caliper housing and install a pipe plug in the tube opening.
3. Remove bolts that attach hose bracket to caliper.
4. Remove bolts that attach caliper to steering knuckle.
5. Remove caliper from brake disc by slowly sliding it up and away from disc.

Disassembling Caliper

1. Referring to Fig. 9, drain caliper, then place it in a vise.
2. Separate caliper halves and remove two crossover seals.
3. Using a screwdriver, pry exposed dust boot out of groove, Fig. 10. Be sure to hold piston compressed during this operation.
4. Remove piston, seal and dust boot from caliper, Fig. 11. Remove piston return spring.
5. Remove piston dust boot by grasping edge and pulling out of its groove, Fig. 12.
6. Remove fingers, roll piston seal out of its groove and discard seal, Fig. 13.
7. Remove remaining pistons in same manner.
8. Remove bleeder screw from inner caliper.

Assembling Caliper

1. Clamp caliper housing in vise and coat cylinder bores with silicone

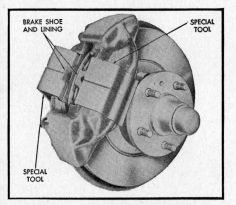

Fig. 20 Piston compression tools installed

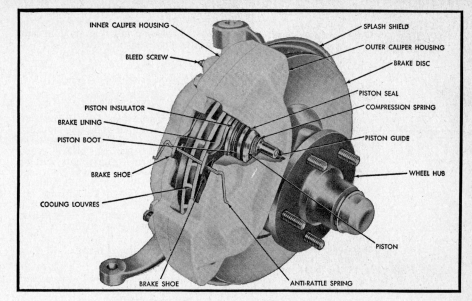

Fig. 19 Budd opposed piston Dics Brake assembly

grease, then install piston return spring with large diameter down and seated in recess at bottom of bore.
2. Coat outside diameter and fill inner diameter of a new piston seal with silicone grease and work over piston land and down into position in groove, using fingers only.
3. Install dust boot on piston with lip of seat toward piston.
4. Using a suitable tapered sleeve, Fig. 14, install piston, seal and boot in sleeve, with lip of seal towards taper. Push in on assembly until seal lip is even with knife edge of sleeve, Fig. 14.

5. Place installing tool over bore opening and return spring. Index with boot in caliper, Fig. 15. Press down on piston, sliding piston out of tool and into caliper bore until bottomed. Remove sleeve tool.
6. Position piston boot sealing lip over groove evenly. Using the tool shown in Fig. 16 or its equivalent, press down on tool, forcing boot sealing lip into caliper groove. Remove tool and install remaining pistons in same manner, Fig. 17.
7. Test pistons for smooth operation in their bores by depressing with fingers.

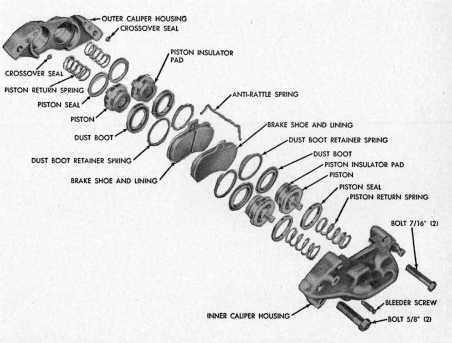

Fig. 21 Budd disc brake caliper disassembled

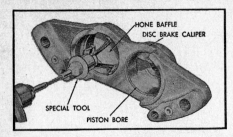

Fig. 22   Honing piston bore

8. Lightly clamp outer caliper half in vise and install new crossover passage seals in position in recess of caliper mating surface, Fig. 17.
9. Place mating caliper half over one clamped in vise, install attaching bolts and torque to 120-140 ft-lbs.
10. Install brake shoes in caliper with curved portion (with tabs) entering first and metal shoe against open ends of pistons. Using fingers, spread linings apart until pistons are seated in their bores, Fig. 18.
11. Install bleeder screw and tighten lightly.

Installing Caliper

1. Check runout of brake disc with dial indicator as outlined previously.
2. Install caliper over disc and align mounting holes. Install bolts and torque to 85-90 ft-lbs. (as caliper is being lowered into place, be sure that linings ride freely over disc.)
3. Connect brake line at caliper housing, then position brake hose bracket. Install bracket and attaching bolts and tighten securely.
4. Follow normal bleeding procedure, being sure all air bubbles have escaped.

5. Replenish brake fluid in master cylinder.
6. Install wheels and road test as suggested previously.

BUDD OPPOSED PISTONS

The Budd Disc brake, Fig. 19, consists of a fixed caliper (inner and outer housing) two friction pads (brake lining) bonded to steel shoes, four pistons, piston return springs, piston seals, dust boots and retainers. The brake disc is made from high grade cast iron and has a series of air vent louvers to provide cooling for the brake aseembly. The splash shield has a series of stamped vents so designed as to supply additional air for cooling.

Removing Lining

1. Remove wheels.
2. Remove brake shoe anti-rattle spring.
3. Slide piston compression tools, Fig. 20, between brake shoes and piston insulator and snap in place. This will hold pistons in a retracted position during removal and installation of brake lining units.
4. Remove bolts that attach caliper assembly to steering knuckle and knuckle arm.
5. Slowly slide caliper up and away from brake shoe.
6. Carefully invert caliper and remove brake shoe assembly (one at a time).

Installing Lining

1. Slide brake disc shoe and lining assembly into position in caliper (one at a time).
2. Slide caliper down into position over brake disc and align mounting holes.
3. Install caliper mounting bolts and

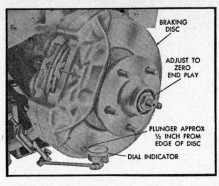

Fig. 23   Checking brake disc for runout

torque to 65 ft-lbs.
4. Remove piston compression tools.
5. Install wheels.

CAUTION: Road test vehicle and apply several heavy 40 mph stops to wear off any foreign material on brakes and to seat units. The vehicle may pull to one side or the other if this is not done. This condition will be more noticeable if only one wheel was worked on.

Removing Caliper

1. Remove wheels.
2. Slide piston compression tools, Fig. 20, between brake shoes and piston pads and snap in place.
3. Disconnect brake line at caliper housing and install a 1/8" pipe plug.
4. Unfasten caliper and slowly slide it up and away from brake disc.

Disassembling Caliper

1. Referring to Fig. 21, remove piston compression tools and four bolts that hold two halves of caliper together.
2. Separate halves and remove two crossover seals.
3. Using a small screwdriver, pry out exposed end of piston dust boot retainer spring and uncoil from its groove to release dust boot.
4. Using same screwdriver, work dust boot out of groove. Be sure to hold piston compressed during this operation.
5. Remove piston, seal and dust boot from caliper. Remove piston return spring.
6. Remove piston dust boot by grasping edge and pulling out of its groove.

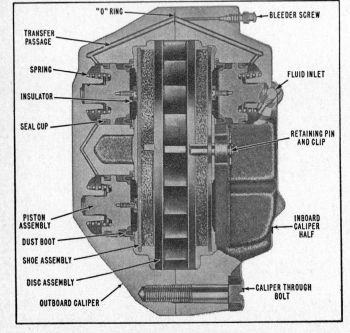

Fig. 24   Delco-Moraine disc brake assembly

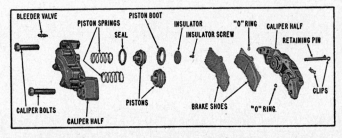

Fig. 27   Delco-Moraine disc brake caliper components

Fig. 25   Installing Delco-Moraine disc brake shoes

7. Pry piston seal out of its groove and discard.
8. Remove remaining three pistons in same manner.
9. Remove bleeder screw from inner caliper housing.

Cleaning & Inspection

1. Clean all parts in brake fluid and wipe dry. Using an air hose, blow out drilled passages and bores.
2. Check dust boots for punctures and tears. If punctures or tears are evident, new boots should be installed.
3. Inspect piston bores in both housings for scoring or pitting. Bores that show light scratches or corrosion can usually be cleaned with crocus cloth. However, bores that have deep scratches or scoring may be honed, Fig. 22, providing the diameter of bore is not increased more than .002". If the bore does not clean up within this specification, a new caliper housing must be installed. Black stains on bore walls are caused by the piston seals and will do no harm.
4. When honing, Fig. 22, be sure to install the hone baffle before honing bore. The baffle is used to protect hone stones from damage.
5. Use extreme care in cleaning the caliper after honing. Remove all dust and grit by flushing caliper with brake fluid. Wipe dry with clean, lintless cloth and then clean a second time in like manner.

Assembling Caliper

1. Referring to Fig. 21, clamp caliper in a vise, then install piston return spring. Be sure spring is seated in recess in bottom of bore.
2. Coat outside diameter and fill inner diameter of a new piston seal with silicone grease and work over piston land and down into position in groove, using fingers only.
3. Install dust boot on piston with lip of boot toward piston pad.
4. Install piston over return spring and press down until piston bottoms in bore.
5. Using a small, blunt screwdriver, work lip of boot into groove, around diameter of bore. Use care so as not to puncture boot during this operation, or a new boot will have to be installed.

6. Install coil spring by inserting one end in position in groove and continue to install around diameter of bore until retainer is fully seated. Be sure boot is completely locked in position by retainer and that retainer is fully seated in groove.
7. Install remaining pistons in same manner, then test pistons for smooth operation in their bores by depressing with fingers.
8. Install piston compression tool over each caliper half to hold pistons in retracted position.
9. Install new crossover passage seals in recess of caliper mating surface.
10. Install brake shoe in caliper and place mating caliper half over one clamped in vise.
11. Install attaching bolts and torque to 55 ft-lbs (7/16") and 150 ft-lbs for 1/2" bolts.
12. Install bleeder screw but do not tighten.

Installing Caliper

1. Before installing caliper over disc, check disc for runout with a dial gauge as shown in Fig. 23. Lateral runout should not exceed .003"; if runout is excessive, remove disc and check its mounting surface on wheel hub. Runout of hub should not exceed .004".
2. Install caliper over disc and torque 7/16" bolts to 65 ft-lbs, and 150 ft-lbs for 1/2" bolts. Remove piston compression tools.
3. Connect brake line at caliper housing and allow caliper to fill with brake fluid then close bleeder screw. Be sure all air bubbles have escaped when bleeding the caliper. Replenish brake fluid in master cylinder.
4. Install wheels and road test vehicle as outlined previously.

DELCO-MORAINE OPPOSED PISTONS

These brakes are used on all four

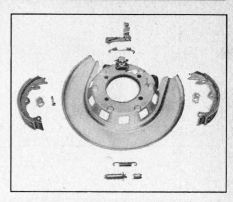

Fig. 26   Delco-Moraine parking brake components

wheels. The components of the disc brake system are shown in Fig. 24. The caliper assemblies replace the conventional wheel cylinder, brake shoes and linings, and the disc replaces the brake drum.

The caliper assembly contains four pistons, two acting on each shoe with one shoe on each side of the disc.

The brake disc is riveted to the hub flange at the front wheel and to the spindle flange at the rear wheel. The disc rotates through the caliper assembly, which is bolted to a support that is attached to the steering knuckle at the front wheel and the spindle support bolts at the rear wheel. The disc has cooling fins between the two shoe reacting surfaces. When a disc must be replaced, the rivets can be drilled out and then the wheel studs will be used for disc retention purposes.

A miniature set of brake shoes, mounted on a flange plate and shield assembly attached to the rear wheel spindle support bolts, are used for vehicle parking, Fig. 25.

Brake Shoes, Replace

To avoid overflow of the master cylinder reservoir, the manufacturer recommends removing only about two-thirds of the fluid in the reservoir when replacing

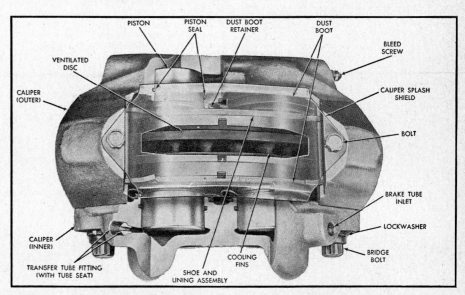

Fig. 28   Kelsey-Hayes opposed piston disc brake

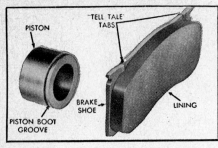

Fig. 29 Brake piston, shoe and lining assembly

Fig. 30 Removing brake shoe and lining

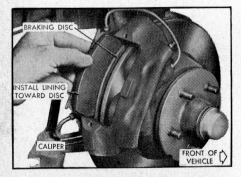

Fig. 31 Installing brake shoe and lining

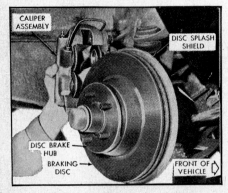

Fig. 32 Replacing brake disc caliper

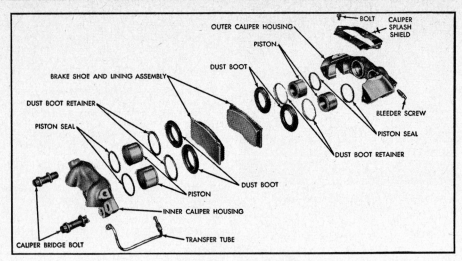

Fig. 33 Caliper disassembled

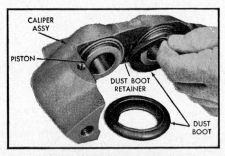

Fig. 34 Removing dust boot from piston and caliper

brake shoe pads.

If all the hydraulic fluid is removed, as previously directed, air can enger the master cylinder when pistons are moved toward the discs, making it necessary to bleed the system.

When replacing brake shoes, Fig. 25, siphon about two-thirds of the brake fluid from the master cylinder (see above) and remove the wheel assembly. Then remove the shoe guide pin and clip after which the shoes can be lifted out.

Before the new shoes can be replaced, the cylinder pistons must be pushed back into their bores and retained with a thin clip to allow clearance for the new shoes to be installed. Pushing the pistons back into the cylinders causes the brake fluid to be forced backward into the master cylinder reservoir. The amount of brake fluid pushed back would overflow the master cylinder, causing fluid spillage around the engine fire wall.

Calipers

The caliper assembly, Fig. 27 comes in two halves assembled by strong bolts at the flange end. The two halves contain fluid crossover passages from one to the other, sealed with "O" rings.

The bleeder screw is threaded into a passage drilled to intersect the fluid crossover passage. The bleeder screws are located at the front of each caliper. There are two bleeder screws, one inboard, one outboard at the rear wheels, and one bleeder screw at the inboard side at the front wheel. It is necessary, therefore, to remove the rear wheel when bleeding the rear caliper.

Service Summary

1. There is no brake shoe adjustment on the disc brakes.
2. The groove in the brake shoe is an indicator of brake wear. When the groove is just about gone it is time for shoe replacement.
3. When replacing shoes it is necessary to siphon fluid from master cylinder reservoir to make room for fluid return to the reservoir when pushing the caliper pistons back into their bores to make room for the thickness of the new shoes.
4. The shoes have a directional arrow on the back of the shoe plate. This arrow points to the forward rotation of the disc, and the purpose is for aligning the grain of the lining material in relation to the disc.
5. When bleeding the calipers, the rear wheel must be removed to reach the outboard bleeder screw.
6. A retaining clip of thin metal is used to hold the pistons into the bores while installing the new brake shoes.
7. The caliper assembly is removable, after disconnecting the brake line, by removing the two mounting bolts and lifting the assembly off the disc.
8. The disc is riveted to the spindle flange in production. However, the rivets may be drilled out and the wheel studs and nuts are sufficient to hold the new disc in place when replacing the disc.
9. The rear wheel spindle must be removed to gain access to the parking brake shoes. It is necessary then to remove the caliper, the axle drive shaft, the spindle drive shaft yoke and remove the spindle and disc as an assembly from the wheel support. You now have access to the parking brake shoes the same as any other conventional bendix type brake shoe, Fig. 26.
10. If the car is equipped with the special optional knock-off hub assemblies, the adapters must be removed to gain access to the parking brake adjustment.

KELSEY-HAYES OPPOSED PISTON TYPE BRAKE

This type brake, Fig. 28, is a fixed cali-

Fig. 35   Removing pistons from caliper

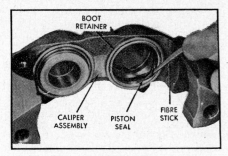

Fig. 36   Removing piston seals
from caliper

per, opposed piston, non-energized, ventilated type, actuated by the hydraulic system. There is no lateral movement of either the disc or the caliper. The caliper assembly consists of two caliper housings bolted together. Each half contains two cylinder bores. Each cylinder contains a seal, piston and externally attached molded rubber dust boot to seal the cylinder bore from contamination. The pistons are sealed by rubber piston seals hositioned in grooves machined in the cylinder bores which provide hydraulic seaing between pistons and cylinder bores.

An additional feature of this brake system is a "tell-tale" tab sounding device which indicates when replacement of the shoe and lining assemblies are required, Fig. 29. The tabs on the shoes create an audible metallic scraping noise from the brake by metal-to-metal contact on the braking disc. This warns the driver that the lining has worn to a minimum thickness, at which time it should be replaced.

Checking Running Clearance

To check the lining-to-disc running clearance, remove wheel and caliper splash shield. Insert a feeler gauge between lining and disc. Clearance ordinarily should be .003-.006". However, if the vehicle was stopped by a brake application just prior to checking the clearance, it is considered normal for the brakes to drag slightly.

Brake Shoe Replace

1. Raise vehicle on hoist or stands.
2. Remove wheel assembly.

3. Remove caliper splash shield and anti-rattle spring.
4. Using two pairs of pliers, grasp tabs on outer ends of shoes and remove shoe and lining by pulling outward, Fig. 30.

NOTE: Due to a ridge of rust that may have formed on the disc surface outside of lining contact area, it may be necessary to force the piston back slightly into its bore. This is done by forcing the shoe back with water pump pliers placed on corner of shoe and caliper housing as shown, Fig. 30.

Installation
1. Push all pistons back into their bores until bottomed to allow for installation of new shoes. This can be done by placing a flat-sided metal bar against piston and exerting a steady force until bottomed.
2. Slide new shoe and lining into caliper with ears of shoe resting on bridges of caliper, Fig. 31. Be sure shoe is fully seated and lining is facing disc.
3. Slide remaining shoe and lining into caliper, using same procedure as above.
4. Place caliper splash shield and anti-rattle spring in position on caliper and install attaching bolts securely.
5. Pump brake pedal several times until a firm pedal has been obtained and shoe and linings have been properly seated.
6. Install wheel. Replenish master cylinder fluid as required.

CAUTION: Road test vehicle and make several heavy 40 m.p.h. stops to wear off any foreign material on the brakes and to seat the units. The vehicle may pull to one side or the other if this is not done. It should not be necessary to bleed the system after replacing linings.

Servicing Caliper

Removal
1. Raise car on hoist or stands.
2. Remove wheel assembly.
3. Disconnect front brake flexible hose from brake tube at frame mounting bracket. Plug tube to prevent loss of fluid.
4. Remove bolts that attach caliper to steering knuckle.

NOTE: Should it become necessary to install a new flexible brake hose, scribe a mark on hose bracket on side where hose enters, and position of hose retaining clip underneath. When reassembling, be sure open end of retaining clip is facing out an away from caliper.

5. Slowly slide caliper up and away from brake disc, Fig. 32.

Disassembly
1. Referring to Fig. 33, remove splash shield and anti-rattle spring.
2. Remove jumper tube at caliper.
3. Mount caliper in a vise with soft jaws and remove transfer tube.
4. Remove shoe and lining units.

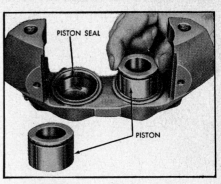

Fig. 37   Installing piston in caliper

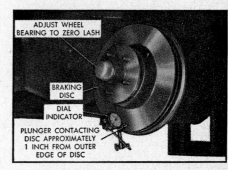

Fig. 38   Checking brake disc runout

5. Remove bridge bolts and separate caliper halves.
6. Peel dust boot out and away from caliper housing retainer and out of piston groove, Fig. 34. Remove remaining boots in same manner.
7. Using Tool C-3999, remove each piston, Fig. 35.

CAUTION: Care must be used so as not to scratch, burr or otherwise damage piston on outside diameter. To do so effects sealing qualities of piston. Draw piston straight out of its bore. If a piston becomes cocked, removal is more difficult and piston or bore may be damaged.

8. Using a small pointed wooden or plastic tool, remove piston seals from grooves in cylinder bore, Fig. 36. Discard old seals.

Assembling Caliper
1. Clamp inner caliper half in a vise (with protector jaws) by mounting lugs.
2. If it was necessary to install a new dust boot retainer ring, contact area on housing should be cleaned and Loctite Sealant Grade H (or equivalent) applied to retainer ring on surface where it seats in housing, then install retainer ring.
3. Dip new piston seals in brake fluid and install in caliper grooves. Seal should be positioned at one area in groove and gently worked around cylinder bore with a finger until properly seated. *Be sure seals are not twisted or rolled.*
4. Coat outside diameter of pistons with brake fluid and install them in cylinder bores, Fig. 37, with open end of piston and boot retaining groove facing out of cylinder.
5. Position piston squarely in bore and

Fig. 39   Single piston disc brake (typical)

apply slow steady pressure. *If piston will not position itself, remove it and check seal for proper position in groove.*

6. Install new dust boot over caliper retaining ring and in piston groove. Install remaining boots in same manner.

7. Install caliper half on one clamped in vise. Assemble with bridge bolts and torque to 70-80 ft-lbs.

CAUTION: Under no circumstances should the bridge bolts be substituted or replaced by inferior bolts as this could cause caliper failure, resulting in an accident.

8. Install and tighten transfer tube.
9. Install bleeder screw loosely.

Installation

1. Before installing caliper, check brake disc for runout. Mount a dial indicator as shown in Fig. 38 and check lateral runout, which should not exceed .0025". If runout is excessive, install

a new disc. *Be sure wheel bearings are adjusted to zero end play during this check. Readjust wheel bearings after checking runout.*

2. Install caliper over disc. Install mounting bolts and torque as indicated:

Dodge & Plymouth:
1966-68 . . . . . . .45-60 ft-lbs.
1969-70 . . . . . . .50-80 ft-lbs.

Ford & Mercury:
1966 . . . . .90-115 ft-lbs.
1967 . . . . .120-130 ft-lbs.

Lincoln Continental:
1966 . . . . .90-115 ft-lbs.
1967 . . . . .120-130 ft-lbs.

Mustang:
1966-67 . . . . . .45-60 ft-lbs.

T-Bird:
1966 . . . . .90-115 ft-lbs.
1967 . . . . .120-130 ft-lbs.

Toronado:
1967 . . . . .54 ft-lbs.
1968 . . . . .165 ft-lbs.

NOTE: A check should be made to be sure that brake disc runs squarely and centrally within caliper opening. There should be .090" to .120" clearance between outside diameter of disc and caliper. There should also be a minimum of .050" from either disc face to machined groove in outboard caliper.

3. Install shoe and lining units.
4. Install caliper splash shield.
5. Open bleeder screw, then connect brake line to caliper housing. Allow caliper to fill with brake fluid, then close bleeder screw. Be sure all air bubbles have escaped when bleeding caliper. Replenish fluid in master cylinder.
6. Pump brake pedal several times to actuate piston seals and to position linings.
7. Road test vehicle as outlined previously.

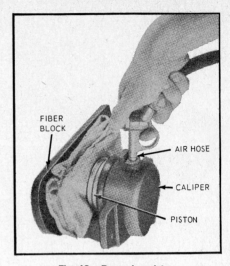

Fig. 42   Removing piston with air pressure

KELSEY-HAYES SINGLE PISTON TYPE

This type brake is a floating caliper, single piston, ventilated unit, actuated by the hydraulic system, Fig. 39. The caliper assembly, Fig. 40, is made up of a floating caliper assembly and an anchor plate. The anchor plate is bolted to the wheel spindle arm by two bolts. The caliper is attached to the anchor plate through two spring steel stabilizers. The caliper slides on two guide pins which also attach to the stabilizers. A single piston is used. The cylinder bore contains a piston with a molded rubber dust boot to seal the cylinder bore from contamination and also to return the piston to the released position when hydraulic pressure is released. Also a rubber piston seal is used to provide sealing between cylinder and piston.

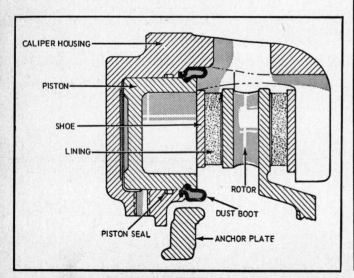
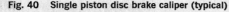

Fig. 40   Single piston disc brake caliper (typical)

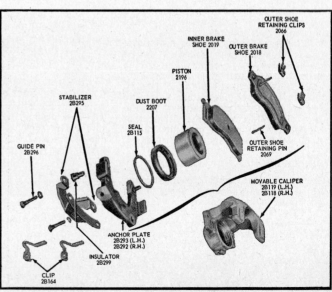

Fig. 41   Single piston disc brake caliper disassembled (typical)

Service Precautions

In addition to the precautions described at the beginning of this chapter, the following must be observed.
1. If the piston is removed for any reason the piston seal must be replaced.
2. During removal and installation of a wheel assembly, use care not to interfere with and damage the caliper splash shield or the bleeder screw fitting.
3. Be sure the vehicle is centered on the hoist before servicing any front end components to avoid bending or damaging the rotor splash shield on full right or left wheel turns.
4. The proportioning valve should not be disassembled or adjustments attempted on it.
5. The wheel and tire must be removed separately from the brake rotor.
6. The caliper assembly must be removed from the spindle prior to removal of shoe and lining assembly.
7. Do not attempt to clean or restore oil or grease soaked brake linings. When contaminated linings are found, linings must be replaced in complete axle sets.

Remove & Disassemble Caliper

1. Raise vehicle and remove front wheels.
2. On Mark III and Mercury models, remove inboard shoe hold down clips and slide outer retaining clips from shoe retaining pins, Fig. 41.
3. Disconnect brake line.
4. Remove guide pins and bolts, if necessary, and remove caliper assembly from stabilizer.
5. Lift caliper away from disc.
6. Slide shoes and lining assemblies out of caliper.
7. Remove guide pin insulators from anchor plate.

NOTE: If necessary to remove the piston, apply air pressure to the fluid port in the caliper, Fig. 42, to remove the piston. Place a cloth over the piston to prevent damage to the piston. If the piston is seized and cannot be forced from the caliper, tap lightly around the piston before applying air pressure. Care should be taken because the piston can develop considerable force due to pressure build-up.

8. Remove dust boot from caliper.
9. Remove rubber piston seal from cylinder and discard it.

Assemble & Install Caliper

1. Apply a film of clean brake fluid to the new caliper piston seal and install it in cylinder bore. Be sure seal does not become twisted and that it is seated fully in the groove.
2. Install a new dust boot by setting the flange squarely in the outer groove of the caliper bore.
3. Coat piston with brake fluid and install in cylinder bore. Spread dust boot over piston as it is installed. Seat dust boot in piston groove.
4. Position inner brake shoe so that ears of shoe rests on top of anchor plate bosses and beneath hold-down springs.

5. Install new caliper guide pin insulators in anchor plate.
6. Position caliper on anchor plate.
7. Install guide pins loosely in anchor plate, being sure guide pins are free of oil, grease or dirt.
8. Install caliper on spindle.

Brake Shoes & Linings, Install

NOTE: When new shoe and lining assemblies are being installed to replace worn linings it will be necessary to push the piston all the way into the caliper bore. This will displace fluid from the caliper into the master cylinder reservoir. Check the primary (front) brake system reservoir level and remove fluid to approximately half full before replacing brake shoes. This will prevent overflow. Do not reuse the removal fluid.

1. Install new caliper guide pin insulators in anchor plate.
2. Position caliper in anchor plate.
3. Install caliper guide pins loosely in anchor plate, being sure they are free of oil, grease or dirt.
4. Position outer brake shoe on caliper and install two retaining pins and clips.
5. Install inner brake shoe so that ears of shoe are on top of anchor plate bosses and under shoe hold-down springs.
6. Position shoe and lining assemblies so that caliper can be placed over rotor. Rotate hammer handle between linings to provide proper clearance.
7. Install caliper over rotor and on spindle. Install and tighten the two caliper bolts, tightening the upper bolt first. Install safety wire and twist ends at least five turns. With moderate pres-

sure applied to brake pedal, tighten stabilizer attaching screws and caliper guide pins.

DELCO-MORAINE SINGLE PISTON

The caliper, Fig. 43, is constructed from a single casting which contains one large piston bore in the inboard section of the casting. The fluid inlet hole and bleeder valve hole are machined into the inboard section of the caliper and connect directly to the piston bore.

The caliper is free to slide on its mounting bolts. Upon application, fluid pressure against the piston forces the inboard shoe and lining against the inboard side of the disc. This action causes the caliper assembly to slide on its mounting bolts until the outboard lining comes into contact with the disc. As pressure builds up, the linings are pressed against the disc with increased force.

Caliper Removal

1. Siphon enough brake fluid out of the master cylinder to bring fluid level to 1/3 full to avoid fluid overflow when the caliper piston is pushed back into its bore.
2. Raise vehicle and remove front wheels.
3. Using a "C" clamp, as illustrated in Fig. 44, push piston back into its bore.
4. Remove two mounting bolts and lift caliper away from disc.

Brake Shoe Removal

1. Remove caliper assembly as outlined above.
2. Remove inboard shoe. Dislodge out-

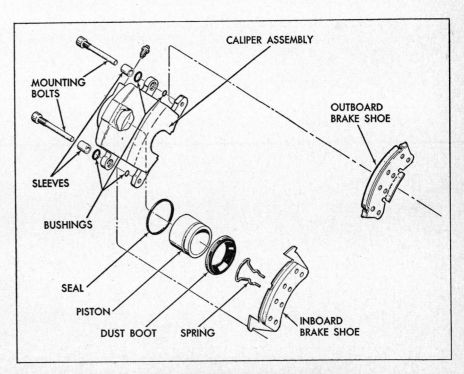

Fig. 43 Single piston caliper. Exploded

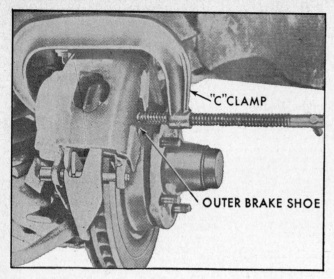

Fig. 44   Compressing piston and shoes with "C" clamp

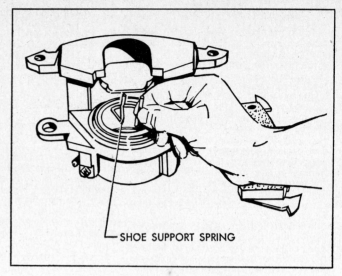

Fig. 45   Installing support spring

board shoe and position caliper on the front suspension so the brake hose will not support the weight of the caliper.
3. Remove shoe support spring from piston.
4. Remove two sleeves from inboard ears of the caliper.
5. Remove four rubber bushings from the grooves in each of the caliper ears.

Brake Shoe Installation

1. Lubricate new sleeves, rubber bushings, bushing grooves and mounting bolt ends with Delco Silicone Lube or its equivalent.
2. Install new bushings and sleeves in caliper ears.

NOTE: Position the sleeve so that the end toward the shoe is flush with the machined surface of the ear.

3. Install shoe support spring in piston cavity, Fig. 45.
4. Position inboard shoe in caliper so spring ends centrally contact shoe edge. Initially, this will place the shoe on an angle. Push upper edge of shoe down until shoe is flat against caliper. When properly seated, spring ends will not extend past shoe more than .100".
5. Position outboard shoe in caliper with shoe ears over caliper ears and tab at bottom of shoe engaged in caliper

cutout.
6. With shoes installed, lift caliper and rest bottom edge of outboard lining on outer edge of brake disc to be sure there is no clearance between outboard shoe tab and caliper abutment.
7. Using a $\frac{1}{4}$" x 1" x $2\frac{1}{2}$" metal bar to bridge caliper cutout, clamp outboard shoe to caliper with a "C" clamp.
8. Bend both ears of outboard shoe over caliper until clearance between shoe ear and caliper (measured at both the edge and side of the caliper) is .005" or less, Fig. 46.
9. Remove "C" clamp and install caliper.

Disassembling Caliper

1. Remove caliper as outlined above.
2. Disconnect hose from steel line, remove U shaped retainer and withdraw hose from frame support bracket.

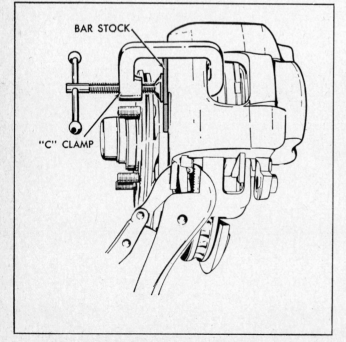

Fig. 46   Fitting shoe to caliper

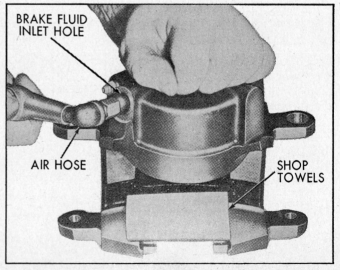

Fig. 47   Removing piston from caliper

Fig. 48   Installing boot to piston

3. After cleaning outside of caliper, remove brake hose and discard copper gasket.
4. Drain brake fluid from caliper.
5. Pad caliper interior with clean shop towels and use compressed air to remove piston, Fig. 47.

NOTE: Use just enough air pressure to east piston out of bore. Do not blow piston out of bore.

CAUTION: Do not place fingers in front of piston in an attempt to catch or protect it when applying compressed air. This could result in serious injury.

6. Carefully pry dust boot out of bore.
7. Using a small piece of wood or plastic, remove piston seal from bore.

NOTE: Do not use a metal tool of any kind to remove seal as it may damage bore.

8. Remove bleeder valve.

Assembling Caliper

1. Lubricate caliper piston bore and new piston seal with clean brake fluid. Position seal in bore groove.
2. Lubricate piston with clean brake fluid and assemble a new boot into the groove in the piston so the fold faces the open end of the piston, Fig. 48.
3. Using care not to unseat the seal, insert piston into bore and force the piston to the bottom of the bore.
4. Position dust boot in caliper counterbore and install, Fig. 49.

NOTE: Check the boot installation to be sure the retaining ring moulded into the boot is not bent and that the boot is installed below the caliper face and evenly all around. If the boot is not fully installed, dirt and moisture may enter the bore and cause corrosion.

5. Install the brake hose in the caliper

using a new copper gasket.
6. Install shoes and re-install caliper assembly.

Caliper Installation

1. Position caliper over disc, lining up holes in caliper with holes in mounting bracket. If brake hose was not disconnected during removal, be sure not to kink it during installation.
2. Start mounting bolts through sleeves in inboard caliper ears and the mounting bracket, making sure ends of bolts pass under ears on inboard shoe.

NOTE: Right and left calipers must not be interchanged.

3. Push mounting bolts through to engage holes in the outboard ears. Then thread mounting bolts into bracket.
4. Torque mounting bolts to 30-40 ft. lbs.
5. If brake hose was removed, reconnect it and bleed the calipers.
6. Replace front wheels, lower vehicle and add brake fluid to master cylinder to bring level to $\frac{1}{4}$" from top.

NOTE: Before moving vehicle, pump brake pedal several times to be sure it is firm. Do not move vehicle until a firm pedal is obtained.

FORD CENTER ABUTMENT TYPE

This is a single piston, sliding caliper

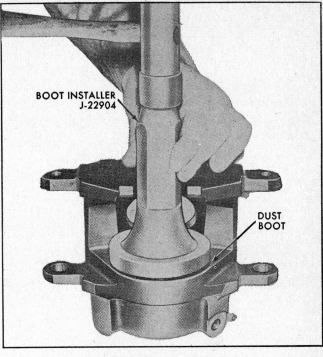

Fig. 49   Installing boot to caliper

type brake but instead of the torque being taken by the caliper assembly, it is transmitted directly to the U-shaped anchor plate. The caliper housing performs only the necessary clamping action against the disc, Fig. 50.

Caliper Removal

NOTE: Siphon a portion of the brake fluid from the larger master cylinder reservoir before servicing unit.

1. Remove wheel and tire and remove cotter pins from caliper support key.
2. Using a drift and a light hammer, remove caliper support key, being careful to avoid damaging key or machined surfaces, Fig. 51.
3. Rotate lower end of caliper housing toward the rear and upward and remove caliper from anchor plate. It is not necessary to disconnect hydraulic line for this operation.
4. Suspend caliper housing with wire or lay caliper on support strut. Do not let caliper hang by its own weight from hydraulic line.

Caliper Disassembly

1. With caliper removed as described previously, disconnect brake hose. Cap hose and plug caliper inlet to prevent fluid loss.
2. With caliper on work bench, remove inlet plug and drain fluid from housing.
3. Position caliper as in Fig. 52, and place shop cloths as shown.
4. Apply air pressure slowly to caliper inlet port to remove piston.

NOTE: If high pressure is applied quickly, piston may pop out and cause injury. A cocked or seized piston can be eased out by rapping sharply on piston end with a soft brass hammer.

5. Remove boot from piston and seal from caliper cylinder bore, Fig. 53.

Caliper Overhaul

1. Remove any rust or corrosion from machined surfaces of caliper housing.
2. Clean housing and piston with iso-propyl alcohol. Clean and dry out grooves and passages with compressed air. Make sure cylinder bore is free of all foreign material.
3. Check cylinder bore, seal groove and piston for wear or damage. Replace piston if pitted or worn.
4. Remove any rust or corrosion from machined surfaces of anchor plate still mounted on car and inspect plate for damage.
5. Inspect anti-rattle clips for damage. Clips should have four tabs, Fig. 53, and a looped type spring. Replace any damaged parts.

Brake Shoe and Lining, Replace

1. Remove caliper housing as outlined previously.

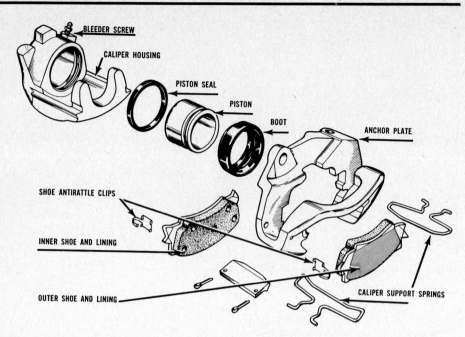

Fig. 50   Center abutment disc brake exploded

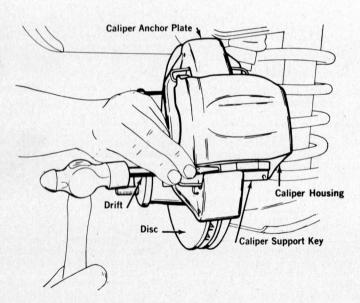

Fig. 51   Removing caliper support key

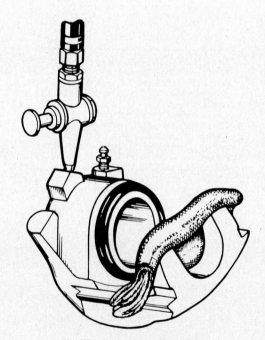

Fig. 52   Removing caliper piston with air pressure

Fig. 53   Caliper piston assembly

2. As shoe and lining assemblies are now exposed, tilt upper edge of shoes away from disc and then take out shoe and lining assemblies, Fig. 54. Shoes are identical and interchangeable.
3. Take three thickness & measurements of each shoe and lining with a micrometer.
4. If there is less than .030" of lining above rivet heads, replace shoes on both front wheels.

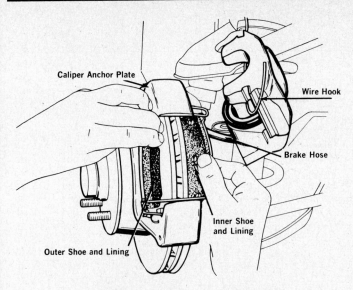

Fig. 54   Removing shoe and lining assemblies

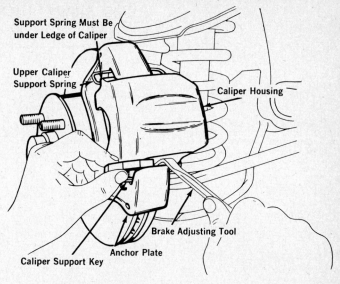

Fig. 55   Positioning caliper housing on anchor plate

5. Position new shoe and lining assemblies in anchor plate by tilting the shoe and sliding the bottom edge into place.
6. Rotate shoes into correct positions, making sure the lining side is next to disc.

Caliper Housing Assembly

1. Lubricate piston seal with clean brake fluid and position seal in its cylinder bore groove.
2. Assemble dust boot on caliper housing by seating boot flange in the outer groove of cylinder bore, making sure it is fully seated.
3. Coat piston with clean brake fluid and install in cylinder bore.
4. Spread dust boot over piston as piston is installed and then bottom piston in the bore. Seat dust boot in its piston groove.

Caliper Housing Installation

1. Assemble anti-rattle clips in anchor plate, making sure that tabs on clips are positioned properly and the loop type springs are positioned on the anchor plate side, away from the disc.
2. Position shoe and lining assemblies as described previously.
3. Place a thin coat of high-temperature lubricant on anchor plate and caliper surfaces that will be in contact after caliper is installed. Avoid getting lubricant on linings.
4. Position caliper in anchor plate, making sure that the top, trailing edge, of the caliper is properly positioned and the caliper support spring is under the projecting ledge of the caliper.
5. Insert a brake adjusting tool, or wide blade screwdriver, between the bottom, leading edge, of the caliper and adjacent anchor plate surface. Pry downward so that caliper housing is pressed upward and inward toward the spindle, Fig. 55.
6. Insert caliper support key between caliper housing and anchor plate. Be

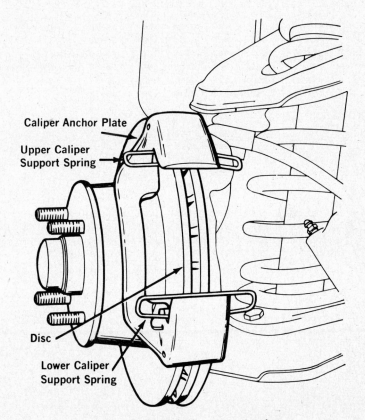

Fig. 56   Position of caliper support springs

sure key is properly positioned and that caliper support springs are still in proper position, Fig. 56.
7. Center the support key so that cotter pin holes are on each side of the anchor plate and insert a new cotter pin in each hole.
8. Connect brake hose to caliper inlet port. Bleed system.

Anchor Plate

1. In the event the anchor plate was removed position it on steering arm and install both mounting bolts finger tight. Tighten upper bolt first to 90-120 ft. lbs. and then tighten lower bolt to 55-75 ft. lbs.
2. Replace caliper housing as described previously.

DISC BRAKES

DISC BRAKE ROTOR SPECIFICATIONS

CAR	Year	Nominal Thickness	Minimum Thickness	Thickness Variation Parallelism	Runout (T.I.R.)	Finish (Micro-In.)	CAR	Year	Nominal Thickness	Minimum Thickness	Thickness Variation Parallelism	Runout (T.I.R.)	Finish (Micro-In.)
American Mtrs.	1966–70	.500	.450	.0005	.005	15–80	Fairlane, Falcon	1966–67	.810	.780	.0007	.002	15–80
	1971	1.000	.940	.0005	.005	15–80	Mustang &	1968–69	.940	.895	.0007	.002	15–80
Belvedere &	1966–69	.886	.816	.0005	.005	40	Torino	1970–71	.935	.875	.0007	.002	15–80
Satellite	1970–71	1.000	.980	.0005	.002	15–80	Ford &	1966–67	1.245	1.215	.0007	.002	15–80
Buick & Riviera	1967–69	1.000	.965	.0005	.005	30–50	Mercury	1968–69	1.185	1.140	.0007	.002	15–80
	1970	1.000	.965	.0005	.004	30–50		1970–71	1.180	1.120	.0007	.003	15–80
	1971	1.290	1.230	.0005	.004	30–80	Imperial	1967–68	.869	.829	.0005	.005	30–60
Buick Special	1967–70	1.000	.965	.0005	.004	30–50		1969	.877	—	—	.005	30–60
	1971	1.040	.980	.0005	.004	30–80		1970–71	1.250	1.200	.0005	.002	15–80
Cadillac	1968	1.250	1.230	.0005	.005	30–40	Lincoln	1966–69	1.245	1.215	.0007	.002	15–80
	1969–71	1.250	1.230	.0007	.002	15–80		1970–71	1.180	1.120	.0007	.003	15–80
Camaro	1967–69	1.000	.965	.0005	.004	30–50	Mark III	1968–69	1.185	1.140	.0007	.002	15–80
	1970	1.000	.965	.0005	.002	30–50		1970–71	1.180	1.120	.0007	.003	15–80
	1971	1.035	.980	.0005	.005	20–60	Oldsmobile	1967–69	1.250	1.215	.0005	.004	30–50
Challenger	1970–71	1.000	.980	.0005	.002	15–80		1970	1.250	1.215	.0007	.002	30–50
Charger	1966–69	.886	.816	.0005	.005	40		1971	1.290	1.215	.0005	.002	30–50
	1970–71	1.000	.980	.0005	.002	15–80	Olds F-85	1967–69	1.000	.965	.0005	.004	30–50
Chevelle	1967–69	1.000	.965	.0005	.004	30–50		1970	1.035	.965	.0005	.004	30–50
	1970	1.000	.965	.0005	.002	30–50		1971	1.040	.965	.0005	.004	30–50
	1971	1.035	.980	.0005	.005	20–60	Olds Toronado	1967–68	1.245	1.215	.0007	.002	15–80
Chevrolet	1967–69	1.250	1.215	.0005	.004	30–50		1969	1.250	1.215	.0005	.004	30–50
	1970	1.250	1.215	.0005	.002	30–50		1970	1.250	1.215	.0005	.002	30–50
	1971	1.285	1.230	.0005	.005	20–60		1971	1.245	1.170	.0005	.002	30–50
Chevy II	1967–69	1.000	.965	.0005	.004	30–50	Pinto	1971	.750	.685	.001	.003	
	1970	1.000	.965	.0005	.002	30–50	Plymouth	1966–68	.869	.829	.0005	.005	30–60
	1971	1.035	.980	.0005	.005	20–60		1969–71	1.250	1.200	.0005	.002	15–80
Chrysler	1966	.869	.829	.0005	.005	30–60	Pontiac	1967–68	1.250	1.215	.0005	.004	20–60
	1969–71	1.250	1.200	.0005	.002	15–80		1969	1.240	1.195	.0007	.004	20–60
Comet, Montego	1967	.810	.780	.0007	.002	15–80		1970–71	1.250	1.215	.0007	.004	20–60
& Cougar	1968–69	.940	.895	.0007	.002	15–80	Tempest/Fire-	1967–68	1.000	.965	.0005	.004	20–60
	1970–71	.935	.875	.0007	.002	15–80	bird	1969	1.000	.960	.0007	.004	20–60
Coronet	1966–69	.886	.816	.0005	.005	40		1970–71	1.085	.965	.0007	.004	20–60
	1970–71	1.000	.980	.0005	.002	15–80	Thunderbird	1966–67	1.245	1.215	.0007	.002	15–80
Corvette	1966–70	1.250	1.215	.0005	.004	30–50		1968–69	1.185	1.140	.0007	.002	15–80
	1971	1.285	1.230	.0005	.002	20–60		1970–71	1.180	1.120	.0007	.003	15–80
Dart	1966–71	.810	.780	.0005	.002	15–80	Valiant &	1966–71	.810	.780	.0005	.002	15–80
Dodge	1966–68	.869	.829	.0005	.005	30–60	Barracuda	1970–71	1.000	.980	.0005	.002	15–80
	1969–71	1.250	1.200	.0005	.002	15–80	Vega	1971	.500	.470	.0005	.002	20–60
Eldorado	1967–68	1.250	1.215	.0007	.002	15–80	Ventura II	1971	1.035	.980	.0005	.004	20–60
	1969–71	1.210	1.190	.0005	.008	15–80							

ANTI-SKID BRAKE SYSTEMS

FORD "SURE TRACK"

This system is designed to keep the rear end of a vehicle tracking the front end correctly by controlling rear brake lockup during "panic stops." The system consists of sensors, valves, an actuator and a tiny computer to control the rate of deceleration of the rear wheels. The rate of deceleration of a rotating wheel is measured in terms of "slip" relative to the vehicle speed. If the car is traveling at 50mph and the wheel with the brakes applied is turning at 40mph, there is a 20 percent slip. The 10 to 20 percent slip range is just short of locking the brakes and it is in this range that maximum braking is accomplished. Ideally, the 10 to 20 percent slip should be maintained throughout the speed range as the vehicle slows down, so the relationship between vehicle speed and wheel speed is constantly changing and must be constantly corrected.

In the Sure Track system, this relationship is controlled electrically by automatically pumping the brakes in cycles when the rear wheels begin to lock up under heavy braking. By this rapid application and release of the brakes the locking point is never reached or is reached and released so fast that the wheels do not stop turning.

Sensor 1969 & Early 1970: A mechanically driven electro magnetic sensor is located at each rear wheel. Each sensor consists of a rotor, which is pressed onto the axle shaft outboard of the wheel bearing and a stator which bolts to the brake backing plate, Fig. 1. When the axle turns, teeth of the rotor pass the teeth of the stator, cutting magnetic lines of force and setting up an electrical current, in proportion to the speed of the rear wheels. Two wires from each of the sensors conduct impulses to the control module.

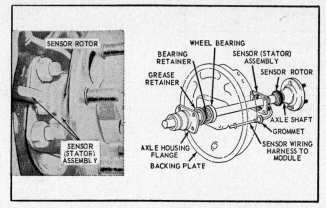

Fig. 1   Sensor components. 1969 & Early 1970 Sure Track

Sensor Late 1970 & 1971: A single sensor stator assembly, Fig. 2, is mounted on the rear axle drive pinion housing with the sensor rotor pressed onto the companion flange outboard of the grease seal. This unit operates in the same manner as the two wheel sensors used on 1969 units to generate electric current. The AC voltage, generated in proportion to driveshaft speed, is conducted from the sensor to the control module.

Control Module: The control module is mounted under the glove box in the passenger compartment and operates on the sum of the signals from the sensor(s).

When the sum of the signals drops abruptly below a predetermined level due to rapid deceleration, the module sends an electrical signal to the actuator solenoid to release the rear brakes. Then, when rear wheel speed increases again, the module de-energizes the solenoid, allowing the brakes to reapply. This cycle continues until the driver releases the brake pedal past the full pressure point

or the vehicle slows to less than 4 mph.

Actuator: The vacuum operated actuator, Fig. 3, is mounted on the vehicle right frame rail under the toe board. The actuator is divided into two chambers by a diaphragm with a spring positioned ahead of the diaphragm.

In addition, the actuator contains a hydraulic cylinder, a solenoid and a time delay switch, all functioning together to regulate pressure to the rear brakes upon control of the control module.

The actuator is connected to the brake hydraulic system between the pressure differential valve and the rear brake hydraulic system.

Electrical power is provided to the Sure Track system when the ignition switch is turned to any position except "Off" and "Accessory". The circuit is protected by a 3-amp fuse in the fuse box.

CAUTION: Do not use a fuse of higher rating than 3-amp to prevent damage to the control module. This fuse is identified by a red cover.

Vacuum for the operation of the actuator is supplied from the engine intake manifold. Atmospheric pressure is provided from an air filter mounted on the right hood hinge bracket. A vacuum check is included in the actuator.

Brake Warning Light: Illumination of the brake warning switch indicates a malfunction in the brake hydraulic system or in the Sure Track unit and requires immediate service of the brake system.

As a test, the warning light will go on when the ignition key is in the start position and will go out when the key is returned to the run position.

To determine if the trouble is in the Sure Track system or the brake hydraulic system, disconnect the switch plug from the hydraulic system differential switch. If the light now goes out the brake hydraulic system is at fault. If the light remains on, check Sure Track system.

Functional Testing

1. Turn ignition key to "On" and listen for solenoid click and actuator cycle.

NOTE: It may be necessary to run

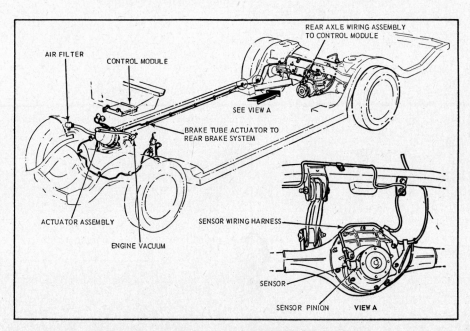

Fig. 2   Sensor components. Late 1970 & 1971 Sure Track

engine prior to performing this check to assure a vacuum supply in the actuator.

2. Raise rear wheels to clear floor.
3. With engine at operating temperature, place transmission in Drive and accelerate to approximately 25 mph. It may be necessary to increase engine speed slightly to obtain sufficient cycling of the Sure Track system for easy observation of its operation.
4. Apply the brakes quickly and firmly. If the Sure Track is functioning properly, it will cycle five or six times or until the brake pedal is released.

NOTE: Both wheels must be turning for this test or the system will not operate.

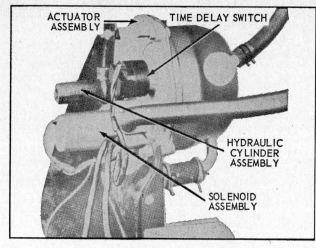

Fig. 3 Actuator assembly. Sure Track

GM SKID CONTROL
Operation

This system combines speed sensors at each wheel, a controller under the instrument panel and a modulator on the cowl in the engine compartment to control rear wheel lock-up.

The sensors produce an electrical signal that is proportional to wheel speed. This signal is monitored by the controller. A wheel that is not locking during brake application will gradually decelerate. When a wheel has started to lock, it will decelerate abruptly at a rate much greater than the car's deceleration. When the controller determines that the signal from the sensors changes too rapidly, and the car is approaching a skid, the controller energizes the modulator solenoid.

The modulator, Figs. 4 and 5, contains a diaphragm both sides of which are exposed to intake manifold vacuum as long as the solenoid is not energized. When the solenoid is energized, atmospheric pressure is allowed to reach the top side of the diaphragm, forcing it down against the support spring. The displacement piston is lowered along with the diaphragm. This seals off hydraulic pressure from the master cylinder to the rear wheel cylinders by closing the hydraulic check valve. The lowering of the displacement piston also increases the area in the hydraulic chamber immediately below the check valve. This increased area results in decreased hydraulic pressure and partial brake release.

With the brakes partially released, the wheels accelerate and, as car speed is approached, the controller senses the condition and de-energizes the modulator, allowing full brake application until a locking condition is again sensed.

The entire cycle of brake release and re-application occurs in about 1/3 second. During a stop where brake pressure is sufficient to cause lock-up, the cycling will continue until the car is slowed to approximately 5 mph or until the brakes are released by the driver.

The brake system warning light also operates in conjunction with the modulator travel switch in case of system malfunctions. When the switch is open for more than approximately four seconds, except during a skid controlled stop, the controller turns on the warning light. An exception to this is an open in the 4 amp feed circuit from the ignition switch, which is indicated without the four second delay. When a malfunction is indicated, the lamp remains lighted until the ignition is turned off.

Trouble Shooting

Brake Warning Light Does Not Light (Check When Ignition Switch Is In Start Position):
1. Burned out bulb.
2. Blown instrument fuse.
3. Open in bulb circuit.

Immediate Brake Light When Ignition Is Turned To On Position:
1. Leak in hydraulic system.
2. Blown skid control fuse.
3. Open in controller circuit.
4. Faulty controller.

NOTE: For the following conditions, it is assumed that the brake lamp circuit operates normally and there are no hydraulic leaks or air trapped in the brake system. All following conditions are with ignition switch ON or engine running.

No Brake Light System Inoperative, Exercise Cycle OK:
1. Wheel sensor not being driven due to missing dust cap or sensor quill.
2. Both sensor leads shorted to each other (not shorted to ground).

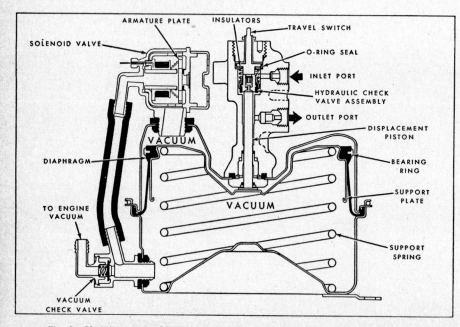

Fig. 4 Modulator assembly during normal braking. G.M. Computerized Skid Control

No Brake Light, System Inoperative, No Exercise Cycle:
1. Loss of ground to controller.
2. Bad connection at controller or modulator.
3. Modulator seized in de-energized position.
4. Faulty controller.

Brake Light Lights After 2-5 Second Delay, System Inoperative, Exercise Cycle O.K.
1. Speed sensor leads open.
2. Speed sensor leads shorted to ground.
3. Modulator travel switch open.
4. Faulty connection at travel switch.
5. Faulty controller.

Brake Light Lights After 2-5 Second Delay, System Inoperative, No Exercise Cycle:
1. Solenoid leads open.
2. Faulty controller.

False Releases While Car Is In Motion:
1. Frayed shield leads causing intermittent short.
2. Sensor drive shaft rubbing in wheel spingle.
3. Missing or damaged insulators.
4. Sensor damper deteriorated.
5. Bad electrical connections.
6. Faulty controller.

False Releases While Vehicle Is Parked:
1. Bad electrical connections.
2. Faulty controller.

Does Not Cycle Down To 5 MPH During Maximum Braking:
1. Insufficient operating vacuum.
2. Faulty controller.

Brake Light On 2-5 Seconds After High Brake Pressure Is Applied:
1. Defective differential and proportioning valve.

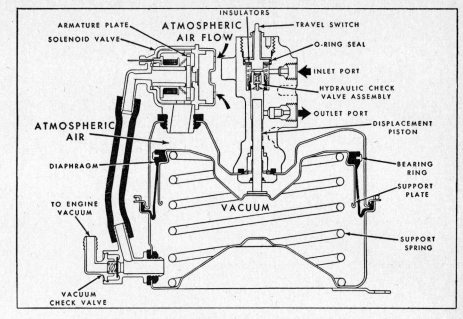

Fig. 5   Modulator assembly during release. G.M. Computerized Skid Control

CHRYSLER SURE BRAKE

This system is designed to prevent any wheel from locking up during brake applications above a speed of about 5mph. The system reduces skid potential of a locked wheel and still maintains brake pressure for maximum stopping effort. The end result is to improve directional control and steerability of the vehicle, and in many cases to reduce the distance required to bring the vehicle to a stop.

The major components of the system are shown in Fig. 6. These include a mechanically driven speed sensor at each wheel, a logic controller located inside the right rear quarter panel and three pressure modulators; one modulator is under each front fender ahead of the wheels and one is in the engine compartment next to the radiator on the right side of the vehicle.

OPERATION

Engine Running—Vehicle Not in Motion

The wheel sensors do not generate any signals for transmission to the logic controller when the vehicle is not in motion. Hence, the logic controller sends no commands to the pressure modulator.

Engine Running—Vehicle in Motion

With the vehicle in motion, alternating current voltage is generated at each wheel sensor and sent to the logic controller. The logic controller processes the signals received from the wheel sensors to sample the speed of each wheel. If the brakes are not applied or if they are applied lightly, the controller does not send any commands to the pressure modulator.

When the brakes are applied with greater force, the controller, based on wheel sensor signals, determines the rate at which each wheel is decelerating. If the rate is great and might produce wheel slippage or lockup, the controller sends a command to the modulator that controls the braking for the wheel or wheels concerned.

Exercise Cycle

If the engine is started with the brake pedal depressed, the pressure modulators go through two exercise cycles. When the ignition switch is turned from OFF to START all three modulators cycle once, and when the switch returns from START to ON the modulators cycle again. These cycles are to insure that the system is working properly. The cycles can be heard under some conditions, but should not be a cause for concern.

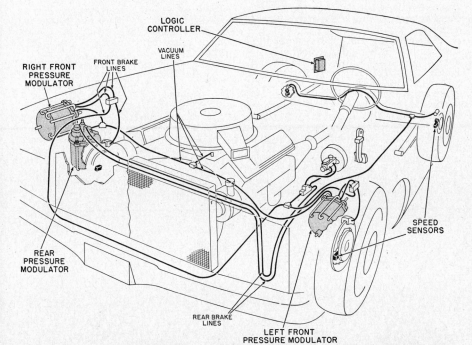

Fig. 6   Chrysler Sure Brake system components

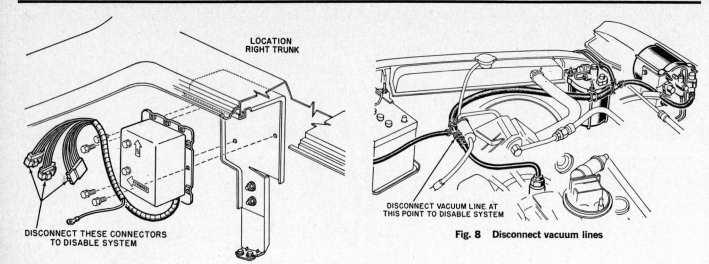

LOCATION
RIGHT TRUNK

DISCONNECT THESE CONNECTORS
TO DISABLE SYSTEM

Fig. 7   Disconnecting logic controller

DISCONNECT VACUUM LINE AT
THIS POINT TO DISABLE SYSTEM

Fig. 8   Disconnect vacuum lines

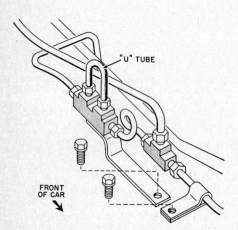

"U" TUBE

FRONT
OF CAR

Fig. 9   Placing "U" tube in system to disable front wheel modulators

3. If the electrical continuity of the air valve lead wire is broken.
4. If all speed sensor signals are not received at the controller, or if the signals are not properly converted in the controller at speeds above 15 mph.

NOTE: Due to the complexities of testing this system and the various voltage charts necessary, it is recommended the unit be returned to a dealer for service. For this reason, a procedure for disabling the Sure Brake System to allow the car to be operated safely, follows.

DISABLING THE SURE BRAKE SYSTEM

If necessary parts or service is not available, the system should be disabled. The brakes will then function the same as those on cars without this system. Proceed as follows:

Disconnect the logic controller (all three connectors), Fig. 7, and the vacuum supply hose. The vacuum hose should be separated at the "T" connection leading to the modulator, Fig. 8. The line to the intake manifold should be plugged and the line to the modulators should be taped to keep out the dirt.

An additional step may be necessary to disable the system. If a pressure modulator diaphragm plate sticks in the retracted or partially retracted position the basic hydraulic brake system will be affected. Test for this by placing car on a hoist and spin wheels by hand to insure they

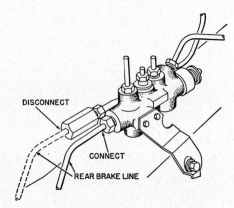

DISCONNECT

CONNECT

REAR BRAKE LINE

Fig. 10   Connections at safety tee to disable rear wheel modulators

are free. With the brakes applied, attempt to spin wheels, release brakes and spin wheels again. If a wheel spins with the brakes applied or does not rotate with brakes released, the modulator for that wheel must be by-passed. This can be accomplished as follows:

1. On front wheel modulators, a "U" tube should be placed in the system after the modulator tubes have been removed, Fig. 9.
2. On rear wheel modulator, route the brake line from rear wheels directly into the rear of safety tee after modulator line has been disconnected, Fig. 10. Also, both hydraulic tubes should be disconnected at the brake warning switch metering valve. This completely by-passes the modulator for the rear brakes.

Warning System

The Sure Brake System includes a secondary system to warn the driver of certain types of failures in the system. The warning system uses the brake warning light. The warning light will be on under the following conditions:

1. It the pressure modulator is activated in the absence of a brake light signal.
2. If the controller sends a signal to open the air valve on a modulator in the absence of a signal to open the by-pass valve.

MANUAL STEERING GEARS

STEERING GEAR ADJUSTMENT SPECIFICATIONS

CAR MAKE	GEAR TYPE	WORM BEARING PRELOAD	CROSS SHAFT PRELOAD
BUICK			
1966-67	Ball & Nut	2 to 7[1]	6 to 15[1]
1968-69	Ball & Nut	5 to 9[1]	10 to 20[1]
1970-71	Ball & Nut	2 to 7[1]	7 to 18[1]
BUICK SPECIAL			
1966-67	Ball & Nut	2 to 7[1]	6 to 15[1]
1968-69	Ball & Nut	5 to 9[1]	10 to 20[1]
1970-71	Ball & Nut	2 to 7[1]	7 to 18[1]
CAMARO & CHEVELLE			
1966	Ball & Nut	4 to 7[1]	8 to 17[1]
1967-71	Ball & Nut	5 to 8[1]	9 to 18[1]
CHEVROLET			
1966	Ball & Nut	4 to 7[1]	8 to 17[1]
1967-71	Ball & Nut	5 to 8[1]	9 to 18[1]
CHEVY II & NOVA			
1966	Ball & Nut	8 to 14[1]	8 to 20[1]
1967-71	Ball & Nut	5 to 8[1]	9 to 18[1]
CHRYSLER			
1966-71	Ball & Nut	1 to 4[1]	8 to 11[1]
COMET & COUGAR			
1966-71	Ball & Nut	4 to 5[1]	9 to 10[1]
CORVAIR			
1966-69	Ball & Nut	3½-4½[1]	11½-14½[1]
CORVETTE			
1966	Ball & Nut	8 to 14[1]	8 to 20[1]
1967-69	Ball & Nut	5 to 8[1]	9 to 18[1]
1970-71	Ball & Nut	4 to 7[1]	8 to 17[1]
DODGE & DART			
1966-71	Ball & Nut	1 to 4[1]	8 to 11[1]
FAIRLANE & TORINO			
1966-71	Ball & Nut	4 to 5[1]	9 to 10[1]
FALCON			
1966-70	Ball & Nut	4 to 5[1]	9 to 10[1]
FORD			
1966-71	Ball & Nut	4 to 5[1]	9 to 10[1]
MERCURY			
1966-71	Ball & Nut	4 to 5[1]	9 to 10[1]
MONTEGO			
1968-71	Ball & Nut	4 to 5[1]	9 to 10[1]
MUSTANG			
1966-71	Ball & Nut	4 to 5[1]	9 to 10[1]
OLDSMOBILE			
1966-71	Ball & Nut	4 to 7[1]	8 to 17[1]
OLDS F-85			
1966-71	Ball & Nut	4 to 7[1]	8 to 17[1]
PLYMOUTH			
1966-71	Ball & Nut	1 to 4[1]	8 to 11[1]
PONTIAC			
1971	Ball & Nut	5 to 8[1]	4 to 10[1]
1968-70	Ball & Nut	7[1]	16[1]
1966-67	Ball & Nut	5 to 9[1]	9 to 18[1]
PONTIAC TEMPEST, GTO, T-37 & FIREBIRD			
1966-67	Ball & Nut	5 to 9[1]	9 to 14[1]
1968-70	Ball & Nut	7[1]	16[3]
1971	Ball & Nut	5 to 8[1]	4 to 10[1]
RAMBLER			
1966-67	Ball & Nut	2 to 6[2]	12 to 18[2]
1968-71	Ball & Nut	⅛ to ⅜[1]	¾ to 1⅛[1]
RAMBLER AMERICAN			
1966-68	Worm & Roller	4 to 10[2]	16 to 18[2]
1968	Ball & Nut	⅛ to ⅜[1]	¾ to 1⅛[1]
VALIANT			
1966-71	Ball & Nut	1 to 4[1]	8 to 11[1]

[1]—Measured with inch-pound torque wrench attached to steering wheel nut.

[2]—Measured in ounces pull on spring scale attached to rim of steering wheel.

[3]—Firebird with V8 engine and A/C. Others 14 in-lbs.

Recirculating Ball Worm & Nut Gear

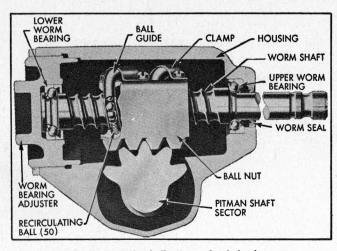

Fig. 1   Recirculating ball-worm and nut steering gear

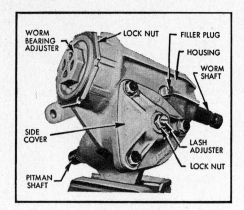

Fig. 2   Steering gear adjustments

DESCRIPTION

As shown in Fig. 1, the worm on the lower end of the steering shaft and the ball nut which is mounted on the worm have mating spiral grooves in which steel balls circulate to provide a low friction drive between worm and nut.

Two sets of balls are used, ranging in number from approximately 20 to 30 to a set, depending upon the size of the steering gear unit. Each set of balls operate independently of the other. The circuit through which each set of balls circulates includes the grooves in the worm and ball nut and a ball return guide attached to the outer surface of the nut.

When the wheel and steering shaft turn to the left, the ball nut is moved downward by the balls which roll between the worm and nut. As the balls reach the outer surface of the nut they enter the return guides which direct them across and down into the ball nut where they enter the circuit again.

When a right turn is made the ball nut moves upward and balls circulate in the reverse direction.

The teeth on the ball nut engage teeth on the sector which is forged integral with the pitman shaft. The teeth on the ball nut are made so that a "high

point" or tighter fit exists between the ball nut and pitman shaft sector teeth when the front wheels are in the straight-ahead position. The teeth on the sector are tapered slightly so that a proper lash may be obtained by moving the pitman shaft endwise by means of a lash adjuster screw which extends through the gear housing side cover. The head of the lash adjuster and the selectively fitted shim fit snugly into a T-slot in the end of the pitman shaft so that the screw also controls end play of the shaft. The screw is locked by an external lock nut.

GEAR ADJUSTMENTS

There are two adjustments on the steering gear: worm bearing preload and pitman shaft overcenter preload, Fig. 2. **Important:** Never attempt to adjust the steering gear while it is connected to the steering linkage. The gear must be free of all outside load in order to properly make any steering gear adjustment.

Preliminary

1. Tighten steering gear mounting bolts.
2. Disconnect steering linkage from steering arm or gear.
3. Turn wheel slowly from one extreme to the other.
   Caution: Never turn the wheel hard against the stopping point in the gear as damage to the ball nut assembly may result.
4. Steering wheel should turn freely and smoothly throughout its entire range.
   Note: Roughness indicates faulty internal parts requiring disassembly of gear unit. Hard pull or binding indicates an excessively tight adjustment of the worm bearings, or excessive misalignment of the steering shaft. Any excessive misalignment must be corrected before the gear can be properly adjusted.

given in inch pounds as measured with a torque wrench pulling on steering wheel nut, Fig. 3, or with a spring scale, measured in ounces, attached to rim of steering wheel, Fig. 4.

Checking Worm Bearing Preload

1. Turn steering wheel gently in one direction until it stops. This positions gear away from "high point" load.
2. Attach torque wrench or spring scale and check the torque or pull required to turn the wheel steadily in the range where lash exists between ball nut and pitman shaft sector.
3. If adjustment is not within specified limits, adjust worm bearing preload.

Adjust Worm Bearing Preload

1. Loosen worm bearing adjuster lock nut, using a drift, Fig. 2.
2. Turn bearing adjuster as required to bring the adjustment within specified limits.
3. Tighten lock nut and recheck preload.

Checking Pitman Shaft Over-Center Preload

1. Turn steering wheel from one ex-

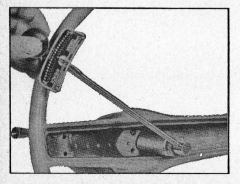

Fig. 3   Checking adjustments with inch-pound torque wrench

NOTE: .Specifications in the Steering Gear Adjustment Specifications chart are

Spring Scale

Fig. 4   Checking adjustments with spring scale

treme to the other while counting the total turns, then turn wheel back ½ the number of turns. This positions steering gear on "high point" where a preload should exist between ball nut and pitman shaft teeth.

2. Attach torque wrench or spring scale and check torque or pull required to turn the wheel through the "high point" range.

3. If adjustment is not within the specified limits, adjust as follows:

Adjust Pitman Shaft Overcenter Preload

1. Loosen lock nut and turn pitman shaft lash adjuster screw as required to bring the adjustment within specified limits.

2. After tightening lock nut, rotate steering wheel back and forth through the "high point" and through the entire range to check for tight spots.

NOTE: If lash cannot be removed at the "high point", or if gear load varies greatly and feels rough, the gear should be removed for inspection of internal parts.

3. Attach linkage to steering gear when adjustments have been completed.

STEERING GEAR REPAIRS

1. Referring to Fig. 5, loosen adjusting screw lock nut and remove housing side cover by unscrewing adjusting screw.

2. Loosen lock nut and back off worm bearing adjuster several turns, then remove housing end cover and gasket.

3. Remove lower thrust bearing, steering shaft and upper bearing from housing.

4. Remove ball return guide clamps and guides from ball nut, turn ball nut over to remove balls and remove ball nut from steering shaft worm.

Inspection of Parts

1. Clean and inspect all ball and roller bearings and races, including race in housing.

2. Inspect pitman shaft bushings in gear housing and end cover. Replace bushings in housing and replace end cover if bushings are worn excessively.

3. It is advisable to replace pitman shaft grease seal in housing to avoid possible leakage of lubricant. Seal must be installed with feather edge toward inside of housing.

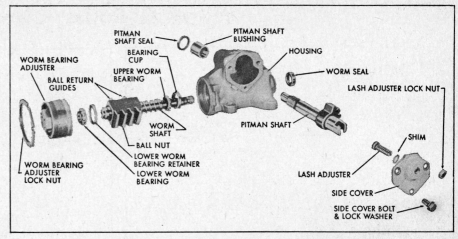

Fig. 5   Recirculating ball-worm and nut gear disassembled

4. Inspect steering shaft for wear or pits in bearing races, which would require replacement of shaft.

5. Check shaft for straightness.

6. Inspect teeth of ball nut and pitman shaft. If scored or excessively worn it is advisable to replace both parts to insure proper mating of teeth.

7. Check serrations of pitman shaft; if twisted, replace shaft.

8. Check fit of pitman shaft adjusting screw and shim in slot in end of pitman shaft. *With shim in place, screw head must be free to turn in slot with zero to .002" end play.* If end play is excessive, selectively fit a new shim, which are furnished in four different thicknesses.

9. Inspect steering column jacket for distortion. A ripple or wavy feeling of jacket surface, particularly at lower end, will usually indicate a sprung jacket. Replace jacket if sprung or otherwise damaged.

10. Inspect control shaft bearing in tube of gear housing, and steering shaft upper bearing in control lever housing support. Replace worn or damaged parts.

Reassemble

Note: Lubricate all seals, bushings, bearings and gears with multi-purpose gear lube prior to installation.

1. Position ball nut over worm shaft so that deep side of teeth will be toward side cover when installed in gear housing.

2. Install exactly ½ the total number of balls in each circuit, rocking worm shaft slightly to aid in installing balls.

3. Place about six balls in each return guide, using grease to hold balls in place.

4. Install return guides, clamp and screw.

5. Rotate worm through its complete travel several times to be sure balls are installed correctly and rotate freely.

6. Place upper bearing on worm shaft and slide worm shaft assembly into housing.

7. Place lower bearing in worm bearing adjuster and install bearing retainer.

8. Install adjuster assembly and lock nut in housing. Tighten adjuster only enough to hold worm bearings in place. Final adjustment will be made later.

9. Turn worm shaft until center groove in ball nut lines up with center of pitman shaft bushing.

10. Install pitman shaft and lash adjuster with shim so that center tooth meshes with center groove in ball nut.

11. Install side cover with gasket on lash adjuster by turning adjuster counterclockwise.

12. Install side cover bolts and washers.

13. Turn lash adjuster so that teeth on shaft and ball nut engage but do not bind.

14. Install lash adjuster lock nut loosely.

15. To protect pitman shaft seal from damage, cover shaft splines with masking tape. Slide new seal into place and seat it against shoulder in housing.

16. Install new worm shaft seal flush with surface of housing.

17. Fill gear housing with multi-purpose lubricant and adjust gear assembly as outlined previously.

Worm & Roller Gear

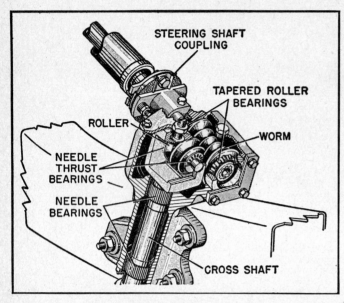

Fig. 6 Worm and roller steering gear

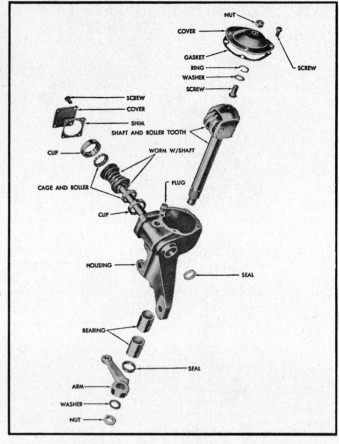

Fig. 7 Worm and roller gear unit disassembled

DESCRIPTION

In this type steering gear, Fig. 6, the worm is integral with the steering shaft and is supported on each end by opposed tapered roller bearings. The triple tooth roller is attached to the roller shaft by means of a steel shaft. Two needle bearing assemblies are installed between this shaft and the roller.

The roller shaft is mounted in the steering gear housing on two needle bearing assemblies which are pressed into the housing. The housing cover is attached to the housing by four cap screws. An adjustment screw, mounted in the cover, controls roller shaft end play and worm and roller mesh adjustment.

The steering wheel and roller shaft arm (pitman arm) are splined to the steering shaft and roller shaft respectively. Both the pitman arm and steering wheel have master splines to insure correct installation.

ADJUSTMENTS

Worm End Play, Adjust

1. Free the steering gear of all load by disconnecting the linkage and loosening the steering column braces.
2. Loosen the four cover screws about ⅛".
3. Use a knife to separate the top shim, passing the blade all the way around between the shims, being careful not to damage the remaining shims.
4. Remove one shim at a time between inspections to remove the end play.
5. The adjustment is correct when there is no end play and no stiffness in the steering gear throughout the complete range of its travel.

Roller Shaft End Play, Adjust

1. Turn the steering gear to either extreme and back off ⅛ of a turn.
2. Gripping the pitman arm at the hub, the roller shaft should rotate freely without a particle of end play.
3. If end play exists, adjust as required by means of the roller shaft adjusting screw in the side cover.
4. Be sure to tighten the lock nut securely and inspect for end play and free rotation throughout the entire range of steering gear travel.

Worm & Roller Mesh, Adjust

1. Loosen the roller shaft adjusting screw lock nut.
2. With the steering gear in its central position (linkage disconnected) tighten the roller shaft adjusting screw just enough to remove play between the roller shaft roller tooth and worm.
3. Check this by the amount of play felt at the pitman arm. It is better to leave a slight amount of play at this point than to tighten too much.
4. If tightened beyond the point where the lash is removed, serious results will occur which will cause poor steering operation.
5. Tighten the adjusting screw lock nut.

GEAR REPAIRS

1. Referring to Fig. 7, use a suitable puller to remove gear oil seal from housing. If shaft is corroded or dirty, clean the portion between oil seal and serrations to avoid binding in bearings.
2. Place a suitable arbor over cross shaft threads while withdrawing cross shaft, following with the arbor. This arbor will keep bearing rollers from dropping out of their cages.
3. Remove cross shaft adjusting screw lock nut. Remove cover and shims from bottom cover gasket and cross shaft.
4. Remove shaft-worm, bearings and cups.
5. If necessary, drive needle bearings from housing.
6. Clean all parts and inspect for wear.
7. Assemble parts without lubrication. Lubrication should be done after adjustments are completed. The needle bearings are grease-packed at the factory.
8. If either of the worm thrust bearings is damaged, replace both bearings. Use new oil seals.

American Motors

INDEX OF SERVICE OPERATIONS

AMERICAN MOTORS

SERIAL NUMBER LOCATION: 1966-68 Stamped on plate attached to top of right front wheelhouse panel under hood.

1969-72: Plate is attached to top of instrument panel, on driver's side.

ENGINE IDENTIFICATION

6-199 & 6-232 (1966-69): The engine code number is located on a machined pad adjacent to the distributor. The letter contained in the code number identifies the cubic inch displacement of the engine. The letter "J" denotes the 199 engine with 8.5 compression ratio. The letter "L" denotes the 232 engine with 8.5 compression ratio.

6-199 & 6-232 (1970): The engine code number is located on a machined pad adjacent to the distributor. The letter "A" denotes the 199 engine. The letter "E" denotes the 232 engine with 1 barrel carburetor while the letter "G" denotes the 232 engine with 2 barrel carburetor.

6-232 & 6-258 (1971-72): The engine code is located on a pad between number two and three cylinders. The letter "A" denotes the 258 engine. The letter "E" denotes the 232 engine.

V8-287 & 327: The engine code number is located on a tag attached to the alternator mounting bracket. The letter contained in the code denotes the size of the cylinder bore and compression ratio. The letter "E" denotes the 4" bore with 8.7 compression ratio (327 engine). The letter "F" denotes the 4" bore with 9.7 compression ratio (327 engine). The letter "G" denotes the 3¾" bore with 8.7 compression ratio (287 engine).

V8-290, 343 & 390 (1966-69): The engine code is located on a plate attached to the front of the right-hand rocker arm cover. The letter "H" four-barrel carburetor. The letter "Z" is for the 243 engine with four-barrel carburetor; "S" for two-barrel carburetor. The letter "W" is for the 390 engine with two-barrel carburetor in 1968 and four-barrel in 1969; "X" with four-barrel carburetor in 1968.

V8-304, 360, 390, & 401 (1970-72): The engine code is located on a tag attached to the right bank rocker cover. The letter "H" denotes the 304 engine. The letter "N" denotes the 360 engine with 2 barrel carburetor while the letter "P" denotes the 360 engine with 4 barrel carburetor. The letter "X" denotes the 390 engine. The letter "Z" denotes the 401 engine.

GRILLE IDENTIFICATION

1966 American

1966 Classic

1966 Ambassador

1966 Marlin

1967 American

1967 Rebel

1967 Rebel SST

1967 Ambassador

GRILLE IDENTIFICATION—Continued

1967 Marlin & DPL

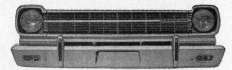

1968 American

1968 Rebel

1968 Ambassador

1968-69 Javelin

1968-69 AMX

1969 Rambler

1969 Rebel

1969 Ambassador

1970-72 Hornet

1970 Rebel

1970 Ambassador

1970 AMX

1970 Javelin

1970-72 Gremlin

1971 Javelin

1971-72 AMX

1971-72 Ambassador

1971 Matador

1972 Javelin

1972 Matador

GENERAL SPECIFICATIONS

Year	Engine	Car-buretor	Bore and Stroke	Piston Dis-place-ment, Cubic Inches	Com-pres-sion Ratio	Maximum Brake H.P. @ R.P.M.	Maximum Torque Lbs. Ft. @ R.P.M.	Normal Oil Pressure Pounds
1966	128 H.P. 6-199	1 Barrel	3.7500 x 3.00	199	8.5	128 @ 4400	180 @ 1600	50
	145 H.P. 6-232	1 Barrel	3.7500 x 3.50	232	8.5	145 @ 4300	215 @ 1600	50
	155 H.P. 6-232	2 Barrel	3.7500 x 3.50	232	8.5	155 @ 4400	222 @ 1600	50
	198 H.P. V8-287	2 Barrel	3.7500 x 3.25	287	8.7	198 @ 4700	280 @ 2600	50
	200 H.P. (Late 1966)..........V8-290	2 Barrel	3.75 x 3.28	290	9.0	200 @ 4600	285 @ 2800	50
	225 H.P. (Late 1966)..........V8-290	4 Barrel	3.75 x 3.28	290	10.0	225 @ 4700	300 @ 3200	50
	250 H.P. (1966)...............V8-327	2 Barrel	4.0000 x 3.25	327	8.7	250 @ 4700	340 @ 2600	55
	270 H.P. V8-327	4 Barrel	4.0000 x 3.25	327	9.7	270 @ 4700	360 @ 2600	55
1967	128 Horsepower................6-199	1 Barrel	3.75 x 3.00	199	8.5	128 @ 4400	182 @ 1600	75
	145 Horsepower................6-232	1 Barrel	3.75 x 3.50	232	8.5	145 @ 4300	215 @ 1600	75
	155 Horsepower................6-232	2 Barrel	3.75 x 3.50	232	8.5	155 @ 4400	222 @ 1600	75
	200 Horsepower...............V8-290	2 Barrel	3.75 x 3.28	290	9.0	200 @ 4600	285 @ 2800	75
	225 Horsepower...............V8-290	4 Barrel	3.75 x 3.28	290	10.0	225 @ 4700	300 @ 3200	75
	280 Horsepower...............V8-343	4 Barrel	4.08 x 3.28	343	10.2	280 @ 4800	365 @ 3000	75
1968–69	128 Horsepower................6-199	1 Barrel	3.75 x 3.00	199	8.5	128 @ 4400	182 @ 1600	75
	145 Horsepower................6-232	1 Barrel	3.75 x 3.50	232	8.5	145 @ 4300	215 @ 1600	75
	155 Horsepower................6-232	2 Barrel	3.75 x 3.50	232	8.5	155 @ 4400	222 @ 1600	75
	200 Horsepower...............V8-290	2 Barrel	3.75 x 3.28	290	9.0	200 @ 4600	285 @ 2800	75
	225 Horsepower...............V8-290	4 Barrel	3.75 x 3.28	290	10.0	225 @ 4700	300 @ 3200	75
	235 Horsepower...............V8-343	2 Barrel	4.08 x 3.28	343	9.0	235 @ 4400	345 @ 2600	75
	280 Horsepower...............V8-343	4 Barrel	4.08 x 3.28	343	10.2	280 @ 4800	365 @ 3000	75
	315 Horsepower...............V8-390	4 Barrel	4.165 x 3.574	390	10.2	315 @ 4600	425 @ 3200	75
1970	128 Horsepower................6-199	1 Barrel	3.75 x 3.00	199	8.5	128 @ 4400	182 @ 1600	75
	145 Horsepower................6-232	1 Barrel	3.75 x 3.50	232	8.5	145 @ 4300	215 @ 1600	75
	155 Horsepower................6-232	2 Barrel	3.75 x 3.50	232	8.5	155 @ 4400	222 @ 1600	75
	210 Horsepower...............V8-304	2 Barrel	3.75 x 3.44	304	9.0	210 @ 4400	305 @ 2800	75
	245 Horsepower...............V8-360	2 Barrel	4.08 x 3.44	360	9.0	245 @ 4400	365 @ 2400	75
	290 Horsepower...............V8-360	4 Barrel	4.08 x 3.44	360	10.0	290 @ 4800	395 @ 3200	75
	325 Horsepower...............V8-390	4 Barrel	4.156 x 3.574	390	10.0	325 @ 5000	420 @ 3200	75
	340 Horsepower①...........V8-390	4 Barrel	4.165 x 3.574	390	10.0	340 @ 5100	430 @ 3600	75
1971	135 Horsepower................6-232	1 Barrel	3.75 x 3.50	232	8.0	135 @ 4000	210 @ 1600	75
	150 Horsepower................6-258	1 Barrel	3.75 x 3.90	258	8.0	150 @ 3800	240 @ 1800	75
	210 Horsepower...............V8-304	2 Barrel	3.75 x 3.44	304	8.4	210 @ 4400	300 @ 2600	75
	245 Horsepower...............V8-360	2 Barrel	4.08 x 3.44	360	8.5	245 @ 4400	365 @ 2600	75
	285 Horsepower...............V8-360	4 Barrel	4.08 x 3.44	360	8.5	285 @ 4800	390 @ 3200	75
	330 Horsepower...............V8-401	4 Barrel	4.17 x 3.68	401	9.5	330 @ 5000	430 @ 3400	75
1972	100 Horsepower②...........6-232	1 Barrel	3.75 x 3.50	232	8.0	100 @ 3600	185 @ 1800	75
	110 Horsepower②...........6-258	1 Barrel	3.75 x 3.895	258	8.0	110 @ 3500	195 @ 2000	75
	150 Horsepower②...........V8-304	2 Barrel	3.75 x 3.44	304	8.3	150 @ 4200	245 @ 2500	75
	175 Horsepower②...........V8-360	2 Barrel	4.08 x 3.44	360	8.3	175 @ 4000	285 @ 2400	75
	195 Horsepower②...........V8-360	4 Barrel	4.08 x 3.44	360	8.3	195 @ 4400	295 @ 2900	75
	220 Horsepower②③.........V8-360	4 Barrel	4.08 x 3.44	360	8.3	220 @ 4400	315 @ 3100	75
	255 Horsepower③...........V8-401	4 Barrel	4.165 x 3.68	401	8.5	255 @ 4600	345 @ 3300	75

①—Rebel Machine.
②—Ratings are net (as installed in the vehicle).
③—With dual exhausts.

TUNE UP SPECIFICATIONS

OLD CAR SPECIFICATIONS: For 1946-65 Tune Up Specifications see back of book.

★When using a timing light, disconnect vacuum hose or tube at distributor and plug opening in hose or tube so idle speed will not be affected.

●When checking compression, lowest cylinder must be within 80 percent of highest.

Year	Engine	Spark Plug		Distributor		Firing Order	Ignition Timing ★		Hot Idle Speed ③		Fuel Pump Press. Lbs.
		Type M	Gap Inch	Point Gap Inch	Dwell Angle Deg.		BTDC ①	Mark	Std. Trans.	Auto. Trans. ②	
1966	6-199	N14Y	.035	.016	31–34	Fig. C	10°⑥	Fig. K	550⑤	550N⑤	4–5½
	6-232	N14Y	.035	.016	31–34	Fig. C	5°⑥	Fig. K	550⑤	550N⑤	4–5½
	V8-287, 327	H14Y	.035	.016	28–32	Fig. L	5°⑥	Fig. J	550⑤	550N⑤	4–5½
	V8-290 200 H.P.	N12Y	.035	.016	29–31	Fig. E	TDC	Fig. J	500⑤	500N⑤	4–5½
	V8-290 225 H.P.	N12Y	.035	.016	29–31	Fig. E	TDC	Fig. J	500⑤	500N⑤	4–5½
1967	6-199 Delco-Remy	N14Y	.035	.016	31–34	Fig. C	3°⑥	Fig. K	600⑤	525D⑤	4–5½
	6-199 Prestolite	N14Y	.035	.019	36–42	Fig. C	3°⑥	Fig. K	600⑤	525D⑤	4–5½
	6-232 Delco-Remy	N14Y	.035	.016	31–34	Fig. C	5°⑥	Fig. K	600⑤	600N⑤	4–5½
	6-232 Prestolite	N14Y	.035	.020	36–42	Fig. C	5°⑥	Fig. K	600⑤	600N⑤	4–5½
	V8s Delco-Remy	N12Y	.035	.016	29–31	Fig. E	TDC	Fig. G	600⑤	600N⑤	5–6½
	V8s Prestolite	N12Y	.035	.016	27–32	Fig. E	TDC	Fig. G	600⑤	600N⑤	5–6½
1968–69	6-199, 232 Std. Tr.	N14Y	.035	.016	31–34	Fig. C	TDC	Fig. K	600⑤	—	4–5½
	6-199, 232 Auto. Tr.	N14Y	.035	.016	31–34	Fig. C	5°	Fig. K	—	525D⑤	4–5½
	V8-290, 343, 390	N12Y	.035	.016	29–31	Fig. E	TDC	Fig. G	650⑤	550D⑤	5–6½
1970	6-199, 232	N14Y	.035	.016	31–34	Fig. C	3°	Fig. K	600	550D	4–5½
	V8-304, 360, 390	N12Y	.035	.016	29–31	Fig. E	5°④	Fig. G	650	600D	5–6½
1971	6-232 Std. Tr.	N12Y	.035	.016	31–34	Fig. C	3°	Fig. K	700	—	4–5½
	6-232 Auto Tr.	N12Y	.035	.016	31–34	Fig. C	5°	Fig. K	—	600D	4–5½
	6-258	N12Y	.035	.016	31–34	Fig. C	5°	Fig. K	700	600D	4–5½
	V8-304, 360, 401	N12Y	.035	.016	29–31	Fig. E	2½°	Fig. G	750	650D	5–6½
1972	6-232 Exc. Calif.	N12Y	.035	.016	31–34	Fig. C	5°	Fig. K	600	550D	4–5½
	6-232 Calif.	N12Y	.035	.016	31–34	Fig. C	5°	Fig. K	700	600D	4–5½
	6-258 Exc. Calif.	N12Y	.035	.016	31–34	Fig. C	3°	Fig. K	600	550D	4–5½
	6-258 Calif.	N12Y	.035	.016	31–34	Fig. C	3°	Fig. K	700	600D	4–5½
	V8-304 Exc. Calif.	N12Y	.035	.016	29–31	Fig. E	5°	Fig. G	750	650D	5–6½
	V8-304 Calif.	N12Y	.035	.016	29–31	Fig. E	5°	Fig. G	750	700D	5–6½
	V8-360	N12Y	.035	.016	29–31	Fig. E	5°	Fig. G	750	700D	5–6½
	V8-401 Exc. Calif.	N12Y	.035	.016	29–31	Fig. E	5°	Fig. G	700	650D	5–6½
	V8-401 Calif.	N12Y	.035	.016	29–31	Fig. E	5°	Fig. G	700	700D	5–6½

①—BTDC: Before top dead center.
②—D: Drive. N: Neutral.

③—Where two speeds are listed, lower speed indicates idle solenoid disconnected.

④—V8-390 with distributor 1111948 set at TDC.
⑤—If air conditioned turn A/C switch full on.
⑥—California vehicle TDC.

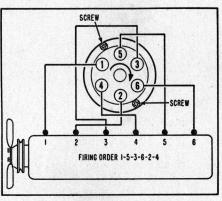

Fig. C

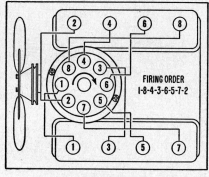

Fig. E

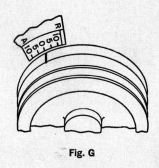

Fig. G

Continued

TUNE UP NOTES—Continued

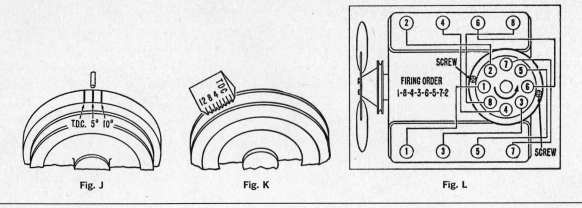

Fig. J   Fig. K   Fig. L

PISTONS, PINS, RINGS, CRANKSHAFT & BEARINGS

Year	Model	Piston Clearance Top of Skirt	Ring End Gap① Comp.	Oil	Wrist-pin Diam-eter	Rod Bearings Shaft Diameter	Bearing Clearance	Main Bearings Shaft Diameter	Bearing Clearance	Thrust on Bear. No.	Shaft End Play
1966	6-199	.0009–.0015	.010	.015	.9306	2.0948–2.0955	.001–.002	2.4988–2.4995	.001–.002	3	.003–.007
	6-232	.0009–.0015	.010	.015	.9306	2.0948–2.0955	.001–.002	2.4988–2.4995	.001–.002	3	.003–.007
	V8-287	.0009–.0015	.010	.015	.9306	2.2483–2.2490	.001–.002	2.4988–2.4995	.001–.002	1	.003–.007
	V8-290	.0009–.0015	.010	.015	.9306	2.0934–2.0955	.001–.002	2.7474–2.7489	.001–.002	3	.003–.008
	V8-327	.0009–.0015	.010	.015	.9306	2.2483–2.2490	.001–.002	2.4988–2.4995	.001–.002	1	.003–.007
1967–68	6-199, 232	.0003–.0009	.010	.015	.9306	2.0934–2.0955	.001–.002	2.4981–2.5001	.001–.002	3	.004–.008
	V8-290	.0009–.0015	.010	.015	.9306	2.0934–2.0955	.001–.002	②	.001–.002	3	.003–.008
	V8-343	.0009–.0015	.010	.015	.9306	2.0934–2.0955	.001–.002	②	.001–.002	3	.003–.008
	V8-390	.0009–.0015	.010	.015	1.000	2.2471–2.2492	.001–.002	②	.001–.002	3	.003–008
1969	6-199, 232	.0005–.0013	.010	.015	.9306	2.0934–2.0955	.001–.002	2.4981–2.5001	.001–.002	3	.0015–.007
	V8-290	.001–.0018	.010	.015	.9306	2.0934–2.0955	.001–.002	②	.001–.002	3	.003–008
	V8-343	.0012–.002	.010	.015	.9306	2.0934–2.0955	.001–.002	②	.001–.002	3	.003–.008
	V8-390	.001–.0018	.010	.015	1.000	2.2471–2.2492	.001–.002	②	.001–.002	3	.003–.008
1970	6-199, 232	.0005–.0013	.010	.015	.9306	2.0934–2.0955	.001–.002	2.4981–2.5001	⑤	3	.0015–.007
	V8-304	.001–.0018	.010	.015	.9306	2.0934–2.0955	.001–.002	④	⑤	3	.003–.008
	V8-360	.0012–.002	.010	.015	.9306	2.0934–2.0955	.001–.002	④	⑤	3	.003–.008
	V8-390	.0012–.002	.010	.015	1.000	2.2402–2.2471	.001–.002	④	⑤	3	.003–.008
	V8-390③	.001–.0018	.010	.015	1.000	2.2402–2.2471	.001–.002	④	⑤	3	.003–.008
1971	6-232, 258	.0005–.0013	.010	.015	.9306	2.0934–2.0955	.001–.002	2.4986–2.5001	.001–.002	3	.0015–.007
	V8-304	.001–.0018	.010	.015	.9306	2.0934–2.0955	.001–.002	④	⑤	3	.003–008
	V8-360	.0012–.002	.010	.015	.9306	2.0934–2.0955	.001–.002	④	⑤	3	.003–.008
	V8-401	.001–.0018	.010	.015	1.000	2.2471–2.2485	.001–.002	④	⑤	3	.003–.008
1972	6-232, 258	.0009–.0017	.010	.015	.9306	2.0934–2.0955	.001–.002	2.4986–2.5001	.001–.002	3	.0015–.007
	V8-304	.001–.0018	.010	.010	.9306	2.0934–2.0955	.001–.002	④	⑤	3	.003–.008
	V8-360	.0012–.002	.010	.015	.9306	2.0934–2.0955	.001–.002	④	⑤	3	.003–.008
	V8-401	.001–.0018	.010	.015	1.000	2.2464–2.2485	.001–.002	④	⑤	3	.003–.008

①—Fit rings in tapered bores for clearance listed in tightest portion of ring travel.
②—Rear main 2.7464–2.7479″, others 2.7469–2.7489″.
③—Rebel machine.
④—Rear main 2.7479–2.7464″, others 2.7489–2.7474″.
⑤—Rear main .002–.003″, others .001–.002″.

VALVE SPECIFICATIONS

Year	Model	Valve Lash		Valve Angles		Valve Spring Installed Height	Valve Spring Pressure Lbs. @ In.	Stem Clearance		Stem Diameter	
		Int.	Exh.	Seat	Face			Intake	Exhaust	Intake	Exhaust
1966	6-199	Hydraulic③		①	②	1¹³⁄₁₆	155 @ 1⁷⁄₁₆	.001–.003	.001–.003	.3715–.3725	.3715–.3725
	6-232	Hydraulic③		①	②	1¹³⁄₁₆	155 @ 1⁷⁄₁₆	.001–.003	.001–.003	.3715–.3725	.3715–.3725
	V8-267	Hydraulic③		①	②	1¹³⁄₁₆	155 @ 1⁷⁄₁₆	.001–.003	.001–.003	.3718–.3725	.3718–.3725
	V8-290	Hydraulic③		①	②	1¹³⁄₁₆	195 @ 1¹³⁄₃₂	.001–.003	.001–.003	.3715–.3725	.3715–.3725
	V8-327	Hydraulic③		①	②	1¹³⁄₁₆	155 @ 1⁷⁄₁₆	.001–.003	.001–.003	.3718–.3725	.3718–.3725
1967–68	6-199, 232	Hydraulic③		①	②	1¹³⁄₁₆	195 @ 1⁷⁄₁₆	.001–.003	.001–.003	.3715–.3725	.3715–.3725
	8-290, 343	Hydraulic③		①	②	1¹³⁄₁₆	194 @ 1¹³⁄₃₂	.001–.003	.001–.003	.3715–.3725	.3715–.3725
	8-390	Hydraulic③		①	②	1¹³⁄₁₆	250 @ 1²¹⁄₆₄	.001–.003	.001–.003	.3715–.3725	.3715–.3725
1969	6-199, 232	Hydraulic③		④	②	1¹³⁄₁₆	195 @ 1⁷⁄₁₆	.001–.003	.001–.003	.3715–.3725	.3715–.3725
	8-290, 343, 390	Hydraulic③		①	⑤	1¹³⁄₁₆	200 @ 1²⁵⁄₆₄	.001–.003	.001–.003	.3715–.3725	.3715–.3725
1970	6-199, 232	Hydraulic③		④	②	1¹³⁄₁₆	195 @ 1⁷⁄₁₆	.001–.003	.001–.003	.3715–.3725	.3715–.3725
	V8-304, 360, 390	Hydraulic③		①	⑦	1¹³⁄₁₆	200 @ 1²⁵⁄₆₄	.001–.003	.001–.003	.3715–.3725	.3715–.3725
	8-390⑥	Hydraulic③		①	⑦	1¹³⁄₁₆	189 @ 1²³⁄₆₄	.001–.003	.001–.003	.3715–.3725	.3715–.3725
1971	6-232, 258	Hydraulic③		⑦	②	1¹³⁄₁₆	195 @ 1⁷⁄₁₆	.001–.003	.001–.003	.3715–.3725	.3715–.3725
	V8-304, 360, 401	Hydraulic③		①	⑤	1¹³⁄₁₆	189 @ 1²³⁄₆₄	.001–.003	.001–.003	.3715–.3725	.3715–.3725
1972	6-232, 258	Hydraulic③		⑦	②	1¹³⁄₁₆	195 @ 1⁷⁄₁₆	.001–.003	.001–.003	.3715–.3725	.3715–.3725
	V8-304, 360, 401	Hyrdaulic③		①	⑤	1¹³⁄₁₆	218 @ 1²³⁄₆₄	.001–.003	.001–.003	.3715–.3725	.3715–.3725

①—Intake 30°, exhaust 45°.
②—Intake 29°, exhaust 44°.
③—No adjustment.
④—Intake 30°, exhaust 44°.
⑤—Intake 29°, exhaust 44½°.
⑥—Rebel Machine.
⑦—Intake 30°, exhaust 44½°.

ENGINE TIGHTENING SPECIFICATIONS★

★Torque specifications are for clean and lightly lubricated threads only. Dry or dirty threads produce increased friction which prevents accurate measurement of tightness.

Year	Engine Model	Spark Plugs Ft. Lbs.	Cylinder Head Bolts Ft. Lbs.	Intake Manifold Ft. Lbs.	Exhaust Manifold Ft. Lbs.	Rocker Arm Shaft Bracket Ft. Lbs.	Rocker Arm Cover Ft. Lbs.	Connecting Rod Cap Bolts Ft. Lbs.	Main Bearing Cap Bolts Ft. Lbs.	Flywheel to Crankshaft Ft. Lbs.	Vibration Damper or Pulley Ft. Lbs.
1966–68	6-199, 6-232	25–30	80–85	20–25	20–25	...	40–45①	27–30	75–85	100–110	70–80
1969	6-199, 232	25–30	80–85	20–25	20–25	...	45–55①	26–30	75–85	100–110	50–60
1970	6-199, 232, 258	25–30	75–85	20–25	20–25	...	45–55①	26–30	75–85	100–110	50–60
1971–72	6-232, 258	25–30	80–85	20–25	20–25	...	45–55①	26–30	75–85	100–110	50–60
1966	V8-287, 327	25–30	58–62	20–25	20–25	...	3–5	46–50	③	100–110	70–80
1966–68	V8-290, 343	25–30	90–100	40–45	30–35	65–70②	20–30①	27–30	95–105	100–110	45–55
1969	V8-290, 343	25–30	90–100	40–45	30–35	65–70②	20–30①	26–30	95–105	100–110	50–60
1970–71	V8-304, 360	25–30	105–115	40–45	30–35	65–70②	20–30①	26–30	95–105	100–110	50–60
1972	V8-304, 360	25–30	105–115	40–45	30–35	65–70②	45–55①	26–30	95–105	100–110	50–60
1968–69	V8-390	25–30	90–100	40–45	30–35	65–70②	20–30①	35–40	95–105	100–110	50–60
1970–71	V8-390, 401	25–30	105–115	40–45	30–35	65–70②	20–30①	35–40	95–105	100–110	50–60
1972	V8-401	25–30	105–115	40–45	30–35	65–70②	45–55①	35–40	95–105	100–110	50–60

①—Inch pounds. ②—Rocker arm stud. ③—Rear 50 to 55, others 80 to 85.

DISTRIBUTOR SPECIFICATIONS

★If advance is checked on vehicle, double the R.P.M. and degrees advance to get crankshaft figures.

Year	Model	Distributor Part No.①	Breaker Gap	Dwell Angle Deg.	Breaker Arm Spring Tension	Centrifugal Advance Degrees @ RPM. of Distributor★		Vacuum Advance		Dist. Retard
						Advance Starts	Full Advance	Inches of Vacuum To Start Plunger	Max. Adv. Dist. Deg. @ Vacuum	Max. Ret. Dist. Deg. @ Vacuum
1966	6-199, 232	1110340	.016	31–34	17–21	2 @ 475	13 @ 2200	5–7	11 @ 16	—
	V8-287, 327	1111025	.016	28–32	17–21	2 @ 350	18 @ 1900	5–7	10 @ 15	—
	6-199, 232	1110366	.016	31–34	17–21	2 @ 400	16 @ 2200	5–7	11 @ 16	—
	V8-287, 327	1111130	.016	28–32	17–21	1 @ 325	20 @ 1850	5–7	10 @ 15	—
	V8-290	1111106	.016	29–31	17–21	1 @ 400	16 @ 2200	4–6	12 @ 18	—
1967	6-199, 232	1110340	.016	31–34	17–21	1 @ 475	13 @ 2200	5–7	11 @ 17	—
	6-199, 232	1110366	.016	31–34	17–21	2 @ 400	15½ @ 2200	5–7	11 @ 17	—
	6-199, 232	1DC-4601A	.019	36–42	17–21	1 @ 470	13 @ 2200	5–7	11 @ 17	—
	8-290 (9.0 C.R.)	1111106	.016	29–31	17–21	1 @ 400	16 @ 2200	4–6	12 @ 19	—
	8-290 (9.0 C.R.)	1BP-4201	.016	27–32	17–21	1 @ 435	16 @ 2200	4–6	12 @ 19	—
	8-290 (10.0 C.R.)	1111198	.016	29–31	17–21	1 @ 375	15 @ 1950	4–6	12 @ 19	—
	8-343	1111191	.016	29–31	17–21	1 @ 450	14 @ 2200	8–10	12 @ 19	—
	8-343	1BP-4201A	.016	27–32	17–21	1 @ 490	14 @ 2200	8–10	12 @ 19	—
1968–69	6-199, 232	1110444	.016	31–34	17–21	0 @ 350	13 @ 2000	5–7	11 @ 16½	—
	8-290 2 Bar. Carb.	1111106	.016	29–31	17–21	0 @ 400	16 @ 2200	4–6	12 @ 18½	—
	8-290 4 Bar. Carb.	1111198	.016	29–31	17–21	0 @ 375	15 @ 1950	4–6	12 @ 18½	—
	8-343 2 Bar. Carb.	1111472	.016	29–31	17–21	0 @ 450	14 @ 2200	4–6	12 @ 18½	—
	8-343 4 Bar. Carb.	1111191	.016	29–31	17–21	0 @ 450	14 @ 2200	8–10	12 @ 19½	—
	V8-343 4 Bar. Carb.	1111948	.016	29–31	17–21	1 @ 400	16 @ 2200	8–10	12 @ 20½	—
	V8-390	1111473	.016	29–31	17–21	0 @ 400	15 @ 2200	8–10	12 @ 19	—
1970	6-199, 232	1110481	.016	31–34	17–21	1 @ 450	13 @ 2250	5–7	9 @ 14½	4 @ 9
	6-232	1110444	.016	31–34	17–21	2 @ 450	14 @ 2200	5–7	11 @ 17	—
	8-304	1112018	.016	29–31	17–21	1 @ 500	14 @ 2200	—		5 @ 9
	8-304, 360 2 B. Carb.	1111988	.016	29–31	17–21	1 @ 500	14 @ 2100	5–7	9 @ 14½	5 @ 9
	8-360, 390 4 B. Carb.	1111987	.016	29–31	17–21	1 @ 450	13 @ 2000	5–7	9 @ 14½	5 @ 9
	8-390	1111473	.016	29–31	17–21	1 @ 400	16 @ 2200	8–10	12 @ 20½	5 @ 9
	8-390	1111948	.016	29–31	17–21	1 @ 400	16 @ 2200	4–6	12 @ 18½	—
1971	6-232, 258	1110340	.016	31–34	17–21	1 @ 450	13½ @ 2000	5–7	11½ @ 17	—
	8-304	1112028	.016	29–31	17–21	1 @ 450	14½ @ 2000	5–6	12½ @ 19	—
	8-360 2 B. Carb.②	1112028	.016	29–31	17–21	1 @ 450	14½ @ 2000	5–6	12½ @ 19	—
	8-360 2 B. Carb.③	1111948	.016	29–31	17–21	1 @ 400	16 @ 2200	4–6	12 @ 18½	—
	8-360 4 B. Carb.	1111948	.016	29–31	17–21	1 @ 400	16 @ 2200	4–6	12 @ 18½	—
	8-401	1111948	.016	29–31	17–21	1 @ 400	16 @ 2200	4–6	12 @ 18½	—
1972	6-232, 258	1110497	.016	31–34	17–21	½ @ 500	14 @ 2000	5–7	9 @ 11	—
	8-304, 360	1112111	.016	29–31	17–21	1 @ 550	15 @ 2000	5–7	9 @ 16	—
	8-401	1112112	.016	29–31	17–21	½ @ 450	14 @ 2000	5–7	9 @ 16	—

①—Stamped on distributor housing plate. ②—Synchromesh trans. ③—Automatic trans.

ALTERNATOR SPECIFICATIONS

| Year | Alternator | | | | | | | | Regulator | | | |
| | Make | Model | Ground Polarity | Rated Output | | Field Current | | Model | Regulator Test @ 120° F. | | |
				Amperes	Volts	Amperes ①	Volts		Ampere Load	Altern. R.P.M.	Volts
1966–68	Motorola	A-12NAM 453	Negative	35	15	2.0–2.6		R2AM 1②	10	1500	13.7–14.5
	Motorola	A-12NAM 552	Negative	40	15	1.8–2.4		R2AM 1②	10	1500	13.7–14.5
1967–68	Motorola	A-12NAM 455	Negative	35	12	2.0–2.6		R2AM 1②	10	1500	13.7–14.5
	Motorola	A-12NAM 553	Negative	40	12	1.8–2.4		R2AM 1②	10	1500	13.7–14.5
1969–71	Amer. Mtrs.	3195534	Negative	35	15	2.4–2.5	10	3195003②	10	2000	13.7–14.5
	Motorola	A-12NAM 456	Negative	35	14.2	2.0–2.6		R2AM 4②	10	2000	13.7–14.5
	Motorola	A-12NAM 606	Negative	55	15	1.8–2.4		R2AM 4②	10	2000	13.7–14.5

①—Excessive current drawn indicates shorted field winding. No current draw indicates an open winding.
②—Regulator is a sealed assembly, requiring no adjustments.

STARTING MOTOR SPECIFICATIONS

| Year | Part No. ② | Rotation ① | Brush Spring Tension, Ounces | No Load Test | | | Torque Test | | |
				Amperes	Volts	R.P.M.	Amperes	Volts	Torque, Lbs. Ft.
1966	1107282	C	35 Min.	65-100	10.6	3600–5100	470	5.1	12
	1107349	C	35 Min.	49–76	10.6	6200–9400	270–310	4.3	—
	1107731	C	35 Min.	64	10.6	7800	290	4.25	10.5
	C6FF-11001B	C	40	70	12	9500	180–220	—	
1967	1107349	C	35	49–76	10.6	6200–9400	270–310	4.3	—
	110832	C	35	49–87	10.6	6200–10700	290–425	4.2	—
	MDY-6112	C	35	80	10.0	4000 Min	405	4.0	—
	C6FF-11001B	C	40	70	12	9500	180–220	—	
1968	1108384	C	35	49–87	10.6	6200–10700	290–425	4.2	—
	MDY-6113	C	35	80	10.0	4000	405	4.0	—
	C7FF-11001B	C	40	70	12	9500	500	4.5	—
1969–70	C7FF-11001-B	C	40	65	12	9250	500	4.5	—
	C9FF-11001-A	C	40	65	12	9250	500	4.5	—
1971	—	C	40	65	12	9250	600	3.4	—
1972	—	C	40	65	12	9250	600	4.5	—

①—As viewed from drive end.   C—Clockwise.   ②—Stamped on plate riveted to side of housing.

REAR AXLE SPECIFICATIONS

Year	Model	Carrier Type ②	Ring Gear & Pinion Backlash		Pinion Bearing Preload			Differential Bearing Preload		
			Method	Adjustment	Method	New Bearings Inch-Lbs.	Used Bearings Inch-Lbs.	Method	New Bearings Inch-Lbs.	Used Bearings Inch-Lbs.
1966	Amb. 6	Integral	Shims	.006–.009	Shims	17–28①	17–28①	Shims	.004–.008	.004–.008
	Other 6s	Integral	Shims	.006–.009	Shims	15–25①	15–25①	Shims	.004–.008	.004–.008
	V8s	Integral	Shims	.006–.009	Shims	17–28①	17–28①	Shims	.004–.008	.004–.008
1967–68	6 Cyl.	Integral	Shims	.006–.009	Shims	15–25①	15–25①	Shims	.004–.009	.004–.009
	V8s	Integral	Shims	.006–.009	Spacer	17–28①	17–28①	Shims	.005–.010	.005–.010
1969	6 Cyl.	Integral	Shims	.005–.009	Shims	15–25①	15–25①	Shims	.008	.008
	V8s	Integral	Shims	.005–.009	Spacer	17–28①	17–28①	Shims	.008	.008
1970	7 7/16" Dr. Gr.	Integral	Shims	.005–.009	Sleeve	15–25①	15–25①	Shims	.008	.008
	8 7/8" Dr. Gr.	Integral	Shims	.005–.009	Sleeve	17–28①	17–28①	Shims	.008	.008
1971–72	7 9/16" Dr. Gr.	Integral	Shims	.005–.009	Sleeve	15–25①	15–25①	Shims	.008	.008
	8 7/8" Dr. Gr.	Integral	Shims	.005–.009	Sleeve	17–28①	17–28①	Shims	.008	.008

①—Adjust at drive pinion flange nut with inch-pound torque wrench. 　②—Axle shaft end play .006".

WHEEL ALIGNMENT SPECIFICATIONS

OLD CAR SPECIFICATIONS: For 1946–65 Wheel Alignment Specifications see back of book.

Year	Model	Caster Angle, Degrees		Camber Angle, Degrees				Toe-In. Inch	Toe-Out on Turns, Deg.①	
				Limits		Desired				
		Limits	Desired	Left	Right	Left	Right		Outer Wheel	Inner Wheel
1966	Man. Steer.	0 to +½	+¼	−¼ to +¼	−¼ to +¼	Zero	Zero	1/16–3/16	17¾⑤	20
	Power Steer.	+¾ to +1½	+1½	−¼ to +¼	−¼ to +¼	Zero	Zero	1/16–3/16	17¾⑤	20
1967	Man. Steer.	−½ to +½	Zero	−3/8 to +3/8	−3/8 to +3/8	Zero	Zero	1/8	—	—
	Power Steer.	+½ to +1½	+1	−3/8 to +3/8	−3/8 to +3/8	Zero	Zero	1/8	—	—
1968	American ②	−½ to +½	Zero	−3/8 to +3/8	−3/8 to +3/8	Zero	Zero	1/8	18' 40"	20
	American ③	+½ to +1½	+¾	−3/8 to +3/8	−3/8 to +3/8	Zero	Zero	1/8	18' 40"	20
	Rebel, Amb.	0 to −1	−½	−3/8 to +3/8	−3/8 to +3/8	Zero	Zero	1/8	17' 46"	20
	AMX, Javelin②	−½ to +½	Zero	−3/8 to +3/8	−3/8 to +3/8	Zero	Zero	1/8	18	20
	AMX, Javelin③	+½ to +1½	+¾	−3/8 to +3/8	−3/8 to +3/8	Zero	Zero	1/8	18	20
1969	Rebel, Amb.	0 to −1	−½	−3/8 to +3/8	−3/8 to +3/8	Zero	Zero	1/8	22	25
	Others②	−½ to +½	Zero	−3/8 to +3/8	−3/8 to +3/8	Zero	Zero	1/8	22	25
	Others③	+½ to +1½	+¾	−3/8 to +3/8	−3/8 to +3/8	Zero	Zero	1/8	22	25
1970	Man. Steer.④	−½ to +½	Zero	−3/8 to +3/8	−3/8 to +3/8	Zero	Zero	1/16–3/16	22	25
	Power Steer.④	+½ to 1½	+1	−3/8 to +3/8	−3/8 to +3/8	Zero	Zero	1/16–3/16	22	25
	Javelin	+½ to +1½	+1	−3/8 to +3/8	−3/8 to +3/8	Zero	Zero	1/16–3/16	22	25
1971	All Models	+½ to +1½	+1	−3/8 to +3/8	−3/8 to +3/8	Zero	Zero	1/16–3/16	22	25
1972	All Models	—	+1	—	—	+3/8	+1/8	1/8	22	25

①—Incorrect toe-out when other adjustments are correct, indicates bent steering arms. 　④—Except Javelin.
②—Manual steering. 　⑤—American 18⅔°.
③—Power Steering.

BRAKE SPECIFICATIONS

Year	Model	Brake Drum Inside Diameter	Wheel Cylinder Bore Diameter			Master Cylinder Bore Diameter		
			Disc Brake	Front Drum Brake	Rear Drum Brake	Disc Brakes	Drum Brakes	Power Brakes
1966	American	9	—	1 3/8	15/16	—	1	1
	Marlin	10	2	1 3/16	15/16	—	1	1
	Classic 6	9	2	1 1/8	15/16	—	1	1
	Classic V8	10	2	1 3/16	15/16	—	1	1
	Ambassador 6	10	2	1 3/32	15/16	—	1	1
	Ambassador V8	10	2	1 3/16	15/16	—	1	1
1967	American 6-Cyl.	9	—	1 1/8	15/16	—	7/8	7/8
	All Other 6-Cyl.	9	—	1 1/8	15/16	—	1	1
	Rogue V8	10	—	1 3/16	29/32	—	1	1
	Ambassador & Marlin V8	9	—	1 3/16	15/16	—	1	1
	Rebel Wagon	9	—	1 3/32	15/16	—	1	1
	Cars with Disc Brakes	10	2	—	1	1	—	1
	6-Cyl. Wagons, Disc Brakes	10	2	—	1 1/8	1	—	1
	V8 Wagons, Disc Brakes	10	2	—	15/16	1	—	1
1968	American, Javelin 6-Cyl.	9	—	1 1/8	15/16	—	1	1
	Rebel (Except Wagon) 6-Cyl.	9	—	1 1/8	15/16	—	1	1
	All V8s & Rebel 6 Wagon	10	—	1 3/16②	15/16①	—	1	1
	All V8s with Disc Brakes	10	2	—	15/16	1	—	1
1969	American, Javelin 6-Cyl.	9	—	1 1/8	15/16	—	1	1
	Rebel (Except Wagon) 6-Cyl.	9	—	1 1/8	15/16④	—	1	1
	All V8s & Rebel 6 Wagon	10	—	1 3/16③	15/16④	—	1	1
	All V8s with Disc Brakes	10	2	—	1	1	—	1
1970	Gremlin	9	—	1 1/8	15/16	—	1	1
	Hornet, Javelin 6-Cyl.	9	—	1 1/8	15/16	—	1	1
	Ambassador, Rebel 6-Cyl.	10	—	1 1/8	15/16	—	1	1
	AMX, Hornet, Javelin V8	10	—	—	—	—	1	1
	Rebel V8	10	—	—	—	—	1	1
	All with Disc Brakes	10	2	—	1	1	—	1
1971	Gremlin	9	—	1 1/8	7/8	—	1	1
	Hornet, Javelin 6-Cyl.	9	—	1 1/8	7/8	—	1	1
	Matador, Amb. 6-Cyl.	10	—	1 3/32	15/16	—	1	1
	Hornet, Javelin V8	10	2 3/4	1 3/16	7/8	⑤	1	1
	Matador, Amb. V8	10	2 3/4	1 3/16	15/16⑥	1 1/8	1	1
1972	Gremlin 6-Cyl.	9	2 3/4	1 1/8	13/16	1⑦	1	1
	Gremlin V8	9	2 3/4	1 3/16	7/8	1 1/16	1	1
	Hornet, Javelin 6-Cyl.	9	2 3/4	1 1/8	7/8	1⑦	1	1
	Hornet, Javelin V8	10	2 3/4	1 3/16	7/8	1⑦	1	1
	Matador, Amb. 6-Cyl.	10	2 3/4	1 3/32	15/16	1 1/8	1	1
	Matador, Amb. V8	10	2 3/4	1 3/16	15/16	1 1/8	1	1

①—7/8″ on American, AMX and Javelin V8.
②—3/32″ on Rebel Six.
③—3/32″ on V8-343, 390 wagons.
④—7/8″ on Rambler, Javelin and AMX.
⑤—Manual 1 1/16″, power 1″.
⑥—1″ on wagons.
⑦—Non power disc brakes 1 1/16″.

American Motors

COOLING SYSTEM & CAPACITY DATA

★NOTE: Alcohol should not be used in Rambler engines having aluminum components in contact with the coolant. When only water is used a good corrosion inhibitor must be added to the system. Failure to use an inhibited coolant may result in severe corrosion damage to the cooling system components.

Year	Model or Engine	Cooling Capacity, Qts.			Radiator Cap Relief Pressure, Lbs.		Thermo. Opening Temp. ①	Fuel Tank Gals.	Engine Oil Refill Qts. ②	Transmission Oil			Rear Axle Oils Pint
		No Heater	With Heater	With A/C	With A/C	No. A/C				3 Speed Pints	4 Speed Pints	Auto. Trans. Qts. ⑩	
1966	American 6	9½	10½	10½	14	14	195	16	4	1½	—	9	3
	American V8	13	14	14	14	14	195	16	4	—	3½	9	4
	Rambler 6	9½	10½	10½	14	14	195	19⑦	4	2¼	—	9	4
	V8-287, 327	18	19	19	14	14	195	19⑦	4	4	3½	11	4
1967	American 6 Cyl.	9½	10½	10½	14	14	195	16	4	1½	—	9	3
	Other 6 Cyl.	9½	10½	10½	14	14	195	16	4	1½	—	9	4
	V8-290	13	14	14	14	14	195	21½⑧	4	2½	3½	9	4
	V8-343	12	13	13	14	14	195	21½⑧	4	—	3½	10	4
1968	6-199, 232	9½	10½	10½	14	14	195	⑨	4	1½	—	9	3
	V8-290	12	13	13	14	14	195	⑨	4	2½	3½	10	4
	V8-343, 390	13	14	14	14	14	195	⑨	4	2½	3½	10	4
1969	6-199, 232	9½	10½	10½	14	14	195⑪	⑫	4	1½⑬	—	9	3
	V8-290	13	14	14	14	14	195	⑫	4	3	2½	⑭	4
	V8-343, 390	12	13	13	14	14	195	⑫	4	—	2½	11	4
1970	6-199, 232	9½	10½	10½	14	14	195	⑮	4	1½⑬	—	9½	3
	V8-304	13	14	14	14	14	195	⑮	4	3	2½	9½	4
	V8-360, 390	12	13	13	14	14	195	⑮	4	—	2½	10	4
1971	6-232	9½	10½	10½	14	14	205	③	4	1½⑬	—	9½	④
	6-258	9½	10½	10½	14	14	205	③	4	2½	—	9½	④
	V8-304	13	14	14	14	14	195	③	4	2½	2½	9½	4
	V8-360, 401	12	13	13	14	14	195	③	4	3	2½	10	4
1972	6-232	9½	10½	10½	14	14	205	⑤	4	1½⑬	—	8½	④
	6-258	9½	10½	10½	14	14	205	⑤	4	1½⑬	—	8½	④
	V8-304	13	14	14	14	14	195	⑤	4	3	2½	9½	4
	V8-360, 401	12	13	13	14	14	195	⑤	4	3	2½	9½	4

①—With alcohol-type anti-freeze use a 170° unit.
②—Add one quart with filter change.
③—Gremlin, 21; Hornet & Javelin, 16; Ambassador wagons & Matador 3 seat wagon, 17; all others, 19½.
④—Matador & Ambassador, 4; all others, 3.
⑤—Hornet, 16; Gremlin, 21; Javelin, 16; Matador & Ambassador sedans, 19½; Matador 2 seat wagons, 19½; Matador 3 seat wagons, 21½; Ambassador wagons, 21½.

⑦—17 gals. for 3-seat wagon.
⑧—19 gals. for 3-seat wagon.
⑨—American 16.
AMX and Javelin 19.
Rebel & Ambassador 21½.
3-Seat Wagon 19.
⑩—Approximate. Make final check with dipstick.
⑪—Rambler Rogue with 6-232 uses 205°.

⑫—Rambler 16.
AMX and Javelin 19.
Rebel 3-seat wagon and Amb. wagon 19.
All Others 21½.
⑬—Fully synchronized 2½.
⑭—With 2 barrel carb. 9; with 4 barrel carb. 11.
⑮—Rebel and Ambassador sedans, 21½, Rebel 2 seat wagons, 21½. All others 19. California vehicles about 2 gal. less.

Electrical Section

DISTRIBUTOR, REPLACE

1. Disconnect distributor primary wire from coil terminal.
2. Remove distributor cap and rotor. *Mark position of rotor arm on distributor housing so distributor can be installed in same position.*
3. Remove vacuum line from distributor.
4. Remove distributor hold-down clamp.
5. Note relative position of distributor in block, then work it out of the engine.

Installation

1. Turn rotor about 1/8 of a turn counterclockwise past the mark previously placed on the distributor housing.
2. Push the distributor down into the block with the housing in the normal "installed" position. *On gear-driven distributors, it may be necessary to move the rotor slightly to start gear into mesh with camshaft gear, but rotor should line up with mark when distribuor is down in place.*
3. Tighten distributor clamp screw snugly and connect vacuum line, primary wire to coil, and install cap.

V8 Note

If the engine was disturbed while the distributor was removed from the engine, first crank the engine to bring No. 1 piston up on its compression stroke and continue cranking until the timing mark is adjacent to the timing indicator. Then rotate the distributor cam until the rotor is in position to fire No. 1 cylinder. Install the distributor as outlined above and set the ignition timing as directed in front of this manual.

STARTER, REPLACE

To remove starter, disconnect cable from battery. Disconnect cable and solenoid lead wire from solenoid switch. Remove starter attaching bolts and take off starter.

IGNITION SWITCH, REPLACE

1970-72

The ignition switch on all models is mounted on the lower section of the steering column and is connected to the lock by a remote control rod. To remove switch, place key in Off-Lock position and remove mounting screws. Disconnect switch from remote control rod, remove wire harness and remove switch. When installing switch, place switch and ignition lock in Off-Lock position and insert a 3/32" drill into the switch aligning

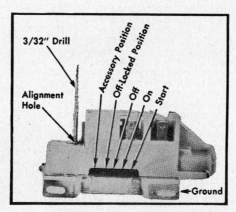

Fig. 1   Ignition switch alignment. 1970-72

hole, Fig. 1. With drill in place, install switch on remote control rod. Remove all slack by sliding switch toward the steering wheel. Install mounting screws, remove drill and connect wire harness.

1969 Rebel & Ambassador

1. Remove escutcheon nut from switch.
2. Disconnect wires and remove switch.

1967-68 All; 1969 AMX, Javelin & Rambler

Remove ignition switch from rear of instrument panel by holding switch escutcheon while pressing switch assembly toward instrument panel and turning counterclockwise.

The multi-wire connector on the switch should be removed after the switch is removed from the instrument panel. The multi-wire connector is locked to the switch by plastic fingers which are part of the connector and must be released before removing the connector.

NOTE: The AMX and Javelin have a separate ground wire added to the ignition switch plate.

All 1966

1. Disconnect a battery cable.
2. Disconnect switch wires.
3. Compress switch from rear, turn clockwise and remove switch from rear. Switch bezel is removed from front.

NOTE: After the switch is removed the lock cylinder can be removed from the switch by inserting a paper clip through the small hole in the face or side of the switch. Then depress the lock pin and remove the lock.

LIGHT SWITCH, REPLACE
1971-72 Javelin

1. Remove knob from toggle switch by depressing a small spring steel retaining tab up toward the handle.
2. Remove seven screws from steering column lower cover and remove cover.
3. Remove wire connections, two retaining screws and remove switch.

1966-70 & 1971-72 Except Javelin

1. Disconnect a battery cable.
2. With switch in full "Off" position ("On" position for 1969-72 models) press button on side or top of switch to release shaft and knob assembly.
3. Remove switch mounting sleeve nut.
4. Disconnect wire harness connector.
5. Reverse procedure to install. Position switch so that shaft is lined up properly before tightening.

STOP LIGHT SWITCH, REPLACE

When replacing the switch, have the new switch ready for installation as soon as the old switch is removed from the master cylinder to avoid undue loss of brake fluid.

NEUTRAL SAFETY SWITCH
1966-72 Console Type

The switch is located on the right side of the selector shaft under the console. It also functions as a back-up light switch, therefore, the following adjustments will automatically adjust the back-up light switch for proper contact when the shift lever is in the "R" position.
1. Remove selector knob from shaft.
2. Unfasten and lift console up and over selector shaft.
3. Place selector lever in neutral.
4. Use a 3/32" drill as an aligning pin. Insert the pin in the hole on the face of the switch. If necessary, move switch until pin enters freely into hole in switch toggle. *Switch toggle must enter into slot of actuating tab.*
5. Secure two screws that fasten switch to pivot bracket and remove aligning pin.
6. When switch is adjusted properly, engine will start only in Park or Neutral.

1966-72 Steering Column Type

The neutral safety switch also functions as a back-up light switch (when the car is so equipped). Therefore, the following adjustments will automatically adjust the back-up light switch for proper contact when the gear selector lever is

in the "R" position.
1. Loosen two screws that secure switch to steering jacket tube.
2. Place selector lever in "N".
3. Using a 3/32" drill as an aligning pin, insert the pin in the hole on the face of the switch. If necessary, rotate the switch until the pin enters freely in the hole in the switch toggle.
4. Tighten the switch screws and remove aligning pin.

TURN SIGNAL SWITCH, REPLACE

1970-72

1. Disconnect negative battery cable.
2. Remove steering wheel.
3. Loosen anti-theft cover retaining screws and lift cover from column. *It is not necessary to remove these screws completely as they are held on the cover by plastic retainers.*
4. Using a suitable tool, depress lock plate and pry out snap ring from steering shaft groove.
5. Remove tool, lock plate, cancelling cam, upper bearing preload spring and thrust washer.
6. Place directional signal lever in right turn position and remove lever.
7. Depress hazard warning light switch and remove the button by turning in a counterclockwise direction.
8. Remove directional signal wire harness from mounting bracket on lower column. On Shift Command, column shift, use a stiff wire to depress lock tab which retains the shift quadrant light wire in connector block.
9. Remove directional signal switch screws and remove switch.

1967-68 Tilt Column; 1969 All

1. Perform steps 1 to 5 as outlined for non-tilt columns.
2. Remove turn signal cover, switch retaining screws and switch.
3. Reverse procedure to install.

1967-68 Non-Tilt Column

1. Disconnect a battery cable.
2. Remove cover and pull off steering wheel.
3. Remove cancelling cam, turn signal switch lever, hazard warning knob and light shield (if equipped).
4. Remove plastic trim that covers column support plate. Remove signal switch wiring harness protector from lower side of column. *Do not remove column support plate.*
5. Disconnect signal switch connector from main harness. Remove terminals from switch harness. *Do not cut switch harness wires.*
6. Remove upper bearing snap ring and flat and wave washers.
7. Remove turn signal cover by loosening switch screws until cover can be rotated counterclockwise and remove cover from column.
8. Remove switch from turn signal cover, noting position of shift gate, springs and upper bearing retainer.
9. Reverse procedure to install.

1966

The turn signal switch is mounted to a bracket at the upper end of the jacket tube just below the steering wheel, which must be removed to get at the switch.

The signal switch cam is installed with an interference fit in the lower section of the steering wheel.

In diagnosing turn signal problems, the fuse, bulbs, wiring a good ground should be checked. A known good signal switch can be connected to the signal switch wire harness connector to determine whether the switch is defective.

On models having a wire harness attach a piece of string or fine wire to the signal switch harness. Leaving the string or wire in the steering column serves as an aid in replacement of the switch.

HORN SOUNDER & STEERING WHEEL

Disconnect battery. Remove horn button or ring. This is retained by screws from under the steering wheel on some models and is rubber mounted and can be pulled up on others. Remove steering wheel with a puller. Note line up of dash marks on steering shaft and wheel and align these marks when wheel is installed.

INSTRUMENT CLUSTER

1971 Hornet & Gremlin

1. If so equipped, the package tray must be removed to gain access to speedometer cable, light switch and wiper control.
2. Disconnect battery.
3. Remove wiper control knob and spanner nut.
4. Disconnect speedometer cable at rear of cluster.
5. Remove three top and two side screws from cluster overlay.
6. Partially remove cluster from instrument panel to gain access to harness connectors. **NOTE:** If equipped with low fuel warning system, remove relay mounting screw at lower left side of panel and remove complete system with the cluster.

1971 Matador & Ambassador

1. Disconnect battery and remove screws from cluster overlay.
2. Remove A/C thermostat control knob if so equipped.
3. Remove overlay.
4. Remove screws securing cluster to panel.
5. Disconnect speedometer cable from behind panel.
6. Remove cluster disconnect plug and flasher unit.
7. Remove low fuel warning relay mounting screw at lower side of panel, if so equipped.
8. Remove cluster assembly.

1971 Javelin

1. Disconnect battery.
2. Cover painted surface of column

with a cloth.
3. Remove the top, side and lower screws around bezel.
4. If equipped with radio, remove control knobs and retaining nuts.
5. Remove knobs from four instrument panel switches.
6. If equipped with A/C, release the speedometer cable hold-down clip on wheelhouse panel to allow movement of cable.
7. Move bezel and cluster out of opening far enough to reach in and disconnect speedometer cable, wire harness plug and wire connections.
8. The cluster can be removed from bezel by removing eight screws from reverse side.

1970 Hornet & Gremlin

1. Disconnect negative battery cable.
2. Cover steering column to prevent scratching and remove package tray if so equipped.
3. Disconnect speedometer cable.
4. Remove control knobs and retaining nuts from wiper and headlight switch.
5. Remove bezel retaining screws and remove bezel and cluster toward the center of the car as an assembly.
6. Disconnect all wires and lamps from rear of cluster.

1967-68 American; 1969 Rambler

1. Disconnect battery.
2. Remove cigar lighter and ignition switch.
3. Remove W/S wiper switch knob.
4. Remove light switch knob and shaft.
5. Remove flasher unit.
6. Disconnect speedometer cable housing at rear of cluster.
7. Remove two Phillips head screws at top of cluster overlay.
8. Partially remove cluster from instrument panel to gain access for removal of cluster pin plug.
9. Remove cluster assembly.
10. Reverse procedure to install.

1967-68 Except American; 1969 Except Rambler 1970 Except Hornet & Gremlin

1. Disconnect battery.
2. Remove screws from cluster overlay.
3. Remove overlay.
4. Remove screws securing cluster to instrument panel.
5. Remove pin plug and cluster.
6. Disconnect speedometer cable and parking brake light.

IMPORTANT: Spring metal grounding clip is required between cluster and Weather-eye controls. Also between clock or tachometer of AMX, Javelin. Be sure to install clip upon assembly of cluster if it was removed.

1966 American

1. Disconnect battery.
2. Remove ash tray and bracket, radio and instrument cluster overlay panel.
3. Remove Weather Eye console, bulb and socket.
4. On A/C cars, the air discharge outlet assembly and glove box must

be removed. For access to the center attaching screw of the air discharge outlet, remove center discharge outlet bezel and vent assembly.

5. Disconnect speedometer cable and printed circuit plug. Remove wire harness clips attached to cluster.
6. The light switch, ignition switch and windshield wiper control need only be removed from the mounting on the panel and placed aside to provide clearance for removal of cluster.
7. Mask or tape cluster lens to prevent scratches.
8. Pull down on cluster to remove two upper tabs from slotted rubber mounting brackets.
9. Route cluster through rear of instrument panel and remove at bottom center. On A/C cars the cluster must be routed over the A/C evaporator and removed through glove box opening.

1966 Classic

1. Disconnect battery.
2. Remove flasher harness and printed circuit connectors and speedometer cable.
3. Remove two $5/16$" hex screws holding wire harness to rear of cluster.
4. Remove instrument cluster opening moulding with a fiber stick.
5. Remove four screws holding instrument panel bezel overlay to panel.
6. Mask panel lens to prevent scratches.
7. Remove four screws that hold cluster to panel.
8. On air conditioned cars remove discharge grille assembly.
9. Cluster and bezel assembly is then removed from front of panel.

1966 Ambassador & Marlin

1. Disconnect battery.
2. Remove flasher harness and printed circuit connectors and speedometer cable.
3. Remove two $5/16$" hex screws holding wire harness to rear of cluster.
4. Remove windshield wiper control.
5. Remove cluster opening inner and outer mouldings with a fiber stick.
6. Remove two cluster bezel screws.
7. Remove screws holding cluster bezel to panel.
8. If equipped with air conditioning, remove discharge grille or cover used in its place when not so equipped.
9. On cars with automatic transmission column shift and adjustable tilt wheel, steering column mounting bracket bolts should be loosened to allow clearance for cluster and bezel to be removed.
10. Remove cluster from bezel.

W/S WIPER MOTOR, REPLACE

1966-68 Rambler, 1969-71 Rebel, Ambassador & Matador

1. Remove wiper arms and blades and cowl air intake cover.

2. Slide link to motor retainer clip off motor arm stud which is accessible through cowl top opening. Remove link from motor.
3. On vacuum type motor, disconnect control cable and hose from motor, then remove motor and mounting plate from dash panel.
4. On models with electric wiper, disconnect switch-to-motor female connectors at switch and remove through main wire harness grommet. Remove wiper motor and mounting plate.

1966-68 American, AMX & Javelin; 1969-71 Rambler, AMX, Javelin & Gremlin

1. To remove wiper motor, remove four screws holding motor to dash panel.
2. Remove hose and control cable from vacuum type motor. On electric motors, separate wiper harness plug under instrument panel.
3. Tilt motor and slide link-to-motor retaining clip off of stud and remove motor.

W/S WIPER TRANSMISSION, REPLACE

1966-68 Rambler, 1969-71 Rebel, Ambassador & Matador

1. Remove wiper arms and blades.
2. Remove cowl air intake cover.
3. Disconnect link-to-motor retainer and link from wiper arm through cowl top opening.
4. Close hood and remove two capscrews holding each pivot shaft body to cowl top.
5. Remove both pivot body and link assemblies as a unit through cowl top opening.
6. Pivot shaft bodies may than be removed by sliding retainer off stud.

NOTE

When installing pivot shaft bodies to cowl top, the assist spring must be in a position to engage rubber sleeved stud on vacuum wiper. There are no assist springs on electric wipers.

1966-68 American, AMX & Javelin; 1969-71 Rambler, AMX, Javelin, Hornet & Gremlin

1. Remove wiper arms and blades.
2. Remove pivot shaft-to-cowl top nuts.
3. Remove wiper motor.
4. Slide pivot shaft body and link assembly to the left to clear right pivot shaft opening and move assembly to the right side of car to remove as a unit.

NOTE

When installing pivot shafts to cowl top, flat side of pivot shaft indexes flat side of hole in cowl top when pivot shaft is in up position.

W/S WIPER CONTROL, REPLACE

1970-71 Ambassador, Rebel & Matador

1. Disconnect negative battery cable.
2. Cover steering column to prevent scratching.
3. If so equipped, remove package tray and disconnect speedometer cable.
4. Remove control knob and retaining nut from the wiper control.
5. On vacuum wiper systems, disconnect control at the wiper motor.
6. Remove instrument cluster retaining screws and pull out cluster as a unit.
7. Remove vacuum wiper control.
8. On electrical systems, disconnect the electrical connections to the switch and remove switch.

1966-69 All, 1970-71 AMX, Javelin, Hornet & Gremlin

1. Remove control knob. The knob is retained either by a set screw or by a spring retainer. The spring retainer is released as follows: turn knob fully to right and insert Allen wrench in notch at small end of knob. Push toward shaft to raise spring out of groove and at same time pull knob off shaft.
2. On all models, after the knob has been removed, disconnect control cable from motor on vacuum wipers. On electric wipers, disconnect three female connectors from switch. Remove French nut to disengage switch from instrument panel.

NOTE: On vacuum wipers the control cable must be installed with the washer at the end of the control wire inserted in slot in slide valve. The conduit must butt against the shoulders of the anchoring slot and be fastened securely to assure positive opening and closing of the valve for efficient operation.

RADIO

NOTE: When installing radio, be sure to adjust antenna trimmer for peak performance.

1971 Matador & Ambassador

1. The radio is retained to the cluster by three screws adjacent to the face of the radio.
2. Disconnect battery.
3. Disconnect antenna and speaker leads from radio.
4. Remove instrument cluster overlay.
5. Remove radio lead from fuse panel.
6. Remove radio mounting screws and remove radio.

1971 Javelin

1. Disconnect battery.
2. Remove six attaching screws that lie next to lower edge at windshield.
3. Remove radio knobs and two retaining nuts.
4. Open the right door and remove the two panel attaching screws at the door pillar area.

5. Remove five attaching screws in the upper flange of the instrument cluster bezel.
6. Remove the moulding attaching screws and assist handle at lower right half of crash pad assembly and remove.
7. Remove three attaching screws in speaker mounting plate.
8. Remove speaker (AM radio only).
9. Slide radio back and lift up to disconnect speaker and bulb wires.
10. Remove radio power lead from fuse panel. Tie a heavy string to the wire to aid in dressing the wire back through the wiring and duct assemblies.
11. Remove radio.

1970-71 Hornet & Gremlin

1. Disconnect battery.
2. Remove package tray if so equipped.
3. Remove ash tray and bracket.
4. Remove radio knobs and shaft nuts.
5. Remove bezel retaining screws and bezel.
6. Disconnect antenna, speaker and power lead.
7. Remove radio.

1970 AMX & Javelin

1. Disconnect battery.
2. Remove four bezel retaining screws.
3. Remove knobs and shaft nuts.
4. Remove bezel.
5. Removing retaining screw from rear or radio.
6. Disconnect leads and remove radio.

1968-69 Javelin & AMX

1. Remove the ash tray.
2. Remove the retaining bolt in the ash tray which is threaded into the radio. With AM-Tapeplayer combination this bolt is not used. A retaining nut is used on the rear of the radio and must be removed.
3. Remove the shaft retaining nuts.
4. Disconnect all leads from radio and tip the rear of the radio up and to the toe board and remove from the rear edge of the panel.

NOTE: If equipped with A/C the air discharge duct must be removed to gain clearance.

1968 American; 1969 Rambler

1. Disconnect battery and remove antenna lead from radio.
2. Disconnect power lead from radio and unplug radio-to-speaker cable.
3. Remove control knobs and control shaft bushing retainer nuts.
4. Remove ash tray.
5. Remove phillips head screw which is threaded into cage nut on radio.
6. Radio can now be removed toward back and down from panel.

NOTE: If equipped with A/C it will be necessary to remove the glove box.

1968 Rambler
1969-70 Rebel & Ambassador

1. The radio is retained to the instru-

ment cluster by four screws adjacent to the face of the radio and a brace rod from the rear of the radio down to the instrument panel flange.
2. Disconnect the battery.
3. Disconnect antenna, power, ground and speaker leads from radio.
4. On 1968, remove brace bracket rod from instrument panel flange.
5. Remove instrument panel overlay and on 1968 models, remove instrument cluster.
6. Remove radio mounting screws and remove radio.

NOTE: Leads attached to radio must be drawn carefully through the opening while removing the radio to prevent damage to the wiring.

1966-67

1. Radio is retained to instrument panel by the control shaft bushing nuts.
2. Disconnect battery and remove antenna lead from radio.
3. Disconnect power lead from radio and unplug radio-to-speaker cable.
4. Pull knobs from radio and remove control shaft bushing retainer nuts.
5. Radio can now be removed toward back and down from instrument panel.

NOTE: On Rambler models with A/C, it will be necessary to remove the A/C discharge outlet assembly and connecting duct. On American models with A/C it will be necessary to remove the glove box.

HEATER CORE REMOVAL
1970-71 Hornet & Gremlin

1. Open heater valve and drain about 2 qts. from cooling system.
2. Disconnect heater hoses and plug heater core tubes.
3. Remove blower motor and fan.
4. Remove package tray if so equipped.
5. Disconnect wire connector at resistor.
6. Remove instrument panel bezel, outlet and duct.
7. Disconnect control cables from damper levers.

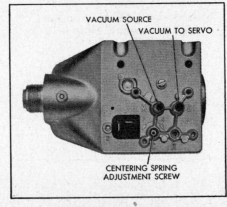

Fig. 1   Centering spring adjustment. 1967-71

8. Remove right side windshield pillar moulding and the instrument panel upper attaching screws and right side cap screw at the door hinge post.
9. Remove right side kick panel and heater housing attaching screws.
10. Pull the right side of the instrument panel slightly rearward and remove the housing.

1966-68 American, 1969 Rambler, 1968-70 AMX & Javelin

1. Open heater water valve and drain about 2 qts from cooling system.
2. After disconnecting hoses from heater core, install cork plugs in hoses and core tubes.
3. Disconnect blower motor wires and ground wire to dash panel.
4. Remove glove box and its door. On AMX and Javelin, it is necessary to remove glove box hinge bracket.
5. Disconnect outside air control cable at damper lever.
6. Remove three heater housing attaching screws in front compartment and lift out heater core and blower housing assembly.
7. Heater core is now accessible for removal.

1966-68 Except American; 1969-71 Rebel, Ambassador & Matador

1. Disconnect outside air damper cable at heater housing under dash.
2. Drain system and disconnect hoses.
3. Remove two lower attaching nuts for blower housing in engine compartment.
4. Remove glove box and door in order to remove remaining heater housing screws and lower heater and core housing as an assembly.
5. Slide heater core out of housing.

SPEED CONTROL
1967-71

Brake Release Switch, Adjust

1. Disconnect multiple connector at regulator.
2. Turn ignition switch to accessory position.
3. Using a test lamp, ground one test lamp lead and touch the other to terminal No. 2 in harness connector.
4. Adjust switch so that lamp will light when brake pedal is fully released and will go out when brake pedal is depressed about $1/4$ inch.
5. If switch cannot be adjusted, it is defective and should be replaced. Install new switch and repeat Step 4.
6. Remove test lamp, turn off ignition key and plug connector to regulator.

Chain Linkage, Adjust

Chain linkage should never be taut. To adjust, start engine, set carburetor at hot idle with anti-stall plunger backed off so as not to affect idle speed. Hook chain to accelerator linkage, pull taut, then loosen by length of one ball and *taut, do not pull so far as to cause throttle to open.*

Centering Springs, Adjust

If speed control system holds speed three or more mph higher than selected speed, turn centering spring adjusting screw (C) toward (S) $1/32''$ or less, Fig. 1.

If speed control system holds speed three or more mph below selected speed, turn centering spring adjusting screw (C) toward (F) $1/32''$ or less. *Do not move adjustment screw (R).*

Engine Section

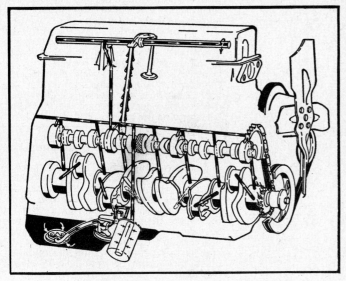

Engine oiling system.   6-199, 232, 258 engines

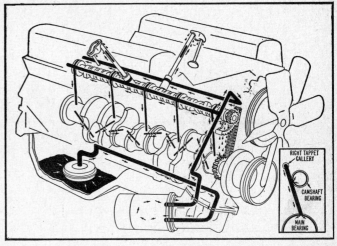

Engine oiling system.   V8-290, 304, 343, 360, 390, 401 engines

ENGINE MARKINGS

Engines are stamped with a three-letter code which is stamped adjacent to the engine identification code number. The code is as follows:

First letter means size of bore.

Second letter means size of main bearings.

Third letter means size of rod bearings.

Letter "A" means standard size.

Letter "B" means .010" undersize.

Letter "C" means .010" oversize.

Engines not so marked are standard in all respects.

On six-cylinder engines a five digit engine code number is located on a machined surface on the upper left corner of the engine block. On V8 engines the engine code number is stamped on a tag attached to the generator mounting bracket.

ENGINE REPLACE
All Models

1. Mark hood hinge location on hood panel to aid in installation and remove hood.
2. Remove battery and drain cooling system, crankcase and transmission.
3. Disconnect all wiring, tubing, hoses and linkage.
4. Disconnect exhaust pipe.
5. Remove radiator and air cleaner.
6. If so equipped, remove power steering pump, Air Guard pump and air conditioning compressor and condenser.
7. Support engine with lifting fixture.
8. Remove rear crossmember and disconnect torque tube, where used, from transmission extension.
9. On 1966 V8, disconnect brake tube bracket fastened to underside of body, disconnect shock absorbers at lower bracket, parking brake cable at equalizer and cable housing at torque tube bracket.
10. Also on 1966 V8, move rear axle rearward to remove front U-joint from transmission mainshaft.
11. Disconnect speedometer cable.
12. Disconnect gearshift linkage. On floor shift units, remove gear selector lever.

NOTE: On pre-1970 units, the selector lever is removed by removing boot then removing the two attaching bolts. On 1970 models, remove the boot then insert a .015"-.020" thick feeler blade alongside the driver's side of the lever between the spring steel barb and the lower part of the shaft lever.

13. Disconnect front engine support cushions from engine and lift engine forward and upward through hood opening while supporting driveshaft.

CYLINDER HEAD

Tighten cylinder head bolts a little at a time in three steps in the sequence shown in the illustrations. Final tightening should be to the torque specifications listed in the *Engine Tightening* table.

V8-290, 304, 343, 360, 390, 401

The cylinder block has two locating dowels on each bank to assist in lining up and holding the cylinder head and gasket in position during installation.

IMPORTANT: The No. 7 bolt shown in Fig. 5, second from front on the left bank, must have the threads sealed to prevent coolant leakage. Permatex No. 2 or equivalent is recommended.

V8-287, 327

The cylinder head block surface has two locating dowels to assist in lining up and holding the position of the head and gasket during installation and removal.

After installing push rods, rocker arms and cylinder head cap screws, tighten the cap screws in the sequence shown in Fig. 1, and to the torque values given in the *Engine Tightening Chart*.

The cylinder head and rocker arm cap screws are of various lengths and design, among which are two special tapped heads to accommodate the retaining screws that hold the rocker arm cover; three long plain cap screws to retain rocker arms and cylinder head, and one special bolt to index with oil holes for rocker arm lubrication. *This special $6\,3/8''$ long drilled bolt is part of the lubrication system and must be installed in the rear position to index with oil passages in the tappet area.*

6-199, 6-232, 258 Engines

IMPORTANT: The cylinder head bolt

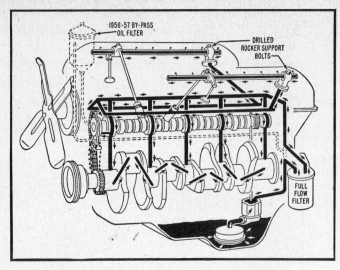

Engine oiling system. V8-287, 327

located at the left front corner of the head (No. 11, Fig. 4) must have the threads sealed to prevent coolant leakage. Permatex No. 2 or equivalent is recommended.

VALVE ARRANGEMENT
Front to Rear

All V8s . . . . E-I-I-E-E-I-I-E
6-199, 232, 258 . . . . . E-I-I-E-I-E-E-I-E-I-E

VALVE LIFT SPECS.

Year	Engine	Intake	Exhaust
1966-68	6-199, 232	.375	.375
1969-72	6-199, 232, 258	.381	.381
1966	V8-287	.375	.375
1966-67	V8-290	.425	.425
1966	V8-327	.375	.375
1967	V8-343	.425	.425
1968-69	V8-290, 343, 390	①	①
1970	V8 Except Machine	.425	.425
1970	Machine	.457	.457

①—Standard cam .425"; Hi-Perf. cam .477".

VALVE TIMING
Intake Opens Before TDC

Year	Engine	Degrees
1966-72	6-199, 232, 258	12½
1966	V8-287, 327	12½
1967-69	V8-290, 343	18½
1968-69	V8-390	18½
1970	V8 Exc. Machine	18½
1970	Machine	18
1971-72	V8-304, 360	14¾
1971	V8-401	25½

ROCKER ARMS
V8-290, 304, 343, 360, 390, 401

These engines have individually mounted rocker arms consisting of a rocker arm retaining stud, rocker arm pivot ball,

---

rocker arm and retaining nut to operate each valve, Fig. 6.

The rocker arm studs are threaded into the cylinder head. The threads are of such design to cause an interference fit; therefore, care must be taken that replacement studs be installed until the hexagon head is flush with the cylinder head and torqued to 65-70 ft-lbs.

The push rods are hollow, serving as oil galleries for lubricating each individual rocker arm assembly. Prior to installing, the push rods should be cleaned thoroughly, inspected for wear and deposits which may restrict the flow of oil to the rocker arm assembly.

The push rods also serve as guides to maintain correct rocker arm to valve stem relationship; therefore, a contact pattern on the push rods where they contact the cylinder head is normal.

When installing the rocker arm retaining nut, it is important that they be tightened until bottomed, using a torque of 20-25 ft-lbs.

Lubrication to each rocker arm is supplied by the corresponding hydraulic valve lifter. A metering system located in each valve lifter consists of a stepped lower surface on the push rod cap that contacts a flat plate, causing a restriction, Fig. 7. The restriction meters the amount of oil flow through the push rod cap, hollow push rod, and upper valve train components. A loss of lubrication to the rocker arm could be caused by a

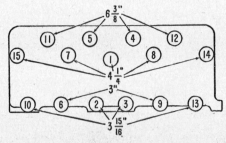

Fig. 1 Cylinder head tightening sequence and bolt length chart. 8-287, 327

---

restricted or plugged push rod or a defective hydraulic valve lifter.

CAUTION: Correct installation of push rods in these engines is critical and more than normal care must be taken upon installation. When placing the push rods through the guide hole in the cylinder head, it is important that the push rod end is inserted in the plunger cap socket. It is possible that the push rod may seat itself on the edge of the plunger cap which will restrict valve lifter rotation and lubrication to rocker arms.

It is recommended that, just prior to installation of the cylinder head covers, the engine be operated and the supply of lubrication to each rocker arm be visually inspected. If inspection reveals that an individual rocker arm is not being supplied with lubrication, the push rod and/or valve lifter must be inspected to determine the cause.

6-199, 6-232, 258 Engines

The pressure supply for each rocker arm is obtained from No. 5 camshaft bearing location where the camshaft meters the flow of oil from the main lubrication gallery through a groove in the camshaft bearing surface to a gallery extending upwards to the cylinder head gasket surface, Fig. 9. When installing the rocker arm shaft the oil holes must face down to the cylinder head, Fig. 10.

V8-287, 327 Engines

The rocker arm shaft assemblies are secured to the cylinder head with four long cylinder head and rocker arm shaft retaining screws, Fig. 11. The shafts are hollow and plugged at each end, serving as oil galleries for rocker arm, push rod end and valve stem lubrication.

Two different rocker arms are used to accommodate the angle from the shaft support to valve stems. However, the shaft assemblies are interchangeable from one cylinder bank to the other.

VALVE GUIDES
V8-290, 304, 343, 360, 390, 401 6-199, 6-232, 258 Engines

Excessive valve stem-to-guide clearance will cause lack of power, rough idling and noisy valves, and may cause valve breakage. Insufficient clearance will result in noisy and sticky functioning of valves and disturb engine smoothness of operation.

Valve stem-to-guide clearances are listed in the *Engine Valve Specifications* table. By using a micrometer and a suitable telescope hold gauge, check the diameter of the valve stem in three places (top, center and bottom). Insert telescope hole gauge in valve guide bore, measuring at the center. Subtract the highest reading of valve stem diameter from valve guide bore center diameter to obtain valve-to-guide clearance. If clearance is not within specified limits, use the next oversize valve and ream bore to fit. Valves with oversize stems are available in .003", .015" and .030".

V8-287, 327

Valve guides are removed and replaced with special pullers and drivers made for the purpose. If this equipment is not available, carefully measure with a steel scale the amount each guide projects from the valve port before removing it so that the position of the new guide will be properly located when it is driven in. After the new guides are installed, they should be reamed to provide the clearance within the limits given in the *Valve Specifications* chart.

VALVE LIFTERS

Mechanical Lifters

Since these lifters are of the mushroom type and the guides are cast integral with the cylinder block, it is necessary to remove the camshaft before the lifters can be taken out. Follow the instructions for removing the camshaft under that heading; then remove the oil pan and take the lifters out through the bottom.

To make removal of the camshaft easier, hold up the lifters with rubber bands on overhead valve engines.

Hydraulic Lifters

Valve lifters may be removed from their bores after removing the rocker arms and push rods. Adjustable pliers with taped jaws may be used to remove lifters that are stuck due to varnish, carbon, etc. Fig. 12 illustrates the type of lifter used.

TIMING CHAIN COVER

6-199, 232, 258

1. Remove drive belts, fan and pulley.
2. Remove vibration damper.
3. Remove oil pan-to-timing chain cover screws and cover-to-block screws.
4. Raise the cover and pull the oil pan front seal up enough to pull the retaining nibs from the holes in the cover.
5. Remove timing chain cover gasket from block. Cut off seal tab flush with front face of cylinder block. Clean gasket surfaces.
6. Remove oil seal.
7. Place gasket in position on cylinder block. Install new oil pan front seal, cut off protruding tab of seal to match portion of the original seal.
8. Insert suitable aligning tool in cover seal bore and on crankshaft. Install cover-to-oil pan screws and tighten lightly. Install cover screws and tighten.
9. Retighten all screws and install new cover seal.

V8-287, 327

1. Remove water pump, fuel pump and vibration damper.
2. Remove cover bolts and remove cover.

V8-290, 304, 343, 360, 390, 401

The timing chain cover is a die casting

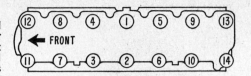

Fig. 4 Cylinder head tightening sequence. 6-199, 232, 258 engines. The No. 11 bolt must be sealed to prevent coolant leakage

THREADS MUST BE SEALED TO PREVENT COOLANT LEAKAGE

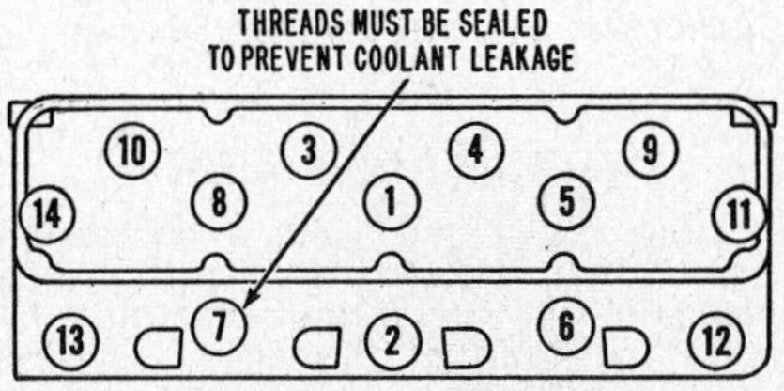

Fig. 5 Cylinder head tightening sequence on V8-290, 304, 343, 360, 390. The No. 7 bolt indicated (second from front on left bank only) must be sealed to prevent coolant leakage

incorporating an oil seal at the vibration damper hub, Fig. 13. The crankshaft front seal is installed from the back side of the cover, therefore, it is necessary to remove the cover when replacement of the seal is required. To remove cover, proceed as follows:

1. Drain cooling system completely.
2. Remove lower radiator hose and by-pass hose from cover.
3. Remove distributor, fuel pump, drive belts, fan and hub assembly and vibration damper, using a suitable puller.

NOTE: It is not necessary to disconnect power steering or discharge air conditioning system (if equipped). Remove units from their mounting brackets and place them aside.

4. Remove two front oil pan bolts and the eight hex head bolts retaining the cover to the cylinder block.

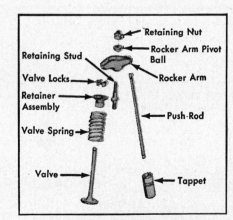

Fig. 6 Valve train on V8-290, 304, 343, 360, 390, 401 engines

5. Pull cover forward until free from locating dowel pins.
6. Remove used seal and clean seal bore and gasket surface of cover.
7. Apply sealing compound to outer surface of seal and a film of Lubriplate or equivalent to seal lips. Drive seal into cover bore until seal contacts outer flange of cover.

Installation of Cover

1. Prior to installation of cover, remove lower dowel pin from cylinder block.
2. Using a sharp knife or razor blade, cut oil pan gasket flush with cylinder block on both sides of oil pan.
3. Cut corresponding pieces of gasket from the replacement oil pan gasket set. Cement gasket to cover. Install replacement Neoprene oil pan seal into cover and align cork gasket tabs to the pan seal.
4. Apply a strip of sealing compound to both the cut-off oil pan gaskets at the oil pan to cylinder block location.
5. Place cover in position, install oil pan bolts in cover, tighten evenly and slowly until cover aligns with upper dowel. Then install lower dowel through cover. Drive dowel in corresponding hole in cylinder block.
6. Install cover attaching bolts and torque to 20-30 ft-lbs.

Six Cylinder

NOTE: On 1966 models it is not necessary to remove the cover in order to replace the cover oil seal.

When installing the cover it is important that the cover be properly aligned when installing the vibration damper to prevent damage to the oil seal. This is accomplished by leaving the cover-to-block cap screws loose until the vibration damper has been partially installed. Then tighten the cover screws.

TIMING CHAIN

When installing a timing chain, see that the timing marks on the sprockets are in line as shown in Fig. 14 and 15.

CAMSHAFT

6-199, 232, 258

1. Remove cylinder head.
2. Remove value lifters.
3. Remove radiator and, if so equipped, air conditioning condenser.
4. Remove timing chain cover.
5. Rotate crankshaft until timing marks on sprockets are aligned, Fig. 15.
6. Remove sprockets and chain.
7. Lower front bumper by removing forward back bar-to-side sill bolts.
8. Remove crankshaft.

V8-287, 327

1. Remove cylinder head covers, ignition wires, rocker arm assemblies, intake manifold and carburetor.
2. Remove lifter cover.
3. Remove push rods and lifters.
4. Remove fuel pump, vibration damper

and timing chain cover.
5. Remove water pump and water distribution manifold.
6. Rotate engine until timing marks align, Fig. 14.
7. Remove fuel pump eccentric, sprockets and timing chain.
8. Remove camshaft thrust plate and camshaft.

V8-290, 304, 343, 360, 390, 401

1. Disconnect battery ground cable.
2. Disconnect transmission cooler lines at radiator if so equipped.
3. Remove radiator.
4. Remove distributor, wires and coil.
5. Remove intake manifold and carburetor as an assembly.
6. Remove cylinder head covers, loosen rocker arms and remove push rods and lifters.
7. Dismount power steering pump.
8. Remove fan and hub, fuel pump and heater hose at water pump.
9. Remove alternator.
10. Remove vibration damper and pulley and lower radiator hose at water pump.
11. Remove timing chain cover, distributor-oil pump drive gear, fuel pump eccentric sprockets and chain.
12. Remove hood latch support bracket upper retaining screws and move bracket as required to allow removal of camshaft.

PISTONS & RODS, ASSEMBLE

V8 Engines

Assemble piston to connecting rod as shown in Figs. 16 to 21D.

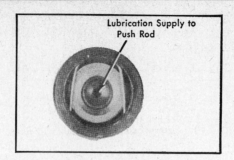

Fig. 7   Hydraulic lifter identification. V8-290, 304, 343, 360, 390, 401 engines

Overhead Valve 6-Cyl.

Pistons are marked with a depression notch on the top perimeter, Fig. 22. When installed in the engine this notch must be toward the front of the engine. Always assemble rods and caps with the cylinder numbers facing the camshaft side of engine.

PISTONS, PINS & RINGS

Pistons are furnished in standard sizes and oversizes of .002, .005. .010 and .020".

Piston pins are furnished in oversizes of .003 and .005".

Piston rings are available in .020" oversizes. On 1966 V8s a .030" oversize is also available.

MAIN & ROD BEARINGS

Both main and rod bearings are supplied in undersizes of .001, .002, .010 and .012".

CRANKSHAFT REAR OIL SEAL

199, 232, 290, 304, 343, 360, 390 Engines

1. To replace the seal, Fig. 23, remove oil pan and scrape oil pan surfaces clean.
2. Remove rear main bearing cap.
3. Remove and discard old seals.
4. Clean cap throughly.
5. Loosen all remaining main bearing cap screws.
6. With a brass drift and hammer, tap upper seal until sufficient seal is protruding to permit pulling seal out completely with pliers.
7. Wipe seal surface of crankshaft clean, then oil lightly.
8. Coat back surface of upper seal with soap, and lip of seal with engine oil.
9. Install upper seal into cylinder block. *Lip of seal must face to front of engine.*
10. Coat cap and cylinder block mating surface portion of seal with Permatex No. 2 or equivalent, being careful not to apply sealer on lip of seal.
11. Coat back surface of lower seal with soap, and lip of seal with No. 40 engine oil. Place into cap, seating seal firmly into seal recess in cap.
12. Place Permatex No. 2 or equivalent on both chamfered edges of rear main bearing cap.
13. Install main bearings and install cap. Tighten all caps to correct torque as listed in the *Engine Tightening Specifications* table.
14. Cement oil pan gasket to cylinder block with tongue of gasket at each end coated with Permatex or equivalent before installing into rear main bearing cap at joint of tongue and oil pan front neoprene seal.
15. Coat oil pan rear seal with soap. Place into recess of rear main bearing cap, making certain seal is firmly and evenly seated.
16. Install oil pan and tighten drain plug securely.

287, 327 Engines

A braided oil seal is pressed into the upper and lower grooves behind the rear main bearing. Directly in front of this seal is an oil slinger which deflects the oil back into the oil pan. Should the braided seal require replacement, the installation of the lower half is accomplished as follows:

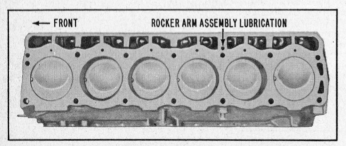

Fig. 9   Rocker arm lubrication gallery. 6-199, 232, 258 engines

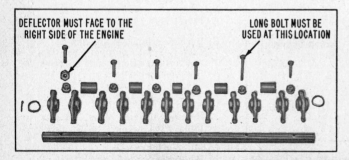

Fig. 10   Rocker arm assembly. 6-199, 232, 258 engines

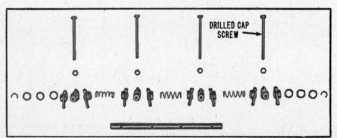

Fig. 11   Rocker arm assembly. V8-287, 327 engines

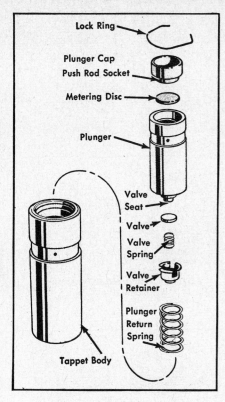

Fig. 12   Hydraulic valve lifter

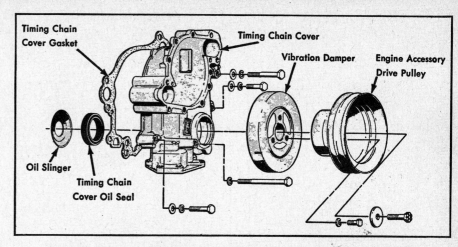

Fig. 13   Timing chain cover assembly. V8-290, 304, 343, 360, 390, 401 engines

With the bearing cap and lower bearing half removed, install a new seal so that both ends protrude above the cap. Tap the seal down into position or roll it snugly in its groove with a smooth rounded tool. Then cut off the protruding ends of the seal with a sharp knife or razor blade.

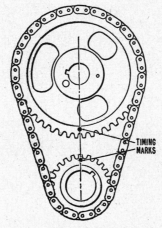

Fig. 14   Valve timing. V8 engines

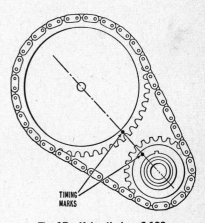

Fig. 15   Valve timing. 6-199, 232, 258 engines

OIL PAN
1969 V8, 1970-71 All

1. Disconnect battery ground cable.

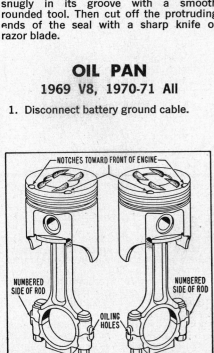

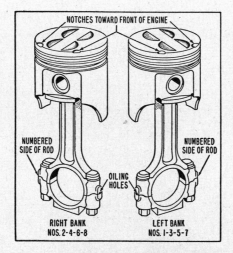

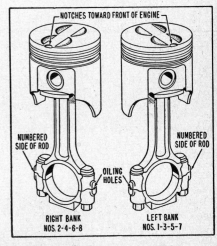

Fig. 16   Piston and rod assembly. 1967 V8-290, 1968-69 Low Compression V8-290, 343

Fig. 17   Piston and rod assembly. 1967 V8-290 High Compression

Fig. 18   Piston and rod assembly. 1967 V8-343. 1968-69 High Comp. V8-343

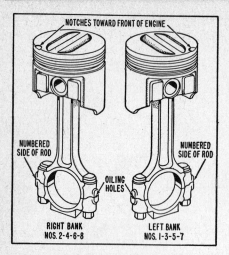

Fig. 19 Piston and rod assembly. 1968-69 V8-390

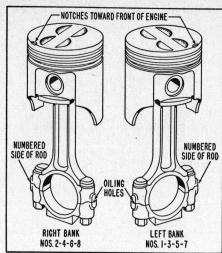

Fig. 20 Piston and rod assembly. 1968-69 V8-290 High Comp.

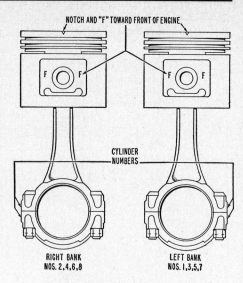

Fig. 21 Piston and rod assembly. V8-287, 327 engines

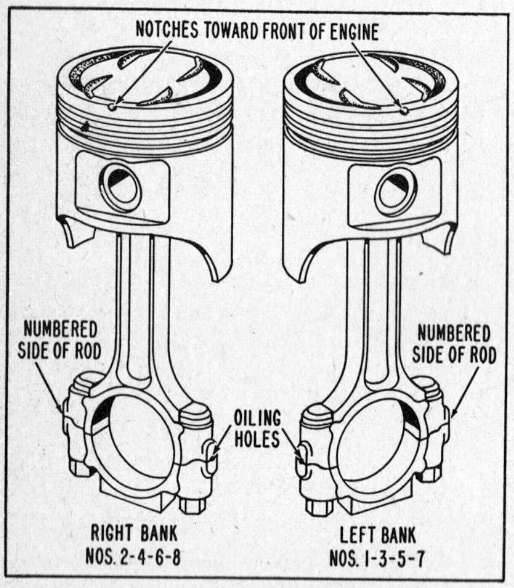

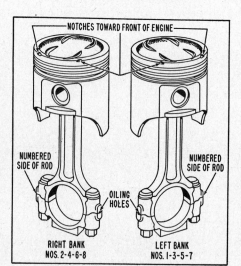

Fig. 21A Piston and rod assembly. 1970-71 V8-304

Fig. 21B Piston and rod assembly. 1970-71 V8-360 Std. Compression

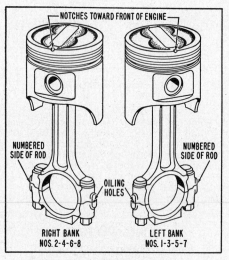

Fig. 21C Piston and rod assembly. 1970 V8-360 High Compression

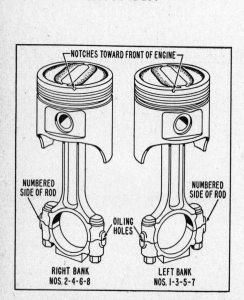

Fig. 21D Piston and rod assembly. 1970-71 V8-390, 401

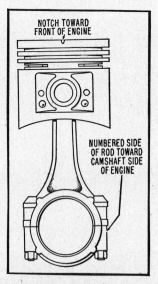

Fig. 22 Piston and rod assembly. 6-199, 232, 258 engines

2. Support engine with lifting fixture, Fig. 24.
3. Raise car and support on side sills.
4. Disconnect engine mounts at engine brackets.
5. Disconnect idler arm at sill. Disconnect body ground cables if so equipped.
6. Loosen sway bar if so equipped. On 1969 V8 except Ambassador, disconnect shock absorbers at lower control arms.
7. Remove front crossmember-to-sill bolts, pull crossmember down and place 2"x4"x6" blocks between crossmember and sills.
8. On six cylinder, remove right engine mount bracket from engine. On V8, remove starter.
9. Drain and remove oil pan.

1968-69 Six

1. Disconnect front cushions from engine bracket.

2. Remove right bracket from engine.
3. Disconnect ground strap.
4. Remove cylinder head cover and air cleaner.
5. Disconnect fan shroud if so equipped.
6. Raise engine as far as possible.
7. Disconnect stabilizer bar from side sill if so equipped.
8. Loosen strut rod bolts at lower control arms.
9. Remove crossmember-to-side sill bolts.
10. With weight of car on wheels pry down crossmember, use wooden blocks to hold crossmember down.
11. Drain engine oil, remove oil pan.

1968 V8

1. Turn crankshaft until mark on damper is 180° from timing marks on cover.
2. Disconnect cushions from crossmember.
3. Disconnect ground strap.
4. On American, remove cushion brackets from cylinder block.
5. Remove starter.
6. Remove idler arm from side sill.
7. On Ambassador, disconnect stabilizer bar at side sills. On other models, loosen stabilizer bar links to control arms as far as possible.
8. Attach lifting fixture to engine and raise engine as far as possible.
9. Loosen strut rod bolts at control arms.
10. Remove crossmember-to-sill bolts

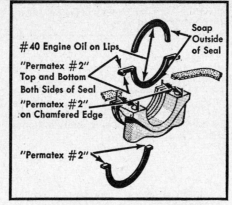

Fig. 23   Rear main bearing sealing. 199, 232, 290, 304, 343, 360, 390, 401 engines

and pry crossmember down and insert wooden blocks to hold it down.
11. Drain oil and remove pan.

1967 Six and V8s

1. Remove front springs. Then support weight of car at front.
2. Support front of engine above engine compartment.
3. Remove front support cushions at engine.
4. Remove idler arm from bracket.

5. Remove front stabilizer bar (if equipped).
6. Unfasten front crossmember and pry it down to gain clearance for oil pan removal. Wooden spacer blocks installed between crossmember and body side sill will assist in holding crossmember down.
7. On six-cylinder models, remove flywheel dust cover.
8. Drain engine oil and remove pan.

1966 Ambassador V8

1. Drain engine oil and remove flywheel dust cover.
2. Disconnect front suspension stabilizer bar at rear mounting locations and allow bar to hang down.
3. Unfasten and remove oil pan.

1966 American, Classic & Marlin & Ambassador 6 Cyl.

1. Remove front springs, then support weight of car at front.
2. Support front of engine from above engine compartment.
3. Remove support cushion at engine.
4. Remove steering idler arm from bracket.
5. On Rambler models, remove sway stabilizer bar (if equipped).
6. Unfasten front suspension crossmember from body side sills.
7. Pry crossmember down to obtain

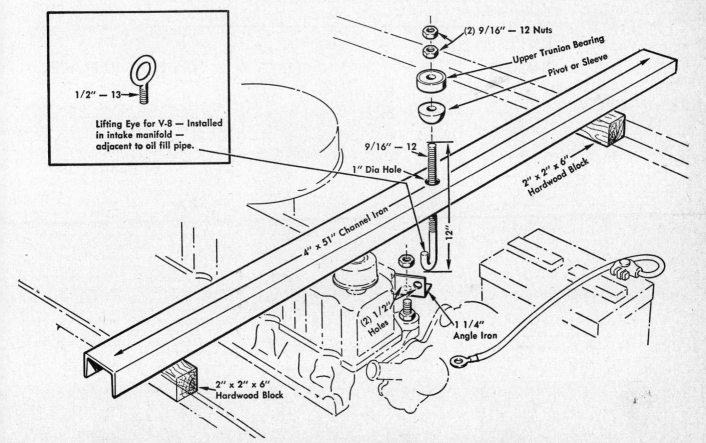

Fig. 24   Engine lifting fixture

clearance for oil pan removal.

NOTE: Wooden spacer blocks installed between crossmember and body side sill will assist in holding corssmember down.

8. Remove flywheel underpan.
9. Remove oil pan.

OIL PUMP
6-199, 6-232, 258 & V8s

Oil pump removal or replacement will not affect distributor timing as the distributor drive gear remains in mesh with the camshaft gear.

Upon disassembly of the oil pump, locate a straight edge across the pump body and gears in the body and check the gear-to-cover clearance, which should

not exceed .004". A clearance of .008" maximum should exist between gears and walls of pump body.

The pump cover should be installed with the pump out of the engine and pump checked for freedom of operation before installation.

The oil pressure relief valve, which is built into the pump, is not adjustable, the correct pressure being built into the relief valve spring.

WATER PUMP

1. To remove the water pump, drain cooling system.
2. Remove fan belt, fan and pulley.
3. Unfasten and remove water pump from water manifold.

FUEL PUMP, REPLACE

1. Remove all gasket material from the pump and block gasket surfaces. Apply sealer to both sides of new gasket.
2. Position gasket on pump flange and hold pump in position against its mounting surface. Make sure rocker arm is riding on camshaft eccentric.
3. Press pump tight against its mounting. Install retaining screws and tighten them alternately.
4. Connect fuel lines. Then operate engine and check for leaks.

SERVICE NOTE: Before installing the pump, it is good practice to crank the engine so that the nose of the camshaft eccentric is out of the way of the fuel pump rocker arm when the pump is installed. In this way there will be the least amount of tension on the rocker arm, thereby easing the installation of the pump.

Clutch and Transmission Section

> **NOTE:** 1972 Linkage adjustment information is in this section. Repair procedures on both automatic and manual shift transmissions are covered elsewhere in this manual. Procedures for removing automatic transmissions as well as linkage adjustments on 1966-71 models are included in the automatic transmission chapters. See Chapter Index.

CLUTCH PEDAL, ADJUST
Pedal Height

1966-68 & 1969 6-199

Adjust clutch pedal stop bracket to obtain a dimension of 6" for 1966-67 and 6½" for 1968 all and 1969 6-199 from the bare floor to the bottom of the clutch pedal.

NOTE: 1966 units with 6-232 engine are equipped with a self-adjusting clutch.

1969-71 6-232, 258 & V8

Insert a 5/16" pin, approximately 4½" long, through holes in pedal support bracket. Adjust pedal support until pin slides through all three holes.

1970 6-199

This clutch is not adjustable.

Pedal Free Play

NOTE: *See below for models equipped with the "E-Stick" Clutch and Shifting mechanism.*

In order to provide sufficient free movement of the clutch release bearing when the clutch is engaged and pedal fully released, free pedal play should be 7/8" to 1⅛" with 1" desired.
Adjustment for free pedal play is made

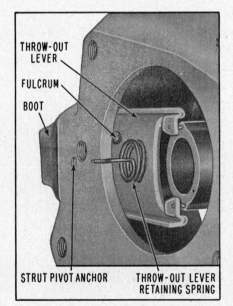

THROW-OUT LEVER
FULCRUM
BOOT
STRUT PIVOT ANCHOR
THROW-OUT LEVER RETAINING SPRING

Fig. 1   Clutch throw-out bearing and lever assembly

by varying the length of the beam or link to the release lever rod. Lengthening this rod reduces pedal travel; shortening it increases pedal play.

CLUTCH, REPLACE
Removal

Disconnect the release fork pull-back spring and remove the clevis pin from the end of the release fork rod. Disconnect the release fork at the pivot and pull the fork out as far as possible. Remove the transmission as described under *Transmission, Remove & Replace.*

Remove the clutch housing pan and mark the clutch cover and flywheel so that the clutch may be installed in the same relative position. Loosen the clutch cover bolts gradually and evenly until the clutch spring pressure is entirely relieved. Remove the bolts, and the clutch assembly may be removed from below.

Unless special clutch rebuilding equipment is available, it is recommended that the clutch assembly be exchanged for a rebuilt unit should the clutch require rebuilding. The driven disc, however, may be replaced without special equipment. If clutch rebuilding equipment is available, follow the equipment manufacturer's instructions.

SERVICE BULLETIN

Lubricates Clutch Cover: Three felt pads in the clutch cover are lubricated in production before they are assembled over the eyebolts. A squeak that may occur during clutch operation after mileage

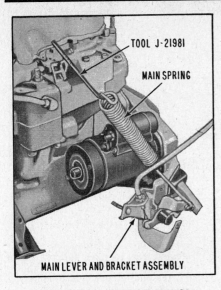

Fig. 2 Main lever bracket assembly

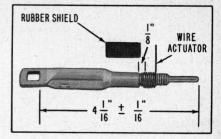

Fig. 3 Self-adjuster

has accumulated can be eliminated by relubricating the felt pads.

To do this, remove the cover pan from the clutch housing. Next, with a squirt-type oil can, carefully apply a mixture of heavy oil and mineral spirits to the three felt pads. Use only a small amount of lubricant, and make certain the lubricant does not get on the clutch driven member. Then apply a thin coating of a suitable light grease to the sides of the pressure plate lugs, where the lugs extend through the clutch cover. Install the pan to complete the job.

Clutch, Install

1. Very sparingly apply front wheel bearing lubricant to the clutch shaft pilot bearing in the crankshaft. If too much lubricant is used, it will run out of face of flywheel when hot and ruin driven plate facings. Make certain that flywheel surface is clean and dry.
2. Make sure that splines in driven plate hub are clean, and apply a

light coating of lubriplate. Driven plate facings must be clean and dry.
3. Place driven plate on pressure plate, then place clutch assembly in position on flywheel, being sure to align marks made on flywheel and cover before removal.
4. Install cover bolts with washers but do not tighten.
5. Insert a spare clutch shaft through hub of driven plate and into pilot bearing.
6. Tighten each clutch cover bolt several turns at a time to draw cover evenly to flywheel and avoid distortion of cover.
7. While tightening cover bolts, move clutch shaft from side to side to center driven plate with pilot bearing. If driven plate is not centered, it will be difficult to slide the transmission into place. Make sure all cover bolts are uniformly tightened.
8. Remove aligning clutch shaft and install transmission, clutch linkage and adjust clutch pedal free play.

SELF-ADJUSTING CLUTCH
Clutch Removal

Clutch removal requires prior removal of the main spring, main lever assembly and the clutch housing. Always index mark the clutch cover assembly and flywheel on original production assemblies before removal so these parts can be assembled in the same relative position.

NOTE: When necessary to replace the clutch driven plate after accumulated mileage, a new self-adjuster link must also be installed.

Clutch Installation

1. Bolt cover to flywheel. Install rubber dust shield on opening in clutch housing.
2. Position throw-out bearing and lever assembly with strut in clutch housing. Lubricate strut seat in throw-out lever with engine oil. Secure throw-out lever assembly with retaining

spring, Fig. 1.
3. Secure clutch housing to engine with main lever and bracket assembly in proper position, Fig. 2. Tighten upper bracket bolt to 40-45 ft-lbs and lower bolt 35-40 ft lbs.
4. Place lower end of cable in mounting hole in main bracket. Place cable and fitting over pin on bellcrank and secure in place.
5. Install self-adjuster on the headed pin on bellcrank and insert threaded end of self-adjuster with flat washer and seal in socket on end of throw-out lever, Fig. 3.
6. When in proper position, wire extension on threaded portion of self-adjuster will be in opening of actuator. Remove instruction tape from self-adjuster.
7. Use a suitable clutch aligner to position clutch driven plate.
8. Install main spring, Fig. 2.
9. Remove aligning tool and install transmission.
10. Install cable adjuster gauge on main bracket, Fig. 4.
11. With clutch pedal secured in extended position on toeboard, adjust cable to obtain a snug fit on cable adjuster gauge by adjusting the upper cable retaining nut. After this adjustment is made, secure cable in position with the lower cable retaining lock nut and remove gauge.

NOTE: Operate clutch pedal in normal manner until automatic self-adjuster

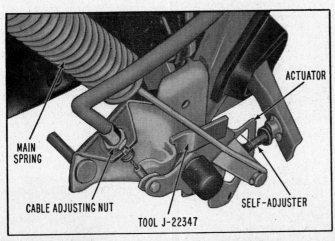

Fig. 4 Cable adjustment

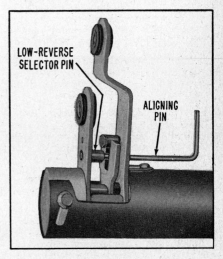

Fig. 5 Aligning pin used when adjusting Ainsworth type shift mechanism. 1966

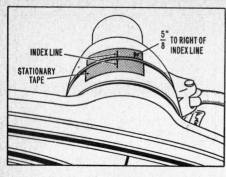

Fig. 6 Aligning shift bowl. 1967 gearshift

reaches normal operating position. This position is reached when the wire extension, being actuated by clutch pedal movement, has extended the threaded portion of the self-adjuster rearward until the wire does not contact the opening of the actuator. This will require 10 to 20 strokes of the pedal. No clutch pedal free play will be present as the fingers of the clutch cover are in contact with the face of the throw-out bearing at all times.

MANUAL TRANS.
Three Speed, Replace

1969-72

1. Raise car and support engine.
2. Mark rear U-joint yoke to aid in assembly, and disconnect propeller shaft from rear axle.
3. Slide front U-joint from transmission mainshaft.
4. Remove screws from rear engine support cushion at extension housing.
5. Remove bolts that secure rear corssmember to sills and remove crossmember.

NOTE: Before removing rear member on Javelin and AMX with power steering, open hood to avoid damage from pump reservoir wing nut.

6. Disconnect speedometer cable and shift rods from transmission.
7. On models with floor shift, remove shift lever bezel, boot, retainer and shift lever.
8. When removing transmission, use guide pins in place of two lower cap screws so as not to damage clutch shaft.

1967 American & 1968 All Models

1. Jack up or support engine.
2. Unfasten rear engine support cushion from extension housing (2 capscrews).
3. Unfasten and remove rear crossmember. *An additional body crossmember is used on Convertible models. Therefore, it is also necessary to remove crossmember tie plate when removing transmission.*
4. Remove propeller shaft.
5. Disconnect speedometer cable and gearshift rods from transmission levers.
6. Unfasten and remove transmission.
7. Reverse procedure to install.

1967 Rambler

1. Unfasten and remove exhaust pipes from exhaust manifolds.
2. Remove propeller shaft.
3. Jack up or support engine.
4. Unfasten rear engine support cushion from extension housing (2 capscrews).
5. Unfasten and remove crossmember.
6. Disconnect speedometer cable and gearshift rods from transmission levers.
7. Unfasten and remove transmission.
8. Reverse procedure to install.

1966 American

1. Jack up or support engine.
2. Unfasten rear engine support cushion from extension housing or torque tube adapter (2 capscrews). *On Convertible models, an additional crossmember is used; therefore, it is also necessary to remove crossmember tie plate when removing transmission.*
3. On 6-199 engine, raise and support rear of body at side sills. Disconnect rear shocks at rear axle tubes, hand brake cable at adjusting yoke, and rear brake hose clip from body floor pan. Remove rear spring U-bolts and move rear axle to rear and remove front U-joint from transmission mainshaft.
   On 6-232 engine, remove propeller shaft by separating rear U-joint and sliding front U-joint from transmission mainshaft.
4. On all models, disconnect speedometer cable and gearshift rods from transmission levers.
5. Unfasten and remove transmission.
6. Reverse procedure to install.

1966 Rambler

1. On V8s, unfasten exhaust pipes from exhaust manifolds.
2. Jack up or support engine.
3. Unfasten rear engine support cushion from extension housing or torque tube adapter (2 capscrews).
4. Unfasten and remove crossmember.
5. Lower jack supporting engine so extension housing or torque tube adapter clears reinforcing rib in floor pan.
6. Disconnect brake tube bracket from underside of body.
7. Disconnect shock absorbers at lower bracket. Then disconnect torque tube at rear of transmission extension housing.
8. Disconnect parking brake cable at equalizer and brake cable housing at torque tube bracket.
9. Move rear axle rearward to remove front U-joint from transmission mainshaft.
10. Disconnect speedometer cable and gearshift rods from transmission levers.
11. Unfasten and remove transmission.
12. Reverse procedure to install.

Four Speed, Replace

1966-67 & 1969 All Models

1. Remove chrome trim ring that secures rubber boot to floor pan and slide boot up on shift lever.
2. Unfasten and remove shift lever from cross shaft (2 capscrews).
3. Raise vehicle.

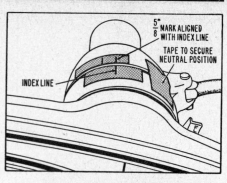

Fig. 7 Locating neutral position of shift bowl. 1967 gearshift

4. Unfasten and remove exhaust pipes from exhaust manifolds.
5. Jack up or support engine.
6. Unfasten rear engine support cushion from crossmember.
7. Unfasten and remove crossmember.

NOTE: Before removing crossmember on Javelin and AMX models with power steering, open hood to avoid damage from pump reservoir wing nut.

8. Remove propeller shaft.
9. Disconnect speedometer cable from transmission.
10. Lower engine until adequate clearance is obtained to permit transmission removal.
11. Reverse procedure to install.

1968 & 1970-72 All Models

The procedure to remove the transmission is the same as that given previously for the three speed transmission.

MANUAL TRANS.
SHIFT LINKAGE

1969-72 Three Spd. Floor Shift

NOTE: For 1969 models, omit Steps 1-4.

1. Loosen reverse trunnion nuts.
2. Shift transmission into reverse and lock steering column.

NOTE: It may be necessary to move the lower column shift lever upward until it is in the locked position.

3. Tighten lower trunnion lock nut until it contacts the trunnion then tighten upper lock nut while holding trunnion centered in lever.
4. Unlock steering column.
5. Shift transmission into neutral.
6. Loosen 2-3 lever attaching nut and adjusting bolt.
7. With 1st-Reverse shift rod in neutral, align the 2-3 shift rod so the shift notch is exactly aligned with the 1st-Reverse shift notch. Tighten adjusting bolt and attaching nut.
8. On 1970-71 units, shift transmission into reverse and lock steering column. Column must lock without any binding.

1969-72 Three Spd. Column Shift

NOTE: For 1969 models, omit Steps 1-3.

1. With shift rods disconnected from levers, place column lever in reverse position and lock column.
2. Place transmission levers in reverse position and adjust shift rod trunnion for a free pin fit in the lever. Tighten trunnion. Unlock column.
3. Shift transmission into neutral.
4. Insert a 3/16" drill bit through the aligning holes of the two shift levers, shift gate and the bracket on the jacket tube.
5. With the shift levers in the neutral position, carefully adjust the trunnions to a free fit in the shift levers and secure the trunnion in this position with the lock nuts. Use care when tightening the lock nuts so a binding condition does not exist.

1967 Three Speed

1. Place shift levers on transmission in neutral.
2. Loosen all shift rod trunnion lock nuts about four turns.
3. Align center-line of column gearshift lever with center-line of hazard warning light switch knob.
4. Place a 2" piece of masking tape along top edge of shift bowl adjacent to the gap between the shift bowl and the turn signal switch cover.
5. Place a second piece of tape along the lower edge of the turn signal switch cover and directly across the gap from the first tape. Draw a line across both pieces of tape, Fig. 6.
6. Measure 5/8" to the right of the line on the shift bowl tape and draw another line as shown.
7. Raise the shift lever to align the 5/8" line on the shift bowl tape with the index line on the stationary tape. This is the proper neutral position.
8. Hold the shift bowl in this position by taping the bowl to the switch housing, Fig. 7.
9. With the shift levers and transmission levers in the proper neutral

position, adjust the trunnions to a free fit in the levers while holding the low-reverse lever aligned with the second-high lever. When tightening the lock nuts, maintain proper trunnion alignment to prevent binding.
10. Remove tape and check shifting operation in all gears.

1968-72 Four Speed

NOTE: On some units, it is necessary to lower the rear of the transmission before adjusting the linkage.

1. Loosen the transmission shift lever nuts (two on each lever) and loosen the lock nuts on the reverse shift rod at the trunnion.
2. Install a 1/4" drill bit through the selector lever retainer, through the levers, spacer plate, and through the aligning hole in the mounting bracket.
3. This is the neutral position. Place all three transmission levers in the neutral position.
4. Adjust the trunnion on the reverse shift rod to enter freely into the reverse lever. Lock the check nuts on the reverse rod and secure with washer and cotter pin.
5. Tighten the lower nuts of the shift levers first, being careful not to move the outer levers out of position.
6. Tighten the upper "hug nuts" to 10 ft. lbs. Do not overtighten or the shift shafts could be broken. Remove the aligning pin.

1966-67 Four Speed

1. Loosen transmission shift lever nuts (2 for each lever) and remove trunnion from reverse shift lever.
2. Remove access cover from left side of console.
3. Install a 5/16" drill bit through selector lever retainer, through the levers, spacer plate and through the align-

ing hole in shift lever pivot bracket. This is neutral position for the three selector levers.
4. Place all three transmission levers in neutral. Adjust trunnion on inner reverse shift rod to enter freely into reverse lever. Lock check nut on reverse rod and secure with washers and cotter pins.
5. The outer levers on transmission side cover plate will be in proper position as the two nuts were loose when the aligning pin was installed. Tighten lower nuts first, being careful not to move outer levers out of position. Then torque upper "hug" nuts to 8-10 ft-lbs. Do not over-torque these nuts as the shift shafts could be broken.
6. Remove aligning pin and check shift operation in all positions.

1966 Three Speed (Ainsworth Type)

1. Loosen trunnion lock nuts on shift rods.
2. Use a 3/16" diameter rod as an aligning pin. Insert pin as shown in Fig. 5. This is neutral position of operating levers.
3. Adjust trunnions on shift rods so they enter freely into operating levers while transmission shift levers are in neutral position.
4. Tighten trunnion lock nuts and remove aligning pin.

1972 AUTO. TRANS. LINKAGE ADJUST

Place transmission selector lever in Park position and place transmission shift lever in Park and adjust shift rod trunnion to a free pin fit. Place transmission selector lever in Park and check column lock for ease of operation.

For Trouble Shooting and "In Car Repairs" refer to the Chrysler Torqueflite transmission section in the front of this manual.

Rear Axle, Propeller Shaft & Brakes

REAR AXLES

Fig. 1 illustrates the rear axle assembly used on these cars. When necessary to overhaul the unit, refer to the *Rear Axle Specifications* table in this chapter.

Description

In these rear axles, Fig. 1, the drive pinion is mounted in two tapered roller bearings. These bearings are preloaded by a washer behind the front bearing. The pinion is positioned by shims located in front of the rear bearing. The differential is supported in the carrier by two tapered roller side bearings. These bear-

ings are preloaded by shims located between the bearings and carrier housing. The differential assembly is positioned for proper ring gear and pinion backlash by varying the position of these shims. The differential case houses two side gears in mesh with two pinions mounted on a pinion shaft which is held in place by a lock pin. The side gears and pinions are backed by thrust washers.

On all 1966 models and 1967 American, the rear axle assembly must be removed from the chassis to perform any major service work.

On 1967 except American and all 1968-72, it is not necessary to remove the rear axle assembly. However, the underbody should be washed to prevent particles of road dirt from contaminating the parts.

REAR AXLE & PROP. SHAFT, REPLACE

1968 American, AMX & Javelin; 1969-72 Hornet, Rambler, AMX, Javelin & Gremlin

1. Remove axle shaft nuts prior to raising the car weight from the wheels.
2. Remove the axle housing cover to drain the lubricant.
3. Raise and support the rear of the body.
4. Remove the rear wheels and rear wheel hubs and drums.
5. Disconnect rear parking brake cables at equalizer.

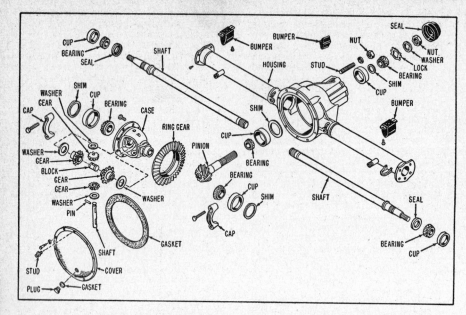

Fig. 1 Rear axle assembly. For 1967-72 V8s the pinion bearing preload is adjusted by means of a collapsible spacer instead of the shim shown

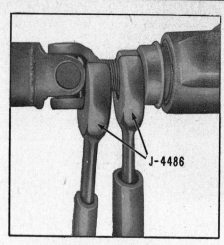

Fig. 2 Loosening propeller shaft coupling 1966 American with 199 engine

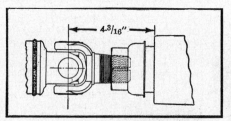

Fig. 3 Correct propeller shaft coupling location. 1966 American with 199 engine

6. Remove the brake support plates.

NOTE: Retain the shims located between the left support plate and axle tube for use on reassembly.

7. Remove the axle shafts from the axle.
8. Mark the universal joint yoke and bearing before separating to insure same alignment at time of assembly. Disconnect the propeller shaft at the rear universal joint.
9. Disconnect the rear shocks at the axle.
10. Disconnect the brake line at the body floor pan bracket.
11. Remove the rear spring U bolts and the axle may now be removed.

1968-72 Rebel, Ambassador & Matador

1. Remove axle shaft nuts prior to raising the car weight from the wheels.
2. Raise and support the rear of the car.
3. Remove the axle housing cover and drain the lubricant.
4. Mark the rear universal joint and bearing and disconnect the propeller shaft at the rear universal joint.
5. Disconnect the parking brake cable at the equalizer.

NOTE: The left cable is routed to upper long end of equalizer. Disconnect the brake lines at the support plates.

6. Remove the wheels, hubs, drums, support plates, seals, axle shafts and bearings.
7. Support the axle assembly and disconnect the shocks at the axle tubes.
8. Lower axle assembly until it is supported by the control arms.
9. Pull one axle tube down and remove the spring. Pull the other axle tube and remove the other spring.

10. Support the axle assembly and disconnect the upper control arms at the axle housing.
11. Disconnect the lower control arms at the axle tubes and the axle may now be removed.

1966 American

1. To remove, first raise and support rear of body.
2. Disconnect and remove hand brake cables from brake assemblies.
3. On cars with 199 engine, use the type wrenches shown in Fig. 2 to remove the propeller shaft. The coupling nut dust shield will serve as a puller to partially remove the propeller shaft from the rear axle pinion.
4. On cars with 6-232 engine the propeller shaft is removed by separating the rear universal joint by removing the two U-bolts. The drive pinion yoke is removed by removing the cap screw that holds the yoke to the pinion shaft.
5. Disconnect rear shock absorbers, rear brake line at bracket on body floor pan and rear springs from body.
6. Move axle and springs back far enough to permit the propeller shaft to be slipped out of the front universal joint.
7. Separate axle from springs and slide axle back and out from under car.

NOTE: On cars with 199 engine, install the propeller shaft and coupling on the rear axle pinion shaft until the center of the universal joint yoke is positioned as shown in Fig. 3, measured from the front face of the rear axle housing.

1966-67 Rambler & 1967 American

1. To remove propeller shaft, first raise and support rear of body.
2. Disconnect parking brake cable at equalizer and parking brake cable housing at torque tube bracket.

3. Disconnect torque tube from transmission, rear brake hose at bracket on body floor pan, shock absorbers at shock mounting bracket, and stabilizer bar at axle tube. The rear springs are held in position in spring seats by car weight and shock absorber travel limits.
4. Roll axle free from car and disconnect truss rods, torque tube and propeller shaft from rear axle.

NOTE: A "slip" or "union" type coupling is used, Fig. 4. On cars with 6-199 engine with standard and automatic transmission, and 6-232 engine with automatic transmission incorporate a vibration damper as part of the slip-type propeller shaft coupling assembly. The propeller shaft and coupling can be slipped off the pinion shaft when disconnecting the propeller shaft and rear axle.

SERVICE BULLETIN

Pinion Leak: Incorrect reinstallation of a propeller shaft and torque-tube assembly can cause a leakage of rear axle lubricant past the pinion oil seal.

A correct positioning of the propeller shaft coupling on the rear axle pinion shaft must be made when the torque tube and propeller shaft are assembled to the rear axle housing. This will assure proper contact of the pinion oil seal with the seal area of the slip-type coupling for the propeller shaft, Fig. 5.

To check for proper positioning of the coupling, measure from the flange of the torque tube trunnion to the forward

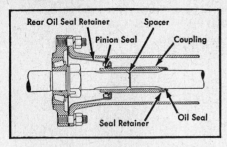

Fig. 4 Slip-type propeller shaft coupling. 1966 Classic, Marlin and Ambassador

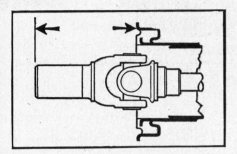

Fig. 5 Arrows indicate where to measure for correct positioning of propeller shaft coupling on rear axle pinion shaft. 1966 Marlin, Classic and Ambassador

edge of the universal joint yoke. This dimension should be 4¹/₁₆ in. for 1966 Classic 6 cyl. cars and 6 in. on 1966 Classic and Marlin V8's and 1966 Ambassadors.

AXLE SHAFTS

The hub and drum are separate units. The drum is attached to the hub by cap screws on V8s and by speed nuts on sixes. Also, the hub and axle shaft are serrated to mate and fit together on the

taper. Both are punch marked to insure correct assembly, Fig. 5A. The axle shaft is removed as follows:

1. Remove the wheel and then remove the brake drum which is retained by cap screws on V8s and speed clips on Sixes.
2. Remove the hub with a suitable puller. *Do not use a knock-out type puller as damage to the wheel bearings or thrust block may result.*
3. Remove brake support plate, oil seal and shims.
4. Remove axle shaft with a puller.

When installing hub onto axle, install two well lubricated thrust washers and axle shaft nut. Tighten axle shaft nut until hub is installed to the dimensions shown in Fig. 5A. Remove axle shaft nut and one thrust washer. Reinstall axle shaft nut and tighten to 250 ft. lbs. If cotter pin hole is not aligned, tighten the nut to the next castellation and install cotter pin.

NOTE

Do not use an original hub on a replacement axle shaft; use a new hub. A new hub may be installed on an original axle shaft providing the serrations on the shaft are not worn or damaged. Be certain that the hub and axle shaft are punch marked to insure proper alignment on installation. A replacement hub, which is not serrated, can be installed and serrations will be cut in the hub when installed on the shaft due to the difference in hardness of the shaft and the hub.

Assembly

Replace the parts in the reverse order of their removal. If the old parts are replaced and the shims have not been disturbed, the axle shaft end play should be correct when the parts are assembled. However, if a new shaft, bearing, differential carrier or housing has been installed, it will be necessary to check the end play.

The end play can be checked when all

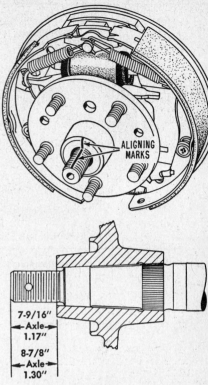

Fig. 5A Installing hub on axle shaft

7-9/16" Axle 1.17"

8-7/8" Axle 1.30"

parts have been replaced except the wheel and hub. To make this check, rap each axle shaft after the nuts are tight to be sure the bearing cups are seated. Then place a dial indicator so that its stem contacts the end of the shaft and work the shaft in and out to determine the amount of existing end play. If an adjustment is necessary, remove the outer oil seal and brake support and add or remove shims as required. When making this adjustment, an equal thickness of shims should be removed or added on each side of the axle housing to maintain

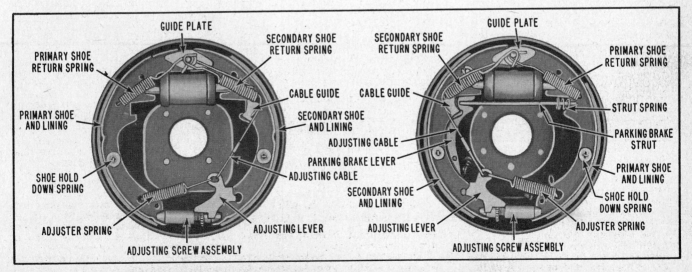

Fig. 6 Bendix Duo-Servo Brake. Left view is a left front brake. Right view is a right rear brake

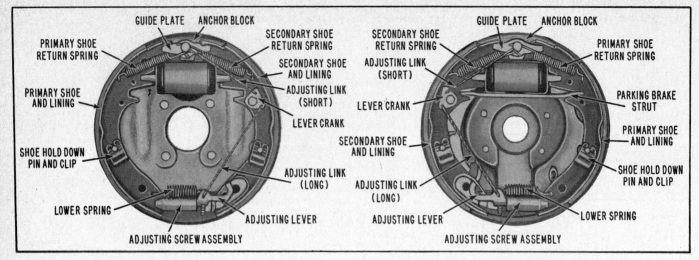

Fig. 7 Wagner Compound Shoe-Type Brake. Left view is a left front brake. Right view is a right rear brake

a central position of the differential thrust block.

NOTE

The application of a bead of sealing material such as "Pliobond" or "Permatex" to the outer diameter of axle tube flange and the brake support contact area is recommended. The sealing material will be used in addition to the gasket for improved sealing.

BRAKE ADJUSTMENTS

SERVICE BULLETIN

To Stop Brake Squeal: A brake squeal which may occur on a Classic or Ambassador V8 having 10 in. Bendix Duo-Servo type brakes with bonded lining is usually confined to the front wheels. The noise can be eliminated by installing heavier hold-down springs on the front shoes, and a drum spring on the front drums.

To make the correction, remove the black-colored springs which hold the brake shoes to the support plates, and replace them with heavier springs available for the purpose.

A simple method of installing the springs on the drums, if a special tool is not available, is to cut the top off a tapered metal pail so that the cut edge just covers the outer edge of the drum. Place the pail on the drum, hook the spring ends together, and slip the spring over the narrow end of the pail. Then roll the spring over the pail and into position against the drum flange.

1966-72 Self-Adjusting Brakes

These brakes, Figs. 6 and 7 have self-adjusting mechanisms that assure correct lining-to-drum clearances at all times. The automatic adjusters operate only when the brakes are applied as the car is moving rearward.

Although the brakes are self-adjusting, an initial adjustment is necessary after the brake shoes have been relined or re-

placed, or when the length of the star wheel adjusting screw has been changed during some other service operation.

Frequent usage of an automatic transmission forward range to halt reverse vehicle motion may prevent the automatic adjusters from functioning, thereby inducing low pedal heights. Should low pedal heights be encountered on these models, it is recommended that numerous forward and reverse stops be made until satisfactory pedal height is obtained.

NOTE

If a low pedal condition cannot be corrected by making numerous stops (provided the hydraulic system is free of air) it indicates that the self-adjusting mechanism is not functioning. Therefore, it will be necessary to remove the brake drum, clean, free up and lubricate the adjusting mechanisms. Then adjust the brakes as follows, being sure the parking brake is fully released.

Adjustment

1. When the brake parts have been installed in their correct position, initially adjust the star wheel assembiles to a point where $3/16''$ to $1/4''$ of threads are exposed between star wheel and star wheel nut on Series 10, $3/8''$ of threads exposed on American, Ambassador and Rebel models.
2. Following the initial adjustment and final assembly, check the brake pedal height to insure brake operation. Then drive the car forward and reverse, making 10 to 15 brake applications prior to road testing. This action balances the adjustment of the four brake units and raises the brake pedal.

PARKING BRAKE, ADJUST

1968 American; 1969 Rambler

1. With service brakes properly adjusted, pull parking brake handle to

the third notch from the released position.
2. Tighten the parking brake cable at the equalizer to a point where the rear wheels are locked from forward rotation.
3. Release brake handle and check for rear brake drag—wheels should rotate freely.

1966-67 Rambler; 1968 Except American; 1969 Except Rambler; 1970-72 All

1. With service brakes properly adjusted, set parking brake pedal on the first notch from fully released position.
2. Tighten parking brake cable at equalizer to a point where the rear wheels are locked in forward rotation.
3. Release pedal and check for rear wheel drag—wheels should rotate freely.

1966-67 American

1. With service brakes properly adjusted, pull parking brake handle to fifth notch from fully released position.
2. Tighten parking brake cable at equalizer to a point where the rear wheels are locked in forward rotation.
3. Release brake handle and check for rear brake drag—wheels should rotate freely.

BRAKE MASTER CYLINDER, REPLACE

To remove the master cylinder, disconnect the brake lines from the connections on the master cylinder. Unfasten the cylinder from its mounting and remove from the car.

Install in the reverse order of removal and bleed the brake system.

Front End and Steering Section

1970-72

The front suspension, Fig. 1, is an independent linked type, with the coil springs located between seats in the wheel house panels and seats attached to the upper control arms.

Direct acting telescoping shock absorbers are located inside the coil springs.

Each upper control arm assembly has two rubber bushings attached to the wheel house panel and a ball joint attached to the steering knuckle.

Each lower control arm has a rubber bushing attached to the front crossmember and a ball joint attached to the steering knuckle.

The lower control arm strut rods are attached to the lower control arms and body side sill brackets.

1966-69

The front suspension, Fig. 2, is an independent link type. The right and left assemblies may be disassembled on the car or removed for bench overhaul.

The coil springs are located between the upper seats of the steering knuckle pins and a seat in the wheelhouse panel. Transmission of road noise through the springs is minimized by insulating the springs from the body with rubber cushions.

The shock absorbers are the direct-acting type with built-in rebound bumper control. The end mountings of the shocks are retained in rubber grommets.

The upper control arms contain rubber insulated bushings installed in the inner end of the arms. The control arms are attached to the mounting bracket on the wheelhouse panel and the trunnion at the outer end.

The lower control arms are attached to a removable crossmember at the pivot ends. The outer ends are attached to the steering knuckle pin with a ball joint stud.

LUBRICATION

Rambler 1966-72 models and American 1966-68 are equipped with plugs which must be removed and a hand-operated grease gun used with special grease to lubricate the suspension at 32,000-mile intervals or three years, whichever occurs first under normal driving conditions.

Under severe driving conditions, such as dusty or extreme wet conditions, earlier lubrication is recommended. Under these conditions the suspension system should be inspected every 12,000 miles or one year whichever occurs first, and lubricated as required.

WHEEL ALIGNMENT
1966-67 American & 1968-72 All

Caster is obtained by moving the two adjusting nuts on the threaded strut rod, Fig. 2. One nut is on each side of the

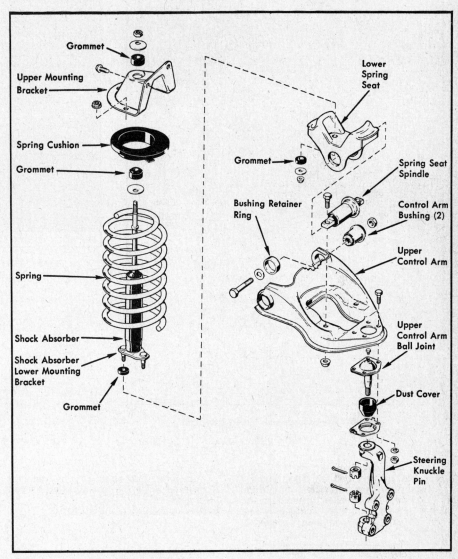

Fig. 1   1970-72 front suspension. Lower control arm (not shown) is the same as used on previous models

mounting bracket. Therefore, moving the nuts on the rod will move the lower control arm to front or rear for desired caster angle. After adjustment, torque nuts to 85 ft-lbs.

Camber is obtained by turning on the eccentric lower control arm bolt, Fig. 3. after adjustment, torque lock nut to 95 ft-lbs.

1966-67 Rambler

The upper control arm attaching bolts are provided with eccentric washers, one attached to the bolt and the other keyed to the threaded end of the bolt.

Loosening the attaching bolt nuts will permit turning the bolt and the eccentrics to provide caster and camber adjustment. Tool J-9447, Fig. 4, which is a special $\frac{7}{8}$"

box ratchet wrench, may be used on the eccentric bolts and nuts with a combination $\frac{7}{8}$" open end and box wrench.

After adjustment, the eccentric bolt nuts should be tightened 50-55 ft-lbs torque. A torque limiting type wrench should be used to measure the torque effort accurately.

TOE-IN, ADJUST

To adjust toe-in, loosen the clamps at both ends of the adjustable tubes on each tie rod. Turn the tubes an equal amount until the toe-in is correct. Turning the right tube in the direction the wheels revolve when the car is going forward increases the toe-in and turning the left tube in the opposite direction increases

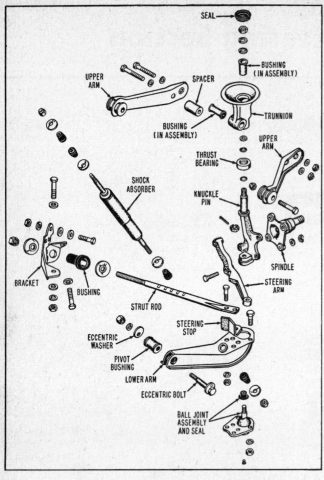

Fig. 2   Front suspension. 1966-69 (typical)

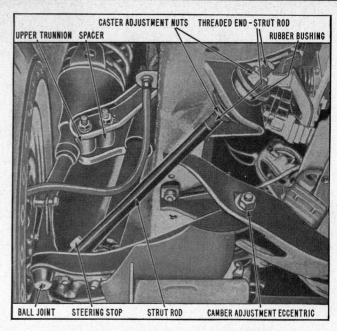

Fig. 3   Front suspension (rear view) showing caster and camber adjustments. 1966-67 American & 1968-72 All

1966-67

1. To adjust bearings, tighten spindle nut to 20 ft-lbs torque while rotating hub to seat bearings, Fig. 6.
2. Place nut retainer on adjusting nut so tabs of retainer cover cotter pin hole in spindle.
3. Back off adjusting nut and nut retainer together to the second slot. This will provide the desired .001″ to .006″ end play.
4. Install cotter pin and dust cap.

NOTE: To check end play, install a dial indicator on wheel hub or stud and set the sensing tip of indicator against spindle. An alternate method is to mount the indicator on the spindle nut and sensing tip against face of hub. Grasp tire and gently push and then pull outward. The end play will register on dial.

toe-in. To decrease toe-in turn the right tube backward and the left tube forward. It is important that both tubes be turned an equal amount in order to maintain the correct position of the steering wheel. When adjustment is complete, tighten all clamp bolts.

NOTE: *In performing service operations on the steering linkage or when adjusting toe-in, be sure to square the tie rod ball sockets on the studs and align the tie rod stud in the center, or slightly above center, of the cross tube opening, before tightening the steering linkage adjusting tube. This will prevent the stud from contacting the side of the cross tube opening, which would otherwise result in noise problems or damage.*

WHEEL BEARINGS, ADJUST

1968-72

1. To adjust bearings, tighten spindle nut to 20 ft-lbs torque while rotating the wheel to seat bearings.
2. Then loosen spindle nut ⅓ turn and with the wheel rotating retorque the spindle nut to 12 inch pounds.

3. Place the nut retainer on spindle nut with the slots of the retainer aligned with the cotter pin hole on the spindle.
4. Install cotter pin and dust cap.

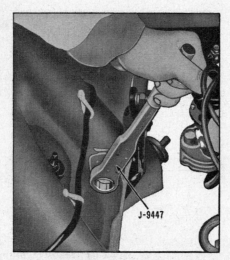

Fig. 4   Caster and camber eccentric adjusting tool. 1966-67 Rambler

WHEEL BEARINGS, REPLACE

(Disc Brakes)

1. Remove two thirds of the total fluid capacity of the master cylinder reservoir to prevent fluid overflow when the caliper pistons are pushed back on their bores.
2. Raise car and remove front wheels.
3. Disconnect hydraulic tube from mounting bracket. Do not disconnect any hydraulic fitting.
4. Holding the lower edge of the caliper, remove the lower bolt. Any shims that fall out at this point should be labeled to insure that they be replaced in their original position.
5. Holding the upper edge of the caliper, remove the upper bolt, tag these shims.

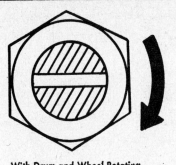

With Drum and Wheel Rotating,
Torque the Adjusting Nut 20 Ft. Lbs.

Install Lock Retainer on Nut so that
the Retainer Tabs Cover the Cotter
Pin Hole

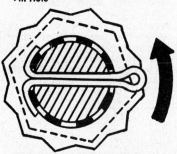

Back off Nut and Nut Retainer to the
Second Slot, and Install Cotter Pin

Fig. 6   Front wheel bearing
adjustment. 1966-67

6. Hang caliper from upper suspension to prevent strain being placed on brake hose.
7. Remove spindle nut and hub and disc assembly. Grease retainer and inner bearing can now be removed.

CHECKING BALL JOINTS FOR WEAR
1966-72

Before checking ball joints for wear, make sure the front wheel bearings are properly adjusted and that the control arms are tight.

Referring to Fig. 7, raise wheel with a jack placed under the frame as shown. Then test by moving the wheel up and down to check axial play, and rocking it

at the top and bottom to measure radial play.

Any noticeable looseness at a ball joint indicates a faulty joint.

BALL JOINT, REPLACE

1. Drill out the two rivets that attach ball joint to lower control arm.
2. Remove two strut rod mounting bolts.
3. Remove steering knuckle arm and stud nut and remove ball joint from knuckle pin with a suitable ball joint remover.
4. When installing new ball joints, note that two bolts, lockwashers and nuts are furnished to replace rivets that were removed.

SHOCK ABSORBER, REPLACE

After disconnecting the shock from the wheelhouse panel at the top and from the lower control arm at the bottom, collapse the unit, work to one side and remove from out of the lower control arm.

Reverse the foregoing procedure to install.

SPRING, REPLACE
1970-72

1. Remove shock absorber.
2. Install spring compressor (J-23474) through upper spring seat opening, Fig. 8. Place tool lower attaching screws through shock absorber mounting holes in the lower spring seat. Install tool lower retainer.
3. Remove lower spring seat pivot retaining nuts.
4. Tighten compressor until spring is compressed approximately 1".
5. Raise and support front of car under frame allowing control arms to fall free of lower spring seat. Remove wheel.
6. Pull lower spring seat away from car. Loosen compressor and allow lower spring seat to come out.
7. When all spring tension is released, remove tool lower retainer spring seat and spring.

Fig. 8   Installation of spring compressor. 1970-72

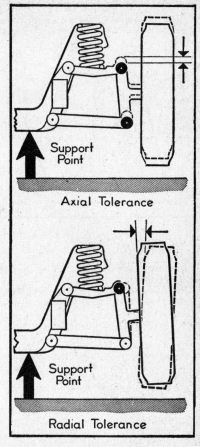

Fig. 7   Checking ball joints for wear. 1966-72

1966-69

1. To remove a spring, raise rear end of car opposite from side from which spring is to be removed. Additional pressure may be gained by leaning on fender over the spring.
2. Install hooks in holes on ears of spring seats. Hooks will hold spring in compressed position to allow removal from vehicle. A service spring may be installed as follows:
3. Install upper and lower cushions and upper and lower spring seats on spring. Align holes in ears of upper and lower spring seats.
4. Compress spring by suitable means (arbor press or hydraulic jack) and install hook on spring seats. Spring can then be installed on spring support.

CAUTION: Lip of lower spring seat must engage seat support to prevent spring from shifting during operation.

5. Hooks are released from spring seat by raising opposite near end of vehicle.

STEERING GEAR, REPLACE
1967-72 All Models

1. Remove flexible coupling bolts.

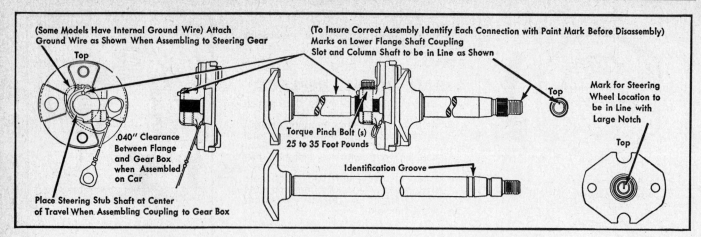

Fig. 9 Line up of steering wheel and shaft through to steering gear. 1966 American

2. Remove pitman arm, using a suitable puller.
3. Remove mounting screws and lower steering gear from vehicle.

1966 Rambler

1. Disconnect battery.
2. Remove horn blowing ring by pressing down at center and turning counterclockwise.
3. Remove steering wheel with a suitable puller.
4. Remove jacket tube support plate screws. Loosen steering jacket tube bracket-to-instrument panel bolts.
5. Remove pitman arm with a suitable puller.
6. Unfasten steering gear from mounting plate (3 screws) and remove gear from below car.

1966 American

1. Remove steering wheel and pitman arm, using suitable pullers.
2. Loosen steering jacket tube at support plate and at instrument panel mounting bracket.
3. Unfasten steering gear and remove it from below the car.

NOTE: On some 1966 models, two flexible couplings are used in steering shaft assembly, Fig. 9.

POWER STEERING
1966-72
Steering Gear, Replace

1. Disconnect pressure and return hoses from gear. Raise hoses above pump level to keep oil from draining out of pump.
2. On 1966, remove lower flange pinch bolt. On 1967-72, remove flexible coupling bolt nuts, noting the different nut sizes to insure correct assembly.
3. Remove pitman arm with a suitable puller.
4. Remove gear attaching bolts.
5. Slide lower shaft free of coupling flange, then remove gear.
6. Reverse procedure to install. On 1966 American models, after gear is installed, do not tighten mounting bolts until clearance between coupling hub and gear housing is checked; it must be a minimum of .040", Fig. 9.

BUICK
All Intermediate & Full Size Models

OLD CAR SPECIFICATIONS: For 1946-65 Tune Up and Wheel Alignment Specifications see back of book.

*This material covered only in the "Service Trade Edition" of this manual.

INDEX OF SERVICE OPERATIONS

1966 Special & Std. Skylark

1966 Skylark Gran Sport

1966 LeSabre

1966 Electra

1966 Wildcat

1966 Riviera

1967 Sportwagon, Special

1967 Gran Sport

1967 LeSabre & Electra

1967 Wildcat

1967 Riviera

1968 Sportwagon, Special, Skylark

1968 Gran Sport

1968 LeSabre

1968 Electra

1968 Riviera

1968 Wildcat

1969 Sportwagon, Special

1969 Gran Sport

1969 LeSabre

1969 Wildcat

1969 Skylark

1969 Electra

1969 Riviera

1970 Skylark, Sportwagon

1970 Gran Sport

1970 LeSabre

1970 Wildcat

1970 Electra

1970 Riviera

1970 Estate Wagon

1971 Skylark

1971 Gran Sport 400

1971 Gran Sport Stage 1

1971 Centurion

1971 Electra

1971 Riviera

1971 LeSabre

1972 Gran Sport

1972 Centurion

1972 Riviera

ENGINE IDENTIFICATION

Buick engines are stamped with two different sets of numbers. One is the engine production code which identifies the engine and its approximate production date. The other is the engine serial number which is the same number that is found on the vehicle identification plate attached to the left body hinge pillar. To identify an engine, look for the production code prefix letters, then refer to the following table for its identification.

On 1968-72 V8 350, 400, 430, 455 on left bank cylinder head.

On V8-400, 401, 425 engines the code is stamped upside down on front of cylinder block when viewed from front of engine.

On V6-225, V8-300 and 340 engines the code is stamped on right side of crankcase between middle branches of right exhaust manifold.

Engine	Code Prefix
1966 V6-225	MH
V8-300	ML
V8-340 2 Bar. Carb.	MA
V8-340 4 Bar. Carb.	MB
V8-400	MR
V8-401	MT
V8-425	MW
1967 V6-225	NH
V8-300	NL
V8-340 2 Bar. Carb.	NA
V8-340 4 Bar. Carb.	NB
V8-400	NR
V8-430	MD, or ND
1968 6-250	
V8-350 2 Bar. Carb.	PO
V8-350 4 Bar. Carb.	PP
V8-400	PR
V8-430	PD

Engine	Code Prefix
1969 6-250	
V8-350 2 Bar. Carb.	RO
V8-350 4 Bar. Carb.	RP
V8-400	RR
V8-430	RD
1970 6-250	
V8-350 2 Bar. Carb.	SO
V8-350 4 Bar. Carb.	SB, P
V8-455	SF, R, S
1971 6-250	
V8-350 2 Bar. Carb.	TC, TO
V8-350 4 Bar. Carb.	TB, TP
V8-455	TA, R, S
1972 V8-350 2 Bar. Carb.	WC
V8-350 4 Bar. Carb.	WB
V8-455	WF
V8-455 (Stage I)	WS
V8-455 (Riviera G.S.)	WA

GENERAL ENGINE SPECIFICATIONS

Year	Engine	Carburetor	Bore and Stroke	Piston Displacement, Cubic Inches	Compression Ratio	Maximum Brake H.P. @ R.P.M.	Maximum Torque Lbs. Ft. @ R.P.M.	Normal Oil Pressure Pounds
1966	160 Horsepower............V6-225	2 Barrel	3.750 x 3.40	225	9.0	160 @ 4200	235 @ 2400	33
	210 Horsepower............V8-300	2 Barrel	3.750 x 3.40	300	9.0	210 @ 4600	310 @ 2400	33
	220 Horsepower............V8-340	2 Barrel	3.750 x 3.85	340	9.0	220 @ 4000	340 @ 2400	33
	260 Horsepower............V8-340	4 Barrel	3.750 x 3.85	340	10.25	260 @ 4000	365 @ 2800	33
	325 Horsepower............V8-401	4 Barrel	4.1875 x 3.64	401	10.25	325 @ 4400	445 @ 2800	40
	340 Horsepower............V8-425	4 Barrel	4.3125 x 3.64	425	10.25	340 @ 4400	465 @ 2800	40
	360 Horsepower............V8-425	Two 4 Bar.	4.3125 x 3.64	425	10.25	360 @ 4400	465 @ 2800	40
1967	160 Horsepower............V6-225	2 Barrel	3.750 x 3.40	225	9.0	160 @ 4200	235 @ 2400	33
	210 Horsepower............V8-300	2 Barrel	3.750 x 3.40	300	9.0	210 @ 4400	310 @ 2400	33
	220 Horsepower............V8-340	2 Barrel	3.750 x 3.85	340	9.0	220 @ 4200	340 @ 2400	33
	260 Horsepower............V8-340	4 Barrel	3.750 x 3.85	340	10.25	260 @ 4200	365 @ 2800	33
	340 Horsepower............V8-400	4 Barrel	4.040 x 3.90	400	10.25	340 @ 5000	440 @ 3200	30
	360 Horsepower............V8-430	4 Barrel	4.1875 x 3.90	430	10.25	360 @ 5000	475 @ 3200	30
1968	155 Horsepower............①6-250	1 Barrel	3.875 x 3.53	250	8.5	155 @ 4200	235 @ 1600	30—45
	230 Horsepower............V8-350	2 Barrel	3.800 x 3.85	350	9.0	230 @ 4400	350 @ 2400	37
	280 Horsepower............V8-350	4 Barrel	3.800 x 3.85	350	10.25	280 @ 4800	375 @ 3200	37
	340 Horsepower............V8-400	4 Barrel	4.040 x 3.90	400	10.25	340 @ 5000	440 @ 3200	30
	360 Horsepower............V8-430	4 Barrel	4.1875 x 3.90	430	10.25	360 @ 5000	475 @ 3200	30
1969	155 Horsepower............①6-250	1 Barrel	3.875 x 3.53	250	8.5	155 @ 4200	235 @ 1600	30—45
	230 Horsepower............V8-350	2 Barrel	3.800 x 3.85	350	9.0	230 @ 4400	350 @ 2400	37
	280 Horsepower............V8-350	4 Barrel	3.800 x 3.85	350	10.25	280 @ 4600	375 @ 3200	37
	340 Horsepower............V8-400	4 Barrel	4.040 x 3.90	400	10.25	340 @ 5000	440 @ 3200	40
	360 Horsepower............V8-430	4 Barrel	4.1875 x 3.90	430	10.25	360 @ 5000	475 @ 3200	40
1970	155 Horsepower............①6-250	1 Barrel	3.875 x 3.53	250	8.5	155 @ 4200	235 @ 1600	30—45
	260 Horsepower............V8-350	2 Barrel	3.800 x 3.85	350	9.0	260 @ 4600	360 @ 2600	37
	285 Horsepower............V8-350	4 Barrel	3.800 x 3.85	350	9.0	285 @ 4600	375 @ 3000	37
	315 Horsepower............V8-350	4 Barrel	3.800 x 3.85	350	10.25	315 @ 4800	410 @ 3200	37
	350 Horsepower............V8-455	4 Barrel	4.3125 x 3.90	455	10.00	350 @ 4600	510 @ 2800	40
	360 Horsepower............V8-455	4 Barrel	4.3125 x 3.90	455	10.00	360 @ 4600	510 @ 2800	40
	370 Horsepower............V8-455	4 Barrel	4.3125 x 3.90	455	10.00	370 @ 4600	510 @ 2800	40

Continued

GENERAL ENGINE SPECIFICATIONS—Continued

Year	Engine	Car-buretor	Bore and Stroke	Piston Dis-place-ment, Cubic Inches	Com-pres-sion Ratio	Maximum Brake H.P. @ R.P.M.	Maximum Torque Lbs. Ft. @ R.P.M.	Normal Oil Pressure Pounds
1971	145 Horsepower.............①6-250	1 Barrel	3.875 x 3.53	250	8.5	145 @ 4000	235 @ 2400	30–45
	230 Horsepower.............V8-350	2 Barrel	3.800 x 3.85	350	8.5	230 @ 4400	350 @ 2400	37
	260 Horsepower.............V8-350	4 Barrel	3.800 x 3.85	350	8.5	260 @ 4600	360 @ 3000	37
	315 Horsepower.............V8-455	4 Barrel	4.3125 x 3.90	455	8.5	315 @ 4400	450 @ 2800	40
	330 Horsepower.............V8-455	4 Barrel	4.3125 x 3.90	455	8.5	330 @ 4600	455 @ 2800	40
	345 Horsepower.............V8-455	4 Barrel	4.3125 x 3.90	455	8.5	345 @ 5000	460 @ 3000	40

①—See Chevrolet chapter for service procedures on this engine.

VALVE SPECIFICATIONS

Year	Model	Valve Lash Int.	Valve Lash Exh.	Valve Angles Seat	Valve Angles Face	Valve Spring Installed Height ③	Valve Spring Pressure Lbs. @ In.	Stem Clearance Intake	Stem Clearance Exhaust	Stem Diameter Intake	Stem Diameter Exhaust
1966	V6-225	Hydraulic⑥		45	45	1.727	164 @ 1.34	.002–.0025①	.0025–.003①	.3407–.3412②	.3402–.3407②
	V8-300, 340	Hydraulic⑥		45	45	1.727	164 @ 1.34	.0012–.0032	.0025–.003①	.3405–.3415②	.3402–.3407②
	V8-401, 425	Hydraulic⑥		45	45	1.60	101 @ 1.16	.002–.003①	.0025–.0035①	.3720–.3730②	.3715–.3720②
1967	V6-225	Hydraulic⑥		45	45	1.727	168 @ 1.25	.0012–.0032	.0015–.0035①	.3405–.3415	.3402–.3407②
	V8-300, 340	Hydraulic⑥		45	45	1.727	164 @ 1.34	.0012–.0032	.0015–.0035①	.3405–.3415	.3402–.3407②
	V8-400, 430	Hydraulic⑥		45	45	1.89	177 @ 1.45	.0015–.0035	.0015–.0035①	.3720–.3730	.3720–.3730②
1968–69	6-250④	1 Turn⑤		46	45	1.66	185 @ 1.27	.001–.0027	.001–.0027	.3410–.3417	.3410–.3417
	V8-350	Hydraulic⑥		45	45	1.72	180 @ 1.34	.0015–.0035	.0015–.0035①	.3720–.3730	.3720–.3730②
	V8-400, 430	Hydraulic⑥		45	45	1.89	177 @ 1.45	.0015–.0035	.0015–.0035①	.3720–.3730	.3720–.3730②
1970–71	6-250④	1 Turn⑤		46	45	1.66	185 @ 1.27	.001–.0027	.001–.0027	.3410–.3417	.3410–.3417
	V8-350	Hydraulic⑥		45	45	1.72	180 @ 1.34	.0015–.0035	.0015–.0035①	.3720–.3730	.3720–.3730②
	V8-455	Hydraulic⑥		45	45	1.89	177 @ 1.45	.0015–.0035	.0015–.0035①	.3720–.3730	.3720–.3730②
1972	V8-350	Hydraulic⑥		45	45	1.72	180 @ 1.34	.0015–.0035	.0015–.0032①	.3720–.3730	.3723–.3730②
	V8-455	Hydraulic⑥		45	45	1.89	177 @ 1.45	.0015–.0035	.0015–.0032①	.3720–.3730	.3723–.3730②

①—Plus or minus .001″. Guide tapers top to bottom with larger dimension at bottom.
②—Plus or minus .0005″. Guide tapers top to bottom with larger dimension at top.
③—Outer spring.
④—See Chevrolet chapter for service procedures on this engine.
⑤—Turn rocker arm stud nut until all lash is eliminated, then tighten nut the additional turn listed.
⑥—No adjustment.

TUNE UP SPECIFICATIONS

OLD CAR SPECIFICATIONS: For 1946-65 Tune Up Specifications see back of book.

★When using a timing light, disconnect vacuum tube or hose at distributor and plug opening in hose or tube so idle speed will not be affected.

| Year | Engine | Spark Plug | | Distributor | | Firing Order | Ignition Timing★ | | Hot Idle Speed | | Comp. Press. Lbs. [3] | Fuel Pump Press. Lbs. |
		Type AC	Gap Inch	Point Gap Inch	Dwell Angle Deg.		BTDC [1]	Mark	Std. Trans.	Auto. Trans. [2]		
1966	V6-225	44S	.035	.016[5]	30	Fig. G	5°	Fig. E	550[4]	550D[4]	165	4¼-5¾
	V8-300, 340 2 B.C.	45S	.035	.016[5]	30	Fig. C	2½°	Fig. E	550[4]	550D[4]	165	4¼-5¾
	V8-340 4 Bar. Carb.	44S	.035	.016[5]	30	Fig. C	2½°	Fig. E	550[4]	550D[4]	180	5½-7
	V8-401, 425	44S	.035	.016[5]	30	Fig. D	2½°[6]	Fig. A	500[4]	500D[4]	180	5½-7
1967	6-225 Except Cal.	44S	.035	.016[5]	30	Fig. G	5°	Fig. E	550[4]	550D[4]	165	4¼-5¾
	6-225 California[7]	44S	.035	.016[5]	30	Fig. G	5°	Fig. E	650[4]	600D[4]	165	4¼-5¾
	8-300 Except Cal.	[10]	.035	.016[5]	30	Fig. B	2½°	Fig. E	550[4]	550D[4]	165	4¼-5¾
	8-300 California[7]	[10]	.035	.016[5]	30	Fig. B	2½°	Fig. E	650[4]	600D[4]	165	4¼-5¾
	8-340 Except Cal.	[10]	.035	.016[5]	30	Fig. B	2½°	Fig. E	550[4]	550D[4]	165	4¼-5¾
	8-340 California[7]	[10]	.035	.016[5]	30	Fig. B	2½°	Fig. E	650[4]	600D[4]	165	4¼-5¾
	8-400 Except Cal.	44TS	.035	.016[5]	30	Fig. B	2½°	Fig. E	500[4]	500D[4]	180	5½-7
	8-400 California[7]	44TS	.035	.016[5]	30	Fig. B	2½°	Fig. E	600[4]	550D[4]	180	5½-7
	8-430 Except Cal.	44TS	.035	.016[5]	30	Fig. B	2½°	Fig. E	550[4]	550D[4]	180	5½-7
	8-430 California[7]	44TS	.035	.016[5]	30	Fig. B	2½°	Fig. E	600[4]	550D[4]	180	5½-7
1968	6-250[8] Std. Tr.	46N	.030	.019	32	153624	TDC	Damper	700[4]	—	130	4-5
	6-250[8] Auto. Tr.	46N	.030	.019	32	153624	4°	Damper	—	600D[4]	130	4-5
	V8-350	45TS	.030	.016	30	Fig. B	TDC	Fig. E	700[4]	550D[4]	165	4¼-5¾
	V8-400	44TS	.030	.016	30	Fig. B	TDC	Fig. E	700[4]	600D[4]	180	5½-7
	V8-430	44TS	.030	.016	30	Fig. B	TDC	Fig. E	—	550D[4]	180	5½-7
1969	6-250[8] Std. Tr.	R46N	.035	.019	32	153624	TDC	Damper	700	—	130	4-5
	6-250[8] Auto Tr.	R46N	.035	.019	32	153624	4°	Damper	—	500D[4]	130	4-5
	V8-350	R45TS	.030	.016	30	Fig. B	TDC[9]	Fig. E	700	600D	165	4¼-5¾
	V8-400 Std. Tr.	R44TS	.030	.016	30	Fig. B	2½ ATDC	Fig. E	700	—	180	5½-7
	V8-400 Auto Tr.	R44TS	.030	.016	30	Fig. B	TDC	Fig. E	—	600D	180	5½-7
	V8-400 G.S. Stage I	R44TS	.030	.016	30	Fig. B	10°	Fig. E	700	600D	180	6-8
	V8-430	R44TS	.030	.016	30	Fig. B	TDC	Fig. E	—	550D	180	5½-7
1970	6-250[8]	R46N	.035	.019	32	153624	[12]	Damper	700	550D	130	4-5
	V8-350	R45TS	.030	.016	30	Fig. B	6°	Fig. F	700	600D	165	4¼-5¾
	V8-455	R44TS	.030	.016	30	Fig. B	6°[14]	Fig. F	700	600D	180	4¼-5¾
1971	6-250[8]	R46TS	.035	.019	32	153624	4°	Damper	550	500D		4-5
	V8-350 Std. Tr.	R45TS	.030	.016	30	Fig. B	6°	Fig. F	800	—		4¼-5¾
	V8-350 Auto. Tr.	R45TS	.030	.016	30	Fig. B	[11]	Fig. F	—	600D		4¼-5¾
	V8-455 Std. Tr.	R44TS	.030	.016	30	Fig. B	6°	Fig. F	700	—		4¼-5¾
	V8-455 Auto. Tr.	R44TS	.030	.016	30	Fig. B	4°	Fig. F	—	600D		4¼-5¾
	V8-455 Stage I	R44TS	.030	.016	30	Fig. B	10°	Fig. F	700	600D		4¼-5¾
1972	V8-350	R45TS	.040	.016	30	Fig. B	4°	Fig. F	800	650D		3
	V8-455	R45TS	.040	.016	30	Fig. B	4°	Fig. F	900	650D		4½
	V8-455 Stage 1	R45TS	.040	.016	30	Fig. B	[13]	Fig. F	900	650D		4½

[1]—BTDC: Before top dead center.
[2]—D: Drive. N: Neutral.
[3]—Plus or minus 20 lbs.
[4]—If air conditioned, turn A/C switch to "Full On" position.
[5]—Turn adjusting screw in (clockwise) until engine misfires; then turn screw out ½ turn.
[6]—12° BTDC for V8-425 with 2 carbs and automatic transmission.
[7]—Air Injector Reactor (A.I.R.).
[8]—See Chevrolet chapter for service procedures on this engine.
[9]—5° BTDC for LeSabre.
[10]—2 barrel 45S, 4 barrel 44S.
[11]—4 Barrel carburetors and all LeSabres 4°; All others 10°.
[12]—Std. trans. TDC: Auto. Trans. 4°.
[13]—Manual trans., 8°; Automatic trans., 10°.
[14]—Early Gran Sport models set at TDC.

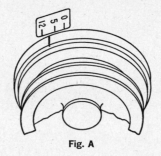

Fig. A

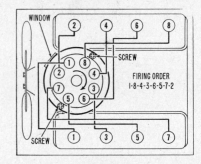

WINDOW SCREW FIRING ORDER 1-8-4-3-6-5-7-2 SCREW

Fig. B

Continued

TUNE UP NOTES—Continued

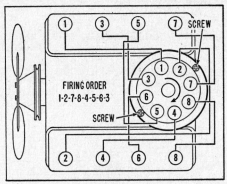

Fig. D

FIRING ORDER
1-2-7-8-4-5-6-3

SCREW

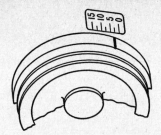

Fig. E

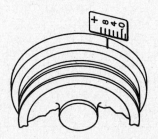

Fig. F

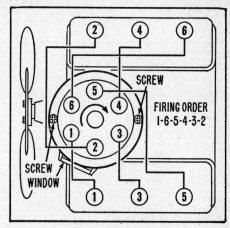

Fig. G

FIRING ORDER
1-6-5-4-3-2

SCREW

SCREW
WINDOW

DISTRIBUTOR SPECIFICATIONS

★NOTE: If advance is checked on the vehicle, double the R.P.M. and degrees advance to get crankshaft figures.

Year	Model	Distributor Part No.①	Breaker Gap	Dwell Angle Deg.	Breaker Arm Spring Tension	Centrifugal Advance Degrees @ R.P.M. of Distributor★		Vacuum Advance		Dist. Retard
						Advance Starts	Full Advance	Inches of Vacuum To Start Plunger	Max. Adv. Dist. Deg. @ Vacuum	Max. Ret. Dist. Deg. @ Vacuum
1966	V6-225	1110342	.016③	30	19–23	1 @ 500	13 @ 2100	6 to 8	8 @ 15	—
	V8-300	1111147	.016③	30	19–23	1 @ 325	17 @ 2300	6 to 8	8 @ 16	—
	V8-340	1111144	.016③	30	19–23	1 @ 325	16 @ 2300	6 to 8	9 @ 15	—
	V8-401, 425	1111055	.016③	30	19–23	1 @ 400	15 @ 1950	6 to 8	8 @ 16	—
	V8-425 Two Carbs.	1111058	.016③	30	19–23	1 @ 450	10 @ 1900	6 to 8	8 @ 16	—
1967	V6-225	1110342	.016③	30	19–23	1 @ 500	13 @ 2100	6 to 8	8 @ 15	—
	V8-300	1111147	.016③	30	19–23	1 @ 325	17 @ 2300	6 to 8	8 @ 16	—
	V8-340	1111144	.016③	30	19–23	1 @ 325	16 @ 2300	6 to 8	9 @ 15	—
	V8-400, 430	1111149	.016③	30	19–23	1 @ 425	16 @ 1850	6 to 8	8 @ 15	—
1968	6-250 Std. Tr.	1110439	.019	32	19–23	1 @ 450	16 @ 2100	6 to 8	11 @ 17	—
	6-250 Auto. Tr.	1111339	.019	32	19–23	1 @ 450	15 @ 2100	6 to 8	11 @ 17	—
	V8-350	1111330	.016③	30	19–23	1 @ 550	14 @ 2300	6 to 8	8 @ 16	—
	V8-400, 430	1111285	.016③	30	19–23	1 @ 550	16 @ 2300	6 to 8	8 @ 16	—
1969	6-250 Std. Tr.	1110463	.019	32	19–23	1 @ 400	17 @ 2100	6 to 8	12 @ 17	—
	6-250 Auto. Tr.	1110464	.019	32	19–23	1 @ 400	15 @ 2100	6 to 8	12 @ 17	—
	V8-350-2 Bar. Carb.	1111938	.016③	30	19–23	1 @ 375	17 @ 2300	6 to 8	9 @ 16	—
	V8-350-4 Bar. Carb.	1111334	.016③	30	19–23	1 @ 500	15 @ 2300	6 to 8	9 @ 16	—
	V8-400, 430	1111335	.016③	30	19–23	1 @ 500	17 @ 2300	6 to 8	9 @ 16	—
	V8-400 G.S. Stage I	1111962	.016③	30	19–23	1 @ 500	12 @ 2300	6 to 8	9 @ 16	—
1970	6-250 Std. Tr.	1110463	.019	32	19–23	1 @ 400	17 @ 2100	6 to 8	12 @ 17	—
	6-250 Auto. Tr.	1110464	.019	32	19–23	1 @ 400	15 @ 2100	6 to 8	12 @ 17	—
	V8-350 2 Bar. Carb.	1111986	.016③	30	19–23	1 @ 375	17 @ 2300	6 to 8	9 @ 16	—
	V8-350 4 Bar. Carb.	1112006	.016③	30	19–23	1 @ 450	9 @ 2300	6 to 8	9¾ @ 25	—
	V8-455	1111984	.016③	30	19–23	1 @ 500	17 @ 2300	6 to 8	9 @ 16	—
	V8-455 Stage I	1111962	.016③	30	19–23	1 @ 500	12 @ 2300	6 to 8	9 @ 16	—

Continued

DISTRIBUTOR SPECIFICATIONS—Continued

★NOTE: If advance is checked on the vehicle, double the R.P.M. and degrees advance to get crankshaft figures.

Year	Model	Distributor Part No.①	Breaker Gap	Dwell Angle Deg.	Breaker Arm Spring Tension	Centrifugal Advance Degrees @ R.P.M. of Distributor★		Vacuum Advance		Dist. Retard
						Advance Starts	Full Advance	Inches of Vacuum To Start Plunger	Max. Adv. Dist. Deg. @ Vacuum	Max. Ret. Dist. Deg. @ Vacuum
1971	6-250	1110489	.019	32	19–23	1 @ 500	13 @ 2050	8	11½ @ 16	—
	V8-350 Std. Tr.	1112006	.016③	30	19–23	1 @ 450	9 @ 2300	6 to 8	9¾ @ 25	—
	V8-350 Auto. Tr.	1112037	.016③	30	19–23	1 @ 750	6 @ 2300	6 to 8	9¾ @ 25	—
	V8-350	1112080	.016③	30	19–23	1 @ 750	11 @ 2400	6½ to 8½	9¾ @ 25	—
	V8-455	1112077	.016③	30	19–23	1 @ 750	12 @ 2300	6 to 8	9¾ @ 25	—
1972	V8-350	1112109	.016③	30	19–23	1 @ 400	8 @ 1500	6 to 8	9 @ 16	—
	V8-455	1112110	.016③	30	19–23	1 @ 500	9 @ 1450	6 to 8	9 @ 13	—
	V8-455 Stage 1	1112016	.016③	30	19–23	1 @ 350	12 @ 2300	6 to 8	9 @ 16	—

①—Located on distributor housing plate. ③—Turn adjusting screw in (clockwise) until engine misfires; then turn screw out ½ turn.

PISTONS, PINS, RINGS, CRANKSHAFT & BEARINGS

Year	Engine	Piston Clearance	Ring End Gap①		Wrist-pin Diameter	Rod Bearings		Main Bearings			
			Comp.	Oil		Shaft Diameter	Bearing Clearance	Shaft Diameter	Bearing Clearance	Thrust on Bear. No.	Shaft End Play
1966	V6-225	.0005–.0011	.010	.015	.9394	2.000	.0002–.0023	2.4995	.0004–.0015	2	.004–.008
	V8-300, 340	.0005–.0011	.010	.015	.9394	2.000	.0002–.0023	2.9995	.0004–.0015	3	.004–.008
	V8-401	.001–.0016	.015	.015	.9995	2.2495	.0002–.0023	2.4985	.0001–.0019	3	.004–.008
	V8-425	.0013–.0019	.015	.015	.9995	2.2495	.0002–.0023	2.4985	.0001–.0019	3	.004–.008
1967	V6-225	.0011–.0027	.010	.015	.9394	2.000	.0002–.0023	2.4995	.0004–.0015	2	.004–.008
	V8-300	.0011–.0017	.010	.015	.9394	2.000	.0002–.0023	2.4995	.0004–.0015	3	.004–.008
	V8-340	.0011–.0017	.010	.015	.9394	2.000	.0002–.0023	2.9995	.0004–.0015	3	.004–.008
	V8-400, 430	.0007–.0023	.013	.015	.9994	2.249–2.250	.0002–.0023	3.2500	.0007–.0018	3	.003–.009
1968–69	6-250②	.0005–.0011	.010	.015	.9271	1.999–2.000	.0007–.0027	2.3004	.0003–.0029	7	.002–.006
	V8-350	.0008–.0014	.013	.015	.9394	2.0000	.0002–.0023	2.9995	.0004–.0015	3	.003–.009
	V8-400, 430	.0007–.0013	.013	.015	.9994	2.249–2.250	.0002–.0023	3.2500	.0007–.0018	3	.003–.009
1970	6-250②	.0005–.0011	.010	.015	.9271	1.999–2.000	.0007–.0027	2.3004	.0003–.0029	7	.002–.006
	V8-350	.0008–.0014	.013	.015	.9394	2.0000	.0002–.0023	2.9995	.0004–.0015	3	.003–.009
	V8-455	.0010–.0022	.013	.015	.9994	2.249–2.250	.0002–.0023	3.2500	.0007–.0018	3	.003–.009
1971–72	V8-350	.0008–.0020	.013	.015	.9394	2.000	.0002–.0023	2.9995	.0004–.0015	3	.003–.009
	V8-455	.0010–.0016	.013	.015	.9994	2.249–2.250	.0002–.0023	3.250	.0007–.0018	3	.003–.009

①—Fit rings in tapered bores for clearance given in tightest portion of ring travel.
②—See Chevrolet chapter for service procedures on this engine.

ALTERNATOR & REGULATOR SPECIFICATIONS

Year	Model	Rated Hot Output Amps.	Field Current 12 Volts @ 80 F.	Cold Output @ 14 Volts 2000 R.P.M. Amps.	5000 R.P.M. Amps.	Model	Field Relay Air Gap In.	Point Gap In.	Closing Voltage	Voltage Regulator Air Gap In.	Point Gap In.	Voltage @ 125° F.
1966	1100691	42	2.2–2.6	28	40	1119515	.015	.030	1.5–2.7	.067	.014	13.5–14.4
	1100705	37	2.2–2.6	25	35	1119515	.015	.030	1.5–2.7	.067	.014	13.5–14.4
	1100708	42	2.2–2.6	28	40	1119515	.015	.030	1.5–2.7	.067	.014	13.5–14.4
	1100709	55	2.2–2.6	32	50	1119515	.015	.030	1.5–2.7	.067	.014	13.5–14.4
	1100710	55	2.2–2.6	32	50	1119515	.015	.030	1.5–2.7	.067	.014	13.5–14.4
1967	1100691	42	2.2–2.6	28	40	1119515	.015	.030	1.5–2.7	.067	.014	13.5–14.4
	1100761	37	2.2–2.6	25	35	1119515	.015	.030	1.5–2.7	.067	.014	13.5–14.4
	1100774	55	2.2–2.6	32	50	1119515	.015	.030	1.5–2.7	.067	.014	13.6–14.4
1968–69	1100762	37	2.2–2.6	25	35	1119515	.015	.030	1.5–3.2	.067	.014	13.6–14.4
	1100761	37	2.2–2.6	25	35	1119515	.015	.030	1.5–3.2	.067	.014	13.6–14.4
	1100802	55	2.2–2.6	32	50	1119515	.015	.030	1.5–3.2	.067	.014	13.6–14.4
	1100691	42	2.2–2.6	28	40	1119515	.015	.030	1.5–3.2	.067	.014	13.6–14.4
	1100774	55	2.2–2.6	32	50	1119515	.015	.030	1.5–3.2	.067	.014	13.6–14.4
1970	1100761	37	2.2–2.6	29	—	1119515	.015	.030	1.5–3.2	.067	.014	13.6–14.4
	1100888	37	2.2–2.6	29	—	1119515	.015	.030	1.5–3.2	.067	.014	13.6–14.4
	1100691	42	2.2–2.6	32	—	1119515	.015	.030	1.5–3.2	.067	.014	13.6–14.4
	1100774	55	2.2–2.6	44	—	1119515	.015	.030	1.5–3.2	.067	.014	13.6–14.4
	1100892	55	2.2–2.6	44	—	1119515	.015	.030	1.5–3.2	.067	.014	13.6–14.4
	1100860	61	2.2–2.6	47	—	1119515	.015	.030	1.5–3.2	.067	.014	13.6–14.4
1971	1100891	—	2.2–2.6	—	—	1119515	.015	.030	1.5–3.2	.067	.014	13.6–14.4
	1100905	37	2.2–2.6	—	—	1119515	.015	.030	1.5–3.2	.067	.014	13.6–14.4
	1100924	55	4.0–4.5	—	—	1116384	—	—	—	—	—	13.5–14.5
	1100926	42	4.0–4.5	—	—	1116384	—	—	—	—	—	13.5–14.5
	1100931	42	2.2–2.6	—	—	1119515	.015	.030	1.5–3.2	.067	.014	13.6–14.4
	1100932	—	2.2–2.6	—	—	1119515	.015	.030	1.5–3.2	.067	.014	13.6–14.4
	1100943	42	2.2–2.6	—	—	1119515	.015	.030	1.5–3.2	.067	.014	13.6–14.4
1972	1102449	37	2.2–2.6	7①	29②	1119515	.015	.030	1.5–3.2	.067	.014	13.5–14.5
	1102443	42	2.2–2.6	9①	32②	1119515	.015	.030	1.5–3.2	.067	.014	13.5–14.5
	1102448	55	2.2–2.6	9①	44②	1119515	.015	.030	1.5–3.2	.067	.014	13.5–14.5
	1102442	55	2.2–2.6	9①	44②	1119515	.015	.030	1.5–3.2	.067	.014	13.5–14.5
	1102450	61	2.2–2.6	12①	47②	1119515	.015	.030	1.5–3.2	.067	.014	13.5–14.5
	1102447	63	2.8–3.2	13①	51②	1119519	.015	.030	1.5–3.2	.067	.014	13.5–14.5

①—At 500 engine R.P.M.   ②—At 1500 engine R.P.M.

REAR AXLE SPECIFICATIONS

Year	Model	Carrier Type	Ring Gear & Pinion Backlash Method	Adjustment	Pinion Bearing Preload Method	Adjustment New Bearings Inch-Lbs.	Adjustment Used Bearings Inch-Lbs.	Differential Bearing Preload Method	Adjustment New Bearings Inch-Lbs.	Adjustment Used Bearings Inch-Lbs.
1966–67	43-44-45000	Integral	Shims	.007–.009	Spacer	20–30①	12–20①	Shims	35–40③	20–25③
	46-48-49000	Integral	Shims	.007–.009	Spacer	25–30①	10–15①	Shims	35–40③	25–30③
1968–70	43-44-45000	Integral	Shims	.006–.008	Spacer	20–25①	10–15①	Shims	35–40③	20–25③
	46-48-49000	Integral	Shims	.007–.009	Spacer	25–30①	10–15①	Shims	35–40③	25–30③
1971–72	All	Integral	Shims	.006–.008	Spacer	20–25①	10–15①	Shims	35–40③	20–25③

①—Measured with torque wrench at pinion flange nut.
②—Measured with torque wrench at ring gear bolt.
③—Total preload measured with torque wrench at pinion flange nut with new seal installed.

STARTING MOTOR SPECIFICATIONS

Year	Model	Starter Number	Brush Spring Tension Oz①	Free Speed Test			Resistance Test③	
				Amps.	Volts	R.P.M.	Amps. ①	Volts
1966	V6-225	1107259	35	65–100②	10.6	3600–5100	300–360	3.5
	V8-300, 340	1107374	35	65–100②	10.6	3600–5100	300–360	3.5
	V8-401	1107361	35	70–105②	10.6	3800–6200	480–540	3.0
	V8-401, 425	1107313	35	70–105②	10.6	3800–6200	480–540②	3.0
1967	V6-225, V8-300	1107596	35	49–87②	10.6	6200–10700	—	—
	V8-340	1107374	35	65–100②	10.6	3600–5100	300–360	3.5
	V8-400, 430	1107385	35	70–105②	10.6	3800–6200	480–540	3
1968	6-250	1108365	35	49–87②	10.6	6200–10700	290–425②	4.2
	V8-350	1108380	35	65–100②	10.6	3600–5100	300–360②	3.5
	V8-400, 430	1108354	35	70–105②	10.6	3800–6200	480–540②	3.0
1969–72	6-250	1108365	35	49–87②	10.6	6200–10700	290–425②	4.2
	V8-350	1108391	35	55–85③	9	3100–4900	—	—
	V8-400, 430, 455	1108392	35	48–74②	9	4100–6300	—	—

①—Minimum. ②—Includes solenoid.
③—Check capacity of motor by using a 500 ampere meter and a carbon pile rheostat to control voltage. Apply volts listed across motor with armature locked. Current should be as listed.

BRAKE SPECIFICATIONS

Year	Model	Brake Drum Inside Diameter	Wheel Cylinder Bore Diameter			Master Cylinder Bore Diameter		
			Front Disc Brake	Front Drum Brake	Rear Drum Brake	With Disc Brakes	With Drum Brakes	With Power Brakes
1966	Special (Except Below)	9.495–9.505	—	1 1/16	15/16	—	1.00	1.00
	Sportwagon	9.495–9.505	—	1 1/16	1.00	—	1.00	1.00
	Skylark Gran Sport	9.495–9.505	—	1 1/8	15/16	—	1.00	1.00
	Senior Models	11.997–12.002	—	1 1/8	1.00	—	1.00	1.00
1967	Le Sabre, Wildcat, Electra	11.997–12.002	—	1 3/16	1.00	1 1/8	1.00	1.00
	Riviera	11.997–12.002	—	①	15/16	1 1/8	1.00	1.00
	Special, Skylark	9.495–9.505	—	1 1/8	15/16	1 1/8	1.00	1.00
	G.S. 400	9.495–9.505	—	1 1/8	7/8	1 1/8	1.00	1.00
	Sportwagon	9.495–9.505	—	1 1/8	1.00	1 1/8	1.00	1.00
1968	Special, Skylark	9.495–9.505	—	1 1/8	7/8	1 1/8	1.00	1.00
	Sportwagon	9.495–9.505	—	1 1/8	1.00	1 1/8	1.00	1.00
	GS-350, GS-400	9.495–9.505	—	1 1/8	7/8	1 1/8	1.00	1.00
	Le Sabre, Wildcat, Electra	11.997–12.022	—	1 3/16	1.00	1 1/8	1.00	1.00
	Riviera	11.997–12.022	—	1 3/16	15/16	1 1/8	1.00	1.00
1969	Special, Skylark	9.495–9.505	—	1 1/8	7/8	1 1/8	1.00	②
	Sportwagon	9.495–9.505	—	1 1/8	1.00	1 1/8	1.00	②
	GS-350, GS-400	9.495–9.505	—	1 1/8	7/8	1 1/8	1.00	②
	LeSabre, Wildcat, Electra	11.997–12.022	2 15/16	1 3/16	1.00	1 1/8	1.00	②
	Riviera	11.997–12.022	2 15/16	1 3/16	15/16	1 1/8	1.00	②
1970	Skylark, GS, GS-455	9.495–9.505	—	1 1/8	7/8	1 1/8	1.00	②
	Sportwagon	9.495–9.505	—	1 1/8	7/8	1 1/8	1.00	②
	Le Sabre, Wildcat, Electra, Wagon	11.997–12.022	2 15/16	1 3/16	1.00	1 1/8	1.00	②
	Riviera	11.997–12.022	2 15/16	1 3/16	15/16	1 1/8	1.00	②

Continued

BRAKE SPECIFICATIONS—Continued

Year	Model	Brake Drum Inside Diameter	Wheel Cylinder Bore Diameter			Master Cylinder Bore Diameter		
			Front Disc Brake	Front Drum Brake	Rear Drum Brake	With Disc Brakes	With Drum Brakes	With Power Brakes
1971–72	Skylark, GS, GS-455	9.495–9.505	—	1⅛	⅞	1⅛	1.00	②
	Sportwagon	9.495–9.505	—	1⅛	⅞	1⅛	1.00	②
	Le Sabre, Centurion, Electra	10.997–11.007	2¹⁵⁄₁₆	—	¹⁵⁄₁₆	1⅛	—	②
	Estate Wagon	11.997–12.007	2¹⁵⁄₁₆	—	¹⁵⁄₁₆	1⅛	—	②
	Riviera	10.997–11.007	2¹⁵⁄₁₆	—	¹⁵⁄₁₆	1⅛	—	②

①—First type 1⅛", second type 1³⁄₁₆".   ②—Drum brakes 1", disc brakes 1⅛".

ENGINE TIGHTENING SPECIFICATIONS*

★Torque specifications are for clean and lightly lubricated threads only. Dry or dirty threads produce increased friction which prevents accurate measurement of tightness.

Year	Engine	Spark Plugs Ft. Lbs.	Cylinder Head Bolts Ft. Lbs.	Intake Manifold Ft. Lbs.	Exhaust Manifold Ft. Lbs.	Rocker Arm Shaft Bracket Ft. Lbs.	Rocker Arm Cover Ft. Lbs.	Connecting Rod Cap Bolts Ft. Lbs.	Main Bearing Cap Bolts Ft. Lbs.	Flywheel to Crankshaft Ft. Lbs.	Vibration Damper or Pulley Ft. Lbs.
1966	V6-225	25–35	65–80	45–55	10–15	25–35	3–5	30–40	95–120	50–65	—
	300, 340	25–35	65–80	45–55	10–15	25–35	3–5	30–40	95–120	50–65	140 min.
	400, 401, 425	25–35	65–80	25–35	10–15	25–35	3–5	40–50	80–110	50–65	200 min.
1967	V6-225	25–35	65–80	45–55	15–20	25–35	3–5	30–40	95–120	50–65	—
	300, 340	25–35	65–80	45–55	15–20	25–35	3–5	30–40	95–120	50–65	140 min.
	400, 430	15	100–120	45–55	15–20	25–35	3–5	45–50	80–115	50–65	200 min.
1968–69	6-250	25	95	④	④	—	5	35	65	60	⑤
	V8-350	15	75	55	18	30	4	35	95	60	140 min.
	V8-400, 430	15	100	55	18	30	4	45	110	60	200 min.
1970	6-250	25⑥	95	④	④	—	5	35	65	60	⑤
	V8-350	15	75	55	18	25	4	35	95	60	120 min.
	V8-455	15	100	55	18	25	4	45	110	58	200 min.
1971–72	V8-350	15	75	55	18	25	4	35	95	60	120 min.
	V8-455	15	100	65	18	25	4	45	110	58	200 min.

①—Rear bearing cap 100–110 ft.-lbs.   ②—Rear bearing cap 65–70 ft. Lbs.   ③—Rear bearing cap 60–70 ft. lbs.
④—End clamps 20, center bolts 30.   ⑤—Pressed on.   ⑥—1971 use 15 ft.-lbs.

WHEEL ALIGNMENT SPECIFICATIONS

OLD CAR SPECIFICATIONS: For 1946-65 Wheel Alignment Specifications see back of book.

Year	Model	Caster Angle, Degrees Limits	Desired	Camber Angle, Degrees Limits Left	Right	Desired Left	Right	Toe-In. Inch	Toe-Out on Turns, Deg. Outer Wheel	Inner Wheel
1966	Special, Skylark	−1 to 0	−½	0 to +1	0 to +1	+½	+½	⅛−¼	20	21¼
	Le Sabre	+½ to +1½	+1	0 to +1	0 to +1	+½	+½	⁷⁄₃₂−⁵⁄₁₆	20	①
	Wildcat	+½ to +1½	+1	0 to +1	0 to +1	+½	+½	⁷⁄₃₂−⁵⁄₁₆	20	②
	Electra 225	+½ to +1½	+1	0 to +1	0 to +1	+½	+½	⁷⁄₃₂−⁵⁄₁₆	20	21° 47′
	Riviera	+½ to +1½	+1	0 to +1	0 to +1	+½	+½	⁷⁄₃₂−⁵⁄₁₆	20	22° 50′
1967	Special, Skylark	−1 to 0	−½	0 to +1	0 to +1	+½	+½	⅛−¼	18° 38′	20
	G.S. 400	−1 to 0	−½	0 to +1	0 to +1	+½	+½	⅛−¼	18° 38′	20
	Le Sabre	+½ to +1½	+1	0 to +1	0 to +1	+¼	+¼	⁷⁄₃₂−⁵⁄₁₆	18° 9′	20
	Wildcat	+½ to +1½	+1	0 to +1	0 to +1	+¼	+¼	⁷⁄₃₂−⁵⁄₁₆	16° 58′	20
	Electra 225	+½ to +1½	+1	0 to +1	0 to +1	+¼	+¼	⁷⁄₃₂−⁵⁄₁₆	16° 58′	20
	Riviera	+½ to +1½	+1	0 to +1	0 to +1	+¼	+¼	⁷⁄₃₂−⁵⁄₁₆	17° 5′	20
1968	Intermediates	−1 to 0	−½	0 to +1	0 to +1	+½	+½	⅛−¼	18° 8′	20
	Le Sabre	+½ to +1½	+1	−¼ to +¾	−¼ to +¾	+¼	+¼	⁷⁄₃₂−⁵⁄₁₆	18° 9′	20
	Wildcat	+½ to +1½	+1	−¼ to +¾	−¼ to +¾	+¼	+¼	⁷⁄₃₂−⁵⁄₁₆	16° 58′	20
	Electra 225	+½ to +1½	+1	−¼ to +¾	−¼ to +¾	+¼	+¼	⁷⁄₃₂−⁵⁄₁₆	16° 58′	20
	Riviera	+½ to +1½	+1	−¼ to +¾	−¼ to +¾	+¼	+¼	⁷⁄₃₂−⁵⁄₁₆	17° 5′	20
1969–70	Intermediates	−1 to 0	−½	0 to +1	0 to +1	+½	+½	⅛−¼	18½	20
	Le Sabre	+¼ to +1¼	+¾	−½ to +½	−½ to +½	0	0	⁷⁄₃₂−⁵⁄₁₆	19½	20
	Estate Wagon	+¼ to +1¼	+¾	−½ to +½	−½ to +½	0	0	⁷⁄₃₂−⁵⁄₁₆	19½	20
	Wildcat	+¼ to +1¼	+¾	−½ to +½	−½ to +½	0	0	⁷⁄₃₂−⁵⁄₁₆	19½	20
	Electra 225	+¼ to +1¼	+¾	−½ to +½	−½ to +½	0	0	⁷⁄₃₂−⁵⁄₁₆	19½	20
	Riviera	+½ to +1½	+1	−¼ to +¾	−¼ to +¾	+¼	+¼	⁵⁄₃₂−¼	16¾	20
1971	Intermediates	0 to +1	+½	0 to +1	0 to +1	+½	+½	⅛−¼	—	—
	Le Sabre	+½ to +1½	+1	−¼ to +¾	−¼ to +¾	+¼	+¼	⅛−¼	—	—
	Estate Wagon	+½ to +1½	+1	−¼ to +¾	−¼ to +¾	+¼	+¼	⅛−¼	—	—
	Centurion	+½ to +1½	+1	−¼ to +¾	−¼ to +¾	+¼	+¼	⅛−¼	—	—
	Electra 225	+½ to +1½	+1	−¼ to +¾	−¼ to +¾	+¼	+¼	⅛−¼	—	—
	Riviera	+½ to +1½	+1	−¼ to +¾	−¼ to +¾	+¾	+¼	⅛−¼	—	—
1972	Intermediates	+½ to −1½	−½	+1¼ to −¼	+1¼ to −¼	+½	+½	¹⁄₁₆−⁵⁄₁₆	18½	20
	Le Sabre	0 to +2	+1	+1 to −½	+1 to −½	+½	+½	¹⁄₁₆−⁵⁄₁₆	18½	20
	Estate Wagon	0 to +2	+1	+1 to −½	+1 to −½	+½	+½	¹⁄₁₆−⁵⁄₁₆	18½	20
	Centurion	0 to +2	+1	+1 to −½	+1 to −½	+½	+½	¹⁄₁₆−⁵⁄₁₆	18½	20
	Electra 225	0 to +2	+1	+1 to −½	+1 to −½	+½	+½	¹⁄₁₆−⁵⁄₁₆	18½	20
	Riviera	0 to +2	+1	+1 to −½	+1 to −½	+½	+½	¹⁄₁₆−⁵⁄₁₆	18½	20

①—Manual steering 23° 32′, power steering 22° 46′. ②—Manual steering 23°, power steering 21° 47′.

COOLING SYSTEM & CAPACITY DATA

Year	Model or Engine	Cooling Capacity, Qts.			Radiator Cap Relief Pressure, Lbs.		Thermo. Opening Temp. [1]	Fuel Tank Gals.	Engine Oil Refill Qts. [3]	Transmission Oil			Rear Axle Oil Pints
		No Heater	With Heater	With A/C	With A/C	No A/C				3 Speed Pints	4 Speed Pints	Auto. Trans. Qts. [13]	
1966	V6-225	10½	11.2	11.2	15	15	180	20	4	3⅜	—	[5]	2½
	V8-300	12.2	12.7	14.0	15	15	180	20	4	3⅜	—	[5]	2½
	V8-340[11]	12.2	12.7	14.7	15	15	180	20	4	3⅜	—	[5]	2½
	V8-340[10]	13.7	14.5	14.5	15	15	180	25	4	3⅜	—	[5]	2½
	V8-401[6]	17½	18½	18½	15	15	180	20	4	3½	—	[5]	2½
	V8-401[4]	17	18	18.3	15	15	180	25	4	3½	—	[7]	2
	Riviera	17	18	18.3	15	15	180	21	4	—	—	[7]	2
1967	V6-225	10½	11.2	11.2	15	15	190	20	4	3⅜	—	[12]	2¾
	V8-300	12.2	12.7	14.0	15	15	190	20	4	3⅜	—	[12]	2¾
	V8-340[11]	12.2	12.7	14.7	15	15	190	20	4	3⅜	—	[12]	2¾
	V8-340[10]	12.2	12.7	14.7	15	15	190	25	4	3⅜	—	[12]	2¾
	V8-400[6]	17.0	18.0	18¼	15	15	190	20	4	3½	3	[7]	2¾
	V8-430[4]	17.0	18.0	18¼	15	15	190	25	4	—	—	[7]	4¼
	Riviera	17.0	18.0	18¼	15	15	190	21	4	—	—	[7]	4¼
1968	6-250	10.00	11.30	13.00	15	15	195	20	4	3⅜	—	[12]	2.9
	V8-350[11]	12.62	13.50	13.52	15	15	190	20	4	3⅜	—	[12]	2.9
	GS-350	12.62	13.45	13.52	15	15	190	20	4	3.4	3	[12]	2.9
	GS-400	15.34	16.17	16.67	15	15	190	20	4	3.5	3	[7]	2.9
	V8-350[10]	12.34	13.20	13.55	15	15	190	25	4	3⅛	—	[12]	2.9
	V8-430[4]	15.84	16.70	17.00	15	15	190	25	4	3½	—	[7]	4¼
	Riviera	15.84	16.70	17.00	15	15	190	21	4	—	—	[7]	4¼
1969	6-250	10.0	11.3	13.0	15	15	195	20	4	3⅜	—	[12]	2.9
	V8-350[11]	12.6	13.5	13.5	15	15	190	20	4	3⅜	—	[14]	2.9
	GS-350	12.6	13.5	13.5	15	15	190	20	4	3.4	3	[15]	2.9
	GS-400	15.3	16.2	16.7	15	15	190	20	4	3.5	3	[16]	2.9
	V8-350[10]	12.3	13.2	13.6	15	15	190	25	4	3.5	—	[17]	2.9
	V8-430	16.0	16.7	17.0	15	15	190	25	4	—	—	[16]	4¼
	Riviera	16.0	16.7	17.0	15	15	190	21	4	—	—	[16]	4¼
1970	6-250	—	16.04	16.04	15	15	190	20	4	3½	3	[15]	3
	V8-350[11]	—	16.45	16.52	15	15	190	20[18]	4	3½	3	[15]	3
	GS-455	—	19.17	19.67	15	15	190	20	4	4	3	[16]	3
	V8-350[10]	—	16.20	16.55	15	15	190	25[19]	4	3½	—	[15]	3
	V8-455	—	19.70	20.0	15	15	190	25[19]	4	3½	—	[16]	4¼
	Riviera	—	19.70	20.0	15	15	190	21	4	—	—	[16]	4¼
1971	6-250	—	16.04	16.04	15	15	195	20	4	3½	3	[15]	4¼
	V8-350[11]	—	16.5	16.5	15	15	190	20[18]	4	3½	3	[16]	4¼
	GS-455	—	19.0	19.5	15	15	190	20	4	3½	3	[16]	4¼
	V8-350[10]	—	16.2	16.55	15	15	190	25[19]	4	3½	—	[15]	4¼
	V8-455	—	19.7	20.0	15	15	190	25[19]	4	3½	—	[16]	5½
	Riviera	—	19.7	20.0	15	15	190	21	4	—	—	[16]	5½
1972	V8-350[11]	—	16.45	16.85	15	15	190	20[18]	4	3½	3	[21]	4¼
	V8-350[10]	—	18.90	19.30	15	15	190	25	4	—	—	[21]	4¼
	Estate Wagon	—	16.20	16.60	15	15	190	23	4	—	—	[22]	[20]
	V8-455	—	16.20	16.60	15	15	190	25	4	—	—	[22]	5½
	Riviera	—	18.70	19.0	15	15	190	24	4	—	—	[22]	5½

[1]—For permanent type anti-freeze. If alcohol is used, install a 160° unit.
[2]—Super Turbine 400, 11½ qts.
[3]—Add one quart with filter change.
[4]—Wildcat and Electra.
[5]—Total 9½ qts.; oil pan only 4 qts.
[6]—Skylark Gran Sport.
[7]—Total 11½ qts.; oil pan only 2½ qts.
[8]—Buick Special and LeSabre passenger cars.
[9]—LeSabre Station Wagon, Wildcat and Electra.

[10]—LeSabre.
[11]—Special, Skylark and Sportwagon.
[12]—Total 9½ qts. Oil pan only 2½ qts.
[13]—Approximate. Make final check with dipstick.
[14]—Two speed unit 9½ qts. total. Oil pan only 2½ qts.
    Three speed unit 10 qts. total. Oil pan only 3 qts.
[15]—Total 10 qts. Oil pan only 3 qts.
[16]—Total 11½ qts. Oil pan only 3½ qts.

[17]—Two speed unit 9½ qts. total. Oil pan only 2½ qts.
    Three speed unit 11½ qts. total. Oil pan only 3½ qts.
[18]—Sportwagon 23 gallons.
[19]—Estate Wagon 24 gallons.
[20]—With V8-350, 4¼ pints; with V8-455, 5½ pints.
[21]—Total 10 qts. Oil pan only 2½ qts.
[22]—Total 11½ qts. Oil pan only 3 qts.

Electrical Section

DISTRIBUTOR, REPLACE

1. Disconnect primary wire from distributor and disconnect pipe from vacuum control unit.
2. Remove distributor cap.
3. Crank engine until distributor rotor is in position to fire No. 1 cylinder and the timing mark (see *Tune Up Chart*) is aligned with the timing indicator.
4. Remove distributor clamp and lift the distributor out of the crankcase.

NOTE: Before installation of either a new or repaired distributor apply a few drops of engine oil to the drain hole near the lower end of the housing and apply oil to the oiler on the housing. Rotate the distributor shaft several times by hand to distribute the oil and to make sure that the shaft turns freely.

1. Check to make sure that the timing mark is aligned with the timing indicator with No. 1 piston on the compression stroke in position to fire.
2. Place a new seal on distributor housing.
3. Rotate distributor cam in direction of arrow on cam until rotor is in position to fire No. 1 cylinder.
4. Rotate oil pump shaft with screwdriver to align slot in shaft with tongue on lower end of distributor shaft.
5. Install distributor in crankcase with vacuum control pointing to right side of engine, in position to connect to vacuum pipe.
6. Install distributor clamp and bolt with lockwasher, leaving bolt just loose enough to permit movement of distributor.
7. Rotate distributor housing until breaker points just start to open and tighten clamp bolt. This will permit starting engine for setting timing.
8. Connect pipe to vacuum control and primary wire to terminal stud.
9. Install distributor cap. If spark plug wires are disconnected from cap make certain that wires are connected in accordance with firing order.
10. Check and set ignition timing as given below.

STARTER, REPLACE

To remove the starter, disconnect battery cable from battery. Disconnect cable and solenoid lead wire from solenoid switch. Remove starter attaching bolts and take off starter.

LIGHT SWITCH, REPLACE
1966-72

1968 Special and Skylark

If air conditioned, remove two screws at left A/C duct and remove duct. Then remove switch as outlined below.

Fig. 1   Ignition switch in "Lock" position. 1969-72

1966-67 Riviera

1. Remove ash receiver.
2. Remove instrument panel molding.
3. Remove steering column lower cover.
4. Lower steering column.
5. Remove instrument panel lower housing.
6. Remove switch as directed below.

1971 Senior Models

1. Remove left trim panel by pulling headlight knob out to last detent and depress clip on back of knob.
2. Pull trim panel out and pull wires out of connectors.
3. Then remove switch as directed below.

1972 Models

1. Remove switch knob as described further on.
2. Remove left instrument cluster trim panel.
3. Remove switch as directed below.

All Models

1. After performing the necessary preliminary operations given above, pull switch knob out to the last notch, then depress latch button and pull knob and rod assembly out of swtich.
2. Remove switch escutcheon.
3. Pull switch down and unplug from connector.
4. Reverse procedure to install.

IGNITION SWITCH, REPLACE
1969-72

The ignition switch is located on the top of the steering column under the instrument panel. To replace it the steering column must be lowered as follows:
1. Disconnect shift indicator link.
2. Remove nuts securing bracket to dash panel and carefully lower column.
3. Unplug connectors from switch and be sure switch is in "accessory" position.
4. Remove two screws securing switch and remove switch.
5. When installing switch, it must be positioned in "Lock", Fig. 1, as well as the lock cylinder.
6. Fit actuator rod into switch and assemble to column.
7. Complete assembly in reverse of removal procedure.

1968

1. Except Riviera, if air conditioned, remove left A/C distribution duct.
2. On all models, remove lock cylinder (in accessory position).
3. Remove switch retaining nut.
4. Lower switch and unplug from connector by depressing retainer tabs.
5. Reverse procedure to install.

1966-67 Special, Skylark, G.S. 400

1. Turn key to accessory position and remove lock cylinder.
2. Remove switch retaining nut and pull switch down and unplug from connector.
3. Reverse procedure to install.

1966-67 LeSabre, Wildcat, Electra

1. Remove ash receiver.

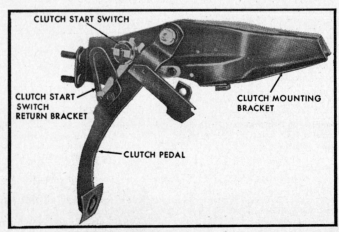

Fig. 2   Clutch start switch in start position. 1969-72

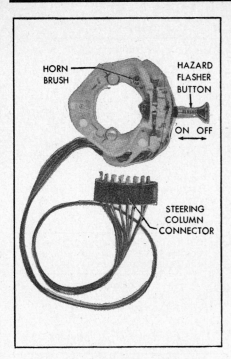

Fig. 3 Turn signal and hazard warning flasher switch assembly. 1967-72

2. Turn key to accessory position and remove lock cylinder.
3. Remove switch retaining nut.
4. Lower switch into ash receiver hole and unplug from connector.
5. Reverse procedure to install.

1966-67 Riviera

1. Remove ash receiver.
2. Remove instrument panel molding.
3. Remove column lower cover.
4. Lower steering column.
5. Remove instrument panel lower housing.
6. Turn key to accessory position and remove lock cylinder.
7. Remove switch retaining nut.
8. Lower switch and unplug connector.
9. Reverse procedure to install.

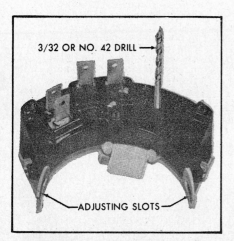

Fig. 6 Adjusting neutral safety switch. 1967-72

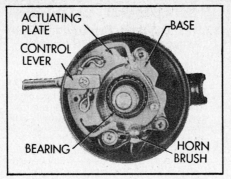

Fig. 4 Top view of turn signal switch control. 1966

STOP LIGHT SWITCH, REPLACE
1966-72

The stop lights are controlled by a mechanical switch mounted on the brake pedal bracket. This spring loaded switch makes contact whenever the brake pedal is applied. When the brake pedal is released it depresses the switch to open the contacts and turn brake lights off.

CLUTCH START SWITCH
1969-72

A clutch start switch is installed on all manual transmission cars. The switch is mounted on the clutch pedal bracket and it prevents the car from being started until the clutch pedal is depressed, Fig. 2.

TURN SIGNAL SWITCH, REPLACE
1967-72

As shown in Fig. 3, the assembly is a turn signal switch and hazard warning switch. It is mounted in a housing at the upper end of the steering column mast jacket, just below the steering wheel. Therefore to get at the switch the steering wheel will have to be removed.

1966 All

The turn signal switch is mounted in a housing at the upper end of the steering column mast jacket just below the steering wheel. Therefore to get at the switch the steering wheel will have to be removed, Figs. 4 and 5.

NEUTRAL START & BACK-UP LIGHT SWITCH

To check operation of switch after adjustments are made as outlined below, proceed as follows:
1. With shift lever in Park starter should operate.
2. With shift lever in Reverse back-up lights should light but starter should not operate.

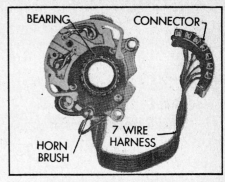

Fig. 5 Turn signal switch plate and wiring. 1966

3. With shift lever in Neutral starter should operate but back-up lights should be out.
4. With shift lever in Drive, starter should not operate and back-up lights should be out.

1966-72

1. Place shift lever in Drive (Neutral for 1972).
2. Attempt to insert a 3/32" or a No. 42 drill through gauging hole in switch body into inner hole in sliding part of switch, Fig. 6.
3. If drill does not enter inner hole, loosen two switch mounting screws and slide switch body as required to allow drill to enter inner hole. Tighten screws and remove drill.

1966 Senior Cars

1. Referring to Fig. 7, place shift control lever in *Park* position.
2. Insert a 3/32" rod through gauging hole in operating lever and through gauging hole in switch body.
3. If gauging rod will not go through holes or is not parallel, loosen two switch mounting screws and move switch sidewise until gauge is parallel. Then retighten screws.

1966 Special Series

1. Place shift control lever in *Drive*.
2. Insert a 3/32" rod through gauging hole in right forward face of switch and into gauging hole in center of switch slide.

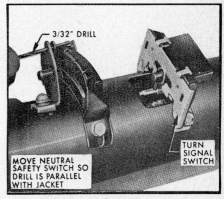

Fig. 7 Checking neutral safety switch adjustment. 1966 Senior cars

3. If gauging rod will not enter hole in switch slide, loosen two switch mounting screws and move switch sidewise until gauge enters hole. Tighten switch screws.

HORN SOUNDER & STEERING WHEEL

1968-72

1. Remove horn cap or actuator bar.
2. On deluxe wheels, pull horn wire from steering wheel and back off wheel nut flush with top of steering shaft.
3. Use a suitable puller to remove wheel.

1967

1. Unplug curved connector from switch on lower end of steering column.
2. On 43000 and 44000 Series with standard steering wheel, pry off cap, remove three screws and take off bushing spacer, receiver cup and Belleville spring.
3. On all other Series cars, remove screws from underside of steering wheel that secure horn actuator bar, partially lift off bar, pull lead connector from canceling cam, then fully lift off bar.
4. Remove nut and pull off steering wheel.

1966

1. Unplug large curved connector on mast jacket to prevent horn from blowing. Connector has locking tabs on outside edges; lift tabs to release.
2. On standard Special series wheels, pry off cap, remove three screws and take off spacer bushing receiver cup and Belleville spring.
3. On 43000 and 44000 Series, remove actuator bar cap and pull out lead plug in steering wheel.
4. On 45-46 and 48000 Series, remove actuator bar cap, bushing and screw assembly, adapter springs and contact plate.
5. On 49000 Series, remove cap and lens assembly and pull out lead plug in steering wheel. On 49000 Series with optional wheel, remove cap and lens assembly.
6. On all Series, loosen steering wheel nut several turns (do not remove). Attach a puller to wheel hub and pull wheel up to nut. Then remove nut and lift off wheel.

NOTE: Location marks for proper installation of steering wheel are provided to insure a straight-ahead position when front wheels are in straight-ahead position. When installing Belleville spring on standard wheels, be sure concave side of spring faces inward. Also locate receiver cup so that slot in cup is uppermost.

INSTRUMENT CLUSTER
1971-72 LeSabre, Centurion. Estate Wagon, Electra & Riviera

1. Disconnect battery ground cable.
2. Remove cluster trim panels as follows:
   Left Trim Panel—pull headlight knob out to last detent and depress clip on back of knob to remove. Pull trim panel out and pull wires out of connectors.
   Right Trim Panel—Remove radio knobs and escutcheons. Remove trip set and speed alert knobs, if equipped. Pull trim panel out and pull wire from connector.
3. Speedometer removal is accomplished as follows: Remove lower instrument panel filler panel. Disconnect shift pointer cable with shift lever in L1. Remove speedo face glass by removing two screws on top of glass and remove speedometer by removing three screws on speedo face.
4. Fuel & Temperature Gauges: After removal of speedometer these gauges can be removed by pulling out of connector.

1969-72 Special & Skylark

CAUTION: If equipped with Cruise Control, disconnect speedometer cable from transducer to prevent damage when cluster housing is pulled back.

1. Remove glove box (9 screws).
2. Remove instrument panel upper cover (2 screws thru cluster housing and 2 nuts above glove box opening). Pull cover rearward to disengage three guide pins from clips.
3. Remove steering column opening filler (4 screws). On air conditioned units, drop left plastic duct by removing 2 screws and disconnecting inner end from center distribution duct.
4. Lower steering column by removing 2 nuts and disconnecting shift indicator link. Pad column to avoid marring paint.
5. Pull cluster housing back after removing eight screws. Rest housing on column and rotate so back of cluster is visible.
6. Disconnect speedometer cable and wires from cluster. On air conditioned units, disconnect left air hose from left outlet by twisting "quick-connect" coupling counterclockwise. Disconnect heater control panel.
7. Remove cluster by removing four cluster to housing screws.
8. Reverse above procedure to install.

1969-70 LeSabre, Wildcat & Electra

CAUTION: If equipped with Cruise Control, disconnect speedometer cable from transducer to prevent damage when cluster housing is pulled back.

1. Remove lower instrument panel filler (4 screws), then slide filler forward and down.
2. Remove glove box (5 screws).

NOTE: Do not remove glove box door

as it comes off with cover along with ash tray assembly.

3. Remove instrument panel cover (2 nuts above glove box opening and 3 screws thru cluster housing) and remove all screws along bottom edge of cover.
4. Lower steering column by removing two nuts and disconnecting shift indicator link. Pad column to avoid marring paint.
5. Pull cluster housing back after removing eight screws. Rest housing on column and rotate so back of housing is visible.
6. Disconnect speedometer cable and wires.
7. Disconnect heater-air conditioner control panel.

NOTE: Do not distrub cables and vacuum hoses or adjustment will be required after reassembly.

8. Remove instrument cluster (6 cluster to housing screws).
9. Reverse procedure to install.

1968 Special & Skylark

CAUTION: If equipped with Cruise Control, the upper speedometer cable must be disconnected from the transducer before cluster housing is pulled back.

1. Remove instrument panel compartment body (6 screws).
2. Remove radio knobs and escutcheons.
3. Remove radio filler plate (2 nuts and 2 screws). Do not remove radio.
4. Remove four hex nuts at top underside of dash and two screws at housing. Pull instrument panel upper cover rearward to remove.
5. Remove steering column filler (4 screws). If air conditioned, remove one screw at left A/C duct and remove duct from instrument panel housing.
6. Remove four nuts from lower edge of instrument panel housing.
7. Remove four screws across upper edge of instrument panel housing.
8. Remove two nuts from steering column mounting bracket and disconnect shift quadrant link wire at steering column. Lower steering column.
9. Pull instrument panel rearward and rotate it so back of cluster is visible.
10. Remove two nuts from heater control installation and separate front instrument panel housing.
11. Disconnect speedometer cable (from below).
12. Disconnect wiring harness clip, printed circuit connector and clock connector from instrument cluster.
13. Disconnect accessory switch and Cruise Control switch wires from top side of instrument panel housing.
14. Disconnect headlight switch connector.
15. Disconnect W/S wiper-washer switch connector.
16. Disconnect cigar lighter connector.
17. Remove instrument panel housing.
18. Remove cluster from panel housing (4 screws).
19. Reverse procedure to install.

1968 LeSabre, Wildcat & Electra

CAUTION: If equipped with Cruise Control the upper speedometer cable must be disconnected from transducer before cluster housing is pulled back.

1. Remove instrument panel compartment body (8 screws).
2. Remove three hex nuts at top underside of dash and four screws at instrument panel housing. Pull instrument panel upper cover rearward to remove.
3. Remove steering column filler (2 screws). Disconnect shift quadrant link wire at steering column. Remove two nuts from steering column mounting bracket and one bolt from column wedge. Lower steering column.
4. Remove two nuts from lower edge of instrument panel housing at steering column.
5. Remove four screws across upper edge of instrument panel housing.
6. Remove two screws at heater control installation and separate from instrument panel housing.
7. Remove ash receiver (4 screws).
8. Remove one nut at lower right side of instrument housing.
9. Remove headlight switch from instrument panel housing; do not unplug connector.
10. Remove one nut at lower left side of instrument panel housing.
11. Protect steering column so that instrument panel housing will not mar column when housing is tilted back.
12. Remove two screws at center A/C duct (lower) and remove duct.
13. Disconnect from instrument cluster the speedometer cable (from below), printed circuit connector (from above), wiring harness clip (from below), clock connector and two clock bulbs (from above), Cruise Control switch connector (from above), courtesy light connector (from above), W/S wiper-washer switch connector (from below), antenna and accessory switch connectors (from above), and cluster ground wire (from above).
14. Remove complete instrument panel housing, then separate cluster from panel housing (6 screws).
15. Reverse procedure to install.

1968-70 Riviera

CAUTION: If equipped with Cruise Control the upper speedometer cable must be disconnected from the transducer before cluster housing is pulled back.

1. Remove instrument panel compartment body (8 screws).
2. Remove four nuts at right underside of dash and four screws at housing. Pull instrument panel upper cover rearward to remove.
3. Remove steering column filler (2 screws). If column shift, disconnect shift quadrant link wire at steering column. Remove two nuts from column mounting bracket and one nut from column wedge. Lower steering column.
4. Remove two nuts from lower edge of instrument panel housing at steer-

ing column. Remove four screws across upper edge of instrument panel housing.
5. Remove one nut at lower left side of instrument housing.
6. Remove ash receiver (4 screws).
7. Remove one nut at lower right side of instrument housing.
8. Remove two screws at heater control installation and separate from instrument panel housing.
9. Protect steering column so panel housing will not mar column when housing is tilted back.
10. Disconnect from cluster the speedometer cable, two wiring harness clips, printed circuit connector (all from above).

NOTE: If equipped with Cruise Control, disconnect speedometer cable at Cruise Control transducer located at rear of engine compartment. This will allow instrument housing to be pulled rearward.

11. Disconnect from instrument housing the clock connector and two clock bulbs, Cruise Control switch connector, courtesy light connector, W/S wiper-washer switch connector, antenna and accessory switch connectors, cluster ground wire, A/C hose and headlight connector (all from above).
12. Remove instrument panel housing.
13. Separate panel housing from cluster (6 screws).
14. Reverse procedure to install.

1966-67 Special, Skylark, G.S. 400

1. Disconnect battery ground strap.
2. Remove five screws and pull instrument panel upper cover rearward to remove.
3. Lower steering column and remove $\frac{1}{4}$" hex screw (in column cutout) from lower edge of instrument panel housing.
4. Remove one $\frac{1}{4}$" hex screw from lower edge of instrument panel housing through glove box hole.
5. Remove four remaining $\frac{1}{4}$" hex screws from lower edge of instrument panel housing.
6. Remove six screws across upper edge of instrument panel housing.
7. Disconnect speedometer cable.
8. Pull instrument panel rearward and rotate it so back of cluster is visible.
9. Disconnect from cluster: printed circuit connector, clock connector, shift quadrant light.
10. Remove four $\frac{1}{4}$" hex screws and remove instrument panel cluster.

NOTE: To remove speedometer or printed circuit, first remove instrument cluster. The fuel gauge is accessible from below without removing any other parts. Bulbs in the left half of the cluster can be removed from below without removing any other parts. To remove bulbs from the right half of the cluster, however, the left defroster duct must be removed to provide working clearance.

1966-67 LeSabre, Wildcat, Electra

1. Disconnect battery ground strap.
2. Remove two windshield side garnish moldings.

3. Remove six screws and pull instrument panel upper cover rearward. Disconnect radio speaker wire and remove cover.
4. Remove ash receiver.
5. Remove one $\frac{3}{8}$" hex nut through hole in glove box.
6. Remove either radio bracket screw.
7. Remove two $\frac{3}{8}$" hex head bolts from outer ends of instrument panel housing.
8. Remove A/C hose from center distribution duct and push hose to left of steering column.
9. Remove light switch from instrument panel housing (do not unplug connector).
10. Protect steering column. Then tilt instrument panel housing back and place $1\frac{1}{2}$" spacer blocks ($\frac{7}{8}$" on 1966) under each end of housing at attaching points.
11. Disconnect from cluster: shift indicator link, printed circuit connector, clock connector, Cruise switch connector, Cruise speedometer connector and speedometer cable.
12. From below, remove two $\frac{1}{4}$" hex head screws from bottom edge of instrument cluster.
13. From above, remove three $\frac{1}{4}$" hex head screws from bottom edge of cluster, being careful not to lose two spacers.
14. Disconnect ground wire from upper edge of cluster.
15. Shift cluster to the right and lift out. It may be necessary to depress Cruise engage knob for clearance.

NOTE: To remove speedometer or printed circuit the cluster must first be removed. To remove the fuel gauge, perform Steps 1, 2 and 3 above, then remove gauge (3 screws).

1966-67 Riviera

1. Disconnect battery ground strap.
2. Remove ash receiver.
3. Remove center air outlet and duct.
4. Remove radio.
5. Remove upper cover by removing three screws at cluster housing and two $\frac{3}{8}$" nuts at glove box opening.
6. Pry out instrument panel molding.
7. Remove steering column lower cover.
8. Remove two $\frac{11}{16}$" nuts and lower steering column.
9. Remove instrument panel lower housing by removing five $\frac{1}{4}$" screws across bottom and six across top. Electro-Cruise amplifier connector must be unplugged (if equipped).
10. To loosen upper housing, protect steering column, then remove two $\frac{3}{8}$" nuts from below (one from each end of housing). Remove four $\frac{1}{4}$" screws across top of housing. Pull housing out to rest on steering column and knees.
11. Rotate upper housing so that cluster retaining screws can be seen. Disconnect speedometer cable, unplug cluster connector, Cruise connector, courtesy light and clock connectors. Remove two wiring harness clamp screws.
12. Remove five $\frac{1}{4}$" screws across bottom of cluster and five $\frac{3}{8}$" nuts across top of cluster. Then remove cluster assembly.

NOTE: To remove speedometer or printed circuit, the cluster assembly must first be removed.

To remove oil pressure or temperature gauge, pry off instrument panel molding, remove steering column lower cover and lower steering column, remove ash receiver, instrument panel lower housing (5 screws), light switch, and gauges as required.

To remove ammeter or fuel gauge, remove ash receiver, center air outlet and duct, radio, and gauges as required.

W/S WIPER MOTOR, REPLACE

1972

1. Disconnect battery and remove cowl screen.
2. Loosen nuts on wiper drivelink to motor cranking arm and slip drivelink off cranking arm.
3. Disconnect washer hoses and electrical connections.
4. Unfasten motor and remove.

1966-71

1. With wiper motor in Park position, remove washer hoses and electrical connections from motor.
2. On Special and Riviera, remove the air intake grille. On LeSabre, Wildcat and Electra, remove plastic access cover.
3. Loosen nuts which retain drive link to crank arm ball stud or remove nut retaining crank arm to motor, depending on model.
4. Remove motor retaining bolts and remove motor.

CAUTION: Wiper motor must be in Park position prior to installation on the cowl.

W/S WIPER TRANSMISSION

1972

1. Disconnect battery and remove cowl screen.
2. If necessary, disconnect washer hoses from nozzles.
3. Remove wiper arm and blade assemblies.
4. On Intermediate models; remove two screws from right and left transmission pilot shaft. The third screw on left side is removed last. With transmission loose, rotate it towards front of car and remove through access hole in right side of cowl.
5. On Senior models; remove six bolts securing transmission to cowl, three on each side at the serrated head of output shaft.

1966-71

1. Make sure motor is in Park position.
2. Remove arm and blade assemblies.
3. Remove air intake grille or screen (if equipped).
4. Disconnect drive rod from motor crank.

5. Remove transmission retaining nuts or bolts and lower drive rods into plenum chamber.
6. Remove transmission assemblies through cowl opening.

W/S WIPER SWITCH, REPLACE

1971-72 Senior Models

1. Remove left trim panel as described previously.
2. Remove switch by pulling out of connector.

1970 LeSabre, Estate Wagon, Wildcat & Electra

1. Remove lower instrument panel filler (4 screws) then slide filler forward and down.
2. Lower steering column by removing two nuts and disconnecting shift indicator link.
3. Unplug connector from switch.
4. Remove wiper knob.
5. Remove switch (two screws).

1969 LeSabre, Wildcat & Electra

1. Pry wiper-washer switch from cluster housing.
2. Remove switch by unplugging switch connector.
3. Reverse procedure to install.

1968-72 Special & Skylark

1. If air conditioned, remove two screws at left A/C distribution duct and remove duct.
2. Remove steering column filler (4 screws).
3. Unplug connectors from wiper-washer switches.
4. Remove screws from switches and pull switches down.
5. Reverse procedure to install.

1968 LeSabre, Wildcat & Electra

1. Remove steering column filler (2 screws).
2. Disconnect shift quadrant link wire at steering column. Remove two nuts from steering column mounting bracket and one bolt from column wedge. Lower steering column to gain access to switch attaching screw.
3. Unplug connectors from wiper-washer switches.
4. Unfasten and pull switches down (2 screws).
5. Reverse procedure to install.

1968-70 Riviera

1. Pull instrument panel housing assembly out to rest on column and knees.
2. Unplug connectors from wiper-washer switches.
3. Unfasten and pull switches out (2 screws).
4. Reverse procedure to install.

1966-67 Except Riviera

1. Loosen set screw and remove knob.
2. Unscrew switch escutcheon.
3. Pull switch down and unplug from connector.

1966-67 Riviera

The windshield wiper and washer switches are removed together by prying with a small screwdriver in a notch at the bottom edge of the switch housing. The faulty switch can then be disconnected and removed from the assembly.

RADIO, REPLACE

1972 Senior Models

NOTE: When installing radio, be sure to adjust antenna trimmer for peak performance.

1. Remove knobs and escutcheons. If equipped with trip-set and speed alert, unscrew the cone shaped knobs.
2. Remove right trim panel.
3. Remove retaining nuts from shafts.
4. Remove ash tray and separate connectors and antenna lead in from radio.

1971 Senior Models

1. Remove right trim panel as described previously.
2. Remove ash tray assembly.
3. Disconnect antenna lead-in and radio connector.
4. Loosen radio side brace.
5. Remove radio retaining nuts on front of panel.
6. Disconnect center A/C duct behind ash tray.
7. Remove radio.

1970 LeSabre, Estate Wagon, Wildcat & Electra

1. Remove instrument panel lower filler (4 screws) then slide filler forward and down.
2. Remove radio ground strap screws.
3. Remove radio knobs, escutcheons, hex nuts and lower radio downward.

NOTE: On air condition cars, remove center distributor duct for clearance.

4. Disconnect antenna and leads and remove radio.

1969-72 Special & Skylark

1. Remove radio knobs, escutcheons and two hex nuts.
2. Remove filler plate (2 screws).
3. Remove ash tray and slide (4 screws).
4. Remove radio support (2 screws). If air conditioned, remove center distributor duct.
5. Remove two nuts attaching radio face to instrument panel and move radio downward.
6. Disconnect antenna lead and wiring and remove radio.
7. Reverse procedure to install.

1969 LeSabre, Wildcat & Electra

1. On A/C models, remove center distribution duct.
2. Remove right instrument trim panel and remove screw in bottom of radio.
3. Remove radio knobs and escutcheons and nuts. Unplug antenna lead and wires from radio.
4. Remove radio downward.
5. Reverse procedure to install.

1969-70 Riviera

1. Remove ash tray assembly (4 screws).
2. Remove radio knobs, escutcheons and hex nuts.
3. Unplug antenna and leads from radio.
4. Remove radio downward through ash tray opening.
5. Reverse procedure to install.

1968 Special & Skylark

1. Remove radio knobs and escutcheons.
2. Remove radio filler plate (2 nuts and 2 screws).
3. Remove ash receiver.
4. If air conditioned, remove two screws at lower center A/C duct and remove duct.
5. Remove radio bracket-to-radio screw and two bracket screws at instrument panel and remove bracket.
6. Remove two instrument panel attaching nuts at radio face.
7. Disconnect radio wiring and remove radio downward.
8. Reverse procedure to install.

1968 Senior Models

1. Remove ash receiver.
2. If air conditioned (except Riviera), remove two screws at center A/C duct and remove duct.
3. Remove radio knobs and escutcheons.
4. Remove two hex nuts.
5. Unplug antenna lead from radio.
6. Unplug three wire and single wire connector from radio.
7. Remove radio downward.
8. Reverse procedure to install.

1967 Special & Skylark

Without Air Conditioning
1. Disconnect ground strap from battery.
2. Pull off radio control knobs and unscrew two nuts holding radio to instrument panel.
3. Disconnect radio and speaker lead connectors and antenna cable.
4. Remove screw holding support to radio and remove radio from underside of dash.

With Air Conditioning
1. Disconnect ground cable from battery.
2. Pull off radio control knobs and unscrew nuts securing radio to instrument panel.
3. Remove clamps connecting A/C outlet hoses to distribution duct. Remove two screws securing duct to heater and lower out duct.

4. Pry open two spring clips holding center duct to instrument panel and remove center duct.
5. Disconnect radio and speaker leads and antenna cable.
6. Remove screw holding support to radio and remove radio.

1967 LeSabre, Wildcat & Electra

1. Pull off radio control and unscrew nuts securing radio to instrument panel.
2. Unfasten instrument panel cover to panel (6 screws). Then pull cover rearward and raise it enough so that any connectors attached to underside of cover may be disengaged. Complete removal of cover.
3. Remove left and right radio mounting bracket screws. Disengage radio-speaker lead and antenna cable at rear of radio and remove radio.

1967 Riviera

1. Open and remove three screws from upper portion of ash tray and three screws from underside of assembly. Partially withdraw ash tray and disconnect lamp and cigar lighter leads, then complete removal of ash tray.
2. Pry out chrome trim strip at center of instrument panel.
3. Remove two screws securing center outlet, lift off center outlet and pull out plastic duct.
4. Pull off radio knobs, unscrew two nuts holding radio to instrument panel and take off escutcheon.
5. Disconnect radio-speaker lead and antenna cable.
6. Remove radio support (2 nuts and two screws).
7. Lower radio through ash tray opening.

1966 Special & Skylark

1. Remove ash receiver.
2. Remove radio-to-bracket screw.
3. Remove knobs and escutcheons and two $5/8''$ nuts.
4. Remove radio downward.

1966 LeSabre, Wildcat & Electra

1. Remove two windshield side garnish moldings.
2. Remove six screws and pull instrument panel upper cover rearward. Disconnect speaker wire and remove cover.
3. Remove ash receiver.
4. Remove A/C center outlet and duct.
5. Remove radio-to-bracket screw.
6. Remove knobs and escutcheons and two $5/8''$ nuts.
7. Remove radio upward.

1966 Riviera

1. Remove ash receiver.
2. Remove center air outlet and duct.
3. Remove brace from underside of radio.
4. Remove radio knobs and escutcheons and two $5/8''$ nuts.
5. Unplug feed and speaker wire connector and antenna cable from radio.

6. Remove radio through ash receiver opening.

HEATER CORE REMOVAL

After draining radiator and disconnecting heater hoses, proceed as follows:

1969-72 Special & Skylark

Without Air Conditioning
1. Remove right front fender skirt.
2. Disconnect control cables from lever of defroster door and outside air inlet door on heater.
3. Disconnect temperature control cable from lever of temperature door on heater.
4. Remove attaching nuts from heater studs.
5. Remove connector from blower motor resistor.
6. Remove screws from lower part of defroster outlet to top of heater.
7. Work heater rearward until studs clear dash and remove.
8. Reverse procedure to install.

With Air Conditioning
1. Remove instrument panel cover with right side A/C outlet and hose attached.
2. Remove center A/C duct, left A/C outlet duct, A/C distributor duct and defroster assembly.
3. Disconnect defroster and temperature control wires.
4. Unfasten and remove air conditioner-heater assembly from dash.
5. Heater core can now be removed from assembly.

1972 All Senior Models
1969-71 LeSabre, Wildcat & Electra

Without Air Conditioning
1. Disconnect vacuum hoses from defroster door and outside air inlet door actuator diaphrams and control cable from temperature door lever.
2. Unfasten connector from blower motor resistor.
3. Remove nuts securing heater to dash.
4. Remove screws securing defroster outlet adapter to heater and raise adapter away from heater.
5. Work heater rearward until studs clear dash and remove.
6. Reverse procedure to install.

With Air Conditioning
1. Remove instrument panel cover with center A/C outlet and right A/C outlet and hose attached.
2. Remove center A/C duct, A/C distributor duct and defroster outlet manifold assembly.
3. Disconnect defroster and temperature control wires and pink hose from mode door diaphragm.
4. Unfasten and remove air conditioner-heater assembly from dash.
5. Heater core can now be removed from assembly.

1969-71 Riviera

Without Air Conditioning
1. Remove right front fender.

2. Disconnect blower motor wire and resistor connectors.
3. Disconnect temperature door cable.
4. Disconnect vacuum hoses attached to outside door and vent heater door vacuum diaphrams.
5. Remove screws securing blower and heater assembly to dash and remove.
6. Reverse procedure to install.

With Air Conditioning
1. Disconnect temperature door control cable and blower resistor connector.
2. Unfasten and remove air conditioner-heater assembly from dash.
3. Remove air distributor duct and heater core.

1966-68 Full Size Cars

NOTE: On air conditioned models it will be necessary to remove the air conditioner-heater assembly to gain access to the heater core.

1. Remove nuts securing heater-defroster assembly to cowl.
2. Disconnect all control cables from defroster door, outside air door and temperature door levers.
3. Disconnect electrical connector from blower motor resistor.
4. Remove screws securing the defroster outlet adapter-to-heater core and raise adapter away from heater.
5. Heater core can now be worked away from cowl and removed.

1966-68 Intermediate Cars

NOTE: On air conditioned models it will be necessary to remove the air conditioner-heater assembly to gain access to the heater core.

NOTE: On 1968 models, the right front fender skirt must be removed before all

attaching nuts can be taken off heater core studs. The balance of the removal procedure is the same as previous models as outlined below. The screw securing the defroster to the top of the heater may have to be removed as for 1967 models.

1. Remove right front wheel and draw an arc on the inside of the fender skirt 11" from the upper bolt of the wheel opening. Then draw another arc 16¾" from the lower wheel opening bolt. Drill a ¾" hole at the intersection of the two arcs and remove the lower right attaching nut from the heater core through this hole.
2. Disconnect all control wires from levers of defroster door, outside air door and the lever of the temperature control door.
3. Remove connector from blower resistor and take off nuts from remaining studs that retain heater core to cowl.
4. On 1967 models, remove the screw securing defroster outlet to top of heater. Heater core may now be worked rearward until studs clear cowl and lifted out.

SPEED CONTROLS
1969-72 Cruise Master

Bead Chain Adjustment
1. Adjust engine hot idle speed and mixture, then shut off engine.
2. Check slack in chain by unsnapping swivel from ball stud and holding chain taut at ball stud; center of swivel should extend ⅛" beyond center of ball stud.
3. Adjust bead chain slack by sliding sleeve back on chain and removing loose rivet. Move swivel on ball chain until slack is correct. Then

reinstall rivet and slide sleeve over rivet.

Cruise Speed Adjustment
The cruise speed adjustment can be set as follows:
1. If car cruises below engagement speed, screw orifice tube on transducer outward.
2. If car cruises above engagement speed, screw orifice tube inward.

NOTE: Each ¼ turn of the orifice tube will change cruise speed about one mile per hour. Snug up lock nut after each adjustment.

Brake Release Switch Adjustment
1. Turn on ignition switch and connect a test light between one terminal of brake release switch and ground; select terminal where light goes out when pedal is depressed.
2. Loosen screw that retains switch to pedal support bracket. Position switch so circuit opens (light goes out) when pedal is depressed ¼". Tighten screw and recheck.

1968 Cruise Master
Servo Unit Adjustment
Adjust the bead chain so that it is as tight as possible without holding the throttle open when the carburetor is set at its lowest idle throttle position.

When connecting the bead chain (engine stopped) manually set the fast idle cam at its lowest step and connect the chain so that it does not hold the idle screw off the cam. If the chain needs to be cut, cut it three beads beyond the bead that pulls the linkage.

Regulator Unit Adjustment
To remove any difference between engagement and cruising speed, one adjustment is possible. However, no adjustment should be made until the following items have been checked or serviced.
1. Bead chain properly adjusted.
2. All hoses in good condition, properly attached, not leaking, pinched or cracked.

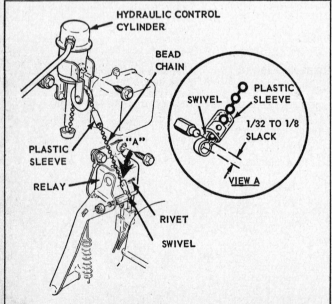

Fig. 8 Auto Cruise bead chain adjustment

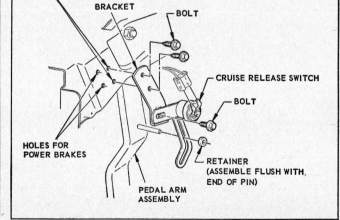

Fig. 9 Auto Cruise brake release switch adjustment

3. Regulator air filter cleaned and properly oiled.
4. Electric and vacuum switches properly adjusted.

Engagement—Cruising Speed Zeroing

If the cruising speed is lower than the engagement speed, loosen the orifice tube locknut and turn the tube outward; if higher turn the tube inward. Each ⅛ turn will alter the engagement-cruising speed difference one mph. Tighten locknut after adjustment and check the system operation at 50 mph.

1967 Auto Cruise

Bead Chain Adjustment

To check the bead chain adjustment, snap swivel off stud and check measurement shown in Fig. 8. If chain is too loose or too tight, adjustments can be made in ⅛″ increments by sliding plastic sleeve off swivel, removing rivet, repositioning chain and inserting rivet in nearest open hole. Recheck adjustment. Snap swivel onto stud and slide plastic sleeve over swivel body to retain rivet.

Brake Release Switch Adjustment

Turn on ignition switch and connect a test lamp between one terminal of the brake release switch and ground. Select terminal where light goes out when brake pedal is depressed.

Loosen screw that retains brake release switch to brake pedal support bracket. Position switch so that circuit opens (light goes out) when brake pedal is depressed ¼″, Fig. 9.

1966-67 AC Electro Cruise

Power Unit Ball Chain, Adjust

IMPORTANT: Do not lubricate power unit ball chain or its pulley.
1. Loosen jam nut on threaded stud attached to end of ball chain.
2. With carburetor set on slow idle cam, rotate threaded stud so that chain is just taut without advancing idle speed of engine with engine running, then back off one full turn.
3. Tighten jam nut against rivnut on throttle bracket.
4. This adjustment should always be checked whenever carburetor linkage is adjusted.

Brake Release Switch, Adjust

1. Disconnect wiring harness connector from brake release switch.
2. Connect test lamp across switch terminals.

NOTE: If desired, the cruise lamp in the engagement switch may be used as a test lamp by unplugging connector to speed transducer in speedometer and leaving release switch wiring connector on switch. Then turn ignition switch on and press control knob which will cause Cruise light to be on.

3. Loosen screw that retains switch to brake pedal support bracket. Position switch to open the circuit at ½ inch brake pedal travel. An open circuit will be indicated by an unlit test lamp. If Cruise lamp is used, an open circuit will be indicated when light goes out.
4. When brake pedal is at released position, the circuit must be closed for the Electro-Cruise to operate.
5. Tighten adjusting screw and recheck switch adjustment by depressing brake pedal several times with test lamp connected.

Engine Section

NOTE:—SEE CHEVROLET CHAPTER FOR SERVICE ON THE 6-250 ENGINE

ENGINE, REPLACE

1. Drain cooling system and remove radiator.
2. Disconnect linkage at transmission and clutch (if equipped).
3. Remove transmission.
4. Remove hood and battery.
5. Disconnect exhaust pipes from manifolds.
6. Disconnect usual items under hood such as fuel lines, radiator hoses, wires, etc.
7. If equipped with an oil cooler, disconnect cooler lines.
8. Raise car and place on jack stands.
9. Support transmission with suitable jack.
10. Remove flywheel cover pan, converter-to-flex plate bolts and transmission-to-engine bolts.
11. Attach a suitable chain to engine, remove front engine mount through bolts and remove engine.

CYLINDER HEADS

Some cylinder head gaskets are coated with a special lacquer to provide a good seal once the parts have warmed up. Do not use any additional sealer on such gaskets. If the gasket does not have this lacquer coating, apply suitable sealer to both sides.

1967-72

1. Drain coolant and disconnect battery.
2. Remove intake manifold.
3. When removing right cylinder head, remove Delcotron and/or A/C compressor with mounting bracket and move out of the way. *Do not disconnect hoses from air compressor.* Disconnect A.I.R. pipe assembly if so equipped.
4. When removing left cylinder head, remove oil dipstick, power steering pump and/or A.I.R. pump with mounting bracket (if equipped) and move out of the way with hoses attached. Disconnect A.I.R. pipe if so equipped.
5. Disconnect exhaust manifold from head to be removed.
6. Remove rocker arm shaft and lift out push rods.
7. Remove cylinder head.
8. Reverse procedure to install and tighten bolts gradually and evenly in the sequence shown in Figs. 1 through 6.

1966 V8-401, 425

1. Drain cooling system.

2. Remove air cleaner and disconnect all pipes from carburetor and intake manifold.
3. Disconnect wires from accelerator vacuum switch and remove throttle return spring.
4. Remove ignition coil and equalizer shaft bracket from engine.
5. Take off intake manifold and carburetor as an assembly.
6. When removing *right* cylinder head, remove air conditioning compressor (if equipped), exercising care.
7. When removing *left* cylinder head, remove power steering gear pump with mounting bracket (if equipped) and move it out of the way with hoses attached.
8. Disconnect wires from plugs.
9. Disconnect water manifold from both cylinder heads and disconnect exhaust manifold from head to be removed.
10. With air hose and cloths, clean dirt off cylinder head and adjacent area to avoid getting dirt into engine, and

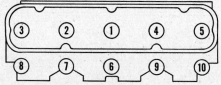

Fig. 1 Cylinder head tightening sequence. 1968-69 V8-350, 400, 430

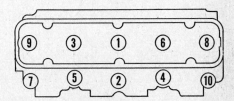

Fig. 1A Cylinder head tightening sequence. 1970-72 V8-350, 455

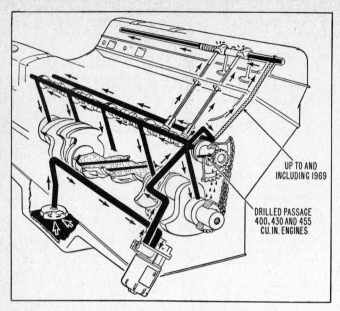

Engine lubrication system.   6-225; 8-300, 340, 350, 400, 430, 455

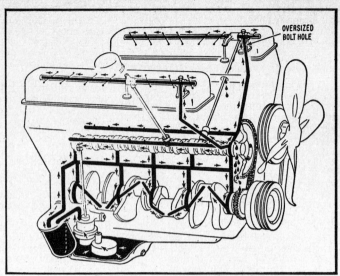

Engine oiling system.   V8-401, 425

particularly into the hydraulic valve lifters.

11. Remove rocker arm cover and rocker arm and shaft assembly.
12. Lift out push rods. *Due to close tolerance in the engine compartment it is necessary to leave some of the bolts and push rods in the head during removal. The push rods should be pulled up and taped in position while cylinder is being removed. The same parts must be in the head during installation.*
13. Remove cylinder head attaching bolts and lift off head.
14. Installation is made in the reverse order of removal. Tighten head bolts in the sequence shown in Fig. 7.

ROCKER ARMS
1970-72, V8-350, 455

A nylon retainer is used to retain the rocker arm. Break them below their head with a chisel, Fig. 8. When replacing rocker assembly position rocker arms so that external rib on each arm points away from rocker shaft bolt, Fig. 9.

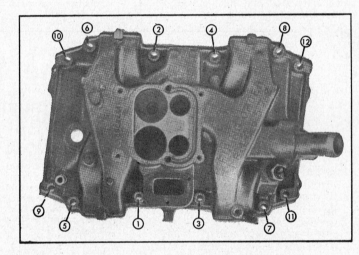

Fig. 2   Intake manifold tightening sequence. V8-350, 400, 430, 455

1968-69 V8-350, 400, 430

When installing rocker arm shaft, be sure that drill mark is facing up and toward rear of left cylinder head and toward front on right cylinder head, Fig. 10.

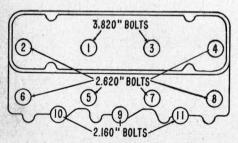

Fig. 3   Cylinder head tightening sequence. V6 engines

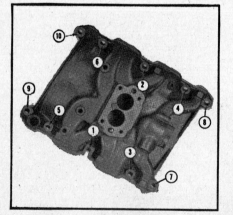

Fig. 4   Intake manifold tightening sequence. V6-225

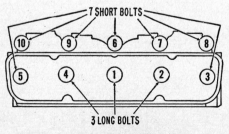

Fig. 5   Cyl. head tightening sequence. V8-300, 340

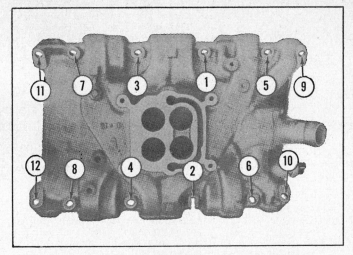

Fig. 6   Intake manifold tightening sequence. V8-300, 340

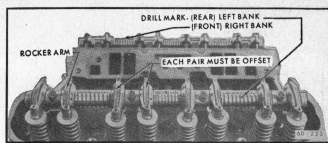

Fig. 10   Rocker arms positioned on shaft. V8-350, 400, 430

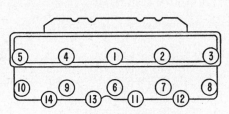

Fig. 7   Cylinder head tightening
sequence. V8-401, 425

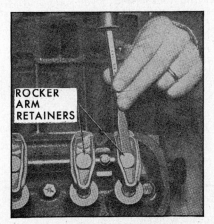

Fig. 8   Removing nylon retainer.
1970-72 V8-350, 455

Fig. 9   Rocker arm positioned on
shaft. 1970-72 V8-350, 455

6-225; 8-300, 340

1. To disassemble, remove cotter pin, plain washer and spring washer from each end of rocker arm shaft.
2. Remove bracket bolts and slide rocker arms and brackets off shaft.
3. Clean and inspect all parts, taking care to clean out all oil holes. Replace parts that are excessively worn.
4. Assemble springs, rocker arms and brackets.

Note that two different rocker arms are used and that the valve ends of rocker arms slant away from the brackets.

5. Install spring washer, flat washer and cotter pin on each end of shaft in the order named.
6. Install bolts with plain washers through brackets and shaft so the notches are positioned as shown in Fig. 11.

V8-401, 425

1. To disassemble, remove cotter pin, flat washer and spring washer from each end of the rocker arm shaft and remove bolts from brackets. Remove rocker arms, springs and brackets from shaft.
2. Clean and inspect all parts and replace those that are excessively worn.
3. Assemble springs, rocker arms and brackets on shaft, Fig. 12. Note that the long spring is at the middle of the shaft, the valve ends of all rocker arms slant toward middle of shaft, and a bracket is located between each pair of rocker arms.
4. Install spring washer, flat washer and cotter pin on each end of the shaft in the order named.
5. Install bolts with plain washers through brackets and shaft so that the notch on one end of the shaft is *upward* in line with bolt heads. This places the oil holes on lower side of shaft in proper relationship to rocker arms.

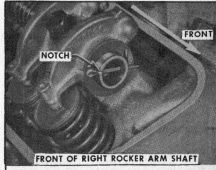

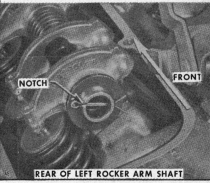

Fig. 11   Rocker arm shaft installation.
6-225; 8-300, 340

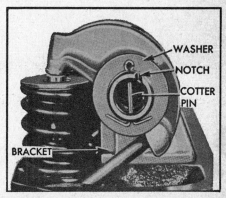

Fig. 12   Rocker arm shaft installation.
V8-401, 425

VALVE ARRANGEMENT
Front to Rear

V6 Left Head	E-I-E-I-I-E
V6 Right Head	E-I-I-E-I-E
V8-350, 400, 430, 455	E-I-I-E-E-I-I-E
Other V8s	E-I-E-I-I-E-I-E

VALVE LIFT SPECS.

Engine	Year	Intake	Exhaust
V6-225	1966-67	.401	.401
6-250	1968-71	.388	.388
V8-300	1966-67	.3931	.401
V8-340	1966-67	.3992①	.3992①
V8-350	1968-70	.3766	.384
V8-350	1971	.388	.388
V8-350	1972	.3818	.3984
V8-400	1967	.4214	.4498
V8-400	1968-69	.4187	.4482
V8-401	1966	.431	.431
V8-425	1966	.439	.441
V8-430	1967	.4214	.4498
V8-430	1968-69	.4187	.4482
V8-455	1970	.3891	.4602
V8-455	1971-72	.387	.456

①—1966 LeSabre; intake .393, exhaust .401.

VALVE TIMING
Intake Opens Before TDC

Engine	Year	Degrees
V6-225	1966-67	24
6-250	1968-70	16
V8-300	1966-67	30
V8-340	1966-67	32
V8-350	1968-70	24
V8-350	1971	28
V8-350	1972	24
V8-400	1967-69	14
V8-401	1966	28

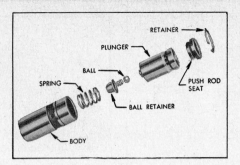

Fig. 13 Hydraulic valve lifter parts

V8-425	1966	29
V8-430	1967-69	14
V8-455	1970	17
V8-455	1971	12
V8-455	1972	12①

①—California engine 14.

VALVE GUIDES

The valves operate in guides pressed into the cylinder head.

HYDRAULIC VALVE LIFTERS

Failure of an hydraulic valve lifter, Fig. 13, is generally caused by an inadequate oil supply or dirt. An air leak at the intake side of the oil pump or too much oil in the engine will cause air bubbles in the oil supply to the lifters, causing them to collapse. This is a probable cause of trouble if several lifters fail to function, but air in the oil is an unlikely cause of failure of a single unit.

The valve lifters may be lifted out of their bores after removing the rocker arms and push rods. Adjustable pliers with taped jaws may be used to remove lifters that are stuck due to varnish, carbon, etc. Fig. 13 illustrates the type of lifter used.

TIMING CHAIN COVER
V8-401, 425

1. To remove the timing chain, drain cooling system, then remove radiator, shroud, fan belt, fan and pulley, and vibration damper.
2. Remove all bolts that attach timing chain cover and water manifold to engine. *Do not remove five small bolts attaching water pump to chain cover.* Remove cover and manifold, using care to avoid damaging oil pan gasket.

V6-225, V8-300, 340, 350, 400, 430, 455

1. Drain cooling system and remove radiator.
2. Remove fan, pulleys and belts.
3. Remove crankshaft pulley and reinforcement.
4. If equipped with power steering, remove any pump bracket bolts attached to timing chain cover and loosen and remove any other bolts necessary that will allow pump and brackets to be moved out of the way.
5. Remove fuel pump.
6. Remove Delcotron and brackets.
7. Remove distributor cap and pull spark plug wire retainers off brackets on rocker arm cover. Swing distributor cap with wires attached out of the way. Disconnect distributor pri-

REMOVE BOLTS MARKED * FOR COMPLETE REMOVAL REVERSE PROCEDURE FOR INSTALLATION

Fig. 14 Timing chain cover installation. V8-400, 430, 455

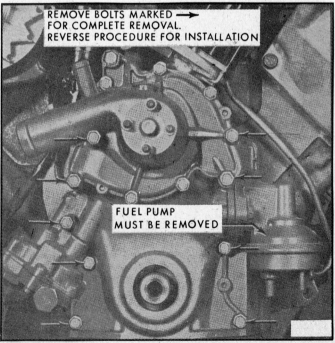

REMOVE BOLTS MARKED → FOR COMPLETE REMOVAL. REVERSE PROCEDURE FOR INSTALLATION

FUEL PUMP MUST BE REMOVED

Fig. 15 Timing chain cover installation. 1968 V8-350, 1967 V6-225

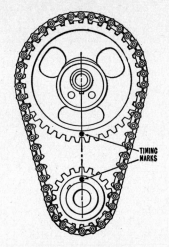

Fig. 16   Valve timing marks. V8-401, 425

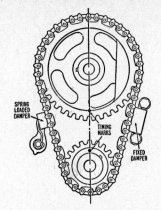

Fig. 17   Valve timing marks. V6-225

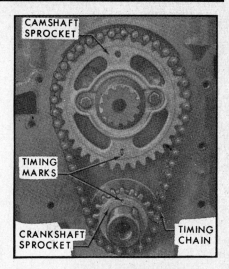

Fig. 18   Valve timing marks. V8-300, 340, 350, 400, 430, 455

mary lead. On 400, 430, remove coil.

8. Remove distributor. *If chain and sprockets are not to be disturbed, note position of distributor rotor for installation in the same position.*

9. Loosen and slide clamp on thermostat by-pass hose rearward.

10. Remove bolts attaching chain cover to block.

11. On 225, 300, 340, 350 engines, remove two oil pan-to-chain cover bolts and remove cover.

12. On 400, 430, 455 engines, remove four oil pan-to-chain cover bolts. *Do not remove the five bolts attaching water pump to chain cover.* Remove cover, using care to avoid damaging oil pan gasket.

13. Reverse procedure to install, noting data shown in Figs. 14 and 15.

IMPORTANT

Remove the oil pump cover and pack the space around the oil pump gears completely full of vaseline. There must be no air space left inside the pump. Re-install the cover using a new gasket.

This step is very important as the oil pump may lose its prime whenever the pump, pump cover or timing chain cover is disturbed. If the pump is not packed it may not begin to pump oil as soon as the engine is started.

TIMING CHAIN
225, 300, 340, 350, 400, 430, 455

1. With the timing case cover removed as outlined above, temporarily install the vibration damper bolt and washer in end of crankshaft.

2. Turn crankshaft so sprockets are positioned as shown in Figs. 17, 18. Use a sharp rap on a wrench handle to start the vibration damper bolt out without disturbing the position of the sprockets.

3. Remove front oil slinger.

NOTE: On V8-400, 430, 455 it will be necessary to first remove the oil pan.

4. Remove camshaft distributor drive gear and fuel pump eccentric.

5. Use two large screwdrivers to alternately pry the camshaft sprocket then the crankshaft sprocket for-

ward until the camshaft sprocket is free. Then remove camshaft sprocket and chain, and crankshaft sprocket off crankshaft.

6. To install, assemble chain on sprockets and slide sprockets on their respective shafts with the "O" marks on the sprockets lined up as shown.

7. Complete the installation in the reverse order of removal.

V8-401, 425

1. Remove oil slinger from crankshaft and remove bolt, lockwasher and plain washer that attaches fuel pump operating eccentric and camshaft sprocket to camshaft.

2. If there has been doubt about the valve timing, turn the crankshaft until the camshaft sprocket keyway is straight down toward the crankshaft and the timing marks on both sprockets are as shown in Fig. 16.

3. Using two large screwdrivers, al-

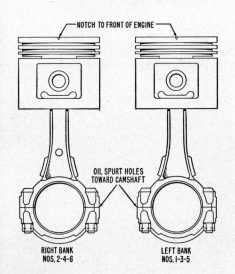

Fig. 19   Piston and rod assembly. V6-225

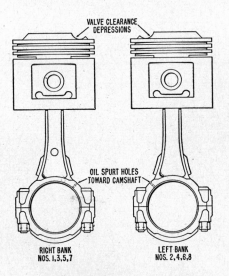

Fig. 20   Piston and rod assembly. V8-401, 425

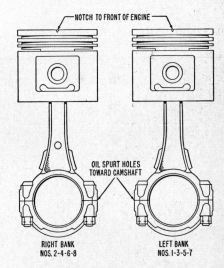

Fig. 21   Piston and rod assembly. V8-300, 340, 350, 400, 430, 455

ternately work the sprockets outward until the camshaft sprocket is free of the camshaft. Remove this sprocket and chain, then remove the other sprocket from the crankshaft.

4. Thoroughly clean all sludge from cover and front face of crankcase. Inspect crankshaft oil seal in chain cover and replace if worn.
5. When ready to install the chain, turn crankshaft until Nos. 1 and 4 pistons are on top dead center. Turn camshaft so that sprocket key points straight down toward crankshaft.
6. Place timing chain over sprockets so that timing marks are located as shown in Fig. 16. Install sprockets with chain on the two shafts.
7. Install fuel pump eccentric and oil slinger. Then complete the installation in the reverse order of removal.

CAMSHAFT

1. To remove camshaft, remove rocker arm shaft assemblies, push rods and valve lifters.
2. Remove timing chain and sprockets.
3. Slide camshaft out of engine, using care not to mar the bearing surfaces.

PISTONS & RODS, ASSEMBLE

Rods and pistons should be assembled and installed as shown in Figs. 19, 20, 21.

PISTONS, PINS & RINGS

Pistons are available in standard sizes and oversizes of .001, .005, .010, .020 and .030 inch.

Rings are furnished in standard sizes and oversizes of .010, .020 and .030 inch.

Piston pins are supplied in standard sizes and oversizes of .003 and .005 inch.

MAIN & ROD BEARINGS

Main bearings are available in standard sizes and undersizes of .001, .002, .003 and .010 inch.

Rod bearings are furnished in standard sizes and undersizes of .001, .002 and .010", Fig. 22.

Fig. 22   Location of undersize mark on main and rod bearing shell

CRANKSHAFT OIL SEAL

A braided oil seal is pressed into the upper and lower grooves behind the rear main bearing.

OIL PAN
6-250

To remove oil pan it is necessary to remove the engine from the chassis.

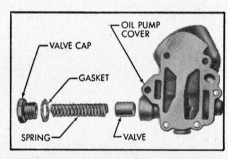

Fig. 24   Oil pump cover and by-pass valve. 225, 300, 340, 350, 400, 430, 455

1970-72 V8-350, 455

1. Disconnect battery and drain oil.
2. Remove fan shroud to radiator tie bar screws.
3. Remove air cleaner and disconnect linkage to throttle.
4. Raise and support car on stands.
5. With manual transmission, loosen clutch equalizer bracket to frame bolts. Disconnect crossover pipe at engine.
6. With automatic transmission, remove lower flywheel housing. Remove shift linkage attaching bolt and swing out of way. Disconnect crossover pipe at engine. Disconnect idler arm at frame and push steering linkage forward to crossmember. Remove front engine mount bolts and raise engine by placing jack under crankshaft pulley mounting.

NOTE: If car is air conditioned, at this point it will be necessary to place a support under right side of transmission prior to raising engine to prevent transmission from cocking to the right when raised.

7. Remove oil pan. It may be necessary to position crankshaft so 1 and 2 crankpin and counterweight will not interfere with front of pan.

1968-69 V8-350, 400, 430

1. Disconnect battery and drain oil.
2. Raise and support car on stands.
3. With manual transmission, loosen clutch equalizer bracket-to-frame bolts. Remove exhaust crossover pipe, and front engine mounting bolts. Remove fan shroud-to-radiator tie bar screws.
4. With automatic transmission, remove lower flywheel housing. Remove shift linkage attaching bolts and swing out of the way (LeSabre only). Remove front engine mounting bolts. Remove fan shroud-to-radiator tie bar screws.
5. Raise engine by placing jack under crankshaft pulley mounting.
6. Unfasten and remove pan.
7. Reverse procedure to install.

1967 V8-400, 430

1. Disconnect ground strap at battery.
2. Raise car and drain oil.
3. With manual shift transmission,

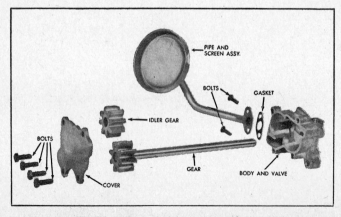

Fig. 23   Oil pump disassembled. V8-401, 425

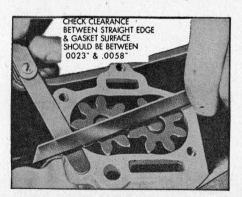

Fig. 25   Checking oil pump gear end clearance. 225, 300, 340, 350, 400, 430, 455

loosen clutch equalizer bracket-to-frame bolts. Remove lower flywheel housing, exhaust crossover pipe, front engine mount bolts and fan shroud-to-radiator tie bar screws.

4. With automatic transmission, remove lower flywheel housing, loosen shift linkage bolts, remove steering idler arm bracket-to-right front frame bolts, front engine mount bolts and fan shroud-to-radiator tie bar screws.

5. Raise engine with jack under crankshaft pulley mounting.

6. Unfasten and remove oil pan.

V8-401, 425

On single exhaust models the exhaust crossover pipe must be removed. On some models, it may be necessary to remove the flywheel housing lower cover and starter splash shield. It may also be necessary to disconnect the steering idler arm bracket from the right frame side rail and lower the steering linkage for clearance. *The idler arm bracket should be fastened in its relative position to the idler arm while disconnected from the frame. This will prevent turning and possible changing of toe-in adjustment.*

6-225; 8-300, 340

1. Remove air cleaner and drain oil from oil pan.
2. Loosen clutch equalizer bracket-to-frame bolts (if equipped).
3. Loosen shift linkage attaching bolts.
4. Remove steering idler arm bracket-to-suspension crossmember attaching bolts.
5. Support engine either with a jack under the oil pan or with chains around exhaust manifold.
6. Remove engine mounting bolts.
7. Raise engine and insert bolts through engine mount bracket bolt holes, then lower engine so mounts rest on bolts.
8. Remove lower flywheel housing.
9. Remove oil pan bolts and lower pan enough to remove oil pump pipe and screen-to-cylinder block bolts.
10. Rotate crankshaft to provide maximum clearance at forward end of oil pan. Move front of pan to the right and lower through opening between crossmember and steering linkage intermediate shaft.
11. Reverse removal procedure to install pan.

OIL PUMP
V8-401, 425

1. Referring to Fig. 23, remove pipe and screen. Take off cover and slide gears out of body. Wash all parts and blow dry.

2. Replace any parts not serviceable.
3. Install gear and shaft and idler gear in body.
4. Check for clearance between gears and cover using a straightedge. Clearance should be .0005″ to .005″.
5. Pack cavity and space between gears and body with vaseline, not chassis lube.
6. Install pump cover with side having grooves toward gears.
7. Complete assembly and install pump.
8. Install pump with new gasket and tighten bolts a little at a time while turning pump shaft through gear lash. If pump shaft tends to bind when bolts are tightened, it may be freed up by tapping body with a mallet.

225, 300, 340, 350, 400, 430, 455

1. To remove pump, take off oil filter.
2. Disconnect wire from oil pressure indicator switch in filter by-pass valve cap (if so equipped).
3. Remove screws attaching oil pump cover to timing chain cover. Remove cover and slide out pump gears. Replace any parts not serviceable.
4. Remove oil pressure relief valve cap, spring and valve, Fig. 24. Remove oil filter by-pass valve cap, spring and valve. Replace any parts of valve not serviceable.
5. Check relief valve in its bore in cover. Valve should have no more clearance than an easy slip fit. If any perceptible side shake can be felt, the valve and/or cover should be replaced.
6. The filter by-pass valve should be flat and free of nicks and scratches.

Assembly & Installation

1. Lubricate and install pressure relief valve and spring in bore of pump cover. Install cap and gasket. Torque cap to 30-35 ft-lbs.
2. Install filter by-pass valve flat in its seat in cover. Install spring, cap and gasket. Torque cap to 30-35 ft-lbs.
3. Install pump gears and shaft in pump body section of timing chain cover to check gear end clearance. Check clearance as shown in Fig. 25. If clearance is less than .0018″ check timing chain cover for evidence of wear.
4. If gear end clearance is satisfactory, remove gears and pack gear pocket *full* of vaseline, not chassis lube.
5. Reinstall gears so vaseline is forced into every cavity of gear pocket and between teeth of gears. *Unless pump is packed with vaseline, it may not prime itself when engine is started.*
6. Install cover and tighten screws alternately and evenly. Final tighten-

ing is 10-15 ft-lbs. torque. Install filter on nipple.

WATER PUMP, REPLACE

Drain cooling system, being sure to drain into a clean container if antifreeze solution is to be saved. Remove the fan belt and disconnect all hoses from water pump. Remove water pump.

FUEL PUMP, REPLACE
1969-70 Riviera Electric Pump

These models have a turbine type electric pump located at the lower end of the fuel pick-up pipe in the bottom of the tank. This pump runs continuously whenever the engine is running thus maintaining a steady pressure whether fuel is needed or not. To replace, proceed as follows:

1. Raise car, disconnect two terminal connector at tank and remove ground wire screw.
2. Lower car and pull back trunk floor mat.
3. Remove five screws from access hole cover and remove cover.
4. Disconnect fuel hose from tank unit.
5. Unscrew retaining cam ring and remove fuel pump-tank unit assembly.
6. To remove pump from tank unit, remove flat wire conductor from plastic clip on fuel tube.
7. Squeeze clamp and pull pump straight back about ½″.
8. Remove two nuts and washers from pump terminals.
9. Squeeze clamp and pull pump straight back, take care to prevent bending of circular support bracket.
10. Reverse procedure to install.

All Models-Mechanical Pump

NOTE: Before installing the pump, it is good practice to crank the engine so that the nose of the camshaft eccentric is out of the way of the fuel pump rocker arm when the pump is installed. In this way there will be the least amount of tension on the rocker arm, thereby easing the installation of the pump.

1. Remove all gasket material from the pump and block gasket surfaces. Apply sealer to both sides of new gasket.
2. Position gasket on pump flange and hold pump in position against its mounting surface. Make sure rocker arm is riding on camshaft eccentric.
3. Press pump tight against its mounting. Install retaining screws and tighten them alternately.
4. Connect fuel lines. Then operate engine and check for leaks.

Clutch and Transmission Section

> NOTE: 1972 linkage adjustment information is in this section. Repair procedures on both automatic and manual shift transmissions are covered elsewhere in this manual. Procedures for removing automatic transmissions as well as linkage adjustments on 1966-71 models are included in the automatic transmission chapters. See Chapter Index.

CLUTCH PEDAL, ADJUST
1969-72

Adjust linkage to provide ⅝" to ⅞" pedal free play. On LeSabre, Wildcat and G.S. 400 units, remove swivel retainer, disconnect swivel from equalizer arm and turn swivel to obtain proper adjustment. On other units, loosen lock nut and turn rod. When proper clearance is reached, tighten lock nut.

1967-68 Intermediates

With clutch pedal at full release position contacting rubber bumper stop, adjust clutch release rod to give zero lash at clutch pedal. Back off release rod approximately two turns to give ⅝ to ⅞ inch lash at pedal pad. Tighten lock nut on clutch release rod.

1967-68 LeSabre & Wildcat

With clutch pedal at full release position contacting rubber bumper stop, assemble all linkage parts except clutch release rod clevis so clevis pin will just assemble in equalizer inner lever with zero lash at clutch pedal. Lengthen release rod by turning clevis off rod approximately three turns to give ⅝ to ⅞ inch lash at pedal pad.

1966 Special, Skylark & LeSabre

1. Before making clutch adjustment, make certain clutch fork is on ball stud.
2. Unhook spring from clutch fork.
3. Push and hold equalizer and release rod toward front of car.
4. Pull and hold clutch fork toward rear of car.
5. If clutch is properly lashed there will be 1/16" to ⅛" clearance between clutch fork and rod.
6. To adjust clutch lash, loosen nut and turn clutch release rod as required.
7. Install spring to clutch fork.

1966 Skylark Gran Sport

1. Hold clutch pedal at full release position, contacting rubber bumper stop.
2. Adjust lower release rod clevis so clevis pin will just assemble into equalizer outer lever, with zero lash at clutch pedal.
3. Shorten lower clutch release rod by turning clevis on rod about two turns to give ⅝" to ⅞" lash at pedal.

1966 Wildcat

1. With clutch pedal at full release position, contacting rubber bumper stop and load removed from clutch over-center spring, adjust turnbuckle to obtain zero lash at pedal.
2. Lengthen rod by turning turnbuckle about two turns to give ⅞" to 1⅛" lash at pedal pad.
3. Tighten lock nut on rod and on over-center spring eyebolt.

CLUTCH, REPLACE
1969-72

1. Remove transmission.
2. Remove pedal return spring from clutch fork. *On LeSabre, Wildcat and G.S. 400, disconnect rod assembly from clutch fork.*
3. Remove flywheel housing.
4. Remove clutch throw-out bearing from clutch fork.
5. Disconnect clutch fork from ball stud by moving it toward center of flywheel housing.
6. Mark clutch cover and flywheel so it can be installed in the same position.
7. Loosen clutch cover to flywheel bolts one turn at a time to avoid bending of clutch cover flange until spring pressure is released.
8. Support pressure plate and cover assembly while removing last bolts, then remove pressure plate and driven plate.
9. Reverse procedure to install being sure to line up marks made in removal.

1967-68 Special, Skylark, G.S. 350, 400, LeSabre & Wildcat

1. Remove transmission. *On LeSabre the equalizer assembly must be released first.*
2. Remove pedal return spring from clutch fork. *On LeSabre disconnect rod assembly from clutch fork.*
3. Remove flywheel housing.
4. Remove clutch release bearing.
5. Disconnect clutch fork from ball stud by forcing it toward center of flywheel housing.
6. Mark clutch cover and flywheel so that cover can be reinstalled in the same position on flywheel to preserve engine balance.
7. Loosen clutch cover-to-flywheel bolts one turn at a time each to avoid bending clutch cover flange until spring pressure is released.
8. Support pressure plate and cover assembly while removing last bolts, then remove assembly with driven disc.

9. Reverse procedure to install, being sure to align marks on clutch cover with mark made on flywheel during removal. Adjust pedal lash as directed above.

1966 Skylark Gran Sport

1. Remove transmission.
2. Disconnect lower clutch release rod from equalizer.
3. Loosen nut on frame side of equalizer and remove equalizer.
4. Remove ball stud from clutch release shaft.
5. Remove release lever and seal.
6. Remove flywheel housing.
7. Remove nylon bushing from flywheel housing.
8. Remove socket head capscrew on clutch release shaft; from same hole remove second socket head capscrew (cone point).
9. Pull clutch release shaft out about three inches. Slide release yoke, release bearing, woodruff key and return spring off end of release shaft. Remove release shaft.
10. Mark clutch cover and flywheel with a center punch so that cover can be reinstalled in same position on flywheel.
11. Loosen each clutch cover bolt one turn at a time in order to relieve clutch spring pressure evenly, thereby avoid distortion of cover.
12. Support clutch cover and pressure plate while removing last bolts, then remove cover and driven plate.
13. Reverse procedure to install.

1966 Wildcat

1. Remove propeller shaft and transmission.
2. Remove clutch equalizer shaft.
3. Remove ball stud from clutch release shaft.
4. Remove clutch release lever.
5. Remove clutch release seal.
6. Remove nylon bushing.
7. Remove socket head capscrew on clutch release shaft. From same hole remove second socket head (cone point).
8. Pull clutch release shaft out about three inches. Slide release yoke, key, release bearing and return spring off end of release shaft. Remove release shaft.
9. Mark clutch cover and flywheel with center punch for assembly purposes to preserve engine balance.
10. Loosen clutch cover bolts a little at a time until spring pressure is relieved, then completely remove bolts

and take out clutch and driven plate.

11. Reverse procedure to install.

1966 Special, Skylark & LeSabre

1. Remove transmission.
2. Remove clutch release bearing.
3. Remove pedal return spring from fork.
4. Remove flywheel housing.
5. Disconnect fork from ball stud by forcing it toward center of vehicle.
6. Mark clutch cover and flywheel for assembly purposes in order to maintain engine balance.
7. Loosen clutch cover bolts a little at a time until spring pressure is released. Then completely remove bolts and take out clutch and driven plate.
8. Reverse procedure to install.

3 SPEED TRANS. REPLACE
All 1966-72

1. Disconnect speedometer cable from driven gear fitting.
2. Disconnect shift control rods from shifter levers at transmission.
3. Remove propeller shaft.
4. Support rear of engine and remove transmission crossmember.
5. Remove two top transmission attaching bolts and insert guide pins in these holes.
6. Remove two lower bolts and slide transmission straight back and out of vehicle.
7. Reverse procedure to install.

3 SPEED TRANS. SHIFT LINKAGE
1969-72

Column Shift

1. Place column selector lever in Reverse detent, making sure the steering column selector plate engages lower most column lever (1st-reverse).
2. Loosen 1st-reverse adjusting clamp.
3. Shift transmission lever into reverse and tighten the 1st-reverse clamp to 17-23 ft-lbs.
4. Shift transmission levers into neutral and loosen 2nd-3rd clamp.
5. Install 3/16" diameter rod through 2nd-3rd lever selector plate and the 1st-reverse lever and alignment plate.
6. Tighten 2nd-3rd shift rod clamp to 17-23 ft-lbs.

Floor Shift

1. Place transmission levers in Neutral.
2. Loosen shift rod adjusting clamp bolts on shifter assembly.
3. Insert 1/4" drill rod through shift as-

sembly and shift levers.

4. Tighten clamp bolts to 17-23 ft-lbs.
5. To adjust back drive linkage, shift transmission into Reverse. *This must be done using selector lever inside the car.* Loosen clamp bolt.
6. Push back drive rod up against stop in steering column. Tighten clamp bolt.

1968

Column Shift

1. Place transmission levers in neutral.
2. Loosen shift rod adjusting clamps.
3. Install a 3/16" drill rod through 2-3 lever, selector plate and 1st-reverse lever and align plate.
4. Tighten shift rod clamp bolts to 17-23 ft-lbs.
5. To check the cross-over, find the neutral detent in the 1st-reverse position and mark the mast jacket.
6. Move shift lever down to the 2nd-3rd position and find the neutral detent position. Check to see if the two detents line up as shown by the mark made on the mast jacket.
7. If they do not line up, shorten the 1st-reverse rod by pulling it through the swivel by no more than 3/16".

Floor Shift

1. Place transmission levers in neutral.
2. Loosen shift rod adjusting clamp bolts on shifter assembly.
3. Place a 1/4" drill rod through shift assembly and shift levers.
4. Tighten clamp bolts to 17-23 ft-lbs.

1967 LeSabre

1. Place transmission levers in neutral.
2. Loosen shift rod adjusting clamp bolts.
3. Install a 3/16 diameter rod through 1st-reverse rod.
4. Tighten clamp bolts.

1966-67 Special & Skylark

1. Place transmission levers in neutral.
2. Loosen shift rod adjusting clamps.
3. Install a 3/16" diameter rod through low-reverse lever and selector plate.
4. Push 2-3 shift rod through adjusting clamp until 1/4" exists from bottom of adjusting clamp to bottom of shift rod.
5. Tighten shift rod clamps.

1966-67 G.S. 400

1. Place transmission levers in neutral.
2. Loosen shift rod adjusting clamp bolts.
3. Place a 5/16" bolt or drill rod in notch in rear portion of shift lever bracket.
4. Move both levers back against the 5/16" tool.
5. Tighten adjusting clamp bolts.

1966 LeSabre & Wildcat

1. Place transmission levers in neutral.
2. Loosen shift rod adjusting clamp bolts.
3. Install a 1/4" drill rod into bearing tab and low-reverse lever.
4. Place screwdriver beneath selector plate and the 2-3 lever until selector plate engages tang on both shift levers.
5. Tighten adjusting clamps.

4 SPEED TRANS. REPLACE
1966-72 G.S. 350, 400, 455

1. Disconnect speedometer cable and remove driven gear.
2. Disconnect shift control rods from transmission.
3. Remove propeller shaft.
4. Support rear of engine and remove transmission support.
5. Remove two top transmission-to-flywheel housing bolts and insert guide pins.
6. Remove two lower bolts.
7. Slide transmission back and out.
8. Reverse procedure to install.

4 SPEED TRANS. SHIFT LINKAGE
1968-72 G.S. 350, 400, 455

Floor Shift

1. Place transmission in neutral.
2. Adjust all three shift rods so a 1/4" drill rod can be installed through shifter assembly and shift levers.
3. Tighten swivel nuts to 17-23 ft-lbs.
4. On 1969-71 models, using shaft handle inside car only, shift transmission into Reverse, loosen clamp bolt and push back drive rod up against stop in steering column. Tighten clamp bolt.

1966-67 G.S. 400

1. With transmission in neutral, loosen shift rod adjusting clamp bolts.
2. Place a 5/16" bolt or drill rod in notch in rear lower portion of shift bracket.
3. Move all three shift levers back against the 5/16" tool.
4. Tighten adjusting clamps.

1972 AUTO TRANS. LINKAGE ADJUST

This adjustment is the same as that described for previous models and is found in the front section of this manual.

Rear Axle, Propeller Shaft & Brakes

REAR AXLES

Figure 1 illustrates the type rear axle assemblies used on Buicks. When necessary to overhaul any of these units, refer to the *Rear Axle Specifications* table in this chapter.

NOTE: Canadian built Specials and Skylarks may use a "C" type axle. This design axle employs "C" locks to retain the axle shafts. Service on this type axle is covered in the Chevrolet section of this manual.

1966-72 All

In this rear axle, Fig. 1, the drive pinion is mounted in two tapered roller bearings which are preloaded by two selected spacers at assembly. The pinion is positioned by shims located between a shoulder on the drive pinion and the rear bearing. The front bearing is held in place by a large nut.

The differential is supported in the carrier by two tapered roller side bearings. These are preloaded by inserting shims between the bearings and the pedestals. The differential assembly is positioned for proper ring gear and pinion backlash by varying these shims. The ring gear is bolted to the case. The case houses two side gears in mesh with two pinions mounted on a pinion axle which is anchored in the case by a spring pin. The pinions and side gears are backed by thrust washers.

REAR AXLE ASSEMBLY, REPLACE

1970-72

It is not necessary to remove the rear axle assembly for any normal repairs but if the housing must be replaced the assembly may be removed as follows:

1. Raise car high enough and support using jack stands under both frame side rails.
2. Mark rear universal joint and flange for proper reassembly and disconnect rear joint. On Riviera, mark flanged ball stud yoke and rear flange and disconnect rear joint from flange.
3. Push propeller shaft as far forward as possible and wire up out of way.
4. Disconnect parking brake cables and rear brake hose. Cover brake hose opening to prevent entrance of dirt.
5. Support axle with jack and disconnect shock absorbers at lower ends.

On Estate Wagons, disconnect right side of exhaust system by removing exhaust hanger screw to rear frame crossmember. Remove lower spring plate attaching nuts and remove front and rear attaching bolts and remove spring.
6. On Riviera, disconnect track bar at axle housing.

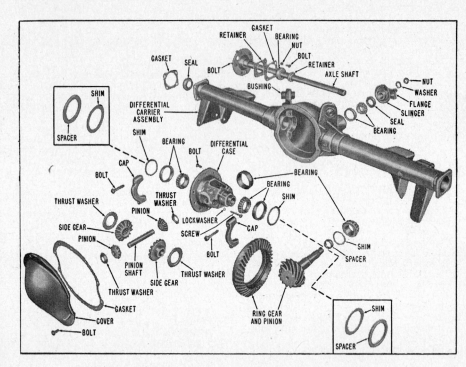

Fig. 1   Rear axle assembly. Roller bearings are used in the axle shafts of some 1969-72 models

7. Disconnect upper control arms at axle housing.
8. Disconnect lower control arms and remove axle assembly.

1966-69 All

It is not necessary to remove the rear axle assembly for any normal repairs. The axle shafts and carrier assembly can easily be removed from the vehicle, leaving the axle housing in place.

1. Raise rear end of car with rear axle hanging on shock absorbers.
2. Mark rear universal joint and pinion flange for proper reassembly. *These parts are carefully balanced in production and assembled with heavy sides opposite. For this reason they should be reassembled the same way.*
3. Disconnect rear universal joint from pinion flange by removing two U-bolts. Wire propeller shaft to exhaust pipe to support it out of the way.
4. Remove rear wheels and brake drums.
5. Remove axle shafts as outlined below.
6. Remove all cover bolts and break cover loose at the bottom to allow lubricant to drain.
7. Remove carrier assembly by prying or by use of a slide hammer.
8. Reverse foregoing procedure to install the carrier assembly, being sure to connect the rear universal joint to the pinion flange according to the alignment marks made previously.

AXLE SHAFT, REPLACE

1966-72 All Except "C" Type

IMPORTANT

Design allows for axle shaft end play up to .042" (.018" on 1969-72). This end play can be checked with the wheel and brake drum removed by measuring the difference between the end of the housing and the axle shaft flange while moving the axle shaft in and out by hand.

End play over this is excessive. Compensating for all the end play by inserting a shim inboard of the bearing in the housing is not recommended since it ignores the end play of the bearing itself, and may result in improper seating of the gasket or backing plate against the housing. If end play is excessive, the axle shaft and bearing assembly should be removed and the cause of the excessive end play determined and corrected.

Removing Axle Shaft

1. Remove wheels and brake drums.
2. Remove nuts holding retainer plates to brake backing plates. Pull retainers clear of bolts and reinstall two lower nuts finger tight to hold brake backing plate in position.
3. Use a slide hammer type puller to pull out axle shaft, if bearing is a tight fit in axle housing, using care not to cut lip of oil seal as shaft is being withdrawn from axle housing.

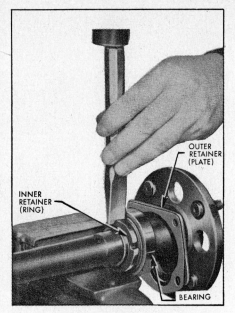

Fig. 2   Removing axle shaft bearing retainer

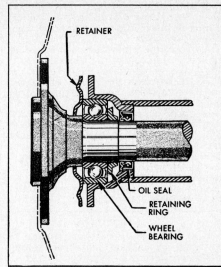

Fig. 3   Axle shaft bearing and oil seal. 1966-67 axle shaft. 1969-72 Senior Series except Estate Wagon

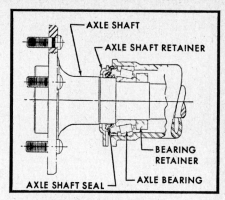

Fig. 4   Axle shaft, bearing and oil seal. 1969-72 Special and Skylark and 1970-72 Estate Wagon

Replacing Shaft Bearings

1. Nick bearing retainer in three or four places with a chisel deep enough to spread ring, Fig. 2. Retainer will then slip off.
2. Press bearing off shaft.
3. Press new bearing against shoulder on axle shaft. *Retainer plate which retains bearing in housing must be on axle shaft before bearing is installed; retainer gasket can be installed after bearing.*
4. Press new retainer ring against bearing.

Replacing Oil Seal

1. Insert axle shaft so that splined end is just through seal.
2. Using axle shaft as a lever, push down on shaft until seal is pried from housing.
3. Apply sealer to outside diameter of new seal.
4. Position seal over a suitable installer and drive seal straight into axle housing until seated.

Axle Shaft, Install

1. Apply a coat of wheel bearing grease in bearing recesses of housing.
2. Install new outer retainer gaskets.
3. To help prevent damage to lip of oil seal when installing axle shaft and to ensure lubricant on seal lip during the first few miles of operation, the axle shaft should be lightly lubricated with axle lubricant from the sealing surface to about 6″ inboard of the shaft.
4. Insert axle shafts carefully until splines engage in differential to avoid damage to seals.

PROPELLER SHAFT
1966-72 Senior Series

NOTE

When service is required, the propeller shaft must be removed from the car as a complete assembly. While handling it

out of the car, the assembly must be supported on a straight line as nearly as possible to avoid jamming or bending any of the parts. Figs. 5 and 6 show the components of the assemblies.

1. To remove the assembly, remove center bearing attaching bolts.
2. At rear pinion flange, remove U-bolt clamps from rear U-joint.
3. Mark both flange and shaft to assemble in the same position.

CAUTION: If rear U-joint bearings are not retained on the spider by a connecting strap, use tape or wire to secure bearings.

4. Support rear end of propeller shaft to avoid damage to constant velocity joint and slide complete assembly rearward until front yoke slips from transmission shaft splines.
5. Protect oil seal surface on front slip yoke by taping or wiring a cloth over the complete front U-joint.
6. Slide complete propeller shaft rearward through frame tunnel (if present). Do not bend constant velocity U-joint to its extreme angle at any time.

Installation

The propeller shaft must be handled carefully during its installation to avoid bending any of the parts, Figs. 5 and 6.

1. Protect oil seal diameter on front

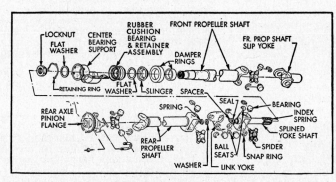

Fig. 5   Propeller shaft assembly. 1966-68 LeSabre, Wildcat and Electra. A one-piece propeller shaft is used in 1969-72

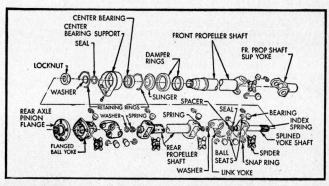

Fig. 6   Propeller shaft assembly. 1966-72 Riviera

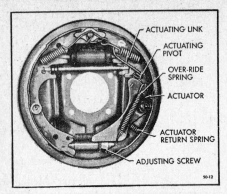

Fig. 7   Left rear wheel brake. 1966-72

The automatic adjusters operate only when the brakes are applied as the car is moving rearward or when the car comes to an uphill stop.

Although the brakes are self-adjusting, an initial adjustment is necessary after the brake shoes have been relined or replaced, or when the length of the adjusting screw has been changed during some other service opration.

Frequent usage of an automatic transmission forward range to halt reverse vehicle motion may prevent the automatic adjusters from functioning, thereby inducing low pedal heights. Should low pedal heights be encountered, it is recommended that numerous forward and reverse stops be made until satisfactory pedal height is obtained.

NOTE

If a low pedal condition cannot be corrected by making numerous reverse stops (provided the hydraulic system is free of air) it indicates that the self-adjusting mechanism is not functioning. Therefore, it will be necessary to remove the brake drum, clean, free up and lubricate the adjusting mechanism. Then adjust the brakes as follows, being sure the parking brake is fully released.

Adjustment

1. Remove adjusting hole cover from backing plate. Turn brake adjusting screw to expand shoes until wheel can just be turned by hand.
2. Using suitable tool to hold actuator away from adjuster, Fig. 8, back off adjuster 30 notches. If shoes still drag, back off one or two additional notches.

NOTE: Brakes should be free of drag when adjuster has been backed off approximately 12 notches. Heavy drag at this point indicates tight parking brake cables.

3. Install adjusting hole cover and check parking brake adjustment.

CAUTION

If finger movement will not turn the screw, free it up. If this is not done, the actuator will not turn the screw during subsequent vehicle operation. Lubricate the screw with oil and coat with wheel bearing grease. Any other adjustment procedure may cause damage to the adjusting screw with consequent self-adjuster problems.

4. Install wheel and drum, and adjusting hole cover. Adjust brakes on remaining wheels in the same manner.
5. If pedal height is not satisfactory, drive the vehicle and make sufficient reverse stops until proper pedal height is obtained.

PARKING BRAKE, ADJUST
1967-72 All;
1966 Special, Skylark, G.S. 350, 400

Need for parking brake adjustment is indicated if the service brake operates

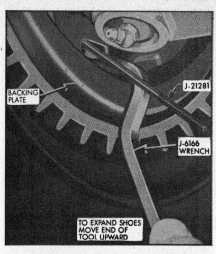

Fig. 8   Adjusting brakes. 1966-72

with good pedal reverse but the parking brake pedal can be depressed more than eight ratchet clicks under heavy foot pressure. After making certain that service brakes are properly adjusted, adjust parking brake mechanism as follows:

1. Depress parking brake pedal exactly three ratchet clicks.
2. Loosen jam nut located at rear of equalizer adjusting nut.
3. Tighten adjusting nut until rear wheels can just be turned rearward, using two hands, but are locked when forward motion is attempted.
4. Release parking brake ratchet one click. At this two-click engagement the rear wheels should rotate forward with a light drag and rearward freely.
5. Release mechanism one more click. At this engagement as well as with mechanism totally disengaged, rear wheels should turn freely in either direction.

1966 Senior Series

Adjustment of the parking brake is necessary whenever the rear brake cables have been disconnected or when the cables have stretched due to extended use. Also to insure proper functioning of the parking brake, the idler lever must have approximately 3/8 in. clearance in slot in frame when parking lever is fully released. Need for parking brake adjustment is indicated if service brake operates with a good pedal reserve but the parking brake ratchets more than eight clicks when depressed.

1. Make brake adjustment as outlined above.
2. Check for correct position of idler lever in frame with parking brake fully released. If necessary, adjust front cable clevis.
3. Depress parking brake pedal exactly two ratchet clicks.
4. Tighten rear cable adjusting nut until rear wheels can just be turned forward using both hands (heavy two-hand drag).
5. Release parking brake lever and check both rear wheels to make sure they turn freely in either direction.

---

slip yoke by taping or wiring a cloth over the entire front U-joint.
2. Slide complete propeller shaft forward through frame tunnel.
3. Remove protecting cover from front U-joint. Fill space between lips of transmission seal with wheel bearing grease and apply a thin coat of the same grease to the seal surface of the front U-joint.
4. Slide front U-joint yoke forward over splines of transmission shaft.
5. Compress two loose bearings of rear U-joint toward each other using a 4" C-clamp. This allows the bearings to seat in the pinion flange without the snap rings gouging the locating surfaces of the pinion flange while entering.
6. Install U-bolt clamps, lock plates and nuts. Draw nuts up evenly and torque to 13 ft. lbs, using a 1/2" extension. *Over-tightening U-bolt nuts distorts the bearings, causing a binding on the spider which can cause drive line shudder and also reduce the life of bearings and spider.*
7. Bend lock plate tabs against nuts.
8. Install two bolts in center bearing support and torque to 20 ft. lbs.
9. Make certain propeller shaft slip spline and center ball stud seat are fully lubricated.

REAR U-JOINT ANGLE

If drive line shudder, roughness, vibration, or rumble is experienced, it may be due to incorrect rear universal joint angle and this angle should be checked. Also, if there is a severe rear end collision, or if the axle housing or any control arms are replaced, the tear universal joint angle should be checked and corrected if necessary. To make the check, however, special Alignment Set No. J-8973 must be used. Inasmuch as this equipment is not likely to be found in general repair shops, it is recommended that a Buick dealer having this equipment do the work.

BRAKE ADJUSTMENTS
1966-72 Self-Adjusting Brakes

These brakes, Fig. 7, have self-adjusting shoe mechanisms that assure correct lining-to-drum clearances at all times.

MASTER CYLINDER, REPLACE
1967-72

1. Disconnect brake pipes from master cylinder and tape end of pipes to prevent entrance of dirt.
2. On manual brakes, disconnect brake pedal from master cylinder push rod.
3. Remove two nuts holding master cylinder to dash or power cylinder and remove master cylinder from car.

1966

1. Remove connector from stop light switch. Disconnect brake pipe from master cylinder and tape end of pipe to prevent entrance of dirt.
2. Disconnect brake pedal from master cylinder push rod by removing safety washer and retainer.

3. Remove nuts holding master cylinder to dash panel and remove cylinder from car.

POWER BRAKE UNIT
1967-72

1. Disconnect brake pipes from master cylinder and tape ends of pipes to prevent entrance of dirt. Disconnect vacuum hose from cylinder.
2. Remove four nuts holding power unit to dash.
3. Remove retainer and washer from brake pedal pin and disengage push rod eye or clevis.
4. Remove power unit from car.

1966 Senior Series

1. Remove connector from stop light switch and disconnect brake pipe from master cylinder.

2. Remove retainer and special washer from brake pedal pin and disengage push rod eye.
3. Remove four nuts holding power cylinder to dash panel.
4. Disconnect vacuum hoses from tee.
5. Remove power cylinder.

1966 Special & Skylark

1. To remove unit, first remove stop light switch wires.
2. Disconnect hydraulic line. Plug or tape line to prevent dirt from entering hydraulic system.
3. Disconnect vacuum hoses from top of bellows unit.
4. Disconnect air supply hose from unit.
5. Disconnect pedal push rod from pedal.
6. Unfasten and remove brake nut from cowl.
7. Reverse removal procedure to install the unit and bleed the system in the conventional manner.

Front End and Steering Section

FRONT SUSPENSION
1971-72 Senior Series

The strut rod and lower control arm used previously are replaced by a wide span lower control arm. The brake reaction rod is no longer used.

1966-72 G.S. 350, 400, Special, Skylark

Referring to Fig. 1, the upper control arms have threaded steel bushings that are screwed into the inner ends of the arms (1969-72 models use rubber bushings at these locations). A ball joint is riveted to the outer end of the upper arm and is spring loaded to insure proper alignment of the ball in the socket.

The inner end of the lower control arm has pressed-in bushings. Two bolts, passing through the bushings, attach the arm to the frame. The lower ball joint is a press fit in the arm and attaches to the steering knuckle with a castellated nut that is retained with a cotter pin.

Rubber seals are provided on upper and lower shafts and at ball socket assemblies to exclude dirt and moisture from bearing surfaces. Grease fittings are provided at all bearing locations.

SERVICE BULLETIN

Wheel Bolt Replaced: Wheel bolts should not be pressed out of a front hub. A shoulder is formed on each bolt by a swaging operation when the bolts are pressed into the hub and drum during manufacture. Pressing out a swaged bolt enlarges the bolt hole in the hub and drum, making it impossible to install the new bolt tightly.

The method recommended to remove the bolt is to secure the hub and drum in a vise, and mark the center of the bolt head with a center punch. Drill a $\frac{1}{8}$ in. pilot hole in the head of the bolt, and then redrill with a $\frac{9}{16}$ in. bit. Use a chisel to cut off a portion of the bolt head, and then drive out the bolt with a drift. Press the new wheel bolt into place to complete the job.

1966-70 Senior Series

Referring to Fig. 2, the lower control arm assembly consists of two stamped steel plates welded together. The inner ends of the lower control arms are bolted to the frame front crossmember through rubber bushings. The outer end of each arm is connectd to the steering knuckle with a ball joint assembly pressed into the lower control arm and bolted to the steering knuckle. The lower ball joint can be removed for service replacement. Position of the lower control arms is maintained by a brake reaction rod mounted between the lower control arm and frame.

To resist fore and aft movement of the lower control arm in relation to the frame, two solid steel brake reaction rods are positioned between the lower control arms and front of frame side rails. The forward ends of the rods are rubber mounted to hold securely to the frame bracket with nuts and cotter pins. The rearward end of the brake reaction rod attaches to the lower control arm with two bolts.

Special hardened flat washers are used under the bolts and nuts to aid in maintaining required torque. The brake reaction rod must be properly installed and secured prior to checking caster and camber.

The upper control arms consist of a single stamped steel plate. Two replaceable hardened steel bushings are threaded into the inner end of each assembly. 1969 models use rubber bushings at these locations. A ball joint is positioned through the outer end of each arm.

NOTE

The upper ball joint is pressed into the control arm and is serviced only as part of the control arm-ball joint assembly.

IMPORTANT

The front suspension is initially lubricated with a special lubricant (Buick Specification No. 742). Every 6000 miles or six months, whichever occurs first, this lubricant or its equivalent should be used. If lubricants other than this type is used the lubrication interval should be shortened and should not exceed 2000 miles.

WHEEL ALIGNMENT
1966-72

Caster and camber are adjusted by shimming at the upper control arm shaft attaching points.

Adding shims at the front locations will change caster toward negative with practically no change in camber. Adding shims at the rear locations will change caster toward positive and camber toward negative. Adding equal shims at both front and rear locations will not change caster but will change camber toward negative.

To adjust, loosen both front and rear bolts to free shims for removal or addition. After installing or removing shims

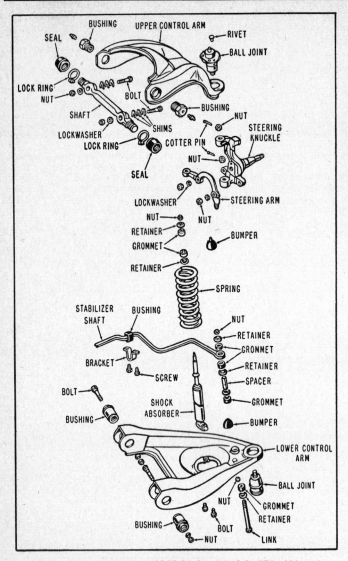

Fig. 1 Front suspension. 1966-68 Special, G.S. 350, 400 and Skylark. For 1969-72, rubber bushings are used at the upper shaft ends

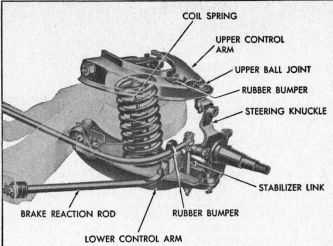

Fig. 2 Front suspension. 1966-70 Senior Series. Rubber bushings are used at upper shaft ends in 1969-70

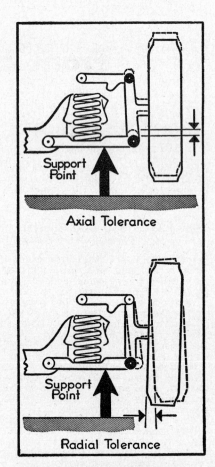

Fig. 3 Checking ball joints for wear

(limit to .380″ in any one stack) tighten and torque shaft bolts to 75 ft. lbs.

TOE-IN, ADJUST
1966-72

IMPORTANT

Car must be at curb weight and running height; bounce front end and allow it to settle at running height. Steering gear and front wheel bearings must be properly adjusted with no looseness at tie rod ends. The car should be moved forward one complete revolution of the wheels before the toe-in check and adjustment is started and the car should never be moved backward while making the check and adjustment.

With front wheels in the straight ahead position, toe-in is adjusted by turning the tie rod adjusting sleeves as required. Left and right adjusting sleeves must be turned exactly the same amount but in opposite directions in order to maintain front wheels in straight ahead position when steering wheel is in straight ahead position.

IMPORTANT

The steering knuckle and steering arm "rock" or tilt as front wheel rises and falls. Therefore, it is vitally important to position the bottom face of the tie rod end parallel with the machined surface at the outer end of the steering arm when tie rod length is adjusted. Severe damage and possible failure can result unless this precaution is taken. The tie rod sleeve clamps must be straight down to 45° forward to provide clearance.

WHEEL BEARINGS, ADJUST
1969-72 All

1. Hand spin wheel in a forward direction and while wheel is spinning, snug up spindle nut to 19 ft. lbs. to fully seat bearings.
2. Back off nut ¼ to ½ turn and retorque to 11 ft. lbs.
3. Snug up spindle nut by hand. Do not install cotter pin if hole in spindle lines up with a slot in spindle nut.
4. Loosen spindle nut 1/12 to 1/6 turn then insert cotter pin.

5. With bearings properly adjusted, there will be from .002-.006" end play.

1966-68 Special, G.S. 350, 400, Skylark

1. Torque spindle nut to 19 ft-lb while rotating wheel. Back off nut and re-torque to 11 ft-lb.
2. If spindle hole lines up a nut slot, back off nut 1/6 turn and insert cotter pin.
3. If neither spindle hole lines up with nut slot, back off nut a maximum of 3/12 of a turn and install cotter pin.
4. Before installation of grease cap in hub, make sure end of spindle and inside of cap are free of grease so that radio static collector makes good contact. Make sure that static collector is properly shaped to provide good contact between end of spindle and grease cap.

1966-68 Senior Series

1. Torque spindle nut to 19 ft-lb while rotating wheel.
2. Back off nut until bearings are loose.
3. Retighten nut to 11 ft-lb while rotating wheel.
4. If either cotter pin hole in spindle lines up with slot in nut, back off nut 1/12 turn and install cotter pin. A 1/6 turn is maximum allowable back-up to align hole with slot.
5. Before installing grease cap in hub, make sure that end of spindle and inside of cap are free of grease so radio static collector makes good contact. Be sure static collector is properly shaped to provide good contact.

WHEEL BEARINGS, REPLACE

(Disc Brakes)

1. Raise car and remove front wheels.
2. Remove tube support bracket bolt. Do not disconnect hydraulic tube or hose.
3. Remove cliper to mounting bracket bolts. Hang caliper from upper suspension.

NOTE: Do not place strain on brake line.

4. Remove spindle nut and hub and disc assembly. Inner wheel bearing and grease retainer can now be removed.

CHECKING BALL JOINTS FOR WEAR

If loose ball joints are suspected, first be sure front wheel bearings are properly adjusted and that control arms are tight. Then check ball joints as follows: Referring to Fig. 3, raise the wheel with a jack placed under the lower control arm at the point shown. Then test by moving the wheel up and down to check

axial play, and rocking it at the top and bottom to measure radial play.

1. Upper ball joint should be replaced if there is any noticeable looseness at this joint.
2. Lower ball joint should be replaced if radial play exceeds .250".
3. Lower ball joint should be replaced if axial play between lower control arm and spindle exceeds the following tolerances:
   1966-70 Senior Series . . . . .100"
   1966-72 Intermediate Models .070"
   1971-72 Senior Series 1
1—With ball joint dislodged from steering knuckle, install stud nut. Rotating torque should be 2-10 ft. lbs.

BALL JOINTS, REPLACE

NOTE: On all models the upper ball joint is spring-loaded in its socket. If the ball stud has any perceptible shake or if it can be twisted with the fingers, the ball joint should be replaced.

The lower ball joint is not spring-loaded and depends upon car weight to load the ball. The lower ball joint should never be replaced merely because it "feels" loose when in an unloaded condition.

Upper ball joints are pressed into the control arm and are not serviced separately. Lower ball joints are also pressed in but can be replaced.

CAUTION: When servicing lower ball joints, be sure to support lower control arm with a suitable jack. If lower control arm is not supported and steering knuckle is disconnected from control arm, the heavily compressed front spring will be completely released.

SHOCK ABSORBER, REPLACE

Unfasten shock absorber top and bottom and remove it through the spring seat. Check shock absorber for obvious physical damage or oil leakage. Push and pull shock absorber in an upright position. If smooth hydraulic resistance is not present in both directions, replace shock absorber.

SPRING, REPLACE

1. Raise car and support with jack stands under frame. Remove wheel with hub and drum.
2. Disconnect stabilizer link from lower control arm and remove shock absorber.
3. Support lower control arm with a suitable floor jack to take up tension of front spring. Disconnect lower control arm ball joint stud from steering knuckle.

CAUTION: Be sure lower control arm is properly supported before disconnecting ball stud.

4. Lower floor jack under spring until

spring is fully extended and remove spring.
5. Complete the installation in the reverse order of removal.

MANUAL STEERING GEAR, REPLACE

1966-72 All Models

1. Remove two nuts or pinch bolt securing lower coupling to steering shaft flange.
2. Use a suitable puller to remove pitman arm.
3. Unfasten gear (3 bolts) from frame and remove from car.

POWER STEERING, REPLACE

1967-72

1. Disconnect pressure and return line hoses at steering gear and elevate ends of hoses higher than pump to prevent oil from draining out of pump.
2. Remove pinch bolt securing coupling to steering gear.
3. Jack up car and remove pitman shaft nut, then use a suitable puller to remove pitman arm.
4. On Senior models, remove sheet metal baffle that covers frame-to-gear attaching bolts.
5. Loosen the three frame-to-steering gear bolts and remove steering gear.

1966 Special & Skylark

1. Disconnect pressure and return line hoses at steering gear and elevate ends of hoses higher than pump to prevent oil from draining out of pump.
2. Remove two nuts securing gear coupling lower flange to steering shaft coupling.
3. Jack up car and remove pitman shaft nut, then remove pitman arm with a puller.
4. Unfasten gear from frame and remove from car.

1966 Senior Series

1. To remove the assembly, disconnect pressure and return line hoses at steering gear and elevate ends of hoses higher than pump to prevent oil from draining out of pump.
2. Disconnect flexible coupling by removing two bolts which attach coupling to steering shaft or flanges. (Flexible coupling is installed on gear box spline and secured by one pinch bolt.)
3. Remove pitman arm.
4. Unfasten and remove steering gear from frame.
5. To install, reverse removal procedure.
6. Check toe-in after installation.
7. Bleed system by turning steering wheel throughout its range until all air bubbles cease to appear in power steering oil reservoir.

CADILLAC

OLD CAR SPECIFICATIONS: For 1946-65 Tune Up and Wheel Alignment Specifications see back of book.

*This material covered only in the "Service Trade Section" of this manual.

INDEX OF SERVICE OPERATIONS

VEHICLE IDENTIFICATION NUMBER LOCATION: 1966-67 On rear portion of block behind intake manifold and on top surface of right frame side rail.

On 1968-72 models the Vehicle identification Number is located on rear upper portion of cylinder block, behind intake manifold and on left side of transmission.

ENGINE UNIT NUMBER LOCATION: 1966-67 Rear of left cylinder bank below Cylinder head. On 1968-72 at rear of cylinder block.

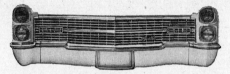

1966

1967 Eldorado

1967 Except Eldorado

1968 Eldorado

1968 Except Eldorado

1969 Eldorado

1969 Except Eldorado

1970 Eldorado

1970 Except Eldorado

1971 Except Eldorado

1971 Eldorado

1972 Eldorado

1972 Except Eldorado

CADILLAC

GENERAL ENGINE SPECIFICATIONS

Year	Engine	Carburetor	Bore and Stroke	Piston Displacement, Cubic Inches	Compression Ratio	Maximum Brake H.P. @ R.P.M.	Maximum Torque Lbs. Ft. @ R.P.M.	Normal Oil Pressure Pounds
1966–67	340 Horsepower..............V8-429	4 Barrel	4.1300 x 4.000	429	10.50	340 @ 4600	480 @ 3000	30–35
1968–69	375 Horsepower..............V8-472	4 Barrel	4.3000 x 4.060	472	10.50	375 @ 4400	525 @ 3000	30–35
1970	375 Horsepower..............V8-472	4 Barrel	4.3000 x 4.060	472	10.00	375 @ 4400	525 @ 3000	35–40
	400 Horsepower..............V8-500	4 Barrel	4.3000 x 4.304	500	10.00	400 @ 4400	550 @ 3000	35–40
1971	345 Horsepower..............V8-472	4 Barrel	4.3000 x 4.060	472	8.50	345 @ 4400	500 @ 2800	35–40
	365 Horsepower..............V8-500	4 Barrel	4.3000 x 4.304	500	8.50	365 @ 4400	535 @ 2800	35–40
1972	220 Horsepower① V8-472	4 Barrel	4.300 x 4.060	472	8.50	220 @ 4000	365 @ 2400	35–40
	235 Horsepower① V8-500	4 Barrel	4.300 x 4.304	500	8.50	235 @ 3800	385 @ 2400	35–40

①—Net rating—as installed in the vehicle.

VALVE SPECIFICATIONS

Year	Model	Valve Lash	Valve Angles		Valve Spring Installed Height	Valve Spring Pressure Lbs. @ In.	Stem Clearance		Stem Diameter	
			Seat	Face			Intake	Exhaust	Intake	Exhaust
1966–70	All	Hydraulic①	45	44	1¹⁵⁄₁₆	160 @ 1½	.0005–.0025	.001–.0025	.3415–.3425	.3415–.3420
1971	All	Hydraulic①	45	44	1¹⁵⁄₁₆	160 @ 1½	.0005–.0025	.001–.0025	.3413–.3420	.3415–.3420
1972	All	Hydraulic①	45	44	1⁶¹⁄₆₄	168 @ 1½	.0010–.0027	.0012–.0027	.3413–.3420	.3413–.3418

①—No adjustment.

DISTRIBUTOR SPECIFICATIONS

★NOTE: If advance is checked on vehicle, double the R.P.M. and degrees advance to get crankshaft figures.

Year	Model	Distributor Part No.①	Breaker Gap	Dwell Angle Deg.	Breaker Arm Spring Tension	Centrifugal Advance Degrees @ R.P.M. of Distributor★		Vacuum Advance		Dist. Retard
						Advance Starts	Full Advance	Inches of Vacuum To Start Plunger	Max. Adv. Dist. Deg. @ Vacuum	Max. Ret. Dist. Deg. @ Vacuum
1966		1111131	②	30	19–23	1 @ 400	8 @ 2000	7.5–9.5	12 @ 15	—
1967	Early	1111259	②	30	19–23	1 @ 400	8 @ 2000	7.5–9.5	12 @ 15	—
	Late	1111262	②	30	19–23	1 @ 400	7 @ 2000	7.5–9.5	12 @ 15	—
1968	All	1111239	②	30	19–23	1 @ 400	13 @ 2000	8–10	12 @ 13	—
1969–70	All	1111939	②	30	19–23	1 @ 400	13 @ 2000	8–10	12 @ 13	—
1971	All	1112065	②	30	19–23	1 @ 400	13 @ 2000	8–10	12¾ @ 16	—
1972	All	1112108	②	30	19–23	1 @ 400	13 @ 2000	8–10	12¾ @ 16	—

①—Stamped on distributor housing plate.   ②—Turn adjusting screw to the right until engine misfires. Then turn screw ½ turn to the left.

TUNE UP SPECIFICATIONS

OLD CAR SPECIFICATIONS: For 1946-65 Tune Up Specifications see back of book.

★When using a timing light, disconnect vacuum hose or tube at distributor and plug opening in hose or tube so idle speed will not be affected.

Year	Engine	Spark Plug		Distributor		Firing Order	Ignition Timing ★		Hot Idle Speed		Comp. Press. Lbs. ③	Fuel Pump Press. Lbs.
		Type AC	Gap Inch	Point Gap Inch	Dwell Angle Deg.		BTDC ①	Mark	Std. Trans.	Auto. Trans. ②		
1966	Standard Cars	44	.035	⑤	30	Fig. D	5°	Fig. B	—	480D④	175	5¼–6½
	With A.I.R.	44	.035	⑤	30	Fig. D	5°	Fig. B	—	550D④	175	5¼–6½
	With A.I.R. and A/C	44	.035	⑤	30	Fig. D	5°	Fig. B	—	550D④	175	5¼–6½
1967	Without A.I.R.	44	.035	⑤	30	Fig. D	5°	Fig. B	—	480D④	175	5¼–6½
	With A.I.R.	44	.035	⑤	30	Fig. D	5°	Fig. B	—	550D④	175	5¼–6½
	With A.I.R. and A/C	44	.035	⑤	30	Fig. D	5°	Fig. B	—	550D④	175	5¼–6½
1968	All	44N	.035	⑤	30	Fig. C	5°	Fig. B	—	550D④	175	5¼–6½
1969	All	R44N	.035	⑤	30	Fig. C	5°	Fig. B	—	550D④	175	5¼–6½
1970	All	R46N	.035	⑤	30	Fig. C	7½°	Fig. A	—	600D④	220	5¼–6½
1971–72	All	R46N	.035	⑤	30	Fig. C	8°	Fig. E	—	600D④	220	5¼–6½

①—BTDC: Before top dead center.

②—D: Drive. N: Neutral.

③—Plus or minus 20 lbs.

④—When making adjustments, air conditioner must be turned off (if equipped). Also, hose must be disconnected at vacuum release cylinder. The hot idle compensator must be closed; this can be done by pressing finger or eraser end of pencil on compensator. On 1968 units, compensator pin is just in front of primary throttle bores; on 1967 compensator is located in air horn vent stack just to left rear of secondary metering rod hanger; on 1966 units brass valve located in secondary side of unit.

On 1966 models, to set stator blades for proper performance, remove pink wire from contact fitting on transmission downshift switch and connect to white wire fitting with alligator clip; this will activate stator switch.

⑤—Turn adjusting screw in (clockwise) until engine begins to misfire; then back screw out ½ turn.

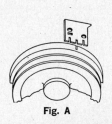

Fig. A

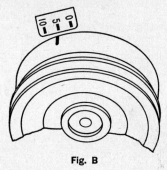

Fig. B

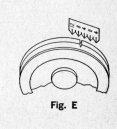

Fig. E

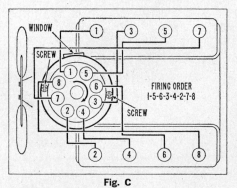

Fig. C

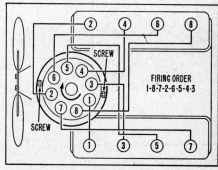

Fig. D

CADILLAC

STARTING MOTOR SPECIFICATIONS

Year	Model	Starter Number	Brush Spring Tension Oz①	Free Speed Test			Resistance Test③	
				Amps.	Volts	R.P.M.	Amps.	Volts
1966-67	Exc. 75, Eldo.	1107367	35	70–105②	10.6	7800–12000	480–540②	3.0
1966	Series 75	1107368	35	70–105②	10.6	7800–12000	480–540②	3.0
1967	Eldorado	1107389	35	70–99②	10.6	7800–12000	435–535②	3.0
1968-70;	Std. Cars	1108381	35	70–99②	10.6	7800–12000	435–455②	3.0
1972	Eldorado	1108352	35	70–99②	10.6	7800–12000	435–455②	3.0
1971	Std. Cars	1108371	—	—	—	—	—	—
	Eldorado	1107389	35	70–99②	10.6	7800–12000	435–535②	3.0

①—Minimum. ②—Includes solenoid.
③—Check capacity of motor by using a 500-ampere meter and a carbon pile rheostat to control voltage. Apply volts listed across motor with armature locked. Current should be as listed.

ENGINE TIGHTENING SPECIFICATIONS★

★Torque specifications are for clean and lightly lubricated threads only. Dry or dirty threads produce increased friction which prevents accurate measurement of tightness.

Year	Spark Plugs Ft. Lbs.	Cylinder Head Bolts Ft. Lbs.	Intake Manifold Ft. Lbs.	Exhaust Manifold Ft. Lbs.	Rocker Arm Shaft Bracket Ft. Lbs.	Rocker Arm Cover Ft. Lbs.	Connecting Rod Cap Bolts Ft. Lbs.	Main Bearing Cap Bolts Ft. Lbs.	Flex Plate to Crankshaft Ft. Lbs.	Vibration Damper or Pulley Ft. Lbs.
1966	25	60	②	60④	75	28①	40	95	75	15③
1967	25	60	②	60④	—	28①	40	95	75	15③
1968-72	25	115	30	35	—	24①	40	90	75	17

①—Inch pounds. Retorque after engine has been run. ②—Bolt 30, nut 25. ③—Pulley to damper screws. ④—50 ft.-lbs. on engines with no gaskets.

WHEEL ALIGNMENT SPECIFICATIONS

OLD CAR SPECIFICATIONS: For 1946-65 Wheel Alignment Specifications see back of book.

Year	Model	Caster Angle, Degrees		Camber Angle, Degrees				Toe-In. Inch	Toe-Out on Turns, Deg.	
		Limits	Desired	Limits		Desired			Outer Wheel	Inner Wheel
				Left	Right	Left	Right			
1966	All	−1½ to −½	−1	−⅛ to +⅜	−⅜ to +⅛	Zero	−¼	3/16 to ¼	20	20°11'
1967-68	Eldorado	−⅜ to +⅜	Zero	−1½ to +2½	−1½ to −2½	Zero	Zero	0 to ⅛	18⅙	20
	All Others	−½ to −1½	−1	+⅜ to −⅛	+⅛ to −⅜	Zero	−¼	3/16 to ¼	18⅙	20
1969-70	Eldorado	−1½ to −2½	−2	+⅜ to −⅜	+⅜ to −⅜	Zero	Zero	0 to ⅛	18⅙	20
	All Others	−½ to −1½	−1	+⅜ to −⅜	+⅜ to −⅜	Zero	Zero	⅛ to ¼	18⅙	20
1971-72	Eldorado	−½ to −1½	−1	+⅜ to −⅜	+⅜ to −⅜	Zero	Zero	0 to 1/16	—	—
	All Others	−½ to −1½	−1	+⅜ to −⅜	+⅝ to −⅜	Zero	−¼	⅛ to ¼	—	—

BRAKE SPECIFICATIONS

Year	Model	Brake Drum Inside Diameter	Wheel Cylinder Bore Diameter			Master Cylinder Bore Diameter		
			Disc Brake	Front Drum Brake	Rear Drum Brake	Disc Brakes	Drum Brakes	Power Brakes
1966	All	12④	—	1 3/16	1	—	1	1
1967	Series 75	12	—	1 3/16	1	—	1	1
	Eldorado	11	1 15/16	1 1/8	7/8	1	1	1
	All Others	12	—	1 3/16	15/16	—	1	1
1968	Series 75	12	2 3/4	1 3/16	7/8 ②	1	1	1
	Eldorado	11	1 15/16	1 1/8	13/16 ③	1	1	1
	All Others	12	2 3/4	1 3/16	13/16 ①	1	1	1
1969–70	Series 75	12	2 3/4	—	7/8	1	—	1
	Eldorado	11	2 15/16	—	7/8	1	—	1
	All Others	12	2 3/4	—	13/16	1	—	1
1971–72	Eldorado	11	2 15/16	—	15/16	1 1/8	—	1 1/8
	Others	12	2 15/16	—	15/16	1 1/8	—	1 1/8

①—Cars with front drums 15/16".
②—Cars with front drums 1".
③—Cars with front drums 7/8".
④—Plus or minus .005".

COOLING SYSTEM & CAPACITY DATA

Year	Model or Engine	Cooling Capacity, Qts.			Radiator Cap Relief Pressure, Lbs.		Thermo. Opening Temp. ①	Fuel Tank Gals.	Engine Oil Refill Qts. ③	Transmission Oil			Rear Axle Oil Pints
		No Heater	With Heater	With A/C	With A/C	No. A/C				3 Speed Pints	4 Speed Pints	Auto. Trans. Qts. ⑩	
1966	Except 75	—	17.2	18.2	15	15	175	26	4	—	—	⑥	5
	Series 75	—	—	20.7	15	15	175	26	4	—	—	⑥	5
1967	Eldorado	16	17	17 1/2	15	15	⑦	24	4	—	—	⑨	4 1/2 ⑭
	Series 75	—	18	19	15	15	⑦	20	4	—	—	⑥	5
	Others	16	18	20 1/2	15	15	⑦	26	4	—	—	⑧	5
1968–69	Eldorado	—	20.3	20.8	15	15	195	24	5	—	—	⑨	4 1/2 ⑭
	Series 75	—	23.8 ⑬	23.8 ⑬	15	15	195	20	4	—	—	⑧	5
	Others	—	20.3 ⑪	20.8 ⑫	15	15	195	26	4	—	—	⑧	5
1970	Eldorado	—	21.3	21.3	15	15	180	24 ⑮	5	—	—	⑯	4 1/2 ⑭
	Series 75	—	21.8	21.8	15	15	180	26 ⑮	4	—	—	⑰	5
	Others	—	21.3	21.3	15	15	180	26 ⑮	4	—	—	⑰	5
1971–72	Eldorado	—	21.3	21.8	15	15	180	27	5	—	—	⑯	4 ⑭
	Series 75	—	—	24.8	15	15	180	27	4	—	—	⑰	5
	Others	—	21.3	21.8	15	15	180	27	4	—	—	⑰	5

①—For permanent anti-freeze.
③—Add one quart with filter change.
⑥—Oil pan 3 qts. Total capacity 11 qts.
⑦—With A/C 185° without A/C 195°
⑧—Oil pan 2 qts. Total capacity 12 1/2 qts.
⑨—Oil pan 5 qts. Total capacity 13 qts.
⑩—Approximate. Make final check with dipstick.
⑪—1969, 21.3 qts.
⑫—1969, 21.8 qts.
⑬—1969, 24.8 qts.
⑭—Front drive axle.
⑮—California vehicles approx. 2 gallons less.
⑯—Oil pan 6 qts. Total capacity 13 qts.
⑰—Oil pan 4 qts. Total capacity 12 1/2 qts.

CADILLAC

ALTERNATOR & REGULATOR SPECIFICATIONS

| Year | Model | Alternator |||| Regulator |||||||
| | | Rated Hot Output Amps. | Field Current 12 Volts @ 80° F. | Output @ 14 Volts || Model | Field Relay ||| Voltage Regulator |||
				2000 R.P.M. Amps.	5000 R.P.M. Amps.		Air Gap In.	Point Gap In.	Closing Voltage	Air Gap In.	Point Gap In.	Voltage @ 125° F.
1966–70	1100742	63	2.8–3.2	35	59	1119519	.015	.030	1.5–2.7	.067	.014	13.5–14.3
1967–70	1100696	42	2.2–2.6	28	40	1119515	.015	.030	2.3–3.7	.060	.014	13.5–14.4
	1100694	55	2.2–2.6	32	50	1119515	.015	.030	2.3–3.7	.060	.014	13.5–14.4
1966	1100691	42	2.2–2.6	28	40	1119515	.015	.030	2.3–3.7	.060	.014	13.5–14.4
	1100692	55	2.2–2.6	32	50	1119515	.015	.030	2.3–3.7	.060	.014	13.5–14.4
1971–72	1100558	42	2.2–2.6	—	—	1119515	.015	.030	2.3–3.7	.060	.014	13.8–14.8
	1100940	42	2.2–2.6	—	—	—	—	—	—	—	—	
	1100557	63	2.8–3.2	—	—	1119519	—	—	—	—	—	13.8–14.8
	1100937	63	2.8–3.2	—	—	—	—	—	—	—	—	
	1101015	80	4.0–4.5	—	—	—	—	—	—	—	—	

PISTONS, PINS, RINGS, CRANKSHAFT & BEARINGS

| Year | Model | Fitting Pistons || Ring End Gap① || Wrist-pin Diameter | Rod Bearings || Main Bearings ||||
		Shim To Use	Pounds Pull On Scale	Comp.	Oil		Shaft Diameter	Bearing Clearance	Shaft Diameter	Bearing Clearance	Thrust on Bear. No.	Shaft End Play
1966–67	All	②	②	.013	.015	.9995	2.2488–2.2493	.0005–.0021	3.000	.0008–.0029	3	.001–.007
1968–70	All	②	②	.013	.015	.9995	2.500	.0005–.0028	3.250	.0003–.0026	3	.002–.012
1971–72	All	②	②	.013	.015	.9995	2.500	.0005–.0028	3.250	.0001–.0026	3	.002–.012

①—Fit rings in tapered bores for clearance given in tightest portion of ring travel.   ②—See text under "Pistons".

Electrical Section

DISTRIBUTOR, REPLACE

1. Remove distributor cap.
2. Disconnect primary wire from coil.
3. Disconnect vacuum advance pipe or hose from distributor.
4. Crank engine until rotor is pointing to No. 1 spark plug wire position on cap.
5. Remove distributor hold-down nut and clamp.
6. Lift distributor from engine.
7. Note that the rotor will turn slightly as the drive gear becomes disengaged from the camshaft gear. Therefore, when installing the distributor, the rotor should be turned slightly counter-clockwise from No. 1 spark plug position to insure proper engagement of gears. When properly installed, rotor should point directly to No. 1 spark plug position.

STARTER, REPLACE
1972

1. Disconnect battery ground cable at battery.
2. On Eldorado, disconnect starter harness at connector at right rear of engine.
3. Raise front end of car.
4. On models except Eldorado, disconnect battery lead at starter solenoid terminal and disconnect neutral switch wire and coil feed wire at starter solenoid terminals.
5. On Eldorado, remove spring clip securing wire to solenoid housing.
6. Remove screw and nut securing support bracket to starter and crankcase.
7. Unfasten starter motor from crankcase and remove starter by pulling it forward, then toward RH front wheel and up over steering linkage toward rear of car.

1967 Eldorado, All 1968-71

1. Disconnect ground strap at battery.
2. Raise and support front end of car.
3. Disconnect battery lead at starter solenoid terminal.
4. Disconnect neutral safety switch wire and coil feed wire at starter solenoid.
5. Remove spring clip securing wires to solenoid housing.
6. Unfasten starter (2 screws) and remove starter by pulling it forward and then lowering it straight down.
7. Reverse procedure to install.

1966-67 Except Eldorado

1. Disconnect battery ground cable.
2. Raise front of car and place on jack stands.
3. Disconnect battery lead at starter solenoid.
4. Disconnect neutral safety switch wire and coil feed wire at starter solenoid terminals.
5. Remove spring clip securing wires to solenoid housing.

6. Remove two screws that hold starter motor lower brace between starter housing and transmission on lower cover and remove brace.
7. Remove starter upper mounting bolt.
8. Remove two special screws that hold starter to engine.
9. Remove starter by pulling it forward and over transmission cooler pipes, then lower it between idler arm and frame. *It may be necessary to turn front wheels several times to allow starter to be lowered between idler arm and frame.*
10. Reverse procedure to install.

IGNITION SWITCH, REPLACE
1969-72

1. Disconnect battery cable and position ignition key in "Lock".
2. Remove steering column lower cover.
3. Loosen two upper column support nuts and allow column to drop as far

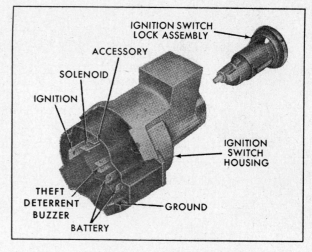

Fig. 1 Ignition switch. 1967-68

as possible without removing the nuts.

NOTE: Do not remove nuts as column may bend under its own weight.

4. Disconnect switch connector and remove switch. Fig. 1A.
5. When reassembling, make sure the ignition key is in the "Lock" position. Assemble switch on actuator rod. Hold rod stationary and move switch towards bottom of column then back off on detent. Install screws and torque to 35 inch lbs.

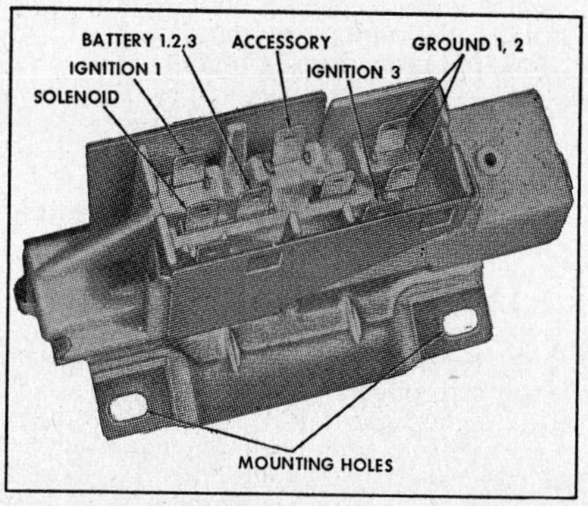

1967-68

1. Remove steering column lower cover.
2. Remove switch lock cylinder by using a paper clip to depress tumbler pin while turning ignition key to the left from accessory position and pulling outward, Fig. 1.
3. Disconnect connector at rear of switch housing.
4. Remove switch mounting nut.
5. Disconnect dial bulb socket at rear of ignition switch housing and remove switch through rear of instrument panel.
6. Reverse procedure to install.

1966

1. Disconnect battery ground cable.
2. Remove right and left windshield garnish moldings (4 screws each side).
3. Separate upper panel cover from upper panel (6 screws).
4. Raise upper panel high enough to disconnect wire connectors at radio speaker, courtesy lights, and for Twilight Sentinel Photocell and Comfort Control sensor (if so equipped).
5. Pull upper panel cover rearward to disengage three hooks at front of

Fig. 1A Ignition switch. 1969-72

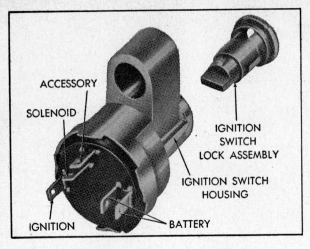

Fig. 2   Ignition switch. 1966

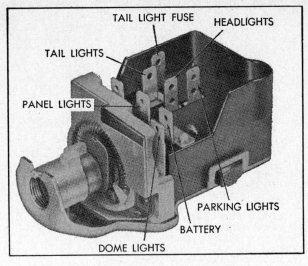

Fig. 3   Headlight switch. 1966-69 1970-72 has no parking light terminal

cover and remove cover.

6. Remove switch lock from switch housing, using a .035″ diameter wire (paper clip) to depress tumbler pin while turning ignition key to the left and pulling outward.
7. Disconnect 4-way connector at rear of ignition switch housing.
8. Remove ignition switch spanner nut.
9. Disconnect dial bulb socket at rear of ignition housing and remove switch through rear of instrument panel.
10. Reverse above procedure to install.

LIGHT SWITCH, REPLACE
1970-72

1. Remove steering column lower cover.
2. Unfasten wiring harness retainer running below switch.
3. Depress button on top of switch and remove knob and rod.
4. Remove screw with ground wire at bottom of switch housing.
5. Pull switch down and rearward and disconnect wire and bulbs.
6. Remove hex head sleeve securing switch to housing case and remove switch.

5/64 INCH ALLEN WRENCH

Fig. 4   Loosening headlight control set screw. 1966

1969

1. Remove instrument panel top cover and steering column lower cover.
2. Remove left A/C duct and outlet and disconnect wiring harness below headlight switch.
3. Depress button on top of switch and remove knob and rod assembly.
4. Remove attaching screws, pull switch rearward and disconnect bulbs and wires and remove switch, Fig. 3.

1967-68

1. Remove steering column lower cover.
2. On Eldorado, remove hoses at vacuum valve, which is integral with headlight valve.
3. Remove lower right screw securing switch housing to lower instrument panel. *This screw has a special ¾″ head and may be removed with a ¼″ socket.*
4. If equipped with Automatic Climate Control, remove left outlet hose at inboard side to gain access to upper left screw.
5. Remove upper left screw securing light switch housing to lower instrument panel. *This screw has a special ¾″ head and may be removed with a ¼″ socket.*
6. Pull light switch rearward, disconnect wire harness connectors, two bulbs and remove switch, Fig. 3.
7. Reverse procedure to install.

1966

1. Disconnect battery ground cable.
2. Loosen set screw securing switch housing to cluster bezel, Fig. 4.
3. Lift upward on bottom of switch housing to disengage upper retainer clip from locating slot in bezel opening, then pull control switch straight out to remove.
4. Disconnect switch housing dial bulb socket from top of housing case.
5. Disconnect trunk warning lens dial bulb socket from bottom of case (if so equipped).

6. If equipped with Guide-Matic and/or Twilight Sentinel, disconnect switch lead connectors.
7. Disconnect multiple wire connector from top of switch and remove switch assembly, Fig. 3.
8. On cars *without* Guide-Matic or Twilight Sentinel, depress spring-loaded release button on bottom of headlight switch and remove switch operating shaft on knob assembly. Remove know and sleeve from switch, Fig. 5.
9. On cars *with* Guide-Matic and/or Twilight Sentinel, depress spring-loaded release button on bottom of switch and remove switch operating shaft and knob. Remove upper retainer clip from housing case (2 screws). Remove housing case from housing (2 screws) with switch attached. Remove hex head sleeve securing switch to case and remove switch from case.
10. Reverse removal procedure to install.

CAUTION: Be sure that tang on switch is aligned with locating notch in housing case before tightening knob and sleeve assembly (hex head sleeve on cars with Guide-Matic and/or Twilight Sentinel). Be sure that Guide-Matic and/or Twi-

7/32 INCH ALLEN WRENCH

Fig. 5   Removing light switch knob and sleeve assembly. 1966

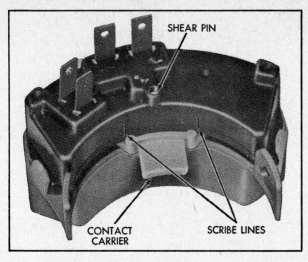

Fig. 6   Switch in neutral position. 1967-72

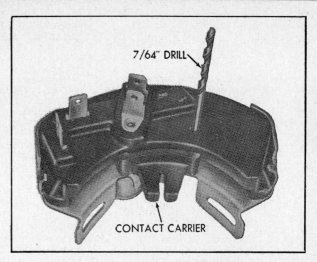

Fig. 7   Switch in neutral position. 1966

light Sentinel control switch leads extend through notch in side of case.

STOP LIGHT SWITCH
1970-72

The stoplight is retained to the brake pedal bracket. To adjust, pull the brake pedal fully up to its stop. This action automatically adjusts the switch.

1966-69

1. Disconnect two leads wires from switch on brake pedal flange.
2. Remove locking nut from switch.
3. Remove stop light switch.
4. Reverse procedure to install.

NOTE: Adjust switch action so that stop light is on when brake pedal is depressed ½". Loosen front and rear nuts that hold switch and move switch up or down until this action is obtained. Tighten switch lock nuts securely to prevent loss of adjustment.

NEUTRAL START SWITCH

NOTE: On all models the neutral switch, back-up light switch and parking brake vacuum release valve are combined into one unit mounted on the steering column under the instrument panel.

1967-72

Removal
1. Place transmission shift lever in neutral.
2. Remove switch from column, being careful not to disturb neutral position of contact carrier, Fig. 6.
3. Mark neutral position of contact carrier.
4. Mark top vacuum hose for identification and remove hoses.
5. Disconnect two wiring connectors from switch.

Installation
1. Place transmission shift lever in neutral detent.
2. Connect two wires to switch.
3. Move contact carrier on switch to neutral position as marked during removal.

NOTE: If necessary to install a new switch, the switch will be secured in neutral by a shear pin. Do not break pin.

4. Install switch on steering column, aligning contact carrier blade with slot in shift tube.
5. Secure switch to steering column with two mounting nuts, making sure that shift lever is in neutral detent while this operation is performed.
6. Connect vacuum hoses to switch as marked during removal.
7. Switch should now be properly adjusted. If new switch was installed, a slightly greater effort to position

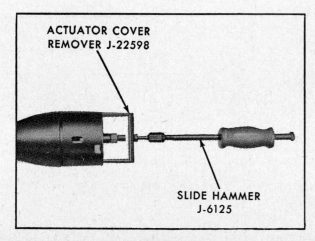

Fig. 8   Removing actuator cover. 1967-68

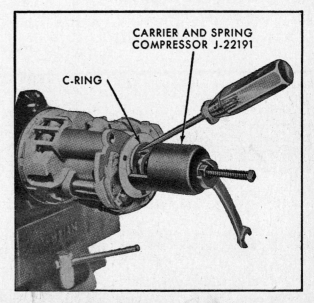

Fig. 9.   Removing C-ring. 1967-72

the shift lever in any position besides neutral will be necessary to break the shear pin.

1966

The removal procedure of the switch assembly is the same as outlined for later models. To install the switch, proceed as follows:

1. Place transmission shift lever in neutral detent.
2. Move contact carrier on switch to neutral position. Neutral position is obtained when a $7/64''$ drill fits hole in contact carrier, Fig. 7.
3. Connect two wires to switch.
4. Install switch on steering column, aligning slot in contact carrier with blade on inner shift tube.
5. Secure switch with two screws, making sure shift lever is centered in neutral detent position while this operation is being performed.
6. Connect vacuum hoses to switch as marked during removal.
7. Remove drill from hole in contact carrier. Switch should now be properly adjusted.
8. Check adjustment by inserting $7/64''$ drill into hole in contact carrier. Drill enters about $3/8''$ into housing when properly aligned. If drill does not enter about $3/8''$, move switch slightly until entry is obtained. Remove drill.

TURN SIGNAL SWITCH, REPLACE

1969-72

Standard Wheel

1. Remove battery cable.
2. Remove steering wheel.
3. Remove lock plate cover screws and cover.
4. With a suitable compressor, compress lock plate and spring and remove snap ring from shaft.
5. Remove lock plate, cancelling cam, preload spring and thrust washer.
6. Remove turn signal lever.
7. Disconnect switch wiring connector and wrap a piece of tape around connector and harness to facilitate removal.
8. Remove upper mounting bracket from column.
9. Remove three retaining screws and remove switch. Reverse procedure to install.

Tilt & Telescope Wheel

1. Disconnect battery cable and remove steering wheel and rubber bump stop.
2. With a suitable tool, compress upper steering shaft pre-load spring and remove C ring, Fig. 9.
3. Remove compressor, lock plate, horn contact, and upper shaft pre-load spring.
4. Disconnect switch wiring connector and wrap a piece of tape around connector and harness to facilitate removal.
5. Remove upper mounting bracket and switch wiring protector.
6. Position shift bowl in "Park" and remove turn signal lever.

7. On Eldorado, disconnect switch and Cruise Control connectors on column and attach a piece of piano wire to connector on Cruise Control harness, unscrew signal lever and gently pull Cruise Control harness up through and out of column. Secure piano wire in column to aid in reassembly.
8. Push hazard warning flasher button in then unscrew and remove button.
9. Remove retaining screws and remove switch.
10. Reverse procedure to install. On Eldorado, use the piece of piano wire previously installed to draw the Cruise Control harness through the column.

1968

Standard Wheel

1. Disconnect battery ground cable.
2. Remove lower steering column cover.
3. Disconnect turn signal switch and cornering switch multiple connectors at lower end of steering column.
4. Cut turn and cornering multiple connectors from wiring harnesses and harness strap on steering column.
5. Remove steering wheel.
6. Slide upper bearing preload spring and turn cancelling cam off steering shaft.
7. Remove turn signal lever.
8. Remove cap from hazard warning switch button. Push switch button in and, after removing screw remove button.
9. Remove snap ring from steering shaft.
10. Slide thrust washer and wave washer off shaft.
11. Loosen three switch mounting screws until assembly can be rotated counterclockwise. It may be necessary to push on top of screws to loosen assembly.
12. Rotate cover counterclockwise and pull assembly off top of jacket.
13. Remove three screws from engagement with lock plate.
14. Remove switch and housing assemblies from cover and separate them.
15. Reverse procedure to install.

Tilt & Telescope Wheel

1. Perform Steps 1 through 5 above.
2. Remove tilt release lever and signal switch lever.
3. Remove cap from hazard warning switch knob.
4. Push in on hazard warning knob and remove screw and knob.
5. Remove actuator cover, using a suitable slide hammer. Rotate slide hammer after each hammer blow to distribute forces evenly around cover, Fig. 8.
6. Remove C-ring as shown in Fig. 9.
7. Remove carrier and spring compressor from column.
8. Remove horn contact carrier.
9. Remove signal switch and hazard warning switch screws.

1967

1. Disconnect battery ground cable.
2. Remove steering column lower cover.
3. Disconnect turn signal harness 9-way and cornering light 3-way "half-moon" connectors.

4. Remove steering wheel horn pad. On T & T column, also remove telescope lock lever.
5. Scribe mark for alignment of steering wheel when replacing, then remove steering wheel.
6. Remove turn signal lever and hazard warning knob. On T & T column, also remove tilt lever, shift lever and actuator cover, Fig. 8.
7. On standard column, remove "C" retaining ring and thrust and wave washers. On T & T column, snip wiring harness at switch, then remove "C" retaining ring, carrier, contact and bumper, and remove switch, Fig. 9.
8. Remove column mounting support bracket and carefully support column with a wood block.
9. Remove wire cover clips from column jacket. On T & T column, pull loose connector and harness out from below. On standard column, remove upper end assembly, pulling wiring up through top of column and remove switch from upper end assembly.
10. Reverse procedure to install.

1966

Standard Wheel

1. Remove steering column lower cover.
2. Remove transmission shift indicator.
3. Remove steering wheel.
4. Remove column lower cover plate.
5. Loosen column upper clamp.
6. Disconnect turn signal switch wires and horn contact wire at connectors under instrument panel.
7. Remove plastic cam from upper end of column shaft.
8. Remove wiring harness shield from jacket.
9. Remove six wires from turn signal-stop light connector by prying collapsible edge of each lead inboard until wire can be pulled through connector. Repeat procedure for three wires at cornering light connector.
10. Separate switch housing from lock plate (6 screws) and pull housing up to remove guide wires through carrier.

NOTE: When performing Step 10 it will be necessary to pull signal switch housing up on shaft until upper bearing seat is free from upper bearing and remove upper bearing seat.

11. Remove wire harness clamp on reverse side of turn signal switch housing.
12. Separate switch from housing (3 screws).
13. Reverse above procedure to install.

Tilt & Telescoping Wheel

1. Disconnect multiple connectors from turn signal switch on side of steering column jacket.
2. Remove turn signal switch from jacket.
3. Disconnect cable from switch by removing one self-tapping screw, and slip coil end of cable off post.

NOTE: When installing switch, raise tilt lever, place tilt mechanism in maximum "down" position and attach cable to switch. Coil end of cable should be slipped over post on switch with wire next to base of post and coil extending outward. Do not twist cable. Install cable in its natural position.

Insert clamp tang in mounting hole and install retaining screw through flag-shaped terminal into switch, locking them together. With turn signal lever in "off" position, install switch on steering column jacket, being certain that switch is centered properly and secured with two screws.

It is not necessary to apply extra tension on cable after switch is installed. Switch should function properly without further adjustment.

HORN SOUNDER & STEERING WHEEL

1969-72

1. Remove three screws from back of spokes and lift pad assembly from wheel.
2. On tilt and telescope wheels remove three screws securing lever and knob assembly to flange and screw assembly. Unscrew flange and screw assembly from steering shaft and remove. Remove lever and knob assembly.
3. On standard wheels, scribe an alignment mark on wheel hub in line with slash mark on steering shaft to be used upon installation.
4. Loosen steering shaft nut, apply a suitable puller to loosen wheel; then remove puller, nut and wheel.
5. Remove three screws securing three contact wires to wheel.
6. Reverse procedure to install.

1966

1. Remove cap from horn control shroud by prying it off carefully.
2. Remove steering shaft nut and washer.
3. Lift horn control shroud and switch assembly from steering wheel. If horn control shroud is to be replaced, remove three screws from underside of horn control and remove control, which is serviced only as an assembly.
4. Remove horn contact cartridge from wheel hub.
5. Scribe an alignment mark on wheel hub in line with slash mark on end of steering shaft to be used at installation.
6. Reinstall nut on steering shaft so that nut is flush with end of shaft.
7. Then use a suitable puller to remove wheel.

INSTRUMENT CLUSTER

1972

1. Disconnect battery ground cable.
2. Remove instrument panel top cover.
3. Remove steering column lower cover.

4. Disconnect speedo cable from speedometer.
5. Remove left hand air conditioner outlet hose from behind cluster.
6. Disconnect cluster connector.
7. Disengage wiring harness from clip at back of cluster and position out of way.
8. Remove screw securing shift pointer to column and remove pointer.
9. Remove four screws (2 upper and 2 lower) securing cluster to bezel.
10. Move cluster back and to right. Tip right hand corner of cluster upward and remove cluster out through top of panel.

1969-71

1. Disconnect battery cable.
2. Remove instrument panel top cover, clock, radio and steering column lower cover.
3. Remove shift indicator pointer.
4. Remove odometer reset knob by pulling if off shaft.
5. Remove four cluster-to-bezel screws.
6. Move cluster forward and to the right. Tip right hand corner of cluster downward and remove cluster from under panel.

1968

1. Remove instrument panel top cover.
2. Remove steering column lower cover.
3. Remove transmission shift indicator pointer with an Allen wrench. Locking screw is accessible through slot on lower edge of shift bowl.
4. Disconnect multiple connector at instrument panel cluster case and remove instrument panel harness from cluster attachment.
5. Disconnect speedometer cable from speedometer head by depressing risers on wave washer. Feed cable back through firewall to protect cable.
6. If equipped with Automatic Climate Control, remove the control left air outlet hose at outboard end.
7. Remove two upper screws that secure panel cluster to bezel.
8. If equipped with Automatic Climate Control, remove two screws securing center outlet duct to bezel and remove duct.
9. Remove two lower cluster-to-bezel screws. One screw is located below clock, the other is between headlight switch and left A/C air outlet duct.
10. Remove radio knobs, springs and rings. Remove radio control shaft nuts.
11. Remove screw on right side that secures radio to bracket.
12. Carefully pull radio out of bezel to disengage control shafts and lower radio slightly to permit removal of cluster.
13. If equipped with Rear Window Defogger, Seat Warmer or convertible top, disconnect connectors.
14. Loosen upper left and right bezel-to-bracket screws.
15. Pry left corner of bezel forward and pull cluster up to remove.

1967

1. Remove upper instrument panel cover.

2. Remove steering column lower cover.
3. Remove transmission shift indicator pointer.
4. Disconnect multiple connector at instrument panel cluster case and remove panel harness from cluster attachment.
5. Disconnect speedometer cable by depressing risers on wave washer. Then risers are 180° apart.
6. Separate instrument panel cluster from bezel (3 screws).
7. Remove right and center lower screws that secure panel cluster to bezel. Center screw is located below clock.
8. If equipped with Automatic Climate Control, remove center air outlet boot.
9. Remove center air outlet (2 screws).
10. If equipped with Automatic Climate Control, remove left air outlet boot at inboard end.
11. Using a flexible hex driver, remove lower left instrument panel cluster-to-bezel screw.
12. If equipped with Rear Window Defogger, Seat Warmer or convertible top, disconnect connectors.
13. Disconnect map light switch connector.
14. Loosen upper left and right bezel-to-bracket screws.
15. Pry left corner of bezel forward and pull instrument panel cluster up to remove.
16. Reverse procedure to install.

1966

1. Remove upper instrument panel cover.
2. Remove headlamp switch, clock and steering column.
3. Remove steering column upper cover (2 screws).
4. Disconnect seven cluster bulb sockets, fuel gauge, temperature gauge and transmission stator switch connectors.
5. Disconnect cable from speedometer.
6. Working through headlamp switch opening in cluster bezel, remove screw that holds cluster bezel right lower mounting bracket to right mounting bracket on instrument panel center brace.
7. Remove two screws that hold cluster bezel to upper instrument panel center moulding and remove bezel and cluster from panel.
8. Remove trip odometer reset shaft knob.
9. Separate bezel from cluster panel (4 screws).

RADIO, REPLACE

NOTE: When installing radio, be sure to adjust antenna trimmer for peak performance.

1970-72

1. Remove steering column lower cover.
2. If necessary, remove defroster hose from behind radio.
3. Remove radio knobs, washers and control rings.

4. Remove spanner nuts that hold shafts to panel.
5. Disconnect wires and antenna lead from radio.
6. Remove two hex head screws that hold lower support bracket to radio and instrument panel center support and remove bracket.
7. Pull radio back from panel to disengage shafts and lower to gain access to dial bulb.
8. Disconnect dial bulb and remove radio.

1968-69

1. On 1968, remove instrument panel top cover. On 1969, remove steering column lower cover. If necessary, remove defroster hose from behind radio.
2. On 1968, remove A/C center duct (2 screws).
3. Remove radio knobs, springs and rings.
4. Remove spanner nuts that hold radio control shafts to instrument panel.
5. Remove screw on right side that secures radio to bracket and loosen screw that secures bracket to brace.
6. Pull radio rearward to disengage control shafts and drop radio slightly to gain access to wiring connectors.
7. On AM/FM Stereo radio, disconnect audio-amplifier unit connector.
8. Disconnect antenna lead-in cable and connector at radio.
9. Disconnect light bulb socket from radio.
10. Disconnect foot control cable plug from radio if equipped.
11. On stereo radio, remove tape securing speaker leads: Two pieces on instrument panel cluster and two pieces at instrument panel frame above glove box door.
12. Remove radio. On 1968 units, radio is removed by working it out through top of instrument panel.

1967

1. Remove upper instrument panel cover.
2. Remove ash tray housing.
3. Unfasten ash tray frame from retaining plate (4 screws), disconnect frame multiple connector and remove frame.
4. Remove radio knobs, springs and rings.
5. Remove spanner nuts that hold control shafts to instrument panel.
6. Unfasten radio bracket from frame (screw on right side).
7. Pull radio rearward to disengage control shafts and drop radio slightly to gain access to wiring connectors.
8. Remove radio through ash tray opening.
9. Reverse procedure to install.

1966

1. Remove upper instrument panel cover.
2. Remove radio knobs, springs and rings, using Allen wrench to loosen knob retainer screws.
3. Disconnect dial bulb socket from radio.

4. Disconnect antenna lead-in cable and five-way wire connector at radio.
5. Disconnect floor control cable plug from radio (if equipped).
6. Using spanner wrench, remove nuts that hold control shafts to upper panel right moulding and remove escutcheons.
7. Remove lock nut securing radio front side bracket to mounting stud.
8. Loosen screw securing radio rear side bracket to radio and remove screw securing rear side bracket to upper instrument panel.
9. Carefully pull radio rearward to disengage control shafts and front side bracket from upper panel.
10. Remove radio through opening in top of upper instrument panel.

W/S WIPER MOTOR
1972

1. Raise hood and remove cowl screen.
2. Reach opening and loosen transmission drive link to crank arm nuts.
3. Remove transmission drive link from motor crankarm.
4. Disconnect wiring and washer hoses.
5. Remove motor attaching screws.
6. Remove motor while guiding crankarm through hole.

1966-71

1. Disconnect battery ground cable.
2. Disconnect three washer hoses from washer control valve. *Mark small outlet hoses and corresponding control valve nozzles for identification.*
3. Disconnect two-way wire connector at washer unit and three-way wire connector at wiper unit.
4. Remove cover on 1967-70 from opening in left side of cowl to gain access to wiper crank arm. *Cover is located above wiper-washer assembly.*
5. Loosen two lock nuts securing wiper unit crank arm to ball socket on end of transmission drive linkage, then disengage crank arm from ball socket. *Do not remove lock nuts from ball sockets.*

NOTE: On 1968-70 Eldorado, access to the crank arm is gained by removing the air inlet screen.

6. Remove three screws that hold wiper-washer assembly to cowl and remove assembly.
7. Reverse procedure to install.

W/S WIPER TRANSMISSION
1972

1. Raise hood and remove cowl vent screen.
2. Remove wiper arm and blade from transmission to be removed.
3. Loosen attaching nuts securing transmission drive link to motor crankarm.

NOTE: If only left side is to be removed, it will not be necessary to loosen nuts securing right drive link to motor crankarm.

4. Disconnect transmission drive link from crankarm.
5. Remove attaching screws securing transmission to body.
6. Remove transmission and linkage assembly through plenum chamber opening.

1968-71 Except Eldorado

1. Remove both wiper arms.
2. Remove six clips securing rubber hood seal to cowl and position seal out of the way.
3. Remove cowl ventilator screen (12 screws).
4. Unfasten left wiper transmission from cowl (3 screws).
5. Repeat Step 4 for right side.
6. Allow transmissions, linkage and bellcrank to lie in cowl plenum.
7. Remove ball socket cover (2 screws). Cover is located on top of cowl directly behind wiper-washer assembly.
8. Loosen two lock nuts securing crank arm to ball socket on end of drive linkage, then disengage crank arm from ball socket. Do not remove locknuts from ball socket studs.
9. Slide linkage to one side to allow one end of linkage to be drawn out through opening in cowl and remove linkage.
10. Reverse procedure to install.

1968-71 Eldorado

1. Remove both wiper arms.
2. Remove cowl air inlet screen.
3. Remove access hole cover from opening in center of cowl to gain access to wiper unit crank arm.
4. Remove lock nut securing crank arm to ball socket stud.
5. Remove three transmission mounting screws on right and left transmissions.
6. Disengage ball socket stud at wiper unit and remove transmissions and linkages as a complete assembly.
7. Reverse procedure to install.

1966-67 Except Eldorado

1. Remove shroud top ventilator frame and grille assembly.
2. Remove rubber grommet (1966) or cover (1967) from opening in left side of cowl to gain access to wiper unit crank arm.
3. Loosen (do not remove) two retaining nuts that secure drive linkage ball socket to motor crank arm, then disengage linkage from crank arm ball.
4. Remove mounting screws from right and left transmissions.
5. Remove four screws at bellcrank, then remove transmissions and linkage as an assembly.
6. Reverse procedure to install.

1967 Eldorado

1. Remove top shroud ventilator frame and grille assembly.
2. Remove access hole cover (2 screws) from opening in center of cowl to gain access to wiper unit crank arm.
3. Remove lock nut securing crank arm to ball socket stud.

4. Remove mounting screws on right and left transmissions.
5. Disengage ball socket stud at wiper unit and remove transmissions and linkage as a unit.
6. Reverse procedure to install.

W/S WIPER SWITCH

1969-72

1. Open left front door to gain access to screw securing control switch to instrument panel extension on door.
2. Loosen screw securing control switch to extension. *Screw is trapped and cannot be removed.*
3. Pull control switch out and disconnect electrical connector.

1967-68

1. Remove steering column lower cover.
2. Remove two screws and clip securing switch to panel.
3. Pull switch rearward to disengage from instrument panel.
4. Disconnect dial bulb socket and wiring harness connector from back of switch.
5. Reverse procedure to install.

1966

1. Disconnect negative battery cable.
2. Using a screwdriver, carefully pry frame and switch assembly from lower instrument panel to disengage snap-in mounting studs on frame from stud retainers in lower instrument panel.
3. Disconnect dial bulb socket and four-way wire harness connector from back of switch, then remove frame and switch assembly.
4. Remove switch from frame.

HEATER CORE REMOVAL

After draining radiator and disconnecting heater hoses proceed as follows:

1972

With Air Conditioning

1. Remove blower evaporator assembly.
2. Remove 29 screws and 4 nuts securing evaporator together.
3. Remove clamp and screw securing high pressure line to bottom of case.
4. Remove sealing grommet around heater inlet and outlet pipes.
5. Remove 6 screws (3 each side) securing heater core and baffle to case.
6. Lift heater core and baffle from case.
7. Remove screws securing baffle to heater core and remove baffle.

Without Air Conditioning

Refer to procedure given for 1971 models to remove heater core.

1971

With Air Conditioning

1. Remove instrument panel top cover.
2. Remove right and left outlet A/C hoses and center outlet connector.
3. Remove two screws securing A/C distributor to heater case and remove distributor.
4. Remove one screw securing defroster nozzle to heater case and remove nozzle from under clips and out of car.
5. Remove glove compartment liner.
6. Disconnect vacuum hoses at recirc door, water valve, control head and supply hose.
7. Disconnect aspirator hose from in-car sensor.
8. Remove instrument panel center vertical brace.
9. Remove instrument panel horizontal brace.
10. Remove four nuts securing heater case to cowl on engine side of dash.
11. Remove heater case from position under panel being careful to hold case as upright as possible to avoid spilling coolant.
12. Remove rubber seal from around core water nipples.
13. Remove screw and clip from under seal.
14. Remove two screws and clip from opposite end of case and remove core.

Without Air Conditioning

1. Remove instrument panel top cover.
2. Remove two screws and position center ventilation duct and sleeve out of way.
3. Remove vacuum hoses from diverter door and defroster door vacuum actuators.
4. Remove Bowden cable from temperature door arm and remove screw securing cable to heater case. Reposition cable out of way.
5. Remove two screws and nuts securing heater case to cowl and pull case away from cowl.
6. Remove heater case from position under panel being careful to hold in upright position to avoid spilling coolant.
7. Remove two screws and retainer at each side of core securing core to case and remove core.

1966-70 All Models

With Air Conditioning

1. Working in engine compartment, disconnect vacuum hoses and wiring from servo units being sure to mark them for proper installation.
2. On 1966-69 models remove fender to cowl tie struts. If car is equipped with Auto Level Control position left tie strut with compressor attached.
3. To gain access to the Heater & Air Modulator assembly, remove the vacuum storage tank and disconnect master switch, control cables and vacuum hoses again being sure to mark them for ease of assembly.
4. Unfasten and remove Heater & Air Modulator assembly from engine compartment.
5. The heater core can now be removed from this assembly.

1966-70 Except Eldorado

Without Air Conditioning

1. Blower motor and heater-blower assembly must be removed to get at the heater core. To do this, first disconnect electrical connector to blower on cowl in engine compartment. Then remove five screws securing blower motor to its case and remove motor.
2. Disconnect cable at temperature valve at pivot point on heater and remove cable clamp.
3. Remove screw securing vacuum manifold to heater and move manifold and hoses out of the way.
4. Remove seven screws securing bottom of heater to cowl and six screws securing top of heater to cowl, and take out heater assembly.
5. To remove heater core, remove four screws (two each side) that secure wire retaining clamp to heater blower case and remove clamps.
6. Heater core can now be pulled out of case and rubber grommets removed from inlet and outlet fittings.

1967-70 Eldorado

Without Air Conditioning

1. Before removing heater blower and motor, disconnect rubber cooling hose from nipple on blower motor.
2. The left cowl-to-fender shield strut rod must also be removed before taking out heater-blower assembly.

SPEED CONTROL

1970-72

Bead Chain Adjustment

1. Adjust engine hot idle speed and mixture, then shut off engine.
2. Check slack in chain by unsnapping swivel from ball stud and holding chain taut at ball stud; center of swivel should extent 1/8" beyond center of ball stud.
3. Adjust bead chain slack by sliding sleeve back on chain and removing loose rivet. Move swivel on ball chain until slack is correct. Then reinstall rivet and slide sleeve over rivet.

Cruise Speed Adjustment

The cruise speed adjustment can be set as follows:
1. If car cruises below engagement speed, screw orifice tube on transducer outward.
2. If car cruises above engagement speed, screw orifice tune inward.

NOTE: Each 1/4 turn of the orifice tube will change cruise speed about one mile per hour. Snug up lock nut after each adjustment.

Brake Release Switch Adjustment

1. Turn on ignition switch and connect a test light between one terminal of brake release switch and ground; select terminal where light goes out when pedal is depressed.
2. Loosen screw that retains switch to pedal support bracket. Position switch so circuit opens (light goes out) when pedal is depressed 1/4". Tighten screw and recheck.

Control Cable Adjustment, 1966-69

The cable is preset at the factory and should not require adjustment unless a new cable is installed. This adjustment

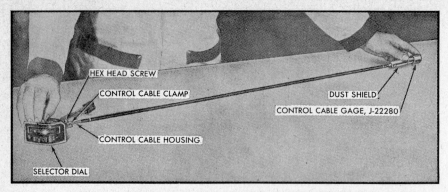

Fig. 10 Control cable adjustment for Slide Switch Speedostat

Fig. 11 Accelerator linkage adjustment
for Slide Switch type Speedostat

must be performed off the car as follows:

1. Remove the selector assembly.
2. Rotate selector dial to low speed position until it is positioned against its stop but do not force beyond its stop.
3. Position assembly flat on workbench and make certain there are no kinks in cable.
4. Loosen hex head set screw at cable clamp on selector control.
5. Pull cable housing until it is approximately half-way out of cable clamp. Position control cable gauge shown in Fig. 10 in end of dust shield. Hold dust shield and gauge and push toward selector control assembly until gauge bottoms. While holding in this position, tighten set screw at cable clamp.

Accelerator Linkage

1. Adjust throttle rod.
2. Start engine and operate at slow idle with transmission lever in "Park".
3. Separate linkage from exterior arm.
4. Adjust trunnion so that when it is installed through exterior arm, the stop stud will be aligned with locating notch and throttle valves will be closed.

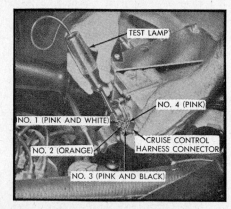

Fig. 12 Electrical connections on
Slide Switch type Speedostat

5. Install washer on trunnion and secure with cotter pin.

NOTE: Due to the angle at which the trunnion enters hole in exterior arm, it is necessary to rotate the exterior arm slightly forward when inserting the trunnion. Repeat this operation until proper alignment is obtained. Be care-

ful not to turn trunnion too far back or throttle valves will unseat and cause an incorrect adjustment. Insert the gauge shown in Fig. 11 (or small diameter pipe) over stop stud to check alignment.

Brake Release Switch

1. Turn on ignition but do not start engine.
2. Momentarily move slide switch to AUTO position until red indicator light glows.
3. Using a test lamp, ground one lead and touch the other lead to terminal No. 4, Fig. 12.
4. Loosen mounting screw securing release switch to brake pedal mounting bracket.
5. Adjust release switch so that lamp will light when brake pedal is fully released, and will go out when brake pedal is depressed about 1/4 inch. Tighten switch mounting screw. If switch cannot be adjusted, it is defective and should be replaced.

Engine Section

ENGINE, REPLACE

1970-72

1. Disconnect battery ground cable.
2. Remove hood and carburetor air cleaner with hoses.
3. Disconnect carburetor linkage at pedal lever.
4. Disconnect Cruise Control vacuum hoses if so equipped.
5. Remove clamp securing upper radiator hose to cradle.
6. Disconnect and/or remove all necessary wiring, pipes, hoses, linkage, etc.
7. Remove fan and A/C compressor.
8. Partially remove power steering pump, laying it aside so hoses are above fluid level in reservoir.
9. Drain radiator and disconnect hoses.
10. Proceed with steps 13 through 32 as described for 1968-69 models.

1968-69

NOTE: Disregard optional equipment items mentioned in the following if the car being serviced is not so equipped.

1. Disconnect battery ground cable.
2. Remove hood, air cleaner and automatic level control hoses.
3. Disconnect carburetor linkage at pedal lever.
4. Disconnect Cruise Control linkage.
5. Remove radiator shroud and clamp securing radiator upper hoses to cradle.
6. Disconnect and/or remove all necessary wiring, pipes, hoses, linkage, etc.
7. Remove fan. On Eldorado, remove studs from water pump shaft hub.
8. Remove Cruise Control power head.
9. Remove A/C compressor.
10. Partially remove power steering pump, laying it aside so that pressure and return hoses are above the fluid level in pump reservoir.
11. Position power steering cooler out of the way.
12. Loosen A.I.R. pump and remove belt.
13. Remove water pump pulley and alternator.
14. Remove two upper transmission-to-engine screws. Right screw secures transmission dipstick and modulator line to engine.
15. Remove A/C power servo from heater air selector. On cars other than Eldorado, remove blower relay and master switch from heater air selector.
16. Remove dust shield-to-cowl tie struts.
17. Position a lifting bracket to rear intake manifold attaching screws on Cruise Control cars. Bracket is in place on all others.
18. Raise car and place on jack stands.
19. Remove front engine mount nuts.
20. Remove oil filter.
21. On Eldorado, remove right output shaft.

22. Unfasten starter and allow it to hang by its cables.
23. Remove converter inspection pan.
24. Disconnect exhaust pipes from manifolds.
25. Place a jack under exhaust pipes to support system while engine is removed.
26. Support transmission with a jack.
27. Remove four lower transmission-to-engine screws.
28. Remove three screws securing converter to flex plate.
29. With lifting rig attached, pry engine forward while raising it as far as possible.
30. Lower transmission and again raise engine.
31. Remove flex plate and lift engine free of car.
32. Reverse procedure to install.

1967 Except Eldorado

NOTE: Engine must be removed with transmission attached as follows:

1. Lower radio antenna.
2. Remove hood.
3. Raise and support car (front and rear).
4. Disconnect negative battery cable.
5. Remove carburetor air cleaner.
6. Disconnect and/or remove all necessary wiring, pipes, hoses, linkage, etc.
7. If equipped with A/C, remove compressor.
8. Disconnect transmission fluid cooler lines at radiator, plug lines to prevent loss of fluid and remove radiator.
9. Remove fan blade assembly.

NOTE: Fan clutches used on A/C cars are always to be in an "in car position." When removed from car, support assembly to keep clutch disc in a vertical plane to prevent leaks of silicone fluid from clutch mechanism.

10. Disconnect exhaust pipe components as required.
11. Disconnect speedometer cable at transmission.
12. Unfasten and position steering idler arm to one side.
13. Disconnect propeller shaft, transmission shift linkage and electrical wires from transmission.
14. With hoisting equipment secured, tilt rear of engine down at a 45° angle and lift engine and transmission straight out.

1967 Eldorado

NOTE: The general procedure for removing the engine is similar to standard models up to a point from where it continues as follows:

1. Remove one screw securing brace to final drive.
2. Unfasten right exhaust pipe clamp at exhaust manifold.
3. Remove four screws securing transmission front cover to transmission. *Upper left screw is accessible with an extension and universal socket.*
4. Remove three converter-to-flex plate attaching screws. *This is done by removing cork in vibration damper and inserting a screw in damper. Rotate the screw to gain access to converter-to-flex plate screws. Do not pry on flex plate ring gear to rotate converter as flex plate may become damaged.*
5. Remove vacuum modulator line at transmission and at engine.
6. Working through center crossmember, loosen (do not remove) two transmission mounting nuts.
7. Remove two nuts securing engine mounting studs to front frame crossmember.

CAUTION: There is one bolt left securing the final drive housing to the engine support bracket and two screws securing the transmission to the spacer to the engine. Do not proceed further until chain hoist cable is connected to the engine as engine may shift.

8. Attach chain hoist cable to engine and take up slack.
9. Remove lower right and left transmission-to-adapter-to cylinder block screws.
10. Place small jack under final drive housing to support final drive and transmission.
12. Remove engine by pulling it slightly forward to disengage from transmission and up from engine compartment. Turn engine slightly clockwise while removing to clear engine compartment.
13. Secure a holding strap to transmission to prevent converter from falling out.

1966

NOTE: Engine must be removed with transmission attached.

1. Lower radio antenna.
2. Place car on jack stands (front and rear).
3. Disconnect positive battery cable.
4. Remove carburetor air cleaner.
5. Drain cooling system.
6. Disconnect wires, tubing, hoses and linkage attached to engine and transmission.
7. Unfasten and move power steering pump to one side without disconnecting hoses.
8. Remove fan blade, spacer and pulley.
9. On air conditioned cars, remove compressor.
10. Remove crossover pipe.

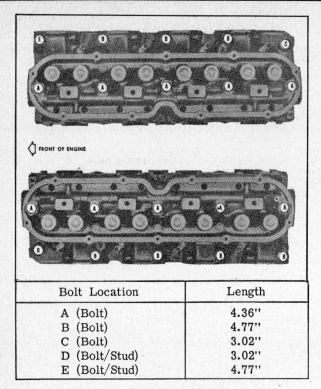

Bolt Location	Length
A (Bolt)	4.36"
B (Bolt)	4.77"
C (Bolt)	3.02"
D (Bolt/Stud)	3.02"
E (Bolt/Stud)	4.77"

Fig. 2   Location and length of cylinder head screws. 1968-72

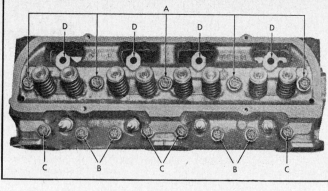

Fig. 3   Cylinder head bolt locations on 1966-67 engines (see Service Bulletin)

11. Unfasten and move steering idler arm to one side.
12. Unfasten engine front supports from frame.
13. Disconnect propeller shaft.
14. Remove hood.
15. Place jack with wood block cushion under transmission and take load from rear engine crossmember.
16. Remove two rear engine support mount - to - transmission extension housing screws.
17. Remove rear engine support crossmember.
18. Support engine with a hoist and remove jack from under transmission.
19. With all wires, tubing, straps, etc. disconnected, tilt rear of engine down at a 45-degree angle and lift engine and transmission straight out.
20. Reverse procedure to install.

CYLINDER HEAD, REPLACE
1968-72

1. Remove intake manifold.
2. Drain coolant from radiator.
3. Disconnect ground strap at rear of cylinder heads from cowl.
4. Disconnect wiring connector for high engine temperature warning system from sending unit at rear of left cylinder head.
5. Remove alternator if working on right cylinder head, or partially remove power steering pump if working on left cylinder head.
6. Remove A.I.R. manifold from both cylinder heads if equipped.
7. Unfasten wiring harness from cylinder head and position out of the way.

8. Unfasten exhaust manifold from cylinder head.
9. Remove rocker arm cover.
10. Remove rocker arm assemblies and lift out push rods.
11. Unfasten and lift off cylinder head.
12. After carefully removing all gasket material from mating surfaces of head and block, position new gasket over dowels and install cylinder head in reverse order of removal, being sure to install the screws as indicated in Fig. 2.

1966-67

NOTE: On cars equipped with A.I.R. System, release hose clamps and disconnect air delivery hose at check valve fitting. If working on left cylinder head, remove bolt that holds air pump to rear air pump mounting bracket. Remove pump filter from left rocker arm cover and set aside with hoses attached. If working on right cylinder head, release hose clamp and disconnect intake air bleed valve hose at check valve fitting.

If left cylinder head on the Eldorado with Cruise Control is to be removed, the control power unit and bracket must be removed from back of cylinder head.

On cars equipped with A.I.R. System, lift intake manifold with carburetor and air bleed valve attached.

1. Disconnect battery positive cable, remove carburetor air cleaner and drain cooling system. On air conditioned cars, remove compressor.
2. If the right-hand head is to be removed, disconnect vacuum hose and both heater inlet hoses from water control valve. Also remove the capscrew that holds the transmission filler tube bracket to the exhaust manifold.
3. If left-hand head is to be removed, remove power steering pump and bracket and position to one side (do not disconnect hoses).
4. If both heads are to be removed, first disconnect all necessary wiring, carburetor linkage, vacuum lines, fuel lines, etc.
5. Remove rocker arm covers, secondary ignition wiring and distributor cap as a unit.
6. Unfasten and lift intake manifold off

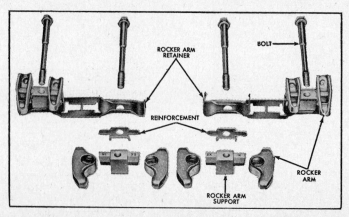

Fig. 4   Rocker arm components disassembled. 1967-72

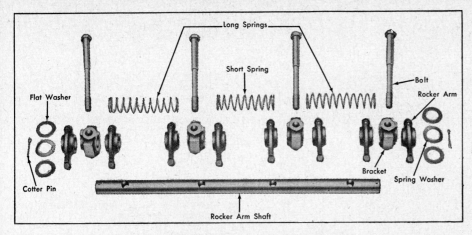

Fig. 6   Rocker arm assembly disassembled. 1966

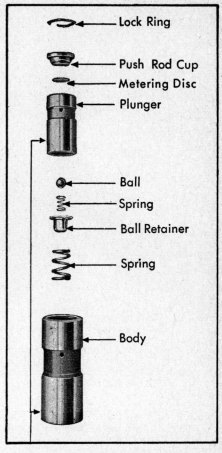

Fig. 7   Hydraulic valve lifter

locating dowels on cylinder heads and remove manifold with carburetor attached.

7. Disconnect exhaust pipe from exhaust manifolds and remove heat control valve from left manifold.

8. Remove rocker arm assembly. *If equipped with air conditioning, the right bank rocker arm assembly must be removed with cylinder head because of interference between rear rocker arm mounting screw and blower motor.*

9. Remove push rods and remaining cylinder head bolts.

10. Remove No. 1 and 5 spark plugs from left bank head (2 and 6 for right head) and install lifting hooks in spark plug holes. Lift head off dowels.

11. Reverse removal procedure to install cylinder heads, being sure to use all new gaskets.

12. On cars with air conditioning, the right rocker arm assembly must be installed with cylinder head because of interference between rear rocker arm screw and blower motor.

13. Be sure face of manifold heat valve stamped "TOP" is next to left manifold.

SERVICE BULLETIN

Care should be taken when installing cylinder head bolts on 1966-67 engines to make certain they are installed in the proper holes, otherwise the threads can be stripped when the bolts are tightened. Information pertaining to head bolt locations and bolt lengths is given below and in conjunction with Fig. 3 when installing head bolts.

Location	Length
A	4.06″
B	2.75″
C	3.69″
D	5.94″

VALVE ARRANGEMENT
Front to Rear

All Models . . . . E-I-I-E-E-I-I-E

VALVE LIFT SPECS.

Engine	Year	Intake	Exhaust
V8-429	1966	.427	.466
V8-429	1967	.440	.440
V8-472	1968-71	.440	.454
V8-500	1970-71	.440	.454
V8-472	1972	.490	.490
V8-500	1972	.490	.490

VALVE TIMING
Intake Opens Before TDC

Engine	Year	Degrees
V8-429	1966	34
V8-429	1967	39
V8-472	1968-70	18
V8-472	1971	38
V8-500	1970	18
V8-500	1971-72	34
V8-472	1972	34

ROCKER ARMS
1967-72

When disassembling the rocker arm assembly, be sure to keep the supports and rocker arms in order so they can be installed in the exact same position.

Install rocker arms on supports and place supports in retainers as shown in Fig. 4. *Be sure that the "EX" on support is positioned toward the exhaust valve and "IN" toward the intake valve.*

Place capscrews through the reinforcements, supports and retainers and position assemblies on cylinder head. Make sure that push rods are properly seated in the lifter seats and in the rocker arms. Lubricate rocker arm bearing surfaces before assembling in order to prevent wear.

1966

1. If a new rocker shaft is necessary, install new cotter pin on end of shaft (end without chamfered edge).
2. Assemble as shown in Fig. 6.

Oil grooves in rocker shaft should face toward cylinder head and notches in end of shafts should face

engine when assembly is installed on head.
Line up mounting holes in rocker shaft with holes in brackets and install mounting bolts.

VALVE GUIDES

Removable valve guides are used. If a special tool is not available to control the position of the guides when they are installed, carefully measure that portion of the guide that protrudes from the cylinder head and install the new guides accordingly.

VALVE LIFTERS

The valve lifters may be lifted out of their bores after removing the rocker arms and push rods. Adjustable pliers with taped jaws may be used to remove lifters that are stuck due to varnish, carbon, etc. Fig. 7 illustrates the type of lifter used.

ENGINE FRONT COVER
1970-72

1. On Eldorado, remove engine from chassis.
2. Remove vibration damper.

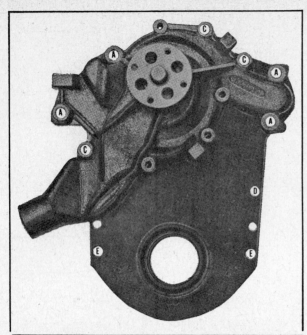

Key	(No.)	Size	Torque
A	(4)	3/8-16 x 1-3/8	25 Foot-Pounds
C	(3)	5/16-18 x 1-1/4	15 Foot-Pounds
D	(1)	5/16-18 x 5/8	15 Foot-Pounds
E	(2)	3/8-16 x 5/8	25 Foot-Pounds

Fig. 8   Engine front cover attaching screws. 1968-72

3. Drain oil and remove oil pan.
4. Drain radiator and remove lower radiator from water pump.
5. Unfasten and remove front cover.
6. Reverse procedure to install, referring to Fig. 8.

1968-69

1. Disconnect battery ground cable. On 1969 Eldorado, remove engine from chassis.
2. Remove carburetor air cleaner.
3. Drain cooling system.
4. Remove oil pan.
5. Remove upper radiator hose.
6. Remove fan. *On A/C cars, keep fan clutch in "on car" position when removed to prevent leaks of silicone fluid from clutch mechanism.*
7. Remove all drive belts.
8. Remove lower radiator hose.
9. Remove four capscrews that hold crankshaft pulley to vibration damper. *Place scribe marks on pulley and damper for proper installation.*
10. Remove plug from end of crankshaft.
11. Use a suitable puller to remove vibration damper.

NOTE: Use of shop air pressure through a spark plug port to hold one piston within its compression stroke will make it possible to remove vibration damper without turning the crankshaft.

12. Unfasten and remove front cover.

13. Reverse procedure to install, being careful to install the attaching screws as shown in Fig. 8.

1967

1. Disconnect negative battery cable.
2. Remove carburetor air cleaner.
3. Remove two oil pan-to-front cover nuts and studs.
4. Remove fan hub spacer and fan. On A/C cars remove fan.

NOTE: Fan clutches used on air conditioned cars are always to be in an "in car position". When removed from car, support assembly to keep clutch disc in a vertical plane to prevent leaks of silicone fluid from clutch mechanism.

5. Remove power steering drive belt, alternator belt and pulley.
6. Without disconnecting hoses, detach power steering pump and bracket and position to one side.
7. Detach alternator and bracket and position to one side.
8. On Eldorado with air conditioning, partially remove compressor. Also remove compressor lower mounting bracket from engine front cover.
9. Remove ignition distributor.
10. Remove fuel pump.
11. Remove vibration damper.
12. If equipped with A.I.R. System, detach air pump and bracket and swing to one side.
13. Remove oil filter, Fig. 9.
14. Unfasten and remove engine front cover, using care to protect front oil pan seal and gaskets from damage during cover removal.
15. Reverse procedure to install. Tighten cover screws as indicated in Fig. 10.

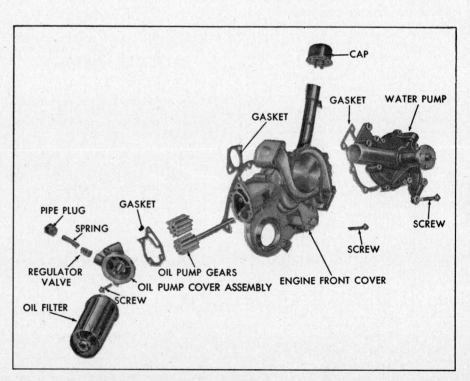

Fig. 9   Engine front cover disassembled. 1967

1966

1. Referring to Figs. 11 and 12, remove carburetor air cleaner. Drain cooling system and remove radiator and oil pan.
2. Remove fan blade. If equipped with air conditioning, remove compressor.
3. Remove power steering and alternator belts and pulley.
4. Unfasten power steering pump and bracket and position to one side (do not disconnect hoses).
5. Unfasten and position alternator and support bracket away from engine.
6. Remove distributor and fuel pump.
7. Unfasten and lower stabilizer bar.
8. Remove four screws from crankshaft pulley.
9. Remove cork plug from end of crankshaft. Then pull off vibration damper with puller.
10. Disconnect heater inlet hose at cylinder head water outlet pipe and heater outlet hose at water pump.
11. Remove oil filter.
12. Remove water outlet pipe from cylinder heads.
13. Remove capscrew holding fuel filter to bracket on oil filler tube.
14. Remove 12 screws that hold front cover to block and take off cover with water pump attached.
15. Reverse removal procedure to install the assembly, referring to Fig. 12 for attaching screw locations and torque specifications.

FRONT COVER OIL SEAL

1970-72

1. Remove vibration damper.
2. With a thin blade screw driver or similar tool, pry out front cover oil seal.
3. Lubricate new seal and fill cavity with wheel bearing grease. Position seal on end of crankshaft with garter spring side toward engine.
4. Using a suitable installer drive seal into cover until it bottoms against cover.

1968-69

1. Disconnect battery ground cable.
2. Remove carburetor air cleaner.
3. Raise front of car.
4. Remove alternator drive belt.
5. Remove air pump drive belt.
6. Remove power steering pump belt.
7. Working under car, remove four screws that hold crankshaft pulley to vibration damper. Place scribe marks on pulley and damper for proper installation.
8. Remove plug from end of crankshaft.
9. Use a suitable puller to remove vibration damper.
10. Pry out seal.
11. Lubricate new oil seal by filling cavity between lips with wheel bearing grease. Position seal on end of crankshaft with garter spring side toward engine.
12. Using a suitable seal installer, drive seal into front cover until it bottoms against cover.

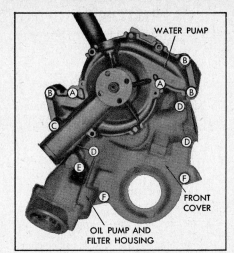

Fig. 10   Front cover attaching screws. 1967

Key	(No.)	Size	Torque
A	(2)	5/16-18 x 3-1/4	10 Foot-Pounds
B	(3)	3/8-16 x 3-5/8	20 Foot-Pounds
C	(1)	3/8-16 x 5	20 Foot-Pounds
D	(3)	5/16-18 x 2-1/8	10 Foot-Pounds
E	(1)	5/16-18 x 2-1/2	10 Foot-Pounds
F	(2)	5/16-18 x 1	10 Foot-Pounds

1966-67

The seal may be replaced without removing the front cover as follows:
1. Remove carburetor air cleaner and all drive belts.
2. Raise front of car and place jack stands under frame near cowl.
3. Working under car, scribe a locating mark shim spacer, crankshaft pulley and vibration damper so that damper may be reinstalled in same position on crankshaft.
4. Remove shim and pulley from vibration damper (6 screws).

5. Remove cork from end of crankshaft.
6. Pull vibration damper off crankshaft.
7. With screwdriver, pry out oil seal.
8. Lubricate new seal with wheel bearing grease and install on crankshaft with garter spring side toward engine.
9. Using a seal driver, drive seal into front cover until it bottoms against shoulder in bore.
10. Lubricate bore of vibration damper with E.P. lube to prevent seizure to crankshaft. Then reassemble parts removed.

Service Bulletin

1966: When it is necessary to replace a single lip front cover oil seal due to oil leakage, it has been the practice also to replace the vibration damper if the damper has been scored or grooved by the seal.

It is no longer necessary to replace the grooved vibration damper now that the new dual lip seal is available. The dual lip seal straddles any groove that may have been worn in the damper and thus provides a good seal.

TIMING CHAIN

1. Remove engine front cover as outlined above.
2. Remove two capscrews and washers that hold sprocket to camshaft.
3. Remove camshaft sprocket with chain.
4. Remove crankshaft sprocket.
5. To install, reverse removal procedure, being sure to line up the timing marks as shown in Fig. 13.

CAMSHAFT

1970-72

1. Remove engine front cover.
2. Remove distributor and oil pump.

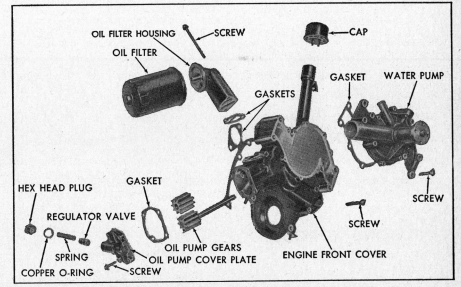

Fig. 11   Engine front cover disassembled. 1966

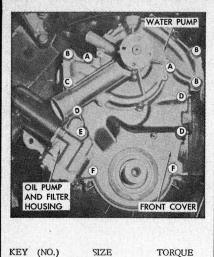

KEY	(NO.)	SIZE	TORQUE
A	(2)	5/16-18 x 3-1/4	10 foot-pounds
B	(3)	3/8-16 x 3-5/8	20 foot-pounds
C	(1)	3/8-16 x 5	20 foot-pounds
D	(3)	5/16-18 x 2-1/8	10 foot-pounds
E	(1)	5/16-18 x 2-1/2	10 foot-pounds
F	(2)	5/16-18 x 1	10 foot-pounds

Fig. 12 Engine front cover
attaching screws. 1966

3. Remove oil slinger from crankshaft.
4. Remove fuel pump and fuel pump eccentric.
5. Unfasten and remove camshaft sprocket with chain attached.
6. Remove valve lifters.
7. Remove radiator.
8. Carefully slide camshaft forward until it is out of engine.

1968-69

In order to replace the camshaft, it is necessary to remove the engine on all 1968 and 1969 Eldorado. Then follow the procedure outlined for 1967 models.

1966-67

1. To remove camshaft, take off engine front cover, timing chain and sprockets.
2. If equipped with air conditioner, remove condenser.
3. Remove hood lock plate support.
4. Remove valve lifters.
5. Slide camshaft out of engine carefully. *Use extreme care to keep cam lobes from scratching camshaft bearings.*
6. When installing camshaft, apply a coating of rear axle lubricant to camshaft bearing journals and camshaft lobes.

PISTONS & RODS ASSEMBLE

On all engines, assemble and install the piston and rod assemblies as shown in Fig. 14.

PISTONS

Service Bulletin

In 1966 engines on cars after approximate V.I. No. 202250, (also 1967) the piston diameters are slightly larger for a better piston to cylinder bore fit.

In determining the piston size to order, the diameters of the cylinder bores must be known. Identification of cylinder bore diameters can be made on any Cadillac engine by noting the letter stamped on the valve lifter compartment cover rail, next to the lower inside edge of the cylinder head.

The identification of the letters are grouped in twos, such as "AB", for two adjacent cylinders to which they refer. The letter denotes the diameter size, as shown in the table in Fig. 17, and applies to the letters in the piston size chart shown below.

New Piston Sizes

Letter	Piston Size
A	4.1282-4.1284
B	4.1284-4.1286
C	4.1286-4.1288
D	4.1288-4.1290
E	4.1290-4.1292
H	4.1292-4.1294
J	4.1294-4.1296
K	4.1296-4.1298
L	4.1298-4.1300
M	4.1300-4.1302
AA	4.1382-4.1384
BB	4.1384-4.1386
CC	4.1386-4.1388
DD	4.1388-4.1390
EE	4.1390-4.1392
HH	4.1392-4.1392
JJ	4.1394-4.1396
KK	4.1396-4.1398
LL	4.1398-4.1400
MM	4.1400-4.1402

1966-72

Pistons should be measured for size as shown in Fig. 15. Cylinders should be measured 1⅛" from the top, crosswise to the cylinder block. The clearance should be .0003 to .0007" in this position at room temperature (70°F). Subtract .0001" from measurement for every 6° above 70°.

An identification letter is stamped on the valve lifter compartment cover next to lower inside edge of cylinder head. The letters are in groups of two for adjacent cylinders (such as "A" "B") midway between the two cylinders. This letter denotes the cylinder size as shown in Figs. 16, 17. The table indicates ten piston sizes to match ten bore sizes. This makes it possible to maintain the proper clearance between block and piston.

If double letters (such as "AA" "BB") appear, it indicates that the cylinder has been bored .010" over the diameter indicated by the single letter in the chart.

PISTON RINGS

Replacement rings are available from Cadillac in standard size and .010" oversize.

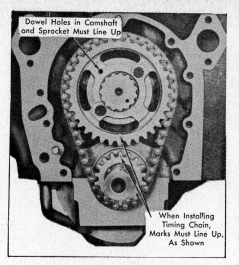

Fig. 13 Timing gear locating
marks. 1966-72

PISTON PINS

Piston pins are a matched fit with the piston and are not available separately. Piston pins are pressed in the connecting rods and will not become loose enough to cause a knock or tapping until after very high mileages. In such cases a new piston and pin assembly should be installed.

MAIN & ROD BEARINGS

Main and rod bearings are supplied by Cadillac in standard sizes only.

CRANKSHAFT OIL SEAL
1966-72

The two seal halves are identical and can be used in either the lower or upper location. However, both seal halves are pre-lubricated with a film of wax for break-in. Do not remove or damage this film. Fig. 18 shows the construction of the main bearing cap and seal.

NOTE: The seal installation cannot properly be made without the use of the "shoehorn" tool shown in Fig. 19. This tool can be made out of metal banding strap or similar shim stock of .020" thickness.

To install the lower half of the seal into the bearing cap, slide either end of seal into position at one end of bearing cap and place tool on seal land at other end of bearing, Fig. 20. Make sure seal is positioned over bearing ridge and lip of seal is facing forward (car position).

Hold thumb over end of seal that is flush with split line to prevent it from slipping upward, and push seal into seated position by applying pressure to the other end. Make sure seal is pressed down firmly and is flush on each side to avoid possibility of a leak at seal split line. Avoid pressing on lip as damage to sealing edge could result.

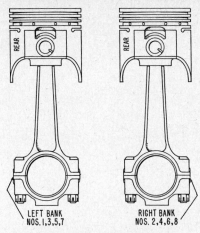

**Fig. 14   Piston and rod assembly
1966-67. For 1968-72 odd numbers
on right bank**

Letter	Cylinder Sizes (In Inches)	Piston Sizes (In Inches)
A	4.1290 - 4.1292	4.1280 - 4.1282
B	4.1292 - 4.1294	4.1282 - 4.1284
C	4.1294 - 4.1296	4.1284 - 4.1286
D	4.1296 - 4.1298	4.1286 - 4.1288
E	4.1298 - 4.1300	4.1288 - 4.1290
H	4.1300 - 4.1302	4.1290 - 4.1292
J	4.1302 - 4.1304	4.1292 - 4.1294
K	4.1304 - 4.1306	4.1294 - 4.1296
L	4.1306 - 4.1308	4.1296 - 4.1298
M	4.1308 - 4.1310	4.1298 - 4.1300
AA	4.1390 - 4.1392	4.1380 - 4.1382
BB	4.1392 - 4.1394	4.1382 - 4.1384
CC	4.1394 - 4.1396	4.1384 - 4.1386
DD	4.1396 - 4.1398	4.1386 - 4.1388
EE	4.1398 - 4.1400	4.1388 - 4.1390
HH	4.1400 - 4.1402	4.1390 - 4.1392
JJ	4.1402 - 4.1404	4.1392 - 4.1394
KK	4.1404 - 4.1406	4.1394 - 4.1396
LL	4.1406 - 4.1408	4.1396 - 4.1398
MM	4.1408 - 4 1410	4.1398 - 4.1400

**Fig. 17   Cylinder and piston sizes.
1966. See Service Bulletin for late
1966 and 1967 pistons**

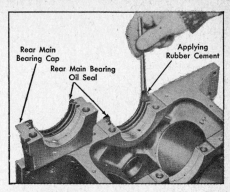

**Fig. 18   Rear main bearing
cap and seal. 1966-72**

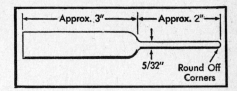

**Fig. 19   Rear main bearing oil seal
"shoehorn" installer. 1966**

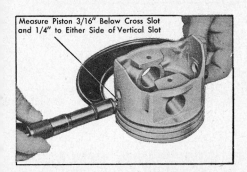

Fig. 15   Measuring piston diameter. 1966-72

To install upper half of seal in cylinder block (with crankshaft in car), position "shoehorn" tool on land of block. Start seal into groove in block with lip facing forward and rotate seal into position. Do not press on lip or sealing edge may be damaged. Both ends of seal must be flush at seal split line to avoid leaks. If necessary, Lubriplate or its equivalent may be used to facilitate installation of both upper and lower seal halves. Do not use silicone or a leak may result.

OIL PAN, REPLACE
1968-72 Except Eldorado

NOTE: For easier removal of the oil pan past the stabilizer bar, first remove the two *front* dowel studs from the block by running a jam nut on each stud to lock the pan nut on the stud. Working over the front frame crossmember, use a socket to remove the stud with the two nuts attached. On engines prior to 1968 with studs further rearward, this procedure is not necessary.

1. Disconnect battery ground cable.
2. Drain engine oil.
3. Remove "Y" exhaust pipe at exhaust manifold.
4. Remove starter.
5. Unfasten and lower idler arm support.
6. Disconnect pitman arm at center link and lower steering linkage.
7. Remove transmission lower cover.
8. Unfasten and lower oil pan.

NOTE: To align the oil pan at the rear and prevent damage from the flywheel teeth during installation, first locate the oil pan on the crankcase with two screws at mid-point. Then install two screws at the rear while checking gasket alignment.

1967-72 Eldorado

To remove the oil pan it is necessary to

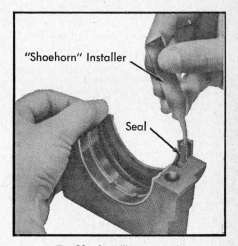

**Fig. 20   Installing rear main
bearing oil seal. 1966-72**

remove the engine as described previously.

1966-67 Except Eldorado

1. Disconnect battery positive cable.
2. Drain engine oil.
3. Disconnect exhaust crossover pipe at exhaust manifold.
4. Disconnect exhaust support bracket at transmission extension housing and position exhaust system to one side.
5. Remove starting motor.
6. Unfasten and lower steering idler arm support.
7. Disconnect pitman arm at drag link and lower steering linkage.
8. Remove transmission lower cover.
9. Unfasten and remove oil pan from cylinder block and engine front cover.

Cylinder and piston sizes (as indicated by letters stamped on the cylinder head gasket surface). The letters are in groups of two for adjacent cylinders (such as "H" and "B") midway between the two cylinders. The letters denote the cylinder piston sizes as shown below).

Letter	Cylinder Size (Diameter in Inches)	Piston Size (Diameter in Inches)
A	4.3000 - 4.3002	4.2992 - 4.2994
B	4.3002 - 4.3004	4.2994 - 4.2996
C	4.3004 - 4.3006	4.2996 - 4.2998
D	4.3006 - 4.3008	4.2998 - 4.3000
E	4.3008 - 4.3010	4.3000 - 4.3002
H	4.3010 - 4.3012	4.3002 - 4.3004
J	4.3012 - 4.3014	4.3004 - 4.3006
K	4.3014 - 4.3016	4.3006 - 4.3008
L	4.3016 - 4.3018	4.3008 - 4.3010
M	4.3018 - 4.3020	4.3010 - 4.3012
AA	4.3100 - 4.3102	4.3092 - 4.3094
BB	4.3102 - 4.3104	4.3094 - 4.3096
CC	4.3104 - 4.3106	4.3096 - 4.3098
DD	4.3106 - 4.3108	4.3098 - 4.3100
EE	4.3108 - 4.3110	4.3100 - 4.3102
HH	4.3110 - 4.3112	4.3102 - 4.3104
JJ	4.3112 - 4.3114	4.3104 - 4.3106
KK	4.3114 - 4.3116	4.3106 - 4.3108
LL	4.3116 - 4.3118	4.3108 - 4.3110
MM	4.3118 - 4.3120	4.3110 - 4.3112

Fig. 16   Cylinder and piston sizes. 1968-72

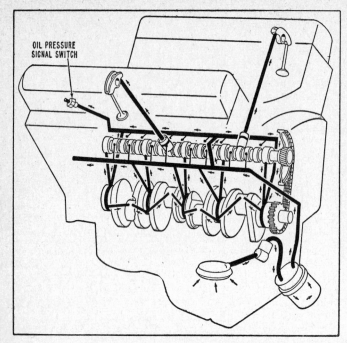

Engine oiling system. 1968-72

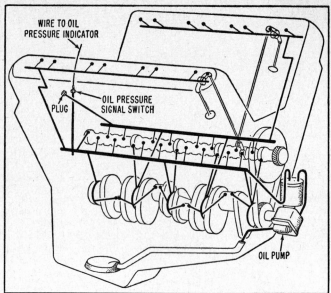

Engine oiling system. 1966-67 (typical)

10. Reverse procedure to install pan.

NOTE: Install new oil pan front and rear seals by pulling locating tangs on seals through locating holes in seal flange. Make sure seals are firmly positioned on flange surfaces with ends of each seal properly located in cut-out notches in side gaskets. Seal all four corner notch openings with a coating of rubber cement. Clean out notches in block where ends of oil pan rear seal fit. Fill this rectangular cavity with Transmission Cooler Hose Cement.

OIL PUMP
1968-72

1. Raise car and remove oil filter.
2. Remove five screws securing pump to engine. *The screw nearest the pressure regulator should be removed last, allowing the pump to come down with screw.*
3. Remove pump drive shaft.
4. Reverse procedure to install, being sure to pack the pump with petrolatum.

1966-67

The oil pump housing is an integral part of the engine front cover, Figs. 8, 9, and 10. Whenever the oil pump housing components require service, the front cover must be removed from the engine. Refer to "Engine Front Cover" for procedure.

Inspect strainer screen for dirt and float for leaks. Look for nicks or burrs or nicks on pressure regulator valve which might cause leaks or binding in pump body. Inspect pump gears for

nicks and burrs. Inspect bottom cover for wear and dress down on a surface plate if necessary. Place bottom cover on pump and check drive shaft end play. If end play exceeds .006 in., replace drive and idler gears. Assemble and install oil pump in the reverse order of its removal and disassembly.

Before installing the oil filter, fill oil passages in filter support bracket with engine oil. This will allow oil pump to prime itself when engine is started.

WATER PUMP, REPLACE
1968-72

1. Disconnect battery ground cable.
2. Drain radiator and remove fan shroud.
3. Remove fan assembly. *On A/C cars, be sure to keep the fan clutch in the "on car" position when removed to prevent leakage of silicone fluid into clutch mechanism.*
4. Remove all drive belts.
5. Pull pump pulley off shaft.
6. Disconnect water inlet from pump.
7. Unfasten and remove pump from front cover.
8. Reverse procedure to install, being sure to install bolts as shown in Fig. 21.

1966-67

1. Disconnect battery positive cable.
2. Drain radiator. On air conditioned cars, partially remove compressor.
3. Remove fan blades, spacer, and drive belts.
4. Unfasten and move generator and support bracket away from engine.
5. Remove oil filter and support bracket.

6. Remove water hose and water outlet pipe.
7. Unfasten water pump from engine.
8. Reverse removal procedure to install pump, tightening mounting bolts to the torque indicated in Fig. 22.

FUEL PUMP, REPLACE
1968-72

1. Raise car and disconnect fuel line at pump and plug line.
2. Disconnect fuel pipe to fuel filter at pump.
3. Remove mounting screw on upper pump flange.
4. Remove nut from mounting stud at lower pump flange.
5. Tipping pump upward, pull pump straight out from engine and remove.
6. Reverse procedure to install.

1967

NOTE: On cars equipped with A.I.R. system except Eldorado, it is necessary to remove the air pump and the bolt that holds the strut to the pump front mounting bracket. Swing front of strut out of the way to gain access to the fuel pump.

1. Connect a jumper wire from coil primary negative terminal (on distributor side) to a good ground to prevent engine from starting.
2. Loosen two capscrews holding fuel pump to engine front cover.
3. Crank engine until camshaft eccentric is at its low point of contact with fuel pump arm, and pump has minimum pressure on mounting screws.
4. Release clamp securing rubber hose to fuel pump inlet and plug hose opening to prevent fuel drainage. *On Eldorado equipped with A.I.R. System, remove corded rubber baffle*

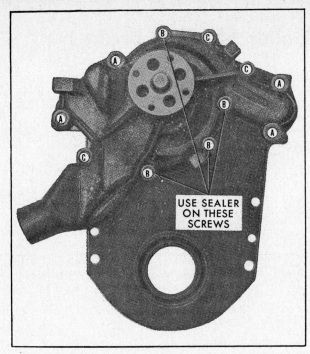

Fig. 21   Water pumping attaching screws. 1968-72

Key	Size	Torque
A	1/4-20x1-1/4	5 foot-pounds
B	5/16-18x3-1/4	10 foot-pounds
C	3/8-16x3-5/8	15 foot-pounds
D	3/8-16x3-7/8	15 foot-pounds

Fig. 22   Water pump screws. 1966-67

from front crossmember and rubber hose from connector located on crossmember instead of at fuel pump inlet.

5. *Remove mounting screws and pump. On Eldorado equipped with A.I.R. System, remove power steering pump belt to make pump removal easier.*

1966

NOTE: On cars equipped with A.I.R. System, it is necessary to remove the air pump and the bolt that holds strut to pump front mounting bracket. Swing front of strut out of the way to gain access to the fuel pump.

1. Disconnect fuel line between fuel filter and pump. Release clamp securing hose to pump. Plug end of hose to prevent drainage.
2. Unfasten and remove pump from engine.
3. To install, crank engine until camshaft eccentric is at its highest point.
4. Place gasket on engine and install pump. Loosely install screws. Then lift pump and tighten screws.
5. Remove plug from hose and install hose and fuel line. Then operate engine and check for leaks.

Automatic Transmission

1972 AUTO. TRANS. LINKAGE ADJUSTMENTS

Linkage adjustment procedures for 1972 models are the same as those for 1971 models as outlined in the front of this manual.

NOTE: 1972 linkage adjustment information is in this section. Repair procedures on both automatic and manual shift transmissions are covered elsewhere in this manual. Procedures for removing automatic transmissions as well as linkage adjustments on 1966-71 models are included in the automatic transmission chapters. See Chapter Index.

Rear Axle, Propeller Shaft & Brakes

REAR AXLE

1967-72 Eldorado

The rear axle used on these models is a welded assembly of the beam type with a drop center. The rear wheel spindles are a press fit and bolted to the rear axle assembly, Fig. 1. As shown, tapered roller bearings are used in the rear wheels. These bearings do not require regularly scheduled repacking. When major brake service work is to be performed, however, it is recommended that the bearings be cleaned and repacked.

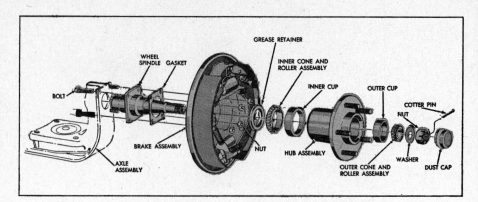

Fig. 1   Rear wheel spindle disassembled. 1967-72 Eldorado

Wheel Bearing Adjustment

Adjustment of the rear wheel bearings should be made while revolving the wheel at least three times the speed of the nut rotation when taking torque readings.
1. Check to make sure that hub is completely seated on wheel spindle.
2. While rotating wheel, tighten spindle nut to 30 ft-lbs. Make certain all parts are properly seated and that threads are free.
3. Back off spindle nut ¼ turn and install cotter pin. *If cotter pin cannot be installed in either the available holes in the spindle with nut in the above position, loosen spindle nut until cotter pin can be installed.*
4. Peen end of cotter pin snug against side of nut. If it can be moved with a finger, vibration may cause it to wear and break.

Wheel Spindle, Replace

1. Raise and support rear of car and remove hub.
2. Disconnect brake line at wheel cylinder.
3. Unfasten and remove brake backing plate and position out of the way.
4. Place jack under rear axle.
5. Remove four nuts from center spring clamp and lower rear axle until spindle is accessible.
6. Remove lower spring insulator from rear axle.
7. Drive spindle out of rear axle.

Installation

1. Start new spindle, with keyway up, into axle and install four backing plate to spindle nuts.
2. Progressively tighten nuts until spindle is fully seated and then remove attaching nuts and bolts.
3. Position lower spring insulator to rear axle.
4. Position rear axle to center spring clamp, making sure that spring aligning pin locates into axle. See that lower insulator is properly positioned and that center spring clamp bolts engage rear axle mounting holes.
5. Install four nuts securing center spring clamp to rear axle, tightening to 30 ft-lbs.
6. Install new gasket on wheel spindle.
7. Install brake backing plate and tighten nuts to 40 ft-lbs.
8. Connect brake line to wheel cylinder, tightening fitting to 14 ft-lbs.
9. Install rear hub.

Rear Axle, Replace

1. Raise and support rear of car with

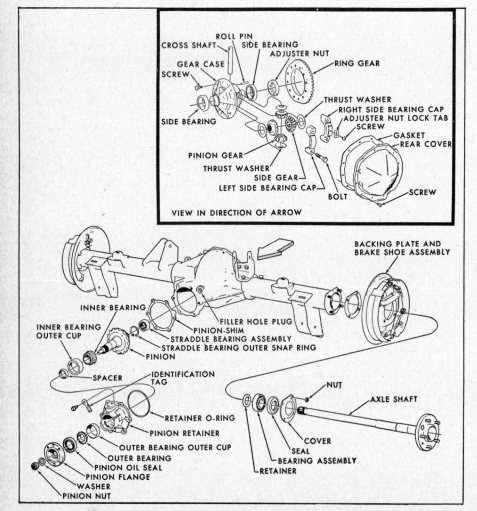

Fig. 1A   Rear axle assembly. 1970-72 standard cars

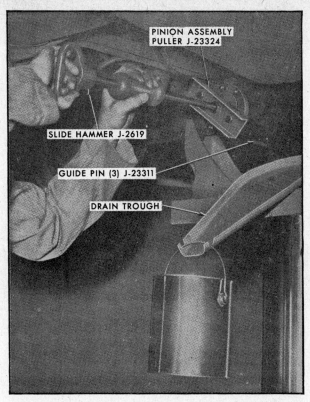

Fig. 2   Removing pinion assembly. 1970-72 standard cars

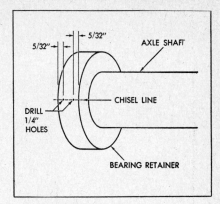

Fig. 2A   Removing bearing retainer. 1970-72 standard cars

jack stands at rear frame pads ahead of rear wheel opening.
2. Remove rear wheels and hubs.
3. Disconnect brake lines at wheel cylinders.
4. Disconnect parking brake cable at equalizer.
5. Disconnect rubber brake hose at underbody connector.
6. Disconnect overtravel lever link from bracket on rear axle.
7. Remove spring guides retaining parking brake cable to center spring clamp.
8. If rear axle is being replaced, remove brake backing plates.
9. Supporting rear axle at center with a jack, remove eight nuts (4 each side) from center spring clamp assemblies.
10. Lower rear axle with jack and remove from car.
11. Remove lower spring insulators from rear axle.
12. If rear axle is being replaced, remove bolt securing brake line junction fitting to axle. Remove brake line, overtravel lever link bracket, and drive spindles from axle.
13. Reverse procedure to install.

1970-71 Standard Cars

This axle design, Fig. 1A, uses two tapered roller bearings and a straight roller straddle bearing to support the pinion and provide rigidity. Adjustment of the pinion is done by the use of shims at the pinion retainer to differential carrier connection. Pinion-ring gear backlash adjustment of .005-.010" is accomplished through the use of a shim lo-

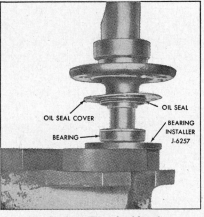

Fig. 3   Installing wheel bearing. 1970-72 standard cars

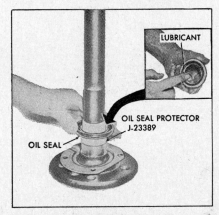

Fig. 3A   Installing rear wheel oil seal. 1970-72 standard cars

cated to the left of the left side bearing. The differential preload is adjusted by means of an adjuster nut that is retained under the right side bearing cap which in addition to the shim provides the correct backlash.

The rear wheel bearing is called a "unit bearing". It is a tapered roller bearing that is completely assembled as a unit.

Differential Removal

1. Raise car on a hoist.
2. Remove wheel shields, discs, wheels and brake drums.
3. Remove four nuts that secure retainer and backing to rear axle housing.
4. Attach a suitable to axle shaft and remove axle shafts.
5. Install two nuts on backing plate mounting studs to prevent plates from falling and damaging brake lines.
6. Remove two attaching screws and lockwashers that secure differential carrier nose bumper arm.
7. Support propeller shaft with a chain and disconnect propeller shaft at axle flange.
8. Place a drain pan under differential and remove axle housing cover.
9. Remove five pinion retainer to carrier screws and loosen remaining screw.

CAUTION: Do not remove remaining screw.

10. Install guide pins, Fig. 2.
11. Position drain pan under pinion retainer and attach puller.
12. Using slide hammer, unseat pinion from carrier, removing remaining screw and slide pinion assembly over guide pins and out of carrier.
13. Remove adjuster lock tab, bearing caps, adjuster nut and remove carrier case.

Axle Shaft, Replace

1. Raise car and remove wheel and brake drum.
2. Remove axle retaining nuts and lockwashers.
3. Attach slide type puller and remove axle shaft.

NOTE: When removing axle shaft,

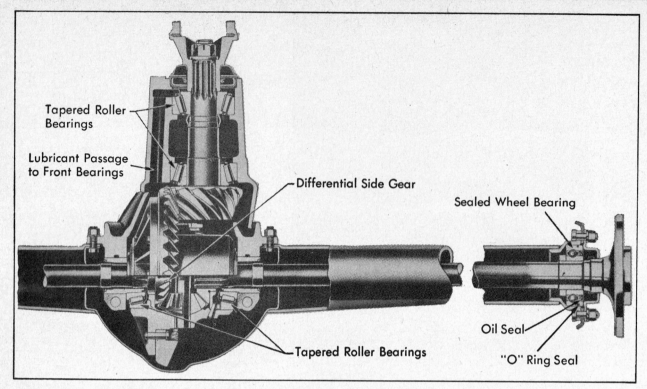

Fig. 3B   Rear axle assembly. 1966-69 standard cars

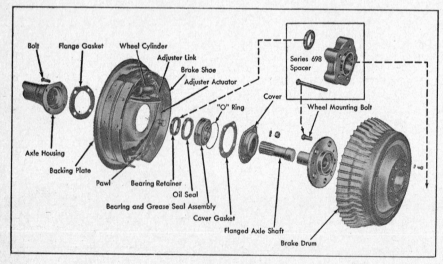

Fig. 4   Rear wheel disassembled. 1966-69

the bearing may separate leaving the outer race in the housing. This is normal and does not indicate failure. If the bearing is to be replaced, make sure the old bearing outer race is removed from the housing.

Removing Bearings

1. To remove bearing retainer, drill holes as in Fig. 2A being sure not to drill more than ½" deep to avoid damaging shaft.
2. Using a cold chisel, notch retainer next to bearing, being careful not to damage shaft.

NOTE: Retainer need not be completely split. Drive chisel into retainer only until retainer can be slipped off shaft.

3. Stand axle upright on flanged end and using two screwdrivers pry seal away from bearing.
4. Position shaft in a press and press shaft out of bearing.

Installing Bearing

1. Install bearing cover on shaft with raised side of cover against shaft flange, Fig. 3.
2. Install seal protector on shaft with

small end of protector toward splined end of shaft, Fig. 3A.

3. Lubricate lip of seal and install by pressing down over protector. Seal is properly installed when the lip of the seal clears the large end of the protector.
4. Position bearing on shaft with narrow ring of bearing facing flanged end of shaft.
5. Press bearing on shaft until bearing bottoms against shoulder on shaft.
6. Position retainer on shaft with chamfer on retainer next to bearing.
7. Press retainer on shaft until retainer bottoms against bearing.

1966-69 Standard Cars

The design of the rear axle carrier assembly is shown in Fig. 3B. The axle shafts are supported at the outer ends by ball bearings which are lubricated from the differential carrier. The axle shaft oil seals are an integral part of the bearings and they are not servicable separately from the bearing. An "O" ring seal is located in the grooved outer surface of the bearing.

Any service on the differential carrier assembly, except drive pinion oil seal or yoke replacement, should be handled by replacement of the complete assembly. No disassembly or adjustment of this unit should be attempted because special equipment is used at the factory for selection of mating parts and setting side bearing preload.

Whenever a carrier is removed because of scored gears, worn bearings, or any failure which causes dirt or metal chips, it will be necessary to remove the housing from the car for thorough clean-

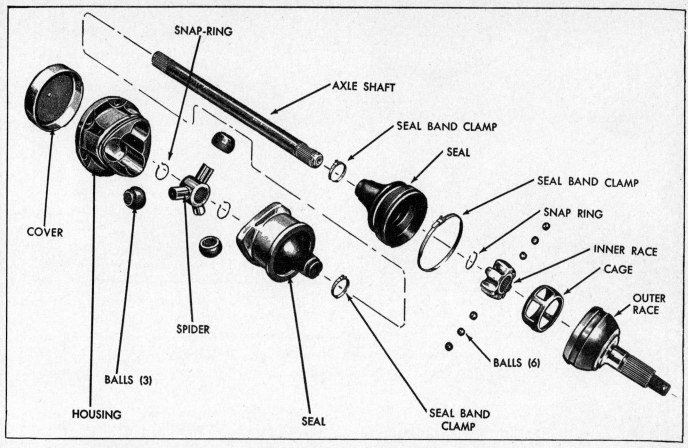

Fig. 5 Eldorado drive axle, exploded

ing before the new carrier is installed. Also check axle shaft bearings for metal chips and clean if necessary.

In case of lubricant leakage between differential carrier and axle housing, check first to make sure that the nuts are tightened to the recommended torque of 37 ft. lbs. If tightening the nuts does not stop the leak, an extra gasket should be installed, using a non-hardening sealer. The additional sealing effect of the extra gasket should prevent further leakage. If a replacement differential is installed, the special lubricant shipped with the new differential must be used.

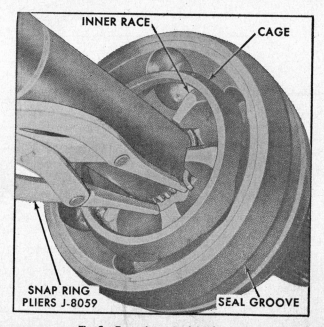

Fig. 6 Removing outer joint from axle

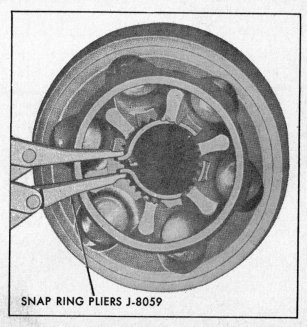

Fig. 7 Removing and installing inner snap ring

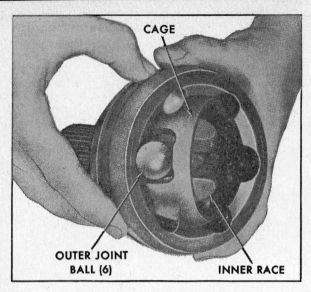

Fig. 8   Removing balls from outer joint

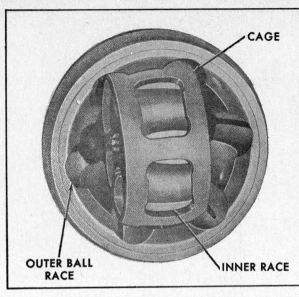

Fig. 9   Removing cage and inner race

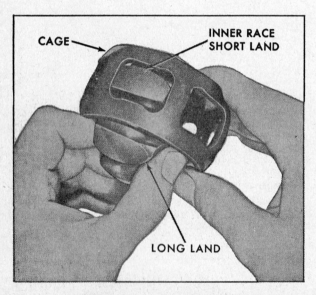

Fig. 10   Removing inner race from cage

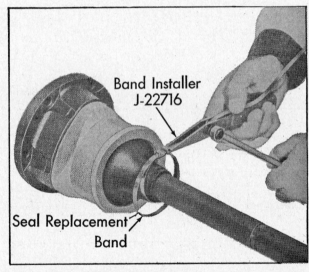

Fig. 11   Installing new seal clamp

Removal

1. Disconnect rear universal joint at pinion yoke. Use suction gun to remove grease from differential carrier.
2. Remove axle shafts as outlined below.
3. Remove nuts and washers that hold carrier to axle housing and remove entire assembly with gasket.

Installation

NOTE: Use a new carrier-to-housing gasket and new "O" ring seals on axle shaft bearings.

1. Place gasket on housing, install carrier, nuts and washers, and torque nuts to 37 ft. lbs.
2. Install axle shafts as explained below.

3. Install lubricant in differential to filler plug level.
4. Connect rear universal joint at pinion yoke.

Axle Shaft, Replace

1. Raise car and remove wheel.
2. Remove brake drum.
3. Remove four axle retaining nuts and lockwashers.
4. Using slide hammer type puller, remove axle shaft.

Removing Bearings

1. Using a chisel and hammer, groove spacer next to bearing. The spacer need not be split. Drive chisel into spacer only enough to allow spacer to be slipped from shaft.

NOTE: On Eldorado models, before notching retainer, drill two $\frac{1}{4}$" holes

along chisel line. Be sure not to drill any deeper than $\frac{1}{2}$" as axle shaft may be damaged.

2. Press shaft through bearing. *If bearing has been removed because of failure, inspect axle housing and differential carrier for metal chips and, if necessary, clean thoroughly.*

Installing Bearing

1. Install new bearing on shaft so that bearing seal is toward flange end of shaft.
2. Press bearing on shaft so that it is located 3.180" from outer surface of axle shaft flange to inner end of bearing inner race.
3. Install oil ring seal on bearing.

Install Axle Shaft

1. Apply film of differential lube to

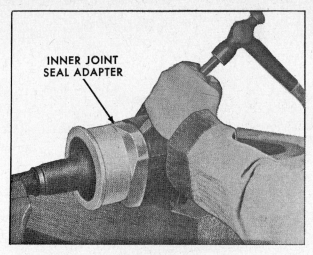

Fig. 12 Removing seal adapter

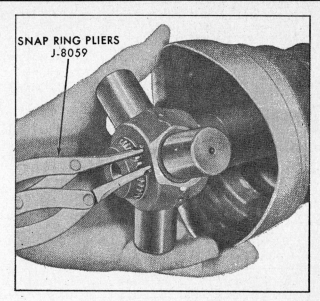

Fig. 13 Removing spider snap ring

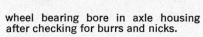

Fig. 14 Installing seal adapter on joint housing

Fig. 15 Rubber hose location

wheel bearing bore in axle housing after checking for burrs and nicks.

2. Use a new "O" ring seal on wheel bearing and install axle shaft (shorter one on left side), being careful not to damage "O" ring seal.

3. Install brake backing plate and bearing retainer.

4. Install nuts and lockwashers on housing bolts and tighten by inserting socket wrench through rear axle flange.

5. Install brake drum and wheel.

PROPELLER SHAFT
Two Piece Type

Removal

1. With car raised, remove two center bearing support-to-frame bolts.

2. Remove U-bolts and locks at rear axle pinion.

3. Slide propeller shaft and front yoke off transmission output shaft and through frame tunnel section, removing it at the rear. *Slide spare yoke into transmission extension*

housing to prevent oil from leaking out.

Installation

1. Lubricate front propeller shaft yoke with automatic transmission oil and remove spare yoke from transmission extension housing that had been installed to prevent oil leaking out.

2. Slide propeller shaft and front yoke into transmission output shaft through frame tunnel section, being careful not to nick yoke. *Be sure to reinstall any shims that may have been removed from between propeller shaft center support and frame tunnel.*

3. Install two center bearing support-

CADILLAC

to-frame bolts. Install U-bolts and locks at rear axle pinion and torque U-bolt nuts to 15 ft. lbs.

IMPORTANT

If drive line shudder, roughness, vibration or rumble is experienced, it may be due to misalignment of the propeller shaft assembly. To make this check, however, a special Propeller Shaft Alignment Gauge Set. No. J-8905 must be used. Inasmuch as this equipment is not likely to be found in general repair shops, it is recommended that a Cadillac dealer having this equipment do the work.

One Piece Type

Removal

1. Raise car on hoist.
2. Remove flange attaching bolts and lower propeller shaft.

   NOTE: Do not allow shaft to hang on front constant velocity joint.

3. Push shaft forward so rear universal joint flange clears pinion shaft, then remove shaft by pulling rearward to disengage slip yoke. Install spare yoke into transmission extension housing to prevent loss of oil.

Installation

1. Remove spare yoke and insert front yoke of propeller shaft into extension housing, engaging transmission shaft splines.
2. Install rear flange attaching bolts and torque to 65 ft. lbs.
3. Check transmission oil.

ELDORADO DRIVE AXLES

General Description

Each drive axle, Fig. 5, consists of an axle shaft, with a ball type constant velocity joint at the outboard end and a tri-pot type at the inboard end. The torsional damper on the right hand shaft is not serviceable and must be replaced as a unit.

The inboard joint is not only flexible to operate at various angles, but can also move in and out as required by suspension movement.

Right Drive Axle

1. Disconnect negative battery cable.
2. Raise car and remove wheel. Remove drive axle spindle nut.
3. Using a block of wood and a hammer, tap on end of drive axle to unseat axle at hub assembly.

   NOTE: Install a short piece of rubber hose on the lower control arm torsion bar connector to prevent damage to the drive axle seals.

4. Remove six drive axle-to-output shaft screws and lock washers.
5. Remove two output shaft support-to-engine bolts and one support-to-brace self tapping screw.
6. Rotate inboard end of drive axle

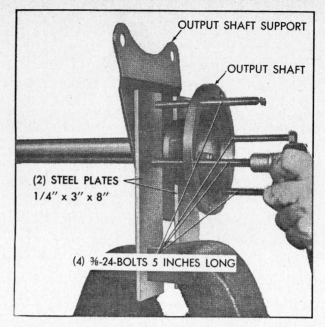

Fig. 16   Removing right hand output shaft support and bearing

rearward toward starter.
7. Slide shaft straight out toward side of car and remove output shaft from underside of car.
8. Remove drive axle by rotating axle inboard and toward front of car.
9. Reverse procedure to install.

NOTE: When attaching right hand output shaft support to the engine, do not allow the shaft and support assembly to hang in the final drive unit. Install support bolts and washers loosely and by moving the flange end of the shaft up and down, and back and forth, find the center location. Hold shaft in this position and tighten bolts to 50 ft-lbs.

Left Drive Axle

Perform steps 1-4 of removal of right axle then proceed as follows:

1. Loosen shock absorber upper mounting bolt.
2. Remove stabilizer bar link bolt cotter pin and nut.
3. Remove upper ball joint cotter pin and nut. Using a hammer, strike knuckle to disengage upper ball joint then remove ball joint stud from knuckle and brake line clip from stud.
4. Remove brake hose bracket from frame.
5. Carefully tip disc and knuckle assembly out at upper end to extent of brake hose.

   NOTE: Wire assembly to upper control arm so brake does not support weight of knuckle assembly.

6. Rotate inner end of drive axle toward front of car.
7. Guide drive axle out of knuckle and remove axle from car.
8. Reverse procedure to install, being careful not to damage brake line

when installing upper ball joint stud.

Outer Constant Velocity Joint

1. Remove inner and outer seal clamps by cutting with a chisel and slide seal down axle shaft to gain access to joint.
2. Wipe excess grease from joint and spread snap ring and slide joint off spline, Fig. 6.
3. Remove inner race snap ring, Fig. 7.
4. Hold constant velocity joint in one hand then tilt cage and inner race so that one ball can be removed, Fig. 8. Continue until all balls have been removed.

   NOTE: It may be necessary to tap the outer cage to rotate it.

5. Turn cage 90° with slot in cage aligned with short land on outer race and lift cage out of race, Fig. 9.
6. Turn short land of inner race 90° in line with hole in cage. Lift land on inner race up through hole in cage, then turn up and out to separate, Fig. 10.
7. Reverse procedure to install, using new seal clamps, Fig. 11. Cut off excess strap.

Inner Constant Velocity Joint

1. Remove small seal clamp bank by cutting it with a chisel.
2. Remove large end of seal from joint housing by prying up crimped edge on seal adapter. Drive seal adapter and seal off of joint housing with hammer and chisel, Fig. 12.

   NOTE: Use care when removing seal adapter not to damage it or the seal.

3. Slide seal and adapter down axle

shaft until joint is exposed.

NOTE: Do not allow spider leg balls to fall off by accident as adapter is moved.

4. Remove spider leg balls.
5. Remove spider outer snap ring, Fig. 13.
6. Tap spider assembly from shaft.
7. Reverse procedure to install, being sure to stake seal adapter to joint housing, Fig. 14.

Right Hand Output Shaft

1. Disconnect negative battery cable.
2. Raise car and install a short length of rubber hose on lower control arm torsion bar connector, Fig. 15.
3. Remove six drive axle-to-output shaft bolts and lock washers.
4. Remove output shaft support mounting bolts.
5. Rotate inboard end of drive axle rearward.
6. Pull output shaft out until it clears final drive then lower splined end and remove from car.

Right Hand Output Shaft Bearing, Replace

1. Remove output shaft as described above.
2. Remove three output shaft bearing retainer-to-support bolts.
3. Using two fabricated steel plates and four $\frac{3}{8}$ x 24 bolts five inches long illustrated in Fig. 16, tighten bolts alternately to press out bearing.

Left Hand Output Shaft

1. Remove left drive axle.
2. Remove output shaft retaining bolt and pull shaft out of final drive.

Final Drive, Replace

The final drive unit is not serviced but

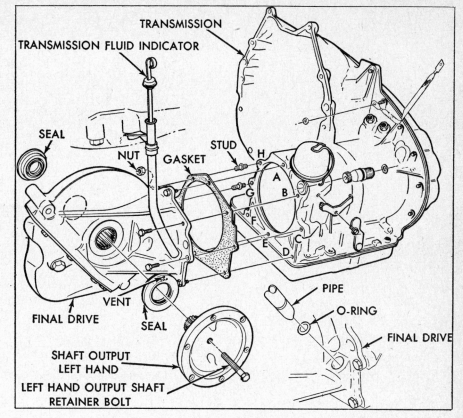

Fig. 17   Final drive attachment

is replaced as a unit.

1. Disconnect negative battery cable.
2. Remove approximately one gallon of fluid from transmission then remove transmission filler tube and plug tube hole.
3. Remove bolts "A" and "B" and nut "H", Fig. 17.
4. Remove bolt securing transmission oil cooler lines to final drive.
5. Remove nut from large through bolt, final drive support bracket to final drive.
6. Disconnect left front engine mount support bracket from engine. And final drive support bracket from left front engine mount support.
7. Remove right output shaft as outlined above.
8. Remove six left output shaft-to-drive axle bolts and lock washers.
9. Loosen final drive cover screws and drain fluid, then remove cover.
10. Compress left hand inner constant velocity joint and secure drive axle to frame with a piece of wire to provide clearance.
11. Remove final drive support bracket.
12. Remove remaining final drive-to-transmission bolts and nut "G".
13. Disengage final drive splines from transmission.

NOTE: To avoid damage to seals, final drive unit should be supported by a suitable jack and proper alignment must be maintained throughout removal.

14. Remove final drive unit from underside of car by sliding unit toward front of car, permitting ring gear to rotate up over steering linkage and work unit free from car.
15. Reverse procedure to install, being very careful to maintain proper final drive-to-transmission alignment to prevent seal damage.

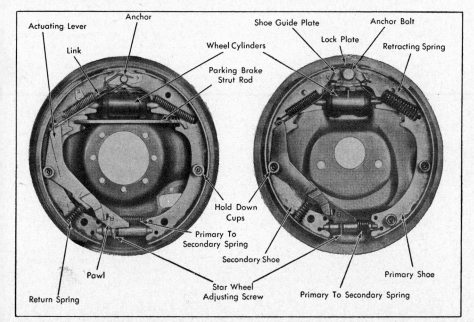

Fig. 18   Right front and rear brake mechanism, 1966-68. Rear only 1969-72

Fig. 19 Adjusting front brakes through holes in brake drums. Hooked tool shown is used to hold pawl free of star wheel while adjusting front brakes on 1966-68 models

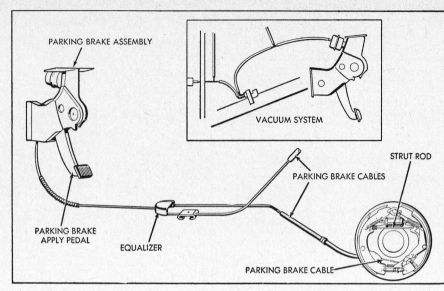

Fig. 21 Parking brake linkage. 1966-72

BRAKE ADJUSTMENTS
1966-72 Self-Adjusting Brakes

These brakes, Fig. 18, have self-adjusting shoe mechanisms that assure correct lining-to-drum clearances at all times. The automatic adjusters operate only when the brakes are applied as the car is moving rearward or when the car comes to an uphill stop.

Although the brakes are self-adjusting, an initial adjustment is necessary after the brake shoes have been relined or replaced, or when the length of the star wheel adjuster has been changed during some other service operation.

Frequent usage of an automatic transmission forward range to halt reverse vehicle motion may prevent the automatic adjusters from functioning, thereby inducing low pedal heights. Should low pedal heights be encountered, it is recommended that numerous forward and reverse stops be made with a moderate pedal effort until satisfactory pedal height is obtained.

NOTE

If a low pedal height condition cannot be corrected by making numerous reverse stops (provided the hydraulic system is free of air) it indicates that the self-adjusting mechanism is not functioning. Therefore, it will be necessary to remove the brake drum, clean, free up and lubricate the adjusting mechanism. Then adjust the brakes, being sure the parking brake is fully released.

Manual Shoe Adjustment

1. Check fluid level in master cylinder and add fluid as necessary to a level 1/4" below top of reservoir.
2. Check front wheel bearing adjustment.
3. Check to make certain that parking brake cable and linkage, including levers on rear secondary shoes, are free.
4. Tighten star wheel until brake drums can just be rotated forward with a two-foot bar placed between wheel studs.
5. Disengage adjusting pawl from star wheel with a hooked tool and back off star wheel 40 notches, Fig. 19.
6. Install wheels and drive car alternately forward and backward, applying brakes moderately in each direction until pedal travel is normal and brakes are adjusted satisfactorily.

PARKING BRAKE, ADJUST
1968-72

1. With service brakes properly adjusted, lubricate parking brake linkage at equalizer and cable stud with heat-resistant lubricant, and check for free movement of cables.
2. Depress parking brake pedal about 1 3/4" from full released position.
3. Raise rear wheels off floor.
4. Hold brake cable and stud from turning and tighten equalizer nut until a slight drag is felt on either wheel (going forward). After each turn of equalizer nut, check to see if either wheel begins to drag.
5. Release parking brake. No brake drag should be felt at either rear wheel. Operate several times to check adjustment. After adjustment is completed, parking brake pedal should travel 1 3/4" to 2 3/4".

VACUUM RELEASE PARKING BRAKE
1966-72

The foot-operated parking brake is mounted on the cowl to the left of the steering column. It incorporates a vacuum release, Fig. 21, operated by a vacuum diaphragm that is connected to the parking brake mechanism. When the transmission selector is moved into any Drive position, a vacuum valve in the neutral safety switch opens, allowing diaphragm to be actuated by engine vacuum.

The diaphragm is connected by a link to a release mechanism on the parking brake. Vacuum acting on the diaphragm unlocks the parking brake pedal, permitting it to return to the release position by spring action. Any abnormal leaks in the vacuum release system will prevent proper brake release. A manual release is provided and may be used if the automatic release is inoperative or if manual release is desired at any time.

Testing Vacuum Release

1. If the mechanism is inoperative, first check for damaged or kinked vacuum hoses and for loose hose connections at the diaphragm, vacuum release valve at neutral safety switch, and at engine manifold connection.
2. Check adjustment of neutral safety switch and operation of vacuum release valve.
3. Check diaphragm piston travel by running engine and moving transmission selector lever from drive to neutral. The manual release lever should move up and down as vacuum is applied and released. If no movement is observed, or if movement is slow (more than 1 or 2 seconds to complete the full stroke) diaphragm is leaking and should be replaced.
4. Check brake release with vacuum applied. If diaphragm piston completes full stroke but does not release brake, a malfunction of the pedal assembly is indicated, and the complete parking brake assembly should be replaced.
5. Check operation of parking brake with engine off. Parking brake should remain engaged regardless of transmission selector lever position. If not, replace parking brake assembly.

POWER BRAKE, REPLACE

Service Bulletin

A sign of brake fluid dampness below the master cylinder at the power brake unit or on wheel cylinders at the bottom of the boot, does not necessarily indicate that these cylinders are leaking.

A small amount of fluid leakage at these areas can occur due to the creeping action of a very light film of fluid on the cylinder bores around the seals. This action provides proper seal lubrication. In addition, normal brake heat will pro-duce a slight escape of lubricant from the impregnated, porous-metal wheel cylinder pistons.

Normal dampness at the master cylinder or wheel cylinders is not easily distinguishable from a definite leak. Therefore, this condition must be checked carefully.

If there is sufficient dampness to form a "teardrop" of fluid at the bottom of the master cylinder or on the bottom of the wheel cylinders at the boot area, the rate of fluid seepage is too high and the cause should be determined and corrected.

1966-71

1. Disconnect hydraulic lines from master cylinder on power unit. Cap line fittings to prevent dirt entering system.
2. Disconnect vacuum hose from vacuum check valve on power unit. On 1967-71, remove steering column lower cover.
3. Remove cotter pin and spring spacer that attach power unit push rod to brake pedal relay lever.
4. Unfasten and remove power unit from cowl.

Front End and Steering Section

FRONT SUSPENSION 1966-72 STANDARD CARS

The front suspension system consists of two upper and lower control arm assemblies, steel coil springs, shock absorbers, front diagonal tie struts, and a stabilizer bar. Rubber bushings are used at all frame attaching points.

Ball joints are used at the outer ends of the upper and lower control arms. The upper ball joint is pressed into the upper control arm and tack-welded to the arm at two points. It connects the upper control arm to the steering knuckle through a camber adjustment eccentric. The lower ball joint, a tension type joint, is pressed into the lower control arm. It connects the lower control arm to the steering knuckle.

Beginning with 1970 models the steering knuckle is a combination steering knuckle, brake caliper support and steering arm.

The upper control arms pivot at their inner ends on two flanged rubber bushings, one at each end of the one-piece control arm shaft which is bolted to the top surface of the spring tower on the front frame crossmember. The lower control arms pivot on a single rubber bushing that is bolted to the front suspension frame crossmember. Diagonal tie struts are used to control the fore and aft movement of the wheels. The struts are bolted to the outer ends of the lower control arms and extend through the frame crossmember. Rubber bushings and a steel spacer are used at the frame mount.

Lubrication

The ball joints are packed with lubricant and sealed at assembly and should not require further lubrication throughout their service life under normal driving conditions. The only maintenance they normally require is an inspection of the seals for physical damage each time the engine oil is changed.

Service plugs are provided in the ball joint covers so that the joints may be packed in the event a seal should become damaged and require replacement. Both the seals and plugs are serviceable.

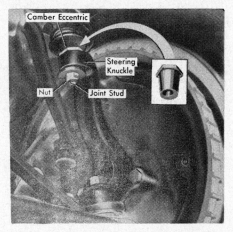

Fig. 1   Camber adjustment eccentric. 1966-72

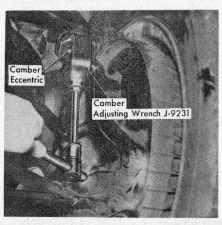

Fig. 2   Adjusting camber. 1966-72

Wheel Alignment, 1966-72 Standard Cars

Camber, Adjust

Adjustment is made at the camber eccentric located in the steering knuckle upper support, Fig. 1. The upper ball joint stud fits through the camber eccentric and knuckle support. Turning the eccentric repositions the upper ball joint stud.

To adjust camber, loosen the ball joint stud nut one turn and tap bottom of stud with soft mallet to loosen eccentric. Using a suitable wrench, Fig. 2, turn the eccentric as required to obtain the camber specifications listed in the *Wheel Alignment* chart. The final position of the stud should be in the rear portion of the camber eccentric in order to keep steering angle correct. After proper adjustment has been established, torque stud nut to 60 ft. lbs.

NOTE

If the camber eccentric is too tight to be adjusted a tool can easily be made by cutting a piece of 7/16" diameter steel rod about 20" long, chamfering it on one end and rounding it off on the other end.

If the eccentric must be freed for a camber adjustment, position the car on a wheel alignment machine, backing off the self-locking nut on the ball joint stud one turn, and thread a standard nut halfway on the stud. Insert the rounded end of the tool inside the nut and against the bottom of the stud. Then pound on the end of the tool with a heavy hammer to break the camber eccentric loose.

In cases where the eccentric is to be removed but comes loose from the stud instead of the knuckle, place a washer against the bottom of the eccentric and drive the eccentric out from below, using the same tool as described above. When the eccentric must be removed in this manner, inspect it for damage and replace if necessary.

Caster, Adjust

Adjustment is made by turning the retaining nuts on the forward ends of the

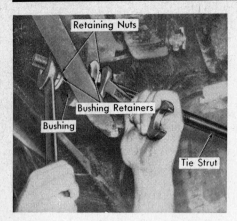

Fig. 3 Adjusting caster. 1966-72

tie-struts at the frame front crossmember, Fig. 3. To gain access to the retaining nuts, it is necessary to remove the splash shield.

Proper caster adjustment is obtained by shortening or lengthening the struts between the lower suspension arms and the frame front crossmember. To provide more negative caster, lengthen the struts by loosening the front bushing retaining nuts and tightening the rear bushing retaining nuts. One turn of the nuts results in approximately $\frac{1}{2}°$ change in caster.

To provide more positive caster, shorten the struts by loosening the rear bushing retaining nuts and tightening the front bushing retaining nuts.

After proper adjustment has been made, tighten front retaining nuts to 60 ft. lbs., being sure to hold the rear nut with a wrench so as not to disturb the adjustment.

Toe-In, Adjust

Toe-in is adjusted by turning the tie rod adjusters at the outer ends of each tie rod after loosening the clamp bolts. (Both right and left pivot ends have right-hand threads.) Be sure to turn both adjusters an equal amount so that the relation of the steering gear high spot to the straight ahead position of the front wheels will not be changed.

When adjustment has been completed according to the specification listed in the *Wheel Alignment* chart, tighten nuts on clamp bolts to 20 ft. lbs. torque.

NOTE

Make certain that both inner and outer tie rod ball pivots are centered in their respective housings prior to tightening the tie rod adjusting clamps.

If the tie rods are not properly positioned, a binding condition may occur, resulting in poor return of wheels to the straight ahead position.

Each tie rod should be checked after adjustment by grasping the center of the tie rod and rotating it fore and aft. The movement should be equal in both directions. If not, it indicates that the pivot studs are not properly positioned.

Wheel Bearings, Adjust

Service Bulletin

Looseness at a front wheel does not necessarily indicate worn bearings or a loose spindle nut, since the tapered roller bearings used on front wheels of all 1966-70 standard Cadillacs should not be pre-loaded and normally can have up to .004″ end play.

When adjusting the front wheel bearings, raise the front of the car and make sure that the wheel is completely seated on the spindle. Tighten the adjusting nut to 30 ft. lbs. torque and rotate the drum to be sure all parts are properly seated and the threads are free. Then back off the nut $\frac{1}{4}$ turn. If the cotter pin cannot be installed in either of the two available holes in the spindle with the nut in this position, loosen the adjusting nut until the cotter pin can be installed. The wheel should spin freely.

Wheel Bearings, Replace (Disc Brakes)

1968-72

1. Remove two thirds of the total fluid capacity in the front master cylinder reservoir to prevent fluid overflow when the piston is pushed back in its bore.
2. Raise car and remove front wheels.
3. Position 7 inch "C" clamp on the caliper so that solid side rests against the back of the caliper. The screw end rests against the back of the outboard shoe.
4. Tighten "C" clamp until caliper moves out far enough to bottom the piston in its bore. This will release the pressure on the shoe and lining assemblies.
5. Remove "C" clamp.
6. Remove two bolts which hold caliper to support plate.

NOTE: It is not necessary to remove brake hose from caliper during this operation.

7. Slide caliper off of disc. Do not allow caliper to hang from brake hose.
8. Remove spindle nut and hub and disc assembly. Grease retainer and inner bearing can now be removed.

1967

1. Raise car and remove front wheels.
2. Remove two bolts securing caliper to steering knuckle and remove caliper.

NOTE: Disconnect brake line only where necessary.

3. Remove spindle nut and hub and disc assembly. Grease retainer and inner bearing can now be removed.

Checking Ball Joints For Wear 1966-72 Std. Cars

Upper Ball Joint

Using the regular ball joint stud nut and a second nut as a lock nut, turn joint in its socket with a torque wrench. If the torque is not within the limits of 2 to 4 ft-lbs, the joint should be replaced.

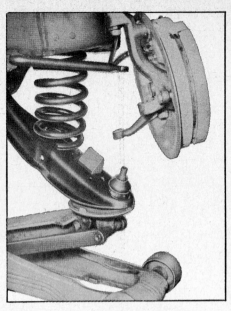

Fig. 6 Coil spring installation. 1966-72

Lower Ball Joint

The lower ball joint is designed to turn freely in its socket and cannot be checked with a torque wrench. It should be checked by noting the amount of free play as the joint is worked vertically in its socket. Free play should not exceed $\frac{1}{16}$″. Replace joint if it exceeds this limit.

Ball Joints, Replace

The upper ball joints are pressed into the upper control arm and tack-welded to the arm. Therefore, the upper ball joints are supplied only with the upper control arm. The lower ball joints are pressed into the lower control arms but they are replaceable.

Shock Absorber, Replace

The shock absorbers are removed through the bottom of the lower control arm after unfastening it at the top and bottom.

To install, place the retainer and rubber grommet on the upper stem and fully extend the shock absorber rod. Insert the shock absorber up into the coil spring and guide the stem through the tower in the crossmember. Then place the lower end in position on the lower control arm. Install bolt, washer and nut and torque nut to 90-110 ft. lbs. Fasten shock absorber at top.

Tie-Strut & Bushings 1970-72 Std. Cars

Raise car and disconnect stabilizer link from lower arm on side from which tie-strut is to be removed. Remove strut and bushings and replace as follows:

1. Replace rear locknut on threaded end of tie-strut and run nut about $\frac{3}{4}$″ from end of thread.
2. Install rear bushing retainer on tie-strut with concave side against nut.
3. Insert metal spacer part way through conical shaped bushing from small end and install on tie-

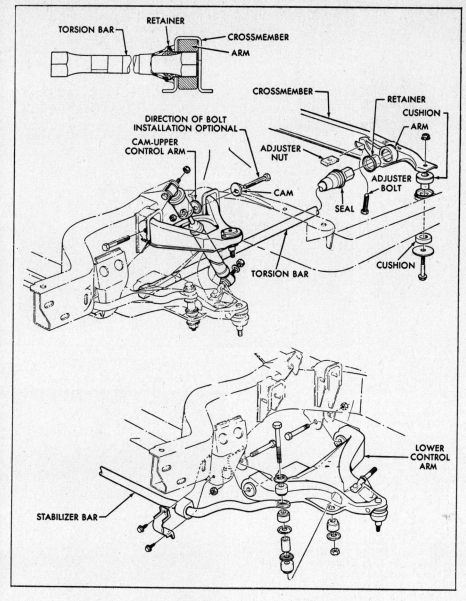

Fig. 7 Front suspension disassembled. 1967-72 Eldorado

5. Install front bushing on end of strut and slide bushing into position in frame crossmember. Front bushing should lock in rear bushing.
6. Install front bushing retainer on threaded end of strut with flat side against bushing. Start front nut on end of strut but do not tighten.
7. Secure opposite end of strut to lower control arm and torque bolts to 55 ft. lbs.
8. Connect stabilizer link.
9. Lower car and with car weight on all four wheels, tighten front nut to 55-70 ft. lbs.
10. Tighten rear nut, compressing bushing until retainer bottoms on metal spacer in bushing.
11. Adjust caster as outlined previously.
12. Install splash shield.

Coil Spring, Replace

1. Disconnect shock absorber at upper end.
2. Raise front of car and place jack stands under frame side rails.
3. Disconnect stabilizer link from side from which spring is to be removed.
4. Disconnect tie strut at lower arm.
5. Remove shock absorber.
6. Remove wheel and brake drum.
7. Place a floor jack under outer end of lower control arm, then separate lower ball joint from steering knuckle.
8. Lower floor jack and remove spring, Fig. 6.
9. Reverse procedure to install.

ELDORADO FRONT SUSPENSION

The front suspension consists of two upper and two lower control arms, a stabilizer bar, shock absorbers and a right and left torsion bar, Fig. 7. Torsion bars are used instead of the conventional coil springs. The front end of the torsion bar is attached to the lower control arm. The rear of the torsion bar is mounted into an adjustable arm in the torsion bar crossmember. The standing height of the car is controlled by this adjustment.

Standing Height, Adjust

The standing height must be checked and adjusted if necessary before checking and adjusting front wheel alignment. The standing height is controlled by the adjustment setting of the torsion bar adjusting bolt, Fig. 7. Clockwise rotation of the bolt increases standing height: counterclockwise rotation decrease standing height.

To check, measure from top of the upper shock absorber mounting bolt to the top of the lower shock mount bolt. As shown in Fig. 8, this dimension should be 14.6". If dimensions are not correct, adjust as required.

Wheel Alignment, Adjust

After checking and, if necessary, adjusting standing height, check camber and caster as follows:

Camber is adjusted by turning the upper control arm rear cam bolt, Fig. 9. Caster is adjusted by turning the upper

strut with small end toward front of car.
4. With strut held in horizontal position install threaded end through frame front cross member.
5. Position opposite end of strut on lower arm with pointed end inward, and install attaching bolts and nuts loosely.
6. Install front bushing on end of strut, cupped side toward frame, and slide bushing against cross member.
7. Install front bushing retainer on strut with concave side against bushing.
8. Start new locknut on threaded end of strut and connect stabilizer link to lower arm.
9. Lower car and with car weight on all four wheels, position front bushing on metal spacer and tighten locknut on front end of strut to 35 ft. lbs.

10. Tighten tie-strut to lower arm nuts and bolts to 55 ft. lbs.

Tie-Strut & Bushings 1966-69 Std. Cars

Raise car and jack up under frame side rails. Remove splash shield and disconnect stabilizer link from lower control arm on side tie-strut is to be removed. Remove strut and bushings. Then replace as follows:
1. Insert spacer in rear bushing and install bushing and spacer in frame through rear side of crossmember.
2. Install nut on tie-strut and run nut to bottom of thread.
3. Install rear bushing retainer on strut with concave side toward nut.
4. With strut held in horizontal position, install threaded end of strut through rear bushing in frame crossmember.

Fig. 8   Checking standing height. 1967-72 Eldorado

Fig. 9   Caster-camber cam locations. 1967-72 Eldorado

Fig. 10   Horizontal check for ball joint wear. 1967-72 Eldorado

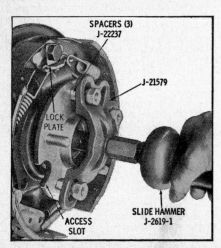

Fig. 12   Removing hub assembly. Eldorado

control arm front and rear cam bolts. Wheels must be in straight ahead position. Use camber reading scale for making this adjustment.
1. Turn rear cam bolt so camber reading is 1/4° more than original setting for every 1° of caster change required for a correct reading. Turn to plus side of camber if caster is negative and to the negative side of camber if caster is positive.
2. Turn front cam bolt so camber will return to original setting.
3. Recheck caster reading.

NOTE: If a problem arises where there is not enough cam adjustment remaining to obtain correct reading:
1. Turn front cam bolt so high part of cam is pointing up.
2. Turn rear cam bolt so high part of cam is pointing down. This is a location to start from and a correct reading can be obtained with the above procedure.
3. Tighten upper control arm cam nuts to 75 ft-lbs. Hold bolt head securely as any movement of the cam will affect the final setting and will require a recheck of camber and caster adjustments.

Toe-In, Adjust

Toe-in is adjusted by turning the tie rod adjusting tubes at outer ends of each tie rod after loosening clamp bolts. Readings should be taken only when front wheels are straight ahead and steering gear is on its high spot.
1. Center steering wheel, raise car and check wheel run-out.
2. Loosen tie rod adjuster nuts and adjust tie rods to obtain the specified toe-in.
3. Tighten tie rod adjuster nuts to 20 ft-lbs.

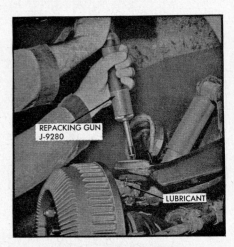

Fig. 11   Repacking upper ball joint. 1967-72 Eldorado

Fig. 13   Removing front wheel bearing. Eldorado

4. Position adjuster clamps so that opening of clamps are facing up. Interference with front suspension components could occur while turning if clamps are facing down.

Wheel Bearings, Replace

1. Raise car and remove front wheels.
2. Remove drum.

NOTE: For disc brakes remove two bolts securing caliper to steering knuckle and remove caliper.

3. Remove drive axle pin, nut and washer.
4. Position access slot in hub so that each of the attaching bolts can be removed.

NOTE: On disc brakes the attaching bolts are removed from behind the splash shield.

5. Using slide hammer puller, remove hub, Fig. 12.
6. Remove bearing from hub with puller, Fig. 13.
7. Press new bearing into hub.

Ball Joints

Vertical Check for Wear
1. Raise car and position jack stands under lower control arms as near as possible to each ball joint.
2. Clamp vise grips on end of drive axle and position a dial indicator so that dial indicator ball rests on vise grip.
3. Place a pry bar between lower control arm and outer race and pry down on bar. Reading must not exceed 1/8".

Horizontal Check for Wear
1. With car raised as above, position dial indicator as shown in Fig. 10.
2. Grasp front wheel and push in on bottom of tire while pulling out at top. Read dial gauge, then reverse push-pull procedure.
3. Horizontal deflection on gauge should not exceed 1/8" at wheel rim. This procedure checks both the upper and lower ball joints.

Upper Ball Joint, Replace
1. Remove upper control arm and grind head off three rivets. Using a hammer and punch, drive out rivets.
2. Install new ball joint, securing it in place with three bolts and nuts contained in the kit.
3. Install upper control arm and lubricate ball joint fitting until grease escapes between seal and steering knuckle, Fig. 11.

Lower Ball Joint, Replace
1. Remove lower control arm and cut off two rivet heads from sides of control arm. Grind off head of rivet at bottom of control arm, then drive rivet out of arm.
2. Install service ball joint, securing it to control arm with bolts and nuts contained in kit.

Torsion Bar, Replace
1. Raise and place car on jack stands.

2. Remove wheel, the install one or two nuts to prevent drum from falling off car.
3. Remove hub cotter pin, nut and washer, and brake line clip attached to frame.
4. Place jack under lower control arm on side torsion bar is to be removed.
5. Disconnect upper ball joint and remove nut and brake line clip.
6. Disconnect shock absorber at lower end.
7. Pull tie rod from steering knuckle.
8. Disconnect stabilizer bar.
9. Disconnect lower ball joint.
10. Disengage brake backing plate from drive axle and wire it to upper control arm.
11. Remove lower control arm-to-frame attaching nuts. *Do not remove bolts yet.*
12. Lower jack from under lower control arm. The torsion bar is now unloaded and lower control arm is hanging free.
13. Remove torsion bar adjusting bolt.
14. Pull down on outer end of lower control arm with one hand, while reaching back with the other hand to remove torsion bar adjusting nut from frame crossmember.
15. Remove lower control arm-to-frame attaching bolts and disengage arm from frame mounts.
16. Slide lower control arm off torsion bar and slide bar out of frame crossmember retainer and remove from car.

Inspection
1. Check rubber seal for damage and replace if necessary.
2. A new retainer must be used when torsion bar is replaced.
3. Check torsion bar for nicks, scratches or dents. If any of these conditions exist the torsion bar must be replaced.

Installation
1. Lubricate both ends of bar for about 3" with lubriplate.
2. Lubricate bar retainer in crossmember.
3. Place torsion bar in retainer. *Torsion bar ends are marked and must be installed as indicated as it is possible to reverse bar when installing.*
4. Lubricate lower control arm torsion bar connector and position control arm on bar. *When installing control arm, make sure that arm is installed in the "on car position" and is level. Also check torsion bar, making certain that it is fully seated in crossmember.*
5. With a jack, raise lower control arm and install in chassis mounts. Do not tighten nuts yet.
6. Pull down on lower control arm with one hand, and with the other hand, install torsion bar lock nut through chassis crossmember and under arm. Lubricate adjusting bolt with E.P. chassis lube and install bolt. Do not tighten bolt yet.
7. Install brake backing plate.
8. Install lower ball joint, tighten nut to 40 ft-lbs and install cotter pin.
9. Install lower ball joint, tighten nut to 40 ft-lbs and install cotter pin.
10. Install upper ball joint to steering knuckle.
11. Complete the installation and lower car. Tighten nuts that were left

loose. Finally, check standing height and wheel alignment as outlined previously.

POWER STEERING, REPLACE

Service Bulletin
Whenever steering or front end work is being performed on a 1966-1968 car, it is good practice to check the three steering gear mounting screws, and retorque them to 45 ft-lbs. Any mounting screw that is found below 5 ft-lbs or over-torqued above 60 ft-lbs should be replaced.

1968-72 Standard Cars
1. Disconnect pressure and return line hoses at steering gear. Have container ready to catch dripping oil. Secure hoses in raised position to prevent loss of fluid.
2. Raise car and use a puller to disconnect pitman arm from steering linkage.
3. Remove screw that holds flexible coupling to steering shaft.
4. Unfasten gear from frame side rail, lower gear down and out of car with pitman arm attached.
5. Reverse procedure to install.

1967-72 Eldorado
1. Disconnect hydraulic hoses at rear of pump reservoir. Cap pump fittings to prevent drainage of fluid from pump. Also, cap or tape hose fittings. If equipped with steering pump cooler, disconnect return hose at cooler.
2. Pull pitman arm from drag link.
3. Remove two bolts holding flexible coupling together.
4. Unfasten gear from frame and move gear forward and down out of car.
5. Reverse procedure to install. Check fluid level and bleed hydraulic system as outlined for standard cars.

1966-67 Standard Cars
1. Disconnect pressure and return line hoses at rear of pump reservoir. Cap pump fittings to prevent drainage of fluid from pump.
2. Jack up car and place jack stands near outer ends of lower suspension arms.
3. Disconnect pitman arm from steering gear.
4. Remove screw that holds flexible coupling to upper steering shaft.
5. Remove three screws that hold gear housing to frame and remove gear.
6. Reverse foregoing procedure to install the steering gear. Fill reservoir to level mark. Replace filler cap, start engine and idle for three minutes, then check for leaks in reservoir shell.
7. Any air trapped in the system should be bled out by running engine at a fast idle for about two minutes. Turn wheels occasionally from right to left without hitting the stops. Recheck fluid level after bleeding system.

CAMARO · CHEVELLE · CHEVROLET
CHEVY II · CORVETTE

OLD CAR SPECIFICATIONS: For 1946-65 Tune Up and Wheel Alignment Specifications see back of book.
*This material covered only in the "Service Trade Edition" of this manual.

INDEX OF SERVICE OPERATIONS

SERIAL NUMBER LOCATION: Plate on left front door pillar or top of left side instrument panel

ENGINE NUMBER LOCATION

4 & 6 CYL.: Pad at front righthand side of cylinder block at rear of distributor

V8 ENGINES: Pad at front righthand side of cylinder block

ENGINE IDENTIFICATION CODE

Engines are identified in the following table by the code letter or letters immediately following the engine serial number.

CAMARO

CODE			CODE			CODE		
AM	6-230 with M/T	1969	CKB	8-350 165 H.P.	1972	JJ	8-396 with A/H	1969
AN	6-230 with P/G, T/D	1969	CKK	8-350 with M/T, 175, 200 H.P.	1972	JL	8-396 with SHPE, T/H	1969
AO	6-230 with T/H	1969	CKD	8-350 with T/H, 175, 200 H.P.	1972	JM	8-396 with A/H, T/H	1969
AP	6-230 with A/C	1969	CKS	8-350 with M/T, 255 H.P.	1972	LA	6-230 with M/T	1967
AQ	6-230 with P/G, T/D, A/C	1969	CLD	8-400 with M/T, 350 H.P.	1971	LB	6-230 with M/T, A/C	1967
AR	6-230 with A/C, T/H	1969	CLC	8-400 with M/T, 350 H.P.	1971	LC	6-230 with AIR	1967
BA	6-230 with M/T	1968	CNC	8-307 with M/T	1970	LD	6-230 with AIR, A/C	1967
BB	6-230 with M/T, A/C	1968	CND	8-307 with 4 sp. tr.	1970	LE	6-230 with P/G	1967
BB	6-250 with P/G, T/D	1969	CNE	8-307 with P/G	1970	LF	6-230 with P/G, A/C	1967
BC	6-230 with HDC	1968	CNF	8-307 with T/H	1970	LG	6-230 with P/G, AIR	1967
BC	6-250 with P/G, T/D, A/C	1969	CNI	8-350 with M/T, 250 H.P.	1970	LH	6-230 with AIR, A/C, P/G	1967
BD	6-230 with A/C	1968	CNJ	8-350 with M/T, 300 H.P.	1970	LN	6-250 with M/T	1967
BD	6-250 with T/H	1969	CNK	8-350 with P/G, 300 H.P.	1970	LO	6-250 with M/T, A/C	1967
BE	6-250 with M/T	1969	CNM	8-350 with P/G, 250 H.P.	1970	LP	6-250 with AIR	1967
BF	6-230 with P/G	1968	CNN	8-350 with T/H, 250 H.P.	1970	LQ	6-250 with AIR, A/C	1967
BF	6-250 with A/C	1969	CRE	8-350 with T/H, 300 H.P.	1970	LR	6-250 with M/T, A/C	1967
BH	6-230 with P/G, A/C	1968	CRF	6-250 with M/T	1970	LS	6-250 with AIR	1967
BH	6-250 with T/H, A/C	1969	CRG	6-250 with M/T	1970	LT	6-250 with AIR, A/C	1967
CM	6-250 with M/T	1968	CTB	8-350 with M/T, 320 H.P.	1970	LU	6-250 with P/G	1967
CN	6-250 with A/C	1968	CTC	8-350 with T/H, 320 H.P.	1970	MA	8-327 with 2 BC, M/T	1967-68
CQ	6-250 with P/G	1968	CTW	8-400 with T/H, 350 H.P.	1970	MB	8-327 with 2 BC, AIR	1967
CR	6-250 with P/G, A/C	1968	CTX	8-400 with M/T, 350 H.P.	1970	MD	8-283 with 2 BC, 4 sp. tr.	1967
CAA	6-250 with M/T	1971	CTY	8-400 with T/H, 375 H.P.	1970	ME	8-327 with 2 BC, P/G	1967-68
CAB	6-250 with P/G	1971	DA	8-307 with M/T	1969	MF	8-327 with 2 BC, P/G, AIR	1967
CBG	6-250 with M/T	1972	DC	8-307 with P/G	1969	MJ	8-283 with 2 BC, P/G	1967
CBJ	6-250 with P/G	1972	DD	8-307 with T/H	1969	MK	8-327 with M/T	1967
CCA	8-307	1971	DE	8-307 with 4 sp. tr.	1969	ML	8-327 with AIR	1967
CCG	6-250 with M/T	1970	DZ	8-302 with 4 BC	1969	MM	8-327 with P/G	1967
CCK	6-250 with T/H, taxi & police	1970	EI	8-396 Hi Perf.	1967	MN	8-327 with P/G, AIR	1967
CCL	6-250 with M/T, taxi & police	1970	EQ	8-396 with Hi Perf.	1967	MO	8-302 with 4 BC	1967-68
CCM	6-250 with P/G, taxi & police	1970	EY	8-396 with Hi Perf., Air	1967	MP	8-302 with 4 BC, AIR	1967
CCZ	6-250 with M/T	1970	FA	8-327 with M/T	1969	MQ	8-396 HPE	1967-68
CGB	8-350 with P/G, 250 H.P.	1971	FB	8-327 with P/G	1969	MR	8-396 with AIR, HPE	1967-68
CGB	8-350 with P/G	1972	FC	8-327 with T/H	1969	MS	8-350 with M/T	1967-68
CGK	8-350 with M/T, 300 H.P.	1971	FH	8-327 with T/H	1969	MT	8-350 with AIR	1967
CGL	8-350 with T/H, 300 H.P.	1971	HA	8-350 with M/T	1969	MT	8-396 with SHPE, A/H	1968
CGP	8-350 with M/T, 360 H.P.	1971	HB	8-350 with T/H	1969	MU	8-350 with P/G	1967-68
CGR	8-350 with T/H, 360 H.P.	1971	HC	8-350 with 2 BC	1969	MV	8-350 with P/G, AIR	1967
CJF	8-396 with T/H, 350 H.P.	1970	HD	8-350 with 2 BC, T/H	1969	MW	8-396 with M/T, A/T	1967-68
CJH	8-396 with M/T, 375 H.P.	1970	HE	8-350 with P/G	1969	MX	8-396 with HPE	1967-68
CJI	8-396 with T/H, 350 H.P.	1970	HF	8-350 with 2 BC, P/G	1969	MY	8-396 with T/H	1967-68
CJL	8-396 with T/H, 375 H.P.	1970	JB	8-396 with P/G	1969	MZ	8-396 with T/H, AIR	1967
CKG	8-307 with M/T	1972	JF	8-396 with HPE	1969	CLA	8-400 with M/T	1972
CKH	8-307 with P/G	1972	JG	8-396 with T/H	1969	CLB	8-400 with T/H	1972
CKO	8-400 with M/T, 375 H.P.	1970	JH	8-396 with SHPE	1969			
CKT	8-350 with T/H, 255 H.P.	1972	JI	8-396 with HPE, T/H	1969			

ENGINE IDENTIFICATION CODE—Continued

CHEVROLET

CODE		
BA	6-250 with M/T	1969
BG	6-250 with M/T, A/C	1969
CA	6-250 with M/T	1968
CC	6-250 with A/C	1968
CJ	6-250 with HDC	1968
CK	6-250 with HDC, A/C	1968
CM	6-250 with M/T	1968
CN	6-250 with A/C	1968
CQ	6-250 with P/G	1968
CR	6-250 with P/G, A/C	1968
CAA	6-250 with M/T	1971
CAB	6-250 with P/G, T/D	1971
CAC	6-250 with M/T, taxi & police	1971
CAD	6-250 with P/G, taxi & police	1971
CBH	6-250 with M/T, taxi & police	1972
CBJ	6-250 with P/G	1972
CBK	6-250 with P/G, taxi & police	1972
CNJ	6-250 with M/T	1972
CCM	6 cyl. with P/G, taxi & police	1970
CCG	6 cyl. with 3 sp. tr.	1970
CCH	6 cyl. with 3 sp. tr.	1970
CCK	6 cyl. T/H, taxi & police	1970
CCZ	6 cyl. with 3 sp. tr.	1970
CCL	6 cyl. with 3 sp. tr., taxi & police	1970
CAR	8-350 with T/H, taxi & police	1972
CKB	8-350 with M/T	1972
CSH	8-350 with M/T, police	1972
CSJ	8-350 with M/T	1972
CGA	8-350, with M/T, 250 H.P.	1971
CGB	8-350, with P/G, 250 H.P.	1971
CGC	8-350 with M/T, 250 H.P.	1971
CGJ	8-350 with T/H, taxi & police, 250 H.P.	1971
CJB	8-350 with M/T, police, 300 H.P.	1971
CKP	8-400 with T/H, 170 H.P.	1972
CLB	8-400 with T/H, 210, 240 H.P.	1972
CLR	8-400 with M/T, police	1972
CLK	8-400 with T/H, 265 H.P.	1971
CLP	8-400 with T/H, 300 H.P.	1971
CPD	8-454 with M/T, 390 H.P.	1971
CPG	8-454 with M/T, police, 390 H.P.	1971
CPD	8-454 with M/T	1972
CPG	8-454 with M/T, police	1972
CRF	6 cyl. with M/T	1970
CRG	6 cyl. with M/T	1970
CND	8-350 with M/T, 250 H.P.	1970

CODE		
CNP	8-350 with M/T, taxi & police, 250 H.P.	1970
CNQ	8-350 with M/T, 300 H.P.	1970
CNR	8-350 with T/H, 300 H.P.	1970
CNS	8-350 with P/G, police, 300 H.P.	1970
CNT	8-350 with T/H, police, 300 H.P.	1970
CNU	8-350 with P/G, 250 H.P.	1970
CNV	8-350 with T/H, 250 H.P.	1970
CNW	8-350 P/G, taxi & police, 250 H.P.	1970
CNX	8-350 T/H, taxi & police, 250 H.P.	1970
CGR	8-400 with M/T, 265 H.P.	1970
CGV	8-454 with M/T, 345 H.P.	1970
CGS	8-454 M/T, police, 345 H.P.	1970
CGT	8-454 with M/T, police, 390 H.P.	1970
CGU	8-454 with M/T, 390 H.P.	1970
DO	8-307 with M/T	1968
DP	8-307 with 4 sp. tr. S.S.	1968
DQ	8-307 with HDC	1968
DR	8-307 with P/G	1968
DS	8-307 with T.H.	1968
FA	6 cyl. with 3 sp. tr.	1966-67
FA	8-327 with M/T	1969
FB	8-327 with P/G	1969
FC	8-327 with T/H	1969
FE	6 cyl. with HDC	1966-67
FF	6 cyl. with HDC, A/C	1966-67
FH	8-327 with T/H	1969
FK	6 cyl. taxi	1966-67
FL	6 cyl. with 3 sp. tr., A/C	1966-67
FM	6 cyl. with P/G	1966-67
FP	6 cyl. taxi	1966-67
FR	6 cyl. with P/G, A/C	1966-67
FV	6 cyl. with AIR	1966-67
FW	6 cyl. with AIR, HDC	1966
FX	6 cyl. with AIR, HDC, A/C	1966
FY	6 cyl. with AIR, A/C	1966-67
FZ	6 cyl. taxi with AIR	1966-67
GA	8-283 with 3 sp. tr.	1966-67
GC	8-283 with 4 sp. tr.	1966-67
GF	8-283 with P/G	1966-67
GK	8-283 with AIR	1966-67
GP	6 cyl. with P/G, AIR	1966-67
GQ	6 cyl. with P/G, A/C, AIR	1966-67
GR	6 cyl. taxi with P/G, AIR	1966-67

CODE		
GS	8-283 with 4 sp. tr., AIR	1966-67
GT	8-283 with P/G, AIR	1966-67
GU	8-283 with HDC	1967
HA	8-327 with 3 sp. tr.	1966-68
HB	8-327 with 3 sp. tr., HPE	1966
HB	8-327 with AIR	1967
HB	8-327 with HDC	1968
HC	8-327 with P/G	1966-68
HF	8-327 with P/G, AIR	1966-67
HF	8-327 with T/H	1968
HG	8-350 with M/T	1969
HH	8-350 with M/T	1969
HI	8-327 with 4 BC	1968
HI	8-350 with 2 BC	1969
HJ	8-327 with 4 BC, P/G	1968
HJ	8-350 with 2 BC, T/H	1969
HK	8-350 with P/G	1969
HL	8-327 with 4 BC, HDC	1968
HL	8-350 with 2 BC, P/G	1969
HM	8-327 with 4 BC, T/H	1968
HM	8-350 with 2 BC, T/H	1969
HN	8-350 with T/H	1969
IA	8-396 with M/T	1966-68
IB	8-396 with AIR	1966-67
IC	8-396 with P/G, AIR	1966-67
ID	8-327 with SHPE	1966-68
IG	8-396 with P/G	1966-68
IH	8-427 with M/T	1966-68
II	8-427 with AIR	1966-67
IJ	8-427 with T/H	1966-67
IJ	8-427 with T/H	1968
IN	8-396 with T/H, AIR	1967
IO	8-427 with T/H, AIR	1967
IV	8-396 with T/H	1966-68
JN	8-396 with 2 BC	1969
JQ	8-396 with 2 BC, T/H	1969
KE	8-327 with 4 sp. tr.	1967
LA	8-427 with HPE	1969
LB	8-427 with 4 BC	1969
LC	8-427 with HPE, T/H	1969
LD	8-427 with SHPE	1969
LE	8-427 with 4 BC, T/H	1969
LH	8-427 with HPE	1969
LI	8-427 with T/H	1969
LS	8-427 with SHPE, T/H	1969

CHEVELLE & MONTE CARLO

CODE		
AA	6-194 with M/T	1966
AC	6-194 with HDC	1966
AD	6-230 with T/H	1969
AG	6-194 with A/C	1966
AH	6-194 with HDC, A/C	1966
AK	6-194 taxi	1966
AL	6-194 with P/G	1966
AM	6-230 with M/T	1969
AN	6-230 with P/G, T/D	1969
AN	6-194 taxi with P/G	1966
AP	6-230 with A/C	1969
AQ	6-230 with P/G, T/D, A/C	1969
AR	6-230 with T/H, A/C	1969
AR	6-194 with P/G, A/C	1966
AS	6-194 with AIR	1966
AT	6-194 with A/C, AIR	1966
AU	6-194 with HDC, A/C, AIR	1966
AV	6-194 taxi with AIR	1966
AW	6-194 with HDC, AIR	1966

CODE		
AX	6-194 with P/G, AIR	1966
AY	6-194 with P/G, AIR, A/C	1966
AZ	6-194 taxi with P/G, AIR	1966
BA	6-230 with M/T	1968
BB	6-230 with HDC, A/C	1967-68
BB	6-250 with P/G, T/D	1969
BC	6-250 with P/G, T/D, A/C	1969
BC	6-230 with HDC	1967-68
BD	6-230 with A/C	1968
BD	6-250 with T/H	1969
BE	6-250 with M/T	1969
BF	6-250 with A/C	1969
BF	6-230 with P/G	1968
BH	6-230 with P/G, A/C	1968
BH	6-250 with T/H, A/C	1969
BL	6-230 with P/G, AIR	1966-67
BM	6-230 with P/G, A/C, AIR	1966-67
BN	6-230 with P/G, P/V	1966
BN	6-230 with AIR	1967

CODE		
BO	6-230 with A/C, AIR	1966-67
CA	6-230 with M/T	1966-67
CB	6-230 with M/T, A/C	1966
CB	6-230 with A/C	1967
CC	6-230 with P/G	1966-67
CD	6-230 with P/G, A/C	1966-67
CM	6-250 with 3 sp. tr.	1967-68
CN	6-250 with A/C	1967-68
CO	6-250 with AIR	1967
CP	6-250 with AIR, A/C	1967
CQ	6-250 with P/G	1967-68
CR	6-250 with P/G, A/C	1967-68
CS	6-250 with P/G, AIR	1967
CT	6-250 with P/G, AIR, A/C	1967
CAA	6-250 with M/T	1971
CBG	6-250 with M/T	1972
CBJ	6-250 with A/T	1972

Continued

ENGINE IDENTIFICATION CODE—Continued

CHEVELLE & MONTE CARLO—Continued

CODE		
CCA	8-307 with M/T	1971
CCM	6-250 P/G, police & taxi	1970
CCK	6-250 T/H, police & taxi	1970
CCL	6-250 M/T, police & taxi	1970
CDA	8-350 with M/T	1972
CDB	8-350 with P/G	1972
CKA	8-350 with M/T	1972
CGA	8-350 with M/T, 250 H.P.	1971
CGB	8-350 with P/G, 250 H.P.	1971
CGK	8-350 with M/T, 300 H.P.	1971
CGL	8-350 with T/H, 300 H.P.	1971
CKG	8-307 with M/T	1972
CKH	8-307 with A/T	1972
CLA	8-400 with M/T, 330 H.P.	1971
CLB	8-400 with M/T, 300 H.P.	1971
CLJ	8-400 with M/T, 265 H.P.	1971
CLK	8-400 with T/H, 265 H.P.	1971
CLL	8-400 with M/T, 300 H.P.	1971
CLP	8-400 with T/H, 300 H.P.	1971
CLA	8-400 with M/T	1972
CLB	8-400 with T/H	1972
CLJ	8-400 with M/T	1972
CLK	8-400 with T/H	1972
CLL	8-400 with 4 sp. tr.	1972
CLR	8-400 with M/T, police	1972
CLS	8-400 with M/T	1972
CNC	8-307 with M/T	1970
CND	8-307 with 4 sp. tr.	1970
CNE	8-307 with P/G	1970
CNF	8-307 with T/H	1970
CNI	8-350 with M/T, 250 H.P.	1970
CNJ	8-350 with M/T, 300 H.P.	1970
CNK	8-350 with P/G, 300 H.P.	1970
CPA	8-454 with M/T, 390 H.P.	1971
CPG	8-454 with M/T, 390 H.P.	1971
CPP	8-454 with M/T, 460 H.P.	1971
CPR	8-454 with T/H, 460 H.P.	1971
CPA	8-454 with M/T	1972
CPD	8-454 with T/H, 230, 270 H.P.	1972
CRE	8-350 with T/H, 300 H.P.	1970
CNM	8-350 with P/G, 250 H.P.	1970

CODE		
CTW	8-396 with T/H, 350 H.P.	1970
CTX	8-396 with M/T, 350 H.P.	1970
CTY	8-396 with T/H, 375 H.P.	1970
CTZ	8-396 with HDC, 350 H.P.	1970
CKN	8-400 with T/H, 325 H.P.	1970
CKD	8-396 with M/T, 375 H.P.	1970
CKP	8-396 with T/H, 375 H.P.	1970
CKQ	8-396 with HDC, 375 H.P.	1970
CKR	8-400 with T/H, 330 H.P.	1970
CKS	8-400 with HDC, 330 H.P.	1970
CKT	8-396 with M/T, 375 H.P.	1970
CKU	8-396 with HDC, 375 H.P.	1970
CZX	8-400 with M/T, 265 H.P.	1970
CRH	8-400 with T/H, 265 H.P.	1970
CRN	8-454 with M/T, 390 H.P.	1970
CRQ	8-454 with T/H, 390 H.P.	1970
CRR	8-454 with T/H, 450 H.P.	1970
CRS	8-454 T/H alum. heads, 450 H.P.	1970
CRT	8-454 with M/T, 390 H.P.	1970
CRU	8-454 with HDC, 390 H.P.	1970
CRV	8-454 with M/T, 450 H.P.	1970
CRW	8-454 M/T, alum. heads, 450 H.P.	1970
CRX	8-454 with HDC, 450 H.P.	1970
CRY	8-454 HDC, alum. heads, 450 H.P.	1970
DA	8-283 with 3 sp. tr.	1966-67
DA	8-307 with M/T	1968
DA	8-307 with M/T	1969
DB	8-283 with 4 sp. tr.	1966-67
DB	8-307 with 4 sp. tr.	1968
DC	8-307 with P/G	1969
DD	8-307 with T/H	1969
DE	8-307 with 4 sp. tr.	1969
DE	8-283 with P/G	1967
DE	8-307 with P/G	1968
DF	8-283 with P/G	1966
DI	8-283 with AIR	1966-67
DJ	8-283 with P/G, AIR	1966-67
DK	8-283 with 4 sp. tr., AIR	1966-67
DN	8-283 with HDC	1967
DN	8-307 with HDC	1968
EA	8-327 with M/T	1966-68

CODE		
EA	8-327 with 4 BC	1967
EB	8-327 with AIR	1967
EB	8-327 with HPE	1966
EC	8-327 with SHPE	1966
EC	8-327 with P/G, AIR	1967
ED	8-396 with M/T, P/G	1967
ED	8-396 with T/I	1966
ED	8-396 with P/G	1968
EE	8-327 with P/G	1966-68
EF	8-396 with P/G, HPE	1966
EF	8-396 HPE	1968
EG	8-396 Special HPE	1966-68
EH	8-327 with 4 BC	1968
EH	8-396 with AIR	1966-67
EI	8-327 with 4 BC, P/G	1968
EJ	8-327 with 4 BC, HDC	1968
EJ	8-396 with HPE, AIR	1966
EK	8-396 with P/G	1966-68
EL	8-396 with P/G, HPE	1966-68
EM	8-396 with P/G, AIR	1966-67
EN	8-396 with P/G, HPE, AIR	1966
EO	8-327 with HDC	1968
EP	8-327 with SHPE	1967-68
EQ	8-327 with HDC	1967
ER	8-327 with SHPE, AIR	1967
ES	8-327 with SHPE, HDC	1967-68
ET	8-396 with T/H	1968
EU	8-396 with T/H, HPE	1968
HA	8-350 with M/T	1969
HB	8-350 with T/H	1969
HC	8-350 with 2 BC	1969
HD	8-350 with 2 BC, T/H	1969
HE	8-350 with P/G	1969
HF	8-350 with 2 BC, P/G	1969
JA	8-396 with M/T	1969
JC	8-396 with HPE	1969
JD	8-396 with SHPE	1969
JE	8-396 with HPE, T/H	1969
JK	8-396 with T/H	1969

CHEVY II & NOVA

CODE		
AA	4-153 with M/T	1969
AB	4-153 with T/D	1969
AM	6-230 with M/T	1969
AN	6-230 with P/G, T/D	1969
AO	6-230 with T/H	1969
AP	6-230 with A/C	1969
AR	6-230 with T/H, A/C	1969
BA	6-230 with M/T	1968
BB	6-230 with A/C, HDC	1968
BB	6-250 with P/G, T/D	1969
BC	6-230 with HDC	1968
BC	6-250 with P/G, T/D, A/C	1969
BD	6-230 with A/C	1968
BD	6-250 with T/H	1969
BE	6-250 with M/T	1969
BF	6-230 with M/T	1968
BF	6-250 with A/C	1969
BH	6-230 with P/G, A/C	1968
BH	6-250 with T/H, A/C	1969
CAA	6-250 with M/T	1971
CAB	6-250 with P/G, T/D	1971
CBG	6-250 with M/T	1972
CBJ	6-250 with P/G, T/D	1972
CCA	8-307 with M/T	1971
CCA	4-153 with M/T	1970

CODE		
CCB	4-153 with T/D	1970
CCC	8-307 with P/G	1971
CCD	6-230 with T/D	1970
CCM	6-250 with P/G, police & taxi	1970
CCG	6-250 with M/T	1970
CCK	6-250 with T/H, police & taxi	1970
CCI	6-250 with M/T	1970
CCL	6-250 with M/T, police & taxi	1970
CGB	8-350 with P/G	1972
CKA	8-350 with M/T, 165 H.P.	1972
CKB	8-350 with T/H, 165 H.P.	1972
CKK	8-350 175, 200 H.P.	1972
CGB	8-350 with P/G, 250 H.P.	1971
CGK	8-350 with M/T, 300 H.P.	1971
CGL	8-350 with T/H, 300 H.P.	1971
CKG	8-307 with M/T	1972
CKH	8-307 with P/G	1972
CKO	8-400 with M/T, 375 H.P.	1970
CKP	8-400 T/H, alum. heads, 375 H.P.	1970
CKQ	8-400 with HDC, 375 H.P.	1970
CKR	8-400 with M/T, 330 H.P.	1970
CKS	8-400 with HDC, 330 H.P.	1970
CKT	8-400 M/T, alum. heads, 375 H.P.	1970
CKU	8-400 HDC, alum. heads, 375 H.P.	1970
CM	6-250 with M/T	1968

CODE		
CN	6-250 with A/C	1968
CNC	8-307 with M/T	1970
CND	8-307 with 4 sp. tr.	1970
CNE	8-307 with P/G	1970
CNF	8-307 with T/H	1970
CNI	8-350 with M/T, 250 H.P.	1970
CNJ	8-350 with M/T, 300 H.P.	1970
CNK	8-350 with P/G, 300 H.P.	1970
CNM	8-350 with P/G, 250 H.P.	1970
CNN	8-350 with T/H, 250 H.P.	1970
CPT	8-454 with T/H	1971
CPS	8-454 with M/T	1971
CQ	6-250 with P/G	1968
CR	6-250 with P/G, A/C	1968
CRE	8-350 with T/H, 300 H.P.	1970
CRF	6-250 with M/T	1970
CTB	8-350 with M/T, 320 H.P.	1970
CTC	8-350 with T/H, 320 H.P.	1970
CTW	8-400 with T/H, 350 H.P.	1970
CTX	8-400 with M/T, 350 H.P.	1970
CTY	8-400 with T/H, 375 H.P.	1970
CTZ	8-400 with HDC, 350 H.P.	1970

Continued

ENGINE IDENTIFICATION CODE—Continued

CHEVY II & NOVA—Continued

CODE		
DA	8-307 with M/T	1968-69
DB	8-307 with 4 sp. tr.	1968
DC	8-307 with P/G	1969
DD	8-307 with T/H	1969
DE	8-307 with P/G	1968
DE	8-307 with 4 sp. tr.	1969
EA	8-327 with M/T	1968
EE	8-327 with P/G	1968
EP	8-327 with SHPE	1968
HA	8-350 with M/T	1969
HB	8-350 with T/H	1969
HC	8-350 with 2 BC	1969
HD	8-350 with 2 BC, T/H	1969
HE	8-350 with P/G	1969
HF	8-350 with 2 BC, P/G	1969
JF	8-396 with HPE	1969
JH	8-396 with SHPE	1969
JI	8-396 with HPE, T/H	1969
JL	8-396 with SHPE, T/H	1969
MK	8-327 with M/T	1968
ML	8-327 with SHPE	1968
MM	8-327 with P/G	1968
OA	4-153 with M/T	1966-68
OC	4-153 with HDC	1966-68
OG	4-153 taxi	1966

CODE		
OH	4-153 with P/G	1966-68
OJ	4-153 taxi with P/G	1966
OK	6-194 with M/T	1966-67
OM	6-194 with HDC	1966-67
OQ	6-194 taxi	1966
OR	6-194 with P/G	1966-67
OS	6-194 with P/G, AIR	1966
OT	6-194 taxi with P/G	1966
PC	6-230 with AIR	1966-67
PD	8-283 with M/T	1966-67
PE	8-283 with 4BC	1966
PE	8-283 with AIR	1967
PF	8-283 with A/C	1966-67
PG	8-283 with AIR, A/C	1966
PI	6-230 with P/G, AIR	1966-67
PL	8-283 with 4 sp. tr.	1966-67
PM	8-283 with 4 sp. tr., A/C	1966-67
PN	8-283 with P/G	1966-67
PO	8-283 with P/G, 4BC	1966
PP	8-283 with P/G, A/C	1966-67
PQ	8-283 with 4 sp. tr., AIR	1966-67
PS	8-283 with 4 sp. tr., AIR, A/C	1966
PU	8-283 with P/G, AIR	1966-67
PV	6-230 with M/T	1966-67

CODE		
PX	6-230 with P/G	1966-67
ZA	8-327 with M/T	1966
ZA	8-327 with 4BC	1967
ZB	8-327 with AIR	1967
ZB	8-327 with M/T, HPE	1967
ZC	8-327 with A/C, AIR	1966
ZD	8-327 with P/G, AIR	1966
ZE	8-327 with M/T, A/C	1966
ZE	8-327 with A/C	1967
ZF	8-327 with M/T, A/C, HPE	1966
ZG	8-327 with SHPE, AIR	1966-67
ZH	8-327 with SHPE, A/C, AIR	1966
ZI	8-327 with SHPE	1966-67
ZJ	8-327 with SHPE, A/C	1966-67
ZK	8-327 with P/G	1966-67
ZL	8-327 with P/G, HPE	1966
ZM	8-327 with P/G, A/C	1966-67
ZN	8-327 with P/G, HPE, A/C	1966
ZV	6-194 with HDC, AIR	1966
ZW	6-194 taxi with AIR	1966
ZX	6-194 with P/G, AIR	1966-67
ZY	6-194 with HDC, AIR	1966
ZY	6-194 with AIR	1967

CORVETTE

CODE		
CGS	8-350 with M/T, 300 H.P.	1971
CGT	8-350 with T/H, 300 H.P.	1971
CGW	8-454 with HPE, T/H	1970
CGW	8-350 with M/T, 350 H.P.	1971
CGX	8-350 with M/T, 350 H.P.	1971
CGY	8-350 with M/T, 370 H.P.	1971
CGZ	8-350 with M/T, 370 H.P.	1971
CPH	8-454 with M/T, 390 H.P.	1971
CPJ	8-454 with T/H, 390 H.P.	1971
CPK	8-454 with M/T, 460 H.P.	1971
CPL	8-454 with T/H, 460 H.P.	1971
CPW	8-454 with M/T, 450 H.P.	1971
CPX	8-454 with T/H, 450 H.P.	1971
CRI	8-454 with HPE, T/I	1970
CTL	8-350 with M/T	1970
CTM	8-350 with T/H	1970
CTN	8-350 with HPE	1970
CTO	8-350 with HPE, A/C	1970
CTP	8-350 with HPE, T/I	1970
CTQ	8-350 with HPE, T/I, A/C	1970
CTR	8-350 with SHPE	1970
CTU	8-350 with SHPE, T/I	1970
CTV	8-350 with SHPE, T/I, 4 sp. tr.	1970

CODE		
CZL	8-454 with H/D	1970
CZN	8-454 with H/D, T/H	1970
CZU	8-454 with HPE	1970
HD	8-327 with SHPE, AIR	1966-67
HE	8-327 with M/T	1966-68
HH	8-327 with AIR	1966-67
HO	8-327 with P/G	1966-67
HO	8-327 with T/H	1968
HP	8-327 with P/S, SHPE, A/C	1967-68
HR	8-327 with P/G, AIR	1966-67
HT	8-327 with SHPE, H/L	1966-68
HW	8-350 with HPE	1969
HX	8-350 with HPE, A/C	1969
HY	8-350 with M/T	1969
HZ	8-350 with T/H	1969
IK	8-427 with SHPE, H/L	1966
IL	8-427 with HPE	1966-68
IL	8-427 with 4 sp. tr., P/G	1967
IM	8-427 with AIR	1966-67
IM	8-427 HPE, 3 Carbs	1968
IO	8-427 HPE, T/H, 3 Carbs	1968
IQ	8-427 with H/T	1967-68
IR	8-427 with P/G, AIR	1967

CODE		
IR	8-427 HPE, 3 Carbs	1968
IT	8-427 Heavy Duty	1967-68
IU	8-427 with Alum. Heads	1967-68
JA	8-427 with SHPE, AIR, Tri-Carbs	1967
JC	8-427 with Tri-Carbs	1967
JD	8-427 with P/G, Tri-Carbs	1967
JE	8-427 SHPE, Tri-Carbs	1967
JF	8-427 Tri-Carbs., AIR	1967
JG	8-427 Tri-Carbs	1967
JH	8-427 Alum. Heads, AIR	1967
KH	8-327 with SHPE, A/C, AIR	1967
LL	8-427 with HPE, T/H	1969
LM	8-427 with HPE	1969
LN	8-427 with HPE, T/H, 3 Carbs	1969
LO	8-427 with HD	1969
LP	8-427 with A/H	1969
LQ	8-427 with HPE, 3 Carbs	1969
LR	8-427 with SHPE, 3 Carbs	1969
LT	8-427 with SHPE, 3 Carbs, HDC	1969
LU	8-427 with A/H, HDC	1969
LV	8-427 with T/H	1969
LW	8-427 with A/H, T/H	1969
LX	8-427 with SHPE, 3 Carbs, T/H	1969

NOTES

A/C: Air Conditioned	H/D: Heavy Duty	P/S: Power steering
A/H: Aluminum Heads	HDC: Heavy duty clutch	P/V: Positive crankcase ventilation
A/S: Air suspension	HPE: High performance engine	SHPE: Special high perf. engine
AIR: Air injection reactor	H/L: Hydraulic lifters	S.S.: Super Sport
A/T: Automatic transmission	M/T: Manual transmission	T/D: Torque Drive
4BC: Four barrel carburetor	O/D: Overdrive	T/H: Turbo Hydramatic
F/I: Fuel injection	P/G: Powerglide	T/I: Transistor ignition

GRILLE IDENTIFICATION

1966 Chevelle

1966 Chevrolet

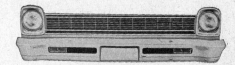

1966 Chevy II

1966-67 Corvette

1967 Chevelle

1967 Chevrolet

1967 Camaro

1967 Camaro Super Sport

1967 Chevy II

1968 Camaro

1968 Camaro Rally Sport

1968 Chevelle

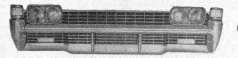

1968 Chevrolet

1968 Chevy II

1968 Corvette

1969 Camaro

1969 Camaro S. S.

1969 Chevy Nova

1969 Chevelle

1969 Chevelle S. S.

1969 Chevrolet

1969 Corvette

1970 Chevrolet

1970-72 Chevy Nova

GRILLE IDENTIFICATION—Continued

1970-71 Camaro

1970-71 Camaro S. S.

1970 Monte Carlo

1970 Chevelle

1970 Chevelle S. S.

1970-72 Corvette

1971 Chevelle

1971 Chevelle S. S.

1971 Monte Carlo

1971 Chevrolet

1971 Caprice & Estate Wagon

1972 Camaro

1972 Chevelle

1972 Monte Carlo

1972 Chevrolet

1972 Caprice & Estate Wagon

GENERAL ENGINE SPECIFICATIONS

Year	Engine	Carburetor	Bore and Stroke	Piston Displacement, Cubic Inches	Compression Ratio	Maximum Brake H.P. @ R.P.M.	Maximum Torque Lbs. Ft. @ R.P.M.	Normal Oil Pressure Pounds
1966	90 Horsepower..............4-153	1 Barrel	3.875 x 3.25	153	8.5	90 @ 4000	152 @ 2400	30–45
	120 Horsepower..............6-194	1 Barrel	3.5635 x 3.25	194	8.5	120 @ 4400	177 @ 2400	30–45
	140 Horsepower..............6-230	1 Barrel	3.875 x 3.25	230	8.5	140 @ 4400	220 @ 1600	30–45
	155 Horsepower..............6-250	1 Barrel	3.875 x 3.53	250	8.5	155 @ 4200	235 @ 1600	30–45
	195 Horsepower..............V8-283	2 Barrel	3.875 x 3.00	283	9.25	195 @ 4800	285 @ 2400	30–45
	220 Horsepower..............V8-283	4 Barrel	3.875 x 3.00	283	9.25	220 @ 4800	295 @ 3200	30–45
	275 Horsepower..............V8-327	4 Barrel	4.001 x 3.25	327	10.5	275 @ 4800	355 @ 4200	30–45
	300 Horsepower..............V8-327	4 Barrel	4.001 x 3.25	327	10.5	300 @ 5000	360 @ 3400	30–45
	325 Horsepower..............V8-396	4 Barrel	4.094 x 3.76	396	10.25	325 @ 4800	410 @ 3200	50–75
	350 Horsepower..............V8-327	4 Barrel	4.001 x 3.25	327	11.0	350 @ 5800	360 @ 3600	30–45
	360 Horsepower..............V8-396	4 Barrel	4.094 x 3.76	396	10.25	360 @ 5200	420 @ 3600	50–75
	390 Horsepower..............V8-427	4 Barrel	4.251 x 3.76	427	10.25	390 @ 5200	470 @ 3600	50–75
	425 Horsepower..............V8-427	4 Barrel	4.251 x 3.76	427	11.0	425 @ 5600	460 @ 4000	50–75
1967	90 Horsepower..............4-153	1 Barrel	3.875 x 3.25	153	8.50	90 @ 4000	152 @ 2400	30–45
	120 Horsepower..............6-194	1 Barrel	3.563 x 3.25	194	8.50	120 @ 4400	177 @ 2400	30–45
	140 Horsepower..............6-230	1 Barrel	3.875 x 3.25	230	8.50	140 @ 4400	220 @ 1600	30–45
	155 Horsepower..............6-250	1 Barrel	3.875 x 3.53	250	8.50	155 @ 4200	235 @ 1600	30–45
	195 Horsepower..............V8-283	2 Barrel	3.875 x 3.00	283	9.25	195 @ 4800	285 @ 2400	30–45
	290 Horsepower..............V8-302	4 Barrel	4.000 x 3.00	302	11.00	290 @ 5800	290 @ 4200	30–45
	210 Horsepower..............V8-327	2 Barrel	4.001 x 3.25	327	8.75	210 @ 4600	320 @ 2400	30–45
	275 Horsepower..............V8-327	4 Barrel	4.001 x 3.25	327	10.00	275 @ 4800	355 @ 3200	30–45
	295 Horsepower..............V8-350	4 Barrel	4.001 x 3.48	350	10.25	295 @ 4800	380 @ 3200	30–45
	300 Horsepower..............V8-327	4 Barrel	4.001 x 3.25	327	10.00	300 @ 5000	360 @ 3400	30–45
	325 Horsepower..............V8-327	4 Barrel	4.001 x 3.25	327	11.00	325 @ 5600	355 @ 3600	30–45
	325 Horsepower..............V8-396	4 Barrel	4.094 x 3.76	396	10.25	325 @ 4800	410 @ 3200	30–35
	350 Horsepower..............V8-327	4 Barrel	4.001 x 3.25	327	11.00	350 @ 5800	360 @ 3600	30–45
	350 Horsepower..............V8-396	4 Barrel	4.094 x 3.76	396	10.25	350 @ 5200	415 @ 3400	30–35
	375 Horsepower..............V8-396	4 Barrel	4.094 x 3.76	396	11.00	375 @ 5600	415 @ 3600	30–35
	385 Horsepower..............V8-427	4 Barrel	4.251 x 3.76	427	10.25	385 @ 5200	460 @ 3400	30–35
	390 Horsepower..............V8-427	4 Barrel	4.251 x 3.76	427	10.25	390 @ 5400	460 @ 3600	30–35
	400 Horsepower..............V8-427	3 Carbs.	4.251 x 3.76	427	10.25	400 @ 5400	460 @ 3600	30–35
	425 Horsepower..............V8-427	4 Barrel	4.251 x 3.76	427	N.A.	N.A.	N.A.	30–35
	435 Horsepower..............V8-427	3 Carbs.	4.251 x 3.76	427	11.00	435 @ 5800	460 @ 4000	30–35
1968	90 Horsepower..............4-153	1 Barrel	3.875 x 3.25	153	8.50	90 @ 4000	152 @ 2400	30–45
	140 Horsepower..............6-230	1 Barrel	3.875 x 3.25	230	8.50	140 @ 4400	220 @ 1600	30–45
	155 Horsepower..............6-250	1 Barrel	3.875 x 3.53	250	8.50	155 @ 4200	235 @ 1600	30–45
	290 Horsepower..............V8-302	4 Barrel	4.000 x 3.00	302	11.00	290 @ 5800	290 @ 4200	30–45
	200 Horsepower..............V8-307	2 Barrel	3.875 x 3.25	307	9.00	200 @ 4600	300 @ 2400	30–45
	210 Horsepower..............V8-327	2 Barrel	4.001 x 3.25	327	8.75	210 @ 4600	320 @ 2400	30–45
	250 Horsepower..............V8-327	4 Barrel	4.001 x 3.25	327	8.75	250 @ 4800	325 @ 3200	30–45
	275 Horsepower..............V8-327	4 Barrel	4.001 x 3.25	327	10.00	275 @ 4800	355 @ 3200	30–45
	300 Horsepower..............V8-327	4 Barrel	4.001 x 3.25	327	10.00	300 @ 5000	360 @ 3400	30–45
	325 Horsepower..............V8-327	4 Barrel	4.001 x 3.25	327	11.00	325 @ 5600	355 @ 3600	30–45
	350 Horsepower..............V8-327	4 Barrel	4.001 x 3.25	327	11.00	350 @ 5800	360 @ 3600	30–45
	295 Horsepower..............V8-350	4 Barrel	4.001 x 3.48	350	10.25	295 @ 4800	380 @ 3200	30–45
	325 Horsepower..............V8-396	4 Barrel	4.094 x 3.76	396	10.25	325 @ 4800	410 @ 3200	30–35
	350 Horsepower..............V8-396	4 Barrel	4.094 x 3.76	396	10.25	350 @ 5200	415 @ 3400	30–35
	375 Horsepower..............V8-396	4 Barrel	4.094 x 3.76	396	11.00	375 @ 5600	415 @ 3600	30–35
	385 Horsepower..............V8-427	4 Barrel	4.251 x 3.76	427	10.25	385 @ 5200	460 @ 3400	30–35
	390 Horsepower..............V8-427	4 Barrel	4.251 x 3.76	427	10.25	390 @ 5400	460 @ 3600	30–35
	400 Horsepower..............V8-427	3 Carbs.	4.251 x 3.76	427	10.25	400 @ 5400	460 @ 3600	30–35
	425 Horsepower..............V8-427	4 Barrel	4.251 x 3.76	427	11.00	425 @ 5600	460 @ 4000	30–35
	430 Horsepower..............V8-427	4 Barrel	4.251 x 3.76	427	12.50	430 @ 5200	450 @ 4400	30–35
	435 Horsepower..............V8-427	3 Carbs.	4.251 x 3.76	427	11.00	435 @ 5800	460 @ 4000	30–35

Continued

GENERAL ENGINE SPECIFICATIONS

Year	Engine	Carburetor	Bore and Stroke	Piston Displacement, Cubic Inches	Compression Ratio	Maximum Brake H.P. @ R.P.M.	Maximum Torque Lbs. Ft. @ R.P.M.	Normal Oil Pressure Pounds
1969	90 Horsepower..............4-153	1 Barrel	3.875 x 3.25	153	8.50	90 @ 4000	152 @ 2400	30—45
	140 Horsepower..............6-230	1 Barrel	3.875 x 3.25	230	8.50	140 @ 4400	220 @ 1600	30—45
	155 Horsepower..............6-250	1 Barrel	3.875 x 3.53	250	8.50	155 @ 4200	235 @ 1600	30—45
	290 Horsepower...........V8-302	4 Barrel	4.000 x 3.00	302	11.00	290 @ 5800	290 @ 4200	30—45
	200 Horsepower...........V8-307	2 Barrel	3.875 x 3.25	307	9.00	200 @ 4600	300 @ 2400	30—45
	210 Horsepower...........V8-327	2 Barrel	4.001 x 3.25	327	9.00	210 @ 4600	320 @ 2400	30—45
	235 Horsepower...........V8-327	2 Barrel	4.001 x 3.25	327	9.00	235 @ 4800	325 @ 2800	30—45
	255 Horsepower...........V8-350	4 Barrel	4.001 x 3.48	350	9.00	255 @ 4800	365 @ 3200	30—45
	300 Horsepower...........V8-350	4 Barrel	4.001 x 3.48	350	10.25	300 @ 4800	380 @ 3200	30—45
	350 Horsepower...........V8-350	4 Barrel	4.001 x 3.48	350	11.00	350 @ 5600	380 @ 3600	30—45
	370 Horsepower...........V8-350	4 Barrel	4.001 x 3.48	350	11.00	370 @ 5800	380 @ 4000	30—45
	265 Horsepower...........V8-396	2 Barrel	4.094 x 3.76	396	9.00	265 @ 4800	400 @ 2800	30—35
	325 Horsepower...........V8-396	4 Barrel	4.094 x 3.76	396	10.25	325 @ 4800	410 @ 3200	30—35
	350 Horsepower...........V8-396	4 Barrel	4.094 x 3.76	396	10.25	350 @ 5200	415 @ 3200	30—35
	375 Horsepower...........V8-396	4 Barrel	4.094 x 3.76	396	11.00	375 @ 5600	415 @ 3600	30—35
	335 Horsepower...........V8-427	4 Barrel	4.251 x 3.76	427	10.25	335 @ 4800	470 @ 3200	30—35
	390 Horsepower...........V8-427	4 Barrel	4.251 x 3.76	427	10.25	390 @ 5400	460 @ 3600	30—35
	400 Horsepower...........V8-427	4 Barrel	4.251 x 3.76	427	10.25	400 @ 5400	460 @ 3600	30—35
	425 Horsepower...........V8-427	4 Barrel	4.251 x 3.76	427	11.00	425 @ 5600	460 @ 4000	30—35
	430 Horsepower...........V8-427	4 Barrel	4.251 x 3.76	427	12.00	430 @ 5200	450 @ 4400	30—35
	435 Horsepower...........V8-427	3 Carbs.	4.251 x 3.76	427	11.00	435 @ 5800	460 @ 4000	30—35
1970	90 Horsepower..............4-153	1 Barrel	3.875 x 3.25	153	8.50	90 @ 4000	152 @ 2400	30—45
	140 Horsepower..............6-230	1 Barrel	3.875 x 3.25	230	8.50	140 @ 4400	220 @ 1600	30—45
	155 Horsepower..............6-250	1 Barrel	3.875 x 3.53	250	8.50	155 @ 4200	235 @ 1600	30—45
	200 Horsepower...........V8-307	2 Barrel	3.875 x 3.25	307	9.00	200 @ 4600	300 @ 2400	30—45
	250 Horsepower...........V8-350	2 Barrel	4.001 x 3.48	350	9.00	250 @ 4800	345 @ 2800	30—45
	300 Horsepower...........V8-350	4 Barrel	4.001 x 3.48	350	10.25	300 @ 4800	380 @ 3200	30—45
	350 Horsepower...........V8-350	4 Barrel	4.001 x 3.48	350	11.00	350 @ 5600	380 @ 3600	30—45
	360 Horsepower...........V8-350	4 Barrel	4.001 x 3.48	350	11.00	360 @ 6000	380 @ 4000	35—45
	370 Horsepower...........V8-350	4 Barrel	4.001 x 3.48	350	11.00	370 @ 6000	380 @ 4000	30—45
	350 Horsepower...........V8-396	4 Barrel	4.125 x 3.76	①	10.25	350 @ 5200	415 @ 3400	30—35
	375 Horsepower...........V8-396	4 Barrel	4.125 x 3.76	①	11.00	375 @ 5600	415 @ 3600	30—35
	265 Horsepower...........V8-400	2 Barrel	4.125 x 3.75	400	9.00	265 @ 4400	400 @ 2400	30—35
	330 Horsepower...........V8-400	4 Barrel	4.125 x 3.75	400	10.25	330 @ 4800	410 @ 3200	30—35
	345 Horsepower...........V8-454	4 Barrel	4.251 x 4.00	454	10.25	345 @ 4400	500 @ 3000	30—35
	360 Horsepower...........V8-454	4 Barrel	4.251 x 4.00	454	10.25	360 @ 4400	500 @ 3200	30—35
	390 Horsepower...........V8-454	4 Barrel	4.251 x 4.00	454	10.25	390 @ 4800	500 @ 3400	30—35
	450 Horsepower...........V8-454	4 Barrel	4.251 x 4.00	454	11.25	450 @ 5600	500 @ 3600	30—35
	460 Horsepower...........V8-454	4 Barrel	4.251 x 4.00	454	11.25	460 @ 5600	490 @ 3000	30—35
1971	145 Horsepower..............6-250	1 Barrel	3.875 x 3.53	250	8.50	145 @ 4200	230 @ 1600	30—45
	200 Horsepower...........V8-307	2 Barrel	3.875 x 3.25	307	8.50	200 @ 4600	300 @ 2400	30—45
	245 Horsepower...........V8-350	2 Barrel	4.00 x 3.48	350	8.50	245 @ 4800	350 @ 2800	35—45
	270 Horsepower...........V8-350	4 Barrel	4.00 x 3.48	350	8.50	270 @ 4800	360 @ 3200	35—45
	330 Horsepower...........V8-350	4 Barrel	4.00 x 3.48	350	9.0	330 @ 5600	360 @ 4000	35—45
	255 Horsepower...........V8-400	2 Barrel	4.125 x 3.76	400	8.50	255 @ 4400	390 @ 2400	35—45
	300 Horsepower...........V8-396	4 Barrel	4.126 x 3.76	①	8.50	300 @ 4800	400 @ 3200	35—45
	365 Horsepower...........V8-454	4 Barrel	4.251 x 4.00	454	8.50	365 @ 4800	465 @ 3200	35—45
	425 Horsepower...........V8-454	4 Barrel	4.251 x 4.00	454	9.0	425 @ 5600	475 @ 4000	35—45
1972	110 Horsepower②..............6-250	1 Barrel	3.875 x 3.53	250	8.50	110 @ 3800	185 @ 1600	30—45
	130 Horsepower②...........V8-307	2 Barrel	3.875 x 3.25	307	8.50	130 @ 4000	230 @ 2400	30—45
	165 Horsepower②...........V8-350	2 Barrel	4.00 x 3.48	350	8.50	165 @ 4000	280 @ 2400	35—45
	175 Horsepower②...........V8-350	4 Barrel	4.00 x 3.48	350	8.50	175 @ 4000	280 @ 2400	35—45
	200 Horsepower②...........V8-350	4 Barrel	4.00 x 3.48	350	8.50	200 @ 4400	300 @ 2800	35—45

Continued

GENERAL ENGINE SPECIFICATIONS—Continued

Year	Engine	Car-buretor	Bore and Stroke	Piston Dis-place-ment, Cubic Inches	Com-pres-sion Ratio	Maximum Brake H.P. @ R.P.M.	Maximum Torque Lbs. Ft. @ R.P.M.	Normal Oil Pressure Pounds
1972	255 Horsepower②............V8-350	4 Barrel	4.00 x 3.48	350	9.0	255 @ 5600	280 @ 4000	35–45
	170 Horsepower②............V8-400	2 Barrel	4.126 x 3.75	400	8.50	170 @ 3400	325 @ 2000	35–45
	210 Horsepower②............V8-402	4 Barrel	4.126 x 3.76	402	8.50	210 @ 4400	320 @ 2400	35–45
	240 Horsepower②............V8-402	4 Barrel	4.126 x 3.76	402	8.50	240 @ 4400	345 @ 3200	35–45
	230 Horsepower②............V8-454	4 Barrel	4.251 x 4.00	454	8.50	230 @ 4000	360 @ 3200	35–45
	270 Horsepower②............V8-454	4 Barrel	4.251 x 4.00	454	8.50	270 @ 4000	390 @ 3200	35–45

①—Marketed as 396 cu. in. but actually 402 cu. in.

②—Ratings are net—As installed in the vehicle.

TUNE UP SPECIFICATIONS

OLD CAR SPECIFICATIONS: For 1946-65 Tune Up Specifications see back of book.

★When using a timing light, disconnect vacuum hose or tube at distributor and plug opening in hose or tube so idle speed will not be affected.

●When checking compression, lowest cylinder must be within 80 percent of highest.

Year	Engine Model	Spark Plugs Type AC	Spark Plugs Gap Inch	Distributor Point Gap Inch	Distributor Dwell Angle Deg.	Firing Order	Ignition Timing★ BTDC ①	Ignition Timing★ Mark	Hot Idle Speed③ Std. Trans.	Hot Idle Speed③ Auto. Trans. ②	Fuel Pump Press. Lbs.
CAMARO											
1967	6-230	46N	.035	.019	31–34	Fig. G	4°	Fig. A	500⑪	500D⑪	3–4½
	6-230⑫	46N	.035	.019	31–34	Fig. G	4°	Fig. A	700⑯	500D⑯	3–4½
	6-250	46N	.035	.019	31–34	Fig. G	4°	Fig. A	500⑪	500D⑪	3–4½
	6-250⑫	46N	.035	.019	31–34	Fig. G	4°	Fig. A	700⑯	500D⑯	3–4½
	8-302	43	.035	.019	28–32	Fig. E	6°	Fig. A	800⑪	—	5–6½
	8-327, 210 H.P.	44	.035	.019	28–32	Fig. E	2°	Fig. A	500⑪	600D⑪	5–6½
	8-327, 210 H.P.⑫	44	.035	.019	28–32	Fig. E	2°	Fig. A	700⑯	600D⑯	5–6½
	8-327, 275 H.P.	44	.035	.019	28–32	Fig. E	8°	Fig. A	500⑪	500D⑪	5–6½
	8-327, 275 H.P.⑫	44	.035	.019	28–32	Fig. E	6°	Fig. A	700⑯	600D⑯	5–6½
	8-327, 350 H.P.	44	.035	.019	28–32	Fig. E	10°	Fig. A	700⑪	—	5–6½
	8-327, 350 H.P.⑫	44	.035	.019	28–32	Fig. E	10°	Fig. A	750⑪	—	5–6½
	8-396, 375 H.P.	43N	.035	.019	28–32	Fig. E	6°	Fig. A	750⑪	—	5–6½
	8-350	44	.035	.019	28–32	Fig. E	4°	Fig. A	500⑪	500D⑪	5–6½
	8-350⑫	44	.035	.019	28–32	Fig. E	4°	Fig. A	700⑪	500D⑪	5–6½
1968	6-230, 250 Std. Tr.	46N	.035	.019	31–34	Fig. G	TDC	Fig. A	700⑯	—	3–4½
	6-230, 250 Auto Tr.	46N	.035	.019	31–34	Fig. G	4°	Fig. A	—	600D⑪	3–4½
	8-302	43	.035	.019	28–32	Fig. E	4°	Fig. A	900⑯	—	5–6½
	8-327, 210 H.P.⑱	44	.035	.019	28–32	Fig. E	2° ATC	Fig. A	700⑪	—	5–6½
	8-327, 210 H.P.⑲	44	.035	.019	28–32	Fig. E	2°	Fig. A	—	600D⑯	5–6½
	8-327, 275 H.P.⑱	44	.035	.019	28–32	Fig. E	TDC	Fig. A	700⑪	—	5–6½
	8-327, 275 H.P.⑲	44	.035	.019	28–32	Fig. E	4°	Fig. A	—	600D⑯	5–6½
	8-350, 295 H.P.⑱	44	.035	.019	28–32	Fig. E	TDC	Fig. A	700⑯	—	5–6½
	8-350, 295 H.P.⑲	44	.035	.019	28–32	Fig. E	4°	Fig. A	—	600D⑯	5–6½
	8-396, 325 H.P.	43N	.035	.019	28–32	Fig. E	4°	Fig. A	700⑯	600D⑯	5–8½
	8-396, 375 H.P.	43N	.035	.019	28–32	Fig. E	10°	Fig. A	750⑪	—	5–8½

Continued

TUNE UP SPECIFICATIONS—Continued

OLD CAR SPECIFICATIONS: For 1946-65 Tune Up Specifications see back of book.

★When using a timing light, disconnect vacuum tube or hose at distributor and plug opening in hose or tube so idle speed will not be affected.
●When checking compression, lowest cylinder must be within 80 percent of highest.

Year	Engine Model	Spark Plugs Type AC	Gap Inch	Distributor Point Gap Inch	Dwell Angle Deg.	Firing Order	Ignition Timing★ BTDC ①	Mark	Hot Idle Speed③ Std. Trans.	Auto. Trans. ②	Fuel Pump Press. Lbs.
1969	6-230, 250⑱	R46N	.035	.019	31–34	Fig. G	TDC	Fig. A	700⑯	—	3–4½
	6-230, 250⑲	R46N	.035	.019	31–34	Fig. G	4°	Fig. A	—	550D⑯	3–4½
	8-302	R43	.035	.019	28–32	Fig. E	4°	Fig. A	900⑯	—	5–6½
	8-307	R45S	.035	.019	28–32	Fig. E	2°	Fig. A	700⑯	600D⑯	5–6½
	8-327, 210 H.P.⑱	R45S	.035	.019	28–32	Fig. E	2° ATC	Fig. A	700⑯	—	5–6½
	8-327, 210 H.P.⑲	R45S	.035	.019	28–32	Fig. E	2°	Fig. A	—	600D⑯	5–6½
	8-350, 255 H.P.⑱	R44	.035	.019	28–32	Fig. E	TDC	Fig. A	700⑯	—	5–6½
	8-350, 255 H.P.⑲	R44	.035	.019	28–32	Fig. E	4°	Fig. A	—	600D⑯	5–6½
	8-350, 300 H.P.⑱	R44	.035	.019	28–32	Fig. E	TDC	Fig. A	700⑯	—	5–6½
	8-350, 300 H.P.⑲	R44	.035	.019	28–32	Fig. E	4°	Fig. A	—	600D⑯	5–6½
	8-396, 325 H.P.	R44N	.035	.019	28–32	Fig. E	4°	Fig. A	800⑯	600D⑱	5–8½
	8-396, 350 H.P.⑱	R43N	.035	.019	28–32	Fig. E	TDC	Fig. A	800⑯	—	5–8½
	8-396, 350 H.P.⑲	R43N	.035	.019	28–32	Fig. E	4°	Fig. A	—	600D⑯	5–8½
	8-396, 375 H.P.	R43N	.035	.019	28–32	Fig. E	4°	Fig. A	750⑯	700D⑱	5–8½
1970	6-250 Std. Tr.	R46T	.035	.019	31–34	Fig. G	TDC	Fig. A	750	—	3½–4½
	6-250 Auto. Tr.	R46T	.035	.019	31–34	Fig. G	4°	Fig. A	—	600D/400	3½–4½
	8-307 Std. Tr.	R43	.035	.019	29–31	Fig. E	2°	Fig. A	700	—	5–6½
	8-307 Auto. Tr.	R43	.035	.019	29–31	Fig. E	8°	Fig. A	—	600D/450	5–6½
	8-350, 250 H.P.⑱	R44	.035	.019	29–31	Fig. E	TDC	Fig. A	750	—	7–8½
	8-350, 250 H.P.⑲	R44	.035	.019	29–31	Fig. E	4°	Fig. A	—	600D/450	7–8½
	8-350, 300 H.P.⑱	R44	.035	.019	29–31	Fig. E	TDC	Fig. A	700	—	7–8½
	8-350, 300 H.P.⑲	R44	.035	.019	29–31	Fig. E	4°	Fig. A	—	600D	7–8½
	8-350, 360 H.P.	R43	.035	.019	29–31	Fig. E	8°	Fig. A	800	750D/500	7–8½
	8-396, 350 H.P.⑱㉑	R44T	.035	.019	29–31	Fig. E	TDC	Fig. A	700	—	5–8½
	8-396, 350 H.P.⑲㉑	R44T	.035	.019	29–31	Fig. E	4°	Fig. A	—	600D	5–8½
	8-396, 375 H.P.㉑	R43T	.035	.019	29–31	Fig. E	4°	Fig. A	750	700D	5–8½
	8-454, 450 H.P.	R43T	.035	.019	29–31	Fig. E	4°	Fig. A	750	700D	5–8½
1971	6-250	R46TS	.035	.019	31–34	Fig. G	4°	Fig. A	550	550D	3½–4½
	8-307 Std. Tr.	R45TS	.035	.019	29–31	Fig. E	4°	Fig. A	550	—	5–6½
	8-307 Auto. Tr.	R45TS	.035	.019	29–31	Fig. E	8°	Fig. A	—	550D	5–6½
	8-350, 245 H.P.⑱	R45TS	.035	.019	29–31	Fig. E	2°	Fig. A	600	—	7–8½
	8-350, 245 H.P.⑲	R45TS	.035	.019	29–31	Fig. E	6°	Fig. A	—	550D	7–8½
	8-350, 270 H.P.⑱	R44TS	.035	.019	29–31	Fig. E	4°	Fig. A	600	—	7–8½
	8-350, 270 H.P.⑲	R44TS	.035	.019	29–31	Fig. E	8°	Fig. A	—	550D	7–8½
	8-350, 330 H.P.⑱	R43TS	.035	.019	29–31	Fig. E	8°	Fig. A	700	—	7–8½
	8-350, 330 H.P.⑲	R43TS	.035	.019	29–31	Fig. E	12°	Fig. A	—	700D	7–8½
	8-396, 300 H.P.	R44TS	.035	.019	29–31	Fig. E	8°	Fig. A	600	600D	7–8½
1972	6-250	R46T	.035	.019	31–34	Fig. G	4°	Fig. A	700	600D	3½–4½
	8-307 Std. Tr.	R44T	.035	.019	29–31	Fig. E	4°	Fig. A	900	—	5–6½
	8-307 Auto. Tr.	R44T	.035	.019	29–31	Fig. E	8°	Fig. A	—	600D	5–6½
	8-350, 165 H.P.	R44T	.035	.019	29–31	Fig. E	6°	Fig. A	900	600D	7–8½
	8-350, 200 H.P.⑱	R44T	.035	.019	29–31	Fig. E	4°	Fig. A	800	—	7–8½
	8-350, 200 H.P.⑲	R44T	.035	.019	29–31	Fig. E	8°	Fig. A	—	600D	7–8½
	8-350, 255 H.P.⑱	R44T	.035	.019	29–31	Fig. E	4°	Fig. A	900	—	7–8½
	8-350, 255 H.P.⑲	R44T	.035	.019	29–31	Fig. E	8°	Fig. A	—	700D	7–8½
	8-402	R44T	.035	.019	29–31	Fig. E	8°	Fig. A	750	600D	7–8½

TUNE UP SPECIFICATIONS—Continued

OLD CAR SPECIFICATIONS: For 1946-65 Tune Up Specifications see back of book.

★When using a timing light, disconnect vacuum tube or hose at distributor and plug opening in hose or tube so idle speed will not be affected.

●When checking compression, lowest cylinder must be within 80 percent of highest.

Year	Engine Model	Spark Plugs		Distributor		Firing Order	Ignition Timing★		Hot Idle Speed③		Fuel Pump Press. Lbs.
		Type AC	Gap Inch	Point Gap Inch	Dwell Angle Deg.		BTDC ①	Mark	Std. Trans.	Auto. Trans. ②	
CHEVELLE											
1966	6-194 Std. Eng.	46N	.035	④	31–34	Fig. G	8°	Fig. A	500⑪	500D⑪	3–4½
	6-194 Man. Tr.⑫	46N	.035	④	31–24	Fig. G	3°	Fig. A	700⑪	—	3–4½
	6-194 Auto. Tr.⑫	46N	.035	④	31–34	Fig. G	8°	Fig. A	—	600D⑪	3–4½
	6-230 Std. Eng.	46N	.035	④	31–34	Fig. G	4°	Fig. A	500⑪	500D⑪	3–4½
	6-230⑫	46N	.035	④	31–34	Fig. G	4°	Fig. A	700⑪	600D⑪	3–4½
	8-283 Std. Eng.	45	.035	④	28–32	Fig. E	4°	Fig. A	500⑪	500D⑪	5–6½
	8-283⑫	45	.035	④	28–32	Fig. E	4°	Fig. A	700⑪	600D⑪	5–6½
	8-327, 275 H.P.	44	.035	④	28–32	Fig. E	8°	Fig. A	500⑪	500D⑪	5–6½
	8-327, 275 H.P.⑬	44	.035	④	28–32	Fig. E	8°	Fig. A	700⑪	—	5–6½
	8-327, 275 H.P.⑭	44	.035	④	28–32	Fig. E	2°⑮	Fig. A	—	600D⑪	5–6½
	8-396, 325 H.P.	43N	.035	④	28–32	Fig. E	4°	Fig. A	500⑪	500D⑪	5–6½
	8-396, 325 H.P.⑫	43N	.035	④	28–32	Fig. E	4°	Fig. A	500⑪	500D⑪	5–6½
	8-396, 360 H.P.	43N	.035	④	28–32	Fig. E	4°	Fig. A	550⑪	600D⑪	5–6½
	8-396, 360 H.P.⑫	43N	.035	④	28–32	Fig. E	4°	Fig. A	550⑪	550D⑪	5–6½
1967	6-230	46N	.035	.019	31–34	Fig. G	4°	Fig. A	500⑪	500D⑪	3–4½
	6-230⑫	46N	.035	.019	31–34	Fig. G	4°	Fig. A	700⑯	500D⑯	3–4½
	6-250	46N	.035	.019	31–34	Fig. G	4°	Fig. A	500⑪	500D⑪	3–4½
	6-250⑫	46N	.035	.019	31–34	Fig. G	4°	Fig. A	700⑯	500D⑯	3–4½
	8-283	45	.035	.019	28–32	Fig. E	4°	Fig. A	500⑪	500D⑪	5–6½
	8-283 Std. Tr.⑫	45	.035	.019	28–32	Fig. E	TDC	Fig. A	700⑯	600D⑯	5–6½
	8-283 Auto. Tr.⑫	45	.035	.019	28–32	Fig. E	4°	Fig. A	700⑯	600D⑯	5–6½
	8-327, 275 H.P.	44	.035	.019	28–32	Fig. E	8°	Fig. A	500	500	5–6½
	8-327, 275 H.P.⑫	44	.035	.019	28–32	Fig. E	6°	Fig. A	700	600	5–6½
	8-327, 325 H.P.	44	.035	.019	28–32	Fig. E	10°	Fig. A	700⑪	—	5–6½
	8-327, 325 H.P.⑫	44	.035	.019	28–32	Fig. E	10°	Fig. A	750⑪	—	5–6½
	8-396, 325 H.P.	43N	.035	.019	28–32	Fig. E	4°	Fig. A	500⑪	500D⑪	5–6½
	8-396, 325 H.P.⑫	43N	.035	.019	28–32	Fig. E	4°	Fig. A	700⑪	500D⑪	5–6½
	8-396, 350 H.P.	43N	.035	.019	28–32	Fig. E	4°	Fig. A	550⑪	550D⑪	5–6½
	8-396, 350 H.P.⑫	43N	.035	.019	28–32	Fig. E	4°	Fig. A	700⑪	500D⑪	5–6½
1968	6-230, 250 Std. Tr.	46N	.035	.019	31–34	Fig. G	TDC	Fig. A	700⑯	—	3–4½
	6-230, 250 Auto. Tr.	46N	.035	.019	31–34	Fig. G	4°	Fig. A	—	600D⑪	3–4½
	8-307	45S	.035	.019	28–32	Fig. E	2°	Fig. A	700⑱	600D⑯	5–6½
	8-327, 275 H.P.⑱	44	.035	.019	28–32	Fig. E	TDC	Fig. A	700⑪	—	5–6½
	8-327, 275 H.P.⑲	44	.035	.019	28–32	Fig. E	4°	Fig. A	—	600D⑪	5–6½
	8-327, 325 H.P.	44	.035	.019	28–32	Fig. E	4°	Fig. A	750⑪	—	5–6½
	8-396, 350 H.P.⑱	43N	.035	.019	28–32	Fig. E	TDC	Fig. A	700⑯	—	5–8½
	8-396, 350 H.P.⑲	43N	.035	.019	28–32	Fig. E	4°	Fig. A	—	600D⑯	5–8½
1969	6-230, 250⑱	R46N	.035	.019	31–34	Fig. G	TDC	Fig. A	700⑯	—	3–4½
	6-230, 250⑲	R46N	.035	.019	31–34	Fig. G	4°	Fig. A	—	550D⑯	3–4½
	8-307	R45S	.035	.019	28–32	Fig. E	2°	Fig. A	700⑯	600D⑯	5–6½
	8-350, 255 H.P.⑱	R44	.035	.019	28–32	Fig. E	TDC	Fig. A	700⑯	—	5–6½
	8-350, 255 H.P.⑲	R44	.035	.019	28–32	Fig. E	4°	Fig. A	—	600D⑯	5–6½
	8-350, 300 H.P.⑱	R44	.035	.019	28–32	Fig. E	TDC	Fig. A	700⑯	—	5–6½
	8-350, 300 H.P.⑲	R44	.035	.019	28–32	Fig. E	4°	Fig. A	—	600D⑯	5–6½
	8-396, 325 H.P.	R44N	.035	.019	28–32	Fig. E	4°	Fig. A	800⑯	600D⑯	5–8½
	8-396, 350 H.P.⑱	R43N	.035	.019	28–32	Fig. E	TDC	Fig. A	800⑯	—	5–8½
	8-396, 350 H.P.⑲	R43N	.035	.019	28–32	Fig. E	4°	Fig. A	—	600D⑯	5–8½
	8-396, 375 H.P.	R43N	.035	.019	28–32	Fig. E	4°	Fig. A	750⑯	750D⑯	5–8½

Continued

TUNE UP SPECIFICATIONS—Continued

OLD CAR SPECIFICATIONS: For 1946-65 Tune Up Specifications see back of book.

★When using a timing light, disconnect vacuum tube or hose at distributor and plug opening in hose or tube so idle speed will not be affected.

●When checking compression, lowest cylinder must be within 80 percent of highest.

Year	Engine Model	Spark Plugs		Distributor		Firing Order	Ignition Timing★		Hot Idle Speed③		Fuel Pump Press. Lbs.
		Type AC	Gap Inch	Point Gap Inch	Dwell Angle Deg.		BTDC ①	Mark	Std. Trans.	Auto. Trans. ②	
1970	6-250 ⑱	R46T	.035	.019	31–34	Fig. G	TDC	Fig. A	750	—	3–4½
	6-250 ⑲	R46T	.035	.019	31–34	Fig. G	4°	Fig. A	—	600D/400	3–4½
	8-307 ⑱	R43	.035	.019	28–32	Fig. E	2°	Fig. A	700	—	5–6½
	8-307 ⑲	R43	.035	.019	28–32	Fig. E	8°	Fig. A	—	600D/450	5–6½
	8-350 ⑱	R44	.035	.019	28–32	Fig. E	TDC	Fig. A	700	—	5–6½
	8-350 ⑲	R44	.035	.019	28–32	Fig. E	4°	Fig. A	—	600D	5–6½
	8-400, 265 H.P. ⑱	R44	.035	.019	28–32	Fig. E	4°	Fig. A	700	—	5–8½
	8-400, 265 H.P. ⑲	R44	.035	.019	28–32	Fig. E	8°	Fig. A	—	600D	5–8½
	8-400, 330 H.P.	R44T	.035	.019	28–32	Fig. E	4°	Fig. A	700	600D	5–8½
	8-396, 350 H.P. ⑱	R44T	.035	.019	28–32	Fig. E	TDC	Fig. A	700	—	5–8½
	8-396, 350 H.P. ⑲	R44T	.035	.019	28–32	Fig. E	4°	Fig. A	—	600D	5–8½
	8-396, 375 H.P.	R43T	.035	.019	28–32	Fig. E	4°	Fig. A	750	700D	5–8½
	8-454, 360 H.P.	R43T	.035	.019	28–32	Fig. E	6°	Fig. A	700	600	5–8½
	8-454, 390 H.P.	R43T	.035	.019	28–32	Fig. E	6°	Fig. A	700	600D	5–8½
	8-454, 450 H.P.	R43T	.035	.019	28–32	Fig. E	4°	Fig. A	700	700D	5–8½
1971	6-250	R46TS	.035	.019	31–34	Fig. G	4°	Fig. A	550	500D	3½–4½
	8-307 ⑱	R45TS	.035	.019	29–31	Fig. E	4°	Fig. A	550	—	5–6½
	8-307 ⑲	R45TS	.035	.019	29–31	Fig. E	8°	Fig. A	—	500D	5–6½
	8-350, 245 H.P. ⑱	R45TS	.035	.019	29–31	Fig. E	2°	Fig. A	600	—	7–8½
	8-350, 245 H.P. ⑲	R45TS	.035	.019	29–31	Fig. E	6°	Fig. A	—	600D	7–8½
	8-350, 270 H.P. ⑱	R44TS	.035	.019	29–31	Fig. E	4°	Fig. A	600	—	7–8½
	8-350, 270 H.P. ⑲	R44TS	.035	.019	29–31	Fig. E	8°	Fig. A	—	600D	7–8½
	8-400	R44TS	.035	.019	29–31	Fig. E	8°	Fig. A	600	600D	7–8½
	8-454, 365 H.P.	R43TS	.035	.019	29–31	Fig. E	8°	Fig. A	600	600D	7–8½
	8-454, 425 H.P. ⑱	R44TS	.035	.019	29–31	Fig. E	8°	Fig. A	700	—	7–8½
	8-454, 425 H.P. ⑲	R44TS	.035	.019	29–31	Fig. E	12°	Fig. A	—	700D	7–8½
1972	6-250	R46T	.035	.019	31–34	Fig. G	4°	Fig. A	700	600D	3½–4½
	8-307 Std. Tr.	R44T	.035	.019	29–31	Fig. E	4°	Fig. A	900	—	5–6½
	8-307 Auto. Tr.	R44T	.035	.019	29–31	Fig. E	8°	Fig. A	—	600D	5–6½
	8-350, 165 H.P.	R44T	.035	.019	29–31	Fig. E	6°	Fig. A	900	600D	7–8½
	8-350, 175 H.P. ⑱	R44T	.035	.019	29–31	Fig. E	4°	Fig. A	800	—	7–8½
	8-350, 175 H.P. ⑲	R44T	.035	.019	29–31	Fig. E	8°	Fig. A	—	600D	7–8½
	8-402	R44T	.035	.019	29–31	Fig. E	8°	Fig. A	750	600D	7–8½
	8-454	R44T	.035	.019	29–31	Fig. E	8°	Fig. A	750	600D	7–8½

CHEVY II & NOVA

Year	Engine Model	Spark Plugs		Distributor		Firing Order	Ignition Timing★		Hot Idle Speed③		Fuel Pump Press. Lbs.
		Type AC	Gap Inch	Point Gap Inch	Dwell Angle Deg.		BTDC ①	Mark	Std. Trans.	Auto. Trans. ②	
1966	4-153	46N	.035	④	31–34	Fig. H	4°	Fig. A	500⑪	500D⑪	3–4½
	6-194 Std. Eng.	46N	.035	④	31–34	Fig. G	8°	Fig. A	500⑪	500D⑪	3–4½
	6-194 Std. Tr.⑫	46N	.035	④	31–34	Fig. G	3°	Fig. A	700⑪	—	3–4½
	6-194 Auto Tr.⑫	46N	.035	④	31–34	Fig. G	8°	Fig. A	—	600D⑪	3–4½
	6-230 Std. Eng.	46N	.035	④	31–34	Fig. G	4°	Fig. A	500⑪	500D⑪	3–4½
	6-230⑫	46N	.035	④	31–34	Fig. G	4°	Fig. A	700⑪	600D⑪	3–4½
	8-283 Std. Eng.	45	.035	④	28–32	Fig. E	4°	Fig. A	500⑪	500D⑪	5–6½
	8-283⑬	45	.035	④	28–32	Fig. E	4°	Fig. A	700⑪	600D⑪	5–6½
	8-327, 275 H.P.	44	.035	④	28–32	Fig. E	8°	Fig. A	500⑪	500D⑪	5–6½
	8-327, 275 H.P.⑲	44	.035	④	28–32	Fig. E	8°	Fig. A	700⑪	—	5–6½
	8-327, 275 H.P.⑭	44	.035	④	28–32	Fig. E	2°⑯	Fig. A	—	600D⑪	5–6½

Continued

TUNE UP SPECIFICATIONS—Continued

OLD CAR SPECIFICATIONS: For 1946-65 Tune Up Specifications see back of book.

★When using a timing light, disconnect vacuum hose or tube at distributor and plug opening in hose or tube so idle speed will not be affected.

●When checking compression, lowest cylinder must be within 80 percent of highest.

| Year | Engine Model | Spark Plugs | | Distributor | | Firing Order | Ignition Timing★ | | Hot Idle Speed③ | | Fuel Pump Press. Lbs. |
		Type AC	Gap Inch	Point Gap Inch	Dwell Angle Deg.		BTDC ①	Mark	Std. Trans.	Auto. Trans. ②	
1966	8-327, 350 H.P.	44	.035	④	28–32	Fig. E	10°	Fig. A	700⑪	—	5–6½
	8-327, 350 H.P.⑫	44	.035	④	28–32	Fig. E	10°	Fig. A	750⑪	—	5–6½
	8-396, 325 H.P.	43N	.035	④	28–32	Fig. E	4°	Fig. A	500⑪	500D⑪	5–6½
	8-396, 325 H.P.⑫	43N	.035	④	28–32	Fig. E	4°	Fig. A	500⑪	500D⑪	5–6½
1967	4-153	46N	.035	.019	31–34	Fig. H	4°	Fig. A	500⑪	500D⑪	3–4½
	6-194	46N	.035	.019	31–34	Fig. G	4°	Fig. A	500⑪	500D⑪	3–4½
	6-194 Std. Tr.⑫	46N	.035	.019	31–34	Fig. G	2°	Fig. A	700⑯	—	3–4½
	6-194 Auto. Tr.⑫	46N	.035	.019	31–34	Fig. G	4°	Fig. A	—	600D⑯	3–4½
	6-250	46N	.035	.019	31–34	Fig. G	4°	Fig. A	500⑪	500D⑪	3–4½
	6-250⑫	46N	.035	.019	31–34	Fig. G	4°	Fig. A	700⑯	500D⑯	3–4½
	8-283	45	.035	.019	28–32	Fig. E	4°	Fig. A	500⑪	500D⑪	5–6½
	8-283 Std. Tr.⑫	45	.035	.019	28–32	Fig. E	TDC	Fig. A	700⑯	—	5–6½
	8-283 Auto. Tr.⑫	45	.035	.019	28–32	Fig. E	4°	Fig. A	—	600D⑯	5–6½
	8-327, 275 H.P.	44	.035	.019	28–32	Fig. E	8°	Fig. A	500⑪	500D⑪	5–6½
	8-327, 275 H.P.⑫	44	.035	.019	28–32	Fig. E	6°	Fig. A	700⑯	600D⑯	5–6½
1968	4-153 Std. Tr.	46N	.035	.019	31–34	Fig. H	TDC	Fig. A	750⑯	—	3–4½
	4-153 Auto. Tr.	46N	.035	.019	31–34	Fig. H	4°	Fig. A	—	600D⑯	3–4½
	6-230, 250 Std. Tr.	46N	.035	.019	31–34	Fig. G	TDC	Fig. A	700⑯	—	3–4½
	6-230, 250 Auto. Tr.	46N	.035	.019	31–34	Fig. G	4°	Fig. A	—	600D⑪	3–4½
	8-307	45S	.035	.019	28–32	Fig. E	2°	Fig. A	700⑯	600D⑯	5–6½
	8-327, 275 H.P.⑱	44	.035	.019	28–32	Fig. E	TDC	Fig. A	700⑪	—	5–6½
	8-327, 275 H.P.⑲	44	.035	.019	28–32	Fig. E	4°	Fig. A	—	600⑯	5–6½
	8-350 Std. Tr.	44	.035	.019	28–32	Fig. E	TDC	Fig. A	700⑯	—	5–6½
	8-350 Auto. Tr.	44	.035	.019	28–32	Fig. E	4°	Fig. A	—	600⑯	5–6½
1969	4-153⑱	R46N	.035	.019	31–34	Fig. H	TDC	Fig. A	750⑯	—	3–4½
	4-153⑲	R46N	.035	.019	31–34	Fig. H	4°	Fig. A	—	600D⑯	3–4½
	6-230, 250⑱	R46N	.035	.019	31–34	Fig. G	TDC	Fig. A	700⑯	—	3–4½
	6-230, 250⑲	R46N	.035	.019	31–34	Fig. G	4°	Fig. A	—	550D⑯	3–4½
	8-307	R45S	.035	.019	28–32	Fig. E	2°	Fig. A	700⑯	600D⑯	5–6½
	8-327, 210 H.P.⑱	R45S	.035	.019	28–32	Fig. E	2° ATC	Fig. A	700⑯	—	5–6½
	8-350, 255 H.P.⑱	R44	.035	.019	28–32	Fig. E	TDC	Fig. A	700⑯	—	5–6½
	8-350, 255 H.P.⑲	R44	.035	.019	28–32	Fig. E	4°	Fig. A	—	600D⑯	5–6½
	8-350, 300 H.P.⑱	R44	.035	.019	28–32	Fig. E	TDC	Fig. A	700⑯	—	5–6½
	8-350, 300 H.P.⑲	R44	.035	.019	28–32	Fig. E	4°	Fig. A	—	600D⑯	5–6½
	8-396, 350 H.P.⑱	R43N	.035	.019	28–32	Fig. E	TDC	Fig. A	800⑯	—	5–8½
	8-396, 350 H.P.⑲	R43N	.035	.019	28–32	Fig. E	4°	Fig. A	—	600D⑯	5–8½
	8-396, 375 H.P.	R43N	.035	.019	28–32	Fig. E	4°	Fig. A	750⑯	750D⑯	5–8½
1970	4-153⑱	R46N	.035	.019	31–34	Fig. H	TDC	Fig. A	750	—	3–4½
	4-153⑲	R46N	.035	.019	31–34	Fig. H	4°	Fig. A	—	650D	3–4½
	6-230, 250⑱	R46T	.035	.019	31–34	Fig. G	TDC	Fig. A	750	—	3–4½
	6-230, 250⑲	R46T	.035	.019	31–34	Fig. G	4°	Fig. A	—	600D/400	3–4½
	8-307⑱	R43	.035	.019	28–32	Fig. E	2°	Fig. A	700	—	5–6½
	8-307⑲	R43	.035	.019	28–32	Fig. E	8°	Fig. A	—	600D/450	5–6½
	8-350, 250 H.P.⑱	R44	.035	.019	28–32	Fig. E	TDC	Fig. A	750	—	5–6½
	8-350, 250 H.P.⑲	R44	.035	.019	28–32	Fig. E	4°	Fig. A	—	600D/450	5–6½
	8-350, 300 H.P.⑱	R44	.035	.019	28–32	Fig. E	TDC	Fig. A	700	—	5–6½
	8-350, 300 H.P.⑲	R44	.035	.019	28–32	Fig. E	4°	Fig. A	—	600D	5–6½
	8-396, 350 H.P.	R44T	.035	.019	28–32	Fig. E	TDC	Fig. A	700	—	5–8½
	8-396, 375 H.P.⑱	R43T	.035	.019	28–32	Fig. E	4°	Fig. A	750	—	5–8½
	8-396, 375 H.P.⑲	R43T	.035	.019	28–32	Fig. E	4°	Fig. A	—	700D	5–8½

Continued

TUNE UP SPECIFICATIONS—Continued

OLD CAR SPECIFICATIONS: For 1946-65 Tune Up Specifications see back of book.

★When using a timing light, disconnect vacuum hose or tube at distributor and plug opening in hose or tube so idle speed will not be affected.

●When checking compression, lowest cylinder must be within 80 percent of highest.

Year	Engine Model	Spark Plugs		Distributor		Firing Order	Ignition Timing★		Hot Idle Speed③		Fuel Pump Press. Lbs.
		Type AC	Gap Inch	Point Gap Inch	Dwell Angle Deg.		BTDC①	Mark	Std. Trans.	Auto. Trans.②	
1971	6-250	R46TS	.035	.019	31–34	Fig. G	4°	Fig. A	550	500D	3½–4½
	8-307, 200 H.P.⑱	R45TS	.035	.019	29–31	Fig. E	4°	Fig. A	550	—	5–6½
	8-307, 200 H.P.⑲	R45TS	.035	.019	29–31	Fig. E	8°	Fig. A	—	550D	5–6½
	8-350, 245 H.P.⑱	R44TS	.035	.019	29–31	Fig. E	2°	Fig. A	600	—	7–8½
	8-350, 245 H.P.⑲	R44TS	.035	.019	29–31	Fig. E	6°	Fig. A	—	550D	7–8½
	8-350, 270 H.P.⑱	R44TS	.035	.019	29–31	Fig. E	4°	Fig. A	600	—	7–8½
	8-350, 270 H.P.⑲	R44TS	.035	.019	29–31	Fig. E	8°	Fig. A	—	550D	7–8½
1972	6-250	R46T	.035	.019	31–34	Fig. G	4°	Fig. A	700	600D	3½–4½
	8-307, Std. Tr.	R44T	.035	.019	29–31	Fig. E	4°	Fig. A	900	—	5–6½
	8-307, Auto. Tr.	R44T	.035	.019	29–31	Fig. E	8°	Fig. A	—	600D	5–6½
	8-350, 165 H.P.	R44T	.035	.019	29–31	Fig. E	6°	Fig. A	900	600D	7–8½
	8-350, 200 H.P.⑱	R44T	.035	.019	29–31	Fig. E	4°	Fig. A	800	—	7–8½
	8-350, 200 H.P.⑲	R44T	.035	.019	29–31	Fig. E	8°	Fig. A	—	600D	7–8½

CHEVROLET

Year	Engine Model	Spark Plugs		Distributor		Firing Order	Ignition Timing★		Hot Idle Speed③		Fuel Pump Press. Lbs.
1966	6-250 Std. Eng.	46N	.035	④	31–34	Fig. G	6°	Fig. A	500⑪	500D⑪	3–4½
	6-250⑫	46N	.035	④	31–34	Fig. G	6°	Fig. A	700⑪	600D⑪	3–4½
	8-283 Std. Eng.	45	.035	④	28–32	Fig. E	4°	Fig. A	500⑪	500D⑪	5–6½
	8-283⑫	45	.035	④	28–32	Fig. E	4°	Fig. A	700⑪	600D⑪	5–6½
	8-327, 275 H.P.	44	.035	④	28–32	Fig. E	8°	Fig. A	500⑪	500D⑪	5–6½
	8-327, 275 H.P.⑬	44	.035	④	28–32	Fig. E	8°	Fig. A	700⑪	—	5–6½
	8-327, 275 H.P.⑭	44	.035	④	28–32	Fig. E	2°⑮	Fig. A	—	600D⑪	5–6½
	8-396, 325 H.P.	43N	.035	④	28–32	Fig. E	4°	Fig. A	550⑪	500D⑪	5–6½
	8-396, 325 H.P.⑫	43N	.035	④	28–32	Fig. E	4°	Fig. A	500⑪	500D⑪	5–6½
	8-427, 390 H.P.	43N	.035	—	—	Fig. E	4°	Fig. A	550⑪	550D⑪	5–6½
	8-427, 390 H.P.⑫	43N	.035	—	—	Fig. E	4°	Fig. A	550⑪	550D⑪	5–6½
	8-427, 425 H.P.	43N	.035	—	—	Fig. E	10°	Fig. A	800⑪	—	5–6½
1967	6-250	46N	.035	.019	31–34	Fig. G	4°	Fig. A	500⑪	500D⑪	3–4½
	6-250⑫	46N	.035	.019	31–34	Fig. G	4°	Fig. A	700⑪	500D⑯	3–4½
	8-283	45	.035	.019	28–32	Fig. E	4°	Fig. A	500⑪	500D⑪	5–6½
	8-283 Std. Tr.⑫	45	.035	.019	28–32	Fig. E	TDC	Fig. A	700⑯	600D⑯	5–6½
	8-283 Auto. Tr.⑫	45	.035	.019	28–32	Fig. E	4°	Fig. A	700⑯	600D⑯	5–6½
	8-327, 275 H.P.	44	.035	.019	28–32	Fig. E	8°	Fig. A	500⑪	500D⑪	5–6½
	8-327, 275 H.P.⑫	44	.035	.019	28–32	Fig. E	6°	Fig. A	700⑯	600D⑯	5–6½
	8-396, 325 H.P.	43N	.035	.019	28–32	Fig. E	4°	Fig. A	500⑪	500D⑪	5–6½
	8-396, 325 H.P.⑫	43N	.035	.019	28–32	Fig. E	4°	Fig. A	700⑪	500D⑪	5–6½
	8-427, 385 H.P.	43N	.035	.019	28–32	Fig. E	4°	Fig. A	550⑪	550D⑪	5–6½
	8-427, 385 H.P.⑫	43N	.035	.019	28–32	Fig. E	4°	Fig. A	700⑪	550D⑪	5–6½
1968	6-250 Std. Tr.	46N	.035	.019	31–34	Fig. G	TDC	Fig. A	700⑯	—	3–4½
	6-250 Auto. Tr.	46N	.035	.019	31–34	Fig. G	4°	Fig. A	—	600D⑪	3–4½
	8-307	45S	.035	.019	28–32	Fig. E	2°	Fig. A	700⑯	600D⑯	5–6½
	8-327, 250 H.P.	44S	.035	.019	28–32	Fig. E	4°	Fig. A	700⑪	600D⑯	5–6½
	8-327, 275 H.P.⑱	44	.035	.019	28–32	Fig. E	TDC	Fig. A	700⑪	—	5–6½
	8-327, 275 H.P.⑲	44	.035	.019	28–32	Fig. E	4°	Fig. A	—	600D⑯	5–6½
	8-396, 325 H.P.	43N	.035	.019	28–32	Fig. E	4°	Fig. A	700⑯	600D⑯	5–8½
	8-396, 375 H.P.	43N	.035	.019	28–32	Fig. E	4°	Fig. A	750⑯	—	5–8½
	8-427, 385 H.P.	43N	.035	.019	28–32	Fig. E	4°	Fig. A	700⑯	600D⑯	5–8½

Continued

TUNE UP SPECIFICATIONS—Continued

OLD CAR SPECIFICATIONS: For 1946-65 Tune Up Specifications see back of book.

★When using a timing light, disconnect vacuum hose or tube at distributor and plug opening in hose or tube so idle speed will not be affected.

●When checking compression, lowest cylinder must be within 80% of highest.

Year	Engine	Spark Plug Type AC	Gap Inch	Distributor Point Gap Inch	Dwell Angle Deg.	Firing Order	Ignition Timing★ BTDC①	Mark	Hot Idle Speed③ Std. Trans.	Auto. Trans.②	Fuel Pump Press. Lbs.
1969	6-250⑱	R46N	.035	.019	31–34	Fig. G	TDC	Fig. A	700⑯	—	3–4½
	6-250⑲	R46N	.035	.019	31–34	Fig. G	4°	Fig. A	—	550D⑯	3–4½
	8-327, 325 H.P.⑱	R45S	.035	.019	28–32	Fig. E	2° ATC	Fig. A	700⑯	—	5–6½
	8-327, 235 H.P.⑲	R45S	.035	.019	28–32	Fig. E	2°	Fig. A	—	600D⑯	5–6½
	8-350, 255 H.P.⑱	R44	.035	.019	28–32	Fig. E	TDC	Fig. A	700⑱	—	5–6½
	8-350, 255 H.P.⑲	R44	.035	.019	28–32	Fig. E	4°	Fig. A	—	600D⑯	5–6½
	8-350, 300 H.P.⑱	R44	.035	.019	28–32	Fig. E	TDC	Fig. A	700⑯	—	5–6½
	8-350, 300 H.P.⑲	R44	.035	.019	28–32	Fig. E	4°	Fig. A	—	600D⑯	5–6½
	8-396, 265 H.P.⑱	R44N	.035	.019	28–32	Fig. E	TDC	Fig. A	700⑯	—	5–6½
	8-396, 265 H.P.⑲	R44N	.035	.019	28–32	Fig. E	4°	Fig. A	—	600D⑯	5–6½
	8-427, 335 H.P.	R44N	.035	.019	28–32	Fig. E	4°	Fig. A	800⑯	600D⑯	5–8½
	8-427, 390 H.P.	R43N	.035	.019	28–32	Fig. E	4°	Fig. A	800⑪	600D⑪	5–8½
	8-427, 425 H.P.	R43N	.035	.019	28–32	Fig. E	4°	Fig. A	750⑯	750D⑯	5–8½
1970	6-250⑱	R46T	.035	.019	31–34	Fig. G	TDC	Fig. A	750	—	3–4½
	6-250⑲	R46T	.035	.019	31–34	Fig. G	4°	Fig. A	—	600D/400	3–4½
	8-350, 250 H.P.⑱	R44	.035	.019	28–32	Fig. E	TDC	Fig. A	750	—	5–6½
	8-350, 250 H.P.⑲	R44	.035	.019	28–32	Fig. E	4°	Fig. A	—	600D/450	5–6½
	8-350, 300 H.P.⑱	R44	.035	.019	28–32	Fig. E	TDC	Fig. A	700	—	5–6½
	8-350, 300 H.P.⑲	R44	.035	.019	28–32	Fig. E	4°	Fig. A	—	600D	5–6½
	8-400, 265 H.P.⑱	R44	.035	.019	28–32	Fig. E	4°	Fig. A	700	—	5–8½
	8-400, 265 H.P.⑲	R44	.035	.019	28–32	Fig. E	8°	Fig. A	—	600D/450	5–8½
	8-454, 345 H.P.	R44T	.035	.019	28–32	Fig. E	6°	Fig. A	—	600D	5–8½
	8-454, 360 H.P.	R43T	.035	.019	28–32	Fig. E	6°	Fig. A	700	600	5–8½
	8-454, 390 H.P.	R43T	.035	.019	28–32	Fig. E	6°	Fig. A	700	600D	5–8½
1971	6-250	R46TS	.035	.019	31–34	Fig. G	4°	Fig. A	550	550D	3½–4½
	8-350, 245 H.P.⑱	R44TS	.035	.019	31–34	Fig. E	2°	Fig. A	550	—	7–8½
	8-350, 245 H.P.⑲	R44TS	.035	.019	31–34	Fig. E	6°	Fig. A	—	550D	7–8½
	8-350, 270 H.P.	R44TS	.035	.019	31–34	Fig. E	8°	Fig. A	—	550D	7–8½
	8-400, 255 H.P.⑱	R44TS	.035	.019	31–34	Fig. E	4°	Fig. A	550	—	7–8½
	8-400, 255 H.P.⑲	R44TS	.035	.019	31–34	Fig. E	8°	Fig. A	—	550D	7–8½
	8-400, 300 H.P.	R44TS	.035	.019	31–34	Fig. E	8°	Fig. A	—	600D	7–8½
	8-454, 365 H.P.	R43TS	.035	.019	31–34	Fig. E	8°	Fig. A	—	600D	7–8½
1972	6-250	R46T	.035	.019	31–34	Fig. G	4°	Fig. A	700	600D	3½–4½
	8-350	R44T	.035	.019	29–31	Fig. E	6°	Fig. A	—	600D	7–8½
	8-400	R44T	.035	.019	29–31	Fig. E	6°	Fig. A	—	600D	7–8½
	8-402	R44T	.035	.019	29–31	Fig. E	8°	Fig. A	—	600D	7–8½
	8-454	R44T	.035	.019	29–31	Fig. E	8°	Fig. A	—	600D	7–8½

CORVETTE

Year	Engine	Spark Plug Type AC	Gap Inch	Distributor Point Gap Inch	Dwell Angle Deg.	Firing Order	Ignition Timing★ BTDC①	Mark	Hot Idle Speed③ Std. Trans.	Auto. Trans.②	Fuel Pump Press. Lbs.
1966	8-327, 300 H.P.	44	.035	④	28–32	Fig. E	6°	Fig. A	500	500D	5–6½
	8-327, 300 H.P.⑬	44	.035	④	28–32	Fig. E	4° ATC	Fig. A	700	—	5–6½
	8-327, 300 H.P.⑭	44	.035	④	28–32	Fig. E	4° ATC	Fig. A	—	600D	5–6½
	8-327, 350 H.P.	44	.035	④	28–32	Fig. E	10°	Fig. A	700	—	5–6½
	8-327, 350 H.P.⑫	44	.035	④	28–32	Fig. E	10°	Fig. A	700	—	5–6½
	8-427, 390 H.P.	43N	.035	—	—	Fig. E	4°	Fig. A	550	550D	5–6½
	8-427, 390 H.P.⑫	43N	.035	—	—	Fig. E	4°	Fig. A	600	550D	5–6½
	8-427, 425 H.P.	43N	.035	—	—	Fig. E	8°	Fig. A	800	—	5–6½
1967	8-327, 300 H.P.	44	.035	.019	28–32	Fig. E	6°	Fig. A	500⑪	500D⑪	5–6½
	8-327, 300 H.P.⑬	44	.035	.019	28–32	Fig. E	4° ATC	Fig. A	500⑯	600D⑯	5–6½
	8-327, 300 H.P.⑭	44	.035	.019	28–32	Fig. E	4° ATC	Fig. A	700⑯	600D⑯	5–6½

Continued

TUNE UP SPECIFICATIONS—Continued

OLD CAR SPECIFICATIONS: For 1946-65 Tune Up Specifications see back of book.

★When using a timing light, disconnect vacuum hose or tube at distributor and plug opening in hose or tube so idle speed will not be affected.

●When checking compression, lowest cylinder must be within 80 percent of the highest.

Year	Engine Model	Spark Plugs Type AC	Gap Inch	Point Gap Inch	Dwell Angle Deg.	Firing Order	Ignition Timing★ BTDC①	Mark	Hot Idle Speed③ Std. Trans.	Auto. Trans.②	Fuel Pump Press. Lbs.
1967	8-427, 390 H.P.	43N	.035	.019	28–32	Fig. E	4°	Fig. A	550⑪	550D⑪	5–6½
	8-427, 390 H.P.⑫	43N	.035	.019	28–32	Fig. E	4°	Fig. A	700⑪	550D⑪	5–6½
	8-427, 400 H.P.	43N	.035	.019	28–32	Fig. E	4°	Fig. A	550⑪	550D⑪	5–6½
	8-427, 400 H.P.⑫	43N	.035	.019	28–32	Fig. E	4°	Fig. A	750⑪	600D⑪	5–6½
	8-427, 425 H.P.	43N	.035	.019	28–32	Fig. E	12°⑰	Fig. A	1000⑪	—	5–6½
	8-427, 435 H.P.	43N	.035	.019	28–32	Fig. E	5°	Fig. A	750⑪	—	5–6½
	8-427, 435 H.P.⑫	43N	.035	.019	28–32	Fig. E	5°	Fig. A	750⑪	—	5–6½
1968	8-327, 300 H.P.	44	.035	.019	28–32	Fig. C	4°	Fig. A	700⑪	600D⑯	5–6½
	8-327, 350 H.P.	44	.035	.019	28–32	Fig. C	4°	Fig. A	750⑪	—	5–6½
	8-427, 390 H.P.	43N	.035	.019	28–32	Fig. E	4°	Fig. A	1000⑪	600D⑯	5–8½
	8-427, 400 H.P.	43N	.035	.019	28–32	Fig. E	4°	Fig. A	1000⑪	600D⑯	5–8½
	8-427, 425 H.P.	43N	.035	.019	28–32	Fig. E	4°	Fig. A	750⑯	—	5–8½
	8-427, 430 H.P.	43XL	.035	.019	28–32	Fig. E	12°	Fig. A	1000⑯	—	5–8½
	8-427, 435 H.P.	43N	.035	.019	28–32	Fig. E	4°	Fig. A	750⑯	—	5–8½
1969	8-350, 300 H.P.⑱	R44	.035	.019	28–32	Fig. E	4°	Fig. A	700⑯	—	5–6½
	8-350, 300 H.P.⑲	R44	.035	.019	28–32	Fig. E	4°	Fig. A	—	600D⑯	5–6½
	8-350, 300 H.P.	R44	.035	.019	28–32	Fig. E	8°	Fig. A	750⑯	—	5–6½
	8-350, 370 H.P.	R43	.035	.019	28–32	Fig. E	⑳	Fig. A	750⑯	—	5–6½
	8-427, 390 H.P.	R43N	.035	.019	28–32	Fig. E	4°	Fig. A	800⑪	600D⑪	5–8½
	8-427, 400 H.P.	R43N	.035	.019	28–32	Fig. E	4°	Fig. A	800⑪	600D⑪	5–8½
	8-427, 425 H.P.	R43N	.035	.019	28–32	Fig. E	4°	Fig. A	750⑯	750D⑯	5–8½
	8-427, 430 H.P.	R43XL	.035	—	—	Fig. E	12°⑤	Fig. A	1000⑯	—	5–8½
	8-427, 435 H.P.	R43N	.035	—	—	Fig. E	4°	Fig. A	750⑯	750D⑯	5–8½
1970	8-350, 300 H.P.	R44	.035	.019	29–31	Fig. E	4°	Fig. A	700	600	7½–9
	8-350, 350 H.P.	R44	.035	.019	29–31	Fig. E	8°	Fig. A	750	—	7½–9
	8-350, 370 H.P.	R43	.035	—	—	Fig. E	8°	Fig. A	900	—	7½–9
	8-454, 360 H.P.	R43T	.035	.019	28–32	Fig. E	6°	Fig. A	700	600	5–8½
	8-454, 390 H.P.	R43T	.035	.019	29–31	Fig. E	6°	Fig. A	700	600	7½–9
	8-454, 460 H.P.	R43XL	.035	—	—	Fig. E	8°	Fig. A	700	600	7½–9
1971	8-350, 270 H.P.	R44TS	.035	.019	29–31	Fig. E	8°	Fig. A	600	550D	7–8½
	8-350, 330 H.P.	R43TS	.035	—	—	Fig. E	8°	Fig. A	700	—	7–8½
	8-454, 365 H.P.	R43TS	.035	.019	29–31	Fig. E	8°	Fig. A	600	600D	7–8½
	8-454, 425 H.P.⑱	R44TS	.035	—	—	Fig. E	8°	Fig. A	700	—	7–8½
	8-454, 425 H.P.⑲	R44TS	.035	—	—	Fig. E	12°	Fig. A	—	700D	7–8½
1972	8-350, 200 H.P.	R44T	.035	.019	29–31	Fig. E	8°	Fig. A	800	600D	7–8½
	8-350, 255 H.P.	R44T	.035	.019	29–31	Fig. E	4°	Fig. A	900	—	7–8½
	8-454	R44T	.035	.019	29–31	Fig. E	8°	Fig. A	750	600D	7–8½

①—BTDC: Before top dead center.

②—D: Drive. N: Neutral.

③—Where two speeds are listed, lower speed indicates idle solenoid disconnected.

④—New points, .019", used .016". On V8s, turn adjusting screw in (clockwise) until engine misfires; then back off ½ turn.

⑤—Adjust timing at 800 R.P.M.

⑥—Early production 750 R.P.M. Engine date stamped to 1118 QA or QB, 950–1000 R.P.M.

⑩—Transistorized ignition 6° BTDC.

⑪—With A/C "ON".

⑫—With Air Injection Reactor System.

⑬—Manual transmission and Air Injection Reactor System.

⑭—Automatic transmission and Air Injection Reactor System.

⑮—After top dead center.

⑯—With A/C "OFF".

⑰—At 800 R.P.M.

⑱—With standard transmission.

⑲—With automatic transmission.

⑳—With distributor 1111496 set at 14°. All others set at 4°.

㉑—Marketed as 396 but actually 402 cu. in.

"0" is TDC
Marks 2° Increments

Fig. A

Continued

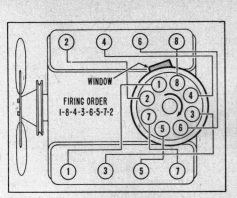

Fig. C

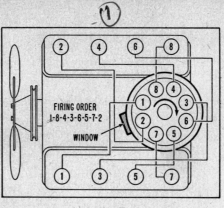

Fig. E

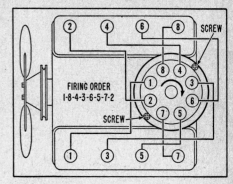

Fig. F

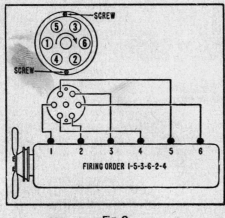

Fig. G

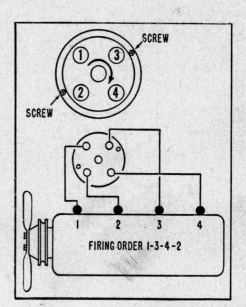

Fig. H

REAR AXLE SPECIFICATIONS

Year	Model	Carrier Type	Ring Gear & Pinion Backlash		Pinion Bearing Preload			Differential Bearing Preload		
			Method	Adjustment	Method	New Bearings Inch-Lbs.	Used Bearings Inch-Lbs.	Method	New Bearings Inch-Lbs.	Used Bearings Inch-Lbs.
1966–72	All	Integral	Shims	.005–.008	Spacer	20–25①	5–10①	Shims	.010	.010

①—Use inch-pound torque wrench on pinion shaft nut.

VALVE SPECIFICATIONS

★Adjust hydraulic lifters by tightening rocker arm stud nut just to the point where all lash is eliminated. Then turn nut the additional turns listed. See Valves Adjust text for details.

Year	Engine Model	Valve Lash★ Int.	Exh.	Valve Angles Seat	Face	Valve Spring Installed Height	Valve Spring Pressure Lbs. @ In.	Stem Clearance Intake	Exhaust	Stem Diameter Intake	Exhaust
1966	4-153	1 Turn⑤		46	45	1.66	175 @ 1.26	.001–.0027	.0015–.0032	.3410–.3417	.3410–.3417
	6-194	1 Turn⑤		46	45	1.66	175 @ 1.33	.001–.0027	.0015–.0032	.3410–.3417	.3410–.3417
	6-230	1 Turn⑤		46	45	1.66	175 @ 1.33	.001–.0027	.0015–.0032	.3410–.3417	.3410–.3417
	6-250	1 Turn⑤		46	45	1.66	185 @ 1.27	.001–.0027	.0015–.0032	.3410–.3417	.3410–.3417
	8-283	1 Turn⑤		46	45	1.66	175 @ 1.26	.001–.0027	.001–.0027	.3410–.3417	.3410–.3417
	8-327, 275, 300 H.P.	1 Turn⑤		46	45	1.66	175 @ 1.26	.001–.0027	.001–.0027	.3410–.3417	.3410–.3417
	8-327, 350 H.P.	1 Turn⑤		46	45	1.66	182 @ 1.21	.001–.0027	.001–.0027	.3410–.3417	.3410–.3417
	8-396, 325 H.P.	1 Turn⑤		46	45	1.88	220 @ 1.46	.001–.0025	.0012–.0027	.3715–.3722	.3713–.3720
	8-396, 360 H.P.	1 Turn⑤		46	45	1.88	315 @ 1.38	.001–.0025	.0012–.0027	.3715–.3722	.3713–.3720
	8-427, 390 H.P.	1 Turn⑤		46	45	1.88	315 @ 1.38	.001–.0025	.0012–.0027	.3715–.3722	.3713–.3720
	8-427, 425 H.P.	.020H	.024H	46	45	1.88	315 @ 1.38	.001–.0025	.0012–.0027	.3715–.3722	.3713–.3720
1967	4-153	1 Turn⑤		46	45	1 21/32	175 @ 1.26	.001–.0027	.0015–.0032	.3410–.3417	.3410–.3417
	6-194, 230	1 Turn⑤		46	45	1 21/32	177 @ 1.33	.001–.0027	.0015–.0032	.3410–.3417	.3410–.3417
	6-250	1 Turn⑤		46	45	1 21/32	186 @ 1.27	.001–.0027	.0015–.0032	.3410–.3417	.3410–.3417
	8-283, 327, 350	1 Turn⑤		46	45	1 5/32	200 @ 1.25	.001–.0027	.0012–.0027	.3410–.3417	.3410–.3417
	8-302	.030H	.030H	46	45	1 5/32	200 @ 1.25	.001–.0027	.0012–.0027	.3410–.3417	.3410–.3417
	8-396, 325 H.P.	1 Turn⑤		46	45	1 7/8	222 @ 1.46	.001–.0025	.0012–.0027	.3715–.3722	.3713–.3720
	8-396, 350 H.P.	1 Turn⑤		46	45	1 7/8	315 @ 1.38	.001–.0025	.0012–.0027	.3715–.3722	.3713–.3720
	8-396, 375 H.P.	.020H	.024H	46	45	1 7/8	315 @ 1.38	.001–.0025	.0012–.0027	.3715–.3722	.3713–.3720
	8-427⑥	1 Turn⑤		46	45	1 7/8	315 @ 1.38	.001–.0025	.0012–.0027	.3715–.3722	.3713–.3720
	8-427, 425 H.P.	.022H	.024H	46④	45	1 7/8	193 @ 1.32	.001–.0025	.0012–.0027	.3715–.3722	.3713–.3720
	8-427, 435 H.P.	.024H	.028H	46④	45	1 7/8	315 @ 1.38	.001–.0025	.0012–.0027	.3715–.3722	.3713–.3720
1968	4-153	1 Turn⑤		46	45	1.66	175 @ 1.26	.001–.0027	.0017–.0027	.3410–.3417	.3410–.3417
	6-230, 250	1 Turn⑤		46	45	1.66	186 @ 1.27	.001–.0027	.0017–.0027	.3410–.3417	.3410–.3417
	8-302	.030H	.030H	46	45	1.56	200 @ 1.25	.001–.0027	.0017–.0027	.3410–.3417	.3410–.3417
	8-307, 327, 350	1 Turn⑤		46	45	1.70	198 @ 1.25	.001–.0027	.0017–.0027	.3410–.3417	.3410–.3417
	8-396, 325 H.P.	1 Turn⑤		46	45	1 7/8	215 @ 1.48	.001–.0027	.0015–.0032	.3715–.3722	.3713–.3722
	8-396, 350 H.P.	1 Turn⑤		46	45	1 7/8	315 @ 1.38	.001–.0027	.0015–.0032	.3715–.3722	.3713–.3722
	8-396, 375 H.P.	.024H	.028H	46④	45	1 7/8	315 @ 1.38	.005–.0025	.0012–.0027	.3715–.3722	.3713–.3720
	8-427⑥	1 Turn⑤		46	45	1 7/8	315 @ 1.38	.001–.0027	.0015–.0032	.3715–.3722	.3713–.3722
	8-427, 430 H.P.	.022H	.024H	46	45	1 7/8	193 @ 1.32	.001–.0025	.0012–.0027	.3715–.3722	.3713–.3722
	8-427, 425, 435 H.P.	.024H	.028H	46	45	1 7/8	315 @ 1.38	.001–.0027	.0015–.0032	.3715–.3722	.3713–.3722
1969	4-153	1 Turn⑤		46	45	1.66	175 @ 1.26	.001–.0027	.0015–.0032	.3410–.3417	.3410–.3417
	6-230	1 Turn⑤		46	45	1.66	175 @ 1.33	.001–.0027	.0015–.0032	.3410–.3417	.3410–.3417
	6-250	1 Turn⑤		46	45	1.66	186 @ 1.27	.001–.0027	.0015–.0032	.3410–.3417	.3410–.3417
	8-302	.030H	.030H	46	45	1.70	200 @ 1.25	.001–.0027	.001–.0027	.3410–.3417	.3410–.3417
	8-307, 327, 350①	1 Turn⑤		46	45	1.70	200 @ 1.25	.001–.0027	.001–.0027	.3410–.3417	.3410–.3417
	8-350, 370 H.P.	.030H	.030H	46	45	1.70	200 @ 1.25	.001–.0027	.001–.0027	.3410–.3417	.3410–.3417
	8-396, 265, 325 H.P.	1 Turn⑤		46	45	1.88	220 @ 1.46	.001–.0025	.0012–.0027	.3715–.3722	.3713–.3722
	8-396, 350	1 Turn⑤		46	45	1.88	312 @ 1.38	.001–.0025	.0012–.0027	.3715–.3722	.3713–.3722
	8-396, 375	.024H	.028H	46	45	1.88	312 @ 1.38	.001–.0025	.0012–.0027	.3715–.3722	.3713–.3722
	8-427⑥	1 Turn		46	45	1.88	312 @ 1.38	.001–.0025	.0012–.0027	.3715–.3722	.3713–.3722
	8-427, 425 H.P.	.024H	.028H	46	45	1.88	312 @ 1.38	.001–.0025	.0012–.0027	.3715–.3722	.3713–.3722
	8-427, 430 H.P.	.022H	.024H	46④	45	1.88	198 @ 1.32	.001–.0025	.0012–.0027	.3715–.3722	.3713–.3722
	8-427, 435 H.P.	.024H	.028H	46④	45	1.88	312 @ 1.38	.001–.0025	.0012–.0027	.3715–.3722	.3713–.3722
1970	4-153	1 Turn⑤		46	45	1.66	175 @ 1.26	.001–.0027	.0015–.0032	.3410–.3417	.3410–.3417
	6-230	1 Turn⑤		46	45	1.66	177 @ 1.33	.001–.0027	.0015–.0032	.3410–.3417	.3410–.3417
	6-250	1 Turn⑤		46	45	1.66	186 @ 1.27	.001–.0027	.0015–.0032	.3410–.3417	.3410–.3417
	8-307	1 Turn⑤		46	45	1.70	200 @ 1.25	.001–.0027	.0012–.0029	.3410–.3417	.3410–.3417
	8-350, 250, 300 H.P.	1 Turn⑤		46	45	1.70	200 @ 1.25	.001–.0027	.0012–.0029	.3410–.3417	.3410–.3417
	8-350, 360 H.P.	.024H	.030H	46	45	1.70	200 @ 1.25	.001–.0027	.0012–.0029	.3410–.3417	.3410–.3417
	8-350, 370 H.P.	.020H	.025H	46	45	1.70	200 @ 1.25	.001–.0027	.0012–.0029	.3410–.3417	.3410–.3417

Continued

VALVE SPECIFICATIONS—Continued

★Adjust hydraulic lifters by tightening rocker arm stud nut just to the point where all lash is eliminated. Then turn nut the additional turns listed. See Valves Adjust text for details.

Year	Engine Model	Valve Lash ★		Valve Angles		Valve Spring Installed Height	Valve Spring Pressure Lbs. @ In.	Stem Clearance		Stem Diameter	
		Int.	Exh.	Seat	Face			Intake	Exhaust	Intake	Exhaust
1970	8-396, 350 H.P.⑦	1 Turn⑤		46	45	1.88	240 @ 1.38	.001–.0027	.0012–.0027	.3715–.3722	.3715–.3722
	8-396, 375 H.P.⑦	.024H	.028H	46	45	1.88	240 @ 1.38	.001–.0027	.0012–.0027	.3715–.3722	.3715–.3722
	8-400, 265 H.P.	1 Turn⑤		46	45	1.70	200 @ 1.25	.001–.0027	.0012–.0027	.3410–.3417	.3410–.3417
	8-400, 330 H.P.	1 Turn⑤		46	45	1.88	240 @ 1.38	.001–.0027	.0012–.0027	.3715–.3722	.3715–.3722
	8-454, 345 H.P.	1 Turn⑤		46	45	1.88	240 @ 1.38	.001–.0027	.0012–.0027	.3715–.3722	.3715–.3722
	8-454, 360, 390 H.P.	1 Turn⑤		46	45	1.88	240 @ 1.38	.001–.0027	.0012–.0027	.3715–.3722	.3715–.3722
	8-454, 450 H.P.	.024H	.028H	46	45	1.88	240 @ .138	.001–.0027	.0012–.0027	.3715–.3722	.3715–.3722
1971	6-250	1 Turn⑤		46	45	1.66	186 @ 1.27	.001–.0027	.001–.0027	.3410–.3417	.3410–.3417
	8-307	1 Turn⑤		46	45	1.70	200 @ 1.25	.001–.0027	.001–.0027	.3410–.3417	.3410–.3417
	8-350, 245, 270 H.P.	1 Turn⑤		46	45	1.70	200 @ 1.25	.001–.0027	.001–.0027	.3410–.3417	.3410–.3417
	8-350, 330 H.P.	.020H	.025H	46	45	1.70	200 @ 1.25	.001–.0027	.001–.0027	.3410–.3417	.3410–.3417
	8-396⑦	1 Turn⑤		46	45	1.88	240 @ 1.38	.001–.0027	.001–.0027	.3715–.3722	.3715–.3722
	8-400	1 Turn⑤		46	45	1.70	200 @ 1.25	.001–.0027	.001–.0027	.3410–.3417	.3410–.3417
	8-454, 365 H.P.	1 Turn⑤		46	45	1.88	240 @ 1.38	.001–.0027	.001–.0027	.3715–.3722	.3715–.3722
	8-454, 425 H.P.	.024H	.028H	46	45	1.88	240 @ 1.38	.001–.0027	.001–.0027	.3713–.3720	.3713–.3720
1972	6-250	1 Turn⑤		46	45	1.66	186 @ 1.27	.001–.0027	.001–.0027	.3410–.3417	.3410–.3417
	8-307	1 Turn⑤		46	45	1.68	200 @ 1.17	.001–.0027	.001–.0027	.3410–.3417	.3410–.3417
	8-350, 165 H.P.	1 Turn⑤		46	45	1.70	200 @ 1.25	.001–.0027	.001–.0027	.3410–.3417	.3410–.3417
	8-350, 175, 200 H.P.	1 Turn⑤		46	45	1.70	200 @ 1.25	.001–.0027	.001–.0027	.3410–.3417	.3410–.3417
	8-350, 255 H.P.	.024H	.030H	46	45	1.70	200 @ 1.25	.001–.0027	.001–.0027	.3410–.3417	.3410–.3417
	8-400	1 Turn⑤		46	45	1.70	200 @ 1.25	.001–.0027	.001–.0027	.3410–.3417	.3410–.3417
	8-402	1 Turn⑤		46	45	1.88	215 @ 1.48	.001–.0027	.001–.0027	.3715–.3722	.3713–.3720
	8-454	1 Turn⑤		46	45	1.88	240 @ 1.38	.001–.0027	.001–.0027	.3715–.3722	.3713–.3720

①—255, 300, 350 H.P.
②—Early production: intake, .012H, exhaust .020H. Engines date stamped TO-1118 QA or QB: intake .018H, exhaust .030H.
③—Tapers .3414" at top to .3404" at bottom.
④—Aluminum heads 45°.
⑤—Turn rocker arm stud nut until all lash is eliminated, then tighten nut the additional turn listed.
⑥—335, 385, 390, 400 H.P.
⑦—Marketed as 396 but actually 402 cu. in.

PISTONS, PINS, RINGS, CRANKSHAFT & BEARINGS

Year	Engine Model	Piston Clearance	Ring End Gap①		Wrist-pin Diameter	Rod Bearings		Main Bearings		Thrust on Bear. No.	Shaft End Play
			Comp.	Oil		Shaft Diameter	Bearing Clearance	Shaft Diameter	Bearing Clearance		
1966–67	4-153	.0005–.0011	.010	.015	.927	1.999–2.000	.0007–.0027	2.2983–2.2993	.0003–.0029	5	.002–.006
1968	4-153	.0005–.0011	.010	.015	.927	1.999–2.000	.0007–.0027	2.3004	.0003–.0029	5	.002–.006
1969–70	4-153	.0005–.0015	.010	.015	.927	1.999–2.000	.0007–.0027	2.983–2.2993	.0003–.0029	5	.002–.006
1966–67	6-194	.0005–.0011	.010	.015	.927	1.999–2.000	.0007–.0027	2.2983–2.2993	.0003–.0029	7	.002–.006
1966–67	6-230	.0005–.0011	.010	.015	.927	1.999–2.000	.0007–.0027	2.2983–2.2993	.0003–.0029	7	.002–.006
1968	6-230	.0005–.0011	.010	.015	.927	1.999–2.000	.0007–.0027	2.3004	.0003–.0029	7	.002–.006
1966–67	6-250	.0005–.0011	.010	.015	.927	1.999–2.000	.0007–.0027	2.2983–2.2993	.0003–.0029	7	.002–.006
1968	6-250	.0005–.0011	.010	.015	.927	1.999–2.000	.0007–.0027	2.3004	.0003–.0029	7	.002–.006
1969–70	6-230, 250	.0005–.0015	.010	.015	.927	1.999–2.000	.0007–.0027	2.2983–2.2993	.0003–.0029	7	.002–.006
1971–72	6-250	.0005–.0015	.010	.015	.927	1.999–2.000	.0007–.0027	2.3004	.0003–.0029	7	.002–.006
1966–67	8-283	.0005–.0011	.010	.015	.927	1.999–.2000	.0007–.0027	⑨	.0003–.0029	5	.003–.011

Continued

PISTONS, PINS, RINGS, CRANKSHAFT & BEARINGS—Continued

Year	Engine Model	Piston Clearance	Ring End Gap①		Wrist-pin Diameter	Rod Bearings		Main Bearings		Thrust on Bear. No.	Shaft End Play
			Comp.	Oil		Shaft Diameter	Bearing Clearance	Shaft Diameter	Bearing Clearance		
1967	8-302	.0024–.0030	.013	.015	.927	1.999–2.000	.0007–.0028	2.2984–2.2993	.0008–.0030	5	.003–.011
1969	8-302	.0024–.0030	.013	.015	.927	1.999–2.000	.0007–.0028	2.4479–2.4488	.0008–.0030	5	.003–.011
1968	8-307	.0005–.0011	.010	.015	.927	2.099–2.100	.0007–.0027	⑫	.004 Max.	5	.002–.006
1969	8-307	.0005–.0011	.010	.015	.927	2.099–2.100	.0007–.0027	2.4479–2.4488	.0008–.0020	5	.003–.011
1970	8-307	.0005–.0011	.010	.015	.927	2.099–2.100	.0007–.0028	②	㉘	5	.002–.006
1971–72	8-307	.0005–.0011	.010	.015	.927	2.099–2.100	.0013–.0035	⑫	㊟	5	.002–.006
1966–67	8-327⑤	.0005–.0011	.013	.015	.927	1.999–2.000	.0007–.0027	⑨	.004 Max.	5	.003–.011
1966–67	8-327⑥	.0024–.0030	.010	.015	.927	1.999–2.000	.0007–.0027	⑨	.004 Max.	5	.003–.011
1968	8-327⑬	.0005–.0011	.013	.015	.927	2.099–2.100	.0007–.0028	⑫	.004 Max.	5	.002–.006
1968	8-327⑭	.0024–.0030	.010	.015	.927	2.099–2.100	.0007–.0028	⑫	.004 Max.	5	.002–.006
1969	8-327	.0005–.0011	.013	.015	.927	2.099–2.100	.0007–.0028	2.4479–2.4488	.0008–.0020	5	.003–.011
1967	8-350	.0005–.0011	.010	.015	.927	2.099–2.100	.0007–.0028	⑮	.004 Max.	5	.003–.011
1968	8-350	.0007–.0013	.010	.015	.927	2.099–2.100	.0007–.0028	⑫	.004 Max.	5	.002–.006
1969	8-350㉖	.0005–.0011	.010	.015	.927	2.099–2.100	.0007–.0028	2.4479–.24488	㉗	5	.003–.011
1969	8-350㉖	.0024–.003	.010	.015	.927	2.099–2.100	.0007–.0028	2.4479–2.4488	㉗	5	.003–.011
1970	8-350㉕	.0007–.0013	.010	.015	.927	2.099–2.100	.0007–.0028	②	㉘	5	.002–.006
1970	8-350㉙	.0020–.0026	.010	.015	.927	2.009–2.100	.0007–.0028	②	㉘	5	.002–.006
1970	8-350㉚	.0036–.0042	.010	.015	.927	2.099–2.100	.0007–.0028	②	㉘	5	.002–.006
1971	8-350㊵	.0007–.0017	.010	.015	.927	2.099–2.100	.0013–.0035	②	㊟	5	.002–.006
	8-350㊶	.0036–.0046	.010	.015	.927	2.099–2.100	.0013–.0035	2.4503–2.4508	㊟	5	.002–.006
1972	8-350㊸	.0007–.0017	.010	.015	.927	2.099–2.100	.0013–.0035	㊻	㊟	5	.002–.006
	8-350㊹	.0036–.0046	㊺	.015	.927	2.099–2.100	.0013–.0035	㊻	㊟	5	.002–.006
1966–67	8-396⑦	.0007–.0013	.010	.010	.989	2.199–2.200	.0009–.0029	⑩	.004 Max.	5	.006–.010
1968	8-396	.0010–.0016	.010	.015	.989	2.199–2.200	.0009–.0029	③	.004 Max.	5	.006–.010
1969	8-396⑰	.001 –.0018	.010	.010	.989	2.199–2.200	.0009–.0025	⑲	.004 Max.	5	.006–.010
	8-396⑱	.0036–.0044	.010	.010	.989	2.198–2.199	.0014–.003	④	.004 Max.	5	.006–.010
1970	8-396㉙㊳	.0018–.0026	.010	.010	.989	2.199–2.200	.0009–.0025	2.750	㉝	5	.006–.010
	8-396⑱㊳	.0036–.0046	.010	.010	.989	2.1985–2.1995	.0014–.0030	2.750	㉞	5	.006–.010
1971	8-396㊳	.0018–.0028	.010	.015	.989	2.199–2.200	.0009–.0025	2.7505–2.751	㊷	5	.006–.010
1970	8-400㉛	.0014–.0020	.010	.015	.989	2.099–2.100	.0009–.0030	2.650	㉘	5	.002–.006
	8-400㉜	.0018–.0026	.010	.015	.989	2.199–2.200	.0009–.0025	2.650	㉝	5	.006–.010
1971	8-400	.0014–.0024	.010	.015	.927	2.099–2.100	.0013–.0035	2.650	㊟	5	.002–.006
1972	8-400	.0014–.0024	.010	.010	.927	2.099–2.100	.0013–.0035	㊼	㊟	5	.002–.006
1972	8-402	.0018–.0028	.010	.010	.989	2.199–2.200	.0009–.0025	2.7504	㉝	5	.006–.010
1966	8-427⑦	.0009–.0015	.010	.010	.989	2.199–2.200	.0009–.0029	⑩	.004 Max.	5	.006–.010
	8-427⑧	.0037–.0043	.010	.010	.989	2.199–2.200	.0009–.0029	⑩	.004 Max.	5	.006–.010
1967	8-427⑧	.0054–.0053	.010	.010	.989	2.199–2.200	.0009–.0029	⑩	.004 Max.	5	.006–.010
	8-427⑪	.0037–.0043	.010	.010	.989	2.199–2.200	.0009–.0029	⑩	.004 Max.	5	.006–.010
1968	8-427⑯	.0012–.0018	.010	.010	.989	2.199–2.200	.0009–.0029	③	.004 Max.	5	.006–.010
	8-427⑪	.0040–.0046	.010	.010	.989	2.199–2.200	.0014–.0034	③	.004 Max.	5	.006–.010
1969	8-427⑳	.0012–.002	.010	.010	.989	2.199–2.200	.0009–.0025	㉑	.004 Max.	5	.006–.010
	8-427㉒	.0037–.0043	.010	.010	.989	2.1985–2.1995	.0014–.003	㉑	.004 Max.	5	.006–.010
	8-427㉓	.0058–.0066	.010	.010	.989	2.1985–2.1995	.0014–.003	㉑	.004 Max.	5	.006–.010
	8-427㉔	.004 –.0048	.010	.010	.989	2.1985–2.1995	.0014–.003	㉑	.004 Max.	5	.006–.010
1970	8-454㉟	.0024–.0034	.017	.010	.989	2.199–2.200	.0009–.0025	④	㊲	5	.006–.010
	8-454㊱	.0040–.0050	.017	.010	.989	2.1985–2.1995	.0014–.0030	㉑	㉞	5	.006–.010
1971	8-454⑦	.0024–.0034	.010	.015	.989	2.199–2.200	.0009–.0025	2.7503–2.751	㊷	5	.006–.010
	8-454⑧	.0040–.0050	.010	.015	.989	2.199–2.200	.0009–.0025	2.7503–2.751	㊷	5	.006–.010
1972	8-454	.0024–.0034	.010	.010	.989	2.199–2.200	.0009–.0025	㊽	㉝	5	.006–.010

①—Fit rings in tapered bores to the clearance listed in tightest portion of ring travel.
②—No. 1, 2, 3, 4: 2.4484–2.4493; No. 5: 2.4479–2.4488.
③—No. 1–2: 2.7507
  No. 3–4: 2.7505
  No. 5: 2.7506
④—1: 2.7484–2.7493
  2, 3 & 4: 2.7481–2.7490
  5: 2.7478–2.7488
⑤—With 2 bar. carb.
⑥—With 4 bar. carb.
⑦—Except 425 H.P.
⑧—425 H.P.
⑨—Front: 2.2984–2.2993
  Rear: 2.2978–2.2988
  Others: 2.2983–2.2993
⑩—1 & 2: 2.7487–2.7497
  3 & 4: 2.7482–2.7492
  5: 2.7478–2.7488

Continued

PISTONS, PINS, RINGS, CRANKSHAFT & BEARINGS NOTES—Continued

⑪—435 H.P.
⑫—Front: 2.4502
Rear: 2.4507
Others: 2.4505
⑬—Except 325 H.P.
⑭—325 H.P.
⑮—Rear: 2.4478–2.4488
Others: 2.4483–2.4493
⑯—385, 390, 400 H.P.
⑰—Except 375 H.P.
⑱—375 H.P.
⑲—1 & 2: 2.7484–2.7493
3 & 4: 2.7481–2.7490
5: 2.7478–2.7488
⑳—335, 390, 400 H.P.
㉑—1, 2, 3 & 4: 2.7481–2.7490
5: 2.7478–2.7488
㉒—425 H.P.
㉓—430 H.P.
㉔—435 H.P.

㉕—250, 255 & 300 H.P.
㉖—350 & 370 H.P.
㉗—No. 1, 2, 3, 4: .0008–.002; No. 5: .0018–.0034.
㉘—No. 1: .0003–.0015; No. 2, 3, 4: .0006–.0018; No. 5: .0008–.0023.
㉙—350 H.P.
㉚—360 & 370 H.P.
㉛—265 H.P.
㉜—330 H.P.
㉝—No. 1: .0007–.0019; No. 2, 3, 4: .0013–.0025; No. 5: .0024–.0040.
㉞—No. 1, 2, 3, 4: .0013–.0025; No. 5: .0029–.0045.
㉟—Except 450 H.P.
㊱—450 H.P.
㊲—No. 1, 2, 3, 4: .0013–.0025; No. 5: .0024–.0040.

㊳—Marketed as 396 but actually 402 cu. in.
㊴—No. 1: .0008–.002; No. 2, 3, 4: .0011–.0023; No. 5: .0017–.0033.
㊵—240 & 270 H.P.
㊶—330 H.P.
㊷—No. 1: .0007–.0019; No. 2, 3, 4: .0013–.0025; No. 5: .0019–.0035.
㊸—165, 175, 200 H.P.
㊹—255 H.P.
㊺—Top ring, .010, lower ring, .013".
㊻—No. 1, 2, 3, 4: 2.4502; No. 5: 2.4508".
㊼—No. 1, 2, 3, 4: 2.6503; No. 5: 2.6509".
㊽—No. 1: 2.7492; No. 2, 3, 4: 2.7504; No. 5: 2.7499".

BRAKE SPECIFICATIONS

Year	Model	Brake Drum Inside Diameter	Wheel Cylinder Bore Diameter			Master Cylinder Bore Diameter		
			Disc Brake	Front Drum Brake	Rear Drum Brake	Disc Brakes	Drum Brakes	Power Brakes
1966–67	Chevy II	9½	—	1 1/16	7/8	—	1①	1
	Chevelle	9½	—	1 1/8	15/16	—	1①	1
	Chevrolet	11	—	1 3/16	1	—	1①	1
	Corvette	11¾	1 7/8	—	1 3/8	1	1	1
	Camaro	9½	—	1 1/8	15/16	—	1	1
1968–69	Camaro	9½	2 1/16④	1 1/8	7/8	—	1	1
	Chevelle	9½	2 1/16	1 1/8	②	1 1/8	1⑤	1
	Chevy II	9½	2 1/16	1 1/8	7/8	—	1⑤	1
	Chevrolet	11	2 1/16	1 3/16	1	1	1⑤	1
	Corvette	—	③	—	—	1	—	1
1970–72	Camaro	9½	2 15/16	—	7/8	1 1/8	—	1 1/8
	Chevelle⑥	9½	2 15/16	1 1/8	7/8	1 1/8	1	1
	Chevy II	9½	2 15/16	1 1/8	7/8	1 1/8	1	1
	Chevrolet	11⑦	2 15/16	1 3/16	1⑧	1 1/8	1	1
	Corvette	—	③	—	—	1	—	1⑨

①—7/8" with metallic linings.
②—1968 15/16; 1969 7/8.
③—Front 1 7/8; Rear 1 3/8.
④—Front discs only. For 4 wheel disc option, see Corvette.
⑤—1968, 7/8 with metallic linings.
⑥—Includes Monte Carlo.
⑦—1971–72 Wagon, 12.
⑧—1971–72 Sedans and Coupes 15/16".
⑨—1972 power brakes 1 1/8".

ENGINE TIGHTENING SPECIFICATIONS★

★Torque specifications are for clean and lightly lubricated threads only. Dry or dirty threads produce increased friction which prevents accurate measurement of tightness.

Year	Engine Model	Spark Plugs Ft. Lbs.	Cylinder Head Bolts Ft. Lbs.	Intake Manifold Ft. Lbs.	Exhaust Manifold Ft. Lbs.	Rocker Arm Stud Ft. Lbs.	Rocker Arm Cover Ft. Lbs.	Connecting Rod Cap Bolts Ft. Lbs.	Main Bearing Cap Bolts Ft. Lbs.	Flywheel to Crankshaft Ft. Lbs.	Vibration Damper or Pulley Ft. Lbs.
1966–70	4-153	25	95	[3]	[3]	—	55[4]	35	65	60	[2]
1966–67	6-194	25	95	[3]	[3]	—	55[4]	35	65	60	[2]
1966–69	6-230	25	95	[3]	[3]	—	55[4]	35	65	60	[2]
1970	6-230	15	95	[3]	[3]	—	55[4]	35	65	60	[2]
1966–69	6-250	25	95	[3]	[3]	—	55[4]	35	65	60	[2]
1970	6-250	15	95	[3]	[3]	—	55[4]	35	65	60	[2]
1971–72	6-250	15	95	[3]	[3]	—	45[4]	35	65	60	60
1966–67	8-283	25	65	30	20	—	55[4]	35	80	60	[2]
1967	8-302	25	65	30	20	—	55[4]	[10]	80	60	60
1968–69	8-302	25	65	30	20	—	55[4]	45	80	60	60
1968	8-307	25	65	30	20[1]	—	55[4]	45	80	60	60
1969–70	8-307	25	65	30	20[1]	—	55[4]	45	75	60	[2]
1971–72	8-307	15	65	30	20[1]	—	45[4]	45	75[12]	60	60
1966–67	8-327	25	65	30	20	—	55[4]	35	80	60	60
1968–69	8-327	25	65	30	20	—	55[4]	[10]	80	60	60
1967	8-350	25	65	30	20	—	55[4]	35	80	60	[2]
1968	8-350	25	65	30	20	—	55[4]	45	80	60	[2]
1969–70	8-350	25	65	30	20[1]	—	55[4]	45	75	60	60
1971–72	8-350	15	65	30	20[1]	50	45[4]	45	75[12]	60	60
1966–67	8-396	25	80	30	20	50	50[4]	50	[5]	60	85
1968–69	8-396	25	80	30	20	50	50[4]	45	[5]	60	85
1970	8-396[11]	15	80	30	20	50	50[4]	50	105	65	85
1970–72	8-400[6]	25	65	30	20	—	55[4]	45	75	60	60
1970	8-400[7]	15	80	30	20	50	50[4]	50	105	65	85
1971–72	8-402	15	80	30	20	50	50[4]	50	105	65	85
1966	8-427	25	80	30	20	50	50[4]	50	[5]	60	85
1967	8-427	25	80[8]	30	20	50[9]	50[4]	50	[5]	60	85
1968–69	8-427	25	80[8]	30	20	50[9]	50[4]	45	[5]	60	85
1970–72	8-454	15	80	30	20	50	50[4]	50	105	65	85

①—Inside bolts 30 ft. lbs.
②—Pressed on.
③—End clamp bolts 20, center bolts 30.
④—Inch lbs.
⑤—2 bolt caps 95 ft.-lbs., 4 bolt caps 105 ft.-lbs.
⑥—265 H.P.
⑦—330 H.P.
⑧—Aluminum Head—Short bolts 65 ft. lbs Long bolts 75 ft. lbs.
⑨—Aluminum Head—60 ft. lbs.
⑩—For 3/8" bolts 45 ft.-lbs.; for 11/32" bolts 35 ft.-lbs.
⑪—Marketed as 396 but actually 402 cu. in.
⑫—Outer bolts on engines with 4 bolt caps 65 ft. lbs.

DISTRIBUTOR SPECIFICATIONS

★NOTE: If advance is checked on vehicle, double the R.P.M. and degrees advance to get crankshaft figures.

Year	Model	Distributor Part No.②	Breaker Gap	Dwell Angle Deg.	Breaker Arm Spring Tension	Centrifugal Advance Degrees @ R.P.M. of Distributor★		Vacuum Advance		Dist. Retard
						Advance Starts	Full Advance	Inches of Vacuum To Start Plunger	Max. Adv. Dist. Deg. @ Vacuum	Max. Ret. Dist. Deg. @ Vacuum

CAMARO, CHEVROLET, CHEVELLE, CHEVY II & NOVA

Year	Model	Distributor Part No.②	Breaker Gap	Dwell Angle Deg.	Breaker Arm Spring Tension	Advance Starts	Full Advance	Inches of Vacuum To Start Plunger	Max. Adv. Dist. Deg. @ Vacuum	Max. Ret. Dist. Deg. @ Vacuum
1966	4-153	1110292	③	31–34	19–23	0 @ 300	14 @ 1850	6	11 @ 12	—
	6-250	1110351	③	31–34	19–23	0 @ 450	14 @ 1400	6	10 @ 14	—
	6-194	1110360	③	31–34	19–23	0 @ 450	13 @ 1150	6	10 @ 14	—
	6-230	1110362	③	31–34	19–23	0 @ 450	15 @ 1600	6	10 @ 14	—
	8-396, 325 H.P.	1111109	③	28–32	19–23	0 @ 450	15 @ 2500	8	10 @ 17	—
	8-427, 390 H.P.	1111112	③	28–32	19–23	0 @ 450	15 @ 2500	6	7 @ 12	—
	8-427, 425 H.P.	1111113	—	—	—	—	—	—	—	—
	8-396, 325 H.P.	1111137	③	28–32	19–23	0 @ 450	15 @ 2500	8	10 @ 17	—
	8-396, 360 H.P.	1111138	③	28–32	19–23	0 @ 450	15 @ 2500	7	6 @ 12	—
	8-396, 360 H.P.	1111139	③	28–32	19–23	0 @ 450	15 @ 2500	7	6 @ 12	—
	8-427, 390 H.P.	1111140	—	—	—	0 @ 450	15 @ 2500	6	7 @ 12	—
	8-427, 425 H.P.	1111143	—	—	—	—	—	—	—	—
	8-283	1111150	③	28–32	19–23	0 @ 450	14 @ 2200	8	7 @ 15	—
	8-327, 275 H.P.	1111152	③	28–32	19–23	0 @ 450	13 @ 2050	8	7 @ 15	—
	8-327, 350 H.P.	1111154	③	28–32	19–23	0 @ 450	15 @ 2550	6	7 @ 12	—
	8-327, 350 H.P.	1111155	③	28–32	19–23	0 @ 450	15 @ 2550	6	7 @ 12	—
1967	4-153	1110292	.019	31–34	19–23	0 @ 300	14 @ 1850	6	12 @ 12	—
	6-194	1110388	.019	31–34	19–23	0 @ 450	14 @ 1900	6	11 @ 14	—
	6-230	1110362	.019	31–34	19–23	0 @ 450	15 @ 1600	6	11 @ 14	—
	6-230 With A.I.R.	1110387	.019	31–34	19–23	0 @ 475	13 @ 2000	6	11 @ 14	—
	6-250	1110351	.019	31–34	19–23	0 @ 450	14 @ 1400	6	11 @ 14	—
	8-283	1111150	.019	28–32	19–23	0 @ 450	14 @ 2100	8	8 @ 15	—
	8-283 With A.I.R.	1111256	.019	28–32	19–23	0 @ 450	15 @ 2050	8	8 @ 15	—
	8-302, 290 H.P.	1111266	.019	28–32	19–23	0 @ 500	16 @ 2075	10	7½ @ 17	—
	8-302, 290 H.P.	1111467	.019	28–32	19–23	0 @ 625	12 @ 1100	10	7½ @ 17	—
	8-327, 210 H.P.	1111101	.019	28–32	19–23	0 @ 450	16 @ 1975	8	8 @ 15	—
	8-327, 275 H.P.	1111249	.019	28–32	19–23	0 @ 450	13 @ 2050	8	8 @ 15	—
	8-327, 275 H.P.④	1111150	.019	28–32	19–23	0 @ 450	14 @ 2100	8	8 @ 15	—
	8-327, 325 H.P.	1111195	.019	28–32	19–23	0 @ 450	15 @ 2550	6	8 @ 12	—
	8-350	1111168	.019	28–32	19–23	0 @ 450	13 @ 2350	10	8 @ 17	—
	8-396, 325 H.P.	1111169	.019	28–32	19–23	0 @ 450	16 @ 2500	8	8 @ 15	—
	8-396, 350 H.P.	1111170	.019	28–32	19–23	0 @ 450	16 @ 2500	7	6 @ 12	—
	8-427, 385 H.P.	1111170	.019	28–32	19–23	0 @ 450	16 @ 2500	7	6 @ 12	—
1968	4-153	1110447	.019	31–34	19–23	0 @ 450	14 @ 1850	7	12 @ 15	—
	4-153	1110246	.019	31–34	19–23	0 @ 450	12 @ 1800	7	12 @ 15	—
	6-230	1110436	.019	31–34	19–23	0 @ 500	18 @ 2300	7	11½ @ 16	—
	6-230	1110433	.019	31–34	19–23	0 @ 500	16 @ 2300	7	11½ @ 16	—
	6-250	1110439	.019	31–34	19–23	0 @ 450	16 @ 2100	7	11½ @ 16	—
	6-250	1110399	.019	31–34	19–23	0 @ 450	14 @ 2100	7	11½ @ 16	—
	8-302	1111467	.019	28–32	19–23	0 @ 625	16 @ 2200	10	7½ @ 17	—
	8-307	1111257	.019	28–32	19–23	0 @ 500	14 @ 2150	6	7½ @ 12	—
	8-327, 210 H.P.	1111440	.019	28–32	19–23	0 @ 500	18 @ 1975	6	7½ @ 12	—
	8-327, 210 H.P.	1111443	.019	28–32	19–23	0 @ 450	16 @ 1975	6	7½ @ 12	—
	8-327, 275 H.P.	1111298	.019	28–32	19–23	0 @ 450	17 @ 2050	8	7½ @ 15½	—
	8-327, 275 H.P.	1111297	.019	28–32	19–23	0 @ 450	15 @ 2050	10	7½ @ 17	—
	8-327, 250 H.P.	1111150	.019	28–32	19–23	0 @ 450	14 @ 2100	8	7½ @ 15½	—
	8-327, 325 H.P.	1111444	.019	28–32	19–23	0 @ 475	15 @ 2350	8	7½ @ 15½	—
	8-350, 295 H.P.	1111264	.019	28–32	19–23	0 @ 475	15 @ 2350	10	7½ @ 17	—
	8-350, 295 H.P.	1111168	.019	28–32	19–23	0 @ 450	13 @ 2350	10	7½ @ 17	—

Continued

DISTRIBUTOR SPECIFICATIONS—Continued

★NOTE: If advance is checked on the vehicle, double the R.P.M. and degrees advance to get crankshaft figures.

Year	Model	Distributor Part No.②	Breaker Gap	Dwell Angle Deg.	Breaker Arm Spring Tension	Centrifugal Advance Degrees @ R.P.M. of Distributor★		Vacuum Advance		Dist. Retard
						Advance Starts	Full Advance	Inches of Vacuum To Start Plunger	Max. Adv. Dist. Deg. @ Vacuum	Max. Ret. Dist. Deg. @ Vacuum

CAMARO, CHEVROLET, CHEVELLE, CHEVY II & NOVA—Continued

Year	Model	Distributor Part No.②	Breaker Gap	Dwell Angle Deg.	Breaker Arm Spring Tension	Advance Starts	Full Advance	Inches of Vacuum To Start Plunger	Max. Adv. Dist. Deg. @ Vacuum	Max. Ret. Dist. Deg. @ Vacuum
1968	8-396, 325, 350 H.P.	1111169	.019	28–32	19–23	0 @ 450	16 @ 2500	8	7½ @ 15½	—
	8-396, 325, 350 H.P.	1111445	.019	28–32	19–23	0 @ 450	18 @ 2500	8	7½ @ 15½	—
	8-427, 385 H.P.	1111169	.019	28–32	19–23	0 @ 450	16 @ 2500	8	7½ @ 15½	—
	8-396, 375 H.P.	1111170	.019	28–32	19–23	0 @ 450	16 @ 2500	7	6 @ 12	—
	8-427, 425 H.P.	1111170	.019	28–32	19–23	0 @ 450	16 @ 2500	7	6 @ 12	—
1969–70	4-153	1110457	.019	31–34	19–23	0 @ 450	14 @ 1850	7	12 @ 15	—
	4-153	1110458	.019	31–34	19–23	0 @ 450	12 @ 1800	7	12 @ 15	—
	6-230	1110459	.019	31–34	19–23	0 @ 500	18 @ 2300	7	11½ @ 16	—
	6-230	1110460	.019	31–34	19–23	0 @ 500	16 @ 2300	7	11½ @ 16	—
	6-250	1110463	.019	31–34	19–23	0 @ 450	16 @ 2100	7	11½ @ 16	—
	6-250	1110464	.019	31–34	19–23	0 @ 450	14 @ 2100	7	11½ @ 16	—
1969	8-302	1111480	.019	28–32	19–23	0 @ 625	16 @ 2200	8	7½ @ 15½	—
	8-307	1111481	.019	28–32	19–23	0 @ 500	14 @ 2100	6	7½ @ 12	—
	8-327	1111482	.019	28–32	19–23	0 @ 500	16 @ 2100	6	7½ @ 12	—
	8-327	1111483	.019	28–32	19–23	0 @ 450	14 @ 2100	6	7½ @ 12	—
	8-350	1111486	.019	28–32	19–23	0 @ 400	18 @ 2050	7	6½ @ 17	—
	8-350	1111487	.019	28–32	19–23	0 @ 450	16 @ 2200	7	6½ @ 17	—
	8-350, 255 H.P.	1111955	.019	28–32	19–23	0 @ 450	16 @ 2200	7	6½ @ 17	—
	8-350, 255 H.P.	1111956	.019	28–32	19–23	0 @ 450	16 @ 2200	7	12 @ 13	—
	8-350, 300 H.P.	1111488	.019	28–32	19–23	0 @ 475	15 @ 2360	10	5 @ 17	—
	8-350, 300 H.P.	1111489	.019	28–32	19–23	0 @ 450	13 @ 2360	10	5 @ 17	—
	8-396, 265 H.P.	1111949	.019	28–32	19–23	0 @ 450	19 @ 2100	8	7½ @ 15½	—
	8-396, 265 H.P.	1111950	.019	28–32	19–23	0 @ 450	17 @ 2150	8	7½ @ 15½	—
	8-396, 325 H.P.	1111497	.019	28–32	19–23	0 @ 450	16 @ 2500	8	7½ @ 15½	—
	8-427, 335 H.P.	1111497	.019	28–32	19–23	0 @ 450	16 @ 2500	8	7½ @ 15½	—
	8-396, 350 H.P.	1111498	.019	28–32	19–23	0 @ 450	18 @ 2500	8	7½ @ 15½	—
	8-396, 350, 375 H.P.	1111499	.019	28–32	19–23	0 @ 450	16 @ 2500	6	7½ @ 12	—
	8-396, 390 H.P.	1111925	.019	28–32	19–23	0 @ 400	13 @ 1900	8	7½ @ 15½	—
1970	8-307	1111995	.019	28–32	19–23	0 @ 500	14 @ 2150	6	7½ @ 12	—
	8-307	1112005	.019	28–32	19–23	0 @ 400	12 @ 2150	8	10 @ 17	—
	8-350, 250 H.P.	1112001	.019	28–32	19–23	0 @ 400	18 @ 2050	7	12 @ 17	—
	8-350, 250 H.P.	1112002	.019	28–32	19–23	0 @ 450	16 @ 2200	7	12 @ 17	—
	8-350, 300 H.P.	1111996	.019	28–32	19–23	0 @ 475	15 @ 2350	10	7½ @ 17	—
	8-350, 300 H.P.	1111997	.019	28–32	19–23	0 @ 450	13 @ 2350	10	10 @ 17	—
	8-350, 360 H.P.	1112019	.019	29–31	19–23	0 @ 575	13 @ 2500	8	7½ @ 15½	—
	8-400, 265 H.P.	1111492	.019	28–32	19–23	0 @ 400	16 @ 2200	6	7½ @ 12	—
	8-400, 265 H.P.	1111494	.019	28–32	19–23	0 @ 350	14 @ 2200	6	7½ @ 12	—
	8-396, 330 H.P.①	1111998	.019	28–32	19–23	0 @ 450	16 @ 2500	8	7½ @ 15½	—
	8-396, 350 H.P.①	1111999	.019	28–32	19–23	0 @ 450	18 @ 2500	8	7½ @ 15½	—
	8-396, 350, 375 H.P.①	1112000	.019	28–32	19–23	0 @ 450	16 @ 2500	6	7½ @ 12	—
	8-454, 345 H.P.	1111436	.019	28–32	19–23	0 @ 410	13 @ 2000	8	7½ @ 15½	—
	8-454, 390 H.P.	1111963	.019	28–32	19–23	0 @ 410	13 @ 2000	8	7½ @ 15½	—
	8-454, 450 H.P.	1111437	.019	28–32	19–23	0 @ 400	13 @ 1900	—	—	—
1971	6-250	1110489	.019	31–34	19–23	0 @ 465	12 @ 2050	8	11½ @ 16	—
	8-307	1112005	.019	29–31	19–23	0 @ 400	12 @ 2150	8	10 @ 17	—
	8-307	1112039	.019	29–31	19–23	0 @ 340	10 @ 2100	8	10 @ 17	—
	8-350, 240 H.P.	1112005	.019	29–31	19–23	0 @ 400	12 @ 2150	8	10 @ 17	—
	8-350, 240 H.P.	1112042	.019	29–31	19–23	0 @ 440	14 @ 2150	8	10 @ 17	—

Continued

DISTRIBUTOR SPECIFICATIONS—Continued

★NOTE: If advance is checked on the vehicle, double the R.P.M. and degrees advance to get crankshaft figures.

Year	Model	Distributor Part No.②	Breaker Gap	Dwell Angle Deg.	Breaker Arm Spring Tension	Centrifugal Advance Degrees @ R.P.M. of Distributor★		Vacuum Advance		Dist. Retard
						Advance Starts	Full Advance	Inches of Vacuum To Start Plunger	Max. Adv. Dist. Deg. @ Vacuum	Max. Ret. Dist. Deg. @ Vacuum
CAMARO, CHEVROLET, CHEVELLE, CHEVY II & NOVA—Continued										
1971	8-350, 270 H.P.	1112044	.019	29–31	19–23	0 @ 420	11 @ 2100	8	7½ @ 15½	—
	8-350, 270 H.P.	1112045	.019	29–31	19–23	0 @ 430	9 @ 2100	8	7½ @ 15½	—
	8-350, 330 H.P.	1112049	.019	29–31	19–23	0 @ 535	12 @ 2500	8	7½ @ 15½	—
	8-350, 330 H.P.	1112074	.019	29–31	19–23	0 @ 520	10 @ 2500	8	7½ @ 15½	—
	8-396, 380 H.P.	1112057	.019	28–30	28–32	0 @ 465	15 @ 2200	8	10 @ 8½	—
	8-400, 255 H.P.	1112056	.019	29–31	19–23	0 @ 465	12 @ 2250	10	9 @ 17	—
	8-400, 300 H.P.	1112057	.019	28–30	28–32	0 @ 465	15 @ 2200	8	10 @ 17	—
	8-454, 365 H.P.	1112052	.019	28–30	28–32	0 @ 430	11 @ 1950	8	10 @ 17	—
	8-454, 425 H.P.	1112054	.019	28–30	28–32	0 @ 545	14 @ 2500	7	6 @ 12	—
	8-454, 425 H.P.	1112075	.019	28–30	28–32	0 @ 650	8 @ 2500	7	6 @ 12	—
1972	6-250	1110489	.019	31–34	19–23	0 @ 465	12 @ 2050	8	11½ @ 16	—
	8-307	1112005	.019	29–31	19–23	0 @ 400	12 @ 2150	8	10 @ 17	—
	8-307	1112039	.019	29–31	19–23	0 @ 340	10 @ 2100	8	10 @ 17	—
	8-350, 165 H.P.	1112005	.019	29–31	19–23	0 @ 400	12 @ 2150	8	10 @ 17	—
	8-350, 175, 200 H.P.	1112044	.019	29–31	19–23	0 @ 420	11 @ 2100	8	7½ @ 15½	—
	8-350, 175, 200 H.P.	1112045	.019	29–31	19–23	0 @ 430	9 @ 2100	8	7½ @ 15½	—
	8-350, 255 H.P.	1112049	.019	29–31	19–23	0 @ 535	12 @ 2500	8	7½ @ 15½	—
	8-350, 255 H.P.	1112095	.019	29–31	19–23	0 @ 545	14 @ 2500	8	7½ @ 15½	—
	8-400	1112055	.019	29–31	19–23	0 @ 500	14 @ 2250	10	9 @ 17	—
	8-400	1112099	.019	29–31	19–23	0 @ 465	12 @ 2250	8	10 @ 17	—
	8-402	1112057	.019	29–31	19–23	0 @ 465	15 @ 2200	8	10 @ 17	—
	8-454	1112052	.019	29–31	19–23	0 @ 430	11 @ 1950	8	10 @ 17	—
CORVETTE										
1966	8-427, 390 H.P.	1111141	③	28–32	19–23	0 @ 450	15 @ 2500	6	7 @ 12	—
	8-427, 390 H.P.	1111142	—	—	—	0 @ 450	15 @ 2500	6	7 @ 12	—
	8-427, 425 H.P.	1111145	—	—	—	—	—	—	—	—
	8-327, 300 H.P.	1111153	③	28–32	19–23	0 @ 450	13 @ 2050	6	7 @ 12	—
	8-327, 350 H.P.	1111156	③	28–32	19–23	0 @ 450	15 @ 2550	4	8 @ 8	—
	8-327, 350 H.P.	1111157	③	28–32	19–23	0 @ 450	15 @ 2550	4	8 @ 8	—
1967	8-327, 300 H.P.④	1111117	.019	28–32	19–23	0 @ 450	20 @ 2550	6	8 @ 12	—
	8-327, 350 H.P.	1111157	—	—	—	0 @ 450	14 @ 2300	4	8 @ 7	—
	8-327, 300 H.P.	1111194	.019	28–32	19–23	0 @ 450	15 @ 2550	6	8 @ 12	—
	8-237, 350 H.P.	1111196	.019	28–32	19–23	0 @ 450	15 @ 2550	4	8 @ 7	—
	8-427, 390, 400 H.P.	1111247	.019	28–32	19–23	0 @ 450	16 @ 2500	7	6 @ 12	—
	8-427, Tri-Carb.	1111248	.019	28–32	19–23	0 @ 450	16 @ 2500	7	6 @ 12	—
	8-427, 435 H.P.	1111258	—	—	—	0 @ 450	15 @ 1900	8	8 @ 15	—
1968	8-327, 300 H.P.	1111194	.019	28–32	19–23	0 @ 450	15 @ 2550	6	7½ @ 12	—
	8-327, 350 H.P.	1111438	.019	28–32	19–23	0 @ 450	15 @ 2550	6	7½ @ 12	—
	8-327, 350 H.P.	1111441	.019	28–32	19–23	0 @ 450	15 @ 2200	8	7½ @ 15½	—
	8-427, 390, 400 H.P.	1111293	.019	28–32	19–23	0 @ 450	16 @ 2500	7	6 @ 12	—
	8-427, 435 H.P.	1111296	.019	28–32	19–23	0 @ 450	15 @ 1900	8	7½ @ 15½	—
	8-427, 430 H.P.	1111295	.019	28–32	19–23	0 @ 600	15 @ 2500	—	—	—
	8-427, 390, 400 H.P.	1111294	.019	28–32	19–23	0 @ 450	16 @ 2500	7	6 @ 12	—

Continued

DISTRIBUTOR SPECIFICATIONS—Continued

★NOTE: If advance is checked on the vehicle, double the R.P.M. and degrees advance to get crankshaft figures.

Year	Model	Distributor Part No.②	Breaker Gap	Dwell Angle Deg.	Breaker Arm Spring Tension	Centrifugal Advance Degrees @ R.P.M. of Distributor★		Vacuum Advance		Dist. Retard
						Advance Starts	Full Advance	Inches of Vacuum To Start Plunger	Max. Adv. Dist. Deg. @ Vacuum	Max. Ret. Dist. Deg. @ Vacuum
CORVETTE—Continued										
1969	8-350, 300 H.P.	1111490	.019	28–32	19–23	0 @ 450	16 @ 2550	8	5 @ 17	—
	8-350, 350 H.P.	1111491	—	—	—	0 @ 500	13 @ 2500	7	7½ @ 12	—
	8-350, 350 H.P.	1111493	.019	28–32	19–23	N.A.	N.A.	7	7½ @ 12	—
	8-350, 370 H.P.	1111496	.019	28–32	19–23	0 @ 600	10 @ 2300	7	6 @ 12	—
	8-350, 370 H.P.	1111971	—	—	—	0 @ 475	10 @ 2300	7	6 @ 12	—
	8-427, 390, 400 H.P.	1111926	.019	28–32	19–23	0 @ 400	13 @ 1900	7	6 @ 12	—
	8-427, 390, 400 H.P.	1111954	—	—	—	0 @ 450	13 @ 1850	7	6 @ 12	—
	8-427, 430 H.P.	1111927	—	—	—	0 @ 600	14½ @ 2500	—	—	—
	8-427, 435 H.P.	1111928	—	—	—	0 @ 450	15 @ 1900	8	7½ @ 15½	—
1970	8-350, 300 H.P.	1111490	.019	29–31	19–23	0 @ 450	16 – 2550	8	9½ @ 17	—
	8-350, 350 H.P.	1111493	.019	29–31	19–23	N.A.	N.A.	8	9½ @ 17	—
	8-350, 370 H.P.	1111491	—	—	—	0 @ 500	13 @ 2500	8	7½ @ 12	—
	8-454, 390 H.P.	1111464	.019	28–30	28–32	0 @ 545	11 @ 1600	7	6 @ 12	—
	8-454, 460 H.P.	1112026	—	—	—	0 @ 500	10½ @ 1150	7	6 @ 12	—
1971	8-350, 270 H.P.	1112050	.019	29–30	19–23	0 @ 430	9 @ 2100	8	6 @ 15½	—
	8-350, 330 H.P.	1112038	—	—	19–23	0 @ 535	12 @ 2500	8	7½ @ 15½	—
	8-454, 365 H.P.	1112051	.019	28–30	28–32	0 @ 428	11 @ 1500	8	10 @ 17	—
	8-454, 425 H.P.	1112053	—	—	28–32	0 @ 545	14 @ 2500	7	6 @ 12	—
	8-454, 425 H.P.	1112076	.019	28–30	28–32	0 @ 550	16 @ 2500	7	6 @ 12	—
1972	8-350, 200 H.P.	1112050	.019	29–31	19–23	0 @ 430	9 @ 2100	8	6 @ 15½	—
	8-350, 255 H.P.	1112101	.019	29–31	19–23	0 @ 545	14 @ 2500	8	7½ @ 15½	—
	8-454	1112051	.019	29–31	19–23	0 @ 430	11 @ 1950	7	10 @ 17	—

①—Marketed as 396 but actually 402 cu. in.
②—Stamped on distributor housing plate.
③—New points .019", used points .016".
④—With A.I.R. System.

STARTING MOTOR SPECIFICATIONS

Year	Model	Starter Number	Brush Spring Tension Oz①	Free Speed Test			Resistance Test③	
				Amps.	Volts	R.P.M.①	Amps.	Volts
1966	V8-283	1107247	35	49–76②	10.6	6200–9400	270–310③	4.3
	4 & 6 Cyl.	1107259	40	49–76②	10.6	6200–9400	270–310③	4.3
	4 & 6 Cyl.	1107260	35	49–76②	10.6	6200–9400	270–310③	4.3
1966–67	V8-327	1107320	35	65–100②	10.6	3600–5100	300–360③	3.5
1966	V8-409	1107342	35	70–105②	10.6	3800–6200	480–540②	3.0
1966	V8-327	1107320	35	65–100②	10.6	3600	300–360	3.5
1966	V8-396, 427	1107352	35	65–100②	10.6	3600–5100	300–360②	3.5
1966–68	V8-396, 427	1107365	35	65–100②	10.6	3600–5100	300–360②	3.5
1966–68	6-230, 250	1107372	35	55–95③	10.6	3800–6000	300–360	3.5
1966	6-250	1107374	35	65–100②	10.6	3600–5100	300–360	3.5
1967	4 & 6 Cyl.	1107399	35	49–87②	10.6	6200–10700	290–425②	4.2
	4 & 6 Cyl. P.G.	1107400	35	49–87②	10.6	6200–10700	290–425②	4.2
	V8-283	1107496	35	49–87②	10.6	6200–10700	290–425②	4.2
	V8-283, 327, 350	1107388	35	65–100②	10.6	3600–5100	300–360	3.5

Continued

STARTING MOTOR SPECIFICATIONS—Continued

Year	Model	Starter Number	Brush Spring Tension Oz[1]	Free Speed Test			Resistance Test[3]	
				Amps.	Volts	R.P.M.[1]	Amps.	Volts
1968–69	8-307, 327, 350	1107368	35	65–100[2]	10.6	3600–5100	300–360	3.5
	8-327, 427	1108351	35	70–99[2]	10.6	7800–12000	300–360	3.5
	8-327, 350	1108361	35	65–100[2]	10.6	3600–5100	300–360[2]	3.5
	4-153, 6-230, 250	1108365	35	49–87[2]	10.6	6200–10700	290–425[2]	4.2
	4-153	1108366	35	49–87[2]	10.6	6200–10700	290–425[2]	4.2
	8-307, 302, 327	1108367	35	49–87[2]	10.6	6200–10700	290–425[2]	4.2
	8-350	1108338	35	55–85[2]	9	3100–4900	—	—
	8-396, 427	1108418	35	65–95[2]	9	7500–10500	—	—
	8-327	1108382	35	53–69[2]	9	6400–8600	—	—
	6-250	1107372	35	55–95[2]	9	3000–4800	—	—
	8-427	1108400	35	65–95[2]	9	7500–10500	—	—
1970	4 & 6 Cyl.	1108365	35	50–80[2]	9	5500–10500	—	—
	6-250	1107372	35	55–95[2]	9	3000–4800	—	—
	8-307	1108367	35	50–80[2]	9	5500–10500	—	—
	8-350	1108338	35	55–80[2]	9	3500–6000	—	—
	8-350	1108427	35	55–80[2]	9	3500–6000	—	—
	8-454	1108430	35	65–95[2]	9	7500–10500	—	—
	8-400	1108418	35	65–95[2]	9	7500–10500	—	—
	8-454	1108400	35	65–95[2]	9	7500–10500	—	—
1971–72	6-250	1108365	35	50–80[2]	9	5500–10500	—	—
	8-307	1108367	35	50–80[2]	9	5500–10500	—	—
	[4]	1108418	35	65–95[2]	9	7500–10500	—	—
	[4]	1108430	35	65–95[2]	9	7500–10500	—	—
	8-454	1108429	35	65–95[2]	9	7500–10500	—	—
	8-454	1108400	35	65–95[2]	9	7500–10500	—	—

[1]—Minimum.　　　　[2]—Includes solenoid.　　　　[4]—Used on V8-350, 400, 402, and 454 engines.
[3]—Check capacity of motor by using a 500 ampere meter and a carbon pile rheostat to control voltage. Apply the volts listed across motor with armature locked. Current should be as listed.

ALTERNATOR & REGULATOR SPECIFICATIONS

Year	Alternator					Regulator						
	Model	Rated Hot Output Amps.	Field Current 12 Volts @ 80° F.	Output @ 14 Volts		Model	Field Relay			Voltage Regulator		
				2000 R.P.M. Amps.	5000 R.P.M. Amps.		Air Gap In.	Point Gap In.	Closing Voltage	Air Gap In.	Point Gap In.	Voltage @ 125° F.
1966–68	1100693	37	2.2–2.6	25	35	1119515	.015	.030	1.5–3.2	.067	.014	13.5–14.4
	1100694	55	2.2–2.6	32	50	1119515	.015	.030	1.5–3.2	.067	.014	13.5–14.4
1966–67	1100695	32	2.2–2.6	21	30	1119515	.015	.030	1.5–3.2	.067	.014	13.5–14.4
1966–68	1100696	42	2.2–2.6	28	40	1119515	.015	.030	1.5–3.2	.067	.014	13.5–14.4
1966	1100697	60	2.8–3.2	36	58	1116368	.015	.025	2.5–3.5	—	—	13.4–14.3
1966–67	1100742	63	2.85–3.15	35	59	1119519	.015	.030	1.5–3.2	.067	.014	13.5–14.4
1966–68	1100750	61	2.2–2.6	33	58	1119515	.015	.030	1.5–3.2	.067	.014	13.5–14.4
1966–67	1117754	62	3.7–4.4	20	55	1116378	.015	.025	2.5–3.5	—	—	13.4–14.3
1967	1117777	62	4.14–4.62	20	55	1116378	.015	.025	2.5–3.5	—	—	13.4–14.3

Continued

ALTERNATOR & REGULATOR SPECIFICATIONS—Continued

Year	Alternator					Regulator						
				Output @ 14 Volts			Field Relay			Voltage Regulator		
	Model	Rated Hot Output Amps.	Field Current 12 Volts @ 80° F.	2000 R.P.M. Amps.	5000 R.P.M. Amps.	Model	Air Gap In.	Point Gap In.	Closing Voltage	Air Gap In.	Point Gap In.	Voltage @ 125° F.
1968	1100794	37	2.2–2.6	25	35	1119515	.015	.030	1.5–3.2	.067	.014	13.4–14.3
	1100795	42	2.2–2.6	28	40	1119515	.015	.030	1.5–3.2	.067	.014	13.4–14.3
	1100796	61	2.2–2.6	33	58	1119515	.015	.030	1.5–3.2	.067	.014	13.4–14.3
	1100810	63	2.2–2.6	35	59	1119515	.015	.030	1.5–3.2	.067	.014	13.4–14.3
	1100813	37	2.2–2.6	25	35	1119515	.015	.030	1.5–3.2	.067	.014	13.4–14.3
	1100814	37	2.2–2.6	25	35	1119515	.015	.030	1.5–3.2	.067	.014	13.4–14.3
	1100815	42	2.2–2.6	28	40	1119515	.015	.030	1.5–3.2	.067	.014	13.4–14.3
	1100817	61	2.2–2.6	33	58	1119515	.015	.030	1.5–3.2	.067	.014	13.4–14.3
	1100818	63	2.2–2.6	35	59	1119515	.015	.030	1.5–3.2	.067	.014	13.4–14.3
1969–70	1100825①	61	4.0–4.5	—	—	—	—	—	—	—	—	—
	1100833①	42	4.0–4.5	—	—	—	—	—	—	—	—	—
	1100834	37	2.2–2.6	—	—	1119515	.015	.030	1.5–3.2	.067	.014	13.4–14.3
	1100836	37	2.2–2.6	25	35	1119515	.015	.030	1.5–3.2	.067	.014	13.4–14.3
	1100837	37	2.2–2.6	25	35	1119515	.015	.030	1.5–3.2	.067	.014	13.4–14.3
	1100839	42	2.2–2.6	—	—	1119515	.015	.030	1.5–3.2	.067	.014	13.4–14.3
	1100841	42	2.2–2.6	—	—	1119515	.015	.030	1.5–3.2	.067	.014	13.4–14.3
	1100843	61	2.2–2.6	33	58	1119515	.015	.030	1.5–3.2	.067	.014	13.4–14.3
	1100845	61	2.2–2.6	—	—	1119515	.015	.030	1.5–3.2	.067	.014	13.4–14.3
	1100846	63	2.2–2.6	—	—	1119515	.015	.030	1.5–3.2	.067	.014	13.4–14.3
	1100847	61	2.2–2.6	—	—	1119515	.015	.030	1.5–3.2	.067	.014	13.4–14.3
	1100859①	42	4.0–4.5	—	—	—	—	—	—	—	—	—
	1100896	61	2.2–2.6	—	—	1119515	.015	.030	1.5–3.2	.067	.014	13.4–14.3
	1100897	61	2.2–2.6	—	—	1119515	.015	.030	1.5–3.2	.067	.014	13.4–14.3
	1100900①	42	—	—	—	—	—	—	—	—	—	—
	1100901①	42	—	—	—	—	—	—	—	—	—	—
	1100950①	42	—	—	—	—	—	—	—	—	—	—
1971	1100543①	42	4–4.5	—	37	—	—	—	—	—	—	—
	1100544①	61	4–4.5	—	55	—	—	—	—	—	—	—
	1100566	37	2.2–2.6	25	35	1119515	.015	.030	1.5–3.2	.067	.014	13.8–14.8
	1100567	42	2.2–2.6	28	40	1119515	.015	.030	1.5–3.2	.067	.014	13.8–14.8
	1100836	37	2.2–2.6	25	35	1119515	.015	.030	1.5–3.2	.067	.014	13.8–14.8
	1100837	37	2.2–2.6	25	35	1119515	.015	.030	1.5–3.2	.067	.014	13.8–14.8
	1100843	61	2.2–2.6	33	58	1119515	.015	.030	1.5–3.2	.067	.014	13.8–14.8
	1100917	63	2.8–3.2	35	59	1119519	.030	.030	1.5–3.2	.067	.014	13.8–14.8
	1100950①	42	4–4.5	—	37	—	—	—	—	—	—	—
1972	1100543	42	4–4.5	—	37	—	—	—	—	—	—	—
	1100544	61	4–4.5	—	55	—	—	—	—	—	—	—
	1100950	42	4–4.5	—	37	—	—	—	—	—	—	—
	1102440	37	2.2–2.6	25	35	1119515	.015	.030	1.5–3.2	.067	.014	13.5–14.4
	1102452	37	2.2–2.6	25	35	1119515	.015	.030	1.5–3.2	.067	.014	13.5–14.4
	1102453	37	2.2–2.6	25	35	1119515	.015	.030	1.5–3.2	.067	.014	13.5–14.4
	1102454	37	2.2–2.6	25	35	1119515	.015	.030	1.5–3.2	.067	.014	13.5–14.4
	1102456	37	2.2–2.6	25	35	1119515	.015	.030	1.5–3.2	.067	.014	13.5–14.4
	1102458	42	2.2–2.6	28	40	1119515	.015	.030	1.5–3.2	.067	.014	13.5–14.4
	1102459	42	2.2–2.6	28	40	1119515	.015	.030	1.5–3.2	.067	.014	13.5–14.4
	1102463	61	2.2–2.6	33	58	1119515	.015	.030	1.5–3.2	.067	.014	13.5–14.4
	1102464	63	2.8–3.2	35	59	1119519	.030	.030	1.5–3.2	.067	.014	13.5–14.5

①—Integral System.

WHEEL ALIGNMENT SPECIFICATIONS

OLD CAR SPECIFICATIONS: For 1946-65 Wheel Alignment Specifications see back of book.

Year	Model	Caster Angle, Degrees		Camber Angle, Degrees				Toe-In. Inch	Toe-Out on Turns, Deg.①	
		Limits	Desired	Limits		Desired			Outer Wheel	Inner Wheel
				Left	Right	Left	Right			
CAMARO										
1967	All	0 to +1	+½	−¼ to +½	−¼ to +½	+¼	+¼	⅛ to ¼	—	—
1968-79	All	0 to +1	+½	−¼ to +¾	−¼ to +¾	+½	+½	⅛ to ¼	—	20
1970	Z-28	−¾ to +¼	−¼	+¼ to +1¼	+¼ to +1¼	+¾	+¾	⅛ to ¼	—	—
	Others	0 to +1	+½	+½ to +1½	+½ to +1½	+1	+1	⅛ to ¼	—	—
1971-72	Z-28	−½ to +½	Zero	−1¼ to −¼	−1¼ to −¼	−¾	−¾	⅛ to ¼	—	—
	Others	−1 to +1	Zero	+¼ to +1¾	+¼ to +1¾	+1	+1	1/16 to 5/16	—	—
CHEVELLE										
1966	Super Sport	0 to −½	−½	0 to +1	0 to +1	+½	+½	⅛ to ¼	18.4	20
	Others	−½ to −1½	−1	0 to +1	0 to +1	+½	+½	⅛ to ¼	18.4	20
1967-70	S.S., M. Carlo	−1 to 0	−½	0 to +1	0 to +1	+½	+½	⅛ to ¼	18.4	20
	Others	−1½ to −½	−1	0 to +1	0 to +1	+½	+½	⅛ to ¼	18.4	20
1971	All	−½ to −1½	−1	+¼ to +1¼	+¼ to +1¼	+¾	+¾	⅛ to ¼	—	—
1972	All	−2 to 0	−1	0 to +1½	0 to +1½	+¾	+¾	1/16-5/16	—	—
CHEVY II & NOVA										
1966-67	All	+½ to +1½	+1	0 to +1	0 to +1	+½	+½	¼ to ⅜	18.7	20
1968-71	All	0 to +1	+½	−¼ to +¾	−¼ to +¾	+½	+½	⅛ to ¼	—	20
1972	All	−1 to +1½	+½	−½ to +1	−½ to +1	+¼	+¼	1/16-5/16	—	—
CHEVROLET										
1966-70	All	+¼ to +1¼	+¾	−¼ to +¾	−¼ to +¾	+¼	+¼	⅛ to ¼	20	22½
1971-72	All	−2 to Zero	−1	+¼ to +1¼	+¼ to +1¼	+½	+½	1/16 to 5/16	—	—
CORVETTE										
1966-67	All	+½ to +1½	+1	+¼ to +1¼	+¼ to +1¼	+¾	+¾	3/16 to 5/16	18½	20
1968	Manual Steer.	+½ to +1½	+1	+¼ to +1¼	+¼ to +1¼	+¾	+¾	3/16 to 5/16	—	20
	Power Steer.	+1¾ to +2¾	+2¼	+¼ to +1¼	+¼ to +1¼	+¾	+¾	3/16 to 5/16	—	20
	Rear Wheel Align.	—	—	−⅜ to −1⅜	−⅜ to −1⅜	−¾	−¾	1/32 to 3/32	—	—
1969-72	Manual Steer.	+½ to +1½	+1	+¼ to +1¼	+¼ to +1¼	+¾	+¾	3/16 to 5/16②	—	20
	Power Steer.	+1¾ to +2¾	+2¼	+¼ to +1¼	+¼ to +1¼	+¾	+¾	3/16 to 5/16②	—	20
	Rear Wheel Align.	—	—	−⅜ to −1⅜	−⅜ to −1⅜	−⅞	−⅞	1/32 to 3/32	—	—

①—Incorrect toe-out, when other adjustments are correct, indicates bent steering arms.
②—1971 ⅛" to ⅜".

COOLING SYSTEM & CAPACITY DATA

Year	Model or Engine	Cooling Capacity, Qts.			Radiator Cap Relief Pressure, Lbs.		Thermo. Opening Temp. [1]	Fuel Tank Gals.	Engine Oil Refill Qts. [2]	Transmission Oil			Rear Axle Oil Pints
		No Heater	With Heater	With A/C	With A/C	No A/C				3 Speed Pints	4 Speed Pints	Auto. Trans. Qts. [15]	
CAMARO													
1967	6-230, 250	10	11	11	15	15	195	18	4	3	3	[6]	3½
	V8-327	14	16	16	15	15	180	18	4	3	3	[12]	4
	V8-350	15	16	16	15	15	180	18	4	3½	3	[12]	4
1968	6-230, 250	11	12	12	15	15	195	18	4	3	3	[6]	3½
	8-327	15	16	16	15	15	195	18	4	3	3	[6]	3½
	8-350	14	15	16	15	15	195	18	4	3[8]	3	[6]	3½
	8-396	22	23	23	15	15	195	18	4	3[8]	3	[12]	3½
1969	6-230, 250	11	13	13	15	15	195	18	4	3[8]	3	[19]	3½
	8-327	16	17	17	15	15	195	18	4	3[8]	3	[19]	3½
	8-350	15	16	17	15	15	195	18	4	3[8]	3	[19]	3½
	8-396	22	23	23	15	15	195	18	4	3[8]	3	[19]	4
1970	6-250	11	12	13	15	15	195	19	4	3	—	[19]	3½
	8-307	14	15	16	15	15	195	19	4	3	—	[19]	3½
	8-350 Exc. 360 H.P.	15	16	16	15	15	195	19	4	—	3	[19]	3½
	8-350, 360 H.P.	15	16	16	15	15	180	19	4	—	3	[19]	3½
	8-396[25]	22	23	23	15	15	195	19	4	—	3	[19]	3½
1971	6-250	11	12	12	15	15	195	18	4	3	—	[19]	3½
	8-307	14	15	15	15	15	195	18	4	3	—	[19]	3½
	8-350 Exc. 330 H.P.	14	15	15	15	15	195	18	4	—	3	[19]	[26]
	8-350, 330 H.P.	14	15	15	15	15	180	18	4	—	3	[19]	[26]
	8-396[25]	23	24	24	15	15	195	18	4	—	3	[19]	[26]
1972	6-250	11	12	13	15	15	195	18	4	3	—	[19]	4¼
	8-307	14	15	16	15	15	195	18	4	3	—	[19]	4¼
	8-350 Exc. 255 H.P.	15	16	16	15	15	195	18	4	—	3	[19]	4¼
	8-350, 255 H.P.	15	16	16	15	15	180	18	4	—	3	[19]	4¼
	8-402	23	24	24	15	15	195	18	4	—	3	[19]	4¼
CHEVELLE													
1966	6-194	11	12	12	15	15	180	20	4	2	—	[4]	3½
	6-230	11	12	12	15	15	180	20	4	2	—	[4]	3½
	8-283	15	16	17	15	15	180	20	4	2	2½	[5]	3½
	8-327	14	15	16	15	15	180	20	4	2	2½	[5]	4
	8-396	22	23	24	15	15	180	20	4	2	2½	[12]	4
1967	6-230, 250	10	11	11	15	15	195	20	4	3	—	[6]	3½
	V8-283	15	16	16	15	15	180	20	4	3	3	[6]	4
	V8-327	15	16	16	15	15	180	20	4	3	3	[12]	4
	V8-396	21	23	23	15	15	180	20	4	3	3	[12]	4
1968	6-230, 250	11	12	12	15	15	195	20	4	3	—	[6]	3½
	8-307	16	17	18	15	15	195	20	4	3[8]	3	[6]	3½
	8-327, 275 H.P.	15	16	17	15	15	195	20	4	3[8]	3	[12]	4
	8-327, 325 H.P.	16	17	17	15	15	195	20	4	3[8]	3	[12]	4
	8-396	23	24	24	15	15	195	20	4	3[8]	3	[12]	4
1969	6-230, 250	11	13	13	15	15	195	20[20]	4	3[8]	—	[19]	3½
	8-307	16	17	18	15	15	195	20[20]	4	3[8]	3	[19]	3½
	8-350	15	16	17	15	15	195	20[20]	4	3[8]	3	[19]	4
	8-396	22	23	23	15	15	195	20[20]	4	3[8]	3	[19]	4
1970	6-250	11	12	13	15	15	195	20[22]	4	3[8]	—	[19]	[9]
	8-307	14	15	16	15	15	195	20[22]	4	3[8]	3	[19]	[9]
	8-350	15	16	16	15	15	195	20[22]	4	3[8]	3	[19]	[9]
	8-400	22	23	24	15	15	195	20[22]	4	3[8]	3	[19]	[9]
	8-454	21	22	23	15	15	195	20[22]	4	3[8]	3	[19]	[9]

Continued

COOLING SYSTEM & CAPACITY DATA—Continued

Year	Model or Engine	Cooling Capacity, Qts.			Radiator Cap Relief Pressure, Lbs.		Thermo. Opening Temp. ①	Fuel Tank Gals.	Engine Oil Refill Qts. ②	Transmission Oil			Rear Axle Oil Pints
		No Heater	With Heater	With A/C	With A/C	No A/C				3 Speed Pints	4 Speed Pints	Auto. Trans. Qts. ⑮	
CHEVELLE—Continued													
1971	6-250	11	12	12	15	15	195	18	4	3	—	⑲	㉖
	8-307	15	16	16	15	15	195	18	4	3	—	⑲	㉖
	8-350	15	16	16	15	15	195	18	4	3	3	⑲	㉖
	8-396㉕	22	23	23	15	15	195	18	4	3	3	⑲	㉖
	8-454, 365 H.P.	21	22	22	15	15	195	18	4	—	3	⑲	㉖
	8-454, 425 H.P.	21	22	22	15	15	180	18	4	—	3	⑲	㉖
1972	6-250	11	12	12	15	15	195	㉘	4	3	—	⑲	㉙
	8-307	14	15	16	15	15	195	㉘	4	3	—	⑲	㉙
	8-350	15	16	16	15	15	195	㉘	4	3	3	⑲	㉙
	8-402	22	23	24	15	15	195	㉘	4	3	3	⑲	㉙
	8-454	21	22	23	15	15	195	㉘	4	—	3	⑲	㉙
CHEVY II & NOVA													
1966	4-153	8	9	9	15	15	180	16	3½⑪	2	...	④	3½
	6-194	11	12	12	15	15	180	16	4	2	...	④	3½
	6-230	11	12	12	15	15	180	16	4	2	...	④	3½
	8-283	15	16	17	15	15	180	16	4	2	2½	⑤	3½
	8-327, 275 H.P.	14	15	16	15	15	180	16	4	2	2½	⑤	3½
	8-327, 350 H.P.	15	16	17	15	15	180	16	4	2	2½	⑤	3½
1967	4-153	8	9	9	15	15	195	16	3½⑪	3	3	⑥	3½
	6-194, 250	10	11	11	15	15	195	16	4	3	3	⑥	3½
	V8-283	15	16	16	15	15	180	16	4	3	3	⑥	4
	V8-327	15	16	16	15	15	180	16	4	3	3	⑫	4
1968	4-153	8	9	9	15	15	195	18	4	3	—	⑥	3½
	6-230, 250	11	12	12	15	15	195	18	4	3	—	⑥	3½
	8-307	16	17	17	15	15	15	18	4	3	3	⑥	3½
	8-327, 350	15	16	16	15	15	195	18	4	3⑧	4	⑥	3½
1969	4-153	8	9	9	15	15	195	18	4	3⑧	—	⑲	3½
	6-230, 250	11	13	13	15	15	195	18	4	3⑧	—	⑲	3½
	8-307	16	17	17	15	15	195	18	4	3⑧	3	⑲	3½
	8-350	15	16	16	15	15	195	18	4	3½	3	⑲	4
	8-396	22	23	23	15	15	195	18	4	3½	3	⑲	4
1970	4-153	8	9	9	15	15	195	18㉓	3½⑪	3	—	⑲	⑨
	6-230, 250	11	12	13	15	15	195	18㉓	4	3	—	⑲	⑨
	8-307	14	15	16	15	15	195	18㉓	4	3⑧	3	⑲	⑨
	8-350	15	16	16	15	15	195	18㉓	4	3⑧	3	⑲	⑨
1971	6-250	11	12	12	15	15	195	18	4	3	—	⑲	㉖
	8-307	15	16	16	15	15	Temp.	18	4	3	—	⑲	㉖
	8-350	15	16	16	15	15	195	18	4	3	3	⑲	㉖
1972	6-250	11	12	12	15	15	195	16	4	3	—	⑲	4¼
	8-307	14	15	16	15	15	195	16	4	3	—	⑲	4¼
	8-350	15	16	15	15	15	195	16	4	3	3	⑲	4¼
CHEVROLET													
1966	6-250	12	13	14	15	15	180	20⑦	4	2	—	⑯	3½
	8-283	16	17	18	15	15	180	20⑦	4	2	2½	⑯	3½
	8-327	14	15	16	15	15	180	20⑦	4	2	2½	⑤	4

Continued

COOLING SYSTEM & CAPACITY DATA—Continued

Year	Model or Engine	Cooling Capacity, Qts.			Radiator Cap Relief Pressure, Lbs.		Thermo. Opening Temp. [1]	Fuel Tank Gals.	Engine Oil Refill Qts. [2]	Transmission Oil			Rear Axle Oil Pints
		No Heater	With Heater	With A/C	With A/C	No A/C				3 Speed Pints	4 Speed Pints	Auto. Trans. Qts. [15]	
CHEVROLET—Continued													
1966	8-396, 325 H.P.	22	23	23	15	15	180	20[7]	4	2	2½	[12]	4
	8-396, 390 H.P.	21	22	22	15	15	180	20[7]	4	2	2½	[12]	4
	8-427, 425 H.P.	22	23	23	15	15	180	20[7]	4	2	2½	[12]	4
1967	6-250	11	12	12	15	15	195	24	4	3	—	[16]	3½
	V8-283	16	17	17	15	15	180	24	4	3	3	[16]	4
	V8-327	14	15	15	15	15	180	24	4	3	3	[12]	4
	V8-396	21	22	22	15	15	180	24	4	3½	3	[12]	4
	V8-427	21	22	22	15	15	180	24	4	3½	3	[12]	4
1968	6-250	11	12	13	15	15	195	24	4	3	—	[6]	3½
	8-307	16	17	18	15	15	195	24	4	3	3	[12]	3½
	8-327	14	15	16	15	15	195	24	4	3	3	[12]	3½
	8-396, 427	21	22	22	15	15	195	24	4	3[8]	3	[12]	3½
1969	6-250	11	12	13	15	15	195	24	4	3[8]	—	[19]	3½
	8-327	16	17	18	15	15	195	24	4	3[8]	3	[19]	3½
	8-350	14	15	16	15	15	195	24	4	3½	3	[19]	4
	8-396	22	23	23	15	15	195	24	4	3½	3	[19]	4
	8-427	21	22	22	15	15	195	24	4	3½	3	[19]	4
1970	6-250	11	12	12	15	15	195	25[24]	4	3[8]	—	[19]	[9]
	8-350, 250 H.P.	15	16	16	15	15	195	25[24]	4	3[8]	—	[19]	[9]
	8-350, 300 H.P.	15	16	17	15	15	195	25[24]	4	3[8]	—	[19]	[9]
	8-400	15	16	17	15	15	195	25[24]	4	3[8]	—	[19]	[9]
	8-454	21	22	22	15	15	195	25[24]	4	3[8]	—	[19]	[9]
1971	6-250	11	12	12	15	15	195	23[27]	4	3	—	[19]	[20]
	8-350	15	16	16	15	15	195	23[27]	4	3	—	[19]	[20]
	8-396[25]	22	23	23	15	15	195	23[27]	4	—	—	[19]	[20]
	8-400	15	16	16	15	15	195	23[27]	4	3	—	[19]	[20]
	8-454	21	22	22	15	15	195	23[27]	4	—	—	[19]	[26]
1972	6-250	11	12	12	15	15	195	23[20]	4	3	—	[19]	[29]
	8-350	15	16	17	15	15	195	23[20]	4	—	—	[19]	[29]
	8-400	15	16	17	15	15	195	23[20]	4	—	—	[19]	[29]
	8-402	22	23	24	15	15	195	23[20]	4	—	—	[19]	[29]
	8-454	21	22	23	15	15	195	23[20]	4	—	—	[19]	[29]
CORVETTE													
1966	8-327, 300 H.P.	15	16	16	15	15	180	20[18]	4	2	2½	[5]	3.7
	8-327, 350 H.P.	15	16	16	15	15	180	20[18]	5	—	2½	—	3.7
	8-427, 425 H.P.	22	23	23	15	15	180	20[18]	5	—	2½	—	3.7
1967	V8-327—300 H.P.	15	16	16	15	15	180	20[18]	4	2	3	[12]	4
	V8-327—350 H.P.	15	16	16	15	15	180	20[18]	5	2	3	[12]	4
	V8-427	22	23	23	15	15	180	20[18]	5	2	3	[12]	4
1968	8-327	14	15	15	15	15	195	20	4	3	3	[12]	3.7
	8-427	21	22	22	15	15	195	20	5	3	3	[12]	3.7
1969	8-350	14	15	15	15	15	195	20	4	3	3	[21]	4
	8-427	21	22	22	15	15	195	20	5	3	3	[21]	4
1970	8-350 Exc. 370 H.P.	14	15	21	15	15	195	20	4	—	3	[4]	4
	8-350, 370 H.P.	17	18	22	15	15	180	20	4	—	3	[4]	4
	8-454	21	22	—	15	15	195	20	5	—	3	[4]	4

COOLING SYSTEM & CAPACITY DATA—Continued

Year	Model or Engine	Cooling Capacity, Qts.			Radiator Cap Relief Pressure, Lbs.		Thermo. Opening Temp. ①	Fuel Tank Gals.	Engine Oil Refill Qts. ②	Transmission Oil			Rear Axle Oil Pints
		No Heater	With Heater	With A/C	With A/C	No A/C				3 Speed Pints	4 Speed Pints	Auto. Trans. Qts. ⑮	

CORVETTE—Continued

Year	Model or Engine	No Heater	With Heater	With A/C	With A/C	No A/C	Thermo. Opening Temp.	Fuel Tank Gals.	Engine Oil Refill Qts.	3 Speed Pints	4 Speed Pints	Auto. Trans. Qts.	Rear Axle Oil Pints
1971	8-350 Exc. 330 H.P. ⑬	14	15	15	15	15	195	18	4	—	3	—	4
	8-350 Exc. 330 H.P. ⑭	17	18	18	15	15	195	18	4	—	—	⑲	4
	8-350, 330 H.P.	17	18	18	15	15	180	18	4	—	3	⑲	4
	8-454, 365 H.P.	21	22	22	15	15	195	18	5	—	3	⑲	4
	8-454, 425 H.P. ⑬	19	20	20	15	15	180	18	5	—	3	—	4
	8-454, 425 H.P. ⑭	21	22	22	15	15	180	18	5	—	—	⑲	4

①—For permanent type anti-freeze.
②—Add one quart with filter change.
③—Refill 1¾ qts. Total capacity 10½ qts.
④—Refill 1½ qts. Total capacity 7½ qts.
⑤—Refill 1½ qts. Total capacity 9 qts.
⑥—Refill 1½ qts. Total capacity 8½ qts.
⑦—Wagons 24 gallons.
⑧—Heavy duty unit 3½.
⑨—3¾ for 8⅛" ring gear and 4¼ for 8⅞" ring gear.
⑩—Wagons 19 gallons.
⑪—Add one pint with filter change.
⑫—Powerglide: Refill 1½ qts. Total capacity 9½ qts. Turbo Hydramatic: Refill 2 qts. Total capacity 13 qts.
⑬—Standard trans.
⑭—Auto. trans.
⑮—Approximate. Make final check with dipstick.

⑯—Refill 1½ qts. Total capacity 8¾ qts.
⑰—Refill 1½ qts. Total capacity 10 qts.
⑱—36 gallon tank also available.
⑲—Powerglide & Torque Drive: Refill 3 qts. Total capacity 8½ qts. Turbo-Hydramatic 350: Refill 2½ qts. Total capacity 10 qts. Turbo-Hydramatic 400: Refill 4 qts. Total capacity 11 qts.
⑳—Wagons 22 gallons.
㉑—Refill 4 qts. Total capacity 11 qts.
㉒—California vehicles about 2 gallons less.
㉓—California vehicles about 1 gallon less.
㉔—Wagons 22 gallons. California vehicles about 2 gallons less.
㉕—Marketed as 396 but actually 402 cu. in.
㉖—3½ for 8⅛" ring gear and 4 for 8⅞" ring gear.
㉗—Wagons 20 gallons.
㉘—Wagons 19 gallons; others 18 gallons.
㉙—4¼ for 8⅛" and 8½" ring gears and 4.9 for 8⅞" ring gear.

Electrical Section

DISTRIBUTOR
Removal

1. Disconnect distributor primary wire from coil terminal.
2. Remove distributor cap and rotor. *Mark position of rotor arm on distributor housing so distributor can be installed in same position.*
3. Remove vacuum line and distributor hold-down clamp.
4. Note relative position of distributor in block, then work it out of the engine.

Installation

1. Turn rotor about ⅛ of a turn counterclockwise past the mark previously placed on the distributor housing.
2. Push the distributor down into the block with the housing in the normal "installed" position. *It may be necessary to move the rotor slightly to start gear into mesh with camshaft gear, but rotor should line up with mark when distributor is down in place.*

NOTE: Because the lower end of the distributor shaft drives the oil pump, use extra care when installing the distributor to be sure it is completely seated and engaged in oil pump.

3. Tighten distributor clamp screw snugly and connect vacuum line, primary wire to coil, and install cap.

NOTE

If the engine was disturbed while the distributor was removed from the engine, first crank the engine to bring No. 1 piston up on its compression stroke and continue cranking until the timing mark is adjacent to the timing indicator. Then rotate the distributor cam until the rotor is in position to fire No. 1 cylinder. Install the distributor and set the ignition timing.

STARTER, REPLACE
1966-72 All Models

1. Disconnect ground cable at battery.
2. Raise vehicle to working height.
3. Disconnect all wires at solenoid.

NOTE: Reinstall terminal nuts as each wire is disconnected as thread size is different but may be mixed and stripped.

4. Loosen starter front bracket (nut on V8 and bolt on Sixes) then remove two mounting bolts. *On 1968 Chevelle V8 with single exhaust, it is necessary to disconnect and lower the exhaust crossover pipe.*

On V8 engines using solenoid heat remove front bracket upper bolt

and detach bracket from starter.

5. Remove front bracket bolt or nut and rotate bracket clear of work area. Then lower starter from vehicle by lowering front end first (hold starter against bell housing and sort of roll end-over end).
6. Reverse removal procedure to install and torque mount bolts to 25-35 ft-lbs.

IGNITION SWITCH, REPLACE
1969-72

The ignition switch is mounted on top of the mast jacket inside the brake pedal support and is actuated by a rod and rack assembly.

1. Disconnect battery cable.
2. Disconnect and lower steering column.
3. The switch should be in the "Lock" position before removal. If lock cylinder has been removed, the actuating rod is pulled up to the stop then back one detent, to place it in the "Lock" position. Remove retaining screws and switch.
4. Reverse procedure to install being sure that the switch is in the "Lock" position before installing.

1968 Except Corvette

1. Disconnect battery ground cable.
2. On Chevelle and Chevy II, remove ash tray and retainer. Remove radio knobs, nuts, connectors, bracket and radio.

NOTE: On Chevy II, the radio does not have to be removed. Access can be gained by removing the ash tray only.

3. On all models, remove lock cylinder by positioning in "ACC" position and inserting a wire in small hole in cylinder face. Push in on wire to

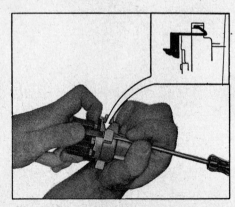

Fig. 1   Unlocking ignition switch connector. 1966-68

depress plunger and continue turning key counter-clockwise until lock cylinder can be removed.
4. Remove switch bezel nut and pull switch out from under dash.
5. Using a screwdriver, unsnap the "theft resistant" locking tangs on the connector from the position on the switch shown in Fig. 1. Unplug the connector.
6. Reverse procedure to install.

1968 Corvette
With Air Conditioning

1. Disconnect battery ground cable.
2. Remove screws securing mast jacket trim covers and remove covers.
3. Remove left side console forward trim panel.
4. Lower steering column.
5. Remove screws securing left instrument panel to door opening, top of dash and left side of center instrument panel.
6. Pull cluster assembly down and tip forward for access to switch.
7. Remove switch as outlined above for other 1968 models.

Less Air Conditioning

1. Disconnect battery cable.
2. Remove screws securing "Corvette" cover plate in top center of cluster.
3. Remove switch as outlined above for other 1968 models.

1966-67 Chevelle

1. Disconnect battery ground cable.
2. Remove ash tray and retainer.
3. Remove A/C distributor duct.
4. Unfasten and push A/C and/or heater control panel from console. *If interference between control panel and radio is encountered, loosen radio retaining nuts.*
5. Remove radio knobs, bezels and nuts.
6. Disconnect wiring harness and antenna lead-in.
7. Remove radio rear brace attaching screw and remove radio from vehicle.
8. Remove ignition switch bezel nut and push switch rearward from panel opening. Disconnect wiring connector from rear of switch.
9. Reverse removal procedure to install.

1966-67 Except '66 Chevelle

1. Disconnect battery ground cable.
2. Remove lock cylinder by positioning switch in "off" position and inserting a paper clip in small hole in cylinder face.
3. Push in on wire to depress plunger and continue to turn ignition key counter-clockwise until lock cylinder can be removed.
4. Remove switch nut from passenger side of dash.
5. Pull switch out from under dash and remove wiring connectors.

NOTE: To remove "theft resistant" connector, use a screwdriver to un-

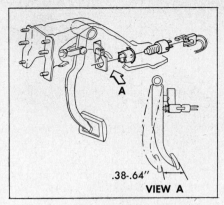

Fig. 2 Stop light switch. All 1967;
1968-72 Chevelle

snap the locking tangs on the connector from their position on the switch, Fig. 1. Then unplug the connector.

6. Reverse above procedure to install.

LIGHT SWITCH, REPLACE
1968-72 Corvette

1. Disconnect battery cable.
2. Remove screws securing mast jacket trim covers and remove covers.
3. Remove left side console forward trim panel.
4. Lower steering column.
5. Remove screws securing left instrument panel to door opening, top of dash and left side of center instrument panel.
6. Pull cluster down and tip forward for access.
7. Depress switch shaft retainer and remove the knob and shaft assembly. Remove switch retaining bezel.
8. Disconnect vacuum hoses from switch, tagging them for assembly. Pry the connector from the switch and remove the switch.

1970-72 Camaro

1. Disconnect battery ground cable.
2. Remove steering column lower cover.
3. Reach up under cluster and depress lighting switch shaft retainer while pulling gently on shaft.
4. Remove nut securing switch to carrier.
5. Remove cluster carrier screws and tilt right side of cluster out.

NOTE: Grounding ring at cigar lighter may have to be freed for further movement of carrier.

6. Unplug connector and remove switch.

1968-72 Except Corvette & 1970-72 Camaro

1. Disconnect battery ground cable.

NOTE: On Chevy II remove the parking brake bracket and lower to the floor. Heater on air

conditioning control head must also be removed.

2. Pull switch knob to "ON" position.
3. Reach up under instrument panel and depress switch shaft retainer, then remove knob and shaft assembly.
4. Remove ferrule nut and switch from panel.

NOTE: Remove vacuum hoses from Camaro and Chevrolet optional headlight switches. Tag location of hoses for assembly.

5. Disconnect multi-contact connector from light switch.
6. Reverse procedure to install.

1966-67 All Cars

1. Disconnect battery ground cable.
2. Pull control knob to headlight "ON" position.
3. Reach under instrument panel and depress switch shaft retainer and remove knob and shaft assembly.
4. Remove retaining ferrule and bezel.
5. Remove switch from panel.
6. Disconnect multi-plug connector from lighting switch.
7. Reverse above procedure to install.

STOP LIGHT SWITCH, REPLACE
1968-72

1. Disconnect wiring harness connector from switch, Fig. 3.
2. Remove retaining nut (if equipped) and unscrew switch from bracket.

NOTE: On Corvettes, remove screw holding switch bracket to brake pedal housing.

3. On Chevelles, depress brake pedal and push new switch into clip until shoulder bottoms out.
4. On Corvettes, align switch bracket on brake pedal housing and install screw.
5. On all other models, install inboard adjusting nut, install switch through bracket and install retaining nut.
6. Plug connector onto switch.

1966 Chevrolet, Chevy II & Corvette

1. From under instrument panel adjacent to brake pedal, disconnect two connectors from switch.
2. Remove lock nut from plunger end of switch and remove switch.
3. Locate new switch in same position on mounting bracket or brace and install connectors to switch.
4. Adjust switch position. Electrical contact should be made when brake pedal is depressed $\frac{3}{8}$" to $\frac{1}{2}$" from fully released position.

1966 Chevelle & All 1967

1. Disengage retaining fingers, disconnect wiring harness connector from switch and unscrew switch from its mounting clip, Fig. 2.

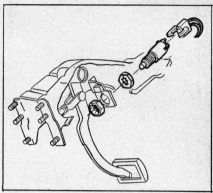

Fig. 3 Stop light switch. 1968-72
Camaro, Chevrolet and Chevy II

2. Depress brake pedal and push new switch into clip until shoulder bottoms out against clip.
3. Check switch for proper position. Electrical contact should be made when brake pedal is depressed $\frac{3}{8}$" to $\frac{5}{8}$" from fully released position.

CLUTCH START SWITCH
1969

1. Unplug connector from switch.
2. Remove retainer from pins or link on clutch pedal arm.
3. Remove retaining screw and switch.

1970-72

1. Unplug connector from switch.
2. Compress switch actuating shaft retainer and remove shaft with switch attached from switch bracket.

NEUTRAL SAFETY SWITCH, REPLACE
1966-72 Column Shift

1. Disconnect wiring connectors at switch terminals.
2. Unfasten and remove switch from mast jacket.
3. To install, locate shift lever in "Drive" and locate lever tang against transmission selector plate.
4. If provided for, align slot in contact support with hole in switch and insert a $\frac{3}{32}$" rod to hold support in place. Switch is now in drive position.
5. Place contact support drive slot over shifter tube drive tang and tighten screws. Remove clamp and $\frac{3}{32}$" rod.
6. Connect wiring harness and check operation of switch.

1966-68 Floor Shift Except Corvette

1. Position shift lever in "Drive" position. Remove ash tray, trim plate, and indicator lens and housing from console.
2. Disconnect bulbs from housing. Disconnect multiple connector at switch terminals (on Camaro models from

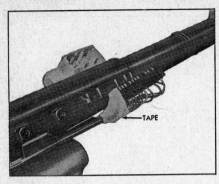

Fig. 4 Taping turn signal connector and wires. 1969-72

5. Disconnect shifter boot and retainer.
6. Disconnect switch from shifter and cut electrical leads approximately 4" from switch.
7. Splice wires from new switch to existing harness. Solder spliced connections and wrap with electrician's tape.
8. Install and adjust switch as outlined below.

TURN SIGNAL SWITCH, REPLACE

1969-72

1. Disconnect battery cable and remove steering wheel.
2. Remove cover from shaft. *The cover retaining screws need not be completely removed from the cover.*
3. Using a suitable tool, compress lock plate (horn contact carrier on tilt models) and remove snap ring ("C" ring on tilt models).
4. Remove lock plate, cancelling cam, spring, thrust washer and signal lever.
5. Push hazard warning knob in and unscrew knob.
6. Pull connector from bracket and wrap upper part of connector with tape to prevent snagging the wires during removal. On Tilt models, position shifter housing in "Low" position. Remove harness cover.
7. Remove retaining screws and remove switch, Figs. 4 and 5.

1968

1. Disconnect steering column harness at connector.
2. Disconnect neutral safety switch and back-up lamp switch connectors.
3. Remove steering wheel.
4. Slide upper bearing preload spring and cancelling cam off end of shaft.
5. Remove turn signal lever retaining screw and remove lever.
6. Push hazard warning switch in, unscrew and remove knob.
7. Drive out shift lever retaining pin and remove shift lever.
8. Remove "C" retaining ring from upper steering shaft.
9. Slide thrust washer and wave washer off upper steering shaft.
10. Loosen three turn signal mounting screws until switch cover can be rotated counter-clockwise. It may be necessary to push on top of screws to loosen cover.
11. Rotate turn signal switch cover counter-clockwise and pull cover off top of jacket.
12. Remove shift lever bowl from top of jacket.
13. If necessary, pry upper shift lever spring from bowl and discard spring. Remove bowl washer.
14. If necessary to service components within signal switch cover, remove three signal switch mounting screws completely from engagement with the lock plate. Use care to control the three springs as screws are removed.
15. Remove turn signal switch and upper bearing housing from cover.
16. Reverse procedure to install.

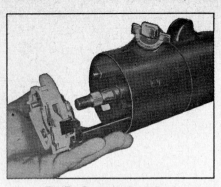

Fig. 5 Removing turn signal switch. 1969-72

1967 Except Corvette

All Columns Except Tilt & Telescoping
1. Disconnect battery ground cable.
2. Disconnect signal switch wiring from chassis harness at multiple connector under instrument panel.
3. Remove steering wheel.
4. Remove shift lever roll pin and lever from column (if applicable).
5. Push in hazard warning switch knob and unscrew knob.
6. Remove switch lever arm.
7. On Chevy II and Camaro with automatic transmission, remove column-mounted dial indicator housing and lamp assembly (if applicable).
8. Remove mast jacket lower trim cover(s).
9. On Chevrolet and Chevelle with automatic transmission, remove quadrant dial pointer (if applicable).
10. Remove retaining "C" ring from upper steering shaft and slide thrust and wave washers from steering shaft.
11. Loosen signal switch screws until assembly can be rotated counterclockwise. *Do not completely remove screws until unit is on work bench.*
12. Rotate switch counterclockwise and pull unit from top of mast jacket. Allow unit to hang from top of column.
13. Remove upper support bracket. *Do not suspend column by lower reinforcement only.*
14. Reinforce column and remove wire harness protector and clip, then position bracket and reinstall bolts finger tight.
15. Remove shift lever bowl from mast jacket and disengage from wire harness.
16. Remove three screws from engagement with lock plate, using care not to lose three springs as screws are removed.
17. Disassemble switch and upper bearing housing from switch cover.
18. Reverse procedure to install, using a new switch as it is not repairable.

Tilt Column
1. Disconnect battery ground cable.
2. Disconnect signal wire harness from body harness at multiple connector under instrument panel.
3. Remove steering wheel.
4. Remove preload spring and cancelling cam from end of shaft.
5. Remove shift lever pin and lever from steering column (except floor

---

wiring harness at the in-line connector).
3. Remove retaining nuts and switch.
4. To install new switch, clamp pawl rod against contact point of detent and align slot in contact support with drive hole in switch. Insert a 3/32" rod to hold in place. Switch is now in drive position.
5. Position switch to lever and bracket assembly with lever engaged in contact support and install retaining nuts.
6. Remove clamp and 3/32" rod, connect wiring and check switch operation.
7. Install bulbs, housing, lens, ash tray and trim plate.

1966-68 Corvette, 1969-72 All Floor Shift

1. Disconnect shift control lever arm from transmission control rod.
2. Remove shift control knob.
3. Remove trim plate.
4. Remove control assembly from seal and cut switch wiring.
5. Remove switch from control assembly.
6. To install, position gearshift in Drive position, align hole in contact support with hole in switch and insert a pin (3/32") to hold support in place.
7. Place contact support drive slot over drive tang and tighten switch mounting screws.
8. Connect wiring harness to switch wiring.
9. Install trim plate control knob and connect shift lever arm to transmission control rod.

1966 Corvette

Service Note

The neutral safety switch on these models is serviced with 95 inches of wire attached to the switch. The following procedure for replacing the switch permits cutting and splicing the wire approximately 4 inches from the switch rather than replace the entire assembly.

1. Disconnect battery ground cable.
2. Raise rear of vehicle and place on stands.
3. Disconnect shifter arm at clevis.
4. Remove center console trim plate.

shift).
6. Remove turn signal lever.
7. Push in and remove hazard warning knob.
8. On Camaro with automatic transmission, remove quadrant dial and lamp assembly from column.
9. Remove mast jacket trim cover(s).
10. On Chevrolet and Chevelle with automatic transmission, remove quadrant dial pointer.
11. Assemble a suitable slide hammer to turn signal cover, place a cover remover over turn signal cover, tighten clamp and pull cover from end of column with slide hammer.
12. Remove three switch mounting screws, *noting short length of top screw.*
13. Cut multiple connector from switch wiring and slide switch from end of column.

Installation

1. Feed wiring through bearing housing, around support and through shift bowl and shroud.
2. Feed through wiring protector. If clearance is not sufficient, loosen mast jacket bracket retaining bolts.
3. Insert switch wiring terminals in multiple connector. *Use old connector and wiring for color guide.*
4. Position switch and install three mounting screws with short screw in top position.
5. Complete the installation in reverse order of removal.

1967 Corvette

Standard & Telescoping Column
1. Disconnect battery ground cable.
2. Disconnect signal switch harness wiring from chassis wire harness at multiple connector under instrument panel.
3. Remove steering wheel.
4. Remove preload spring and cancelling cam.
5. Remove turn signal lever.
6. Push in and unscrew hazard warning knob.
7. Remove lower trim cover.
8. Remove retaining ring, thrust and wave washers from upper end of shaft.
9. Cut wiring above connector.
10. Remove three switch mounting screws and slide switch, cover and upper bearing housing from column, pulling wire through protector and escutcheon.
11. Reverse procedure to install.

1966 Chevrolet

1. Remove steering wheel.
2. Remove lever from cancelling mechanism.
3. Remove shift lever retaining pin and lever.
4. Disconnect turn signal wiring from harness quick disconnect.
5. Remove lower trim cover plate and mast jacket upper clamp.
6. With Powerglide, remove dial indicator retaining screws.
7. Separate turn signal control from signal housing (3 screws).
8. Remove wiring clamps (slide components upward on column to expose

upper clamp).
9. Remove turn signal assembly and housing, shift lever housing and mast jacket cover extension from steering column.
10. Remove turn signal from housings and mast jacket.

CAUTION: Turn signal control assembly must be in neutral position when assembling steering wheel to prevent damage to cancelling cam and control assembly.

1966 Chevelle

1. Remove steering wheel.
2. Remove cancelling cam, spring, turn signal lever screw and lever.
3. Remove shift lever pin and lever from shift bowl.
4. Disconnect signal wiring from instrument panel harness at multiple connector.
5. Disconnect mast jacket upper clamp and bend away from column. Remove wiring harness retainer and cover.
6. Remove three screws and take off switch, housing and shift bowl from steering column. Disengage switch and wiring harness from other units. On cars with Powerglide, the dial quadrant lamp and socket must be detached from signal housing first.
7. Reverse above procedure to install.

CAUTION: Turn signal control assembly must be in neutral position when assembling steering wheel to prevent damage to cancelling cam and control assembly.

1966 Chevy II

1. Remove steering wheel.
2. Remove lever from cancelling mechanism.
3. Remove control lever retaining pin and lever.
4. Remove mast jacket upper support clamp.
5. Disconnect turn signal, horn and shift indicator light (Powerglide) wiring at chassis harness quick disconnect and disconnect plastic harness cover attaching harness to mast jacket.
6. Separate turn signal control from switch housing (3 screws).
7. Remove turn signal, housing and shift bowl from steering column.
8. Disconnect shift indicator light (Powerglide only) and horn wires from multiple connector. Disengage turn signal from signal and shift lever housings.
9. Reverse above procedure to install.

CAUTION: Turn signal control assembly must be in neutral position when assembling steering wheel to prevent damage to cancelling cam and control assembly.

1966 Corvette

Standard Steering
1. Remove steering wheel.
2. Remove terminal leads from multiple connector and disconnect harness cover from mast jacket.
3. Remove control lever, three screws retaining control unit to housing re-

tainer plate and slide control unit from steering shaft.
4. Remove retainer plate, housing and control unit from mast jacket.

CAUTION: Wiring terminals must be individually pulled through slot in mast jacket escutcheon to prevent damage to harness assembly.

5. Transfer wiring harness cover to new control unit and reverse above procedure to install new unit.

Telescoping Steering
1. Disconnect battery ground cable.
2. Remove steering wheel and hub.
3. Remove spring and cancelling cam from steering shaft.
4. Remove signal lever.
5. Remove signal control from retaining plate.
6. Remove clamp and cover from signal wire harness.
7. Remove terminals from plastic connectors.
8. Guiding wiring, pull signal switch out of housing.
9. Reverse above procedure to install.

HORN SOUNDER & STEERING WHEEL

1970-72 Camaro

1. Disconnect battery ground cable.
2. Remove two steering wheel shroud screws at underside of steering wheel and remove shroud.
3. Remove three spacer screws, spacer, plate and belleville spring.
4. Remove steering wheel nut and washer and, using a suitable puller, remove steering wheel.

1969-72 Deluxe Wheel

1. Disconnect battery ground cable.
2. Remove four attaching screws on underside of steering wheel, Fig. 6.
3. Lift steering wheel shroud and pull horn wires from cancelling cam tower.
4. Remove steering wheel nut and washer, and use a suitable puller to remove steering wheel.

1968 Deluxe Wheel

1. Disconnect battery ground cable.
2. Disconnect steering column wiring harness from chassis harness at connector.
3. Remove three screws from underside of steering wheel.
4. Remove four screws securing both horn blowing buttons. This will permit wires to hang loose.
5. Remove steering wheel shroud.
6. Remove wheel nut and washer.
7. Use a puller to remove wheel.
8. Reverse procedure to install.

1967-69 Standard Wheel

1. Disconnect battery ground cable and steering column harness from chassis wiring harness.
2. Pull out horn button cap or center ornament and retainer.
3. Remove three screws from receiving

cup.
4. Remove receiving cup, belleville spring, bushing and pivot ring.
5. Remove wheel nut and washer and use a suitable puller to remove wheel.

CAUTION: Turn signal control assembly must be in neutral position when assembling steering wheel to prevent damage to cancelling cam and control assembly.

1967-72 Simulated Wood Wheel

1. Disconnect steering column harness from chassis wiring harness at connector.
2. Disconnect battery ground cable.
3. Remove horn cap by pulling up.
4. Remove screws and contact assembly.

NOTE: If steering wheel only is to be replaced, perform Step 4. If turn signal cancelling cam is to be replaced, omit Step 4 and proceed with Steps 5 and 6.

5. Remove retaining screws and remove wheel from hub assembly.
6. Remove wheel nut and washer.
7. Use a suitable puller to remove wheel.

NOTE: Turn signal control assembly must be in neutral position when assembling the hub to prevent damage to cancelling cam and control assembly.

8. Reverse procedure to install.

1967-72 Corvette Telescoping Wheel

1. Disconnect steering column harness at wiring connector. Disconnect battery ground cable.
2. Pry off horn button cap.
3. Remove three screws securing horn contact to spacer and hub.
4. Remove two screws securing lock screw to lock knob and remove screw, knob and spacer.

NOTE: If wheel only is to be replaced, perform Step 5. If turn signal cancelling cam is to be replaced, omit Step 5 and proceed with Steps 6 and 7.

5. Remove wheel from hub (6 screws).
6. Remove nut and washer from shaft and use a suitable puller to remove wheel and hub.
7. Slide cancelling cam and spring off shaft.

1967-68 Tilt Type

On vehicles with tilt steering columns, it will be necessary to install steering column upper bearing preload spring prior to the cancelling cam. This differs from all other steering upper bearing preload springs as they are installed after the cancelling cam.

1967 Deluxe Wheel

1. Disconnect battery ground cable.
2. Pull out horn button center ornament.

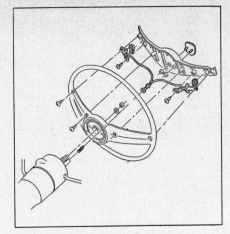

Fig. 6   Steering wheel and horn attachments. 1969-72

3. Remove receiving cup (3 screws).
4. Remove wheel nut and washer.
5. Remove three screws securing spoke ornament with horn tabs. Remove ornament with belleville spring and insulator still installed inside.
6. Remove steering wheel with a puller.

1966 (Except Corvette)

1. Disconnect turn signal switch harness from chassis wiring harness at connector.
2. On standard models, pull out horn button. On other models pull out center ornament from horn ring.
3. Remove receiving cup or horn ring (3 screws), spring, and bushing; on deluxe wheels also remove pivot ring.
4. Remove steering wheel nut and use a puller to remove wheel.

CAUTION: Turn signal control assembly must be in neutral position when assembling steering wheel to prevent damage to cancelling cam and control assembly.

Chevelle Note

Before installing steering wheel, make certain steering shaft stop clamp at bottom of mast jacket is secured and that steering shaft is 1-3/4" above top of turn signal housing.

1966 Corvette

1. Pry off horn cap.
2. Remove washer and nut from steering shaft.
3. Use a suitable puller to remove wheel.

INSTRUMENT CLUSTER
1971-72 Chevrolet

1. Disconnect battery ground cable.
2. Remove cigar lighter knob and hidden screw in shroud where knob was.
3. Pull on headlamp switch shaft then remove hidden screw above middle of shaft.
4. Remove two screws at bottom

corners of shroud and lift off shroud.
5. To service instruments, remove clock stem set knob.
6. Remove lens retaining strip secured by three screws at top of lens. Be careful not to mar lens.
7. Lift off lens carefully—guide pins are on bottom of lens.
8. Gently lift up on bottom of filter housing and rotate housing up and rearward, toward technician on front seat. Top of housing should clear top of instrument carrier. Use care around PRNDL housing and lift filter assembly off. Speedometer, fuel gauge and clock can now be removed.

1970-72 Camaro

1. Disconnect battery ground cable.
2. Remove 6 screws securing trim cover beneath steering column. Two of these screws are located above the ash tray.
3. Remove headlamp switch retaining nut.
4. From behind panel, disconnect cigar lighter and unscrew retainer. Note grounding ring.
5. From under lower edge of cluster, remove screw on either side of column.
6. Remove 4 screws visible on front of carrier.
7. Remove screw retaining ground wire for wiper switch. Screw is fastened under top left corner of switch.
8. Carefully tilt carrier out of access to the connectors on headlamp and wiper switches.
9. Remove lens screws then cluster screws.
10. Disconnect shift indicator from steering column.
11. Disconnect speedometer cable and tilt cluster forward and remove remaining connectors.
12. Lift cluster out.

1970-72 Chevy Nova

1. Disconnect battery ground cable.
2. Lower steering column and apply protective covering to mast jacket to protect paint.
3. Remove three screws above front of heater control securing it to instrument cluster.
4. Remove radio control knobs, washers, bezel nuts and front support at lower edge of cluster. This will allow radio to remain in panel.
5. Remove screws at top, bottom and sides of cluster securing it to panel.
6. Tilt console forward and reach behind to disconnect speedometer cable and all other connections and lift instrument panel out of carrier after removing screws.

1970-72 Chevelle (W/Standard Panel)

1. Disconnect battery ground cable.
2. Lower steering column.
3. Disconnect parking brake hand release rod attachment.
4. Disconnect speedometer cable from speedometer.
5. Remove instrument panel pad (six screws).
6. Disconnect radio speaker bracket

from instrument panel.

7. Disconnect A/C center outlet (three screws).
8. Disconnect A/C control head (four screws).
9. Disconnect radio speaker connector from radio.
10. Remove radio knobs, washers, bezels and wiring and remove bolts from braces securing radio; roll radio out from under panel.
11. Remove six instrument panel attaching bolts and roll out instrument panel. **NOTE: Two men are needed.**
12. Pop out three telltale snap covers and remove three telltale housing attaching screws, remove telltale housing.
13. Remove clock stem set knob and separate cluster from carrier (8 screws).

1970-72 Chevelle S.S. & Monte Carlo & Optional Panel

1. Disconnect battery ground cable.
2. Remove instrument panel pad (6 screws).
3. Disconnect A/C center outlet (3 screws).
4. Disconnect A/C control head (4 screws).
5. Disconnect radio speaker and brackets from cluster.
6. Disconnect speaker leads from radio and remove radio knobs, washers, bezels and wiring including antenna lead.
7. Unfasten radio and roll radio out from under instrument panel.
8. Remove steering column cover.
9. Remove two steering column attaching bolts. Note shims.
10. Disconnect PRNDL cable from column housing and lower column.
11. Disconnect parking brake hand release rod attachment.
12. Remove six instrument panel attaching bolts and roll out panel. **NOTE: Two men are needed.**
13. Disconnect speedometer cable.
14. Remove cluster lamp sockets, clock, fuel gauge, and all connectors from rear of panel.
15. Remove screws retaining printed circuit and lift off circuit panel.

1969-70 Chevrolet

1. Disconnect battery ground cable.
2. If air conditioned, remove lap cooler from under steering column.
3. Remove column mast jacket trim cover.
4. Lower steering column.

CAUTION: *Do not allow column to hang from dash or distortion to the column will result.*

5. If equipped with Comfortron, remove the in-car sensor.
6. Remove instrument panel pad and if air conditioned, disconnect center outlet hose when removing pad.
7. Disconnect transmission indicator cable on column.
8. Remove indicator bulb bezel by pushing in at right side of the four bezel screw covers to access to screws.
9. Remove transmission indicator lamp housing.

10. Remove radio knobs and nuts. Remove rear brace, antenna lead and move radio back away from instrument carrier assembly.
11. Remove instrument panel trim plate by inserting a hooked tool such as a cotter pin remover, behind the trim plate and pulling the plate forward enough to release it from its retainers.
12. Remove air conditioning and/or heater control retaining screws and move control back away from instrument carrier assembly.
13. Remove screws retaining instrument carrier to panel lower reinforcement and to parking brake pedal bracket.
14. Remove ash tray and retaining bracket.
15. Remove three screws at top of instrument carrier and tilt the carrier assembly forward.
16. Disconnect speedometer cable. Disconnect panel harness by removing six screws that hold illumination cover to rear of carrier and remove all other connections.
17. Remove carrier assembly from panel opening and remove eight screws retaining cluster to carrier.

1968 Chevrolet

1. Disconnect battery ground cable.
2. Unplug forward wiring harness connector from fuse panel under hood.
3. Remove fuse panel from firewall.
4. Unfasten instrument cluster from instrument panel (8 screws).
5. Remove screw retaining column mounted automatic transmission pointer cable from mast jacket.
6. Reaching behind cluster, disconnect speedometer cable, chassis harness connector, clock, speed warning device connections, defogger, convertible top or tail gate switches and vacuum hose connections (if so equipped). *On models with gauge pack, disconnect oil pressure line also.*
7. After all disconnects are made, tip cluster forward and remove.
8. Reverse procedure to install.

1968-69 Chevelle

1. Disconnect battery ground cable.
2. Remove ash tray and retainer.
3. Remove radio knobs, nuts, electrical connections, aerial plug and radio rear support, then lift out radio.
4. Remove heater control screws, then push control head out of instrument panel.
5. Lower steering column. If equipped, remove automatic transmission indicator cable on steering column.
6. Remove instrument panel retaining screws at top, sides and bottom of panel. Also remove any attachments to underside of panel such as speedometer stem, defogger or tail gate control switch.
7. Lift loosened instrument panel up and back slightly, reach behind cluster and remove speedometer cable housing retaining nut, then support instrument panel on protected steering column.
8. Remove clips on top of instrument cluster rear cover and remove all connectors at back of cover and oil

pressure pipe fitting from rear of oil pressure gauge (if so equipped).
9. Remove five screws securing twin window cluster to back of instrument panel and remove cluster.
10. Reverse procedure to install.

1968-72 Corvette

Left Hand Side
1. Disconnect battery ground cable.
2. Lower steering column.
3. Remove screws and washers securing left instrument panel to door opening, top of dash and left side of center instrument panel.
4. Unclip and remove floor console trim panel.
5. Pull cluster slightly forward to obtain clearance for removal of speedometer cable housing nut, tachometer cable housing nut, headlamp and ignition switch connectors and panel illuminating lamps.
6. Reverse procedure to install.

Center Cluster
1. Disconnect battery positive cable at battery.
2. Remove wiper switch trim plate screws and tip plate forward for access to switch connector. Lift trim plate out from cluster.
3. Unclip and remove right and left console forward trim pads to gain access to studs at lower edge of cluster.
4. Remove nuts from studs at lower edge of cluster.
5. Remove remaining screws retaining cluster to instrument panel.
6. Remove right instrument panel pad.
7. Remove radio knobs, bezel retaining nuts and one radio support bolt (from behind cluster).
8. Slide radio back towards firewall and pull cluster forward. Reach behind cluster, disconnect oil pressure line, wiring harness and bulbs.

CAUTION: The center cluster trim plate is designed to collapse under impact, Consequently, do not try to deflect the cluster plate forward to gain access to back of gauges.

9. Lift cluster assembly up and forward to remove.
10. Reverse procedure to install cluster.

1968-69 Camaro

1. Disconnect battery ground cable.
2. On 1969, remove instrument panel pad, A/C attachments and radio brace attachments.
3. Remove mast jacket supports at toe pan and dash, and lower column. *Both supports must be detached to prevent distortion of mast jacket.*
4. Remove cluster retaining screws from face of panel and partially remove assembly from console opening.
5. Reaching behind cluster assembly, disconnect speedometer cable, speed warning device (if equipped) and chassis harness connector at rear of panel.
6. Remove assembly from console.
7. Reverse procedure to install.

1968-69 Chevy II & Nova

1. Disconnect battery.
2. Unfasten heater control from cluster (2 screws).
3. Remove radio knobs, bezel nuts and front support at lower edge of cluster. This will allow radio to remain in instrument panel during cluster removal.
4. On 1968, remove mast jacket from trim cover. Disengage Powerglide range indicator cable (if equipped). On 1969, disconnect and lower column.
5. Remove toe pan trim cover.
6. Remove bolts securing steering column retainer to toe pan. Loosen bolts securing retainer halves.
7. Remove bolts at top, bottom and sides of cluster securing it to instrument panel.
8. Remove steering column-to-dash panel bracket nuts and carefully lower column. Be careful not to jar or apply any load on column during this operation.
9. Remove ignition switch tumbler and bezel through cluster and leave hanging.
10. Tilt cluster forward and disconnect speedometer cable and necessary electrical connectors. Then remove cluster.
11. Reverse procedure to install and align steering column.

1967 Chevrolet

1. Disconnect battery ground strap.
2. Remove four screws retaining instrument bezel to top edge of instrument console. Disengage tabs on bezel lower section from clips on instrument console and remove bezel.
3. Remove eight screws retaining leading edges of instrument cluster to console and pull cluster forward from console opening.
4. Reaching behind cluster, disconnect speedometer cable, chassis harness connector, clock and speed warning device connections (if equipped) at rear of cluster. *On models with gauge pack, disconnect oil pressure line also.*
5. When all disconnections are made, remove cluster.
6. Reverse above procedure to install. Make sure ground strap between cluster case and center right lower attachment is properly installed.

1967 Camaro

1. Disconnect battery ground cable.
2. Remove mast jacket lower support screws at toe pan.
3. Remove mast jacket upper support bolts and allow steering wheel to rest on seat cushion. *Both supports must be detached to prevent distortion of mast jacket.*
4. Remove cluster attaching screws from face of panel and partially remove assembly from console opening.
5. Reaching behind cluster assembly, disconnect speedometer cable, speed warning device (if equipped) and chassis harness connector at rear of panel.
6. Remove cluster from console open-

ing.
7. Reverse procedure to install.

1966 Chevrolet

1. Disconnect battery ground cable.
2. Remove A/C hose connecting left outlet to distributor duct (if equipped).
3. Disconnect speedometer cable at cluster.
4. Disconnect panel wiring harness connector and clock or tachometer wiring lead connections at rear of cluster housing.
5. Remove radio knobs, bezels and retaining nuts. Push radio in to disengage shafts from panel openings. *On rear seat speaker models, make sure speaker fader control wiring is disconnected from radio harness wiring.*
6. Remove instrument panel compartment door and compartment retaining screws.
7. Remove upper and lower instrument panel console screws.
8. Protect mast jacket and outer edges of console.
9. Open right front door, roll console forward and slide to right to remove assembly from vehicle.
10. Reverse procedure to install.

1966-67 Chevelle

1. Disconnect battery ground cable.
2. Separate steering shaft from coupling.
3. Loosen mast jacket lower clamp.
4. Remove A/C center distributor duct (if equipped).
5. Remove radio rear support bracket screw.
6. On 1966 models, remove mast jacket trim cover and upper support clamp. On 1967 models, remove mast jacket upper support clamp and retaining bolts from lower support.
7. On 1966 models, loosen set screw and remove Powerglide dial indicator (if equipped).
8. Disconnect speedometer cable.
9. Remove instrument panel retaining screws (9 upper and 5 lower).
10. Working underneath console, remove four lower screws from instrument cluster housing.
11. Pull instrument panel from console and lay it forward on protected mast jacket.
12. Disconnect wiring harness, cluster lamps and wiring terminals from rear of cluster.
13. Remove four screws retaining upper section of cluster housing to panel and remove cluster from instrument panel.
14. Reverse procedure to install.

1966-67 Chevy II

1. Disconnect battery ground cable.
2. On 1966 models, remove Powerglide dial indicator (if equipped) and mast jacket upper support clamp. On 1967 models, remove mast jacket upper support clamp.
3. Disconnect retaining collar securing speedometer cable to speedometer head.
4. Separate cluster from console.
5. Pull cluster forward of console open-

ing and disconnect all wiring and lamp connections.
6. Remove cluster from vehicle.

CAUTION: Do not pull cluster outward further than slack in wire will permit, otherwise wiring and lamp connections may be damaged.

1966-67 Corvette

1. Remove mast jacket assembly.
2. Disconnect tachometer drive cable at distributor.
3. Disconnect cowl vent control cable brackets and headlamp panel control switch from instrument cluster.
4. Remove light switch.
5. Remove ignition switch. Disconnect ignition switch lamp support at instrument panel.
6. On 1966 models, disconnect parking brake lever support at cowl crossmember.
7. Disconnect pressure line at oil gauge, then remove lead wires from ammeter, wiper switch and cigar lighter. Disconnect trip odometer at mast jacket support.
8. Remove cluster-to-dash screws and pull cluster slightly forward to obtain clearance for removal of speedometer cable, tachometer cable, cluster ground wire, fuel gauge lead wires and remaining lamps.
9. Reverse procedure to install.

W/S WIPER MOTOR
1971-72

1. Raise hood and remove cowl screen or grille.
2. Disconnect wiring and washer hoses.
3. Reaching through cowl opening, loosen transmission drive link attaching nuts to motor crankarm.
4. Disconnect drive link from motor crankarm.
5. Remove motor attaching screws.
6. Remove motor while guiding crankarm through hole.

1970 Camaro

1. Remove two cowl screen attaching screws from center of cowl then pry up screen at eight clips and remove.
2. Reaching through cowl opening, loosen the two crank arm attaching nuts.
3. Remove transmission crank arm.
4. Disconnect wiring and washer hoses.
5. Remove motor attaching screws and remove motor while guiding crank arm through hole.

1970 Except Camaro

The procedure is the same as for previous models except that the plastic access cover is now used on Chevrolet, Chevelle and Monte Carlo models.

1968-69

1. Make sure wiper motor is in park position.
2. Disconnect washer hoses and electrical connectors from assembly.
3. Remove the air intake grille on

Chevy II, Camaro and Corvette models. On Chevrolet models, remove plastic access cover.
4. Loosen nuts which retain the drive link to the crank arm ball stud on Chevrolet models. On all other models, remove the nut which retains the crank arm to the motor.
5. On Corvette, it is necessary to remove the ignition shield and distributor cap to gain access to the motor retaining screws or nuts.

NOTE: *Remove left bank spark plug wires from the cap and mark both cap and wires for aid in reinstallation.*

6. Remove three motor retaining screws or nuts and remove motor.

CAUTION: Wiper motor must be in the park position prior to installation on the cowl. Do not install a motor that was dropped or hung by the drive link.

1967 Camaro & Chevrolet

1. Make certain motor is in Park position.
2. Disconnect washer hoses and electrical connectors from assembly.
3. On Chevrolet models, remove plenum chamber side cover and loosen nuts retaining drive rod ball stud to crank arm.
4. Remove three mounting bolts and motor. On Camaro models, pull motor from cowl opening and loosen nuts retaining drive rod ball stud to crank arm.
5. Reverse procedure to install.

CAUTION: Motor must be in Park position prior to installation to cowl. Do not install a motor that has dropped or hung from drive link.

1967 Chevelle

1. Make certain motor is in Park position.
2. Disconnect washer hoses and all electrical connectors.
3. Remove three motor mounting bolts, carefully remove motor from firewall and detach clip retaining drive arm to motor crank arm.

CAUTION: Motor must be in Park position prior to installation to cowl. Do not install motor that has dropped or hung from drive link.

1967 Chevy II

1. Make certain motor is in Park position.
2. Working under instrument panel, remove special retainer clip securing transmission linkage to motor crank arm.
3. Disconnect linkage, electrical connectors and washer hoses.
4. Unfasten (3 bolts) and remove motor from cowl opening.

CAUTION: Motor must be in Park position prior to installation to cowl. Do not install motor that has dropped or hung from drive link.

1966 Chevrolet

1. To remove motor, first make certain it is in park position, then remove wiper arm and blade assemblies.
2. Remove plenum chamber side cover.
3. Loosen nuts retaining drive rod to crank arm.
4. Disconnect battery ground cable, then remove washer hoses, if present, and all electrical connectors.
5. Unfasten and remove motor (3 bolts).

1966 Chevy II

1. Make certain wiper motor is in park position.
2. Remove special clip retaining transmission linkage to motor crank arm. Then remove linkage, electrical connectors and washer hoses (if equipped).
3. Unfasten and remove motor (3 screws).
4. Install in reverse order of removal. Check and replace motor gasket if necessary. Use seal compound in screw holes.

1966-67 Corvette

1. Disconnect ground lead at battery.
2. Remove engine distributor shield and left-bank spark plug wiring vertical shield.
3. Disconnect left-bank spark plug wire bracket-to-manifold and position to one side.
4. Disconnect ignition resistor at firewall, then remove washer pump inlet and outlet hose at pump valve.
5. Remove ignition distributor cap and position to one side, then disconnect washer pump and motor lead wires.
6. Remove glove box door and compartment.
7. Make sure wiper arms and blades are in parked position, then remove transmission clip and disconnect both transmission and spacer from crank arm.

1966 Chevelle

1. Make certain motor is in parked position.
2. Disconnect electrical connections and washer hoses (if equipped).
3. Remove motor retaining bolts. Carefully pull motor from firewall and detach clip retaining wiper transmission drive rod to crank arm.
4. To install, check sealing gaskets at motor and retaining bolts and replace if necessary. Then reverse removal procedure to install.

W/S WIPER TRANSMISSION

1971-72 W/Rectangular Motor

1. Remove wiper arms and blades.
2. Raise hood and remove cowl vent screen or grille.
3. Disconnect wiring from motor.
4. Loosen, but do not remove, transmission drive link to motor crankarm attaching nuts and disconnect drive link from crankarm.

5. Remove right and left transmission to body attaching screws and guide transmission and linkage through cowl opening.

NOTE: When installing, motor must be in Park position.

1971-72 W/Round Motor

1. Raise hood and remove cowl vent screen.
2. On Chevelle, Monte Carlo and Camaro models, remove right and left wiper arm and blades.
3. On Chevrolet models, remove arm and blade only from transmission to be removed.
4. Loosen, do not remove, attaching nuts securing drive link to motor crankarm.
5. Disconnect transmission drive link from motor crankarm.
6. On Chevelle, Monte Carlo and Camaro models, remove right and left transmission to body screws.
7. On Chevrolet models, remove attaching screws securing only the transmission to be removed.
8. Remove transmission and linkage through cowl opening.

NOTE: When installing, motor must be in Park position.

1968-70

1. Make sure wiper motor is in park position.
2. On Corvette only, remove rubber plug from front of wiper motor actuator, then insert a screwdriver, pushing internal piston rearward to actuate wiper door open.
3. On all models, remove wiper arm and blade assembly from one transmission. On articulated left-hand arm assemblies, remove clip retaining pinned arm to blade arm.
4. Remove air intake grille or screen (if equipped).
5. Loosen nuts retaining drive rod ball stud-to-crank arm and detach rod from arm.
6. Remove transmission retaining screws, or nuts, then lower drive rod assemblies into plenum chamber.
7. Remove transmission and linkage through cowl opening.
8. Reverse procedure to install. Make sure wiper blades are installed in the park position (plus or minus $3/8$" from top of reveal molding on recessed wiper arms).

1967 Chevy II

1 Make certain wiper motor is in park position. Remove wiper arm and blade assembly from transmission shaft.
2. From under left side of dash, remove special retainer clip securing transmission linkage to wiper crank arm and remove linkage from crank.
3. Remove glove box door and interior. Remove screws securing defroster duct to fire wall and lower duct. Remove retainer clip securing crank link to right transmission and remove linkage from right transmission.

4. Remove retaining capscrews securing transmission to cowl (2 each side). Remove right and left transmission with connector link still attached through glove box opening. Disconnect connecting link from the transmission being replaced.
5. Reverse procedure to install. Check and replace gasket if necessary. Use waterproof cement to seal screw holes.

1966-67 Chevrolet & 1967 Camaro

1. Make certain motor is in park position, then remove wiper arm and blade assemblies.
2. Remove plenum chamber ventilator grille.
3. Loosen nuts retaining drive rod to crank arm and detach rod from arm.
4. Remove transmission retaining screws and lower transmission and drive rod assemblies into plenum chamber.
5. Remove transmission and linkage from plenum chamber through cowl opening.

1966-67 Chevelle

1. Make certain motor is in park position, then remove wiper arm and blade assemblies.
2. Remove plenum chamber grille.
3. Remove clip retaining transmission drive rod to crank arm and detach rod from arm.
4. Remove transmission retaining screws, lower assembly into plenum chamber and remove unit from chamber.

1966 Chevy II

1. Make certain motor is in park position, then remove wiper arm and blade.
2. Remove special retainer clip securing transmission linkage to wiper crank arm and remove linkage from crank.
3. Remove retainer clip securing left transmission link to right transmission and remove link from right transmission.
4. Remove two retaining screws securing transmission to cowl (one side) and remove transmission from under dash.

1966 Corvette

1. Remove wiper block and arm from transmission.
2. Remove glove box.
3. Remove three transmission-to-cowl screws.
4. Unclip and remove transmission from crank arm.
5. Remove transmission through glove box opening.
6. To install reverse removal procedure.

W/S WIPER SWITCH

1970-72 Camaro

1. Disconnect battery ground cable.
2. Remove trim plate and A/C outlet

from below steering column if so equipped.
3. Remove light switch.
4. Remove 6 screws securing instrument carrier. Two of these are behind the cluster on either side of steering column.

NOTE: Cigar lighter grounding ring may have to be removed with lighter housing to gain access to left side of carrier.

5. Disconnect wiper switch wiring.
6. Tilting carrier forward, reach behind and remove 3 switch retaining screws and lift out switch.

1968 (Except Chevelle) 1969 Chevrolet 1970-72 Chevelle & Chevrolet

1. Disconnect battery ground cable.
2. On 1968 Chevy II, remove parking brake and heater control assemblies.
3. On 1968, remove left A/C outlet duct. On 1969-72, remove trim plate and lap cooler outlet.
4. On 1968, loosen set screw and remove knob.
5. Disconnect and remove switch from rear of panel.
6. Reverse procedure to install.

1969 Camaro, Chevelle, Nova 1970-72 Chevy Nova

1. Disconnect battery ground cable.
2. On Chevelle, remove left air outlet and headlight switch.
3. Disconnect and remove switch from rear of panel.
4. Reverse procedure to install.

1969-72 Corvette

1. Disconnect battery ground cable.
2. Remove screws from upper part of center console marked "Corvette".
3. Disconnect and remove switch and plate.
4. Carefully pry knob from switch then remove switch from plate.
5. To install, insert a small rod in the switch arm before pushing the knob on the arm outside of the trim plate then reverse the above procedure.

1967-68 Chevelle

1. Disconnect battery ground cable.
2. Remove wiper knob.
3. Slip a section of wiper hose about 3 feet long, over the end of the stem of the switch. Make sure it fits tightly on the shaft.
4. Remove bezel nut and push switch down and out of instrument panel, guiding it through the wiring.
5. Bring switch down far enough to remove electrical connector.
6. Then remove hose from switch and remove switch.
7. Reverse foregoing to install the switch.

1967 Except Chevelle

1. Disconnect battery ground cable.
2. Remove connectors from rear of switch.
3. On A/C models it is necessary to remove the left A/C outlet duct to

gain access to rear of switch.
4. Loosen set screw and pull knob from switch.
5. Withdraw switch from behind console.
6. Reverse procedure to install.

1966 Chevrolet, Chevy II & Chevelle

1. Disconnect battery ground cable.
2. Remove connector(s) from rear of switch.
3. Remove small set screw from bottom of wiper knob and remove knob.
4. Remove retaining nut and withdraw switch from under dash panel.
5. Reverse above procedure to install.

RADIO, REPLACE

NOTE: When installing radio, be sure to adjust antenna trimmer for peak performance.

1970-72 Chevelle, Chevrolet & Nova

1. Disconnect battery ground cable.
2. Remove ash tray and retainer.
3. Remove radio knobs, washers, controls, trim plate and nuts from radio bushings.
4. Remove hoses from center A/C duct if equipped.
5. Disconnect all leads to radio.
6. Remove screw from radio rear mounting bracket and lower radio.

1968-69 Except Corvette

1. Disconnect battery ground cable.
2. On Chevelle and Chevrolet, remove ash tray and retainer.
3. Remove radio knobs, nuts, electrical connections, rear support and lift radio out.

1968-72 Corvette

Coupe
1. Disconnect battery ground cable.
2. Remove left and right door sill plates and kick pads. Disconnect radio to speaker connectors (left and right side).
3. Remove right side dash pad.
4. Remove right and left console forward trim pads.
5. Remove one bolt securing heater floor outlet duct to center distributor assembly.
6. Remove floor outlet duct by pulling it through left hand opening.
7. From front of console, tape radio push buttons in depressed position. From rear of console, disconnect electrical connector, brace and antenna.
8. Remove radio knobs and bezel retaining nuts. Push radio forward (towards front of car). From rear of console, tip back of radio up and remove from right side opening.
9. Reverse procedure to install.

Convertible
1. Disconnect battery cable.
2. Remove right instrument panel pad.
3. Disconnect speaker connectors.

NOTE: On some vehicles it may be

necessary to remove kick panels to gain access to speaker connectors.

4. Remove wiper switch trim plate screws and tip plate for access to switch connector. Remove switch connector and trim plate from cluster assembly.
5. Unclip and remove right and left console forward trim pads. Remove forwardmost screw on each side of console.
6. Insert a flexible drive socket between the console and metal horseshoe brace, remove the nuts from the two studs on the lower edge of the console cluster.
7. Remove remaining screws retaining cluster to instrument panel.
8. From rear of console, disconnect radio connector, brace and antenna lead.
9. Remove radio knobs and bezel retaining nuts.
10. Pull top of console forward. Separrate radio from console and remove it from the right side opening.

NOTE: The center instrument cluster trim plate is designed to collapse under impact. Consequently, do not try to deflect the cluster plate forward to gain more access to remove the radio. Also use care so as not to damage the plastic oil pressure line when pulling console forward.

1966-67 Chevy II

1. Disconnect battery ground cable.
2. Remove radio knobs and retaining nuts, including trim plate.
3. Remove glove box door (including one upper left screw retaining compartment interior box) for access to radio brace retaining screw.
4. Remove two instrument panel radio braces and retaining screws and nuts, including one radio rear brace retaining screw.
5. Disconnect electrical connections and remove radio through front of dash panel.
6. Reverse procedure to install.

1967 Camaro & Chevrolet

1. Disconnect battery ground cable.
2. Remove ash tray and retainer.
3. Where necessary, disconnect A/C center duct hoses.
4. Remove radio knobs, retaining nuts and support bolt.
5. Disconnect electrical connector and antenna lead.
6. Remove radio from under dash.

1966-67 Chevelle

1. Disconnect battery ground cable.
2. Remove ash tray and retainer.
3. On A/C models, remove center air distributor duct.
4. Remove heater and A/C control panel.
5. Remove radio knobs, retaining nuts and support bolts.
6. Remove radio electrical connector and antenna lead.
7. Remove radio from under dash.

HEATER CORE REMOVAL

1971-72 L/Air Cond.

1. Disconnect battery ground cable.
2. Drain radiator, disconnect heater hoses at core and plug openings to prevent spillage of water.
3. Remove nuts from air distributor duct studs on engine side of firewall.
4. On Chevrolet, remove distributor duct retaining screw.
5. On Chevelle, from under dash, drill out lower right hand distributor stud with a 1/4" drill.
6. On Nova, remove glove box and door and drill out lower right hand distributor stud with a 1/4" drill.
7. On Camaro, remove glove box, radio, and defroster duct to distributor duct screw.
8. On Corvette, remove right instrument panel pad, right hand dash braces, center dash console duct and floor outlet duct, radio and center dash console.
9. On all models, pull distributor duct from firewall being careful not to bend cable.
10. On Camaro, disconnect cable and resistor wires and remove distributor and core.
11. On all other models, remove core assembly from duct.

1971-72 W/Air Cond.

Chevrolet

1. Disconnect battery ground cable.
2. Drain radiator and disconnect heater hoses from core. Plug openings to prevent spillage of coolant.
3. Remove nuts from selector duct studs projecting through firewall.
4. Remove glove box and door.
5. Remove center distributor duct hoses, duct cable, center distributor duct to selector duct screws and remove center duct.
6. Inside car, drill out lower right hand case stud using a 1/4" drill.
7. Remove floor distributor duct.
8. Unfasten and remove selector duct from firewall.
9. Disconnect wiring, vacuum lines and cables and remove from vehicle.
10. Scribe location of temperature door camming plate on selector duct and remove camming plate. Remove core and core housing from duct.

Chevelle

1. Disconnect battery ground cable.
2. Drain radiator and disconnect heater hoses from core and plug openings to prevent spillage of coolant.
3. Remove nuts from distributor case studs projecting through firewall.
4. Remove right lap cooler and right kick pad cover.
5. Disconnect center duct hoses, remove center distributor duct to selector duct screws and remove center duct.
6. Remove floor distributor duct.
7. Drill out lower right hand selector duct stud from inside car.
8. Remove retaining screws securing air selector to firewall and lower selector assembly. Remove all wiring, vacuum lines and cables and scribe location of temperature door camming plate on

selector duct and remove camming plate. Remove core and housing from selector assembly.

Chevy Nova

1. Disconnect battery ground cable and drain radiator.
2. Disconnect heater hoses from core and plug openings to prevent spillage of coolant.
3. Remove accessible nuts from air selector duct studs.
4. Remove right fender skirt to fender and skirt reinforcing screws. Lower skirt to wheel and remove remaining stud nut.
5. Remove glove box and door.
6. Remove right kick pad recirculating air valve.
7. Remove center duct and floor duct. Remove screws securing left half of selector duct to right half and separate.
8. Remove screws securing right half of selector to firewall and remove duct. Disconnect wiring, and cables.
9. Scribe location of temperature door camming plate on selector duct and remove camming plate.
10. Lay selector duct on floor and remove core.

Camaro

1. Disconnect battery ground cable.
2. Drain radiator and disconnect heater hoses from core. Plug openings to prevent spillage of coolant.
3. Remove nuts from distributor studs on engine side of firewall.
4. Remove glove box and radio.
5. Remove defroster duct to distributor duct screw. With radio removed, the defroster duct can be pulled rearward to gain clearance for distributor duct removal.
6. Carefully pull distributor from firewall and disconnect wiring and cables. Remove duct and core from vehicle.

Corvette

1. Disconnect battery ground cable. Drain radiator and disconnect heater hoses from core. Plug openings to prevent spillage of coolant.
2. Remove nuts from engine side distributor duct.
3. Remove right hand dash pad and center instrument cluster. Remove dash braces.
4. Disconnect right dash outlet duct from center duct. Remove screws attaching center duct to selector duct and remove center duct.
5. Remove screws attaching selector duct to firewall and pull selector rearward and to the right. Disconnect cables and wiring.
6. Remove selector duct from car. Remove temperature door camming plate from duct and remove core and housing.

1968-70

1. Disconnect battery ground cable. Drain radiator.
2. Disconnect heater hoses and plug heater outlets to prevent coolant spillage.
3. Remove nuts from air distributor duct studs on engine side of firewall.

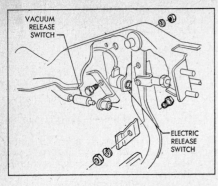

Fig. 7 Release switches and brackets. 1968-70

4. On Chevrolet and Nova, remove glove box and door assembly. On Corvette, remove right instrument panel pad, right hand dash braces, center dash console duct and floor outlet duct.
5. Except Corvette: from under dash, drill out lower right distributor stud. Corvette: remove radio and center dash console.
6. Pull distributor duct from firewall mounting, remove resistor wires and lay distributor duct on floor.

NOTE: Use care to avoid bending bowden cables.

7. Remove core from distributor duct.

1966-67 Chevrolet, Chevelle, Camaro

1. Remove all cables except defroster cable on Chevrolet, and all electrical connectors from heater and defroster assembly.
2. From engine side of dash, remove two screws and stud nuts attaching air inlet assembly to dash.

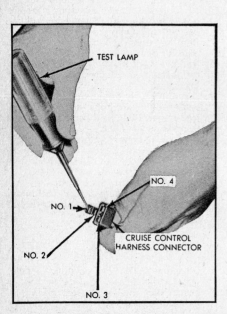

Fig. 9 Electrical connection on Slide Switch type Speedostat

3. From inside of car, pull entire heater and defroster assembly from firewall, removing defroster cable on Chevrolet at this time.
4. On 1967-68 models, three case-to-firewall mounting screws must be removed before assembly can be removed from firewall.
5. With heater on bench, remove heater core springs and lift out core.

1966-67 Chevy II

1. Remove three nuts from blower motor that attach heater to dash.
2. From inside of car, remove glove box and its door.
3. Remove screw attaching distributor bracket to dash.
4. Remove screw attaching heater case bracket to adapter bracket, pull heater from dash and lower it to the floor.
5. Cables, wiring connector and defroster hoses may now be removed.
6. With heater removed, take out screws attaching core cover to heater.
7. Remove core mounting screws and lift it out.

1966-67 Corvette

1. Drain radiator and remove radiator supply tank from support and move it out of the way.
2. Remove battery.
3. Disconnect heater hoses.
4. Remove seven stud nuts attaching blower and air inlet to dash panel.
5. Remove blower and air inlet assembly from beneath fender.
6. Remove glove box and panels on either side of the instrument panel console.
7. Place a waterproof covering over carpeting under heater.
8. Disconnect bowden cables and wiring.
9. Carefully work heater assembly out from under dash.
10. Core can now be removed.

SPEED CONTROLS
1967-72 Cruise Master

Servo Unit Adjustment

Adjust the bead chain so that it is as

Fig. 8 Accelerator linkage adjustment for Slide Switch type Speedostat

tight as possible without holding the throttle open when the carburetor is set as its lowest idle throttle position.

When connecting the bead chain (engine stopped) manually set the fast idle cam at its lowest step and connect the chain so that it does not hold the idle screw off the cam. If the chain needs to be cut, cut it three beads beyond the bead that pulls the linkage.

Regulator Unit Adjustment

To remove any difference between engagement and cruising speed, one adjustment is possible. However, no adjustment should be made until the following items have been checked or serviced.

1. Bead chain properly adjusted.
2. All hoses in good condition, properly attached, not leaking, pinched or cracked.
3. Regulator air filter cleaned and properly oiled.
4. Electric and vacuum switches properly adjusted.

Engagement - Cruising Speed Zeroing

If the cruising speed is lower than the engagement speed, loosen the orifice tube locknut and turn the tube outward; if higher turn the tube inward. Each ¼ turn will alter the engagement-cruising speed difference one mph. Tighten lock-

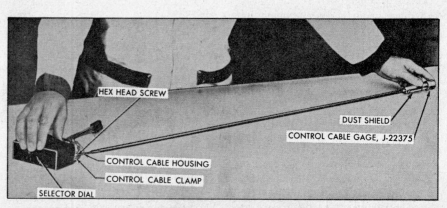

Fig. 10 Control cable adjustment for Slide Switch Speedostat

nut after adjustment and check the system operation at 50 mph.

Brake Release Switch

The brake switch plunger must be clear of the pedal arm when the arm is moved ¼" (electric switch) and 5/16" (vacuum switch) measured at the switch, Fig. 7.

1966-67 Speedostat

Accelerator Linkage

1. Adjust throttle rod.
2. Start engine and operate at slow idle with transmission lever in "Park".
3. Separate linkage from exterior arm.
4. Adjust trunnion so that when it is installed through exterior arm, the stop stud will be aligned with locating notch and throttle valves will be closed.
5. Install washer on trunnion and secure with cotter pin.

NOTE: Due to the angle at which the trunnion enters hole in exterior arm, it is necessary to rotate the exterior arm slightly forward when inserting the trunnion. Repeat this operation until proper alignment is obtained. Be careful not to turn trunnion too far back or throttle valves will unseat and cause an incorrect adjustment. Insert the gauge shown in Fig. 8 (or small diameter pipe) over stop stud to check alignment.

Brake Release Switch

1. Turn on ignition but do not start engine.
2. Momentarily move slide switch to AUTO position until red indicator light glows.
3. Using a test lamp, ground one lead and touch the other lead to terminal No. 4, Fig. 9.
4. Loosen mounting screw securing release switch to brake pedal mounting bracket.
5. Adjust release switch so that lamp will light when brake pedal is fully released, and will go out when brake pedal is depressed about ¼ inch. Tighten switch mounting screw. If switch cannot be adjusted, it is defective and should be replaced.

Control Cable Adjustment, 1966-67

The cable is preset at the factory and should not require adjustment unless a new cable is installed. This adjustment must be performed off the car as follows:

1. Remove the selector assembly.
2. Rotate selector dial to low speed position until it is positioned against its stop but do not force beyond its stop.
3. Position assembly flat on workbench and make certain there are no kinks in cable.
4. Loosen hex head set screw at cable clamp on selector control.
5. Pull cable housing until it is approximately half-way out of cable clamp. Position control cable gauge shown in Fig. 10 in end of dust shield. Hold dust shield and gauge and push toward selector control assembly until gauge bottoms. While holding in this position, tighten set screw at cable clamp.

NOTE: The gauge shown in Fig. 10 is used on Chevrolet and Chevelle. The .090" end of the tool is used for Chevrolet adjustment; the .125" end for Chevelle.

Engine Section

NOTE

Throughout the engine section there will be references to Small V8s and Mark IV V8s. These can be distinguished as follows:

Small V8s: V8-283, 302, 307, 327, 350 and 265 H.P. V8-400.

Mark IV V8s: V8-396, other V8-400s, V8-427, 454.

ENGINE, REPLACE

NOTE: Starting with 1968, V8 engines are equipped with two strap type lifting rings, one at the right front the other at the left rear of the engine. Use of these rings eliminates the need to remove the rocker arm covers to install lifting adapters.

1966-72 Except Corvette

NOTE: The engine and transmission are removed as a unit. First disconnect and/or remove as required wires, tubes, hoses and linkage attached to engine and transmission. Then do the following:

1. Remove hood, radiator and fan. Also power steering pump and A/C compressor (if equipped).
2. On V8-409, detach power brake unit and move it aside.
3. Remove drive shaft.
4. Unfasten and lower exhaust pipes.
5. Remove rocker arm cover (s) and attach lifting device.
6. Remove front mount through bolts.
7. Raise engine to take weight off mounts, then remove rear mount bolts and crossmember. On Chevrolet models it will be necessary to

remove mount from transmission before crossmember can be removed. On Chevrolet it will be necessary to remove mount from transmission and loosen rear frame cushion bolts before crossmember can be removed. On 1968-72 Camaro, it is not necessary to remove the crossmember completely; after removing the bolts, slide it back.

8. Remove engine and transmission assembly.

1966-72 Corvette

When necessary to remove the engine, it is recommended that the engine and transmission assembly be lifted from the vehicle as a unit. It takes considerably less time to remove the engine and transmission as a unit than it would to "split" the engine from the transmission in the vehicle and remove the engine alone.

CYLINDER HEAD

1966-72 Four & Six Cylinder

1. Drain cooling system and remove air cleaner.
2. Disconnect choke rod or choke cable, accelerator pedal rod at bellcrank on manifold, and fuel and vacuum lines at carburetor.
3. Disconnect exhaust pipe at manifold flange, then unfasten and remove manifolds and carburetor as an assembly.
4. Remove fuel and vacuum line retaining clip from water outlet and disconnect wire harness from temperature sending unit and coil, leaving harness clear of clips on rocker arm cover.

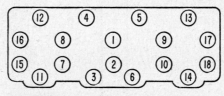

Fig. 1 Cylinder head tightening sequence. 4-153 engine

Fig. 2 Cylinder head tightening sequence. 6-194, 230, 250

Fig. 3 Cylinder head tightening sequence. Small V8 engines

Fig. 4 Cylinder head tightening sequence. V8-409 engines

5. Disconnect radiator hose at water outlet housing and battery ground strap at cylinder head.
6. Remove spark plugs and coil.
7. Remove rocker arm cover. Back off rocker arm nuts, pivot rocker arms to clear push rods and lift out push rods.
8. Unfasten and remove cylinder head.
9. Reverse procedure to install and tighten head bolts in the sequence shown in Figs. 1 and 2.

1966-72 V8s

NOTE: On Camaro and Chevy II with V8-396 and air conditioning it is necessary to remove the battery, A/C compressor, radiator shroud, air injector pump and starter. As the engine must be raised 2½" to remove the exhaust manifold it will be necessary to remove the engine mount through bolts and loosen transmission mount bolts.

When removing left head, power steering pump or air suspension compressor must be removed if so equipped.

On all other models, proceed as follows:
1. Remove intake and exhaust manifolds.
2. Remove rocker arm covers.
3. Back off rocker arm nuts, pivot rocker arms to clear push rods and remove push rods.
4. Unfasten and remove cylinder heads.
5. Reverse procedure to install and tighten head bolts in the sequence shown in Figs. 3 to 6.

VALVES, ADJUST
Hydraulic Lifters

NOTE: *After the engine has been thoroughly warmed up the valves may be adjusted with the engine shut off as follows: With engine in position to fire No. 1 cylinder the following valves may be adjusted: Exhaust 1-3-4-8, intake 1-2-5-7. Then crank the engine one more*

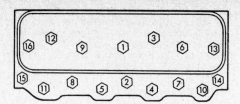

Fig. 5 Cylinder head tightening sequence. Mark IV V8 engines

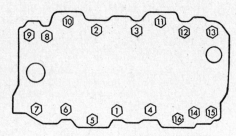

Fig. 6 Intake manifold tightening sequence. Mark IV V8 engines

complete revolution which will bring No. 6 cylinder to the firing position at which time the following valves may be adjusted: Exhaust 2-5-6-7, intake 3-4-6-8.

The following procedure, performed with the engine running should be done only in case readjustment is required.
1. After engine has been warmed up to operating temperature, remove valve cover and install a new valve cover gasket on cylinder head to prevent oil from running out.
2. With engine running at idle speed, back off valve rocker arm nut until rocker arm starts to clatter.
3. Turn rocker arm nut down slowly until the clatter just stops. This is the zero lash position.
4. Turn nut down ¼ additional turn and pause 10 seconds until engine runs smoothly. Repeat additional ¼ turns, pausing 10 seconds each time, until nut has been turned down the

number of turns listed in the *Valve Specifications Chart* from the zero lash position.

NOTE

This preload adjustment must be done slowly to allow the lifter to adjust itself to prevent the possibility of interference between the intake valve head and top of piston, which might result in internal damage and/or bent push rods. Noisy lifters should be replaced.

Mechanical Lifters

With the engine warmed to operating temperature as described above, turn rocker arm stud nut as required to obtain the clearances given in *Valve Specifications* table.

VALVE ARRANGEMENT
Front to Rear

4 Cylinder	E-I-I-E-I-I-E
6 Cylinder	E-I-I-E-E-I-I-E-E-I-I-E
Small V8	E-I-I-E-E-I-I-E
Mark IV V8	I-E-I-E-I-E-I-E

ROCKER ARM STUDS

Rocker arm studs that have damaged threads may be replaced with standard studs. If studs are loose in the head, oversize studs (.003" or .013") may be installed after reaming the holes with a proper size reamer.
1. Remove the old stud by placing a suitable spacer, Fig. 8, over stud. Install nut and flat washer and remove stud by turning nut.
2. Ream hole for oversize stud.
3. Coat press-fit area of stud with rear axle lube. Then install new stud, Fig. 9. If tool shown is used, it should bottom on the head.

NOTE: 1970-71 V8-350 cu. in., 360 and 370 H.P. engines are equipped with threaded rocker arm studs.

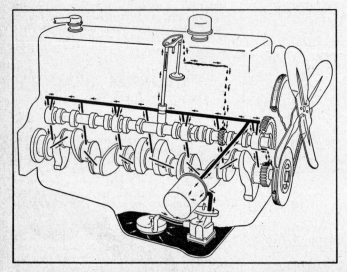

Engine oiling system. 6-194, 230, 250. Four cylinder is similar

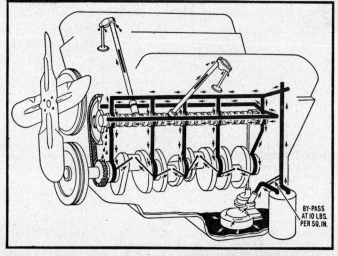

Engine oiling system. Small V8 engines

Fig. 8   Removing valve rocker arm stud

8-454	1970 ㉓	.3983	.4300
	1970 ⑭⑤	.4614	.480
	1971 ⑩	.5197	.5197
	1972 ㉚	.4614	.480
	1972 ㉛	.3983	.480

②—250 H.P.	⑰—370 H.P.
③—300 H.P.	⑱—265 H.P.
④—350 H.P.	⑲—375 H.P.
⑤—365 H.P.	⑳—335 H.P.
⑥—275 H.P.	㉑—430 H.P.
⑦—210 H.P.	㉒—330 H.P.
⑧—295 H.P.	㉓—345 H.P.
⑨—325 H.P.	㉔—360 H.P.
⑩—425 H.P.	㉕—245 H.P.
⑪—340 H.P.	㉖—270 H.P.
⑫—400 H.P.	㉗—California vehicles
⑬—385 H.P.	㉘—165, 200 H.P.
⑭—390 H.P.	㉙—255 H.P.
⑮—435 H.P.	㉚—230 H.P.
⑯—255 H.P.	㉛—270 H.P.

Fig. 9   Installing valve rocker arm stud

VALVE LIFT SPECS

Engine	Year	Intake	Exhaust
4-153	1966-70	.3973	.3973
6-194	1966-67	.3318	.3318
6-230	1966	.3349	.3349
	1967	.388	.388
	1968-70	.3317	.3317
6-250	1967-72	.388	.388
	1972 ㉗	.388	.4051
8-283	1966	.3987	.3987
	1967	.390	.410
8-302	1968-69	.4851	.4851
8-307	1968	.390	.410
	1969 ③⑯	.3945	.3945
	1970-72	.390	.410
	1972 ㉗	.4006	.4100
8-327	1966 ②	.3987	.3987
	1966 ③	.3987	.3987
	1966-68 ④	.4472	.4472
	1966 ⑥	.3987	.3987
	1967-68 ⑦	.390	.410
	1967-68 ⑥	.390	.410
	1967-68 ③	.390	.410
	1967-68 ⑧	.390	.410
	1967-68 ⑨	.4472	.4471
	1969	.3945	.3945
8-350	1967-68	.390	.410
	1969 ③⑯	.3945	.3945
	1969 ④	.4500	.4600
	1969 ⑰	.4851	.4851
	1970 ③③	.390	.410
	1970 ④	.4500	.4600
	1970-71 ⑰㉒㉔	.4586	.4850
	1971 ㉕㉖	.390	.410
	1972 ㉘	.390	.4100
	1972 ㉗㉘	.4006	.4100
	1972 ㉙	.4586	.4850
8-396	1966-69 ⑨⑱	.398	.398
	1967-69 ④	.4614	.4800
	1969 ⑲	.5197	.5197
8-400	1970 ⑱	.390	.410
	1970 ㉒	.3983	.3983
	1970 ④	.4614	.480
	1971 ③	.3983	.430
	1972	.390	.410
	1972 ㉗	.4006	.410
8-402	1972	.3983	.430
8-427	1966-68 ⑬	.4614	.4800
	1966-69 ⑭	.4614	.4800
	1967-69 ⑭	.4614	.4800
	1966-69 ⑮	.5917	.5917
	1966-69 ⑯	.5197	.5197
	1969 ⑳	.398	.398
	1969 ㉑	.5586	.580

VALVE TIMING

Intake Opens Before TDC
All Except Corvette

Engine	Year	Degrees
4-153	1966-67	33½
	1968-70	17½
6-194	1966-67	62
6-230	1966-67	62
	1968-70	16
6-250	1966-67	62
	1968-72	16
8-283	1966	32½
	1967 Chevrolet	38
	1967 Chevelle	38
	1967 Chevy II	36
8-307	1968-72	28
	1972 Calif.	44
8-327	1966	32½
	1967 Chevrolet	38
	1967 Chevelle	38
	1967 Camaro	36
	1967-68 325 H.P.	54
	1968-69	28
8-350	1968	28
	1969-70 255, 300 H.P.	28
	1969 350 H.P.	52
	1970 250, 300 H.P.	28
	1970 360 H.P.	42½
	1971 245, 270 H.P.	28
	1971 330 H.P.	42⅔
	1972 165, 200 H.P.	28
	1972 165, 200 H.P. Calif.	44
	1972 255 H.P.	42⅔
8-396	1969 265, 325 H.P.	28
	1969 350 H.P.	56
	1968	28
	1966-68 325, 350 H.P.	40
	1966-67 360 H.P.	56
8-400	1970 265, 330 H.P.	28
	1970 350 H.P.	56
	1971 300 H.P.	28
	1972	28
	1972 Calif	44
8-402	1972	30
8-427	1966-67 385, 390 H.P.	56
	1966 425 H.P.	54
	1969 390, 400 H.P.	56
	1969 435 H.P.	44
8-454	1970 360 H.P.	56
	1971 365 H.P.	56
	1971 425 H.P.	44
	1972	56

Corvette

Engine	Year	Degrees
8-327	1966 250, 300 H.P.	32½
	1966-67 350 H.P.	54
	1967 300 H.P.	38
	1967-68 435 H.P.	44
	1968 300 H.P.	28
	1968 350 H.P.	40
8-350	1969-70 300 H.P.	28
	1969-70 350 H.P.	52
	1970 370 H.P.	42½
	1971 270 H.P.	28
	1971 330 H.P.	42⅔
	1972 200 H.P.	28
	1972 200 H.P. Calif.	44
	1972 255 H.P.	42¾
8-427	1966-67 390, 400 H.P.	56
	1966 425 H.P.	54
	1967-69 435 H.P.	44
	1968 390, 400 H.P.	40
	1969 390, 400 H.P.	56
	1969 435 H.P.	44
8-454	1970 390 H.P.	56
	1970 460 H.P.	62
	1971 365 H.P.	56
	1971 425 H.P.	44
	1972	56

PUSH RODS

On engines that use push rods with a hardened insert at one end, the hardened end is identified by a color stripe and should always be installed toward the rocker arm during assembly. The V8-409 engine exhaust push rods are longer than the intake and carry different color stripe for further identification.

Service Bulletin

On 6-cylinder engines with air conditioning, it is not necessary to remove the distributor wires, etc. to replace the valve push rod cover and/or gasket.

1. Remove coil and bracket from block.
2. Remove distributor hold-down clamp.
3. Lift distributor up for clearance (do not disengage from cam gear), then remove push rod cover.
4. Use new gasket and reverse procedure to install.

VALVE GUIDES

On all engines valves operate in guide holes bored in the head. If clearance be-

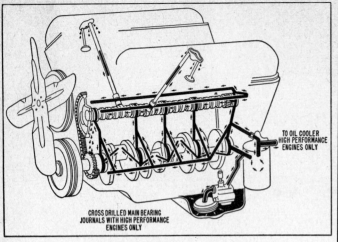

Engine lubrication. Mark IV V8 engines

Engine oiling system. V8-409

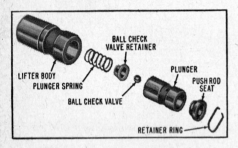

Fig. 11 Hydraulic valve lifter

comes excessive, use the next oversize valve and ream the bore to fit. Valves with oversize stems are available in .003, .015 and .030".

HYDRAULIC LIFTERS

Valve lifters may be lifted from their bores after removing rocker arms and push rods. Adjustable pliers with taped jaws may be used to remove lifters that are stuck due to varnish, carbon, etc. Fig. 11 illustrates the type of lifter used.

TIMING CASE COVER

NOTE: On all engines the cover oil seal may be replaced without taking off the timing gear cover. After removing the vibration damper, pry out the old seal with a screwdriver. Install the new seal with the lip or open end toward inside of cover and drive it into position.

1966-72 Four & Six Cylinder

1. To remove cover, remove radiator.
2. Remove vibration damper (6-cyl.) or pulley (4-cyl.).
3. Remove oil pan.
4. Unfasten and remove cover.
5. Pry oil seal out of cover with a large screwdriver. Install new seal with open side of seal inside of cover and drive

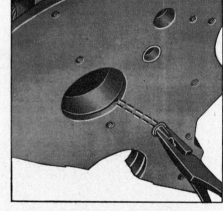

Fig. 12 Timing gear oil nozzle removal. 4-153, 6-194, 230, 250

Fig. 13 Installing timing case cover. 4-153, 6-194, 230, 250

Fig. 14 Removing camshaft gear from camshaft. 4-153 and all 6 cylinder engines

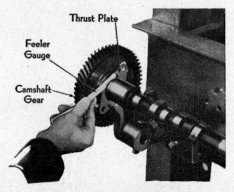

Fig. 15 Checking camshaft end play which should be .001 to .005". 4-153 and all 6 cylinder engines

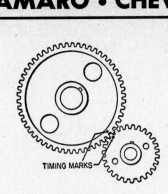

Fig. 16 Timing gear locating marks. 4-153 and all 6 cylinder engines

Fig. 17 Checking timing gear backlash with feeler gauge. Lash should be .004 to .006". 4-153 and all 6 cylinder engines

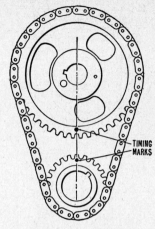

Fig. 18 Timing gear locating marks. V8 engines

or press seal into place.

6. If oil nozzle is to be replaced, remove it with pliers as shown in Fig. 12. Drive new nozzle in place, using a suitable light plastic or rubber hammer.
7. Clean gasket surfaces.
8. Install a suitable centering tool over end of crankshaft.
9. Coat gasket with light grease and stick it in position on block.
10. Install cover over centering tool, Fig. 13, and install cover screws, tightening them to 6 to 8 ft. lbs. *It is important that the centering tool be used to align the cover so the vibration damper installation will not damage the seal and position seal evenly around damper hub surface.*

1966-71 V8s

Remove vibration damper, oil pan, heater hose from water pump, and water pump from cylinder block. Unfasten and remove cover and gaskets.

Pry old seal out of cover from the front with a large screwdriver. Install the new seal so the open end of the seal is toward the inside of the cover and drive it into position with a suitable driver, being sure to support cover at sealing area.

1. Make certain that the mating faces of cover and block are clean and flat.
2. Make certain oil slinger is in place against crankshaft sprocket.
3. Coat oil seal with light grease and, using a new cover gasket, install cover and gasket over dowel pins in cylinder block.
4. Install and tighten cover screws to 6-8 lb. ft. torque.
5. Install oil pan, harmonic balancer and water pump.
6. Start engine and check for leaks.

TIMING GEARS
4-153 & All 6 Cyl. Engines

When necessary to install a new camshaft gear, the camshaft will have to be removed as the gear is a pressed fit on the shaft. The camshaft is held in position by a thrust plate which is fastened to the crankcase by two capscrews which are accessible through two holes in the gear web.

Use an arbor press to remove the gear and when doing so, a suitable sleeve, Fig. 14, should be employed to support the gear properly on its steel hub.

Before installing a new gear, assemble a new thrust plate on the shaft and press the gear on just far enough so that the thrust plate has practically no clearance, yet is free to turn. The correct clearance is from .001" to .005", Fig. 15.

The crankshaft gear can be removed by utilizing the two tapped holes in conjunction with a gear puller.

When the timing gears are installed, be sure the punch-marks on both gears are in mesh, Fig. 16. Backlash between the gears should be from .004" to .006", Fig. 17. Check the run-out of the gears, and if the camshaft gear run-out exceeds .004" or the crank gear run-out is in excess of .003", remove the gear (or gears) and examine for burrs, dirt or some other fault which may cause the run-out. If these conditions are not the cause, replace the gear (or gears).

TIMING CHAIN
V8 Engines

1. Remove timing chain cover as outlined previously.
2. Remove crankshaft oil slinger.
3. Crank engine until "O" marks on sprockets are in alignment, Fig. 18.
4. Remove three camshaft-to-sprocket bolts.
5. Remove camshaft sprocket and timing chain together. Sprocket is a light press fit on camshaft for approximately ⅛". If sprocket does not come off easily, a light blow with a plastic hammer on the lower edge of the sprocket should dislodge it.
6. If crankshaft sprocket is to be replaced, remove it with a suitable gear puller. Install new sprocket, aligning key and keyway.
7. Install chain on camshaft sprocket. Hold sprocket vertical with chain hanging below and shift around to align the "O" marks on sprockets.
8. Align dowel in camshaft with dowel hole in sprocket and install sprocket on camshaft. *Do not attempt to*

drive sprocket on camshaft as welch plug at rear of engine can be dislodged.
9. Draw sprocket onto camshaft, using the three mounting bolts. Tighten to 15-20 lb. ft. torque.
10. Lubricate timing chain and install cover.

CAMSHAFT
Service Bulletin
Camaro Camshaft Removal: On 6-cylinder jobs, it has been found that it is much easier to remove the engine from the chassis rather than performing the operation with the engine in the car. Once the engine is removed, take out the camshaft as outlined below.

4-153, 6-194, 6-230, 6-250

To remove the camshaft, remove radiator, grille, push rods, valve lifters, oil pan, vibration damper (6 cyl) or pulley (4 cyl), and timing case cover. Then pull out camshaft and gear assembly.

If necessary to replace bearings, the engine will have to be removed from the chassis. Then remove camshaft, flywheel and crankshaft. Drive out the expansion plug at the rear of the rear camshaft bearing and use suitable equipment to remove and replace the bearings.

V8 Engines

To remove the camshaft, remove valve lifters, fuel pump and its push rod, radiator, timing chain and camshaft sprocket. Install two ⁵⁄₁₆"-18 x 4" bolts in two camshaft bolt holes. Using these bolts as a puller, remove camshaft.

PISTONS & RODS, ASSEMBLE
1966-71

Assemble pistons to connecting rods as shown in Fig. 21 to 29.

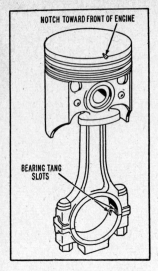

Fig. 21 Piston and rod assembly. 6-194 engine

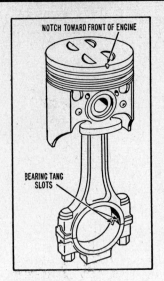

Fig. 22 Piston and rod assembly. 4-153 and 6-230 engines

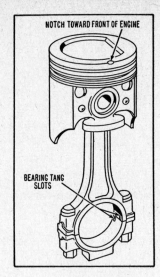

Fig. 23 Piston and rod assembly. 6-250 engine

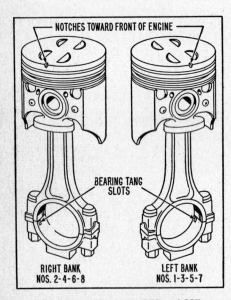

Fig. 24 V8-283, 307, 350 and 327 (except 325 and 350 H.P.)

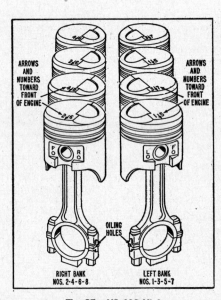

Fig. 25 V8-409 High performance engine

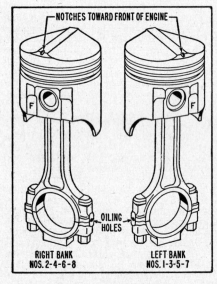

Fig. 26 V8-409 standard engine

PISTON OVERSIZES

```
4-153 ........ .001, .020, .030, .040"
6 Cyl. ........ .001, .020, .030, .040"
V8-283 ........ .001, .020, .030, .040"
V8-302, 307, 327, 350 ..001, .020, .030"
V8-396, 310, 350 H.P. .001, .020, .030"
V8-396 375 H.P. ........ .001, .030"
V8-400 ........ .001, .020, .030"
V8-427 390 H.P. ........ .001, .020, .030"
V8-427, 425, 435 H.P. .001, .030, .060"
V8-454 345, 390 H.P. .001, .020, .030"
V8-454 450, 460 H.P. .001, .030, .060"
V8-454 465 H.P. ... .001, .030, .060"
```

RING OVERSIZES

```
4-153, 6-230, 6-250 .020, .030, .040"
V8-327, 350 ............ .020, .030"
6-194 .................. .020, .040"
V8-283 ............ .020, .030, .040"
```

```
V8-396 ................ .020, .030"
V8-400 ................ .020, .030"
V8-427 390 H.P. ........ .020, .030"
V8-427, 425, 435 H.P. .... .030, .060"
V8-454 ............ .020, .030, .060"
```

MAIN & ROD BEARINGS
Undersizes

On all engines main and rod bearings are available in undersizes of .001, .002, .010 and .020".

SERVICE BULLETIN

Connecting rod type noise correction on 6-194 and 6-230 engines may be made as follows:

Remove connecting rod cap and Plastigage the bearings. If clearance is within .001 to .002", reinstall cap and retaining nuts. Then tighten nuts to the proper torque as listed in the *Engine Tightening Specifications* table.

NOTE 4-153 & All 6 Cyl.

The rear main bearing journal has no oil hole drilling. To remove the upper bearing half (bearing half with oil hole) proceed as follows after cap is removed:

1. Use a small drift punch and hammer to start the bearing rotating out of the block.
2. Use a pair of pliers (tape jaws) to hold the bearing thrust surface to the oil slinger and rotate the crankshaft to pull the bearing out.
3. To install, start the bearing (side not notched) into side of block by hand, then use pliers as before to turn

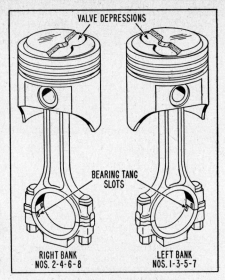

Fig. 27 V8-302, 327
(325 and 350 H.P.)

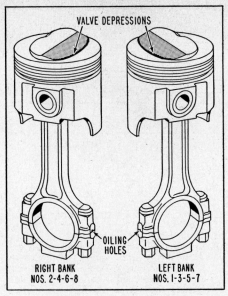

Fig. 27A V8-302, 350 Z-28
High performance

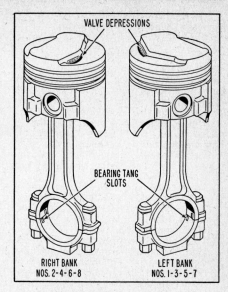

Fig. 28 V8-396, 454 engines

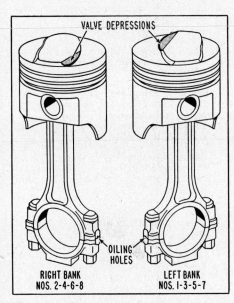

Fig. 28A V8-400 High performance

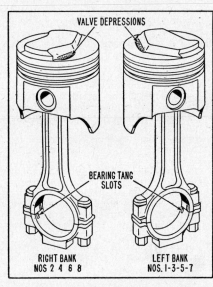

Fig. 28B V8-427 engine, 1966-68

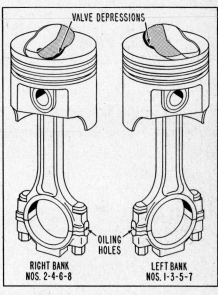

Fig. 29 V8-427 engine, 1969-70

bearing half into place.
4. The last ¼" movement may be done by holding just the slinger with the pliers or tap in place with a drift punch.

CRANKSHAFT REAR OIL SEAL

NOTE: On engines equipped with helix type rear seal, a seal starting tool, Fig. 31, must be used to prevent the upper seal half from coming into contact with the sharp edge of the block. Place the tip of the tool into the seal channel and "shoehorn" the seal into the upper seal channel.

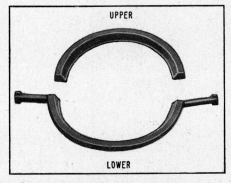

Fig. 30 Crankshaft rear oil seal.
4-153, 6-194, 230, 250

4-153, 6-194, 230, 250

Both halves of the seal Fig. 30 can be removed without removal of the crankshaft. Always replace upper and lower seal as a unit.
1. Remove oil pan and rear main bearing cap.
2. Remove seal from groove, prying from bottom with a small screwdriver.
3. Clean crankshaft surface. Then insert a new seal, well lubricated with engine oil, in bearing cap groove. *Keep oil off parting line surface as this surface is treated with glue.*
4. Gradually push with a hammer handle until seal is rolled into place.
5. To replace upper half of seal, use a small hammer and brass pin punch to tap one end of seal until it protrudes far enough to be removed with

pliers. Install the new seal.
6. Install bearing cap and oil pan.

1966-72 V8

When necessary to correct an oil leak due to a defective seal, always replace the upper and lower seal halves as a unit. *When installing either half, lubricate the lip portion only with engine oil, keeping oil off the parting line surface as this is treated with glue.* Always clean crankshaft surface berore installing a new seal. Be careful of seal retainer tang while inserting a new seal so that it doesn't cut the seal.

1. To replace the lower seal, remove seal from groove in bearing cap, using a small screwdriver to pry it out.
2. Insert new seal and roll it in place with finger and thumb.
3. To replace the upper seal (with engine in car) use a small hammer and tap a brass pin punch on one end of the seal until it protrudes far enough to be removed with pliers.
4. Insert the new seal, gradually pushing with a hammer handle until seal is rolled into place.
5. Install bearing cap with new seal and tighten bearing cap bolts.

OIL PAN
1971-72 Six

1. Disconnect battery positive cable.
2. Remove radiator upper mounting panel or side mount bolts.
3. Place a piece of heavy cardboard between fan and radiator.
4. Disconnect fuel suction line at fuel pump.
5. Raise vehicle on hoist and drain oil.
6. Disconnect and remove starter.
7. Remove either flywheel underpan or converter housing underpan and splash shield.
8. On all vehicles except Chevelle and Chevrolet, disconnect steering rod at idler lever, than position steering linkage to one side for clearance.
9. Rotate crankshaft until timing mark on damper is at 6 o'clock position.
10. Remove bolts attaching brake line to

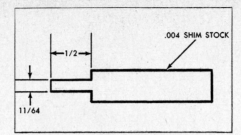

Fig. 31 Fabricated seal starting tool for helix type seal

front crossmember and move brake line away from member.
11. Remove through bolts from engine front mounts.
12. Remove oil pan bolts.
13. On Chevelle and Chevrolet, raise engine slowly until motor mounts can be removed from frame brackets, remove mount and continue to raise engine until it is about three inches up.
14. On all models except Chevelle and Chevrolet, raise engine enough to insert 2" x 4" wood blocks under engine mounts, then lower engine onto blocks.
15. Lower oil pan and remove.

1971-72 V8 Except Chevelle with Mark IV Engines

1. Disconnect battery ground cable.
2. Remove distributor cap.
3. Remove fan shroud retaining bolts.
4. On Mark IV engines, place a heavy piece of cardboard between fan and radiator.
5. Raise vehicle on hoist and drain oil.
6. Disconnect exhaust or crossover pipes.
7. On vehicles with automatic transmission, remove converter housing underpan and splash shield.
8. On all models except Chevelle and Chevrolet, disconnect steering idler lever at frame and swing linkage down for clearance.
9. Rotate crankshaft until timing mark on damper is at 6 o'clock position.

10. On small V8 engines, disconnect starter brace at starter. Remove inboard starter bolt and loosen outboard starter bolt. Starter can be swung out for clearance.
11. Remove through bolts from engine front mounts.
12. Use a suitable jack and a block of wood and raise engine until blocks of wood 2" on Chevrolet and Nova and 3" on Chevelle can be inserted under mounts. Lower engine until supported by blocks.
13. Remove oil pan.

1971-72 Chevelle with Mark IV Engines

1. Disconnect battery positive cable.
2. Remove air cleaner, dipstick and disconnect distributor cap from distributor.
3. Disconnect radiator shroud and upper mounting panel. This allows radiator to move up and down freely in later steps.
4. Place a heavy piece of cardboard between fan and radiator.
5. Disconnect engine ground straps at engine.
6. Disconnect accelerator control cable from engine.
7. Place a hook and chain over cowl, Fig. 32.
8. Raise vehicle on hoist and drain oil.
9. Remove propeller shaft and plug rear of transmission.
10. On floor shift models, remove two bolts securing shift lever to linkage. On all other models, disconnect linkage at transmission.
11. Disconnect speedometer cable and back-up lamp switch connector.
12. On manual transmissions, disconnect clutch cordon shaft at frame. On automatics, disconnect cooler lines, detent cable, rod or switch wire and modulator pipe.
13. Remove crossmember bolts and place jack under engine. Raise engine and move crossmember toward rear of car.
14. On engines with single exhaust, remove crossover pipe. On dual exhaust models, disconnect exhaust pipes.

PLACE FABRICATED STRAP OVER COWL

INSTALL BOLT THROUGH CENTER LINK OF CHAIN

Fig. 32 Install strap over cowl

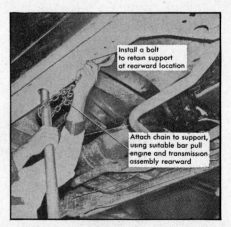

Install a bolt to retain support at rearward location

Attach chain to support, using suitable bar pull engine and transmission assembly rearward

Fig. 33 Prying engine/transmission assembly rearward. 1967 Chevelle V8-283, 327 with Auto. Trans. & 1968-69 Chevelle V8-307, 327, 350 with Std. Trans.

15. Remove flywheel housing cover. Remove transmission attaching bolts and remove transmission. On manual transmission models, remove flywheel housing, throwout bearing and flywheel.
16. Remove engine mount through bolts.
17. Raise rear of engine about 4 inches. Attach each end of chain to engine using bell housing bolts or transmission mounting bolts. Lower engine jack and move to front of engine.
18. Raise front of engine and insert 2" blocks of wood under front mounts.
19. Rotate crankshaft until timing mark on damper is at 6 o'clock position.
20. Remove oil pan.

1970 Camaro

1. Disconnect battery ground cable.
2. Remove distributor cap on V8 units to prevent damage when engine is raised.
3. On Mark IV engines, remove dipstick and tube.
4. Raise car and drain crankcase.
5. Disconnect exhaust crossover pipe at manifolds if necessary.
6. Remove automatic transmission converter under pan if so equipped.
7. Rotate crankshaft so timing mark is at 6 o'clock position.
8. Remove front engine mount through bolts.
9. Raise engine and insert 3" wood blocks under engine mounts. Lower engine until it is supported by blocks.
10. Remove oil pan bolts and oil pan.

1970 Chevrolet Six

1. Disconnect battery ground cable, starter wires and starter brace attaching bolt.
2. Loosen fan belt.
3. Raise vehicle and drain crankcase.
4. Remove starter, flywheel underpan and engine mount through bolts. Rotate crankshaft so timing mark is positioned at 6 o'clock position.
5. Position fan so the widest openings between the blades are at the top and bottom.
6. Raise the front of the engine and remove the engine mounts at the frame brackets.
7. Insert 5" wood blocks between the engine mount brackets and the frame brackets.
8. Remove oil pan bolts and oil pan.

1970 Chevrolet V8, 1966-69 Chevrolet All, 1967-69 Camaro, 1968-70 Chevelle V8 with Auto. Trans. Exc. V8-396 1968-70 Chevy II & Nova

1. Disconnect battery ground cable.
2. On V8s, lift cap off distributor to prevent damaging cap when engine is raised.
3. Remove through bolts from engine front mounts.
4. Remove fan blade and starter.
5. Disconnect cooler lines (if equipped) at transmission and remove converter housing underpan.
6. Disconnect steering linkage at idler lever and swing linkage for pan clearance.

7. Rotate crankshaft until timing mark on vibration damper is at 6 o'clock position.
8. Use a suitable jack and a block of wood to prevent damage to oil pan and raise engine enough to insert 2" x 4" wood blocks under engine mounts; then lower engine to blocks. On 1968-69 Chevy II, attach a cantilever hoist or chain-fall to engine. If chain-fall is used, disconnect and move hood out of the way.

NOTE: If 2" x 4" wood blocks are cut 5½" long they can be used on all Chevrolet engines. The 5½" length up for 4 and 6 cylinder engines and the 4" side for V8 engines.

9. On Camaro six-cylinder models, after oil pan bolts are removed and oil pan lowered, remove the oil pump, then remove the pan. On all other models, remove the pan without removing the pump.

NOTE: On 396 and 427 engines the oil pan has three ¼"-20 attaching bolts at the crankcase front cover—one at each corner and one at lower center.

1968-70 Chevelle V8-307, 327, 350 with Std. Trans. & 1967 Chevelle V8-283, 327 with Auto. Trans.

1. Disconnect battery positive cable and remove air cleaner. Remove distributor cap.
2. Remove radiator upper mounting panel. On 1967, remove radiator retaining bolts and place a piece of heavy cardboard between the radiator and fan blade to avoid damage.
3. Remove fuel pump and left rear engine mount bolt. Remove fan belt.
4. On floor shift, remove shift lever and floor plate.
5. Raise vehicle on hoist and drain oil.
6. Remove crankshaft pulley and starter motor.
7. Remove flywheel underpan, disconnect transmission linkage and remove shift bracket assembly.
8. Remove drive shaft, disconnect exhaust pipes from manifolds and remove front engine mounts to block bolts.
9. Rotate crankshaft until timing mark on harmonic balancer is at 6 o'clock position.
10. Remove bolts attaching transmission crossmember to frame. Remove two bolts attaching brake line to front crossmember and move brake line from crossmember.
11. Raise front of engine at harmonic balancer until clearance between engine mounts and block is approximately ½ inch.
12. Using a chain and bar as illustrated in Fig. 33, pull the engine/transmission assembly rearward and insert a bolt through the forward mounting hole in the crossmember and the rearward hole in the frame on each side.

NOTE: Use extreme caution during this step as the engine is "free" in the chassis.

13. Raise front of engine approximately 2 additional inches. Remove oil pan bolts and lower oil pan.
14. Remove front main bearing cap and remove oil pan.

1968-70 Chevelle V8-396 1967 Chevelle Six with Std. Trans.

The engine must be completely disconnected from its mounts, front and rear, and the crossmember disconnected and moved rearward to allow the engine to be raised high enough to provide clearance for the oil pan to be removed. The engine therefore, must be supported by a fabricated hook and a suitable chain, hung over the cowl, Fig. 32, or by removing the hood and attaching a chain hoist to raise the engine. *Because the engine is free and the crossmember removed, use caution.*

Once the engine has been raised and secured, proceed as outlined for Chevelle V8 with auto. trans.

1968-69 Chevelle Six

1. Remove radiator upper mounting panel. Disconnect battery positive cable.
2. Disconnect fuel line. Raise vehicle and remove splash shield, underpan and starter motor.
3. Remove through bolts from front engine mounts.
4. Rotate crankshaft until timing mark on harmonic balancer is at 6 o'clock position.
5. Remove brake line retainer bolts at crossmember and move line out of the way. Remove oil pan bolts.
6. Raise engine slowly until engine mounts can be removed from frame brackets. Continue to raise engine until it has been raised approximately 3 inches.
7. Lower oil pan and remove.

1967 Chevelle Six with Auto. Trans.

1. Disconnect battery positive cable.
2. Remove radiator upper mounting panel.
3. Disconnect tank to pump fuel line and remove starter.
4. Raise vehicle on hoist and drain oil. Remove underpan and splash shield.
5. Remove engine mount through bolts.
6. Raise front of engine until mounts separate from frame brackets. Remove right mount bracket from engine and install two bolts in the bracket mounting holes so the engine can be supported on wood blocks.
7. Continue raising the engine until a 4½" block can be inserted between the bolts and frame bracket on the right side and a 4" block inserted on the left side between the mount and frame bracket.
8. Rotate crankshaft until the timing mark on the harmonic balancer is at the 6 o'clock position and remove the oil pan bolts.
9. Lower pan, remove front main bearing cap and remove oil pan.

1966 Chevelle All
1967 Chevelle V8-283, 327 with Std. Trans.

1. Remove engine from vehicle.
2. Remove flywheel or converter housing underpan.
3. Remove starter and oil pan.

1966-67 Chevy II

1. Disconnect battery ground cable.
2. Remove starter.
3. Disconnect steering idler arm bracket at right frame side rail and swing linkage down for pan clearance.
4. On 6-cylinder engines, remove front crossmember. On Station Wagons, let stabilizer bar hang down while removing crossmember.
5. On V8s, disconnect exhaust pipes from manifolds and allow pipes to hang.
6. Remove oil pan.

1966-72 Corvette

1. Disconnect battery and remove oil dipstick and tube.
2. Remove starter and flywheel underpan.
3. Disconnect steering linkage idler arm at frame and lower linkage.
4. Remove oil pan.
5. On high performance engines, the oil baffle must be removed before additional operations can be performed.

NOTE: On 427 engines the oil pan has three 1/4"-20 bolts at the crankcase front cover—one at each corner and one at lower center.

OIL PUMP
4-153, 6-194, 6-230, 6-250

The pumps used in these engines are of the positive gear type. After disassembling the pump, examine the shaft and gears for excessive wear and replace where necessary, or better still, install a new pump. When assembling the pump, be sure the ground side of the idler gear is toward the cover.

The gasket used between the pump cover and the body is special in that it controls the clearance in the pump. If the relief valve parts show wear, install new parts. Be sure that the tapered set screw which holds the pump in place is fully seated and locked with its lock nut.

V8 Engines

After removing the oil pan, unfasten pump from rear main bearing cap. Disconnect pump shaft from extension by removing clip from collar. Remove pump cover and take out idler gear, drive gear and shaft.

Should any of the following conditions be found it is advisable to replace the pump assembly.

1. Inspect pump body for cracks or wear.
2. Inspect gears for wear or damage.
3. Check shaft for looseness in housing.
4. Check inside of cover for wear that would permit oil to leak past the ends of gear.
5. Check oil pick-up screen for damage to screen, by-pass valve or body.
6. Check for oil in air chamber.

WATER PUMP, REPLACE
All Models

1. Drain radiator and break loose fan pulley bolts.
2. Disconnect heater hose at water pump.
3. Loosen Delcotron and remove fan belt, then unfasten and remove pump. On 6-cylinder engines, pull pump straight out of block first to prevent damage to impeller.
4. Reverse procedure to install.

FUEL PUMP, REPLACE
1966-72

1. Disconnect fuel lines at pump.

2. Unfasten and remove pump.
3. If push rod is to be removed on 396, 400, 427 and 454 engines, remove pipe plug, then remove push rod. On 283, 302, 307, 327, 350 and 265 H.P. V8-400, remove fuel pump adapter and gasket then remove push rod.
4. Reverse procedure to install. On V8 engines, a pair of mechanical fingers may be used to hold fuel pump push rod up while installing pump.

NOTE

Installation of the pump on V8-283 and 327 engines can be performed faster by using the following means of retaining the fuel pump push rod in the engine during pump replacement.

1. Before removing the pump, remove upper bolt from engine front mount boss located to the right of the timing chain cover on the front of the engine. This bolt enters the push rod bore acting as a plug.
2. Remove the original bolt and install one that is 1-3/4" long. Turn it down by hand until it is stopped by the push rod. Do not use a wrench to turn in this bolt as it may damage the push rod, necessitating its replacement.
3. The fuel pump can then be removed without the push rod slipping from its installed position. After installing the pump, the original shorter bolt must be reinstalled to avoid oil leakage.

Service Bulletin

On Mark IV engines the access hole for removal of the fuel pump push rod is located below the fuel pump mounting bolts. This access hole, which permits removal of the push rod after the pump has been removed, has a threaded plug with a square recessed hole. The plug may be removed by using a hand-made tool. A 5/16" square end for inserting and turning the plug for removal is required. A piece of bar stock, approximately 1-1/2" long is suggested.

Clutch and Transmission Section

NOTE: 1972 linkage adjustment information is in this section. Repair procedures on both automatic and manual shift transmissions are covered elsewhere in this manual. Procedures for removing automatic transmissions as well as linkage adjustments on 1966-71 models are included in the automatic transmission chapters. See Chapter Index.

CLUTCH PEDAL, ADJUST
1968-72 Chevrolet & Corvette

1. Disconnect spring between clutch push rod and cross shaft lever.
2. With clutch pedal against stop, loosen jam nuts just enough to allow adjusting rod to move against the clutch fork until the release bearing contacts the pressure plate fingers lightly.
3. Rotate upper nut against swivel and back off 4-1/2 turns. Tighten lower nut to lock swivel against nut.
4. Install return spring and check clutch pedal free travel:
   Chevrolet 1 to 1-1/2".
   Corvette standard clutch 1-1/4 to 2".
   Corvette heavy duty clutch 2 to 2-1/2".

1968-72 Chevelle, Camaro, Chevy II

1. Disconnect return spring at clutch fork.
2. With clutch pedal against stop, loosen lock nut just enough to allow the adjusting rod to be turned out off swivel and against clutch fork until release bearing contacts pres-

3. Rotate push rod into swivel three turns and tighten lock nut.

NOTE: Chevy II and Camaro V8 models use a two-piece push rod. Turn adjusting rod portion of push rod three turns into rod end and tighten lock nut.

4. Reinstall return spring and check clutch pedal free travel:
Chevelle $1\frac{1}{8}$ to $1\frac{3}{4}$".
Chevy II and Camaro 1 to $1\frac{1}{8}$".

1966-67 Models

There is one linkage adjustment (clutch fork push rod or pedal push rod) to compensate for all normal clutch wear.

The clutch pedal should have 1 to $1\frac{1}{4}$" free travel (measured at clutch pedal pad) before the clutch release bearing engages the clutch diaphragm levers. Lash is required to prevent clutch slippage that would occur if the bearing was held against the diaphragm levers and to prevent the bearing from running continually until failure occurs.

CLUTCH, REPLACE

Clutch Disc Installation

On all 4 and 6-cylinder engines the clutch disc is installed with the damper springs to the flywheel side. On V8's install clutch disc with damper springs and grease slinger to transmission side.

1966-72

1. Support engine and remove transmission as outlined further on.
2. Disconnect clutch fork push rod and spring.
3. Remove flywheel housing.
4. Slide clutch fork from ball stud and remove fork from dust boot.

NOTE: Look for "X" mark on flywheel and on clutch cover. If "X" mark is not evident, prick punch marks on flywheel and clutch cover for indexing purposes during installation.

5. Loosen clutch-to-flywheel attaching bolts evenly one turn at a time until spring pressure is released. Then remove bolts and clutch assembly.
6. Reverse procedure to install.

THREE SPEED TRANSMISSION, REPLACE

1968-69 Corvette

1. Disconnect battery ground cable.
2. Remove shift ball.
3. Remove console trim plate.
4. Raise vehicle on a hoist.
5. Remove right and left exhaust pipes. *In order to remove the exhaust pipes on 8-396 and 427 engines, it will be necessary to remove the forward stud on each manifold.*
6. Disconnect and lower front of propeller shaft. Remove slip yoke from

transmission.

7. Remove bolts retaining rear mounts to bracket. Raise engine, lifting transmission off mount bracket.
8. Unfasten transmission linkage mounting bracket from frame.
9. Detach gearshift from mounting bracket and remove bracket. Remove shifter mechanism with rods attached.
10. Disconnect shifter levers at transmission. Disconnect speedometer cable.
11. Unfasten and remove transmission mount bracket. Unfasten rear mount cushion and exhaust pipe yoke.
12. Unfasten transmission from clutch housing.
13. Pull transmission rearward and rotate clockwise until it is clear of clutch housing. *To allow room for transmission removal, slowly lower rear of engine until tachometer drive cable at the distributor just clears horizontal ledge across front of dash.*

CAUTION: The tachometer cable can be easily damaged by heavy contact with the dash. Slide transmission rearward out of the clutch, then tip front end of transmission downward and lower assembly from vehicle.

14. Reverse procedure to install.

1968-72 Except Corvette

1. On floor shift models, remove shift knob and console trim plate.
2. Disconnect speedometer cable at transmission and on floor shift models, disconnect back-up lamp switch. Disconnect T.C.S. switch wire if so equipped.
3. Remove drive shaft.
4. On 1967-69 Camaro, disconnect exhaust pipe at manifold.
5. Remove crossmember-to-frame attaching bolts. On floor shift models, remove crossmember-to-control lever support attaching bolts. On Chevelle, also remove control lever brace-to-crossmember attaching bolt.
6. Remove bolts retaining transmission mount to crossmember.
7. Support engine and raise slightly until crossmember may be slid rearward or removed.

NOTE: On some Camaros, it may be necessary to remove the right rear body mount bolt then, using a suitable tool, pry the right rear portion of the frame downward and insert a block of wood to maintain enough of a gap so the crossmember can be removed.

8. Remove shift levers at transmission side cover. On floor shift models, remove stabilizer-to-control lever retaining nut. Push bolt toward transmission until stabilizer rod may be disconnected.
9. Remove transmission-to-clutch housing upper retaining bolts and install guide pins in holes, then remove lower bolts.
10. Slide transmission rearward and remove from vehicle.
11. Reverse procedure to install.

1966-67 Corvette

1. Disconnect battery ground cable.
2. Disassemble shift lever.
3. Raise front and rear of vehicle.
4. Insert a block of wood between top of differential carrier housing and underbody to prevent upward travel of carrier when carrier front support is disconnected.
5. Disconnect differential carrier front support from its frame bracket by removing nut on underside of biscuit mount.
6. Pry carrier downward to relieve load while removing two center mounting bolts from carrier front support.

NOTE: To pry carrier downward, insert crowfoot end of a pry bar through opening in carrier front support, hooking end of bar over top of center mounting bolt pad cast in underside of carrier.

7. Pivot carrier support downward for access to propeller shaft U-joint.
8. Disconnect propeller shaft front and then rear U-bolts.
9. Disconnect parking brake cable from ball socket at idler lever, located near center of underbody.
10. Move propeller shaft forward to remove from car.
11. Remove heat deflectors from right and left exhaust pipes.
12. Remove left bank exhaust pipe.
13. Remove right bank exhaust pipe and heat riser.
14. Disassemble transmission mount, supporting engine with a jack and wood block under oil pan. Raise engine to remove load from rear mount cushion.
15. Remove transmission - to - mount bracket bolts. Remove two bolts from mount pad-to-transmission case and remove rubber mount cushion and exhaust pipe "yoke".
16. Disconnect shift levers from transmission side cover.
17. Disconnect speedometer cable.
18. Remove transmission output shaft slip yoke. *Yoke is removed to prevent tearing deflecting pad on underbody when transmission is being removed.*
19. Disconnect transmission shift control lever and bracket assembly from adapter plate on side of transmission.
20. Lower transmission, letting shift lever slide down and through dust boot in console.
21. Remove transmission-to-clutch housing bolts.
22. Slide transmission rearward from clutch and rotate it for access to three flat head machine screws in control lever bracket adapter plate. Then rotate transmission back to upright position.
23. To allow room for transmission removal, slowly lower rear of engine until tachometer drive cable at distributor just clears horizontal ledge across front of dash.

CAUTION: The tachometer cable can easily be damaged by heavy contact with dash. Slide transmission rearward out of clutch, then tip front end of transmission downward and lower assembly from vehicle.

24. Reverse procedure to install.

1966-67 Except Corvette

1. Remove propeller shaft.
2. Disconnect speedometer cable at transmission.
3. Disconnect shift rods at transmission levers.
4. Support engine.
5. Remove transmission - to - flywheel housing bolts.
6. Remove transmission crossmember-to-mount bolts.
7. Loosen transmission crossmember and move it rearward to allow ample room to remove the transmission.

NOTE: On Camaro models moving the crossmember rearward is not possible because the crossmember is mounted in a recess in the frame which is enclosed by the underbody of the car. Consequently, rather than moving the crossmember rearward, it must be completely removed during transmission assembly removal.

8. Slide transmission rearward and remove.
9. Reverse procedure to install.

FOUR SPEED TRANSMISSION, REPLACE

1968-72 All Models

The procedure for removing this transmission is similar to that described for the 1968-70 3-speed units.

1966-67 Corvette

The procedure for removing these transmissions is similar to that described for the 3-speed units of the corresponding year.

1966-67 Except Corvette

1. Remove shift lever trim plate and dust boot.
2. Remove shift lever assembly.
3. Raise vehicle to working height.
4. Disconnect speedometer cable from driven gear fitting.
5. Remove propeller shaft.
6. Support engine at oil pan rail with a suitable jack or other device capable of supporting engine when transmission is removed.
7. Disconnect shift lever bracket from extension housing and remove all three shift levers from shifter shafts and remove bracket, levers and linkage.
8. Remove extension mount-to-cross member bolts.
9. Loosen transmission crossmember and move it rearward or remove it entirely.
10. Remove transmission-to-clutch housing bolts and install guide pins in the two top holes.
11. Slide transmission rearward enough to allow sufficient clearance of input shaft and clutch housing. Then tilt input shaft end of transmission

downward and withdraw transmission from vehicle.
12. Reverse procedure to install.

THREE SPEED SHIFT LINKAGE, ADJUST

1969-72 Except Corvette

Column Shift

1. Place shift lever in "Reverse" position and ignition switch in "Lock".
2. Raise vehicle on a hoist.
3. Loosen shift control rod swivel lock nuts. Pull down slightly on 1/R rod attached to column lever to remove any slack and then tighten clevis lock nut at transmission lever.
4. Unlock ignition switch and shift column lever to "Neutral". Position column lower levers in "Neutral", align gauge holes in levers and insert gauge pin.

NOTE: Alignment holes are on the lower side of levers on Chevelle and Nova models.

5. Support rod and swivel to prevent movement and tighten 2/3 shift control rod lock nut.
6. Remove alignment tool from column lower levers and check operation. Then place column lever in "Reverse" and check interlock control.

Floor Shift

1. Turn ignition switch to "Lock" position and raise vehicle on hoist.
2. Loosen lock nuts at swivels on both shift rods and on back drive rod, Fig. 2.
3. Set transmission shift levers in "Neutral".
4. Set shift lever in car in "Neutral" and install locating gauge into control lever bracket assembly.
5. Run 1/R shift rod nut against swivel and tighten locknut against swivel.
6. Run 2/3 shift rod against swivel and tighten locknut against swivel.
7. Remove gauge pin and shift lever into "Reverse", then pull down slightly on rod to remove any slack and tighten clevis jam nut. Ignition switch should move freely in and out of "Lock".

1969-72 Corvette

1. Turn ignition switch to "Lock" and raise vehicle on a hoist.
2. Loosen swivel lock nuts on both shift rods and disconnect back drive cable from column lock tube lever, Fig. 3.
3. Place shift control in car into "Neutral" and insert a locking gauge (.644") in notch of lever and bracket assembly.
4. Place transmission levers into "Neutral".
5. Hold 1/R rod and lever against locating gauge and tighten locknut against swivel.
6. Hold 2/3 rod and lever against locating gauge and tighten the forward nut against swivel and then the aft. Remove locating gauge.
7. Check operation of linkage. *Caution:*

Shift lever must be properly centered in console to prevent fore and aft and side contact with console. Shim lever support bracket as required but be sure to maintain support to extension clearance.

8. From inside vehicle, loosen two nuts at steering column to dash panel bracket.
9. Place transmission shift lever into "Reverse".
10. Rotate the lock tube lever counterclockwise to remove free play. Reposition the cable bracket until the cable eye passes over the retaining pin on the bracket.
11. Hold the bracket in position and have an assistant tighten the steering column to dash panel bracket retaining nuts.
12. Reinstall the cotter pin and washer retaining the back drive cable.

1968 (Also Late 1967) Chevrolet, Camaro, Chevelle, Chevy II

Column Shift

1. Loosen swivel locking clamps on both shift rods. Shift rods must pass freely through swivels.
2. Place shift lever handle in neutral. Insert fabricated L-shaped tool, Fig. 1, through 1/R lever, the relay lever and the 2/3 lever and then into the hole in the alignment plate bolted to the mast jacket.
3. Place transmission shift levers in neutral position.
4. Tighten both swivel clamp nuts on the rods, supporting swivels with one hand while tightening to insure against any movement of the swivels or rods.
5. Remove alignment tool from levers. Shift transmission through all ranges, then return to neutral. Reinsert tool; if it does not pass freely through alignment holes and bracket, loosen clamps and readjust linkage.

1966 & Early 1967 Chevrolet, Camaro, Chevelle, Chevy II

Column Shift

1. Move both transmission shift levers until transmission is in neutral. Neutral detents in transmission cover must both be engaged to make this adjustment correctly. To check, start engine with clutch disengaged, and release clutch slowly.
2. Move selector lever to neutral position. Also align low-reverse tube lever with 2-3 shifter tube lever on mast jacket.
3. Align shift control rods and levers in neutral position.
4. Move selector levers through all positions to check adjustment and to insure over-travel in all positions.

1968 Chevelle, Camaro, Chevy II

Floor Shift

1. Loosen swivel locking clamps on both shift rods. Shift rods must pass freely through swivel.
2. Set shift lever in neutral and install

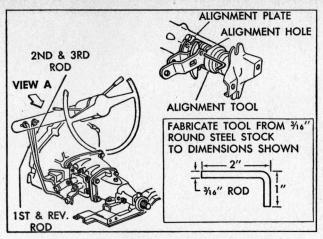

Fig. 1   Three-speed column shift linkage adjustment. Late 1967 and 1968-72 Chevrolet, Chevy II, Chevelle and Camaro

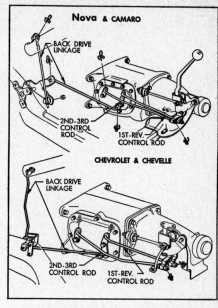

Fig. 2   3-Speed floor shift linkage. 1969-72 except Corvette

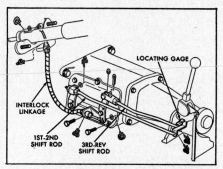

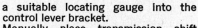

Fig. 3   3 Speed linkage. 1969-72 Corvette

neutral detent and insert a locating pin into notch of lever and bracket assembly.
3. Install nut and clevis on rod loosely.
4. With lever against locating pin, adjust clevis at lever until clevis pin passes freely through holes and secure with washer and cotter pin.
5. Install nuts and swivel loosely on rod, attach rod to lever and secure with retainer.
6. With lever against locating pin, attach swivel to lever and secure with retainer. Tighten nuts against swivel.
7. Remove locating pin and check shifts to insure proper operation.

FOUR SPEED SHIFT LINKAGE, ADJUST
1969-72

The procedure, Figs. 5 and 6, is the same as that for Three Speed transmissions described previously.

a suitable locating gauge into the control lever bracket.
3. Manually place transmission shift levers in neutral.
4. Run 1/R shift rod nut against swivel and tighten lock nut against swivel.
5. Run 2/3 shift rod nut against swivel, then tighten lock nut against swivel.
6. Remove locating gauge and check operation.

1968 Corvette
1. Loosen swivel locking clamps on both shift rods. Shift rods must pass freely through swivels.
2. Place shift lever in neutral. Insert a $\frac{41}{64}''$ locating gauge in notch of lever and bracket assembly.
3. Manually place transmission levers in neutral position.
4. With 1/R rod and lever against locating gauge, tighten lock nut against swivel.
5. With 2/3 rod and lever against locating gauge, run forward nut against swivel and then tighten other nut against swivel.
6. Remove gauge and check shifts. Return to neutral position and re-insert locating gauge. If gauge does not freely enter bracket, readjust linkage.

1966-67 Corvette
1. Set transmission levers in neutral.
2. Move transmission control lever to

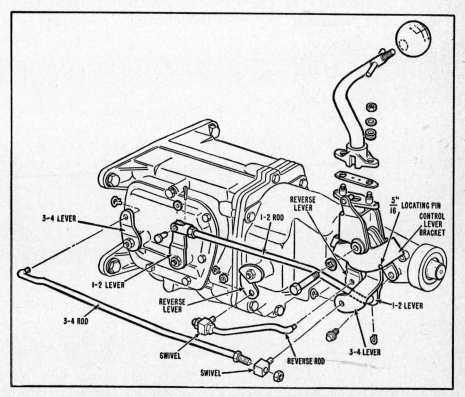

Fig. 4   Four speed transmission linkage. 1966-67 (typical)

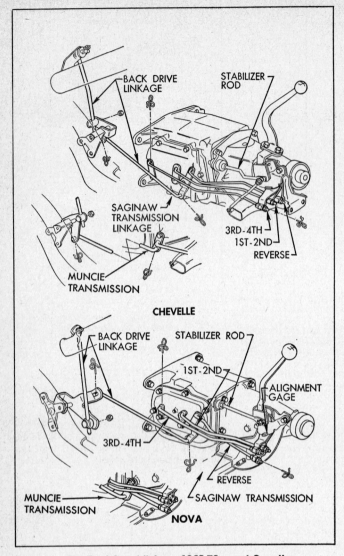

Fig. 5   4 Speed linkage. 1968-72 except Corvette

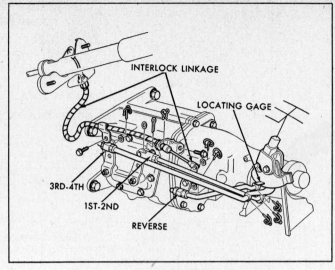

Fig. 6   4 Speed linkage. 1968-70 Corvette

1967-68

1. Loosen swivel locking clamps on both shift rods. Shift rods must pass freely through swivels.
2. Set transmission shift levers in neutral detent position.
3. Move shift control lever to neutral detent position and insert a suitable locating gauge into control lever bracket.
4. Tighten reverse lever swivel lock nuts.
5. Repeat step 4 for the $\frac{1}{2}$ shift rod and the $\frac{3}{4}$ rod.
6. Remove locating gauge. After removing locating gauge on Camaro with Muncie transmission, readjust rod by shortening the rod three turns by use of jam nuts. Check shift for proper operation and readjust if necessary.

1966

Two makes of transmissions are used in 1966, the Muncie and the Saginaw. Linkage adjustments are similar to the 1965 procedure except that a locating gauge ($\frac{1}{8}$" thick to $\frac{41}{64}$" wide and 3" long) is placed in the slot of the control lever bracket. Use Fig. 4 as a guide only.
1. Referring to Fig. 4, set transmission levers in neutral detent position.
2. Move shift lever to neutral position and insert a $\frac{5}{16}$" locating pin into control lever bracket.
3. Install 1-2 shift rod into 1-2 shift control lever. Holding lever against lo-cating pin, adjust clevis at lever until clevis pin freely passes through holes in clevis and lever. Tighten jam nut.
4. Install reverse rod into reverse shift control lever. With jam nuts and swivel loose on rod, attach swivel to level. Maintaining reverse lever against locating pin and while holding swivel, run jam nut against swivel until it contacts swivel. Then tighten jam nut against swivel.
5. Install 3-4 rod to 3-4 transmission level. With jam nuts and swivel loose on 3-4 rod, attach swivel to lever. Holding 3-4 control level against locating pin and while holding swivel, tighten jam nut against swivel.
6. Remove locating pin and check shifts to insure proper operation. Readjust clevis and swivel if necessary.

1972 AUTO. TRANS. LINKAGE, ADJUST

The 1972 linkages are basically the same as those used in 1971 and the adjustment procedures are covered in the front of this manual.

However, for 1972 Chevrolet models with Turbo Hydra-Matic, the detent cable adjustment is changed and is accomplished as follows:
1. Install detent cable through lower opening of accelerator lever.
2. Position retainer "A" on cable and install in hole in lever.
3. Position retainer "B" on cable to the dimension shown in view B, Fig. 7.
4. With accelerator cable connected at carburetor and accelerator pedal lever, fully depress accelerator pedal to automatically adjust retainer.

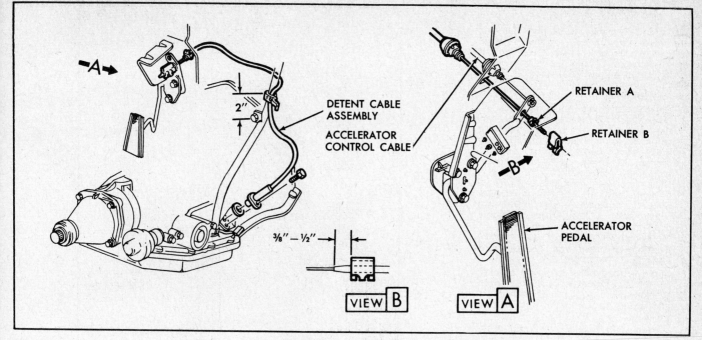

Fig. 7   Detent cable adjustment. 1972 Chevrolet with T. H. 350

Rear Axle, Propeller Shaft & Brakes

REAR AXLE

Figs. 1 and 2 illustrate the rear axle assemblies used. When necessary to overhaul any of these units, refer to the *Rear Axle Specifications* table in this chapter.

1966-72 Corvette

In this axle, the drive pinion is mounted in two tapered roller bearings that are preloaded by a spacer. The pinion is positioned by a shim located between the head of the drive pinion and the rear pinion bearing. The front bearing is held in place by a large washer and a locking pinion nut.

The differential is supported in the carrier by two tapered roller side bearings.

The differential side bearings are preloaded by shims between the bearings and carrier housing, Fig. 2. The differential assembly is positioned for proper ring gear and pinion backlash by varying the position and thickness of these shims.

The ring gear is bolted to the case. The case houses two side gears in mesh with two pinions mounted on a pinion shaft which is held in place by a lock screw. The side gears are backed by thrust washers.

The differential side gears drive two splined yokes which are retained by snap rings located on the yoke splined end. The yokes are supported on caged needle bearings pressed into the carrier, adjacent to the differential bearings. A lip seal, pressed into the carrier outboard of the bearing, prevents oil leakage and dirt entry.

On 1966-69 models, Positraction type differential is optional. Positraction is standard on 1970-72 units.

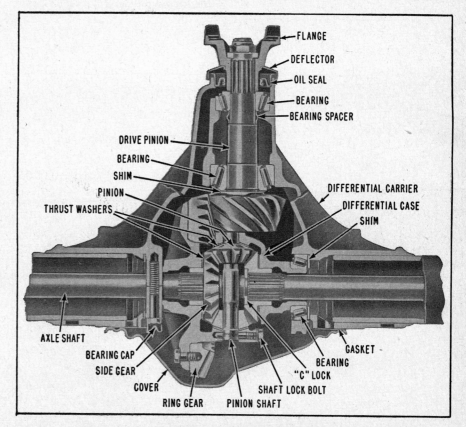

Fig. 1   Rear axle. 1967-72 Camaro, 1966-72 Chevrolet, 1966-72 Chevelle and Chevy II

Remove & Replace

It is not necessary to remove the rear axle assembly for any normal repairs. The axle shafts and carrier assembly can easily be removed from the vehicle, leaving the rear axle housing in place.

Corvette 1966-72

1. Disconnect spring and spring links.
2. Disconnect axle drive shafts at carrier by removing U-bolts securing trunnion to side gear yoke, Fig. 2.
3. Disconnect carrier front support bracket at frame crossmember. Remove bolts and bracket.
4. Disconnect propeller shaft at transmission and at companion flange. Slide transmission yoke forward into transmission. Drop propeller shaft down and out toward the rear.
5. Mark camber cam and bolt relative location on strut rod bracket and loosen cam bolts, Fig. 3.
6. Remove four bolts securing bracket to carrier lower surface and drop bracket. Remove camber cam bolts and swing strut rods up and out of the way.
7. Loosen carrier-to-cover bolts gradually to allow grease to drain out.
8. With mounting bolts removed, pull carrier partially out of cover, drop nose to clear crossmember and gradually work carrier down and out.

CAUTION: *When removing carrier, use care so as not to scrape or gouge gasket mounting surface on cover with ring gear. A deep scratch or gouge at this point may cause a lubricant leak after assembly.*

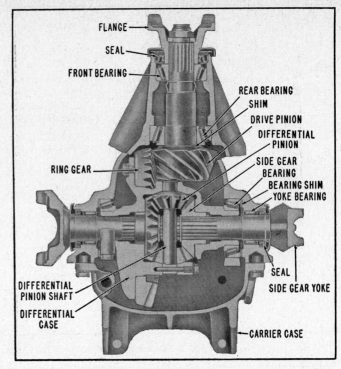

Fig. 2   Rear axle. 1966-72 Corvette

9. Reverse removal procedure to install carrier, *being sure to move the camber cams to marked location before tightening nuts.*

REAR AXLE

1967-72 Camaro, 1966-72 Chevrolet, Chevelle & Chevy II

In these rear axles, Fig. 1, the rear axle housing and differential carrier are cast into an integral assembly. The drive pinion assembly is mounted in two opposed tapered roller bearings. The pinion bearings are preloaded by a spacer behind the front bearing. The pinion is positioned by a washer between the head of the pinion and the rear bearing.

The differential is supported in the carrier by two tapered roller side bearings. These bearings are preloaded by spacers located between the bearings and carrier housing. The differential assembly is positioned for proper ring gear and pinion backlash by varying these spacers. The differential case houses two side gears in mesh with two pinions mounted on a pinion shaft which is held in place by a lock pin. The side gears and pinions are backed by thrust washers.

Remove & Replace

Construction of the axle assembly is such that service operations may be performed with the housing installed in the vehicle or with the housing removed and installed in a holding fixture. The following procedure is necessary only when the housing requires replacement.

1. Raise vehicle and place stand jacks under frame side rails.
2. Remove rear wheels.
3. Support rear axle assembly with a

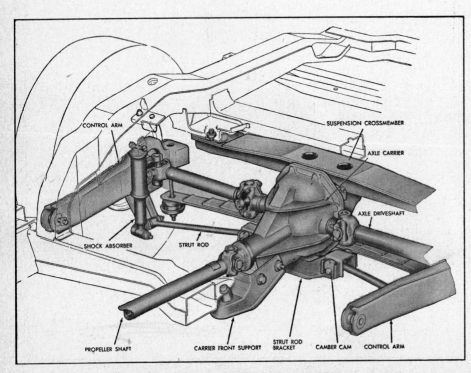

Fig. 3   Rear suspension. 1966-72 Corvette

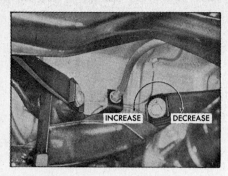

Fig. 4   Rear universal joint angle adjusting cams. Chevelle

suitable jack so that tension is relieved in springs and tie rod.

4. Disconnect tie rod at axle housing bracket.
5. Remove trunnion bearing "U" bolts from rear yoke, split universals joint, position propeller shaft to one side and tie it to frame side rail.
6. Remove axle "U" bolt nuts and allow control arm and shock absorbers to hang freely so that they do not interfere with axle.
7. Disconnect hydraulic brake hose at connector on axle housing.
8. Remove brake drum and disconnect parking brake cable at lever and at flange plate.
9. Lower axle and remove from vehicle.
10. Reverse foregoing procedure to install axle assembly.

AXLE SHAFT
1967-70 Camaro, 1966-70 Chevrolet, Chevelle & Chevy II

1. Raise vehicle and remove wheel and brake drum.

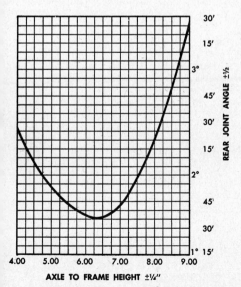

Fig. 6   Rear universal joint angle curve. Chevelle

2. Drain lube from carrier and remove cover.
3. Remove differential pinion shaft lock screw and remove differential pinion shaft.
4. Pull flanged end of axle shaft toward center of vehicle and remove "C" lock from button end of shaft.
5. Remove axle shaft from housing, being careful not to damage seal.
6. Reverse foregoing procedure to install the axle shaft.

Corvette 1966-72

1. Disconnect inboard drive shaft trunnion from side gear yoke, Fig. 3.
2. Remove four bolts securing shaft flange to spindle drive flange.
3. Pry drive shaft out of outboard drive flange pilot and remove by withdrawing outboard end first.
4. If necessary, overhaul universal joints as described in the *Universal Joint* chapter.
5. Install axle shaft in reverse order of removal, *being certain to rotate yokes so that trunnion seats are phased 90 degrees apart.* Torque drive flange bolts to 70-90 ft-lbs and U-bolt nuts to 14-18 ft-lbs.

PROPELLER SHAFT
1966-72

These models use a one-piece propeller shaft. Powerglide models use a propeller shaft tube which incorporates rubber insulators for quieter operation. These insulators, which are bonded to the smaller tube, press fit to the larger tube.

BRAKE ADJUSTMENTS
1966-72 Self Adjusting Brakes

These brakes, Fig. 7, have self-adjusting shoe mechanisms that assure correct lining-to-drum clearances at all times. The automatic adjusters operate only when the brakes are applied as the car is moving rearward or when the car comes to an uphill stop.

Although the brakes are self-adjusting, an initial adjustment is necessary after the brake shoes have been relined or replaced, or when the length of the adjusting screw has been changed during some other service operation.

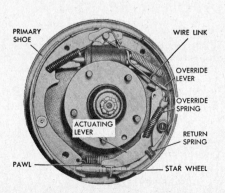

Fig. 7   Left front brake. 1966-72

Fig. 5   Measuring pinion angle with bubble protractor

Frequent usage of an automatic transmission forward range to halt reverse vehicle motion may prevent to automatic adjusters from functioning, thereby inducing low pedal heights. Should low pedal heights be encountered, it is recommended that numerous forward and reverse stops be made until satisfactory pedal height is obtained.

NOTE

If a low pedal condition cannot be corrected by making numerous reverse stops (provided the hydraulic system is free of air) it indicates that the self-adjusting mechanism is not functioning. Therefore it will be necessary to remove the brake drum, clean, free up and lubricate the adjusting mechanism. Then adjust the brakes, being sure the parking brake is fully released.

Adjustment

A lanced "knock out" area, Fig. 8, is provided in the web of the brake drum for servicing purposes in the event retracting of the brake shoes is required in order to remove the drum.

1. With brake drum off, disengage the actuator from the star wheel and rotate the star wheel by spinning or turning with a screwdriver.
2. Using the brake drum as an adjustment fixture, turn the star wheel until the drum slides over the brake shoes with a slide drag.
3. Turn the star wheel 1¼ turns to retract the brake shoes. This will allow sufficient lining-to-drum clear-

Fig. 8   Brake drum access hole

Fig. 9   Aligning drum tang with wheel hub. 1966-72

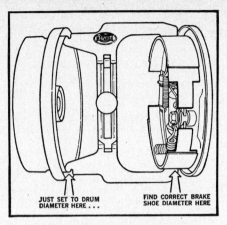

Fig. 10   Use of Drum-to-Brake Shoe Clearance Gauge (J-21177)

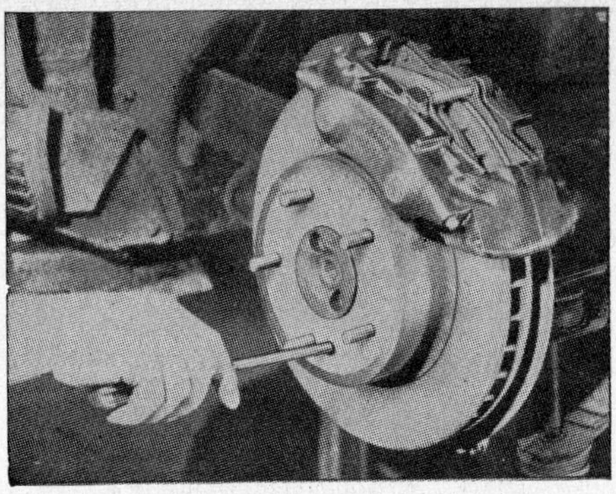

JUST SET TO DRUM DIAMETER HERE . . .

FIND CORRECT BRAKE SHOE DIAMETER HERE

Fig. 11   Adjusting parking brake shoes. 1966-72 Corvette

ance so final adjustment may be made.

4. Install drum and wheel.

NOTE: *If lanced area in brake drum was knocked out, be sure all metal has been removed from brake compartment. Install new hole cover in drum to prebent contamination of brakes. Make certain that drums are installed in the same position as when removed with the drum locating tang in line with the locating hole in the wheel hub, Fig. 9.*

5. Make final adjustment by driving and stopping in forward and reverse until satisfactory pedal height is obtained.

NOTE: *The recommended method of adjusting the brakes is by using the Drum-to-Brake Shoe Clearance Guage shown in Fig. 10 to check the diameter of the brake drum inner surface. Turn the tool to the opposite side and fit over the brake shoes by turning the star wheel until the gauge just slides over the linings. Rotate the gauge around the brake shoe lining surface to assure proper clearance.*

PARKING BRAKE, ADJUST

1966-72 Except Corvette

1. Jack up both rear wheels.
2. Apply parking brake two notches from fully released position.
3. Loosen equalizer forward check nut and tighten rear nut until a light to moderate drag is felt when rear wheels are rotated.
4. Tighten check nuts securely.
5. Fully release parking brake and rotate rear wheels; no drag should be present.

1966-72 Corvette

1. With car on lift or jack stands, remove wheel. (On optional knock-off wheels, the adapter bracket must be removed to gain access to the hole in the hat section of the disc.)
2. Turn disc until the adjusting screw can be seen through hole in disc.
3. Insert a screwdriver through hole in disc and tighen adjusting screw by moving your hand away from the floor on both the left and right sides, Fig. 11.
4. Tighten until disc will not move, then back off ten notches.
5. Apply emergency brake four notches from inside of car.
6. Tighten brake cables at equalizer to produce a light drag with wheels mounted.
7. Fully released parking brake handle and rotate rear wheels. No drag should be evident with handle released.

MASTER CYLINDER, REPLACE

1966-72

Disconnect hydraulic lines from master cylinder. Unfasten and remove cylinder from its mounting.

POWER BRAKE UNIT

1966-72

1. Remove vacuum hose from vacuum check valve.
2. Disconnect hydraulic line at main cylinder.
3. On 1968-72 Chevelle with standard transmission, remove main cylinder from power unit and from inside vehicle remove nuts holding unit to firewall. Push brake pedal to floor. There is now enough clearance to remove the pivot pin.
4. On all other models, disconnect push rod at brake pedal and unfasten and remove power unit.

1966-72 CORVETTE REAR WHEEL ALIGNMENT

Rear wheel camber and toe-out should be inspected and corrected if rear tires show unusual wear.

Camber, Adjust

Wheel camber is obtained by adjusting the eccentric cam and bolt assembly located at the inboard mounting of the strut rod (see Fig. 2). Place rear wheels on alignment machine and determine camber angle.

To adjust, loosen cam bolt nut and rotate cam and bolt assembly until the camber angle is minus $1/3$ degree (plus or minus $1/2$ degree). Tighten nut securely and torque to 55-70 ft-bls.

Toe-Out, Adjust

Rear wheel toe-out is adjusted by inserting slotted shims of varying thickness inside the frame side member on both sides of the torque control arm pivot bushing. Shims are available in thicknesses of $1/32''$, $1/8''$ and $1/4''$.

To adjust, loosen torque arm pivot bolts until shims are free enough to remove. Position torque arm assembly to obtain toe-out of $1/32''$ to $3/32''$ per wheel. Shim gap toward vehicle centerline between end of control arm bushing and frame side inner wall.

Front End and Steering Section

FRONT SUSPENSION

All front suspension systems are basically similar, being of the S.L.A. (short-long arm) type with independent coil springs. In Camaro, Chevrolet, Chevelle, Chevy II (1968-72) and Corvette the springs ride on the lower control arms. In the Chevy II (to 1967) the springs ride on the upper control arms. Ball joints connect the upper and lower control arms to the steering knuckles. See Figs. 1, 2 and 3.

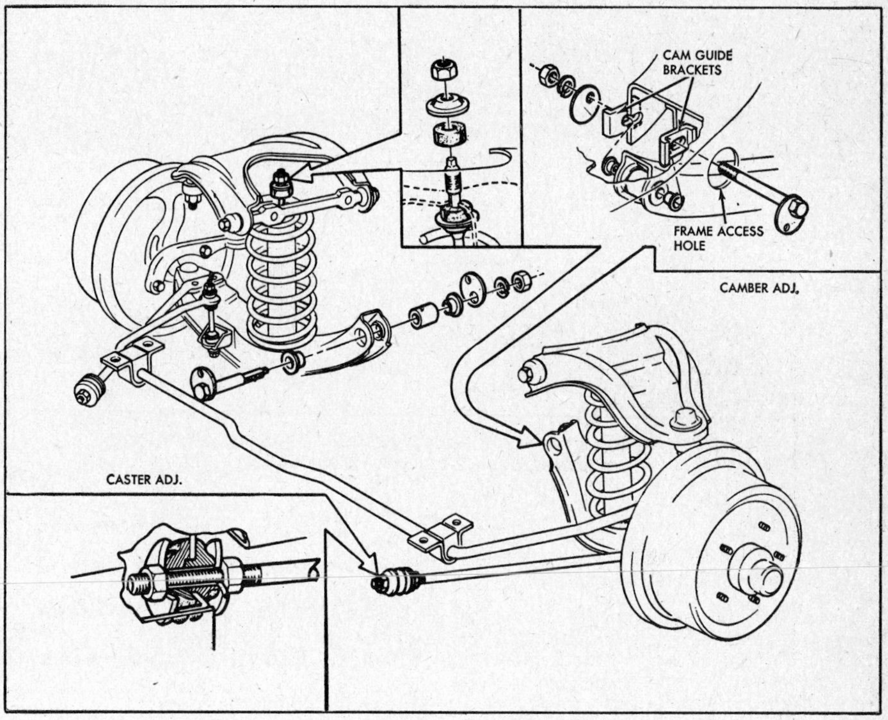

LUBRICATION

IMPORTANT

On models that have a recommended chassis lubrication period of 6000 miles, the car should be warmed up before lubricating the front suspension ball joints. If the car has been outdoors in extreme cold weather it should be allowed to warm up to at least 10°F. above zero before this job is started. Inadequate ball joint lubrication or seal damage can result should the job be done while the parts are at lower temperatures.

Fig. 1   Front suspension. 1966-72 Chevrolet

WHEEL ALIGNMENT

NOTE: Before adjusting caster and camber angles after complaint of excessive tire wear or poor handling, the front bumper should be raised and quickly released to allow car to return to its normal height.

1966-72 Chevrolet & 1966-67 Chevy II

The caster angle is adjusted by turning the two nuts at the front of the lower control arm strut rod, Fig. 1. Shortening this rod will increase caster, lengthening it will decrease caster.

Camber angle is adjusted by loosening the lower control arm pivot bolt and rotating the cam located on the pivot, Fig. 1. This eccentric cam action will move the lower control arm in or out, thereby varying camber.

1968-72 Chevy II
1967-72 Camaro
1966-72 Chevelle
1966-72 Corvette

Caster and camber adjustments are made by means of shims between the upper control arm inner support shaft and the support bracket attached to the frame. Shims may be added, subtracted or transferred to change the readings as follows:

Caster, Adjust

Transfer shims from front to rear or rear to front. The transfer of one shim to the front bolt from the rear bolt will decrease positive caster. On shim (1/32") transferred from the rear bolt to the front bolt will change caster about 1/2 degree.

Camber, Adjust

Change shims at both the front and rear of the shaft. Adding an equal number of shims at both front and rear of the support shaft will decrease positive camber. One shim (1/32") at each location will move camber approximately 1/5 degree on Camaro, Chevelle and Chevy II; on Chevrolet and Corvette the change will be about 1/6 degree.

Fig. 2   Front suspension. 1966-67 Chevy II

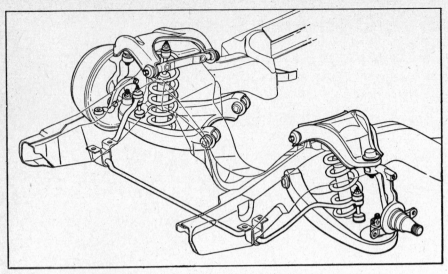

Fig. 3 Front suspension. 1968-72 Chevy II, 1967-72 Camaro, 1966-72 Chevelle. Typical of 1966-72 Corvette

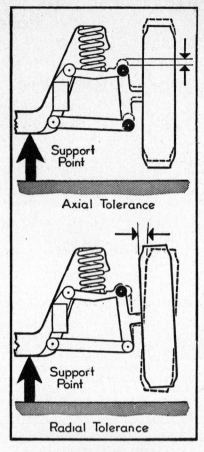

Fig. 4 Checking ball joints for wear. 1966-67 Chevy II

TOE-IN, ADJUST

Toe-in can be adjusted by loosening the clamp bolts at each end of each tie rod and turning each tie rod to increase or decrease its length as necessary until proper toe-in is secured and the steering gear is on the high point for straight-ahead driving.

WHEEL BEARINGS, ADJUST

1966-72

1. While rotating wheel, tighten spindle nut to 12 ft-lbs torque.
2. Back off adjusting nut one flat and insert cotter pin. If slot and pin hole do not line up, back off adjusting nut an additional 1/2 flat or less as required to insert cotter pin.
3. Spin wheel to see that it turns freely, then spread cotter pin.
4. Bearings should have zero preload and .001 to .008" end movement when properly adjusted.

WHEEL BEARINGS, REPLACE

Disc Brakes

1. Raise car and remove front wheels.
2. Remove bolts holding brake caliper to its mounting and insert a fabricated block (1 1/16 x 1 1/16 x 2 inches in length) between the brake pads as the caliper is being removed. Once removed, the caliper can be wired or secured in some manner away from the disc.
3. Remove spindle nut and hub and disc assembly. Grease retainer and inner wheel bearing can now be removed.

CHECKING BALL JOINTS FOR WEAR

1966-72 Except 1966-67 Chevy II

Upper Ball Joint

The upper ball joint is checked for wear by checking the torque required to rotate the ball stud in the assembly. To make this type of check it will be necessary to remove the stud from the steering knuckle.

Install a nut on the ball stud and measure the torque required to turn the stud in the assembly with a torque wrench. Specified torque for a new ball joint is 3 to 10 ft-lbs. If torque readings are excessively high or low, replace the ball joint. If excessive wear is indicated in the upper ball joint, both upper and lower ball joints should be replaced.

Lower Ball Joint

Raise car and support lower control arm so spring is compressed in the same manner as if the wheels were on the ground and check axial (up and down) play at ball joint. If play exceeds 1/16", replace the joint.

Another indication of lower ball joint excessive wear is when difficulty is experienced when lubricating the joint. If the liner has worn to the point where the lubrication grooves in the liner have been worn away, then abnormal pressure is required to force lubricant through the joint. Should this condition be evident, replace both lower ball joints.

Chevy II, 1966-67

With front wheel bearings properly adjusted and control arms tight, refer to Fig. 4 and raise wheel with a jack under the frame as shown. Then test by moving the wheel up and down to check axial play, and rocking the wheel at the top and bottom to measure radial play.

1. Lower ball joint should be replaced if there is any noticeable looseness

at this joint.
2. Upper ball joint should be replaced if radial play exceeds .250".
3. Upper ball joint should be replaced if axial play between upper control arm and spindle exceeds .0625".

UPPER BALL JOINT REPLACE

1966-72 Except 1966-67 Chevy II

1. Support weight of vehicle at outer end of lower control arm.
2. Remove wheel assembly.
3. Remove nut from upper ball joint stud.
4. Remove stud from knuckle.
5. Cut off ball rivets with a chisel.
6. Enlarge ball stud attaching holes in control arm (if necessary) to accept the bolts included in the ball joint replacement kit.
7. Install and tighten new ball joint.
8. Reassemble ball joint to steering knuckle.

1966-67 Chevy II

1. With wheels on floor, install spacer support as shown in Fig. 5 between upper control arm and frame side rail. Then raise vehicle.
2. Remove wheel and tire.
3. Disconnect stabilizer link (if so

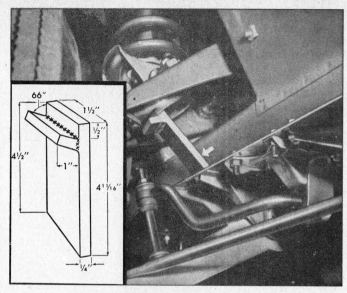

Fig. 5 Chevy II (to 1967 only) upper control arm support installed. Right side control arm support bracket is shown. For left side, angled support should be welded to reverse side of plate

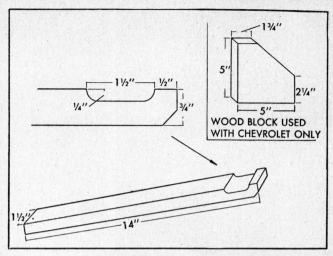

Fig. 6 Spring removal tools. 1966-72 Chevrolet

equipped) and strut rod at lower control arm.

4. Remove nut from upper ball stud.
5. Strike upper part of steering knuckle with a hammer (backing up with another hammer). Drop lower control arm, steering knuckle and brake assembly with an adjustable jack until upper ball joint is easily accessible.
6. Chisel off three ball joint retaining rivet heads.
7. Attach replacement ball joint to control arm, using special bolts furnished with the replacement kit. Torque to 20-25 ft. lbs. *Do not attempt to use any bolts other than those in the kit as they are special hardened bolts.*
8. Raise lower control arm and steering knuckle in position. Insert upper ball stud into knuckle and torque stud nut to 42-47 ft. lbs.
9. Lubricate ball stud and complete the installation. Then check caster and camber.

LOWER BALL JOINT, REPLACE

1966-72 Chevrolet & Corvette

1. Support lower control arm at outer end on floor jack with hoist or jack pad clear of lower ball stud nut and seal.
2. If equipped with disc brakes, remove caliper assembly.
3. Remove upper and lower ball stud nuts, free ball studs from steering knuckle and wire knuckle and brake drum or disc assembly out of the way.
4. Being careful not to enlarge holes in control arm, cut off rivets.

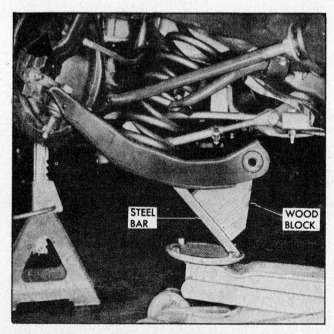

Fig. 7 Removing front spring. 1966-72 Chevrolet

Fig. 8 Removing front spring. 1968-72 Chevy II, 1967-72 Camaro, 1966-72 Chevelle

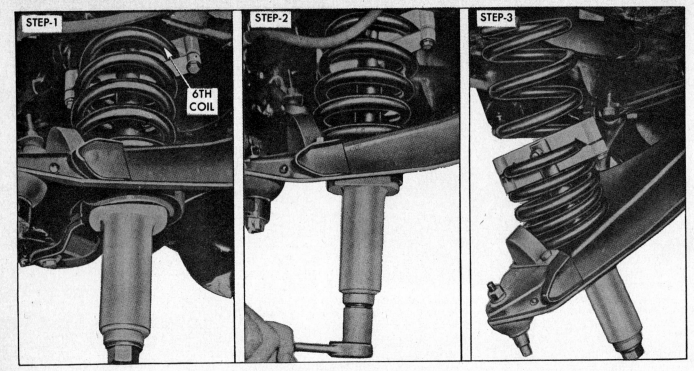

Fig. 9   Removing front spring. 1966-72 Corvette

5. Install new joint against underside of control arm and retain in place with special bolts supplied with replacement ball joint kit. Use only the alloy bolts supplied for this operation. The special thick headed bolt must be installed in the forward side of the control arm.
6. Tighten bolts and nut on ball stud and lubricate joint.

1966-72 Chevelle, Camaro, & 1968-72 Chevy II

1. Support lower control arm at outer end of floor jack with hoist or jack pad clear of lower ball stud and remove wheel. If equipped with disc brakes, remove caliper assembly.
2. Remove upper and lower ball stud nuts, free ball studs from steering knuckle and wire knuckle and brake drum or disc assembly out of the way.
3. Use a screwdriver to pry out seal and retainer. Use a suitable extractor to push out ball joint.
4. Start replacement ball joint into control arm and use a suitable puller tool to pull the ball joint into position. Be sure to position air vent in rubber boot inboard.
5. Install stud into steering knuckle and secure in place.

1966-67 Chevy II

1. With car weight on front wheels, position support between upper control arm and frame side rail, Fig. 5.
2. Raise vehicle and remove nut from ball stud.
3. Disconnect stabilizer at upper link. Break loose lower ball stud and drop lower control arm until lower ball joint is accessible.

4. Cut off rivets from retaining plate.
5. Remove ball joint from arm.
6. Install new ball joint in arm, using special bolts furnished with repair kit.
7. Raise lower control arm and insert ball stud into knuckle. Secure with nut and cotter pin and connect stabilizer.

SHOCK ABSORBER, REPLACE

1966-67 Chevy II

1. With car weight on floor, place support as shown in Fig. 5.
2. Raise car and remove wheel.
3. Disconnect shock absorber lower mounting nuts.
4. Remove shock absorber upper mounting bracket bolts.
5. Lift bracket and shock from car.
6. Reverse above procedure to install.

1966-72 Except 1966-67 Chevy II

1. Hold shock upper stem from turning with a suitable wrench and remove nut and grommet.
2. Unfasten lower shock pivot from lower control arm and pull shock and mounting out through bottom of spring housing.
3. Reverse removal procedure to install. Tighten upper retaining nut until it bottoms on shoulder of stem.

COIL SPRING, REPLACE

1966-67 Chevy II

1. Remove wheel and tire.
2. Support lower control arm with an

adjustable jack and raise slightly from full rebound position.
3. Remove shock absorber.
4. With a suitable spring compressor, compress spring.
5. Remove lower spring seat retaining nuts and lift spring and seat from control arm and guide it down and out through fender skirt.
6. When installing new spring, see that the spring coil ends are against spring stops in upper and lower seats. Locating tab on upper spring seat may be flattened before installing spring.

1966-72 Chevrolet

1. With suitable wrench, hold shock absorber upper stem from turning, then remove retaining nut, retainer and upper grommet.
2. With car supported by the frame so that control arms hang free, remove wheel assembly. Replace one wheel nut to hold brake drum.
3. Remove shock absorber, stabilizer bar-to-lower control arm link, strut rod-to-lower control arm attaching nuts and tie rod end.
4. Install a steel bar (made to the dimensions shown in Fig. 6) through shock absorber mounting hole in lower control arm so that notch seats over bottom spring coil and bar extends inboard and under inner bushing.
5. Fit a 5" wood block, Fig. 7, between bar and bushing.
6. With suitable jack or hoist, lift up slightly on end of bar to remove tension from inner pivot cam bolt, which can then be removed.
7. Lower inner end of lower control arm. Tension on spring will be re-

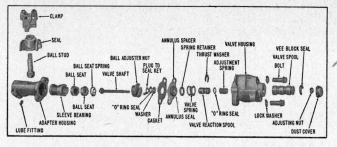

Fig. 10   Power steering control valve and adapter assembly. 1966-72

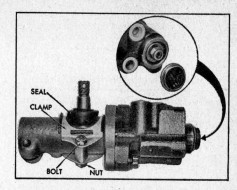

Fig. 11   Power steering control valve ball stud seal replacement. Chevy II 1966-67

moved before spring can be removed from vehicle.

8. Reverse procedure to install and check wheel alignment.

1966-72 Chevelle, Camaro, 1968-72 Chevy II

1. Perform Steps 1, 2 and 3 as outlined for 1966 Chevrolet. However, place the bar, Fig. 8, in the shock absorber mounting hole in the lower control arm so that the notch seats over the bottom spring coil and the bar extends outboard beyond the end of the control arm and slightly toward the front of the car.
2. Remove ball stud from knuckle, using extreme care not to damage the seal.
3. Reverse above procedure to install.

1966-72 Corvette

Remove and install the front spring in the conventional manner and as suggested by Fig. 9. It may be necessary to assist the spring out of its tower with a pry bar.

Disconnect the lower ball joint from the steering knuckle and lower the control arm with the compressed spring. *Immediately* release compression on the spring by backing off the long screw. Release spring and tool and withdraw spring.

CAUTION

The spring force under compression is very great. Exercise every safety precaution when performing this operation to see that individuals and materials subject to damage are removed from the path of the spring when the control arm is being lowered. Also, the compressed spring should be relaxed immediately after lowering the control arm to reduce the time of exposure to the great compressive force.

STEERING GEAR, REPLACE
1968-72 All Models

1. Remove nuts, washers and bolts at steering coupling.
2. Remove pitman arm nut and washer from sector shaft and mark relation of arm position to shaft.
3. Use a suitable puller to remove pitman arm. On Camaro models, use care not to bend or facture brake

pipe when removing steering gear.
4. Unfasten gear from frame and remove assembly.
5. Reverse procedure to install.

1966-67 Camaro, Chevrolet, Chevelle & Corvette

1. Remove steering coupling lower clamp bolt and spread clamp slightly.
2. Remove pitman arm nut. Scribe mark on arm and shaft for assembly and then use a suitable puller to remove arm.
3. On Chevelle only, remove stabilizer bar-to-frame mounting brackets. Remove left front bumper arm-to-frame rear attaching bolt. Mark eccentric washer-to-frame location and loosen front attaching bolt enough to release eccentric washer from notches in arm.
4. While supporting steering gear, remove three gear-to-frame bolts and washers. Then lower assembly down and out of vehicle.

1966-67 Chevy II

1. Remove steering wheel and mast jacket.
2. Remove remaining gear-to-frame mounting bolt and pull gear assembly out of vehicle through engine compartment.

NOTE: It will be necessary to move steering gear towards engine in order to allow the steering shaft to clear front seat cushion.

INTEGRAL POWER STEERING
1968-72 Chevrolet, Camaro, Chevelle, Chevy II

To remove gear assembly, disconnect pressure and return hoses from gear housing and cap both hoses and steering gear outlets to prevent foreign material from entering system, then follow procedure as outlined under *Steering Gear, Replace.*

1967 Camaro, 1966-67 Chevrolet, 1966-67 Chevelle

1. To remove the gear assembly, disconnect pressure and return hoses from gear housing and cap both hoses

and steering gear outlets to prevent foreign material from entering system.
2. Remove steering shaft coupling clamp bolt.
3. Remove pitman arm nut. Scribe a mark on arm and shaft for assembly and use a suitable puller to remove pitman arm.
4. On Chevelle only, remove stabilizer bar-to-frame mounting brackets. Remove left front bumper arm-to-frame rear attaching bolt. Mark eccentric washer-to-frame location and loosen front attaching bolt enough to release eccentric washer from notches in arms.
5. While supporting steering gear, remove gear housing-to-frame bolts, then lower assembly down and out of vehicle.

LINKAGE TYPE POWER STEERING
1966-72

Power steering equipment consists of a recirculating ball type steering gear and linkage to which a hydraulic power mechanism has been added as part of the steering linkage. The hydraulic mechanism furnishes additional power to *assist* the manual operation so that the turning effort at the steering wheel is greatly reduced. The hydraulic mechanism consists of three basic units: a hydraulic pump and reservoir, a control valve, and a power cylinder.

Control Valve, Adjust

1. Disconnect cylinder rod from frame bracket.
2. With car on a hoist, start the engine. One of the following two conditions will exist:
   a. If piston rod remains retracted, turn the adjusting nut clockwise until the rod begins to move out. Then turn the nut counterclockwise until the rod just begins to move in. Now turn the nut clockwise to exactly one half the rotation needed to change the direction of shaft movement.
   b. If the rod extends upon starting the pump, move the nut counterclockwise until the rod begins to retract, then clockwise until the rod begins to move out again. Now

turn the rod to exactly one half the rotation needed to change the direction of shaft movement.

Do not turn the nut back and forth more than is absolutely necessary to balance the valve.

3. Restart engine. Front wheels should not turn from center if valve has been properly balanced.

Power Cylinder Repairs

Removal

1. Disconnect two hydraulic lines at power cylinder.
2. Unfasten power cylinder rod from brace at frame.
3. Unfasten power cylinder from relay rod bracket.
4. Remove power cylinder from car.

Inspection

1. Inspect seals for leaks around cylinder rod and if leaks are present, replace seals as follows:
2. Use a hook tool to remove retaining ring. Remove wiper ring, back-up washer, back-up ring and seal. *Piston rod seal should not be removed unless there are signs of leakage*

along the piston shaft at shaft seal.

3. Examine brass fitting hose connection seats for cracks or damage and replace if necessary.
4. For service other than seat or seal replacement, replace the power cylinder.

Installation

1. Install power cylinder on car by reversing removal procedure.
2. Reconnect two hoses, fill system with fluid and bleed system as outlined below.

Filling & Bleeding System

1. Fill reservoir to proper level with Automatic Transmission Fluid and let fluid remain undisturbed for about two minutes.
2. Raise front wheels off floor.
3. Run engine at idle for two minutes.
4. Increase engine speed to about 1500 rpm.
5. Turn wheels from one extreme to the other, lightly contacting stops.
6. Lower wheels to floor and turn wheels right and left.
7. Recheck for leaks.
8. Check oil level and refill as required. Pump pressure should be 870 lbs.

Control Valve Repairs

Removal, Fig. 10

1. Loosen relay rod-to-control valve clamp.
2. Disconnect hose connections at control valve.
3. Disconnect control valve from pitman arm.
4. Unscrew control valve from relay rod.
5. Remove control valve from car.

Ball Stud Seal, Replace

In servicing the control valve, refer to Fig. 10. To replace the ball stud seal, refer to Fig. 11 and proceed as follows:
1. Remove pitman arm with a suitable puller.
2. Remove clamp by removing nut, bolt and spacer. If crimped type clamp is used, straighten clamp end and pull clamp and seal off end of stud.
3. Install new seal and clamp over stud so lips on seal mate with clamp. (A nut and bolt attachment type clamp replaces the crimped type for service, Fig. 11).
4. Center the ball stud, seal and clamp in opening in adapter housing, then install spacer, bolt and nut.

CHEVROLET CORVAIR

OLD CAR SPECIFICATIONS: For 1946-65 Tune Up and Wheel Alignment Specifications see back of book.

*This material covered only in the "Service Trade Edition" of this manual.

INDEX OF SERVICE OPERATIONS

SERIAL NUMBER LOCATION

1966-67: Left-hand top of frame side rail rearward of battery bolts.

1968-69: Top of instrument panel on left front side.

ENGINE NUMBER LOCATION

1966-68: Top of engine block behind oil pressure sending unit.

1969: Top of engine block forward of oil filter adapter.

ENGINE IDENTIFICATION

Engines are identified in the following table by the code letter
or letters immediately following the engine serial number.

CODE		
RL 6-164 with T/C 1966	RY 6-164 with P/G, A/C, SHPE . 1966-67	QO 6-164 with P/G, A.I.R., A/C . . . 1967
RM 6-164 with M/T, SHPE 1966-67	RZ 6-164 with SHPE, A/C 1966-67	QP 6-164 with HPE, P/G, A.I.R., A/C 1967
RN 6-164 with SHPE, P/G 1966-67	RA 6-164 with M/T and A/T . . . 1966-67	QQ 6-164 with SHPE, A.I.R., A/C . 1967
RQ 6-164 with SHPE, A.I.R. . . . 1966-67	RB 6-164 1966	QR 6-164 with SHPE, A.I.R., A/C, P/G 1967
RR 6-164 with A/C 1966	RD 6-164 with HPE 1966-67	QS 6-164 with HPE, A.I.R., A/C . . 1967
RS 6-164 with M/T, A.I.R. 1966-68	RE 6-164 with A/C 1966-68	AC 6-164 with M/T 1969
RS 6-164 with A.I.R. 1966	RF 6-164 with HPE, A/C 1966-68	AD 6-164 with HPE 1969
RU 6-164 with M/T, HPE, A.I.R. 1966-68	RG 6-164 with P/G 1966-67	AE 6-164 with P/G 1969
RV 6-164 with P/G, A.I.R. 1966-68	RH 6-164 with P/G, HPE 1966-67	AF 6-164 with P/G, HPE 1969
RW 6-164 with HPE, A.I.R., P/G 1966-68	RJ 6-164 with P/G, A/C 1966-68	AG 6-164 with SHPE 1969
RX 6-164 with P/G, HPE, A.I.R. 1966-67	RK 6-164 with P/G, HPE, A/C . 1966-68	AH 6-164 with P/G, HPE 1969

A/C: Air conditioned	HPE: High performance engine	P/G: Powerglide
A.I.R.: Air injection reactor	M/T: Manual transmission	SHPE: Special Hi Perf. engine
A/T: Automatic transmission		T/C: Turbocharged

FRONT VIEW IDENTIFICATION

1966-69

GENERAL ENGINE SPECIFICATIONS

Year	Engine	Car-buretor	Bore and Stroke	Piston Dis-place-ment, Cubic Inches	Com-pres-sion Ratio	Maximum Brake H.P. @ R.P.M.	Maximum Torque Lbs. Ft. @ R.P.M.	Normal Oil Pressure Pounds
1966	95 Horsepower..............6-164	2 One Bar.	3.4375 x 2.94	164	8.25	95 @ 3600	154 @ 2400	40
	110 Horsepower..............6-164	2 One Bar.	3.4375 x 2.94	164	9.25	110 @ 4400	160 @ 2800	40
	140 Horsepower..............6-164	4 One Bar.	3.4375 x 2.94	164	9.25	140 @ 5200	160 @ 3600	40
	Turbocharged 180 H.P..........6-164	1 One Bar.	3.4375 x 2.94	164	8.25	180 @ 4000	265 @ 3200	40
1967–69	95 Horsepower..............6-164	2 One Bar.	3.4375 x 2.94	164	8.25	95 @ 3600	154 @ 2400	40
	110 Horsepower..............6-164	2 One Bar.	3.4375 x 2.94	164	9.25	110 @ 4400	160 @ 2800	40
	140 Horsepower..............6-164	4 One Bar.	3.4375 x 2.94	164	9.25	140 @ 5200	160 @ 3600	40

DISTRIBUTOR SPECIFICATIONS

★Note: If advance is checked on vehicle, double the R.P.M. and degrees advance to get crankshaft figures.

Year	Model	Distributor Part No.①	Rotation ②	Breaker Gap	Dwell Angle Deg.	Breaker Arm Spring Tension	Centrifugal Advance Degrees @ R.P.M. of Distributor★		Vacuum Advance	
							Advance Starts	Full Advance	Inches of Vacuum To Start Plunger	Max. Adv. Dist. Deg. @ Vacuum
1966–67	95 H.P.-Std. Tr.	1110310	C	③	31–34	19–23	1 @ 450	14 @ 2100	5 to 7	12 @ 15
	95 H.P.-Auto. Tr.	1110311	C	③	31–34	19–23	1 @ 975	10 @ 2100	6 to 8	12 @ 15
	110 Horsepower	1110319	C	③	31–34	19–23	1 @ 500	10 @ 2400	6 to 8	12 @ 15
1966	Turbo-Charged	1110329	C	③	31–34	19–23	1 @ 2050	9 @ 2450	None	None
	4 Carb. Eng.	1110330	C	③	31–34	19–23	1 @ 500	9 @ 1400	None	None
1967	95 H.P. With A.I.R.	1110369	C	③	31–34	19–23	0 @ 450	20 @ 2200	7	12 @ 15
	110 H.P. With A.I.R.	1110389	C	③	31–34	19–23	0 @ 450	20 @ 2200	7	12 @ 15
1968	95 H.P.-Std. Tr.	1110434	C	③	31–34	19–23	0 @ 450	14 @ 2100	7	12 @ 15
	95 H.P.-Auto. Tr.	1110311	C	③	31–34	19–23	0 @ 850	10 @ 2100	7	12 @ 15
	110 H.P.-Std. Tr.	1110389	C	③	31–34	19–23	0 @ 450	13 @ 2200	7	12 @ 15
	110 H.P.-Auto. Tr.	1110319	C	③	31–34	19–23	0 @ 400	10 @ 2400	7	12 @ 15
	140 H.P.	1110371	C	③	31–34	19–23	0 @ 450	16 @ 1500	6	11 @ 14
1969	95 H.P.-Std. Tr.	1110452	C	③	31–34	19–23	0 @ 450	14 @ 2100	7	12 @ 16
	95 H.P.-Auto. Tr.	1110453	C	③	31–34	19–23	0 @ 850	10 @ 2100	7	12 @ 16
	110 H.P.-Std. Tr.	1110454	C	③	31–34	19–23	0 @ 450	13 @ 2200	7	12 @ 16
	110 H.P.-Auto. Tr.	1110455	C	③	31–34	19–23	0 @ 400	10 @ 2400	7	12 @ 16
	140 H.P.	1110454	C	③	31–34	19–23	0 @ 450	13 @ 2200	7	12 @ 16

①—Stamped on distributor housing plate.　②—As viewed from above.　③—New points .019″, used .016″.

TUNE UP SPECIFICATIONS

OLD CAR SPECIFICATIONS: For 1946–65 Tune Up Specifications see back of book.

★Because of the difference in rate of expansion between aluminum head and steel spark plug it is advisable to allow engine to cool before removing plugs.

●When using a timing light, disconnect vacuum hose at distributor and plug opening in hose so idle speed will not be affected.

| Year | Model | Spark Plug ★ | | Distributor | | Firing Order | Ignition Timing ● | | Hot Idle Speed | | Comp. Press. Lbs. ③ | Fuel Pump Press. Lbs. |
		Type AC	Gap Inch	Point Gap Inch	Dwell Angle Deg.		BTDC ①	Mark	Std. Trans.	Auto. Trans. ②		
1966	95 H.P. Std. Trans.	46FF	.035	④	31–34	Fig. D	6°	Fig. B	475⑥	—	130	4–5
	95 H.P. Std. Trans.⑨	46FF	.035	④	31–34	Fig. D	6°	Fig. B	700⑥	—	130	4–5
	95 H.P. Auto. Tr.	46FF	.035	④	31–34	Fig. D	14°	Fig. B	—	475D⑥	130	4–5
	95 H.P. Auto. Tr.⑨	46FF	.035	④	31–34	Fig. D	14°	Fig. B	—	600D⑥	130	4–5
	110 H.P. Std. Tr.	44FF	.030	④	31–34	Fig. D	14°⑦	Fig. B	625⑥	—	130	4–5
	110 H.P. Std. Tr.⑨	44FF	.030	④	31–34	Fig. D	14°⑦	Fig. B	700⑥	—	130	4–5
	110 H.P. Auto. Tr.	44FF	.030	④	31–34	Fig. D	14°⑦	Fig. B	—	475D⑥	130	4–5
	110 H.P. Auto. Tr.⑨	44FF	.030	④	31–34	Fig. D	14°⑦	Fig. B	—	600D⑥	130	4–5
	140 H.P. Std. Tr.	44FF	.030	④	31–34	Fig. D	18°⑧	Fig. B	625⑥	—	130	4–5
	140 H.P. Std. Tr.⑨	44FF	.030	④	31–34	Fig. D	18°⑧	Fig. B	700⑥	—	130	4–5
	140 H.P. Auto. Tr.	44FF	.030	④	31–34	Fig. D	18°⑧	Fig. B	—	475D⑥	130	4–5
	140 H.P. Auto. Tr.⑨	44FF	.030	④	31–34	Fig. D	18°⑧	Fig. B	—	600D⑥	130	4–5
	Turbocharged Eng.	44FF	.030	④	31–34	Fig. D	24°	Fig. A	825⑥	—	130	4–5
1967	95 H.P. Std. Tr.	46FF	.035	④	31–34	Fig. D	6°	Fig. B	500⑥	—	130	3½–5
	95 H.P. Auto. Tr.	46FF	.035	④	31–34	Fig. D	14°	Fig. B	—	500D⑥	130	3½–5
	95 H.P.⑨	44FF	.035	④	31–34	Fig. D	TDC	Fig. B	700⑥	500D⑥	130	3½–5
	110 H.P.	44FF	.030	④	31–34	Fig. D	14°	Fig. B	650⑥	500D⑥	130	3½–5
	110 H.P. with P/G, A/C	44FF	.030	④	31–34	Fig. D	24°	Fig. B	—	500D⑥	130	3½–5
	110 H.P.⑨	44FF	.030	④	31–34	Fig. D	4°	Fig. B	700⑥	600D⑥	130	3½–5
1968	95 H.P.	46FF	.035	④	31–34	Fig. D	⑩	Fig. B	700⑥	600D⑥	130	5½–6¾
	110 H.P.	44FF	.030	④	31–34	Fig. D	⑪	Fig. B	700⑥	600D⑥	130	5½–6¾
	140 H.P.	44FF	.030	④	31–34	Fig. D	4°	Fig. B	650⑥	550D⑥	130	5½–6¾
1969	95 H.P. Std. Tr.	R44FF	.035	④	31–34	Fig. D	6°	Fig. B	700	—	130	5½–6¾
	95 H.P. Auto. Tr.	R44FF	.035	④	31–34	Fig. D	14°	Fig. B	—	600D	130	5½–6¾
	110 H.P. Std. Tr.	R44FF	.035	④	31–34	Fig. D	4°	Fig. B	700	—	130	5½–6¾
	110 H.P. Auto. Tr.	R44FF	.035	④	31–34	Fig. D	12°	Fig. B	—	600D	130	5½–6¾
	140 H.P.	R44FF	.035	④	31–34	Fig. D	4°	Fig. B	650	550D	130	5½–6¾

① —BTDC-Before top dead center.
② —D-Drive
③ —Plus or minus 20 lbs.
④ —New points .019″, used .016″.
⑥ —If air conditioned, turn A/C switch to Full" On" position and add 50 R.P.M. to idle speed listed.
⑦ —1966 with A/C 24°.
⑧ —With head gasket (Part No. 3891552) set at 14°.
⑨ —With A.I.R. system.

⑩ —Manual trans. 6°; automatic trans. 14°.
⑪ —Manual trans. 4°; automatic trans. 12°.

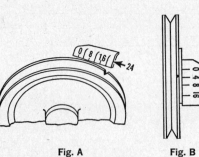

Fig. A

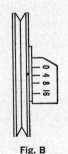

Fig. B

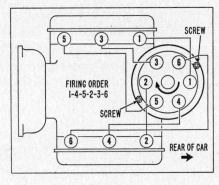

FIRING ORDER 1-4-5-2-3-6

SCREW

SCREW

REAR OF CAR

Fig. D

PISTONS, PINS, RINGS, CRANKSHAFT & BEARINGS

Year	Model	Piston Clearance	Ring End Gap① Minimum		Wrist-pin Diameter	Rod Bearings		Main Bearings			
			Comp.	Oil		Shaft Diameter	Bearing Clearance	Shaft Diameter	Bearing Clearance	Thrust on Bearing No.	Shaft End Play
1966–67	All	.0011–.0017②	.013	.015	.8001	1.799–1.800	.003 Max.	③	.003 Max.	1	.002–.006
1968	All	.0011–.0017②	.010	.015	.8001	1.799–1.800	.0007–.0028	④	.003 Max.	1	.002–.007
1969	All	.0011–.0017②	.013	.015	.8001	1.799–1.800	.0004–.0025	③	.003 Max.	1	.002–.006

①—Oversize rings not furnished.   New rings should be fitted to tightest part of cylinder if cylinder is tapered.
②—Cylinder and piston must be replaced as a unit if bore is worn or tapered in excess of .005".
③—No. 1 and 2: 2.0978–2.0988.   No. 3 and 4: 2.0983–2.0993.
④—No. 2: 2.0991, all others 2.0996.

REAR AXLE & BRAKE SPECIFICATIONS

Year	Model	Carrier Type	Diff. Bear. Preload		Ring Gear & Pinion Backlash		Pinion Bear. Preload		Brake Drum Dia.	Brake Cyl. Bore Diameter		
			Method	Adjust.	Method	Adjust.	Method	Adjust.		Wheel Cylinders		Master Cylinder
										Front	Rear	
1966–69	All	Integral	①	②	①	.005–.008	①	③	9½	⅞	15/16	1

①—Threaded adjuster.
②—2 to 3 notches tight.
③—New bearings 5–10 inch-lbs.

ENGINE TIGHTENING SPECIFICATIONS★

★Torque specifications are for clean and lightly lubricated threads only. Dry or dirty threads produce increased friction which prevents accurate measurement of tightness.

Year	Spark Plugs Ft. Lbs.	Cylinder Head Bolts Ft. Lbs.	Exhaust Manifold Ft. Lbs.	Rocker Arm Stud Nut Ft. Lbs.	Rocker Arm Stud Ft. Lbs.	Rocker Arm Cover Ft. Lbs.	Connecting Rod Cap Bolts Ft. Lbs.	Crankcase Bolts Ft. Lbs.	Flywheel to Crankshaft Ft. Lbs.	Vibration Damper or Pulley Ft. Lbs.
1966–69	20	40	25	100①	40	50①	25	55	45	45

①—Inch lbs.

ALTERNATOR & REGULATOR SPECIFICATIONS

| Year | Alternator | | | | | Regulator | | | | | | |
| | | | | Output @ 14 Volts | | | Field Relay | | | Voltage Regulator | | |
	Model	Rated Hot Output Amps.	Field Current 12 Volts @ 80° F.	2000 R.P.M. Amps.	5000 R.P.M. Amps.	Model	Air Gap In.	Point Gap In.	Closing Voltage	Air Gap In.	Point Gap In.	Voltage @ 125° F.
1966-69	1100639	37	2.2-2.6	25	35	1119515	.015	.030	1.5-3.2	.067	.014	13.5-14.4
	1100698	47	2.8-3.2	31	45	1119515	.015	.030	1.5-3.2	.067	.014	13.5-14.4

STARTER MOTOR SPECIFICATIONS

| Year | Model | Part No. | Brush Spring, Tension, Ounces | No Load Test | | | Resistance Test③ | |
				Amperes	Volts	R.P.M.	Amperes	Volts
1966	Standard Trans.	1108306	35①	58-80②	10.6	6750-10500	280-320	4
	Automatic Trans.	1108307	35①	58-80②	10.6	6750-10500	280-320	4
1967-69	Standard Trans.	1108317	35	58-80②	10.6	6750-10500	280-320	4
	Automatic Trans.	1108318	35	58-80②	10.6	6750-10500	280-320	4

①—Minimum. ②—Includes solenoid.
③—Check capacity of motor by using a 500 ampere meter and a carbon pile rheostat to control voltage. Apply volts listed across motor with armature locked. Current should be as listed.

VALVE SPECIFICATIONS

| Year | Engine Model | Valve Lash | Valve Seat Angle | Valve Face Angle | Valve Spring Installed Height | Valve Spring Pressure Lbs. @ In. | Valve Stem Clearance | | Valve Stem Diameter | |
							Intake	Exhaust	Intake	Exhaust
1966-67	Turbo-Charged	1 Turn①	44	44	1²¹⁄₃₂②	175 @ 1.26②	.001-.0027	.0014-.0029	.3414-.3422	.3407-.3418
	All Others	1 Turn①	44	44	1²¹⁄₃₂②	175 @ 1.26②	.001-.0027	.0014-.0029	.3414-.3422	.3707-.3418
1968	All	1 Turn①	45	44	1.66②	175 @ 1.26②	.001-.0027	.0014-.0035	.3414-.3422	.3407-.3418
1969	All	1 Turn①	46	45	1²¹⁄₃₂②	175 @ 1.26②	.001-.0028	.0014-.0029	.3414-.3422	.3407-.3418

①—Tighten adjusting screw until all clearance between valve stem and rocker arm has been eliminated. Then tighten screw the additional number of turns listed to center the lifter plunger. See details under "Valves, Adjust" in text.
②—Outer spring.

CAPACITY DATA

| Year | Model | Fuel Tank Gallons | Engine Oil | | | 3 Speed Trans. Pints | 4 Speed Trans. Pints | Powerglide, Quarts③ | Differential, Pints |
			Refill, Qts. ①	Summer Grade	Winter Grade				
1966	All	14	4	30	10W	3.1	3.6	②	4
1967	All	14	4	30	10W	3.7	3.7	②	4
1968	All	14	4	30	10W	3.1	3.5	②	4
1969	All	14	4	30	10W	3.7	3.7	②	2.7

①—Add ½ quart for filter change.   ②—Oil pan 3 qts. Total capacity 6½ qts.   ③—Approximate. Make final check with dipstick.

WHEEL ALIGNMENT SPECIFICATIONS

OLD CAR SPECIFICATIONS: For 1946–65 Wheel Alignment Specifications see back of book.

Year	Model	Front Wheel Alignment			Rear Wheel Alignment			Toe-Out on Turns, Deg.	
		Caster Degrees	Camber Degrees	Toe-In Inch	Caster Degrees	Camber Degrees	Toe-In Inch	Outer Wheel	Inner Wheel
1966	All	+3	+1	¼	—	+1	—	18.4	20
1967–69	All	+1½ to +2¼	+½ to +1½	3/16 to 5/16	—	+½ to +1½	3/16 to 5/16	18.4	20

Electrical Section

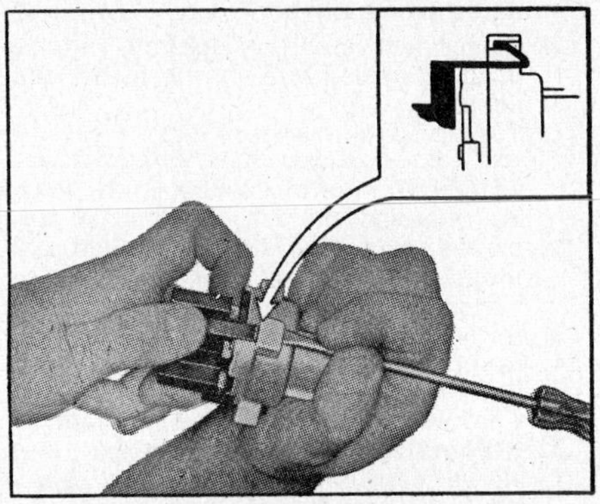

STARTER, REPLACE
1966-69

1. Disconnect battery ground cable.
2. Raise and support car.
3. Observe and record color coding at solenoid connections, then disconnect all wire from solenoid.

NOTE: Reinstall nut as each wire is disconnected as thread size is different and may be mixed and stripped.

4. Unfasten and pull starter forward to clean housing and remove starter.
5. Reverse procedure to install.

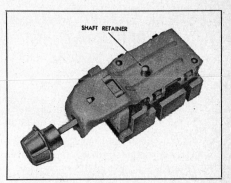

Fig. 2   Light switch shaft retainer

Fig. 1   Unlocking ignition switch connector. 1966-69

IGNITION SWITCH, REPLACE
1966-69

1. Disconnect battery ground cable.

2. Remove lock cylinder by positioning switch in "Off" position.
3. Insert a paper clip in small hole in cylinder face.
4. Push in on wire to depress plunger and continue to turn ignition key counter-clockwise until lock cylinder can be removed.
5. Using a suitable spanner wrench, remove front attaching nut.
6. Pull switch out from under dash and remove wiring connectors.
7. To remove "theft resistant" connector, use a screwdriver to unsnap locking tangs on connector, Fig. 1. Unplug connector.
8. Reverse above procedure to install.

DISTRIBUTOR, REPLACE

To remove distributor, disconnect primary wire from coil. Remove distributor cap and vacuum line from distributor. Mark position of rotor arm on housing so that distributor may be reinstalled in same position. Unfasten and remove distributor from engine.

If necessary to remove secondary leads from distributor cap, mark position on cap tower for lead to No. 1 cylinder.

When installing distributor, turn rotor about ⅛ turn counterclockwise past the mark previously placed on distributor housing. Push distributor down into position in block with housing in normal installed position. It may be necessary to move the rotor slightly to start gear into mesh with camshaft gear but rotor should line up and mark when distributor is down in place. Fasten distributor in place and check ignition timing.

GENERATOR, REPLACE
1966-69 Delcotron

1. Disconnect battery ground cable.
2. Disconnect wiring leads at Delcotron.
3. Remove blower belt.
4. Unfasten and remove Delcotron.

VIEW A

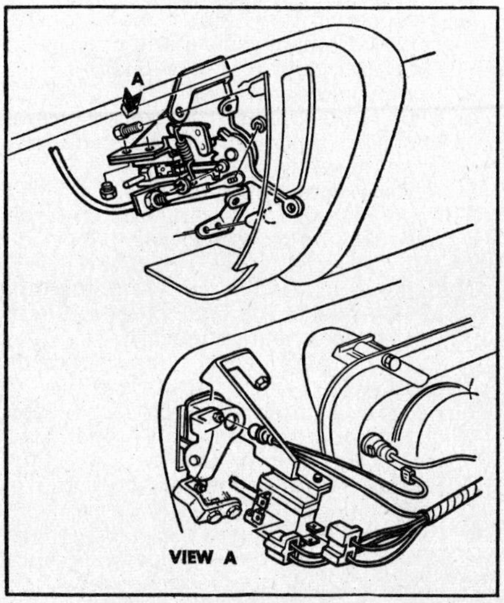

Fig. 3   Neutral safety switch installation. 1966-69

LIGHT SWITCH, REPLACE
1966-69

1. Disconnect battery ground cable.
2. Pull switch knob out to "On" position.
3. Reach under instrument console and depress switch shaft retainer, Fig. 2.
4. With retainer depressed, pull knob and shaft from switch.
5. Disconnect multi-plug connector from switch. A screwdriver may be inserted in side of switch to pry plug from switch.
6. Reverse above procedure to install.

STOP LIGHT SWITCH, REPLACE

1966-69

1. Disconnect two connectors from switch terminals, located under instrument panel adjacent to brake pedal.
2. Remove lock nut from plunger end of switch and remove switch from bracket or brace.
3. Remove second lock nut from switch and install on new switch.
4. Position switch on bracket or brace and install remaining lock nut.
5. Install two electrical connectors.
6. Check operation of switch and adjust as required. Electrical contact should be made when brake pedal is depressed $\frac{3}{8}$" to $\frac{1}{2}$" from fully released position.

NEUTRAL SAFETY SWITCH, REPLACE

1966-69, Fig. 3

1. Disconnect battery ground cable.
2. Remove instrument cluster.
3. Remove retaining ring securing switch lever arm to range selector.
4. Unfasten switch from range selector (2 screws).
5. Lower switch and disconnect wiring harness connectors from switch terminals.
6. Install wiring harness connectors onto new switch.
7. Extend switch plunger to its outer most position and insert gauge block (.68") in switch case.
8. Position switch plunger pin to range selector and loosely install attaching screws.
9. Install retainer securing plunger pin to range selector.
10. Place transmission range selector in "N".
11. Push forward on switch case until contact carrier is against gauge block.
12. Tighten switch screws and remove gauge block.
13. Test operation of switch. Engine must start in "N" position only. Check operation of back-up lamps (if used).

TURN SIGNAL SWITCH, REPLACE

1966, Fig. 4

STANDARD MODELS

1. Disconnect battery ground cable.
2. Remove steering wheel.
3. Disconnect signal wiring at harness connector.
4. Remove steering column mast jacket upper support clamp.
5. Remove signal lever and three screws attaching control to retaining plate.
6. Remove retaining plate and signal housing from steering column, and disengage wiring from housing.
7. Reverse above procedure to install.

CAUTION: Turn signal control assembly

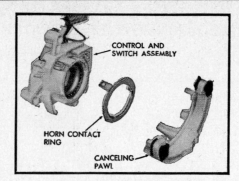

Fig. 4 Turn signal control. 1966

must be in neutral position when assembling steering wheel to prevent damage to cancelling cam and control assembly.

TELESCOPING WHEEL

1. Disconnect battery ground cable.
2. Remove steering wheel and hub.
3. Remove spring and cancelling cam from steering shaft.
4. Remove turn signal lever.
5. Unfasten signal control from retaining plate (3 screws).
6. Remove wiring clamp and cover from signal wiring harness.
7. Remove wire terminals from plastic connectors, using a screwdriver. *To facilitate reassembly, record color code of wires.*
8. Guiding wiring, carefully pull signal switch out of housing.
9. Reverse above procedure to install.

CAUTION: Turn signal control assembly must be in neutral position when assembling steering wheel to prevent damage to cancelling cam and control assembly.

1967-69

1. Disconnect battery ground cable.
2. Disconnect turn signal multiple connector from chassis harness connector under instrument panel.
3. Remove steering wheel.
4. Slide upper bearing preload spring and turn signal cancelling cam from upper steering shaft.
5. Remove turn signal lever.
6. Push in hazard warning switch knob, unscrew and remove knob.
7. Remove mast jacket trim cover.
8. Remove retaining ring and steering shaft upper wave and thrust washers.
9. Cut harness near connector.
10. Loosen mast jacket upper support bolts.
11. Remove three switch mounting screws and slide assembly from mast jacket and steering shaft.
12. Remove wire connector, clip and/or cover.
13. Reverse procedure to install. Turn signal should be in neutral position before installing steering wheel. Install connector to wiring and connect turn signal wire harness to chassis harness connector.

HORN SOUNDER & STEERING WHEEL

1967-69

Standard Wheel

1. Disconnect steering column wire harness from chassis wire harness at connector.
2. Pull horn button cap or center ornament and retainer.
3. Remove receiving cup or horn ring, Belleville spring, bushing and pivot ring (3 screws).
4. Remove wheel nut and washer and use a suitable puller to remove wheel.
5. Reverse procedure to install. *Turn signal control assembly must be in neutral position when assembling steering wheel to prevent damage to cancelling cam and control assembly.*

Simulated Wood Wheel

1. Disconnect steering column harness from chassis wire harness at connector.
2. Pull up to remove horn cap.

NOTE: If steering wheel only is to be removed perform Step 4. If turn placed, skip Step 4 and proceed with Step 5.

3. Remove horn contact assembly.
4. Remove steering wheel.
5. Pull off wheel hub.
6. Remove turn signal cancelling cam.
7. Reverse procedure to install. *Turn signal control assembly must be in neutral position when assembling wheel hub to prevent damage to cancelling cam and control assembly.*

Telescoping Wheel

1. Disconnect column harness at wiring connector.
2. Pry off horn button cap and remove retainer.
3. Remove control lever.
4. Remove spacer, cup, spring and insulator from center of wheel (3 screws).
5. Pull off steering wheel.
6. If necessary, remove spring and cancelling cam.
7. Reverse procedure to install.

1966

1. Disconnect horn wire at chassis wiring harness.
2. Pull out horn button on standard models. On other models pull out center ornament from horn ring.
3. Remove contact assembly (3 screws).
4. Use a suitable puller to remove steering wheel.

INSTRUMENT CLUSTER

1967-69

1. Disconnect battery ground cable.
2. Remove light and wiper switch bezel nuts.
3. On Powerglide models, remove shift lever knob.

4. Remove heater or A/C control retaining screws and allow control to hang below instrument console. On A/C models remove air outlet from panel.
5. Disconnect speedometer cable. If equipped, disconnect trip odometer and speed warning unit.
6. On Powerglide models, remove upper mast jacket support clamp and lower support bolts.

NOTE: On 1968-69 models the instrument panel center pad must be removed. This pad overlaps the edge of the instrument cluster bezel, preventing direct removal of the cluster. To remove the center pad, proceed as follows:
1. Remove radio bezel or radio hole plate to gain access to the center pad retaining rivets.
2. Using a #25 or #26 drill, drill out rivets (one at each upper corner of opening).
3. Remove two screws securing pad at lower edge of instrument panel and remove center pad.
When installing, use suitable tapping screws in place of the rivets. An oval Phillips head screw is best for this application because the height of the screw head must be kept at a minimum to prevent interference with the radio bezel or hole cover.

7. *Allow steering wheel to rest on seat cushion to prevent distortion to the mast jacket.*
8. Unfasten cluster from console.
9. Pull instrument cluster forward from console and disconnect cluster wiring harness from panel wiring harness at multiple connector.
10. On Powerglide models, remove shift lever mechanism from rear of cluster housing.
11. Remove cluster from console.
12. Reverse procedure to install.

1966

1. Disconnect battery ground cable.
2. Remove steering wheel.
3. Remove light and wiper switch bezel nuts.
4. On Powerglide models, remove shift lever knob.
5. Remove heater or air conditioning control retaining screws and allow control to hang below instrument console.
6. Disconnect speedometer cable.
7. Remove screws retaining instrument cluster to console.
8. Pull instrument cluster forward from console and disconnect cluster wir-

ing from panel wiring harness at multiple disconnect.
9. On Powerglide models, remove shift lever mechanism from rear of cluster housing.
10. Remove cluster from console completely.

W/S WIPER MOTOR
1968-69

1. If possible, place motor in park position and disconnect battery ground cable.
2. Remove wiper blades and arms.
3. Remove plenum chamber grille.
4. Loosen nuts retaining drive link to crank arm ball stud.
5. Disconnect all wiring and washer hose connections at motor and pump.
6. Unfasten and remove motor from firewall.
7. Reverse procedure to install.

1966-67

1. Remove retainer securing drive link to wiper motor drive arm.
2. If equipped with a washer, note location of washer hoses to wiper motor then remove hoses from motor from inside front compartment. Also remove electrical connectors from motor.
3. Remove screws securing motor to the body and remove motor.
4. To install, reverse above procedure. *It is important that the three screws attaching motor be fully tightened so that the sleeves surrounding the screws bottoms to prevent "floating" of the motor.*

W/S WIPER TRANSMISSION
1968-69

1. Make certain motor is in park position, then remove wiper arm and blades.
2. Remove plenum chamber grille.
3. Loosen nuts retaining drive link to crank arm ball joint and disconnect drive link from crank arm.
4. Remove transmission retaining screws, lower assembly into plenum chamber and remove complete unit from chamber.
5. Reverse procedure to install.

1966-67

1. Position wiper in park position. Then remove wiper arms and blades.
2. Remove retainer securing drive link to wiper motor drive arm.
3. Remove retainers securing ends of link to each wiper transmission and remove link.
4. Unfasten and remove transmission (3 screws each side).
5. To install reverse removal procedure. Apply sealer to weld nuts before tightening transmission retaining screws. Tips of wiper blades should be 1½" above lower windshield opening with motor in park position. Arms and blades should be parallel. Operate wipers and check linkage for running clearance.

W/S WIPER SWITCH
1966-69

1. Disconnect battery ground cable.
2. Loosen small set screw at bottom of wiper arm and remove knob.
3. Remove bezel, lock nut and washer.
4. Withdraw wiper switch from instrument panel and remove connector from rear of switch. A single connector is used on units without a windshield washer. Two connectors are used with windshield washer.
5. Reverse above procedure to install.

RADIO REMOVAL

NOTE: When installing radio, be sure to adjust antenna trimmer for peak performance.

1967-69 With A/C

1. Disconnect battery ground cable.
2. Remove ash tray and bracket.
3. Remove radio attaching bracket and light from radio. Disconnect radio electrical connector and antenna lead.
4. Disconnect center air conditioning flexible hose at evaporator case.
5. Remove cigar lighter and ignition switch.
6. Remove radio knobs, bezel and retaining nuts.
7. Lower and remove radio.

Fuel Pump, Accelerator Linkage & Turbocharger

FUEL PUMP, REPLACE

1. Disconnect fuel lines at pump. Leave "T" connector and pipe in pump.
2. Loosen lock nut and remove set screw holding pump in place.
3. Remove fuel pump and push rod.

INSTALLATION

1. If removed, install "T" connector and pipe in outlet connection.
2. Install pump into housing with outlet connection to front. Carefully feel pump position with set screw, being sure set screw pilots in locking hole.
3. Tighten set screw and then lock nut.
4. Install fuel lines. Then operate engine and check for leaks

TURBOCHARGER

The turbocharger is an exhaust driven unit that forces air-fuel mixture into the intake manifold at higher than atmospheric pressure, thereby improving engine breathing and power output. It consists of a precision-balanced rotating group with a turbine wheel at one end and a centrifugal impeller at the other, each wheel enclosed in a contoured housing.

The hot exhaust gases are directed against the turbine wheel blades, spinning the wheel, shaft and impeller wheel at a high rate of speed. The impeller, in the compressor housing, draws air-fuel mixture from the carburetor and passes it to the intake manifold under a higher than atmospheric pressure. This increases the amount of air-fuel mixture available to the cylinder, resulting in a greater horsepower output.

Under heavy load, the turbocharger speed automatically increases due to increase in exhaust gases, providing more fuel-air mixture to meet the engine's demand.

The turbocharger is provided with a semi-floating sleeve bearing which is lubricated with engine oil taken from the oil filter adapter and drained through a large tube into the rocker arm area of the right cylinder head.

Inspection

If trouble is suspected in the turbocharger, it should be inspected and serviced as follows:

1. Disconnect oil drain line at elbow. Connect a hose from the elbow to a container placed at side of engine. Start engine and run at idle speed for one minute to determine oil flow (should be about one quart per minute at idle).
2. Remove turbocharger and carburetor from engine and separate the two units.
3. Inspect the turbine wheel for damage, carbon build-up on blades, and carbon accumulation on back face of turbine wheel. Check for free rotation by depressing the shield against the spring ring, then rotating the wheel.

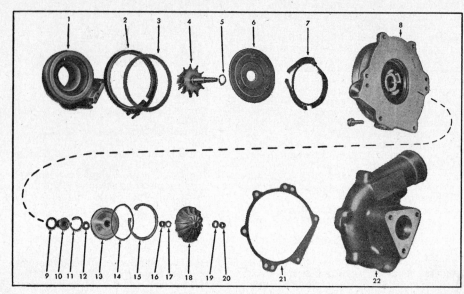

Fig. 1   Disassembled view of turbocharger

1. Turbine housing	12. Mating ring (washer)
2. Charger housing clamp	13. Oil seal
3. Gasket	14. "O" ring seal
4. Turbine wheel and shaft	15. Seal retaining ring
5. Oil seal ring	16. Shaft sleeve
6. Shield plate	17. Impeller shim
7. Spring ring	18. Impeller
8. Bearing housing	19. Impeller special washer
9. Bearing shim	20. Nut
10. Bearing	21. Gasket
11. Bearing retaining ring	22. Compressor housing

If the wheel does not rotate freely, disassemble the unit and inspect for damaged parts or foreign material causing the interference.

Service, Fig. 1

1. Remove compressor housing. Inspect it for signs of damage on the inner contour.
2. Inspect impeller wheel for damaged blades or evidence of rubbing in the housing.
3. Note any oil accumulation in housing or on impeller, indicating a defective oil seal.
4. If impeller requires cleaning, use a nylon bristle brush and a solvent such as diesel fuel or kerosene to remove accumulated dirt. Thoroughly clean impeller and compressor housing. *Failure to remove all dirt may result in a more severe unbalance than existed prior to cleaning.*
5. Measure turbine shaft end play with a dial indicator attached to the bearing housing so that indicator point is resting on impeller nut.
6. Rest assembly squarely on hub of turbine wheel, then push down on housing and record indicator reading. Release pressure on housing and check measurement again. Allowable end play is .005" to .008". If end play is excessive, the unit should be rebuilt.
7. Check turbine shaft radial play, the maximum allowable being .022". If excessive, unit should be rebuilt.
8. If unit is in satisfactory condition, install compressor housing, using a new gasket, and torque the bolts to 80 in-lb.
9. Install carburetor to turbocharger, then install assembly on vehicle.

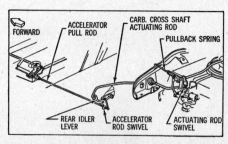

Fig. 2   Accelerator linkage adjustment. 1966-69

ACCELERATOR LINKAGE
1966-69

NOTE: Accelerator linkage should be adjusted to get simultaneous full throttle position at the accelerator pedal, the linkage idler lever and the carburetor throttle lever. The pedal downward travel stop (at idler lever at transmission) is adjustable to furnish a pedal angle comfortable to the driver.

1. To adjust, disconnect accelerator pull rod swivel from rear idler lever, Fig. 2.

2. Disconnect carburetor pull-back spring. Remove carburetor cross shaft actuating rod swivel from cross shaft.
3. Pull carburetor cross shaft actuating rod rearward until rear idler lever hits stop on its bracket. Rotate carburetor cross shaft to move L.H. primary carburetor into wide open throttle position (thru detent on Powerglide).
4. With carburetor cross shaft and its actuating rod held in the foregoing positions, align actuating rod swivel until it freely engages its mating hole in cross shaft lever. Remove swivel and back it off five full turns and replace it in lever hole.

5. Connect pull-back spring.
6. Depress pedal to within 1⅛″ of floor carpet and block pedal in this position. *This pedal setting is measured from the underside of the rubber flange at the top of the pedal.*
7. Rotate rear idler lever into wide open throttle position and reconnect accelerator pull rod after adjusting rod swivel so it freely engages its mating hole in idler lever.
8. Remove pedal block and check complete accelerator control linkage adjustment by depressing pedal and inspecting carburetor throttle valve to be sure it is at wide open position.

Engine Section
"In Car" Operations

ENGINE SEAL & SHIELDS
Seal & Retainer

REMOVAL, Fig. 1

1. Remove spare tire and air cleaner.
2. Remove retainer-to-body screws.
3. Disconnect seal from engine shields by pushing groove of seal off shield flange.
4. Remove seal and retainer.

INSTALLATION

1. Lubricate groove of seal with liquid soap or silicone and place seal and retainer in position over shields.
2. While guiding groove of seal on shield flange (with one hand) press seal in place, using a block of wood or hammer handle.
3. Install all screws finger tight, then tighten them securely.

Front Shield

REMOVAL, Fig. 2

1. Disconnect battery positive cable.
2. Remove spare tire and air cleaner.
3. Remove vacuum balance tube.
4. Disconnect heater hose at upper shroud.
5. Remove grommet for Powerglide dipstick tube (if equipped).
6. Disconnect seal from flange of front shield.
7. Remove grommet (for starter wiring and fuel line) from front shield.
8. Disconnect starter wiring (engine side).
9. From underside of vehicle disconnect accelerator rod at transmission bellcrank and fuel line at flex hose (plug fuel line from tank), then disconnect axle dipstick tube at differential carrier.
10. Disconnect accelerator rod at carburetor cross shaft, then remove rod and bellows from front shield.
11. Disconnect grommet from front shield and remove axle dipstick tube.
12. Disconnect fuel line at fuel pump, then remove fuel line from front shield.

13. Remove attaching bolts and front shield.

INSTALLATION

1. Install front shield by guiding it over starter wiring and Powerglide dipstick tube (if equipped).
2. Install front shield bolts finger tight, then tighten them securely.
3. Install fuel line through front shield, then connect fuel line at fuel pump.
4. Install accelerator rod through front shield, then connect bellows to front shield and connect accelerator rod at carburetor cross shaft.
5. Install axle dipstick tube through front shield and connect grommet in front shield.
6. Connect starter wiring.
7. Install grommet (for starter wiring and

fuel line) in front shield.
8. Lubricate groove of seal with liquid soap or silicone. Then, while guiding groove of seal onto flange (with one hand), press seal in place with a block of wood or hammer handle.
9. Install grommet for Powerglide dipstick tube (if equipped).
10. Connect heater hose at upper shroud.
11. Install vacuum balance tube.
12. From underside of vehicle connect fuel line at flex hose, accelerator rod at transmission bellcrank and axle dipstick tube at differential carrier.

Left Shield

REMOVAL, Fig. 2

1. Remove bolts attaching left side of

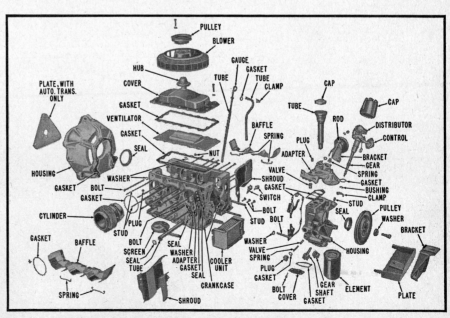

Engine block and attaching parts

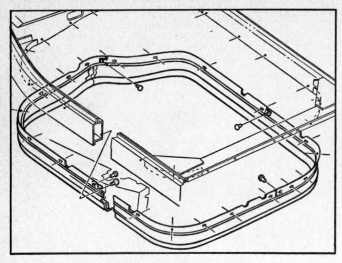

Fig. 1   Engine seal and retainer

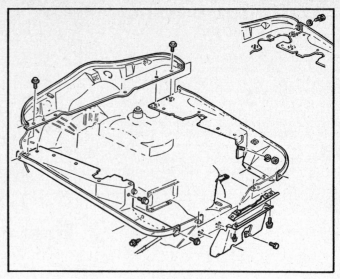

Fig. 2   Engine shields

upper shroud and left shield to cylinder head.
2. Remove bolts attaching left shield to left exhaust duct.
3. Remove bolt attaching left shield and oil cooler to cylinder head.
4. Remove bolts attaching left shield to front shield and (if equipped) remove screw from ground strap.
5. Disconnect seal from flange of left shield.
6. Remove left shield by pulling from under upper shroud, front shield and oil cooler flange.

INSTALLATION

1. Place left shield in position under upper shroud, front shield and oil cooler flange.
2. Install all bolts attaching left shield finger tight, then tighten them securely.
3. Lubricate groove of seal with liquid soap or silicone. Then, while guiding groove of seal onto shield flange (with one hand), press seal in place with a block of wood or hammer handle.
4. Connect ground strap (if equipped).

Right Shield

REMOVAL, Fig. 2

1. Remove spare tire, then remove bolts attaching right side of upper shroud and right shield to cylinder head.
2. Remove bolts attaching right shield to right exhaust duct.
3. Remove ignition coil and bracket.
4. Remove bolts attaching right shield to front shield and (if equipped) remove screw from ground strap.
5. Disconnect seal from flange of right shield.
6. Remove bolt attaching muffler bracket to right shield.
7. Remove muffler.
8. Remove right shield by pulling from under upper shroud and front shield.

INSTALLATION

1. Place right shield in position under upper shroud and front shield.
2. Install all bolts attaching right

shield finger tight, then tighten them securely.
3. Lubricate groove of seal with liquid soap or silicone. Then, while guiding groove of seal onto shield flange (with one hand), press seal in place with a block of wood or hammer handle.
4. Connect ground strap (if equipped).
5. Install ignition coil and bracket, then spare tire.

Rear Center Shield

NOTE: The rear center shield is two pieces. The engine seal is connected to the upper half, which need not be removed under normal conditions.

LOWER HALF, Fig. 2

1. Remove bolts attaching rear center shield to skid plate and exhaust ducts.
2. Remove rear center shield.
3. Place rear center shield in position

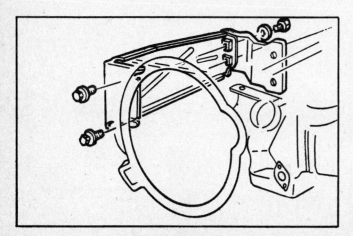

Fig. 3   Muffler heat shield

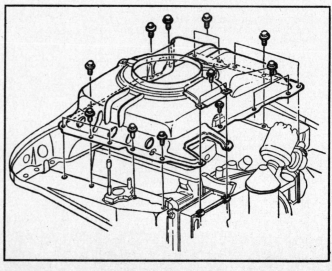

Fig. 4   Upper shroud

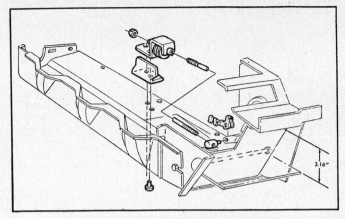

Fig. 5   Lower shroud and thermostat

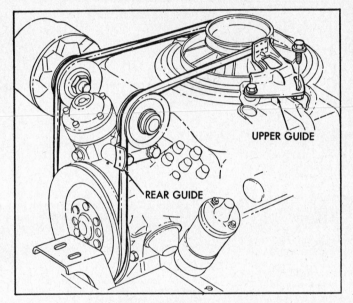

Fig. 6   Blower belt and guides

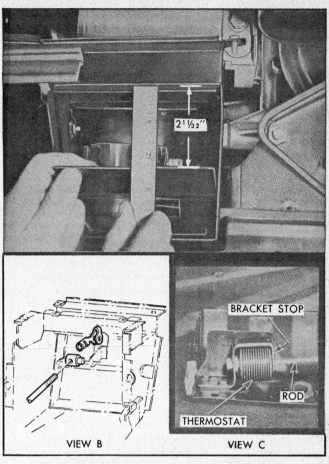

Fig. 5A   Adjusting cooling air damper door opening

with attaching bolts finger tight, then tighten bolts securely.

UPPER HALF
1. Remove lower half of center shield.
2. Disconnect seal from flange of rear center shield.
3. Remove bolts and upper half.
4. Install upper half and tighten securely.
5. Install lower half (see above).
6. Lubricate groove of seal with liquid soap or silicone. Then, while guiding groove of seal onto shield flange (with one hand), press seal in place with a block of wood or hammer handle.

Muffler Heat Shield

REMOVAL, Fig. 3
1. Remove two bolts attaching heat shield to muffler hanger.
2. Loosen two bolts attaching rear of heat shield and right rear shroud to cylinder head.
3. Remove heat shield.

INSTALLATION
1. Install heat shield in position under

head of two bolts in rear of cylinder head.
2. Install bolts attaching heat shield to muffler hanger and tighten securely.
3. Tighten two bolts attaching rear of heat shield and right rear shroud to cylinder head.

ENGINE COOLING COMPONENTS
Upper Shroud

REMOVAL, FIG. 4
1. Remove spare tire and air cleaner.
2. Disconnect fuel lines at fuel pump and carburetors, then remove fuel lines to carburetors.
3. Disconnect vacuum advance hose at right carburetor.
4. Disconnect accelerator rod at carburetor cross shaft, and choke control rods at choke levers. Then remove upper choke control rods.
5. Remove carburetors with cross shaft and linkage attached.
6. Remove blower belt.
7. Disconnect crankcase ventilation

tube at upper shroud. Then disconnect vacuum balance tube at bracket and cylinder heads.
8. Remove vacuum balance tube and crankcase ventilation tube and hoses as an assembly.
9. Remove generator with bracket attached.
10. Disconnect heater hose at upper shroud.
11. Remove oil cooler access hole cover and oil dipstick.
12. Remove distributor cap. Then remove spark plug wires and cap as an assembly.
13. Remove bolts attaching upper shroud. Then remove shroud by raising front of shroud and rotating clockwise to clear oil filter and generator adapter.

INSTALLATION
1. Install upper shroud in position and install attaching bolts finger tight. Then rotate blower, checking clearance while tightening bolts securely.
2. Install oil cooler access hole cover and oil dipstick. Then install spark plug wires and distributor cap.
3. Connect heater hose to upper shroud.
4. Install generator and bracket.
5. Install vacuum balance tube and crankcase ventilation tube and hoses.
6. Install blower belt and adjust.
7. Install carburetors and cross shaft. Then connect vacuum advance hose at right carburetor.

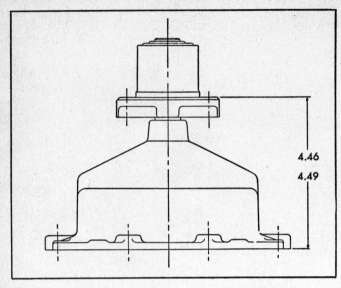

Fig. 7   Blower bearing replacement, 1966-68

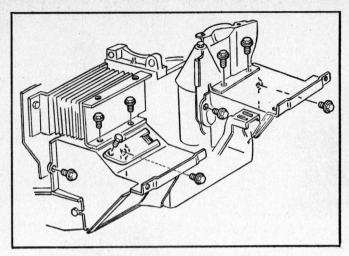

Fig. 8   Oil cooler and exhaust ducts

8. Install, adjust and connect upper choke control rods. Then adjust and connect accelerator rod.
9. Install and connect fuel lines.
10. Install air cleaner and spare tire.

Lower Shrouds & Thermostats

REMOVAL, FIG. 5

1. Remove bolts attaching lower shroud to crankcase, cylinder head, front shroud and exhaust duct.
2. Drop lower shroud until swivel on thermostat rod can be disconnected from exhaust duct damper.
3. Disconnect swivel and remove lower shroud and thermostat assembly.

THERMOSTAT, REPLACE

NOTE: In the event of a failed thermostat bellows, the exhaust duct damper will remain in the open position, allowing a maximum air flow over engine to prevent overheating.

1. Remove lower shroud (see above).
2. Using an open end wrench on the flat provided, hold thermostat and remove its actuating rod and swivel assembly.
3. Remove nut attaching thermostat to bracket, then remove thermostat.
4. Install new thermostat and tighten securely.
5. Install thermostat actuating rod and swivel and tighten securely.

CAUTION: To prevent damage to thermostat bellows while tightening actuating rod, hold flat on thermostat with an open end wrench.

COOLING AIR DAMPER

The rate of engine cooling is regulated by a bellows type thermostat mounted in the lower part of each engine lower shroud and exhaust duct, Fig. 5A. The exhaust duct damper doors in the duct are controlled by the thermostat to start opening at 195° and are fully open at 210° F. In normal operation, the damper door angles will vary between full open and closed to maintain engine temperature in operating range.

To check the operation of the damper doors, have the engine at operating temperature. Open the damper door until the bellows is stopped within its mounting bracket. Measure the opening of the damper door from its upper edge as shown and, if necessary, adjust the swivel to obtain approximately $2\frac{11}{32}$".

THERMOSTAT, ADJUST

1. Install lower shroud with two bolts (one to crankcase and one to cylinder head).
2. Hold exhaust duct damper in fully open position and pull thermostat actuating rod out to maximum travel (thermostat against bracket stop).
3. Adjust swivel until it just enters hole provided in exhaust duct damper.
4. Remove lower shroud and connect retaining clip, then install lower shroud.

INSTALLATION

1. Connect swivel to exhaust duct damper. Then install all lower shroud attaching bolts and tighten securely.
2. Check adjustment, verifying that thermostat bottoms at bracket before damper hits stop.

Front Shrouds

REMOVAL

1. Remove lower shroud (see above).
2. Remove exhaust manifold.
3. Disconnect heater hose at elbow on front shroud.
4. Remove bolts attaching front shroud to cylinder head and upper shroud. Then remove front shroud and heater elbow as a unit.

NOTE: On left front shroud, one attaching bolt (to cylinder head) is reached through heater elbow.

INSTALLATION

1. Install and tighten front shroud.
2. Connect heater hose.
3. Install exhaust manifold.
4. Install lower shroud.

Exhaust Ducts

REMOVAL

1. Disconnect seal from flange of exhaust duct and rear center shield.
2. Remove ignition coil and bracket (for right exhaust duct).
3. Remove grille, then remove rear center shield.
4. Remove lower shroud.
5. Unfasten and remove exhaust duct.

INSTALLATION

1. Install exhaust duct with all bolts finger tight, then tighten bolts securely.
2. Install lower shroud.
3. Install rear center shield and grille.
4. Lubricate groove of seal with liquid soap or silicone. Then, while guiding groove of seal onto rear center shield and exhaust duct flange (with one hand), press seal in place with a block of wood or hammer handle.
5. Install ignition coil and bracket (if removed).

Rear Shrouds

REMOVAL

1. Remove oil cooler (for left rear shroud) or remove ignition coil and bracket (for right rear shroud).
2. Remove lower shroud.
3. Remove exhaust duct.

NOTE: For right rear shroud it is necessary to disconnect wiring at cylinder head temperature and oil pressure sending units. Then disconnect at harness quick-disconnect so harness may be removed with shroud.

INSTALLATION

1. Install rear shroud. Then install exhaust duct and lower shroud.
2. Install oil cooler and/or ignition coil and bracket.

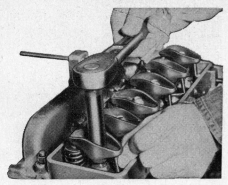

Fig. 9 Adjusting valves

Blower Belt, Idler Pulley & Belt Guides

REMOVAL, Fig. 6

1. Loosen bolt and nut at idler pulley and remove blower belt.
2. If necessary, remove bolt and idler pulley and rear belt guide as a unit.
3. If necessary, remove bolts attaching upper belt guide and remove guide.

INSTALL & ADJUST

1. If removed, install upper guide, leaving bolts finger tight.
2. If removed, install rear guide and idler pulley as a unit and leave bolt and nut finger tight.
3. Install blower belt over pulleys (generator pulley last).
4. Adjust blower belt as follows: Place a $\frac{1}{16}$" shim between belt and rear guide. Then, using a bar and a strand tension gauge, adjust blower belt to 55 lbs for a used belt, or 75 lbs for a new belt (plus or minus 5 lbs). Tighten bolt and nut securely. Remove shim from between blower belt and rear guide. Then, using shim as a gauge, adjust upper guide and tighten securely.

Blower

1. Remove upper shroud.
2. Remove bolts from blower pulley. Then remove pulley and blower from blower bearing hub.
3. Reverse procedure to install.

Exhaust Manifolds

REMOVAL

1. Remove lower shroud.
2. Remove nuts at exhaust manifold flange (retaining exhaust pipe).
3. Remove nuts, locks and clamps.
4. Using a soft hammer, tap exhaust manifold off exhaust port sleeves and remove and discard all packings.

INSTALLATION

1. Using new packings, install manifold over exhaust port sleeves, then install clamps, locks and nuts.
2. Tighten manifold clamp nuts a little at a time until specified torque is reached. Tap manifold in place over exhaust port sleeves with a soft hammer while tightening nuts.
3. Install lower shrouds.

4. Using a new packing, connect exhaust pipe to manifold.

CRANKCASE COVER & BLOWER BEARING

REMOVAL

1. Remove upper shroud.
2. Remove retaining bolts from blower pulley and remove pulley and blower from bearing hub.
3. Remove crankcase vent tube retainer, vent tube and O-ring seal.
4. Remove attaching bolts and take off crankcase cover and blower bearing assembly.
5. Remove crankcase vent and crankcase cover gaskets.

BLOWER BEARING, REPLACE

1969

1. Remove center four crankcase cover bolts and install tool, J-22894.
2. Measure distance from lower edge of tool bridge to bearing flange. Record this dimension.
3. Place puller fingers under bearing flange and remove bearing.

1966-68

1. While supporting crankcase cover, press blower bearing shaft out of cover.
2. Coat new bearing shaft with hypoid lube. Then, while supporting crankcase cover, press bearing hub into cover to specified height, Fig. 7.

CAUTION: Press on shaft of blower bearing. Do not press on bearing outer race or bearing seal.

INSTALLATION

1. Clean all gasket surfaces.
2. Install crankcase cover gasket and vent, then second crankcase cover gasket.
3. Install crankcase cover.
4. Install crankcase vent tube, using a new O-ring seal.
5. Install blower and pulley.
6. Install upper shroud.

OIL FILTER & GENERATOR ADAPTER

REMOVAL

1. Remove blower belt.
2. Disconnect and remove generator.
3. Disconnect fuel lines at fuel pump.
4. Remove bolts from around oil filler tube, then remove all remaining bolts from adapter.
5. Remove adapter from fuel pump, oil filter, idler pulley and belt guide as a unit.

INSTALLATION

1. Check surface of engine rear housing and adapter for nicks or cracks.
2. Install a new adapter gasket.
3. Place bolts and flat washers (3) in adapter around oil filler tube.
4. Start fuel pump push rod and return spring into push rod guide.
5. Hold adapter cover in place and

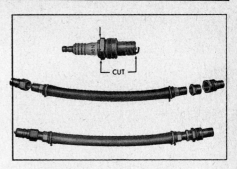

Fig. 10 Air adapter tool

tighten bolts around oil filler tube finger tight.
6. Install remaining bolts and washers, then tighten all bolts securely.
7. Install and connect generator and fuel lines.
8. Start engine and check for leaks.

OIL COOLER

REMOVAL

1. Remove cooler access hole cover, Fig. 8.
2. Unfasten and remove cooler from shroud, shield and cylinder head.
3. Remove mounting bolt and take off cooler and seals.

INSTALLATION

1. Install new seals on cooler adapter.
2. Install cooler, tightening bolt securely.
3. Install all screws and bolts to shroud, shield and cylinder head, then tighten securely.
4. Install cooler access hole cover.
5. Start engine and check for leaks.

OIL PUMP

GEAR REMOVAL

1. Drain engine oil.
2. Support engine with a jack with a piece of hardwood positioned between oil pan rails adjacent to engine skid plate.
3. Remove grille and rear center shield and disconnect rear mount. Then lower engine about one inch (to clear rear mount bracket).
4. Remove rear mount bracket and engine skid plate.
5. Remove oil pump cover and gasket.

GEAR INSTALLATION

1. Install pump gears. Then, using a new gasket, install pump cover.
2. Install skid plate and rear mount bracket.
3. Raise engine and connect rear mount.
4. Install rear center shield and grille.
5. Remove jack and wood block.
6. Fill with oil, start engine and check for leaks.

Oil Pressure Regulator

1. Drain engine oil.
2. Remove left lower shroud and left exhaust duct.
3. Remove pressure regulator plug, gasket, spring and valve.

Fig. 11 Measuring valve spring installed height

4. Reverse procedure to install.
5. Start engine and check for leaks.

NOTE: To check oil pressure regulator, remove oil pressure sending unit and connect oil pressure gauge. Accelerate engine until pressure gauge stops increasing. The regulator should regulate at 35 psi.

Oil Pan

1. Drain engine oil and remove pan.
2. Clean gasket surfaces and install pan with new gasket.
3. Fill with oil, start engine and check for leaks.

CRANKSHAFT PULLEY OR VIBRATION DAMPER

REMOVAL

1. Disconnect engine seal from rear center shield and remove rear half of left and right side shield flanges.
2. Remove blower belt and oil filter.
3. Drain oil, then place engine jack under engine.
4. Remove grille and rear center shield.
5. Disconnect engine rear mount, then lower engine far enough to remove engine rear mount bracket.
6. Remove attaching bolt and use a suitable puller to remove crankshaft pulley or vibration damper.

INSTALLATION

1. Position pulley or vibration damper on end of crankshaft with key lined up.
2. Using retaining bolt and flat washer, pull pulley or damper in place, then back bolt out ½ turn and torque to specifications.

CAUTION: Do not drive pulley or damper onto crankshaft. To do so may damage crankshaft thrust bearing and crankcase.

3. Install engine rear mount bracket.
4. Raise engine and connect rear mount.
5. Remove engine jack.

6. Install rear center shield and grille.
7. Install new oil filter.
8. Install blower belt.
9. Lubricate groove of oil seal with liquid soap or silicone. Then, while guiding groove of seal onto shield flange (with one hand) press seal into place with a block of wood or a hammer handle.
10. Fill with oil, start engine and check for leaks.

ENGINE REAR HOUSING SEAL

1. Remove crankshaft pulley or vibration damper.
2. Remove seal by prying on outer edge of seal with two screwdrivers.
3. Install new seal over crankshaft and tap in place with a block of hardwood.
4. Install pulley or vibration damper.

ENGINE REAR HOUSING

1. Remove distributor cap and note position of rotor, then disconnect and remove distributor.
2. Remove oil filter and generator adapter.
3. Drain engine oil.
4. Install a suitable engine lift under engine with a piece of hardwood positioned between oil pan rails adjacent to engine skid plate. (Installation of wood block will allow removal of engine skid plate.)
5. Remove rear center shield and disconnect rear mount, then lower engine about 1″ to clear rear mount bracket.
6. Remove rear mount bracket and engine skid plate.
7. Remove crankshaft pulley or vibration damper.
8. Remove engine rear housing.
9. Reverse procedure to install.

DISTRIBUTOR DRIVE GEAR & FUEL PUMP ECCENTRIC

1. Remove engine rear housing.
2. Remove distributor drive gear, then remove spacer and fuel pump eccentric.
3. When installing, first be sure woodruff keys are in place in crankshaft, then position fuel pump eccentric and spacer on crankshaft.
4. Lubricate crankshaft and distributor drive gear with engine oil and install gear until it bottoms.
5. Install engine rear housing.

CYLINDER HEAD & VALVE SERVICE

Valves, Adjust

NOTE: In order to adjust valves, the lower shrouds and muffler heat shield must be removed. Then remove rocker arm covers and adjust valves as follows:

1. Remove distributor cap and rotate

Fig. 12 Rocker arm studs and push rod guides

crankshaft to bring No. 1 piston up on top dead center of its compression stroke. Rotor should be pointing to No. 1 position and timing mark at "O" on timing tab.
2. In this position, valves that can be adjusted are:
   No. 1 intake and exhaust.
   No. 3 intake, No. 5 exhaust.
   No. 4 exhaust, No. 6 intake.
3. To make the adjustment, turn adjusting nut out until there is end play in the push rod. Then turn adjusting nut in until push rod end play is eliminated. Finally, turn adjusting nut in one additional turn to center the plunger in the hydraulic lifter, Fig. 9.
4. Turn crankshaft one revolution to bring No. 2 piston to top dead center on its compression stroke. Then adjust the following valves in the same manner.
   No. 2 intake and exhaust.
   No. 3 exhaust, No. 5 intake.
   No. 4 intake, No. 6 exhaust.

Valve Seals

NOTE: Intake valves are provided with valve stem oil seals. These seals can be replaced with cylinder head installed as follows:

1. Remove spark plug, rocker arm and push rod on cylinder to be serviced.
2. Apply compressed air to spark plug hole to hold valve in place. (A tool to apply air to cylinder is available through local jobbers or it may be manufactured from parts shown in Fig. 10.)
3. Use a suitable compressor to compress valve spring. Then remove valve locks, valve cap, valve spring and damper assembly.
4. Remove seal from valve guide.
5. Install new seal, using a special plastic sleeve to prevent seal damage as seal passes over valve lock grooves. Push seal on guide until it bottoms on guide end.
6. Install valve parts, using grease to hold valve locks in place while releasing valve spring compressor.
7. Adjust valve as outlined previously and complete the installation.

Checking Valve Spring Installed Height

NOTE: Follow procedure for installing

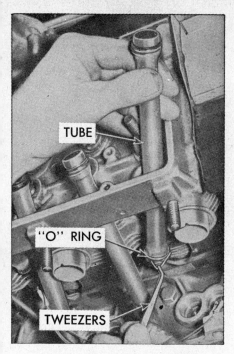

Fig. 13 Removing push rod tubes

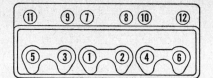

Fig. 14 Cylinder head tightening sequence

Fig. 15 Push rod installation

valve stem seals. Then check valve spring height as follows:

1. Install spring cap and valve locks without spring.
2. Hold spring cap and pull valve against seat. Then measure distance between spring cap and spring seat, Fig. 11. This locates spring cap in installed position.
3. Remove valve locks and spring cap and, if necessary, shim spring.

NOTE: Spring shims are available in .030" thickness. Do not use shim if it will bring spring height below specification listed in Valve Specifications table.

4. Reassemble and adjust valve.

Valve Lifters, Replace

REMOVAL

1. Drain engine oil.
2. Remove lower shrouds (1966-68).
3. For right bank, remove muffler heat shield.
4. Remove valve rocker arm covers.
5. Remove rocker arms and push rods.
6. Remove rocker arm studs and push rod guides, then remove rocker arm stud O-ring seals, Fig. 12.
7. Pull push rod tubes from crankcase bore and remove inner O-ring seal, Fig. 13. Then remove push rod tube from cylinder head and remove O-ring seal.
8. Remove valve lifters with a magnet or a wire hook.
9. Place valve lifters, rocker arm parts and push rods in racks so they may be installed in original locations.

INSTALLATION

1. Lubricate valve lifters and install in crankcase bores.

2. Install new O-ring seals (lightly coated with oil) on long end of push rod tubes, then install tubes through bore in cylinder head. Install new O-ring seals on inner end of tubes.
3. Start push rod tubes into bores in cylinder head and crankcase, then seat tubes with a 9/16" deep socket place against cylinder head end of tube and tap lightly with a hammer.
4. Install new O-ring seals into rocker arm stud bore in cylinder head.
5. Install push rod guides, then rocker arm studs.
6. Torque rocker arm studs to 10 ft-lbs below specifications. Then tighten cylinder head nuts and rocker arm studs a little at a time in the sequence shown in Fig. 14 until specified torque is reached.
7. Install push rods with side hole out, Fig. 15. Then install rocker arms, balls and nuts.
8. Adjust valves as outlined.
9. Install rocker arm covers with new gaskets. Torque to specifications.
10. Install lower shrouds and muffler heat shield as outlined.
11. Fill with oil, start engine and check for leaks.

Cylinder Heads, Replace

SERVICE BULLETIN

New Head Gasket and Timing: On 1966 Corvair 500 and Monzas with 4 x 1 (140 H.P.) engines, air conditioning and Powerglide, use new cylinder head gaskets No. 3891552, which are copper flashed for identification, on these engines.

The thicker gasket has been designed to obtain the desired compression ratio of 8.75:1. In conjunction with the cylinder head and latest gasket design, the distributor timing has been changed from 18° BTDC to 14° BTDC for the above models only.

1966-69

1. Drain engine oil.
2. Disconnect battery cable.
3. Remove spare tire and air cleaner.
4. Remove from cylinder head:
   a. Carburetor, carburetor mounting studs and upper choke control rods.
   b. Ignition coil and bracket (right head). Air Injector pump, tubes and hoses.
   c. Side shield, lower shroud and exhaust duct.
   d. Oil cooler (left head).
   e. Muffler, muffler shield and muf-

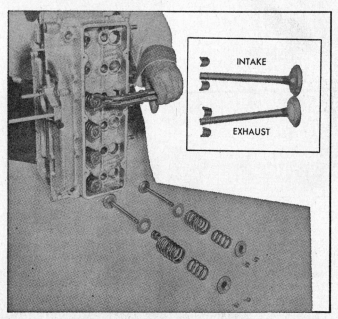

Fig. 16 Compressing valve springs

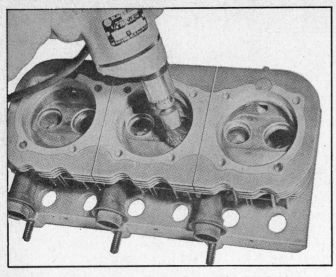

Fig. 17   Removing carbon from combustion chambers

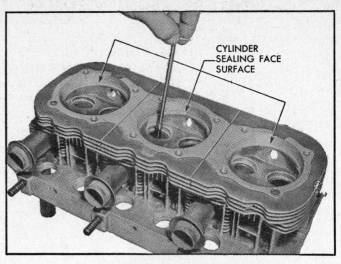

CYLINDER
SEALING FACE
SURFACE

Fig. 18   Cleaning valve guides

fler hanger (right head).
f. Spark plugs and vacuum advance tube hose at cylinder head.
g. Bolts attaching upper shroud to front and rear shrouds and bolts attaching front and rear shrouds to cylinder head.
h. Exhaust manifolds. *On front shroud for 1966-68, it will be necessary to disconnect heater hose to gain access to one bolt.*

NOTE: On left rear shroud it will be necessary to disconnect heater hose at elbow to gain access to one bolt.

5. On right head, disconnect wire to cylinder head temperature sending unit.
6. Remove rear center shield.
7. On 1966-69, disconnect engine at rear mount and lower engine several inches.
8. Remove rocker arms and push rods as outlined under *Valve Lifters, Replace,* then unfasten and remove cylinder head.
9. Reverse procedure to install.

Cylinder Head, Disassemble

1. Compress valve springs and remove valve locks, Fig. 16. It may be necessary to tap valve spring caps lightly to loosen valve locks.
2. Release compressor and remove valve spring cap, spring (and damper if used), valve and spring shims.
3. Remove remaining valves.
4. Remove valve stem oil seals from intake valve guides.

NOTE: Under ordinary circumstances no further disassembly of the head is necessary. If cylinder head is to be replaced, transfer or install carburetor studs, exhaust manifold studs, choke coil and control rod assembly, vacuum balance tube, carburetor mounting pad plug and cylinder head temperature sending unit.

5. Clean carbon from combustion chambers, Fig. 17, and clean valve guides, Fig. 18.

INSPECTION

1. Check cylinder heads for damage. Check fit of exhaust manifold sleeves; if loose or cracked, replace as outlined.
2. Inspect valves for burned faces, excessive seat pound 'in, cracked faces or badly scuffed or worn valve stems.
3. Inspect valve seats for cracks or burnt seats, and valve guides for cracks or excessive wear.

NOTE: If valve seats are beyond repair, cylinder head replacement is necessary. Excessive valve-to-bore clearance may cause oil consumption. Insufficient clearance will result in noisy and sticky functioning of valve and disturb smoothness of operation.

4. Measure valve stem clearance with a dial indicator as shown in Fig. 19. With valve head dropped about $1/16''$ off its seat, move stem of valve from side to side, using light pressure to obtain a clearance reading. If clearance exceeds specifications, it will be necessary to ream valve guides for oversize valve or replace valve guides.
5. Check valve spring tension; if not within 5 lbs of specifications, replace spring or springs.
6. Clean air circulating passages formed by cooling fins, Fig. 20.

Reconditioning Valve Seats

Regardless of the methods used for valve seat reconditioning, the final seat width in cylinder head should be $1/32''$ to $1/16''$ on the intake and $1/16''$ to $3/32''$ on exhaust valves. Valve seat angle on all seats should be as specified and should be concentric within .002" dial indicator reading.

Reconditioning Valve Faces

Valve facing machine should be set as specified for grinding valves. After grinding, if the edge of the valve head is less than $1/32''$ thick, replace the valve, Fig. 21.

Exhaust Manifold Sleeves

NOTE: Do not remove exhaust manifold sleeves unless absolutely necessary. If sleeves are removed they should be replaced with the next largest diameter sleeve.

1. Warm cylinder head to 200°F. Then remove exhaust manifold sleeves with a pipe wrench by turning gradually, Fig. 22. *Do not tap or pry sleeves from cylinder head.*
2. Check sleeve installation holes in head for nicks or damage.
3. Coat new sleeves with anti-freeze compound and locate flat side parallel to exhaust push rod tube hole.

NOTE: Sleeves are installed in cylinder head with a press fit and must be started into place square with the exhaust bore in head. Sleeves are available in standard, .002" and .010" oversize for service.

4. Place sleeve in container of dry ice for about 10 minutes.
5. Warm cylinder head to about 200°F. *Do not use an open flame.*
6. Remove sleeves one at a time from the dry ice and tap into place with a soft-faced hammer.

Reaming Valve Guides

Oversize valves can be utilized to obtain proper valve-to-guide clearance in all cases except when guide is either cracked or is worn to the extent that reaming will not clean up the guide bore to permit use of the largest oversize valve available. Valves are available in standard, .003", .010" and .020" oversize stems.

Valve Guides, Replace

Replacement valve guides on all engines except turbocharged engine are

Fig. 19   Measuring valve stem clearance

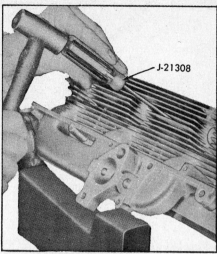

Fig. 20   Cleaning cooling fins

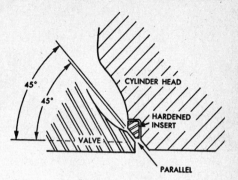

Fig. 21   Relation of valve and seat angles

available in oversizes of .002" (standard replacement), .010" and .020". Service guides are bored to permit use of valves with standard diameter stems.

Remove valve guide as shown in Fig. 23 and install as shown in Fig. 24.

VALVE LIFT SPECS.

Year and Model	Intake	Exhaust
1966-67 95 H.P.	385	.385
1966-67 110, 140 H.P.	.390	.390
1966-67 180 H.P.	.390	.390
1968 95 H.P.	.403	.403
1968 110, 140 H.P.	.409	.409
1969 95 H.P.	.385	.385
1969 110, 140 H.P.	.390	.390

VALVE TIMING
Intake Opens Before TDC

Year and Model	Degrees
1966 95 H.P.	44
110, 140 H.P.	55
180 H.P.	82
1967 95 H.P.	44
110 H.P.	55
1968 95 H.P.	26
110 H.P.	37
140 H.P.	70
1969 95 H.P.	26
110 H.P.	37
140 H.P.	26

Fig. 22   Removing exhaust manifold sleeve

PISTON RINGS, REPLACE

Bear in mind that cylinders and pistons are serviced as a unit and the operation outlined below is for replacing one or more pistons in one bank requiring ring replacement. It is not intended for complete piston and ring replacement.

1. Drain crankcase oil and remove cylinder head.
2. Remove cylinder from piston requiring new rings.
3. Remove old and install new rings. Position oil control ring gap towards top of engine and compression rings with gap 45° from oil ring gap location. Rings must be installed with markings and inside bevel toward top of piston. Lubricate piston rings with engine oil and slide ring compressing tool, Fig. 25, over rings just enough to compress rings into piston.
4. Reverse above procedure to install parts removed. Add engine oil, start engine and check for oil leaks.

ROD BEARINGS, REPLACE

1. Remove air cleaner element and carburetor intake hose.
2. Remove choke heat tube, choke

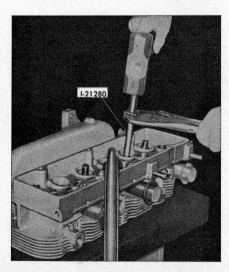

Fig. 23   Removing valve guide

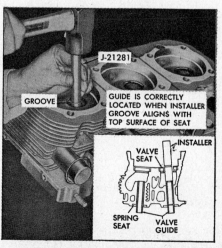

Fig. 24   Installing new valve guide

Fig. 25   Installing piston rings with aid of ring compressor (J-8356)

fresh air hose and carburetor linkage.

3. Disconnect fuel lines at carburetor.
4. Remove left bank carburetor.
5. Disconnect choke link to choke assembly. Remove choke and air horn by removing nuts at legs of air horn support.
6. Disconnect spark plug wires.
7. Remove blower drive belt.
8. Disconnect fuel lines at fuel pump.
9. Remove carburetor cross shaft and vacuum balance tube.
10. Remove all engine upper shroud bolts and screws.
11. Remove screws on each side of front engine shield.

12. Disconnect cooling air throttle valve thermostat rod and remove cooling air throttle valve.
13. Remove all fuel lines.
14. Remove engine upper shroud, tipping front lip up so it clears front engine shield.
15. Remove blower pulley and blower.
16. Remove crankcase cover, gaskets and crankcase vent.
17. Remove spark plug from cylinder requiring new rod bearing and remove rod cap and bearing insert. Use a piece of $5/16''$ plastic hose on each rod bolt to protect crankshaft journals from being scratched.
18. Reverse above procedure to install parts removed. While tightening

upper shroud bolts, rotate blower and check for interference at blower to upper shroud. Add engine oil, start engine and check for oil leaks.

Rod bearing inserts are available in standard sizes and undersizes of .001″, .002″, .010″ and .020″. These bearings are not shimmed and when clearance becomes excessive the next undersize bearing insert should be used. *Do not file rod or caps in an attempt to fit bearings.*

Rod bearing clearance is checked with Plastigage in the same manner outlined for main bearings. If flattened Plastigage measurement is not over .003″ (worn) or .002″ (new) or not less than .001″ the fit is satisfactory.

Repairs Requiring Engine Removal

ENGINE, REPLACE
Power Train

1. Remove shrouds and shields as required and as outlined previously.
2. Back car into place so that rear bumper is under a chain hoist.
3. Use holes provided to attach a chain to bumper.
4. Raise car with hoist and install jack stands.
5. Disconnect all necessary wires, hoses, pipes, linkage, etc.
6. Loosen (do not remove) bolts attaching engine to mounts.
7. Lower car so that engine rests absolutely flat on two 6 x 6 inch blocks.
8. Reach under car and remove loosened bolts from mounts.
9. Raise car body to clear engine.
10. Slide power train out from under car.
11. Reverse procedure to install.

SERVICE BULLETIN
DIFFICULTY INSTALLING STRUT RODS: On 1966-69 models, some difficulty has been experienced connecting the rear strut rod brackets to the differential carrier during engine installation. The procedure is as follows:

1. With spring compressed to curb height, position strut bracket to differential carrier. To prevent distortion to strut bracket it is recommended that the retaining bolts be installed in the following manner.
2. Using a long drift, align bracket with differential carrier and install forward bolt on side of carrier. Do not tighten bolt. Remaining bolts will require further alignment.
3. Align bracket with rear bolt on underside of carrier, using drift to align bracket during bolt installation.
4. Install rear bolt on side of carrier, then install remaining bolt to underside of carrier.
5. Alternately tighten all bolts a little at a time to permit an even draw against bracket. Then tighten bolts snugly and check bracket for proper seating against carrier. *It is*

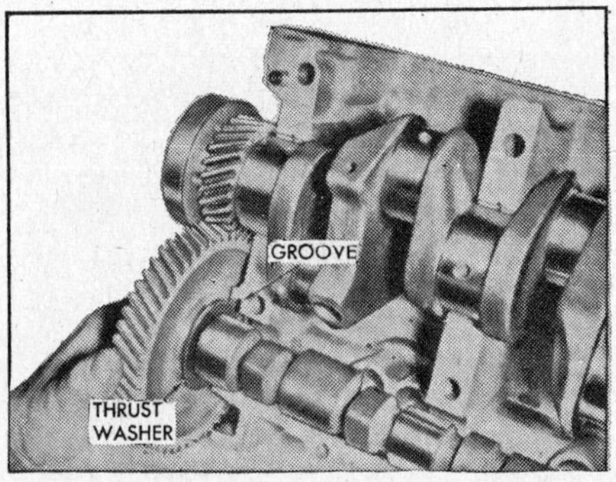

Fig. 27   Installing camshaft in crankcase

recommended that the strut rods be installed before installing the axle drive shafts.

ENGINE DISASSEMBLY

1. Remove transmission from power train.
2. Remove differential carrier from engine.
3. Remove clutch from engine (if equipped).
4. Remove carburetor linkage and related parts.
5. Remove blower belt.
6. Remove fuel pump.
7. Remove generator.
8. Remove engine front shield.
9. Remove vacuum balance tube.
10. Remove both carburetors.
11. Remove fuel lines and oil level gauge.
12. Remove distributor and spark plugs.
13. Remove coil and generator brace from cylinder head.
14. Remove engine upper shroud and side shields.
15. Remove oil filter and generator adapter.
16. Remove blower and pulley.
17. Remove crankcase vent tube.
18. Remove crankcase cover and blower bearing.
19. Remove engine front and lower

shrouds and exhaust ducts.
20. Remove oil pan.
21. Remove exhaust manifold.
22. Remove choke heat tube at right cylinder head.
23. Remove engine rear mounting bracket and skid plate at engine rear housing.
24. Remove cylinder heads. *When crankshaft is turned for further disassembly cylinders will need a holding fixture which can readily be made. Six $1/2''$ x $4 1/4''$ long steel tubes to be used on long cylinder studs (one on each cylinder) and six $1/2''$ x $3 1/2''$ long tubes for each short stud. Slip the tubes on the studs and keep them in place by means of the stud nuts.*
25. Remove valve lifters with a magnet or wire hook.
26. Remove connecting rod caps, being sure they are marked so that they will be returned to the correct connecting rod.
27. Remove spring retainers and take off cylinder air baffle.
28. Remove each cylinder with piston and connecting rod as a unit.
29. Push piston out of cylinder with a hammer handle. *Ridges and/or deposits on upper end of cylinder can be removed after piston has been removed from cylinder with a cylinder mounted ridge reamer.*
30. Remove crankshaft pulley.
31. Remove engine rear housing.

ENGINE, REASSEMBLE
Crankshaft

1. To install crankshaft gear, mount shaft in an arbor press and support it between front crankshaft throw and front journal.
2. Press on crankshaft gear and install two woodruff keys.
3. Position fuel pump eccentric and spacer on shaft.
4. Lubricate crankshaft and distributor drive gear and install distributor drive gear.
5. Install oil slinger with concave side

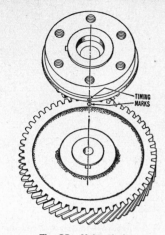

Fig. 28   Valve timing

away from distributor drive gear.
6. Install crankshaft and main bearings.

Camshaft

Camshaft bearing journal clearance should be .0015" to .0035" new and .002" to .004" used. If clearance is not within limits either the crankcase or camshaft should be replaced.

1. To assemble camshaft gear and thrust washer to camshaft, firmly support shaft at back of front journal in an arbor press.
2. Place thrust washer over end of shaft and install woodruff key in keyway.
3. Lubricate camshaft with hypoid lubricant.
4. Install camshaft gear and press into place until it bottoms against thrust washer.

Timing Gear Marks

1. Install camshaft, guiding camshaft thrust washer into groove in crankcase, Fig. 27, while indexing camshaft gear to crankshaft gear so that valve timing marks line up as shown in Fig. 28.
2. Install other half of crankcase onto crankshaft and camshaft and fasten both halves together. Tighten bolts to the proper torque and in proper sequence.
3. Check camshaft end play, which should be .003" to .007".

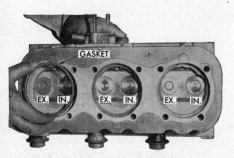

Fig. 30   Installing cylinder head gaskets

4. Check timing gear backlash which should be .002" to .004".
5. Install front crankshaft oil slinger on crankshaft gear with flange side toward crankcase. Install slinger retaining snap ring, using care to avoid scratching sealing surface.
6. Install main oil gallery plugs with Permatex 404 anti-freeze compound or its equivalent.
7. Install flywheel housing with new gasket and torque bolts to 20-30 ft. lbs.

Pistons, Cylinders and Rods

NOTE: When installing the 1966-69 type (notched) engine cylinder over piston and rings, position the oil control ring gap toward the top of the engine. Place the compression rings with the gap 45° from the oil ring gap, and on the opposite side of the piston from the notch in the cylinder. Installing the cylinder with the ring gaps in line with the cylinder notch could result in broken rings.

1. Push piston into cylinder with hammer handle while holding cylinder in one hand until it is slightly below top of cylinder bore. *Notch on piston top must be installed towards front of engine (flywheel end) on both banks.*
2. With pistons and cylinders installed, install rod bearings.
3. Position crankcase pins by turning crankshaft with pulley so that crankshaft journal is in line with piston and rod to be installed.
4. Place a piece of plastic hose with at least a 5/16" diameter over each rod bolt to protect shaft journal.
5. Install a new copper cylinder gasket over cylinder pilot, Fig. 29.
6. Push piston with hammer handle while guiding cylinder bore pilot into crankcase. Remove plastic hose from rod bolts and install rod bearing and cap. Torque rod nuts to 20-26 ft. lbs.
7. Install cylinder holding tubes (used previously on disassembly) on cylinder studs to hold cylinder in place. Continue procedure until all cylinders and pistons are installed.
8. Install cylinder air baffles with retaining springs. Fig. 29. *Air baffles are not interchangeable.*

Crankcase Cover and Blower Bearing

1. Install new gasket on crankcase.
2. Install crankcase vent and another crankcase gasket.
3. Install crankcase cover and blower bearing and torque bolts to 7-13 ft. lbs.
4. Install crankcase vent tube and gasket.

Oil Pump Screen and Tube

If the original or a new oil pump screen and tube assembly is to be installed in the original crankcase, the outside diameter of the end of the tube will have to be tinned with solder before installing in crankcase.

1. Install oil pump screen and pick-up tube into cylinder case with pick-up screen positioned parallel to oil pan rails. Secure tube with clamp.

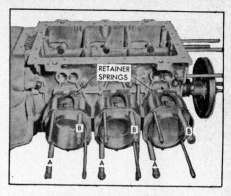

Fig. 29   Installing cylinder and piston. Tubes "A" and "B" are holding cylinders in place

2. Coat threads on engine temperature and oil pressure sending units with anti-seize compound (Permatex 404) or its equivalent. Torque oil pressure unit to 45-65 ft. lbs. and temperature unit 35-45 ft. lbs.

Cylinder Head

Be sure all cylinder head gaskets are in cylinder head combustion chambers as shown in Fig. 30. Remove all cylinder retaining tubes from cylinder bank to which cylinder head is to be installed.

1. Install cylinder head, Fig. 31.
2. Install six flat washers and nuts on long studs, adjacent to intake manifold.
3. Install six new "O" rings, lubricated with lubriplate, in counterbore of cylinder head (location for rocker arm studs) and coat rocker stud bore with anti-seize compound.
4. Install rocker arm studs, with threads coated with anti-seize compound.
5. Tighten nuts and rocker studs in sequence shown in Fig. 14. Torque nuts and rocker studs to 27-33 ft. lbs.

Push Rod Oil Drain Tubes

1. Lightly oil hydraulic lifters and in-

Fig. 31   Installing cylinder head

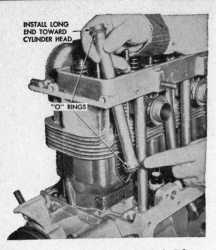

Fig. 34 Installing push rod drain tubes

5. Install oil filter and generator adapter.
6. Install sheet metal removed.
7. Install wires, fuel lines, etc.
8. Install spark plugs.
9. Install oil pan. Check parting line to see if flywheel housing gasket is far enough up for good sealing.
10. Install fuel pump and add engine oil.

CRANKCASE
Engine Disassembled

1. Remove two oil gallery plugs located at flywheel housing end of crankcase. These passages should be cleaned with solvent.
2. Check cylinder pilot bores and bearing surfaces in each half of crankcase for nicks, cracks or other damage that would interfere with the proper fit of component parts.
3. Do not use scrapers or other sharp tools to clean gasket surfaces. A good cleaning solvent should be used to dissolve gasket material or varnish that may adhere to the surfaces.

Stud and Thread Repairs

Always use anti-seize compound (Permatex 404 or equivalent) on all threads entering aluminum.

To replace crankcase studs, install long and short studs as indicated in Fig. 35. Studs are available in oversizes of .003", .006" and .009".

It should require a torque of 10 to 30 ft. lbs. to install studs. If torque is less than 10, another selected stud should be used.

Heli-coils for thread repairs are available at local auto parts jobbers and should be installed to Heli-Coil prescribed methods.

All cylinder studs installed in crankcase adjacent to the main bearing webs have blind holes while the others do not.

MAIN BEARINGS
Engine Disassembled

Whenever the crankcase is parted, the bearings and crankshaft journals should

Fig. 35 Installed length of crankcase and rear housing studs

be inspected. If upon inspection one half shows evidence of fatigue, distress, abrasion, erosion, scoring or the like, both crankcase halves should be replaced. *Never should one half be replaced without replacing the other half.*

If the running clearance of a bearing is too great with used bearing inserts, it will be necessary to replace both bearing halves. Should this become necessary, the crankshaft journal should be checked with a micrometer for out-of-round, taper or undersize dimensions.

When replacing rear main bearing, install the flanged bearing shell in the left half of the case only. Install the unflanged shell in the right half.

Main Bearing Clearance

Main bearing clearance is checked with Plastigage, a wax-like material, available at auto parts jobbers.

To assure proper seating of the bearings, all crankcase bolts must be at their specified torque. Eight long 7/16" bolts 42-48 ft. lbs., and three 5/16" bolts 7-13 ft. lbs. Hold bolt head on 7/16" bolts while tightening the nut. Do not tighten at bolt head. Fig. 36 shows tightening sequence. To check main bearing clearance, proceed as follows:
1. Starting with rear main bearing,

stall in their proper bores.
2. Install push rod oil drain tubes through cylinder head, Fig. 34. Place "O" rings, one on each end of drain tube as shown. Oil "O" rings and push in place at lifter bore in crankcase and cylinder head.
3. Install push rods with side oil hole up into valve rocker socket.
4. On early production engines, install push rod guides in place over rocker studs and push rods and tighten bolts. *On late production engines, push rod guides are installed under valve rocker studs.*
5. Install rocker arms, balls and nuts loosely in place. Adjust valve lash as outlined elsewhere in this section, after installing distributor.

Final Assembly

1. Install engine rear housing.
2. Install crankshaft pulley. After pulley bottoms in place, back off retaining bolt one turn and then torque it to 60-80 ft. lbs. *Do not drive pulley shaft thrust bearing and crankcase.*
3. Install oil cooler.
4. Install exhaust manifolds.

Fig. 36 Crankcase tightening sequence

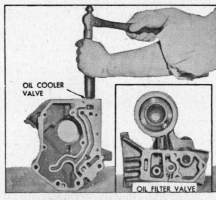

Fig. 37 Oil filter and oil cooler by-pass valve installation

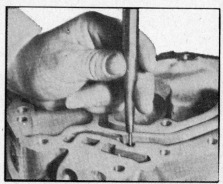

Fig. 38 Installing oil pressure regulator stop groove pin

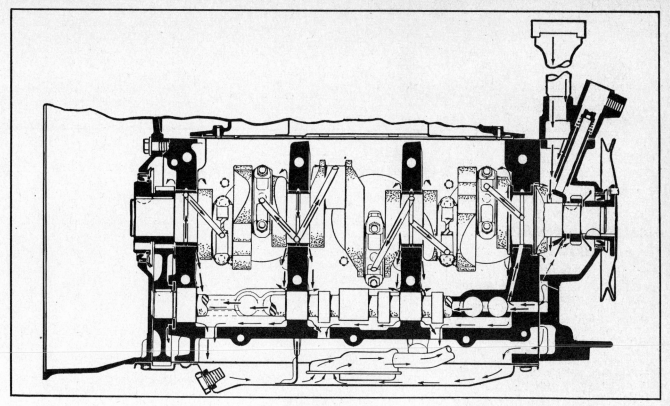

Engine lubrication

remove one half of the crankcase while the other is supported on its side. Wipe oil from bearings and journal.

2. Place a strip of Plastigage the full width of the bearing (parallel to crankshaft on journal). *Crankcase split line surfaces must be free of nicks and foreign matter.*

3. Install other half of crankcase with bearings and evenly tighten crankcase bolts to proper torque. *Do not rotate crankshaft while Plastigage is between bearing and journal.*

4. Remove one half of crankcase. Then measure the width of the flattened Plastigage with the graduated scale on the edge of the Plastigage envelope.

5. If the flattened Plastigage is not over .004″ (worn) or .003″ (new) or less than .001″ the bearing insert is satisfactory. If not within these limits replace bearing insert.

6. A .002″ undersize bearing may produce the proper clearance. If not, it will be necessary to regrind the crankshaft journal for use with the next undersize bearing. Bearings are available in undersizes of .001″, .002″, .010″ and .020″.

7. Proceed to the next bearing. After all bearings have been checked and installed, rotate the crankshaft to see that there is no excessive drag.

8. Check the end play by forcing the crankshaft to the extreme forward position. End play should be .002″ to .006″.

OIL PUMP REPAIRS
Engine Disassembled

1. When assembling the oil pump to the engine rear housing, install the idler gear on the shaft. Idler gear shaft should be .010″ to .020″ below gasket surface.

2. Place drive gear and shaft in pump housing.

3. Check projection of oil pump gears above gasket surface; this should be

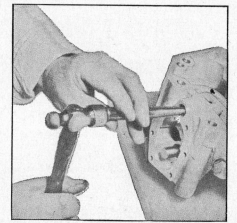

Fig. 39   Installing oil gallery plug

.0045″ maximum and .0025″ minimum. Clearance between gears and housing should be .005″.

4. Lubricate pump gears before installation. Install pump cover and tighten bolts.

5. Install a long screwdriver down the distributor mounting hole in the engine rear housing and turn oil pump drive shaft to see that pump turns freely.

6. Install pressure regulator valve, spring, gasket and plug.

OIL COOLER & BY-PASS VALVES
Engine Disassembled

1. Referring to Fig. 37, remove oil filter by-pass valve by catching the inner edge of the valve with a suitable hook or small screwdriver.

2. Install the new filter valve with the spring *up* in the adapter housing.

3. Remove the oil cooler valve in the same manner as the filter valve. However, the valve spring should be installed *down*.

ENGINE REAR HOUSING
Engine Disassembled

When replacing the engine rear housing as a new unit, the following opera-

tions are required.
1. Install groove pin, Fig. 38, which holds oil pump pressure regulator valve in place.
2. Install oil pump gallery plug flush with counterbore, using sealing compound, Fig. 39.
3. Install new rear housing seal.
4. Install distributor holding stud 1⅛" measured from distributor pad on engine rear housing.

FLYWHEEL HOUSING SEAL

Engine Disassembled

1. Tap seal out of housing with a wood or fibre drift.
2. Clean flywheel housing seal surface with solvent and check surface for nicks or damage.

3. Lubricate outer seal surface (beaded area) with lubriplate or petrolatum and install with suitable driver. *If seal is removed and still usable, pack sealing lips with a good grade of cup grease with a high melting point (350°). New seals are packed with this type grease to last the life of the seal.*

Clutch and Manual Transmission Section

NOTE: Transmission repair procedures are covered in separate sections.

CLUTCH LINKAGE, ADJUST
1966-69

1. Referring to Fig. 1, drive nut (8) to within ⅛" of threads on clutch cable rod assembly.
2. Tension clutch cable rod to 15 lbs and thread swivel (7) to line up with shaft (1) inboard lever with lever located to dimension shown from transmission crossmember. Assemble swivel (7) to lever with clip (2).
3. Torque nut (8) to swivel (7) to 7-12 ft-lbs.
4. Install spring (5) to bracket (6) and to shaft (1).
5. Manually pull clutch pull rod (4) forward until slack is taken up at clutch fork. With clutch pull rod in this position, align swivel (3) with hole in outboard to shaft lever. Back off swivel two turns and assemble to lever with clip (2).

CLUTCH, REPLACE

1. Remove engine, axle and transmission from the car and separate the axle and transmission from the engine as outlined in the *Power Train Section.*
2. The clutch fork, ball stud and clutch release bearing are removed with the axle housing.
3. Disconnect clutch fork from ball stud and remove clutch release bearing from shaft.
4. Remove 6 clutch attaching bolts, one turn at a time, until clutch spring pressure is released. Then remove clutch from engine.
5. Reverse above procedure to install the clutch, being sure the cushion springs of the clutch disc are located on the flywheel side of the driven plate hub.

3 & 4 SPEED TRANS., REPLACE
1966-69

NOTE: Either transmission can be removed from the vehicle, leaving the engine in the chassis as follows:

1. Disconnect engine seal (both sides) at front shield. *This is done by grasp-*

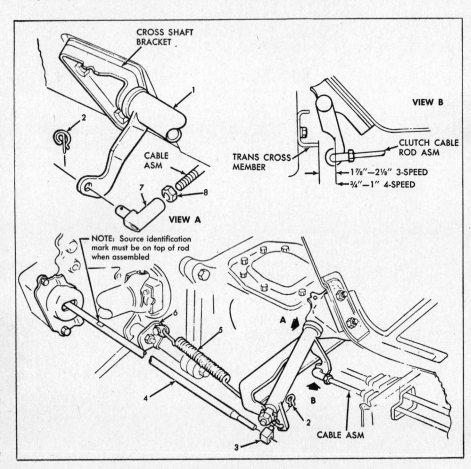

Fig. 1   Clutch linkage adjustment. 1966-68. Dimension shown is ⅜" for 1969

ing at lower edge and pulling groove of seal off shield flanges.
2. Disconnect starter motor wires at quick disconnect. Disconnect both battery cables at battery to avoid battery post damage when engine is lowered.
3. Disconnect radio ground straps (if equipped) at left and right shields.
4. Raise vehicle and support on jack stands, then remove rear-center shield.
5. Support weight of engine with a suitable lift.
6. Loosen two engine rear mount nuts until they are flush with end of stud.
7. Disconnect fuel line from body clip

so that line can swing away from floor pan.
8. To allow clearance for transaxle to swing down, loosen front upper bolt from each rear strut rod bracket at differential a few turns to relieve tension on lockwasher. Remove the three others on each side.
9. Disconnect accelerator rods at transmission bellcrank.
10. Disconnect left and right front strut rod brackets at engine front mount bracket.
11. Disconnect clutch fork pull rod and spring at clutch cross shaft. Loosen nut attaching cross shaft to engine front mount. Cross shaft can be ro-

tated and pushed up out of the way.

12. Disconnect shift rod coupling at transmission shift rod.
13. Disconnect emergency brake return spring at front mount bracket.
14. Remove back-up lamp switch wiring (if equipped).
15. Lower front of engine enough for transmission to clear underbody on removal. Remove bolts retaining transmission to differential, allowing transaxle to partially drain; then remove transmission from differential.

NOTE: Transmission input shaft remains engaged in clutch and will protrude out through differential. Transmission is removed with front mount bracket attached. To install transmission, reverse removal procedure. If the replacement transmission is being installed in a vehicle without back-up lights, be sure an expansion plug is installed in the lamp switch hole.

SHIFT LINKAGE, ADJUST
1966-69

To adjust the linkage, see Figs. 2 and 3 for details on the installation and for adjustment procedure.

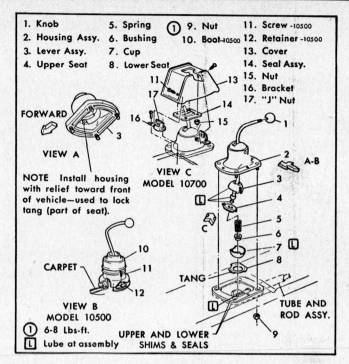

1. Knob
2. Housing Assy.
3. Lever Assy.
4. Upper Seat
5. Spring
6. Bushing
7. Cup
8. Lower Seat
9. Nut
10. Boot -10500
11. Screw -10500
12. Retainer -10500
13. Cover
14. Seal Assy.
15. Nut
16. Bracket
17. "J" Nut

FORWARD

VIEW A

NOTE Install housing with relief toward front of vehicle—used to lock tang (part of seat).

VIEW C
MODEL 10700

A-B

C

TANG

CARPET

VIEW B
MODEL 10500

① 6-8 Lbs-ft.
Ⓛ Lube at assembly

UPPER AND LOWER SHIMS & SEALS

TUBE AND ROD ASSY.

Fig. 2   Three and four-speed transmission gearshift control. 1966-69

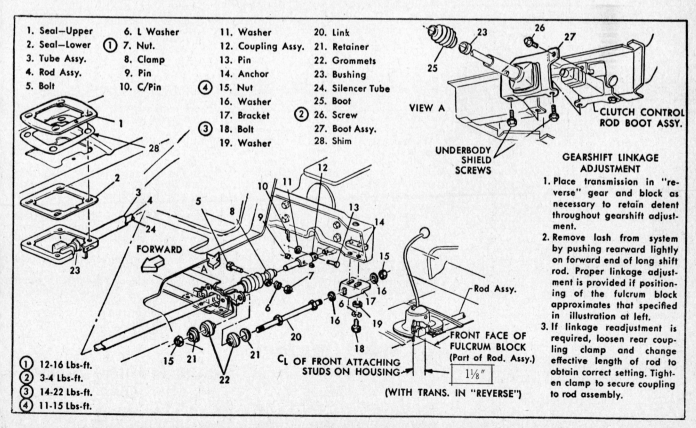

1. Seal—Upper
2. Seal—Lower
3. Tube Assy.
4. Rod Assy.
5. Bolt
6. L Washer
7. Nut.
8. Clamp
9. Pin
10. C/Pin
11. Washer
12. Coupling Assy.
13. Pin
14. Anchor
15. Nut
16. Washer
17. Bracket
18. Bolt
19. Washer
20. Link
21. Retainer
22. Grommets
23. Bushing
24. Silencer Tube
25. Boot
26. Screw
27. Boot Assy.
28. Shim

VIEW A

CLUTCH CONTROL ROD BOOT ASSY.

UNDERBODY SHIELD SCREWS

FORWARD

A

Rod Assy.

FRONT FACE OF FULCRUM BLOCK (Part of Rod. Assy.)

1⅛"

(WITH TRANS. IN "REVERSE")

CL OF FRONT ATTACHING STUDS ON HOUSING

① 12-16 Lbs-ft.
② 3-4 Lbs-ft.
③ 14-22 Lbs-ft.
④ 11-15 Lbs-ft.

GEARSHIFT LINKAGE ADJUSTMENT

1. Place transmission in "reverse" gear and block as necessary to retain detent throughout gearshift adjustment.
2. Remove lash from system by pushing rearward lightly on forward end of long shift rod. Proper linkage adjustment is provided if positioning of the fulcrum block approximates that specified in illustration at left.
3. If linkage readjustment is required, loosen rear coupling clamp and change effective length of rod to obtain correct setting. Tighten clamp to secure coupling to rod assembly.

Fig. 3   Three and four-speed transmission shift linkage installation and adjustment. 1966-69

Rear Axle and Brake Section

AXLE DESCRIPTION

The Corvair rear axle is of the straddle-mounted hypoid type which embodies a differential carrier mounted rigidly to the engine; no rear axle housing is used, Figs. 1 and 2. Independently suspended axle shafts are attached to universal joints which, in turn, are splined into the differential side gears.

A hollow shaft is used with the drive pinion to permit passage of the engine output shaft forward to the transmission. To permit the axial hole in the pinion shaft, the drive pinion and gear are two pieces coupled together. The drive pinion shaft is directly connected to the transmission output member. Preloaded tapered roller bearings support the drive pinion at fore and aft locations in the differential carrier. The ring gear is bolted to the differential case which is mounted on preloaded tapered roller bearings on each side of the differential carrier.

Components of the differential assembly are conventional with the exception of the side gears which have integral elongated splined hubs which project to the outboard extremity of the differential case and cover to receive the axle shaft universal joints.

WHEEL BEARINGS, ADJUST
1966-69

NOTE: The wheel spindle, spindle support, spindle bearings and spacer are the various items that affect wheel bearing end play. Therefore, when replacing any of these items, it will be necessary to ascertain proper adjusting shim thickness to maintain specified end play. Tool J-21836 is available to ascertain the shim thickness required. To use the tool, proceed as follows:

1. Remove knurled nut from each end of the gauge tool.
2. Position spindle inner bearing on small end of gauge (small end of bearing toward pin on gauge). Then finger tighten knurled nut against bearing, Fig. 3.
3. Position gauge and bearing assembly through inboard side of spindle support.
4. Install bearing spacer over large end of gauge, then position spindle outer bearing on gauge and against spacer, Fig. 4. Install undercut end of knurled nut against bearing and hand tighten nut so that there is no play in gauge body.
5. Install dial indicator as shown in Fig. 4 with gauge finger against movable shaft of tool J-21836.
6. Move shaft of tool so that it travels the maximum permissible distance limited by spacer and inner bearing. Record reading obtained and recheck to ensure accuracy.
7. To the reading obtained, add .097". The total obtained is the required shim thickness necessary to maintain specified end play.

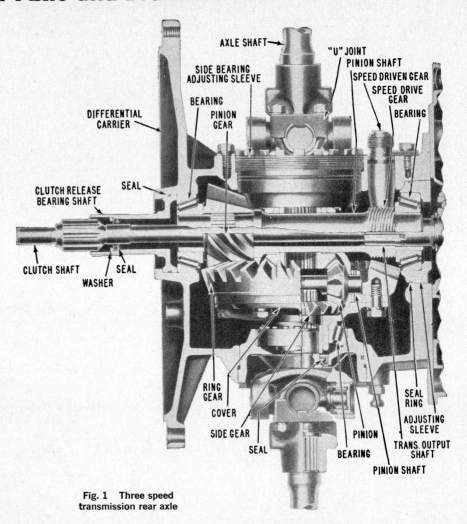

Fig. 1 Three speed transmission rear axle

EXAMPLE: If the dial indicator reading is .026" and we add .097", the total shim thickness is .123". The shim to be installed would be .124" thick since this is the shim with a thickness nearer to the value as computed above. The gauge is constructed to represent the smallest shim, which is .097".

8. Disassemble gauge and install spindle outer bearing. Pack both wheel bearings with the recommended grease prior to installation.
9. Position support outer seal on a suitable tool and install seal in support. Connect brake line.
10. Reassemble spindle to support.
11. Reassemble axle shaft, brake drum and wheel.

AXLE SHAFT, BEARING & U-JOINT
1966-69

1. Raise vehicle and support with jack stands at jacking pads on underbody.
2. Position hydraulic jack under torque arm bracket and raise jack until drive shaft is at or near curb position.
3. Bend lock tabs downward from their position against trunnion retaining bolts.
4. Disconnect inboard drive shaft trunnion from side gear yoke by removing the four bolts, retaining straps and bolt locks.
5. Remove four bolts, retaining straps and bolt locks securing outboard drive shaft trunnion to drive spindle flange.
6. Pry drive shaft out of flange or yoke and remove shaft.
7. Reverse procedure to install. Rotate drive shaft so that loose ends of trunnion are in a horizontal position, then tighten retaining bolts alternately until both ends of drive shaft are seated in trunnion seats.

SIDE BEARING SLEEVE SEAL
1966-69

1. Raise vehicle and remove axle drive

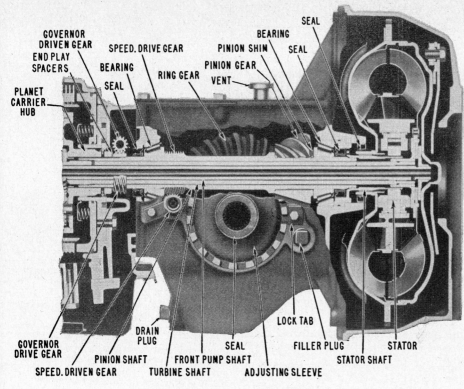

Fig. 2 Powerglide transmission rear axle

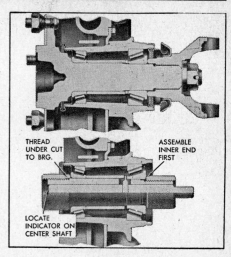

Fig. 3 Spindle bearing gauge installation. 1966-69

shaft and differential side bearing yoke.

2. Mark relationship of side bearing adjusting sleeve to differential carrier, making sure that these marks are easily identified as they are to be used to re-align sleeve to maintain differential side bearing preload.
3. Remove adjusting sleeve lock tab and sleeve. Record the number of turns necessary to remove sleeve from carrier, using marks scribed in Step 2 as a reference.
4. Remove damaged seal ring and install a new one in the groove. Apply a thin coating of vaseline to seal after installation in groove.
5. Install sleeve in carrier, making sure that sleeve is turned to correspond with the number of turns recorded in Step 3.
6. Back off the number of turns to relieve seal windup, then reposition to original setting and install lock tab.
7. Install side bearing yoke and axle drive shaft.

DIFFERENTIAL CARRIER

1. After removing the engine from the car, the differential is then removed from the engine. Disassemble differential carrier by first removing speedometer driven gear.
2. Remove differential carrier cover.
3. Remove side gear adjusting sleeves, Fig. 5.
4. Remove pinion adjusting sleeve, Fig. 6.
5. Remove pinion drive gear with bearings attached, Fig. 7.
6. Remove differential from carrier by shifting differential to one side of carrier and then turning 90 degrees in order to remove via the cover hole in carrier.

Inspection

1. Inspect all bearing cups, races and rollers for damage and wear, especially large end of rollers as this is where wear is most evident on taper roller bearings. The rear axle pinion bearings are of the pre-loaded type, and the natural wear pattern is a slightly frosted condition with occasional slight scratches on races and rollers. This does not indicate a defective bearing.
2. On Powerglide axles, inspect oil seal in stator support and at converter hub for evidence of wear or damage.
3. Inspect pinion splines for evidence of excessive wear.
4. Inspect ring gear and pinion teeth for scoring, chipping or cracking.
5. Check fit of differential side gears in case.
6. Check fit of side gear and U-joint shaft splines.
7. Inspect differential pinion shaft for scoring or evidence of excessive wear.
8. Inspect differential carrier for cracks or crossed threads.

AXLE REPAIRS
For Three Speed and Powerglide Axles

NOTE—*Repairs required on three speed*

Fig. 4 Gauging rear wheel bearing shim requirements 1966-69

Fig. 5 Removing side bearing adjusting sleeve

Fig. 6   Removing pinion adjusting sleeve

axles only, and those for Powerglide axles only are outlined further on. Refer to Fig. 8 for relationship of parts.

Pinion Bearing, Replace

When it becomes necessary to replace pinion bearings and/or ring gear and drive pinion, it is necessary to re-establish the pinion mounting distance.

Pinion bearings may be removed with the aid of a press. It will be noted that a shim or shims are used between the pinion rear bearing and pinion. To determine the shim thickness to be used when installing new parts special gauges are required, Fig. 9. Lacking this equipment, check the ring gear contact pattern as shown in Fig. 10. To do this the differential carrier must be assembled. If a change is indicated, disassemble the parts and change the shimming as required to obtain the proper tooth contact pattern. Shims are available in thicknesses of .006, .009, .012, .015 and .018".

Pinion Front Bearing Race

1. Thread adjusting sleeve and race assembly into carrier until finger tight and remove old race with a punch or other suitable tool. On Powerglide models it is necessary to remove the seal.

CAUTION: Adjusting sleeve should engage sufficient threads in carrier to prevent

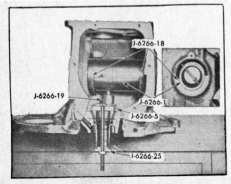

Fig. 9   Pinion depth shim selection gauges

possible thread damage when driving out race.

2. Install new race in pinion adjusting sleeve.

Side Bearing Adjusting Sleeve Bearing Race

1. Thread side bearing adjusting sleeve and race assembly into carrier until finger tight and drive out old race with a punch or other suitable tool.

CAUTION: Adjusting sleeve should engage sufficient threads in carrier to prevent possible thread damage when driving out race.

2. Install new bearing race in adjusting sleeve, using a suitable flat plate as a driver. Drive bearing race until it is flush with sleeve face.

Differential Overhaul

Disassemble the differential as suggested by Fig. 11. To remove the differential pinions after the case has been separated, drive out the roll pin securing the differential pinion shaft to the case. Before separating the differential case halves, punch mark the rim of both halves so that they may be attached in the original position, Fig. 12. When securing the ring gear to the case, tighten all bolts to a torque of 40-60 ft. lbs. in a criss-cross pattern.

REPAIRS ON 3 SPEED TRANS. AXLES ONLY

Clutch Release Bearing Shaft Seal

Remove split ring and old seal from clutch release bearing shaft by prying out with a punch. Install the new seal, open side inward, using a suitable socket (¾") and socket extension. Drive seal until it bottoms, then install split ring in clutch release bearing shaft.

Clutch Release Bearing Shaft and/or Pinion Bearing Rear Race

1. Place differential carrier in arbor press and press out shaft and race.
2. If a new shaft is being installed, first install the inner seal. Install a new seal ring in groove on outer diameter of bearing shaft and lubricate with vaseline.
3. Support differential carrier only on boss at clutch release bearing location with a suitable cylinder; then place bearing race on shaft and press both into differential carrier. Press until cup is flush with adjacent surface inside carrier.

REPAIRS ON POWERGLIDE AXLES ONLY

Pinion Shaft Front Oil Seal and/or Converter Hub Oil Seal

The pinion shaft front oil seal and the converter hub oil seal are located dia-

Fig. 7   Removing pinion from carrier

metrically opposite fore and aft respectively, in the differential carrier.

Remove the oil seal by prying out with a punch or similar tool. Coat outer diameter of new seal with a non-hardening sealer and install seal. The converter hub seal is mounted flush. A special driver is available to install the pinion seal. A stop is provided on this driver which insures the seal being installed to the proper depth. This same driver (J-8340) is also used to drive the converter hub seal.

Pinion Shaft Rear Oil Seal

Drive out the old seal with a pin punch inserted through access hole in stator shaft. Install new seal as shown in Fig. 13 until it bottoms.

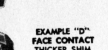

Fig. 10   Ring gear contact patterns

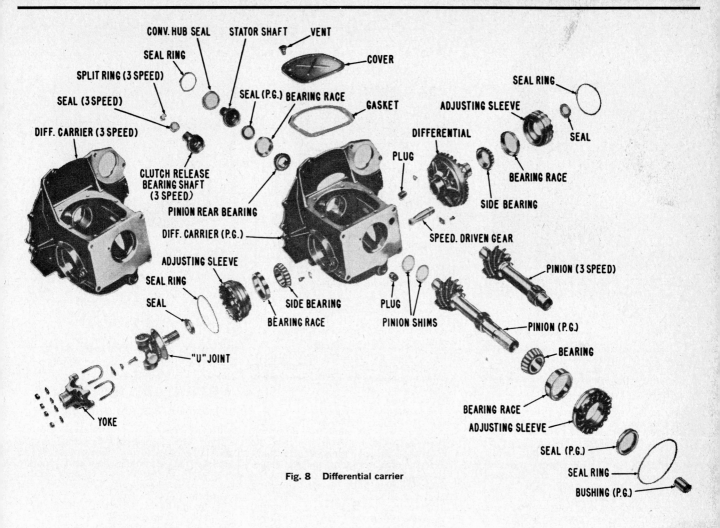

Fig. 8   Differential carrier

Pinion Shaft Bushing

Remove old bushing from inside diameter of pinion shaft using a chisel or other suitable tool. Use care not to damage the bushing mating surfaces in pinion shaft during removal.

Install new bushing with a suitable driver. Special tool J-8333 is available for this operation; it has a stop provided thereon to press the bushing to the proper depth.

Stator Shaft and/or Pinion Rear Bearing Race

1. Remove stator shaft and pinion bearing cup from carrier by placing carrier in a press and pressing downward on end of stator shaft. Replace parts removed.
2. Install seal ring in groove on outside diameter of stator shaft and lubricate with vaseline. *Outer diameter seal is not used on later production*

stator shafts.
3. If a new stator shaft is being installed, it will be necessary to install a new pinion rear oil seal as previously described.
4. Align notch in stator shaft, Fig. 13, with drain back passage boss in dif-

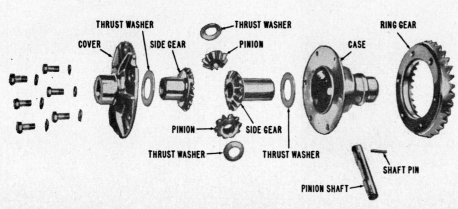

Fig. 11   Differential assembly

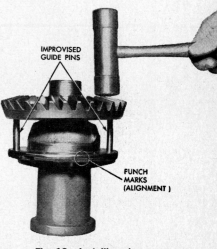

Fig. 12   Installing ring gear on differential case and cover, using improvised guide pins

Fig. 13   Installing pinion rear oil seal in stator shaft

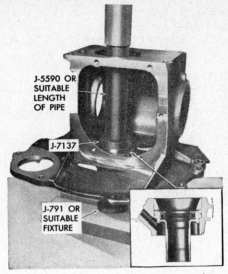

J-5590 OR
SUITABLE
LENGTH
OF PIPE

J-7137

J-791 OR
SUITABLE
FIXTURE

Fig. 14   Installing stator shaft and pinion rear bearing race

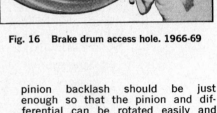

Fig. 16   Brake drum access hole. 1966-69

ferential carrier. Place bearing race on stator shaft and press race and shaft into housing, Fig. 14. *Carrier must be supported only at stator shaft boss for this operation.*

ASSEMBLE DIFFERENTIAL CARRIER

1. Referring to Fig. 8, insert differential into carrier with side bearing cones installed on differential hubs.
2. While differential is loose in carrier, insert pinion into carrier through cover hole. Then engage pinion with ring gear and carefully position pinion rear bearing in race. On Powerglide models, care must be used not to damage seal at this loca-

tion when pinion is installed.
3. Install new O-ring seals in side bearing adjusting sleeves. Coat adjusting sleeve threads with a non-hardening pipe thread compound. Loosely install sleeves in carrier with side bearings positioned in sleeves.
4. On Powerglide models, install a new O-ring seal in pinion adjusting sleeve. Position pinion so that its front bearing will pick up the bearing race in sleeve and loosely install sleeve in carrier. Use care not to damage seal lips when inserting pinion shaft over adjusting sleeve.
5. Tighten both side bearing adjusting sleeves and pinion adjusting sleeve to the point of contact between bearings and races. At this point, there should be no preload on any of the bearings and ring gear and

pinion backlash should be just enough so that the pinion and differential can be rotated easily and smoothly. The assembly is now ready for ring gear and pinion adjustment.

BRAKE ADJUSTMENTS
1966-69 Self-Adjusting Brakes

These brakes, Fig. 15, have self-adjusting shoe mechanisms that assure correct lining-to-drum clearances at all times. The automatic adjusters operate only when the brakes are applied as the car is moving rearward or when the car comes to an uphill stop.

Although the brakes are self-adjusting, an initial adjustment is necessary after the brake shoes have been relined or replaced, or when the length of the star wheel adjuster has been changed during some other service operation.

Frequent usage of an automatic transmission forward range to halt reverse vehicle motion may prevent the automatic adjusters from functioning, thereby inducing low pedal heights. Should

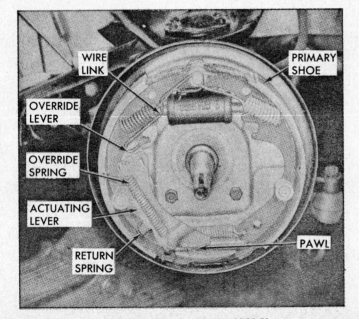

WIRE LINK

PRIMARY SHOE

OVERRIDE LEVER

OVERRIDE SPRING

ACTUATING LEVER

RETURN SPRING

PAWL

Fig. 15   Right front brake. 1966-69

drum locating tang

Fig. 17   Aligning drum tang with wheel hub. 1966-69

low pedal heights be encountered, it is recommended that numerous forward and reverse stops be made until satisfactory pedal height is obtained.

NOTE

If a low pedal height condition cannot be corrected by making numerous reverse stops (provided the hydraulic system is free of air) it indicates that the self-adjusting mechanism is not functioning. Therefore, it will be necessary to remove the brake drum, clean, free up and lubricate the adjusting mechanism. Then adjust the brake, being sure the parking brake is fully released.

Adjustment

A lanced "knock out" area, Fig. 16, is provided in the web of the brake drum for servicing purposes in the event retracting of the brake shoes is required in order to remove the drum.

1. With brake drum off, disengage the actuator from the star wheel and rotate the star wheel by spinning or turning with a screwdriver.
2. Using the brake drum as an adjustment fixture, turn the star wheel until the drum slides over the brake shoes with a slide drag.
3. Turn the star wheel $1\frac{1}{4}$ turns to retract the brake shoes. This will allow sufficient lining-to-drum clearance so final adjustment may be made.
4. Install drum and wheel. *NOTE: If lanced area in brake drum was knocked out, be sure all metal has been removed from brake compartment. Install new hole cover in drum to prevent contamination of brakes. Make certain that drums are installed in the same position as when removed with the drum locating tang in line with the locating hole in the wheel hub, Fig. 17.*
5. Make final adjustment by driving and stopping vehicle forward and reverse until satisfactory pedal height is obtained.

PARKING BRAKE, ADJUST

1. With service brakes properly adjusted and rear wheels raised, pull parking brake lever up one notch from fully released position.
2. Loosen forward check nut on equalizer and tighten rear nut until a heavy drag is felt when rear wheels are rotated.
3. Tighten check nuts securely.
4. Fully release parking brake and rotate rear wheels; no drag should be present.

MASTER CYLINDER, REPLACE

1. Disconnect hydraulic lines from outlet end of cylinder.
2. Remove pedal return spring.
3. Unfasten mounting nuts from dash wall and remove cylinder.

Suspension and Steering Section

FRONT WHEEL BEARINGS
1966-69

1. With spindle nut loosened slightly, rotate wheel while applying 12 ft-lbs torque to spindle nut.
2. To align cotter pin hole, back off spindle nut more than one nut flat but less than $1\frac{1}{2}$ flats. Then insert cotter pin. Spindle nut back-off must exceed one flat in order to achieve the .001 to .008" bearing end play required.

FRONT WHEEL ALIGNMENT
1966-69

CAMBER ADJUST

Camber angle is adjusted by loosening the lower control arm pivot bolt and rotating the cams located on this pivot, Fig. 1. The eccentric cam action will move the lower control arm in or out, thereby varying camber.

CASTER ADJUST

Caster is adjusted by turning the two nuts at the rear of the strut rod, Fig. 2. Lengthening this rod by turning the nuts increases caster. Shortening the rod by turning the nuts decreases caster.

REAR WHEEL ALIGNMENT
1966-69

CAMBER ADJUST

1. Camber angle of rear wheels should be $+\frac{1}{2}°$ to $+1\frac{1}{2}°$. Adjustment is made by rotating the eccentric cam and bolt assembly, located at the

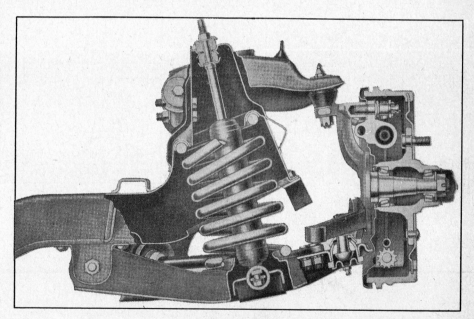

Front suspension

outboard mounting of rear strut rod, Fig. 3.
2. Place rear wheels on an alignment machine and determine camber angle.
3. Loosen cam bolt and rotate cam and bolt assembly to obtain the specified camber. Tighten nut on bolt securely.

TOE-IN, ADJUST

1. Total toe-in of rear wheels is $\frac{1}{8}$" to $\frac{3}{8}$". It is adjusted by moving the torque arm-to-underbody bracket horizontally as required, Fig. 3.
2. To adjust, loosen front strut rod inner bracket-to-transmission support bolts so that bracket is loose on slots. Then loosen bracket-to-underbody attaching bolts until bracket is free enough to be moved.
3. Position torque arm to obtain specified toe-in and tighten bolts securely.

CHECKING BALL JOINTS FOR WEAR

Before checking, make sure front wheel bearings are properly adjusted and that control arms are tight.

Referring to Fig. 4, raise wheel with

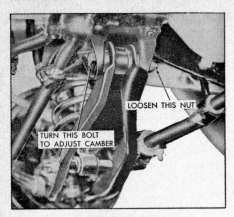

Fig. 1 Front wheel camber adjustment. 1966-69

a jack placed under the lower control at the point shown. Then test by moving the wheel up and down to check axial play, and rocking it at the top and bottom to measure radial play.

1. Upper ball joint should be replaced if there is any noticeable looseness at the joint.
2. Lower ball joint should be replaced if radial play exceeds .250".
3. Lower ball joint should be replaced if the axial play between lower control arm and spindle exceeds the following:
   1966-69 . . . . .060".

BALL JOINTS, REPLACE

On all models the upper ball joints are riveted to the upper control arm. All service ball joints, however, are provided with bolt, nut and washer assemblies for replacement purposes.

On all models, the lower ball joints

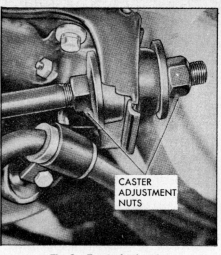

Fig. 2 Front wheel caster adjustment. 1966-69

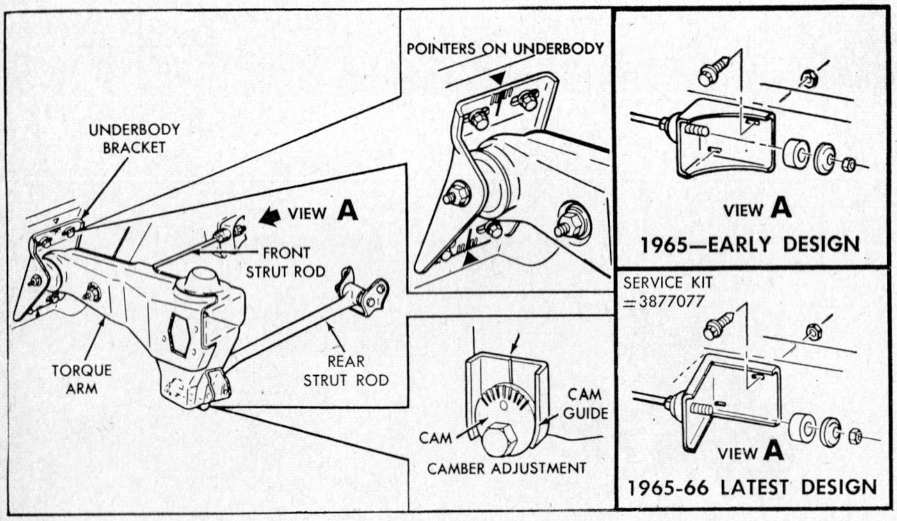

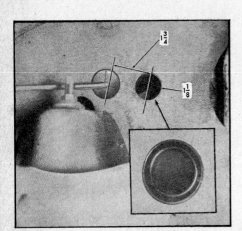

Fig. 3 Rear wheel adjusting bracket. 1966-69

COIL SPRING, REPLACE

1. Raise vehicle and allow front control arms to swing free.
2. Remove shock absorber.
3. Remove strut rod nuts (pressed in).
4. *Loosen but do not remove lower*

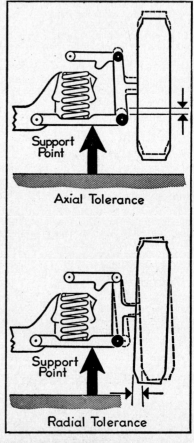

Fig. 4 Checking ball joints for wear

are pressed into the lower control arms.

In servicing the front suspension, it will be desirable to raise the car on a hoist and the suspension allowed to swing free. If a twin post hoist or similar equipment is used, support the front of the vehicle at the forward end of the body side rail extension (each side) with jackstands and lower front of hoist.

SHOCK ABSORBER, REPLACE

1. With vehicle supported and front end hanging free, remove upper attaching nut, cup washer and grommet.
2. Remove two lower attaching bolts.
3. Withdraw shock absorber through lower control arm.
4. Reverse above procedure to install, extending shock absorber shaft to its full length to facilitate installation.

Fig. 5 Drill hole in location shown to provide an access hole for removal of steering gear, 1966 only. Insert shows plug used to close hole after gear is installed.

control arm inner pivot nut.

5. Place jackstand under inner end of control arm under bushing.

6. Remove control arm pivot nut and tap out pivot pin.

7. Lower hoist or jackstand until spring is free and take it out. *A bar placed through control arm and in-spring tower will retain spring and keep it from slipping until free. Otherwise, keep clear of suspension until all compression is removed from spring.*

Reverse above procedure to replace the spring. When installing, place rubber spacer in place on top of spring and secure it with friction tape. Step in spacer must contact end of spring.

STEERING GEAR
1966-69

1. To remove steering gear, raise front of vehicle and (1966 only) drill a $1\frac{1}{8}''$ diameter hole in left front splash shield, Fig. 5.

2. Remove steering coupling clamp bolt.

3. Use a puller to remove pitman arm.

4. Unfasten and remove steering gear from below vehicle.

5. Reverse procedure to install. From below vehicle, guide steering gear and shaft into position carefully to align coupling with notch in steering shaft. Insert plug in access hole drilled in splash shield.

CHEVROLET VEGA

OLD CAR SPECIFICATIONS: For 1946-65 Tune Up and Wheel Alignment Specifications see back of book.

*This material covered only in the "Service Trade Edition" of this manual.

INDEX OF SERVICE OPERATIONS

SERIAL NUMBER LOCATION

On top of instrument panel, left front.

1971-72

ENGINE NUMBER LOCATION

On pad at right side of cylinder block, above starter.

GENERAL ENGINE SPECIFICATIONS

Year	Engine	Car- buretor	Bore and Stroke	Piston Dis- place- ment, Cubic Inches	Com- pres- sion Ratio	Maximum Brake H.P. @ R.P.M.	Maximum Torque Lbs. Ft. @ R.P.M.	Normal Oil Pressure Pounds
1971-72	80 Horsepower①...............4-140	1 Barrel	3.501 x 3.625	140	8.00	80 @ 4400	121 @ 2400	40
	90 Horsepower①...............4-140	2 Barrel	3.501 x 3.625	140	8.00	90 @ 4800	121 @ 2800	40

①—Ratings Net—as installed in the vehicle.

TUNE UP SPECIFICATIONS

OLD CAR SPECIFICATIONS: For 1964—65 Tune Up Specifications see back of book.

★When using a timing light, disconnect vacuum hose or tube at distributor and plug opening in hose or tube so idle speed will not be affected.

Year	Engine Model	Spark Plug		Distributor		Firing Order	Ignition Timing★		Hot Idle Speed		Comp. Press. Lbs. ③	Fuel Pump Press. Lbs.
		Type AC	Gap Inch	Point Gap Inch	Dwell Angle Deg.		BTDC ①	Mark	Std. Trans.	Auto. Trans. ②		
1971	80 Horsepower	R42TS	.035	.019	31-34	Fig. A	6°	Fig. B	850⑤	650D⑤	140	3-4½
	90 Horsepower	R42TS	.035	.019	31-34	Fig. A	④	Fig. B	1200⑥	700D⑥	140	3-4½
1972	80 Horsepower	R42TS	.035	.019	31-34	Fig. A	6°⑦	Fig. B	850⑥	700D⑧	140	3-4½
	90 Horsepower	R42TS	.035	.019	31-34	Fig. A	8°	Fig. B	1200	700D⑧	140	3-4½

①—BTDC—Before top dead center.
②—D—Drive.
③—Plus or minus 20 lbs.
④—With synchromesh trans. 6°; with automatic trans. 10°.
⑤—Solenoid disconnected.
⑥—1200 R.P.M. in California.
⑦—4° for California vehicles w/manual trans.

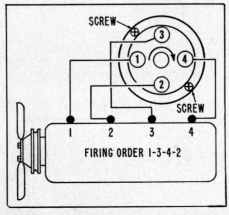

SCREW

SCREW

FIRING ORDER 1-3-4-2

Fig. A

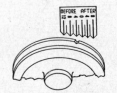

BEFORE AFTER

Fig. B

CHEVROLET VEGA

VALVE SPECIFICATIONS

Year	Engine Model	Valve Lash		Valve Angles		Valve Spring Installed Height	Valve Spring Pressure Lbs. @ In.	Stem Clearance		Stem Diameter	
		Int.	Exh.	Seat	Face			Intake	Exhaust	Intake	Exhaust
1971-72	80 Horsepower	.015C	.030C	46	45	1.746	186 @ 1.29	.001-.0027	.001-.0027	.3410-.3417	.3410-.3417
	90 Horsepower	.015C	.030C	46	45	1.746	190 @ 1.31	.001-.0027	.001-.0027	.3410-.3417	.3410-.3417

DISTRIBUTOR SPECIFICATIONS

★NOTE: If advance is checked on vehicle, double the R.P.M. and degrees advance to get crankshaft figures.

Year	Model	Distributor Part No.①	Breaker Gap	Dwell Angle Deg.	Breaker Arm Spring Tension	Centrifugal Advance Degrees @ R.P.M. of Distributor★		Vacuum Advance			Dist. Retard
						Advance Starts	Full Advance	Inches of Vacuum To Start Plunger	Max. Adv. Dist. Deg. @ Vacuum		Max. Ret. Dist. Deg. @ Vacuum
1971-72	Std. Trans.	1110492	.019	31-34	19-23	0 @ 590	12 @ 2000	7	12 @ 15		—
	Auto. Trans.	1110435	.019	31-34	19-23	0 @ 470	11 @ 2000	7	12 @ 17		—

ALTERNATOR & REGULATOR SPECIFICATIONS

Year	Alternator					Regulator							
				Cold Output @ 14 Volts			Field Relay			Voltage Regulator			
	Model	Rated Hot Output Amps.	Field Current 12 Volts @ 80 F.	2000 R.P.M. Amps.	5000 R.P.M. Amps.	Model	Air Gap In.	Point Gap In.	Closing Voltage	Air Gap In.	Point Gap In.	Voltage @ 125° F.
1971-72	1100545	32	4-4.5	—	31	—	—	—	—	—	—	—
	1100546	55	4-4.5	—	50	—	—	—	—	—	—	—
	1100559	32	4-4.5	—	31	—	—	—	—	—	—	—
	1100560	55	4-4.5	—	50	—	—	—	—	—	—	—

STARTING MOTOR SPECIFICATIONS

Year	Model	Starter Number	Brush Spring Tension Oz.①	Free Speed Test			Resistance Test	
				Amps.	Volts	R.P.M.①	Amps.	Volts
1971-72	Std. Trans.	1108195	—	50-75	9	6500-10000	—	—
	Auto. Trans.	1108196	—	50-75	9	6500-10000	—	—

①—Minimum.

2-212

ENGINE TIGHTENING SPECIFICATIONS★

★Torque specifications are for clean and lightly lubricated threads only. Dry or dirty threads produce increased friction which prevents accurate measurement of tightness.

Year	Engine Model	Spark Plugs Ft. Lbs.	Cylinder Head Bolts Ft. Lbs.	Intake Manifold Ft. Lbs.	Exhaust Manifold Ft. Lbs.	Rocker Arm Stud Ft. Lbs.	Cam Cover Ft. Lbs.	Connecting Rod Cap Bolts Ft. Lbs.	Main Bearing Cap Bolts Ft. Lbs.	Flywheel to Crankshaft Ft. Lbs.	Vibration Damper or Pulley Ft. Lbs.
1971–72	4-140	15	60	30	30	—	35①	35	65	60	80

①—Inch pounds.

PISTONS, PINS, RINGS, CRANKSHAFT & BEARINGS

Year	Engine Model	Piston Clearance	Ring End Gap① Comp.	Ring End Gap① Oil	Wrist-pin Diameter	Rod Bearings Shaft Diameter	Rod Bearings Bearing Clearance	Main Bearings Shaft Diameter	Main Bearings Bearing Clearance	Thrust on Bear. No.	Shaft End Play
1971–72	4-140	.0020–.0028	.009	.010	.927	1.999–2.000	.0007–.0027	2.2983–2.2993	.0003–.0029	4	.002–.007

①—Fit rings in tapered bores for clearance listed in tightest portion of ring travel.

WHEEL ALIGNMENT SPECIFICATIONS

OLD CAR SPECIFICATIONS: For 1946-65 Wheel Alignment Specifications see back of book.

Year	Model	Caster Angle, Degrees Limits	Caster Angle, Degrees Desired	Camber Angle, Degrees Limits Left	Camber Angle, Degrees Limits Right	Camber Angle, Degrees Desired Left	Camber Angle, Degrees Desired Right	Toe-In. Inch	Toe-Out on Turns, Deg.① Outer Wheel	Toe-Out on Turns, Deg.① Inner Wheel
1971–72	All	— ¼ to − 1¼	− ¾	− ¼ to + ¾	− ¼ to + ¾	+ ¼	+ ¼	³⁄₁₆ to ⁵⁄₁₆	—	—

①—Incorrect toe-out when other adjustments are correct, indicates bent steering arms.

COOLING SYSTEM & CAPACITY DATA

Year	Model or Engine	Cooling Capacity, Qts. No Heater	Cooling Capacity, Qts. With Heater	Cooling Capacity, Qts. With A/C	Radiator Cap Relief Pressure, Lbs. With A/C	Radiator Cap Relief Pressure, Lbs. No A/C	Thermo. Opening Temp. ①	Fuel Tank Gals.	Engine Oil Refill Qts. ②	Transmission Oil 3 Speed Pints	Transmission Oil 4 Speed Pints	Transmission Oil Auto. Trans. Qts. ③	Rear Axle Oil Pints
1971–72	4-140	5.7	6.5	6.5	15	15	195	11	3	2.4	3	③	2.5

①—For permanent type anti-freeze.   ②—Add 1 quart with filter change.   ③—Refill 3 qts.   Total capacity 8½ qts.

REAR AXLE SPECIFICATIONS

Year	Model	Carrier Type	Ring Gear & Pinion Backlash		Pinion Bearing Preload			Differential Bearing Preload		
			Method	Adjustment	Method	New Bearings Inch-Lbs.	Used Bearings Inch-Lbs.	Method	New Bearings Inch-Lbs.	Used Bearings Inch-Lbs.
1971-72	All	Integral	Shims	.005–.008	Spacer	25	10	Shims	—	—

BRAKE SPECIFICATIONS

Year	Model	Brake Drum Inside Diameter	Wheel Cylinder Bore Diameter			Master Cylinder Bore Diameter		
			Disc Brake	Front Drum Brake	Rear Drum Brake	Disc Brakes	Drum Brakes	Power Brakes
1971-72	All	9	1⅞	—	¾	¾	—	¾

Electrical Section

DISTRIBUTOR

Removal

1. Release distributor cap hold-down screws and remove cap.
2. Disconnect distributor primary lead from coil terminal.
3. Scribe an alignment mark on the distributor and engine in line with the rotor.
4. Remove distributor hold-down bolt and clamp and remove distributor.
   CAUTION: Avoid rotating engine while distributor is removed.

Installation

1. Turn rotor about ⅛ turn in a clockwise direction past the mark previously made to locate rotor.
2. Push distributor down into position in cylinder head with distributor housing in a normal installed position.

NOTE: It may be necessary to move rotor slightly to start gear into mesh with camshaft gear, but rotor should line up with the mark when distributor is down in place.

3. Tighten distributor clamp bolt and connect vacuum line, primary wire and install the cap.

NOTE

If the engine was disturbed while the distributor was removed, it will be necessary to crank the engine to bring No. 1 cylinder piston up on the compression stroke. Continue cranking until timing mark is adjacent to pointer. Then rotate the distributor cam until rotor is in position to fire No. 1. Install distributor in this position and tighten clamp bolt and check timing.

STARTER, REPLACE

NOTE: The following procedure may vary slightly depending on model and series of vehicle.

1. Disconnect battery ground cable at battery.
2. Disconnect all wires at solenoid terminals.

NOTE: Reinstall the nuts on the terminals as each wire is removed as thread size is different and if mixed, stripping of threads may occur.

3. Loosen starter front bracket then remove two mount bolts, Fig. 1.
4. Remove front bracket bolt and rotate bracket clear of work area then lower starter from vehicle by lowering front end first.
5. Reverse procedure to install.

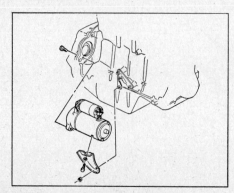

Fig. 1   Starter motor installation

IGNITION SWITCH, REPLACE

The ignition switch is mounted on the top of the steering column jacket near the front of the dash. It is located inside the channel section of the brake pedal support and is completely inaccessible without first lowering the steering column.

1. Lower the steering column and be sure it is properly supported before proceeding.
2. The switch should be positioned in Lock position before removing, Fig. 2.
3. Unfasten and remove the switch, detaching it from the actuating rod.
4. When installing, make sure the lock and the switch are in the Lock position. Then install the activating rod into the switch and fasten the switch.

LIGHT SWITCH, REPLACE

1. Disconnect ground cable at battery.
2. Pull headlamp switch knob to "ON" position.

Fig. 2   Ignition switch assembly

3. Reach under instrument panel and depress switch shaft retainer button while pulling on the switch control shaft knob.
4. With a large bladed screwdriver, remove the light switch ferrule nut from front of instrument panel.
5. Disconnect the multi-contact connector from side of switch and remove switch.

STOP LIGHT SWITCH

1. Reach under right side of instrument panel at brake pedal support and release wiring harness connector at switch.
2. Pull switch from mounting bracket.
3. When installing switch, adjust by bringing brake pedal to normal position. Electrical contact should be made when pedal is depressed as shown in Fig. 4. To adjust, the switch may be rotated or pulled in the clip.

CLUTCH START SWITCH

NOTE: The clutch pedal must be fully depressed and the ignition switch in START position for the vehicle to start.

The clutch switch assembly mounts with two tangs to the clutch pedal brace switch pivot bracket and the clutch pedal

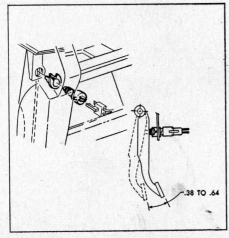

Fig. 4   Stop light switch replacement

arm, Fig. 5.
1. Under the instrument panel on the clutch pedal support remove the multi-contact connector from switch.
2. Compress switch assembly actuating shaft barb retainer and push out of clutch pedal.
3. Compress switch assembly pivot bracket barb and lift off switch.
4. When installing new switch, no adjustments are necessary as the switch is self aligning.

NEUTRAL SAFETY SWITCH, REPLACE

1. Remove four screws securing floor console, Fig. 6.
2. Disconnect electrical plugs on back-up contacts and neutral start contacts of switch assembly.
3. Place shift lever in Neutral.
4. Remove two screws securing shift indicator plate.
5. Remove two screws securing shift lever curved cover.
6. Remove two screws securing switch to lever assembly.

NOTE: Screws are hidden beneath lever cover.

7. Tilt switch to right as you lift switch out of lever hole.
8. When installing switch, make sure it is in Neutral position. When switch is installed, shifting out of Neutral will shear the switch plastic locating pin.

TURN SIGNAL SWITCH, REPLACE

1. Remove steering wheel with suitable puller.
2. Remove three cover screws and lift cover off the shaft. **NOTE:** These screws have plastic retainers on the back of the cover so it is not necessary to completely remove these screws.
3. Place Lock Plate Compressing Tool J-23653, Fig. 7, on end of steering shaft and compress the lock plate as far as possible using the shaft nut as shown. Pry the round wire snap ring out of the shaft groove and discard the ring. Remove tool and lift lock plate off end of shaft.
4. Slide the signal cancelling cam, upper bearing preload spring and thrust washer off the end of shaft.
5. Remove turn signal lever screw and remove the lever.
6. Push hazard warning knob in and unscrew the knob.
7. Wrap upper part of connector with tape, Fig. 8, to prevent snagging of wires during switch removal.
8. Remove three screws on switch and pull switch straight up through housing.

HORN SOUNDER & STEERING WHEEL

1. Disconnect battery ground cable.

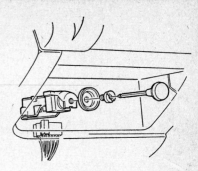

Fig. 3   Light switch replacement

2. On regular production steering wheel models, remove the two screws securing the steering wheel shroud from beneath the wheel and remove the shroud. On GT or optional wheel models, pry off horn button cap.
3. Remove steering wheel nut and use a suitable puller to remove the steering wheel.

INSTRUMENT CLUSTER

Standard Cluster

The instrument cluster bezel is retained by nine screws. After removal of bezel, remove cluster lens-light shield combination (2 screws at top of lens and 2 screws at bottom of light shield). The lens tips out at the top and then lifts off. Instruments are then easily removed.

GT Cluster

The cluster bezel is retained by six screws. After removal of bezel, remove the lens light shield (6 screws). Then lift lens and light shield straight out. Instruments are then accessible for replacement.

W/S WIPER MOTOR

1. Raise hood.
2. Reaching through cowl opening,

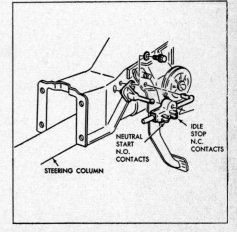

Fig. 5   Clutch operated neutral start switch

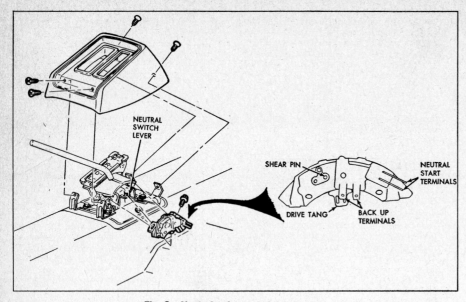

Fig. 6   Neutral safety switch installation

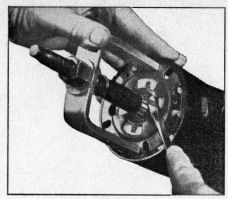

Fig. 7   Removing lock plate retaining ring

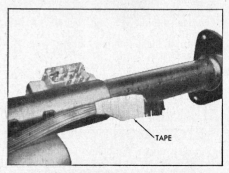

Fig. 8   Taping turn signal connector and wires

loosen the two transmission drive link attaching nuts to motor crankarm.
3. Remove transmission drive link from motor crankarm.
4. Disconnect wiring and unfasten motor and remove.

W/S WIPER SWITCH

1. Beneath instrument panel, unplug the headlamp switch multi-connector for clearance to wiper switch screw.
2. Unplug connector on bottom of wiper switch.
3. Remove two screws mounting washer pump.

NOTE: Do not remove washer pump hoses.

4. Remove two remaining mounting screws from wiper switch and drop switch from behind instrument panel.

RADIO, REPLACE

NOTE: When installing radio, be sure to adjust antenna trimmer for peak performance.

1. Remove battery ground cable.
2. Remove knobs, controls, washers and nuts from radio bushings.
3. Disconnect antenna lead, power connector and speaker connectors from rear of radio.

4. Remove two screws securing radio mounting bracket to instrument panel lower reinforcement and lift out radio.

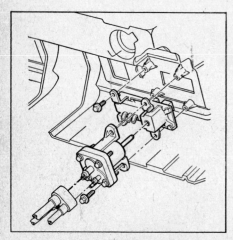

Fig. 9   Wiper-washer control switch

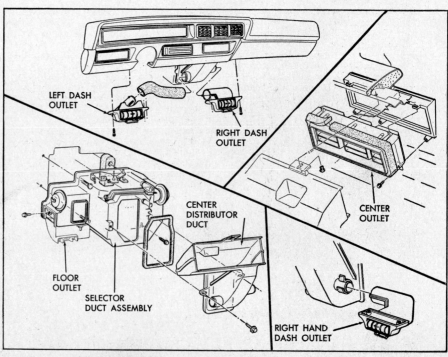

Fig. 10   Air distributor ducts and outlets on air conditioned cars

HEATER CORE REMOVAL

Without Air Conditioning

1. Disconnect battery ground cable.
2. Disconnect blower motor lead wire.
3. Place a pan under vehicle and disconnect heater hoses at core connections and secure ends of hoses in a raised position.
4. Remove the coil bracket to dash panel stud nut and move coil out of way.
5. Remove the blower inlet to dash panel screws and nuts and remove the blower inlet, blower motor and wheel as an assembly.
6. Remove the core retainer strap screws and remove the core.
7. When replacing core, be sure the blower inlet sealer is intact.

With Air Conditioning

1. Disconnect battery ground cable.
2. Place a pan under heater core tubes, disconnect heater hoses at the core and secure ends of hoses in a raised position. Cap or tape the core tubes to prevent coolant spillage during selector duct removal.
3. Referring to Fig. 10, remove nuts from selector duct studs on engine side of dash.
4. Disconnect left hand dash outlet flexible hose at center distributor duct.

Fig. 11   Removing temperature door bell crank on air conditioned cars

5. Remove the right hand dash outlet assembly.
6. Remove instrument cluster bezel screws and remove the bezel and center outlet as an assembly.
7. Remove ash tray and retainer.
8. Remove the radio as outlined previously.
9. Remove control assembly to instrument panel screws and lower the control assembly.
10. Remove cigarette lighter assembly.

11. Remove the screw securing the right end of the instrument panel carrier reinforcement.
12. Pry out the clip retaining the center distributor duct to the instrument panel. Remove the center duct to selector duct screws and remove the center distributor duct. Rotate the duct clockwise and then pull down and to the left to remove. It may be necessary to pull rearward on the instrument panel to remove the duct.
13. Remove the defroster duct to selector duct screws.
14. Remove the remaining selector duct to dash panel screws and pull the duct rearward far enough to disconnect all electrical and vacuum lines. Mark these lines for proper installation.
15. Disconnect temperature door cable, all vacuum and electrical connections and remove selector duct assembly. Mark vacuum hoses for proper installation.
16. If the core must be replaced, pry off or punch out the temperature door bell crank, Fig. 11.

CAUTION: Use care to prevent bending the arm or damaging the selector case. Then remove the screws securing the backing plate and the temperature door cable retainer and remove the core and backing plate as an assembly.

Engine Section

ENGINE, REPLACE

1. Raise hood to fully open position and install a bolt through the hood hold-open link to hold hood in wide open position, Fig. 1.
2. Disconnect battery positive cable at battery and negative cable at engine block (except on air conditioned vehicles).
3. Drain cooling system and disconnect hoses at radiator. Disconnect heater hoses at water pump and at heater

inlet (bottom hose).
4. Disconnect emission system hoses: PCV at cam cover; cannister vacuum hose at carburetor; PCV vacuum at inlet manifold and bowl vent at carburetor.
5. Remove radiator panel or shroud and remove radiator, fan and spacer.
6. Remove air cleaner, disconnecting vent tube at base of cleaner.
7. Disconnect electrical leads at: Delcotron, ignition coil, starter solenoid, oil pressure switch, engine temperature switch, transmission controlled spark switch at transmission, transmission controlled spark solenoid and engine ground strap at cowl.
8. Disconnect: Automatic transmission throttle valve linkage at manifold mounted bellcrank, fuel line at rubber hose to rear of carburetor,

transmission vacuum modulator and air conditioning vacuum line at inlet manifold, accelerator cable at manifold bellcrank.
9. On air conditioned cars, disconnect compressor at front support, rear support, rear lower bracket and remove drive belt from compressor.
10. Move compressor slightly forward and allow front of compressor to rest on frame forward brace, then secure rear of compressor to engine compartment so it is out of way.
11. Disconnect power steering pump, if equipped, and position it out of way.
12. Raise car on a hoist and disconnect exhaust pipe at manifold.
13. Remove engine flywheel dust cover

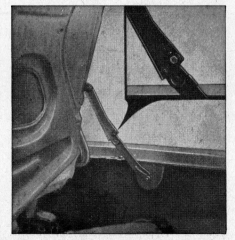

Fig. 1   Hood hold-open bolt installed

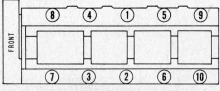

Fig. 2   Cylinder head tightening sequence

Fig. 3   Adjusting valve lash

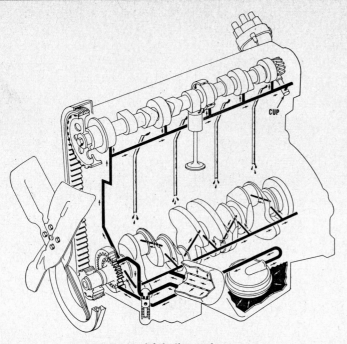

Engine lubrication system

with inverted "V" notch on timing belt upper cover. The following valves can be adjusted with cam in this position (number one firing).
Number one cylinder—Intake and Exhaust
Number two cylinder—Intake
Number three cylinder—Exhaust

b. Use a feeler gauge and measure clearance between tappet and cam lobe. Adjust clearance by turning adjusting screw in tappet.

NOTE: It is mandatory that the adjusting screw, Fig. 4, be turned one complete revolution to maintain proper stem-to-screw relationship. Each revolution of screw alters clearance by .003".

c. Rotate camshaft timing sprocket 180 degrees so timing mark is at 12 o'clock position and in line with notch on timing belt upper cover. The following valves can be adjusted with camshaft in this position (number four firing).
Number two cylinder—Exhaust
Number three cylinder—Intake
Number four cylinder—Intake and Exhaust

VALVE ARRANGEMENT
Front to Rear

4-cylinder . . . . I-E-I-E-I-E-I-E

CAMSHAFT COVER

1. Raise hood to fully open position and install bolt through the hood hold-open link, Fig. 1.
2. Disconnect battery negative cable at battery.
3. Remove air cleaner wing nut. Disconnect ventilation tube at camshaft cover or at air cleaner; then remove air cleaner.
4. Remove PCV valve from grommet at front of cover.
5. Remove cover-to-cylinder head screws and withdraw cover from head.

CAMSHAFT, REMOVAL

1. Remove hood.
2. Remove camshaft timing sprocket.
3. Remove timing belt upper cover and

---

or converter underpan.

14. On automatic transmission cars, remove converter-to-flywheel retaining bolts and nuts and install coverter safety strap.
15. Remove converter housing or flywheel housing-to-engine retaining bolts.
16. Loosen engine front mount retaining bolts at frame attachment and lower vehicle.
17. Install floor jack under transmission.
18. Install suitable engine lifting equipment and raise engine slightly to take weight from engine mounts and remove engine front mount retaining bolts.
19. Remove engine and pull forward to clear transmission while slowly lifting engine from car.

CYLINDER HEAD

1. Remove engine front cover and camshaft cover as outlined further on.
2. Remove timing belt and camshaft sprocket.
3. Remove intake and exhaust manifolds.

4. Disconnect hose at thermostat housing.
5. Remove cylinder head bolts and with the aid of an assistant lift head and gasket from engine. Place head on two blocks of wood to prevent damage to valves.
6. Reverse procedure to install and tighten head bolts in sequence shown in Fig. 2.

VALVES, ADJUST

1. To adjust valves, the tappet must be on the base circle of the cam lobe. Do this as follows:
a. Rotate camshaft timing sprocket to align timing mark on sprocket

Fig. 5   Camshaft removal tool installed

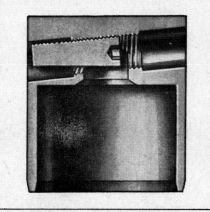

Fig. 4   Tappet and adjusting screw assembly. Screw is threaded in all areas except in valve stem contact surface

Fig. 6   Depressing valve tappets

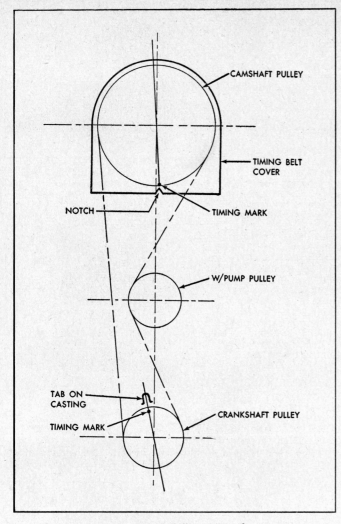

Fig. 7 Sprocket alignment marks

Fig. 7A Checking sprocket alignment. 1972

NOTE: Use a torque wrench to tighten screws the final few turns. About 10 ft. lbs. is required to depress tappets.

10. At this point the camshaft can be removed by sliding it forward from the head.

CAMSHAFT BEARINGS

After removal of the camshaft as described previously, the bearings can be removed without removing the camshaft end plug.

CAM LOBE LIFT SPECS.

		Intake (B1)	Exhaust (B1)
80 H.P.	1971	.4199	.4301
90 H.P.	1971	.4365	.4365
80 H.P. [1]	1972	.4199	.4302
80 H.P. [2]	1972	.4367	.4379
90 H.P.	1972	.4367	.4379

[1]—Except California vehicles.
[2]—California vehicles.

cam retainer and seal assembly.
4. Remove camshaft cover.
5. Disconnect fuel line at carburetor and remove idle solenoid from bracket.
6. Remove carburetor choke coil, cover and rod assembly.
7. Remove distributor.
8. Raise vehicle on a hoist, disconnect engine front mounts at body attachment, raise front of engine and install wood blocks, about 1½″ thick, between engine mounts and body. Lower vehicle.
9. Install camshaft removal tool as shown in Fig. 5, to cylinder head as follows:
   a. Position tool to cylinder head so attaching holes align with cam cover lower attaching holes.
   b. Align tappet depressing levers on tool so each lever will depress both intake and exhaust valve for their respective cylinder. Lever should fit squarely in notches adjacent to valve tappets.
   c. With tool aligned, make sure screws in bottom of tool are backed off so they do not make contact with bosses beneath tool.
   d. Install hardened screws supplied with tool, to attach tool to head. Torque screws securely.
   e. Turn screws in bottom of tool downward until they just seat against corresponding bosses on head.
   f. Apply a heavy body lubricant to ball end of lever depressing screws and proceed to tighten screws to depress tappets, Fig. 6.

Fig. 9 Removing oil pan baffle

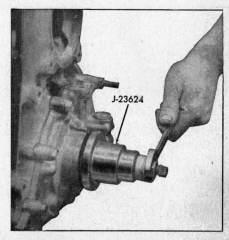

Fig. 8 Installing crankshaft front seal

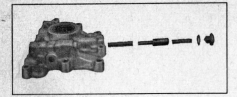

Fig. 10   Oil pump pressure regulator

Fig. 11   Checking driven gear-to-housing clearance

VALVE TIMING

Intake Open Before TDC

80 H.P.	1971	22
90 H.P.	1971	25
80 H.P.①	1972	22
80 H.P.②	1972	28
90 H.P.	1972	28

①—Except California vehicles.
②—California vehicles.

VALVE GUIDES

On all engines, valves operate in guide holes bored in the cylinder head. If clearance becomes excessive, use the next oversize valve and ream toe bore to fit. Valves with oversize stems are available in .003, .015 and 030".

ENGINE FRONT COVER

1. Raise hood to fully open position and install hood hold-open bolt.
2. Disconnect battery ground cable at battery.
3. Remove fan and spacer.
4. Loosen, but do not remove, the two cover lower screws. Cover is slotted to permit easy removal.
5. Remove the two cover upper retaining screws and remove cover.

TIMING BELT & WATER PUMP

1. Remove engine front cover as previ-

ously described.
2. Remove accessory drive pulley or damper.
3. Drain coolant and loosen water pump bolts to relieve tension on belt.
4. Remove timing belt lower cover, then remove belt from sprockets.
5. Remove water pump bolts and lift off pump.

CAMSHAFT SPROCKET

After removal of timing belt, the camshaft sprocket can be removed as follows:
1. Align one hole in sprocket with bolt head behind sprocket, then using a socket on bolt head to prevent cam from turning, remove sprocket retaining bolt and withdraw sprocket from camshaft.
2. When installing, be sure timing marks are aligned as in Fig. 7.

NOTE: For 1972 a simplified method is provided for checking camshaft and crankshaft alignment. Proper alignment is assured by making sure hole in left rear of the timing belt upper cover is in line with the corresponding hole in the camshaft sprocket. Check alignment by inserting a pencil or other similar tool through the hole in cover. If alignment is correct, tool will also enter small hole in cam gear, Fig. 7A.

CRANKSHAFT SPROCKET

1. Remove engine front cover, accessory drive pulley, timing belt and timing belt lower cover.
2. Install suitable puller to crankshaft sprocket and remove sprocket.

OIL PUMP (CRANKCASE FRONT COVER) SEAL

1. Remove engine front cover, accessory dirve pulley, timing belt and timing belt lower cover and crankshaft sprocket.
2. Pry old seal from front cover being careful not to damage seal housing or seal lip contact surfaces.
3. Coat seal with light engine oil and apply an approved sealing compound to outside diameter of seal.
4. Position seal, closed end outward,

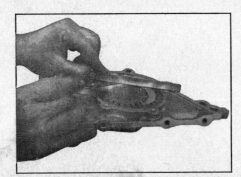

Fig. 14   Checking gear end clearance

Fig. 12   Checking drive gear-to-crescent clearance

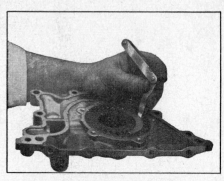

Fig. 13   Checking driven gear-to-crescent clearance

onto crankshaft. Then install seal into bore using tool J-23624, Fig. 8.

PISTONS & RODS, ASSEMBLE

The "F" on the front of the piston must face the front of the engine when the piston and road assembly is installed in its proper cylinder.

Piston Oversizes

Oversize pistons are not available since bore reconditioning is not recommended. Production pistons are available in four size ranges so pistons can be select fitted to the bores. Cylinder bore repairs, such as glaze busting, honing or reboring will destroy the electro-chemically treated finish necessary for proper piston-to-bore operation. Therefore, if cylinder bores are unserviceable, a new cylinder case and piston assembly should be installed.

MAIN & ROD BEARINGS

Undersizes

Bearings are available in .001, .002, .010 and .020" undersizes.

NOTE: If for any reason main bearing caps are replaced, shimming may be necessary. Laminated shims for each cap are available for service. Shim requirements will be determined by bearing clearance.

Fig. 15 Tensioning adapter locating hole

J—23654

Fig. 16 Adjusting timing belt

Fig. 17 Removing fuel pump and gauge unit

OIL PAN

1. Raise vehicle on a hoist and drain engine oil.
2. Support front of engine so weight is off front mounts, and remove frame crossmember and both front crossmember braces.
3. Disconnect idler arm at frame side rail.

NOTE: On air conditioned vehicles, disconnect idler arm at relay rod.

4. Mark relationship of steering linkage pitman arm to steering gear pitman shaft and remove pitman arm.

NOTE: Do not rotate steering gear pitman shaft while arm is disconnected as this will change steering wheel alignment.

5. Remove flywheel cover or converter underpan.
6. Remove oil pan to cylinder case screws, tap pan lightly to break sealing bond and remove oil pan.
7. Remove pick up screen to baffle support bolts, then remove support from baffle.
8. Remove bolt securing oil pan drain back tube to baffle. Then rotate baffle 90 degrees towards left side of car and remove baffle from pick up screen, Fig. 9.

OIL PUMP (CRANKCASE FRONT COVER)

1. Remove engine front cover, accessory drive pulley, timing belt, timing belt lower cover and crankshaft sprocket.
2. Raise vehicle on a hoist and remove oil pan and baffle.
3. Remove bolts and stud securing oil pump to cylinder case.

Inspection

1. Clean gasket surfaces, then wash parts in approved solvent and blow out all passages.
2. Check pressure regulator for free operation, Fig. 10.
3. Inspect pump gears for nicks, broken parts and other damage.

4. Check clearance between outside diameter of driven gear and pump. Clearance should be .0038-.0068", Fig. 11.
5. Check clearance between outside diameter of drive gear and crescent. Clearance should be .0023-.0093", Fig. 12.
6. Check clearance between inside diameter of driven gear and pump crescent. Clearance should be .0068-.0148", Fig. 13.
7. Check gear end clearance. It should be .0009-.0023", Fig. 14.

NOTE: The pump gears and body are not serviced separately. If pump gears or body are worn, replacement of the entire is necessary.

WATER PUMP, REPLACE

1. Raise hood to fully open position and install hold-open bolt.
2. Disconnect battery ground cable at battery.
3. Remove engine fan and spacer.
4. Loosen, but do not remove, the two cover lower screws. Cover is slotted to permit easy removal.
5. Remove the two cover upper retaining screws and remove cover.
6. Drain coolant and loosen water pump bolts to relieve tension in timing belt.
7. Remove radiator lower hose and heater hose at water pump.
8. Unfasten and remove water pump.

TIMING BELT TENSION, ADJUST

1. Drain coolant at engine block and remove fan and extension.
2. Remove engine front cover.
3. Remove water pump retaining bolts, clean gasket surfaces on block and pump. Install new gasket and loosely install water pump bolts.

NOTE: Apply an approved anti-seize compound to the water pump bolts before installation.

4. Position tool J-23564 in gauge hole

adjacent to left side of pump, Fig. 15.
5. Apply 15 ft. lbs. of torque to water pump as shown in Fig. 16. Tighten water pump bolts while maintaining torque on side of pump.
6. Reinstall front cover, fan, extension and fill cooling system.

FUEL PUMP, REPLACE

Removal

1. Disconnect battery ground cable.
2. Disconnect meter and pump wires at rear wiring harness connector.
3. Raise vehicle on hoist and drain fuel tank.
4. Disconnect fuel line hose at gauge unit pick up line.
5. Disconnect tank vent lines to vapor separator.
6. Remove gauge ground wire screw at underbody floorpan.
7. Remove tank straps bolts and lower tank carefully.
8. Unscrew retaining ring using spanner wrench J-22554, Fig. 17, and remove pump-tank unit assembly.

Replacement

1. Remove flat wire conductor from plastic clip on fuel tube.
2. Squeeze clamp and pull pump straight back about ½ inch.
3. Remove two nuts and lockwashers and conductor wires from pump terminals.
4. Squeeze clamp and pull pump straight back to remove it from tank unit. Take care to prevent bending of circular support bracket.
5. Slide replacement pump through circular support bracket until it rests against rubber coupling. Make sure pump has rubber isolator and saran strainer attached.
6. Attach two conductor wires to pump terminals using lockwashers and nuts being certain flat conductor is attached to terminal located on side away from float arm.
7. Squeeze clamp and push pump into rubber coupling.
8. Replace flat wire conductor in plastic clip on fuel pick up tube.
9. Install unit into tank and replace fuel tank.

Clutch & Transmission Section

CLUTCH PEDAL, ADJUST

Initial adjustment after clutch and/or cable replacement is made at two points, at the ball stud and the lower end of the cable.

1. Ball stud adjustment is made before attaching the cable as follows: using gauge J-23644, place it so flat end is against the front face of the clutch housing and the hooked end is located at the point of cable attachment on the fork, Fig. 1.

2. Turn ball stud inward until clutch release bearing lightly contacts the clutch spring levers, then install the lock nut and tighten being careful not to change the adjustment. Remove the gauge by pulling outward at the housing end.

3. To adjust the cable, place it through the hole in the fork and pull it until the clutch pedal is firmly against the rubber bumper.

4. Push the clutch fork forward until the throwout bearing lightly contacts the clutch spring levers, then screw the lock pin on the cable until it bottoms out on the fork. Turn it ¼ additional clockwise revolution, set pin into groove in the fork and attach return spring. This procedure will produce .90" lash at the pedal.

Adjustment for normal clutch wear is accomplished by loosening the lock nut and by turning the clutch fork ball stud counterclockwise until .90" of free play is obtained at the pedal.

Fig. 1   Clutch adjusting gauge in place

GEARSHIFT

The shift controls for both transmissions are floor mounted, Fig. 2. The shift selector shaft, Fig. 3, located inside the case with the ends extending through the case perpendicular to the mainshaft, has both side to side and angular movement.

Two intermediate shift levers, which

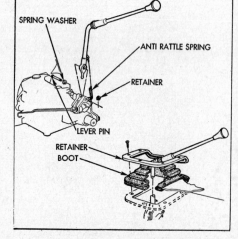

Fig. 2   Gearshift lever installation

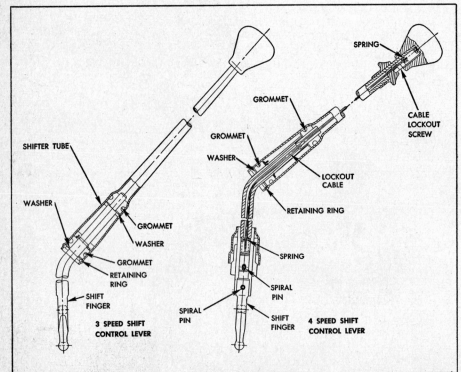

Fig. 4   Shift control lever cross section

Fig. 3   Shift selector shaft

select the gear required, are attached to the selector shaft by means of spiral pins. The side movement of the selector shaft allows the intermediate shift levers to pick up the proper shift shaft. The angular movement positions the shift shaft such that the shift forks (attached to shafts by spiral pins) move the synchronizer sleeves to obtain the required gear.

The 4-speed shift control operation is similar to the 3-speed except for the gear shift lever which has a reverse lockout feature, Fig. 4.

TRANSMISSION, REPLACE

1. Place shift lever in neutral and remove shift lever.

2. Raise vehicle on a hoist and drain lubricant.
3. Remove propeller shaft.
4. Disconnect speedo cable, TCS switch and back-up lamp switch.
5. Remove crossmember to transmission mount bolts.
6. Support engine with an appropriate jack stand and remove crossmember to frame bolts and remove crossmember.
7. Remove transmission to clutch housing upper retaining bolts and install guide pins in holes.
8. Remove lower bolts, then slide transmission rearward and remove from vehicle.

NOTE: Inspect throwout bearing support gasket located beneath lip of support. If necessary, replace gasket before installing transmission.

AUTO. TRANS. LINKAGE, ADJUST

For all practical purposes the adjustments are the same as those described for the Chevy Nova elsewhere in this manual.

Rear Axle, Propeller Shaft & Brakes

REAR AXLE
Description

The rear axle, Fig. 1, is a semi-floating type consisting of a cast carrier and large bosses on each end into which two welded steel tubes are fitted. The carrier contains an overhung hypoid pinion and ring gear. The differential is a two pinion arrangement.

The overhung hypoid drive pinion is supported by two preloaded tapered roller bearings. The pinion shaft is sealed by means of a molded, spring loaded, rubber seal. The seal is mounted on the pinion shaft flange which is splined and bolts to the hypoid pinion shaft.

The ring gear is bolted to a one piece differential case and is supported by two preloaded tapered roller bearings.

Removal

1. Raise vehicle on a hoist.
2. Place adjustable lifting device under axle.
3. Disconnect rear shock absorbers from axle and remove propeller shaft.
4. Disconnect upper control arm from axle and remove both rear wheels.
5. Remove right and left brake drums.
6. Disconnect brake lines from clips on axle tubes.
7. Remove differential cover and drain lubricant.
8. Unscrew differential lock screw, remove pinion shaft and axle shaft "C" locks. Reinstall pinion shaft and tighten lock screw to retain differential gears, Fig. 2.
9. Remove both axle shafts.
10. Remove brake backing plate retaining nuts and remove backing plates, with shoes and brake lines attached, and wire to frame.
11. Remove right and left lower control arm pivot bolts at axle.
12. Lower axle assembly slowly until coil spring tension is released, then remove axle.

AXLE SHAFT

1. Raise vehicle on a hoist and remove

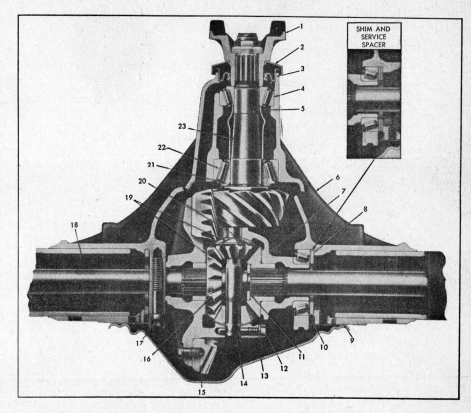

Fig. 1   Rear axle cross section

1. Companion Flange	6. Differential Carrier	11. "C" Lock	15. Ring Gear	20. Differential Pinion
2. Deflector	7. Differential Case	12. Pinion Shaft Lock Bolt	16. Side Gear	21. Shim
3. Pinion Oil Seal	8. Shim	13. Cover	17. Bearing Cap	22. Pinion Rear Bearing
4. Pinion Front Bearing	9. Gasket	14. Pinion Shaft	18. Axle Shaft	23. Drive Pinion
5. Pinion Bearing Spacer	10. Differential Bearing		19. Thrust Washer	

wheel and tire assembly and brake drum.

2. Drain lubricant from axle by removing carrier cover.
3. Unscrew pinion shaft lock screw and remove pinion shaft, Fig. 2.
4. Push flanged end of axle shaft toward center of car and remove "C" lock from button end of shaft.
5. Remove axle shaft from housing being careful not to damage seal.

Oil Seal &/or Bearing Replacement

1. If replacing seal only, remove the seal by using the button end of axle shaft. Insert the button end of shaft behind the steel case of the seal and pry seal out of bore being careful not to damage housing.
2. If replacing bearings, insert tool J-22813 into bore so tool head grasps behind bearing, Fig. 3. Slide washer against seal, or bearing, and turn nut

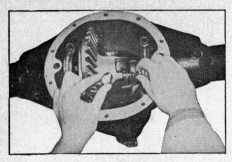

Fig. 2   Differential pinion shaft removal

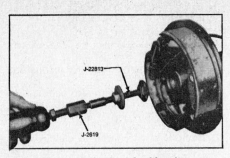

Fig. 3   Removing wheel bearing and seal

Fig. 4   Installation seal and wheel bearing

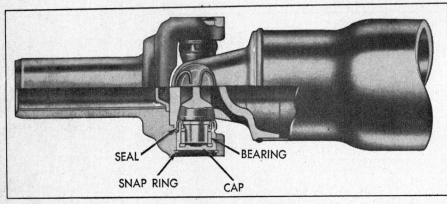

Fig. 5   Propeller shaft cross section

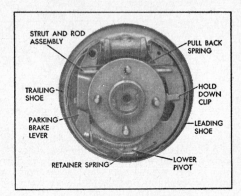

Fig. 6   Rear brake assembly

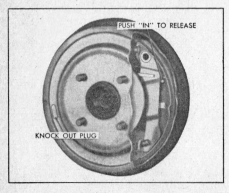

Fig. 7   Drum knock out provision

against washer. Attach slide hammer J-2619 and remove bearing.

3. Pack cavity between seal lips with a high melting point wheel bearing lubricant. Position seal on tool J-21491 and position seal in axle housing bore, tap seal in bore just below end of housing, Fig. 4.

PROPELLER SHAFT

1. Raise vehicle on a hoist. Mark relationship of shaft to companion flange and disconnect the rear universal joint by removing trunnion bearing "U" bolts. Tape bearing cups to trunnion to prevent dropping and loss of bearing rollers.
2. Withdraw propeller shaft front yoke from transmission.
3. When installing, be sure to align

marks made in removal to prevent driveline vibration.

BRAKE ADJUSTMENTS

Disc brakes are used on the front wheels and drum brakes, Fig. 6, are used on the rear wheels. Rear brake adjustment is not automatic. Adjustment takes place, if needed, only when the parking brake is applied. When the parking brake is applied, the strut is pushed against the front shoe and the rod is pulled against the rear shoe. As the shoes spread, a spring lock mounted within the strut and rod assembly, allows the strut and rod assembly to lengthen. When the parking brake is released, the rod connected to the rear shoe is relaxed and brake shoe pressure on the drum is released providing running clearance. Clearance is obtained by the difference in the diameter of the rod and the diameter of the hole in the rear shoe.

NOTE: If the brake drum cannot be removed, it will be necessary to release the brake adjuster. To gain access to the adjuster, knock out the lanced area in web of brake drum, Fig. 3, using a chisel or similar tool. Release the rod from the trailing shoe by pushing in on the rod until it is clear of the shoe. The pull back spring will then pull the shoes toward each other and the drum may be removed.

CAUTION: After knocking out the lanced area, be sure to remove the piece of metal from inside the drum.

Fig. 8   Releasing adjuster on car

Installation

1. To replace rear brake shoes, tool J-23566, must be used to release the adjuster, Fig. 8. The adjuster position for new shoes is shown in Fig. 10.

PARKING BRAKE, ADJUST

1. Place vehicle on a hoist.
2. Apply parking brake one notch from fully released position and raise hoist.
3. Loosen equalizer check nut and tighten the adjusting nut until a slight drag is felt when rear wheels are rotated.
4. Tighten check nut securely.
5. Release parking brake and rotate rear wheels. No drag should be present.

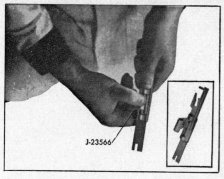

Fig. 9   Releasing adjuster off car

MASTER CYLINDER, REPLACE

1. Disconnect cylinder push rod from brake pedal.
2. Disconnect brake lines from two outlets on cylinder and cover ends of lines to prevent entry of dirt.
3. Unfasten and remove cylinder from dash.

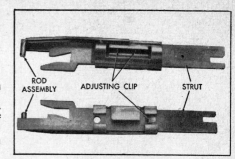

Fig. 10   Adjuster position for new shoes

Front End & Steering Section

FRONT SUSPENSION

The front suspension, Fig. 1, is of the A frame type with short and long control arms. The upper control arm is bolted to the front end sheet metal at each inner pivot point. Rubber bushings are used for mounting.

The lower control arms attach to the front end sheet metal with cam type bolts through rubber bushings. The cam bolts adjust caster and camber.

The upper ball joint is riveted in the upper arm and the lower ball joint is pressed into the lower arm.

Coil springs are mounted between the lower control arms and the shock absorber tower.

WHEEL ALIGNMENT

Caster

Caster angle is adjusted by loosening the rear lower control arm pivot nut and rotating the cam until proper setting is reached.

NOTE: This eccentric cam action will tend to move the lower control arm fore or aft thereby varying the caster. Hold the cam bolt while tightening the nut.

Camber

Camber angle is adjusted by loosening

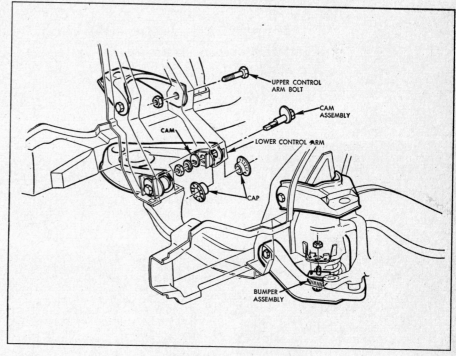

Fig. 1   Front suspension

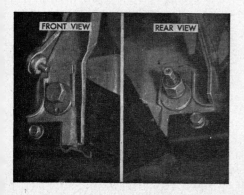

Fig. 2   Caster and camber adjustment

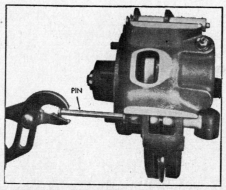

Fig. 3   Removing caliper mounting pins

Fig. 4   Removing upper ball joint stud from knuckle

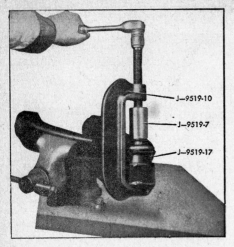

Fig. 5 Removing lower ball joint

the front lower control arm pivot nut and rotating the cam until setting is reached.

NOTE: This eccentric cam action will move the lower arm in or out thereby varying the setting. Hold the cam bolt head while tightening the nut.

TOE-IN, ADJUST

1. Loosen clamp bolt nut at each end of each tie rod and rotate the sleeve until proper toe-in is reached.
2. Position tie rod ball stud assembly straight on a center line through their attaching points.
3. Tighten clamp nuts.

WHEEL BEARINGS, ADJUST

1. With wheel raised, remove hub cap, dust cap and cotter pin from end of spindle.
2. While rotating wheel, tighten spindle nut to 12 ft. lbs.
3. Back off adjusting nut one flat and insert cotter pin. If slot and pin hole do not line up, back off the adjusting nut an additional ½ flat or less as required to insert cotter pin.
4. Spin wheel to check that it rolls

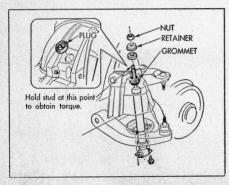

Hold stud at this point to obtain torque.

Fig. 7 Front shock absorber mountings

freely and then lock the cotter pin.

NOTE: Bearing should have zero preload and .001-.008" end movement when properly adjusted.

WHEEL BEARINGS, REPLACE

1. Raise vehicle on a hoist and remove the wheel and tire assembly.
2. Remove the brake caliper from the disc by removing the mounting pins and stamped nuts, Fig. 3.
3. Remove hub grease cap, cotter pin, spindle nut and washer and remove hub and bearings.
4. Remove inner bearing by prying out the grease seal.

CHECKING BALL JOINTS FOR WEAR

Upper Ball Joint

The upper ball joint is checked for wear by checking the torque required to rotate the ball joint stud in the assembly. This is done after first dislodging the ball joint from the steering knuckle.

1. Install the stud nut to the ball stud. in the seat.
2. Check the torque required to turn the ball stud.

NOTE: Specified torque for a new joint is 2 to 4 ft. lbs. rotating torque. If readings are excessively high or low, replace the joint.

Lower Ball Joint

The lower ball joint is checked for wear by checking to be sure torque is present. After dislodging ball joint from steering knuckle perform the following:

1. Install the stud nut to the ball stud.
2. Check the torque required to turn the ball stud in the seat.

NOTE: Some torque is required, if zero torque is observed, sufficient wear has taken place for replacement of the ball joint.

UPPER BALL JOINT, REPLACE

1. Raise vehicle on a hoist and remove wheel and tire assembly.
2. Support lower control arm with a floor jack.
3. Remove upper ball stud nut and remove ball stud from knuckle, Fig. 4.
4. Remove control arm pivot bolts and remove control arm.
5. Grind off rivets securing ball joint to arm.
6. Install new ball joint using bolts and nuts supplied in kit.

LOWER BALL JOINT, REPLACE

1. Place vehicle on hoist and support

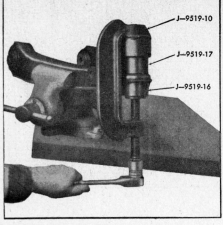

Fig. 6 Installing lower ball joint

lower control arm at outer end on a jack.
2. Free lower ball stud from knuckle.
3. Using tool shown in Fig. 5, press ball joint out of control arm.
4. Position new ball joint so that grease bleed vent in rubber boot is facing inboard.
5. Install tool shown in Fig. 6 and press new joint into arm.
6. Install lube fitting in joint and install stud into steering knuckle.

SHOCK ABSORBER, REPLACE

1. Hold shock absorber stem and remove the nut, upper retainer and rubber grommet, Fig. 7.
2. Raise vehicle on a hoist.
3. Remove bolts from lower end of shock absorber and lower the shock from the vehicle.

COIL SPRING, REPLACE

1. With shock absorber removed and stabilizer bar removed, raise the vehicle and place jackstands under front braces.
2. Remove the wheel and tire assembly.
3. Place a floor jack under the lower

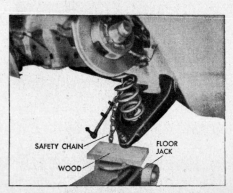

Fig. 8 Removing front coil spring

arm and support the arm. Use a block of wood between the control arm and the jack, Fig. 8.

4. Remove the lower ball stud from the knuckle.
5. Remove the tie rod end from the knuckle.
6. Lower the control arm by slowly lowering the jack until the spring can be removed.

STEERING GEAR, REPLACE

1. Remove the pot joint coupling clamp bolt at the steering gear wormshaft.
2. Remove pitman arm nut and washer from pitman shaft and mark relation of arm position to shaft.
3. Remove pitman arm with suitable puller.
4. Remove bolts securing gear to frame and remove gear assembly.

INTEGRAL POWER STEERING

Replacement procedures for removing the gear assembly are the same as for the manual type gear with the following additions:

1. Disconnect both pressure and return hoses from the gear housing and cap both hoses and steering gear outlets to prevent entry of dirt.

CHRYSLER • DODGE
IMPERIAL • PLYMOUTH

OLD CAR SPECIFICATIONS: For 1946-65 Tune Up and Wheel Alignment Specifications see back of book.

This material covered only in the "Service Trade Edition" of this manual.

INDEX OF SERVICE OPERATIONS

CHRYSLER • DODGE • IMPERIAL • PLYMOUTH

VEHICLE NUMBER LOCATION

1966-67: ON LEFT FRONT DOOR PILLAR.

1968-72: ON PLATE ATTACHED TO DASH PAD AND VISIBLE THROUGH WINDSHIELD.

ENGINE NUMBER LOCATION

1966-72 Six: Right front of block below cylinder head.
1966-72 V8-273, 318, 340, 360: Left front of block below cylinder head.

1966-67 V8-361, 383: Right front of block below distributor.
1966-67 V8-426: Left front of block left of water pump.

1966-67 V8-440: Left front of block below thermostat housing.
1968-72 V8-383, 400, 426, 440: Left side rear of block near oil pan flange.

ENGINE IDENTIFICATION CODE

YEAR	MODEL	ENGINE PREFIX	YEAR	MODEL	ENGINE PREFIX	YEAR	MODEL	ENGINE PREFIX
1966	6-170	B170		V8-426	BH426		V8-383	C383
	6-225	B225		V8-440	B440		V8-426	CH426
	V8-273	B273	1967	6-170	C170		V8-440	C440
	V8-318	B318		6-225	C225			
	V8-361	B361		V8-273	C273			
	V8-383	B383		V8-318 U.S. Built	C318			
				V8-318 Canadian Built	CC318			

1968-72 engines are identified by the cubic inch displacement and prefixed by either the letters PM or PT. These engines are 6-170, 6-198, 6-225, V8-273, 318, 340, 360, 383, 400, 426 and 440.

CHRYSLER GRILLE IDENTIFICATION

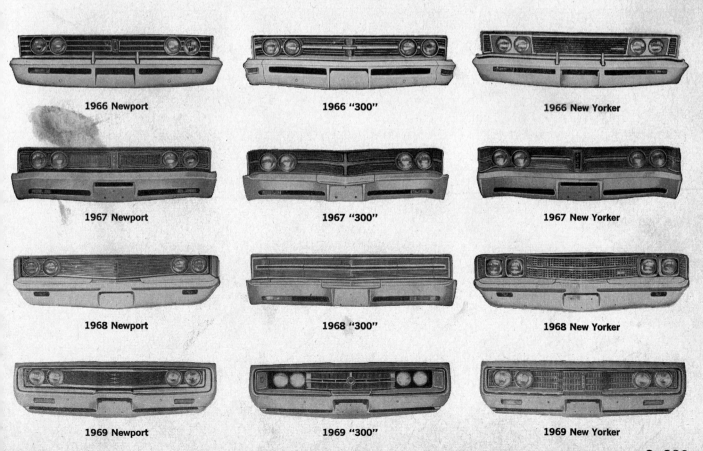

1966 Newport   1966 "300"   1966 New Yorker

1967 Newport   1967 "300"   1967 New Yorker

1968 Newport   1968 "300"   1968 New Yorker

1969 Newport   1969 "300"   1969 New Yorker

CHRYSLER GRILLE IDENTIFICATION—Continued

1970 Newport

1970 "300"

1970 New Yorker

1971 Newport

1971 "300" & New Yorker

1971 New Yorker & Town Country

1972 Newport

1972 New Yorker & Town Country

DODGE GRILLE IDENTIFICATION

1966 Dart

1966 Coronet

1966 Coronet 500

1966 Polara & Monaco

1966-67 Charger

1967 Polara

1967 Dart

1967 Coronet

1967 Coronet "500"

1967 Monaco

1968 Dart

1968 Charger

1968 Coronet

1968 Coronet "500"

1968 Coronet R/T

1968 Polara

1968 Monaco

1969 Dart

1969 Coronet

1969 Coronet "500"

1969 Charger

1969 Polara

1969 Monaco

1970 Dart

1970 Coronet, R/T, Super Bee

1970 Challenger

1970 Charger

1970 Polara

1970 Monaco

1971 Dart & Demon

1971 Challenger

1971 Charger

1971 Coronet

1971 Polara

1971 Monaco

1972 Dart

DODGE GRILLE IDENTIFICATION—Continued

1972 Challenger

1972 Charger

1972 Coronet

1972 Polara

1972 Monaco

IMPERIAL GRILLE IDENTIFICATION

1966

1967

1968

1969

1970

1971

1972

PLYMOUTH GRILLE IDENTIFICATION

1966 Valiant

1966 Barracuda

1966 Belvedere & Satellite

1966 Fury

1967 Valiant

1967 Barracuda

1967 Belvedere

1967 Satellite

1967 Fury

1968 Valiant

1968 Barracuda

1968 Belvedere & Road Runner

1968 Satellite

1968 "GTX"

1968 Fury

1968 Sport Fury

1969 Valiant

1969 Barracuda

1969 Belvedere, Road Runner & Satellite

1969 "GTX"

1969 Sport Satellite

1969 Fury

1969 Sport Fury & VIP

1970 Valiant & Duster

1970 Barracuda

1970 Hemi 'Cuda

1970 Belvedere, Road Runner & Satellite

1970 Sport Satellite

1970 "GTX"

1970 Fury

PLYMOUTH GRILLE IDENTIFICATION—Continued

1970 Sport Fury

1971 Valiant & Duster

1971 Duster 340

1971 Barracuda

1971 Satellite

1971 Road Runner

1971 Fury

1971 Sport Fury

1972 Valiant

1972 Barracuda

1972 Satellite

1972 Road Runner

1972 Sebring

1972 Fury

GENERAL ENGINE SPECIFICATIONS

Year	Engine	Carburetor	Bore and Stroke	Piston Displacement, Cubic Inches	Compression Ratio	Maximum Brake H.P. @ R.P.M.	Maximum Torque Lbs. Ft. @ R.P.M.	Normal Oil Pressure Pounds
CHRYSLER AND IMPERIAL								
1966	270 Horsepower.............V8-383	2 Barrel	4.2500 x 3.375	383	9.2	270 @ 4400	390 @ 2800	45-65
	325 Horsepower.............V8-383	4 Barrel	4.2500 x 3.375	383	10.0	325 @ 4800	425 @ 2900	45-65
	350 Horsepower.............V8-440	4 Barrel	4.3200 x 3.75	440	10.10	350 @ 4400	480 @ 2800	45-65
1967	270 Horsepower.............V8-383	2 Barrel	4.25 x 3.375	383	9.20	270 @ 4400	390 @ 2800	45-65
	325 Horsepower.............V8-383	4 Barrel	4.25 x 3.375	383	10.00	325 @ 4800	425 @ 2800	45-65
	350 Horsepower.............V8-440	4 Barrel	4.32 x 3.75	440	10.10	350 @ 4400	480 @ 2800	45-65
	375 Horsepower.............V8-440	4 Barrel	4.32 x 3.75	440	10.10	375 @ 4600	480 @ 3200	45-65

Continued

GENERAL ENGINE SPECIFICATIONS—Continued

Year	Engine	Car-buretor	Bore and Stroke	Piston Dis-place-ment, Cubic Inches	Com-pres-sion Ratio	Maximum Brake H.P. @ R.P.M.	Maximum Torque Lbs. Ft. @ R.P.M.	Normal Oil Pressure Pounds
CHRYSLER & IMPERIAL—Continued								
1968	290 Horsepower..............V8-383	2 Barrel	4.25 x 3.375	383	9.2	290 @ 4400	390 @ 2800	45–65
	330 Horsepower..............V8-383	4 Barrel	4.25 x 3.375	383	10.0	330 @ 5000	425 @ 3200	45–65
	350 Horsepower..............V8-440	4 Barrel	4.32 x 3.75	440	10.1	350 @ 4400	480 @ 2800	45–65
	375 Horsepower..............V8-440	4 Barrel	4.32 x 3.75	440	10.1	375 @ 4600	480 @ 3200	45–65
1969	290 Horsepower..............V8-383	2 Barrel	4.25 x 3.375	383	9.2	290 @ 4400	380 @ 2400	45–65
	330 Horsepower..............V8-383	4 Barrel	4.25 x 3.375	383	10.0	330 @ 5000	425 @ 3200	45–65
	350 Horsepower..............V8-440	4 Barrel	4.32 x 3.75	440	10.1	350 @ 4400	480 @ 2800	45–65
	375 Horsepower..............V8-440	4 Barrel	4.32 x 3.75	440	10.1	375 @ 4600	480 @ 3200	45–65
1970	290 Horsepower..............V8-383	2 Barrel	4.25 x 3.375	383	8.7	290 @ 4400	380 @ 2800	45–65
	330 Horsepower..............V8-383	4 Barrel	4.25 x 3.375	383	9.5	330 @ 5000	425 @ 3200	45–65
	350 Horsepower..............V8-440	4 Barrel	4.32 x 3.75	440	9.7	350 @ 4400	480 @ 2800	45–65
	375 Horsepower..............V8-440	4 Barrel	4.32 x 3.75	440	9.7	375 @ 4600	480 @ 3200	45–65
1971	275 Horsepower..............V8-383	2 Barrel	4.25 x 3.375	383	8.7	275 @ 4400	375 @ 2800	45–65
	300 Horsepower..............V8-383	4 Barrel	4.25 x 3.375	383	8.7	300 @ 4800	410 @ 3400	45–65
	190 Horsepower①..............V8-400	2 Barrel	4.342 x 3.375	400	8.2	190 @ 4400	310 @ 2400	45–65
	335 Horsepower..............V8-440	4 Barrel	4.32 x 3.75	440	9.0	335 @ 4400	460 @ 3200	45–65
	370 Horsepower..............V8-440	4 Barrel	4.32 x 3.75	440	9.7	370 @ 4600	480 @ 3200	45–65
1972	175 Horsepower①..............V8-360	2 Barrel	4.00 x 3.58	360	8.8	175 @ 4000	285 @ 2400	45–65
	190 Horsepower①..............V8-400	2 Barrel	4.342 x 3.375	400	8.2	190 @ 4400	310 @ 2400	45–65
	225 Horsepower①..............V8-440	4 Barrel	4.32 x 3.75	440	8.2	225 @ 4400	345 @ 3200	45–65
	245 Horsepower①②..............V8-440	4 Barrel	4.32 x 3.75	440	8.2	245 @ 4400	360 @ 3200	45–65
DODGE								
1966	101 Horsepower..............6-170	1 Barrel	3.4000 x 3.125	170	8.50	101 @ 4400	155 @ 2400	45–65
	145 Horsepower..............6-225	1 Barrel	3.4000 x 4.125	225	8.40	145 @ 4000	215 @ 2400	45–65
	180 Horsepower..............V8-273	2 Barrel	3.6250 x 3.31	273	8.80	180 @ 4200	260 @ 1600	40–65
	235 Horsepower..............V8-273	4 Barrel	3.6250 x 3.31	273	10.50	235 @ 5200	280 @ 4000	40–65
	230 Horsepower..............V8-318	2 Barrel	3.91 x 3.31	318	9.00	230 @ 4400	340 @ 2400	45–65
	265 Horsepower..............V8-361	2 Barrel	4.125 x 3.375	361	9.00	265 @ 4400	380 @ 2400	45–65
	270 Horsepower..............V8-383	2 Barrel	4.25 x 3.375	383	9.20	270 @ 4400	390 @ 2800	45–65
	325 Horsepower..............V8-383	4 Barrel	4.25 x 3.375	383	10.00	325 @ 4800	425 @ 2800	45–65
	365 Horsepower..............V8-426	4 Barrel	4.25 x 3.75	426	10.30	365 @ 4800	470 @ 3200	40–60
	350 Horsepower..............V8-440	4 Barrel	4.32 x 3.75	440	10.10	350 @ 4400	480 @ 2800	45–65
1967	115 Horsepower..............6-170	1 Barrel	3.40 x 3.125	170	8.50	115 @ 4400	155 @ 2400	45–65
	145 Horsepower..............6-225	1 Barrel	3.40 x 4.125	225	8.40	145 @ 4000	215 @ 2400	45–65
	180 Horsepower..............V8-273	2 Barrel	3.625 x 3.31	273	8.80	180 @ 4200	260 @ 1600	40–65
	235 Horsepower..............V8-273	4 Barrel	3.625 x 3.31	273	10.50	235 @ 5200	280 @ 4000	40–65
	230 Horsepower..............V8-318	2 Barrel	3.91 x 3.31	318	9.20	230 @ 4400	340 @ 2400	45–65
	270 Horsepower..............V8-383	2 Barrel	4.25 x 3.375	383	9.20	270 @ 4400	390 @ 2800	45–65
	325 Horsepower..............V8-383	4 Barrel	4.25 x 3.375	383	10.00	325 @ 4800	425 @ 2800	45–65
	350 Horsepower..............V8-440	4 Barrel	4.32 x 3.75	440	10.10	350 @ 4400	480 @ 2800	45–65
	375 Horsepower..............V8-440	4 Barrel	4.32 x 3.75	440	10.10	375 @ 4600	480 @ 3200	45–65
	425 H.P. Hemi..............V8-426	Two 4 Bar.	4.25 x 3.75	426	10.25	425 @ 5000	490 @ 4000	40–60
1968	115 Horsepower..............6-170	1 Barrel	3.40 x 3.125	170	8.5	115 @ 4400	155 @ 2400	45–65
	145 Horsepower..............6-225	1 Barrel	3.40 x 4.125	225	8.4	145 @ 4000	215 @ 2400	45–65
	190 Horsepower..............V8-273	2 Barrel	3.625 x 3.31	273	9.0	190 @ 4400	260 @ 2000	45–65
	230 Horsepower..............V8-318	2 Barrel	3.91 x 3.31	318	9.2	230 @ 4400	340 @ 2400	45–65
	275 Horsepower..............V8-340	4 Barrel	4.04 x 3.31	340	10.5	275 @ 5000	340 @ 3200	45–65
	290 Horsepower..............V8-383	2 Barrel	4.25 x 3.375	383	9.2	290 @ 4400	390 @ 2800	45–65
	300 Horsepower..............V8-383	4 Barrel	4.25 x 3.375	383	10.0	300 @ 4400	400 @ 2400	45–65
	330 Horsepower..............V8-383	4 Barrel	4.25 x 3.375	383	10.0	330 @ 5000	425 @ 3200	45–65

Continued

GENERAL ENGINE SPECIFICATIONS—Continued

Year	Engine	Car- buretor	Bore and Stroke	Piston Dis- place- ment, Cubic Inches	Com- pres- sion Ratio	Maximum Brake H.P. @ R.P.M.	Maximum Torque Lbs. Ft. @ R.P.M.	Normal Oil Pressure Pounds
DODGE—Continued								
1968	350 Horsepower..............V8-440	4 Barrel	4.32 x 3.75	440	10.1	350 @ 4400	480 @ 2800	45–65
	375 Horsepower..............V8-440	4 Barrel	4.32 x 3.75	440	10.1	375 @ 4600	480 @ 3200	45–65
	425 Horsepower..............V8-426	Two 4 Bar.	4.25 x 3.75	426	10.25	425 @ 5000	490 @ 4000	40–60
1969	115 Horsepower..............6-170	1 Barrel	3.40 x 3.125	170	8.5	115 @ 4400	115 @ 2400	45–65
	145 Horsepower..............6-225	1 Barrel	3.40 x 4.125	225	8.4	145 @ 4000	215 @ 2400	45–65
	190 Horsepower..............V8-273	2 Barrel	3.63 x 3.31	273	9.0	190 @ 4400	260 @ 2000	45–65
	230 Horsepower..............V8-318	2 Barrel	3.91 x 3.31	318	9.2	230 @ 4400	340 @ 2400	45–65
	275 Horsepower..............V8-340	4 Barrel	4.04 x 3.31	340	10.5	275 @ 5000	340 @ 3200	45–65
	290 Horsepower..............V8-383	2 Barrel	4.25 x 3.38	383	9.2	290 @ 4400	390 @ 2800	45–65
	330 Horsepower..............V8-383	4 Barrel	4.25 x 3.38	383	10.0	330 @ 5000	425 @ 3200	45–65
	335 Horsepower..............V8-383	4 Barrel	4.25 x 3.38	383	10.0	335 @ 5000	425 @ 3400	45–65
	350 Horsepower..............V8-440	4 Barrel	4.32 x 3.75	440	10.1	350 @ 4400	480 @ 2800	45–65
	375 Horsepower..............V8-440	4 Barrel	4.32 x 3.75	440	10.1	375 @ 4600	480 @ 3200	45–65
	390 Horsepower..............V8-440	Three 2 Bar.	4.32 x 3.75	440	10.5	390 @ 4700	490 @ 3200	45–65
	425 Horsepower..............V8-426	Two 4 Bar.	4.25 x 3.75	426	10.25	425 @ 5000	490 @ 4000	45–65
1970	125 Horsepower..............6-198	1 Barrel	3.40 x 3.64	198	8.4	125 @ 4400	180 @ 2000	45–65
	145 Horsepower..............6-225	1 Barrel	3.40 x 4.12	225	8.4	145 @ 4000	215 @ 2400	45–65
	230 Horsepower..............V8-318	2 Barrel	3.91 x 3.31	318	8.8	230 @ 4400	320 @ 2000	45–65
	275 Horsepower..............V8-340	4 Barrel	4.04 x 3.31	340	8.8	275 @ 5000	340 @ 3200	45–65
	290 Horsepower..............V8-383	2 Barrel	4.25 x 3.38	383	8.7	290 @ 4400	390 @ 2800	45–65
	330 Horsepower..............V8-383	4 Barrel	4.25 x 3.38	383	9.5	330 @ 5000	425 @ 3200	45–65
	335 Horsepower..............V8-383	4 Barrel	4.25 x 3.38	383	9.5	335 @ 5200	425 @ 3400	45–65
	425 Horsepower..............V8-426	Two 4 Bar.	4.25 x 3.75	426	10.2	425 @ 5000	490 @ 4000	45–65
	350 Horsepower..............V8-440	4 Barrel	4.32 x 3.75	440	9.7	350 @ 4400	480 @ 2800	45–65
	375 Horsepower..............V8-440	4 Barrel	4.32 x 3.75	440	9.7	375 @ 4600	480 @ 3200	45–65
	390 Horsepower..............V8-440	Three 2 Bar.	4.32 x 3.75	440	10.5	390 @ 4700	490 @ 3200	45–65
1971	125 Horsepower..............6-198	1 Barrel	3.40 x 3.64	198	8.4	125 @ 4400	180 @ 2000	45–65
	145 Horsepower..............6-225	1 Barrel	3.40 x 4.12	225	8.4	145 @ 4000	215 @ 2400	45–65
	230 Horsepower..............V8-318	2 Barrel	3.91 x 3.31	318	8.6	230 @ 4400	320 @ 2000	45–65
	275 Horsepower..............V8-340	4 Barrel	4.04 x 3.31	340	10.2	340 @ 5000	340 @ 3200	45–65
	290 Horsepower..............V8-340	Three 2 Bar.	4.04 x 3.31	340	10.2	290 @ 5000	340 @ 3200	45–65
	255 Horsepower..............V8-360	2 Barrel	4.00 x 3.58	360	8.7	255 @ 4400	360 @ 2400	45–65
	275 Horsepower..............V8-383	2 Barrel	4.25 x 3.38	383	8.5	275 @ 4400	375 @ 2800	45–65
	300 Horsepower..............V8-383	4 Barrel	4.25 x 3.38	383	8.5	300 @ 4800	410 @ 3400	45–65
	425 Horsepower..............V8-426	Two 4 Bar.	4.25 x 3.75	426	10.2	425 @ 5000	490 @ 4000	45–65
	335 Horsepower..............V8-440	4 Barrel	4.32 x 3.75	440	9.0	335 @ 4400	460 @ 3200	45–65
	370 Horsepower..............V8-440	4 Barrel	4.32 x 3.75	440	9.7	370 @ 4600	280 @ 3200	45–65
	385 Horsepower..............V8-440	Three 2 Bar.	4.32 x 3.75	440	10.5	385 @ 4700	490 @ 3200	45–65
1972	100 Horsepower①..............6-198	1 Barrel	3.40 x 3.64	198	8.4	100 @ 4400	160 @ 2400	45–65
	110 Horsepower①..............6-225	1 Barrel	3.40 x 4.12	225	8.4	110 @ 4000	185 @ 2000	45–65
	150 Horsepower①..............V8-318	2 Barrel	3.91 x 3.31	318	8.6	150 @ 4000	260 @ 1600	45–65
	240 Horsepower①..............V8-340	4 Barrel	4.04 x 3.31	340	8.5	240 @ 4800	290 @ 3600	45–65
	175 Horsepower①..............V8-360	2 Barrel	4.00 x 3.58	360	8.8	175 @ 4000	285 @ 2400	45–65
	190 Horsepower①..............V8-400	2 Barrel	4.34 x 3.38	400	8.2	190 @ 4400	310 @ 2400	45–65
	255 Horsepower①②..............V8-400	4 Barrel	4.34 x 3.38	400	8.2	255 @ 4800	340 @ 3200	45–65
	225 Horsepower①..............V8-440	4 Barrel	4.32 x 3.75	440	8.2	225 @ 4400	345 @ 3200	45–65
	245 Horsepower①②..............V8-440	4 Barrel	4.32 x 3.75	440	8.2	245 @ 4400	360 @ 3200	45–65
	330 Horsepower①..............V8-440	Three 2 Bar.	4.32 x 3.75	440	10.3	330 @ 4800	410 @ 3600	45–65

Continued

GENERAL ENGINE SPECIFICATIONS—Continued

Year	Engine	Car-buretor	Bore and Stroke	Piston Dis-place-ment, Cubic Inches	Com-pres-sion Ratio	Maximum Brake H.P. @ R.P.M.	Maximum Torque H.P. @ R.P.M.	Normal Oil Pressure Pounds
PLYMOUTH								
1966	101 Horsepower..............6-170	1 Barrel	3.40 x 3.125	170	8.50	101 @ 4400	155 @ 2400	45–65
	145 Horsepower..............6-225	1 Barrel	3.40 x 4.125	225	8.40	145 @ 4000	215 @ 2400	45–65
	180 Horsepower.............V8-273	2 Barrel	3.625 x 3.31	273	8.80	180 @ 4200	260 @ 1600	40–65
	235 Horsepower.............V8-273	4 Barrel	3.625 x 3.31	273	10.50	235 @ 5200	280 @ 4000	40–65
	230 Horsepower.............V8-318	2 Barrel	3.91 x 3.31	318	9.00	230 @ 4400	340 @ 2400	45–65
	265 Horsepower.............V8-361	2 Barrel	4.125 x 3.38	361	9.00	265 @ 4400	380 @ 2400	45–65
	270 Horsepower.............V8-383	2 Barrel	4.25 x 3.38	383	9.20	270 @ 4400	390 @ 2800	45–65
	325 Horsepower.............V8-383	4 Barrel	4.25 x 3.38	383	10.00	325 @ 4800	425 @ 2800	45–65
	365 Horsepower.............V8-426	4 Barrel	4.25 x 3.75	426	10.30	365 @ 4800	470 @ 3200	40–60
	365 Horsepower.............V8-440	4 Barrel	4.32 x 3.75	440	10.10	365 @ 4600	480 @ 3200	45–65
	425 H.P. Hemi HP2..........V8-426	Two 4 Bar.	4.25 x 3.75	426	10.25	425 @ 5000	490 @ 4000	45–65
1967	115 Horsepower..............6-170	1 Barrel	3.40 x 3.125	170	8.50	115 @ 4400	155 @ 2400	45–65
	145 Horsepower..............6-225	1 Barrel	3.40 x 4.125	225	8.40	145 @ 4000	215 @ 2400	45–65
	180 Horsepower.............V8-273	2 Barrel	3.625 x 3.31	273	8.80	180 @ 4200	260 @ 1600	40–65
	235 Horsepower.............V8-273	4 Barrel	3.625 x 3.31	273	10.50	235 @ 5200	280 @ 4000	40–65
	230 Horsepower.............V8-318	2 Barrel	3.91 x 3.31	318	9.20	230 @ 4400	340 @ 2400	45–65
	270 Horsepower.............V8-383	2 Barrel	4.25 x 3.38	383	9.20	270 @ 4400	390 @ 2800	45–65
	325 Horsepower.............V8-383	4 Barrel	4.25 x 3.38	383	10.00	325 @ 4800	425 @ 2800	45–65
	350 Horsepower.............V8-440	4 Barrel	4.32 x 3.75	440	10.10	350 @ 4400	480 @ 2800	45–65
	375 Horsepower.............V8-440	4 Barrel	4.32 x 3.75	440	10.10	375 @ 4600	480 @ 3200	45–65
	425 H.P. Hemi.............V8-426	Two 4 Bar.	4.25 x 3.75	426	10.25	425 @ 5000	490 @ 4000	40–60
1968	115 Horsepower..............6-170	1 Barrel	3.40 x 3.125	170	8.5	115 @ 4400	155 @ 2400	45–65
	145 Horsepower..............6-225	1 Barrel	3.40 x 4.125	225	8.4	145 @ 4000	215 @ 2400	45–65
	190 Horsepower.............V8-273	2 Barrel	3.625 x 3.31	273	9.0	190 @ 4400	260 @ 2000	45–65
	230 Horsepower.............V8-318	2 Barrel	3.91 x 3.31	318	9.2	230 @ 4400	340 @ 2400	45–65
	275 Horsepower.............V8-340	4 Barrel	4.04 x 3.31	340	10.5	275 @ 5000	340 @ 3200	45–65
	290 Horsepower.............V8-383	2 Barrel	4.25 x 3.375	383	9.2	290 @ 4400	390 @ 2800	45–65
	300 Horsepower.............V8-383	4 Barrel	4.25 x 3.375	383	10.0	300 @ 4400	400 @ 2400	45–65
	330 Horsepower.............V8-383	4 Barrel	4.25 x 3.375	383	10.0	330 @ 5000	425 @ 3200	45–65
	350 Horsepower.............V8-440	4 Barrel	4.32 x 3.75	440	10.1	350 @ 4400	480 @ 2800	45–65
	375 Horsepower.............V8-440	4 Barrel	4.32 x 3.75	440	10.1	375 @ 4600	480 @ 3200	45–65
	425 Horsepower.............V8-426	Two 4 Bar.	4.25 x 3.75	426	10.25	425 @ 5000	490 @ 4000	40–60
1969	115 Horsepower..............6-170	1 Barrel	3.40 x 3.125	170	8.5	115 @ 4400	155 @ 2400	45–65
	145 Horsepower..............6-225	1 Barrel	3.40 x 4.125	225	8.4	145 @ 4000	215 @ 2400	45–65
	190 Horsepower.............V8-273	2 Barrel	3.63 x 3.31	273	9.0	190 @ 4400	260 @ 2000	45–65
	230 Horsepower.............V8-318	2 Barrel	3.91 x 3.31	318	9.2	230 @ 4400	340 @ 2400	45–65
	275 Horsepower.............V8-340	4 Barrel	4.04 x 3.31	340	10.5	275 @ 5000	340 @ 3200	45–65
	290 Horsepower.............V8-383	2 Barrel	4.25 x 3.38	383	9.2	290 @ 4400	390 @ 2800	45–65
	330 Horsepower.............V8-383	4 Barrel	4.25 x 3.38	383	10.0	330 @ 5000	425 @ 3200	45–65
	335 Horsepower.............V8-383	4 Barrel	4.25 x 3.38	383	10.0	335 @ 5000	425 @ 3400	45–65
	350 Horsepower.............V8-440	4 Barrel	4.32 x 3.75	440	10.1	350 @ 4400	480 @ 2800	45–65
	375 Horsepower.............V8-440	4 Barrel	4.32 x 3.75	440	10.1	375 @ 4600	480 @ 3200	45–65
	390 Horsepower.............V8-440	Three 2 Bar.	4.32 x 3.75	440	10.5	390 @ 4700	490 @ 3200	45–65
	425 Horsepower.............V8-426	Two 4 Bar.	4.25 x 3.75	426	10.25	425 @ 5000	490 @ 4000	45–65
1970	125 Horsepower..............6-198	1 Barrel	3.40 x 3.64	198	8.4	125 @ 4400	180 @ 2000	45–65
	145 Horsepower..............6-225	1 Barrel	3.40 x 4.12	225	8.4	145 @ 4000	215 @ 2400	45–65
	230 Horsepower.............V8-318	2 Barrel	3.91 x 3.31	318	8.8	230 @ 4400	320 @ 2000	45–65
	275 Horsepower.............V8-340	4 Barrel	4.04 x 3.31	340	8.8	275 @ 5000	340 @ 3200	45–65
	290 Horsepower.............V8-383	2 Barrel	4.25 x 3.38	383	8.7	290 @ 4400	390 @ 2800	45–65
	330 Horsepower.............V8-383	4 Barrel	4.25 x 3.38	383	9.5	330 @ 5000	425 @ 3200	45–65
	335 Horsepower.............V8-383	4 Barrel	4.25 x 3.38	383	9.5	335 @ 5200	425 @ 3400	45–65
	425 Horsepower.............V8-426	Two 4 Bar.	4.25 x 3.75	426	10.2	425 @ 5000	490 @ 4000	45–65

Continued

GENERAL ENGINE SPECIFICATIONS—Continued

Year	Engine	Car-buretor	Bore and Stroke	Piston Displacement, Cubic Inches	Compression Ratio	Maximum Brake H.P. @ R.P.M.	Maximum Torque H.P. @ R.P.M.	Normal Oil Pressure Pounds
PLYMOUTH—Continued								
1970	350 Horsepower.............V8-440	4 Barrel	4.32 x 3.75	440	9.7	350 @ 4400	480 @ 2800	45–65
	375 Horsepower.............V8-440	4 Barrel	4.32 x 3.75	440	9.7	375 @ 4600	480 @ 3200	45–65
	390 Horsepower.............V8-440	Three 2 Bar.	4.32 x 3.75	440	10.5	390 @ 4700	490 @ 3200	45–65
1971	125 Horsepower.............6-198	1 Barrel	3.40 x 3.64	198	8.4	125 @ 4400	180 @ 2000	45–65
	145 Horsepower.............6-225	1 Barrel	3.40 x 4.12	225	8.4	145 @ 4000	215 @ 2400	45–65
	230 Horsepower.............V8-318	2 Barrel	3.91 x 3.31	318	8.6	230 @ 4400	320 @ 2000	45–65
	275 Horsepower.............V8-340	4 Barrel	4.04 x 3.31	340	10.2	340 @ 5000	340 @ 3200	45–65
	290 Horsepower.............V8-340	Three 2 Bar.	4.04 x 3.31	340	10.2	290 @ 5000	340 @ 3200	45–65
	255 Horsepower.............V8-360	2 Barrel	4.00 x 3.58	360	8.7	255 @ 4400	360 @ 2400	45–65
	275 Horsepower.............V8-383	2 Barrel	4.25 x 3.38	383	8.5	275 @ 4400	375 @ 2800	45–65
	300 Horsepower.............V8-383	4 Barrel	4.25 x 3.38	383	8.5	300 @ 4800	410 @ 3400	45–65
	425 Horsepower.............V8-426	Two 4 Bar.	4.25 x 3.75	426	10.2	425 @ 5000	490 @ 4000	45–65
	335 Horsepower.............V8-440	4 Barrel	4.32 x 3.75	440	9.0	335 @ 4400	460 @ 3200	45–65
	370 Horsepower.............V8-440	4 Barrel	4.32 x 3.75	440	9.7	370 @ 4600	280 @ 3200	45–65
	385 Horsepower.............V8-440	Three 2 Bar.	4.32 x 3.75	440	10.5	385 @ 4700	490 @ 3200	45–65
1972	100 Horsepower①...........6-198	1 Barrel	3.40 x 3.64	198	8.4	100 @ 4400	160 @ 2400	45–65
	110 Horsepower①...........6-225	1 Barrel	3.40 x 4.12	225	8.4	110 @ 4000	185 @ 2000	45–65
	150 Horsepower①...........V8-318	2 Barrel	3.91 x 3.31	318	8.6	150 @ 4000	260 @ 1600	45–65
	240 Horsepower①...........V8-340	4 Barrel	4.04 x 3.31	340	8.5	240 @ 4800	290 @ 3600	45–65
	175 Horsepower①...........V8-360	2 Barrel	4.00 x 3.58	360	8.8	175 @ 4000	285 @ 2400	45–65
	190 Horsepower①...........V8-400	2 Barrel	4.34 x 3.38	400	8.2	190 @ 4400	310 @ 2400	45–65
	255 Horsepower①②.........V8-400	4 Barrel	4.34 x 3.38	400	8.2	255 @ 4800	340 @ 3200	45–65
	255 Horsepower①...........V8-440	4 Barrel	4.32 x 3.75	440	8.2	225 @ 4400	345 @ 3200	45–65
	245 Horsepower①②.........V8-440	4 Barrel	4.32 x 3.75	440	8.2	245 @ 4400	360 @ 3200	45–65
	330 Horsepower①...........V8-440	Three 2 Bar.	4.32 x 3.75	440	10.3	330 @ 4800	410 @ 3600	45–65

①—Ratings are NET—as installed in the vehicle.
②—With dual exhausts.

TUNE UP SPECIFICATIONS

OLD CAR SPECIFICATIONS: For 1946-65 Tune Up Specifications see back of book.

★When using a timing light, disconnect vacuum tube or hose at distributor and plug opening in hose or tube so idle speed will not be affected.

Year	Engine	Spark Plug Type ⑦	Spark Plug Gap Inch	Distributor Point Gap Inch	Distributor Dwell Angle Deg.	Firing Order	Ignition Timing★ BTDC ①	Ignition Timing★ Mark	Hot Idle Speed Std. Trans.	Hot Idle Speed Auto. Trans. ②	Comp. Press. Lbs. ③	Fuel Pump Press. Lbs.
CHRYSLER AND IMPERIAL												
1966	8-383 2 Bar. Carb.⑫	J14Y	.035	.017	28–32	Fig. J	12½°	Fig. F	500⑥	500N⑥	140	4–5½
	8-383 2 Bar. Carb.⑬	J14Y	.035	.017	28–32	Fig. J	5° ATC	Fig. F	600⑥	600N⑥	140	4–5½
	8-383 4 Bar. Carb.⑫	J13Y	.035	.017	28–32	Fig. J	12½°	Fig. F	500⑥	500N⑥	150	4–5½
	8-383 4 Bar. Carb.⑬	J13Y	.035	.017	28–32	Fig. J	5° ATC	Fig. F	650⑥	600N⑥	150	4–5½
	8-440 Chrysler⑫	J13Y	.035	.017	28–32	Fig. J	12½°	Fig. F	500⑥	500N⑥	150	4–5½
	8-440 Chrysler⑬	J13Y	.035	.017	28–32	Fig. J	5° ATC	Fig. F	650⑥	600N⑥	150	4–5½
	8-440 Imperial⑫	J13Y	.035	.017	28–32	Fig. J	12½°⑪	Fig. F	—	500N⑥	150	4–5½
	8-440 Imperial⑬	J13Y	.035	.017	28–32	Fig. J	5° ATC⑪	Fig. F	—	600N⑥	150	4–5½
1967	V8-383 2 Bar. Carb.⑫	J14Y	.035	.017	28–32	Fig. J	12½°	Fig. F	550⑥	550N⑥	140	3½–5
	V8-383 2 Bar. Carb.⑱	J14Y	.035	.017	28–32	Fig. J	5°	Fig. F	—	650N⑥	140	3½–5
	V8-383 2 Bar. Carb.⑲	J14Y	.035	.017	28–32	Fig. J	TDC	Fig. F	600⑥	—	140	3½–5

Continued

TUNE UP SPECIFICATIONS—Continued

OLD CAR SPECIFICATIONS: For 1946-65 Tune Up Specifications see back of book.

★When using a timing light, disconnect vacuum tube or hose at distributor and plug opening in hose or tube so idle speed will not be affected.

Year	Engine	Spark Plug Type ⑦	Spark Plug Gap Inch	Distributor Point Gap Inch	Distributor Dwell Angle Deg.	Firing Order	Ignition Timing★ BTDC ①	Ignition Timing★ Mark	Hot Idle Speed Std. Trans.	Hot Idle Speed Auto. Trans. ②	Comp. Press. Lbs. ③	Fuel Pump Press. Lbs.
CHRYSLER AND IMPERIAL—Continued												
1967	V8-383 4 Bar. Carb.⑫	J13Y	.035	.017	28–32	Fig. J	12½°	Fig. F	500⑥	500N⑥	150	3½–5
	V8-383 4 Bar. Carb.⑱	J13Y	.035	.017	28–32	Fig. J	5°	Fig. F	650⑥	—	150	3½–5
	V8-383 4 Bar. Carb.⑲	J13Y	.035	.017	28–32	Fig. J	TDC	Fig. F	—	650N⑥	150	3½–5
	V8-440 Chrysler⑫	J13Y	.035	.017	28–32	Fig. J	12½°	Fig. F	650⑥	650N⑥	150	3½–5
	V8-440 Chrysler⑱	J13Y	.035	.017	28–32	Fig. J	5°	Fig. F	—	650N⑥	150	3½–5
	V8-440 Chrysler⑲	J13Y	.035	.017	28–32	Fig. J	TDC	Fig. F	650⑥	—	150	3½–5
	V8-440 Imperial⑫	J11Y	.035	.017	28–32	Fig. J	12½°⑪	Fig. F	—	650N⑥	150	3½–5
	V8-440 Imperial⑬	J11Y	.035	.017	28–32	Fig. J	5°⑪	Fig. F	—	650N⑥	150	3½–5
1968	V8-383 Std. Tr.㉑	J14Y	.035	.017	28–33	Fig. J	TDC	Fig. F	650⑧	—	140	3½–5
	V8-383 Auto. Tr.㉑	J14Y	.035	.017	28–33	Fig. J	7½°	Fig. F	—	600N⑥	140	3½–5
	V8-383 Std. Tr.④	J11Y	.035	.017	28–33	Fig. J	TDC	Fig. F	650⑥	—	150	3½–5
	V8-383 Auto. Tr.④	J11Y	.035	.017	28–33	Fig. J	5°	Fig. F	—	650N⑥	150	3½–5
	V8-440 Std. Tr.	J13Y	.035	.017	28–33	Fig. J	7½°	Fig. F	650⑥	—	150	3½–5
	V8-440 Auto. Tr.	J13Y	.035	.017	28–33	Fig. J	TDC	Fig. F	—	550N⑥	150	3½–5
	V8-440 Std. Tr.㉒	J11Y	.035	.017	28–33	Fig. J	5°	Fig. F	650N⑥	—	150	3½–5
	V8-440 Auto. Tr.㉒	J11Y	.035	.017	28–33	Fig. J	TDC	Fig. F	—	650N⑥	150	3½–5
1969	V8-383 Std. Tr.㉑	J14Y	.035	.017	30–35	Fig. J	TDC	Fig. F	700⑥	—	140	3½–5
	V8-383 Auto. Tr.㉑	J14Y	.035	.017	30–35	Fig. J	7½°	Fig. F	—	600⑥	140	3½–5
	V8-383 Auto. Tr.④	J11Y	.035	.017	30–35	Fig. J	5°	Fig. F	700⑥	650⑥	150	3½–5
	V8-440 Auto. Tr.	J13Y	.035	.017	30–35	Fig. J	7½°	Fig. F	—	650⑥	150	3½–5
	V8-440 Auto. Tr.㉒	J11Y	.035	.017	30–35	Fig. J	5°	Fig. F	—	650⑥	150	3½–5
	V8-440 Std. Tr.㉒	J11Y	.035	.017	⑨	Fig. J	TDC	Fig. F	700⑥	—	150	3½–5
1970–71	V8-383 Std. Tr.㉑	J14Y	.035	.019	28½–32½	Fig. J	TDC	Fig. F	750	—	100	3½–5
	V8-383 Auto. Tr.㉑	J14Y	.035	.019	28½–32½	Fig. J	2½°	Fig. F	—	650N	100	3½–5
	V8-383 Std. Tr.④	J11Y	.035	.019	28½–32½	Fig. J	TDC	Fig. F	900	—	110	3½–5
	V8-383 Auto. Tr.④	J11Y	.035	.019	28½–32½	Fig. J	2½°	Fig. F	—	700N	110	3½–5
	V8-400 Auto. Tr.	J11Y	.035	.019	28½–32½	Fig. J	2½°	Fig. F	—	700N	100	3½–5
	V8-440 Auto. Tr.	J13Y	.035	.019	28½–32½	Fig. J	5°	Fig. F	—	650N	110	3½–5
	V8-440 Std. Tr.㉒	J11Y	.035	.019	28½–32½	Fig. J	TDC	Fig. F	900	—	110	3½–5
	V8-440 Auto. Tr.㉒	J11Y	.035	.019	28½–32½	Fig. J	2½°	Fig. F	—	800N	110	3½–5
1972	V8-360	N13Y	.035	.017	30–34	Fig. H	TDC	Fig. E	—	750N	—	5–7
	V8-400	J13Y	.035	.019	28½–32½	Fig. J	5°	Fig. F	—	700N	100	3½–5
	V8-440 Chrysler	J11Y	.035	.019	28½–32½	Fig. J	10°㉗	Fig. F	—	750N㉘	—	3½–5
	V8-440 Imperial	J11Y	.035	—	—	Fig. J	10°	Fig. F	—	750N㉘	—	5½–7
DODGE												
1966	6-170⑫	N14Y	.035	.020	40–45	Fig. G	5°	Fig. E	550⑭	550N⑭	125	3½–5
	6-170⑬	N14Y	.035	.020	40–45	Fig. G	5° ATC	Fig. E	650⑭	650N⑭	125	3½–5
	6-225⑫	N14Y	.035	.020	40–45	Fig. G	2½°	Fig. E	550⑭	550N⑭	125	3½–5
	6-225⑬	N14Y	.035	.020	40–45	Fig. G	5° ATC	Fig. E	650⑭	650N⑭	125	3½–5
	8-273 Std. Trans.⑫	N14Y	.035	.017	28–32	Fig. H	5°	Fig. F	500⑥	—	135	5–7
	8-273 Auto. Trans.⑫	N14Y	.035	.017	28–32	Fig. H	10°	Fig. F	—	500N⑥	135	5–7
	8-273 2 Bar. Carb.⑬	N14Y	.035	.017	28–32	Fig. H	5° ATC	Fig. F	700⑯	650N⑥	135	5–7
	8-273 4 Bar. Carb.⑫	N10Y	.035	.017	⑩	Fig. H	10°	Fig. F	500⑥	500N⑥	135	5–7
	8-273 4 Bar. Carb.⑬	N10Y	.035	.017	⑩	Fig. H	5° ATC	Fig. F	600⑥	600N⑥	135	5–7

Continued

TUNE UP SPECIFICATIONS—Continued

OLD CAR SPECIFICATIONS: For 1946-65 Tune Up Specifications see back of book.

★When using a timing light, disconnect vacuum tube or hose at distributor and plug opening in hose or tube so idle speed will not be affected.

Year	Engine	Spark Plug Type ⑦	Gap Inch	Distributor Point Gap Inch	Dwell Angle Deg.	Firing Order	Ignition Timing★ BTDC ①	Mark	Hot Idle Speed Std. Trans.	Auto. Trans. ②	Comp. Press. Lbs. ③	Fuel Pump Press. Lbs.
DODGE—Continued												
1966	8-318 Std. Trans.⑫	⑩a	.035	.017	28–32	Fig. H	5°	Fig. F	500⑥	—	140	5–7
	8-318 Auto. Trans.⑫	⑩a	.035	.017	28–32	Fig. H	10°	Fig. F	—	500N⑥	140	5–7
	8-318 2 Bar. Carb.⑬	⑩a	.035	.017	28–32	Fig. H	4° ATC	Fig. F	650⑯	600N⑯	140	5–7
	8-361, 383 2 B.C.⑫	J14Y	.035	.017	28–32	Fig. J	12½°	Fig. F	500⑥	500N⑥	140	3½–5
	8-361, 383 2 B.C.⑬	J14Y	.035	.017	28–32	Fig. J	5° ATC	Fig. F	650⑥	600N⑥	140	3½–5
	8-383, 426, 440 4 B.C.⑫	J13Y	.035	.017	28–32	Fig. J	12½°	Fig. F	500⑥	500N⑥	145	3½–5
	8-383, 426, 440 4 B.C.⑬	J13Y	.035	.017	28–32	Fig. J	5° ATC	Fig. F	600⑥	600N⑥	145	3½–5
1967	6-170⑫	N14Y	.035	.020	40–45	Fig. G	5°	Fig. E	550⑭	550N⑭	125	3½–5
	6-170⑬	N14Y	.035	.020	40–45	Fig. G	5° ATC	Fig. E	700⑭	650N⑭	125	3½–5
	6-225⑫	N14Y	.035	.020	40–45	Fig. G	5°	Fig. E	550⑭	550N⑭	125	3½–5
	6-225⑬	N14Y	.035	.020	40–45	Fig. G	TDC	Fig. E	650⑭	650N⑭	125	3½–5
	8-273 Std. Trans.⑫	N14Y	.035	.017	28–32	Fig. H	5°	Fig. F	500⑥	—	135	5–7
	8-273 Auto. Trans.⑫	N14Y	.035	.017	28–32	Fig. H	10°	Fig. F	—	500N⑥	135	5–7
	8-273 Std. Trans.⑬	N14Y	.035	.017	28–32	Fig. H	5° ATC	Fig. F	700⑥	—	135	5–7
	8-273 Auto. Trans.⑬	N14Y	.035	.017	28–32	Fig. H	5° ATC	Fig. F	—	650N⑥	135	5–7
	8-273 4 Bar. Carb.⑫	N10Y	.035	.017	⑩	Fig. H	10°	Fig. F	600⑥	600N⑥	135	5–7
	8-273 4 Bar. Carb.⑬	N10Y	.035	.017	⑩	Fig. H	5° ATC	Fig. F	700⑥	650N⑥	135	5–7
	8-318 Std. Trans.⑫	⑩a	.035	.017	28–32	Fig. H	5°	Fig. F	500⑥	—	140	5–7
	8-318 Auto. Trans.⑫	⑩a	.035	.017	28–32	Fig. H	10°	Fig. F	—	500N⑥	140	5–7
	8-318⑬	⑩a	.035	.017	28–32	Fig. H	5° ATC	Fig. F	650⑥	650N⑥	140	5–7
	8-383 2 Bar. Carb.⑫	J14Y	.035	.017	28–32	Fig. J	12½°	Fig. F	550⑥	550N⑥	140	3½–5
	8-383 2 Bar. Carb.⑱	J14Y	.035	.017	28–32	Fig. J	5°	Fig. F	—	600N⑥	140	3½–5
	8-383 2 Bar. Carb.⑲	J14Y	.035	.017	28–32	Fig. J	TDC	Fig. F	650⑥	—	140	3½–5
	8-383 4 Bar. Carb.⑫	J13Y	.035	.017	28–32	Fig. J	12½°	Fig. F	500⑥	500N⑥	150	3½–5
	8-383 4 Bar. Carb.⑱	J13Y	.035	.017	28–32	Fig. J	5°	Fig. F	—	600N⑥	150	3½–5
	8-383 4 Bar. Carb.⑲	J13Y	.035	.017	28–32	Fig. J	TDC	Fig. F	650⑥	—	150	3½–5
	8-440⑫	J13Y	.035	.017	28–32	Fig. J	12½°	Fig. F	650⑥	650N⑥	150	3½–5
	8-440⑱	J13Y	.035	.017	28–32	Fig. J	5°	Fig. F	—	650N⑥	150	3½–5
	8-440⑲	J13Y	.035	.017	28–32	Fig. J	TDC	Fig. F	650⑥	—	150	3½–5
	8-440 Hi Perf.⑫	J11Y	.035	.017	28–32	Fig. J	12½°	Fig. F	650⑥	650N⑥	150	3½–5
	8-440 Hi Perf.⑱	J11Y	.035	.017	28–32	Fig. J	5°	Fig. F	—	650N⑥	150	3½–5
	8-440 Hi Perf.⑲	J11Y	.035	.017	28–32	Fig. J	TDC	Fig. F	650⑥	—	150	3½–5
	8-426 Hemi⑫	N10Y	.035	.017	⑰	Fig. J	12½°	Fig. F	750⑥	750N⑥	175	3½–5
	8-426 Hemi⑬	N10Y	.035	.017	⑰	Fig. J	TDC	Fig. F	750⑥	750N⑥	175	3½–5
1968	6-170 Std. Trans.	N14Y	.035	.020	40–45	Fig. G	5° ATC	Fig. E	700⑭	—	125	3½–5
	6-170 Auto. Tr.	N14Y	.035	.020	40–45	Fig. G	2½° ATC	Fig. E	—	650N⑭	125	3½–5
	6-225	N14Y	.035	.020	40–45	Fig. G	TDC	Fig. E	650⑭	650N⑭	125	3½–5
	V8-273 Std. Trans.	N14Y	.035	.017	28–33	Fig. H	5° ATC	Fig. F	700⑥	—	135	5–7
	V8-273 Auto. Tr.	N14Y	.035	.017	28–33	Fig. H	2½° ATC	Fig. F	—	650N⑥	135	5–7
	V8-318 Std. Trans.	N14Y	.035	.017	28–33	Fig. H	5° ATC	Fig. F	650⑥	—	140	5–7
	V8-318 Auto. Tr.	N14Y	.035	.017	28–33	Fig. H	2½° ATC	Fig. F	—	600N⑥	140	5–7
	V8-340 Std. Trans.	N9Y	.035	.017	⑰	Fig. H	TDC	Fig. F	700⑥	—	180	5–7
	V8-340 Auto. Tr.	N9Y	.035	.017	⑰	Fig. H	5°	Fig. F	—	650N⑥	180	5–7
	V8-383 Std. Tr.④	J11Y	.035	.017	28–33	Fig. J	TDC	Fig. F	650⑥	—	150	3½–5
	V8-383 Auto. Tr.④	J11Y	.035	.017	28–33	Fig. J	5°	Fig. F	—	650N⑥	150	3½–5
	V8-383 Std. Tr.㉑	J14Y	.035	.017	28–33	Fig. J	TDC	Fig. F	650⑥	—	140	3½–5
	V8-383 Auto. Tr.㉑	J14Y	.035	.017	28–33	Fig. J	7½°	Fig. F	—	600N⑥	140	3½–5
	V8-440 Std. Tr.㉒	J11Y	.035	.017	⑰	Fig. J	TDC	Fig. F	650⑥	—	150	6–7½
	V8-440 Auto. Tr.㉒	J11Y	.035	.017	28–33	Fig. J	5°	Fig. F	—	650N⑥	150	6–7½
	V8-440, 350 H.P.	J13Y	.035	.017	28–33	Fig. J	7½°	Fig. F	—	600N⑥	150	3½–5
	V8-426	N10Y	.035	.017	⑰	Fig. J	TDC	Fig. F	750⑥	750N⑥	175	7–8½

Continued

TUNE UP SPECIFICATIONS—Continued

OLD CAR SPECIFICATIONS: For 1946-65 Tune Up Specifications see back of book.

★When using a timing light, disconnect vacuum hose or tube at distributor and plug opening in hose or tube so idle speed will not be affected.

| Year | Engine | Spark Plug | | Distributor | | Firing Order | Ignition Timing★ | | Hot Idle Speed | | Comp. Press. Lbs. ③ | Fuel Pump Press. Lbs. |
		Type ⑦	Gap Inch	Point Gap Inch	Dwell Angle Deg.		BTDC ①	Mark	Std. Trans.	Auto. Trans. ②		
DODGE—Continued												
1969	6-170 Std. Tr.	N14Y	.035	.020	42–47	Fig. G	5° ATC	Fig. E	750⑭	—	125	3½–5
	6-170 Auto. Tr.	N14Y	.035	.020	42–47	Fig. G	TDC	Fig. E	—	750N⑭	125	3½–5
	6-225	N14Y	.035	.020	42–47	Fig. G	TDC	Fig. E	650⑭	650N⑭	125	3½–5
	V8-273	N14Y	.035	.017	30–35	Fig. H	2½° ATC	Fig. F	700⑭	650N⑭	135	5–7
	V8-318	N14Y	.035	.017	30–35	Fig. H	TDC	Fig. F	700⑭	650N⑭	140	5–7
	V8-340 Std. Tr.	N9Y	.035	.017	⑰	Fig. H	TDC	Fig. F	750⑭	—	155	5–7
	V8-340 Auto. Tr.	N9Y	.035	.017	⑰	Fig. H	5°	Fig. F	—	700N⑭	155	5–7
	V8-383 Std. Tr. ㉑	J14Y	.035	.017	30–35	Fig. J	TDC	Fig. F	700⑭	—	140	3½–5
	V8-383 Auto. Tr. ㉑	J14Y	.035	.017	30–35	Fig. J	7½°	Fig. F	—	600N⑭	140	3½–5
	V8-383 Std. Tr. ④	J11Y	.035	.017	30–35	Fig. J	TDC	Fig. F	700	—	140	3½–5
	V8-383 Auto. Tr. ④	J11Y	.035	.017	30–35	Fig. J	5°	Fig. F	—	650N⑭	140	3½–5
	V8-383 Std. Tr. ㉓	J11Y	.035	.017	⑰	Fig. J	TDC	Fig. F	700	—	140	3½–5
	V8-383 Auto. Tr. ㉓	J11Y	.035	.017	⑰	Fig. J	5°	Fig. F	—	650N⑭	140	3½–5
	V8-440, 350 H.P.	J13Y	.035	.017	30–35	Fig. J	7½°	Fig. F	—	600N⑭	150	3½–5
	V8-440 Std. Tr. ㉒	J11Y	.035	.017	⑰	Fig. J	TDC	Fig. F	700	—	150	6–7½
	V8-440 Auto. Tr. ㉒	J11Y	.035	.017	30–35	Fig. J	5°	Fig. F	—	650N⑭	150	6–7½
	V8-426 Hemi.	N10Y	.035	.017	⑰	Fig. J	TDC	Fig. F	750	750N⑭	175	7–8½
	V8-440, 390 H.P.	J11Y	.035	.017	⑰	Fig. J	5°	Fig. F	900	900	150	6–7½
1970	6-198 Std. Tr.	N14Y	.035	.020	41–46	Fig. G	2½°	Fig. C	750⑥	—	125	3½–5
	6-198 Auto. Tr.	N14Y	.035	.020	41–46	Fig. G	TDC	Fig. C	—	750⑥	125	3½–5
	6-225	N14Y	.035	.020	41–46	Fig. G	TDC	Fig. C	700⑥	650⑥	125	3½–5
	V8-318	N14Y	.035	.017	30–34	Fig. H	TDC	Fig. F	750⑥	700⑥	140	5–7
	V8-340 Std. Tr.	N9Y	.035	.017	⑰	Fig. H	5°	Fig. E	950	—	155	5–7
	V8-340 Auto. Tr.	N9Y	.035	.017	30–34	Fig. H	5°	Fig. E	—	900	155	5–7
	V8-383 Std. Tr. ㉑	J14Y	.035	.017	28–32	Fig. J	TDC	Fig. F	750	—	140	3½–5
	V8-383 Auto. Tr. ㉑	J14Y	.035	.017	28–32	Fig. J	2½°	Fig. F	—	650	140	3½–5
	V8-383 Std. Tr. ④	J11Y	.035	.017	28–32	Fig. J	TDC	Fig. F	750	—	140	3½–5
	V8-383 Auto. Tr. ④	J11Y	.035	.017	28–32	Fig. J	2½°	Fig. F	—	750	140	3½–5
	V8-440, 350 H.P.	J13Y	.035	.017	28–32	Fig. J	5°	Fig. F	—	600	150	3½–5
	V8-440 Std. Tr. ㉒	J11Y	.035	.017	28–32	Fig. J	TDC	Fig. F	900	—	150	3½–5
	V8-440 Auto. Tr. ㉒	J11Y	.035	.017	28–32	Fig. J	2½°	Fig. F	—	800	150	3½–5
	V8-440, 390 H.P.	J11Y	.035	.017	⑰	Fig. J	5°	Fig. F	900	900	150	6–7½
	V8-426 Std. Tr.	N10Y	.035	.017	⑰	Fig. J	TDC	Fig. F	900	—	175	7–8½
	V8-426 Auto. Tr.	N10Y	.035	.017	⑰	Fig. J	5°	Fig. F	—	900	175	7–8½
1971	6-198	N14Y	.035	.020	41–46	Fig. G	2½°	Fig. C	800	800	100	3½–5
	6-225 ㉔	N14Y	.035	.020	41–46	Fig. G	TDC	Fig. C	750	750	100	3½–5
	6-225 ㉕	N14Y	.035	.020	41–46	Fig. G	2½°	Fig. C	750	750	100	3½–5
	V8-318	N14Y	.035	.017	30–34	Fig. H	TDC	Fig. E	750	700	100	5–7
	V8-340 Std. Tr. ④	N9Y	.035	.017	⑰	Fig. H	5°	Fig. E	900	—	110	5–7
	V8-340 Auto. Tr. ④	N9Y	.035	.017	30–34	Fig. H	5°	Fig. E	—	900	110	5–7
	V8-340 Std. Tr. ㉖	N9Y	.035	.017	⑰	Fig. H	2½°	Fig. E	1000	—	110	5–7
	V8-340 Auto. Tr. ㉖	N9Y	.035	.017	30–34	Fig. H	2½°	Fig. E	—	950	110	5–7
	V8-340 ㉛	N9Y	.035	—	—	Fig. H	5°	Fig. E	900	—	110	5–7
	V8-360	N13Y	.035	.017	30–34	Fig. H	2½°	Fig. E	750	700	100	5–7
	V8-383 Std. Tr. ㉑	J14Y	.035	.017	30–34	Fig. J	TDC	Fig. F	750	—	100	3½–5
	V8-383 Auto. Tr. ㉑	J14Y	.035	.017	30–34	Fig. J	2½°	Fig. F	—	700	100	3½–5
	V8-383 Std. Tr. ④	J11Y	.035	.017	30–34	Fig. J	TDC	Fig. F	750	—	110	3½–5
	V8-383 Auto. Tr. ④	J11Y	.035	.017	30–34	Fig. J	2½°	Fig. F	—	700	110	3½–5
	V8-426 Std. Tr.	N10Y	.035	.017	⑰	Fig. J	TDC	Fig. F	900	—	110	7–8½
	V8-426 Auto. Tr.	N10Y	.035	.017	⑰	Fig. J	2½°	Fig. F	—	900	110	7–8½

Continued

TUNE UP SPECIFICATIONS—Continued

OLD CAR SPECIFICATIONS: For 1946-65 Tune Up Specifications see back of book.

★When using a timing light, disconnect vacuum hose or tube at distributor and plug opening in hose or tube so idle speed will not be affected.

Year	Engine	Spark Plug		Distributor		Firing Order	Ignition Timing★		Hot Idle Speed		Comp. Press. Lbs. ③	Fuel Pump Press. Lbs.
		Type ⑦	Gap Inch	Point Gap Inch	Dwell Angle Deg.		BTDC ①	Mark	Std. Trans.	Auto. Trans. ②		
DODGE—Continued												
1971	V8-440	J13Y	.035	.017	28½–32½	Fig. J	5°	Fig. F	—	900	110	3½–5
	V8-440 Std. Tr.㉒	J11Y	.035	.017	28½–32½	Fig. J	TDC	Fig. F	900	—	110	6–7½
	V8-440 Auto. Tr.㉒	J11Y	.035	.017	28½–32½	Fig. J	2½°	Fig. F	—	900	110	6–7½
	V8-440㉖	J11Y	.035	.017	⑰	Fig. J	5°	Fig. F	900	900	110	6–7½
1972	6-198	N14Y	.035	.020	41–46	Fig. G	2½°	Fig. C	800㉘	800N㉘	125	3½–5
	6-225	N14Y	.035	.020	41–46	Fig. G	TDC	Fig. C	750㉘	750N㉘	125	3½–5
	V8-318	N13Y	.035	.017	30–34	Fig. H	TDC	Fig. E	750	750N㉘	140	5–7
	V8-340	N9Y	.035	—	—	Fig. H	2½°	Fig. E	900㉙	750N	155	5–7
	V8-360	N13Y	.035	.017	30–34	Fig. H	TDC	Fig. E	—	750N	100	5–7
	V8-400㉑	J13Y	.035	.019	28½–32½	Fig. J	5°	Fig. F	—	700N	100	3½–5
	V8-400 Std. Tr.④	J11Y	.035	—	—	Fig. J	2½°	Fig. F	900㉚	—	100	3½–5
	V8-400 Auto. Tr.④	J11Y	.035	—	—	Fig. J	10°㉗	Fig. F	—	750N	100	3½–5
	V8-440	J11Y	.035	.019	28½–32½	Fig. J	10°㉗	Fig. F	—	750N㉘	110	3½–5
	V8-440 Std. Tr.㉒	J11Y	.035	—	—	Fig. J	2½°	Fig. F	900㉚	—	110	3½–5
	V8-440 Auto. Tr.㉒	J11Y	.035	—	—	Fig. J	10°㉗	Fig. F	—	900N	110	3½–5
	V8-440㉖	J11Y	.035	—	—	Fig. J	2½°	Fig. F	—	900N	110	3½–5
PLYMOUTH												
1966	6-170⑫	N14Y	.035	.020	40–45	Fig. G	5°	Fig. E	550⑭	550N⑭	125	3½–5
	6-170⑬	N14Y	.035	.020	40–45	Fig. G	5° ATC	Fig. E	650⑭	650N⑭	125	3½–5
	6-225⑫	N14Y	.035	.020	40–45	Fig. G	2½°	Fig. E	550⑭	550N⑭	125	3½–5
	6-225⑬	N14Y	.035	.020	40–45	Fig. G	5° ATC	Fig. E	650⑭	650N⑭	125	3½–5
	8-273 Std. Trans.⑫	N14Y	.035	.017	28–32	Fig. H	5°	Fig. F	500⑥	—	135	5–7
	8-273 Auto. Trans.⑫	N14Y	.035	.017	28–32	Fig. H	10	Fig. F	—	500N⑥	135	5–7
	8-273 2 Bar. Carb.⑬	N14Y	.035	.017	28–32	Fig. H	5° ATC	Fig. F	700⑯	650N⑯	135	5–7
	8-273 4 Bar. Carb.⑫	N10Y	.035	.017	28–32	Fig. H	10°	Fig. F	500⑥	500N⑥	135	5–7
	8-273 4 Bar. Carb.⑬	N10Y	.035	.017	28–32	Fig. H	5° ATC	Fig. F	600⑥	600N⑥	135	5–7
	8-318 Std. Trans.⑫	⑩a	.035	.017	28–32	Fig. H	5°	Fig. F	500⑥	—	140	5–7
	8-318 Auto. Trans.⑫	⑩a	.035	.017	28–32	Fig. H	10°	Fig. F	—	500N⑥	140	5–7
	8-318 2 Bar. Carb.⑬	⑩a	.035	.017	28–32	Fig. H	4° ATC	Fig. F	650⑯	600N⑯	140	5–7
	8-361, 383 2 B.C.⑫	J14Y	.035	.017	28–32	Fig. J	12½°	Fig. F	500⑥	500N⑥	140	3½–5
	8-361, 383 2 B.C.⑬	J14Y	.035	.017	28–32	Fig. J	5° ATC	Fig. F	650⑥	600N⑥	140	3½–5
	8-383, 440 4 B.C.⑫	J13Y	.035	.017	28–32	Fig. J	12½°	Fig. F	500⑥	500N⑥	145	3½–5
	8-383, 440 4 B.C.⑬	J13Y	.035	.017	28–32	Fig. J	5° ATC	Fig. F	600⑥	600N⑥	145	3½–5
	426 Hemi	N10Y	.035	.017	⑰	Fig. J	12½°	Fig. F	750⑥	750N⑥	175	6½–8
1967	6-170⑫	N14Y	.035	.020	40–45	Fib. G	5°	Fig. E	550⑭	550N⑭	125	3½–5
	6-170⑬	N14Y	.035	.020	40–45	Fig. G	5° ATC	Fig. E	700⑭	650N⑭	125	3½–5
	6-225⑫	N14Y	.035	.020	40–45	Fig. G	5°	Fig. E	550⑭	550N⑭	125	3½–5
	6-225⑬	N14Y	.035	.020	40–45	Fig. G	TDC	Fig. E	650⑭	650N⑭	125	3½–5
	8-273 Std. Trans.⑫	N14Y	.035	.017	28–32	Fig. H	5°	Fig. F	500⑥	—	135	5–7
	8-273 Auto. Trans.⑫	N14Y	.035	.017	28–32	Fig. H	10°	Fig. F	—	500N⑥	135	5–7
	8-273 Std. Trans.⑬	N14Y	.035	.017	28–32	Fig. H	5° ATC	Fig. F	700⑥	—	135	5–7
	8-273 Auto. Trans.⑬	N14Y	.035	.017	28–32	Fig. H	5° ATC	Fig. F	—	650N⑥	135	5–7
	8-273 4 Bar. Carb.⑫	N10Y	.035	.017	⑯	Fig. H	10°	Fig. F	600⑥	600N⑥	135	5–7
	8-273 4 Bar. Carb.⑬	N10Y	.035	.017	⑯	Fig. H	5° ATC	Fig. F	700⑥	650N⑥	135	5–7
	8-318 Std. Trans.⑫	N14Y	.035	.017	28–32	Fig. H	5°	Fig. F	500⑥	—	140	5–7
	8-318 Auto. Trans.⑫	N14Y	.035	.017	28–32	Fig. H	10°	Fig. F	—	500N⑥	140	5–7
	8-318⑬	N14Y	.035	.017	28–32	Fig. H	5° ATC	Fig. F	650⑥	650N⑥	140	5–7

Continued

TUNE UP SPECIFICATIONS—Continued

OLD CAR SPECIFICATIONS: For 1946-65 Tune Up Specifications see back of book.

★When using a timing light, disconnect vacuum hose or tube at distributor and plug opening in hose or tube so idle speed will not be affected.

Year	Engine	Spark Plug		Distributor		Firing Order	Ignition Timing★		Hot Idle Speed		Comp. Press. Lbs. [3]	Fuel Pump Press. Lbs.
		Type [7]	Gap Inch	Point Gap Inch	Dwell Angle Deg.		BTDC [1]	Mark	Std. Trans.	Auto. Trans. [3]		

PLYMOUTH—Continued

Year	Engine	Type [7]	Gap Inch	Point Gap Inch	Dwell Angle Deg.	Firing Order	BTDC [1]	Mark	Std. Trans.	Auto. Trans. [3]	Comp. Press. Lbs. [3]	Fuel Pump Press. Lbs.
1967	8-383 2 Bar. Carb.[12]	J14Y	.035	.017	28-32	Fig. J	12½°	Fig. F	550[6]	550N[6]	140	3½-5
	8-383 2 Bar. Carb.[18]	J14Y	.035	.017	28-32	Fig. J	5°	Fig. F	—	600N[6]	140	3½-5
	8-383 2 Bar. Carb.[19]	J14Y	.035	.017	28-32	Fig. J	TDC	Fig. F	650[6]	—	140	3½-5
	8-383 4 Bar. Carb.[12]	J13Y	.035	.017	28-32	Fig. J	12½°	Fig. F	500[6]	500N[6]	150	3½-5
	8-383 4 Bar. Carb.[18]	J13Y	.035	.017	28-32	Fig. J	5°	Fig. F	—	600N[6]	150	3½-5
	8-383 4 Bar. Carb.[19]	J13Y	.035	.017	28-32	Fig. J	TDC	Fig. F	650[6]	—	150	3½-5
	8-440[12]	J13Y	.035	.017	28-32	Fig. J	12½°	Fig. F	650[6]	650N[6]	150	3½-5
	8-440[18]	J13Y	.035	.017	28-32	Fig. J	5°	Fig. F	—	650N[6]	150	3½-5
	8-440[19]	J13Y	.035	.017	28-32	Fig. J	TDC	Fig. F	650[6]	—	150	3½-5
	8-440 Hi Perf.[12]	J11Y	.035	.017	28-32	Fig. J	12½°	Fig. F	650[6]	650N[6]	150	3½-5
	8-440 Hi Perf.[18]	J11Y	.035	.017	28-32	Fig. J	5°	Fig. F	—	650N[6]	150	3½-5
	8-440 Hi Perf.[19]	J11Y	.035	.017	28-32	Fig. J	TDC	Fig. F	650[6]	—	150	3½-5
	8-426 Hemi[12]	N10Y	.035	.017	[17]	Fig. J	12½°	Fig. F	750[6]	750N[6]	175	3½-5
	8-426 Hemi[13]	N10Y	.035	.017	[17]	Fig. J	TDC	Fig. F	750[6]	750N[6]	175	3½-5
1968	6-170 Std. Trans.	N14Y	.035	.020	40-45	Fig. G	5° ATC	Fig. E	700[14]	—	125	3½-5
	6-170 Auto. Tr.	N14Y	.035	.020	40-45	Fig. G	2½° ATC	Fig. E	—	650N[14]	125	3½-5
	6-225	N14Y	.035	.020	40-45	Fig. G	TDC	Fig. E	650[14]	650N[14]	125	3½-5
	V8-273 Std. Trans.	N14Y	.035	.017	28-33	Fig. H	5° ATC	Fig. F	700[6]	—	135	5-7
	V8-273 Auto. Tr.	N14Y	.035	.017	28-33	Fig. H	2½° ATC	Fig. F	—	650N[6]	135	5-7
	V8-318 Std. Trans.	N14Y	.035	.017	28-33	Fig. H	5° ATC	Fig. F	650[6]	—	140	5-7
	V8-318 Auto. Tr.	N14Y	.035	.017	28-33	Fig. H	2½° ATC	Fig. F	—	600N[6]	140	5-7
	V8-340 Std. Trans.	N9Y	.035	.017	[17]	Fig. H	TDC	Fig. F	700[6]	—	180	5-7
	V8-340 Auto. Tr.	N9Y	.035	.017	[17]	Fig. H	5°	Fig. F	—	650N[6]	180	5-7
	V8-383 Std. Tr.[4]	J11Y	.035	.017	28-33	Fig. J	TDC	Fig. F	650[6]	—	150	3½-5
	V8-383 Auto. Tr.[4]	J11Y	.035	.017	28-33	Fig. J	5°	Fig. F	—	650N[6]	150	3½-5
	V8-383 Std. Tr.[21]	J14Y	.035	.017	28-33	Fig. J	TDC	Fig. F	650[6]	—	140	3½-5
	V8-383 Auto. Tr.[21]	J14Y	.035	.017	28-33	Fig. J	7½°	Fig. F	—	600N[6]	140	3½-5
	V8-440 Std. Tr.[22]	J11Y	.035	.017	[17]	Fig. J	TDC	Fig. F	650[6]	—	150	6-7½
	V8-440 Auto. Tr.[22]	J11Y	.035	.017	28-33	Fig. J	5°	Fig. F	—	650N[6]	150	6-7½
	V8-440, 350 H.P.	J13Y	.035	.017	28-33	Fig. J	7½°	Fig. F	—	600N[6]	150	3½-5
	V8-426 Hemi	N10Y	.035	.017	[17]	Fig. J	TDC	Fig. F	750[6]	750N[6]	175	7-8½
1969	6-170 Std. Tr.	N14Y	.035	.020	42-47	Fig. G	5° ATC	Fig. E	750[14]	—	125	3½-5
	6-170 Auto. Tr.	N14Y	.035	.020	42-47	Fig. G	2½° ATC	Fig. E	—	750N[14]	125	3½-5
	6-225	N14Y	.035	.020	42-47	Fig. G	TDC	Fig. E	650[14]	650N[14]	125	3½-5
	V8-273	N14Y	.035	.017	30-35	Fig. H	2½° ATC	Fig. F	700[14]	650N[14]	135	5-7
	V8-318	N14Y	.035	.017	30-35	Fig. H	TDC	Fig. F	700[14]	650N[14]	140	5-7
	V8-340 Std. Tr.	N9Y	.035	.017	[17]	Fig. H	TDC	Fig. F	750[14]	—	155	5-7
	V8-340 Auto. Tr.	N9Y	.035	.017	[17]	Fig. H	5°	Fig. F	—	700N[14]	155	5-7
	V8-383 Std. Tr.[21]	J14Y	.035	.017	30-35	Fig. J	TDC	Fig. F	700[14]	—	140	3½-5
	V8-383 Auto. Tr.[21]	J14Y	.035	.017	30-35	Fig. J	7½°	Fig. F	—	600N[14]	140	3½-5
	V8-383 Std. Tr.[4]	J11Y	.035	.017	30-35	Fig. J	TDC	Fig. F	700	—	140	3½-5
	V8-383 Auto. Tr.[4]	J11Y	.035	.017	30-35	Fig. J	5°	Fig. F	—	650N[14]	140	3½-5
	V8-383 Std. Tr.[23]	J11Y	.035	.017	[17]	Fig. J	TDC	Fig. F	700	—	140	3½-5
	V8-383 Auto. Tr.[23]	J11Y	.035	.017	[17]	Fig. J	5°	Fig. F	—	650N[14]	140	3½-5
	V8-440, 350 H.P.	J13Y	.035	.017	30-35	Fig. J	7½°	Fig. F	—	600N[14]	150	3½-5
	V8-440 Std. Tr.[22]	J11Y	.035	.017	[17]	Fig. J	TDC	Fig. F	700	—	150	6-7½
	V8-440 Auto. Tr.[22]	J11Y	.035	.017	30-35	Fig. J	5°	Fig. F	—	650N[14]	150	6-7½
	V8-440, 390 H.P.	J11Y	.035	.017	[17]	Fig. J	5°	Fig. F	900	900	150	6-7½
	V8-426 Hemi	N10Y	.035	.017	[17]	Fig. J	TDC	Fig. F	750	750N[14]	175	7-8½

Continued

TUNE UP SPECIFICATIONS—Continued

OLD CAR SPECIFICATIONS: For 1946-65 Tune Up Specifications see back of book.

★When using a timing light, disconnect vacuum tube or hose at distributor and plug opening in hose or tube so idle speed will not be affected.

Year	Engine	Spark Plug		Distributor		Firing Order	Ignition Timing★		Hot Idle Speed		Comp. Press. Lbs. ③	Fuel Pump Press. Lbs.
		Type ⑦	Gap Inch	Point Gap Inch	Dwell Angle Deg.		BTDC ①	Mark	Std. Trans.	Auto. Trans. ②		

PLYMOUTH—Continued

Year	Engine	Type ⑦	Gap Inch	Point Gap Inch	Dwell Angle Deg.	Firing Order	BTDC ①	Mark	Std. Trans.	Auto. Trans. ②	Comp. Press. Lbs. ③	Fuel Pump Press. Lbs.
1970	6-198 Std. Tr.	N14Y	.035	.020	41–46	Fig. G	2½°	Fig. C	750⑥	—	125	3½–5
	6-198 Auto. Tr.	N14Y	.035	.020	41–46	Fig. G	TDC	Fig. C	—	750⑥	125	3½–5
	6-225	N14Y	.035	.020	41–46	Fig. G	TDC	Fig. C	700⑥	650⑥	125	3½–5
	V8-318	N14Y	.035	.017	30–34	Fig. H	TDC	Fig. E	750⑥	700⑥	140	5–7
	V8-340 Std. Tr.	N9Y	.035	.017	⑰	Fig. H	5°	Fig. E	950	—	155	5–7
	V8-340 Auto. Tr.	N9Y	.035	.017	30–34	Fig. H	5°	Fig. E	—	900	155	5–7
	V8-383 Std. Tr.㉑	J14Y	.035	.017	28–32	Fig. J	TDC	Fig. F	750	—	140	3½–5
	V8-383 Auto. Tr.㉑	J14Y	.035	.017	28–32	Fig. J	2½°	Fig. F	—	650	140	3½–5
	V8-383 Std. Tr.④	J11Y	.035	.017	28–32	Fig. J	TDC	Fig. F	750	—	140	3½–5
	V8-383 Auto. Tr.④	J11Y	.035	.017	28–32	Fig. J	2½°	Fig. F	—	750	140	3½–5
	V8-440, 350 H.P.	J13Y	.035	.017	28–32	Fig. J	5°	Fig. F	—	600	150	3½–5
	V8-440 Std. Tr.㉒	J11Y	.035	.017	28–32	Fig. J	TDC	Fig. F	900	—	150	3½–5
	V8-440 Auto Tr.㉒	J11Y	.035	.017	28–32	Fig. J	2½°	Fig. F	—	800	150	3½–5
	V8-440, 390 H.P.	J11Y	.035	.017	⑰	Fig. J	5°	Fig. F	900	900	150	6–7½
	V8-426 Std. Tr.	N10Y	.035	.017	⑰	Fig. J	TDC	Fig. F	900	—	175	7–8½
	V8-426 Auto. Tr.	N10Y	.035	.017	⑰	Fig. J	5°	Fig. F	—	900	175	7–8½
1971	6-198	N14Y	.035	.020	41–46	Fig. G	2½°	Fig. C	800	800	100	3½–5
	6-225㉔	N14Y	.035	.020	41–46	Fig. G	TDC	Fig. C	750	750	100	3½–5
	6-225㉖	N14Y	.035	.020	41–46	Fig. G	2½°	Fig. C	750	750	100	3½–5
	V8-318	N14Y	.035	.017	30–34	Fig. H	TDC	Fig. E	750	700	100	5–7
	V8-340 Std. Tr.④	N9Y	.035	.017	⑰	Fig. H	5°	Fig. E	900	—	110	5–7
	V8-340 Auto. Tr.④	N9Y	.035	.017	30–34	Fig. H	5°	Fig. E	—	900	110	5–7
	V8-340 Std. Tr.㉘	N9Y	.035	.017	⑰	Fig. H	2½°	Fig. E	1000	—	110	5–7
	V8-340 Auto. Tr.㉘	N9Y	.035	.017	30–34	Fig. H	2½°	Fig. E	—	950	110	5–7
	V8-340㉛	N9Y	.035	—	—	Fig. H	5°	Fig. E	900	—	110	5–7
	V8-360	N13Y	.035	.017	30–34	Fig. H	2½°	Fig. E	750	700	100	5–7
	V8-383 Std. Tr.㉑	J14Y	.035	.017	30–34	Fig. J	TDC	Fig. F	750	—	100	3½–5
	V8-383 Auto. Tr.㉑	J14Y	.035	.017	30–34	Fig. J	2½°	Fig. F	—	700	100	3½–5
	V8-383 Std. Tr.④	J11Y	.035	.017	30–34	Fig. J	TDC	Fig. F	750	—	110	3½–5
	V8-383 Auto. Tr.④	J11Y	.035	.017	30–34	Fig. J	2½°	Fig. F	—	700	110	3½–5
	V8-426 Std. Tr.	N10Y	.035	.017	⑰	Fig. J	TDC	Fig. F	900	—	110	7–8½
	V8-426 Auto. Tr.	N10Y	.035	.017	⑰	Fig. J	2½°	Fig. F	—	900	110	7–8½
	V8-440	J13Y	.035	.017	28½–32½	Fig. J	5°	Fig. F	—	900	110	3½–5
	V8-440 Std. Tr.㉒	J11Y	.035	.017	28½–32½	Fig. J	TDC	Fig. F	900	—	110	6–7½
	V8-440 Auto. Tr.㉒	J11Y	.035	.017	28½–32½	Fig. J	2½°	Fig. F	—	900	110	6–7½
	V8-440㉖	J11Y	.035	.017	⑰	Fig. J	5°	Fig. F	900	900	110	6–7½
1972	6-198	N14Y	.035	.020	41–46	Fig. G	2½°	Fig. C	800㉘	800N㉘	125	3½–5
	6-225	N14Y	.035	.020	41–46	Fig. G	TDC	Fig. C	750㉘	750N㉘	125	3½–5
	V8-318	N13Y	.035	.017	30–34	Fig. H	TDC	Fig. E	750	750N㉘	140	5–7
	V8-340	N9Y	.035	—	—	Fig. H	2½°	Fig. E	900㉙	750N	155	5–7
	V8-360	N13Y	.035	.017	30–34	Fig. H	TDC	Fig. E	—	750N	100	5–7
	V8-400㉑	J13Y	.035	.019	28½–32½	Fig. J	5°	Fig. F	—	700N	100	3½–5
	V8-400 Std. Tr.④	J11Y	.035	—	—	Fig. J	2½°	Fig. F	900㉚	—	100	3½–5
	V8-400 Auto. Tr.④	J11Y	.035	—	—	Fig. J	10°㉗	Fig. F	—	750N	100	3½–5
	V8-440	J11Y	.035	.019	28½–32½	Fig. J	10°㉗	Fig. F	—	750N㉘	110	3½–5
	V8-440 Std. Tr.㉒	J11Y	.035	—	—	Fig. J	2½°	Fig. F	900㉚	—	110	3½–5
	V8-440 Auto. Tr.㉒	J11Y	.035	—	—	Fig. J	10°㉗	Fig. F	—	900N	110	3½–5
	V8-440㉖	J11Y	.035	—	—	Fig. J	2½°	Fig. F	—	900N	110	3½–5

Continued

TUNE UP DATA—Continued

①—BTDC: Before top dead center.

②—D: Drive. N: Neutral.

③—Plus or minus 20 lbs.

④—Four barrel carburetor.

⑤—With N61Y plugs, 31° at 3000 R.P.M.; with N58R plugs, 34° at 3000 R.P.M.

⑥—Set Idle speed with air conditioning compressor operating.

⑦—Champion.

⑧—Champion N61Y or N58R.

⑨—Each set of points 27–32°; total dwell both sets 34–40°.

⑩—Each set of points 27–31°; total dwell both sets 36–40°.

⑩a—Some Canadian built 318 engines are being used in some American passenger cars. These engines are equipped with J14Y (⅜" reach) spark plugs. The Canadian engine has wide scallop cylinder head covers the U. S. built engines have narrow oblong covers these engines use N14Y plugs (¾" reach).

⑪—Whenever idle speed or ignition timing is adjusted, vacuum line to brake release mechanism must be disconnected and plugged to prevent parking brake from releasing when selector lever is moved to Drive. Set idle speed with A/C compressor operating.

⑫—Without CAP (cleaner air package).

⑬—With CAP (cleaner air package). ATC: After top center.

⑭—Adjust idle speed with headlights on. If air conditioned turn A/C switch to "Full On" position.

⑮—Each set 27–31°. Total dwell both sets 34–38°.

⑯—With A/C switch off.

⑰—Each set of points 27–32°; total dwell both sets 37–42°.

⑱—With CAP (cleaner air package) and Torqueflite.

⑲—With CAP (cleaner air package) and manual transmission.

㉑—Two barrel carburetor.

㉒—High performance engine.

㉓—Formula "S" and Super Bee only.

㉔—Exc. California.

㉕—California only.

㉖—Three Carbs.

㉗—California vehicles with electronic ignition 5°.

㉘—California vehicles 700N.

㉙—California vehicles 850.

㉚—California vehicles 800.

㉛—Electronic ignition.

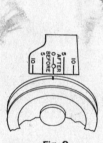

Fig. C

Fig. E

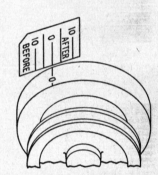

Fig. F

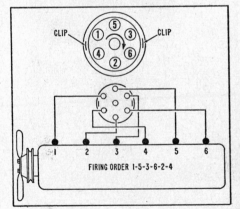

Fig. G

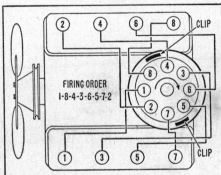

Fig. H

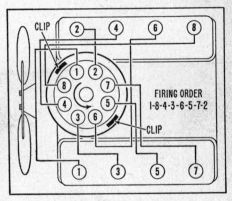

Fig. J

DISTRIBUTOR SPECIFICATIONS

★NOTE: If advance is checked on the vehicle, double the R.P.M. and degrees advance to get crankshaft figures.

Year	Model	Distributor Part No.①	Breaker Gap	Dwell Angle Deg.	Breaker Arm Spring Tension	Centrifugal Advance Degrees @ R.P.M. of Distributor★		Vacuum Advance		Dist. Retard
						Advance Starts	Full Advance	Inches of Vacuum To Start Plunger	Max. Adv. Dist. Deg. @ Vacuum	Max. Ret. Dist. Deg. @ Vacuum
CHRYSLER & IMPERIAL										
1966	V8-383 2 Bar. Carb.③	2642244	.017	28–32	17–20	1 @ 450	11 @ 2150	4.5–8.0	11 @ 13	—
	V8-383 2 Bar. Carb.⑧	2642289	.017	28–32	17–20	4 @ 500	19 @ 2200	4.5–8.0	13 @ 16	—
	V8-383 2 Bar. Carb.⑨	2642373	.017	28–32	17–20	4 @ 500	19 @ 2200	4.5–6.9	13 @ 14	—
	V8-383 4 Bar. Carb.③	2642248	.017	28–32	17–20	1 @ 490	8 @ 2400	6.0–9.0	11 @ 15	—
	V8-383 4 Bar. Carb.⑨	2642367	.017	28–32	17–20	4 @ 500	16 @ 2400	4.5–8.0	14 @ 16	—
	V8-383 4 Bar. Carb.⑧	2642363	.017	28–32	17–20	2 @ 500	16 @ 2400	4.5–8.0	14 @ 16	—
	V8-440③	2642252	.017	28–32	17–20	1 @ 490	8 @ 2400	6.0–9.0	11 @ 15	—
	V8-440⑧	2642365	.017	28–32	17–20	2 @ 500	16 @ 2400	4.5–8.0	14 @ 16	—
	V8-440⑨	2642369	.017	28–32	17–20	3 @ 500	16 @ 2400	4.5–8.0	14 @ 16	—
1967	8-383 2 Bar. Carb.③	2642727	.017	28–32	17–20	1 @ 450	12 @ 2150	5–8	8 @ 10	—
	8-383 2 Bar. Carb.⑧	2642810	.017	28–32	17–20	2 @ 550	16 @ 2200	4.5–8	9 @ 12	—
	8-383 2 Bar. Carb.⑨	2642949	.017	28–32	17–20	3 @ 525	16 @ 2300	4.5–8	9 @ 12	—
	8-383 4 Bar. Carb.③	2642248	.017	28–32	17–20	1 @ 490	9 @ 2400	6–9	11 @ 15	—
	8-383 4 Bar. Carb.⑨	2642949	.017	28–32	17–20	3 @ 525	16 @ 2300	4.5–8	14 @ 16	—
	8-383 4 Bar. Carb.⑧	2642745	.017	28–32	17–20	3 @ 575	12 @ 2450	4.5–8	14 @ 16	—
	8-440③	2642730	.017	28–32	17–20	1 @ 490	10 @ 2300	8–10	12 @ 16	—
	8-440⑧	2642816	.017	28–32	17–20	3 @ 575	14 @ 2400	8–10	14 @ 17	—
	8-440⑨	2642813	.017	28–32	17–20	3 @ 500	16 @ 2300	8–10	14 @ 17	—
	8-440 Hi Perf.③	2642748	.017	28–32	17–20	2 @ 475	10 @ 2200	8–10	12 @ 16	—
	8-440 Hi Perf.⑧	2642822	.017	28–32	17–20	3 @ 475	14 @ 2400	8–10	12 @ 16	—
1968	V8-383 Std. Tr.⑫	2857358	.017	28–33	17–20	3 @ 525	16 @ 2500	5–7.6	12 @ 14¾	—
	V8-383 Auto. Tr.⑫	2857356	.017	28–33	17–20	3 @ 525	18 @ 2500	5–7.6	12 @ 14¾	—
	V8-383 Std. Tr.⑬	2875354	.017	28–33	17–20	0 @ 325	16 @ 2250	5–8	13½ @ 13½	—
	V8-383 Auto. Tr.⑬	2875352	.017	28–33	17–20	3 @ 525	20 @ 2250	5–8	13½ @ 13½	—
	V8-440 Std. Tr.⑮	2875360	.017	28–33	17–20	5 @ 500	16 @ 2500	9–10	12 @ 15.8	—
	V8-440 Auto. Tr.⑯	2875362	.017	28–33	17–20	3 @ 475	12 @ 2450	9–10	12 @ 15.8	—
	V8-440 Std. Tr.⑭	2875102	.017	⑦	17–21	7 @ 500	16 @ 2300	8–9.8	10¾ @ 15	—
	V8-440 Auto. Tr.⑭	2875209	.017	28–33	17–20	5 @ 500	13 @ 2100	8–9.8	10¾ @ 15	—
1969	V8-383 Std. Tr.⑬	2875742	.017	30–35	17–20	1 @ 550	23 @ 2350	8.5	13.5 @ 13.5	—
	V8-383 Auto. Tr.⑬	2875747	.017	30–35	17–20	1 @ 500	19 @ 2350	8.5	13.5 @ 13.5	—
	V8-383 Auto. Tr.⑫	2875731	.017	30–35	17–20	1 @ 550	17 @ 2500	8	12 @ 15	—
	V8-440 Auto. Tr.⑮	2875764	.017	30–35	17–20	1 @ 500	14 @ 2250	11.5	13.5 @ 16	—
	V8-440 Std. Tr.⑭	2875772	.017	⑦	17–20	1 @ 550	19 @ 2500	10.5	12 @ 16	—
	V8-440 Auto. Tr.⑭	2875758	.017	30–35	17–20	2 @ 550	16 @ 2400	10.5	12 @ 16	—
1970	V8-383⑬	3438231	.019	28½–32½	17–20	1 @ 550	16 @ 2200	7.5	11.8 @ 12	2¾②
	V8-383⑫	3438233	.019	28½–32½	17–20	1 @ 600	12 @ 2300	10.5	12 @ 15.5	2¾②
	V8-440	3438219	.019	28½–32½	17–20	1 @ 650	14 @ 2300	10.5	12 @ 15.5	2¾②
	V8-440	3438222	.019	28½–32½	17–20	1 @ 600	12 @ 2300	10.5	12 @ 15.5	2¾②
1971	V8-383, 400⑬	3438534	.019	28½–32½	17–20	1 @ 600	14 @ 2000	9	10 @ 15	—
	V8-383⑬	3438544	.019	28½–32½	17–20	1 @ 700	14 @ 2000	9	10 @ 15	—
	V8-383⑫	3438690	.019	28½–32½	17–20	1 @ 650	14 @ 2400	10.5	10 @ 15	—
	V8-440	3438559	.019	28½–32½	17–20	1 @ 700	12 @ 2400	12	10 @ 16	—
	V8-440	3438572	.019	28½–32½	17–20	1 @ 600	10 @ 2200	10.5	12 @ 15.5	—
	V8-440	3438694	.019	28½–32½	17–20	1 @ 700	10 @ 2200	10.5	12 @ 15.5	—
1972	V8-360	3656272	.017	30–34	17–20	1 @ 550	14 @ 2100	9½	10½ @ 15	—
	V8-360	3656429	—	—	—	1 @ 550	15 @ 1900	9	10 @ 14	—
	V8-360	3656435	—	—	—	1 @ 650	15 @ 1900	9	10 @ 14	—
	V8-400	3656329	.019	28½–32½	17–21	1 @ 650	14 @ 2000	10½	10½ @ 15½	—
	V8-400	3656335	—	—	—	1 @ 650	14 @ 2000	10½	10½ @ 15½	—
	V8-440	3656344	.019	28½–33½	17–21	1 @ 650	12 @ 2000	10½	10½ @ 15½	—
	V8-440	3656341	—	—	—	1 @ 650	12½ @ 2500	10½	10½ @ 15½	—
	V8-440	3656347	—	—	—	1 @ 650	14 @ 2000	10½	10½ @ 15½	—

Continued

DISTRIBUTOR SPECIFICATIONS—Continued

★NOTE: If advance is checked on the car, double the R.P.M. and degrees advance to get crankshaft figures.

Year	Model	Distributor Part No.①	Breaker Gap	Dwell Angle Deg.	Breaker Arm Spring Tension	Centrifugal Advance Degrees @ R.P.M. of Distributor★		Vacuum Advance		Dist. Retard
						Advance Starts	Full Advance	Inches of Vacuum To Start Plunger	Max. Adv. Dist. Deg. @ Vacuum	Max. Ret. Dist. Deg. @ Vacuum
DODGE AND PLYMOUTH										
1966	6-170 Std. Trans.③	2444255	.020	40–45	17–20	1 @ 525	14 @ 2200	5–7	11 @ 12	—
	6-170 Auto. Trans.③	2444256	.020	40–45	17–20	4 @ 475	14 @ 2200	5–7	8 @ 10	—
	6-170 Std. Trans.④	2642349	.020	40–45	17–20	2 @ 500	19 @ 2500	5–7	11 @ 12	—
	6-170 Auto. Trans.④	2642352	.020	40–45	17–20	3 @ 475	19 @ 2500	5–7	8 @ 10	—
	6-225 Std. Trans.③	2444907	.020	40–45	17–20	2 @ 475	12 @ 2200	7–9	7 @ 15	—
	6-225 Auto. Trans.③	2444648	.020	40–45	17–20	2 @ 475	12 @ 2200	5–7	7 @ 13	—
	6-225 Std. Trans.④	2642354	.020	40–45	17–20	2 @ 500	17 @ 2200	5–7	7 @ 13	—
	6-225 Auto. Trans.⑤	2642329	.020	40–45	17–20	4 @ 475	17 @ 2200	5–7	8 @ 10	—
	8-273 Std. Trans.③	2642234	.017	28–32	17–20	1 @ 450	12 @ 1750	5–8	13 @ 13	—
	8-273 Auto. Trans.③	2642238	.017	28–32	17–20	1 @ 475	10 @ 1750	5–8	13 @ 13	—
	8-273 Std. Trans.④	2642356	.017	28–32	17–20	4 @ 500	17 @ 1500	5–8	13 @ 13	—
	8-273 Auto. Trans.④	2642346	.017	28–32	17–20	4 @ 500	17 @ 1900	7–9	13 @ 15	—
	8-273 4 Bar. Carb.③	2642242	.017	⑥	17–21	2 @ 475	9 @ 1800	5–8	11 @ 12	—
	8-273 4 Bar. Carb.④	2642358	.017	⑥	17–21	3 @ 500	16 @ 2000	5–8	11 @ 12	—
	8-318 Std. Trans.③	2444258	.017	28–32	17–20	1 @ 480	12 @ 2300	8–10	12 @ 16	—
	8-318 Auto. Trans.③	2444259	.017	28–32	17–20	1 @ 570	10 @ 2300	8–10	12 @ 16	—
	8-318 Std. Trans.④	2642360	.017	28–32	17–20	3 @ 475	17 @ 2350	8–10	12 @ 16	—
	8-318 Std. Trans.④	2642343	.017	28–32	17–20	2 @ 475	17 @ 2350	8–10	12 @ 16	—
	8-361, 383 2 Bar. Carb.③	2642244	.017	28–32	17–20	1 @ 450	12 @ 2150	5–8	11 @ 13	—
	8-361, 383 2 Bar. Carb.④	2642289	.017	28–32	17–20	4 @ 500	20 @ 2200	5–8	14 @ 16	—
	8-361, 383 2 Bar. Carb.④	2642373	.017	28–32	17–20	4 @ 500	20 @ 2200	5–7	14 @ 14	—
	8-383 4 Bar. Carb.③	2642248	.017	28–32	17–20	1 @ 490	8 @ 2400	6–9	11 @ 15	—
	8-383 4 Bar. Carb.④	2642367	.017	28–32	17–20	4 @ 500	16 @ 2400	4.5–8.0	14 @ 16	—
	8-383 4 Bar. Carb.④	2642363	.017	28–32	17–20	2 @ 500	16 @ 2400	4.5–8.0	14 @ 16	—
	8-426, 440⑩	2642252	.017	28–32	17–20	1 @ 490	8 @ 2400	6.0–9.0	11 @ 15	—
	8-426, 440⑪	2642365	.017	28–32	17–20	2 @ 500	16 @ 2400	4.5–8.0	14 @ 16	—
	8-426, 440⑪	2642369	.017	28–32	17–20	3 @ 500	16 @ 2400	4.5–8.0	14 @ 16	—
	8-426 Hemi	IBS-4006P	.017	⑦	17–21	2 @ 575	9 @ 1400	6–9	11 @ 15	—
1967	6-170 Std. Trans.③	2642758	.020	40–45	17–20	2 @ 525	14 @ 2200	4.5–7.5	10 @ 10	—
	6-170 Auto. Trans.③	2642755	.020	40–45	17–20	3 @ 475	14 @ 2200	5–7.1	8 @ 10	—
	6-170 Std. Trans.④	2642786	.020	40–55	17–20	2 @ 500	18 @ 2200	5–7.1	11 @ 12	—
	6-170 Auto. Trans.④	2642789	.020	40–45	17–20	3 @ 475	18 @ 2200	5–7.1	8 @ 10	—
	6-225 Std. Trans.③	2444907	.020	40–45	17–20	2 @ 475	12 @ 2200	6.9–9.1	7 @ 15	—
	6-225 Auto. Trans.③	2444648	.020	40–45	17–20	2 @ 475	12 @ 2200	4.9–7.1	7 @ 13	—
	6-225 Std. Trans.④	2642792	.020	40–45	17–20	2 @ 500	14 @ 2400	6.9–9.1	8 @ 16	—
	6-225 Auto. Trans.④	2642795	.020	40–45	17–20	3 @ 475	14 @ 2400	5–7.1	8 @ 10	—
	8-273 Std. Trans.⑩	2642234	.017	28–32	17–20	2 @ 450	12 @ 1750	5–8	13 @ 13	—
	8-273 Auto. Trans.⑩	2642238	.017	28–32	17–20	1 @ 475	10 @ 1750	5–8	13 @ 13	—
	8-273 2 Bar. Carb.④	2642805	.017	28–32	17–20	4 @ 500	17 @ 1900	5–8	13 @ 13	—
	8-273 4 Bar. Carb.③	2642242	.017	⑥	17–21	2 @ 475	9 @ 1800	5–8	11 @ 12	—
	8-273 4 Bar. Carb.④	2642358	.017	⑥	17–21	3 @ 500	16 @ 2000	5–8	11 @ 12	—
	8-318 Std. Trans.③	2642721	.017	28–32	17–20	1 @ 475	13 @ 2250	7–9	13 @ 15	—
	8-318 Auto. Trans.③	2642718	.017	28–32	17–20	1 @ 480	12 @ 2350	7–9	13 @ 15	—
	8-318④	2642724	.017	28–32	17–20	3 @ 475	19 @ 2350	7.5–10.5	13 @ 16	—
	8-383 2 Bar. Carb.③	2642727	.017	28–32	17–20	1 @ 450	12 @ 2150	5–8	13 @ 13	—
	8-383 Auto. Trans.⑪	2642810	.017	28–32	17–20	2 @ 550	15 @ 2200	4.5–8	14 @ 16	—
	8-383 Std. Trans.⑪	2642949	.017	28–32	17–20	4 @ 525	15 @ 2300	4.5–8	14 @ 16	—
	8-383 4 Bar. Carb.③	2642248	.017	28–32	17–20	1 @ 490	8 @ 2400	6–9	11 @ 15	—
	8-383 4 Bar. Carb.⑨	2642949	.017	28–32	17–20	3 @ 525	15 @ 2300	4.5–8	14 @ 16	—
	8-383 4 Bar. Carb.⑧	2642745	.017	28–32	17–20	3 @ 575	12 @ 2450	4.5–8	14 @ 16	—

Continued

DISTRIBUTOR SPECIFICATIONS—Continued

★NOTE: If advance is checked on the car, double the R.P.M. and degrees advance to get crankshaft figures.

Year	Model	Distributor Part No.①	Breaker Gap	Dwell Angle Deg.	Breaker Arm Spring Tension	Centrifugal Advance Degrees @ R.P.M. of Distributor★		Vacuum Advance		Dist. Retard
						Advance Starts	Full Advance	Inches of Vacuum To Start Plunger	Max. Adv. Dist. Deg. @ Vacuum	Max. Ret. Dist. Deg. @ Vacuum
DODGE AND PLYMOUTH—Continued										
1967	8-440③	2642730	.017	28–32	17–20	1 @ 490	10 @ 2300	8–10	12 @ 16	—
	8-440 Auto. Trans.④	2642816	.017	28–32	17–20	2 @ 575	14 @ 2400	8–10	14 @ 17	—
	8-440 Std. Trans.④	2642813	.017	28–32	17–20	3 @ 500	16 @ 2300	8–10	14 @ 17	—
	8-440 Hi Perf.③	2642748	.017	28–32	17–20	2 @ 475	10 @ 2200	8–10	12 @ 16	—
	8-440 Hi Perf.⑧	2642822	.017	28–32	17–20	3 @ 475	14 @ 2400	8–10	12 @ 16	—
	8-440 Hi Perf.⑨	2642819	.017	28–32	17–20	4 @ 475	16 @ 2250	8–10	12 @ 16	—
	8-440 Hi Perf.③	2642899	.017	⑦	17–21	2 @ 475	10 @ 2200	8–10	12 @ 16	—
	8-440 Hi Perf.④	2642911	.017	⑦	17–21	3 @ 475	16 @ 2250	8–10	12 @ 16	—
	8-426 Hemi③	IBS-4006P	.017	⑦	17–21	2 @ 575	9 @ 1400	6–9	11 @ 15	—
	8-426 Hemi④	IBS-4006W	.017	⑦	17–21	4 @ 600	16 @ 1550	6–9	11 @ 15	—
1968	6-170 Std. Trans.	2875199	.020	40–45	17–20	3 @ 500	18 @ 2200	5–7.1	8 @ 10	—
	6-170 Auto. Tr.	2875202	.020	40–45	17–20	6 @ 500	15 @ 2200	5–7.1	8 @ 10	—
	6-225 Std. Trans.	2875364	.020	40–45	17–20	3 @ 500	14 @ 2000	6.2–9.7	6 @ 13	—
	6-225 Auto. Tr.	2875366	.020	40–45	17–20	3 @ 500	14 @ 2000	5–7	6 @ 8	—
	V8-273	2875334	.017	28–33	17–21	7 @ 500	16 @ 1900	5–8	13 @ 13	—
	V8-318	2875342	.017	28–33	17–21	5 @ 450	19 @ 2350	8.1–9.8	10 @ 15	—
	V8-340 Std. Trans.	2875086	.017	⑦	17–21	5 @ 500	14 @ 2000	4.5–7.5	10 @ 10	—
	V8-340 Auto. Tr.	2875105	.017	⑦	17–21	3 @ 475	12 @ 2000	4.5–7.5	10 @ 10	—
	V8-383 Std. Tr.⑫	2857356	.017	28–33	17–20	6 @ 525	18 @ 2500	5–7.6	12 @ 14	—
	V8-383 Auto. Tr.⑫	2857358	.017	28–33	17–20	6 @ 525	16 @ 2500	5–7.6	12 @ 14	—
	V8-383 Std. Tr.⑬	2875352	.017	28–33	17–20	6 @ 525	11 @ 760	5–8	13 @ 13	—
	V8-383 Auto. Tr.⑬	2875354	.017	28–33	17–20	0 @ 325	16 @ 2250	5–8	13.5 @ 13.5	—
	V8-440 Std. Tr.⑭	2875102	.017	⑦	17–20	7 @ 500	16 @ 2300	8–9.8	10 @ 15	—
	V8-440 Auto. Tr.⑭	2875209	.017	28–33	17–20	5 @ 500	13 @ 2100	8–9.8	10 @ 15	—
	V8-440, 350 H.P.	2875362	.017	28–33	17–20	3 @ 475	12 @ 2450	9.2–10.7	12 @ 15	—
	V8-426	2875140	.017	⑦	17–21	7 @ 600	16 @ 1550	6–9	11 @ 15	—
1969	6-170 Std. Trans.	2875813	.020	42–47	17–20	2 @ 600	19 @ 2200	7.5	8.5 @ 10	—
	6-170 Auto. Trans.	2875855	.020	42–47	17–20	1 @ 550	16 @ 2200	7.5	8 @ 10	—
	6-225 Std. Trans.	2875822	.020	42–47	17–20	1 @ 550	14 @ 2000	10	8 @ 16	—
	6-225 Auto. Trans.	2875826	.020	42–47	17–20	1 @ 550	14 @ 2000	7	8 @ 10	—
	V8-273	2875790	.017	30–35	17–20	2 @ 550	16 @ 1900	8.5	13.5 @ 13.5	—
	V8-318	2875796	.017	30–35	17–20	1.5 @ 550	19 @ 2400	10.5	10.75 @ 15	—
	V8-340 Std. Trans.	2875782	.017	⑦	17–20	1 @ 550	14 @ 1800	8	10 @ 10.5	—
	V8-340 Auto. Trans.	2875779	.017	⑦	17–20	2 @ 600	12 @ 2000	8	10 @ 10.5	—
	V8-383 Std. Trans.⑬	2875750	.017	30–35	17–20	1 @ 550	19 @ 2500	8	12 @ 15	—
	V8-383 Auto. Trans.⑫	2875731	.017	30–35	17–20	1 @ 550	17 @ 2500	8	12 @ 15	—
	V8-383 Std. Trans.⑬	2875742	.017	30–35	17–20	1 @ 550	23 @ 2350	8.5	13.5 @ 13.5	—
	V8-383 Auto. Trans.⑬	2875747	.017	30–35	17–20	1 @ 500	19 @ 2300	8.5	13.5 @ 13.5	—
	V8-440 Std. Trans.	2875772	.017	⑦	17–20	1 @ 550	19 @ 2500	10.5	12 @ 16	—
	V8-440 Auto. Trans.	2875758	.017	⑦	17–20	2 @ 550	16 @ 2400	10.5	12 @ 16	—
	V8-440 Std. Trans.	2875981	.017	⑦	17–21½	2 @ 610	16 @ 2400	10.5	12 @ 16	—
	V8-440 Auto. Trans.	2875982	.017	⑦	17–21½	1.5 @ 570	14 @ 2400	11	12.5 @ 15.5	—
	V8-426	2875140	.017	⑦	17–21	2.5 @ 650	16 @ 1550	10	11 @ 15	—
	V8-426	IBS-4014A	.017	⑦	17–21	2.5 @ 650	16 @ 1550	10	11 @ 15	—
1970	6-198	3438237	.020	41–46	17–20	1 @ 525	14 @ 1600	7	7.75 @ 10	—
	6-225 Std. Tr.	2875822	.020	41–46	17–20	1 @ 550	14 @ 2000	10	7.75 @ 15	—
	6-198, 225 Auto. Tr.	2875826	.020	41–46	17–20	1 @ 550	14 @ 2000	7	7.75 @ 10	—
	V8-318 Std. Tr.	3438255	.017	30–34	17–20	1 @ 550	16 @ 2100	10.5	10.75 @ 15	—
	V8-318 Auto. Tr.	3438255	.017	30–34	17–20	1 @ 550	14 @ 2100	12	10.75 @ 15	—

Continued

DISTRIBUTOR SPECIFICATIONS—Continued

★NOTE: If advance is checked on the car, double the R.P.M. and degrees advance to get crankshaft figures.

Year	Model	Distributor Part No.①	Breaker Gap	Dwell Angle Deg.	Breaker Arm Spring Tension	Centrifugal Advance Degrees @ R.P.M. of Distributor★		Vacuum Advance		Dist. Retard
						Advance Starts	Full Advance	Inches of Vacuum To Start Plunger	Max. Adv. Dist. Deg. @ Vacuum	Max. Ret. Dist. Deg. @ Vacuum

DODGE & PLYMOUTH—Continued

Year	Model	Distributor Part No.①	Breaker Gap	Dwell Angle Deg.	Breaker Arm Spring Tension	Advance Starts	Full Advance	Inches of Vacuum To Start Plunger	Max. Adv. Dist. Deg. @ Vacuum	Max. Ret. Dist. Deg. @ Vacuum
1970	V8-340 Std. Tr.	3438317	.017	⑦	17–21½	1.5 @ 700	10 @ 900	7.7	10 @ 10.5	—
	V8-340 Std. Tr.	IBS-4015B	.017	⑦	17–21½	1.5 @ 700	10 @ 900	7.7	10 @ 10.5	—
	V8-340 Auto. Tr.	3438325	.017	30–34	17–20	1.5 @ 650	10 @ 850	7.7	10 @ 10.5	—
	V8-383⑪	3438231	.017	28–32	17–20	1 @ 550	16 @ 2200	7.5	11.8 @ 12	2¾②
	V8-383⑫	3438233	.017	28–32	17–20	1 @ 600	12 @ 2300	10.5	12 @ 15.5	2¾②
	V8-440, 350 H.P.	3438219	.017	28–23	17–20	1 @ 650	14 @ 2300	10.5	12 @ 15.5	2¾②
	V8-440, 375 H.P.	3438222	.017	28–32	17–20	1 @ 600	12 @ 2300	10.5	12 @ 15.5	2¾②
	V8-440, 390 H.P.⑨	3438314	.017	⑦	17–21½	1 @ 650	14 @ 2400	11	12.5 @ 15.5	—
	V8-440, 390 H.P.⑨	IBS-4014	.017	⑦	17–21½	1 @ 650	14 @ 2400	11	12.5 @ 15.5	—
	V8-440, 390 H.P.⑨	2875982	.017	⑦	17–21½	1 @ 600	14 @ 2400	11	12.5 @ 15.5	—
	8-426 Std. Tr.	2875987	.017	⑦	17–21½	1 @ 650	16 @ 1600	9	9.2 @ 13.5	—
	8-426 Std. Tr.	IBS-4014E	.017	⑦	17–21½	1 @ 650	16 @ 1600	9	9.2 @ 13.5	—
	8-426 Auto. Tr.	2875989	.017	⑦	17–21½	1 @ 600	13.5 @ 1600	9	9.2 @ 13.5	—
1971	6-198	3438509	.020	41–46	17–20	1 @ 550	14 @ 2000	7	8.5 @ 11	—
	6-198⑤	3438524	.020	41–46	17–20	1 @ 700	14 @ 2000	7	7.75 @ 10	—
	6-225 Std. Tr.	2875822	.020	41–46	17–20	1 @ 550	14 @ 2000	10	7.75 @ 15	—
	6-225 Std. Tr.⑤	3438440	.020	41–46	17–20	1 @ 800	14 @ 2200	10	7.75 @ 15	—
	6-225 Auto. Tr.	2875826	.020	41–46	17–20	1 @ 550	14 @ 2000	7	7.75 @ 10	—
	6-225 Auto. Tr.⑤	3438442	.020	41–46	17–20	1 @ 800	14 @ 2200	7	7.75 @ 10	—
	8-318 Std. Tr.	3438255	.017	30–34	17–20	1 @ 550	16 @ 2100	10.5	10.75 @ 15	—
	8-318 Auto. Tr.	3438225	.017	30–34	17–20	1 @ 550	16 @ 2100	12	10.75 @ 15	—
	8-318⑤	3438453	.017	30–34	17–20	1 @ 600	16 @ 2100	9.5	10.5 @ 15	—
	8-340 Std. Tr.⑫	3438522	.017	⑦	17–21½	1 @ 650	12 @ 2000	7	10 @ 11	—
	8-340 Std. Tr.⑫	IBS-4018C	.017	⑦	17–21½	1 @ 650	12 @ 2000	7	10 @ 11	—
	8-340 Auto. Tr.⑫	3438517	.017	30–34	17–20	1 @ 600	12 @ 2100	9	10 @ 12.5	—
	8-340 Std. Tr.⑯	3438615	.017	⑦	17–21½	1 @ 700	15 @ 2200	7	10 @ 11	—
	8-340 Std. Tr.⑯	1BS-4018D	.017	⑦	17–21½	1 @ 700	15 @ 2200	7	10 @ 11	—
	8-340 Auto. Tr.⑯	3438617	.017	30–34	17–20	1 @ 700	15 @ 2200	9	10 @ 12.5	—
	8-340 Auto. Tr.⑯	1BS-4018E	.017	30–34	17–20	1 @ 700	15 @ 2200	9	10 @ 12.5	—
	8-340	3656151	—	—	—	1 @ 650	12 @ 2000	7	10 @ 11	—
	8-360	3438422	.017	30–34	17–20	1 @ 550	16 @ 2100	9.5	10.5 @ 15	—
	8-360⑤	3438453	.017	30–34	17–20	1 @ 600	16 @ 2100	9.5	10.5 @ 15	—
	8-383⑬	3438534	.019	28½–32½	17–20	1 @ 600	14 @ 2000	9	10 @ 15	—
	8-383⑬⑤	3438544	.019	28½–32½	17–20	1 @ 700	14 @ 2000	9	10 @ 15	—
	8-383⑫	3438690	.019	28½–32½	17–20	1 @ 650	14 @ 2400	10.5	10 @ 15	—
	8-426 Std. Tr.	2875987	.017	⑦	17–21½	1 @ 650	16 @ 1600	9	9.2 @ 13.5	—
	8-426 Std. Tr.	1BS-4017B	.017	⑦	17–21½	1 @ 650	16 @ 1600	9	9.2 @ 13	—
	8-426 Auto. Tr.	3438579	.017	⑦	17–21½	1 @ 600	15 @ 1600	9	9.2 @ 13.5	—
	8-426 Auto. Tr.	1BS-4017E	.017	⑦	17–21½	1 @ 600	15 @ 1600	9	9.2 @ 13.5	—
	8-440 Auto. Tr.	3438559	.019	28½–32½	17–20	1 @ 700	12 @ 2400	12	10 @ 16	—
	8-440 Std. Tr.	3438572	.019	28½–32½	17–20	1 @ 600	10 @ 2200	10.5	12 @ 15.5	—
	8-440 Auto. Tr.	3438694	.019	28½–32½	17–20	1 @ 700	10 @ 2200	10.5	12 @ 15.5	—
	8-440⑯	3438577	.017	⑦	17–21½	1 @ 700	6.5 @ 2200	10.5	10 @ 15	—
1972	6-198	3656237	.020	41–46	17–20	1 @ 550	14 @ 2000	7	8½ @ 11	—
	6-198	3656243	.020	41–46	17–20	1 @ 650	14 @ 2000	7	8½ @ 11	—
	6-225	3656252	.020	41–46	17–20	1 @ 550	14 @ 2000	10	7¾ @ 15	—
	6-225	3656257	.020	41–46	17–20	1 @ 550	14 @ 2000	7	7½ @ 9½	—
	6-225	3656260	.020	41–46	17–20	1 @ 700	14 @ 2000	10	7¾ @ 15	—
	6-225	3656266	.020	41–46	17–20	1 @ 700	14 @ 2000	7	7½ @ 9½	—
	8-318, 360	3656272	.017	30–34	17–20	1 @ 550	16 @ 2100	9½	10½ @ 15	—
	8-318	3656275	.017	30–34	17–20	1 @ 600	16 @ 2100	9½	10½ @ 15	—

Continued

DISTRIBUTOR SPECIFICATIONS—Continued

★NOTE: If advance is checked on the car, double the R.P.M. and degrees advance to get crankshaft figures.

Year	Model	Distributor Part No.①	Breaker Gap	Dwell Angle Deg.	Breaker Arm Spring Tension	Centrifugal Advance Degrees @ R.P.M. of Distributor★		Vacuum Advance		Dist. Retard
						Advance Starts	Full Advance	Inches of Vacuum To Start Plunger	Max. Adv. Dist. Deg. @ Vacuum	Max. Ret. Dist. Deg. @ Vacuum

DODGE AND PLYMOUTH—Continued

Year	Model	Distributor Part No.①	Breaker Gap	Dwell Angle Deg.	Breaker Arm Spring Tension	Advance Starts	Full Advance	Inches of Vacuum To Start Plunger	Max. Adv. Dist. Deg. @ Vacuum	Max. Ret. Dist. Deg. @ Vacuum
1972	8-318	3656390	.017	30–34	17–20	1 @ 550	16 @ 2100	12	10¾ @ 15	—
	8-340	3656278	—	—	—	1 @ 650	13½ @ 2400	9	10 @ 12½	—
	8-360	3656429	—	—	—	1 @ 550	15 @ 1900	9	10 @ 14	—
	8-360	3656435	—	—	—	1 @ 600	15 @ 1900	9	10 @ 14	—
	8-400	3656329	.019	28½–32½	17–20	1 @ 650	14 @ 2000	10½	10½ @ 15½	—
	8-400	3656335	—	—	—	1 @ 650	14 @ 2000	10½	10½ @ 15½	—
	8-400	3656338	—	—	—	1 @ 650	12½ @ 2500	10½	10½ @ 15½	—
	8-440	3656341	—	—	—	1 @ 650	12½ @ 2500	10½	10½ @ 15½	—
	8-440	3656344	.019	28½–32½	17–21	1 @ 650	12 @ 2000	10½	10½ @ 15½	—
	8-440	3656347	—	—	—	1 @ 650	14 @ 2000	10½	10½ @ 15½	—
	8-440	3656353	—	—	—	1 @ 650	10 @ 2150	10½	10½ @ 15½	—

①—Stamped on distributor housing.
②—Solenoid controlled.
③—Without CAP (cleaner air package).
④—With CAP (cleaner air package).
⑤—California only.
⑥—Each set 27–31°; total both sets 36–40°.
⑦—Each set 27–32°; total both sets 37–42°.
⑧—With CAP and Torqueflite.
⑨—With CAP and manual transmission.
⑩—With 2 bar. carb. without CAP.
⑪—With 2 bar. carb. with CAP.
⑫—With 4 bar. carb.
⑬—With 2 bar. carb.
⑭—375 H.P. engine.
⑮—350 H.P. engine.
⑯—Three carbs.

VALVE SPECIFICATIONS

Year	Model	Valve Lash		Valve Angles		Valve Spring Installed Height	Valve Spring Pressure Lbs. @ In.	Stem Clearance		Stem Diameter	
		Int.	Exh.	Seat	Face			Intake	Exhaust	Intake	Exhaust

CHRYSLER AND IMPERIAL

Year	Model	Int.	Exh.	Seat	Face	Valve Spring Installed Height	Valve Spring Pressure Lbs. @ In.	Intake	Exhaust	Intake	Exhaust
1966	2 Bar. Carb.	Hydraulic①	Hydraulic①	45	45	1⁵⁵⁄₆₄	190 @ 1¹⁵⁄₃₂	.001–.003	.002–.004	.372–.373	.371–.372
	4 Bar. Carb.	Hydraulic①	Hydraulic①	45	45	1⁵⁵⁄₆₄	200 @ 1⁷⁄₁₆	.001–.003	.002–.004	.372–.373	.371–.372
1967	8-383, 440 Std.	Hydraulic①	Hydraulic①	45	45	1⁵⁵⁄₆₄	200 @ 1⁷⁄₁₆	.001–.003	.002–.004	.372–.373	.371–.372
	8-440 Hi Perf.	Hydraulic①	Hydraulic①	45	45	1⁵⁵⁄₆₄	246 @ 1²³⁄₆₄	.001–.003	.002–.004	.372–.373	.371–.372
1968–70	8-383, 290 H.P.	Hydraulic①	Hydraulic①	45	45	1.86	200 @ 1.43	.001–.003	.002–.004	.372–.373	.371–.372
	8-383, 330 H.P.	Hydraulic①	Hydraulic①	45	45	1.86	225 @ 1.43	.001–.003	.002–.004	.372–.373	.371–.372
	8-440, 350 H.P.	Hydraulic①	Hydraulic①	45	45	1.86	200 @ 1.43	.001–.003	.002–.004	.372–.373	.371–.372
	8-440, 375 H.P.	Hydraulic①	Hydraulic①	45	45	1.86	230 @ 1.41	.001–.003	.002–.004	.372–.373	.371–.372
1971	8-383, 270 H.P.	Hydraulic①	Hydraulic①	45	45	1⁵⁵⁄₆₄	200 @ 1⁷⁄₁₆	.001–.003	.002–.004	.372–.373	.371–.372
	8-383, 300 H.P.	Hydraulic①	Hydraulic①	45	45	1⁵⁵⁄₆₄	246 @ 1²³⁄₆₄	.001–.003	.002–.004	.372–.373	.371–.372
	8-400	Hydraulic①	Hydraulic①	45	45	1⁵⁵⁄₆₄	200 @ 1⁷⁄₁₆	.001–.003	.002–.004	.372–.373	.371–.372
	8-440, 335 H.P.	Hydraulic①	Hydraulic①	45	45	1⁵⁵⁄₆₄	200 @ 1⁷⁄₁₆	.001–.003	.002–.004	.372–.373	.371–.372
	8-440, 370 H.P.	Hydraulic①	Hydraulic①	45	45	1⁵⁵⁄₆₄	246 @ 1²³⁄₆₄	.001–.003	.002–.004	.372–.373	.371–.372
1972	8-360	Hydraulic①	Hydraulic①	45	45	1.65	195 @ 1.24	.001–.003	.002–.004	.372–.373	.371–.372
	8-400, 440	Hydraulic①	Hydraulic①	45	45	1.86	200 @ 1.42	.001–.003	.002–.004	.372–.373	.371–.372

Continued

VALVE SPECIFICATIONS—Continued

Year	Model	Valve Lash		Valve Angles		Valve Spring Installed Height	Valve Spring Pressure Lbs. @ In.	Stem Clearance		Stem Diameter	
		Int.	Exh.	Seat	Face			Intake	Exhaust	Intake	Exhaust
DODGE AND PLYMOUTH											
1966	6-170, 225	.010H	.020H	45	②	1¹¹⁄₁₆	145 @ 1⁵⁄₁₆	.001–.003	.002–.004	.372–.373	.371–.372
	8-273 2 Bar. Carb.	.013H	.021H	45	45	1¹¹⁄₁₆	145 @ 1⁵⁄₁₆	.001–.003	.002–.004	.372–.373	.371–.372
	8-273 4 Bar. Carb.	.013H	.021H	45	45	1¹¹⁄₁₆	177 @ 1⁵⁄₁₆	.001–.003	.002–.004	.372–.373	.371–.372
	8-318	.013H	.021H	45	45	1¹¹⁄₁₆	145 @ 1⁵⁄₁₆	.001–.003	.002–.004	.372–.373	.371–.372
	8-361, 383	Hydraulic①		45	45	1⁵⁵⁄₆₄	195 @ 1¹⁵⁄₃₂	.001–.003	.002–.004	.372–.373	.371–.372
	8-426	Hydraulic①		45	45	1⁵⁵⁄₆₄	195 @ 1¹⁵⁄₃₂	.001–.003	.002–.004	.372–.373	.371–.372
	8-426 Hemi Char.	.028C	.032C	45	45	1⁵⁵⁄₆₄	266 @ 1.36	.002–.004	.003–.005	.3085–.3095	.3075–.3085
	8-426 Hemi	Hydrualic①		45	45	1⁵⁵⁄₆₄	184 @ 1¹³⁄₃₂	.002–.004	.003–.005	.3085–.3095	.3075–.3085
	8-440	Hydraulic①		45	45	1⁵⁵⁄₆₄	200 @ 1⁷⁄₁₆	.001–.003	.002–.004	.372–.373	.371–.372
1967	6-170, 225	.010H	.020H	45	③	1¹¹⁄₁₆	145 @ 1⁵⁄₁₆	.001–.003	.002–.004	.372–.373	.371–.372
	8-273 2 Bar. Carb.	.013H	.021H	45	45	1¹¹⁄₁₆	145 @ 1⁵⁄₁₆	.001–.003	.002–.004	.372–.373	.371–.372
	8-273 4 Bar. Carb.	.013H	.021H	45	45	1¹¹⁄₁₆	177 @ 1⁵⁄₁₆	.001–.003	.002–.004	.372–.373	.371–.372
	8-318	Hydraulic①		45	45	1¹¹⁄₁₆	148 @ 1⁵⁄₁₆	.001–.003	.002–.004	.372–.373	.371–.372
	8-383	Hydraulic①		45	45	1⁵⁵⁄₆₄	200 @ 1⁷⁄₁₆	.001–.003	.002–.004	.372–.373	.371–.372
	8-440	Hydraulic①		45	45	1⁵⁵⁄₆₄	246 @ 1²³⁄₆₄	.001–.003	.002–.004	.372–.373	.371–.372
	8-426 Hemi	.028C	.032C	45	45	1⁵⁵⁄₆₄	184 @ 1¹³⁄₃₂	.002–.004	.003–.005	.3085–.3095	.3075–.3085
1968	6-170, 225	.010H	.020H	45	②	1.65	145 @ 1⁵⁄₁₆	.001–.003	.002–.004	.372–.373	.371–.372
	8-273, 318	Hydraulic①		45	45	1.65	177 @ 1⁵⁄₁₆	.001–.003	.002–.004	.372–.373	.371–.372
	8-340	Hydraulic①		45	45	1.65	242 @ 1.21	.001–.003	.002–.004	.372–.373	.371–.372
	8-383, 300 H.P.	Hydraulic①		45	45	1.86	225 @ 1.43	.001–.003	.002–.004	.372–.373	.371–.372
	8-383, 290 H.P.	Hydraulic①		45	45	1.86	200 @ 1.43	.001–.003	.002–.004	.372–.373	.371–.372
	8-383, 330 H.P.	Hydraulic①		45	45	1.86	225 @ 1.43	.001–.003	.002–.004	.372–.373	.371–.372
	8-440, 375 H.P.	Hydraulic①		45	45	1.86	230 @ 1.41	.001–.003	.002–.004	.372–.373	.371–.372
	8-440, 350 H.P.	Hydraulic①		45	45	1.86	200 @ 1.43	.001–.003	.002–.004	.372–.373	.371–.372
	8-426	.028C	.032C	45	45	1.86	280 @ 1.37	.001–.003	.002–.004	.372–.373	.371–.372
1969–70	6-170, 198, 225	.010H	.020H	45	②	1¹¹⁄₁₆	145 @ 1⁵⁄₁₆	.001–.003	.002–.004	.372–.373	.371–.372
	8-273, 318	Hydraulic①		45	②	1¹¹⁄₁₆	177 @ 1⁵⁄₁₆	.001–.003	.002–.004	.372–.373	.371–.372
	8-340	Hydraulic①		45	②	1¹¹⁄₁₆	242 @ 1⁷⁄₃₂	.001–.003	.002–.004	.372–.373	.371–.372
	8-383, 290 H.P.	Hydraulic①		45	45	1⁵⁷⁄₆₄	200 @ 1⁷⁄₁₆	.001–.003	.002–.004	.372–.373	.371–.372
	8-383, 330 H.P.	Hydraulic①		45	45	1⁵⁷⁄₆₄	246 @ 1²³⁄₆₄	.001–.003	.002–.004	.372–.373	.371–.372
	8-383, 335 H.P.	Hydraulic①		45	45	1⁵⁷⁄₆₄	246 @ 1²³⁄₆₄	.001–.003	.002–.004	.372–.373	.371–.372
	8-440, 350 H.P.	Hydraulic①		45	45	1⁵⁷⁄₆₄	200 @ 1⁷⁄₁₆	.001–.003	.002–.004	.372–.373	.371–.372
	8-440, 375 H.P.	Hydraulic①		45	45	1⁵⁷⁄₆₄	246 @ 1²³⁄₆₄	.001–.003	.002–.004	.372–.373	.371–.372
	8-440, 390 H.P.	Hydraulic①		45	45	1⁵⁷⁄₆₄	310 @ 1³⁄₈	.001–.003	.002–.004	.372–.373	.371–.372
	8-426	.028C	.032C	45	45	1⁵⁷⁄₆₄	280 @ 1³⁄₈	.001–.003	.002–.004	.372–.373	.371–.372
1971	6-198, 225	.010H	.020H	45	②	1¹¹⁄₁₆	145 @ 1⁵⁄₁₆	.001–.003	.002–.004	.372–.373	.371–.372
	8-318	Hydraulic①		45	②	1¹¹⁄₁₆	177 @ 1⁵⁄₁₆	.001–.003	.002–.004	.372–.373	.371–.372
	8-340	Hydraulic①		45	②	1¹¹⁄₁₆	238 @ 1⁵⁄₁₆	.001–.003	.002–.004	.372–.373	.371–.372
	8-360	Hydraulic①		45	②	1¹¹⁄₁₆	177 @ 1⁵⁄₁₆	.001–.003	.002–.004	.372–.373	.371–.372
	8-383, 2 B. Carb.	Hydraulic①		45	45	1⁵⁵⁄₆₄	200 @ 1⁷⁄₁₆	.001–.003	.002–.004	.372–.373	.371–.372
	8-383, 4 B. Carb.	Hydraulic①		45	45	1⁵⁵⁄₆₄	246 @ 1²³⁄₆₄	.001–.003	.002–.004	.372–.373	.371–.372
	8-440	Hydraulic①		45	45	1⁵⁵⁄₆₄	200 @ 1⁷⁄₁₆	.001–.003	.002–.004	.372–.373	.371–.372
	8-440, Hi Perf.	Hydraulic①		45	45	1⁵⁵⁄₆₄	246 @ 1²³⁄₆₄	.001–.003	.002–.004	.372–.373	.371–.372
	8-440, 3 Carbs.	Hydraulic①		45	45	1⁵⁵⁄₆₄	246 @ 1²³⁄₆₄	.001–.003	.002–.004	.372–.373	.371–.372
	8-426	Hydraulic①		45	45	1⁵⁵⁄₆₄	310 @ 1³⁄₈	.002–.004	.003–.005	.3085–.3095	.3075–.3085
1972	6-198, 225	.010H	.020H	45	③	1.65	160 @ 1.24	.001–.003	.002–.004	.372–.373	.371–.372
	8-318	Hydraulic①		45	③	1.65	189 @ 1.28	.001–.003	.002–.004	.372–.373	.371–.372
	8-340	Hydraulic①		45	③	1.65	238 @ 1.22	.001–.003	.002–.004	.372–.373	.371–.372
	8-360	Hydraulic①		45	③	1.65	195 @ 1.24	.001–.003	.002–.004	.372–.373	.371–.372
	8-400, 2 B. Carb.	Hydraulic①		45	45	1.86	200 @ 1.42	.001–.003	.002–.004	.372–.373	.371–.372
	8-400, 4 B. Carb.	Hydraulic①		45	45	1.86	234 @ 1.40	.001–.003	.002–.004	.372–.373	.371–.372
	8-440	Hydraulic①		45	45	1.86	200 @ 1.42	.001–.003	.002–.004	.372–.373	.371–.372
	8-440, Hi Perf.	Hydraulic①		45	45	1.86	234 @ 1.40	.001–.003	.002–.004	.372–.373	.371–.372
	8-440, 3 Carbs.	Hydraulic①		45	45	1.86	310 @ 1.37	.001–.003	.002–.004	.372–.373	.371–.372

①—No adjustment.   ②—Intake 45°, exhaust 43°.   ③—Intake 45°, exhaust 47°.

PISTONS, PINS, RINGS, CRANKSHAFT & BEARINGS

Year	Model	Piston Clearance Top of Skirt	Ring End Gap①		Wrist-pin Diameter	Rod Bearings		Main Bearings			
			Comp.	Oil		Shaft Diameter	Bearing Clearance	Shaft Diameter	Bearing Clearance	Thrust on Bear. No.	Shaft End Play

CHRYSLER & IMPERIAL

Year	Model	Piston Clearance Top of Skirt	Comp.	Oil	Wrist-pin Diameter	Shaft Diameter	Bearing Clearance	Shaft Diameter	Bearing Clearance	Thrust on Bear. No.	Shaft End Play
1966–67	V8-383	.0005–.0015	.013	.015	1.0936	2.374–2.375	.0005–.0015	2.6245–2.6255	.0005–.0015	3	.002–.007
	V8-440	.0005–.0015	.013	.015	1.0936	2.374–2.375	.0005–.0015	2.7495–2.7505	.0005–.0015	3	.002–.007
1968	8-383	.0002–.0012	.013	.015	1.0936	2.374–2.375	.0005–.003	2.6245–2.6255	.0005–.0015	3	.002–.007
	8-440	.0002–.0012	.013	.015	1.094	2.374–2.375	.0005–.003	2.7495–2.7505	.0005–.0015	3	.002–.007
1969	8-383	.0003–.0013	.013	.015	1.0936	2.374–2.375	.001–.002	2.6245–2.6255	.0005–.0015	3	.002–.007
	8-440	.0003–.0013	.013	.015	1.0936	2.374–2.375	.001–.002	2.7495–2.7505	.0005–.0015	3	.002–.007
1970	8-383, 2 B. C.	.0003–.0012	.013	.015	1.0936	2.374–2.375	.0005–.0015	2.6245–2.6255	.0005–.0015	3	.002–.007
	8-383, 4 B. C.	.0003–.0012	.013	.015	1.0936	2.374–2.375	.001–.002	2.6245–2.6255	.0005–.0015	3	.002–.007
	8-440	.0003–.0012	.013	.015	1.0936	2.374–2.375	.001–.002	2.7495–2.7505	.0005–.0015	3	.002–.007
1971	8-383, 2 B. C.	.0003–.0012	.013	.015	1.0936	2.374–2.375	.0005–.0025	2.6245–2.6255	.0005–.0015	3	.002–.007
	8-383, 4 B. C.	.0003–.0012	.013	.015	1.0936	2.374–2.375	.0007–.0032	2.6245–2.6255	.0005–.0015	3	.002–.007
	8-400	.0003–.0013	.013	.015	1.0936	2.374–2.375	.0005–.002	2.6245–2.6255	.0005–.002	3	.002–.007
	8-440	.0003–.0012	.013	.015	1.0936	2.374–2.375	.0007–.0032	2.7495–2.7505	.0005–.0015	3	.002–.007
1972	8-360	.0005–.0015	.010	—	.9842	2.125	.0005–.0025	2.81	.0005–.0025	3	.002–.010
	8-400	.0002–.0012	.013	—	1.0936	2.374–2.375	.0005–.0025	2.6245–2.6255	.0005–.0025	3	.002–.010
	8-440	.0002–.0012	.013	—	1.0936	2.374–2.375	.0007–.0032	2.7495–2.7505	.0005–.0025	3	.002–.010

DODGE & PLYMOUTH

Year	Model	Piston Clearance Top of Skirt	Comp.	Oil	Wrist-pin Diameter	Shaft Diameter	Bearing Clearance	Shaft Diameter	Bearing Clearance	Thrust on Bear. No.	Shaft End Play
1966	6-170, 225	.0005–.0015	.010	.015	.9008	2.1865–2.1875	.0005–.0015	2.7495–2.7505	.0005–.0015	3	.002–.007
	V8-273, 318	.0005–.0015	.010	.015	.9842	2.124–2.125	.0005–.0015	2.4995–2.5005	.0005–.0015	3	.002–.007
	V8-361, 383	.0005–.0015	.013	.013	1.0936	2.374–2.375	.0005–.0015	2.6245–2.6255	.0005–.0015	3	.002–.007
	V8-426, 440	.0005–.0015	.013	.013	1.0936	2.374–2.375	.0005–.0015	2.7495–2.7505	.0005–.0015	3	.002–.007
	8-426 HP2	.0025–.0035	.013	.015	1.0311	2.374–2.375	.0015–.0025	2.7495–2.7505	.0015–.0025	3	.002–.007
1967	6-170, 225	.0005–.0015	.010	.015	.9008	2.1865–2.1875	.0005–.0015	2.7495–2.7505	.0005–.0025	3	.002–.007
	8-273, 318	.0005–.0015	.010	.015	.9842	2.124–2.125	.0005–.0015	2.4995–2.5005	.0005–.0015	3	.002–.007
	8-383	.0003–.0013	.013	.015	1.0936	2.374–2.375	.0005–.0015	2.6245–2.6255	.0005–.0015	3	.002–.007
	8-440	.0003–.0013	.013	.015	1.0936	2.374–2.375	.0005–.0015	2.7495–2.7505	.0005–.0015	3	.002–.007
	8-426 Hemi	.0025–.0035	.013	.015	1.0311	2.374–2.375	.0015–.0025	2.7495–2.7505	.0015–.0025	3	.002–.007
1968	6-170, 225	.0005–.0015	.010	.015	.9008	2.1865–2.1875	.0002–.0022	2.7495–2.7505	.0005–.0015	3	.002–.007
	8-273, 318	.0005–.0015	.010	.015	.9842	2.124–2.125	.0002–.0022	2.4995–2.5005	.0005–.0015	3	.002–.007
	8-340	.0005–.0015	.013	.015	.9842	2.124–2.125	.0002–.0027	2.4995–2.5005	.0005–.0015	3	.002–.007
	8-383	.0002–.0012	.013	.015	1.0936	2.374–2.375	.0005–.003	2.6245–2.6255	.0005–.0015	3	.002–.007
	8-440	.0002–.0012	.013	.015	1.094	2.374–2.375	.0005–.003	2.7495–2.7505	.0005–.0015	3	.002–.007
	8-426	.0025–.0035	.013	.015	1.0311	2.374–2.375	.001–.0035	2.7495–2.7505	.0005–.0015	3	.002–.007
1969–70	6-170	.0005–.0015	.010	.010	.9008	2.1865–2.1875	.0005–.001	2.7495–2.7505	.0005–.0015	3	.002–.007
	6-198, 225	.0005–.0015	.010	.015	.9008	2.1865–2.1875	.0005–.0015	2.7495–2.7505	.0005–.0015	3	.002–.007
	8-273, 318	.0005–.0015	.010	.015	.9842	2.124–2.125	.0005–.0015	2.4995–2.5005	.0005–.0015	3	.002–.007
	8-340	.0005–.0015	.010	.015	.9842	2.124–2.125	.0005–.0020	2.4995–2.5005	.0005–.0015	3	.002–.007
	8-383, 290 H.P.	.0003–.0013	.013	.015	1.0936	2.374–2.375	.0005–.0015	2.6245–2.6255	.0005–.0015	3	.002–.007
	8-383, 330 H.P.	.0003–.0013	.013	.015	1.0936	2.374–2.375	.001–.002	2.6245–2.6255	.0005–.0015	3	.002–.007
	8-383, 335 H.P.	.0003–.0013	.013	.015	1.0936	2.374–2.375	.001–.002	2.6245–2.6255	.0005–.0015	3	.002–.007
	8-440	.0003–.0013	.013	.015	1.0936	2.374–2.375	.001–.002	2.7495–2.7505	.0005–.0015	3	.002–.007
	8-426	.0025–.0035	.013	.015	1.0311	2.374–2.375	.0015–.0025	2.7495–2.7505	.0015–.0025	3	.002–.007
1971	6-198, 225	.0005–.0015	.010	.015	.9008	2.1865–2.1875	.0005–.002	2.7495–2.7505	.0005–.002	3	.002–.007
	8-318, 340, 360	.0005–.0015	.010	.015	.9842	2.124–2.125	.0005–.002	2.4995–2.5005	.0005–.002	3	.002–.006
	8-383	.0003–.0013	.013	.015	1.0936	2.374–2.375	.0005–.002	2.6245–2.6255	.0005–.002	3	.002–.007
	8-440	.0003–.0013	.013	.015	1.0936	2.374–2.375	.0005–.002	2.7495–2.7505	.0005–.002	3	.002–.007
	8-426	.0025–.0035	.013	.015	1.0311	2.374–2.375	.0015–.0025	2.7490–2.75005	.0015–.003	3	.002–.007

Continued

PISTONS, PINS, RINGS, CRANKSHAFT & BEARINGS—Continued

Year	Model	Piston Clearance Top of Skirt	Ring End Gap①		Wrist-pin Diameter	Rod Bearings		Main Bearings			Shaft End Play
			Comp.	Oil		Shaft Diameter	Bearing Clearance	Shaft Diameter	Bearing Clearance	Thrust on Bear. No.	

DODGE & PLYMOUTH—Continued

Year	Model										
1972	6-198, 225	.0005–.0015	.010	—	.9008	2.1865–2.1875	.0005–.0025	2.7495–2.7505	.0005–.0025	3	.002–.010
	8-318	.0005–.0015	.010	—	.9842	2.124–2.125	.0005–.0025	2.4995–2.5005	.0005–.0025	3	.002–.010
	8-340	.001–.002	.013	—	.9842	2.124–2.125	.0005–.0030	2.4995–2.5005	.0005–.0025	3	.002–.010
	8-360	.0005–.0015	.010	—	.9842	2.124–2.125	.0005–.0025	2.81	.0005–.0025	3	.002–.010
	8-400	.0002–.0012	.013	—	1.0936	2.374–2.375	.0005–.0025	2.6245–2.6255	.0005–.0025	3	.002–.010
	8-440	.0002–.0012	.013	—	1.0936	2.374–2.375	.0007–.0032	2.7495–2.7505	.0005–.0025	3	.002–.010

①—Fit rings in tapered bores for clearance listed in tightest portion of ring travel.

ENGINE TIGHTENING SPECIFICATIONS★

★Torque specifications are for clean and lightly lubricated threads only. Dry or dirty threads produce increased friction which prevents accurate measurement of tightness.

Year	Engine	Spark Plugs Ft. Lbs.	Cylinder Head Bolts Ft. Lbs.	Intake Manifold Ft. Lbs.	Exhaust Manifold Ft. Lbs.	Rocker Arm Shaft Bracket Ft. Lbs.	Rocker Arm Cover Ft. Lbs.	Connecting Rod Cap Bolts Ft. Lbs.	Main Bearing Cap Bolts Ft. Lbs.	Flywheel to Crankshaft Ft. Lbs.	Vibration Damper or Pulley Ft. Lbs.
1966–72	6-170, 198	30	65	200①	10	25	40①	45	85	55	②
1966–72	6-225	30	65	200①	10	25	40①	45	85	55	②
1966–68	8-273	30	85	35	30	15	36①	45	85	55	200①
1969	8-273	30	85	35	30	210①	36①	45	85	55	200①
1966–68	8-318	30	④	35	30	15	36①	45	85	55	200①
1969–72	8-318	30	④	35	30	210①	36①	45	85	55	200①
1968	8-340	30	95	35	30	15	36①	45	85	55	200①
1969–72	8-340, 360	30	95	35	30	210①	36①	45	85	55	200①
1966	8-361	30	70	50	30	25	40①	45	85	55	135
1966–68	8-383	30	70	50	30	25	40①	45	85	55	135
1969–72	8-383, 400	30	70	50	30	25	40①	45	85	55	200①
1966	8-426 Std.	30	70	50	30	25	40①	45	85	70	135
1966–71	8-426 Hemi	30	75	③	35	30	40①	75	100	70	135
1966–68	8-440	30	70	50	30	25	40①	45	85	55	135
1969–72	8-440	30	70	50	30	25	40①	45	85	55	200①

①—Inch pounds.　　③—Tighten 8 (4 each side) center screws to 72 inch-lbs; all others 48 inch-lbs.

②—Press fit.　　④—Composition gasket 95 ft.-lbs. Steel gasket 85 ft.-lbs.

STARTING MOTOR SPECIFICATIONS

Year	Part No.	Rotation ①	Brush Spring Tension, Ounces	No Load Test			Torque Test		
				Amperes	Volts	R.P.M.	Amperes	Volts	Torque, Lbs. Ft.
1966–72	2095150	Clockwise	32–48	85	11	1950	475	4	24.0
	2098500	Clockwise	32–48	90	11	2950	340–420	4	—
	1889100	Clockwise	32–48	78	11	3800	350	4	8.5
	2642930	Clockwise	32–36	78	11	3800	310–445	4	—
	2875560	Clockwise	32–36	90	11	1925–2600	400–450	4	—

①—Viewed from drive end.

ALTERNATOR & REGULATOR SPECIFICATIONS

Year	Unit Number	Ground Polarity	Field Coil Draw Amperes	Current Output			Operating Voltage			Voltage Regulator Point Gap	Regulator Armature Air Gap
				Engine R.P.M.	Amperes	Volts	Engine R.P.M.	Volts	Voltage @ 120° ①		
1966–68	⑥	Negative	2.38–2.75②	1250	26③	15	1250	15	13.3–14.3④	.012–.016	.048–.052⑤
	⑦	Negative	2.38–2.75②	1250	35③	15	1250	15	13.3–14.3④	.012–.016	.048–.052⑤
	⑧	Negative	2.38–2.75②	1250	44③	15	1250	15	13.3–14.3④	.012–.016	.048–.052⑤
	⑨	Negative	2.38–2.75②	1250	51③	15	1250	15	13.3–14.3④	.012–.016	.048–.052⑥
1969	⑥	Negative	2.38–2.75②	1250	26③	15	1250	15	13.3–14.3	.012–.016	.048–.052
	⑦	Negative	2.38–2.75②	1250	34.5③	15	1250	15	13.3–14.3	.012–.016	.048–.052
	⑧	Negative	2.38–2.75②	1250	41③	15	1250	15	13.3–14.3	.012–.016	.048–.052
	⑨	Negative	2.38–2.75②	1250	51③	15	1250	15	13.3–14.3	.012–.016	.048–.052
1970–71	⑥	Negative	2.38–2.75②	1250	26③	15	1250	15	13.3–14.4	—	—
	⑦	Negative	2.38–2.75②	1250	34.5③	15	1250	15	13.3–14.4	—	—
	⑧	Negative	2.38–2.75②	1250	44.5③	15	1250	15	13.3–14.4	—	—
	⑨	Negative	2.38–2.75②	1250	51③	15	1250	15	13.3–14.4	—	—

①—For each 10 degree rise in temperature subtract .04 volt. Temperature is checked with thermometer two inches from installed voltage regulator cover.

②—Current draw at 12 volts while turning rotor shaft by hand.

③—Plus or minus three amperes. If output is low, stator or rectifier is shorted.

④—At 117 degrees F.

⑤—Essex Wire built .032–.042".

⑥—Standard with 6-cyl. engines.

⑦—Standard with V8 engines.

⑧—Heavy duty and/or air conditioning.

⑨—Special equipment.

WHEEL ALIGNMENT SPECIFICATIONS

NOTE: See that riding height is correct before checking wheel alignment.

OLD CAR SPECIFICATIONS: For 1946-65 Wheel Alignment Specifications see back of book.

| Year | Model | Caster Angle, Degrees | | Camber Angle, Degrees | | | | Toe-In. Inch | Toe-Out on Turns, Deg. | |
| | | Limits | Desired | Limits | | Desired | | | Outer Wheel | Inner Wheel |
				Left	Right	Left	Right			
CHRYSLER & IMPERIAL										
1966–68	Manual Steer.	0 to −1	−½	+¼ to +¾	0 to +½	+½	+¼	⅛	18.8①	20
	Power Steer.	+¼ to +1¼	+¾	+¼ to +¾	0 to +½	+½	+¼	⅛	18.8①	20
1969	Manual Steer.	+1/16 to −1 1/16	−½	+¼ to +¾	0 to +½	+½	+¼	⅛	18.8①	20
	Power Steer.	+1/16 to −1 1/16②	−½	+¼ to +¾	0 to +½	+½	+¼	⅛	18.8①	20
1970	Manual Steer.	0 to −1	−½	+¼ to +¾	0 to +½	+½	+¼	⅛	18.8①	20
	Power Steer.	0 to −1③	−½	+¼ to +¾	0 to +½	+½	+¼	⅛	18.8①	20
1971	Manual Steer.	0 to −1	−½	+¼ to +¾	0 to +½	+½	+¼	⅛	—	—
	Power Steer.	+¼ to +1¼③	+¾	+¼ to +¾	0 to +½	+½	+¼	⅛	—	—
1972	All	−1/16 to +1 5/16	+⅝	+⅛ to +⅞	−⅛ to +⅝	+½	+¼	⅛	—	—

①—1967–70 Imperial 17.9°, 1966 18.5°. ②—Imperial +3/16 to +1 5/16 with +¾ preferred. ③—Imperial +¼ to +1¼ with +¾ preferred.

Year	Model	Limits	Desired	Left	Right	Left	Right	Toe-In	Outer	Inner
DODGE										
1966	Man. Steer.①	0 to −1	−½	+½	+¼	+½	+¼	⅛	17.6	20
	Power Steer.①	+¼ to +1¼	+¾	+½	+¼	+½	+¼	⅛	17.6	20
	Man. Steer.②	0 to −1	−½	+½	+¼	+½	+¼	⅛	17.8	20
	Power Steer.②	+¼ to +1¼	+¾	+½	+¼	+½	+¼	⅛	17.8	20
	Man. Steer.③	0 to −1	−½	+½	+¼	+½	+¼	⅛	18.8	20
	Power Steer.③	+¼ to +1¼	+¾	+½	+¼	+½	+¼	⅛	18.8	20
1967	Man. Steer.①	0 to −1	−½	+½	+¼	+½	+¼	⅛	17.6	20
	Power Steer.①	+¼ to +1¼	+¾	+½	+¼	+½	+¼	⅛	17.6	20
	Man. Steer.②	0 to −1	−½	+½	+¼	+½	+¼	⅛	17.8	20
	Power Steer.②	+¼ to +1¼	+¾	+½	+¼	+½	+¼	⅛	17.8	20
	Man. Steer.③	0 to −1	−½	+½	+¼	+½	+¼	⅛	18.8	20
	Power Steer.③	+¼ to +1¼	+¾	+½	+¼	+½	+¼	⅛	18.8	20
1968	Man. Steer.①	0 to −1	−½	+½	+¼	+½	+¼	⅛	18	20
	Power Steer.①	+¼ to +1¼	+¾	+½	+¼	+½	+¼	⅛	18	20
	Man. Steer.②	0 to −1	−½	−½	+½	+½	+¼	⅛	18.1	20
	Power Steer.②	+¼ to +1¼	+¾	+½	+¼	+½	+¼	⅛	18.1	20
	Man. Steer.③	0 to −1	−½	+½	+¼	+½	+¼	⅛	17.7	20
	Power Steer.③	+¼ to +1¼	+¾	+½	+¼	+½	+¼	⅛	17.7	20
1969–70	Man. Steer.①	0 to −1	−½	+¼ to +¾	0 to +½	+½	+¼	⅛	17.6	20
	Power Steer.①	+¼ to +1¼	+¾	+¼ to +¾	0 to +½	+½	+¼	⅛	17.6	20
	Man. Steer.②	0 to −1	−½	+¼ to +¾	0 to +½	+½	+¼	⅛	17.8	20
	Power Steer.②	+¼ to +1¼	+¾	+¼ to +¾	0 to +½	+½	+¼	⅛	17.8	20
	Man. Steer.③	0 to −1	−½	+¼ to +¾	0 to +½	+½	+¼	⅛	18.8	20
	Power Steer.③	0 to −1	−½	+¼ to +¾	0 to +½	+½	+¼	⅛	18.8	20
1971	Man. Steer.	0 to −1	−½	+¼ to +¾	0 to +½	+½	+¼	⅛	—	—
	Power Steer.	+¼ to +1¼	+¾	+¼ to +¾	0 to +½	+½	+¼	⅛	—	—
1972	Man. Steer.	−1 5/16 to +1/16	−⅝	+⅛ to +⅞	−⅛ to +⅝	+½	+¼	⅛	—	—
	Power Steer.	−1/16 to +1 5/16	+⅝	+⅛ to +⅞	−⅛ to +⅝	+½	+¼	⅛	—	—

①—Dart. ②—Coronet, Charger and Challenger. ③—Monaco, Polara, 880.

Continued

WHEEL ALIGNMENT SPECIFICATIONS—Continued

NOTE: See that riding height is correct before checking wheel alignment.

OLD CAR SPECIFICATIONS: For 1946-65 Wheel Alignment Specifications see back of book.

Year	Model	Caster Angle, Degrees		Camber Angle, Degrees				Toe-In. Inch	Toe-Out on Turns, Deg.	
		Limits	Desired	Limits		Desired			Outer Wheel	Inner Wheel
				Left	Right	Left	Right			
PLYMOUTH										
1966–67	Man. Steer.	0 to −1	−½	+½	+¼	+½	+¼	⅛	①	20
	Power Steer.	+¼ to +1¼	+¾	+½	+¼	+½	+¼	⅛	①	20
1968–70	Man. Steer.	+1/16 to −1 1/16	−½	+¼ to +¾	0 to +½	+½	+¼	⅛	②	20
	Power Steer.	+3/16 to +1 5/16	+¾	+0¼ to +¾	0 to +½	+½	+¼	⅛	②	20
1971	Man. Steer.	0 to −1	−½	+¼ to +¾	0 to +½	+½	+¼	⅛	—	—
	Power Steer.	+¼ to +1¼	+¾	+¼ to +¾	0 to +½	+½	+¼	⅛	—	—
1972	Man. Steer.	−1 5/16 to +1/16	−⅝	+⅛ to +⅞	−⅛ to +⅝	+½	+¼	⅛	—	—
	Power Steer.	−1/16 to +1 5/16	+⅝	+⅛ to +⅞	−⅛ to +⅝	+½	+¼	⅛	—	—

①—Fury 18.8°, others 17.8°. ②—Fury 17.7°, others 18°.

BRAKE SPECIFICATIONS

Year	Model	Brake Drum Inside Diameter	Wheel Cylinder Bore Diameter			Master Cylinder Bore Diameter		
			Disc Brake	Front Drum Brake	Rear Drum Brake	Disc Brakes	Drum Brakes	Power Brakes
CHRYSLER & IMPERIAL								
1966	All	11	1.638	1⅛	15/16	1	1	1
1967–68	All	11	2.375	1⅛	15/16	1⅛	1	1
1969	Chrysler	11	2.750	1⅛	15/16	1⅛	1	1
	Imperial	11	2.375	—	15/16	1⅛	—	—
1970	All	11	2.750	1⅛	15/16	1⅛	1	1
1971	All	11	2.750	1 3/16	15/16	1	1	1
1972	All	11	2.750	—	15/16	1 1/32	—	1 1/32
DODGE								
1966–67	Polara, Monaco	11	1.638	1⅛	15/16	1	1	1
	Coronet, Charger	10①	2.00	1⅛	15/16	1⅛	1	1
	Dart 6	9	1.638	1	13/16	—	1	1
	Dart V8	10	1.638	1⅛	15/16	1	1	1
1968–69	Dart 6	9	1.638	1	13/16	1	1	1
	Dart V8	10	1.638	1⅛	15/16	1	1	1
	Coronet Deluxe, 440	10	2.00	1⅛	15/16	1⅛	1	1
	Coronet R/T, 500	11	2.00	1⅛	15/16	1⅛	1	1
	Charger	10	2.00	1⅛	15/16	1⅛	1	1
	Polara, Monaco	11	②	1⅛	15/16	1⅛	1	1
1970	Dart 6	③	1.638	1	13/16	1	1	1
	Dart V8	10	1.638	1⅛	15/16	1	1	1

Continued

BRAKE SPECIFICATIONS—Continued

Year	Model	Brake Drum Inside Diameter	Wheel Cylinder Bore Diameter			Master Cylinder Bore Diameter		
			Disc Brake	Front Drum Brake	Rear Drum Brake	Disc Brakes	Drum Brakes	Power Brakes
DODGE—Continued								
1970	Challenger	10④	2.750	1 3/16	15/16	1 1/8	1	1
	Coronet, Charger	10①	2.750	1 1/8	15/16	1 1/8	1	1
	Monaco, Polara	11	2.750	1 1/8	15/16	1 1/8	1	1
1971	Dart, Demon 6	9	—	1	13/16	—	1	1
	Dart, Demon V8	10	1 5/8	1 3/16	15/16	1	1	1
	Challenger	10④	2.750	1 3/16	15/16	1 1/8	1	1
	Coronet, Charger	10④	2.750	1 3/16	15/16	1 1/8	1	1
	Monaco, Polara	11	2.750	1 3/16	15/16	1	1	1
1972	Dart, Demon 6	9	—	1	13/16	—	15/16	15/16
	Dart, Demon V8	10	1 5/8	1 3/16	15/16	1 1/32	1 1/32	1 1/32
	Challenger	10	2.750	1 3/16	15/16	1 1/32	1 1/32	1 1/32
	Coronet, Charger	10④	2.750	1 3/16	15/16	1 1/32	1 1/32	1 1/32
	Monaco, Polara	11	2.750	1 3/16	15/16	1 1/32	1 1/32	1 1/32
PLYMOUTH								
1966	Fury, VIP	11	1.638	1 1/8	15/16	1	1	1
	Valiant, Barracuda 6	9	1 1/8	1	13/16	1	1	1
	Valiant, Barracuda V8	10	1 1/8	1	13/16	1	1	1
	Belvedere, Satellite	10①	—	1 1/8	15/16	1	1	1
1967–69	Valiant, Barracuda 6	9	1.638	1	13/16	1	1	1
	Valiant, Barracuda V8	10	1.638	1 1/8	15/16	1	1	1
	Belvedere, Satellite	10①	2.00	1 1/8	15/16	1 1/8	1	1
	Fury, VIP	11	②	1 1/8	15/16	1 1/8	1	1
1970	Valiant, Duster 6	③	1.638	1	13/16	1	1	1
	Valiant, Duster V8	10	1.638	1 3/16	15/16	1	1	1
	Barracuda	10④	2.750	1 3/16	15/16	1 1/8	1	1
	Belvedere, Satellite	10①	2.750	1 1/8	15/16	1 1/8	1	1
	Fury	11	2.750	1 1/8	15/16	1 1/8	1	1
1971	Valiant, Duster 6	9	—	1	13/16	—	1	1
	Valiant, Duster V8	10	1 5/8	1 3/16	15/16	1	1	1
	Barracuda	10④	2.750	1 3/16	15/16	1 1/8	1	1
	Satellite	10④	2.750	1 3/16	15/16	1 1/8	1	1
	Fury	11	2.750	1 3/16	15/16	1	1	1
1972	Valiant, Duster 6	9	—	1	13/16	—	15/16	15/16
	Valiant, Duster V8	10	1 5/8	1 3/16	15/16	1 1/32	1 1/32	1 1/32
	Barracuda	10	2.750	1 3/16	15/16	1 1/32	1 1/32	1 1/32
	Satellite	10④	2.750	1 3/16	15/16	1 1/32	1 1/32	1 1/32
	Fury	11	2.750	1 3/16	15/16	1 1/32	1 1/32	1 1/32

①—With 383 Hi Perf., 426 or 440 engine, 11″ drums. ②—For 1968, 2.375. For 1969, 2.757. ③—Front 10″, rear 9″. ④—Heavy duty 11″.

CHRYSLER • DODGE • IMPERIAL • PLYMOUTH

COOLING SYSTEM & CAPACITY DATA

Year	Model or Engine	Cooling Capacity, Qts.			Radiator Cap Relief Pressure, Lbs.		Thermo. Opening Temp. ①	Fuel Tank Gals.	Engine Oil Refill Qts. ②	Transmission Oil			Rear Axle Oil Pints
		No Heater	With Heater	With A/C	With A/C	No A/C				3 Speed Pints	4 Speed Pints	Auto. Trans. Qts. ⑫	
CHRYSLER													
1966	All	—	17	18	16	14	180	25③	4	6	—	9½	4
1967	All	—	17⑨	18⑨	16	16	180	25③	4	6½	9	9¼	4
1968	With 8-383	—	17⑨	18⑨	16	16	180	24③	4	6	—	9¼	4
	With 8-440	—	18⑨	19⑨	16	16	180	24③	4	6	—	9¼	4
1969	8-383	—	16⑨	17	16	16	190	24③	4	6	—	9¼	4
	8-440	—	17⑨	18	16	16	190	24③	4	6	—	9¼	4
1970	8-383, 2 B. Carb.	—	14½⑨	15	16	16	195	24⑰	4	5	—	9½	4.4
	8-383, 4 B. Carb.	—	14½⑨	16	16	16	195	24⑰	4	5	—	8	4.4
	8-440	—	15½⑨	17	16	16	195④	24⑰	4	5	—	9½	4.4
1971	8-383, 2 B. Carb.	13½	14½	15	16	16	185	23	4	4¾	—	9½	4.5
	8-383, 4 B. Carb.	13½	14½	15	16	16	185	23	4	—	—	8	4.5
	8-440	14½	15½	17	16	16	185	23	4	—	—	9½	4.5
1972	8-360	14½	15½	15	16	16	185	23	4	—	—	8	4.5
	8-400	13½	14½	14	16	16	185	23	4	—	—	9½	4.5
	8-440	14½	15½	16	16	16	185	23	4	—	—	9½	4.5
IMPERIAL													
1966	All	—	18	18	16	14	180	23	5	—	—	9½	4
1967	All	—	18⑨	19⑨	16	16	180	25	4	—	—	9¼	4
1968	All	—	17⑨	18⑨	16	16	180	24	4	—	—	9¼	4
1969	All	—	19⑨	19	16	16	190	24	4	—	—	9¼	4
1970	All	—	17½⑨	17½	16	16	195	24	4	—	—	9½	4.4
1971–72	All	16½	17½	17½	16	16	185	23	4	—	—	9½	4.5
DODGE													
1966	Dart 6-170	—	12	—	16	14	180	18	4	6½	—	8	2
	Dart 6-225	—	13	13	16	14	180	18	4	6½	—	8	2
	Dart 8-273	—	18	18	16	14	180	18	4	6	8½	8	2
	Coronet 6-225	—	13	13	16	14	180	19	4	6½	—	8	2
	Cor. & Charg. 8-273	—	19	19	16	14	180	19	4	6	—	8	4
	Cor. & Charg. 8-318	—	21	22	16	14	180	19	4	6	—	9¼	4
	Cor. & Charg. 8-361	—	17	18	16	14	180	19	4	—	8½	9¼	4
	Cor. & Charg. 8-383	—	17	18	16	14	180	19	4	—	8½	9¼	4
	Cor. & Charg. 8-426	—	17	18	16	14	180	19	5	—	8½	9¼	4
	Polara, Monaco 8-318	—	21	22	16	14	180	25③	4	6	—	9¼	4
	Polara, Monaco 8-383	—	17	18	16	14	180	25③	4	6	8½	9¼	4
	Polara, Monaco 8-440	—	17	18	16	14	180	25③	4	—	8½	9¼	4
1967	Dart 6-170	—	12	13	16	16	180	18	4	6½	—	8	2
	Dart 6-225	—	13	14	16	16	180	18	4	6½	—	8	2
	Dart 8-273 (2 B.C.)	—	19	20	16	16	180	18	4	6½	8	8	2
	Dart 8-273 (4 B.C.)	—	19	20	16	16	180	18	4	6½	8	8	4
	Coronet 6-225	—	13	14	16	16	180	19	4	6½	—	8	2
	Cor. & Charg. 8-273	—	19	20	16	16	180	19	4	6½	—	8	4
	Cor. & Charg. 8-318	—	18	19	16	16	180	19	4	6½	—	9¼	4
	Cor. & Charg. 8-383	—	17	18	16	16	180	19	4	—	8½	9¼	4
	Cor. & Charg. 8-426	—	18	19	16	16	180	19	5	—	8½	9¼	4
	Cor. & Charg. 8-440	—	18	19	16	16	180	19	4	—	8½	9¼	4

Continued

COOLING SYSTEM & CAPACITY DATA—Continued

Year	Model or Engine	No Heater	With Heater	With A/C	With A/C	No A/C	Thermo. Opening Temp. ①	Fuel Tank Gals.	Engine Oil Refill Qts. ②	3 Speed Pints	4 Speed Pints	Auto. Trans. Qts. ⑫	Rear Axle Oil Pints
		Cooling Capacity, Qts.			Radiator Cap Relief Pressure, Lbs.					Transmission Oil			

DODGE—Continued

Year	Model or Engine	No Heater	With Heater	With A/C	With A/C	No A/C	Thermo. Opening Temp. ①	Fuel Tank Gals.	Engine Oil Refill Qts. ②	3 Speed Pints	4 Speed Pints	Auto. Trans. Qts. ⑫	Rear Axle Oil Pints
1967	Polara, Monaco 8-318	—	18	19	16	16	180	25③	4	6½	—	9¼	4
	Polara, Monaco 8-383	—	17	18	16	16	180	25③	4	6½	9	9¼	4
	Polara, Monaco 8-440	—	17	18	16	16	180	25③	4	—	9	9¼	4
	8-440 Hi Perf.	—	18	19	16	16	180	25③	4	—	9	9¼	4
1968	Dart 6-170	—	12	13	16	16	180	18	4	6½	—	7¾	2
	Dart 6-225	—	13	14	16	16	180	18	4	6½	—	7¾	2
	Dart 8-273	—	19	20	16	16	180	18	4	6	8	7¾	2
	Dart 8-318	—	18	19	16	16	180	18	4	—	8	9¼	2⑩
	Dart 8-340	—	18	19	16	16	180	18	4	—	8	9¼	4
	Dart 8-383	—	17	18	16	16	180	18	4	—	8	7¾	4
	Coronet 6-225	—	13	14	16	16	180	19	4	6½	—	7¾	2⑦
	Coro. Charger 8-273	—	19	20	16	16	180	19	4	6	—	7¾	4
	Coro. Charger 8-318	—	18	19	16	16	180	19	4	6	—	9¼	4
	Coro. Charger 8-383	—	17	18	16	16	180	19	4	—	9	7¾	4
	Coro. Charger 8-440	—	17⑪	18⑪	16	16	180	19	4	—	9	7¾	4⑬
	Coro. Charger 8-426	—	18	19	16	16	180	19	6	—	9	7¾	4⑬
	Polara, Monaco 8-318	—	18	19	16	16	180	24③	4	6	—	9¼	4
	Polara, Monaco 8-383	—	17	18	16	16	180	24③	4	6	—	7¾	4
	Polara, Monaco 8-440	—	17	18	16	16	180	24③	4	—	9	7¾	4⑭
1969	Dart 6-170	—	12⑮	—	—	16	200	18	4	6½	—	7¾	2
	Dart 6-225	—	13	15	16	16	190	18	4	6½	—	7¾	2
	Dart 8-273	—	17	19	16	16	190	18	4	6	7	7¾	2
	Dart 318	—	16	18	16	16	190	18	4	6	7	7¾	2⑩
	Dart 8-340	—	16	16	16	16	190	18	4	—	7	7¾	4
	Dart 8-383	—	16	16	16	16	190	18	4	—	7	7¾⑯	4
	Coronet 6-225	—	13	15	16	16	190	19	4	6½	—	7¾	2⑦
	Coro. Charger 8-318	—	16	19	16	16	190	19	4	6	—	7¾	4
	Coro. Charger 8-383	—	16	17	16	16	190	19	4	—	7½	7¾⑯	4
	Coro. Charger 8-440	—	17	18	16	16	190	19	4	—	7½	9¼	4⑬
	Coro. Charger 8-426	—	18	—	16	16	190	19	6	—	7½	8	4⑬
	Polara, Monaco 8-318	—	16	19	16	16	190	24③	4	6	—	7¾	4
	Polara, Monaco 8-383	—	16	17	16	16	190	24③	4	6	—	7¾⑯	4
	Polara, Monaco 8-440	—	17	18	16	16	190	24③	4	—	—	9¼	4⑭
1970	Dart 6 Cyl.	12	13	13	16	16	190	18	4	6½	—	8½	2
	Dart 8-318	15	16	16	16	16	195	18	4	4¾	—	8	4
	Dart 8-340	14	15	15	16	16	190	18	4	4¾	7	8	4
	Challenger 6 Cyl.	—	13	14	16	16	190	18	4	6½	—	8½	2
	Challenger 8-318	—	16	17½	16	16	195	18	4	4¾	7	8	4
	Challenger 8-340	—	15½	15½	16	16	190	18	4	4¾	7	8	4
	Challenger 8-383	—	14½	15	16	16	190	18	4	4¾	7	8⑱	4
	Challenger 8-440	—	17	17	16	16	190	18	6	—	7	9	5½
	Challenger 8-426	—	17	17	16	16	190	18	6	—	7	8½	5½
	Coro., Charger 6-225	12	13	13	16	16	190	19	4	4¾	—	8½	2
	Coro., Charger 8-318	15	16	16	16	16	195	19	4	4¾	—	8	4
	Coro., Charger 8-383	13½	14½	15	16	16	190	19	4	4¾	7	8⑱	4
	Coro., Charger 8-440	16	17	17	16	16	190	19	6	—	7	8½	5½
	Coro., Charger 8-426	16	17	17	16	16	190	19	6	—	7	8½	5½
	Polara, Monaco 8-318	16	17	17	16	16	195	24⑰	4	4¾	—	8	4
	Polara, Monaco 8-383	13½	14½	14½	16	16	195	24⑰	4	4¾	—	9½	4
	Polara, Monaco 8-440	14½	15½	15½	16	16	195	24⑰	4	—	—	9½	4

Continued

COOLING SYSTEM & CAPACITY DATA—Continued

Year	Model or Engine	Cooling Capacity, Qts.			Radiator Cap Relief Pressure, Lbs.		Thermo. Opening Temp. ①	Fuel Tank Gals.	Engine Oil Refill Qts. ③	Transmission Oil			Rear Axle Oil Pints
		No Heater	With Heater	With A/C	With A/C	No A/C				3 Speed Pints	4 Speed Pints	Auto. Trans. Qts. ⑫	
DODGE—Continued													
1971	Dart 6 Cyl.	12	13	13	16	16	185	17	4	6½	—	8½	2
	Dart 8-318	15	16	16½	16	16	185	17	4	4¾	—	8½	4½
	Dart 8-340	14	15	15	16	16	185	17	4	4¾	7	8	4½
	Challenger 6 Cyl.	12	13	13	16	16	185	18	4	4¾	—	8½	2
	Challenger 8-318	15	16	16½	16	16	185	18	4	4¾	—	8½	2
	Challenger 8-340	14	15	15	16	16	185	18	4	4¾	7½	8	4½
	Challenger 8-383	13½	14½	15	16	16	185	18	4	4¾	7½	8⑱	4½
	Challenger 8-440	16⑲	17⑲	17⑳	16	16	185	18	4	—	7½	9½	5½
	Challenger 8-426	14½	15½	—	16	16	185	18	6	—	7½	8	5½
	Coro., Charger 6-225	12	13	13	16	16	185	21	4	6½	—	8½	4
	Coro., Charger 8-318	15	16	16½	16	16	185	21	4	4¾	—	8½	4
	Coro., Charger 8-383	13½	14½	15	16	16	185	21	4	4¾	7½	8⑱	4
	Coro., Charger 8-440	14½	15½	17	16	16	185	21	4	—	7½	9½	5½
	Coro., Charger 8-426	14½	15½	—	16	16	185	21	6	—	7½	8	5½
	Polara, Monaco 6-225	12	13	13	16	16	185	23	4	4¾	—	8½	4½
	Polara, Monaco 8-318	15	16	16½	16	16	185	23	4	4¾	—	8½	4½
	Polara, Monaco 8-360	14	15	15	16	16	185	23	4	4¾	—	8	4½
	Polara, Monaco 8-383	13½	14½	15	16	16	185	23	4	4¾	—	8⑱	4½
	Polara, Monaco 8-440	14½	15½	17	16	16	185	23	4	—	—	9½	4½
1972	Dart 6 Cyl.	12	13	13	16	16	185	16	4	6½	—	8½	2
	Dart 8-318	15	16	16	16	16	185	16	4	4¾	—	8½	4½
	Dart 8-340	14	15	15	16	16	185	16	4	4¾	7	8	4¼
	Challenger 6 Cyl.	12	13	13	16	16	185	18	4	4¾	—	8½	2
	Challenger 8-318	15	16	16½	16	16	185	18	4	4¾	—	8½	4½
	Challenger 8-340	14	15	14½	16	16	185	18	4	4¾	7½	8	4½
	Coro., Charger 6-225	12	13	13	16	16	185	21	4	6½	—	8½	4½
	Coro., Charger 8-318	15	16	16½	16	16	185	21	4	4¾	—	8½	4½
	Coro., Charger 8-340	14	15	14½	16	16	185	21	4	—	7½	8	4½
	Coro., Charger 8-400	13½	14½	15	16	16	185	21	4	—	7½	8⑱	4½⑭
	Coro., Charger 8-440	14	15	15	16	16	185	21	4	—	7½	9½	5½
	Polara, Monaco 8-318	15	16	16½	16	16	185	23	4	—	—	8½	4½
	Polara, Monaco 8-360	14½	15½	15	16	16	185	23	4	—	—	8	4½
	Polara, Monaco 8-400	13½	14½	14	16	16	185	23	4	—	—	9½	4½
	Polara, Monaco 8-440	14½	15½	16	16	16	185	23	4	—	—	9½	4½
PLYMOUTH													
1966	Belvedere 6-225	—	13	14	16	14	180	19	4	6½	—	8	2⑦
	8-273⑤	—	18	19	16	14	180	19	4	6	—	8	4
	8-318⑤	—	21	22	16	14	180	19	4	6	—	9¼	4
	8-361, 383⑤	—	17	18	16	14	180	19	4	—	8½	9¼	4
	8-426⑤	—	17	17	16	14	180	19	5	—	8½	9¼	4
	Fury 6-225	—	13	14	16	14	180	25⑧	4	6½	—	8	4
	Fury 8-318	—	21	22	16	14	180	25⑧	4	6	—	9¼	4
	Fury 8-383, 440	—	17	18	16	14	180	25⑧	4	6	8½	9¼	4
1967	Belvedere 6-225	—	13	14	16	16	180	19	4	6½	—	8	2⑦
	8-273⑤	—	18	19	16	16	180	19	4	6½	—	8	4
	8-318⑤	—	21	22	16	16	180	19	4	6½	—	9¼	4
	8-383⑤	—	17	18	16	16	180	19	4	—	8½	9¼	4
	8-426⑤	—	18	19	16	16	180	19	4	—	8½	9¼	4

Continued

COOLING SYSTEM & CAPACITY DATA—Continued

Year	Model or Engine	Cooling Capacity, Qts.			Radiator Cap Relief Pressure, Lbs.		Thermo. Opening Temp. ①	Fuel Tank Gals.	Engine Oil Refill Qts. ②	Transmission Oil			Rear Axle Oil Pints
		No Heater	With Heater	With A/C	With A/C	No A/C				3 Speed Pints	4 Speed Pints	Auto. Trans. Qts. ⑫	

PLYMOUTH—Continued

Year	Model or Engine	No Heater	With Heater	With A/C	With A/C	No A/C	Thermo. Opening Temp.	Fuel Tank Gals.	Engine Oil Refill Qts.	3 Speed Pints	4 Speed Pints	Auto. Trans. Qts.	Rear Axle Oil Pints
1967	Fury 6-225	—	13	14	16	16	180	25③	4	6½	—	8	4
	Fury 8-318	—	18	19	16	16	180	25③	4	6½	—	9¼	4
	Fury 8-383	—	17	18	16	16	180	25③	4	6½	8½	9¼	4
	8-440 Hi Perf.	—	18	19	16	16	180	25③	4	6½	9	9¼	4
1968	Fury, VIP 6-225	—	13	14	16	16	180	24③	4	6½	—	7¾	4
	Others 6-225	—	13	14	16	16	180	19	4	6½	—	7¾	2⑦
	8-273	—	19	20	16	16	180	19	4	6	—	7¾	4
	Fury, VIP 8-318	—	18	19	16	16	180	24③	4	6	—	9¼	4
	Others 8-318	—	18	19	16	16	180	19	4	6	—	9¼	4
	Fury, VIP 8-383	—	17	18	16	16	180	24③	4	—	9	7¾	4
	Others 8-383 2 B.C.	—	17	18	16	16	180	19	4	—	9	7¾	4
	8-383 4 Bar. Carb.	—	17	18	16	16	180	19	4	—	9	7¾	4
	8-426 Hemi.	—	18	19	16	16	180	19	6	—	9	7¾	4⑬
	Fury, VIP 8-440 Std.	—	17	18	16	16	180	24③	4	—	9	7¾	4¼
	Fury, VIP 8-440 Hi Perf.	—	18	19	16	16	180	24③	4	—	9	7¾	4¼
	Others 8-440 Hi Perf.	—	17⑪	18⑪	16	16	180	19	4	—	9	7¾	4⑬
1969	Fury, VIP 6-225	—	13	—	16	—	190	24③	4	6½	—	7¾	4
	Others 6-225	—	13	15	16	16	190	19	4	6½	—	7¾	2⑦
	Fury, VIP 8-318	—	16	19	16	16	190	24③	4	6½	—	7¾	4
	Others 8-318	—	16	19	16	16	190	19	4	6½	—	7¾	4
	Fury, VIP 8-383 2 B.C.	—	16	17	16	16	190	24③	4	—	7¾	9¼	4
	Others 8-383 2 B.C.	—	16	17	16	16	190	19	4	—	7½	9¼	4
	Fury, VIP 8-383 4 B.C.	—	16	17	16	16	190	24③	4	—	7¾	7¾	4
	Others 8-383 4 B.C.	—	16	17	16	16	190	19	4	—	7½	7¾	4
	8-426 Hemi.	—	18	—	16	—	190	19	6	—	7½	8	4⑬
	Fury, VIP 8-440	—	17	18	16	16	190	24③	4	—	7¾	9¼	4
	Others 8-440	—	17	18	16	16	190	19	4	—	7½	9¼	4⑬
1970	Fury 6-225	—	12	14	16	16	190	24③	4	4¾	—	8½	4
	Others 6-225	—	12	14	16	16	190	19	4	4¾	—	8½	2
	Fury 8-318	—	16	17½	16	16	195	24②	4	4¾	—	8	4
	Others 8-318	—	16	17½	16	16	195	19	4	4¾	—	8	4
	Fury 8-383 2 B.C.	—	14½	16	16	16	190	24③	4	4¾	—	9½	4
	Others 8-383 2 B.C.	—	14½	15	16	16	190	19	4	4¾	—	9½	4
	Fury 8-383 4 B.C.	—	14½	16	16	16	190	24③	4	—	—	8	4
	Others 8-383 4 B.C.	—	14½	16	16	16	190	19	4	4¾	7	8	4
	Fury 8-440	—	15½	17	16	16	190	24③	4	—	—	9½	4
	Others 8-440	—	15½	17	16	16	190	19	4	—	7	9½	5½
	8-426 Hemi	—	17	—	16	16	190	19	6	—	7	8½	5½
1971	Fury 6-225	12	13	13	16	16	185	23	4	6½	—	8½	4½
	Others 6-225	12	13	13	16	16	185	21	4	4¾	—	8½	4
	Fury 8-318	15	16	16½	16	16	185	23	4	4¾	—	8½	4½
	Others 8-318	15	16	16½	16	16	185	21	4	4¾	—	8½	4
	Fury 8-360	14	15	15	16	16	185	23	4	4¾	—	8	4½
	Fury 8-383	13½	14½	15	16	16	185	23	4	4¾	—	8⑱	4½
	Others 8-383	13½	14½	15	16	16	185	21	4	4¾	7½	8⑱	4
	Others 8-426	14½	15½	—	16	16	185	21	6	—	7½	8½	5½
	Fury 8-440	14½	15½	17	16	16	185	23	4	—	—	9½	4½
	Others 8-440	14½	15½	17	16	16	185	21	4	—	7½	9½	5½

Continued

COOLING SYSTEM & CAPACITY DATA—Continued

Year	Model or Engine	Cooling Capacity, Qts.			Radiator Cap Relief Pressure, Lbs.		Thermo. Opening Temp. ①	Fuel Tank Gals.	Engine Oil Refill Qts. ②	Transmission Oil			Rear Axle Oil Pints
		No Heater	With Heater	With A/C	With A/C	No A/C				3 Speed Pints	4 Speed Pints	Auto. Trans. Qts. ⑫	
PLYMOUTH—Continued													
1972	Satellite 6-225	12	13	13	16	16	185	21	4	6½	—	8½	4½
	Satellite 8-318	15	16	16½	16	16	185	21	4	4¾	—	8½	4½
	Satellite 8-340	14	15	14½	16	16	185	21	4	4¾	7½	8	4½
	Satellite 8-400	13½	14½	15	16	16	185	21	4	4¾	7½	8⑱	4½
	Satellite 8-440	14	15	15	16	16	185	21	4	—	7½	9½	5½
	Fury 8-318	15	16	16½	16	16	185	23	4	—	—	8½	4½
	Fury 8-360	14½	15½	15	16	16	185	23	4	—	—	8	4½
	Fury 8-400	13½	14½	14	16	16	185	23	4	—	—	9½	4½
	Fury 8-440	14½	15½	16	16	16	185	23	4	—	—	9½	4½
VALIANT AND BARRACUDA													
1966	6-170	—	12	—	16	14	180	18	4	6½	—	8	2
	6-225	—	13	14	16	14	180	18	4	6½	—	8	2
	8-273	—	18	18	16	14	180	18	4	6	8½	8	2
1967	6-170	—	12	—	16	16	180	18	4	6½	—	8	2
	6-225	—	13	14	16	16	180	18	4	6½	—	8	2
	8-273 2 Bar. Carb.	—	19	20	16	16	180	18	4	6½	8	8	2
	8-273 4 Bar. Carb.	—	19	20	16	16	180	18	4	6½	8	8	4
1968	6-170	—	12	13	16	16	180	18	4	6½	—	7¾	2
	6-225	—	13	14	16	16	180	18	4	6½	—	7¾	2
	8-273	—	19	20	16	16	180	18	4	6	8	7¾	2
	8-318	—	17	18	16	16	180	18	4	—	8	9¼	4
	8-340	—	18	19	16	16	180	18	4	—	8	9¼	4
	8-383	—	17	18	16	16	180	18	4	—	8	7¾	4
1969	6-170	—	12	14	16	16	200	18	4	6½	—	7¾	2
	6-225	—	13	15	16	16	190	18	4	6½	—	7¾	2
	8-273	—	17	19	16	16	190	18	4	6½	7	7¾	4
	8-318	—	16	18	16	16	190	18	4	6½	7	9¼	4
	8-340	—	16	—	16		190	18	4	6½	7	9¼	4
	8-383 2 Bar. Carb.	—	16	—	16		190	18	4	6½	7	9¼	4
	8-383 4 Bar. Carb.	—	16	—	16		190	18	4	6½	7	7¾	4
1970	Valiant 6-198, 225	—	13	14	16	16	190	18	4	6½	—	8½	2
	Barracuda 6-225	—	13	14	16	16	190	18	4	4¾	—	8½	2
	8-318	—	16	17	16	16	195	18	4	4¾	7	8½	4
	Valiant 8-340	—	15	17	16	16	190	18	4	4¾	7	8	4
	Barracuda 8-340	—	15½	15½	16	16	190	18	4	4¾	7	8	4
	8-383 2 Bar. Carb.	—	14½	15	16	16	190	18	4	—	—	9½	4
	8-383 4 Bar. Carb.	—	14½	15	16	16	190	18	4	4¾	7	8	4
	8-440	—	17	17	16	16	190	18	6	—	7	9½	5½
	8-426	—	17	—	16	16	190	18	6	—	7	8	5½
1971	Valiant 6 Cyl.	12	13	13	16	16	185	17	4	6½	—	8½	2
	Barracuda 6 Cyl.	12	13	13	16	16	185	18	4	4¾	—	8½	2
	Valiant 8-318	15	16	16½	16	16	185	17	4	4¾	—	8½	4½
	Barracuda 8-318	15	16	16½	16	16	185	18	4	4¾	—	8½	2
	Valiant 8-340	14	15	15	16	16	185	17	4	4¾	7	8	4½
	Barracuda 8-340	14	15	15	16	16	185	18	4	4¾	7½	8	4½
	8-383	13½	14½	15	16	16	185	18	4	4¾	7½	8⑱	4½
	8-440	16⑲	17⑲	17⑳	16	16	185	18	4	—	7½	9½	5½
	8-426	14½	15½	—	16	16	185	18	6	—	7½	8	5½

Continued

COOLING SYSTEM & CAPACITY DATA—Continued

Year	Model or Engine	Cooling Capacity, Qts.			Radiator Cap Relief Pressure, Lbs.		Thermo. Opening Temp. ①	Fuel Tank Gals.	Engine Oil Refill Qts. ②	Transmission Oil			Rear Axle Oil Pints
		No Heater	With Heater	With A/C	With A/C	No A/C				4 Speed Pints	4 Speed Pints	Auto. Trans. Qts. ⑫	

VALIANT AND BARRACUDA—Continued

Year	Model or Engine	No Heater	With Heater	With A/C	With A/C	No A/C	Thermo.	Fuel	Engine Oil	4 Speed	4 Speed	Auto. Trans.	Rear Axle
1972	Valiant 6 Cyl.	12	13	13	16	16	185	16	4	6½	—	8½	2
	Barracuda 6 Cyl.	12	13	13	16	16	185	16½	4	4¾	—	8½	2
	Valiant 8-318	15	16	16	16	16	185	16	4	4¾	—	8½	4½
	Barracuda 8-318	15	16	16½	16	16	185	16½	4	4¾	—	8½	4½
	Valiant 8-340	14	15	15	16	16	185	16	4	4¾	7	8	4½
	Barracuda 8-340	14	15	14½	16	16	185	16½	4	—	7½	8	4½

①—With alcohol type anti-freeze use a 160° unit.
②—Add one qt. with filter change.
③—Wagons 22 gals.
④—440 Hi Perf. uses 190°.
⑤—Wagons 21 gals.
⑥—Polara, Monaco, 880: Cars, 25, Wagons 21. Dart and Coronet: 111" W.B. 18, 106" W.B. 16, 119" W.B. 19, 116" W.B. 21.
⑦—Station Wagon 4 pints.
⑧—Belvedere and Satellite.
⑨—Add 1½ qts. for rear seat heater.
⑩—With manual transmission 4 pints.
⑪—With 4 speed trans., 18 (19 with A/C).
⑫—Approximate. Make final check with dipstick.
⑬—With manual trans. 5½ pints.
⑭—5½ pints for High Perf. engine.
⑮—Add 2 qts. for 22" radiator.
⑯—9¼ qts. for High Perf.
⑰—Wagons 23 gals.
⑱—With 2 bar. carb. 9½ qts.
⑲—Auto. Trans., 1½ qts. less.
⑳—Auto. Trans. 18 qts.

REAR AXLE SPECIFICATIONS

Year	Model	Carrier Type	Ring Gear & Pinion Backlash		Pinion Bearing Preload			Differential Bearing Preload		
			Method	Adjustment	Method	New Bearings Inch-Lbs.	Used Bearings Inch-Lbs.	Method	New Bearings Inch-Lbs.	Used Bearings Inch-Lbs.
1966–72	All	Removable①	②	.006–.008	Shims	20–30④	10–15④	②	③	③
1966–72	Exc. Below	Integral	Shims	.004–.007	Shims	15–25④	8–12④	Shims	③	③
1967–72	⑤	Integral	Shims	.004–.009	Shims	10–20④	10–20④	Shims	③	③
1969–72	8¼" ⑥	Integral	②	.006–.008	⑦	20–35④	10–25④	②	③	③

①—Adjust axle shaft end play to .008–.018".
②—Threaded adjusters.
③—Preload is correct when ring gear and pinion backlash is properly adjusted.
④—Adjust by turning pinion shaft nut with an inch-pound torque wrench and seal removed.
⑤—9¼" and 9¾" axles.
⑥—"C" lock type.
⑦—Collapsible spacer.

Electrical Section

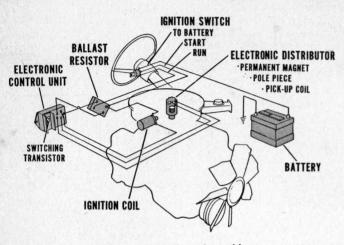

Fig. A Electronic system wiring

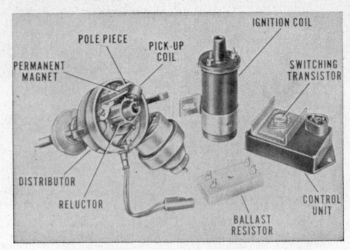

Fig. B Electronic system components

ELECTRONIC IGNITION

This system, Figs. A and B, is composed of a magnetic distributor, an electronic control unit, a wiring harness, a production coil and a dual ballast resistor.

The distributor is essentially the same as the conventional type except the contacts have been replaced by a pickup coil and the cam by a reluctor. With a conventional contact type system, the voltage necessary to fire the spark plugs is developed by interrupting the current flowing through the primary of the ignition coil by opening a set of contacts. With the Electronic System, the voltage is produced the same way except that the current is interrupted by a transistor in the electronic control unit. This happens each time the control unit receives a "timing" pulse from the distributor magnetic pickup.

Since the magnetic pickup, reluctor and the control unit, which replace the contact points and cam, do not normally change or wear out with service, engine timing and dwell does not require periodic adjusting. This minimizes regular ignition maintenance to cleaning and replacing the spark plugs.

TROUBLE SHOOTING

Engine Will Not Start—Fuel System OK

1. Dual ballast.
2. Faulty ignition coil.
3. Faulty pickup or improper pickup air gap.
4. Faulty wiring.
5. Faulty control unit.

Engine Surges Severely—Not Lean Carburetor

1. Wiring.

2. Faulty pickup leads.
3. Ignition coil.

Engine Misses—Carburetion Good

1. Spark plugs.
2. Secondary cables.
3. Ignition coil.
4. Wiring.
5. Control unit.

DISTRIBUTOR, REPLACE
6-170, 198, 225

The distributor rotates clockwise. To remove, take off cap, disconnect primary wire and vacuum line. Remove hold-down bolt and lift out distributor. Install in the following manner.

1. Rotate crankshaft to bring No. 1 piston up on its compression stroke, and position mark on inner edge of crankshaft pulley in line with the "O" (TDC) mark on timing chain cover.
2. With distributor gasket in position, hold distributor over mounting pad.
3. Turn rotor to point forward, corresponding to 4 o'clock piston.
4. Install distributor so that when fully seated on engine, the gear has spiraled to bring rotor to 5 o'clock position.
5. Turn housing until ignition points are separating and rotor is under No. 1 cap tower.
6. Install hold-down bolt.
7. Adjust timing with timing light.

1966-72 V8s

To remove the distributor, disconnect the vacuum control line and low tension wire and remove the cap and lock plate hold-down screw.

When installing the distributor, make sure that No. 1 piston is on top dead center on compression stroke and that the distributor rotor is in No. 1 firing position.

SERVICE BULLETIN

FUSIBLE LINK REPAIR: Alternator equipped 1966-72 cars have charging circuits protected by a fuse-type wire. This fusible link is installed on the starter relay battery terminal.

If the charging circuit becomes overloaded, the inner fuse wire of this link burns out and the insulation heats up and breaks apart. This cuts off the battery from the charging system.

In the event one of these cars has none of its electrical parts functioning, check for a burned out fusible link. After locating and correcting the short, a new fusible link should be installed. Do not allow the insulation to contact any other wiring.

In situations like this, never use an uninsulated wire as a jumper if a fusible link replacement is not available. This can cause a fire in the electrical system.

STARTER, REPLACE
Reduction Gear Type

1. To remove starter, disconnect ground cable at battery.
2. Remove cable at starter.
3. Disconnect wires at solenoid.
4. Remove one stud nut and one bolt attaching starter motor to flywheel housing.
5. Slide transmission oil cooler bracket off stud (if so equipped).
6. Remove starter motor and removeable seal.
7. Reverse above procedure to install.

NOTE: When tightening attaching bolt and nut be sure to hold starter away from engine to insure proper alignment.

Direct Drive Type

1. Disconnect battery ground cable.
2. Remove cable at starter.
3. Disconnect lead wire from solenoid.
4. Unfasten and remove starter and removable seal.

NOTE

Noisy or erratic starter operation may be caused by lack of lubrication or deposits of foreign material on the Bendix driveshaft.

To correct this condition, remove the inspection plate at the bottom of the torque converter or clutch housing. Then apply a suitable upper-cylinder rust inhibitor or SAE 5W or SAE 10W oil to the shaft by means of a 7" piece of tubing attached to the spout of a pressure oil can. In extreme cases, it may be necessary to remove, disassemble and clean the starter.

CLUTCH SWITCH
1970-71

A clutch switch is used which necessitates depressing the clutch pedal before the engine can be started.

IGNITION SWITCH, REPLACE
1971-72

1. Disconnect battery ground cable.
2. Remove steering column cover and remove two screws attaching wiring cover from column.
3. Disconnect wiring connectors at column.
4. Remove horn ring ornament, horn ring or rim blow switch pad and ornament if so equipped.
5. Disconnect horn wires at steering wheel hub.
6. Remove horn ring.
7. Remove steering wheel with suitable puller.
8. Remove screw attaching turn signal lever and remove lever.

NOTE: On Tilt & Tel columns, lever screws out.

9. Attach a string or fine wire to signal switch wiring before removing switch from column. When switch is removed leave wire in column jacket tube as an aid in replacement.
10. Remove screws attaching signal switch and upper bearing retainer screws and remove retainer and signal switch and flasher switch.
11. Remove screw and lift out ignition key lamp assembly.
12. Remove snap ring from upper end of steering shaft.
13. Remove three bearing housing attaching screws.

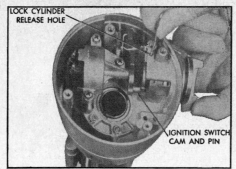

Fig. 1 Lock cylinder removal. 1970-72

14. With tool C-3044 attached to threaded holes for signal switch retaining screws, pull bearing and housing from steering shaft.
15. Remove lower snap ring from steering shaft.
16. Remove lock plate pin retaining ring from lock plate hub.
17. Use tool C-4113 and press steering shaft lock plate pin out of shaft and plate and remove lock plate.

NOTE: Do not use hammer as damage to column may result.

18. Remove lock lever guide plate screws and plate.
19. Depress key cylinder retainer toward the cylinder to disengage it from slot in housing bore, then withdraw key cylinder from lock housing.

1970 With Standard Steering Column

1. Disconnect battery ground cable.
2. Remove steering column cover and remove two screws attaching wiring cover to steering column. Disconnect wiring connectors at column.
3. Remove steering wheel.
4. Remove turn signal lever.
5. Attach a piece of fine wire to signal switch wiring before removing switch. When switch is removed, leave wire in column to aid in replacement of wire.
6. Remove turn signal switch and upper bearing retainer screws and remove switch.
7. Remove ignition key lamp retaining screws and lift out lamp.
8. Remove snap ring from upper end of column.
9. Remove three bearing housing attaching screws and with a suitable puller, pull bearing and housing from steering shaft.
10. Remove lower snap ring from steering shaft.
11. Remove lock plate retaining pin from lock plate hub. *This pin must be pressed out. Do not attempt to hammer on pin or shaft as damage to the collapsible column may result.*
12. Remove lock plate and lock lever guide.
13. Insert a small wire in access hole, depress lock cylinder retainer and withdraw cylinder, Fig. 1.
14. Remove switch retaining screws and remove switch.

1970 With Tilt-O-Scope

The ignition switch is mounted on the steering column lower cover and is actuated by a rod connected to the rack. Before removal or installation, be sure lock cylinder is in the Lock position.

1969 Polara & Monaco

1. Remove center air conditioning duct and left cooler duct.
2. Remove ignition switch bezel nut.
3. Remove ignition switch from under side of panel and disconnect main harness.

1967-69 Chrysler & Imperial

1. Remove switch bezel nut from front of panel.
2. Push switch into and down below panel.
3. Disconnect wiring harness multiple connector and remove switch.

1968-69 Charger

1. Remove lower center A/C duct and left A/C duct (if equipped).
2. Remove steering column cover for visual assist and remove ignition switch spanner.
3. Disconnect wiring connector and remove switch.

1968-69 Coronet & Dart

1. Remove A/C duct (if equipped).
2. Remove switch bezel.
3. On Coronet, loosen harness from clip for access.
4. Disconnect wiring connector and pull switch out from under panel.

1966 Chrysler

All switches in the instrument panel or in the instrument cluster can be serviced from under the instrument panel by removing the switch knob, mounting nut or bezel and disconnecting wiring to switch.

1966 Imperial

1. Remove lower steering column cover plate.
2. Remove accessory switch knobs.
3. Remove screw that attaches left end of switch bezel to instrument panel. This screw can be reached from inside steering column opening.
4. Remove screw in ignition switch well.
5. Lift off switch bezel.
6. Remove mounting nut from ignition switch.
7. From under instrument panel pull switch down, disconnect wiring and remove switch.
8. Reverse above procedure to install.

1967-69 Plymouth & Valiant

1. Where necessary, remove air conditioning elbow. Remove bezel nut and lower switch behind panel far enough to remove multiple connector.
2. Before installing switch, connect multiple connector and position switch in panel.
3. Install and tighten bezel nut.

1966 Plymouth

Valiant, Barracuda and Fury switches are removed from under the panel after disconnecting the multiple connector from the back and removing the bezel on the panel.

In Belvedere and Satellite models, it is necessary to remove the turn signal flasher before disconnecting the multiple connector. The bezel is then removed and the switch is dropped from under the panel.

1966-67 Dart, Charger, Coronet

On all models remove bezel. On Coronet models, loosen the harness from the retaining clip before lowering the switch and disconnecting the multiple connector.

1967-68 Polara & Monaco

1. Remove bezel nut, disconnect multiple connector from switch and remove switch from under panel.
2. Before installing switch, connect multiple connector and insert switch in opening. Install and tighten bezel nut.

1966 Polara & Monaco

The ignition switch is serviced through the instrument cluster opening (see Instrument Cluster Removal). Remove the multiple connector from the back of the switch. The knob is retained by a set screw and is removed before removing the bezel nut.

LIGHT SWITCH, REPLACE

1971-72 Chrysler & Imperial

1. Remove left spotcooler duct.
2. Remove headlamp switch knob and shaft by pulling the switch to on, depressing the release button on bottom of switch case, and pulling on the knob.
3. Remove headlamp sentinel and automatic dimmer control knobs if so equipped.
4. Remove headlamp switch mounting nut.
5. Remove headlamp switch from under instrument panel and disconnect wiring.

1971-72 Coronet, Charger, Polara & Monaco

1. Reaching under instrument panel, disconnect wiring to switch.
2. Remove switch mounting screws and remove switch.

1971-72 Fury & Satellite

1. Reaching under instrument panel, disconnect switch wiring.
2. Unfasten and remove switch.

1970 Coronet & Belvedere

1. Disconnect battery ground cable.
2. Remove mounting screws and move safety relay and vent controls to one side.
3. Remove left air conditioner duct if necessary.

4. Remove two mounting screws, disconnect wire and remove switch. Place wires on switch before installing switch.

1969 Coronet, Belvedere & Satellite

1. Disconnect battery ground cable at battery.
2. Disconnect all wiring connectors from back of switches.
3. Remove switch bezel mounting screws.
4. Remove switches and bezel assembly and remove headlight switch.

NOTE: *Carefully pull trim bezel straight to avoid damaging trim pad.*

5. Reverse procedure to install.

1969-70 Monaco & Polara

1. Remove switch bezel.
2. Remove two mounting screws and remove switch.

1969-70 Chrysler & Imperial

1. Remove lamp panel.
2. Remove instrument cluster to gain access to switch.
3. Remove switch mounting screws and switch.

1967-68 Chrysler & Imperial

The Safeguard Sentinel, headlight, panel dimmer light, windshield washer-wiper switches and rear heater switch (Imperial only) are mounted to the back of the instrument cluster bezels. To service any of these switches, remove the appropriate bezel as outlined under *Instrument Cluster Removal.*

To remove the headlight switch, windshield wiper or washer switch, remove eight adapter plate mounting screws and two rear seat heater switch bezel nuts (Imperial only).

To install, insert threaded shank of switch through respective hole in mounting bracket and fasten with nut.

1968 Monaco & Polara

1. Remove dimmer switch.
2. Remove two light switch mounting screws, disconnect electrical connectors from switch and remove switch from panel.

1968-70 Charger

1. Remove instrument cluster as described further on.
2. Disconnect wiring connector.
3. Disconnect heater vacuum hoses for accessibility.
4. Remove two switch mounting screws.
5. Reverse procedure to install.

1966 Chrysler

All switches in the instrument panel or in the instrument cluster can be serviced from under the instrument panel by removing the switch knob, mounting nut or bezel and disconnecting wire to switch.

1966 Imperial

1. Remove lower steering column cover plate.
2. Remove headlight switch knob and stem and windshield wiper switch knob.
3. Remove screw that attaches right end of switch bezel to instrument panel. This screw can be reached from inside steering column opening.
4. Remove headlamp switch retaining nut and lift off switch bezel.
5. Remove headlamp switch and windshield wiper stem seals.
6. Remove mounting nut from headlamp switch and, from under instrument panel, pull switch down and disconnect wiring.
7. Reverse above procedure to install.

1970-72 Barracuda, Challenger

1. Disconnect battery ground cable.
2. Remove lamp panel retaining screws and carefully slide panel out and lay it on top of instrument panel.
3. Remove bezel retaining screws and slide assembly out and disconnect wiring harness.
4. Remove switch mounting screws and remove switch.

1967-72 Valiant, 1966-72 Dart 1967-69 Barracuda 1967-68 Belvedere & Satellite 1966-68 Coronet, 1967 Charger

1. From under instrument panel, remove screw retaining fuse block to panel and move fuse block out of the way.
2. Reaching under panel, depress release button on right side of switch and pull knob out of switch.
3. Remove bezel nut and lower switch under panel to disconnect multiple connector and remove switch.
4. Reverse procedure to install. Insert switch knob into switch until a "click" is heard.

1967-70 Fury & V.I.P.

1. On models with air conditioning, remove left spot cooler hose from duct and move out of the way.
2. If necessary, remove fuse block retaining screw and move fuse block away to gain access to switch.
3. From under panel, use a magnetic screwdriver to remove two screws retaining switch to rear of panel sheet metal.
4. Move switch down from panel reinforcement far enough to disconnect multiple connector and remove switch.
5. Reverse procedure to install.

1966 Plymouth

The switches on Valiant, Barracuda, Belvedere and Satellite models are serviced from under the instrument panel by disconnecting the multiple connector, removing the knob and bezel.

On Fury models it is necessary to remove the instrument cluster (see Instrument Cluster Removal) far enough from the panel to gain access to the multiple connector and the knob release button on the switch.

1967 Polara & Monaco

The headlight and panel dimmer switch are serviced from under the panel after removal of the fuse block. Remove two screws and take out switch.

1966 Polara & Monaco

The switch is removed through the speedometer cluster opening (see Speedometer Cluster Removal). After removing the cluster and multiple connector, the switch knob is removed by depressing the release button on the terminal side of the switch. Then remove the bezel nut on the front of the panel and withdraw the switch through the cluster opening.

STOP LIGHT SWITCH REPLACE

1966-72 All Cars

To remove the switch, disconnect wires from switch and remove switch from its mounting. Install the new switch and connect the wires.

NEUTRAL SAFETY SWITCH

1966-72 All Cars

1. Unscrew switch from transmission case, allowing fluid to drain onto a container, Fig. 2.
2. Move shift lever to "Park" and then to "Neutral" positions and inspect to see that switch operating lever is centered in switch opening in case.
3. Screw switch into transmission case and torque to 25-35 ft-lbs.
4. Add fluid to proper level.
5. Check to see that switch operates only in "Park" and "Neutral".

HORN SOUNDER & STEERING WHEEL

1967-72 All Cars

1. Disconnect ground cable at battery.
2. Remove horn ring ornament by turning counterclockwise or remove rim blow switch pad and ornament if so equipped.
3. Disconnect wires at horn switch.
4. Remove three screws attaching horn ring and switch to steering wheel, then remove horn ring and switch.
5. Remove wheel nut and use a suitable puller to remove steering wheel.

CAUTION: Do not bump or hammer on steering shaft to remove wheel as damage to shaft may result. See *Steering Gear, Replace* for other precautions.

1966 Chrysler

1. Disconnect battery ground cable.
2. Compress and turn horn button ¼ turn counter-clockwise to remove button.
3. Disconnect horn wire at switch.
4. Remove horn switch-to-steering wheel retaining screws and insulators, then remove horn ring and switch.

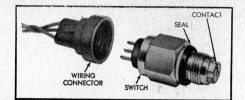

Fig. 2   Neutral safety switch

5. Remove steering shaft nut and use a puller to remove steering wheel.

1966 Imperial

1. Disconnect battery ground cable.
2. Remove two screws from underside of steering wheel. Lift up wheel cover and disconnect ground wire and two horn switch wires.
3. Remove steering wheel retaining nut and use a puller to remove wheel.

1966 Dart, Charger, Coronet

1. Disconnect battery ground cable.
2. Remove horn ring on Coronet models by placing steering wheel in straight-ahead position. Lift horn ring at seven o'clock position and turn counterclockwise ¼ turn.
3. For Dart models, pry cap off horn button with a screwdriver, using care to avoid damaging cap.
4. Disconnect wire at horn switch.
5. Remove three screws and insulators attaching horn ring retainer and switch to steering column. Remove retainer and switch.
6. Loosen steering wheel nut several turns and, with a suitable puller, loosen steering wheel. Then remove nut and steering wheel.

1966 Polara & Monaco

1. Disconnect battery ground cable.
2. Compress and turn horn button ¼ turn counterclockwise to release button from retainer.
3. Disconnect wire at horn switch.
4. Remove three screws and insulators attaching horn ring and switch to steering column. Remove horn ring and switch.
5. Loosen steering wheel nut several turns and, with a suitable puller, loosen wheel. Then remove nut and steering wheel.

1966 Plymouth

1. Disconnect battery ground cable.

2. Remove horn ring on Belvedere, Satellite and Fury models by placing steering wheel in straight-ahead position. Lift horn ring at 7 o'clock position and turn counterclockwise ¼ turn.
3. On Valiant models, pry cap off horn button with a screwdriver.
4. Disconnect wire at horn switch.
5. Remove three screws and insulators attaching horn ring retainer and switch to steering column. Remove retainer and switch.
6. Loosen steering wheel nut several turns and, with a suitable puller, loosen wheel. Then remove nut and steering wheel.

TURN SIGNAL SWITCH

1971-72

1. Disconnect battery ground cable.
2. Remove steering column cover and remove screws attaching wiring through cover from column, Fig. 3.
3. Disconnect wiring connectors at column.
4. Remove horn ring ornament, horn ring or rim blow switch pad and ornament, if so equipped.
5. Disconnect horn wires at steering wheel hub.
6. Remove horn ring.
7. Remove steering wheel with a suitable puller.
8. Remove screw attaching turn signal lever and remove lever. On Tilt and Tel columns, the lever screws out.
9. Attach a piece of string or fine wire, to turn signal wiring before removing switch from column.
10. Remove screws attaching signal switch and upper bearing retainer screws and remove retainer and signal and flasher switch.

1969-70 All Cars

1. Disconnect battery ground cable.
2. Remove steering wheel as outlined above and remove signal operating lever.
3. Disconnect switch wiring multiple connector at steering column jacket. Remove each terminal from connector, tying them together with a piece of string or fine wire, Fig. 3.
4. Remove screws attaching turn signal switch to steering column and remove switch and wires from column. Leave string or wire in column to aid installation.
5. Reverse procedure to install, using wire or string to pull wires through column. Tighten switch lever to 30 inch pounds, steering wheel nut to 24 foot pounds.

1967-68 All Cars

1. Remove steering wheel as outlined previously.
2. Remove snap ring from upper end of steering shaft.
3. Remove turn signal switch and upper bearing retainer screws.
4. Remove retainer and lift out switch.

1966 Chrysler

1. Disconnect battery ground cable.

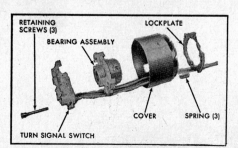

Fig. 3   Turn signal switch. 1969-72

2. Compress and turn horn button ¼ turn counter-clockwise to release button from its retainer.
3. Disconnect horn wire at horn sounding switch.
4. Remove horn ring and switch from steering column (3 screws).
5. Remove steering wheel.
6. Remove turn signal lever.
7. Disconnect turn signal wiring at steering column jacket tube below instrument panel.

NOTE: Attach a piece of string or fine wire to switch wiring before removing switch from steering column. When switch is removed leave string or wire in steering column jacket tube as an aid in replacement of wiring.

8. Remove attaching screws and lift switch off top of steering column.
9. Reverse above procedure to install.

1966 Imperial

1. Disconnect battery ground cable.
2. Remove two screws from underside of steering wheel and remove horn sounding actuator and steering wheel cover.
3. Remove steering wheel.
4. Remove turn signal lever.
5. Remove column lower cover.
6. Remove signal switch and wires (2 screws).
7. Reverse above procedure to install.

1966 Dart & Coronet

1. Remove steering wheel and horn switch as outlined above.
2. Disconnect turn signal switch multiple connector at steering column jacket. Remove each terminal from connector, tying them together with a piece of string.
3. Remove screws from steering column and remove switch and switch wires from column. Leave string in column as an aid in installation.
4. Reverse procedure to install.

1966 Polara & Monaco

1. Remove steering wheel and horn switch as outlined above.
2. Remove turn signal operating lever.
3. Disconnect turn signal wiring at steering column jacket tube below instrument panel.

NOTE: Attach a piece of string to turn signal switch wiring before removing switch from steering column. When switch is removed leave string in column jacket tube as an aid to replacement of wire.

4. Unfasten turn signal switch from steering column and remove switch from top of column.
5. Reverse procedure to install.

1966 Plymouth

1. Remove steering wheel and horn switch as outlined above.
2. Disconnect switch multiple connector at steering column jacket. Remove each terminal from connector, tying them together with a piece of string.

3. Unfasten turn signal switch from steering column and remove switch and switch wires from column. Leave string in column as an aid to installation.

INSTRUMENT CLUSTER REMOVAL

1971 Chrysler & Imperial

1. Remove map lamp, lamp panel end and panel.
2. Remove headlamp switch, radio and A.T.C. controls.
3. Lower steering column cover by removing four screws. Do not disconnect vent control cables.
4. Remove gearshift indicator pointer.
5. Lower steering column and allow steering wheel to rest on seat cushion.
6. Disconnect speedometer cable.
7. Remove five lower cluster mounting screws working through access holes in lower instrument panel.
8. Remove screw holding A.T.C. sensor to instrument cluster bezel and take sensor loose from bezel. On Imperial, remove clock.
9. Working over top of cluster, remove five upper cluster mounting screws.
10. Carefully remove cluster by pulling it rearward in car and rolling the bottom slightly up to clear upper legs on cluster. Disconnect wiring as access is gained.

1971 Coronet, Charger & Satellite

1. Disconnect battery ground cable.
2. Remove ash tray, radio and heater control panel.
3. Remove upper steering column clamp and lower steering column.
4. Remove instrument cluster mounting screws.
5. Disconnect speedometer cable and wiring and remove cluster.

1971 Polara & Monaco

1. Disconnect battery ground cable.
2. Remove lamp panel and steering column cover.
3. Remove radio trim bezel.
4. Remove left trim bezel and/or spot cooler if so equipped.
5. Remove left A/C duct and center A/C connector if so equipped.
6. From under panel disconnect wiring and speedometer cable.
7. Remove gearshift indicator pointer.
8. Tape column to protect finish and remove three column upper clamp nuts and three bolts at lower support at floor.
9. Carefully lower column and allow steering wheel to rest on seat cushion.
10. Remove eight screws mounting cluster to panel and roll cluster out, disconnecting remaining wiring to high beam indicator, fuel gauge, ammeter and temperature gauge and remove cluster to padded work bench for service.

1968 Chrysler

1. Disconnect battery ground cable.

2. Remove steering column cover (4 screws).
3. Disconnect one gear shift indicator mounting nut and disassemble gear shift indicator link from indicator shaft.
4. Remove warning light bezel (8 screws).
5. Pull bezel out slightly to disconnect main wiring harness from bezel, then remove light bezel from panel.
6. Remove cluster bezel (8 screws) and pull bezel out slightly to reach and disconnect wire connectors from headlamp, panel dimmer, washer and wiper switches.
7. Remove cluster bezel from panel.
8. Disconnect odometer reset cable.
9. Disconnect speedometer cable.
10. Remove eight cluster mounting screws.
11. Pull cluster out slightly to reach and disconnect ammeter (2 nuts), gasoline gauge, clock and cluster lighting lamps from main harness.
12. Remove cluster from panel.
13. Reverse procedure to install.

1968-71 Dart

1. Disconnect battery ground cable.
2. Remove column opening cover (4 screws).
3. Remove lower column plate (3 bolts) and upper mounting clamp.
4. Remove six cluster mounting screws.
5. Disconnect speedometer cable.
6. Remove fuse block (1 screw).
7. Rock cluster out and release wiring harness from spring clip at back of cluster, then continue to rock cluster out while using a screwdriver to hold harness clear of speedometer.
8. Disconnect left printed circuit board connector and brake system warning light.
9. From front of panel, disconnect right printed circuit board connector and ammeter leads, then complete cluster roll-out.

1970-71 Barracuda, Challenger

1. Disconnect battery ground cable.
2. Remove lamp panel mounting screws and carefully slide panel out and lay it on top of instrument panel. It is not necessary to disconnect wiring.
3. Remove switch bezel mounting screws and allow bezel to hang loose.
4. Remove steering column plate and disconnect column clamps and allow column to rest on seat.
5. Disconnect speedometer cable.
6. Remove six cluster bezel mounting screws, angle bezel out to clear clock button. Reach behind bezel and disconnect stereo control wiring, if so equipped.
7. On Rallye cluster, remove clock and odometer reset knobs.
8. Remove four cluster-to-panel mounting screws, disconnect wiring harnesses and remove cluster.

1968-70 Belvedere & Satellite, 1968 Coronet 440, 500 & 1969-70 Coronet

1. Disconnect battery ground cable.

2. Remove steering column cover (4 screws).
3. Roll carpeting down and remove steering column cover plate (4 bolts).
4. Remove column clamp at instrument panel (2 nuts).
5. Remove upper trim molding (6 screws if equipped).
6. Remove left side trim molding (1 screw if equipped).
7. Remove left side trim plate (1 screw and 1 T-bolt, if equipped).
8. Remove radio trim plate (2 screws).
9. Remove switch bezel (4 screws).

NOTE: Steps 10-12 do not apply to 1970 models.

10. Remove ignition switch.
11. Remove A/C center opening cover (if equipped).
12. Remove lower left trim pad (6 screws from under panel and 4 screws from front of instrument panel).
13. Disconnect speedometer cable.
14. Remove six screws attaching cluster to panel, rock cluster out far enough to reach and disconnect wiring harness and connectors and remove cluster.
15. Reverse procedure to install.

1968-70 Charger & 1968 Coronet R/T

1. Disconnect battery ground cable.
2. Remove steering column opening cover (4 screws).
3. Remove steering column lower support plate (3 bolts).
4. Remove upper mounting bracket support bolts.
5. Disconnect speedometer cable.
6. Remove five screws mounting cluster to panel. A small screwdriver may be used in removing the medallion from the cluster bezel.
7. Release wire harness from retainer clips and roll cluster out of panel far enough to disconnect wiring from ammeter, switches, tachometer, clock, light bulbs and printed circuit board connectors, then complete cluster roll-out.

1969-70 Monaco & Polara

1. Disconnect battery ground cable.
2. Remove steering column cover.
3. Remove gear shift indicator from the column.
4. Remove lower column floor plate.
5. Remove upper column mounting nuts and lower steering column down to seat.
6. Remove switch and radio bezels, cluster trim pad and trim bezel.
7. Disconnect clock reset cable at the instrument panel lower reinforcement.
8. Disconnect clock lead and remove five cluster mounting screws.
9. Roll cluster out slightly and disconnect the speedometer cable.
10. Disconnect gear shift indicator lamp, main harness and alternator gauge leads and remove cluster.

1970 Chrysler

1. Disconnect battery ground cable.
2. Remove lower steering column cover.
3. Remove three outside floor plate

mounting screws.
4. Remove steering column ground strap, disconnect clamp and lower steering column.
5. Remove left ash tray, radio and heater controls.
6. Remove two vent control screws and allow assembly to hang free.
7. Remove map light.
8. Remove lamp panel and lay it on top of the instrument panel.
9. From under instrument panel, remove four screws from right end accessory switch cover.
10. Disconnect speedometer cable.
11. Remove wiring harness from clip on left side of column support.
12. Remove cluster mounting screws and move cluster to right, rotating right end of cluster towards front of car and down.
13. Roll top of cluster down and rock cluster to left to gain access to wiring.
14. Disconnect wiring and roll cluster out.

1969 Chrysler

1. Disconnect battery ground cable.
2. Remove lower steering column cover and shift indicator pointer.
3. Disconnect turn signal wiring connector.
4. Remove outside floor plate mounting bolts, steering column clamp and ground strap and lower column.
5. Remove ash tray, radio and heater controls.
6. Remove vent control mounting screws and allow vent to hang free.
7. Remove map lamp and lamp panel and lay it on top of instrument panel.
8. From under panel, remove four mounting screws from right and accessory switch cover.
9. Disconnect speedometer cable, remove wiring harness from clip on column and remove cluster mounting screws.
10. Move cluster to right, rotating right end to front of car and down.
11. Roll top of cluster down and rock panel slightly left to gain access to wiring. Disconnect wiring and roll cluster out of panel.

1969-70 Imperial

1. Disconnect battery ground cable.
2. Remove ash tray, radio and heater controls.
3. Disconnect vent control cables at fresh air doors. Remove vent control mounting screws and move control to allow for lamp panel removal.
4. Remove map lamp, lamp panel cluster bezel, steering column cover, steering column cover, shift indicator pointer, steering column clamp at instrument panel and cover screws at floor panel. Lower column.
5. Disconnect speedometer cable.
6. Remove cluster mounting screws.
7. Move cluster to right, pushing right end of cluster to front of car while turning top of cluster down, then pull left end of cluster out of panel.
8. Disconnect wiring and remove cluster.

1969-71 Fury & V.I.P.

1. Disconnect battery ground cable.

2. Remove lamp panel, steering column cover and radio trim bezel.
3. Remove left trim bezel and/or spot cooler if so equipped.
4. Remove left and center A/C duct if so equipped.
5. From under panel, disconnect leads to switches, clock and lamp assemblies and disconnect speedometer cable.
6. Remove shift indicator pointer.
7. Remove steering column upper clamp nuts, three bolts at lower support at floor and lower column. Remove cluster mounting screws, roll cluster out, disconnect leads to high beam indicator, fuel gauge, ammeter and temperature gauge and remove cluster.

1968 Monaco & Polara

1. Disconnect battery ground cable.
2. Remove steering column trim plate (4 screws).
3. Remove gear selector indicator link nut and bolt and slip link off indicator arm.
4. Raise floor carpet and remove three steering column support plate bolts at bulkhead. Remove steering column upper clamp nuts and lower column down to seat cushion.
5. Disconnect left spot cooler hose (if equipped) from A/C and heater housing and move hose out from behind cluster.
6. Disconnect speedometer cable.
7. Disconnect clock reset cable (if equipped).
8. Disconnect main harness connector from printed circuit.
9. Remove eight bezel mounting screws (3 in upper center bezel, 3 in upper right trim bezel and 2 in lower center trim bezel).
10. Pull center bezel out slightly and disconnect fader control harness (if equipped).
11. Remove two screws from rear of fader control housing.
12. Slide center trim bezel out of upper molding toward cluster.
13. Remove left trim bezel from panel (4 screws).
14. Remove four screws and pull cluster out slightly and disconnect alternator indicator leads from rear of cluster housing and remove cluster from panel.
15. Reverse procedure to install.

1968-69 Barracuda

1. Disconnect battery ground cable.
2. Disconnect speedometer cable and multiple connector from left printed circuit board.
3. Remove four cluster screws from underside of crash pad and four screws from lower front face of cluster.
4. Remove clock reset cable.
5. Pull cluster out far enough to reach behind and disconnect right printed circuit board multiple connector, ammeter wires, vacuum gauge hose or tachometer wire and emergency switch flasher connector.
6. Loosen A/C or heater knobs and remove from slide control. Remove A/C or heater mounting screws and move control out of the way.
7. Depress headlight switch knob re-

lease button on bottom side of switch and pull knob and shaft out of switch. Remove switch bezel and allow switch to remain connected to wire harness.

8. Pull w/s wiper knob from shaft. Remove wiper switch bezel nut and allow switch to remain connected to wire harness.

9. Roll cluster out from panel opening, face down and to the right.

1968 Fury & V.I.P.

Bezel Removal

1. Remove instrument cluster light panel (8 screws) and rest panel on top of trim pad. It is not necessary to disconnect feed wire.
2. Remove heater or A/C control knobs.
3. Remove clock reset knob.
4. Remove bezel (6 screws).

Cluster Removal

1. Disconnect battery ground cable.
2. Remove instrument cluster bezel.
3. Remove four screws in steering column cover and drop cover down with vent controls attached.
4. With automatic transmisson and column mounted gear selector, remove gear selector link nut, spring washer and bolt from right side of shift tube.
5. Disconnect speedometer cable.
6. Remove four stereo speaker grille mounting screws and place speaker on top of instrument panel (left side only).
7. Remove five cluster mounting screws, raise up on cluster slightly, roll upper edge out, and disconnect leads at ammeter.
8. With cluster face down, disconnect fuel and temperature gauge wires. Remove high beam, oil pressure and turn signal light sockets.
9. Remove cluster.

1967 Chrysler

1. Disconnect ground cable at battery.
2. Remove steering column cover (4 screws).
3. With automatic transmission and column shift, unfasten and slide shift indicator link off end of indicator quadrant arm.
4. Raise carpet and remove three steering column lower support plate and two column upper clamp bolts.
5. Lower steering column to front seat cushion.
6. Remove seven indicator bezel screws and pull bezel out far enough to disconnect printed circuit board multiple connector and remove bezel.
7. Remove four upper and four lower screws retaining instrument cluster bezel.
8. Pull bezel out far enough to disconnect headlight, panel dimmer, windshield wiper and washer connectors and remove bezel.
9. Remove four upper and four lower cluster mounting screws.
10. Pull cluster out of opening far enough to reach behind cluster to disconnect speedometer cable, ammeter and fuel gauge wires and unplug five cluster bulb sockets.
11. Disconnect speedometer cable by de-

pressing locking tab on flange and pulling straight out of speedometer drive.
12. Remove cluster.

1967-68 Imperial

1. Disconnect ground cable at battery.
2. Tape top of steering column to protect painted finish.
3. Remove steering column trim plate (4 screws).
4. Loosen Allen screw on right underside of column and push gear selector indicator forward and rotate clockwise to remove.
5. Remove steering column upper clamp and allow column to rest in lowered position.
6. If equipped with air conditioning, remove left spot cooler hose at "T" connection under panel by releasing alligator clamp.
7. Remove four upper and lower bezel screws. The four lower screws are located on lower left corner of bezel, each side of column opening and one inside ash receiver.
8. Raise lower edge of bezel and disconnect multiple connectors. Remove vacuum hose from rear air switch (if equipped) by reaching through column opening in panel.
9. Carefully remove bezel with spot cooler hose attached (if A/C equipped).
10. Remove odometer reset cable bezel nut at lower edge of instrument panel and push cable up into panel.
11. Remove eight cluster mounting screws and roll cluster (bottom edge first) out of panel far enough to disconnect multiple connector at printed circuit board. Disconnect speedometer cable by depressing locking tab on ferrule and pulling straight out.
12. Disconnect ammeter wires and remove cluster.

1966 Imperial

NOTE: The instrument cluster contains three separate main groups, speedometer, printed circuit and clock. When servicing the cluster it is necessary to remove only the group containing the desired instrument or gauge.

1. Remove instrument cluster chrome bezel.
2. Remove clock reset knobs and temperature control level knob.
3. Remove lens from cluster.
4. Remove cluster face plate. Then remove desired cluster as follows:

Speedometer

Disconnect speedometer cable from under instrument panel. Unfasten and remove speedometer.

Printed Circuit

Remove screws attaching printed circuit to cluster. Pull assembly forward slightly and disconnect multi-connector. Remove assembly for service of fuel, oil, temperature or ammeter gauges.

Clock

Remove screws attaching clock to cluster. Pull clock forward and disconnect feed wire. Remove clock.

1966 Chrysler

1. Disconnect battery ground cable.
2. Remove steering column cover.
3. Disconnect gear selector indicator link, remove column clamp and loosen steering column lower support plate to partially lower steering column.
4. Disconnect speedometer, odometer cables and multiple connector at printed circuit board.
5. Remove ignition switch bezel and allow switch to hang under panel.
6. From under cluster, remove two lower trim moulding screws and moulding.
7. Loosen three screws retaining cluster upper trim bezel, two screws (under panel) from steering column filler and instrument bezel. Remove filler assembly.
8. Remove four cluster retaining screws and rotate cluster clockwise around steering column 180 degrees.
9. Disconnect two wires at ammeter gauge terminals and remove cluster.

NOTE: Speedometer head and gauges are removed from front of cluster after separating lens from cluster housing.

1967 Dart

1. Disconnect ground cable at battery.
2. Disconnect speedometer cable and left printed circuit board multiple connector.
3. Remove steering column lower support plate and upper column clamp. Lower column out of the way.
4. Remove four screws from underside of upper lip and two screws from lower lip of cluster.
5. Under instrument panel, remove main wire harness from clip on back of cluster housing just above speedometer head drive. Hold wire harness away from speedometer drive while rolling cluster out of panel (top edge first).
6. With cluster face down in panel opening, disconnect ammeter leads and right printed circuit board multiple connector. Remove cluster from vehicle.

1967 Polara & Monaco

1. Disconnect ground cable at battery.
2. Remove steering column trim plate (4 screws).
3. Remove gear selector indicator link nut and bolt and slip link off indicator arm.
4. Remove retaining screw and move fuse block down as an aid in disconnecting speedometer cable. Then remove clock reset cable ferrule nut from bottom of instrument panel.
5. Loosen three steering column support plate bolts at bulkhead.
6. Remove column upper clamp bolts and lower column down to seat cushion.
7. Remove four left bezel retaining screws (two in lower face and two in underside of upper lip) and remove bezel.
8. Remove heater or A/C control knobs and three center retaining screws from underside of upper bezel lip. Re-

move two center bezel lower retaining screws from front face and pull bezel out far enough to disconnect auto pilot light (if equipped) and remove bezel.

9. Remove four cluster retaining screws and pull cluster out of panel opening far enough to reach behind and disconnect two printed circuit board multiple connectors, ammeter wires and clock feed wire (if equipped).

10. Remove cluster from vehicle.

1966 Dart

1. Disconnect battery ground cable.
2. If air conditioned, remove left spot cooler, duct, hose and fuse block.
3. Disconnect speedometer cable.
4. Remove steering column support bracket and lower column support plate at bulkhead.
5. Remove radio control knobs, mounting nuts, ash receiver and housing assembly, and cigar lighter.
6. From under instrument panel, remove nut next to heater blower switch.
7. Remove light switch knob and bezel by depressing release button on switch and pulling out switch knob. Do not remove switch from panel.
8. Remove wiper switch knob and bezel. Do not remove switch from panel.
9. Remove four instrument cluster retaining screws and pull cluster out far enough to disconnect printed circuit board and ignition switch multiple connectors. Disconnect two ammeter wires and remove cluster.

1966-67 Coronet & Charger

1. Disconnect battery ground cable.
2. Remove heater control knobs.
3. Remove radio control knobs and nuts.
4. Open glove box door.
5. Disconnect speedometer cable.
6. Remove wire harness from two clips at steering column bracket.
7. Remove eight cross recessed screws from upper and lower lips of cluster bezel.
8. Carefully pull cluster out to the right, far enough to reach around left end of cluster and disconnect printed circuit board multiple connector.
9. Remove two ammeter wires from terminals, and clock light socket.
10. Roll top of cluster down while working it from the right over open glove box door. Then remove cluster.

1966 Polara, Monaco, 880

Instrument Cluster
1. Disconnect battery ground cable.
2. Remove three screws that mount cluster to housing.
3. Roll cluster out and disconnect printed circuit plug and ammeter wires.
4. Remove cluster.

Speedometer Cluster
1. Disconnect battery ground cable.
2. Disconnect speedometer cable.

3. Unfasten cluster from housing (3 screws).
4. Roll cluster out and disconnect printed circuit plug.
5. Remove cluster.

1967-71 Valiant

1. Disconnect ground cable at battery.
2. Disconnect speedometer cable and printed circuit board multiple connector.
3. Loosen steering column floor plate attaching screws, remove column upper clamp and allow column to rest in lowered position.
4. Remove six mounting screws from cluster (three in underside of cluster bezel and three in lower edge).
5. Before rolling cluster out of instrument panel, reach behind and above cluster and bend three wire harness clips out of the way. Roll upper edge of cluster out far enough to disconnect ammeter wires, emergency flasher, windshield wiper and headlight switch connectors.

1967 Fury & V.I.P.

Bezel Removal
1. Remove eight cluster light panel screws, remove panel and rest it on top of trim pad. It is not necessary to disconnect feed wire.
2. Remove heater or A/C control knobs.
3. Remove bezel (6 screws).

Cluster Removal
1. Disconnect ground cable at battery.
2. Remove steering column cover (4 screws).
3. With automatic transmission and column shift, remove gear selector link nut and bolt from right side of shift tube.
4. Disconnect speedometer cable.
5. Remove seven cluster mounting screws, raise up on cluster slightly and roll upper edge out.
6. With cluster face down, disconnect ammeter, fuel and temperature gauge wires.
7. Remove high beam, oil pressure and turn signal light sockets.
8. Remove cluster from vehicle.

1966 Valiant

1. Disconnect battery ground cable.
2. Disconnect speedometer cable.
3. Remove steering column clamp and lower column support plate at bulkhead to lower column.
4. Remove four screws and pull cluster out far enough to disconnect printed circuit board and ignition switch multiple connectors.
5. Disconnect ammeter wires and remove cluster.

1966 Barracuda

1. Disconnect battery ground cable.
2. Disconnect speedometer cable.
3. Remove heater control knobs.
4. Remove three screws in heater control bezel and remove bezel.
5. Remove ignition switch bezel.
6. Remove steering column clamp and loosen screws in steering column support plate at bulkhead.

7. Remove four screws and pull cluster out far enough to disconnect the two printed circuit multiple connectors, and ammeter gauge wires.
8. Roll cluster out and remove.

1966-67 Belvedere & Satellite

1. Disconnect battery ground cable.
2. Disconnect speedometer cable.
3. Remove steering column cover and clamp.
4. Remove six screws in upper and lower face of cluster bezel. Pull cluster out far enough to remove multiple connectors from headlight and wiper switches and printed circuit board. Next remove two ammeter gauge wires, heater switch wires and control cables.
5. Remove cluster from car.

1966 Fury

Instrument Cluster
1. Disconnect battery ground cable.
2. Remove five screws from bezel and pull cluster out far enough to provide access to multiple connector and ammeter gauge wires.
3. Disconnect printed circuit multiple connector and two ammeter leads.
4. Remove cluster.

Speedometer Cluster
1. Disconnect battery ground cable.
2. Remove instrument cluster.
3. Disconnect speedometer cable, remove steering column cover plate and gear selector indicator. Then remove steering column bracket.
4. Remove four screws and pull cluster out far enough to disconnect multiple connector and turn signal bulbs from printed circuit board.
5. Remove cluster from car.

W/S WIPER MOTOR REPLACE

1971-72 with Non-Concealed Wipers

1. Disconnect battery ground cable.
2. Disconnect wiper motor harness.
3. Remove three motor mounting nuts. On vehicles without A/C it is easier to remove crank arm nut and crank arm from under instrument panel first and omit next two steps.
4. Work motor off mounting studs far enough to gain access to crank arm mounting nut. Do not force or pry motor from studs as drive link can easily be distorted.
5. Using a ½" open end wrench, remove motor crank arm nut. Carefully pry crank arm off shaft and remove motor.

1971-72 with Concealed Wipers

1. Disconnect battery ground cable.
2. Remove wiper arm and blades.
3. Remove cowl screen.
4. Remove drive crank arm retaining nut and drive crank. Disconnect wiring to motor.
5. Unfasten and remove wiper motor.

1966-70 Chrysler & 1967-70 Imperial

1. Remove wiper arms and blades.
2. Remove windshield lower moulding.
3. Remove cowl grille panel.
4. Remove drive crank from motor (one nut) and disconnect wiring to motor.
5. Unfasten motor from dash panel (3 nuts) and remove motor out through cowl grille panel opening.

1966 Imperial

1. Disconnect battery ground cable.
2. If air conditioned, remove right spot cooler hose and distributor duct.
3. From under instrument panel, remove panel lower reinforcement-to-windshield wiper motor mounting bracket pencil brace.
4. Disconnect wiring at motor.
5. From under panel, remove both left and right link-to-pivot retainers.
6. Remove three motor bracket mounting nuts.
7. Carefully work motor and link assembly out from under panel towards right side of car.
8. Remove links and motor mounting bracket.

1970 Barracuda, Challenger

1. Disconnect battery ground cable.
2. Remove wiper arm and blade assemblies.
3. Remove left cowl screen.
4. Remove drive crank arm nut and crank. Disconnect wiring.
5. Remove mounting nuts and remove motor.

1967-69 Barracuda, 1967-70 Dart, Coronet, Charger, Valiant, Belvedere & Satellite

Without Air Conditioning

1. Disconnect ground cable at battery.
2. Disconnect wiper motor wire harness at bulkhead multiple connector.
3. From under instrument panel, remove crank arm nut and arm from motor shaft.
4. Remove mounting nuts and work motor off studs.

With Air Conditioning

1. Disconnect ground cable at battery.
2. Disconnect wiper motor wire harness at bulkhead multiple connector.
3. Remove motor mounting nuts.
4. On 1967-68 Coronet, Charger, Belvedere and Satellite, remove instrument cluster to provide access to left pivot.
5. Disconnect linkage.
6. Work motor off mounting studs far enough to gain access to crank arm mounting nut. *Do not force or pry motor from studs as drive link may be distorted.*
7. Remove motor crank arm nut, pry arm off shaft and remove motor.

1966 Coronet & Charger

1. Disconnect battery ground cable.
2. Disconnect motor multiple connector from engine side of bulkhead.

---

3. Remove three nuts and pull motor out far enough to gain access to drive crank.
4. Rotate crank until drive link retainer is accessible.
5. Using a short screwdriver, carefully pry lip of retainer over drive link pivot pin and remove retainer and spring washer and drive link.
6. Remove motor from car.

1966-70 Polara, Monaco, 880

1. Remove wiper arms and blades.
2. Remove windshield lower moulding.
3. Remove cowl grille panel.
4. Remove nut that mounts drive crank to motor. Remove drive crank and disconnect wiring at motor.
5. Unfasten motor from dash panel (3 nuts) and take motor out through cowl grille panel opening.

1966 Dart

1. Disconnect wiper link at motor.
2. Disconnect motor lead wires at motor.
3. Unfasten motor from cowl panel and pull motor out from underneath instrument panel.

1966 Belvedere & Satellite

Without Air Conditioning

1. Disconnect battery ground cable.
2. Disconnect motor multiple connector from engine side of bulkhead.
3. Remove three mounting nuts and pull motor out far enough to gain access to drive crank.
4. Rotate crank until drive link retainer is accessible.
5. Using a short screwdriver, pry lip of retainer over drive link pivot pin and remove retainer and spring washer.
6. Remove motor from car.

With Air Conditioning

1. Disconnect battery ground cable.
2. Disconnect wiper motor harness at bulkhead multiple connector.
3. Remove three wiper motor mounting nuts.
4. Remove instrument cluster.
5. Reaching through instrument cluster opening, remove the drive link retaining clip from left pivot arm. Remove felt washer and drive link from pivot arm pin.
6. Work motor off mounting studs far enough to gain access to crank arm mounting nut. *Do not force or pry motor from studs as drive link might be distorted.*
7. Remove motor crank arm nut and carefully pry arm off shaft and remove motor.
8. Reverse procedure to install.

1966-70 Fury & V.I.P.

1. Remove wiper arms and blades.
2. Remove windshield lower moulding.
3. Remove cowl grille panel.
4. Remove nut that mounts drive crank to motor. Then remove drive crank and disconnect wiring at motor.
5. Unfasten motor from dash panel (3 nuts) and take motor out through cowl grille panel opening.

1966 Barracuda & Valiant

1. Disconnect wiper link at motor. For variable speed motors, note position of follower cam or spring trip.
2. Disconnect motor lead wires at motor.
3. Remove three nuts attaching motor and bracket to cowl panel and pull motor and bracket down from bracket mounting studs and out from underneath instrument panel.

W/S WIPER TRANSMISSION

1971-72 with Non-Concealed Wipers

1. Disconnect battery ground cable.
2. If A/C equipped, remove duct supplying left spot cooler to provide access to left wiper pivot.
3. Insert a wide blade screwdriver between plastic link bushing and pivot crank arm. Gently twist screwdriver to force bushing and link free of pivot pin.
4. Remove motor mounting nuts, pull motor away from bulkhead and remove motor crank arm retaining nut. After crank arm is removed from motor shaft, remove drive link assembly from under left side of panel.

NOTE: In heater equipped models, remove motor drive crank arm retaining nut and pry crank arm off motor shaft. Gently pry drive link and bushing from left pivot crank arm pin and withdraw assembly from under panel. Remove motor drive crank arm from drive link after removal of assembly from vehicle.

---

5. To remove connecting link from pivots, remove glove box, reach through opening and gently pry bushing and link from right pivot pin. Lift the link from the pivot crank arm pin and repeat operation at left pivot. Withdraw from under left side of panel. The wiper pivots can be removed if required by the removal of the 1/2" mounting nuts at this time.

1971-72 With Concealed Wipers

1. Remove wiper arms and blade assemblies and the cowl screen to provide access.
2. Disconnect battery ground cable.
3. Remove crank arm nut and crank arm from motor shaft.
4. Remove bolts mounting left and right pivots to body.
5. Remove links and pivots through cowl top opening. The linkage and pivots can be serviced on bench after removal from vehicle.

1969-70 Chrysler, Imperial, Polara & Monaco

To service either the drive link or the connecting link, it is necessary to remove the wiper arms and blades, windshield lower moulding and cowl grille panel to gain access to the wiper system. Before starting the installation procedure, make certain the wiper system is in the "Park" position and the battery ground cable disconnected.

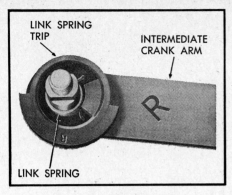

Fig. 4 Variable speed wiper link spring trip installed

1. With connecting and drive links assembled as a unit, insert links through cowl top opening and bolt pivots in position.
2. Position motor crank arm on motor shaft and tighten to 140 inch-pounds. Reconnect battery ground cable.
3. Test wiper system operation and then replace cowl screen and windshield lower moulding.
4. Using a pin or drill, install and adjust wiper arm and blade assemblies.

1970 Barracuda, Challenger, Fury

1. Disconnect battery ground cable.
2. Remove motor crank arm.
3. Remove pivot bolts and remove links and pivots through top cowl opening.

NOTE: If servicing of the mechanism on the 2-speed motor crank is required, be sure that during reassembly, the link is positioned between the ears of the cover retainer.

1969-70 Dart, Coronet, Charger, Valiant, Belvedere, Satellite & 1969 Barracuda

NOTE: On air conditioned models, after disconnecting the battery ground cable, remove left spot cooler duct and carefully pry the link and bushing from the pivot pin. Remove motor mounting nuts, pull motor away from bulkhead and remove motor crank arm retaining nut and crank arm. Remove drive link assembly from under panel.

On models without air conditioning, remove crank arm from motor, remove drive link from left pivot pin and withdraw assembly from under panel. Remove crank arm from drive link after assembly is removed from vehicle. Connecting link can be removed from pivots by removing glove box and reaching through the opening to pry bushing and link from pivot pin. Withdraw from under left side of panel.

1. Install bushing on motor crank arm pin, position drive link on bushing so large side of pivot bushing faces away from drive crank arm. Large side of bushing will be on same side of link as crank arm retainer.
2. Install spring washer with convex side towards link and install retainer. *If retainer was distorted in*

removal, it should be replaced.
3. In heater equipped vehicles, insert drive link assembly under left side of panel, position crank arm on motor shaft, indexing flats on shaft with flats on arm and install retaining nut.

NOTE: On air conditioned models, install drive link from under instrument panel. Install crank arm on motor shaft from engine side of bulkhead. Secure motor with three nuts. Press plastic bushing over pin on left pivot.

4. Insert connecting link into place with "R" (right side) and "L" (left side) facing instrument panel side. Press link bushings onto pivot crank pins.
5. Reconnect battery cable and test operation. Install glove box if necessary.

1967-68 Chrysler, Imperial, Polara & Monaco

To service either the drive link or the connecting link it is necessary to remove the wiper arms and blades, windshield lower moulding and cowl grille panel to gain access to the wiper system. Before starting the installation procedure, make certain the wiper system is in the "Park" position.

1. With connecting and drive links assembled as a unit, insert links through cowl grille panel opening and install felt washer on pin of right pivot and install one felt washer, link, second felt washer, brass washer and retainer clip. Make certain retainer clip is completely seated on pivot pin.
2. Install left pivot.
3. Position motor end of drive link on motor crank pin and install spring washer with convex side towards link and clip retainer in place on pin. *If retainer clip was distorted in removal, it should be replaced.*

1966 Chrysler

To service the drive link or connecting link it is necessary to remove wiper arm and blade assemblies, windshield lower moulding and cowl grille panel to gain access to wiper system. Before starting the installation procedure, make certain the wiper system is in the Park position.

1. With connecting and drive links assembled as a unit, insert links in through cowl grille panel opening and position bushing of connecting link on pin of right pivot and install retainer clip.
2. Install left pivot.
3. Position motor end of drive link on drive crank pin of motor. Make certain "O" ring, release spring, retainer and cam are in proper positions for variable speed wiper systems.
4. Install cover on mechanism on variable speed systems.
5. Install cowl grille panel, windshield lower moulding and wiper arms and blades.

Variable Speed Wiper 1966 Chrysler & Imperial

1. To assemble the linkage, install

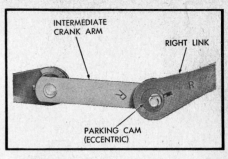

Fig. 5 Variable speed wiper link arm installed

spring washer with concave surface toward crank arm. Install crank pivot coil spring on pivot, and install spring release.
2. Install parking cam to index with spring release and engage spring ends between release and parking cam in openings at point of index, Fig. 4.
3. When assembling to the left link, the "L" on the left crank and on the parking cam should be seen. The cam marked "R" is installed in the same manner. If the intermediate crank is held so that the letter "L" can be seen from this position, the opposite side will show three letters "R".
4. Install link with stop projection on link arm toward cam assembly. Install spring washer with convex surface toward cam assembly.
5. Install retaining nut and bolt, Fig. 5.
6. Assemble left link and cam assembly in the same manner, locking in place with a clip.

Single Speed Wiper 1967-68 Barracuda, Dart, Charger, Coronet, Belvedere, Satellite, Valiant

NOTE: On models with air conditioning, the instrument cluster must be removed to gain access to the wiper system. When installing the links, first make certain that all pins and bushings are lubricated with Multi Purpose lubricant.

1. Install bushing on motor crank arm pin, position drive link on bushing so large side of pivot bushing faces away from drive crank arm. Large side of pivot bushing will be on same side of link as crank arm retainer.
2. Install spring washer with convex side towards link and install retainer. *If retainer was distorted in removal, it should be replaced.*
3. In heater equipped vehicles, insert drive link assembly under left side of instrument panel, position crank arm on motor shaft, indexing flats on motor shaft with flats on crank arm and install crank arm retaining nut.
4. In Coronet, Charger, Belvedere and Satellite models with air conditioning, install drive link through instrument cluster opening. In Dart and Valiant models, install drive link from under instrument panel.
5. Install motor crank arm on motor shaft from engine side of bulkhead.

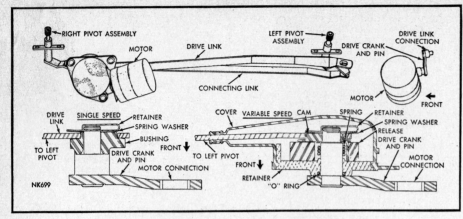

Fig. 6   Windshield wiper system. 1966-68 Chrysler, Imperial, Polara, Monaco, 880, Fury & V.I.P.

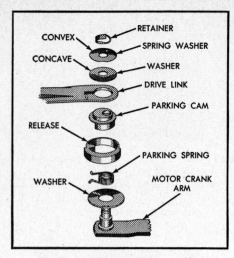

Fig. 7   Variable speed wiper parking mechanism. Dart and Valiant 1966

Position motor on studs and secure with nuts. Install drive link, felt washer and retaining clip on left pivot crank arm.

6. Insert connecting link into place with "R" (right side) and "L" (left side) stamped in link facing instrument panel side.
7. Position felt washers on crank arm pins, install connecting link and felt washers and secure with retainers.

1967-68 Fury & V.I.P.

NOTE: To service either the drive link or the connecting link, it is necessary to remove the wiper arm and blade assemblies, the windshield lower moulding and the cowl grille panel to gain access to the wiper system. The installation is made as follows:

1. Make sure the wiper system is in "Park" position. Then with connecting and drive links assembled as a unit, insert links through cowl grille panel opening.
2. Install one felt washer on pivot pin and position bushing of connecting link on pin of right pivot. Install second felt washer, brass washer and retainer clip, making sure clip is completely seated on pivot pin.
3. Install left pivot.
4. Position motor end of drive link on motor crank pin and install spring washer with convex side toward link and clip retainer in place on pin. If retainer clip was distorted in removal, it should be replaced.

1966 Polara, Monaco, 880 & Fury

NOTE: To service either the drive link or the connecting link it is necessary to remove wiper arm and blade assemblies, windshield lower moulding and cowl grille panel to provide access to wiper system. To make the installation, proceed as follows:

1. With wiper system in "Park" position, insert assembled drive and connecting links through cowl grille panel opening. Position bushing of connecting link on pin of right pivot and install retainer clip.

2. Install left pivot.
3. Position motor end of drive link on drive crank pin of motor. Make certain O-ring, release, spring, retainer and cam are in proper positions for variable speed wiper systems, Fig. 6.
4. Install cover on mechanism on variable speed wiper systems.
5. Install cowl grille panel, windshield lower moulding and install and adjust wiper arm and blade assemblies.

1966 Coronet, Charger, Belvedere & Satellite

REMOVAL: If air conditioned, remove glove box for access to right pivot retainer.
1. Disconnect battery ground cable.
2. Unfasten and move fuse block out of the way.
3. Unfasten motor and pull it out far enough to remove drive link retainer, spring washer and link from drive crank arm. If retainer lip is distorted in removal it should be replaced.
4. From under panel, remove left pivot mounting nuts and right pivot retainer.
5. Remove two links and left pivot as an assembly from under panel or through glove box if air conditioned.

INSTALLATION: The connecting link is marked "R" and "L" (right and left) on side facing bulkhead.
1. Install felt washer on pivot farthest from pivot shaft.
2. Install connecting link with "L" facing away from pivot crank.
3. Install outside felt washer and retainer.
4. Install felt washer on pivot pin closest to pivot shaft.
5. Install drive link (small end) outside felt washer and retainer.
6. Install links and left pivot as an assembly under instrument panel.
7. Install left pivot and mounting nuts, connecting link on right pivot and pivot retainer.
8. Through wiper motor opening in bulkhead, install drive link to crank arm and retainer. Lip of retainer must be tight on pivot shaft.
9. Install motor.

1966 Dart & Valiant

Variable Speed Wiper

1. Install flat washer on motor crank arm pin.
2. Assemble release parking cam and pin of crank arm and install on motor crank arm pin, Fig. 7.
3. Install drive link on motor crank arm pin, making sure parking cam is seated correctly in opening in drive link.
4. Install convex washer and concave spring washer.

Single Speed Wiper

1. Place bushing in end of wiper drive link with spring trip of drive link into keying slot.
2. Install link and bushing on motor crank pin.
3. Install cone washer and retaining clip.

W/S WIPER SWITCH

1971-72 Chrysler & Imperial

1. Remove instrument cluster.
2. Remove screws securing switch and plate to cluster housing.
3. Remove the assembly.
4. Remove screws holding switch to mounting plate and remove switch.

1971-72 Fury, Polara & Monaco

1. Roll cluster down and towards you.

NOTE: It is not necessary to remove bezel assembly, only roll it far enough to gain access to switch mounting screws and wiring.

2. Disconnect leads to switch and unfasten switch.

1970-72 Barracuda, Challenger

1. Disconnect battery ground cable.
2. Remove lamp panel retaining screws and carefully slide panel out and lay it on top of instrument panel.
3. Remove bezel retaining screws and slide assembly out and disconnect wiring harness.
4. Pull control knob from shaft. Remove mounting nut and remove switch from bezel.

1970-72 Coronet & Satellite

1. Remove steering column cover.
2. Lower steering column and allow it to rest on seat.
3. Remove lower trim bezel.
4. Remove switch mounting screws and disconnect wiring. *Place wires on switch before installing switch.*

1969 Coronet, Belvedere & Satellite

The wiper switch is serviced in the same manner as the headlight switch.

1969-72 Dart, 1969 Barracuda & 1969-72 Valiant

1. Remove air conditioning duct (if so equipped).
2. Loosen set screw and remove switch knob.
3. Remove spanner nut.
4. Remove wiring harness from clip. Disconnect wiring and remove switch.

1969-70 Polara & Monaco

The wiper switch is serviced in the same manner as the headlight switch.

1969-70 Fury & V.I.P.

1. Remove all A/C ducts from underside of panel if so equipped.
2. From under panel, disconnect electrical leads.
3. Remove two mounting screws and remove switch.

1969-70 Chrysler & Imperial

1. Remove lamp panel.
2. Remove instrument panel to gain access to switch.
3. Remove two switch mounting screws and remove switch.

1967-68 Chrysler & Imperial

To service the wiper and washer switches it is necessary to remove the instrument cluster bezel as outlined previously. After bezel is removed, the switches are serviced as follows:
1. Remove eight adapter plate mounting screws, and two rear seat heater switch bezel nuts (Imperial only).
2. Separate adapter plate from bezel and remove switch mounting nut from front side of plate and lift switch from plate.

1968-72 Charger

The wiper switch is serviced in the same manner as the headlight switch.

1968 Coronet & Dart

1. Remove A/C duct (if equipped).
2. Loosen set screw and remove switch knob.
3. Remove switch spanner nut.
4. Remove wiring harness from clip to gain access.
5. Disconnect wiring connector at switch and remove switch.

1968 Fury & V.I.P.

1. Remove steering column cover and drop cover down with vent controls attached.
2. Remove ash tray and housing.
3. Remove left spot cooler hose (if equipped).
4. Using a magnetic screwdriver under instrument panel, remove two switch retaining screws.
5. Move switch out of panel reinforcement and down far enough to disconnect multiple connector. When removing washer switch, the button will remain in the panel behind the bezel.
6. To install the washer switch, it will be necessary to locate switch shaft in button before securing switch to rear of panel.

1967 Dart, Coronet & Charger

The wiper switch is serviced in the same manner as the headlight switch except that the knob is retained on the switch by a set screw.

1967-68 Polara & Monaco

To service either the wiper or washer switch the ash receiver and housing assembly must be removed. On air conditioned cars the distribution duct and push button control bracket must be removed before the ash receiver housing. Remove switch retaining screws by reaching up through ash receiver housing.

1967-68 Barracuda, Valiant, Belvedere & Satellite

On Valiant models with air conditioning, it will be necessary to remove the outlet duct from the lower edge of the instrument panel. Unfasten the duct (2 nuts) and pull duct straight down.

To replace the wiper switch, loosen Allen screw in knob and remove knob. Remove bezel nut, lower switch below panel and disconnect multiple connector. Connect multiple connector to replacement switch and position in panel opening. Install bezel nut and tighten securely.

1967 Fury & V.I.P.

From under instrument panel, use a magnetic screwdriver to remove two retaining screws. Move switch out of panel reinforcement and down far enough to disconnect multiple connector.

1966 Chrysler, Dodge & Plymouth

To remove switch, disconnect lead wires at switch, unfasten switch from its mounting and remove it. Be sure to note color code of wires to be sure they are connected to proper terminals when switch is installed.

1966 Imperial

1. Remove lower steering column cover plate.
2. Remove headlamp switch knob and stem and windshield wiper switch knob.
3. Remove screw that attaches right end of switch bezel to instrument panel. This screw can be reached from inside steering column opening.
4. Remove headlamp switch retaining nut.
5. Lift off switch bezel.
6. Remove headlamp and windshield wiper stem seals.
7. Remove mounting nut from windshield wiper switch, pull switch down and disconnect wiring.
8. Remove switch from under panel.

RADIO, REPLACE

NOTE: When installing radio, be sure to adjust antenna trimmer for peak performance.

1971-72 Coronet, Charger & Satellite

1. Disconnect battery ground cable.
2. Remove ash tray.
3. Remove radio knobs and mounting nuts.
4. Remove radio.

1971-72 Polara & Monaco

1. Disconnect battery ground cable.
2. Remove nine lamp panel mounting screws, lower lamp panel slightly, disconnect lamp harness from main harness and remove lamp panel.
3. Remove steering column cover and radio trim bezel.
4. Remove center lower A/C duct, if so equipped.
5. Disconnect wiring and antenna from radio.
6. Remove radio support bracket.
7. Remove radio mounting bolts.
8. Remove radio down through bottom of instrument panel carefully to avoid damage to vacuum hoses and wiring.

1969-70 Polara & Monaco

1. Disconnect battery ground cable.
2. Remove Auto-Temp. control (if so equipped).
3. Remove radio bezel and two radio mounting bolts at front of instrument panel.
4. Remove air conditioning duct (if so equipped).
5. Disconnect electrical leads, loosen radio mounting bracket stud nut and slide radio and stud towards front of car from mounting bracket. Carefully remove radio from under panel.

1969-72 Dart, Challenger, Barracuda, Valiant

1. Disconnect battery ground cable.
2. Disconnect electrical leads and remove knob.
3. From under panel, remove two radio mounting nuts and remove radio mounting bracket. Remove radio down and out from under panel.

1969-72 Chrysler & Imperial

1. Disconnect battery ground cable.
2. Remove left ash receiver and steering column cover.
3. Unscrew stereo tape reset knob if so equipped.
4. Disconnect all electrical leads.
5. Loosen defroster vacuum actuator and move it to facilitate radio removal.
6. Remove two radio mounting screws through access openings in lower panel. On search-tune radios, remove knobs bezels and nuts.
7. Remove support bracket screw from lower reinforcement. *Support radio.*
8. Working through ashtray opening, remove support bracket from radio.
9. Remove radio from under panel.

1968 Chrysler

Without Air Conditioning

1. Disconnect battery ground cable.
2. Remove ash receiver from housing.
3. Remove ash receiver housing (6 screws). Lower housing slightly and disconnect the two lamps, then remove housing.
4. Remove knob from heater temperature control arm.
5. Remove blower switch connector.
6. Remove heater control plate attaching nuts and pull controls out of bezel and drop controls down to ash receiver opening.
7. Disconnect all electrical connections, vacuum switch connector and Bowden cable.
8. Remove heater controls through ash receiver opening.
9. Remove fader cover plate (2 screws).
10. Remove reverberator cover plate (2 screws).
11. Remove center bezel (2 screws upper and 1 screw lower). Open glove box and remove center bezel from panel.
12. Remove two mounting nuts from front of panel (attaching radio).
13. Remove radio mounting bracket (1 screw).
14. Reach up through ash receiver opening and disconnect electrical leads and antenna plug.
15. Remove radio by tilting it towards dash panel and slightly towards the right to disconnect stereo plug at radio (if equipped) and remove radio through ash receiver opening.

With Auto-Temp Air Conditioning

1. Remove ash receiver.
2. Remove A/C controls.
3. Remove Auto-Temp lamp.
4. Remove radio knobs and nuts.
5. If equipped, remove stereo switch, upper left, and cover plate upper right.
6. Remove center bezel. Open glove box door to allow clearance and remove

center bezel far enough to disconnect center air outlet hose and remove bezel from panel.
7. Remove two screws from front of panel (attaching radio to panel).
8. Disconnect radio mounting bracket from back of radio and swing bracket toward glove box.
9. Reach up through ash receiver opening and disconnect all electrical leads and antenna plug.
10. Remove radio by tilting it toward dash panel and slightly toward right to disconnect stereo plug at radio, and remove radio through ash receiver opening.

1967-68 Imperial

1. Disconnect battery ground cable.
2. Remove screws from bottom of A/C distribution duct and hoses from duct (if equipped).
3. Disconnect heater blower motor wire connectors from resistor.
4. From under instrument panel, disconnect radio feed wires and antenna lead from radio.
5. Remove radio support bracket (right side of radio) from radio and instrument panel.
6. Remove radio knobs and mounting nuts and slide radio down and to the right under panel. Rotate front of radio up and remove from under panel.

1968 Polara & Monaco

1. Disconnect battery ground cable.
2. Disconnect cigar lighter lead and remove ash receiver and housing.
3. Remove automatic temperature control.
4. Remove center air outlets (if equipped).
5. Remove radio mounting bracket (loosen one nut at radio, remove one screw in lower reinforcement and swing bracket toward glove box to clear area for radio removal).
6. Remove eight bezel mounting screws. Pull bezel out slightly and disconnect fader control harness and remove two fader control mounting screws from rear of fader and reverberator housing (if equipped).
7. Remove reverberator knob (if equipped).
8. Slide center trim bezel out of upper molding toward cluster.
9. Remove two radio mounting screws.
10. Reach through ash receiver opening and disconnect antenna lead and electrical leads.
11. Remove radio panel by tipping radio down and lowering through ash receiver opening.

1968 Dart

1. Disconnect battery ground cable.
2. Remove instrument cluster.
3. Unfasten and collapse glove box and remove box from panel.
4. Remove temperature control knobs.
5. Working through cluster and glove box openings, remove two heater or A/C mounting stud nuts and move controls out of the way.
6. Remove center bezel (7 screws).
7. Remove radio mounting bracket.
8. Disconnect speaker and antenna

leads.
9. Remove ash receiver (4 screws).
10. Remove two radio mounting screws and remove radio.

1968-70 Charger

1. Disconnect battery ground cable.
2. Remove radio finish plate.
3. On A/C models, remove lower center air duct, left air duct and upper center duct.
4. Remove radio mounting bracket.
5. Unfasten radio from instrument panel (2 screws).
6. Disconnect antenna and speaker leads and remove radio.

1969-72 Fury & V.I.P.

1. Disconnect battery ground cable.
2. Remove lamp panel and steering column cover.
3. Remove radio trim bezel.
4. Remove center lower A/C duct if so equipped.
5. Disconnect electrical leads.
6. Remove radio support bracket and mounting bolts.
7. Remove radio down through bottom of panel carefully to avoid damage to vacuum and electrical connections.

1969-70 Belvedere & Satellite, 1968-70 Coronet

1. Disconnect battery ground cable.
2. Remove radio upper trim panel.
3. Remove radio finish plate.
4. Remove radio rear mounting nut from bracket.
5. Disconnect electrical wiring and antenna lead.
6. Remove two screws from front of instrument panel and remove radio.

1968 Fury & V.I.P.

1. Remove lighting hood and instrument cluster bezel.
2. From under bezel, loosen radio support bracket nut at upper end.
3. If so equipped, remove center A/C spot cooler and disconnect left defroster hose.
4. Disconnect feed wires, speaker wires and antenna cable at radio.
5. From front of instrument panel, remove three radio mounting screws and lift radio out of panel.

1967 Chrysler

Thumbwheel Radio

1. Disconnect ground cable at battery.
2. Remove ash receiver and housing.
3. If air conditioned, pry out on lower edge of outlet hose duct adapter and snap out of distribution duct. Remove hose from adapter and pull hose through ash receiver opening without removing hose from center outlet duct. Remove duct (3 screws).
4. Remove screws in each bezel next to map light and remove bezels.
5. Remove two upper radio bezel screws now exposed and remove screw in lower center of bezel.
6. Disconnect antenna cable.
7. Remove radio mounting screws from instrument panel sheet metal.
8. Remove support bracket screw at lower lip of instrument panel and

loosen nut on mounting stud at back of radio.
9. Rotate edge of radio out and down far enough to disconnect speaker and feed wires before removing from under panel.

Search Tune Radio

The removal procedure on these units is the same as above except that it is not necessary to remove the radio bezel.

1967 Dart

1. Disconnect ground cable at battery.
2. Remove radio control knobs and mounting nuts.
3. On air conditioned models, remove center outlet duct hose and duct. Also remove right defroster hose and hose bracket in back of radio.
4. From under instrument panel, remove radio support bracket lower screw and upper stud nut. Remove bracket.
5. Lower radio and disconnect feed and speaker wires and antenna cable. Remove radio from vehicle.

1967 Polara & Monaco

1. Disconnect ground cable at battery.
2. Remove heater or A/C control knobs.
3. Remove five center bezel screws (3 in underside of upper lip and 2 in face of bezel) and remove bezel.
4. Remove ash receiver and housing.
5. Disconnect right defroster hose at heater outlet and move hose out of the way.
6. Reaching through ash receiver opening, remove two heater or A/C control mounting nuts and move control assembly out of the way. It is not necessary to disconnect control cables.
7. Disconnect radio feed wires and antenna cable from radio.
8. Remove support bracket upper retaining nut and lower retaining screw and remove bracket.
9. Remove two mounting screws from front of panel and remove radio from under panel.

NOTE: If equipped with air conditioning, it is necessary to remove distribution duct and center outlet assembly from instrument panel.

1967 Fury & V.I.P

1. Remove instrument cluster bezel as outlined previously.
2. From under panel, loosen radio support bracket nut at upper end.
3. Disconnect feed wires, speaker wires and antenna cable at radio.
4. From front of instrument panel, remove three mounting screws and lift radio out of panel.

1966 Imperial

1. Disconnect battery ground cable.
2. Unfasten and lower ash receiver and disconnect turn signal flasher and ash receiver lamp wiring.
3. Remove ash receiver.
4. Remove radio-to-instrument panel lower reinforcement mounting bracket and remove bracket.
5. Disconnect antenna lead, speaker leads and radio feed wire.

6. Remove pencil brace from instrument panel lower reinforcement to dash panel. This brace is located just to the left of radio.
7. Remove radio control knobs and mounting nuts.
8. Pull radio out of panel opening and rotate it 90 degrees so its face is to the right of vehicle, then carefully remove radio from under instrument panel.

CAUTION: Do not operate radio with speaker detached, since damage to transistors may result. If rear seat speaker is disconnected from the radio, insert a jumper wire in rear speaker socket to allow receiver to operate.

1966 Chrysler

NOTE: On cars with air conditioning, it is necessary to remove the center air conditioning outlet hose.

1. Disconnect battery ground cable.
2. Remove ash receiver and housing.
3. Remove radio control knobs.
4. Remove radio mounting nuts.
5. Working through ash receiver opening, disconnect speaker leads, radio feed wire and antenna lead cable.
6. Remove radio-to-instrument panel mounting bracket.
7. Remove radio through ash receiver opening.

1966 Dart

1. Disconnect battery ground cable.
2. If air conditioned, remove spot cooler and tubes.
3. Disconnect antenna, speaker and power supply leads.
4. Remove radio control knobs and nuts.
5. Remove radio support bracket.
6. Rotate front edge of radio down and remove from under panel.

1966-67 Charger & Coronet

1. On air conditioned models it is necessary to remove the instrument cluster. Then, after disconnecting the antenna leads and feed wires, loosen radio bracket upper support nut and remove radio through cluster opening. On models without A/C, proceed as follows:
2. Disconnect battery ground cable.
3. Remove upper half of glove box and disconnect speaker leads from speaker terminals.
4. Remove radio control knobs and two mounting nuts.
5. Disconnect both defroster hoses at heater.
6. Disconnect antenna cable and radio feed wires at connector.
7. Loosen radio support bracket retaining nut at radio and remove support bracket mounting screw from lower edge of instrument panel.
8. Remove radio from under instrument panel.

1966 Monaco & Polara

1. Disconnect battery cable.
2. Remove radio control knobs.

3. Remove radio mounting nuts.
4. If air conditioned, remove distributor duct and three spot cooler hoses.
5. From under instrument panel, disconnect speaker leads, radio feed wire and antenna lead cable at radio.
6. Remove radio-to-instrument panel mounting bracket and remove radio.

1966-68 Valiant & Barracuda

NOTE: On air conditioned models it is necessary to remove the two outlet duct retaining nuts and remove duct. Also remove the right defroster hose and hose bracket in back of radio.

1. Disconnect battery ground cable.
2. Remove radio control knobs.
3. Remove bottom screw from radio mounting bracket.
4. Remove left defroster tube.
5. Loosen top screw on radio mounting bracket and remove bracket.
6. Disconnect speaker and antenna leads.
7. Remove mounting nuts from front of radio.
8. Remove radio bezel.
9. Lower radio and disconnect radio power feed cable.
10. Remove radio from under panel.

1966-68 Belvedere & Satellite

1. Disconnect battery ground cable.
2. If air conditioned, remove spot cooler hoses and distribution duct.
3. Remove control knobs, two mounting nuts and bezel.
4. From under instrument panel, disconnect speaker, power and antenna leads.
5. Remove support bracket and radio.

1966 Fury

1. Disconnect battery ground cable.
2. Remove control knobs and two mounting nuts.
3. If air conditioned, remove transition duct and two spot cooler hoses before disconnecting speaker, power supply and antenna leads.
4. Remove radio support bracket.
5. Rotate front end of radio down and remove it from under panel.

HEATER CORE REMOVAL

Before attempting to remove a heater core, disconnect one of the battery cables, drain the radiator and remove inlet and outlet hoses from heater assembly in engine compartment.

1971-72 Dart & Valiant

Less Air Conditioning
1. Remove heater hoses to dash panel seal and retainer plate.
2. Remove heater motor seal retainer plate and seal from dash panel.
3. Disconnect control cables from heater.
4. Remove heater motor resistor wire from resistor.
5. Remove defroster tubes from heater.
6. Disconnect heater housing support rod from outside air duct.
7. Remove heater assembly.

With Air Conditioning
1. Disconnect battery and remove air cleaner.

2. Remove air outlet assembly, glove box and right defroster tube.
3. Disconnect wiring from resistor block, vacuum hoses from outside recirculating air door actuator, temperature control cable, evaporator temperature control switch control cable and heater core ground wire.
4. Remove screw securing heater to evaporator assembly.
5. Disconnect heater housing support rod from outside air duct.
6. Remove heater assembly.
7. Remove outside recirculating air door actuator.
8. Remove operating link between bellcrank and recirculating door.
9. Remove air inlet seal from either front or rear heater housing half only.
10. Remove retainer clips attaching housing halves together and separate halves.
11. Remove screws attaching heater core to heater housing and remove core.

1971-72 Barracuda, Challenger, Coronet & Satellite

Less Air Conditioning

1. Remove three mounting nuts from studs around blower motor and remove flange and air seal.
2. Unplug antenna from radio and place to one side.
3. Remove screw from housing to plenum support rod on right side of housing above fresh air opening.
4. Disconnect three air door cables.
5. Disconnect wires from blower resistor.
6. Tip unit down and out from under panel.

With Air Conditioning

1. Remove air cleaner and slowly discharge refrigerant from system.
2. Disconnect refrigerant lines at dash panel. Leave expansion valve attached to line. Cap all lines.
3. Disconnect blower motor wires and remove motor cooling tube and motor.
4. Remove glove box and appearance shield from lower edge of dash panel.
5. Remove left spot cooler duct and air distribution duct.
6. Disconnect wires from blower resistor and antenna wire from radio.
7. Remove radio.
8. Disconnect vacuum harness from back of control switch.
9. Remove water valve cable from bracket on left end of housing.
10. Remove nuts from housing mounting studs in engine compartment.
11. Remove rubber drain tube.
12. Remove support bracket from housing plenum panel.
13. Carefully remove plenum air seal.
14. Disconnect vacuum hose from inlet air door actuator and by-pass door actuator.
15. Remove air seal from heater and evaporator core tubes.
16. Remove 18 screws holding front and rear covers together and one screw from between core tubes. Separate housings.
17. Remove 3 screws from evaporator core access plate, remove plate, this provides access to two evaporator core mounting screws.

18. Remove four screws holding evaporator core to front cover and remove core. Carefully lift left half of housing seal from rear cover. Do not remove entire seal as bottom portion is a water seal.
19. Remove two core retaining screws from mounting plates and one from between core tubes in back of rear cover. Lift core out of housing.

1971-72 Chrysler, Imperial, Fury, Polara, & Monaco

Less Air Conditioning

1. Remove passenger side housing from vehicle.
2. From inside housing, remove two retaining nuts from right side of heater core and four screws from outside of housing.
3. Remove core tube locating metal screw from top of housing.
4. Carefully pull heater core out of housing.

With Air Conditioning

1. Remove air cleaner.
2. Remove steering column cover and left spot cooling duct.
3. Disconnect two actuator rods at linkage on left side of housing and remove two cover retaining screws.
4. Remove five screws retaining heat distribution duct. When heat duct is removed, three screws in bottom lip of front cover can now be removed.
5. Remove glove box and center spot cooler, air distribution housing and right spot cooler duct.
6. From glove box opening, remove two top retaining screws and three screws from right side of housing.
7. Disconnect wires at resistor block and vacuum hoses from air inlet housing actuator.
8. Remove nut from housing end of support bracket and swing bracket up out of way. Carefully roll front cover and heater core out from under panel.

1966 Imperial

Remove screws attaching heater core housing to dash panel and remove housing and core as a unit. Then remove mastic material covering core mounting screws. Remove screws and lift out heater core.

1969-70 Chrysler, Imperial, Polara, Monaco, Fury & V.I.P

From under dash, remove antenna lead, vacuum hoses from trunk lock and electrical connectors from blower motor resistor block. Remove vacuum hoses from defroster actuator and heater shutoff door actuator. Remove bottom retaining nut from support bracket and swing bracket up out of the way.

In engine compartment, remove retaining nuts from housing. Remove locating bolt from under bottom center of passenger side housing. Roll or tip housing out from under panel and remove temperature control cable from door crank. Remove retaining screws and nuts and remove core.

1966-68 Chrysler, Imperial, Polara, Monaco, Fury & V.I.P.

From under dash remove bracket from top of heater to dash panel, defroster hoses at heater end, actuator vacuum hoses, and wiring at blower motor resistor. Next, remove glove box and then disconnect control cables at heater end. Unclamp flexible connector at right end of heater but do not remove connector from side cowl.

From engine side of dash, remove three nuts that secure heater to dash. Then from inside car, pull heater toward rear of vehicle until studs are clear. Rotate assembly until studs are down and remove heater from car. Take off heater cover plate, remove heater core mounting screws and lift out core.

Chrysler & Imperial Rear Seat Heater

To remove core from rear seat heater on 1966-69 models, from under car, remove heater hose and tubing support clamps at rear of floor pan and drain system. Then remove rear seat cushion and seat back. From inside car remove hoses from heater, and spare tire from trunk. Disconnect motor feed wire, fresh air intake hose and floor air duct hoses from heater. Take out three metal screws from heater mounting brackets and remove heater assembly. With heater on bench, remove 11 screws from end plate and take off plate. Then remove four screws retaining heater core to heater body and lift out core.

1966-70 Dart, Challenger, Barracuda, Valiant

Remove heater motor seal and retainer plate from right side of dash in engine compartment. Then disconnect all control cables from heater assembly, along with heater motor resistor wire and defroster tubes. Remove heater housing support rod from fresh air duct and take out heater assembly.

To get at the core, remove retaining clips from two halves of heater housing and separate halves. Then remove screw attaching seal retainer and seal around the heater core tubes. Take off heater core support clamp, remove screws attaching heater core to heater and lift out core.

1966-70 Belvedere, Satellite, Charger & Coronet

On models equipped with console shift, it is necessary to move console rearward before removing heater. After doing this, remove upper half of glove box and then take off heater-to-cowl support bracket. Next, disconnect defroster hoses, wiring from heater motor resistor, fresh air vent control, and cables for shut-off door at heater end.

Now, reach through glove box door and disconnect cable from temperature control door. From engine compartment, remove three nuts that retain heater assembly to firewall. Then rotate heater assembly until mounting studs are up and lift heater assembly from under dash. To remove core, take off heater cover from front of heater and take out core mounting screws.

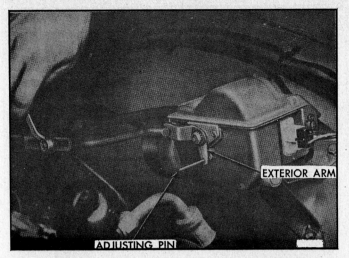

Fig. 9   Auto Pilot accelerator linkage adjustment. 1967

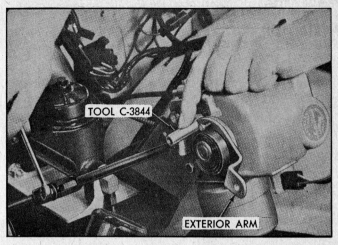

Fig. 10   Auto Pilot accelerator linkage adjustment. 1966

SPEED CONTROLS

1966-67 Auto Pilot Accelerator Linkage

Before attempting to adjust the accelerator linkage, the carburetor must be at curb idle position with the choke completely open. Then operate the linkage by moving the Auto Pilot exterior arm several times, allowing linkage to ease into normal position. *Do not force linkage to close throttle.*

1967 Adjustment, Fig. 9

1. Loosen locknut on Auto Pilot linkage rod and insert a 1/8" diameter rod through hole in exterior arm and into hole in Auto Pilot housing.
2. Hold exterior arm and tighten locknut on linkage.

1966 Adjustment, Fig. 10

1. Loosen locknut on Auto Pilot linkage rod and insert locking arm gauge Tool C-3844 or equivalent over stop stud on Auto Pilot.
2. Hold exterior arm against gauge pin and tighten locknut on linkage. This

will provide proper clearance between stop stud and exterior arm with carburetor in idle position.

Control Cable

1966 Adjustment, Fig. 11

1. Loosen but do not remove set screw on dust shield.
2. Rotate instrument panel control dial counterclockwise until it contacts internal stop.
3. Push in lightly on control cable at dust shield. This will position control rod, to which inner cable attaches, against its upper stop. *Do not force cable beyond this position.*
4. Make certain control dial is still in its extreme counterclockwise stop.
5. Tighten screw on dust shield securely. *A correctly adjusted control cable will not spring back on full rotation in either direction.*

Brake Switch Adjustment

It is important that the brake switch adjustment be carefully performed to insure proper Auto Pilot operation. With a

test lamp connected to the blue wire side of switch, Fig. 12, test lamp should go out with approximately 1/4 to 1/2 inch of brake pedal movement. To replace the brake switch, brake pedal and bracket assembly will have to be removed.

1968-71 Speed Control

Servo Adjustments

There are three adjustment set screws in the servo housing, Figs. 13, 14 and 15. The adjustment of these set screws have been factory set and under normal conditions there should be no need for altering the factory setting during the life of the vehicle.

Need for adjustment can be determined only after accurate diagnosis of the system operation. If adjustment is found to be necessary, perform the appropriate adjustment outlined below; if screw is loose stake side of servo housing adjacent to screw to insure a snug fit.

Lock-In Screw Adjustment, Fig. 13

Lock-in accuracy will be affected by poor engine performance (need for tune-up), loaded gross weight of car (trailering), improper slack in control cable. After the foregoing items have been considered and the speed sags or drops more

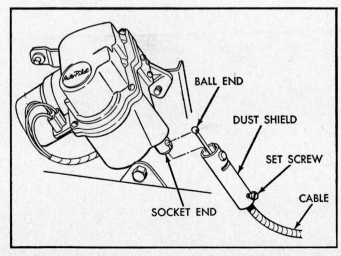

Fig. 11   Auto Pilot control cable and dust shield. 1966

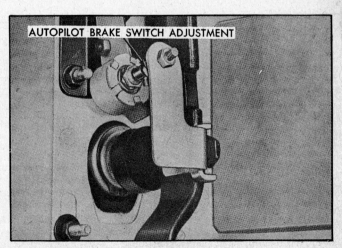

Fig. 12   Auto Pilot brake switch

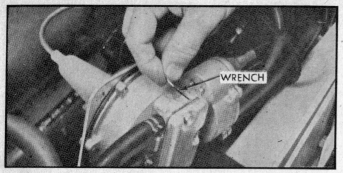

Fig.13   Speed Control lock-in screw adjustment. 1968-71

Fig. 14   Speed Control cut-in screw adjustment. 1968-70

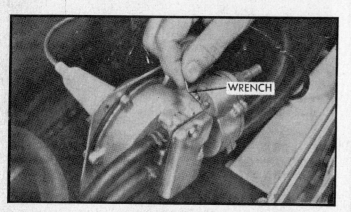

Fig. 15   Speed Control cut-out screw adjustment. 1968-70

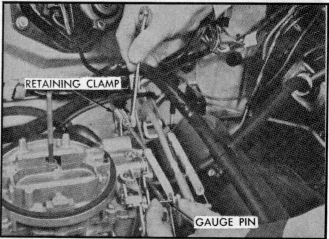

Fig. 16   Speed Control servo cable throttle adjustment. 1968-70

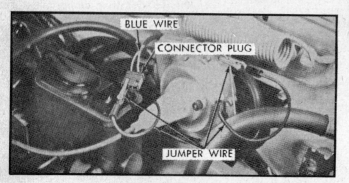

Fig. 17   Speed Control brake switch adjustment. 1968-70

than 2 to 3 mph when the speed control is activated, the lock-in adjusting screw should be turned counter-clockwise approximately $\frac{1}{4}$ turn per one mph correction required.

If a speed increase of more than 2 to 3 mph occurs, the lock-in adjusting screw should be turned clockwise $\frac{1}{4}$ turn per one mph correction required.

CAUTION: This adjustment must not exceed two turns in either direction or damage to the unit may occur.

Cut-In Speed Adjustment, Fig. 14

This adjustment regulates the minimum road speed at which the low speed inhibit switch allows the speed control to be activated. This should range from 25 to 33 mph. If cut-in speed is too low, turn set screw counter-clockwise. If too high,

turn set screw clockwise. Make adjustments in $\frac{1}{8}$ turn increments; total adjustment must not exceed two turns.

Cut-Out Adjustment, Fig. 15

This adjustment affects the road speed at which the system is deactivated during deceleration. Turning the screw clockwise increases road speed at which the system deactivates (cuts out). A counter-clockwise adjustment decreases the cut-out speed. The desired cut-out speed should occur approximately 5 mph below the cut-in setting. Make adjustments in $\frac{1}{8}$ turn increments; total adjustment must not exceed two turns.

Throttle Cable Adjustment, Fig. 16

Optimum servo performance is obtained with a given amount of free play in the throttle control cable. To obtain proper

free play, insert a $\frac{1}{16}$" diameter pin between forward end of slot in cable end of carburetor linkage pin (hair pin clip removed from linkage pin). With choke in full open position and carburetor at curb idle, pull cable back toward dash panel without moving carburetor linkage until all free play is removed. Tighten cable clamp bolt to 45 inch-pounds, remove $\frac{1}{16}$" pin and install hair pin clip.

Brake Switch Adjustment, 1968-69

1. Disconnect harness connector at speed control servo and run a jumper wire from the blue wire terminal of connector to a good ground, Fig. 17.
2. Turn ignition key to accessory position, depress and release turn signal lever push button and check clearance between engaged actuator arm and striker pin on brake pedal, Figs. 18 and 19. Clearance should be .070" to .100".
3. If clearance is not correct, loosen striker pin attaching nut and move pin to obtain this clearance. Then tighten nut securely, insuring that the adjusted clearance is maintained.

NOTE: Before making the low speed inhibit switch adjustment, check speedometer cables to assure proper core length so that both cable drive ends are properly

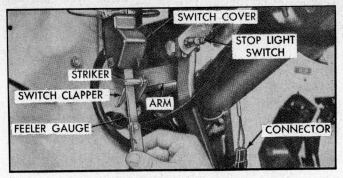

Fig. 18 Checking clapper and striker pin clearance on intermediate size cars. 1968-69 Speed Control

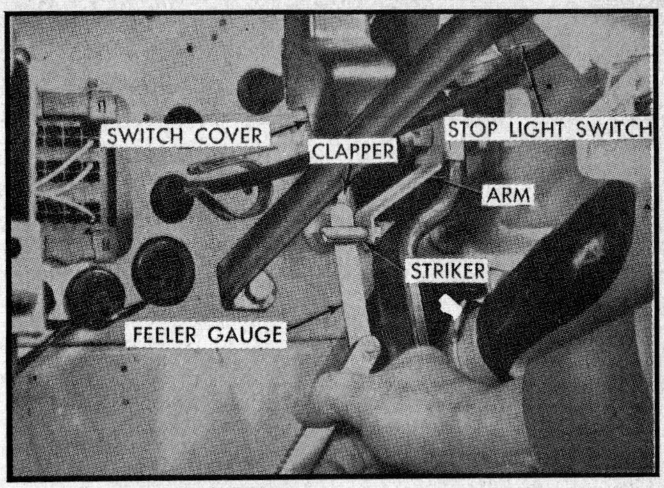

Fig. 19 Checking clapper and striker pin clearance on full size cars. 1968-69 Speed Control

engaged in servo shaft keyways without binding. Also be sure that cable ferrule nuts are properly positioned on servo pilot diameters and nuts properly tightened.

Brake Switch Adjustment, 1970
1. Loosen switch bracket.
2. Insert .140"-.150" spacer gauge between brake push rod and switch with pedal in free position.
3. Push switch bracket assembly toward brake push rod until plunger is fully depressed and switch contacts spacer.
4. Tighten bracket bolt to 100 in-lbs. and remove spacer.

Brake Switch Adjustment, 1971
The procedure is the same as that for 1970 models but the spacer must be .110" for full size cars and .130" for intermediate models.

Engine Section

ENGINE, REPLACE
1966-72 Chrysler & Imperial

In addition to the usual items such as fuel lines, linkage, propeller shaft, etc., perform the following:
1. Scribe a line on hinge brackets on hood to assure proper adjustments when installing. Then remove hood.
2. Remove battery, drain cooling system, remove all hoses, fan shroud, disconnect oil cooler lines and remove radiator.
3. Attach lifting fixture to carburetor flange studs on intake manifold.
4. Raise vehicle on hoist and install an engine support fixture on frame to support rear of engine.
5. Drain transmission and torque converter.
6. Remove engine rear support crossmember and transmission.
7. Lower vehicle and attach chain hoist to fixture eyebolt.
8. Remove engine front mounting bolts. Then raise and work engine out of chassis.

Dodge & Plymouth 1966-72 V8s
1. Scribe hood hinge outlines on hood and remove hood.
2. Drain cooling system and remove battery.
3. Remove fan shroud (if equipped) and radiator.
4. Disconnect fuel lines and wiring to engine.
5. Remove carburetor. Attach engine lifting fixture to carburetor flange studs on intake manifold.

6. Remove engine front mounting nuts.
7. Disconnect propeller shaft and tie out of the way.
8. Disconnect wires and linkage at transmission.
9. Disconnect exhaust pipes at manifold.
10. Attach engine support fixture and remove engine rear crossmember.
11. Remove transmission.
12. Lift engine out of chassis.

6-170, 198, 225
1. Scribe hood hinge outlines on hood and remove hood.
2. Drain cooling system and remove battery and carburetor air cleaner.
3. Disconnect transmission cooler lines at radiator (if equipped).
4. Remove radiator and hoses.
5. Remove outlet vent pipe or closed vent system and rocker arm cover.
6. Disconnect fuel lines, carburetor linkage and wiring to engine.
7. Disconnect exhaust pipe at manifold.
8. Disconnect propeller shaft and tie out of the way.
9. Remove speedometer cable and gearshift rods.
10. Remove clutch torque shaft, brake cables and rods.
11. Remove converter cover plate.
12. Drain converter and transmission. Remove oil cooler lines, filler tube and push button cable (if equipped).
13. Support rear of engine.
14. Remove engine rear support crossmember.
15. Disconnect converter from flexible mounting plate.
16. Remove transmission bolts from

clutch housing.
17. Remove transmission and converter as an assembly. *Do not remove converter from transmission.*
18. Attach lifting fixture to cylinder head and attach chain hoist.
19. Remove engine support and front engine mounting bolts and lift engine from chassis.

CYLINDER HEAD
1966-72 Chrysler & Imperial

Some cylinder head gaskets are coated with a special lacquer to provide a good seal once the parts have warmed up. Do not use any additional sealer on such gaskets. If the gasket does not have this lacquer coating, apply suitable sealer to both sides.
1. Drain cooling system and disconnect battery ground cable.
2. Remove alternator or generator, carburetor air cleaner and fuel line.
3. Disconnect accelerator linkage.
4. Remove vacuum control tube at carburetor and distributor.
5. Disconnect heat indicator sending unit wire.
6. Remove spark plugs.
7. Remove intake manifold, ignition coil and carburetor as a unit.
8. Remove valve lifter chamber cover.
9. Remove rocker arm covers. *On Imperial air conditioned cars prior to 1967 the No. 8 cylinder exhaust valve must be open to allow clearance between rightbank cylinder head cover and heater housing.*
10. Remove exhaust manifolds.

11. Remove rocker arm assemblies.
12. Remove push rods.
13. Remove head attaching bolts and take off heads.
14. Installing the heads is a matter of reversing the removal procedure. Tighten attaching bolts in the sequence shown in Fig. 1.

1966-72 Dodge & Dart Six

1. Drain cooling system.
2. Remove carburetor air cleaner and fuel line.
3. Disconnect accelerator linkage.
4. Remove vacuum control tube at carburetor and distributor.
5. Disconnect spark plug wires, heater hose and clamp holding by-pass hose.
6. Disconnect heat indicator sending unit wire.
7. Disconnect exhaust pipe at manifold.
8. Remove intake and exhaust manifold and carburetor as a unit.
9. Remove closed vent system and rocker arm cover.
10. Remove rocker arms and push rods.
11. Remove head bolts and lift off head.
12. Install the head in the reverse order of removal, and tighten the bolts in the sequence shown in Fig. 2.
13. When installing the manifolds, loosen the three bolts holding the intake and exhaust manifolds together. This is required to maintain proper alignment. Install intake and exhaust manifolds with cup side of the conical washers against the manifolds.

Dodge V8-273, 318, 340, 360

NOTE: The intake manifold attaching bolts on some engines are tilted upward about 30 degrees at an angle to the manifold-to-cylinder head gasket face. The purpose of this design is to provide more effective sealing at the cylinder block end gaskets. If the intake manifold is removed the installation should be such that the bolt tightening is done evenly and in the sequence shown in Fig. 4.

With gaskets in place start all bolts, leaving them loose. Run bolts 1 through 4 down so the heads just touch manifold. Then tighten these four bolts to 25 foot-pounds torque. After checking to see that gaskets are properly seated at all surfaces, tighten remaining bolts to 25 foot-pounds. Finally tighten all bolts in the sequence shown to 35 foot-pounds.

1. Drain cooling system and disconnect battery ground cable.
2. Remove alternator, carburetor air cleaner and fuel line. Disconnect accelerator linkage.
3. Remove vacuum advance hose and distributor cap and wires.
4. Disconnect coil wires, heat indicator wire, heater and by-pass hoses.
5. Remove closed ventilation system and rocker arm covers.
6. Remove intake manifold, coil and carburetor as an assembly.
7. Remove exhaust manifolds.
8. Remove rocker arm and shaft assemblies. Remove push rods.
9. Remove head bolts and lift off cylinder heads.
10. Reverse procedure to install heads and tighten bolts in sequence shown in Fig. 5.

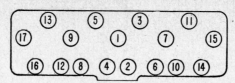

Fig. 1 Cylinder head tightening sequence. V8s with distributor at front of engine

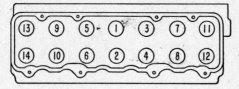

Fig. 2 Cylinder head tightening sequence. 6-170, 198, 225

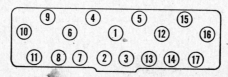

Fig. 3 Cylinder head tightening sequence. V8-426 HP2 engine

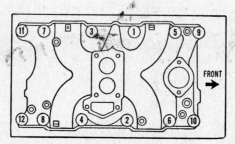

Fig. 4 Intake manifold tightening sequence. V8-273, late 318 & 340, 360

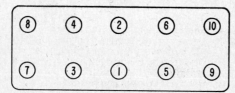

Fig. 5 Cylinder head tightening sequence. V8s with distributor at rear of engine

V8-361, 383, 400, 426, 440

Rocker arm assemblies can be removed without disturbing the cylinder heads or cooling system. To remove the heads, proceed as follows:

1. Drain cooling system, remove air cleaner, fuel line from pump and carburetor, distributor vacuum tube and generator.
2. Disconnect throttle linkage at carburetor, distributor cap, coil wires, heat indicator sending unit wire and heater hoses at engine.
3. Remove spark plugs and cables, and

engine vent pipe or closed vent system.
4. Remove intake manifold, carburetor and coil as an assembly.
5. Remove exhaust manifolds.
6. Remove cylinder head covers and spark plug cable support brackets.
7. Remove rocker shaft assemblies. Do not remove bolts from end brackets.
8. Remove push rods and valve lifter chamber cover.
9. Remove attaching bolts and lift off heads.

NOTE: V8-426 Hemi-Charger engines, in addition to the regular cylinder head bolts, have four stud nuts holding the heads in place. These stud nuts must be removed from inside the tappet chamber before any attempt is made to remove the head.

10. Reverse the foregoing procedure to install the heads and tighten bolts in the sequence shown in Figs. 1 and 3.

V8-426 Hemi-Charger Engine

Cylinder head bolt torque is critical on this engine and in order to obtain proper cylinder head gasket compression, Lubriplate should be applied to the bolt threads and between the bolt head and hardened washer.

NOTE: Care must be taken so as not to get any of the Lubriplate between the hardened washer and bolt boss as this can cause excessive bolt tension and may result in head bolt breakage.

Plymouth 6-170, 198, 225

1. To remove head, drain cooling system.
2. Remove carburetor air cleaner and fuel line.
3. Disconnect accelerator linkage.
4. Remove vacuum control tube at carburetor and distributor.
5. Disconnect spark plug wires, heater hose and clamp holding by-pass hose.
6. Disconnect heat indicator sending unit wire.
7. Disconnect exhaust pipe at manifold.
8. Remove intake and exhaust manifold and carburetor as a unit.
9. Remove vent system and rocker arm cover.
10. Remove thermostat housing and thermostat.
11. Remove rocker arms and push rods.
12. Remove head bolts and lift off head.
13. Check all surfaces of head with a straightedge if there is any reason to suspect leakage. Cylinder head warpage should not exceed .005" lengthwise or .003" crosswise. If there is any reason to suspect restricted water passages, the large recessed screw plug in the rear of the head can be removed.
14. Clean the oil return passages in the head and block.
15. Install the head in the reverse order of removal and tighten the bolts in the sequence shown in Fig. 1 and to the torque listed in the Engine Torque table.
16. When installing the manifolds, loosen the three bolts holding the intake

manifold to the exhaust manifold. *This is required to maintain proper alignment.* Install intake and exhaust manifold with carburetor with the cup side of the conical washers against the manifolds.

Plymouth 1966-72 V8s

NOTE, V8-273: The intake manifold attaching bolts on this engine are tilted upward about 30 degrees at an angle to the manifold-to-cylinder head gasket face. The purpose of this design is to provide more effective sealing at the cylinder block end gaskets. If the manifold is removed the installation should be such that the bolt tightening is done evenly and in the sequence shown in Fig. 4.

With gaskets in place start all bolts, leaving them loose. Run bolts 1 through 4 down so heads just touch manifold. Then tighten these four bolts to 60 inch-pounds torque. After checking to see that gaskets are properly seated at all surfaces, tighten remaining bolts to 60 inch-pounds. Finally, tighten all bolts to 270 inch-pounds.

1. Drain cooling system. Remove air cleaner, fuel line, alternator and distributor vacuum line.
2. Disconnect throttle linkage, coil wires, heat indicator sending unit wire, and heater hoses at engine.
3. Remove distributor cap and spark plug cables.
4. Remove intake manifold, coil and carburetor as an assembly.
5. On 361, 383, 413, 440, 426 engines, remove valve lifter chamber cover and spark plugs located under exhaust manifolds.
6. On all engines, remove rocker arm covers, closed vent system and exhaust manifolds.
7. On 361, 383, 413, 440, 426 engines, remove rocker arms and shaft assemblies. Lift out push rods and place them in a suitable holder in their respective slots. *On 318 engines, push rods and rocker arms are removed with cylinder head.*
8. Remove head bolts from each head and lift off heads.
9. Reverse the removal procedure to install the heads and tighten head bolts in the sequence shown in the diagrams and to the torque listed in the *Engine Tightening Specifications* table.

V8-426 HEMI-CHARGER: Cylinder head bolt torque is critical on this engine and in order to obtain proper cylinder head gasket compression, Lubriplate should be applied to the bolt threads and between bolt head and hardened washer.

NOTE: Care must be taken so as not to get any Lubriplate between hardened washer and bolt boss as this can cause excessive bolt tension and may result in head bolt breakage.

VALVES, ADJUST
6-170, 198, 225

Before the final valve lash adjustment is made, operate the engine for 30 minutes at a fast idle to stabilize engine

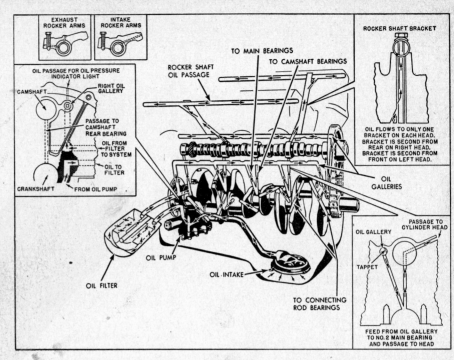

Engine oiling system, V8-273, 318, 340, 360

temperatures.

Before starting the adjustment procedure, make two chalk marks on the vibration damper. Space the marks approximately 120° apart (⅓ of circumference) so that with the timing mark the damper is divided into three equal parts. Adjust the valves for No. 1 cylinder. Repeat the procedure for the remaining valves, turning the crankshaft ⅓ turn in the direction of normal rotation while adjusting the valves in the firing order sequence of 153624.

V8s With Mechanical Lifters

Engines with mechanical lifters can be identified by the rocker arm adjusting screws. These screws are self-locking and when turning them during the process of adjustment they should indicate some resistance to turning (a minimum of 3 lb. ft. tension). If any screw turns too easily it should be replaced and, if necessary, the rocker arm as well.

Valve clearances should be set up after the engine is warmed up to operating temperature and to the clearances listed in the *Valve Specifications* table.

VALVE ARRANGEMENT
Front to Rear

8-318:
Right Bank . . . . I-E-I-E-I-E-I-E
Left Bank . . . . E-I-E-I-E-I-E-I
8-273, 340, 360 . . . . E-I-I-E-E-I-I-E
8-361, 383, 426, 400, 440 . . E-I-I-E-E-I-I-E
6-170, 198, 225 . . . . . E-I-E-I-E-I-I-E-I-E-I

VALVE LIFT SPECS

Engine	Year	Intake	Exhaust
6-170	1966	.375	.365
6-198	1967	.395	.395
	1968	.394	.390
	1969	.395	.395
	1970	.395	.395
	1971-72	.406	.414
6-225	1966-67	.395	.395
	1968	.394	.390
	1969-70	.395	.395
	1971-72	.406	.414
8-273	1966-67[1]	.395	.405
	1966-67[2]	.415	.425
	1968	.372	.400
	1969	.373	.399
8-318	1966	.397	.403
	1967	.390	.390
	1968	.372	.400
	1969-72	.373	.399
8-340	1968[11]	.445	.455
	1968[12]	.430	.445
	1969-72	.429	.444
8-360	1971-72	.410	.412
8-361	1966	.392	.390
8-383	1966[1]	.392	.390
	1966-67[2]	.425	.437
	1968[2]	.425	.437
	1969-71[1][6]	.425	.435
	1969-71[2][9]	.450	.458
8-400	1972[1]	.434	.430
	1972[2]	.449	.464
8-426	1966	.425	.435
	1967	.467	.473
	1968	.490	.480
	1969	.467	.473
	1970-71	.490	.481

8-440	1966	.425	.435
	1967[4]	.425	.435
	1967[5]	.450	.465
	1968[4]	.425	.437
	1968[5]	.450	.465
	1969-71[9]	.425	.435
	1969-71[13]	.450	.458
	1972	.434	.430
	1972[13]	.449	.464
	1972[14]	.449	.464

[1]—2 bar. carb. [2]—4 bar. carb.
[3]—340 H.P.
[4]—350 H.P. [5]—375 H.P.
[6]—330 H.P. [7]—360 H.P.
[8]—Exc. 330 H.P. [9]—Exc. 330 H.P.
[10]—Exc. Hi. Perf. [11]—Man. Trans.
[12]—Auto. Trans.
[13]—Hi Perf.
[14]—3 Carbs.

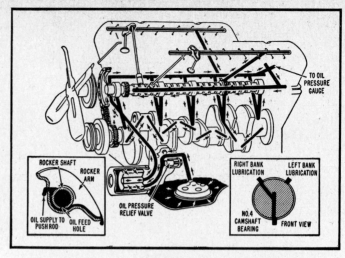

Engine oiling system. V8-361, 383, 400, 413, 426, 440 engines

VALVE TIMING SPECS.
Intake Opens Before TDC

Engine	Year	Degrees
6-170	1966	8
	1967-69	10
6-198	1970	10
	1971-72	16
6-225	1966-70	10
	1971-72	16
8-273	1966-67	14
	1968-69	10
8-318	1966	.19
	1967	14
	1968-72	10
8-340	1968 Man. Tr.	26
	1968 Auto. Tr.	22
	1969-72	22
8-360	1971-72	16
8-361	1966	13
8-383	1966 2 B.C.	13
	1966 4 B.C.	14
	1967	16
	1968	18
	1969-71[1]	18
	1969-71[2]	21

Engine	Year	Degrees
8-400	1972 2 B. C.	18
	1972 4 B. C.	21
8-426	1966-67	30
	1968-71	36
8-440	1966	14
	1967-68 350 H.P.	18
	1967 375 H.P.	19
	1968 375 H.P.	21
	1969-72 L/Hi. Perf.	18
	1969-72 W/Hi. Perf.	21

[1]—2 bar. carb. & 330 H.P.
[2]—4 bar. carb. exc. 330 H.P.

ROCKER ARMS
6-170, 198, 225

1. To remove rocker arms, take off head cover outlet tube.
2. Remove rocker arm cover.
3. Remove rocker shaft bolts and retainers.
4. Lift off rocker arms and shaft.

Inspection

Clean all parts with a suitable solvent. Be sure the inside of the shaft is clean and the oil holes are open. The drilled oil hole in the bore of the rocker arm must be open to the trough and valve end of the arms. The trough also feeds oil to the adjusting screw and push rod.

The shaft should be free from excessive wear in arm contact areas. The shaft should be smooth in retainer contact areas. The adjusting screws in the rocker arms should have a uniform round end. The drag torque should be smooth and uniform. The retainers should be smooth and undamaged in the shaft contact area.

Assemble and Install

1. Referring to Fig. 6, note flat on forward end of rocker shaft which denotes the upper side of the shaft. Rocker arms must be put on the shaft with the adjusting screw to the right side of the engine. Place one of the small retainers on the one long bolt and install the bolt in the rear hole in the shaft from the top side.

2. Install one rocker arm and one spacer; then two rocker arms and a spacer. Continue in same sequence until all rocker arms and spacers are on the shaft.
3. Place a bolt and small retainer in front hole in shaft.
4. Place a bolt and the one *wide* retainer through the center hole in the shaft with six rocker arms on each side of center.
5. Install remaining bolts and retainers, separating the four pairs of rocker arms.
6. Locate the assembly on the cylinder head and position rocker arm adjusting screws in push rods.
7. Tighten bolts finger tight, bringing retainers in contact with the shaft *between rocker arms.*
8. Tighten bolts to specified torque.
9. After running engine to normal operating temperature, adjust valve lash to specifications.
10. Complete the job by installing the remaining parts removed.

V8-273, & 1967-72 V8-318, 340, 360

To provide correct lubrication for the

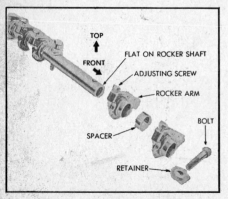

Fig. 6   Rocker arm and shaft assembly. 6-170, 198, 225

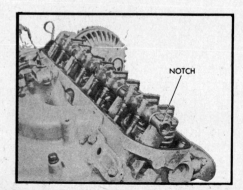

Fig. 7   Notches at end of both rocker arm shafts must face toward center of engine. V8-273 and 1967-72 V8-318, 340, 360

rocker arms on these engines, the rocker shafts have a small notch machined at one end, Fig. 7, and these notches must always face inward toward the center of the engine when installed. In other words, the notched end must be toward the rear of the engine on the right bank, and to the front of the engine on the left bank.

Rocker arms must be correctly positioned on the shaft prior to installation on cylinder head. A good way to do this is to place each rocker arm on the shaft so the adjusting screw is on the same side as the notch of the shaft when the rocker arm is right side up.

It is also important when installing the rocker shaft assembly on the cylinder head to position the short retainers at each end and in the center, and to place long retainers in the two remaining positions.

1966 V8-318 U.S. & 1967 Canadian Built

1. Referring to Fig. 8, slide rocker shaft into bore of strut and at the same time engage intake rocker arm.
2. Install spring and engage exhaust rocker arm.
3. Install remainder of rocker arms in same sequence.

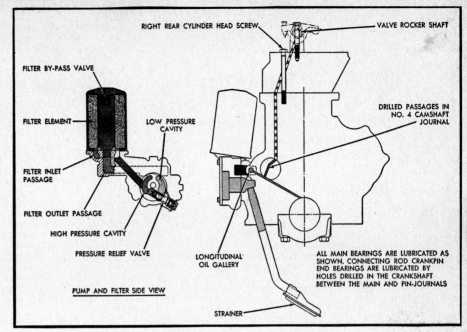

Engine oiling system. 6-170, 198, 225

4. Make sure that head bolt holes in rocker shaft line up with head bolt holes in rocker arm shaft strut. In addition, plug hole in strut must also line up with hole in rocker shaft.
5. Install plugs in both ends of rocker arm shaft.

V8-361, 383, 400, 426, 440

1. Install rocker shafts so that the $3/16''$ diameter rocker arm lubrication holes point downward into rocker arm, and so that the 15 degree angle of these holes point outward toward valve end of rocker arm, Figs. 9 and 9A. The 15 degree angle is determined from the center line of the bolt holes through the shaft which are used to attach the shaft assembly to the cylinder head.
2. On all engines, install rocker arms and shaft assembly, making sure to install long stamped steel retainers

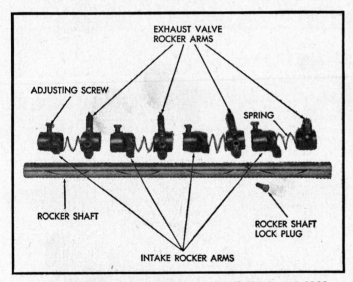

Fig. 8   Rocker arm and shaft assembly. V8-318 through 1966 U.S. and 1967 Canadian built. The 1967 U.S. built 318 and 340 engine is similar to the V8-273 engine

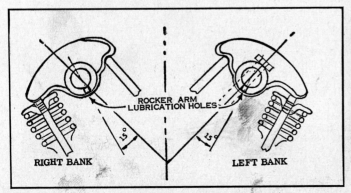

Fig. 9   Rocker arm shaft installation. V8-361, 383, 400, 413, 426, 440

Fig. 10   Rocker arm and shaft assembly installed. 8-273, 361, 383, 400, 413, 426, 440

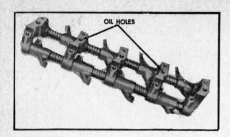

Fig. 9A   Rocker arm shaft assembly. V8-426 HP2 engine

in No. 2 and 4 positions.

NOTE: Use extreme care in tightening the bolts so that valve lifters have time to bleed down to their operating length. Bulged lifter bodies, bent push rods and permanent noisy operation may result if lifters are forced down too rapidly.

3. Installation should be as shown in Fig. 10.

426 Hemi-Charger Service Note

This engine has three different rocker shaft brackets and it is very important that they are positioned as shown in Fig. 11. Because the oil feed holes in the cylinder block are the number 2 and 4 positions, and the number 1 and 3 positions do not have cylinder head gasket beads, mis-location of the brackets can cause either of the following conditions:
1. No. 1 and 3 brackets installed in No. 2 and 4 positions will cause a dry cylinder head.
2. No. 2 and 4 brackets installed in No. 1 and 3 positions will cause a cylinder head gasket leak.

VALVE GUIDES
Non-Removable Type

Valves operate in guide holes bored directly in the cylinder head. When valve stem-to-guide clearance becomes excessive, valves with oversize stems of .005″ .015″ and .030″ are available for service replacement. When necessary to install valves with oversize stems the valve bores should be reamed to provide the proper operating clearance.

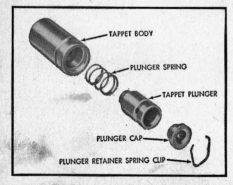

Fig. 12   Hydraulic valve lifter

V8s With Removable Guides

Remove the old guides by driving them out through the top of the cylinder head. Drive the new guides in place by driving them up through the valve port opening.

When installing exhaust valve guides, make certain that the oil holes in the top of the guides are facing up.

After valve guides are properly installed, ream each guide to the clearances listed in the Valve Specification Table.

VALVE LIFTERS
6-170, 198, 225

After taking off rocker arm and shaft assembly, lift out push rods. The valve lifters may then be removed with a suitably long magnet rod. If the lifters cannot be removed with the magnet rod, a special tool (C-3661) may be used, Fig. 13. Insert the tool through the push rod opening in the cylinder head and into lifter. Turn the handle to expand the tool in the lifter, then with a twisting motion remove the lifter from its bore.

NOTE

In the aluminum engine, the valve lifters operate in machined bores in the engine and may be rebored to accommodate oversize lifters of .001″, .008″ and .030″.

HYDRAULIC LIFTERS
Lifter, Replace

Chrysler Tool is available for this operation. To remove the lifter, insert the tool in the lifter body. (This portion of the tool can be used to remove lifters without a varnish build-up around the bottom of the body.) Lift the lifter out of the bore, Fig. 12. If they are struck proceed as follows:

Slide the puller portion of the tool through the cylinder head push rod holes and seat it firmly in the top of the lifter. Insert the puller pin through the body and tool shaft in the holes provided, Fig. 13. Grasp the tool handle and pull the lifter out of the bore as shown.

Checking Hydraulic Lifter Static Clearance

After performing a valve grind job or replacing a cylinder head the hydraulic lifters should be collapsed and the valve stem-to-rocker arm clearance checked. Each lifter should be checked individually to guard against differences in machining or wear variables.

Valve stem-to-rocker arm clearance should check within the limits given in the *Valve Specifications* chart. If the actual measured clearance is less than the minimum specified, very likely the valve has been ground down too much and a new valve should be installed.

When the actual measured clearance is more than the maximum specified, the valve face should be ground down further to bring it at or below the maximum static clearance specified.

To check the clearance a special spanner-type tool is commercially available to apply pressure on the rocker arm to

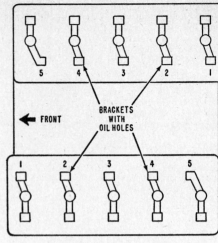

Fig. 11   Valve rocker shaft bracket locations. V8-426 Hemi-Charger engine

bleed down the hydraulic lifter until the plunger is completely bottomed. Of course, checking must be done with the lifter on the heel of the cam. If the special tool is not available, a stiff rod, such as a socket extension, and a length of wire can be used to collapse the lifter. Wire one end of the rod to the rocker arm as close to the valve stem as possible and apply pressure to the other end until the lifter is collapsed.

TIMING CHAIN COVER

NOTE: In order to replace the cover oil seal the cover must be removed from the engine.

6-170, 198, 225

1. To remove cover, drain cooling system and remove radiator and fan.
2. Remove vibration damper with a puller.
3. Loosen oil pan bolts to allow clearance and remove chain case cover.
4. Reverse above procedure to install cover.

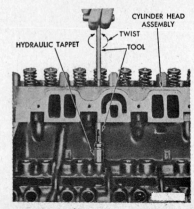

Fig. 13   Removing stuck valve lifter

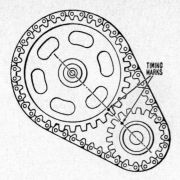

Fig. 15   Valve timing marks aligned for correct valve timing. All Sixes

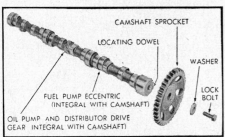

Fig. 17   Camshaft and related parts. 6-170, 198, 225

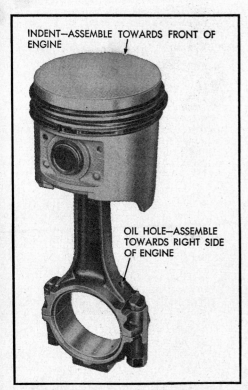

Fig. 19   Piston and rod assembly. 6-170, 198, 225 engines with cast iron block. On aluminum block engines assemble rod to piston with oil hole toward left side of engine

V8-361, 383, 400, 426, 440

1. Drain cooling system.
2. Remove radiator, fan and belt.
3. Remove water pump and housing as an assembly.
4. Remove crankshaft bolt and pulley from vibration damper and remove damper with a puller.
5. Remove key from crankshaft. On V8-426 Hemi-Charger, remove two front pan bolts.
6. Remove chain case cover and gasket. *Use extreme caution to avoid damaging the oil pan gasket; if damaged it will be necessary to remove the oil pan in order to install a new pan gasket.*

V8-273, 318, 340, 360

1. Remove radiator, fan and belt.
2. Remove water pump and housing as a unit.
3. Remove crankshaft pulley.
4. Remove key from crankshaft.
5. Remove fuel pump.
6. Remove chain case cover and gasket, *using extreme caution to avoid damaging oil pan gasket otherwise oil pan will have to be removed. It is normal to find particles of neoprene collected between crankshaft seal retainer and oil slinger.*

TIMING CHAIN
6-170, 198, 225

1. After removing chain case cover as outlined above, take off camshaft sprocket attaching bolt.
2. Remove chain with camshaft sprocket.
3. Clean all parts and dry with compressed air.
4. Inspect timing chain for broken or damaged links. Inspect sprockets for cracks and chipped, worn or damaged teeth.

Installation

1. Turn crankshaft so sprocket timing mark is toward and directly in line with centerline of camshaft.
2. Temporarily install camshaft sprocket. Rotate camshaft to position sprocket timing mark toward and directly in line with centerline of crankshaft; then remove camshaft sprocket.
3. Place chain on crankshaft sprocket and position camshaft sprocket in chain so sprocket can be installed with timing marks aligned without moving camshaft, Fig. 15.
4. Install parts removed in reverse order of removal.

V8 Engines

To install chain and sprockets, lay both the camshaft and crankshaft sprockets on the bench. Position the sprockets so that the timing marks are next to each other. Place the chain on both sprockets, then push the gears apart as far as the chain will permit. Use a straightedge to form a line through the exact centers of both gears. The timing marks must be on this line, Fig. 16.

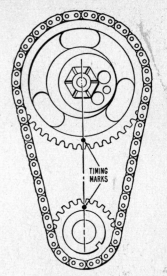

Fig. 16   Valve timing marks aligned for correct valve timing. All V8s

This is the same procedure as in previous models, except that now the alignment is done on the bench rather than on the engine.

Slide the chain with both sprockets on the camshaft and crankshaft at the same time; then recheck the alignment.

CAMSHAFT & BEARINGS
6-170, 198, 225

The camshaft is supported by four precision type, steel backed, babbitt-lined bearings. Rearward thrust is taken by the rear face of the sprocket hub contacting the front of the engine block.

The camshaft, Fig. 17, can be removed

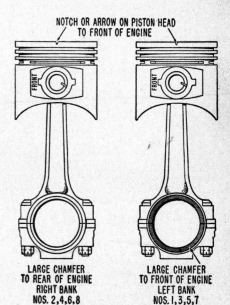

Fig. 20   Piston and rod assembly, V8. On V8-426 Hemi, bearing tangs must face outboard

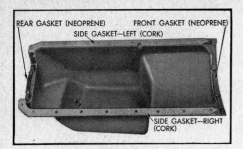

Fig. 21 Location of oil pan gaskets. 6-170, 198, 225

after removing the grille, radiator and timing chain. To remove the camshaft bearings, the torque converter (or flywheel) must also be removed.

1. Remove valve lifters, oil pump and distributor.
2. Slide camshaft out of engine.
3. Remove welch plug back of rear camshaft bearing.
4. Remove bearings with suitable puller equipment.
5. Install new bearings, being sure the oil holes in bearings line up with the corresponding oil holes in the crankcase.

V8 Engines

To remove the camshaft, remove all valve lifters, timing chain and sprockets. Remove distributor and oil pump-distributor drive gear. Remove fuel pump and see that push rod has moved away from eccentric drive cam. Withdraw the camshaft from the engine, using care to see that the cam lobes do not damage the camshaft bearings.

If camshaft bearings are to be replaced, it is recommended that the engine be removed from the chassis and the crankshaft taken out in order that any chips or foreign material may be removed from the oil passages.

PISTON & ROD, ASSEMBLE

6-170, 198, 225

Piston and rod assemblies must be installed as shown in Fig. 19.

V8 Engines

When installing piston and rod assemblies in the cylinders, the compression ring gaps should be diametrically opposite one another and not in line with the oil ring gap. The oil ring expander gap should be toward the outside of the "V" of the engine. The oil ring gap should be turned toward the inside of the engine "V".

Immerse the piston head and rings in clean engine oil and, with a suitable piston ring compressor, insert the piston and rod assembly into the bore. Tap the piston down into the bore, using the handle of a hammer.

Assemble the pistons to the rods as shown in Fig. 20.

PISTONS, PINS & RINGS

Pistons are available in standard sizes and the following oversizes: V8-440: 005, .020". All others: .005, .020, .040".

Pins are available in the following oversizes: V8-273, 318, 426, .003, .008". Not furnished on all other engines.

Rings are available in the following oversizes: 1966-69 Six and all V8s, std. to .009, .020-.029, .040-.049".

MAIN & ROD BEARINGS

Main bearings are furnished in standard sizes and the following undersizes: 1966-72 Six, .001, .002, .010". 1966-72 V8s, 001, .002, .003, .010, .012".

Rod bearings are furnished in standard sizes and the following undersizes: Six, .001, .002, .003, .010". V8s, .001, .002, .003, .010, .012".

CRANKSHAFT REAR OIL SEAL

SERVICE BULLETIN

V8-273, 318 SEAL: When oil seal replacement is necessary on these engines, thoroughly clean the bearing cap and block to assure proper seating of the cap. Install a new rope seal in the conventional manner. Then apply an All Purpose cement (Mopar 1316241) on the joint face on the ends of the rope and 1/4" to each side of the rubber side gaskets. Do not use sealer on the rope where it contacts the crankshaft or near the bearing shell.

This new procedure using sealer at the rear main bearing rope seal and side gasket area entered production (effective November 17, 1964) and all 273 and 318 engines.

SERVICE BULLETIN

V8-361, 383 SIDE SEALS: The side seals used with the crankshaft rear bearing retainer on these engines should be installed in the retainer as rapidly as possible as they are made from a material that expands rapidly when oiled. Apply mineral spirits or kerosene to the seals and install them in the grooves immediately. Install seal retainer and torque to 30 ft-lbs. Failure to pre-oil seals will result in an oil leak.

OIL PAN

CAUTION: *Engine oil pan bolts on all V8-361, 383, 426, 440 engines are 13/16" long with the exception of two bolts at the rear center of the oil pan. The two rear center bolts are 9/16" long and thread into the aluminum seal retainer. Do not use longer bolts than 9/16" at this location as they will bottom in the aluminum seal retainer and, if forced in may strip the threads and damage the seal retainer, causing an oil leak.*

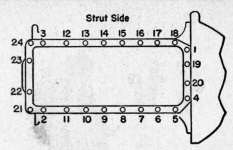

Fig. 22 Tighten oil pan screws to 200 inch pounds in the sequence shown. 6-170, 198, 225

1966-72 Chrysler & Imperial, 1966-72 Dodge & Plymouth V8-361, 383, 400, 426, 440

1. Disconnect battery cable and drain crankcase.
2. Raise car on hoist and disconnect steering linkage from idler arm and pitman arm.
3. Remove outlet vent pipe and disconnect exhaust pipe branches from manifolds.
4. Remove clamp attaching exhaust pipe to extension and remove exhaust pipe.
5. Remove converter dust shield.
6. Remove oil pan bolts and turn flywheel until counterweight and connecting rods at the front end of crankshaft are at their highest position to provide clearance, and lower the pan. Turn the pan to clear oil screen and suction pipe.

1966-72 Dart & Valiant Six

1. Raise car and drain oil pan.
2. Use a puller to remove steering and idler arm ball joints from steering linkage center link.
3. Remove dust shield and engine mount stud nuts.
4. Lower vehicle and remove horns and mounting brackets, then disconnect battery ground cable.
5. Raise engine from 1½ to 2 inches, using a lifting rig.
6. Again raise vehicle, then remove oil pan.
7. When installing pan, refer to Figs. 21 and 22.

1966-72 Dodge & Plymouth Six

1. Remove oil dipstick, disconnect battery ground cable. Raise vehicle and drain oil.
2. Use a puller to remove steering and idler arm ball joints from steering center link. Remove dust shield.
3. Remove oil pan bolts, rotate engine crankshaft to clear counterweights, then remove oil pan.
4. When installing pan, refer to Figs. 21 and 22.

1966-72 V8-273, 318, 340, 360

1. Disconnect battery ground cable.
2. Remove oil level dipstick.
3. Raise vehicle and drain oil.
4. Remove engine-to-torque converter left housing brace.

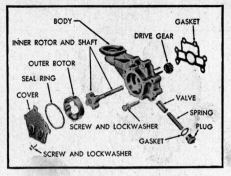

Fig. 23   Oil pump. 6-170, 198, 6-225

5. Remove steering and idler arm ball joints from steering center link.
6. Remove exhaust crossover pipe from exhaust manifolds and leave it hang without disconnecting it from muffler.
7. On some models it will be necessary to remove crossover pipe.
8. Unfasten and remove oil pan.

OIL PUMP, REPLACE

1967-72 Six Cylinder

1. Drain radiator and disconnect upper and lower hoses.
2. Remove fan shroud (if equipped).
3. Raise vehicle on a hoist, support front of engine with a jack stand place under right front corner of engine oil pan. *Do not support engine at crankshaft pulley or vibration damper.*
4. Remove front engine mounts.
5. Raise engine 1½ to 2 inches.
6. Remove oil filter, pump attaching bolts and remove pump assembly.

V8 Engines

On 273, 318, 340, 360 engines, remove oil pump from rear main bearing cap.

On 361, 383, 400, 426, 440 engines, unfasten oil pump from engine and remove pump and filter assembly from bottom of engine.

1966 Six Cylinder

1. Drain radiator and disconnect hoses.
2. Disconnect fuel line at pump inlet, and throttle linkage at carburetor.
3. With car on a hoist, support front of engine with a jack stand placed under right front corner of oil pan (not crankshaft pulley).
4. Cut a piece of 2x4 eight inches long.
5. Raise front of engine just high enough to insert the wood block between front rail and "K" member and right front lower portion of oil pan. Position wood block so one end is against edge of right front engine mount support where it is welded to the "K" member.
6. Lower front of engine so it rests on wood block near right front corner of oil pan.
7. Exert light pressure with a pry bar against right side of engine. This will cause wood block and front of engine to slide to the left about

1½", and will also cause engine to tip slightly toward the left.
8. Remove oil filter, oil pump cover and outer pump rotor. *The outer rotor will drop out when pump cover is removed, so be sure to catch it so it will not be damaged by falling.*
9. There should now be enough clearance between engine and "K" member to allow removal of oil pump.
10. After repairing, install pump, without outer rotor and cover, using a new gasket.
11. Center engine in its original position and, using a jack stand to support it at the front end, install front engine mounts.
12. Connect fuel line, throttle linkage, radiator hoses and refill radiator.

OIL PUMP REPAIRS

6-170, 198, 225

To disassemble, remove the pump cover seal ring, Fig. 23. Press off the drive gear, supporting the gear to keep load off aluminum body. Remove rotor and shaft and lift out outer pump rotor. Remove oil pressure relief valve plug and lift out spring and plunger. Remove oil pressure sending unit.

Inspection

1. The rotor contact area and the bores for the shaft and valve in the pump body should be smooth, free from scratches, scoring or excessive wear.
2. The pump cover should be smooth, flat and free from scoring or ridges. Lay a straightedge across the cover. If a .0015" feeler gauge can be inserted under the straightedge, the cover should be replaced.
3. All surfaces of the outer rotor should be smooth and uniform, free from ridges, scratches or uneven wear. Discard a rotor less than .649" thick and/or less than 2.469" in diameter.
4. The inner rotor and shaft assembly should be smooth, free from scoring and uneven wear. Discard rotors less than .649" thick.
5. Place outer rotor in pump body and measure clearance between rotor and body. Discard pump body if clearance is more than .014".
6. Install inner rotor and shaft in pump body. Shaft should turn freely but without side play. If clearance between rotor teeth is more than .010", replace both rotors.
7. Measure rotor end clearance. If feeler gauge of more than .004" can be inserted between straightedge and rotors, install a new pump body.
8. The oil pressure relief valve should be smooth, free from scratches or scoring, and should be a free fit in its bore.
9. Relief valve springs are painted either gray, red or brown to denote free lengths of 2.19, 2.29 and 2.39 inches. Rather than change the length, replace a spring with one of the same color.

Assemble and Install

1. With pump rotors in body, press drive gear on shaft, flush with end of

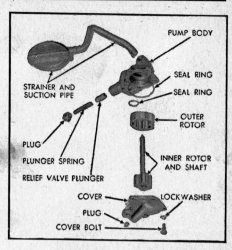

Fig. 24   Oil pump. V8-361, 383, 413, 426, 440

shaft.
2. Install seal ring in groove in body and install cover. Tighten bolts to 10 ft. lbs. Test pump for free turning.
3. Install oil pressure relief valve spring. Use new washer (gasket) and tighten plug securely.
4. If pump shaft turns freely, remove pump cover and outer rotor before installation of pump on engine.
5. Install oil pressure sending unit and tighten to 60 inch lbs. (5 ft. lbs.)
6. Using a new gasket, install pump on engine and tighten bolts to 200 inch lbs. (16 ft. lbs.)
7. Install oil filter reservoir on pump. Install filter element and tighten cover nuts to 25 ft. lbs.
8. Connect oil pressure sending unit wire.
9. Complete the installation by reversing steps as given under Oil Pump, Replace.

V8 Engines

After removing the pump from the engine it should be disassembled, cleaned and inspected for wear, Fig. 24.

1. Remove the cotter pin holding the oil strainer to the oil suction pipe. Then remove the pipe from the pump body.
2. Remove the pump cover and discard the oil seal ring.
3. Remove pump rotor and shaft and lift out rotor body.
4. Remove oil pressure relief valve plug and lift out the spring and plunger.
5. Wash all parts in cleaning solvent and inspect carefully for damage or wear.
6. The mating face of the oil pump cover should be smooth. If it is scratched or grooved, the cover should be replaced with a new one.
7. Check for excessive cover-to-rotor wear by laying a straight edge across the cover surface. If a .0015" feeler gauge can be inserted between cover and straight edge, the cover should be discarded and a new one installed.
8. Slide rotor body and rotor into pump body and then place a straight edge across the face of the pump body

between the bolt holes. If a feeler gauge of less than .003″ or more than .006″ can be inserted between the rotors and straight edge, install a new pump body.

9. Remove the pump rotor and shaft, leaving rotor body in pump cavity. Press rotor body to one side with the fingers and measure the clearance between rotor and pump bodies. If it is more than .014″, install a new pump body.

10. Check the clearance between the pump rotor and rotor body. If the measurement is more than .014″, install a new pump rotor and rotor body.

11. Check the oil pump relief valve plunger for scoring and free operation in its bore. If the plunger is scored, install a new one.

WATER PUMP, REPLACE
Chrysler & Imperial

Drain cooling system, and on air conditioned cars only remove upper half of fan shroud. Loosen power steering pump or idler pulley, and generator. Remove all belts, fan, space and pulley.

On air conditioned cars, remove pulley from water pump fan hub, loosen all nuts from fan and remove the fan drive.

On all models, remove bolts holding water pump body to housing and remove water pump.

Dodge & Plymouth

To remove the water pump, drain cooling system and loosen the fan belt. Remove the fan, spacer, pulley and belt. Remove the pump inlet hose and the heater hose. Remove clamp from by-pass hose. Remove water pump bolts and push pump body down and off the by-pass hose.

Service Bulletin

CORE HOLE PLUG SIZES: When replacing a cup-type core hole plug in an engine, the size of the hole in the cylinder head, water jacket or rear bearing bore for the camshaft should be checked. At these locations a $\frac{1}{16}$″ oversize hole is sometimes bored in production and an oversize core plug installed.

Core plugs $\frac{1}{16}$″ oversize are available for replacement should they be required at these locations.

Service Bulletin

On late 1966 and early 1967 273 and 318 engines, two water pump chain case cover gaskets are used. When necessary to remove and install the water pump on either of these engines, be sure to install two service gaskets for proper sealing.

FUEL PUMP, REPLACE

NOTE: All 1972 Imperials sold in California will be equipped with a Bendix electric fuel pump. The pump is mounted just ahead of the fuel tank on the inside of the main rail.

SERVICE NOTE: Before installing the pump, it is good practice to crank the engine so that the nose of the camshaft eccentric is out of the way of the fuel pump rocker arm when the pump is installed. In this way there will be the least amount of tension on the rocker arm, thereby easing the installation of the pump.

1. Remove all gasket material from the pump and block gasket surfaces. Apply sealer to both sides of new gasket.
2. Position gasket on pump flange and hold pump in position against its mounting surface. Make sure rocker arm is riding on camshaft eccentric.
3. Press pump tight against its mounting. Install retaining screws and tighten them alternately.
4. Connect fuel lines. Then operate engine and check for leaks.

Clutch and Transmission Section

> **NOTE:** 1972 linkage adjustment information is in this section. Repair procedures on both automatic and manual shift transmissions are covered elsewhere in this manual. Procedures for removing automatic transmissions as well as linkage adjustments on 1966-71 models are included in the automatic transmission chapters. See Chapter Index.

CLUTCH PEDAL, ADJUST
1966-72 All Cars

1. Inspect condition of clutch pedal rubber stop, if stop is damaged install a new one.
2. Where necessary, disconnect interlock clutch rod at transmission end.
3. Adjust linkage by turning self-locking adjusting nut to provide $\frac{5}{32}$″ free movement at outer end of fork. This movement will provide the prescribed one-inch free play at pedal.
4. Assemble interlock clutch rod (if used) to transmission pawl.

CLUTCH, REPLACE

Unless special clutch rebuilding equipment is available, it is recommended that the clutch assembly be exchanged for a rebuilt unit should the clutch require rebuilding. The driven disc, however, may be replaced without special equipment. If clutch rebuilding equipment is available, follow the equipment manufacturer's instructions.

Removal

1. Remove transmission and clutch pan.
2. Pull out release bearing and sleeve.
3. Mark clutch cover and flywheel so they may be assembled in the same relative position and thus maintain original balance.
4. Remove cap screws which retain

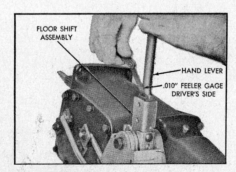

Fig. 1 Removing floor shift handle. 1969-72

clutch cover to flywheel. Loosen each screw a few turns in succession until cover is free.
5. Clutch assembly and driven disc may now be removed from the housing.

Installation

1. Coat the pilot bearing in crankshaft with wheel bearing grease.
2. Clean surfaces of flywheel and pressure plate, making certain no oil or grease remains on these parts.
3. Hold cover plate and disc in place and insert a special clutch aligning tool or a spare clutch shaft through the hub of the disc and into the crankshaft pilot bearing.
4. Bolt clutch cover loosely to flywheel, being sure marks previously made are lined up.
5. To avoid distortion of clutch cover, tighten cover bolts a few turns each in progression until all are tight. The final tightening should be 15-20 ft-lbs. for $\frac{5}{16}$″ bolts and 30 ft-lbs. for $\frac{3}{8}$″ bolts.
6. Install transmission by guiding it into place with guide studs inserted in

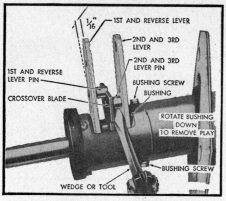

Fig. 2 Gearshift lever adjustment. 1966-69 Three Speed Transmission

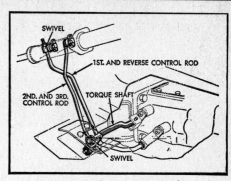

Fig. 3 Gearshift controls. 1966-72 Three Speed Transmission

the two top holes of the housing.

7. Adjust clutch pedal free travel.

THREE SPEED TRANSMISSION, REPLACE

1966-71 Chrysler, 1966-72 Dodge & Plymouth

1. Drain lubricant from transmission.
2. Disconnect propeller shaft, speedometer cable and housing and gearshift control rods.
3. Remove speedometer cable with hand so that housing is not crushed.
4. Disconnect back-up lamp switch leads (if so equipped) and if necessary, loosen exhaust system for clearance.
5. Support engine with a jack or suitable fixture against underside of oil pan flange.
6. Raise engine slightly and disconnect extension housing from removable center crossmember.
7. Support transmission with a suitable jack. Then tap out four long bolts and remove center crossmember. Remove bolts that attach transmission to clutch housing.
8. Slide transmission rearward until clutch shaft clears clutch disc before lowering transmission. Lower and remove transmission.
9. Reverse removal procedure to install.

FOUR SPEED TRANSMISSION, REPLACE

1967-72 Dodge & Plymouth

1. Remove console and shift components.

NOTE: On 1969 models, the shift lever is removed by using a .010" feeler gauge as shown in Fig. 1 to release internal spring clip. When reinstalling lever, push it down into shift unit far enough for spring to click and lock lever in place.

2. Drain fluid from transmission.
3. Disconnect propeller shaft at rear universal joint and carefully pull

yoke out of extension housing. *Be careful not to scratch or nick ground surface on sliding spline yoke during removal and installation of shaft.*

4. Disconnect speedometer cable and stop light switch leads.
5. Disconnect left-hand exhaust pipe (dual exhaust) from manifold.
6. Disconnect parking cable where necessary.
7. Support rear of engine with a jack.
8. Raise engine slightly and disconnect extension housing from removable center crossmember.
9. Support transmission with a suitable jack and remove center crossmember.
10. Remove transmission-to-clutch housing bolts.
11. Slide transmission rearward and out of vehicle.
12. Reverse procedure to install.

1966 Dodge & Plymouth

1. Remove console trim plate.
2. Remove shift lever boot screws and slide boot up on lever.
3. Shift transmission into reverse, lubricate lever opening in lower boot and push boot down over bolt heads. Unscrew two bolts and remove shift lever.
4. On Non-Console type floor shifts, disconnect transmission shift rods.
5. Drain transmission lubricant.
6. Disconnect propeller shaft, speedometer cable and pinion. Remove cable by hand to avoid crushing housing.
7. Disconnect left-hand exhaust pipe (dual exhaust) from exhaust manifold.
8. Disconnect parking brake control cable and backup light switch at connector (if equipped).
9. Support engine against underside of oil pan flange.
10. Raise engine slightly and remove rear crossmember.
11. Support transmission, then remove attaching bolts.
12. Rotate transmission until shift housing and stub lever clear, then slide transmission to the rear and downward out of vehicle.
13. Reverse procedure to install.

SHIFT LINKAGE, ADJUST THREE SPEED TRANS.

1966-72

1. With 2-3 control rod disconnected from lever on steering column and 1st-reverse rod disconnected from transmission lever, position both transmission levers in neutral.

NOTE: The neutral detent balls must be engaged to make this adjustment. To check this, start engine (clutch disengaged) then release clutch slowly.

2. Inspect fore and aft movement of shift levers in steering column. If movement at outer end of levers exceeds $1/16$", loosen two upper bushing screws, Fig. 2, and rotate bushing downward until all free play of levers

has been removed. Then retighten bushing screws.

3. Wedge a screwdriver between crossover blade and the 2-3 lever so that crossover blade is engaged with both lever crossover pins.
4. Adjust length of 2-3 control rod until stud shaft of control rod and swivel enters hole in column lever, Fig. 3. Install washer and clip and tighten swivel lock nut. During the above setting the 2-3 control rod should be adjusted also to position selector lever on column 5°-10° above horizontal.
5. Slide clamp and swivel (on end of 1st-reverse control rod) either in or out until swivel stub shaft enters hole in transmission lever, Fig. 3. Install washers and clip. Determine middle backlash position in linkage, then tighten control rod lock nut.
6. Remove screwdriver from crossover blade and lever. Then move selector lever through all positions to check adjustments and to insure crossover smoothness.

1966 Dodge & Plymouth

1. With 2-3 control rod disconnected from its lever on the steering column and the 1st-reverse control rod disconnected from transmission lever, position both levers in neutral.
2. Check the axial freedom of shift levers in steering column. If outer end of levers move more than $1/16$" as shown in Fig. 2, loosen two upper bushing screws and rotate plastic bushing until all free play of levers has been removed.
3. Tighten bushing screws securely.
4. Install a wedge or screwdriver between cross-over blade and 2-3 lever, Fig. 2, so that cross-over blade is engaged with both lever cross-over pins.
5. Adjust swivel on end of 2-3 control rod until stub shaft of swivel enters hole in column lever. Tighten swivel nut.
6. Slide clamp and swivel on end of 1st-reverse control rod either in or out until swivel stub shaft enters hole in transmission lever.

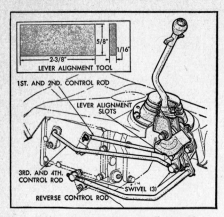

Fig. 6 Gearshift linkage adjustment. 1966-68 four speed transmission

SHIFT LINKAGE, ADJUST FOUR SPEED TRANS.

1966-72 Four Speed Trans.

NOTE: 1970-72 floor shift linkages incorporate a transmission lock rod. This rod is adjusted after the shift linkage as follows:

1. Loosen rod swivel clamp bolt.
2. Place transmission in reverse.
3. Align steering column locating slots and install a suitable tool to hold position.
4. Tighten clamp bolt. Column should now lock in reverse but not in any other gear.

---

1. Install lever alignment tool to hold levers in neutral, Figs. 5, 6.
2. Shift transmission into neutral, then disconnect all control rods from transmission levers.
3. Insert lever alignment tool through slots in levers, making sure it is through all levers and against the back plate.
4. Adjust length of control rods so they enter transmission levers freely without any rearward or forward movement.
5. Secure adjustment and remove tool.
6. Check linkage for ease of shifting into all gears and for crossover smoothness.

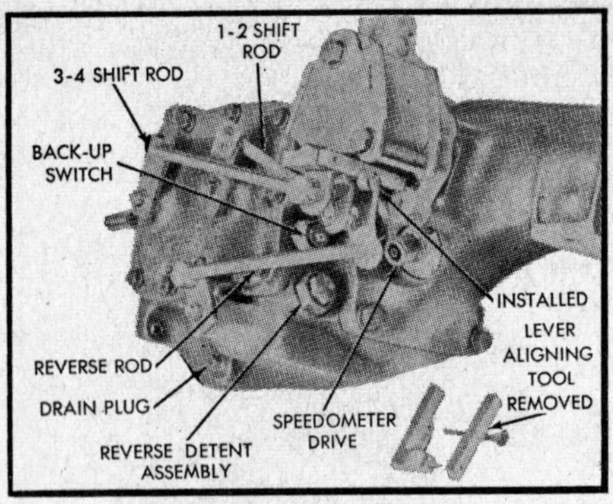

1972 AUTO. TRANS. LINKAGE, ADJUST

Column Shift

1. Place gearshift lever in PARK and lock steering column with key.
2. Move control lever on transmission all the way to rear (PARK).
3. Set adjustable rod to proper length with no load in either direction.
4. Check as follows:
   a. Shift effort must be free and detents feel crisp. All gate stops must be positive.
   b. Detent position must be close enough to gate stops in neutral and drive to assure that hand lever will not remain out of detent when placed against gate and then released.

c. Key start must occur with shift lever held down against PARK gate.

Console Shift

1. At steering column upper end, line up locating slots in bottom of shift housing and bearing housing. Install suitable tool to hold alignment and lock column with ignition key.
2. Place console lever in PARK and move shift control lever on transmission all the way to rear (PARK).
3. Set adjustable rods to proper length with no load applied in either direction.
4. Check adjustment as described above for column shift.

Fig. 5 Gearshift linkage adjustment. 1969 four speed transmission

Labels: 1-2 SHIFT ROD; 3-4 SHIFT ROD; BACK-UP SWITCH; REVERSE ROD; DRAIN PLUG; REVERSE DETENT ASSEMBLY; SPEEDOMETER DRIVE; INSTALLED LEVER ALIGNING TOOL REMOVED

Rear Axle, Propeller Shaft & Brakes

NOTE: Figs. 1 and 2 illustrate the various rear axle assembles used on these cars. When necessary to overhaul any of these units, refer to the **Rear Axle Specifications** table in this chapter.

INTEGRAL TYPE REAR AXLE

Two types of integral carrier axles are used. In both types, the drive pinion is mounted in two opposing tapered roller bearings which are preloaded by a spacer positioned between them.

In the unit shown in Fig. 1, used from 1966 through 1972, the differential is supported by two tapered roller side bearings. These bearings are preloaded by spacers located between the bearings and carrier housing. The differential assembly is positioned for ring and pinion backlash by varying these spacers.

Axle shafts in this unit are held in place by retainers at the outer ends of the shafts. These retainers are bolted through the brake backing plates to the rear axle tubes.

In the unit shown in Fig. 2, introduced in 1969, the differential is also supported by two tapered roller bearings. A threaded differential bearing adjuster is located in each bearing pedestal cap to eliminate differential side play, adjust and maintain ring and pinion backlash and provide a means of obtaining differential bearing preload.

Axles are retained by means of a "C" washer which is installed into a groove in the inner end of the axle shaft inside the differential unit.

On both these units, a removable stamped steel cover, bolted to the rear of the carrier, permits inspection and service of the differential without removal of the complete axle assembly from the vehicle.

Axle Shaft, Renew (Fig. 1 Type)

1. With wheel removed, remove clips holding brake drum on wheel studs and remove drum.
2. Disconnect brake lines at wheel cylinders.
3. Using access hole in axle flange, remove retainer nuts from end of housing.
4. Remove axle shaft and brake as-

sembly, using a slide hammer-type puller.
5. Remove brake assembly from axle shaft with care to avoid damaging shaft in seal contact area.
6. Remove oil seal from axle housing.
7. *Remove axle shaft bearings only when necessary. Removal of bearings makes them unfit for further use.*
8. *Axle shaft end play is pre-set and not adjustable. End play is accomplished by the amount of end play built into the bearings. The two axle housing brake support plate gaskets on each side are used for sealing purposes only. Always replace the gaskets once they have been removed.*
9. Press bearing and collar on shaft firmly against shoulders on shaft.
10. Install new oil seal in housing.
11. Install brake assembly on axle housing and carefully slide axle shaft through oil seal and into side gear splines.
12. Tap end of axle shaft lightly to position axle shaft bearing into bearing bore and attach retainer plate to housing.
13. Install brake drums and wheels.

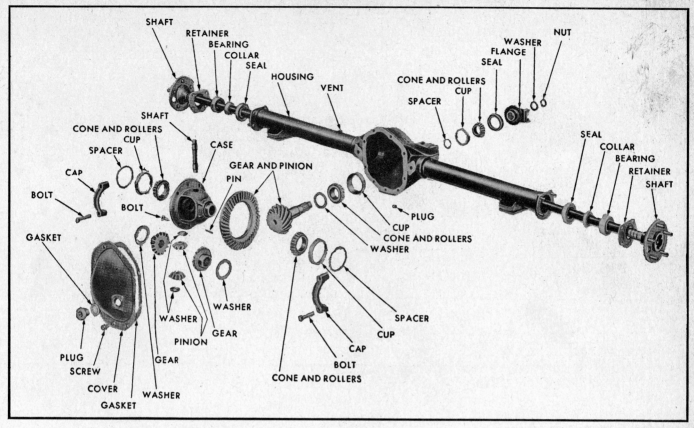

Fig. 1   Integral rear axle. 1966-69

Axle Shaft, Renew (Fig. 2 Type)

1. With wheel and brake drum removed, loosen differential housing cover and drain lubricant. Remove cover.
2. Turn differential case to make pinion shaft lock screw accessible and remove lock screw and shaft.
3. Push axle shaft inward toward center of car and remove "C" washer from groove in axle shaft, Fig. 3.
4. Remove axle shaft from housing, being careful not to damage the axle bearing, which will remain in the housing.
5. The axle bearing and/or seal can now be removed if necessary.
6. Reverse procedure to install.

REMOVABLE CARRIER TYPE

In these rear axles, Figs. 4 and 5, the drive pinion is mounted in two tapered roller bearings. The bearings are preloaded by a spacer and shims behind the front bearing. The drive pinion is positioned by an adjusting washer between the head of the drive pinion and the rear pinion bearing. The front bearing is held in place by a large washer and nut.

The differential is supported in the carrier by two tapered roller side bearings. These bearings are preloaded by two threaded ring nuts between the bearings and the pedestals. The differential assembly is positioned for proper ring gear and pinion backlash by varying the adjustment of these ring nuts. The differential case houses two side gears in mesh with two pinions mounted on a pinion shaft which is held in place by a lock pin. The side gears and pinions are backed up by thrust washers. Side thrust of

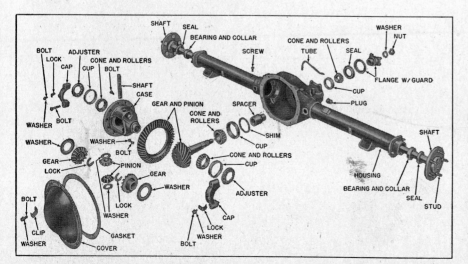

Fig. 2   Integral "C" washer type rear axle. 1969-71

Fig. 3   Location of "C" washer locks

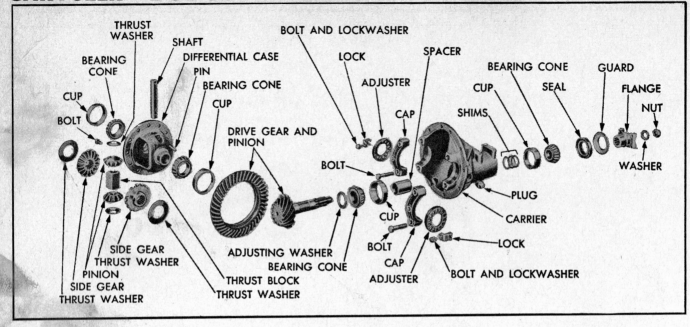

Fig. 4   Removable type rear axle assembly with large pinion

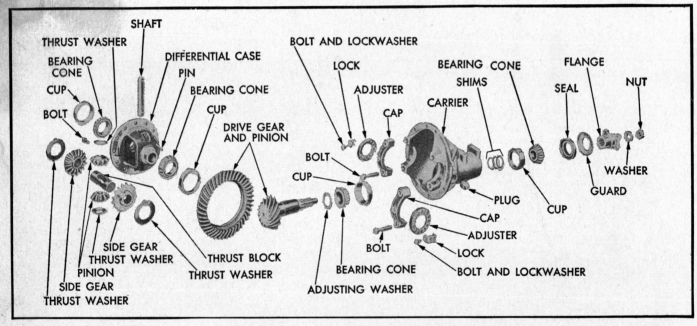

Fig. 5   Removable type rear axle assembly with small pinion

the wheels is transferred from one axle shaft to the other by means of a thrust block in the center of the differential case.

Carrier, Remove & Replace

It is not necessary to remove the rear axle assembly for any normal repairs. The axle shafts and carrier assembly can easily be moved from the vehicle, leaving the rear axle housing in place.
1. Remove axle shafts as outlined below.
2. Disconnect rear universal joint and move propeller shaft out of the way. Support shaft to relieve strain on

the front universal joint.
3. Remove lubricant from axle housing with a suction gun.
4. Remove attaching nuts and lift carrier assembly out of axle housing.
5. Reverse removal procedure to install.

Axle Shaft, Renew (1966-70)

1. With wheels removed, remove clips holding brake drum on axle shaft studs and remove brake drum.
2. Using access hole in axle shaft flange, remove retainer nuts. The right shaft with threaded adjuster in retainer plate will have a lock

under one of the studs that should be removed at this time, Fig. 6.
3. Remove parking brake strut.
4. Attach axle shaft remover tool, Fig. 7, to axle shaft flange and remove axle shaft. Remove brake assembly and foam gaskets.
5. Remove oil seal, Fig. 8.
6. Wipe axle shaft housing seal bore clean and install a new seal, Fig. 9.

Disassembly

To prevent the possibility of damaging axle shaft seal surface, slide a protective sleeve over seal surface next to bearing collar, Fig. 10.

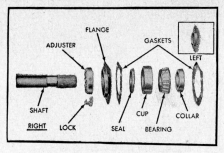

Fig. 6   Axle shaft disassembled

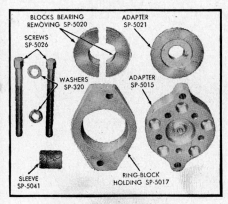

Fig. 7   Tool set for removing axle shaft

1. Position axle shaft bearing collar on a heavy vise and, using a chisel, cut deep grooves into retaining collar at 90-degree intervals, as shown in Fig. 10. This will enlarge bore of collar and permit it to be driven off axle shaft.
2. Remove bearing roller retainer flange by cutting off lower edge with a chisel, Fig. 11.

Fig. 10   Notching bearing retainer collar

Fig. 11   Removing roller retainer

3. Grind a section off flange of inner bearing cone, Fig. 12, and remove bearing rollers, Fig. 13.
4. Pull bearing roller retainer down as far as possible and cut with side cutters and remove, Fig. 14.
5. Remove roller bearing cup and protective sleeve from axle shaft.

CAUTION: Sleeve should not be used as a protector for the seal journal when pressing off bearing cone as it was not designed for this purpose.

6. To avoid scuffing seal journal when bearing cone is being removed, it should be protected by a single wrap of .002" shim stock held in place by a rubber band, Fig. 15.
7. Remove bearing cone with tool set shown in Fig. 7. Tighten bolts of tool alternately until cone is removed, Fig. 16.
8. Remove seal in bearing retainer plate and replace with a new seal.

Assembly

1. Install retainer plate and seal on axle shaft.
2. Install new axle shaft bearing cup, cone and collar on shaft, using tool shown in Fig. 17. Tighten bolts of tool alternately until bearing and collar are seated properly.
3. Inspect axle shaft seal journal for scratches and polish with #600 crocus cloth if necessary.
4. Lubricate wheel bearings with approved grease.

Installation

1. Clean axle shaft flange face and install new gasket followed by brake support plate on left side of axle housing.
2. Install foam gasket on studs of axle housing and slide shaft through oil seal and engage splines in differential side gear.
3. Tap end of axle shaft lightly with a plastic mallet to position axle shaft bearing in housing bearing bore. Position retainer plate over axle housing studs. Install retainer nuts and torque to 30-35 ft-lbs. Start by tightening bottom nut.
4. Repeat Step 1 on right side of axle housing.
5. Back off threaded adjuster on right axle shaft until inner face of adjuster is flush with inner face of retainer plate. Carefully slide axle shaft through oil seal and engage splines in differential side gears.
6. Repeat Step 3.

Axle Shaft End Play

When setting end play both rear wheels must be off the ground, otherwise a false end play setting will occur.
1. Using a dial indicator mounted as shown in Fig. 18, turn the adjuster clockwise until both wheel bearings are seated and there is zero end play in axle shafts. Back off adjuster counterclockwise four notches to establish an axle shaft end play of .013-.023".
2. Tap end of axle shaft lightly with a plastic mallet to seat right wheel bearing cup against adjuster, and rotate axle shaft several revolutions so that a true end play reading is in-

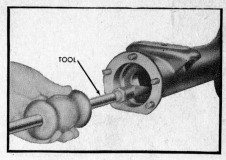

Fig. 8   Removing inner oil seal

Fig. 9   Installing inner oil seal

dicated.
3. Remove one retainer plate nut and install adjuster lock. If tab on lock does not mate with notch in adjuster, turn adjuster slightly until it does. Install nut and torque to 30-35 ft-lbs.
4. Recheck axle shaft end play. If not within prescribed limits, repeat adjustment procedure.

Fig. 12   Flange ground off inner bearing cone

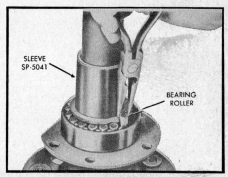

Fig. 13   Removing bearing rollers

Fig. 14   Cutting out bearing retainer

Fig. 15   Seal journal protection

Fig. 16   Removing bearing cone

Fig. 17   Installing bearing and collar

Fig. 18   Measuring axle shaft end play

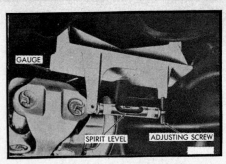

Fig. 20   Measuring rear axle angle. 1966-70 Imperial

Fig. 21   Measuring propeller shaft angle. 1966-70 Imperial

versal to transmission flange and torque retaining nuts to 35 ft. lbs.
4. Align rear of propeller shaft with pinion yoke and position roller and bushing assemblies into seats of pinion yoke.
5. Install bushing clamps and tighten clamp bolts to 170 inch lbs.

Two Piece Shaft, 1966

1. Referring to Fig. 22, remove cross and roller bushing clamps from transmission yoke.
2. Disengage front U-joint cross and roller bushings from yoke.

NOTE: Tie up or otherwise support front end of propeller shaft to prevent damaging center joint.

3. Unfasten rear U-joint from rear axle pinion yoke. Support rear end of shaft.
4. Unfasten center bearing bracket

5. Remove dial indicator and install brake drum, drum retaining clips and wheel.

PROPELLER SHAFT
One Piece Shaft, 1966-69

1. Remove both rear universal joint roller and bushing assembly clamps from pinion yoke. Do not disturb retaining strap holding roller assemblies on cross.
2. If equipped with sliding yoke front joint, lower front of vehicle slightly to prevent loss of transmission oil and pull drive shaft out as an assembly. If equipped with ball and trunnion front joint, disconnect joint from transmission.
3. To install sliding yoke type, carefully slide yoke into splines on transmission output shaft. For ball and trunnion type, connect front uni-

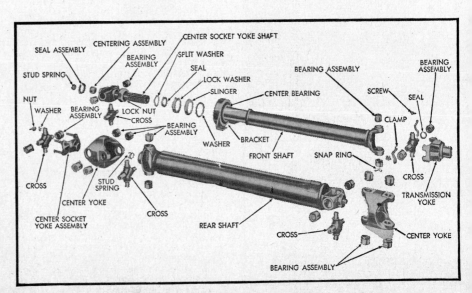

Fig. 22   Two-piece propeller shaft details. 1966 Imperial

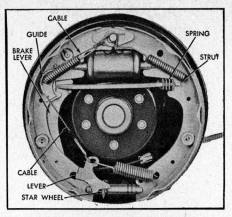

Fig. 23 Right rear brake (10-11 inch) 1966-68. 1969-72 units incorporate overload spring at lever end of cable

from frame crossmember.
5. Reverse procedure to install.

PROP. SHAFT ANGLES
One Piece Shaft, 1966-72

Front Joint Angle
1. Position spirit level gauge and adapter at left side of engine so that adapter pins contact flat surface of engine oil pan flange adjacent to vertical wall of oil pan.
2. Set position of bubble in spirit level.
3. Remove adapter and position gauge firmly along underside of propeller shaft, Fig. 21.
4. Observe position of bubble. Reading should not exceed 2 degrees. If bubble is slightly forward of tolerance, the angle is smaller than specified and need not be corrected. If bubble is rearward of tolerance, angle must be corrected. To reduce angle by one graduation, install ⅛" shim between transmission extension housing and rear engine mount.

Rear Joint Angle
1. Remove pinion bumper plate and position gauge on machined pads with locating pin in rear bolt hole, Fig. 20.
2. Set bubble in spirit level.
3. Remove gauge from carrier and position it firmly along underside of propeller shaft, Fig. 21.
4. Observe position of the bubble. Reading should not exceed 2 degrees. Rear joint angle is corrected by installing wedge type shims between both rear springs and axle housing pads. If bubble is too far forward, insert shim with thick end toward front of car. If bubble is too far rearward, thick end of shim goes to rear of car.

Two Piece Shaft, 1966

When measuring propeller shaft angularity, the vehicle should be in a level position and have no extra weight except that of a full tank of fuel.

CAUTION: The vehicle must be supported

by the wheels or front suspension lower control arms and rear axle housing. Do not use a frame contact hoist.

1. Remove differential carrier rebound bumper and bracket assembly.
2. Hold alignment gauge, Fig. 20, on machined bosses of differential carrier.
3. Adjust the gauge spirit level to center the bubble. The axle pinion housing should be pointing downward at a slight angle. Each time the gauge is used the level must be on the same side of the propeller shaft.
4. Hold gauge on underside of propeller shaft near rear U-joint and note location of bubble in spirit level, Fig. 21. The entire bubble should be within one and three graduations forward from center.
5. If it is necessary to adjust rear joint angle, loosen all U-bolt nuts and install two-degree tapered wedges between both rear springs and axle housing spring pads. If the bubble is forward of the third graduation, install wedges with the thick edge of wedge toward front of vehicle.
6. If the bubble is centered or behind the center graduation, install the wedges with the thick edge toward the rear of the vehicle. Tighten U-bolt nuts to 55 ft-lbs.
7. Temporarily place two passengers in the front seat and one in the rear to load the rear springs.
8. Remeasure rear U-joint angle, then install rebound bumper and plate. Torque attaching screws 200 in-lbs.

BRAKE ADJUSTMENTS
1966-72 Self Adjusting Brakes

These brakes, Fig. 23, have self-adjusting shoe mechanisms that assure correct lining-to-drum clearances at all times. The automatic adjusters operate only when the brakes are applied as the car is moving rearward or when the car comes to an uphill stop.

Although the brakes are self-adjusting, an initial adjustment is necessary when the brake shoes have been relined or replaced, or when the length of the star wheel adjuster has been changed during some other service operation.

Frequent usage of an automatic transmission forward range to halt reverse vehicle motion may prevent the automatic adjusters from functioning, thereby inducing low pedal heights. Should low pedal heights be encountered, it is recommended that numerous forward and reverse stops be made until satisfactory pedal height is obtained.

Service Note

If a low pedal height condition cannot be corrected by making numerous reverse stops (provided the hydraulic system is free of air) it indicates that the self-adjusting mechanism is not functioning. Therefore, it will be necessary to remove the drum, clean, free up and lubricate the adjusting mechanism. Then adjust the brakes, being sure the parking brake is fully released.

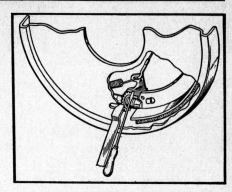

Fig. 24 Releasing brake lever with screwdriver while adjusting star wheel

Adjustment

1. Each backing plate has two adjusting hole covers; remove the rear cover and turn the adjusting screw upward with a screwdriver or other suitable tool to expand the shoes until a slight drag is felt when the drum is rotated.
2. Remove the drum.
3. While holding the adjusting lever out of engagement with the adjusting screw, Fig. 24, back off the adjusting screw about one turn with the fingers.

NOTE: *If finger movement will not turn the screw, free it up. If this is not done, the adjusting lever will not turn the screw during subsequent vehicle operation. Lubricate the screw with oil and coat with wheel bearing grease.*

4. Install wheel and drum, and adjusting hole cover. Adjust brakes on remaining wheels in the same manner.
5. If pedal height is not satisfactory, drive the vehicle and make sufficient reverse stops until proper pedal height is obtained.

PARKING BRAKE, ADJUST
1966-72

1. Release parking brake lever and loosen cable adjusting nut to be sure cable is slack.
2. With rear wheel brakes properly adjusted, tighten cable adjusting nut until a slight drag is felt when the rear wheels are rotated. Then loosen the cable adjusting nut until both rear wheels can be rotated freely.
3. To complete the operation, back off an additional two turns of the cable adjusting nut.
4. Apply and release parking brake several times to be sure rear wheels are not dragging when cable is in released position.

VACUUM RELEASE PARKING BRAKE
1966-72 Imperial

The parking brake is pedal applied

and released by a vacuum chamber. When the engine is started and vacuum is developed, energy is then available to release the parking brake. This is controlled by the transmission push buttons or shift linkage. When the transmission is in "Neutral", vacuum is cut off from the release chamber and there is no action of the parking brake pedal.

When the transmission is shifted into a drive gear (forward or reverse), the vacuum control valve is opened, actuating the vacuum release chamber mounted on the parking brake assembly.

NOTE: *In the event of engine failure and no vacuum, the brake may be released by a manual release lever mounted on the left side of the parking brake pedal assembly. This assembly prevents the vehicle from being driven with the parking brake in the applied position.*

Testing Vacuum Release

1. If the mechanism is inoperative, first check for damaged or kinked vacuum hoses and for loose hose connections at the vacuum chamber, vacuum release valve at neutral safety switch, and at engine manifold connection.
2. Check adjustment of neutral safety switch and operation of vacuum release valve.
3. Check vacuum chamber piston travel by running engine and shifting transmission selector from drive to neutral. The manual release lever should move up and down as vacuum is applied and released. If no movement is observed or if movement is slow (more than 1 or 2 seconds to complete full stroke), the vacuum chamber is leaking and should be replaced.
4. Check brake release with vacuum applied. If vacuum chamber piston completes full stroke but does not release brake, a malfunction of the pedal assembly is indicated.
5. Check operation of parking brake with engine off. Parking brake should remain engaged regardless of transmission selector position.

BRAKE MASTER CYLINDER, REPLACE

1967-72 All Cars

1. Disconnect front and rear brake tubes from master cylinder (residual pressure valves will keep cylinder from draining).
2. Remove nuts that attach master cylinder to cowl panel and/or power brake unit.
3. Disconnect pedal push rod (manual brakes) from brake pedal.
4. Slide master cylinder straight out from cowl panel and/or power brake unit.
5. Reverse procedure to install.

1966 All Cars

To remove the master cylinder, disconnect the master cylinder push rod from brake pedal. Disconnect brake line and stop light wires from cylinder. Remove attaching nuts and remove cylinder from car.

POWER BRAKE

1966-72 Bendix Booster

1. Disconnect brake line(s) from master cylinder.
2. Remove vacuum hose from booster.
3. From under dash, remove brake pedal and push rod attaching bolt.
4. Remove four booster attaching nuts and lift booster from vehicle.
5. Installation is made in the reverse order of removal. Bleed system and check booster operation.

1966-72 Midland-Ross Booster

1. With engine shut off, apply brake several times to balance the internal pressure of the booster.
2. Disconnect hydraulic line at master cylinder and vacuum hose from booster.
3. From underneath dash, remove bolt from plunger and brake pedal linkage.
4. Remove four attaching bolts and lift off booster and master cylinder.

1966 Kelsey Hayes Booster

1. With engine shut off, apply brakes several times to balance internal pressure of brake.
2. Disconnect hydraulic brake line from master cylinder.
3. Disconnect vacuum hose from booster check valve.
4. Unfasten booster push rod from pedal linkage (under instrument panel).
5. Unfasten booster unit from dash panel.
6. Remove booster and master cylinder assembly.

Front End and Steering Section

FRONT SUSPENSION

All Cars Except 1967-72 Imperial

This suspension, Fig. 1, consists of two torsion bar springs (right and left), two sets of upper and lower control arms, four ball joints and two struts.

The front ends of the torsion bar springs engage the lower control arms at the inner pivot points. The rear end of the torsion bars engage adjustable anchor and cam assemblies that are supported by brackets welded to the frame side rails and a removable crossmember.

The upper control arms are mounted on removable brackets that are bolted to the frame side rails. The lower control arms are attached to the frame front crossmember by a pivot shaft and bushing assembly. The pivot shafts are mounted in replaceable rubber bushings.

The steering knuckles are connected to the upper and lower control arms by means of ball joints. To prevent the possibility of fore and aft movement of the lower control arms, a strut is attached to the front crossmember and to the lower control arm.

1967-72 Imperial

The front suspension has a front "K" crossmember that is isolated from the stub frame by four rubber bushing type isolators. The torsion bar rear anchor crossmember is isolated from the stub frame crossmember by two sandwich type rubber insulators. The front anchors are part of the lower control arms and provide the means of adjusting the vehicle front height. The upper control arm is mounted on a pivot bar and the *front* wheel alignment is set by the adjustment of two vertically mounted cam bolts.

LUBRICATION

1966-72

All ball joints and torsion bars are effectively sealed against road splash by tightly fitted balloon type flexible type seals. The ball joints are semi-permanently lubricated with special lubricant, and should not under normal conditions require lubrication before 32,000 miles.

All ball joints, tie rod end seals and protectors should be inspected at all oil change periods. Damaged seals must be replaced to prevent lubricant leakage or contamination and subsequent component failure.

WARNING

Do not use pressure type lubrication equipment as the pressure may damage the balloon type seals. Use a hand type lubrication gun filled only with the special lubricant specified for the job. Fill each unit slowly to avoid rupturing the seal.

Every 32,000 miles remove the plug from the ball joint and install a grease fitting. Using a hand gun, pump the grease into the unit until the seal balloons—indicating fullness. Remove the grease fitting and reinstall the plug.

WHEEL ALIGNMENT

Front suspension height must be correct before measuring caster and camber. After using a suitable solvent to loosen any rust, carefully loosen the upper control arm attaching nuts while holding the bolts from turning. Once caster and camber have been adjusted, Fig. 2, a very small turn of the bolts will affect the gauge readings.

Turning one bolt affects caster more than camber. By bringing caster to approximate specifications, then turning both bolts an equal amount in the same direction to bring camber to the preferred specification, will usually bring caster to the preferred setting.

NOTE: Turning both cams in the same direction an equal amount will change camber with little or no caster change. Turning both cams an equal amount in opposite directions will change caster with little or no change of camber.

TOE-IN, ADJUST
1966-72

With the front wheels in straight

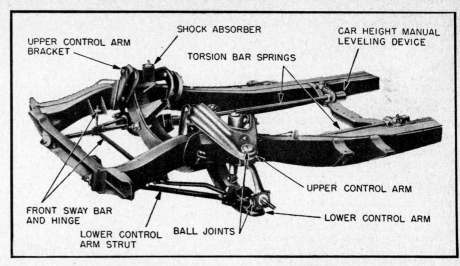

Fig. 1   Torsion bar front suspension. All models except 1967-72 Imperial

ahead position, loosen the clamps at each end of both adjusting tubes. Adjust toe-in by turning the tie rod sleeve which will "center" the steering wheel spokes. If the steering wheel was centered, make the toe-in adjustment by turning both sleeves an equal amount. Position the clamps so they are on the bottom and tighten bolts to 15 ft. lbs.

WHEEL BEARINGS, ADJUST

1. Tighten wheel bearing adjusting nuts to 90 inch pounds on Dodge models (70 on Dart and Valiant) while rotating wheels.
2. Position nut lock on adjusting nut so one pair of cotter pin slots align with pin hole in spindle.
3. Back off adjusting nut and nut lock one slot and install cotter pin. The resulting adjustment should be zero

(no preload) to .003" end play.
4. Clean grease cap, coat inside with wheel bearing grease (do not fill) and install cap.

WHEEL BEARINGS, REPLACE

(Disc Brakes)

1. Raise car and remove front wheels.
2. Remove grease cap, cotter pin, lock nut and bearing adjusting nut.
3. Remove bolts that attach caliper to steering knuckle.
4. Slowly slide caliper up and away from disc and support caliper on steering knuckle arm.

NOTE: Do not allow caliper to hang by brake hose.

5. Remove thrust washer and outer bearing cone. Remove hub and disc assembly. Grease retainer and inner bearing can now be removed.

CHECKING BALL JOINTS FOR WEAR

If loose ball joints are suspected, first

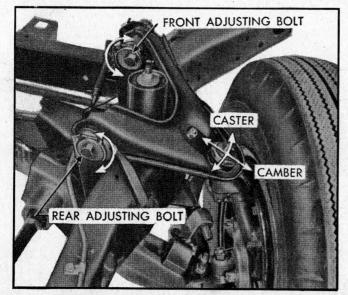

Fig. 2   Camber and caster adjusting bolts. All models except 1967-72 Imperial

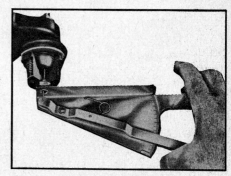

Fig. 3   Scale used to check lower ball joint for wear (tool C-3911)

make sure the front wheel bearings are properly adjusted and that the control arms are tight.

Fig. 3 illustrates tool No. C-3911 which has been developed to measure accurately lower ball joint wear and to eliminate needless replacement of ball joints not excessively worn. Checking procedure is as follows:

1. Raise front of vehicle at lower control arms to bring wheels clear of floor.

   CAUTION—*Lower control arms must be supported sufficiently outboard so that the rebound bumper is not compressed in order to unload lower ball joint.*

2. Remove ball joint plug and screw threaded fitting of tool into ball joint hole until it is firmly seated as shown.

3. Raise and lower wheel either by hand or with a pry bar and note free play indicated on scale of tool. The scale is graduated to indicate free play in minor increments of .010" with the major increments indicating .050" (.070" on 1968-72).

4. Replacement for excessive wear is necessary only when movement of the gauge arm exceeds the above.

NOTE: On 1967-72 Imperial, the lower ball joints are pre-loaded (zero axial end play). Therefore, if any up and down movement is observed the ball joint and lower control arm should be replaced. This is due to the fact that the lower ball joint is a press fit and requires very high removing and installing forces.

BALL JOINTS, REPLACE

On 1966 Imperial, both upper and lower ball joints are threaded into their respective control arms. On 1967-71 Imperial, the upper ball joint is threaded into the control arm and the lower ball joint is serviced as an assembly with the lower control arm. On all other models, the upper ball joint is threaded into the control arm whereas the lower ball joint is furnished as an assembly with the steering arm.

Use a suitable tool to press the ball joints from the steering knuckles, and when installing a ball joint, be sure to start it squarely into the control arm threads.

TORSION BAR, REPLACE

The torsion bars are not interchangeable side for side. The bars are marked either right or left by an "R" or an "L" stamped on one end of the bar. The general procedure for replacing a torsion bar is as follows:

Removal

1. Remove upper control arm rebound bumper.

2. If vehicle is to be raised on a hoist, make sure it is lifted on the body only so suspension is in full rebound position (no load).

3. Release all load from torsion bar by turning anchor adjusting bolt counterclockwise.

NOTE: On 1967-72 Imperial models, load on *both* torsion bars will have to

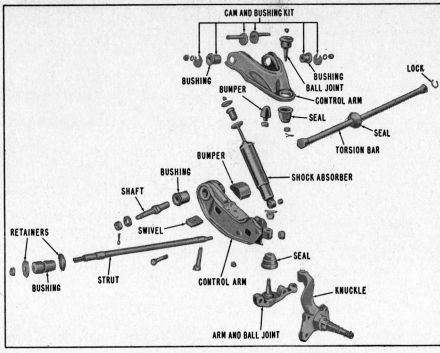

Fig. 4   Front suspension. 1966-72

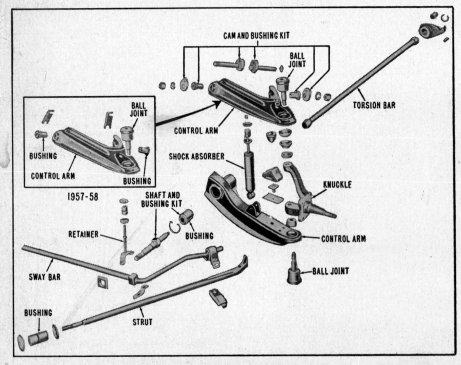

Fig. 5   Front suspension. 1966 Imperial

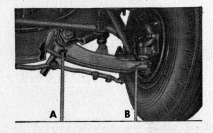

Fig. 6   Measuring front suspension height (typical)

be released by turning the anchor adjusting bolts counterclockwise. This is necessary because the rubber isolator rear crossmember would be under loan and could possibly cause severe damage or personal injury.

4. Slide rear anchor balloon seal off of rear anchor and remove lock ring from anchor.
5. Remove torsion bar, by sliding bar out through rear of rear anchor. Use care not to damage balloon seal when it is removed from torsion bar.

Inspection

1. Inspect balloon seal for damage and replace if necessary.
2. Inspect torsion bar for scores or nicks. Dress down all scratches and nicks to remove sharp edges, then paint repaired areas with a rust preventive.
3. Remove all foreign material from hex openings in anchors and from hex ends of torsion bars.
4. Inspect adjusting bolt and swivel and replace if there is any sign of corrosion or other damage. Lubricate for easy operation.

Installation

1. Insert torsion bar through rear anchor.
2. Slide balloon seal over torsion bar with cupped end toward rear of bar.
3. Coat both ends of torsion bar with a long mileage lubricant.
4. Slide torsion bar in hex opening of lower control arm.
5. Install lock ring, making sure it is seated in groove.
6. Pack annular opening in rear anchor completely full of a long mileage lubricant.
7. Position lip of balloon seal in groove of anchor. *On 1967-72 Imperial models, install balloon seal clamp.*
8. On all models except 1967-72 Imperial, turn adjusting bolt clockwise to place a load on torsion bar. *On 1967-72 Imperial, turn both adjusting bolts clockwise to place a load on both torsion bars.*
9. Lower vehicle to floor and adjust front suspension height.
10. Install upper control arm rebound bumper.

RIDING HEIGHT, ADJUST

Before taking measurements, grasp the bumpers at the center (rear bumper first) and jounce the car up and down several times. Jounce the car at the front bumper the same number of times and release the bumper at the same point in the cycle each time.

1. Measure from the ball joint to the floor (measurement "B"), and from the control arm torsion bar spring anchor housing to the floor (measurement "A"), Fig. 6.
2. Subtract "B" from "A". The distance should be as listed below (plus or minus 1/8").
3. Measure the other side in the same manner.
4. Adjust by turning the torsion bar anchor adjusting nut *clockwise to increase the height and counterclockwise to decrease the height.*

difference from side-to-side should not exceed 1/8".
5. After adjusting, jounce the car and recheck the measurements on both sides, even if only one side may have been adjusted.

Dodge & Dart

1966 Dart (standard)	1 7/8"
Coronet (standard)	1 7/8"
Polara, Monaco	1 1/2"
Dart & Coronet (H.D.)	2 3/8"
1967-68 Dart	2 1/8"
Coronet, Charger	1 7/8"
Polara, Monaco	1 1/8"
1969-70 Dart	2 1/8"
Challenger	1 3/16"
Coronet, Charger	1 7/8"
Polara, Monaco	1 3/8"
1971 Dart 4 Dr.	2 1/8"
Dart 2 Dr.	1 5/8"
Challenger	1"
Coronet, Charger	1 5/8"
Polara, Monaco	1 3/8"

Plymouth

1966 Fury	1 3/8"
Others (standard)	1 7/8"
(heavy duty)	2 3/8"
1967-70 Belvedere, Satellite, Roadrunner	1 7/8"
Fury, V.I.P.	1 3/8"
1971 Satellite	1 5/8"
Fury	1 3/8"

Valiant

1966 (standard)	2"
1966 (heavy duty)	2 3/8"
1967	2 1/8"
1968-69 Barracuda	1 3/8"
Valiant	2 1/8"
1970 Barracuda	1 3/16"
Valiant	2 1/8"
1971 Valiant 4 Dr.	2 1/8"
Valiant 2 Dr.	1 5/8"
Barracuda	1"

Chrysler & Imperial

1966 Chrysler	1 1/8"
Imperial	2"
(heavy duty)	2 3/8"
1967-71 Chrysler	1 1/8"
Imperial	1 3/4"

MANUAL STEERING GEAR, REPLACE

1968-71 Chrysler, Monaco, Polara

1. Use a suitable puller to remove steering arm.
2. Disconnect transmission gear selector linkage (if column mounted).
3. Remove pin from coupling clamp at upper end of steering gear worm shaft.
4. To provide sufficient clearance at coupling, loosen column jacket-to-instrument panel clamp bolts enough to disengage tab on clamp from slot in column jacket. Slide column up far enough to disengage coupling from worm shaft.

5. Raise carpet and remove column lower support plate-to-floor pan bolts.
6. Remove three gear housing mounting bolts and remove gear from under vehicle.

1968-70 Dodge & Plymouth (Except Monaco & Polara)

1. Perform Steps 1 through 4 as described above for other 1968-70 models.
2. Then on Dart and Valiant with 273 engines, from under vehicle remove left front engine mount stud nut and washer. Using a suitable jack, raise engine about 1 1/2 inches. Remove starter. After removing the three steering gear mounting bolts, lower gear through opening.
3. On models with 426 engine, remove battery and battery tray. Remove left front engine mount stud nut and washer. Using a suitable jack, raise engine about 1 1/2 inches. After removing the three gear mounting bolts, rotate gear forward between cylinder head and shock absorber tower, and up through opening left by battery tray removal.
4. On models with 273, 318, 340, 383 and 440 engines (except Dart and Valiant), remove the three steering gear mounting bolts and lower gear from under vehicle.
5. On all 6-cylinder models, remove steering gear mounting bolts and remove gear through engine compartment.

1966-67 Chrysler & 1966-67 Dodge & Plymouth (Except Dart & Valiant With V8-273 Engine)

1. Remove nut and use a puller to take off steering arm.
2. Remove bolt or pin from coupling clamp at upper end of steering worm shaft.
3. To provide sufficient clearance at coupling, loosen column jacket-to-instrument panel clamp bolts enough to disengage tab on clamp from slot in column jacket. Slide column up away from steering gear to disengage coupling from worm shaft.

NOTE: It is not necessary to disconnect shift linkage on models equipped with manual transmission or to remove the floor plate-to-toe board bolts when removing steering gear. If floor plate bolts are loosened, it will be necessary to realign the steering column when reinstalling gear.

---

4. Unfasten and remove gear.

NOTE: On six-cylinder models, gear can be removed through engine compartment. On cars with V8 engines, remove gear from underneath vehicle.

1966-67 Valiant & Dart With V8-273 Engine

1. Disconnect battery ground cable.
2. Loosen worm shaft coupling clamp.

3. Loosen column jacket-to-instrument panel clamp bolts and slide column up far enough to disengage coupling from worm shaft.
4. Raise vehicle and remove left front engine mount stud nut. Jack up engine slightly to provide clearance between left exhaust manifold and body sheet metal to allow removal of gear.
5. Remove starting motor.
6. Remove nut and use a puller to take off steering arm.
7. Unfasten and remove gear from under vehicle.

POWER STEERING, REPLACE

1968-72 Imperial

1. Disconnect battery ground cable.
2. Disconnect pressure and return hoses at steering gear and fasten ends of hoses above oil level in pump reservoir.
3. Remove rubber coupling heat shield.
4. Remove two capscrews attaching rubber coupling to upper flange of steering column shaft.
5. Remove roll pin from pot coupling.
6. Move upper end of intermediate shaft until rubber coupling clears upper flange and carefully tap lower coupling up and off steering gear worm shaft.
7. Using a suitable puller, remove steering gear arm.
8. Disconnect exhaust pipe at ball coupling and exhaust manifold flanges and remove pipe.
9. Disconnect transmission cooler lines from transmission and clamp at starter flange bolt.
10. Remove two steering gear mounting bolts and stud nut. Then remove gear from under vehicle.

1967 Imperial

1. Disconnect battery ground cable.
2. Disconnect pressure and return hoses at steering gear. Fasten hose ends above fluid level in pump.
3. Use a suitable puller to remove steering arm.
4. Remove frame-to-gear mounting bolts and remove gear from under vehicle.

1967-72 Chrysler, Plymouth & Dodge

1. Disconnect battery ground cable.
2. Remove column coupling-to-worm shaft roll pin.

3. Loosen column jacket clamp nuts enough to allow column to be pulled up two inches. On some models it will be necessary to remove column finish plate to get at the clamp.
4. Remove three bolts in lower column support plate at floor pan.
5. Tap coupling and column upward and lift off end of worm shaft.
6. Disconnect pressure and return hoses at gear. Fasten hose ends above fluid level in pump.
7. Use a suitable puller to remove steering arm.
8. Remove gear-to-frame bolts and remove gear from vehicle as follows:
9. On six-cylinder models, remove gear from top of engine compartment.
10. Dart and Valiant with 8-273 engine, remove left front engine mount stud nut. Using suitable jack, raise engine slightly to provide clearance between left exhaust manifold and body sheet metal. Remove starter and then take steering gear out from under vehicle.
11. Dodge and Plymouth with 8-426 engine, remove battery and battery tray. From top side of engine compartment, remove left engine mount insulator stud nut, through bolt and bracket upper bolt. Jack up left side of engine about $1\frac{1}{2}$". Separate engine from engine mount and allow insulator to rest on frame. Rotate steering gear (worm shaft end) up between cylinder head and shock absorber tower and out through battery tray opening.
12. On all other models remove gear from under vehicle.

1966 Imperial

1. Disconnect battery ground cable.
2. Disconnect center link from steering gear.
3. Use puller to remove steering arm.
4. Disconnect pressure and return hoses from gear. Fasten hose ends above fluid level in pump.
5. Drive out roll pin in flexible coupling.
6. Unfasten master cylinder from power brake unit and move master cylinder toward engine.
7. If equipped, unfasten auto pilot from its bracket and lay to one side.
8. Remove steering column cover plate (inside vehicle).
9. Remove three capscrews in lower support plate.
10. Disconnect transmission indicator linkage.
11. Remove column-to-instrument panel clamp while supporting weight of column. Pull up on steering wheel far enough to disengage flexible coupling from worm shaft. Allow steering gear to rest on front seat.

12. Remove gear-to-frame mounting bolts and alignment wedge.
13. Remove gear through engine compartment.

1966 Chrysler, Polara, Monaco, Fury

1. Disconnect battery ground cable.
2. Disconnect pressure and return hoses from gear. Fasten hose ends above fluid level in pump.
3. Remove rubber coupling heat shield.
4. Disconnect rubber coupling from flange of intermediate shaft.
5. Remove roll pin that attaches rubber coupling upper flange to column shaft.
6. Tap rubber coupling as far as it will go upward onto column shaft splines.
7. Remove roll pin that attaches pot coupling to steering worm shaft.
8. Move intermediate shaft until upper flange clears rubber coupling and withdraw from worm shaft splines.
9. Use a suitable puller to remove steering arm.
10. Unfasten gear from crossmember and remove gear from under vehicle.

1966 V8 Valiant, Dart, Coronet, Charger

1. Disconnect battery ground cable.
2. Loosen bolt at worm shaft coupling clamp. Loosen column jacket-to-instrument panel clamp bolts and slide column up far enough to disengage coupling from worm shaft.
3. Disconnect hoses at control valve.
4. On Dart models, raise vehicle and remove left front engine mount stud nut. Jack up engine slightly to provide clearance between left exhaust manifold and body sheet metal to allow removal of gear.
5. Remove starting motor.
6. Remove nut and use a puller to take off steering arm.
7. Unfasten and remove gear.

1966 Six Except Fury

1. Disconnect battery ground cable.
2. Remove worm shaft coupling clamp bolt and roll pin.
3. Loosen column jacket clamp at instrument panel and pull jacket up two inches.
4. Tap coupling upward and lift it off end of worm shaft.
5. Disconnect hoses from gear and fasten ends above oil level in reservoir.
6. Raise vehicle. Remove nut and use a puller to take off steering arm.
7. Unfasten and remove gear through engine compartment.

FORD & MERCURY
Full Size Models

OLD CAR SPECIFICATIONS: For 1946-65 Tune Up and Wheel Alignment Specifications see back of book.

*This material covered only in "Service Trade Edition" of this manual.

INDEX OF SERVICE OPERATIONS

ENGINE & SERIAL NUMBER LOCATION
Plate On Left Front Door Pillar

ENGINE IDENTIFICATION
★Serial number on Vehicle Warranty Plate

Engine code for 1966-72 is the last letter in the serial number.

Year	Engine	Engine Code★	Year	Engine	Engine Code★	Year	Engine	Engine Code★	Year	Engine	Engine Code★
1966–67	6-240	B	1968	6-240	V	1969–70	V8-429①	K	1972	V8-351①	H
	6-240	V		V8-302①	F		V8-429②	N		V8-351④	Q
	V8-289	C		V8-390①	Y	1971	6-240	V		V8-400	S
	V8-352	X		V8-390①	H		V8-302①	F		V8-429	N
	V8-390①	H		V8-390②	Z		V8-351①	H			
	V8-390①	Y		V8-428②	Q		V8-390①	Y			
	V8-390②	Z		V8-427③	R		V8-400①	S			
	V8-410	M	1969–70	6-240	V		V8-429①	K			
	V8-427③	R		V8-302①	F		V8-429②	N			
	V8-427②	W		V8-351 (W)①	H	1972	6-240	V			
	V8-428	P		V8-390①	Y		V8-302①	F			
	V8-428	Q		V8-390⑥	X						

①—Two barrel carburetor.
②—For barrel carburetor.
③—Two 4 barrel carburetors.
④—Four barrel special.
⑤—Premium fuel.
⑥—Two barrel special.

GRILLE IDENTIFICATION

1966 Ford

1968 Ford Custom, Galaxie

1969 Ford "LTD", XL, Squire

1966 Mercury

1968 Ford "LTD", XL, Squire

1969 Mercury Monterey

1967 Ford

1968 Mercury

1969 Mercury Marauder, Marquis

1967 Mercury

1969 Ford Custom, Galaxie

1970 Ford Custom, Galaxie

GRILLE IDENTIFICATION—Continued

1970 Ford "LTD", XL, Squire

1971 Ford Custom, Galaxie

1971 Mercury Monterey

1970 Mercury Marauder, Marquis

1971 Ford "LTD", Squire

1972 Ford Custom, Galaxie

1970 Mercury Monterey

1971 Mercury Brougham, Marquis

1972 Ford "LTD", Squire

1972 Mercury Monterey

1972 Mercury Brougham, Marquis

GENERAL ENGINE SPECIFICATIONS

Year	Engine	Carburetor	Bore and Stroke	Piston Displacement, Cubic Inches	Compression Ratio	Maximum Brake H.P. @ R.P.M.	Maximum Torque Lbs. Ft. @ R.P.M.	Normal Oil Pressure Pounds
FORD								
1966	155 Horsepower...............6-240	1 Barrel	4.00 x 3.18	240	9.2	155 @ 4200	239 @ 2200	35–60
	200 Horsepower............V8-289	2 Barrel	4.00 x 2.87	289	9.3	200 @ 4400	282 @ 2400	35–55
	250 Horsepower............V8-352	4 Barrel	4.00 x 3.50	352	9.3	250 @ 4400	352 @ 2800	35–55
	265 Horsepower............V8-390	2 Barrel	4.05 x 3.78	390	9.5	265 @ 4400	401 @ 2600	35–55
	315 Horsepower............V8-390	4 Barrel	4.05 x 3.78	390	10.5	315 @ 4600	427 @ 2800	35–55
	345 Horsepower............V8-428	4 Barrel	4.13 x 3.98	428	10.5	345 @ 4600	462 @ 2800	35–55
	425 Horsepower............V8-427	Two 4 Bar.	4.23 x 3.78	427	11.1	425 @ 6000	480 @ 3700	40–55
1967	155 Horsepower...............6-240	1 Barrel	4.00 x 3.18	240	9.2	155 @ 4200	239 @ 2200	35–60
	200 Horsepower............V8-289	2 Barrel	4.00 x 2.87	289	9.3	200 @ 4400	282 @ 2400	35–55
	265 H.P., Std. Tr..............V8-390	2 Barrel	4.05 x 3.78	390	9.5	265 @ 4400	401 @ 2600	35–55
	275 H.P., Auto. Tr...........V8-390	2 Barrel	4.05 x 3.78	390	9.5	275 @ 4400	405 @ 2600	35–55
	315 Horsepower............V8-390	4 Barrel	4.05 x 3.78	390	10.5	315 @ 4600	427 @ 2800	35–55
	345 Horsepower............V8-428	4 Barrel	4.13 x 3.98	428	10.5	345 @ 4600	462 @ 2800	35–55
	360 Horsepower............V8-428	4 Barrel	4.13 x 3.98	428	10.5	360 @ 5400	459 @ 3200	35–55
	425 Horsepower............V8-427	Two 4 Bar.	4.23 x 3.78	427	11.1	425 @ 6000	480 @ 3700	40–55
1968	150 Horsepower...............6-240	1 Barrel	4.00 x 3.18	240	9.2	150 @ 4000	234 @ 2200	35–60
	210 Horsepower............V8-302	2 Barrel	4.00 x 3.00	302	9.5	210 @ 4400	295 @ 2400	35–55

Continued

GENERAL ENGINE SPECIFICATIONS—Continued

Year	Engine	Carburetor	Bore and Stroke	Piston Displacement, Cubic Inches	Compression Ratio	Maximum Brake H.P. @ R.P.M.	Maximum Torque Lbs. Ft. @ R.P.M.	Normal Oil Pressure Pounds
FORD—Continued								
1968	270 Horsepower.............V8-390	2 Barrel	4.05 x 3.78	390	9.5	270 @ 4400	403 @ 2600	35–55
	315 Horsepower.............V8-390	4 Barrel	4.05 x 3.78	390	10.5	315 @ 4600	427 @ 2800	35–55
	345 Horsepower.............V8-428	4 Barrel	4.13 x 3.98	428	10.5	345 @ 4600	462 @ 2800	35–55
	390 Horsepower.............V8-427	4 Barrel	4.23 x 3.78	427	10.9	390 @ 5600	400 @ 3200	40–55
1969–70	150 Horsepower.............6-240	1 Barrel	4.00 x 3.18	240	9.2	150 @ 4000	234 @ 2200	35–60
	210 Horsepower.............V8-302	2 Barrel	4.00 x 3.00	302	9.5	210 @ 4400	295 @ 2400	35–60
	250 Horsepower.............V8-351	2 Barrel	4.00 x 3.50	351	9.5	250 @ 4600	355 @ 2600	35–60
	270 Horsepower.............V8-390	2 Barrel	4.05 x 3.78	390	9.5	270 @ 4400	390 @ 2600	35–60
	320 Horsepower.............V8-429	2 Barrel	4.36 x 3.59	429	10.5	320 @ 4400	460 @ 2200	35–60
	360 Horsepower.............V8-429	4 Barrel	4.36 x 3.59	429	11.0	360 @ 4600	476 @ 2800	35–60
1971	140 Horsepower.............6-240	1 Barrel	4.00 x 3.18	240	8.9	140 @ 4000	230 @ 2200	35–60
	210 Horsepower.............V8-302	2 Barrel	4.00 x 3.00	302	9.0	210 @ 4400	296 @ 2600	35–60
	240 Horsepower.............V8-351	2 Barrel	4.00 x 3.50	351	9.0	240 @ 4600	350 @ 2600	35–60
	255 Horsepower.............V8-390	2 Barrel	4.05 x 3.78	390	8.6	255 @ 4400	376 @ 2600	35–60
	260 Horsepower.............V8-400	2 Barrel	4.00 x 4.00	400	9.0	260 @ 4400	400 @ 2200	35–60
	320 Horsepower.............V8-429	2 Barrel	4.36 x 3.59	429	10.5	320 @ 4400	460 @ 2200	35–60
	360 Horsepower.............V8-429	4 Barrel	4.36 x 3.59	429	10.5	360 @ 4600	480 @ 2800	35–60
1972	103 Horsepower[1].............6-240	1 Barrel	4.00 x 3.18	240	8.5	103 @ 3800	170 @ 2200	35–60
	140 Horsepower[1].............V8-302	2 Barrel	4.00 x 3.00	302	8.5	140 @ 4000	239 @ 2000	35–60
	153 Horsepower[1].............V8-351	2 Barrel	4.00 x 3.50	351	8.3	153 @ 3800	266 @ 2000	35–60
	163 Horsepower[1].............V8-351	2 Barrel	4.00 x 3.50	351	8.6	163 @ 3800	277 @ 2000	35–60
	172 Horsepower[1].............V8-400	2 Barrel	4.00 x 4.00	400	8.4	172 @ 4000	298 @ 2200	35–60
	208 Horsepower[1].............V8-429	4 Barrel	4.36 x 3.59	429	8.5	208 @ 4400	322 @ 2800	35–60
MERCURY								
1966	265 H.P. Std. Tr.............V8-390	2 Barrel	4.05 x 3.7800	390	9.5	265 @ 4400	397 @ 2600	35–55
	275 H.P. Auto. Tr...........V8-390	2 Barrel	4.05 x 3.7800	390	10.5	275 @ 4400	405 @ 2600	35–55
	330 Horsepower.............V8-410	4 Barrel	4.05 x 3.9800	410	10.5	330 @ 4600	444 @ 2800	35–55
	345 Horsepower.............V8-428	4 Barrel	4.13 x 3.9800	428	10.5	345 @ 4600	462 @ 2800	35–55
	425 Horsepower.............V8-427	Two 4 Bar.	4.23 x 3.7800	427	11.1	425 @ 6000	480 @ 3700	40–55
1967	270 Horsepower.............V8-390	2 Barrel	4.05 x 3.78	390	9.5	270 @ 4400	403 @ 2600	35–55
	330 Horsepower.............V8-410	4 Barrel	4.05 x 3.98	410	10.5	330 @ 4600	444 @ 2800	35–55
	345 Horsepower.............V8-428	4 Barrel	4.13 x 3.98	428	10.5	345 @ 4600	462 @ 2800	35–55
1968	265 Horsepower.............V8-390	2 Barrel	4.05 x 3.78	390	9.5	265 @ 4400	390 @ 2600	35–55
	280 Horsepower.............V8-390	2 Barrel	4.05 x 3.78	390	10.5	280 @ 4400	403 @ 2600	35–55
	315 Horsepower.............V8-390	4 Barrel	4.05 x 3.78	390	10.5	315 @ 4600	427 @ 2800	35–55
	340 Horsepower.............V8-428	4 Barrel	4.13 x 3.98	428	10.5	340 @ 4600	462 @ 2800	35–55
1969–70	270 Horsepower.............V8-390	2 Barrel	4.05 x 3.78	390	9.5	270 @ 4400	390 @ 2600	35–60
	280 Horsepower (1969).......V8-390	2 Barrel	4.05 x 3.78	390	10.5	280 @ 4400	403 @ 2600	35–60
	320 Horsepower.............V8-429	2 Barrel	4.36 x 3.59	429	10.5	320 @ 4400	460 @ 2200	35–60
	360 Horsepower.............V8-429	4 Barrel	4.36 x 3.59	429	11.0	360 @ 4600	476 @ 2800	35–60
1971	240 Horsepower.............V8-351	2 Barrel	4.00 x 3.50	351	9.0	240 @ 4600	350 @ 2600	35–60
	260 Horsepower.............V8-400	2 Barrel	4.00 x 4.00	400	9.0	260 @ 4400	400 @ 2200	35–60
	320 Horsepower.............V8-429	2 Barrel	4.36 x 3.59	429	10.5	320 @ 4400	460 @ 2200	35–60
	360 Horsepower.............V8-429	4 Barrel	4.36 x 3.59	429	10.5	360 @ 4600	480 @ 2800	35–60
1972	153 Horsepower[1].............V8-351	2 Barrel	4.00 x 3.50	351	8.3	153 @ 3800	266 @ 2000	35–60
	163 Horsepower[1].............V8-351	2 Barrel	4.00 x 3.50	351	8.6	163 @ 3800	277 @ 2000	35–60
	172 Horsepower[1].............V8-400	2 Barrel	4.00 x 4.00	400	8.4	172 @ 4000	298 @ 2200	35–60
	208 Horsepower[1].............V8-429	4 Barrel	4.36 x 3.59	429	8.5	208 @ 4400	322 @ 2800	35–60

[1]—Ratings are NET—as installed in the vehicle.

TUNE UP SPECIFICATIONS

OLD CAR SPECIFICATIONS: For 1946-65 Tune Up Specifications see back of book.

★When using a timing light, disconnect vacuum hose or tube at distributor and plug opening in tube or hose so idle speed will not be affected.

●When checking compression, lowest cylinder must be within 75% of the highest.

Year	Engine	Spark Plug Type ⑤	Gap Inch	Point Gap Inch	Dwell Angle Deg.	Firing Order	BTDC ①	Mark	Hot Idle Speed Std. Trans.	Auto. Trans. ②	Fuel Pump Press. Lbs.
1966	6-240⑬ Auto. Tr.	BF-42	.034	.025	37–42	Fig. H	12°	Fig. J	—	500D⑫	4–6
	6-240⑬ Std. Tr.	BF-42	.034	.025	37–42	Fig. H	6°	Fig. J	525⑫	—	4–6
	6-240⑪ Auto. Tr.	BF-42	.034	.025	37–42	Fig. H	4°	Fig. J	—	500D⑫	4–6
	6-240⑪ Std. Tr.	BF-42	.034	.025	37–42	Fig. H	TDC	Fig. J	600⑫	—	4–6
	V8-289⑬	BF-42	.034	.017	26–31	Fig. N	6°	Fig. K	575⑫	475D⑫	4–6
	V8-289⑪	BF-42	.034	.017	26–31	Fig. N	TDC	Fig. K	625⑫	550D⑫	4–6
	V8-352, 390, 410, 428⑬	BF-42	.034	.017	26–31	Fig. N	10°⑨	Fig. C	575⑫	475D⑫	4½–6½
	V8-352, 390, 410, 428⑪	BF-42	.034	.017	26–31	Fig. N	6°⑨	Fig. C	625⑫	550D⑫	4½–6½
	V8-427	BF-32	.030	.020	22–24	Fig. N	10°	Fig. C	700⑫	—	4½–6½
1967	6-240⑬ Auto. Tr.	BF-42	.034	.025	37–42	Fig. H	10°	Fig. J	—	500D⑫	4–6
	6-240⑬ Std. Tr.	BF-42	.034	.025	37–42	Fig. H	6°	Fig. J	525⑫	—	4–6
	6-240⑪ Auto. Tr.	BF-42	.034	.025	37–42	Fig. H	4°	Fig. J	—	500D⑫	4–6
	6-240⑪ Std. Tr.	BF-42	.034	.025	37–42	Fig. H	TDC	Fig. J	600⑫	—	4–6
	V8-289⑬	BF-42	.034	.017	26–31	Fig. N	6°	Fig. K	575⑫	475D⑫	4–6
	V8-289⑪	BF-42	.034	.017	26–31	Fig. N	TDC	Fig. K	625⑫	550D⑫	4–6
	V8-390, 410, 428⑬	BF-32	.034	.017	26–31	Fig. N	10°⑨	Fig. C	575⑫	475D⑫	4½–6½
	V8-390, 410, 428⑪	BF-32	.034	.017	26–31	Fig. N	6°⑨	Fig. C	625⑫	550D⑫	4½–6½
	V8-427	BF-32	.034	.020	22–24	Fig. N	8°	Fig. C	750⑫	—	4½–6½
1968	6-240	BF-42	.034	.027	35–40	Fig. H	6°	Fig. D	600⑫	500D④	4–6
	V8-302⑬	BF-42	.034	.021	24–29	Fig. N	6°	Fig. F	625⑫	550D④	4–6
	V8-390⑬ Std. Tr.	BF-42	.034	.021	24–29	Fig. N	6°	Fig. I	625⑫	—	4½–6½
	V8-390⑯ Auto. Tr.	BF-42	.034	.017	26–31	Fig. N	6°	Fig. I	—	560D⑫	4½–6½
	V8-428⑬ Std. Tr.	BF-42	.034	.021	24–29	Fig. N	6°	Fig. I	625⑫	—	4½–6½
	V8-428⑯ Auto. Tr.	BF-42	.034	.017	26–31	Fig. N	6°	Fig. I	—	550D⑫	4½–6½
	V8-427⑬	BF-32	.034	.017	26–31	Fig. N	6°	Fig. I	—	600D⑫	4½–6½
1969	6-240	BF-42	.034	.027	35–40	Fig. H	6°	Fig. D	775/500⑭	500D	5
	V8-302 Std. Tr.	BF-42	.034	.021	24–29	Fig. N	6°	Fig. F	650	—	5
	V8-302 Auto. Tr.	BF-42	.034	.017	26–31	Fig. N	6°	Fig. F	—	550D	5
	V8-351	BF-42	.034	.017	26–31	Fig. M	6°	Fig. F	650	550D	5
	V8-390	BF-42	.034	.017	26–31	Fig. N	6°	Fig. I	650	550D	5
	V8-390⑯	BF-42	.034	.021	24–29	Fig. N	6°	Fig. I	—	550D	5
	V8-429	BF-42	.034	.017	26–31	Fig. N	6°	Fig. I	—	550D	5
1970	6-240	BF-42	.035	⑰	⑰	Fig. H	6°	Fig. D	775/500⑭	500④	5
	V8-302	BF-42	.035	.021	24–29	Fig. N	6°	Fig. F	775/500⑭	575④	5
	V8-351	BF-42	.035	.021	24–29	Fig. M	6°	Fig. F	775/500⑭	575④	5
	V8-390 Std. Tr.	BF-42	.035	.021	24–29	Fig. N	6°	Fig. I	775/500⑭	—	5
	V8-390 Auto. Tr.	BF-42	.035	.017	26–31	Fig. N	6°	Fig. I	—	600/500⑭	5
	V8-429⑦	BF-42	.035	.021	24–29	Fig. N	4°	Fig. I	—	600/500⑭	5
	V8-429⑥	BF-42	.035	⑳	⑳	Fig. N	4°	Fig. I	700	600	5
1971	6-240	BRF-42	.034	.027	35–40	Fig. H	6°	Fig. G	800/500⑭	500	5
	V8-302 L/Air Cond.	BRF-42	.034	.021	24–29	Fig. N	6°	Fig. F	800/500⑭	575	5
	V8-302 w/Air Cond.	BRF-42	.034	.021	24–29	Fig. N	6°	Fig. F	800/500⑭	600/500⑭	5
	V8-351 L/Air Cond.㉑	BRF-42	.034	.021	24–29	Fig. M	6°	Fig. F	700/500⑭	575	5
	V8-351 w/Air Cond.㉑	BRF-42	.034	.021	24–29	Fig. M	6°	Fig. F	700/500⑭	600/500⑭	5
	V8-351㉒	ARF-42	.034	.021	24–29	Fig. M	6°	Fig. F	775/500⑭	600/500⑭	5
	V8-390	BRF-42	.034	.021	24–29	Fig. N	6°	Fig. I	—	600/500⑭	5
	V8-400	ARF-42	.034	.021	24–29	Fig. M	③	Fig. I	—	600/500⑭	5
	V8-429⑦ L/Air Cond.	BRF-42	.034	.021	24–29	Fig. N	6°	Fig. I	—	590	5
	V8-429⑦ w/Air Cond.	BRF-42	.034	.021	24–29	Fig. N	6°	Fig. I	—	600/500⑭	5
	V8-429⑥	BRF-42	.034	.021	24–29	Fig. N	4°	Fig. I	700	600	5

Continued

TUNE UP SPECIFICATIONS—Continued

OLD CAR SPECIFICATIONS: For 1946-65 Tune Up Specifications see back of book.

★When using a timing light, disconnect vacuum hose or tube at distributor and plug opening in tube or hose so idle speed will not be affected.

●When checking compression, lowest cylinder must be within 75% of the highest.

| Year | Engine | Spark Plug | | Distributor | | Firing Order | Ignition Timing ★ | | Hot Idle Speed | | Fuel Pump Press. Lbs. |
		Type ⑤	Gap Inch	Point Gap Inch	Dwell Angle Deg.		BTDC ①	Mark	Std. Trans.	Auto. Trans. ②	
1972	6-240	BRF-42	.034	.027	35–39	Fig. H	6°	Fig. G	—	500	5
	V8-302 w/Air Cond.	BRF-42	.034	.017	26–30	Fig. N	6°	Fig. F	—	600/500⑭	5
	V8-302 L/Air Cond.	BRF-42	.034	.017	26–30	Fig. N	6°	Fig. F	—	575	5
	V8-351 w/Air Cond.㉑	BRF-42	.034	.017	26–30	Fig. M	6°	Fig. F	—	600/500⑭	5
	V8-351 L/Air Cond.㉑	BRF-42	.034	.017	26–30	Fig. M	6°	Fig. F	—	575	5
	V8-351㉒	ARF-42	.034	.017	26–30	Fig. M	6°	Fig. F	—	700/500⑭	5
	V8-351 Calif.㉒	ARF-42	.034	.017	26–30	Fig. M	6°	Fig. F	—	625/500⑭	5
	V8-400	ARF-42	.034	.017	26–30	Fig. M	6°	Fig. I	—	625/500⑭	5
	V8-429	BRF-42	.034	.017	26–30	Fig. N	10°	Fig. I	—	600/500⑭	5

①—BTDC: Before top dead center.
②—D: Drive. N: Neutral.
③—California vehicles 6°; all others 10°.
④—With headlights on and A/C off.
⑤—Autolite.
⑥—Four barrel carburetor.
⑦—Two barrel carburetor.
⑧—Conventional ignition 30-33°, transistor ignition 22-24°.

⑨—Whenever idle speed or ignition timing is adjusted, vacuum line to brake release mechanism (if equipped) must be disconnected and vacuum hole plugged to prevent parking brake from releasing when selector lever is moved to Drive.
⑩—If air conditioned, turn A/C switch to "Full On" position.
⑪—With Thermactor Exhaust Emission Control System.
⑫—With Headlights and A/C On.
⑬—Without Thermactor Exhaust Emission Control.

⑭—Higher figure is with throttle modulator energized.
⑮—Premium fuel.
⑯—With IMCO system.
⑰—Dual diaphragm dist., .027 gap, 35°-40° dwell. Single diaphragm dist., .025 gap, 37°-42° dwell.
⑳—Dual diaphragm dist., .021 gap, 24°-29° dwell. Single diaphragm .017 gap, 26°-31° dwell.
㉑—Windsor engine.
㉒—Cleveland engine.

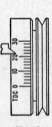

Fig. C

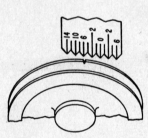

Fig. D

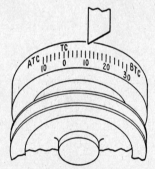

Fig. F

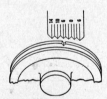

Fig. G

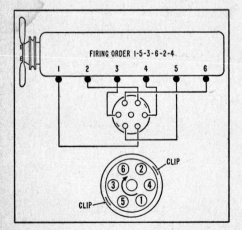

Fig. H

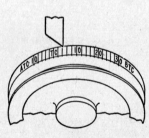

Fig. I

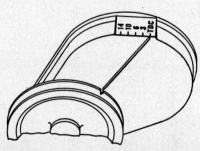

Fig. J

Continued

TUNE UP SPECIFICATIONS—Continued

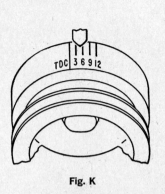

Fig. K

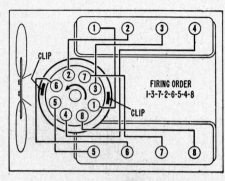

CLIP

FIRING ORDER
1-3-7-2-6-5-4-8

CLIP

Fig. M

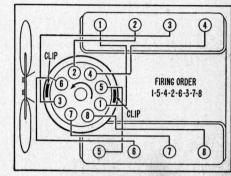

CLIP

FIRING ORDER
1-5-4-2-6-3-7-8

CLIP

Fig. N

DISTRIBUTOR SPECIFICATIONS

★If advance is checked on vehicle, double the R.P.M. and degrees advance to get crankshaft figures.

Year	Model	Basic Distributor Part No.① 12127	Breaker Gap	Cam Angle	Breaker Arm Spring Tension	Centrifugal Advance Degrees @ R.P.M. of Distributor★		Vacuum Advance		Vacuum Retard
						Advance Starts	Full Advance	Inches of Vacuum To Start Plunger	Max. Adv. Dist. Deg. @ Vacuum	Max. Ret. Dist. Deg. @ Vacuum
1966	6-240 Std. Tr.⑩	C6TF-AC	.025	37–42	17–21	None	None	1.2	11 @ 4.9	—
	6-240 Std. Tr.⑤	C6AF-AC	.025	37–42	17–21	½ @ 400	10 @ 1550	5	11 @ 15	—
	6-240 Auto. Tr.⑩	C6AF-Y	.025	37–42	17–21	None	None	.90	10 @ 4.80	—
	6-240 Auto. Tr.⑤	C6AF-AD	.025	37–42	17–21	½ @ 300	11 @ 2000	4	12 @ 18	—
	8-289 Std. Tr.⑩	C5AF-M	.017	26–31	17–21	2 @ 650	13 @ 2000	8	9 @ 14	—
	8-289 Std. Tr.⑤	C6AF-J	.017	26–31	17–21	7 @ 600	15 @ 1800	7	8 @ 16	—
	8-289 Auto. Tr.⑩	C5AF-N	.017	26–31	17–21	2 @ 450	12 @ 2000	8	11 @ 14	—
	8-289 Auto. Tr.⑤	C6AF-S	.017	26–31	17–21	3 @ 600	14 @ 1800	5	10 @ 12	—
	8-352⑩	C5AF-BG	.017	26–31	17–21	1 @ 300	9 @ 2000	10	10 @ 20	—
	8-390⑥⑩	C6AF-A	.017	26–31	17–21	½ @ 400	8 @ 1800	5	10 @ 15	—
	8-390⑤⑥	C6AF-K	.017	26–31	17–21	3 @ 500	13 @ 2000	5	11 @ 17	—
	8-390⑦⑩	C6AF-B	.017	26–31	17–21	2 @ 625	10 @ 2000	5	9 @ 13	—
	8-390⑤⑦	C6AF-T	.017	27–31	17–21	2 @ 475	11 @ 1800	5	11 @ 18	—
	8-390⑧⑩	C6AF-C	.017	26–31	17–21	3 @ 600	10 @ 2000	5	10 @ 17	—
	8-390⑥⑧	C6AF-L	.017	26–31	17–21	3 @ 500	12 @ 2000	6	10 @ 15	—
	8-390⑨⑩	C6AF-D	.017	26–31	17–21	3 @ 500	10 @ 2000	6	12 @ 18	—
	8-390⑧⑨	C6AF-L	.017	26–31	17–21	3 @ 500	12 @ 2000	6	10 @ 15	—
	8-410 Std. Tr.⑩	C6MF-A	.017	26–31	17–21	3 @ 500	10 @ 2000	5	11 @ 18	—
	8-410⑤	C6AF-L	.017	26–31	17–21	3 @ 500	12 @ 2000	6	10 @ 15	—
	8-410 Auto. Tr.⑩	C6AF-D	.017	26–31	17–21	3 @ 500	10 @ 2000	6	12 @ 18	—
	8-427 Transistor⑩	C6AF-F	.020	22–24	22–24	4 @ 650	13 @ 2000	None	None	—
	8-428⑤	C6AF-L	.017	26–31	17–21	3 @ 500	12 @ 2000	6	10 @ 15	—
	8-428⑩	C6AF-E	.017	26–31	17–21	2 @ 500	10 @ 2000	6	10 @ 15	—
1967	6-240 Std. Tr.⑩	C6TF-AC	.025	37–42	17–21	None	None	1.2	11 @ 4.9	—
	6-240 Auto. Tr.⑩	C6AF-Y	.025	37–42	17–21	None	None	.90	10 @ 4.8	—
	6-240 Std. Tr.⑤	C6AF-AC	.025	37–42	17–21	½ @ 400	10 @ 1550	5	11 @ 15	—
	6-240 Auto. Tr.⑤	C6AF-AD	.025	37–42	17–21	½ @ 300	11 @ 2000	4	12 @ 18	—
	8-289 Std. Tr.⑩	C7OF-A	.017	26–31	17–21	½ @ 400	11 @ 1500	5	11 @ 20	—
	8-289 Auto. Tr.⑩	C7OF-B	.017	26–31	17–21	½ @ 300	12 @ 2000	5	12 @ 20	—
	8-289 Std. Tr.⑤	C7OF-D	.017	26–31	17–21	½ @ 300	14 @ 2000	5	12 @ 20	—
	8-289 Auto. Tr.⑤	C7OF-E	.017	26–31	17–21	½ @ 300	13 @ 2000	5	11 @ 20	—
	8-289⑤	C7AF-AH	.017	26–31	17–21	½ @ 300	12 @ 2000	5	10 @ 20	—
	8-289⑩	C7AF-AE	.017	26–31	17–21	½ @ 300	12 @ 2000	5	12 @ 20	—

Continued

DISTRIBUTOR SPECIFICATIONS—Continued

★If advance is checked on vehicle, double the R.P.M. and degrees advance to get crankshaft figures.

Year	Model	Basic Distributor Part No.① 12127	Breaker Gap	Dwell Angle Deg.	Breaker Arm Spring Tension	Centrifugal Advance Degrees @ R.P.M. of Distributor★		Vacuum Advance		Vacuum Retard
						Advance Starts	Full Advance	Inches of Vacuum To Start Plunger	Max. Adv. Dist. Deg. @ Vacuum	Max. Ret. Dist. Deg. @ Vacuum
1967	8-390⑩	C7AF-AB	.017	26–31	17–21	½ @ 300	9 @ 2000	5	11 @ 20	—
	8-390⑩	C7AF-Y	.017	26–31	17–21	½ @ 300	10 @ 2000	5	12 @ 20	—
	8-390⑤⑥	C7AF-Z	.017	26–31	17–21	½ @ 300	12 @ 2000	5	12 @ 20	—
	8-390⑥⑦	C7AF-AA	.017	26–31	17–21	½ @ 300	12 @ 2000	5	11 @ 20	—
	8-428⑥⑧⑨	C7AF-AC	.017	26–31	17–21	½ @ 300	12 @ 2000	5	12 @ 20	—
	8-390⑥⑩	C7AF-A	.017	26–31	17–21	½ @ 300	9 @ 2000	5	12 @ 20	—
	8-390⑦⑩	C7AF-B	.017	26–31	17–21	½ @ 300	10 @ 2000	5	12 @ 20	—
	8-390⑥⑤	C7AF-C	.017	26–31	17–21	½ @ 300	13 @ 2000	5	12 @ 20	—
	8-390⑦⑤	C7AF-D	.017	26–31	17–21	½ @ 300	12 @ 2000	5	12 @ 20	—
	8-390⑧⑩	C7AF-E	.017	26–31	17–21	½ @ 300	10 @ 2000	5	12 @ 20	—
	8-390, 410⑨⑩	C7SF-A	.017	26–31	17–21	½ @ 300	10 @ 2000	5	12 @ 20	—
	8-390, 410⑧⑨⑤	C7SF-B	.017	26–31	17–21	½ @ 300	12 @ 2000	5	12 @ 20	—
	8-410⑧⑩	C7MF-A	.017	26–31	17–21	½ @ 300	10 @ 2000	5	11 @ 20	—
	8-427	CSAF-F	.020	22–24	22–24	4 @ 650	13 @ 2000	None	None	—
	8-428⑩	C7AF-J	.017	26–31	17–21	½ @ 300	10 @ 2000	5	12 @ 20	—
	8-428⑥⑧	C7AF-L	.017	26–31	17–21	½ @ 300	9 @ 1400	5	11 @ 20	—
	8-428⑥⑨	C7SF-B	.017	26–31	17–21	½ @ 300	12 @ 2000	5	12 @ 20	—
1968	6-240 Std. Tr.	C8AF-A	.027	35–40	17–21	½ @ 350	10 @ 2000	5	8 @ 25	6 @ 20
	6-240 Auto. Tr.	C8AF-B	.027	37–40	17–21	½ @ 350	11 @ 2000	5	9 @ 25	6 @ 20
	8-302⑥	C8AF-E	.021	24–29	17–21	½ @ 350	14 @ 2000	5	11 @ 25	6 @ 20
	8-302⑦	C8OF-C	.021	24–29	17–21	½ @ 350	12 @ 2000	5	11½ @ 25	6 @ 20
	8-390⑥	C8AF-M	.021	24–29	17–21	½ @ 350	11 @ 2000	5	12½ @ 25	6 @ 20
	8-390⑦	C8AF-R	.017	26–31	17–21	½ @ 350	14 @ 2000	5	12½ @ 25	6 @ 20
	8-390⑦	C8AF-AA	.017	26–31	17–21	½ @ 350	14 @ 2000	5	11½ @ 20	—
	8-390⑧	C8AF-S	.021	24–29	17–21	½ @ 350	14 @ 2000	5	12½ @ 25	6 @ 20
	8-390⑨	C7AF-AC	.017	26–31	17–21	½ @ 350	14 @ 2000	5	12½ @ 25	—
	8-427	C7OF-F	.017	26–31	17–21	½ @ 300	14½ @ 2000	5	11 @ 20	—
	8-428	C8AF-Y	.017	26–31	19–21	½ @ 350	14 @ 2000	5	12½ @ 25	—
1969	6-240 Std. Tr.	C8AF-A	.027	35–40	17–21	½ @ 350	10 @ 2000	5	8 @ 25	6 @ 20
	6-240 Auto. Tr.	C8AF-B	.027	35–40	17–21	½ @ 350	11 @ 2000	5	9 @ 25	6 @ 20
	8-302 Std. Tr.	C8AF-E	.021	24–29	17–21	½ @ 350	14 @ 2000	5	11 @ 25	6 @ 20
	8-302 Auto. Tr.	C9AF-N	.017	26–31	17–21	½ @ 350	10¾ @ 2000	5	11½ @ 20	—
	8-302 A/C⑦	C9AF-R	.021	24–29	17–21	½ @ 350	10¾ @ 2000	5	11½ @ 20	6 @ 20
	8-351 2 Bar. Carb.	C9OF-M	.017	26–31	17–21	½ @ 350	12¼ @ 2000	5	8 @ 20	—
	8-390 Std. Tr.	C9AF-J	.017	26–31	17–21	½ @ 350	10¾ @ 2000	5	12½ @ 20	—
	8-390 Auto. Tr.	C7AF-AA	.021	24–29	17–21	½ @ 350	12 @ 2000	5	11½ @ 20	—
	8-390 Premium Fuel	C8AF-R	.021	24–29	17–21	½ @ 350	12¼ @ 2000	5	12½ @ 25	6 @ 20
	8-429	C8VF-A	.017	26–31	17–21	½ @ 350	13½ @ 2000	5	9½ @ 25	—
1970	6-240 Std. Tr.	C8AF-A	.027	35–40	17–21	½ @ 350	10 @ 2000	5	8 @ 25	7 @ 20
	6-240 Auto. Tr.	C8AF-B	.027	35–40	17–21	½ @ 350	11 @ 2000	5	9 @ 25	7 @ 20
	8-302 Std. Tr.	D0AF-Y	.021	24–29	17–21	½ @ 350	14 @ 2325	5	11 @ 25	6 @ 20
	8-302 Auto. Tr.	D0AF-T	.021	24–29	17–21	½ @ 350	14 @ 3150	5	11½ @ 25	3½ @ 20
	8-351 Std. Tr.	D0AF-H	.021	24–29	17–21	½ @ 350	14 @ 2375	5	8 @ 25	6 @ 20
	8-351 Auto. Tr.	D0AF-AC	.021	24–29	17–21	½ @ 350	14 @ 2000	5	9½ @ 25	6 @ 20
	8-390 Std. Tr.	C8AF-M	.021	24–29	17–21	½ @ 350	11 @ 2000	5	12½ @ 25	6 @ 20
	8-390 Auto. Tr.	D0OF-Z	.021	24–29	17–21	½ @ 350	14 @ 2000	5	11½ @ 20	3½ @ 20
	8-428	D0AF-M	.021	24–29	17–21	½ @ 350	14 @ 2175	5	12½ @ 25	6 @ 20
	8-429⑥	C8VF-C	.021	24–29	17–21	½ @ 350	14 @ 2975	5	12 @ 25	6 @ 20
	8-429⑧	D0AF-Z	.017	26–31	17–21	½ @ 350	14 @ 2950	5	11 @ 25	—
	8-429⑨	C9AF-Y	.021	24–29	17–21	½ @ 350	14 @ 2775	5	8½ @ 25	6 @ 20
1971	6-240 Std. Tr.	D1AF-CA	.027	35–40	17–21	½ @ 350	18 @ 2500	5	8 @ 25	7 @ 20
	6-240 Auto. Tr.	C8AF-B	.027	35–40	17–21	½ @ 350	11 @ 2000	5	9 @ 25	7 @ 20
	8-302 Std. Tr.	D0AF-Y	.021	24–29	17–21	½ @ 350	14 @ 2325	5	11 @ 25	6 @ 20
	8-302 Auto. Tr.	D0AF-AE	.021	24–29	17–21	½ @ 350	13 @ 2500	5	2½ @ 25	7 @ 20

Continued

DISTRIBUTOR SPECIFICATIONS

★If advance is checked on vehicle, double the R.P.M. and degrees advance to get crankshaft figures.

Year	Model	Basic Distributor Part No.① 12127	Breaker Gap	Dwell Angle Deg.	Breaker Arm Spring Tension	Centrifugal Advance Degrees @ R.P.M. of Distributor★		Vacuum Advance		Vacuum Retard
						Advance Starts	Full Advance	Inches of Vacuum To Start Plunger	Max. Adv. Dist. Deg. @ Vacuum	Max. Ret. Dist. Deg. @ Vacuum
1971	8-351 Std. Tr.	D1AF-GA	.021	24–29	17–21	½ @ 350	13 @ 2500	5	7 @ 25	7 @ 20
	8-351 Auto. Tr.	D1AF-HA	.021	24–29	17–21	½ @ 350	18 @ 2500	5	9½ @ 25	7 @ 20
	8-351 Auto. Tr.	D1AF-KB	.021	24–29	17–21	½ @ 350	15 @ 2500	5	9½ @ 25	7 @ 20
	8-351	D0OF-U	.021	24–29	17–21	1 @ 600	10¼ @ 2000	7	9 @ 16	—
	8-390	D1AF-LB	.021	24–29	17–21	½ @ 350	18 @ 2500	5	9 @ 25	4 @ 20
	8-400	D1MF-AB	.021	24–29	17–21	½ @ 350	14 @ 2500	5	12 @ 25	4 @ 20
	8-400	D1MF-BA	.021	24–29	17–21	½ @ 350	16 @ 2500	5	10 @ 25	4 @ 20
	8-429	C8VF-C	.021	24–29	17–21	½ @ 350	14 @ 2975	5	12 @ 25	6 @ 20
	8-429	D1MF-FA	.021	24–29	17–21	½ @ 350	13 @ 2500	5	11 @ 25	7 @ 20
1972	6-240	D2AF-BA	.027	35–39	17–21	½ @ 500	8½ @ 2000	5	9½ @ 20	7 @ 20
	8-302	D2AF-CA	.017	26–30	17–21	½ @ 500	11 @ 2000	5	5½ @ 20	7 @ 20
	8-351	D2AF-PA	.017	26–30	17–21	½ @ 500	13½ @ 2000	5	9½ @ 20	7 @ 20
	8-351	D2AF-KA	.017	26–30	17–21	1 @ 500	12½ @ 2000	5	13 @ 20	7 @ 20
	8-351	D2ZF-CA	.017	26–30	17–21	½ @ 500	12½ @ 2000	5	10 @ 20	4 @ 20
	8-400	D2AF-RA	.017	26–30	17–21	½ @ 500	12 @ 2000	5	13½ @ 20	4 @ 20
	8-400	D2AF-SA	.017	26–30	17–21	½ @ 500	12 @ 2000	5	13½ @ 20	4 @ 20
	8-429	D2MF-EA	.017	26–30	17–21	½ @ 500	9½ @ 2000	5	11½ @ 20	4 @ 20
	8-429	D2MF-FA	.017	26–30	17–21	½ @ 500	9½ @ 2000	5	11½ @ 20	4 @ 20

①—Stamped on distributor housing plate.
⑤—With Thermactor Exhaust Emission Control System.
⑥—Std. trans. and two-barrel carb.
⑦—Auto. trans. and two-barrel carb.
⑧—Std. trans. and four-barrel carb.
⑨—Auto. trans. and four-barrel carb.
⑩—Without Thermactor Exhaust Emission Control.

ENGINE TIGHTENING SPECIFICATIONS★

★Torque specifications are for clean and lightly lubricated threads only. Dry or dirty threads produce increased friction which prevents accurate measurement of tightness.

Year	Engine Model	Spark Plugs Ft. Lbs.	Cylinder Head Bolts Ft. Lbs.	Intake Manifold Ft. Lbs.	Exhaust Manifold Ft. Lbs.	Rocker Arm Shaft Bracket Ft. Lbs.	Rocker Arm Cover Ft. Lbs.	Connecting Rod Cap Bolts Ft. Lbs.	Main Bearing Cap Bolts Ft. Lbs.	Flywheel to Crankshaft Ft. Lbs.	Vibration Damper or Pulley Ft. Lbs.
1966-68	6-240	15-20	70-75	20-25	20-25	—	7-9	40-45	60-70	75-85	130-145
1969-72	6-240	15-20	70-75	23-28	23-28	—	7-9	40-45	60-70	75-85	130-150
1966-68	V8-289, 302	15-20	65-70	20-22	13-18	—	3-5	19-24	60-70	75-85	70-90
1969-72	V8-302	15-20	65-72	23-25	12-16	—	3-5	19-24	60-70	75-85	70-90
1969-72	V8-351	15-20	95-100	23-25	18-24	—	3-5	40-45	95-105	75-85	70-90
1966-67	V8-352	15-20	80-90	32-35	12-18	40-45	10-12	40-45	95-105	75-85	70-90
1966-68	V8-390	15-20	80-90	32-35	12-18	40-45	4-7	40-45	95-105	75-85	70-90
1969-71	V8-390	15-20	80-90	32-35	18-24	40-45	4-7	40-45	95-105	75-85	70-90
1971-72	V8-400	15-20	95-105	①	12-16	—	3-5	40-45	95-105	75-85	70-90
1966-67	V8-410	15-20	80-90	32-35	12-18	40-45	4-7	40-45	95-105	75-85	70-90
1966-68	V8-427	15-20	100-110	32-35	12-18	40-45	4-7	53-58	95-105	75-85	70-90
1966-68	V8-428	15-20	80-90	32-35	12-18	45-50	4-7	40-45	95-105	75-85	70-90
1969-72	V8-429	15-20	130-140	25-30	28-33	65-75①	5-6	40-45	95-105	75-85	70-90

①—Rocker arm stud to cylinder head.   ②—5/16" bolts 21-25 ft. lbs. 3/8" bolts 27-33 ft. lbs.

VALVE SPECIFICATIONS

Year	Engine Model	Valve Lash		Valve Angles		Valve Spring Installed Height	Valve Spring Pressure Lbs. @ In.	Stem Clearance		Stem Diameter	
		Int.	Exh.	Seat	Face			Intake	Exhaust	Intake	Exhaust
1966	6-240	¾ Turn⑧		45	44	1¹¹⁄₁₆	80 @ 1.70	.001–.0027	.001–.0027	.3416–.3423	.3416–.3423
	8-289	¾ Turn⑧		45	44	1¾	75 @ 1.78	.001–.0027	.002–.0037	.3416–.3423	.3406–.3413
	8-352	.050–.150⑦		45	44	1¹³⁄₁₆	100 @ 1.82	.001–.0024	.001–.0024	.3711–.3718	.3711–.3718
	8-390	.050–.150⑦①		45	44	1¹³⁄₁₆	85 @ 1.82	.001–.0024	.001–.0024	.3711–.3718	.3711–.3718
	8-410	.050–.150⑦①		45	44	1¹³⁄₁₆	85 @ 1.82	.001–.0024	.001–.0024	.3711–.3718	.3711–.3718
	8-427	.025H	.025H	②	③	1¹³⁄₁₆	85 @ 1.82	.001–.0024	.002–.0034	.3711–.3718	.3701–.3708
	8-428	.050–.150⑦①		45	44	1¹³⁄₁₆	85 @ 1.82	.001–.0024	.001–.0024	.3711–.3718	.3711–.3718
1967	6-240	¾ Turn⑧		45	44	1¹¹⁄₁₆	80 @ 1.70	.001–.0027	.001–.0027	.3416–.3423	.3416–.3423
	8-289	¾ Turn⑧		45	44	1²¹⁄₃₂	60 @ 1.64	.001–.0027	.001–.0027	.3416–.3423	.3416–.3423
	8-390, 410	.100–.200⑦		45	44	1¹³⁄₁₆	85 @ 1.82	.001–.0024	.001–.0024	.3711–.3718	.3711–.3718
	8-428	.100–.200⑦		45	44	1¹³⁄₁₆	85 @ 1.82	.001–.0024	.001–.0024	.3711–.3718	.3711–.3718
	8-427	.025H	.028H	②	③	1¹³⁄₁₆	85 @ 1.82	.001–.0024	.002–.0034	.3711–.3718	.3701–.3708
1968	6-240	¾ Turn⑧		45	44	1⁹⁄₁₆	80 @ 1.70	.001–.0027	.001–.0027	.3416–.3423	.3416–.3423
	8-302	¾ Turn⑧		45	44	1⅝	75 @ 1.66	.001–.0027	.0015–.0032	.3416–.3423	.3411–.3418
	8-390	.100–.200⑦		45	44	1⅞	90 @ 1.82	.001–.0024	.0015–.0032	.3711–.3718	.3706–.3713
	8-427	.100–.200⑦		②	③	1¹³⁄₁₆	85 @ 1.82	.001–.0024	.002–.0034	.3711–.3718	.3701–.3708
	8-428	.100–.200⑦		45	44	1¹³⁄₁₆	90 @ 1.82	.001–.0024	.0015–.0032	.3711–.3718	.3706–.3713
1969	6-240	1 Turn⑧		45	44	1⁹⁄₁₆	80 @ 1.70	.001–.0027	.001–.0027	.3416–.3423	.3416–.3423
	8-302	1 Turn⑧		45	44	1⅝	75 @ 1.66	.001–.0027	.0015–.0032	.3416–.3423	.3411–.3418
	8-351	1 Turn⑧		45	44	1²⁵⁄₃₂	83 @ 1.79	.001–.0027	.0015–.0032	.3416–.3423	.3411–.3418
	8-390	.100–.200⑦		45	44	1⅞	90 @ 1.82	.001–.0027	.0015–.0032	.3711–.3718	.3706–.3713
	8-429	1 Turn⑧		45	44	1¹³⁄₁₆	80 @ 1.81	.001–.0027	.001–.0027	.3416–.3423	.3416–.3423
1970	6-240	1 Turn⑧		45	44	1⁹⁄₁₆	80 @ 1.70	.001–.0027	.001–.0027	.3416–.3423	.3416–.3423
	8-302	.067–.167⑧		45	44	1⅝	75 @ 1.66	.001–.0027	.0015–.0032	.3416–.3423	.3411–.3418
	8-351	.083–.183⑧		45	44	1²⁵⁄₃₂	83 @ 1.79	.001–.0027	.0015–.0032	.3416–.3423	.3411–.3418
	8-390	.100–.200⑦		②	44	1⅞	90 @ 1.82	.001–.0027	.0015–.0032	.3711–.3718	.3706–.3713
	8-429	.075–.175⑦		45	44	1⁵¹⁄₆₄	80 @ 1.81	.001–.0027	.001–.0027	.3416–.3423	.3416–.3423
1971–72	6-240	1 Turn⑧		45	44	1⁹⁄₁₆	80 @ 1.70	.001–.0027	.001–.0027	.3416–.3423	.3416–.3423
	8-302	.090–.190⑧		45	44	1⅝	75 @ 1.66	.001–.0027	.0015–.0032	.3416–.3423	.3411–.3418
	8-351⑥	.100–.200⑧		45	44	1²⁵⁄₃₂	83 @ 1.79	.001–.0027	.001–.0027	.3416–.3423	.3411–.3418
	8-351⑨	.100–.200⑧		45	44	1¹³⁄₁₆	80 @ 1.82	.001–.0027	.0015–.0032	.3416–.3423	.3411–.3418
	8-390	.100–.200⑦		45	44	1⅞	90 @ 1.82	.001–.0027	.0015–.0032	.3711–.3718	.3706–.3713
	8-400	.100–.200⑧		45	44	1¹³⁄₁₆	80 @ 1.82	.001–.0027	.0015–.0032	.3416–.3423	.3411–.3418
	8-429	.105–.205⑦		45	44	1⁵¹⁄₆₄	80 @ 1.81	.001–.0027	.001–.0027	.3416–.3423	.3416–.3423

①—Engines built after 12-20-65, .050–.200".
②—Intake 30°, exhaust 45°.   ③—Intake 29°, exhaust 44°.   ④—High performance engines with mechanical lifters.
⑤—Conventional adjustment.
⑥—Windsor engine.
⑦—Clearance specified is obtainable at valve stem tip with lifter collapsed. See "Valves, Adjust" text.
⑧—See text under Valves, Adjust for procedure.
⑨—Cleveland engine.

PISTONS, PINS, RINGS, CRANKSHAFT & BEARINGS

Year	Engine Model	Piston Clearance	Ring End Gap①		Wrist-pin Diameter	Rod Bearings		Main Bearings			
			Comp.	Oil		Shaft Diameter	Bearing Clearance	Shaft Diameter	Bearing Clearance	Thrust on Bear. No.	Shaft End Play
1966–67	6-240	.0014–.0022	.010	.015	.9121	2.1228–2.1236	.0008–.0024	2.3982–2.3990	.0005–.0015	5	.004–.008
	8-289	.0018–.0026	.010	.015	.9121	2.1228–2.1236	.0008–.0026	2.2482–2.2490	.0005–.0015	3	.004–.008
	8-352 (1966)	.0015–.0023	.010	.015	.975	2.4380–2.4388	.0008–.0026	2.7484–2.7492	.0005–.0015	3	.004–.010
	8-390	.0015–.0023	.010	.015	.975	2.4380–2.4388	.0008–.0026	2.7484–2.7492	.0005–.0015	3	.004–.010
	8-410	.0015–.0023	.010	.015	.975	2.4380–2.4388	.0008–.0026	2.7484–2.7492	.0005–.0015	3	.004–.010
	8-427	.0042–.0066	.010	.015	.975	2.4380–2.4388	.0013–.0032	2.7484–2.7492	.0007–.0031	3	.004–.010
	8-428	.0015–.0023	.010	.015	.975	2.4380–2.4388	.0008–.0026	2.7484–2.7492	.0005–.0015	3	.004–.010
1968–72	6-240	.0014–.0022	.010	.015	.9121	2.1228–2.1236	.0008–.0015	2.3982–2.3990	.0005–.0015	5	.004–.008
	8-302	.0018–.0026	.010	.015	.9121	2.1228–2.1236	.0008–.0015	2.2482–2.2490	.0005–.0015	3	.004–.008
	8-351②	.0018–.0026	.010	.015	.912	2.3103–2.3110	.0008–.0015	2.9994–3.0002	.0013–.0025	3	.004–.008
	8-351③	.0014–.0022	.010	.015	.912	2.3103–2.3110	.0008–.0026	2.7484–2.7492	.0009–.0026	3	.004–.008
	8-390	.0015–.0023	.010	.015	.975	2.4380–2.4388	.0008–.0015	2.7484–2.7492	.0013–.0025	3	.004–.010
	8-400	.0014–.0022	.010	.015	.975	2.3103–2.3111	.0008–.0026	2.9994–3.0002	.0009–.0026	3	.004–.010
	8-427	.0030–.0038	.018	.015	.975	2.4380–2.4388	.0008–.0015	2.7484–2.7492	.0005–.0015	3	.004–.010
	8-428	.0015–.0023	.010	.015	.975	2.4380–2.4388	.0008–.0015	2.7484–2.7492	.0005–.0015	3	.004–.010
	8-429	.0014–.0022	.010	.015	1.041	2.4992–2.5000	.0008–.0015	2.994–3.0002	.0005–.0015	3	.004–.008

①—Fit rings in tapered bores for clearance listed in tightest portion of ring travel.
②—Windsor engine.
③—Cleveland engine.

STARTING MOTOR SPECIFICATIONS

Year	Model	Starter Number	Rotation	Brush Spring Tension Ounces	No Load Test			Torque Text		
					Amperes	Volts	R.P.M.	Amperes	Volts	Torque Ft. Lbs.
1966–67	4″ Diameter	—	C	40	70	12	—	460	5.0	9.0
	4½″ Diameter	—	C	40	70	12	—	670	5.0	15.5
1968	6-240, 8-302	C7AF-11001-B	C	40	70	12	9500	670	5.0	15.5
	6-240, 8-302	C7AF-11001-D	C	40	70	12	9500	670	5.0	15.5
	6-240, 8-302	C7AF-11001-F	C	40	70	12	9500	670	5.0	15.5
	8-390, 427, 428	C7AF-11001-C	C	40	70	12	9500	670	5.0	15.5
	8-390, 427, 428	C7AF-11001-E	C	40	70	12	11000	700	4.0	15.5
1969–72	6-240, 8-302, 351	C5TZ-11002-A	C	40	70	12	9500	670	5.0	15.5
	6-240, 8-302, 351	C2OZ-11002-A	C	40	70	12	9500	670	5.0	15.5
	8-390	C3OZ-11002-C	C	40	70	12	9500	670	5.0	15.5
	8-429	C8VY-11002-C	C	40	70	12	10000	700	5.0	15.5

ALTERNATOR & REGULATOR SPECIFICATIONS

Year	Make or Model	Current Rating		Field Current @ 75°F.		Voltage Regulator				Field Relay	
		Amperes	Volts	Amperes	Volts	Make	Voltage @ 75°F.	Contact .Gap	Armature Air Gap	Armature Air Gap	Closing Voltage @ 75°F.
1966–67	Purple①	38	15	2.5	12	Autolite	14.1–14.9	.017–.022	.049–.056	.010–.018	2½–4
	Orange①	42	15	2.9	12	Autolite	14.1–14.9	.017–.022	.049–.056	.010–.018	2½–4
	Black①	45	15	2.9	12	Autolite	14.1–14.9	.017–.022	.049–.056	.010–.018	2½–4
	Red①	55	15	2.9	12	Autolite	14.1–14.9	.017–.022	.049–.046	.010–.018	2½–4
	Green①	60	15	4.6	12	Autolite	14.1–14.9	.017–.022	.049–.056	.010–.018	2½–4
1968	C6AF-10300-A	42	15	2.8–3.3	12	Autolite	13.5–15.3	②	②	②	2.3–4.2
	C6AF-10300-C	42	15	2.8–3.3	12	Autolite	13.5–15.3	②	②	②	2.3–4.2
	C6AF-10300-G	55	15	2.8–3.3	12	Autolite	13.5–15.3	②	②	②	2.3–4.2
	C6TF-10300-E	55	15	2.8–3.3	12	Autolite	13.5–15.3	②	②	②	2.3–4.2
	C6TF-10300-F	55	15	2.8–3.3	12	Autolite	13.5–15.3	②	②	②	2.3–4.2
	C6AF-10300-F	55	15	2.8–3.3	12	Autolite	13.5–15.3	②	②	②	2.3–4.2
	C6AF-10300-D	42	15	2.8–3.3	12	Autolite	13.5–15.3	②	②	②	2.3–4.2
	C6AF-10300-B	42	15	2.8–3.3	12	Autolite	13.5–15.3	②	②	②	2.3–4.2
	C7AF-10300-A	65	15	2.9	12	Autolite	13.5–15.3	②	②	②	2.3–4.2
1969	C6AF-10300-A	55	15	2.8–3.3	12	Autolite	13.5–15.3	②	②	②	2.3–4.2
	C6AF-10300-B	42	15	2.8–3.3	12	Autolite	13.5–15.3	②	②	②	2.3–4.2
	C6AF-10300-F	55	15	2.8–3.3	12	Autolite	13.5–15.3	②	②	②	2.3–4.2
	C6AF-10300-G	55	15	2.8–3.3	12	Autolite	13.5–15.3	②	②	②	2.3–4.2
	C7AF-10300-A	65	15	2.9	12	L-N	14.3–15.1	.045–.052	.010–.015	.015	3.0–4.0
	C9AF-10300-A	42	15	2.8–3.3	12	Autolite	13.5–15.3	②	②	②	2.3–4.2
1970–72	D0ZF-10300-B	38	15	2.4	12	Autolite	13.5–15.3	②	②	②	2.0–4.2
	D0AF-10300-C	42	15	2.9	12	Autolite	13.5–15.3	②	②	②	2.0–4.2
	D0AF-10300-F	42	15	2.9	12	Autolite	13.5–15.3	②	②	②	2.0–4.2
	D0AF-10300-G	42	15	2.9	12	Autolite	13.5–15.3	②	②	②	2.0–4.2
	D0AF-10300-E	55	15	2.9	12	Autolite	13.5–15.3	②	②	②	2.0–4.2
	D0AF-10300-H	55	15	2.9	12	Autolite	13.5–15.3	②	②	②	2.0–4.2
	D0ZF-10300-A	55	15	2.9	12	Autolite	13.6–15.1	.018–.020	.042–.052	.011–.018	6.2–7.2
	D0ZF-10300-C	55	15	2.9	12	Autolite	13.6–15.1	.018–.020	.042–.052	.011–.018	6.2–7.2
	D0SF-10300-A	55	15	2.9	12	Autolite	13.6–15.1	.018–.020	.042–.052	.011–.018	6.2–7.2
	D1ZF-10300-AA	55	15	2.9	12	Autolite	13.5–15.3	②	②	②	2.0–4.2
	D1AF-10300-AA	61	15	2.9	12	Autolite	13.5–15.3	②	②	②	2.0–4.2
	D1AF-10300-BA	65	15	2.9	12	Autolite	13.5–15.3	②	②	②	2.0–4.2
	D0AF-10300-A③	65	15	2.9	12	—	—	—	—	—	—
	C5TF-10300-K	65	15	2.9	12	L-N	—	—	—	—	—

①—Color stamped. Autolite. ②—Not adjustable. ③—Integral regulator.

BRAKE SPECIFICATIONS

Year	Model	Brake Drum Inside Diameter	Wheel Cylinder Bore Diameter			Master Cylinder Bore Diameter		
			Front Disc Brake	Front Drum Brake	Rear Brake	With Disc Brakes	With Drum Brakes	With Power Brakes
1966	All Passenger Cars	11.03	1.9375	1.094	.969	.938	1.00	⅞
	All Wagons	11.03	—	1.062	.969	.938	1.00	⅞
1967–68	With 6-240, 8-289, 8-302 Engines	11.03	1.938	1.094	.969	.9375	1.00	.9375
	All Others	11.03	1.938	1.094	.938	.9375	1.00	.9375
1969–72	All Passenger Cars	11.03	2.755	1.125	.938	1.00	1.00	1.00
	All Wagons	11.03	2.755	1.094	.938	1.00	1.00	1.00

WHEEL ALIGNMENT SPECIFICATIONS

OLD CAR SPECIFICATIONS: For 1946-65 Wheel Alignment Specifications see back of book.

Year	Model	Caster Angle, Degrees		Camber Angle, Degrees				Toe-In. Inch	Toe-Out on Turns, Deg.①	
				Limits		Desired				
		Limits	Desired	Left	Right	Left	Right		Outer Wheel	Inner Wheel
1966	All	+½ to +1½	+½	−¼ to +¾	−¼ to +¾	+¼	+¼	³⁄₁₆	—	20
1967	All	+½ to +1½	+1	0 to +1	0 to +1	+½	+½	³⁄₁₆	18⅛	20
1968	All	0 to +2	+1	−¼ to +1¼	−¼ to +1¼	+½	+½	³⁄₁₆	18⅛	20
1969	All	0 to +2	+1	−¼ to +1¼	−¼ to +1¼	+½	+½	³⁄₁₆	②	20
1970–72	All	0 to +2	+1	−¼ to +1¼	−¼ to +1¼	+½	+½	³⁄₁₆	19⅛	20

①—Incorrect toe-out, when other adjustments are correct, indicates bent steering arms.
②—Manual steering 18.96°; Power steering 19.14°.

REAR AXLE SPECIFICATIONS

Year	Model	Carrier Type	Ring Gear & Pinion Backlash Inch	Nominal Pinion Locating Shim, Inch	Pinion Bearing Preload				Differential Bearing Preload	Pinion Nut Torque Ft.-Lbs.①
					New Bearings With Seal Inch-Lbs.	Used Bearings With Seal Inch-Lbs.	New Bearings Less Seal Inch-Lbs.	Used Bearings Less Seal Inch-Lbs.		
1966	All	Removable	.008–.012	.020	22–32⑤	10–14⑤	—	—	.008–.012③	200
1967–72	④	Integral	.008–.012	.030	15–35	—	12½–32½	—	.008–.012③	175
	Others	Removable	.008–.012	.020	15–35	—	12½–32½	—	.008–.012③	200

①—If torque cannot be obtained, install new spacer.
②—Threaded adjusters—notches tight.
③—Case spread with new bearings; with used bearings .005–.008".

④—8-289, 302 engines with two-barrel carburetor and 6-240 engine.
⑤—Collapsible spacer. With solid spacer 15–35 inch-lbs. with seal in place; 12½–32½ inch-lbs. without seal.

COOLING SYSTEM & CAPACITY DATA

Year	Model or Engine	Cooling Capacity, Qts.			Radiator Cap Relief Pressure, Lbs.		Thermo. Opening Temp. ①	Fuel Tank Gals.	Engine Oil Refill Qts. ②	Transmission Oil			Rear Axle Oil Pints
		No Heater	With Heater	With A/C	With A/C	No A/C				3 Speed Pints	4 Speed Pints	Auto. Trans. Qts. ⑮	
FORD													
1966–67	6-240	12	13	13	12–15	12–15	195	25⑥	4	3½	4	⑫	5⑨
	8-289	14	15	15	12–15	12–15	195	25⑥	4	3½	4	⑫	5⑨
	8-352 (1966)	19½	20½	20½	12–15	12–15	195	25⑥	5	3½	4	13⑧	5½⑩
	8-390, 410, 428	19½	20½	20½	12–15	12–15	195	25⑥	4	3½	4	13⑧	5½⑩
	8-427	19½	20½	20½	12–15	12–15	195	25⑥	5	3½	4	13⑧	5½⑩
1968	6-240	12	13	13	12–15	12–15	195	24⑥	4	3½	4	⑪	4½
	8-302	14	15	15	12–15	12–15	195	24⑥	4	3½	4	⑪	4½
	8-390	19½	20½	20½	12–15	12–15	195	24⑥	4	3½	4	⑬	5
	8-427	19½	20½	20½	12–15	12–15	195	24⑥	5	3½	4	13	5
	8-428	19½	20½	20½	12–15	12–15	195	24⑥	4	3½	4	13	5
1969	6-240	12	13	13	12–15	12–15	195	24⑥	4	3½	4	⑬	4½
	8-302	14	15	15	12–15	12–15	195	24⑥	4	3½	4	⑬	4½
	8-390	19½	20½	20½	12–15	12–15	195	24⑥	4	3½	4	⑭	5
	8-429	19½	20½	20½	12–15	12–15	195	24⑥	4	3½	4	12¾	5

Continued

COOLING SYSTEM & CAPACITY DATA—Continued

Year	Model or Engine	Cooling Capacity, Qts.			Radiator Cap Relief Pressure, Lbs.		Thermo. Opening Temp. ①	Fuel Tank Gals.	Engine Oil Refill Qts. ②	Transmission Oil			Rear Axle Oil Pints
		No Heater	With Heater	With A/C	With A/C	No A/C				3 Speed Pints	4 Speed Pints	Auto. Trans. Qts. ⑮	
FORD—Continued													
1970	6-240	13½	14½	14½	12-15	12-15	195	24⑯	4	3½	4	⑬	4½
	8-302	13½	14½	14½	12-15	12-15	195	24⑯	4	3½	4	⑬	4½
	8-351	15½	16½	16½	12-15	12-15	195	24⑯	4	3½	4	⑬	5
	8-390	19	20	20	12-15	12-15	195	24⑯	4	3½	4	⑬	5
	8-429	17½	18½	18½	12-15	12-15	195	24⑯	4	3½	4	12¾	5
1971	6-240	13	14	14	12-15	12-15	195	23⑯	4	3½	4	⑬	⑤
	8-302	14	15	15	12-15	12-15	195	23⑯	4	3½	4	⑬	⑤
	8-351	15¼	16¼	16¼	12-15	12-15	195	23⑯	4	3½	4	11	5
	8-390	19	20	20	12-15	12-15	195	23⑯	4	3½	4	12¾	5
	8-400	16½	17½	18¼	12-15	12-15	195	23⑯	4	3½	4	12¾	5
	8-429	18	19	19	12-15	12-15	195	23⑯	4	3½	4	12¾	5
1972	6-240	13¼	14¼	14¼	12-15	12-15	195	22④	4	—	—	⑬	⑤
	8-302	14¼	15¼	15¼	12-15	12-15	195	22④	4	—	—	⑬	5
	8-351	15½	16½	16½	12-15	12-15	195	22④	4	—	—	⑬	5
	8-400	16¾	17¾	18¼	12-15	12-15	195	22④	4	—	—	12¾	5
	8-429	17¾	18¾	20	12-15	12-15	195	22④	4	—	—	12¾	5
MERCURY													
1966–67	8-390, 410, 428	19½	20½	20½	12-15	12-15	195	25⑥	4	3½	4	⑭	5½⑩
	8-427	19½	20½	20½	12-15	12-15	195	25⑥	5	3½	4	13⑧	5½⑩
1968	All	19½	20½	20½	12-15	12-15	195	24⑥	4	3½	—	13	5
1969	All	19½	20½	20½	12-15	12-15	195	24⑥	4	3½	—	12¾	5
1970	8-390	19	20	20	12-15	12-15	195	24⑯	4	3½	—	12¾	5
	8-429	17½	18½	18½	12-15	12-15	195	24⑯	4	3½	—	12¾	5
1971	8-351	15¼	16¼	16¼	12-15	12-15	195	23⑯	4	3½	—	11	5
	8-400	16½	17½	18¼	12-15	12-15	195	23⑯	4	3½	—	12¾	5
	8-429	18	19	19	12-15	12-15	195	23⑯	4	3½	—	12¾	5
1972	8-351	15¼	16¼	16¾	12-15	12-15	195	22½⑦	4	—	—	11	5
	8-400	16.6	17.6	18.3	12-15	12-15	195	22½⑦	4	—	—	12¾	5
	8-429	17.8	18.8	19½	12-15	12-15	195	22½⑦	4	—	—	12¾	5

①—For alcohol type anti-freeze use a 160° unit.
②—Add one quart with filter change.
③—V8-352 11 qts., V8-390 11½ qts.
④—Station Wagons 21 gals.
⑤—WER axles 4, all others 5.
⑥—Station Wagons 20 gals.
⑦—Station Wagons 21½ gallons.
⑧—C6 Transmission.
⑨—With limited-slip differential 4½ pints.
⑩—With limited-slip differential 5¼ pints.
⑪—Three spd. 10 qts., C4 8½ qts.
⑫—1966 three spd. 10 qts., 1967 three spd. 11 qts., C4 10¼ qts.
⑬—Three spd. 11 qts., C4 10¼ qts., C6 13 qts.
⑭—Three spd. 11 qts., C6 13 qts.
⑮—Approximate. Make final check with dipstick.
⑯—Station Wagon 22 gals.

IGNITION TIMING

SERVICE BULLETIN

IGNITION TIMING: If you are unable to set the ignition timing to specifications on a 1966 Mercury with air conditioning, the condition may be corrected as follows:

Since the bolt-on accessory drive pulley completely covers the vibration damper, Fig. 1, new timing marks are stamped on the accessory drive pulley. In some cases the bolt-on accessory drive pulley is incorrectly installed so that the timing marks on the drive pulley do not line up with the timing marks on the vibration damper.

NOTE: *The marks on the pulley are 5° in advance of those on the damper in order to facilitate timing operation.*

To remedy the condition, remove the bolt-on accessory drive pulley and reinstall so that the timing marks line up. Before the retaining bolts are installed, rotate the pulley back and forth to be sure the keyway tang is correctly aligned with the damper keyway.

NOTE: *Check the timing pointer to be sure the correct pointer is installed, Fig. 2.*

DISTRIBUTOR, REPLACE
Removal

1. To remove the distributor, disconnect the primary wire and vacuum control pipe. On some models the work may be made easier if the acceleration pull back spring is disconnected.
2. Remove distributor cap.
3. Scribe a mark on the distributor body indicating the position of the rotor, and scribe another mark on the body and engine block indicating position of distributor body in block. These marks can be used as guides when installing distributor in a correctly timed engine.
4. Remove hold down screw or screws and lift distributor out of block. *Do not crank engine while distributor is removed or the initial timing operation will have to be performed.*

Installation

If the crankshaft has not been disturbed, install the distributor, using the scribed marks previously made on the distributor body and engine block as guides.

If the crankshaft has been rotated while the distributor was removed from the engine, it will be necessary to retime the engine. Crank the engine to bring No. 1 piston on top dead center of its compression stroke. Align the timing mark on the vibration damper or pulley with the timing pointer (see *Tune Up* chart). Install the distributor so that the rotor points to the No. 1 spark plug wire terminal in the distributor cap.

NOTE: On all overhead valve engines,

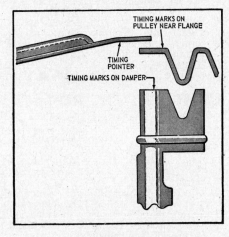

Fig. 1   Installation of bolt-on accessory drive pulley on 1966-67 Mercury with air conditioning

make sure the oil pump intermediate shaft properly engages the distributor shaft. It may be necessary to crank the engine with the starter, after the distributor drive gear is properly engaged, in order to engage the oil pump intermediate shaft.

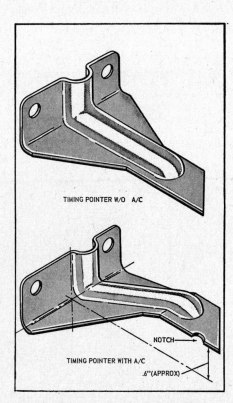

Fig. 2   Timing pointers with and without air conditioning on 1966-67 Mercury

STARTER REPLACE

SERVICE BULLETIN

STARTER PROBLEMS: If the starter is noisy or if it locks up, before condemning the starter, loosen the three mounting bolts enough to hand fit the starter properly into the pilot plate. Then tighten the mounting bolts, starting with the top bolt.

1966-72 Ford & Mercury

1. Disconnect cable at starter terminal.
2. Remove screws and take off starter.
3. Reverse procedure to install and torque bolts to 12-15 ft-lbs.

IGNITION SWITCH, REPLACE

1966 Ford & Mercury

1. Disconnect battery ground cable.
2. Turn ignition key to accessory position. Slightly depress pin with a paper clip, Fig. 3. Turn key counterclockwise and pull key and lock cylinder out of switch. If only lock cylinder is to be replaced, proceed to step 8 below.
3. Press in on rear of switch and rotate it 1/8 turn counter-clockwise (as viewed from terminal end). Remove bezel and switch.
4. Remove insulated plug and wires from rear of switch.
5. If a new switch as well as lock cylinder is to be installed, insert a screwdriver into lock opening of switch and turn slot in switch to full counter-clockwise position.
6. Connect insulated plug and accessory wires to back of switch.
7. Place bezel and switch into switch opening, press switch toward instrument panel and rotate it 1/8 turn to lock in position.
8. If a new lock cylinder is to be installed, insert key in cylinder and turn it to accessory position. Place lock and key in switch, depress pin slightly, Fig. 3, and turn key counter-clockwise. Push lock cylinder into switch, turn key and check lock cylinder operation.
9. Connect battery cable and check operation of switch.

1967 Ford

1. Disconnect ground strap from battery.
2. Remove cigar lighter and radio knobs.
3. Remove instrument cluster trim cover (10 screws).
4. Remove radio rear support nut.
5. Unfasten radio from instrument cluster (2 bolts).
6. Take radio out of cluster and disconnect antenna, speaker and power leads.
7. Remove ignition switch bezel nut.
8. Position ignition switch through ra-

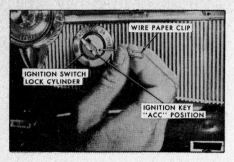

**Fig. 3 Ignition switch lock.
1966-69 Ford and Mercury**

dio opening and remove accessory wire retaining nut.
9. Disconnect ignition switch wire connector from switch and remove switch.
10. Reverse procedure to install.

1967 Mercury

1. Disconnect ground cable from battery.
2. On units equipped with Safety Convenience Panel, lower panel to floor.
3. Remove switch lock cylinder.
4. Remove switch bezel nut by turning to left.
5. Pull ignition switch from back of panel and lower switch. Remove multiple connector retaining nut and disengage connector from ignition switch.

1968-69 Ford & Mercury

1. Disconnect battery ground cable.
2. On Mercury only, remove screw retaining washer valve behind ignition switch and position valve to the side.
3. Insert ignition key in switch. Turn key to accessory position and insert a wire pin in hole on ignition switch. Slightly depress pin while turning counterclockwise past the accessory position; this will release lock cylinder from switch. Pull lock cylinder from switch with the key.
4. Remove bezel nut retaining switch to instrument panel and lower switch.
5. Depress tabs securing multiple connector from switch and remove switch.
6. Reverse procedure to install.

1970-72 Ford & Mercury

1. Remove steering column shroud and lower steering column from brake support bracket.
2. Disconnect battery cable.
3. Disconnect switch wiring and remove two switch retaining nuts. Disconnect switch from actuator and remove switch.
4. Move shift lever to Park position on automatic transmissions and Reverse on standard transmission units. Place ignition key in Lock position and remove the key.

NOTE: New replacement switches are pinned in the Lock position by a plastic shipping pin inserted in a locking hole in the switch. For an existing switch, pull plunger out as far

as it will go then back one detent to Lock position and insert a 3/32" drill in locking hole to retain switch in Lock position.

5. With locking pin in place, install switch on steering column, determine mid position of actuator lash and tighten retaining bolts.
6. Remove locking pin.

LIGHT SWITCH, REPLACE
1966 Ford & Mercury

1. Remove control knob and shaft by pressing knob release button on switch housing, Fig. 4, with knob in full "on" position. Pull knob out of switch.
2. Unscrew mounting nut, remove switch and disconnect wire connector.
3. To install, attach wire connector, insert switch in instrument panel and secure with mounting nut.
4. Install knob and shaft assembly by inserting it all the way into switch until a distinct click is heard. In some instances it may be necessary to rotate switch slightly until it engages switch contact carrier.

1967 Ford

1. Disconnect ground strap from battery.
2. Remove cigar lighter and radio knobs.
3. Remove instrument cluster trim cover (10 screws).
4. Remove set screw from light switch control knob and remove knob.
5. Remove light switch bezel nut.
6. Lower switch and disconnect wiring connector.
7. Reverse procedure to install.

1967 Mercury

1. Disconnect ground cable from battery.
2. Remove light switch knob.
3. Remove bezel nut and bezel.
4. Reach up behind instrument panel

Fig. 4 Light switch. 1966-69 Ford and Mercury

and remove light switch from panel. Lower switch and wiring beneath panel. Disconnect junction block from switch.

1968-69 Ford & Mercury

1. Disconnect battery and ground cable.
2. Remove control knob and shaft by pressing knob release button on switch housing with knob in full on position. Pull knob out of switch.
3. On Mercury only, remove two screws retaining wiring harness bracket at back of switch and remove bracket.
4. Remove bezel nut and lower switch.
5. Disconnect multiple plug to switch. If vehicle has concealed headlamp doors, disconnect the three vacuum hoses and remove switch from vehicle.
6. Reverse procedure to install.

1971-72 Ford & Mercury

1. Disconnect battery ground cable.
2. Remove instrument panel pad.
3. Remove the instrument cluster.
4. Remove switch knob and shaft assembly.
5. Remove three attaching screws and remove switch.

1970 Ford

1. Disconnect battery ground cable.

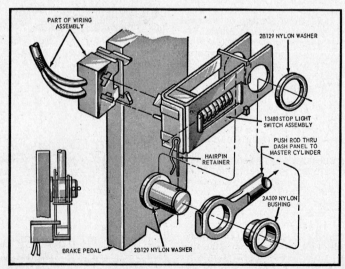

Fig. 5 Mechanical stop light switch. 1966-72 Ford and Mercury

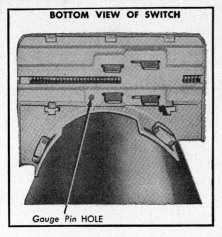

BOTTOM VIEW OF SWITCH

Gauge Pin HOLE

Fig. 6   Neutral safety switch (column shift). All 1967 and 1966 with Cruiseomatic

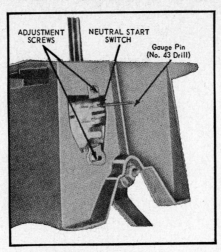

ADJUSTMENT SCREWS   NEUTRAL START SWITCH
Gauge Pin (No. 43 Drill)

Fig. 7   Neutral safety switch (console shift). 1967-69 with C4 and C6 transmissions

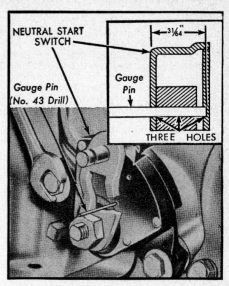

NEUTRAL START SWITCH
Gauge Pin (No. 43 Drill)
Gauge Pin
THREE HOLES

Fig. 8   Neutral safety switch (transmission mounted). 1966 with C4 and C6 transmissions

2. Turn control knob to full ON position and reach up from under the instrument panel and press the release button on the switch housing. With the button pressed in, pull the knob out of the switch.
3. Unscrew bezel nut to detach switch from instrument panel and lower the switch assembly.
4. Disconnect wiring plug and vacuum hoses if so equipped and remove switch.

1970 Mercury

1. Disconnect battery ground cable.
2. From behind instrument panel, disconnect wiring plug and vacuum hoses if so equipped from switch.
3. Remove four retaining screws and pull switch out from behind instrument panel.

STOP LIGHT SWITCH, REPLACE

1966-72 Mechanical Type

1. Referring to Fig. 5, disconnect wires at connector.
2. Remove hairpin retainer and slide switch, push rod and nylon washers and bushing away from pedal, and remove switch.
3. Position the new switch, push rod, bushing and washers on brake pedal pin and secure with hairpin retainer.
4. Connect wires at connector and install wires in retaining clip.

TURN SIGNAL SWITCH, REPLACE

1970-72 Ford & Mercury

1. Remove retaining screw from underside of steering wheel spoke and lift off the pad horn switch/trim cover and medallion as an assembly.
2. Disconnect horn switch wires from terminals.
3. Remove steering wheel retaining nut

and remove steering wheel with a suitable puller.
4. Remove turn signal switch lever by unscrewing it from column.
5. Remove shroud from steering column.
6. Disconnect column wiring connector plug and remove screws that secure switch to column.
7. On tilt column models, remove wires and terminals from column wiring plug.

NOTE: *Record the color code and position of each wire before removing it from plug. A hole provided in the flange casting on fixed column models makes it unnecessary to separate wires from plug. The plug with wires installed can be guided through the hole.*

8. Remove plastic cover sleeve from wiring harness and remove the switch from top of column.

1968-69 Ford & Mercury

Removal

1. Disconnect battery ground cable.
2. Remove horn button and steering wheel.
3. Remove turn indicator handle.
4. Unscrew and remove turn indicator switch from steering column tube.
5. Disconnect connector blocks at the column. Release tabs one at a time and remove wires from block connectors on 1968 models. It is not necessary to remove wires from connectors on 1969 models.
6. From lower portion of column, remove cover from wiring and tie a cord to the wire ends. Remove switch from top of column, feeding wiring and cord up the column.

Installation

1. Attach the wire ends of a new turn indicator switch to the cord and feed wires down through steering column. Remove cord and install cover.
2. Install connector blocks in column. Plug in electrical leads and secure

wiring in retaining clip.
3. Install switch to steering column tube and install indicator handle.
4. Install steering wheel and horn button, and connect battery cable.

SERVICE BULLETIN

1966-67 MODELS: Before judging the turn signal to be the cause of malfunction and replacing as defective, first check the following to make certain that they are not causing the problem:
1. The steering shaft should be centered in the column so that the steering wheel hub canceling fingers are in proper relation to the switch canceling mechanism. This can be accomplished by loosening the column attachment to the dash panel and shifting the tube in relation to the shaft.
2. Make sure that the ignition switch is not sticking between the "Start" and the normal engine "On" position, thereby adversely affecting the electrical circuit.
3. Excessive "Locktite" on the threads of the turn signal lever may be contacting the turn signal switch mechanism, causing a binding condition.
4. The fingers on the steering wheel hub canceling cam may be bent so that proper contact with the canceling mechanism cannot be accomplished.

NOTE: When installing the new switch, make sure the canceling cam on the steering wheel makes contact with the canceling pawls on the switch. The clearance between steering wheel hub and steering shaft housing flange should not be more than 1/16" for proper switch canceling. Reposition steering shaft if necessary.

1966-67 Ford & Mercury

1. Disconnect battery ground cable.
2. Remove horn button.

3. Remove steering wheel.
4. Remove turn signal handle.
5. Remove screws and turn switch from steering column.
6. Remove connector blocks at column. Release tabs one at a time and remove wires from block connectors.
7. From lower portion of column, remove cover from wiring assembly and tie a cord to wire ends. Remove switch from top of column, feeding wire and cord up the column.
8. Attach wire ends of new switch to cord and feed wires down through column. Remove cord and install wiring cover. Then complete the installation in reverse order of removal.

NEUTRAL SAFETY SWITCH
1970-72 Ford & Mercury

Column Shift

The neutral safety switch has been eliminated and is replaced by a series of steps designed into the steering column selector lever hub casting.

Console Shift

1. Remove four screws and plates securing selector lever handle to the lever. Remove handle and detent control.
2. Remove two screws from rear of console top panel. Pull panel back to unhook it from front of console and remove panel.
3. Loosen two switch attaching screws.
4. Move selector lever back and forth until gauge pin (No. 43 drill) can be fully inserted into gauge pin holes.
5. Place selector lever firmly against the stop of the neutral detent position.
6. Slide switch forward or rearward as required until the switch lever contacts the selector lever actuator. If an adjustment cannot be made, loosen the actuating lever attaching screw and adjust the lever.
7. Tighten switch attaching screws and if actuator lever was adjusted tighten the actuator lever bolt.
8. Turn ignition key to ACC position and place selector lever in the reverse position and check operation of back-up lights. Turn key off.
9. Place console top panel on console and install screws.
10. Position selector lever detent control and handle on selector lever and secure with plates and screws.

1969 Ford & Mercury

Column Shift

To adjust the switch proceed as follows:
1. Place transmission selector lever against the stop of the neutral detent.
2. Loosen two retaining screws on the steering column.
3. With the selector lever against neutral stop, rotate the switch until a start in neutral position is obtained. Then tighten the two screws.
4. With the switch properly adjusted in neutral, place the selector lever in the "1" position and push the park reset button, located on the right side of the switch, to the left until it stops.

NOTE: The park reset must be per-

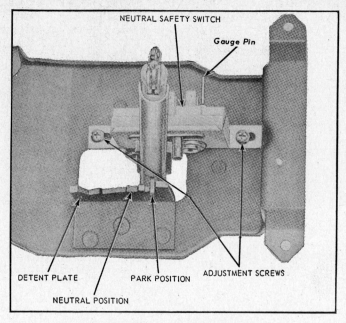

Fig. 9 Neutral safety switch (console shift). 1966 Cruiseomatic

formed whenever the switch has been adjusted.

1968 Ford & Mercury

Column Shift

The redesigned neutral start switch is mounted on top of the steering column but has been moved closer to the toeboard just below the collapsible section of the jacket.

To adjust the switch, it must be removed from the column. Put the selector lever in neutral and set the parking brake. Then disconnect the electrical and vacuum connections, remove the two fastening screws and lift the switch straight up and out.

After removing the switch body, remove the separate actuator lever. Compress the protruding ends of the lever with pliers and lift the lever out of the column. To adjust the switch, proceed as follows:

1. Hold switch with the wire terminal facing toward you, and with actuator lever in place. Move actuator lever all the way to your left, but don't force it or the switch will be damaged internally.
2. Insert a $3/32''$ drill or rod $1/2$ inch into the hole in the boss on the top of the switch.
3. Gently but firmly move actuator lever back to the right until it stops. Excessive pressure on the lever will damage the switch. This will move the Park circuit to its position of minimum travel, which must be done if the switch is to function properly upon installation.
4. Remove the $3/32''$ rod while you align the two gauge pin holes in the switch case. Then reinsert the $3/32''$ rod.
5. Install the actuator lever to the column by squeezing it slightly and pressing it into position in the shift tube.

6. With the transmission selector lever held against the stop in the neutral detent position, fasten switch to column with the two screws.
7. After connecting wiring and any vacuum hose, be sure to remove the $3/32''$ rod.

All 1967 & 1966 Cruiseomatic

Column Shift, Fig. 6

1. With manual linkage properly adjusted, check starter engagement circuit in all transmission selector lever positions. The circuit must be open in all drive positions and closed only in Park and Neutral.
2. To adjust switch, loosen retaining screws that locate switch on steering column.
3. Place transmission selector lever firmly against the stop of the neutral detent position.
4. Rotate switch actuating lever until gauge pin (#43 drill) can be inserted in gauge pin holes.
5. Tighten switch screws and remove gauge pin.

1967-69 C4 & C6 Units

Console Shift, Fig. 7

1. Remove selector lever handle.
2. Unfasten and position console to one side.
3. Loosen adjusting screws.
4. Move selector lever back and forth until gauge pin (#43 drill) can be fully inserted into gauge pin holes.
5. Place transmission selector lever firmly against stop of neutral detent position.
6. Slide combination neutral start and back-up light switch forward or rearward as required until switch actu-

ating lever contacts selector lever.
7. Tighten switch attaching screws, remove gauge pin and check for starting in Park position.

1966 C4 and C6

Replace and Adjust, Fig. 8
1. Apply penetrating oil to outer lever attaching nut to prevent breaking inner lever shaft. Remove transmission downshift outer lever attaching nut and lever.
2. Remove two neutral start switch screws.
3. Disconnect two multiple wire connectors and remove switch from transmission.
4. Install new switch.
5. With transmission manual lever in neutral, check location of switch with gauge pin (#43 drill) and adjust switch if necessary.
6. Tighten switch bolts and remove gauge pin.
7. Install outer downshift lever, and downshift linkage rod to lever.
8. Install switch wires and check operation of switch.

1966 With Cruiseomatic

Console Shift, Fig. 9
1. Remove handle from selector lever.
2. Remove chrome trim panel from top of console.
3. Place lever in neutral position and remove three quadrant attaching screws. Remove indicator light from quadrant base and lift quadrant from console.
4. Loosen two adjustment screws.
5. Move selector lever back and forth until gauge pin (#43 drill) can be fully inserted in gauge pin holes.
6. Place transmission selector lever firmly against stop of neutral detent position.
7. Slide combination neutral start and back-up light switch forward or rearward as required until switch actuating lever contacts selector lever.
8. Tighten switch attaching screws and check for starting in Park position.
9. Complete operation in reverse order.

HORN SOUNDER, REPLACE

1969-72 Rim-Blow Type

The rubber insert and copper strip assembly is not replaceable. Therefore if a new insert assembly is required the entire steering wheel must be replaced.
1. Remove the pad from the steering wheel (three screws).
2. Remove medallion from the pad.
3. After removing the steering wheel nut the wheel can be removed from the shaft with a wheel puller.

1968-72 Except Rim Blow-Type

1. Disconnect battery ground cable.
2. Remove steering column pad (2 screws).
3. Push down and turn horn ring and remove ring and spring.

---

4. Reverse procedure to install.

1966-67 Ford

1. Disconnect horn wire connector that has a yellow and yellow-green wire in it, under instrument panel to the left of steering column.
2. Press down evenly on horn ring and turn counterclockwise until it lifts out from steering wheel.
3. Remove horn ring and spring.
4. The horn ring contacts are integral with the turn signal switch and are removed with the switch.
5. Reverse procedure to install.

1966-67 Mercury

1. Disconnect horn wires at connector at lower end of steering column.
2. Remove hub from steering column by pressing it down and rotating it counterclockwise.
3. Remove screws from center retaining the wires.
4. Remove center screws retaining the ring to the column and from end of ring to steering wheel. A spring will fall out from under each button.
5. Position springs under buttons. Place ring to wheel and install center screws. Install ring to steering column, securing it with a screw at each end of the buttons located in steering spokes. Then complete the installation in reverse order of removal.

INSTRUMENT CLUSTER

1971-72 Ford

Instrument Cluster
1. Disconnect battery ground cable.
2. Remove instrument panel pad.
3. Disconnect speedometer cable and all electrical connections to the instrument cluster.
4. Remove four cluster attaching screws (two at bottom and two at top), and lift the cluster from the instrument panel.

Fuel Gauge & Speedometer
1. Remove instrument cluster as described above.
2. Remove lights, wiper-washer and clock reset knobs.
3. Remove eight screws attaching lens, shield and mask to cluster.
4. Remove two screws attaching speedometer to cluster.
5. To remove fuel gauge, remove two terminal nuts.

1971-72 Mercury

Instrument Cluster
1. Disconnect battery ground cable.
2. Remove instrument panel pad.
3. Disconnect speedometer cable and all wires from back of cluster.
4. Remove four screws from lower edge of cluster and remove cluster.

Fuel Gauge & Speedometer
1. Remove cluster as described above.
2. Remove seven screws attaching the

---

cluster housing and lens and inner mask and the cluster mask.
3. To remove speedometer, remove two screws from rear of cluster housing.
4. To remove fuel gauge, remove terminal nuts and gauge attaching screw.

1969-70 Ford

Fuel Gauge & Speedometer
1. From passenger side of instrument panel, remove lighter element and all of the control knobs, and then remove the cluster trim cover (10 screws).
2. Remove the attaching screws and the lens.
3. Remove attaching screws and lift the mask from the speedometer and fuel gauge.
4. Remove spring washers and nuts (one at each side) and the attaching screw at the bottom, then remove fuel gauge from the studs.
5. Remove attaching screws and pull speedometer head out of cluster far enough to reach the cable disconnect.
6. To disengage the cable, press on the flat surface of the disconnect and at the same time pull the cable from the head.
7. Remove the speedometer.
8. Reverse the procedure to install.

Instrument Cluster
1. Remove the instrument panel pad (20 screws).
2. From behind cluster disconnect all electrical connections to cluster.
3. Disconnect heater, air conditioner and speedometer cables.
4. Remove lighter element and all control knobs from passenger side of cluster.
5. Remove cluster trim cover (10 screws).
6. Remove eight mounting screws and withdraw cluster from panel.
7. Reverse procedure to install.

1969-70 Mercury

Instrument Cluster
1. Remove wiper knob and bezel, cigar lighter element and the finish panel.
2. Remove instrument panel pad.
3. Remove wiper nut and the bracket (3 screws) from left end of pad support.
4. Remove lighter socket and bracket from right end of pad support.
5. Remove five pad support-to-instrument panel screws and three lower left panel-to-instrument panel screws and then remove pad support and lower panel as an assembly.
6. From behind cluster, disconnect all electrical connections to cluster and speedometer cable.
7. Remove the cluster assembly from panel (6 screws).
8. Reverse procedure to install.

Fuel Gauge & Speedometer
After removal of cluster as described above, the speedometer and fuel gauge can be removed from the cluster.

1968 Ford

Fuel Gauge & Speedometer
1. Disconnect battery ground cable.

2. Remove right and left windshield pillar mouldings.
3. Pry moulding from right side of instrument panel pad covering pad screws.
4. Pry off two access covers located above speedometer lens and on underside of pad.
5. Remove instrument panel pad (11 screws).
6. Pull pad off radio control knobs.
7. Remove instrument cluster mask and lens (10 button clips).
8. Disconnect speedometer cable.
9. Remove instrument panel lower pad (5 screws).
10. Remove clock upper retainer (2 screws).
11. Remove two clock screws and position clock forward.
12. Remove plate under speedometer (1 screws).
13. Remove speedometer and black out cover (2 rubber spacers and 5 screws).
14. Remove two fuel gauge screws and position gauge out. Disconnect two wire connectors and remove fuel gauge.
15. Reverse procedure to install.

1968 Mercury

Fuel Gauge

1. Disconnect battery ground cable.
2. Remove control knobs from heater controls, radio, clock, wiper switch (pull off) and headlight switch.
3. Remove speedometer bezel.
4. Remove right and left instrument panel finish panels.
5. Remove speedometer cover lens (4 buttons).
6. Remove fuel gauge cover lens.
7. Remove screws retaining fuel gauge to cluster and position gauge out. Disconnect two push on connectors to gauge and remove gauge.
8. Reverse procedure to install.

Speedometer

1. Disconnect battery ground cable.
2. Remove knobs from heater control, radio and clock.
3. Pull knob from wiper switch.
4. Remove headlight switch knob.
5. Remove speedometer bezel (4 screws).
6. Remove right and left finish panels from cluster.
7. Remove speedometer dial cover (4 buttons).
8. Remove four screws retaining speedometer from cluster and position speedometer out by working speedometer cable out with assembly.
9. Disconnect speedometer cable and also disconnect instrument voltage regulator and remove speedometer and housing.
10. Unfasten speedometer from housing.
11. Reverse procedure to install.

1967 Ford

Fuel Gauge

1. Disconnect ground strap from battery.
2. Remove cigar lighter and radio knobs.
3. Remove instrument trim cover (10 screws).

4. Unfasten warning light housing (4 screws).
5. Disconnect fuel gauge and remove warning light housing.
6. Remove warning light housing lens and mask.
7. Remove fuel gauge from housing.
8. Reverse procedure to install.

Speedometer

1. Disconnect ground strap from battery.
2. Remove instrument panel pad.
3. Remove clock re-set knob.
4. Remove warnings light housing.
5. Remove eight friction pins retaining instrument cluster and mask. Remove lens.
6. Remove four rubber spacers.
7. Remove three screws retaining speedometer to its back can. Position speedometer outward, disconnect cable and remove speedometer.

1967 Mercury

Fuel Gauge

1. Disconnect ground strap from battery.
2. Remove radio knobs.
3. Remove cluster housing screws.
4. Remove speedometer mask and lens (4 friction pins).
5. Remove left hand lens and mask (4 friction pins).
6. Unfasten fuel gauge from instrument cluster rear housing (3 screws). Position fuel gauge outward, disconnect two connectors and remove gauge.
7. Reverse procedure to install.

Speedometer

1. Disconnect ground strap from battery.
2. Remove radio knobs.
3. Remove instrument cluster housing.
4. Remove speedometer mask and lens (4 friction pins).
5. Unfasten speedometer (4 screws). Position speedometer outward, disconnect cable and remove speedometer.
6. Reverse procedure to install.

1966 Ford

Fuel Gauge & Speedometer

1. Disconnect battery ground cable.
2. Remove cluster pad and retainer.
3. Remove upper and lower cluster covers.
4. Remove radio knobs.
5. Remove friction pins retaining cluster lens and mask and remove lens and mask.
6. Disconnect speedometer cable and remove speedometer retaining bracket.
7. Remove left standoffs and speedometer.
8. Remove screws retaining fuel gauge, pull back on left side of speedometer (if not already removed) and ease out fuel gauge. Remove wires and take out fuel gauge.

1966 Mercury

1. Disconnect battery ground cable.
2. Remove headlight, radio, w/s wiper, heater and air conditioner control knobs.

3. Remove screws from instrument cluster center finish panel.
4. Pull finish panel out of instrument panel, disconnect wires from heater and air conditioner switches and remove finish panel.
5. With finish panel removed, all instruments are individually accessible.

W/S WIPER MOTOR

1971-72 Ford & Mercury

1. Disconnect battery ground cable.
2. Remove wiper arm and blade assemblies from pivot shafts.
3. Remove left cowl screen (four screws) for access.
4. Disconnect linkage drive arm from the motor output crankpin by removing retaining clip.
5. From engine side of dash, remove two wire connectors from motor.
6. Remove three bolts that retain motor to dash and remove motor. If output arm catches on dash during removal, handturn the arm clockwise so it will clear opening in the dash. Before installing motor, be sure output arm is in park position.

1969-70 Ford & Mercury

1. Remove wiper arm and blade assemblies from pivot shafts.
2. Remove cowl top grille (10 screws).
3. Disconnect linkage drive arm from motor output arm crankpin by removing clip.
4. Disconnect wire push-on connectors from motor.
5. From engine side of dash, remove bolts retaining motor to dash and remove motor. If output arm catches on dash during removal, hand turn the arm clockwise so it will clear opening in dash.
6. When installing motor, align output arm with opening in dash and turn the arm clockwise as necessary.

1968 Ford & Mercury

1. Remove cowl intake screen.
2. Disconnect wiper links at motor output arm pin. Disconnect motor harness by removing clip.
3. Disconnect motor harness connector and remove motor.
4. Unfasten motor from bracket.

Installation

1. Assemble new motor to bracket. Correctly position vapor seal gasket or replace if required.
2. Connect harness connector to new motor.
3. Position motor and install retaining bolts. Temporarily connect motor wiring connector to motor and run motor so that it is in park position before connecting linkage to motor.
4. Complete installation in reverse order of removal.

1967 Ford & Mercury

1. Remove cowl intake screen.
2. Disconnect wiper links at motor output arm pin. Disconnect motor harness by removing retention clip.
3. Disconnect motor harness connector

and take off motor.

4. Reverse procedure to install, being sure motor is in park position before connecting linkage to motor.

1966 Ford & Mercury

1. To remove wiper motor, disconnect wiper links at motor output arm pins.
2. Unfasten and lower motor.
3. Disconnect motor harness connector and remove motor.

W/S WIPER SWITCH
1971-72 Ford & Mercury

1. Disconnect battery ground cable.
2. Remove instrument panel pad and instrument cluster.
3. Remove three switch attaching screws and remove switch.

1970 Ford

1. Disconnect battery ground cable and remove two piece cover from steering column (2 screws).
2. To allow removal of cluster trim cover, remove radio, wiper, washer, interval, heater and defogger switch knobs and lighter element.
3. Remove screw that retains the PRND21 dial cable to column and loosen set screw that retains the cable pin in the shaft housing.
4. Remove retaining screws and cluster trim cover assembly.
5. Remove the two screws that retain switch to cluster, lower the switch and disconnect multiple connector and hoses.

1969 Ford

1. To allow removal of cluster trim cover, remove the radio, wiper, washer, interval and heater switch knobs and the lighter element.
2. Remove retaining screws and cluster trim cover assembly.
3. Remove screws that retain the switch to the cluster, lower switch and disconnect multiple connector and vacuum hose from switch.

1969-70 Mercury

1. Remove wiper knob and bezel from switch shaft.
2. Remove nut that retains switch to bracket.
3. Lower switch from behind panel and disconnect multiple connector and vacuum hoses from the switch.

1968 Ford

1. Remove wiper and washer control knobs.
2. Reaching under instrument panel, remove two screws retaining switch to lower portion of instrument panel.
3. Disconnect multiple connector and two single connectors from switch.
4. Separate wiper switch from washer switch.

1968 Mercury

1. Disconnect battery ground cable.
2. Remove screw retaining washer co-

ordinator to lower edge of instrument panel and position co-ordinator to the side.
3. Pull off wiper control knob.
4. Remove nut retaining switch to cluster. Lower switch and disconnect multiple connector and five vacuum hoses, then remove switch.

1967 Ford

1. Disconnect ground strap from battery.
2. Remove cigar lighter and radio knobs.
3. Remove instrument cluster trim cover (10 screws).
4. Unfasten switch and bracket from cluster back plate (4 screws).
5. Position switch outward. Disconnect wiring and remove switch and bracket.
6. Remove control knob.
7. Remove bezel nut and remove switch from bracket.
8. Reverse procedure to install.

1967 Mercury

1. Disconnect ground strap from battery.
2. Loosen set screw and remove control knob.
3. Remove switch bezel.
4. Lower switch and remove three vacuum hoses.
5. Unplug connector and remove switch.
6. Reverse procedure to install.

1966 Ford & Mercury

1. Loosen retaining screw and take off switch knob.
2. Remove switch bezel nut.
3. Remove switch from instrument panel.
4. To install reverse removal procedure.

W/S WIPER TRANSMISSION
1971-72 Ford & Mercury

1. Disconnect battery and remove wiper arm and blade assemblies from pivot shafts.
2. Remove cowl screens for access to linkage.
3. Disconnect the left linkage arm from the drive arm by removing the clip.
4. Remove the three bolts retaining the left pivot shaft assembly to the cowl.
5. Remove the left arm and pivot shaft assembly through the cowl opening.
6. Disconnect linkage drive arm from motor crankpin by removing the clip.
7. Remove three bolts that connect drive arm pivot shaft assembly to the cowl and remove the pivot shaft drive arm and right arm as an assembly.

1969-70 Ford & Mercury

1. Remove wiper arm and blades from pivot shafts.
2. Remove cowl top grille.
3. The right pivot shaft and link on Mercury has to be removed before the left assembly or drive arm can

be removed. Remove three retaining screws at right pivot shaft and disconnect the right link from the plate on the inner side of the dash panel by removing the clip. Lift the pivot assembly out of cowl opening.
4. Remove three retaining screws at the left pivot shaft and disconnect the left link from the plate and lift out of cowl opening.
5. Reverse the procedure to install.

1968 Ford & Mercury

1. Remove wiper arms and blades.
2. Remove cowl top ventilator grille, hood pad and windshield washer nozzles.
3. Through cowl opening remove clip retaining wiper arms to motor drive arm.
4. Remove pivot shaft screws, then remove pivot and arms as an assembly from right side of cowl openings.
5. Remove arm to pivot retaining clip.

Installation

1. Install new arm or pivot and clip.
2. Position arm assembly through right side of cowl opening and install screws.
3. On Mercury only, position left hand pivot and pump assembly with hoses through cowl top hole and install grommet. Recouple hoses at connectors after mounting screws are attached.
4. Position wiper arm to motor drive arm and install clip.
5. On Mercury only, disconnect vacuum and washer hoses at plastic connectors; remove grommet around hoses on left side for pivot and pump vibra jet. Removal of right hand pivot shaft is same as Ford.
6. Install washer nozzles, position cowl top hood pad and grille and install retaining screws. Install wiper arms and blades.

1966-67 Ford & Mercury

1. Remove wiper arms and blades.
2. Remove cowl top ventilator grille, hood pad and w/s washer nozzles.
3. Through cowl opening, remove clip from wiper arms-to-drive arms.
4. Remove pivot and arms as an assembly from right side of cowl opening.
5. Remove arm-to-pivot retaining clip.
6. Reverse procedure to install.

RADIO, REPLACE

NOTE: When installing radio, be sure to adjust antenna trimmer for peak performance.

1971-72 Ford & Mercury

1. Disconnect battery ground cable.
2. Remove radio and fader knobs.
3. Remove radio bezel.
4. Remove upper and lower rear radio support bolts and brackets.
5. Disconnect power, antenna and speaker.
6. Remove two nuts retaining radio to instrument panel and remove radio.

1969-70 Ford

1. Remove the trim cover from instrument panel.
2. Remove three nuts retaining front of radio to cluster.
3. Remove screw retaining the rear support to the bottom of the radio.
4. Pull radio from cluster and disconnect wires from chassis.

1969-70 Mercury

1. Disconnect battery ground cable.
2. Remove control knobs from radio.
3. Disconnect all wires from radio and remove nut attaching the rear support to the back of the radio.
4. Remove nut attaching the front edge of radio to instrument panel and remove radio.
5. Remove nut from radio control shaft.

1968 Ford

1. Disconnect battery ground cable.
2. Remove side garnish mouldings from windshield pillars.
3. Unsnap moulding from right side of instrument panel pad to reveal pad attaching screws.
4. Remove two pop-off access covers from instrument panel pad in cluster area.
5. Remove four screws attaching right half of pad to instrument panel.
6. Remove two screws attaching left side of pad to instrument panel above cluster.
7. Remove three screws attaching left side of pad below cluster.
8. Remove one screw attaching each end of instrument panel lower pad to upper pad and remove upper pad.
9. Pull off radio control knobs.
10. Remove lens and mask from cluster (10 buttons).
11. Remove black out cover at right of speedometer (2 screws).
12. Unfasten radio front mounting plate from instrument panel (4 screws).
13. Unfasten radio rear bracket from instrument panel (1 screw).
14. Pull radio part way out and disconnect antenna lead-in cable. Then pull radio out and disconnect power and speaker wires from radio.
15. Remove front mounting plate and rear bracket from radio.
16. Reverse procedure to install.

1968 Mercury

1. Disconnect battery ground cable.
2. Pull off radio control knobs.
3. Remove speedometer bezel (4 screws).
4. Pull W/S wiper knob off shaft.
5. Remove clock and heater knobs.
6. Remove cluster right finish panel (4 screws).
7. Remove nut attaching rear support to radio.
8. Unfasten radio and mounting plate from instrument panel (4 screws). Pull radio out from panel and disconnect radio feed wires, speaker wires and antenna lead from radio.
9. Remove mounting plate from radio.
10. Reverse procedure to install.

Fig. 10 Bead chain adjustment. 1967-68

1967 Ford & Mercury

1. Disconnect ground cable at battery.
2. Remove radio knobs and, on Ford, remove cigar lighter.
3. Remove instrument cluster cover (10 screws on Ford, 13 on Mercury).
4. Remove radio rear support nut.
5. Remove two bolts (Ford) or four screws (Mercury) that retain radio to instrument cluster.
6. Pull radio forward out of cluster and disconnect antenna, speaker and power leads from radio.
7. Reverse procedure to install.

1966 Ford & Mercury

1. Disconnect battery ground cable.
2. If air conditioned, disconnect ducts from plenum and remove nozzle adapter plate.
3. On air conditioned Mercury, remove ash tray and slide bracket.
4. Remove radio knobs.
5. Remove nut from radio bracket and position bracket out of the way (if air conditioned, remove bracket).
6. Disconnect antenna, speaker, power and pilot light leads from radio.
7. On Ford, remove two mounting bolts from under instrument panel and remove radio. On Mercury, remove two mounting nuts and remove radio.

HEATER CORE REMOVAL

1969-72 Ford & Mercury less Air Cond.

1. Drain cooling system and disconnect heater hoses from the core.
2. Remove the core cover and gasket and remove the heater core.

1969-72 Ford & Mercury with Air Cond.

1. Drain cooling system.
2. Remove carburetor air cleaner.
3. Remove vacuum manifold from dash panel.
4. Disconnect heater hoses, remove core cover and remove the core.

1966-68 Ford & Mercury less Air Cond.

1. Drain cooling system and remove heater hoses at core.
2. Remove retaining screws, heater core cover and seal from plenum.
3. Remove heater core from plenum.
4. Before installing new core, apply a thin film of silicone lubricant to pads.

1966-68 Ford & Mercury with Air Cond.

1. Remove the hood, right hinge support bracket and the right hinge and mounting assembly. Do not separate the hinge from the mounting.
2. Loosen the wiring harness from the right fender and move harness to one side.
3. Drain cooling system and disconnect heater hoses from core and move them out of way.
4. Run a strip of masking tape down the leading edge of right front door to protect the edge.
5. Unfasten, at the rear of the right front fender, the bolts holding the fender to the body.
6. Block fender away from body and remove bolts holding heater housing to the dash.
7. Lift the fender and pull out the heater housing and core assembly.
8. Take cover off the housing and remove the core.
9. Reverse the procedure to install.

SPEED CONTOLS

1972

Adjust bead chain to obtain .06-.25" actuator arm free travel when engine is at hot idle. The adjustment should be made to take as much slack as possible out of the chain without restricting the carburetor lever from returning to idle.

On vehicles with a solenoid anti-diesel valve, perform adjustment with ignition switch in the "ON" position.

1969-71

Bead Chain, Adjust

With the engine at hot idle, adjust the bead chain to obtain $\frac{1}{2}$ to 1 ball slack in the chain.

1967-68

Bead Chain, Adjust

With the carburetor set at hot idle, adjust the Bowden cable to provide a $\frac{1}{16}$" clearance between the Bowden cable end "C" washer and the accelerator linkage sleeve, Fig. 10.

1966

Brake Release Switch

1. Remove plug connector from inhibitor switch and install a jumper wire.
2. Remove plug connector from vacuum valve.
3. Ground one lead of a test lamp and touch other lead to red wire from vacuum valve.

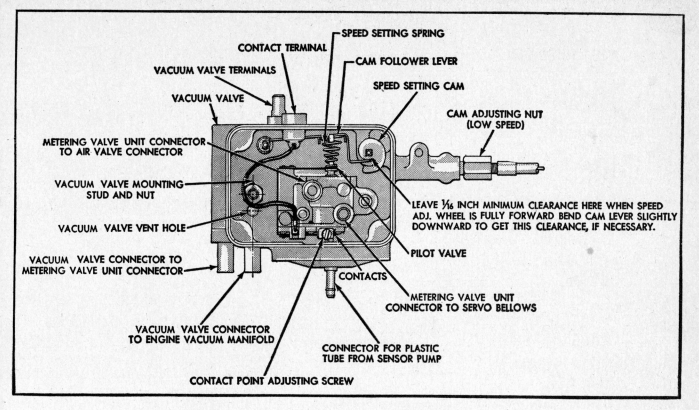

Fig. 11 Metering valve details. The $1/16''$ setting applies to early 1965 units not having an inhibitor switch; otherwise clearance is $3/16''$

4. Turn ignition switch to ACC position. Pull out switch button to ON position.
5. Depress brake pedal; test light should go out within first $1/4$ inch of travel measured at bottom of brake pedal pad.
6. If test lamp does not go out in $1/4$ inch of pedal pad travel, loosen brake pedal bracket attaching bolts and position bracket so it just clears plunger of brake release switch.
7. Vehicles equipped with power brakes should have the engine started and brake pedal depressed several times to assure correct operation of brake release switch with vacuum applied to power brake booster.
8. If brake switch cannot be adjusted, it must be replaced.

Accelerator Linkage, Adjust

Improper accelerator linkage adjustment can result in engine not returning to normal idle, the unit not allowing control at high speeds, or a lag in response to speed changes.
1. Disconnect ball chain from accelerator pedal arm attachment.
2. Check throttle linkage adjustment, being sure that linkage is against normal idle adjusting screw with engine stopped.

3. With vacuum bellows in released position, hold ball chain taut to accelerator pedal arm attachment. Hold attachment up in its normal position.
4. Allow one-half to one ball slack in chain. Cut off extra chain and reconnect chain to accelerator pedal arm attachment. If chain is too short a new chain must be installed.

Control Cable, Adjust
1. Remove two vacuum hoses and air filter from metering valve.
2. Loosen jam nut from cam adjusting nut.
3. Rotate selector dial against low speed stop.
4. Rotate cam adjusting nut until clearance between cam follower lever and speed setting cam is $3/16$ inch. As shown in Fig. 11, the $3/16$ inch clearance applies to early 1965 units without an inhibitor switch.
5. Tighten jam nut snugly against cam adjusting nut. The cam adjusting nut is designed to be loose in the metering valve; it cannot be held tight.
6. Install air filter and the two vacuum hoses.

NOTE: When there is insufficient thread for cable adjustment when installing a new metering valve, proceed as follows:

1. Remove two vacuum hoses and air filter from metering valve.
2. Remove first screw from control cable cover plate and loosen other screw.
3. Rotate cover plate so it faces upward.
4. Remove control cable rack from speed setting cam pinion.
5. Replace metering valve if required.
6. Position speed setting cam to provide approximately $3/16$ clearance to cam follower lever ($1/16$ inch on early 1965 units without inhibitor switch).
7. Rotate selector dial against low speed stop.
8. Loosen jam nut. Position jam nut so that there are three threads visible beyond jam nut. Position cam adjusting nut against jam nut.
9. Install control cable rack onto speed setting cam pinion. Try to maintain $3/16$ inch (or $1/16$ inch on early 1965 units) clearance.
10. With jam adjusting nut in its groove, lower control cable cover plate and install and tighten attaching screws.
11. Final control cable adjustment is made as outlined previously.

Engine Section

ENGINE, REPLACE

NOTE: Because of engine compartment tolerances, the engine should not be removed and installed with the transmission attached.

1. Drain cooling system and crankcase.
2. Remove radiator and air cleaner.
3. Remove hood.
4. Remove fuel and vacuum lines and all hoses, wires and linkage attached to engine.
5. Disconnect exhaust pipe from manifolds.
6. Remove starter and automatic transmission filler tube (if equipped).
7. Remove converter or flywheel housing lower cover.
8. Remove clutch release linkage (if equipped).
9. Support transmission with jack.
10. Unfasten converter or flywheel housing from engine.
11. Remove engine mounting bolts and lift engine out of chassis.

CYLINDER HEAD REPLACE

Tighten cylinder head bolts a little at a time in three steps in the sequence shown in the illustrations. Final tightening should be to the torque specifications listed in the *Engine Tightening* table. After bolts have been tightened to specifications, *they should not be disturbed.*

In instances where cylinder head gasket leakage is hard to control, aluminum paint can be applied to the gasket as a sealer.

Spray one coat of the aluminum paint on both sides of the gasket and allow the paint to dry. Then spray a second coat on both sides and, while the paint is still wet, install the gasket. Torque

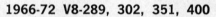

LOCATION FOR $\frac{5"}{16}$-18 LIFTING EYES

Fig. 1   Cylinder head tightening sequence. 6-240 engine

Fig. 2   Cylinder head tightening sequence. V8 engines

the head and manifold bolts to specifications to complete the job.

1966-72 6-240 Engine

1. Drain cooling system and remove air cleaner.
2. Disconnect hoses, tubing, wires and linkage attached to head.
3. Grasp crankcase ventilation regulator valve and pull it from rocker arm cover. Disconnect crankcase vent hose from inlet tube on intake manifold and remove hose and valve.

NOTE: If equipped with Thermactor Exhaust Emission Control System, disconnect air pump outlet hose at air manifold assembly. Remove air manifold. Disconnect anti-backfire valve air and vacuum lines at intake manifold.

4. Remove rocker arm cover. Loosen rocker arm stud nuts so that rocker arms can be rotated to one side.
5. Remove push rods and identify them so they can be installed in their original locations.
6. Disconnect exhaust pipe from engine.
7. Remove head bolts.
8. Install cylinder head lifting eyes in locations shown in Fig. 1.
9. Lift head with intake and exhaust manifolds from engine.
10. Reverse procedure to install and tighten head down in the sequence shown in Fig. 1.

1966-72 V8-289, 302, 351, 400

1. Remove intake manifold and carburetor as an assembly.
2. Disconnect battery ground cable at cylinder head.
3. Remove rocker arm cover.
4. On air conditioned cars, remove compressor.
5. On car with power steering, disconnect pump bracket from left cylinder head and remove drive belt. Wire power steering pump out of the way and in position that will prevent oil from draining out.

NOTE: If left cylinder head is being removed on an engine equipped with Thermactor Exhaust Emission Control System, disconnect hose from air manifold on left head. If a right head is to be removed, remove air pump and bracket and disconnect hose on right head.

6. Remove generator or alternator.

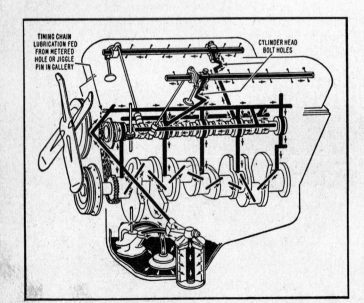

Engine oiling system. V8-352, 390, 410, 427, 428

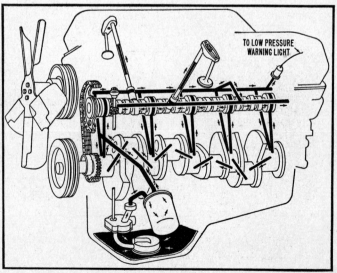

Engine oiling system. V8-429

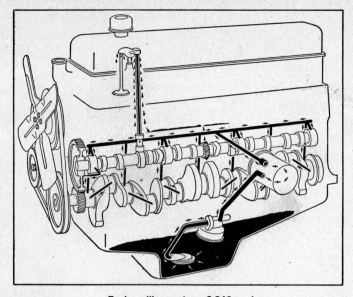

Engine oiling system. 6-240 engine

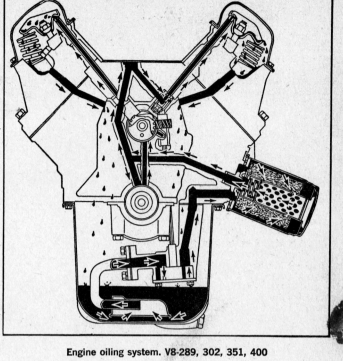

Engine oiling system. V8-289, 302, 351, 400

7. Disconnect exhaust manifold at exhaust pipes.
8. Loosen rocker arm stud nuts so that rocker arms can be rotated to the side.
9. Remove push rods, keeping them in sequence so they may be returned to their original locations.
10. Unfasten and remove cylinder head.
11. Reverse removal procedure to install the head. Tighten cylinder head down in the sequence shown in Fig. 2.

1966-72 V8-352, 390, 410, 427, 428, 429

NOTE

When installing intake manifold attaching bolts on these engines, apply a liberal coat of oil resistant sealer to the underside of bolt heads or to the bolt head bosses on the intake manifold. Failure to to do so can result in oil leakage.

On V8-427 engines, the exhaust manifolds must be detached from the cylinder heads before the heads are removed.

1. Remove intake manifold, carburetor and radiator supply tank as an assembly.

NOTE: If equipped with Thermactor Exhaust Emission Control System, disconnect air lines and hoses as necessary for accessibility. Then remove intake manifold, positive crankcase vent system components (if applicable), carburetor and thermostat housing (or radiator supply tank) as an assembly.

2. Disconnect exhaust pipes from exhaust manifolds.
3. Remove bolts and lift off head.
4. Install cylinder heads in the reverse order of removal and tighten bolts in the sequence shown in Fig. 2.

NOTE

If a noise is encountered after the cylinder head is installed on six-cylinder engines, check for interference between push rod and push rod hole in cylinder head. If interference exists check push rod for straightness. If push rod is straight, then the cylinder head has not been aligned properly during its installation. The use of cylinder head guide pins (one at each end) on cylinder head installation will insure correct head alignment.

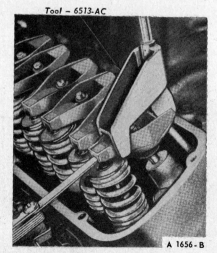

Fig. 3 Checking valve clearance on models with hydraulic lifters

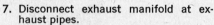

Fig. 4 Inspection of rocker arm stud nut. V8-302, 351

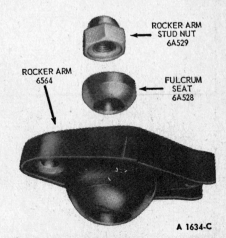

Fig. 5 Valve rocker arm parts. V8-302, 351

VALVE ARRANGEMENT

Front to Rear

```
6-240 . . . . . . . . . . . E-I-E-I-E-I-E-I-E-I
289 Right Bank . . . . . . . . . . . I-E-I-E-I-E-I-E
289 Left Bank . . . . . . . . . . . E-I-E-I-E-I-E-I
302, 351, 429 Right . . . . . I-E-I-E-I-E-I-E
302, 351, 429 Left . . . . . . . . E-I-E-I-E-I-E-I
352, 361, 390 . . . . . . . . . . . E-I-E-I-I-E-I-E
400 Right . . . . . . . . . . I-E-I-E-I-E-I-E
400 Left . . . . . . . . . . E-I-E-I-E-I-E-I
410, 427, 428 . . . . . . . . . . . E-I-E-I-I-E-I-E
```

VALVE LIFT SPECS.

Engine	Year	Intake	Exhaust
6-240	1966-71	.376	.400
	1972	.400	.400
8-289	1966-67	.368	.380
8-302	1968-72	.368	.381
8-351	1969-72[5]	.418	.448
	1971-72[6]	.407	.407
8-352	1966	.408	.408
8-390	1966	.437	.437
	1967[1]	.427	.437
	1967[2]	.437	.437
	1968-71[1]	.427	.430
	1968-69[2]	.440	.440
	1969[4]	.440	.440
8-400	1971	.427	.433
	1972	.422	.427
8-410	1966-67	.437	.437
8-427	1966-67	.524	.524
	1968	.481	.490
8-428	1966	.516	.516
	1967	.437	.437
	1967[3]	.480	.437
	1968	.440	.440
8-429	1969-72	.443	.486

[1]—2 bar. carb. [2]—4 bar. carb.
[3]—Interceptor engine.
[4]—2 bar. carb.-premium fuel.
[5]—Windsor engine.
[6]—Cleveland engine.

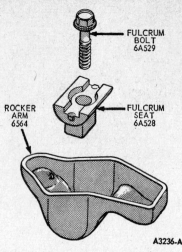

FULCRUM BOLT 6A529

ROCKER ARM 6564

FULCRUM SEAT 6A528

A3236-A

Fig. 6 Rocker arm and related parts. V8-400

VALVE TIMING

Intake Opens Before TDC

Engine	Year	Degrees
6-240	1966-69	12
	1970-71	10
	1972	18
8-289	1966-67	16
8-302	1968-72	16
8-351	1969-72[1]	11
	1971-72[2]	12
8-352	1966	22
8-390	1966-67 4 B.C.	16
	1967 2 B.C.	13
	1968	16
	1969-71 Reg. Fuel	13
	1969 Prem. Fuel	16
8-400	1971-72	17
8-410	1966-67	16
8-427	1968	18
8-428	1966	40½
	1967-68	16
8-429	1969	16

[1]—Windsor engine.
[2]—Cleveland engine.

VALVES, ADJUST

With Mechanical Lifters

If the cylinder head or rocker arm assemblies have been removed and installed, a preliminary (cold) valve lash adjustment should be made before starting the engine. If the adjustment is made in connection with an engine tune-up, the valve lash adjustment should be made with the engine at operating temperature.

To make the "hot" adjustment, operate the engine for a minimum of 30 minutes at a fast idle to stabilize engine temperatures. With the engine idling, check the valve lash with the proper feeler gauge between valve stem and rocker arm. Adjust the lash by means of the adjusting screw to the clearance given in the Valve Specifications table.

To make the "cold" adjustment, first turn over the engine to bring No. 1 piston up on its compression stroke, which will be indicated by the TDC mark on the vibration damper. Then proceed as follows:

V8-352, 390, 406, 427 With Mechanical Lifters

Make three chalk marks on the vibration damper. Space the marks 90 degrees apart (¼ of circumference) so that with the timing mark the damper is divided into four equal parts. Rotate the crankshaft until No. 1 piston is near TDC at the end of the compression stroke and adjust the following valves:

No. 1 intake and exhaust
No. 4 exhaust
No. 5 exhaust
No. 7 intake
No. 8 intake

Rotate the crankshaft 180 degrees (½ turn) which puts No. 4 piston on TDC. Then adjust the following valves:

No. 2 exhaust
No. 4 intake
No. 5 intake
No. 6 exhaust

Rotate the crankshaft 270 degrees (¾ turn), which puts No. 3 piston on TDC.

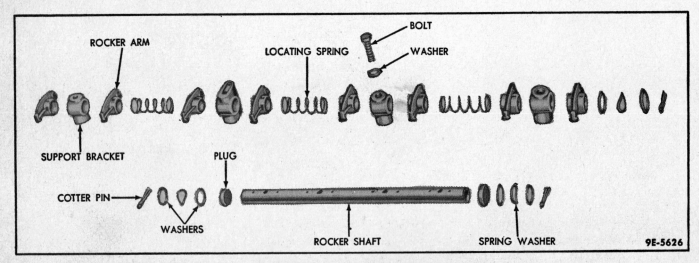

ROCKER ARM

LOCATING SPRING

BOLT

WASHER

SUPPORT BRACKET

PLUG

COTTER PIN

WASHERS

ROCKER SHAFT

SPRING WASHER

9E-5626

Fig. 7 Rocker arm shaft assembly. V8-352, 390, 410, 427 and 428 engines

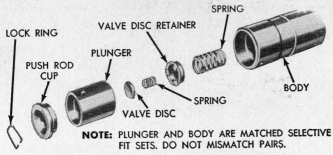

LOCK RING
PUSH ROD CUP
PLUNGER
VALVE DISC RETAINER
SPRING
SPRING
VALVE DISC
BODY

NOTE: PLUNGER AND BODY ARE MATCHED SELECTIVE FIT SETS. DO NOT MISMATCH PAIRS.

Fig. 8 Hydraulic valve lifter disassembled (typical)

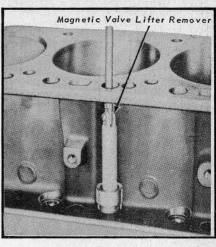

Magnetic Valve Lifter Remover

Fig. 9 Removing valve lifter. 6-240 engine

Then adjust the following valves:
No. 2 intake
No. 3 intake and exhaust
No. 6 intake
No. 7 exhaust
No. 8 exhaust

V8-352 With Rocker Arm Adjusting Screws and Hydraulic Lifters

These engines may be identified by a daub of orange paint on the engine front cover visible from the left side of the engine. In making an adjustment on these valves, follow the procedure outlined above for engines with mechanical lifters insofar as positioning the valves. Then proceed as follows:

1. With lifter being adjusted on base circle of cam on camshaft, turn adjusting screw so that clearance is obtained between push rod and rocker arm adjusting screw.
2. Adjust screw until clearance is just removed.
3. Tighten screw an additional 2½ turns.
4. Apply steady force to the push rod end of the rocker arm, depress the arm until the push rod bottoms in the lifter.
5. Check clearance between end of valve stem and rocker arm. A clearance of at least .060" should exist. If less than .060", back off the adjusting screw until at least .060" clearance is obtained.
6. Repeat adjustment on all other valves in the sequence given for mechanical lifter jobs.

6-240, V8-289, Early 302 & 351

SERVICE BULLETIN

On V8-289 engines to minimize the possibility of burned valves the service procedure has been revised as follows: When the push rod to rocker arm clearance has been eliminated, tighten the rocker arm stud nut an additional ¾ of a turn. The previous procedure required an additional 1½ turn.

With the piston at top dead center of its compression stroke, loosen the rocker arm stud nut until there is end clearance in the push rod. Then tighten the nut just to the point where all end clearance is eliminated. This may be determined by moving the push rod with the fingers as the stud nut is tightened. When the end clearance has been eliminated, tighten the stud nut the additional number of turns listed in the *Valve Specifications Table*.

Operate the engine and check for rough engine idle or noisy lifters. Valve clearance set too tight will cause rough engine idle; if set too loose, noisy lifters will result.

If an adjustment is necessary because of the foregoing conditions, apply pressure on the push rod slowly to bleed down the valve lifter until the plunger is completely bottomed. While holding the lifter in the fully collapsed position, check the available clearance between rocker arm and valve stem tip. If clearance is not within specifications, turn the rocker arm stud nut clockwise to decrease the clearance and counterclockwise to increase clearance.

Late V8-302 & 351

These engines use a new positive stop rocker arm stud. If clearance between valve stem and rocker arm, with lifter collapsed, as in Fig. 3, is not as shown in *Valve Specifications* table a .060" shorter or a .060" longer push rod is available to compensate for dimensional changes in valve train. If clearance is less than specified, install an undersized push rod. If clearance is greater install an oversize push rod.

Valve clearance should be correct when stud nut is tightened until it contacts the stop and torqued to 18-22 ft-lbs. Inspect stud nuts to be sure they are in acceptable condition for re-use, Fig. 4.

V8-352, 390, 400, 410, 427, 428 With Non-Adjustable Hydraulic Lifters

For these engines a .060" shorter push

rod (color coded white) or a .060" longer push rod (color coded yellow) are available for service to provide a means of compensating for dimensional changes in the valve mechanism.

To check the clearance, bring the piston of the cylinder being checked on top dead center of the compression stroke. Then with hydraulic lifter collapsed, check the clearance between valve stem and rocker arm. If the clearance is less than the minimum listed in the *Valve Specifications* table, the .060" shorter push rod should be used. If the clearance is more than the maximum specified, the .060" longer push rod should be used.

SERVICE BULLETIN

New Hydraulic Lifters: A new design hydraulic valve lifter was incorporated in 390, 410 and 428 cubic inch engines built after 12-20-65, identified by an engine date code of 5M20 and higher.

The new design lifter provides for an increased plunger travel to compensate for tolerance stack-up of the various engine components (head gasket thickness, camshaft thickness, valve push rods, etc.). With the new design lifter, it

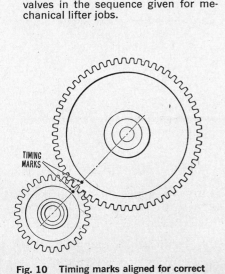

TIMING MARKS

Fig. 10 Timing marks aligned for correct valve timing. 6-240 engine

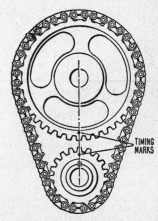

TIMING MARKS

Fig. 11 Timing marks aligned for correct valve timing. V8s

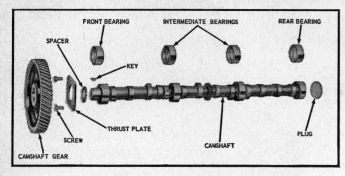

Fig. 12   Camshaft and related parts. 6-240 engine

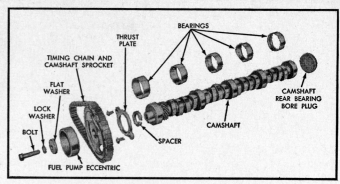

Fig. 13   Camshaft and related parts. V8-289, 302

is no longer necessary to use the .060" oversize push rods as was necessary on some of the earlier engines.

The collapsed lifter specification valve stem to rocker arm clearance for the new design lifter is revised from .050 to .150" to .050 to .200".

VALVE GUIDES
Overhead Valve Engines

Valve guides in these engines are an integral part of the head and, therefore, cannot be removed. For service, guides can be reamed oversize to accommodate one of three service valves with oversize stems (.003", .015" and .030").

Check the valve stem clearance of each valve (after cleaning) in its respective valve guide. If the clearance exceeds the service limits of .004" on the intake or .005" on the exhaust, ream the valve guides to accommodate the next oversize diameter valve.

ROCKER ARMS & SHAFTS

To disassemble the rocker arms, remove cotter pins from each end of the shaft and remove the flat washers and spring washers. Slide rocker arms, springs and supports off shaft, being sure to identify all parts so they can be assembled in the same position.

If it is necessary to remove the plugs from each end of the shaft, drill or pierce one plug, then insert a steel rod through the plug and knock out the plug on the opposite end. Working from the open end, knock out the remaining plug.

Assemble the rocker arms and related parts as indicated by Fig. 7.

ROCKER ARM STUD
6-240, V8-289, 302 (Early)

If necessary to replace a rocker arm stud, a kit is available which contains a stud remover, a stud installer, and two reamers, one .006" and the other 015".

Rocker arm studs that are broken or have damaged threads may be replaced with standard studs. Loose studs in the head may be replaced with .006" or .015" oversize studs which are available for service. *The standard studs have no identification marks, whereas the .006" over-*

size stud has two grooves around the pilot end of the stud. The .015" oversize stud has a step produced by the increased diameter of the stud approximately $1\frac{5}{32}$" from the pilot end.

When going from a standard size stud to a .015" oversize stud, always use a .006" reamer before finish reaming with a .015" reamer.

If a stud is broken off flush with the stud boss, use an easy-out to remove the broken stud, following the instructions of the tool manufacturer.

V8-302 (Late) & V8-351

A new type positive stop rocker arm stud and nut eliminates the need for adjusting valve lash.

Installation

1. Position the piston of the cylinder to be worked on at TDC compression stroke.
2. Locate stud properly with tool T69P-6049D. Make sure tool bottoms on the head.
3. Lubricate rocker arm components and place rocker arm and fulcrum on the stud.
4. Thread nut onto the stud until it contacts the shoulder then tighten nut to 18-22 ft-lbs.

V8-429

The rocker arm support studs are threaded into the cylinder head and can be replaced as follows:
1. Position the piston of the cylinder being worked on the TDC compression stroke.
2. Thread the rocker arm stud into the head until the shoulder contacts the head. Tighten to the torque specified in the *Engine Tightening Table.*
3. Lubricate rocker arm components and position the arm and the fulcrum on the stud.
4. Thread the nut until it contacts the shoulder, then tighten to 18-22 ft. lbs.

HYDRAULIC
VALVE LIFTERS

The internal parts of each hydraulic valve lifter assembly are a matched set. If these are mixed, improper valve operation may result. Therefore, disassemble,

inspect and test each assembly separately to prevent mixing the parts.

Fig. 8 illustrates the type of hydraulic lifter used. See the *Trouble Shooting Chapter* under the heading *Engine Noises* for causes of hydraulic valve lifter noise.

Hydraulic Lifters, Replace
6-240 Engine

1. Remove valve rocker arm cover.
2. Remove valve push rod cover.
3. Loosen rocker arm stud nuts until rocker arms can be disengaged from push rods.
4. Remove push rods, keeping them in a rack so they may be installed in their original location.
5. Remove valve lifters, using the tool shown in Fig. 9 (or equivalent). Place lifters in a rack so they may be installed in their original location.

V8-289, 302, 351, 400

1. Remove intake manifold and related parts.
2. Remove rocker arm covers.
3. Loosen rocker arm stud nuts or bolts and rotate rocker arms to the side.
4. Lift out push rods, keeping them in sequence in a rack so they may be installed in their original location.
5. Using a magnet rod, remove valve lifters and place them in sequence in a rack so they may be installed in their original location.

All V8s With Rocker Arm Shafts

1. Remove intake manifold.
2. Remove rocker arms and shafts.
3. Remove push rods, keeping them in a rack in sequence so they may be installed in their original location.
4. Remove valve lifters with a magnet rod and place them in a rack in sequence so they may be installed in original location.
5. Reverse procedure to install.

TIMING CASE COVER

NOTE: To replace the seal in the timing gear cover, it is necessary to remove the cover as outlined below.

1969-72 V8-302, 351, 400
1. Drain cooling system and oil pan.
2. Disconnect lower radiator hose from water pump.

3. Disconnect heater hose from water pump and slide water pump bypass hose clamp toward pump.
4. Unfasten and position alternator and bracket out of way.
5. If equipped with power steering or air conditioning, remove the drive belts.
6. Remove the fan, spacer, pulley and drive belt.
7. Remove crankshaft pulley and vibration damper.
8. Disconnect fuel pump outlet line from pump and remove pump retaining bolts and lay pump to one side with flex line attached.
9. Remove oil dipstick and the oil pan to front cover attaching bolts.
10. Unfasten and remove the cylinder front cover and water pump as an assembly.
11. Reverse the foregoing to install.

1969-71 V8-390

1. Drain cooling system and oil pan.
2. Disconnect battery ground cable.
3. Disconnect transmission cooler lines from radiator if so equipped and disconnect water hoses from radiator and remove radiator.
4. Remove heater hose from water pump and remove hose from choke housing clamp.
5. Slide water pump bypass hose clamp toward engine.
6. If equipped with power steering, remove pump bracket bolts and position pump to left side to prevent fluid from draining.
7. If air conditioned, remove compressor mounting bolts and lay compressor out of way.
8. Unfasten and position alternator and bracket out of way.
9. Remove water pump and fan assembly.
10. If air conditioned, unfasten condenser attaching bolts and position condenser forward.
11. Remove compressor drive belt and if Thermactor equipped remove the air pump drive belt and the accessory drive pulley.
12. Remove crankshaft pulleys and vibration damper.
13. Disconnect fuel pump outlet line at pump and remove pump attaching bolts and lay pump to one side with flex line attached.
14. Remove crankshaft sleeve.
15. Unfasten and remove the front cover.
16. Reverse the foregoing to install.

V8-429

1. Drain cooling system and oil pan.
2. Remove bolts attaching fan to water pump and remove screws attaching radiator shroud to radiator.
3. Remove fan assembly and radiator shroud.
4. Disconnect radiator hoses at engine and cooler lines at radiator and remove radiator upper support and radiator assembly.
5. Loosen alternator and remove drive belt with pump pulley.
6. If air conditioned, loosen idler pulley and remove compressor support.
7. Remove vibration damper from crankshaft.

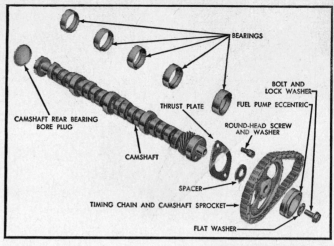

Fig. 14 Camshaft and related parts. V8-352, 390, 410, 427, 428, 429
NOTE: Spacer not used on all models

8. Disconnect power steering lines at pump and unfasten and remove the pump.
9. Loosen bypass hose at pump and disconnect heater return tube at pump.
10. Disconnect and plug fuel inlet line at pump and disconnect fuel outlet line from pump. Unfasten and remove fuel pump.
11. Unfasten and remove cylinder front cover.
12. Reverse procedure to install.

1966-72 6-240

1. Drain cooling system and oil pan.
2. Disconnect automatic transmission oil cooler lines from radiator.
3. Remove radiator.
4. Remove power steering drive belt. Unfasten and position power steering pump and bracket out of the way.
5. Remove fan, spacer, belt and pulley.
6. Remove vibration damper.
7. Remove oil pan, oil pump screen and inlet tube.
8. Unfasten and remove front cover.
9. Reverse procedure to install.

1966-68 V8-289, 302

1. Drain cooling system and crankcase.
2. Unfasten and position alternator and brackets out of the way.
3. Remove all drive belts.
4. Remove fan, spacer and pulley.
5. Remove crankshaft pulley and vibration damper.
6. Unfasten and lay fuel pump to one side with flexible fuel line attached.
7. Remove oil pan-to-front cover bolts.
8. Remove front cover and water pump as an assembly.
9. Reverse procedure to install.

1966-68 V8-352, 390, 410, 427, 428

1. Drain cooling system and crankcase.
2. Disconnect battery ground cable.
3. Disconnect automatic transmission oil cooler lines from radiator.
4. Remove radiator.

5. Unfasten and wire power steering pump to left side of car in a position that will prevent oil from draining out.
6. Unfasten and position air conditioning compressor out of the way.
7. Remove water pump and fan.
8. Remove crankshaft pulley and vibration damper.
9. Unfasten and lay fuel pump to one side with flexible fuel line attached.
10. Remove crankshaft sleeve.
11. Unfasten and remove front cover.
12. Reverse procedure to install.

TIMING GEARS
1966-72 6-240 Engine

CAUTION

When the camshaft and crankshaft lose their timing relationship through removal of the timing gears, interference may occur between crankshaft and cam lobes. Therefore, to prevent possible damage to the camshaft lobes, do not rotate the camshaft or crankshaft in the engine without the timing gears installed.

1. To remove gears, remove cylinder front cover and camshaft.
2. Remove oil slinger from crankshaft.
3. Use a puller to remove crankshaft gear.
4. Press gear off camshaft and remove thrust plate, spacer and key.
5. Reverse procedure to install, being sure timing marks are aligned as shown in Fig. 10.

NOTE: Be sure the camshaft gear and spacer are tight against the shoulder on camshaft and that the thrust plate can be moved freely.

TIMING CHAIN
V8-289, 302, 351, 400

After removing the cover as outlined above, remove the crankshaft front oil slinger. Crank the engine until the tim-

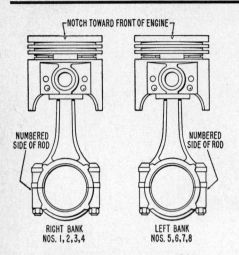

NOTCH TOWARD FRONT OF ENGINE

NUMBERED SIDE OF ROD

NUMBERED SIDE OF ROD

RIGHT BANK NOS. 1, 2, 3, 4

LEFT BANK NOS. 5, 6, 7, 8

Fig. 15 Piston and rod assembly. All V8 engines

ing marks are aligned as shown in Fig. 11. Remove crankshaft sprocket retaining bolt and washer. Slide both sprockets and chain forward and remove them as an assembly.

Reverse the order of the foregoing procedure to install the chain and sprockets, being sure the timing marks are aligned.

V8-352, 390, 410, 427, 428, 429

1. To remove the chain, first take off the front cover as outlined previously.
2. Crank engine until timing marks on camshaft sprocket is adjacent to timing mark on crankshaft sprocket, Fig. 11.
3. Remove camshaft sprocket cap screw and fuel pump eccentric.
4. Slide both sprockets and chain forward and remove as an assembly.
5. Reverse foregoing procedure to install the chain, being sure to align the timing marks as shown.

CAMSHAFT, REPLACE

1966-72 6-240 Engine

1. To remove camshaft, remove radiator and grille.
2. Remove rocker arm cover. Loosen rocker arm stud nuts and move rocker arms to one side and take out push rods. Place push rods in a rack so they can be installed in their original location.
3. Remove valve push rod cover and take out valve lifters. Place valve lifters in a rack so they may be installed in their original location.
4. Remove cylinder front cover.
5. Turn crankshaft to align timing marks as shown in Fig. 10.
6. Carefully remove camshaft with gear attached, Fig. 12.
7. Reverse procedure to install.

V8-289, 302, 351, 400

1. To remove camshaft, remove cylinder front cover and timing chain.
2. Remove distributor cap and spark plug wires, then remove distributor.

3. Disconnect automatic transmission oil cooler lines from radiator and remove radiator.
4. Remove intake manifold and carburetor as an assembly.
5. Remove rocker arm covers.
6. Loosen rocker arm stud nuts or bolts and rotate rocker arms to one side.
7. Remove push rods, keeping them in sequence in a rack so they may be installed in their original location.
8. Using a magnet, remove valve lifters and place them in a rack in sequence so they may be installed in their original location.
9. Remove camshaft thrust plate, Fig. 13, and carefully pull camshaft from engine, using care to avoid damaging camshaft bearings.
10. Reverse procedure to install.

V8-352, 390, 410, 427, 428, 429

1. Remove timing chain cover, chain, sprockets and intake manifold.
2. Remove grille and distributor.
3. Remove rocker arm assembly.
4. Remove push rods.
5. Position an inspection light through push rod opening and into valve push rod valley. Remove valve lifters with a magnet through push rod openings. It may be necessary in some cases to transfer the lifter over to an adjoining push rod opening in order to remove it.
6. Remove oil pan.
7. Slide camshaft out of engine, Fig. 14.

CAMSHAFT BEARINGS

When necessary to replace camshaft bearings, the engine will have to be removed from the vehicle and the plug at the rear of the cylinder block will have to be removed in order to utilize the special camshaft bearing removing and installing tools required to do this job. If properly installed, camshaft bearings require no reaming—nor should this type bearing be reamed or altered in any manner in an attempt to fit bearings.

PISTON & ROD, ASSEMBLE

All V8's

Assemble the pistons to the rods as shown in Fig. 15.

All Sixes

Piston heads are marked for location on the forward side, Fig. 17. Rods and caps are numbered on the same side as the piston they serve.

PISTONS, PINS & RINGS

SERVICE BULLETIN

Piston and Pin Replacement: When servicing engines using press fit piston pins, the piston and pin must be replaced as an assembly if either does not meet specifications. These components are not serviced separately for the principle reason

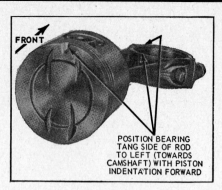

FRONT

POSITION BEARING TANG SIDE OF ROD TO LEFT (TOWARDS CAMSHAFT) WITH PISTON INDENTATION FORWARD

Fig. 17 Piston and rod assembly. 1966-72 6-240 engine

that excess clearances are usually caused by piston wear rather than pin wear. Elimination of excessive clearance by using oversize pins may result in fracture of the connecting rod.

Pistons and rings are available in standard sizes and the following oversizes:

352, 390, 410, 428: .020, .030, .040, .060", 6-240, V8-289, 302, 351, 400, 429: .020, .030, .040".

V8-427: Standard only.

Oversizes piston pins of .001 and .002" are available on 6-240, V8-352 and 390 only.

MAIN & ROD BEARINGS

Front Main Bearing Knock

1967 V8-289 Engines: This problem occurs at 800-1600 rpm under load, and is caused by a high degree of spark advance at idle provided by attachment of the distributor vacuum line to full manifold vacuum; also excessive front main bearing clearance.

To correct the trouble, it is recommended that the distributor vacuum hose be removed from the intake manifold take-off connection and attached to the connection at the base of the carburetor, Fig. 18. Reduce the length of the vacuum hose to provide direct routing to the carburetor connection, free from sharp bends or kinks. The cap removed from the carburetor fitting should be used to close the vacated connection on the manifold.

If the engine knock is not reduced to an acceptable level, then a new front main bearing must be select fitted, utilizing the available .001" or .002" undersize bearing in any combination to provide a desired operating clearance of .0005" to .0015".

Service Bulletin

Undersize Crankshafts: Crankshafts with .010" undersize rod and/or main journals were authorized for use in all 1966-68 engines beginning March 12, 1965. All assemblies containing undersize crankshafts will be identified on the cylinder block date stamp pad with a letter M for undersize main journals and/or a letter P for .010" undersize crankpin (rod) journals. There crankshafts can appear in both production or service engines and

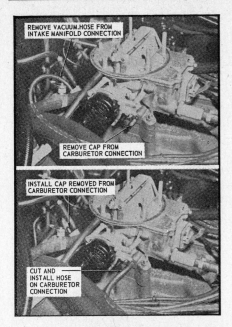

Fig. 18 Procedure for correcting front main bearing knock on 1967 V8-289 engines

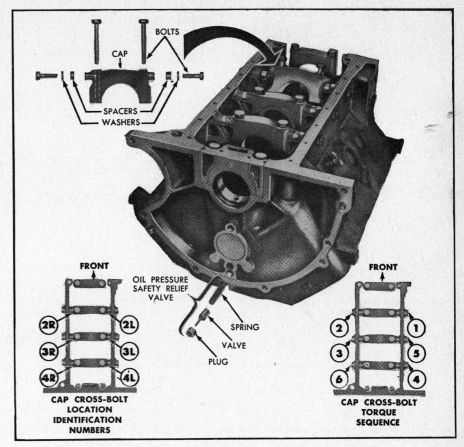

Fig. 19 Cylinder block details. V8-427

short block assemblies. Bearing clearances will remain the same as for standard crankshafts. All rod and/or main journals will be ground undersize if any one of the rod and/or main journals are undersize. This avoids mixing of standard and undersize bearings in the same engine. Three possible combinations can exist on crankshafts with undersize bearing journals:

1. All rod journals .010″ undersize with standard main bearing journals.
2. All rod journals standard with .010″ undersize main journals.
3. Both rod and main bearing journals .010″ undersize.

Main and rod bearings are available in standard sizes and the following undersizes:
V8-352, 390, 410, 428: .002, .010, .020, .030, .040″.
All other engines: .002, .010, .020, .030″.

NOTE

Main and rod bearings are a selective fit. Do not file or lap bearing caps or use bearing shims to obtain proper bearing clearance. Selective fit bearings are available for service in standard sizes only. Standard bearings are divided into two sizes and are identified by a daub of red or blue paint. Red marked bearings increase the clearance; blue marked bearings decrease clearance. When replacing standard bearings with new bearings, it is good practice first to try to obtain the proper clearance with two blue bearing halves.

V8-427 NOTE

Whenever the main bearings are removed, they should be installed as follows, referring to Fig. 19.

1. Torque main bearing cap bolts to 95-105 ft-lbs:

2. Make sure cross-bolt spacers are installed in their proper locations. Production spacers are marked L-2, R-2, L-3, R-3, L-4, R-4.
3. Install and torque cross-bolts in two steps. First torque all cross-bolts to 20 ft-lbs.; then torque them all to 40 ft-lbs.

CRANKSHAFT OIL SEAL
1966-72 6-240 Engine

NOTE: If crankshaft rear oil seal replacement is the only operation being performed, it can be done in the vehicle. If the oil seal is being replaced in conjunction with a rear main bearing replacement, the engine must be removed from the vehicle. To replace the seal only, proceed as follows:

1. Remove starting motor.
2. Disconnect transmission from engine and slide it back. On manual shift transmission, remove clutch assembly.
3. Remove flywheel and engine rear cover plate.
4. Use an awl to punch two holes in crankshaft rear oil seal. Punch holes on opposite sides of crankshaft and just above bearing cap-to-cylinder block split line. Insert a sheet metal screw in each hole.

5. Use two large screwdrivers or pry bars and pry against both screws at the same time to remove seal. It may be necessary to place small blocks of wood against cylinder block to provide a fulcrum point for pry bars. Use caution to avoid scratching or otherwise damaging crankshaft oil seal surfaces.

Installation
1. Clean oil seal recess in cylinder block and rear main bearing cap.
2. Coat new oil seal and crankshaft with a light film of engine oil.
3. Start seal in recess and install it until it is fully seated in seal recess, Fig. 20.
4. Be sure seal was not damaged during installation and reverse the procedure of removal to complete the operation.

V8-289, 302, 351

A braided oil seal is pressed into the upper and lower grooves behind the rear main bearing. Directly in front of this seal is an oil slinger which deflects the oil back into the oil pan. Should the braided seal require replacement, the installation of the lower half is accomplished as follows:

With the bearing cap and lower bearing half removed, install a new seal so that both ends protrude above the cap. Tap the seal down into position or roll it snugly in its groove with a smooth

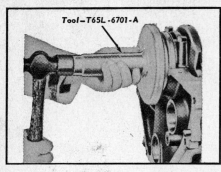

Fig. 20   Crankshaft rear oil seal installation. 6-240 engine

rounded tool. Then cut off the protruding end of the seal with sharp knife or razor blade.

SERVICE BULLETIN

PROTECT OIL SEAL: When replacing a front or rear crankshaft oil seal on a 1966 engine, the surface of the crankshaft contacting the seal must be cleaned with solvent. This will remove any corrosion, sludge or varnish which might be present. In addition, polish the surface with crocus cloth to remove any deposits, burrs or sharp edges that could damage the new seal or cause it to wear prematurely.

Where there is excessive wear on the contact surface, or a satisfactory surface cannot be obtained by polishing, it may be necessary to replace the crankshaft.

Before the new seal is installed, coat it with suitable lubricant along with the contact surface of the shaft. This will prevent damage during installation, and provide lubrication when the engine is first started.

V8-289, 302, 351 NOTE

The crankshaft rear seal is in contact with the outer surface of the flywheel flange rather than on the main bearing journal. In this design, the front face of the flange is exposed to crankcase splash. Therefore, to eliminate the possibility of oil leaks through the threaded holes in the flange, the flywheel attaching capscrews must be coated with an oil resistant sealer.

V8-352, 427

Oil sealing at the rear of the crankshaft is obtained by seal halves in the cylinder block and rear bearing cap. Side seals are also used in the vertical grooves in the bearing cap. Install and test seals in the same manner outlined for other models above.

V8-351, 390, 400, 410, 428

A new rubber split-lip rear crankshaft oil seal is released for service. This seal can be installed without removal of the crankshaft and also eliminates the necessity of seal installation tools.
1. Remove oil pan.
2. Remove rear main bearing cap.
3. Loosen remaining bearing caps, allowing crankshaft to drop down about 1/32".

4. Remove old seals from both cylinder block and rear main bearing cap. Use a brass rod to drift upper half of seal from cylinder block groove. Rotate crankshaft while drifting to facilitate removal.
5. Carefully clean seal groove in block with a brush and solvent. Also clean seal groove in bearing cap. Remove the oil seal retaining pin from the bearing cap if so equipped. *The pin is not used with the split-lip seal.*
6. Dip seal halves in clean engine oil.
7. Carefully install upper seal half in its groove with undercut side of seal toward front of engine, Fig. 21, by rotating it on shaft journal of crankshaft until approximately 3/8" protrudes below the parting surface. *Be sure no rubber has been shaved from outside diameter of seal by bottom edge of groove.*
8. Retighten main bearing caps and torque to specifications.
9. Install lower seal in main bearing cap with undercut side of seal toward front of engine, and allow seal to protrude about 3/8" above parting surface to mate with upper seal upon cap installation.
10. Apply suitable sealer to parting faces of cap and block. Install cap and torque to specifications.

NOTE: If difficulty is encountered in installing the upper half of the seal in position, lightly lap (sandpaper) the side of the seal opposite the lip side using a medium grit paper. After sanding, the seal must be washed in solvent, then dipped in clean engine oil prior to installation.

OIL PAN, REPLACE
1966-72 6-240 Engine

1. Drain crankcase and cooling system.
2. Remove radiator.
3. Disconnect flexible fuel line at fuel pump.
4. With automatic transmission disconnect kickdown rod at bellcrank.
5. With manual shift transmission, disconnect clutch linkage.
6. Raise car and remove starter.
7. Remove engine front support retaining nuts.
8. Raise transmission, remove rear sup-

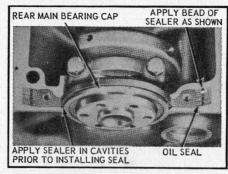

Fig. 22   Oil pan rear seal installation. 6-240 engine

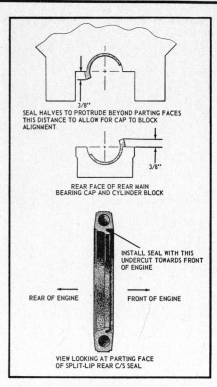

Fig. 21   Split-lip rear crankshaft seal installation on V8-351, 390, 400, 410, 428

port insulator and lower transmission to crossmember.
9. Raise engine and place 3" thick wood blocks between both front support insulators and intermediate support brackets.
10. Remove oil pan bolts and oil pump retaining bolts.
11. Remove oil pump from block and lay it in bottom of oil pan.
12. Rotate crankshaft as required to remove oil pan.
13. Remove inlet tube and screen from pump.

Installation

1. After cleaning, install inlet tube and screen on oil pump, using a new gasket.
2. Clean gasket surfaces of oil pump, pan and block.
3. Remove rear main bearing cap-to-oil pan seal and cylinder front cover-to-oil pan seal. Clean seal grooves.
4. Apply oil-resistant sealer in cavities between bearing cap and cylinder block, Fig. 22.
5. Install new side gaskets on oil pan with oil-resistant sealer.
6. Position a new cylinder front cover seal on oil pan.
7. Place oil pump assembly in pan. Position pan under engine. Install oil pump with new gasket on cylinder block. Install oil pan and tighten screws securely.
8. Complete the operation by reversing the removal procedure.

1966-72 V8-289, 302, 351

1. Drain crankcase and remove dip-

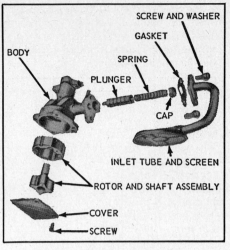

Fig. 23   Oil pump. 6-240 engine

OIL PUMP REPAIRS
Figs. 23, 24, 25

1. With all parts clean and dry, check the inside of the pump housing and the outer race and rotor for damage or excessive wear.
2. Check the mating surface of the pump cover for wear. If this surface is worn, scored or grooved, replace the cover.
3. Measure the clearance between the outer race and housing. This clearance should be .006-.009".
4. With the rotor assembly installed in the housing, place a straight edge over the rotor assembly and housing. Measure the clearance between the straight edge and the rotor and outer race. Recommended limits are .001-.0035". *The outer race, shaft and rotor are furnished only as an assembly.*
5. Check the drive shaft-to-housing bearing clearance by measuring the O.D. of the shaft and the I.D. of the housing bearing. The recommended clearance limits are .0015-.0029".
6. Inspect the relief valve spring for a collapsed or worn condition.
7. Check the relief valve piston for scores and free operation in the bore. The specified piston clearance is .0015-0029".

WATER PUMP, REPLACE
1969-72 Six

1. Drain cooling system.
2. Loosen and remove alternator, power steering and air conditioning belts.
3. Disconnect radiator lower hose and heater hose at pump.
4. Remove fan, spacer, pulley and belt.
5. Unfasten and remove the water pump.

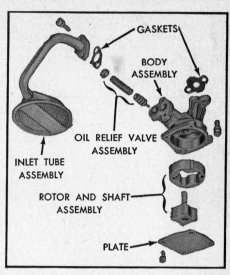

Fig. 24   Oil pump. V8-289, 302, 351

1969-72 V8-429

The water pump is a part of the front cover on this engine and the procedure for removal is found under *Timing Case Cover.*

1966-68 Six

1. Drain cooling system.
2. Remove power steering belt (if equipped). If air conditioned, remove compressor belt.
3. Disconnect radiator lower hose and heater hose at water pump. Remove fan, pulley and drive belt.
4. Remove bolts securing pump to block and remove pump.

1966-72 V8-289, 302, 351, 400

1. Drain cooling system.
2. Remove power steering drive belt (if equipped). If air conditioned, remove compressor belt.
3. Disconnect radiator lower hose and heater hose at water pump.
4. Remove drive belt, fan, spacer or fan drive clutch and pulley.
5. Unfasten and remove water pump from cylinder front cover.

1966-72 V8-352, 390, 410, 427, 428, 429

1. Drain cooling system.
2. Remove power steering drive belt (if equipped). If air conditioned, remove compressor drive belt.
3. Disconnect radiator lower hose and heater hose at water pump.
4. Remove radiator upper support and fan guard.
5. Remove fan belt or belts, fan, spacer or fan drive clutch and pulley.
6. Unfasten and remove water pump.

FUEL PUMP, REPLACE

1. Remove all gasket material from the pump and block gasket surfaces. Apply sealer to both sides of new gasket.

---

stick.
2. Unfasten and position oil pan on No. 2 crossmember.
3. Remove one of the inlet tube retaining bolts and loosen the other. This allows inlet tube to be positioned out of the way when removing oil pan.
4. Crank engine as required to obtain clearance and remove oil pan.
5. Remove oil pump inlet tube and screen.

Installation
1. Position oil inlet tube and loosely install one retaining bolt.
2. Clean gasket surfaces of block and pan.
3. Coat block surface and oil pan gasket with sealer. Position pan gaskets on cylinder block.
4. Position front seal on cylinder front cover, being sure tabs on seal are over oil pan gasket.
5. Position rear oil pan seal on rear main bearing cap, being sure tabs on seal are over oil pan gasket.
6. Place pan on No. 2 crossmember and install other inlet tube retaining bolt.
7. Complete installation in reverse order of removal.

1966-70 V8-352, 390, 410, 427, 428

1. Drain engine oil and disconnect stabilizer bar at connecting links and pull ends down.

NOTE: *To allow clearance for removal of oil pan, remove the front engine mount nuts. Then position floor jack under front leading edge of oil pan (use wood block between pan and jack). Raise engine about 1¼" and insert a 1" block of wood between insulators and frame crossmember. Then remove floor jack.*

2. Remove oil pan screws and lower pan to crossmember.
3. Crank engine to obtain necessary clearance between crankshaft counterweight and rear of oil pan. Then remove pan.

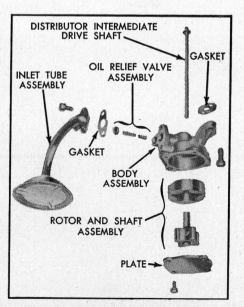

Fig. 25   Oil pump. V8-352, 390, 410, 427, 428, 429

2. Position gasket on pump flange and hold pump in position against its mounting surface. Make sure rocker arm is riding on camshaft eccentric.
3. Press pump tight against its mounting. Install retaining screws and tighten them alternately.

4. Connect fuel lines. Then operate engine and check for leaks.

NOTE: Before installing the pump, it is good practice to crank the engine so that the nose of the camshaft eccentric is out of the way of the fuel pump rocker arm when the pump is installed. In this way there will be the lease amount of tension on the rocker arm, thereby easing the installation of the pump.

Clutch and Transmission Section

NOTE: 1972 linkage adjustment information is in this section. Repair procedures on both automatic and manual shift transmissions are covered elsewhere in this manual. Procedures for removing automatic transmissions as well as linkage adjustments on 1966-71 models are included in the automatic transmission chapters. See Chapter Index.

CLUTCH PEDAL, ADJUST
1969-71

1. Disconnect clutch release lever spring from release lever.
2. Loosen release lever rod locknut and adjusting nut.
3. Move clutch release lever rearward until release bearing lightly touches pressure plate release fingers.
4. Adjust adapter length until adapter seats in release lever pocket.
5. Insert a .194″ feeler against the back face of rod adapter and tighten the adjusting nut finger tight against the feeler gauge.
6. Tighten locknut against adjusting nut being careful not to disturb adjustment.
7. Remove feeler gauge.
8. Install release lever spring and check pedal free travel. Travel should be ⅞″ to 1⅛″.

1966-68

Assist Spring
1. With clutch pedal against its bumper (pedal released), measure distance between assist spring bracket and equalizer upper lever. This distance should be ⅛″. It may be necessary to depress pedal to insert gauge.
2. To decrease gap, loosen rearward nut and tighten front nut.
3. To increase gap, loosen forward nut and tighten rearward nut.
4. Tighten nuts securely, being careful not to change the adjustment.

Free Travel
1. Disconnect clutch return spring from release lever.
2. Loosen release lever rod lock nut 3 or 4 turns.
3. If there is no free travel, shorten rod (by turning at square wrench area) until it is free of clutch release lever.
4. Move clutch release lever rearward until release bearing lightly contacts clutch release fingers.
5. Adjust rod length until rod just contacts its seat in release lever.
6. Adjust lock nut to obtain approximately ³/₁₆″ clearance between nut and rod sleeve end.

7. Turn rod at the square wrench area until nut just contacts rod sleeve end.
8. Tighten lock nut against sleeve while holding rod with wrench.
9. Install clutch return spring.
10. As a final check, measure free travel with engine idling. Dimension should not be less than ½″.

CLUTCH, REPLACE
1966-71

1. Remove transmission as outlined.
2. On cars with aluminum clutch housing, remove starter. Unfasten housing from engine and move housing back just far enough to clear pressure plate, then move it to the right to free the pivot from clutch equalizer bar. Be careful not to lose bushing or disturb linkage or assist spring.
3. Remove flywheel housing cover (cast iron housings only).
4. Remove release lever return spring. Then slide release bearing and hub off release lever (cast iron housings only).
5. Loosen pressure plate attaching bolts gradually and evenly to release spring tension. If same clutch is being installed, first mark clutch cover and flywheel so installation may be made in same position.
6. Remove clutch and driven plate.

MANUAL SHIFT TRANS.
Transmission Replace

Three Speed Units
1. Raise car and drain lube from transmission.
2. Mark drive shaft so that it may be installed in the same relative position.

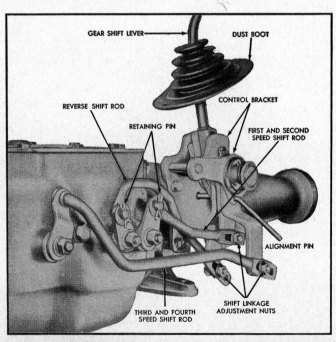

Fig. 1   Shift linkage. 1966-69 four speed transmission

3. Disconnect drive shaft from U-joint flange and slide it out of extension housing.
4. Disconnect speedometer cable.
5. Disconnect shift rods from levers at transmission.
6. Disconnect parking brake cable at equalizer.
7. Unfasten extension from rear support.
8. Raise engine high enough to remove weight from frame crossmember.
9. Support transmission with a jack and detach it from flywheel housing.
10. Slide transmission back and out of car.
11. Reverse removal procedure to install transmission.

Four Speed Units

1. Remove transmission gearshift lever boot retainer. Working under boot, remove shift lever retaining bolts and remove lever. The remaining shift linkage may be left on the transmission during removal.
2. Raise car and disconnect drive shaft from rear U-joint flange and remove drive shaft.
3. Disconnect speedometer cable.
4. Disconnect parking brake cable at equalizer bar and raise rear of engine.
5. Unfasten extension housing from engine rear support.
6. Raise transmission slightly with a jack. Disconnect and remove crossmember and engine rear support as

a unit.
7. Unfasten transmission from clutch housing and install guide pins in the two lower holes.
8. Remove transmission. If necessary, lower engine to gain enough clearance for removal of transmission.
9. Reverse removal procedure to install.

SHIFT LINKAGE, ADJUST

1966-71 3 Speed Units

1. Place selector lever in neutral.
2. Loosen the two shift rod adjusting nuts.
3. Insert a $3/16''$ drill shank through the low-reverse and 2-3 shift levers at steering column. It may be necessary to align levers to insert drill.
4. Tighten adjusting nuts.
5. Remove drill gauge.
6. Start engine and move shift lever to each position to be sure it operates freely.

1966-71 4 Speed Units

1. Loosen three shift linkage adjustment nuts.
2. Install a $1/4''$ diameter alignment tool through control bracket and levers as shown in Fig. 1.

NOTE: An alignment tool can be

made from $1/4''$ diameter drill rod bent to an "L" shape. The extensions should be $1\frac{1}{2}''$ and $3\frac{3}{4}''$ from elbow. Short end of tool should be inserted into control bracket and linkage holes until it bottoms.

3. Tighten three linkage adjusting nuts and then remove alignment tool.
4. Check shift lever for smooth crossover.

NOTE: On 1970-71 models, a transmission lock rod is incorporated in the shift linkage. This link must be adjusted AFTER the shift linkage is properly adjusted.

1. Place shift lever in Neutral and loosen lock rod adjustment nut.
2. Align the hole in the steering column socket casting with the column alignment mark and insert a .180" dia. gauge rod. The column casting must not rotate with the gauge rod installed.
3. Tighten rod lock nut and check for proper operation.

1972 AUTO. TRANS. LINKAGE, ADJUST

Linkage adjustment procedures are the same as those described for 1971 models described in the front section of this manual.

Rear Axle, Propeller Shaft & Brakes

REAR AXLES

Figs. 1 and 3 illustrate the rear axle assemblies used on these cars. When necessary to overhaul either of these units, refer to the *Rear Axle Specifications* table in this chapter.

Integral Carrier Type

The gear set consists of an $8\frac{1}{2}''$ diameter ring gear and an overhung drive pinion which is supported by two opposed tapered roller bearings, Fig. 1. The differential case is a one-piece design with openings allowing assembly of the internal parts and lubricant flow. The differential pinion shaft is retained with a threaded bolt (lock) assembled to the case.

The roller type wheel bearings have no inner race, and the rollers directly contact the bearing journals of the axle shafts. The axle shafts do not use an inner and outer bearing retainer. Rather, they are held in the axle by means of C-locks, Fig. 2. These C-locks also fit into a machined recess in the differential side gears within the differential case. There is no retainer bolt access hole in the axle shaft flange.

Axle Shaft, Bearing & Oil Seal

1. Raise car on hoist and remove wheels.

2. Drain differential lubricant.
3. Remove brake drums.
4. Remove differential housing cover.
5. Position safety stands under rear frame member and lower hoist to allow axle to lower as far as possible.
6. Working through differential case opening, remove pinion shaft lock bolt and pinion shaft.
7. Push axle shaft(s) inward toward center of axle housing and remove C-lock(s) from housing, Fig. 2.
8. Remove axle shaft, using extreme care to avoid contact of shaft seal lip with any portion of axle shaft except seal journal.
9. Use a hook-type puller to remove seal and bearing, Fig. 7.
10. Reverse procedure to install, using suitable driving tools, Fig. 8, to install seal and bearing. New seals are pre-packed with lubricant and do not require oil soaking before installation.

Removable Carrier Type

In these axles, Fig. 3, the drive pinion is straddle-mounted by two opposed tapered roller bearings which support the pinion shaft in front of the drive pinion gear, and straight roller bearing that supports the pinion shaft at the rear of the pinion gear. The drive pinion

is assembled in a pinion retainer that is bolted to the differential carrier. The tapered roller bearings are preloaded by a collapsible spacer between the bearings. The pinion is positioned by a shim or shims located between the drive pinion retainer and the differential carrier.

The differential is supported in the carrier by two tapered roller side bearings. These bearings are preloaded by two threaded ring nuts or sleeves between the bearings and pedestals. The differential assembly is positioned for proper ring gear and pinion backlash by varying the adjustment of these ring nuts. The differential case houses two side gears in mesh with two pinions mounted on a pinion shaft which is held in place by a pin. The side gears and pinions are backed by thrust washers. With high performance engines, an optional rear axle having a four-pinion differential is also used.

The axle shafts are of unequal length, the left shaft being shorter than the right. The axle shafts are mounted in sealed ball bearings that are pressed on the shafts.

Service Bulletin

All Ford Built Rear Axles: Recent manufacturing changes have eliminated the need for marking rear axle drive pinions for individual variations from nominal shim thicknesses. In the past, these pinion markings, with the aid of a shim selection table, were used as a guide to select correct shim thicknesses when a gear set or carrier assembly replacement was performed.

With the elimination of pinion markings, use of the shim selection table is no longer possible and the methods outlined below must be used.

1. Measure the thickness of the original pinion depth shim removed from the axle. Use the same thickness upon installation of the replacement carrier or drive pinion. If any further shim change is necessary, it will be indicated in the tooth pattern check.
2. If the original shim is lost, substitute a nominal shim for the original and use the tooth pattern check to determine if further shim changes are required.

Axle Shaft, Bearing & Seal

1. Remove wheel assembly.
2. Remove brake drum from flange.
3. Working through hole provided in axle shaft flange, Fig. 4, remove nuts that secure bearing retainer.
4. Pull axle shaft out of housing. If bearing is a tight fit in axle housing, use a slide hammer-type puller, Fig. 5. *Brake carrier plate must not be dislodged. Install one nut to hold plate in place after axle shaft is removed.*
5. If axle shaft bearing is to be replaced, loosen inner retainer by nicking it deeply with a chisel in several places, Fig. 6. The bearing will then slide off easily.

NOTE: On 1967-72 models a heavier, hardened retainer ring is used and it is therefore necessary to first drill a $\frac{1}{4}$" hole not more than $\frac{5}{16}$" deep in the retainer ring surface before using a chisel.

6. Press bearing from axle shaft.
7. Inspect machined surfaces of axle shaft and housing for rough spots that would affect the sealing action of the oil seal. Carefully remove any burrs or rough spots.
8. Press new bearing on shaft until it seats firmly against shoulder on shaft.
9. Press inner bearing retainer on shaft until it seats firmly against bearing.
10. If oil seal is to be replaced, use a hook-type tool to pull it out of the housing, Fig. 7. Wipe a small amount of oil resistant sealer on outer edge of seal before it is installed, Fig. 8.

Installation

1. Place a new gasket on each side of brake carrier plate and slide axle shaft into housing. Start the splines into the differential side gear and push the shaft in until bearing bottoms in housing.
2. Install retainer and tighten nuts to 30-40 ft. lbs.
3. Install brake drum and wheel.

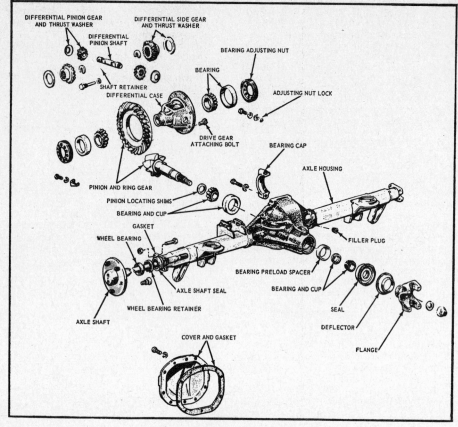

Fig. 1 Integral type rear axle assembly

PROPELLER SHAFT
Remove & Replace

1. Disconnect rear U-joint from drive pinion flange.
2. Pull dirve shaft toward rear of car until front U-joint yoke clears transmission extension housing and output shaft.
3. Install a suitable tool, such as a seal driver, in seal to prevent lube from leaking from transmission.
4. Before installing, check U-joints for freedom of movement. If a bind has resulted from misalignment after overhauling the U-joints, tap the ears of the drive shaft sharply to relieve the bind.
5. If rubber seal installed on end of transmission extension housing is damaged, install a new seal.
6. On a manual shift transmission, lubricate yoke spline with conventional transmission lubricant. On an automatic transmission, lubricate yoke spline with special spline lubricant. *This spline is sealed so that transmission fluid does not "wash" away spline lubricant.*
7. Install yoke on transmission output shaft.
8. Install U-bolts and nuts which attach U-joint to pinion flange. Tighten U-bolts evenly to prevent binding U-joint bearings.

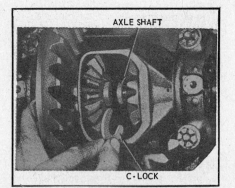

Fig. 2 Axle shaft C-locks. 1967-72 Ford integral type axle

BRAKE ADJUSTMENTS

1. Use the brake shoe adjustment gauge shown in Fig. 9 to obtain the drum inside diameter as shown. Tighten the adjusting knob on the gauge to hold this setting.
2. Place the opposite side of the gauge over the brake shoes and adjust the shoes by turning the adjuster screw until the gauge just slides over the linings. Rotate the gauge around the lining surface to assure proper lining diameter adjustment and clearance.
3. Install brake drum and wheel. Final adjustment is accomplished by mak-

ing several firm reverse stops, using the brake pedal.

Self-Adjusting Brakes

These brakes, Fig. 10, have self-adjusting shoe mechanisms that assure correct lining-to-drum clearances at all times. The automatic adjusters operate only when the brakes are applied as the car is moving rearward or when the car comes to an uphill stop.

Although the brakes are self-adjusting, an initial adjustment is necessary after the brake shoes have been relined or replaced, or when the length of the star wheel adjuster has been changed during some other service operation.

Frequent usage of an automatic transmission forward range to halt reverse vehicle motion may prevent the automatic adjusters from functioning, thereby inducing low pedal heights. Should low pedal heights be encountered, it is recommended that numerous forward and reverse stops be performed with a firm pedal effort until satisfactory pedal height is obtained.

NOTE

If a low pedal height condition cannot be corrected by making numerous reverse stops (provided the hydraulic system is free of air), it indicates that the self-adjusting mechanism is not functioning. Therefore, it will be necessary to remove the brake drums, clean, free up and lubricate the adjusting mechanism. Then adjust the brakes, being sure the parking brake is fully released.

Initial Adjustment

1. Remove adjusting hole cover from brake backing plate and, from the backing plate side, turn the adjusting screw upward with a screwdriver or other suitable tool to expand the shoes until a slight drag is felt when the drums are rotated.
2. Remove the drum.
3. While holding the adjusting lever out of engagement with the adjusting screw, Fig. 11, back off the adjusting screw about one full turn with the fingers.

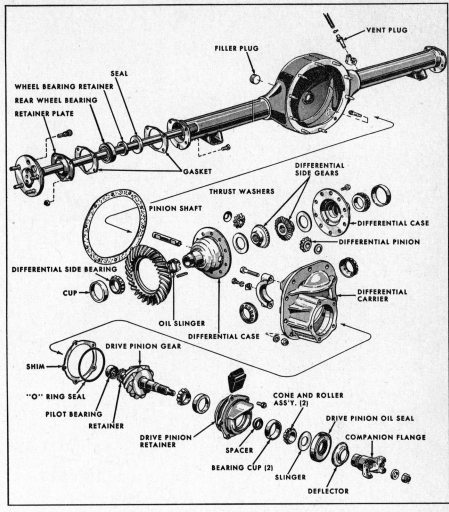

Fig. 3 Removable carrier type of rear axle assembly. On some high performance engines a four-pinion differential is also used

NOTE: If finger movement will not turn the screw, free it up. If this is not done, the adjusting lever will not turn the screw during vehicle operation. Lubricate the screw with oil and coat with wheel bearing grease. Any other adjustment procedure may cause damage to the adjusting screw with consequent self-adjuster problems.

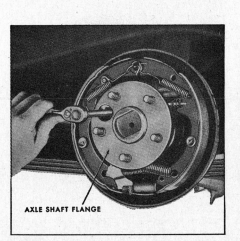

Fig. 4 Removing nuts from rear bearing retainer

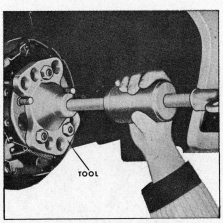

Fig. 5 Removing axle shaft with slide hammer-type puller

Fig. 6 Splitting bearing inner retainer for bearing removal

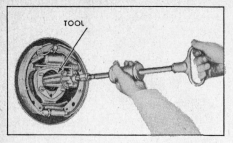

Fig. 7   Using hook-type tool to remove oil seal

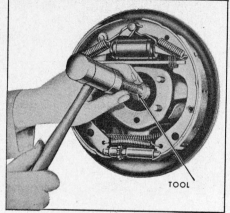

Fig. 8   Using special driver to install oil seal

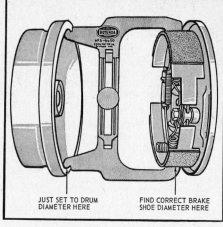

JUST SET TO DRUM DIAMETER HERE

FIND CORRECT BRAKE SHOE DIAMETER HERE

Fig. 9   Brake adjustment gauge

4. Install wheel and drum, and adjusting hole cover. Adjust brakes on remaining wheels in the same manner.
5. If pedal height is not satisfactory, drive the vehicle and make sufficient reverse stops with a firm pedal effort until proper pedal height is obtained.

PARKING BRAKE, ADJUST

Check parking brake cables when brakes are fully released. If cables are loose, adjust as follows:

1968-72 Ford & Mercury

1. Release parking brake pedal.
2. Depress pedal one notch from its normal released position.
3. Raise car.
4. Turn equalizer lever adjusting nut until a moderate drag is felt when turning rear wheels by hand.
5. Release parking brake and make sure that brake shoes return to their fully released position.

1966 Ford & Mercury

1. Fully release parking brake pedal.
2. Depress pedal one notch from its fully released position.

3. Raise car and turn adjusting nut forward against equalizer until a moderate drag is felt when turning rear wheels.
4. Release parking brake and make sure that brake shoes return to fully released position.
5. Turn lock nut forward against equalizer until a moderate drag is felt when turning rear wheels.
6. When cables are properly adjusted, tighten both nuts against equalizer.
7. Release parking brake. Then make sure that there is no drag when turning rear wheels.

VACUUM RELEASE PARKING BRAKE

1966-68 Mercury Parklane

The vacuum power unit will release the parking brakes automatically when the shift lever is moved into any drive position with the engine running. The brakes will not release automatically, however, when the shift lever is in neutral or park position with the engine running, or in any position with the engine off.

The power unit piston rod is attached to the release lever. Since the release lever pivots against the pawl, a slight movement of the release lever will disengage the pawl from the ratchet, allowing the brakes to release. The release lever pivots on a rivet pin in the pedal mount.

As shown in Fig. 13, hoses connect the power unit and the engine manifold to a vacuum release valve in the transmission neutral safety switch. Moving the transmission selector lever into any drive position with the engine running will open the release valve to connect engine manifold vacuum to one side of the actuating piston in the power unit. The pressure differential thus created will cause the piston and link to pull the release lever.

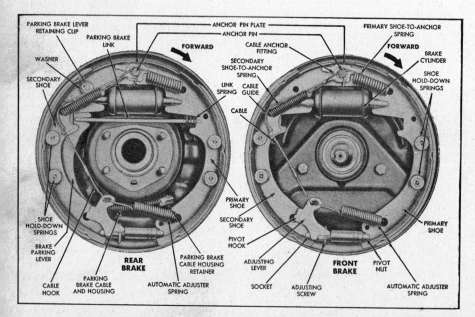

Fig. 10   Right front and rear drum brakes

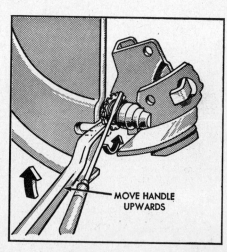

MOVE HANDLE UPWARDS

Fig. 11   Backing off brake adjustment by disengaging adjusting lever with screwdriver

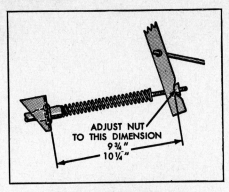

Fig. 12 Parking brake pedal cable adjustment

ADJUST NUT TO THIS DIMENSION 9 ¾" — 10 ¼"

MASTER CYLINDER, REPLACE

1967-72 Ford & Mercury

1. Working from inside of car beneath instrument panel, disconnect master cylinder push rod from brake pedal.
2. Disconnect stop light switch wires at connector. Remove hairpin retainer. Slide stop light switch off brake pedal pin just enough to clear end of pin, then lift switch straight upward from pin.
3. Slide master cylinder push rod, nylon washers and bushings from pedal pin.

4. Remove brake tubes from both outlet ports of master cylinder.
5. Unfasten and remove master cylinder from dash panel.

1966 Ford & Mercury

1. Disconnect rubber boot from rear end of master cylinder in passenger compartment.
2. Disconnect brake line from master cylinder fitting. If stop light switch is attached to cylinder, disconnect wires from switch.
3. Unfasten cylinder from dash panel and lift cylinder away from push rod and out of engine compartment. Remove rubber boot from push rod.

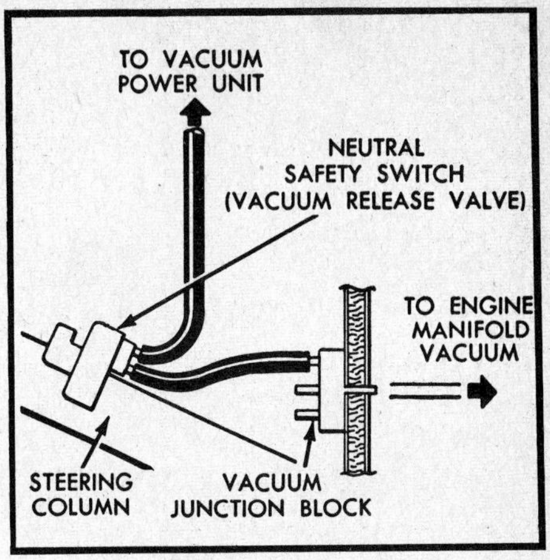

POWER BRAKE UNIT REPLACE

1966-72 Ford & Mercury

1. Working from inside of car under instrument panel, disconnect booster push rod link from brake pedal. To do this, proceed as follows:
2. Disconnect stop light switch wires at connector. Remove hairpin retainer. Slide switch off brake pedal pin just far enough for switch outer hole to clear pin. Then lift switch straight upward from pin. Slide master cylinder push rod and nylon washers and bushing off brake pedal pin.

Fig. 13 Connections for automatic parking brake release. 1966-68 Parklane

TO VACUUM POWER UNIT

NEUTRAL SAFETY SWITCH (VACUUM RELEASE VALVE)

TO ENGINE MANIFOLD VACUUM

STEERING COLUMN

VACUUM JUNCTION BLOCK

3. Open hood and disconnect brake line at master cylinder outlet fitting.
4. Disconnect vacuum hose from booster unit. If equipped with automatic transmission disconnect transmission vacuum unit hose.
5. Remove four attaching nuts and remove booster and bracket from dash panel, slide push rod link out from engine side of dash panel. Remove four spacers.
6. Remove push rod link boot from dash panel.
7. Reverse procedure to install.

Front End and Steering Section

FRONT SUSPENSION
1966-72

Referring to Fig. 1, the construction of the front suspension differs from earlier models in that the lower control arm pivots on a bolt in the front crossmember. The struts, which are connected between the lower control arms and frame crossmember, prevent the control arms from moving forward and backward.

LUBRICATION
1966-72

Ball joints are prelubricated with a special lubricant. The lubricating interval is 36,000 miles. At these intervals, remove the plugs, apply the special lubricant, remove the fittings and replace the plugs.

SERVICE BULLETIN

Some uninformed service people recommend that conventional grease fittings be installed and that the car be lubricated every 1000 miles. This is completely unnecessary and, in fact, may cause damage to the special seals used in the lubrication points.

The use of conventional lubricants not only can do damage to the special seals but is incompatible with the special lubricant. Moreover, after the special sealing plugs have been replaced by conventional grease fittings, dirt and water can enter and cause excessive wear, rendering the units unfit for further service.

SERVICE BULLETIN, 1966-72

BALL JOINT LUBE: The ball joint seals on these models have been redesigned to provide improved sealing and longer life. The new seals can be damaged and the sealing characteristics destroyed if excessive lubricant is used. Specifications call for the addition of only 10 grams (level teaspoon) of lubricant to the ball joints at 36,000 miles intervals. The initial application of 10 grams of lubricant insures forcing grease into the bearing area and still allows for three subsequent lubrications of 10 grams each without ballooning the seals and resultant premature failure.

For the above reasons the ball joint seals on new cars might appear to be collapsed and give the mistaken impression that additional lubricant is required.

This is not the case and under no circumstances should more than 10 grams of lubricant be added to the ball joints at the 36,000 mile intervals.

SERVICE BULLETIN

1966-72 STEERING LINKAGE LUBE: The steering linkage on these models should be lubricated at intervals of 36,000 miles. Normal breathing of socket joints permits moisture condensation within the joint. Moisture inside the joint assembly will cause no appreciable damage and the joint will function normally. However, if the moisture is concentrated in the bearing grease grooves and is frozen at the time of attempted lubrication, grease cannot flow and pressure greasing may damage the joint.

Do not attempt to lubricate the steering linkage on these vehicles if it has set in temperatures lower than 20 deg. above zero F. The vehicle should be allowed to warm up in a heated garage for 30 minutes or until the joints accept lubrication.

IMPORTANT: A torch must not be used to heat joints because this quantity of heat will melt the nylon bearing within the joint.

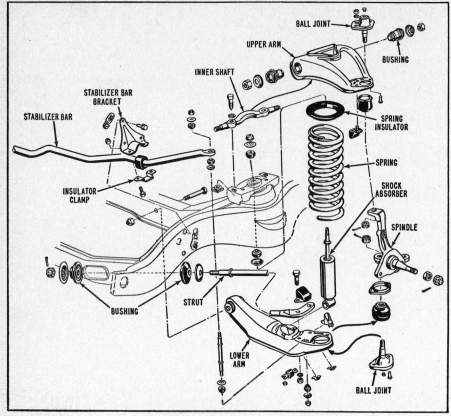

Fig. 1   Front suspension. 1966-72 Ford & Mercury

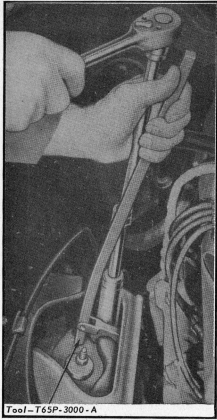

Tool—T65P-3000-A

Fig. 2   Adjusting caster and camber.
1966-72 Ford and Mercury

WHEEL ALIGNMENT

SERVICE BULLETIN

WHEEL BALANCING DIFFERS: On cars with disc brakes, dynamic balancing of the wheel-and-tire assembly on the car should not be attempted without first pulling back the shoe and lining assemblies from the rotor. If this is not done, brake drag may burn out the motor on the wheel spinner.

The drag can be eliminated by removing the wheel, taking out the two bolts holding the caliper splash shield, and detaching the shield. Then push the pistons into their cylinder bores by applying steady pressure on the shoes on each side of the rotor for at least a minute. If necessary, use waterpump pliers to apply the pressure.

After the pistons have been retracted, reinstall the splash shield and wheel. The wheel-and-tire assembly can then be dynamically balanced in the usual way. After the balancing job has been completed, be sure to pump the brake pedal several times until the shoes are seated and a firm brake pedal is obtained.

1966-72 Ford & Mercury

Caster and camber can be adjusted by loosening the bolts that attach the upper suspension arm to the shaft at the frame side rail, and moving the arm assembly in or out in the elongated bolt holes, Fig. 2. Since any movement of the arm af-fects both caster and camber, both factors should be balanced against one another when making the adjustment.

Caster, Adjust

1. To adjust caster, install the adjusting tool as shown in Fig. 2.
2. Loosen both upper arm inner shaft retaining bolts and move either front or rear of the shaft in or out as necessary to increase or decrease caster angle. Then tighten bolt to retain adjustment.

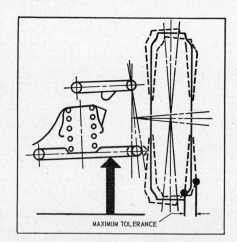

Fig. 3   Measuring lower ball joint radial play, which should not exceed 1/4"

Camber, Adjust

1. Loosen both upper arm inner retaining bolts and move both front and rear ends of shaft inward or outward as necessary to increase or decrease camber angle.
2. Tighten bolts and recheck caster and readjust if necessary.

TOE-IN, ADJUST

Position the front wheels in their straight-ahead position. Then turn both tie rod adjusting sleeves an equal amount until the desired toe-in setting is obtained.

WHEEL BEARINGS, ADJUST

1. Torque adjusting nut 17 to 25 ft-lbs.
2. Back nut off 1/2 turn.
3. Retighten it 10 to 15 inch-lbs (finger tight) and install nut lock and cotter pin.

WHEEL BEARINGS, REPLACE

(Disc Brakes)

1. Raise car and remove front wheels.

2. Remove caliper mounting bolts.

NOTE: It is not necessary to disconnect the brake lines for this operation.

3. Slide caliper off of disc, inserting a spacer between the shoes to hold them in their bores after the caliper is removed. Position caliper assembly out of the way.

NOTE: Do not allow caliper to hang by brake hose.

4. Remove hub and disc assembly. Grease retainer and inner bearing can now be removed.

CHECKING BALL JOINTS FOR WEAR

Upper Ball Joint

1. Raise car on floor jacks placed beneath lower control arms.
2. Grasp lower edge of tire and move wheel in and out.
3. As wheel is being moved in and out, observe upper end of spindle and upper arm.
4. Any movement between upper end of spindle and upper arm indicates ball joint wear and loss of preload. If any such movement is observed, replace upper ball joint.

NOTE: During the foregoing check, the lower ball joint will be unloaded and may move. Disregard all such movement of the lower ball joint. Also, do not mistake loose wheel bearings for a worn ball joint.

Lower Ball Joint

1. Raise car on jacks placed under lower control arms as shown in Fig. 3. This will unload ball joints.
2. Adjust wheel bearings.
3. Attach a dial indicator to lower control arm and position so that its plunger rests against the inner side of the wheel rim adjacent to the lower ball joint.

Fig. 5   Removing and installing coil spring. 1966-72

4. Grasp tire at top and bottom and slowly move it in and out as shown in Fig. 3.
5. If reading on dial indicator exceeds ¼″, replace lower ball joint.

SHOCK ABSORBER, REPLACE

To remove a shock absorber, unfasten it at the top and bottom and lower it through the opening in the lower control arm.

COIL SPRING, REPLACE

1. Support the front of the car at the frame side rails.
2. Place a floor jack under the lower arm. Then unfasten the lower ball joint from the knuckle support.
3. Lower the jack under the lower arm and pull out the coil spring as suggested by Fig. 4.
4. Reverse procedure to install.

BALL JOINTS, REPLACE

The ball joints are riveted to the upper and lower control arms. The ball joints can be replaced on the car by removing the rivets and retaining the new ball joint to the control arm with the attaching bolts, nuts and washers furnished with the ball joint kit.

When removing a ball joint, use a suitable pressing tool to force the ball joint out of the spindle.

STEERING GEAR, REPLACE
1966-72 Ford & Mercury

1. Remove bolt that attaches flex joint to steering gear.
2. Raise front of car and install safety stands.
3. Disconnect pitman arm from sector shaft.
4. If necessary, disconnect muffler inlet pipe.
5. Remove steering gear housing attaching bolts and remove steering gear.

POWER STEERING GEAR
1966-72 Ford & Mercury

1. Disconnect pressure and return lines from steering gear. Plug lines and ports in gear to prevent entry of dirt.
2. Remove two bolts that secure flex coupling to steering gear and to column.
3. Raise car and remove sector shaft nut.
4. Use a puller to remove pitman arm.
5. If car has a standard transmission, remove clutch release lever retracting spring to provide clearance for gear removal.
6. Support steering gear, then remove attaching bolts.
7. Work steering gear free of flex coupling and remove it from car.
8. Reverse procedure to install.

FORD & MERCURY

Compact & Intermediate Models

OLD CAR SPECIFICATIONS: For 1946-65 Tune Up and Wheel Alignment Specifications see back of book.

*This material covered only in the "Service Trade Edition" of this manual.

INDEX OF SERVICE OPERATIONS

ENGINE & SERIAL NUMBER LOCATION: Vehicle warranty plate on rear face of left front door.

ENGINE IDENTIFICATION: Engine code is last letter in serial number on vehicle warranty plate.

Year	Engine	Engine Code	Year	Engine	Engine Code
1966	6-170	U	1970	6-170	U
	6-200	T		6-200	T
	V8-289⑤	A		6-250	L
	V8-289①	C		V8-302	F
	V8-289⑥	K		V8-302 "Boss"	G
	V8-390①	Y		V8-351①	H
	V8-390②	Z		V8-351②	M
	V8-390②	S (GT)		V8-428 CJ	Q
1967	6-170	U		V8-428 CJ⑧	R
	6-200	T		V8-429	N
	V8-289①	C		V8-429 CJ	C
	V8-289⑤	A		V8-429 "Boss"	Z
	V8-289⑥	K	1971	6-170	U
	V8-390①	Y		6-200	T
	V8-390①	H		6-250	L
	V8-390②	Z		V8-302	F
	V8-390②	S (GT)		V8-302 "Boss"	G
1968	6-170	U		V8-351①	H
	6-200	T		V8-351②	M
	V8-289①	C		V8-351②	Q (GT)
	V8-289⑦	K		V8-429 CJ	C
	V8-289⑤	A		V8-429 SCJ	J
	V8-302②	J	1972	6-170	U
	V8-302①	F		6-200	T
	V8-390①	Y		6-250	L
	V8-390①⑤	X		V8-302	F
	V8-390②	S (GT)		V8-351①	H
	V8-427②	W		V8-351②	Q
1969	6-170	U		V8-351⑥	R
	6-200	T		V8-400	S
	6-250	L		V8-429	N
	V8-302①	F			
	V8-351①	H			
	V8-351②	M			
	V8-390②	S			
	V8-427②	W			
	V8-428	Q			
	V8-428⑧	R			

①—Two barrel carburetor.
②—Four barrel carburetor.
④—With transistorized ignition.
⑤—Premium fuel.
⑥—High Performance.
⑦—Special.
⑧—Ram Air.

GRILLE IDENTIFICATION

1966 Falcon

1966 Comet 202, Capri, Caliente & Wagons

1966 Comet Cyclone & GT

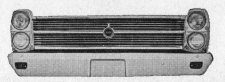

1966 Fairlane

1966 Mustang

1967 Comet, Capri, Caliente, 202, Wagons

FORD & MERCURY — Compact & Intermediate Models

GRILLE IDENTIFICATION—Continued

1967 Cougar

1967 Comet Cyclone & GT

1967 Fairlane

1967 Falcon

1967 Mustang

1968 Falcon

1968 Fairlane

1968 Montego and Comet

1968 Mustang

1968 Cougar 7 Litre

1968 Cougar

1969 Montego and Cyclone

1969 Fairlane, Cobra

1969 Torino GT

1969, 1970 (Early) Falcon

1969 Cougar

1969 Mustang

1970 Torino/Fairlane &
1970 (Late) Falcon

1970 Torino Cobra

1970 Torino GT

1970 Cougar

1970 Cyclone

1970 Montego

1970-72 Maverick

Compact & Intermediate Models — FORD & MERCURY

GRILLE IDENTIFICATION—Continued

1970 Mustang

1970 Mustang Mach 1

1971-72 Maverick Grabber

1971 Cyclone

1971 Montego

1971-72 Cougar

1971-72 Cougar XR7

1971-72 Mustang

1971-72 Mustang Mach 1

1971-72 Comet

1972 Torino

1972 Gran Torino

1971 Torino

1972 Montego

1972 Montego GT

GENERAL ENGINE SPECIFICATIONS

Year	Engine	Car-buretor	Bore and Stroke	Piston Displacement, Cubic Inches	Compression Ratio	Maximum Brake H.P. @ R.P.M.	Maximum Torque Lbs. Ft. @ R.P.M.	Normal Oil Pressure Pounds
1966	105 Horsepower..............6-170	1 Barrel	3.50 x 2.94	170	9.1	105 @ 4400	158 @ 2400	35–55
	120 Horsepower..............6-200	1 Barrel	3.68 x 3.126	200	9.2	120 @ 4400	190 @ 2400	35–55
	200 Horsepower...........V8-289	2 Barrel	4.00 x 2.87	289	9.3	200 @ 4400	282 @ 2400	35–55
	225 Horsepower...........V8-289	4 Barrel	4.00 x 2.87	289	10.0	225 @ 4800	305 @ 3200	35–55
	271 H.P. Hi Perf...........V8-289	4 Barrel	4.00 x 2.87	289	10.5	271 @ 6000	312 @ 3400	35–55
	265 Horsepower...........V8-390	2 Barrel	4.05 x 3.984	390	9.5	265 @ 4400	401 @ 2600	35–55
	315 Horsepower...........V8-390	4 Barrel	4.05 x 3.984	390	10.5	315 @ 4600	427 @ 2800	35–55
	335 Horsepower "GT".......V8-390	4 Barrel	4.05 x 3.984	390	10.5	335 @ 4800	427 @ 3200	35–55
1967	105 Horsepower..............6-170	1 Barrel	3.50 x 2.94	170	9.1	105 @ 4400	158 @ 2400	35–55
	120 Horsepower..............6-200	1 Barrel	4.00 x 2.87	200	9.2	120 @ 4400	190 @ 2400	35–55
	200 Horsepower...........V8-289	2 Barrel	4.00 x 2.87	289	9.3	200 @ 4400	282 @ 2400	35–55
	225 Horsepower...........V8-289	4 Barrel	4.00 x 2.87	289	10.0	225 @ 4800	305 @ 3200	35–55
	265 Horsepower...........V8-390	2 Barrel	4.05 x 3.984	390	9.5	265 @ 4400	401 @ 2600	35–55
	271 H.P., Hi Perf...........V8-289	4 Barrel	4.00 x 2.87	289	10.5	271 @ 6000	312 @ 3400	35–55
	275 Horsepower...........V8-390	2 Barrel	4.05 x 3.984	390	9.5	275 @ 4400	405 @ 2600	35–55
	315 Horsepower...........V8-390	4 Barrel	4.05 x 3.984	390	10.5	315 @ 4600	427 @ 2800	35–55
	320 Horsepower...........V8-390	4 Barrel	4.05 x 3.984	390	10.5	320 @ 4800	427 @ 3200	35–55
	335 Horsepower "GT".......V8-390	4 Barrel	4.05 x 3.984	390	10.5	335 @ 4800	427 @ 3200	35–55
1968	105 Horsepower..............6-170	1 Barrel	3.50 x 2.94	170	9.1	105 @ 4400	158 @ 2400	35–55
	120 Horsepower..............6-200	1 Barrel	3.68 x 3.13	200	9.2	120 @ 4400	190 @ 2400	35–55
	200 Horsepower...........V8-289	2 Barrel	4.00 x 2.87	289	9.3	200 @ 4400	282 @ 4400	35–55
	210 Horsepower...........V8-302	2 Barrel	4.00 x 3.00	302	9.5	210 @ 4400	295 @ 2400	35–55
	230 Horsepower...........V8-302	4 Barrel	4.00 x 3.00	302	10.0	230 @ 4800	310 @ 2800	35–55
	235 Horsepower...........V8-302	4 Barrel	4.00 x 3.00	302	10.5	235 @ 4800	318 @ 3200	35–55
	265 Horsepower...........V8-390	2 Barrel	4.05 x 3.78	390	9.5	265 @ 4400	390 @ 2600	35–55
	270 Horsepower...........V8-390	2 Barrel	4.05 x 3.78	390	9.5	270 @ 4400	403 @ 2600	35–55
	271 Horsepower...........V8-289	4 Barrel	4.00 x 2.87	289	10.5	271 @ 6000	312 @ 3400	35–55
	280 Horsepower...........V8-390	2 Barrel	4.05 x 3.78	390	10.5	280 @ 4400	403 @ 2600	35–55
	320 Horsepower "GT".......V8-390	4 Barrel	4.05 x 3.78	390	10.5	320 @ 4800	427 @ 3200	35–55
	325 Horsepower "GT".......V8-390	4 Barrel	4.05 x 3.78	390	10.5	325 @ 4800	427 @ 3200	35–55
	390 Horsepower...........V8-427	4 Barrel	4.23 x 3.78	427	10.9	390 @ 5600	460 @ 3200	35–55
1969	105 Horsepower..............6-170	1 Barrel	3.50 x 2.94	170	9.1	105 @ 4400	158 @ 2400	35–60
	120 Horsepower..............6-200	1 Barrel	3.68 x 3.13	200	8.8	120 @ 4400	190 @ 2400	35–60
	155 Horsepower..............6-250	1 Barrel	3.68 x 3.91	250	9.0①	155 @ 4000	240 @ 1600	35–60
	210 Horsepower...........V8-302	2 Barrel	4.00 x 3.00	302	9.5	210 @ 4400	295 @ 2400	35–60
	290 Horsepower "H.O.".......V8-302	4 Barrel	4.00 x 3.00	302	10.5	290 @ 5800	290 @ 4300	35–60
	250 Horsepower...........V8-351	2 Barrel	4.00 x 3.50	351	9.5	250 @ 4600	355 @ 2600	35–60
	290 Horsepower...........V8-351	4 Barrel	4.00 x 3.50	351	10.7	290 @ 4800	385 @ 3200	35–60
	320 Horsepower...........V8-390	4 Barrel	4.05 x 3.78	390	10.5	320 @ 4800	427 @ 3200	35–60
	390 Horsepower...........V8-427	4 Barrel	4.23 x 3.78	427	10.9	390 @ 5600	460 @ 3200	35–60
	335 Horsepower...........V8-428	4 Barrel	4.13 x 3.98	428	10.6	335 @ 5200	440 @ 3400	35–60
	Ram Air...............V8-428	4 Barrel	4.13 x 3.98	428	10.6	—	—	35–60
1970	105 Horsepower..............6-170	1 Barrel	3.50 x 2.94	170	9.1	105 @ 4400	158 @ 2400	35–60
	120 Horsepower..............6-200	1 Barrel	3.68 x 3.13	200	8.8	120 @ 4400	190 @ 2400	35–60
	155 Horsepower..............6-250	1 Barrel	3.68 x 3.91	250	9.1	155 @ 4000	240 @ 1600	35–60
	210 Horsepower...........V8-302	2 Barrel	4.00 x 3.00	302	9.5	210 @ 4400	295 @ 2400	35–60
	290 Horsepower "BOSS".......V8-302	4 Barrel	4.00 x 3.00	302	10.5	290 @ 5800	290 @ 4300	35–60
	250 Horsepower...........V8-351	2 Barrel	4.00 x 3.50	351	9.5	250 @ 4600	355 @ 2600	35–60
	300 Horsepower...........V8-351	4 Barrel	4.00 x 3.50	351	11.0	300 @ 5400	380 @ 3400	35–60
	335 Horsepower "CJ".......V8-428	4 Barrel	4.13 x 3.98	428	10.6	335 @ 5200	440 @ 3400	35–60
	Ram Air...............V8-428	4 Barrel	4.13 x 3.98	428	10.6	—	—	35–60
	360 Horsepower...........V8-429	4 Barrel	4.36 x 3.59	429	11.0	360 @ 4600	476 @ 2800	35–60
	345 Horsepower "CJ".......V8-429	4 Barrel	4.36 x 3.59	429	11.5	345 @ 5800	450 @ 3400	35–60
	375 Horsepower "Boss"......V8-429	4 Barrel	4.36 x 3.59	429	10.5	375 @ 5200	450 @ 3400	20–60

Continued

GENERAL ENGINE SPECIFICATIONS—Continued

Year	Engine	Car-buretor	Bore and Stroke	Piston Dis-place-ment, Cubic Inches	Com-pres-sion Ratio	Maximum Brake H.P. @ R.P.M.	Maximum Torque Lbs. Ft. @ R.P.M.	Normal Oil Pressure Pounds
1971	100 Horsepower..............6-170	1 Barrel	3.50 x 2.94	170	8.7	100 @ 4200	148 @ 2600	35—60
	115 Horsepower..............6-200	1 Barrel	3.68 x 3.13	200	8.7	115 @ 4000	180 @ 2200	35—60
	145 Horsepower..............6-250	1 Barrel	3.68 x 3.91	250	9.0	145 @ 4000	232 @ 1600	35—60
	210 Horsepower..........V8-302	2 Barrel	4.00 x 3.00	302	9.0	210 @ 4600	296 @ 2600	35—60
	290 Horsepower "BOSS"......V8-302	4 Barrel	4.00 x 3.00	302	9.4	290 @ 5800	290 @ 4300	35—60
	240 Horsepower..........V8-351	2 Barrel	4.00 x 3.50	351	9.0	240 @ 4600	350 @ 2600	35—60
	285 Horsepower..........V8-351	4 Barrel	4.00 x 3.50	351	10.7	285 @ 5400	370 @ 3400	35—60
	330 Horsepower..........V8-351	4 Barrel	4.00 x 3.50	351	11.7	330 @ 5400	370 @ 4000	35—60
	370 Horsepower "CJ".......V8-429	4 Barrel	4.36 x 3.59	429	11.3	370 @ 5400	450 @ 3400	35—60
	375 Horsepower "SCJ".......V8-429	4 Barrel	4.36 x 3.59	429	11.5	375 @ 5600	450 @ 3400	35—60
1972	82 Horsepower②..............6-170	1 Barrel	3.50 x 2.94	170	8.3	82 @ 4400	129 @ 1800	35—60
	91 Horsepower②.............6-200	1 Barrel	3.68 x 3.13	200	8.3	91 @ 4000	154 @ 2200	35—60
	95 Horsepower②.............6-250	1 Barrel	3.68 x 3.91	250	8.0	95 @ 3600	181 @ 1600	35—60
	98 Horsepower②.............6-250	1 Barrel	3.68 x 3.91	250	8.0	98 @ 3600	183 @ 1600	35—60
	99 Horsepower②.............6-250	1 Barrel	3.68 x 3.91	250	8.0	99 @ 3600	184 @ 1600	35—60
	140 Horsepower②..........V8-302	2 Barrel	4.00 x 3.00	302	8.5	140 @ 4000	230 @ 2200	35—60
	141 Horsepower②..........V8-302	2 Barrel	4.00 x 3.00	302	8.5	141 @ 4000	242 @ 2000	35—60
	143 Horsepower②..........V8-302	2 Barrel	4.00 x 3.00	302	8.5	143 @ 4200	242 @ 2000	35—60
	161 Horsepower②..........V8-351	2 Barrel	4.00 x 3.50	351	8.6	161 @ 4000	276 @ 2000	35—60
	164 Horsepower②..........V8-351	2 Barrel	4.00 x 3.50	351	8.6	164 @ 4000	276 @ 2000	35—60
	177 Horsepower②..........V8-351	2 Barrel	4.00 x 3.50	351	8.6	177 @ 4000	284 @ 2000	35—60
	248 Horsepower② "CJ".......V8-351	4 Barrel	4.00 x 3.50	351	8.6	248 @ 5400	299 @ 3800	35—60
	262 Horsepower②..........V8-351	4 Barrel	4.00 x 3.50	351	8.6	262 @ 5400	299 @ 3600	35—60
	266 Horsepower②..........V8-351	4 Barrel	4.00 x 3.50	351	8.6	266 @ 5400	301 @ 3600	35—60
	168 Horsepower②..........V8-400	2 Barrel	4.00 x 4.00	400	8.4	168 @ 4200	297 @ 2200	35—60
	205 Horsepower②..........V8-429	4 Barrel	4.36 x 3.59	429	8.5	205 @ 4400	322 @ 2600	35—60

①—Mustang "E" Model, 9.5.
②—Ratings are NET—as installed in the vehicle.

TUNE UP SPECIFICATIONS

OLD CAR SPECIFICATIONS: For 1946-65 Tune-Up Specifications see back of book.

★When using a timing light, disconnect vacuum hose or tube at distributor and plug opening in hose or tube so idle speed will not be affected.

●When checking compression, lowest cylinder must be within 75% of the highest.

Year	Engine	Spark Plug		Distributor		Firing Order	Ignition Timing★		Hot Idle Speed⑫		Fuel Pump Press. Lbs.
		Type	Gap Inch	Point Gap Inch	Dwell Angle Deg.		BTDC ①	Mark	Std. Trans.	Auto. Trans. ②	
1966	6-170 Std. Tr.⑬	BF-82	.034	.025	37—42	Fig. H	6°	Fig. A	575⑫	—	4—6
	6-170 Std. Tr.⑭	BF-82	.034	.025	37—42	Fig. H	TDC	Fig. A	625⑫	—	4—6
	6-170 Auto. Tr.⑬	BF-82	.034	.025	37—42	Fig. H	12°	Fig. A	—	500D⑫	4—6
	6-170 Auto. Tr.⑭	BF-82	.034	.025	37—42	Fig. H	TDC	Fig. A	—	550D⑫	4—6
	6-200 Std. Tr.⑬	BF-82	.034	.025	37—42	Fig. H	6°	Fig. A	575⑫	—	4—6
	6-200 Std. Tr.⑭	BF-82	.034	.025	37—42	Fig. H	TDC	Fig. A	625⑫	—	4—6
	6-200 Auto. Tr.⑬	BF-82	.034	.025	37—42	Fig. H	12°	Fig. A	—	500D⑫	4—6
	6-200 Auto. Tr.⑭	BF-82	.034	.025	37—42	Fig. H	TDC	Fig. A	—	550D⑫	4—6

Continued

TUNE UP SPECIFICATIONS—Continued

OLD CAR SPECIFICATIONS: For 1946-65 Tune-Up specifications see back of book.

★When using a timing light, disconnect vacuum hose or tube at distributor and plug opening in hose or tube so idle speed will not be affected.

●When checking compression, lowest cylinder must be within 75% of the highest.

Year	Engine	Spark Plug Type	Spark Plug Gap Inch	Distributor Point Gap Inch	Distributor Dwell Angle Deg.	Firing Order	Ignition Timing★ BTDC [1]	Ignition Timing★ Mark	Hot Idle Speed Std. Trans.	Hot Idle Speed Auto. Trans. [2]	Fuel Pump Press. Lbs.
1966	8-289 Std. Tr.[13]	BF-42	.034	.017	26–31	Fig. E	6°	Fig. F	575[12]	—	4–6
	8-289 Std. Tr.[14]	BF-42	.034	.017	26–31	Fig. E	TDC	Fig. F	625[12]	—	4–6
	8-289 Auto. Tr.[13]	BF-42	.034	.017	26–31	Fig. E	6°	Fig. F	—	475D[12]	4–6
	8-289 Auto. Tr.[14]	BF-42	.034	.017	26–31	Fig. E	TDC	Fig. F	—	625D[12]	4–6
	8-289 Hi Perf.	BF-32	.030	.020	30–33	Fig. E	12°	Fig. F	765[12]	765D[12]	4–6
	8-390[13]	BF-42	.034	.017	26–31	Fig. E	10°	Fig. K	575[12]	475D[12]	4½–6½
	8-390[14]	BF-42	.034	.017	26–31	Fig. E	6°	Fig. K	625[12]	625D[12]	4½–6½
1967	6-170 Std. Tr.[13]	BF-82	.034	.025	37–42	Fig. H	6°	Fig. A	575[12]	—	4–6
	6-170 Std. Tr.[14]	BF-82	.034	.025	37–42	Fig. H	TDC	Fig. A	700[12]	—	4–6
	6-170 Auto. Tr.[13]	BF-82	.034	.025	37–42	Fig. H	12°	Fig. A	—	500D[12]	4–6
	6-170 Auto. Tr.[14]	BF-82	.034	.025	37–42	Fig. H	TDC	Fig. A	—	550D[12]	4–6
	6-200 Std. Tr.[13]	BF-82	.034	.025	37–42	Fig. H	6°	Fig. A	575[12]	—	4–6
	6-200 Std. Tr.[14]	BF-82	.034	.025	37–42	Fig. H	5°	Fig. A	700[12]	—	4–6
	6-200 Auto. Tr.[13]	BF-82	.034	.025	37–42	Fig. H	12°	Fig. A	—	500D[12]	4–6
	6-200 Auto. Tr.[14]	BF-82	.034	.025	37–42	Fig. H	5°	Fig. A	—	550D[12]	4–6
	8-289 Std. Tr.[13][7]	BF-42	.034	.017	26–31	Fig. E	6°	Fig. F	575[12]	—	4–6
	8-289 Std. Tr.[14][7]	BF-42	.034	.017	26–31	Fig. E	TDC	Fig. F	625[12]	—	4–6
	8-289 Auto. Tr.[13][7]	BF-42	.034	.017	26–31	Fig. E	6°	Fig. F	—	475D[12]	4–6
	8-289 Auto. Tr.[14][7]	BF-42	.034	.017	26–31	Fig. E	TDC	Fig. F	—	550D[12]	4–6
	8-289 Std. Tr.[13][8]	BF-42	.034	.017	26–31	Fig. E	6°	Fig. F	600[12]	—	4–6
	8-289 Std. Tr.[14][8]	BF-32	.034	.017	26–31	Fig. E	TDC	Fig. F	625[12]	—	4–6
	8-289 Auto. Tr.[13][8]	BF-42	.034	.017	26–31	Fig. E	6°	Fig. F	—	475D[12]	4–6
	8-289 Auto. Tr.[14][8]	BF-42	.034	.017	26–31	Fig. E	TDC	Fig. F	—	550D[12]	4–6
	8-289[9][13]	BF-42	.030	.020	30–33	Fig. E	12°	Fig. F	750[12]	650D[12]	4–6
	8-289[9][14]	BF-32	.030	.020	30–33	Fig. E	6°	Fig. F	750[12]	650D[12]	4–6
	8-390[13]	BF-32	.034	.017	26–31	Fig. E	10°	Fig. K	575[12]	475D[12]	4½–6½
	8-390[14]	BF-32	.034	.017	26–31	Fig. E	6°	Fig. K	625[12]	550D[12]	4½–6½
1968	6-170	BF-82	.034	.027	37–42	Fig. H	6°	Fig. G	700[16]	550D[16]	4–6
	6-200	BF-82	.034	.027	37–42	Fig. H	6°	Fig. G	700[16]	550D[16]	4–6
	8-289 2 B. Carb.	BF-42	.034	.021	24–29	Fig. E	6°	Fig. B	625[16]	550D[16]	4–6
	8-289 4 B. Carb.	BF-32	.034	.020	30–33	Fig. E	6°	Fig. B	750[16]	650D[16]	4–6
	8-302 2 B. Carb.	BF-42	.034	.021	24–29	Fig. E	6°	Fig. B	625[16]	550D[16]	4–6
	8-302 4 B. Carb.[14]	BF-42	.034	.021	30–33	Fig. E	6°	Fig. B	625[16]	—	4–6
	8-302 4 B. Carb.[4]	BF-42	.034	.017	26–31	Fig. E	6°	Fig. B	—	550D[16]	4–6
	8-390 2 B. Carb.[14]	BF-42	.034	.021	30–33	Highest	6°	Fig. C	625[16]	—	4½–6½
	8-390 2 B. Carb.[4]	BF-42	.034	.017	26–31	Fig. E	6°	Fig. C	—	550D[16]	4½–6½
	8-390 4 B. Carb.[14]	BF-42	.034	.021	30–33	Fig. E	6°	Fig. C	625[16]	—	4½–6½
	8-390 4 B. Carb.[4]	BF-42	.034	.017	26–31	Fig. E	6°	Fig. C	—	550D[16]	4½–6½
	8-390 "GT"	BF-32	.034	.016	26–31	Fig. E	6°	Fig. C	700[16]	550D[16]	4½–6½
	8-427	BF-32	.034	.017	26–31	Fig. E	6°	Fig. C	—	600D[16]	4½–6½
	8-428 Cobra Jet	BF-32	.034	.017	26–31	Fig. E	BTDC	Fig. C	700[16]	650D[16]	5
1969	6-170	BF-82	.034	.027	35–40	Fig. H	6°	Fig. G	750	550D	4½
	6-200	BF-82	.034	.027	35–40	Fig. H	6°	Fig. G	750	550D	4½
	6-250 Less Air Cond.	BF-82[18]	.034	.025	37–42	Fig. H	6°	Fig. G	700	550D	5
	6-250 With Air Cond.	BF-82[18]	.034	.025	37–42	Fig. H	6°	Fig. G	700/500[6]	550/450D[6]	5
	V8-302 Std. Trans.	BF-42	.034	.021	24–29	Fig. E	6°	Fig. C	650	—	5
	V8-302 Auto. Trans.	BF-42	.034	.017	26–31	Fig. E	6°	Fig. C	—	550D	5
	V8-302 "H.O."	AF-32	.030	.020	30–33	Fig. E	16°	Fig. C	800	—	5
	V8-351 2 B. Carb.	BF-42	.034	.017	26–31	Fig. J	6°	Fig. C	650	550D	5
	V8-351 4 B. Carb.	BF-32	.034	.017	26–31	Fig. J	6°	Fig. C	650	550D	5

Continued

TUNE UP SPECIFICATIONS—Continued

OLD CAR SPECIFICATIONS: For 1946-65 Tune-Up specifications see back of book.

★When using a timing light, disconnect vacuum hose or tube at distributor and plug opening in hose or tube so idle speed will not be affected.

●When checking compression, lowest cylinder must be within 75% of the highest.

| Year | Engine | Spark Plug | | Distributor | | Firing Order | Ignition Timing★ | | Hot Idle Speed | | Fuel Pump Press. Lbs. |
		Type	Gap Inch	Point Gap Inch	Dwell Angle Deg.		BTDC ①	Mark	Std. Trans.	Auto. Trans. ②	
1969	V8-390 Std. Trans.	BF-42	.034	.017	26–31	Fig. E	6°	Fig. C	700	—	5
	V8-390 Auto. Trans.	BF-32	.034	.017	26–31	Fig. E	6°	Fig. C	—	550D	5
	V8-427	BF-32	.034	.017	26–31	Fig. E	6°	Fig. C	—	600D	5
	V8-428	BF-32	.034	.017	26–31	Fig. E	6°	Fig. C	700	650D	5
1970	6-170	BF-82	.035	.027	35–40	Fig. H	6°	Fig. G	750	550	4½
	6-200	BF-82	.035	.027	35–40	Fig. H	6°	Fig. G	750	550	4½
	6-250	BF-82	.035	.027	35–40	Fig. H	6°	Fig. G	800/500⑥	500	5
	V8-302	BF-42	.035	.021	24–29	Fig. E	6°	Fig. C	800/500⑥	600/500D⑥	5
	V8-302 "BOSS"	AF-32	.034	.020	30–33	Fig. E	16°	Fig. C	800/500⑥	—	5
	V8-351⑦⑯	AF-42	.034	⑪	⑪	Fig. J	6°	Fig. C	700/500⑥	600/500D⑥	5
	V8-351⑦⑰ Std. Tr.	BF-42	.034	⑪	⑪	Fig. J	6°	Fig. C	700/500⑥	—	5
	V8-351⑦⑰ Auto. Tr.	BF-42	.034	⑪	⑪	Fig. J	10°	Fig. C	700/500⑥	—	5
	V8-351⑧	AF-32	.034	⑪	⑪	Fig. J	6°	Fig. C	800/500⑥	600/500D⑥	5
	V8-428	BF-32	.034	⑪	⑪	Fig. E	6°	Fig. C	800/500⑥	600/500D⑥	5
	V8-429 Auto. Trans.⑧	BF-42	.034	⑪	⑪	Fig. E	4°	Fig. C	700/500⑥	700/500⑥	5
	V8-429 "CJ"	AF-32	.034	⑪	⑪	Fig. E	10°	Fig. C	700	600	6.5-8.5
	V8-429 "BOSS"	AF-32	.034	.020	30–33	Fig. E	10°	Fig. D	700	—	4.5-6.5
1971	6-170	BRF-82	.034	.027	35–40	Fig. H	6°	Fig. L	750③	—	4½
	6-200	BRF-82	.034	.027	35–40	Fig. H	6°	Fig. L	750③	550D③	4½
	6-250	BRF-82	.034	⑤	⑤	Fig. H	6°	Fig. L	750/500⑥	600/500D⑥	5
	V8-302	BRF-42	.034	.021	24–29	Fig. E	6°	Fig. C	800/500⑥	600/500D⑥	5
	V8-302 "BOSS"	AF-32	.034	.020	30–33	Fig. E	16°	Fig. C	800/500⑥	—	5
	V8-351⑦	ARF-42	.034	⑪	⑪	Fig. J	6°	Fig. C	700/500⑥	600D	5
	V8-351⑧	ARF-42	.034	.021	24–29	Fig. J	6°	Fig. C	800/500⑥	600D	5
	V8-429 "CJ"	AF-32	.034	.021	24–29	Fig. E	10°	Fig. C	700/500⑥	650/500D⑥	5
	V8-429 "SCJ"	AF-32	.034	.021	24–29	Fig. E	10°	Fig. C	650/500⑥	700/500D⑥	5
1972	6-170	BRF-82	.034	.027	35–39	Fig. H	6°	Fig. L	750	—	4½
	6-200 Less Air Cond.	BRF-82	.034	.027	35–39	Fig. H	6°	Fig. L	750	550D	4½
	6-200 With Air Cond.	BRF-82	.034	.027	35–39	Fig. H	6°	Fig. L	800/500⑥	600/500D⑥	4½
	6-250	BRF-82	.034	.027	35–39	Fig. H	6°	Fig. L	550	550D	5
	6-250	BRF-82	.034	.027	35–39	Fig. H	6°	Fig. L	750/500⑥	600/500D⑥	5
	V8-302	BRF-42	.034	.017	26–30	Fig. E	6°	Fig. C	575	575D	5
	V8-302	BRF-42	.034	.017	26–30	Fig. E	6°	Fig. C	800/500⑥	600/500D⑥	5
	V8-351⑦	ARF-42	.034	.017	26–30	Fig. J	6°	Fig. C	750/500⑥	575/500D⑥	5
	V8-351⑦ Calif.	ARF-42	.034	.017	26–30	Fig. J	6°	Fig. C	—	625/500⑥	5
	V8-351⑧ Std. Tr.	ARF-42	.034	.020	26–30	Fig. J	10°	Fig. C	900/500⑥	—	5
	V8-351⑧ Auto. Tr.	ARF-42	.034	.017	26–30	Fig. J	16°	Fig. C	—	700/500D⑧	5
	V8-351⑧ Auto. Tr. Calif.	ARF-42	.034	.017	26–30	Fig. J	16°	Fig. C	—	800/500D⑧	5
	V8-351 'BOSS"	ARF-42	.034	.020	26–30	Fig. J	10°	Fig. C	950/500⑥	—	5
	V8-400	ARF-42	.034	.017	26–30	Fig. J	6°	Fig. C	—	625/500D⑧	5
	V8-429	BRF-42	.034	.017	26–30	Fig. E	10°	Fig. C	—	600/500D⑥	5

①—BTDC: Before top dead center.
②—D: Drive.
③—For A/C add 50 R.P.M. Set with headlamps on high beam and A/C off.
④—With IMCO system.
⑤—Dual diaphragm .027 gap, 35–40 dwell. Single diaphragm .025 gap, 37–42 dwell.
⑥—Higher figure is with throttle solenoid energized.

⑦—With two barrel carburetor.
⑧—With four barrel carburetor.
⑨—High performance engine.
⑩—With transistorized ignition.
⑪—Dual diaphragm .021 gap, 24°–29° dwell. Single diaphragm .017 gap, 26°–31° dwell.
⑫—If air conditioned turn A/C switch to "Full On" position.
⑬—Without Thermactor Emission System.

⑭—With Thermactor Emission System.
⑮—On Thermactor equipped engines, adjust idle speed with headlights and with A/C on.
⑯—Fairlane & Montego.
⑰—Mustang & Cougar.
⑱—Mustang "E" BF-92.

Continued

TUNE UP NOTES—Continued

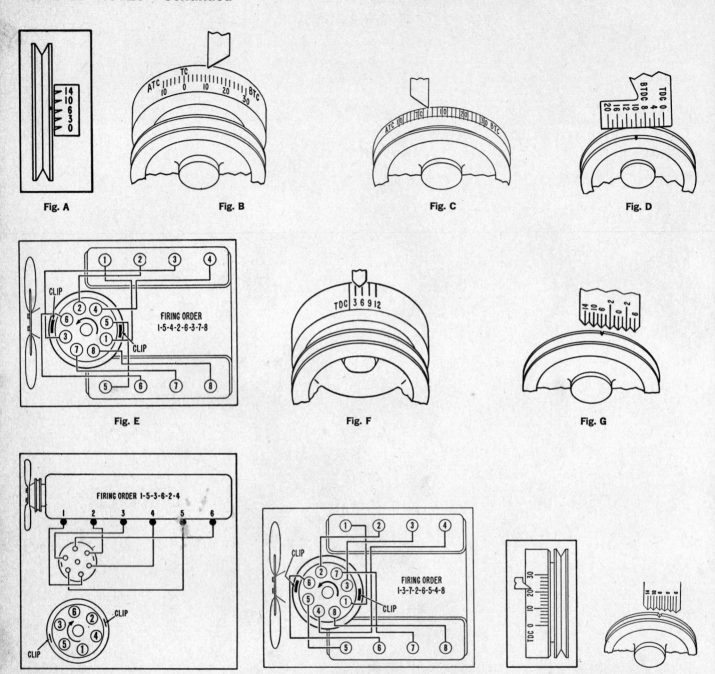

Fig. A Fig. B Fig. C Fig. D

Fig. E Fig. F Fig. G

Fig. H Fig. J Fig. K Fig. L

DISTRIBUTOR SPECIFICATIONS

★If advance is checked on vehicle, double R.P.M. and degrees advance to get crankshaft figures.

Year	Engine	Distributor Basic Part No. 12127	Breaker Gap	Dwell Angle Deg.	Breaker Arm Spring Tension	Centrifugal Advance Degrees @ R.P.M. of Distributor★		Vacuum Advance		Dist. Retard.
						Advance Starts	Full Advance	Inches of Vacuum To Start Plunger	Max. Adv. Dist. Deg. @ Vacuum	Max. Ret. Dist. Deg. @ Vacuum
1966	6-170 Std. Tr.	C5DF-C	.025	37–42	17–21	None	None	0.8	11 @ 3.9	—
	6-170 Std. Tr.③	C6DF-A	.025	37–42	17–21	½ @ 500	13 @ 1800	5.0	10 @ 15	—
	6-170 Auto. Tr.	C5DF-K	.025	37–42	17–21	None	None	.79	8 @ 3.8	—
	6-170 Auto. Tr.③	C6DF-D	.025	37–42	17–21	½ @ 300	13 @ 1800	5.0	6 @ 15	—
	6-200 Std. Tr.	C5DF-E	.025	37–42	17–21	None	None	.44	11 @ 3.8	—
	6-200 Std. Tr.③	C6DF-C	.025	37–42	17–21	½ @ 300	13 @ 1800	4	12 @ 15	—
	6-200 Auto. Tr.	C6DF-K	.025	37–42	17–21	None	None	.79	8 @ 3.8	—
	6-200 Auto. Tr.③	C6DF-E	.025	37–42	17–21	½ @ 300	12 @ 1800	5	10 @ 15	—
	8-289 Std. Tr.	C5AF-M	.017	26–31	17–21	2 @ 650	13 @ 2000	8	9 @ 14	—
	8-289 Std. Tr.③	C6AF-J	.017	26–31	17–21	7 @ 600	15 @ 1800	7	8 @ 16	—
	8-289 Auto. Tr.	C5AF-N	.017	26–31	17–21	2 @ 450	12 @ 2000	8	11 @ 14	—
	8-289 Auto. Tr.③	C6AF-S	.017	26–31	17–21	3 @ 600	14 @ 1800	5	10 @ 12	—
	8-289 Std. Tr.	C5GF-A	.017	26–31	17–21	2 @ 550	10 @ 2000	8	11 @ 20	—
	8-289 Std. Tr.③	C6ZF-A	.017	26–31	17–21	3 @ 475	13 @ 2000	5	7 @ 14	—
	8-289 Auto. Tr.③	C6ZF-B	.017	26–31	17–21	4 @ 650	10 @ 2000	5	9 @ 13	—
	8-289 Hi Perf.	C5OF-E	.020	30–33	27–30	3 @ 650	9 @ 2000	None	None	—
	8-390 Std. Tr.	C6AF-A	.017	26–31	17–21	½ @ 400	8 @ 1800	8	10 @ 15	—
	8-390 Std. Tr.③	C6AF-K	.017	26–31	17–21	3 @ 500	13 @ 2000	5	11 @ 17	—
	8-390 Auto. Tr.	C6AF-B	.017	26–31	17–21	2 @ 625	10 @ 2000	5	9 @ 13	—
	8-390 Auto. Tr.③	C6AF-T	.017	26–31	17–21	2 @ 475	11 @ 1800	5	11 @ 18	—
	8-390 Std. Tr.	C6AF-C	.017	26–31	17–21	3 @ 600	10 @ 2000	5	10 @ 17	—
	8-390 Auto. Tr.③	C6AF-D	.017	26–31	17–21	3 @ 500	10 @ 2000	6	12 @ 18	—
	8-390③	C6AF-L	.017	26–31	17–21	3 @ 500	12 @ 2000	6	10 @ 15	—
	8-390 GT	C6OF-J	.017	26–31	17–21	½ @ 300	12 @ 2000	5	12 @ 20	—
1967	6-170 Std. Tr.	C5DF-C	.025	37–42	17–21	None	None	.80	14 @ 3.90	—
	6-170 Auto. Tr.	C5DF-K	.025	37–42	17–21	None	None	.79	12 @ 3.80	—
	6-170 Std. Tr.③	C7DF-J	.025	37–42	17–21	—	—	—	—	—
	6-170 Auto. Tr.③	C7DF-A	.025	37–42	17–21	2 @ 500	14 @ 2000	5	7 @ 20	—
	6-200 Std. Tr.	C5DF-E	.025	37–42	17–21	None	None	.44	15 @ 3.80	—
	6-200 Auto. Tr.	C5DF-K	.025	37–42	17–21	None	None	.79	12 @ 3.80	—
	6-200 Std. Tr.③	C7DF-C	.025	37–42	17–21	1 @ 500	12 @ 2000	5	12 @ 20	—
	6-200 Auto. Tr.③	C7DF-D	.025	37–42	17–21	5 @ 700	13 @ 2000	5	12 @ 20	—
	8-329 Std. Tr.④	C7OF-A	.017	26–31	17–21	½ @ 400	11 @ 1500	5	11 @ 20	—
	8-289 Auto. Tr.④	C7OF-B	.017	26–31	17–21	½ @ 300	12 @ 2000	5	12 @ 20	—
	8-289 Std. Tr.③④	C7OF-D	.017	26–31	17–21	½ @ 300	14 @ 2000	5	12 @ 20	—
	8-289 Auto. Tr.③④	C7OF-E	.017	26–31	17–21	½ @ 300	13 @ 2000	5	11 @ 20	—
	8-289⑤	C7ZF-A	.017	26–31	17–21	½ @ 300	10 @ 2000	5	11 @ 20	—
	8-289 Std. Tr.③⑤	C7ZF-C	.017	26–31	17–21	½ @ 300	12 @ 2000	5	9 @ 20	—
	8-289 Auto. Tr.③⑤	C7ZF-D	.017	26–31	17–21	½ @ 300	13 @ 2000	5	7 @ 20	—
	8-289 Hi Perf. Eng.	C5OF-E	.020	30–33	27–30	3 @ 650	9 @ 2000	None	None	—
	8-390 Std. Tr.④	C7AF-A	.017	26–31	17–21	1 @ 500	9 @ 2000	5	12 @ 20	—
	8-390 Auto. Tr.④	C7AF-B	.017	26–31	17–21	½ @ 300	10 @ 2000	5	12 @ 20	—
	8-390 Std. Tr.③④	C7AF-C	.017	26–31	17–21	½ @ 300	13 @ 2000	5	12 @ 20	—
	8-390 Auto. Tr.③④	C7AF-D	.017	26–31	17–21	½ @ 300	12 @ 2000	5	12 @ 20	—
	8-390 Std. Tr.⑤	C7AF-E	.017	26–31	17–21	½ @ 300	10 @ 2000	5	12 @ 20	—
	8-390 Auto. Tr.⑤	C7SF-A	.017	26–31	17–21	½ @ 300	10 @ 2000	5	12 @ 20	—
	8-390③⑤	C7SF-B	.017	36–31	17–21	½ @ 300	12 @ 2000	5	12 @ 20	—
	8-390 "GT"	C7AF-U	.017	26–31	17–21	½ @ 300	11 @ 2000	5	11 @ 20	—
	8-390 "GT"③	C7OF-F	.017	26–31	17–21	½ @ 300	14 @ 2000	5	11 @ 20	—
1968	6-170 Std. Trans.	C8DF-A	.027	35–40	17–21	½ @ 350	14 @ 2000	5	8 @ 25	6 @ 20
	6-170 Auto. Tr.	C8DF-B	.027	35–40	17–21	½ @ 350	14 @ 2000	5	9½ @ 25	6 @ 20
	6-200 Std. Trans.	C8DF-C	.027	35–40	17–21	½ @ 350	14 @ 2000	5	12½ @ 25	6 @ 20
	6-200 Auto. Tr.	C8DF-D	.027	35–40	17–21	½ @ 350	14 @ 2000	5	11 @ 25	6 @ 20

Continued

DISTRIBUTOR SPECIFICATIONS—Continued

★If advance is checked on vehicle, double R.P.M. and degrees advance to get crankshaft figures.

Year	Engine	Distributor Basic Part No. 12127	Breaker Gap	Dwell Angle Deg.	Breaker Arm Spring Tension	Centrifugal Advance Degrees @ R.P.M. of Distributor★		Vacuum Advance		Dist. Retard.
						Advance Starts	Full Advance	Inches of Vacuum To Start Plunger	Max. Adv. Dist. Deg. @ Vacuum	Max. Ret. Dist. Deg. @ Vacuum
1968	8-289 Std. Trans.	C8TF-F	.021	24–29	17–21	½ @ 350	11 @ 2000	5	11½ @ 25	6 @ 20
	8-289 Auto. Tr.	C8OF-C	.021	24–29	17–21	½ @ 350	14 @ 2000	5	11½ @ 25	6 @ 20
	8-289 Hi Perf.	C7OF-K	.020	30–33	27–30	½ @ 350	14 @ 2000	—	—	—
	8-302 Std. Trans.⑤	C8ZF-A	.021	24–29	17–21	½ @ 350	11 @ 2000	5	10½ @ 25	6 @ 20
	8-302 Auto. Tr.⑤	C8ZF-D	.017	26–31	17–21	½ @ 350	11 @ 2000	5	9 @ 25	—
	8-302 Std. Trans.④	C8AF-E	.021	24–29	17–21	½ @ 350	14 @ 2000	5	11 @ 25	—
	8-302 Auto. Tr.④	C8OF-C	.021	24–29	17–21	½ @ 350	14 @ 2000	5	11½ @ 25	6 @ 20
	8-390④①	C8WF-B	.017	26–31	17–21	½ @ 350	14 @ 2000	5	12½ @ 25	6 @ 20
	8-390 Std. Trans.④	C8AF-M	.021	24–29	17–21	½ @ 350	11 @ 2000	5	12½ @ 25	6 @ 20
	8-390 Auto. Tr.④	C8AF-AA	.017	26–31	17–21	½ @ 350	14 @ 2000	5	11½ @ 20	—
	8-390 2 Bar. Carb.	C8OF-D	.017	26–31	17–21	½ @ 350	16 @ 2000	5	9½ @ 25	3½ @ 20
	8-427	C7OF-F	.017	26–31	17–21	½ @ 300	14 @ 2000	5	11 @ 20	—
	8-428 Std. Trans.	C8OF-D	.017	26–31	17–21	½ @ 350	16 @ 2375	5	9½ @ 25	3½ @ 20
	8-428 Auto. Trans.	C7OF-F	.017	26–31	17–21	½ @ 350	16 @ 2375	5	11 @ 20	—
1969	6-170 Std. Trans.	C9DF-B	.027	35–40	17–21	½ @ 350	13¾ @ 2000	5	8 @ 25	6 @ 20
	6-170 Auto. Trans.	C8DF-J	.027	35–40	17–21	½ @ 350	14¾ @ 2000	5	11 @ 25	6 @ 20
	6-200 Std. Trans.	C8DF-C	.027	35–40	17–21	½ @ 350	12 @ 2000	5	12½ @ 25	6 @ 20
	6-200 Auto. Trans.	C8DF-D	.027	35–40	17–21	½ @ 350	14 @ 2000	5	11 @ 25	6 @ 20
	6-250	C9OF-R	.025	37–42	17–21	½ @ 350	11½ @ 2000	5	8½ @ 20	—
	8-302 Std. Trans.	C8AF-E	.021	24–29	17–21	½ @ 350	12½ @ 2000	5	11 @ 25	6 @ 20
	8-302 Auto. Trans.	C9AF-N	.017	26–31	17–21	½ @ 350	10¾ @ 2000	5	11½ @ 20	—
	8-302 "H.O."	C9ZF-B	.020	30–33②	17–21	½ @ 350	11 @ 2950	5	11 @ 20	—
	8-302 "H.O."	C9ZF-E	.020	30–33②	17–21	½ @ 350	11 @ 2000	5	7 @ 25	—
	8-351 2 Bar. Carb.	C9OF-M	.017	26–31	17–21	½ @ 350	12¼ @ 2000	5	8 @ 20	—
	8-351 4 Bar. Carb.	C9OF-N	.017	26–31	17–21	½ @ 350	11 @ 2000	5	10½ @ 25	—
	8-390 Std. Trans.	C9AF-R	.017	26–31	17–21	½ @ 350	10¾ @ 2000	5	11½ @ 20	6 @ 20
	8-390 Auto. Trans.	C7AF-AC	.017	26–31	17–21	½ @ 350	12¼ @ 2000	5	12½ @ 20	—
	8-427	C8OF-G	.017	26–31	17–21	½ @ 350	11½ @ 2000	5	11 @ 20	—
	8-428 Std. Trans.	C8OF-H	.017	26–31	17–21	½ @ 350	13½ @ 2000	5	9½ @ 25	3½ @ 20
	8-428 Auto. Trans.	C8OF-J	.017	26–31	17–21	½ @ 350	13½ @ 2000	5	11 @ 20	—
1970	6-170 Std. Trans.	C9DF-B	.027	35–40	17–21	½ @ 350	13¾ @ 2000	5	8 @ 25	6 @ 20
	6-170 Auto. Trans.	D0DF-E	.027	35–40	17–21	½ @ 350	14¾ @ 2000	5	11 @ 25	6 @ 20
	6-200 Std. Trans.	D0DF-C	.027	35–40	17–21	½ @ 350	16 @ 2800	5	7 @ 25	6 @ 20
	6-250	D0OF-A	.027	35–40	17–21	½ @ 350	16 @ 2175	5	9 @ 25	6 @ 20
	8-302 Std. Trans.	D0AF-Y	.021	24–29	17–21	½ @ 350	14 @ 2325	5	11 @ 25	6 @ 20
	8-302 Auto. Trans.	D0AF-T	.021	24–29	17–21	½ @ 350	14 @ 3150	5	11½ @ 25	3½ @ 20
	8-302 "BOSS"	C9ZF-E	.020	30–33②	17–21	½ @ 350	11 @ 2950	5	11 @ 20	6 @ 20
	8-351 Std. Trans.④	D0AF-H	.021	24–29	17–21	½ @ 350	14 @ 2375	5	8 @ 25	6 @ 20
	8-351 Auto. Trans.④	D0AF-AC	.021	24–29	17–21	½ @ 350	14 @ 2000	5	9½ @ 25	6 @ 20
	8-351 Std. Trans.⑤	D0OF-T	.021	24–29	17–21	½ @ 350	14 @ 2300	5	12½ @ 25	6 @ 20
	8-351 Auto. Trans.⑤	D0OF-U	.017	26–31	17–21	½ @ 350	14 @ 2275	5	12½ @ 25	—
	8-428 Std. Trans.	D0ZF-C	.020	30–33②	17–21	½ @ 350	14 @ 2150	5	11 @ 25	3½ @ 20
	8-428 Auto. Trans.	D0ZF-G	.017	26–31	17–21	½ @ 350	14 @ 2075	5	9½ @ 25	—
	8-429 Std. Trans.	C9AF-Y	.021	24–29	17–21	½ @ 350	14 @ 2775	5	8½ @ 25	6 @ 20
	8-429 Auto. Trans.	D0AF-Z	.017	26–31	17–21	½ @ 350	14 @ 2950	5	11 @ 25	—
	8-429 "CJ" Std. Trans.	D0OF-AA	.021	24–29②	17–21	½ @ 350	16 @ 2200	5	8½ @ 25	6 @ 20
	8-429 "CJ" Auto. Tr.	D0OF-AB	.021	24–29	17–21	½ @ 350	—	5	8½ @ 25	6 @ 20
	8-429 "BOSS"	C9ZF-D	.020	30–33②	17–21	½ @ 350	11 @ 2000	5	10 @ 25	6 @ 20
1971	6-170	C9DF-B	.027	35–40	17–21	½ @ 350	13¾ @ 2000	5	8 @ 25	6 @ 20
	6-170	D1DF-FA	.027	35–40	17–21	½ @ 350	14 @ 2500	5	8 @ 25	7 @ 20
	6-200	D0DF-C	.027	35–40	17–21	½ @ 350	16 @ 2800	5	7 @ 25	6 @ 20
	6-200	D1DF-BB	.027	35–40	17–21	½ @ 350	14 @ 2500	5	7½ @ 25	7 @ 20
	6-200	D1DF-CC	.027	35–40	17–21	½ @ 350	—	5	—	—

Continued

DISTRIBUTOR SPECIFICATIONS—Continued

★If advance is checked on vehicle, double R.P.M. and degrees advance to get crankshaft figures.

Year	Engine	Distributor Basic Part No. 12127	Breaker Gap	Dwell Angle Deg.	Breaker Arm Spring Tension	Centrifugal Advance Degrees @ R.P.M. of Distributor★		Vacuum Advance		Dist. Retard.
						Advance Starts	Full Advance	Inches of Vacuum To Start Plunger	Max. Adv. Dist. Deg. @ Vacuum	Max. Ret. Dist. Deg. @ Vacuum
1971	8-302④	D0AF-Y	.021	24–29	17–21	½ @ 350	14 @ 2325	5	11 @ 25	7 @ 20
	8-302④	D0AF-AC	.021	24–29	17–21	½ @ 350	14 @ 2000	5	9½ @ 25	7 @ 20
	8-302④	D0AF-AE	.021	24–29	17–21	½ @ 350	13 @ 2500	5	2½ @ 25	7 @ 20
	8-302④	D0OF-AC	.021	24–29	17–21	½ @ 350	13 @ 2500	5	5 @ 25	7 @ 20
	8-302④	D1DF-EA	.021	24–29	17–21	½ @ 350	13 @ 2500	5	11½ @ 25	7 @ 20
	8-302 "BOSS"	D1ZF-AA	.020	30–33②	17–21	½ @ 350	11 @ 2500	5	2½ @ 25	7 @ 20
	8-351④	D0OF-T	.021	24–29	17–21	½ @ 350	14 @ 2300	5	12½ @ 25	6 @ 20
	8-351④	D0OF-U	.017	26–31	17–21	½ @ 350	14 @ 2275	5	12½ @ 25	—
	8-351④	D1OF-GA	.021	24–29	17–21	½ @ 350	13 @ 2500	5	11 @ 25	4 @ 20
	8-351⑤	D0OF-G	.021	24–29	17–21	½ @ 350	13 @ 2500	5	10½ @ 25	7 @ 20
	8-351⑤	D0OF-V	.021	24–29	17–21	½ @ 350	14 @ 2300	5	10½ @ 25	7 @ 20
	8-351⑤	D1OF-LA	.021	24–29	17–21	½ @ 350	18 @ 2500	5	10½ @ 25	7 @ 20
	8-429	D0OF-AA	.021	24–29	17–21	½ @ 350	16 @ 2200	5	8½ @ 25	7 @ 20
	8-429	D1AF-NA	.021	24–29	17–21	½ @ 350	14 @ 2500	5	8½ @ 25	7 @ 20
1972	6-170	D2DF-AA	.027	35–39	17–21	1 @ 500	13½ @ 2000	5	7½ @ 20	7 @ 20
	6-170	D2DF-BA	.027	35–39	17–21	1 @ 500	13½ @ 2000	5	7½ @ 20	7 @ 20
	6-200	D2DF-CA	.027	35–39	17–21	½ @ 500	12½ @ 2000	5	7½ @ 20	7 @ 20
	6-200	D2DF-DA	.027	35–39	17–21	1 @ 500	13½ @ 2000	5	7½ @ 20	4 @ 20
	6-200	D2DF-EA	.027	35–39	17–21	½ @ 500	12½ @ 2000	5	7½ @ 20	7 @ 20
	6-200	D2DF-FA	.027	35–39	17–21	½ @ 500	13½ @ 2000	5	7½ @ 20	4 @ 20
	6-250	D2OF-DA	.027	35–39	17–21	1 @ 500	13½ @ 2000	5	9½ @ 20	7 @ 20
	6-250	D2OF-EA	.027	35–39	17–21	½ @ 500	10½ @ 2000	5	9½ @ 20	4 @ 20
	6-250	D2OF-PA	.027	35–39	17–21	1 @ 500	10 @ 2000	5	9½ @ 20	7 @ 20
	8-302	D2ZF-LA	.017	26–30	17–21	½ @ 500	13½ @ 2000	5	12½ @ 20	4 @ 20
	8-302	D2OF-HA	.017	26–30	17–21	½ @ 500	11 @ 2000	5	5½ @ 20	7 @ 20
	8-302	D2OF-JA	.017	26–30	17–21	½ @ 500	11 @ 2000	5	5½ @ 20	7 @ 20
	8-302	D2OF-AA	.017	26–30	17–21	½ @ 500	13½ @ 2000	5	12½ @ 20	7 @ 20
	8-302	D2AF-CA	.017	26–30	17–21	½ @ 500	11 @ 2000	5	5½ @ 20	7 @ 20
	8-302	D2OF-RA	.017	26–30	17–21	½ @ 500	11 @ 2000	5	5½ @ 20	7 @ 20
	8-351④	D2ZF-AA	.017	26–30	17–21	½ @ 500	12½ @ 2000	5	12½ @ 20	7 @ 20
	8-351④	D2AF-KA	.017	26–30	17–21	1 @ 500	12½ @ 2000	5	13 @ 20	7 @ 20
	8-351④	D2ZF-CA	.017	26–30	17–21	½ @ 500	12½ @ 2000	5	10 @ 20	4 @ 20
	8-351⑤	D2ZF-EA	.020	26–30	17–21	—	—	—	—	—
	8-351⑤	D2ZF-FA	.020	26–30	17–21	—	—	—	—	—
	8-351⑤	D2ZF-GB	.017	26–30	17–21	½ @ 500	13 @ 2000	5	9½ @ 20	—
	8-351⑤	D2ZF-HA	.017	26–30	17–21	½ @ 500	14½ @ 2000	5	9½ @ 20	—
	8-351⑤	D2ZF-JA	.020	26–30	17–21	½ @ 500	13 @ 2000	5	11½ @ 20	7 @ 20
	8-400	D2AF-RA	.017	26–30	17–21	½ @ 500	12 @ 2000	5	13½ @ 20	4 @ 20
	8-400	D2AF-SA	.017	26–30	17–21	½ @ 500	12 @ 2000	5	13½ @ 20	4 @ 20
	8-429	D2MF-EA	.017	26–30	17–21	½ @ 500	9½ @ 2000	5	11½ @ 20	4 @ 20
	8-429	D2MF-FA	.017	26–30	17–21	½ @ 500	9½ @ 2000	5	11½ @ 20	4 @ 20

①—Premium fuel.
②—Isolate and set individual points to 25–25½° dwell to obtain 30–33° combined dwell.
③—With Thermactor Exhaust Emission Control System.
④—Two barrel carburetor.
⑤—Four Barrel carburetor.

STARTING MOTOR SPECIFICATIONS

Year	Engine Model	Part No.	Brush Spring Tension, Ounces	No Load Test			Torque Test		
				Amperes	Volts	R.P.M.	Amperes	Volts	Torque Lbs. Ft.
1966–67	4½" Dia.	—	40	70	12	—	670	5	15.5
	4" Dia.	—	40	70	12	—	460	5	9.0
1968	6-170, 200	C7ZF-11001-A	40	70	12	8500	460	6	9
	6-170, 200	C7OF-11001-A	40	70	12	9500	670	5	15½
	6-170, 200	C7DF-11001-A	40	70	12	8500	460	6	9
	8-289, 302	C7AF-11001-B	40	70	12	9500	670	5	15½
	8-289, 302	C7AF-11001-D	40	70	12	9500	670	5	15½
	8-289, 302	C7AF-11001-F	40	70	12	9500	670	5	15½
	8-390, 427	C7AF-11001-C	40	70	12	9500	670	5	15½
	8-390, 427	C7AF-11001-E	40	70	12	11000	700	4	15½
1969–71	6-170, 200	C6OZ-11002-A	40	70	12	8500	460	6	9
	6-170	C2DZ-11002-A	40	70	12	8500	460	6	9
	6-200	C3OZ-11002-C	40	70	12	9500	670	5	15½
	6-250	C2OZ-11002-A	40	70	12	9500	670	5	15½
	8-302, 351	C2OZ-11002-A	40	70	12	9500	670	5	15½
	8-302, 351	C5TZ-11002-A	40	70	12	9500	670	5	15½
	8-390, 427	C3OZ-11002-C	40	70	12	9500	670	5	15½
	8-428	C8AZ-11002-A	40	70	12	11000	700	5	15½
	8-429	C8VY-11002-C	40	70	12	10000	700	5	15½

VALVE SPECIFICATIONS

Year	Engine	Valve Lash		Valve Angles		Valve Spring Installed Height	Valve Spring Pressure Lbs. @ In.	Stem Clearance		Stem Diameter, Standard	
		Int.	Exh.	Seat	Face			Intake	Exhaust	Intake	Exhaust
1966	6-170, 200	.067–.200④		45	44	1¹⁹⁄₃₂	150 @ 1.22	.0008–.0025	.001–.0027	.3100–.3107	.3098–.3105
	8-289	¾ Turns①		45	44	1¾	170 @ 1.39	.001–.0027	.002–.0037	.3416–.3423	.3406–.3413
	8-289 Hi Perf.	.018H	.018H	45	44	1¾	247 @ 1.32	.001–.0027	.002–.0037	.3416–.3423	.3406–.3413
	8-390	.050–.150④⑥		45	44	1¹³⁄₁₆	245 @ 1.38	.001–.0024	.001–.0024	.3711–.3718	.3711–.3718
	8-390 "GT"	.050–.200④		45	44	1¹³⁄₁₆	255 @ 1.32	.001–.0024	.001–.0024	.3711–.3718	.3711–.3718
1967	6-170, 200	.066–.216④		45	44	1⁹⁄₁₆	150 @ 1.22	.0008–.0025	.001–.0027	.3100–.3107	.3098–.3105
	8-289	¾ Turns①		45	44	1²¹⁄₃₂	165 @ 1.25	.001–.0027	.001–.0072	.3416–.3423	.3416–.3423
	8-289 Hi Perf.	.018H	.018H	45	44	1¾	245 @ 1.32	.001–.0027	.001–.0027	.3416–.3423	.3416–.3423
	8-390	.100–.200④		45	44	1¹³⁄₁₆	245 @ 1.38	.001–.0024	.001–.0024	.3711–.3718	.3711–.3718
	8-390 "GT"	.100–.200④		45	44	1¹³⁄₁₆	265 @ 1.32	.001–.0024	.001–.0024	.3711–.3718	.3711–.3718
1968	6-170, 200	.066–.166④		45	44	1⁹⁄₁₆	150 @ 1.22	.0008–.0025	.001–.0027	.3100–.3107	.3098–.3105
	8-289, 302	¾ Turns①		45	44	1⅝	180 @ 1.23	.001–.0027	.001–.0032	.3416–.3423	.3411–.3418
	8-289 Special	.018H	.018H	45	44	1⅝	180 @ 1.23	.001–.0027	.002–.0037	.3416–.3423	.3411–.3418
	8-390	.100–.200④		45	44	1⅞	220 @ 1.38	.001–.0024	.0015–.0032	.3711–.3718	.3706–.3713
	8-390 "GT"	.100–.200④		45	44	1¹³⁄₁₆	270 @ 1.32	.001–.0024	.0015–.0032	.3711–.3718	.3706–.3713
	8-427	.100–.200④		⑦	⑦	1¹³⁄₁₆	270 @ 1.32	.001–.0024	.002–.0034	.3711–.3718	.3701–.3708
1969	6-170	.066–.166④		45	44	1⁹⁄₁₆	150 @ 1.22	.0008–.0025	.001–.0027	.3100–.3107	.3098–.3105
	6-200, 250	.095–.195④		45	44	1⁹⁄₁₆	150 @ 1.22	.0008–.0025	.001–.0027	.3100–.3107	.3098–.3105
	8-302	1 Turn①		45	44	1⅝	180 @ 1.23	.001–.0027	.0015–.0032	.3416–.3423	.3411–.3418
	8-302 "H.O."	.025H	.025H	45	44	1¹³⁄₁₆	315 @ 1.32	.001–.0027	.0015–.0032	.3416–.3423	.3411–.3418
	8-351	1 Turn①		45	44	1²⁵⁄₃₂	215 @ 1.34	.001–.0027	.0015–.0032	.3416–.3423	.3411–.3418
	8-390	.100–.200④		45	44	1⅞	220 @ 1.38	.001–.0027	.0015–.0032	.3711–.3718	.3706–.3713
	8-427	.100–.200④		⑦	⑫	1¹³⁄₁₆	270 @ 1.32	.001–.0027	.0015–.0032	.3711–.3718	.3706–.3713
	8-428	.100–.200④		45	44	1¹³⁄₁₆	270 @ 1.32	.001–.0027	.0015–.0032	.3711–.3718	.3706–.3713

Continued

VALVE SPECIFICATIONS—Continued

Year	Engine Model	Valve Lash		Valve Angles		Valve Spring Installed Height	Valve Spring Pressure Lbs. @ In.	Stem Clearance		Stem Diameter Standard	
		Int.	Exh.	Seat	Face			Intake	Exhaust	Intake	Exhaust
1970	6-170	.066–.166④		45	44	1⁹⁄₁₆	150 @ 1.22	.0008–.0025	.001–.0027	.3100–.3107	.3098–.3105
	6-200, 250	.095–.195④		45	44	1⁹⁄₁₆	150 @ 1.22	.0008–.0025	.001–.0027	.3100–.3107	.3098–.3105
	8-302	.067–.167④		45	44	1⅝	180 @ 1.23	.001–.0027	.0015–.0032	.3416–.3423	.3411–.3418
	8-302 "BOSS"	.025H	.025H	45	44	1¹³⁄₁₆	315 @ 1.32	.001–.0027	.0015–.0032	.3416–.3423	.3411–.3418
	8-351⑧	.083–.183④		45	44	1²⁵⁄₃₂	215 @ 1.34	.001–.0027	.0015–.0032	.3416–.3423	.3411–.3418
	8-351⑨⑩	.100–.200④		45	44	1¹³⁄₁₆	210 @ 1.42	.001–.0027	.0015–.0032	.3416–.3423	.3411–.3418
	8-351⑨⑪	.100–.200④		45	44	1¹³⁄₁₆	285 @ 1.32	.001–.0027	.0015–.0032	.3416–.3423	.3411–.3418
	8-428	.100–.200④		45	44	1¹³⁄₁₆	270 @ 1.32	.001–.0027	.0015–.0032	.3711–.3718	.3706–.3713
	8-429 "CJ"	.019H	.019H	⑦	⑫	1¹³⁄₁₆	306 @ 1.36	.001–.0024	.002–.0034	.3416–.3423	.3416–.3418
	8-429 "SCJ"	.019H	.019H	⑦	⑫	1¹³⁄₃₂	306 @ 1.36	.001–.0024	.002–.0034	.3711–.3718	.3701–.3708
	8-429 "BOSS"	.013C	.013C	⑦	⑫	1¹³⁄₃₂	315 @ 1.32	.001–.0024	.002–.0034	.3711–.3718	.3701–.3708
1971	6-170	.066–.166④		45	44	1⁹⁄₁₆	150 @ 1.22	.0008–.0025	.001–.0027	.3100–.3107	.3098–.3105
	6-200	.079–.209④		45	44	1⁹⁄₁₆	150 @ 1.22	.0008–.0025	.001–.0027	.3100–.3107	.3098–.3105
	6-250	.095–.195④		45	44	1⁹⁄₁₆	150 @ 1.22	.0008–.0025	.001–.0027	.3100–.3107	.3098–.3105
	8-302	.090–.190④		45	44	1⅝	180 @ 1.23	.001–.0027	.001–.0027	.3416–.3423	.3411–.3418
	8-302 "BOSS"	.025H	.025H	45	44	1¹³⁄₁₆	315 @ 1.32	.001–.0027	.001–.0027	.3416–.3423	.3411–.3418
	8-351⑧	.100–.200④		45	44	1²⁵⁄₃₂	215 @ 1.34	.001–.0027	.001–.0027	.3416–.3423	.3411–.3418
	8-351⑨⑩	.100–.200④		45	44	1¹³⁄₁₆	210 @ 1.42	.001–.0027	.001–.0027	.3416–.3423	.3411–.3418
	8-351⑨⑪	.100–.200④		45	44	1¹³⁄₁₆	285 @ 1.32	.001–.0027	.001–.0027	.3416–.3423	.3411–.3418
	8-429	.075–.175④		45	44	1¹³⁄₃₂	315 @ 1.32	.001–.0027	.001–.0027	.3416–.3423	.3416–.3423
1972	6-170	.079–.209④		45	45	1¹⁹⁄₃₂	150 @ 1.22	.0008–.0025	.001–.0027	.3100–.3107	.3098–.3105
	6-200	.079–.209④		45	45	1¹⁹⁄₃₂	150 @ 1.22	.0008–.0025	.001–.0027	.3100–.3107	.3098–.3105
	6-250	.095–.195④		45	45	1³⁷⁄₆₄	150 @ 1.22	.0008–.0025	.001–.0027	.3100–.3107	.3098–.3105
	6-250 Calif.	.095–.195④		45	45	1³⁷⁄₆₄	146 @ 1.20	.0008–.0025	.001–.0027	.3100–.3107	.3098–.3105
	8-302	.090–.190④		45	45	1¹¹⁄₁₆	200 @ 1.31	.001–.0027	.0015–.0032	.3416–.3423	.3411–.3418
	8-351⑩	.100–.200④		45	45	1¹³⁄₁₆	210 @ 1.42	.001–.0027	.0015–.0032	.3416–.3423	.3411–.3418
	8-351⑪	.100–.200④		45	45	1¹³⁄₁₆	277 @ 1.34	.001–.0027	.0015–.0032	.3416–.3423	.3411–.3418
	8-351 "BOSS"	.025H	.025H	45	45	1⅝	315 @ 1.32	.001–.0027	.0015–.0032	.3416–.3423	.3411–.3418
	8-400	.100–.200④		45	45	1¹³⁄₁₆	226 @ 1.39	.001–.0027	.0015–.0032	.3416–.3423	.3411–.3418
	8-429	.075–.175④		45	45	1¹³⁄₁₆	229 @ 1.33	.001–.0027	.0015–.0032	.3416–.3423	.3411–.3418

①—Tighten rocker arm adjusting screw to eliminate all push rod end clearance, then tighten screw the number of turns listed.

③—High performance engine.

④—Clearance is obtained at valve stem tip with hydraulic lifter collapsed. If clearance is less than the minimum install an undersize push rod; if clearance is greater than the maximum install an oversize push rod.

⑤—Engines built after 3-29-65.

⑥—Engines built after 12-20-65 .050–.200".

⑦—Intake 30°, Exhaust 45°.

⑧—Windsor engine.

⑨—Cleveland engine.

⑩—2 barrel carb.

⑪—4 barrel carb.

⑫—Intake 29°, exhaust 44°.

REAR AXLE SPECIFICATIONS

Year	Model	Carrier Type	Ring Gear & Pinion Backlash Inch	Nominal Pinion Locating Shim, Inch	Pinion Bearing Preload				Differential Bearing Preload	Pinion Nut Torque Ft.-Lbs.①
					New Bearings With Seal Inch-Lbs.	Used Bearings With Seal Inch-Lbs.	New Bearings Less Seal Inch-Lbs.	Used Bearings Less Seal Inch-Lbs.		
1966–71		Integral	.008–.012	.017	17–27	6–12	—	—	.008–.012③	140
		Removable	.008–.012	④	⑤	8–14	—	—	.008–.012⑥	175

①—If torque cannot be obtained, install new spacer.

③—Case spread with new bearings. With used bearings .003–.005".

④—With 7¾" and 8" ring gear .022". With 8¾" and 9" ring gear .015".

⑤—With 7¾" and 8" ring gear 17–32 inch-lbs. With 8¾" and 9" ring gear 22–32 inch-lbs.

⑥—Case spread with new bearings. With used bearings .005–.008".

PISTONS, PINS, RINGS, CRANKSHAFT & BEARINGS

Year	Engine	Piston Clearance	Ring End Gap[1]		Wrist-pin Diameter	Rod Bearings		Main Bearings			
			Comp.	Oil		Shaft Diameter	Bearing Clearance	Shaft Diameter	Bearing Clearance	Thrust on Bear. No.	Shaft End Play
1966–67	6-170, 200	.0014–.0020	.010	.015	.912	2.1232–2.1240	.0008–.0024	2.2482–2.2490	.0005–.0022	④	.004–.008
	8-289	.0018–.0026	.010	.015	.912	2.1228–2.1236	.0008–.0026	2.2482–2.2490	.0005–.0025	3	.004–.008
	8-289 Hi Perf.	.0030–.0038	.010	.015	.912	2.1228–2.1236	.0008–.0026	2.2482–2.2490	.0005–.0025	3	.004–.008
	8-390	.0015–.0023	.010	.015	.975	2.4380–2.4388	.0008–.0026	2.7484–2.7492	.0005–.0025	3	.004–.010
1968	6-170, 200	.0014–.0020	.010	.015	.912	2.1232–2.1240	.0008–.0015	2.2482–2.2490	.0005–.0015	④	.004–.008
	8-289, 302	.0018–.0026	.010	.015	.912	2.1228–2.1236	.0008–.0015	2.2482–2.2490	.0005–.0015	3	.004–.008
	8-390	.0015–.0023	.010	.015	.975	2.4380–2.4388	.0008–.0015	2.7484–2.7492	.0005–.0015	3	.004–.010
	8-427	.0030–.0038	.018	.015	.975	2.4380–2.4388	.0008–.0015	2.7484–2.7492	.0005–.0015	3	.004–.010
1969	6-170, 200	.0014–.0020	.010	.015	.912	2.1232–2.1240	.0008–.0015	2.2482–2.2490	.0005–.0015	④	.004–.008
	6-250	.0014–.0020	.010	.015	.912	2.1232–2.1240	.0008–.0015	2.3982–2.3990	.0005–.0015	5	.004–.008
	8-302	.0018–.0026	.010	.015	.912	2.1228–2.1236	.0008–.0015	2.2482–2.2490	.0005–.0015	3	.004–.008
	8-302 "H.O."	.0034–.0042	.010	.015	.912	2.1222–2.1230	.001–.0028	2.2482–2.2490	.0005–.0015	3	.004–.008
	8-351	.0018–.0026	.010	.015	.912	2.3103–2.3110	.0008–.0015	2.9994–3.0002	.0013–.0025	3	.004–.008
	8-390	.0015–.0023	.010	.015	.975	2.4380–2.4388	.0008–.0015	2.7484–2.7492	.001–.002	3	.004–.010
	8-427, 428	.0030–.0038	.018	.015	.975	2.4380–2.4388	.002–.003	2.7484–2.7492	.001–.002	3	.004–.010
1970–71	6-170, 200	.0014–.0020	.010	.015	.912	2.1232–2.1240	.0008–.0026	2.2482–2.2490	.0005–.0025	④	.004–.010
	6-250	.0014–.0020	.010	.015	.912	2.1232–2.1240	.0008–.0026	2.3982–2.3900	.0005–.0025	5	.004–.008
	8-302	.0018–.0026	.010	.015	.912	2.1228–2.1236	.0008–.0026	2.2482–2.2400	.0005–.0025	3	.004–.008
	8-302 "BOSS"	.0034–.0042	.010	.015	.912	2.1222–2.1230	.001–.0028	2.2482–2.2490	.0005–.0015	3	.004–.008
	8-351[2]	.0018–.0026	.010	.015	.912	2.3103–2.3110	.0008–.0026	2.9994–3.0002	.0013–.0025	3	.004–.008
	8-351[3]	.0014–.0022	.010	.015	.912	2.3103–2.3110	.0008–.0026	2.7484–2.7492	.0013–.0029	3	.004–.008
	8-428	.003–.0038	.018	.015	.975	2.4380–2.4388	.002–.003	2.7484–2.7492	.001–.002	3	.004–.010
	8-429 "CJ"	.003–.0038	.010	.010	1.040	2.4992–2.5000	.001–.0015	2.9994–3.0002	.0005–.0025	3	.004–.008
	8-429 "BOSS"	.003–.0038	.010	.010	1.040	2.4992–2.5000	.0008–.0026	2.9994–3.0002	.0009–.0025	3	.004–.008
1972	6-170	.0013–.0026	.008	.015	.912	2.1232–2.1240	.0002–.0024	2.2482–2.2490	.0007–.0026	3	.004–.008
	6-200	.0014–.0020	.008	.015	.912	2.1232–2.1240	.0002–.0024	2.2482–2.2490	.0007–.0026	5	.004–.008
	6-250	.0013–.0021	.008	.015	.912	2.1232–2.1240	.0008–.0024	2.3982–2.3900	.0005–.0022	5	.004–.008
	8-302	.0018–.0026	.010	.015	.912	2.1232–2.1240	.0008–.0026	2.2482–2.2490	.0005–.0024	3	.004–.008
	8-351[5]	.0014–.0022	.010	.015	.912	2.3103–2.3110	.0008–.0026	2.7484–2.7492	.0009–.0026	3	.004–.010
	8-351[6]	.0018–.0026	.010	.015	.912	2.3103–2.3110	.0011–.0026	2.7484–2.7492	.0011–.0028	3	.004–.010
	8-400	.0014–.0022	.010	.015	.975	2.3103–2.3110	.0008–.0026	2.9994–3.0002	.0009–.0026	3	.004–.008
	8-429	.0014–.0022	.010	.015	.975	2.4992–2.5000	.0008–.0028	2.9994–3.0002	⑦	3	.004–.008

①—Fit rings in tapered bores for clearance listed in tightest portion of ring travel.
②—Windsor engine.
③—Cleveland engine.
④—No. 3 in 6-170, No. 5 on 6-200.
⑤—Two barrel carburetor.
⑥—Four barrel carburetor.
⑦—No. 1, .0004–.0020; others, .0012–.0028.

ENGINE TIGHTENING SPECIFICATIONS*

★Torque specifications are for clean and lightly lubricated threads only. Dry or dirty threads produce increased friction which prevents accurate measurement of tightness.

Year	Engine	Spark Plugs Ft. Lbs.	Cylinder Head Bolts Ft. Lbs.	Intake Manifold Ft. Lbs.	Exhaust Manifold Ft. Lbs.	Rocker Arm Shaft Bracket Ft. Lbs.	Rocker Arm Cover Ft. Lbs.	Connecting Rod Cap Bolts Ft. Lbs.	Main Bearing Cap Bolts Ft. Lbs.	Flywheel to Crank-shaft Ft. Lbs.	Vibration Damper or Pulley Ft. Lbs.
1966–68	6 Cyl.	15–20	70–75	—	13–18	30–35	3–5	19–24	60–70	75–85	85–100
	8-289	15–20	65–72	20–22	15–20	—	3–5	19–24	60–70	75–85	70–90
	8-302	15–20	65–72	20–22	15–20	—	3–5	19–24	60–70	75–85	70–90
	8-390	15–20	80–90	32–35	18–24[2]	40–45	4–7	40–45	95–105	75–85	70–90
	8-427	15–20	80–90	32–35	18–24	40–45	4–7	53–58	95–105	75–85	70–90
1969–72	6 Cyl.	15–20	70–75	—	13–18	30–35	3–5	[3]	60–70	75–85	85–100
	8-302[4]	15–20	65–72	23–25	12–16	—	3–5	19–24	60–70	75–85	100–130
	8-302[5]	5–10	65–72	[6]	12–16	—	3–5	40–45	60–70[7]	75–85	70–90
	8-351	15–20	95–100	23–25	18–24	—	3–5	40–45	95–105	75–85	70–90
	8-390	15–20	80–90	32–35	18–24	40–45	4–7	40–45	95–105	75–85	70–90
	8-400	10–15	95–105	[6]	[6]	—	3–5	40–45	95–105	75–85	70–90
	8-427	15–20	90–100	32–35	18–24	40–45	4–7	53–58	95–105	75–85	70–90
	8-428	15–20	80–90	32–35	18–24	—	4–7	53–58	95–105	75–85	70–90
	8-429	15–20[8]	130–140	25–30	28–33	—	2½–4	40–45	95–105	75–85	75–90

[2]—Fairlane, Comet, Mustang, Montego, Cougar 15–20.
[3]—6-170, 200 is 19–24; 6-250 is 21–26.
[4]—Except "H.O."
[5]—"H.O."
[6]—5/16 Bolts, 23–25, 3/8 Bolts, 28–32, 1/4 Bolt, 6–9
[7]—Outer bolts on caps 2, 3 & 4—35–40.
[8]—"CJ", "SCJ", "BOSS" use 5-10 ft.-lbs.

ALTERNATOR & REGULATOR SPECIFICATIONS

Year	Make or Model	Current Rating[1] Amperes	Volts	Field Current @ 75°F. Amperes	Volts	Voltage Regulator[2] Make	Voltage @ 75°F.	Contact Gap	Armature Air Gap	Field Relay Armature Air Gap	Closing Voltage @ 75°F.
1966–67	Purple[3]	38	15	2.5	12	Autolite	14.1–14.9	.017–.022	.049–.056	.010–.018	2.5–4.0
	Orange[3]	42	15	2.9	12	Autolite	14.1–14.9	.017–.022	.049–.056	.010–.018	2.5–4.0
	Black[3]	45	15	2.9	12	Autolite	14.1–14.9	.017–.022	.049–.056	.010–.018	2.5–4.0
	Red	55	15	2.9	12	Autolite	14.1–14.9	.017–.022	.049–.056	.010–.018	2.5–4.0
	Leece-Nev.	53	15	2.9	12	Leece-Nev.	14.1–14.9	.018–.020	.042–.052	.009–.011	1.6–2.6
1968	C6AF-10300-A	42	15	2.8–3.3	12	Autolite	13.5–15.3	[4]	[4]	[4]	2.3–4.2
	C6AF-10300-B	42	15	2.8–3.3	12	Autolite	13.5–15.3	[4]	[4]	[4]	2.3–4.2
	C6AF-10300-G	55	15	2.8–3.3	12	Autolite	13.5–15.3	[4]	[4]	[4]	2.3–4.2
	C6DF-10300-A	38	15	2.4	12	Autolite	13.5–15.3	[4]	[4]	[4]	2.3–4.2
	C6TF-10300-F	55	15	2.8–3.3	12	Autolite	13.5–15.3	[4]	[4]	[4]	2.3–4.2
1969	C5TF-10300-K	38	15	2.4	12	Autolite	13.5–15.3	[4]	[4]	[4]	2.3–4.2
	C6AF-10300-B	42	15	2.8–3.3	12	Autolite	13.5–15.3	[4]	[4]	[4]	2.3–4.2
	C6AF-10300-F	55	15	2.8–3.3	12	Autolite	13.5–15.3	[4]	[4]	[4]	2.3–4.2
	C6AF-10300-G	55	15	2.8–3.3	12	Autolite	13.5–15.3	[4]	[4]	[4]	2.3–4.2
	C6DF-10300-A	38	15	2.4	12	Autolite	13.5–15.3	[4]	[4]	[4]	2.3–4.2
	C7AF-10300-A	65	15	2.9	12	Autolite	13.5–15.3	[4]	[4]	[4]	2.3–4.2
	C9AF-10300-A	42	15	2.8–3.3	12	Autolite	13.5–15.3	[4]	[4]	[4]	2.3–4.2
	C9AF-10300-B	55	15	2.8–3.3	12	Autolite	13.5–15.3	[4]	[4]	[4]	2.3–4.2
	C9AF-10300-C	42	15	2.8–3.3	12	Autolite	13.5–15.3	[4]	[4]	[4]	2.3–4.2
	C9SF-10300-A	55	15	2.8–3.3	12	Autolite	13.5–15.3	[4]	[4]	[4]	2.3–4.2
	C9ZF-10300-B	55	15	2.8–3.3	12	Autolite	13.5–15.3	[4]	[4]	[4]	2.3–4.2
	C9ZF-10300-C	55	15	2.8–3.3	12	Autolite	13.5–15.3	[4]	[4]	[4]	2.3–4.2

Continued

FORD & MERCURY — Compact & Intermediate Models

ALTERNATOR & REGULATOR SPECIFICATIONS—Continued

Year	Make or Model	Current Rating① Amperes	Volts	Field Current @ 75°F. Amperes	Volts	Make	Voltage Regulator② Voltage @ 75°F.	Contact Gap	Armature Air Gap	Field Relay Armature Air Gap	Closing Voltage @ 75°F.
1970–72	DOZF-10300-B	38	15	2.4	12	Autolite	13.5–15.3	④	④	④	2.0–4.2
	DOAF-10300-C	42	15	2.9	12	Autolite	13.5–15.3	④	④	④	2.0–4.2
	DOAF-10300-F	42	15	2.9	12	Autolite	13.5–15.3	④	④	④	2.0–4.2
	DOAF-10300-G	42	15	2.9	12	Autolite	13.5–15.3	④	④	④	2.0–4.2
	DOAF-10300-E	55	15	2.9	12	Autolite	13.5–15.3	④	④	④	2.0–4.2
	DOAF-10300-H	55	15	2.9	12	Autolite	13.5–15.3	④	④	④	2.0–4.2
	DOZF-10300-A	55	15	2.9	12	Autolite	13.6–15.1	.018–.020	.042–.052	.011–.013	6.2–7.2
	DOZF-10300-C	55	15	2.9	12	Autolite	13.6–15.1	.018–.020	.042–.052	.011–.013	6.2–7.2
	DOSF-10300-A	55	15	2.9	12	Autolite	13.6–15.1	.018–.020	.042–.052	.011–.013	6.2–7.2
	DOLF-10300A⑤	55	15	2.9	12	—	—	—	—	—	—
	D1ZF-10300AA	55	15	2.9	12	Autolite	13.5–15.3	④	④	④	2.0–4.2
	D1AF-10300AA	61	15	2.9	12	Autolite	13.5–15.3	④	④	④	2.0–4.2
	DOAF-10300A⑤	65	15	2.9	12	—	—	—	—	—	

①—Current rating stamped on housing. ②—Voltage regulation stamped on cover. ③—Color stamp. ④—Not adjustable.
⑤—Integral regulator alternator.

WHEEL ALIGNMENT SPECIFICATIONS

OLD CAR SPECIFICATIONS: For 1946-65 Wheel Alignment Specifications see back of book.

Year	Model	Caster Angle, Degrees Limits	Desired	Camber Angle, Degrees Limits Left	Right	Desired Left	Right	Toe-In. Inch	Toe-Out on Turns, Deg. Outer Wheel	Inner Wheel
1966	Mustang 6	0 to +2	+1	−¼ to +1¼	−¼ to +1¼	+½	+½	¼	18⅞③	20
	Mustang V8	−1 to +1	Zero	−¼ to +1¼	−¼ to +1¼	+½	+½	¼	19⅛④	20
	All Others	−1 to +1	Zero	−½ to +1	−½ to +1	+¼	+¼	¼	17¾	20
1967	Cougar	−¼ to +¾	+¼	+½ to +1¾	+½ to +1¾	+1	+1	3/16	18¾	20
	Mustang	−¼ to +¾	+¼	+½ to +1¾	+½ to +1¾	+1	+1	3/16	18¾	20
	Others	−1 to 0	−½	−¼ to +¾	−¼ to +¾	+¼	+¼	¼	17¾	20
1968	Falcon	−1½ to +½	−½	−½ to +1	−½ to +1	+¼	+¼	¼	18⅛⑤	20
	Montego	−1½ to +½	−½	−½ to +1	−½ to +1	+¼	+¼	¼	18⅛⑤	20
	Fairlane	−1½ to +½	−½	−½ to +1	−½ to +1	+¼	+¼	¼	18⅛⑤	20
	Mustang	−¾ to +1¼	+¼	+¼ to +1¾	+¼ to +1¾	+1	+1	3/16	18¾	20
	Cougar	−¾ to +1¼	+¼	+¼ to +1¾	+¼ to +1¾	+1	+1	3/16	18¾	20
1969	Falcon	−1¾ to +¼	−¾	−½ to +1	−½ to +1	+¼	+¼	3/16	18.1⑤	20
	Fairlane	−1¾ to +¼	−¾	−½ to +1	−½ to +1	+¼	+¼	3/16	18.1⑤	20
	Montego	−1¾ to +¼	−¾	−½ to +1	−½ to +1	+¼	+¼	3/16	18.1⑤	20
	Mustang	−¾ to +1¼	+¼	+¼ to +1¾	+¼ to +1¾	+¾	+¾	3/16	18.68	20
	Cougar	−¾ to +1¼	+¼	+¼ to +1¾	+¼ to +1¾	+¾	+¾	3/16	18.68	20
1970	Maverick	−1½ to +½	−½	−½ to +1	−½ to +1	+¼	+¼	¼	18.48	20
	Falcon	−1¾ to +¾	+¾	−½ to +1	−½ to +1	+¼	+¼	3/16	17.32⑥	20
	Torino	−1¾ to +¾	+¾	−½ to +1	−½ to +1	+¼	+¼	3/16	17.32⑥	20
	Montego	−1¾ to +¾	+¾	−½ to +1	−½ to +1	+¼	+¼	3/16	17.32⑥	20
	Mustang	−1 to +1	Zero	+¼ to +1¾	+¼ to +1¾	+1	+1	3/16	16.68	20
	Cougar	−1 to +1	Zero	+¼ to +1¾	+¼ to +1¾	+1	+1	3/16	16.68	20

Continued

WHEEL ALIGNMENT SPECIFICATIONS—Continued

OLD CAR SPECIFICATIONS: For 1946-65 Wheel Alignment Specifications see back of book.

| Year | Model | Caster Angle, Degrees | | Camber Angle, Degrees | | | | | Toe-In. Inch | Toe-Out on Turns, Deg. | |
| | | Limits | Desired | Limits | | Desired | | | | Outer Wheel | Inner Wheel |
				Left	Right	Left	Right				
1971	Maverick	−2½ to +1½	−½	−¾ to +1¼	−¾ to +1¼	+¼	+¼	³⁄₁₆	18.48	20
	Torino	−2¾ to +1¼	+¾	−¾ to +1¼	−¾ to +1¼	+¼	+¼	³⁄₁₆	17.32⑥	20
	Mustang	−2 to +2	Zero	−½ to +1½	−½ to +1½	+¾	+¾	³⁄₁₆	18.68	20
	Comet	−2½ to +1½	−½	−¾ to +1¼	−¾ to +1¼	+¼	+¼	³⁄₁₆	18.48	20
	Montego	−2¾ to +1¼	+¾	−¾ to +1¼	−¾ to +1¼	+¼	+¼	³⁄₁₆	17.32⑥	20
	Cougar	−2 to +2	Zero	−½ to +1½	−½ to +1½	+¾	+¾	³⁄₁₆	18.68	20
1972	Maverick	−2½ to +1½	−½	−¾ to +1¼	−¾ to +1¼	+¼	+¼	³⁄₁₆	—	—
	Torino	−1¼ to +2¾	+¾	−¼ to +1¾	−¼ to +1¾	+¾	+¾	³⁄₁₆	—	—
	Mustang	−2 to +2	Zero	−½ to +1½	−½ to +1½	+½	+½	³⁄₁₆	—	—
	Comet	−2½ to +1½	−½	−¾ to +1¼	−¾ to +1¼	+¼	+¼	³⁄₁₆	—	—
	Montego	−1¼ to +2¾	+¾	−¼ to +1¼	−¼ to +1¾	+¾	+¾	³⁄₁₆	—	—
	Cougar	−2 to +2	Zero	−½ to +1½	−½ to +1½	+½	+½	³⁄₁₆	—	—

① —Standard steering.
② —Power steering.
③ —With power steering 20⅛°.
④ —Power steering 18¾°.
⑤ —Power steering 17⅞°.
⑥ —Power steering 17.81°.

COOLING SYSTEM & CAPACITY DATA

| Year | Model or Engine | Cooling Capacity, Qts. | | | Radiator Cap Relief Pressure, Lbs. | | Thermo. Opening Temp. ① | Fuel Tank Gals. | Engine Oil Refill Qts. ② | Transmission Oil | | | Rear Axle Oil Pints |
		No Heater	With Heater	With A/C	With A/C	No A/C				3 Speed Pints	4 Speed Pints	Auto. Trans. Qts. ⑨	
1966-67	6-170, 200	8½	9½	9½	12–15	12–15	185	16④	3½	2⑤	4	⑦	2½
	8-289	14	15	15	12–15	12–15	188	16④	4	2⑤	4	⑧	4½
	8-390	19½	20½	20½	12–15	12–15	188	16④	4	2⑤	4	13	5
1968	6-170, 200	8½	9½	9½	12–15	12–15	190	⑥	3½	3½	4	8	2½
	8-289	14	15	15	12–15	12–15	190	⑥	4	3½	4	9	4
	8-302	14	15	15	12–15	12–15	190	⑥	4	3½	4	9	4
	8-390	19½	20½	20½	12–15	12–15	190	⑥	4	3½	4	13	5
	8-427	19½	20½	20½	12–15	12–15	190	⑥	5	3½	4	13	5
1969	6-170, 200	8½	9½	9½	12–15	12–15	190	⑥	3½	3½	4	8	2½
	6-250	9	10	10	12–15	12–15	190	⑥	3½	3½	4	9	4
	8-302	14	15	15	12–15	12–15	190	⑥	4	3½	4	9	4
	8-351	14	15	15	12–15	12–15	190	⑥	4	3½	4	11	5
	8-390	19½	20½	20½	12–15	12–15	190	⑥	4	3½	4	12¾	5
	8-427	19½	20½	20½	12–15	12–15	190	⑥	5	3½	4	12¾	5
	8-428	19½	20½	20½	12–15	12–15	190	⑥	4	3½	4	12¾	5
1970	6-170, 200	9	10	10	12–15	12–15	190	⑫	3½	3½	4	8	2½
	6-250	10½	11½	11½	12–15	12–15	190	⑫	3½	3½	4	9	4
	8-302	14½	15½	15½	12–15	12–15	190	⑫	4	3½	4	9	4
	8-351	15½	16½	16½	12–15	12–15	190	⑫	4	3½	4	⑬	5
	8-428	19	20	20	12–15	12–15	190	⑫	4	3½	4	12¾	5
	8-429	17½	18½	18½	12–15	12–15	190	⑫	4	3½	4	12¾	5
	8-429 "CJ"	18½	19½	19½	12–15	12–15	190	⑫	4	3½	4	12¾	5
	8-429 "BOSS"⑩	18½	19½	19½	12–15	12–15	190	⑫	4	—	4	—	5
	8-429 "BOSS"⑪	18½	19½	19½	12–15	12–15	190	⑫	6	—	4	—	5

Continued

FORD & MERCURY – Compact & Intermediate Models

COOLING SYSTEM & CAPACITY DATA—Continued

Year	Model or Engine	Cooling Capacity, Qts.			Radiator Cap Relief Pressure, Lbs.		Thermo. Opening Temp. ①	Fuel Tank Gals.	Engine Oil Refill Qts. ②	Transmission Oil			Rear Axle Oil Pints
		No Heater	With Heater	With A/C	With A/C	No A/C				3 Speed Pints	4 Speed Pints	Auto. Trans. Qts. ⑨	
1971	6-170	8¼	9¼	9¼	12-15	12-15	190	16	3½	3½	—	8	4
	6-200, 250③	7½	8½	8½	12-15	12-15	190	16	3½	3½	—	8	4
	6-250	7½	8½	8½	12-15	12-15	190	⑭	3½	3½	—	9	4
	8-302	14	15	15	12-15	12-15	190	⑭	4	3½	4	9	4
	8-351	15¼	16¼	16¼	12-15	12-15	190	⑭	4	3½	4	⑬	5
	8-429	18½	19½	19½	12-15	12-15	190	⑭	6	3½	4	12¾	5
1972	Maverick 6-170	8¼	9¼	9¼	12-15	12-15	190	15	3½	3½	—	8	4
	Comet 6-170	8	9	9	12-15	12-15	190	15	3½	3½	—	8	4
	Maverick 6-200	8	9	9	12-15	12-15	190	15	3½	3½	—	8	4
	Comet 6-200	7¾	8¾	9	12-15	12-15	190	15	3½	3½	—	8	4
	Maverick 6-250	9	10	10	12-15	12-15	190	15	3½	3½	—	8	4
	Comet 6-250	8¾	9¾	9¾	12-15	12-15	190	15	3½	3½	—	8	4
	Torino 6-250	10½	11½	12	12-15	12-15	190	⑮	3½	3½	—	9	4
	Montego 6-250	10½	11½	11½	12-15	12-15	190	⑯	3½	3½	—	9	4
	Mustang 6-250	10¼	11¼	11¼	12-15	12-15	190	19½	3½	3½	—	9	4
	8-302③	12½	13½	14¼	12-15	12-15	190	15	4	3½	—	9	4
	Torino 8-302	14¼	15¼	16¼	12-15	12-15	190	⑮	4	3½	4	9	4
	Montego 8-302	14¼	15¼	15¼	12-15	12-15	190	⑯	4	3½	4	9	4
	Mustang 8-302	14¼	15¼	15½	12-15	12-15	190	19½	4	3½	4	9	4
	Torino 8-351	14½	15½	15¾	12-15	12-15	190	⑮	4	3½	4	11	5
	Montego 8-351	14½	15½	15⅞	12-15	12-15	190	⑯	4	3½	4	11	5
	Mustang 8-351	14¾	15¾	15¾	12-15	12-15	190	19½	4⑰	3½	4	11	5
	Cougar 8-351	14¾	15¾	15¾	12-15	12-15	190	16½	4	3½	4	⑱	5
	Torino 8-400	16¾	17¾	17¾	12-15	12-15	190	⑮	4	—	4	12¾	5
	Montego 8-400	16¾	17¾	17¾	12-15	12-15	190	⑯	4	—	4	12¾	5
	Torino 8-429	17¾	18¾	20	12-15	12-15	190	⑮	4	—	4	12¾	5
	Montego 8-429	17⅞	18⅞	18⅞	12-15	12-15	190	⑯	4	—	—	12¾	5

①—Use with permanent type anti-freeze. With alcohol type use a 160° unit.
②—Add 1 qt. with filter change.
③—Maverick and Comet.
④—20 Gallons on Comet, Fairlane, Falcon Wagons.
⑤—With overdrive 3½ pints.
⑥—Falcon cars and Mustang 16, Cougar 17, Fairlane, Montego and Falcon Wagons 20.
⑦—1966 7¾ qts., 1967 8 qts.

⑧—1966 8¾ qts., 1967 9 qts.
⑨—Approximate. Make final check with dipstick.
⑩—Torino & Montego.
⑪—Mustang & Cougar.
⑫—Early Falcon cars & Maverick 16, Mustang, Cougar, Fairlane, Late Falcon & Montego cars 22, Fairlane, Falcon & Montego wagons 19. Subtract 2 gals. for California cars.

⑬—C4 10¼, FMX 11, C6 12¾.
⑭—Torino, Montego, Mustang & Cougar cars, 20. Station wagons, 18.
⑮—Sedans, 22½; wagons, 20½.
⑯—Sedans, 23; wagons, 21.
⑰—"BOSS", 5.
⑱—12" converter, 12¾; others, 11.

BRAKE SPECIFICATIONS

Year	Model	Brake Drum Inside Diameter	Wheel Cylinder Bore Diameter			Master Cylinder Bore Diameter		
			Front Disc Brake	Front Drum Brake	Rear Brake	With Disc Brakes	With Drum Brakes	With Power Brakes
1966	Falcon 6 Cyl.	9.00	—	1.062	.844	—	1.00	—
	Falcon V8	10.00	—	1.125	.906	—	1.00	—
	Mustang 6 Cyl.	9.00	—	1.062	.844	—	1.00	.875
	Mustang V8	10.00	1.636	1.125	.906	.938	1.00	.875
	Comet & Fairlane 6-200, 8-289 Cars	10.00	—	1.125	.906	—	1.00	1.00
	Comet & Fairlane 8-390	10.00	—	1.094	.875	—	1.00	1.00
	Comet & Fairlane Wagons	10.00	—	1.094	.938	—	1.00	1.00
1967	Falcon 6 Cyl. Cars	9.00	1.636	1.062	.844	.9375	1.00	.9375
	Falcon Wagons	10.00	1.636	1.094	.938	.9375	1.00	.9375
	Falcon V8 Cars	10.00	1.636	1.125	.906	.9375	1.00	.9375
	Mustang 6 Cyl.	9.00	1.636	1.062	.844	1.00	1.00	1.00
	Mustang & Cougar 8-390	10.00	1.636	1.094	.813	1.00	1.00	1.00
	Mustang & Cougar 8-289 302①	10.00	1.636	1.125	.875	1.00	1.00	1.00
	Comet & Fairlane 6-200, 8-289, 302	10.00	1.636	1.125	.906	.9375	1.00	.9375
	Comet & Fairlane 8-390 Cars	10.00	1.636	1.094	.875	.9375	1.00	.9375
	Comet & Fairlane 8-289 Convertibles	10.00	1.636	1.094	.906	.9375	1.00	.9375
	Comet & Fairlane 6-200, 8-289 Wagons	10.00	1.636	1.094	.938	.9375	1.00	.9375
	Comet & Fairlane 8-390 Wagons	10.00	1.636	1.094	.938	.9375	1.00	.9375
1968	Falcon 6 Cyl. Cars	9.00	2.375	1.062	.844	.9375	1.00	.9375
	Falcon V8 Cars	10.00	2.375	1.125	.906	.9375	1.00	.9375
	Falcon Wagons	10.00	2.375	1.094	.938	.9375	1.00	.9375
	Mustang 6 Cyl.	9.00	2.375	1.062	.844	1.00	1.00	1.00
	Mustang & Cougar 8-390	10.00	2.375	1.094	.813	1.00	1.00	1.00
	Mustang & Cougar 8-289, 302	10.00	2.375	1.125	.875	1.00	1.00	1.00
	Montego & Fairlane 6-200, 8-289, 302①	10.00	2.375	1.125	.906	.9375	1.00	.9375
	Montego & Fairlane 8-390 Cars	10.00	2.375	1.094	.875	.9375	1.00	.9375
	Montego & Fairlane Convertibles (Exc. 8-390)	10.00	2.375	1.094	.906	.9375	1.00	.9375
	Montego & Fairlane Wagons (Exc. 8-390)	10.00	2.375	1.094	.938	.9375	1.00	.9375
1969–70	Falcon & Maverick 6 Cyl. Cars②	9.00	2.381	1.062	.844	.9375	1.00	.9375
	Falcon V8 Cars	10.00	2.381	1.094	.906	.9375	1.00	.9375
	Falcon Wagons	10.00	2.381	1.125	.938	.9375	1.00	.9375
	Mustang 6 Cyl.	9.00	2.381	1.062	.844	1.00	1.00	1.00
	Mustang & Cougar 8-302	10.00	2.381	1.125	.875	1.00	1.00	1.00
	Mustang & Cougar 8-351, 390	10.00	2.381	1.094	.813	1.00	1.00	1.00
	Montego & Fairlane 6-250, 8-302①③	10.00	2.381	1.125	.096	.9375	1.00	.9375
	Montego & Fairlane 8-351, 390	10.00	2.381	1.094	.875	.9375	1.00	.9375
	Montego & Fairlane Conv. (Exc. 8-351, 390)	10.00	2.381	1.094	.906	.9375	1.00	.9375
	Montego & Fairlane Wagons (Exc. 8-390)	10.00	2.381	1.094	.938	.9375	1.00	.9375
1971	Maverick & Comet 6 Cyl.	9.00	—	1.062	.844	—	1.00	.9375
	Maverick & Comet V8	10.00	—	1.125	.875	—	1.00	.9375
	Torino & Montego Cars	10.00	2.381	1.125	.906	.9375	1.00	.9375
	Torino & Montego Wagons	10.00	2.381	1.125	.968	.9375	1.00	.9375
	Mustang & Cougar 6-250, 8-302	10.00	2.381	1.125	.875	.9375	1.00	1.00
	Mustang & Cougar 8-351, 429	10.00	2.381	1.125	.906	.9375	1.00	1.00
1972	Maverick & Comet 6 Cyl.	9.00	—	1.062	.844	—	1.00	.9375
	Maverick & Comet V8	10.00	—	1.125	.875	—	1.00	.9375
	Torino & Montego	10.00	3.100	—	1.00	1.00	1.00	1.00
	Mustang & Cougar 6-250, 8-302	10.00	2.381	1.125	.875	1.00	1.00	1.00
	Mustang & Cougar 8-351	10.00	2.381	1.125	.906	1.00	1.00	1.00

①—Except convertible.   ②—Includes only early 1970 Falcons.   ③—Includes late 1970 Falcons.

Electrical Section

DISTRIBUTOR, REPLACE

1. To remove the distributor, disconnect the primary wire and vacuum control pipe.
2. Remove distributor cap.
3. Scribe a mark on the distributor body indicating the position of the rotor, and scribe another mark on the body and engine block indicating position of distributor body in block. These marks can be used as guides when installing distributor in a correctly timed engine.
4. Remove hold down screw or screws and lift distributor out of block. *Do not crank engine while distributor is removed or the initial timing operation will have to be performed.*

Installation

If the crankshaft has not been disturbed, install the distributor, using the scribed marks previously made on the distributor body and engine block as guides.

If the crankshaft has been rotated while the distributor was removed from the engine, it will be necessary to retime the engine. Crank the engine to bring No. 1 piston on top dead center of its compression stroke. Align the timing mark on the crankshaft pulley with the timing pointer (see *Tune Up* chart). Install the distributor so that the rotor points to the No. 1 spark plug wire terminal in the distributor cap.

Make sure the oil pump intermediate shaft properly engages the distributor shaft. It may be necessary to crank the engine with the starter, after the distributor drive gear is properly engaged, in order to engage the oil pump intermediate shaft.

STARTER, REPLACE
1966-72

1. On V8 only, raise car on hoist.
2. Disconnect cable at starter terminal.
3. On 1966-68 V8 Comet and all Montego with power steering, disconnect and lower idler arm from frame. Push bolts back through frame.
4. On all models, unfasten and remove starter.

NOISY STARTER OR STARTER LOCKUP: If either of these situations occur, loosen the three mounting bolts enough to hand fit the starter properly into pilot plate. Then tighten starter mounting bolts, starting with top bolt. Starter should not be replaced until it has been proven noisy after proper alignment has been established by the above method.

IGNITION SWITCH, REPLACE
1972 Torino & Montego

The switch is mounted on the steering

Fig. 1   Ignition switch removal. 1966-69

column and is controlled by the lock cylinder through an actuator in the locking mechanism. The switch is connected to the actuator by an actuator rod. Two multiple connector plugs are secured to the switch by snap type retainers. To remove switch, proceed as follows:

1. Disconnect battery ground cable.
2. Remove screws holding instrument panel cluster.
3. Press locking tabs and remove blade type connector on top of switch.
4. Remove two mounting nuts from switch and lift up on switch enough to unhook actuating rod.
5. Remove the switch.

1972 Except Torino & Montego
1970-71 All Except Early 70 Maverick

1. Disconnect battery ground cable.
2. Disconnect switch wiring connector and remove two switch retaining nuts.
3. Detach switch from actuator and remove switch.
4. To install switch, place shift lever in Park (auto. trans.) or Reverse (std. trans.) turn key to Lock position and remove key.

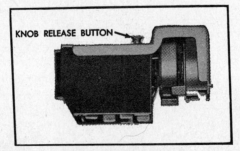

Fig. 2   Light switches. 1966-69

5. New switches are pinned in the Lock position by a plastic shipping pin. For existing switch, pull switch plunger out as far as it will go then back off one detent to Lock position. Insert a $3/32''$ drill in locking hole on top of switch and install switch.

1968-69 All & Early 1970 Maverick

1. Disconnect battery ground cable.
2. Insert key and turn switch to accessory position. Insert a wire pin in hole in switch. Slightly depress pin while turning key counterclockwise past the accessory position. This will release lock cylinder. Pull out lock cylinder with key.
3. Remove bezel nut. Lower switch from instrument panel and remove accessory wire nut. Depress tabs securing multiple connector to rear of switch. Pull multiple connector from switch and remove switch.
4. Reverse procedure to install.

1967

1. Disconnect ground cable from battery.
2. With ignition key, turn switch to the left while inserting a fine wire pin in hole beneath key slot, Fig. 1. Slightly depress pin while turning key. This will release lock cylinder from switch. Pull out lock cylinder with key.
3. Remove switch bezel nut and lower switch from instrument panel. Remove accessory and gauge feed wires from switch, also insulated plug.
4. Reverse procedure to install. Insert key and turn to accessory position. Place cylinder and key in switch. Depress pin slightly while turning key counterclockwise. Push cylinder into switch and remove pin.

1966

1. Disconnect battery ground cable.
2. Turn ignition key to "ACC" position, Fig. 1. Using a paper clip, slightly depress release pin and turn key counter-clockwise. Then pull key and lock cylinder out of switch.
3. Press in on rear of switch and rotate switch $1/8$ turn counter-clockwise (as viewed from terminal end). Remove bezel, switch and spacer.
4. Remove nut from back of switch. Remove accessory and gauge feed wires from accessory terminal of switch. Pull insulated plug from rear of switch.
5. If a new ignition switch is to be installed, insert a screwdriver into lock opening of switch and turn slot in switch to full counter-clockwise position.
6. Connect insulated plug with wires to back of switch. Position accessory and gauge wires on switch stud and install retaining nut.
7. Position spacer on switch with open face away from switch.
8. Place bezel, switch and spacer in

switch opening. Press switch toward instrument panel and rotate it ⅛ turn to lock it in position.
9. If new lock cylinder is to be installed, insert key in cylinder and turn it to "ACC" position. Place lock and key in switch, depress pin slightly with a paper clip and turn key counter-clockwise. Push lock cylinder into switch.
10. Connect battery cable and check switch operation.

LIGHT SWITCH, REPLACE

1968-72 Fairlane, Falcon, Montego, Maverick, Torino & 1971-72 Comet

1. Disconnect battery ground cable.
2. To remove control knob and shaft assembly, place knob in full ON position, then press knob release button on switch and pull out knob and shaft.

NOTE: On air conditioned Mavericks, to gain access to release button, disconnect left AC duct from the register, loosen two register-to-utility shelf retaining nuts and remove the register connector. Turn control knob to full on position and reach behind register to release button.

3. Unscrew mounting nut and remove bezel and switch, then remove junction block from switch.
4. Reverse procedure to install. However, install knob and shaft by inserting all the way into the switch until a distinct click is heard. In some instances it may be necessary to rotate the shaft slightly until it engages the switch contact carrier.

1968-71 Cougar & Mustang

1. Disconnect battery ground cable.
2. Remove two screws and lower parking brake and air control.
3. To remove control knob and shaft assembly, place knob in full ON position, then press knob release button on switch and pull out knob and shaft out of switch.
4. Remove switch bezel (1 nut), then lower switch assembly. Disconnect wire junction block from switch and, on Cougar only, the three vacuum hoses, and remove switch.
5. Reverse procedure to install. However, install knob and shaft assembly by inserting all the way into the switch until a distinct click is heard. In some instances it may be necessary to rotate the shaft slightly until it engages the switch contact carrier.

1967 Cougar & Mustang

1. Disconnect ground cable at battery.
2. Remove control knob and shaft by pressing knob release button on switch housing with knob in "ON" position. Pull knob out of switch.
3. Unfasten and lower parking brake and air control (2 screws).
4. Remove bezel nut and lower switch. Disconnect junction block from

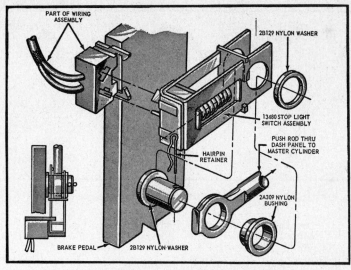

Fig. 3   Mechanical stop light switch.   1966-72

switch.
5. Reverse procedure to install. Insert knob and shaft all the way into switch until a click is heard. In some cases it may be necessary to rotate shaft slightly until it engages switch contact carrier.

All 1966 & 1967-68 Montego, Comet, Falcon, Fairlane

1. Disconnect battery ground cable.
2. Remove control knob and shaft by pressing knob release button on switch housing, Fig. 2, with knob in full "ON" position. Pull knob out of switch.
3. Unscrew mounting nut, remove switch, then remove fuse block from switch.
4. To install, connect fuse block to switch, position switch in instrument panel and install mounting nut.
5. Install knob and shaft by inserting it all the way into switch until a distinct click is heard. In some instances it may be necessary to rotate shaft slightly until it engages switch contact carrier.
6. Connect battery cable.

STOP LIGHT SWITCH, REPLACE

1966-72 Mechanical Type

1. Disconnect wires at connector.
2. Remove hairpin retainer and slide stop light switch, push rod, nylon washers and bushings away from brake pedal, and remove switch, Fig. 3.
3. Reverse above procedure to install.

NEUTRAL SAFETY SWITCH, REPLACE

Column Shift 1969 & Early 1970 Maverick

Removal

1. Disconnect the switch wires at plug

connector.
2. Remove two screws securing switch to column and lift switch from column.

NOTE: Check the switch actuator to be sure it is secure to the shift tube and seated as far forward against shift tube bearing as possible. If the actuator is broken or damaged, replace it.

3. Before installing a new switch, check to see that the red neutral position gauge pin is properly inserted in the neutral pinning hole. If the pin is missing, align the two holes at the neutral pinning hole on top of the switch and install a No. 43 drill.
4. While holding selector lever against the stop in neutral position, place switch on column and install attaching screws.
5. Remove the gauge pin and connect the wires to the switch.

Adjustment

1. With selector lever against neutral stop, loosen two switch retaining screws.
2. Rotate switch until a start is obtained and tighten switch screws.
3. Place selector lever in "1" position and push the park reset button, located on right side of switch, to the left until it stops.

1969-72 Cougar & Mustang 1971-72 Comet & Maverick Console

Removal & Adjustment

1. Place selector lever in neutral.
2. Raise car and remove manual lever control rod attaching nut.
3. Lower car and remove selector lever handle.
4. Unfasten and remove dial housing.
5. Disconnect dial light and switch wires at connectors at dash panel.
6. Unfasten and remove selector lever and housing assembly.
7. Remove pointer back up shield screws and remove the shield.

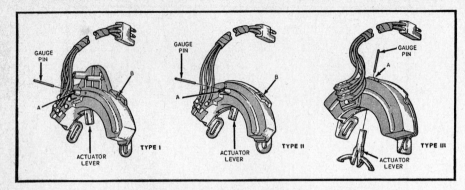

Fig. 3A   Neutral start switch adjustments. 1968 column shift

8. Remove the two switch screws, push the switch harness plug inward and remove the switch and harness assembly.
9. When installing switch, hold it with wires facing down and move the actuator lever all the way to the left. Then return it to neutral positon, Fig. 4A.
10. Position the harness and secure the switch to the housing.
11. Install pointer back up shield.
12. Position selector lever and housing assembly on console and fasten.
13. Connect dial light and switch wires.
14. Install dial housing and selector lever handle.
15. Raise car and attach manual lever control rod.
16. Lower car and check operation of switch in Park position.

1968 Column Shift

Column mounted neutral start switches are located on top of the steering column

jacket but have been moved closer to the toeboard just below the collapsible section of the jacket.

Removal

To adjust the switch, it must be removed from the column. Place the selector lever in neutral and set the parking brake. Then disconnect the electrical and vacuum connections and remove the two fastening screws which will allow you to lift the switch straight up and out.

After removing the switch body of the type 3 switch used on some models, compress the protruding ends of the actuator lever with pliers and lift the lever out of the column. All other types of switches have actuating levers that are integral with the switches, Fig. 3A.

Adjustment

To properly adjust any of the column mounted switches, it is necessary to use a 3/32″ pin gauge or rod to adjust the switch.

1. Hold switch with wire terminal

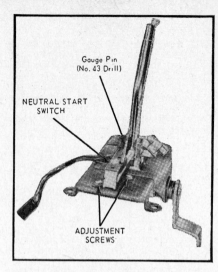

Fig. 4   Neutral safety switch (console shift). 1967-72 Comet, Fairlane and Montego

facing you (and with separate actuator lever in place in the type 3 switch). Move actuator lever all the way to your left, but don't use force as the switch will be damaged internally.
2. Insert gauge pin in hole in tapered round boss facing you on all switches except type 3. On the type 3 switch, insert the gauge pin 1/2 inch into the hole in the boss on the top of the switch.
3. Gently move actuator lever back to the right until it stops. This will move the Park circuit to its position of minimum travel, which must be done if the switch is to function properly upon installation.
4. Pull out gauge pin and fit it in the hole on top of the switch case to engage the switch internal carrier in the neutral position. For type 3 switches, remove the gauge pin while you align the two gauge pin holes in the switch case. Then reinsert the pin.
5. If a type 3 switch is being serviced (with separate actuator lever) install the actuator lever in the column by squeezing it slightly and pressing it carefully into position in the shift tube.
6. With transmission selector lever held against the stop in the neutral detent position, set the switch in place on the column and fasten it with two screws.
7. Connect the electrical connector and vacuum hose, and be sure to remove the gauge pin before operating the selector lever.

1967-70 Montego, Comet, Fairlane & 1971-72 Montego & Torino

Console Shift, Fig. 4

1. Remove handle from selector lever.
2. Remove trim panel from top of console.
3. Remove cover and dial indicator as a unit.
4. Unfasten and remove selector lever

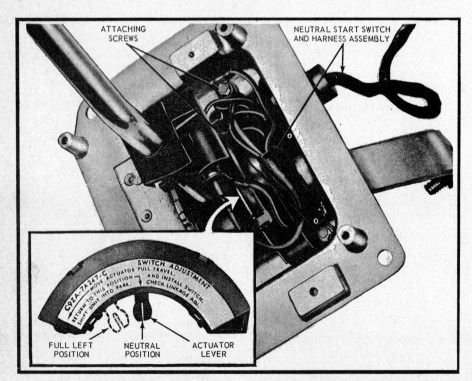

Fig. 4A   Neutral switch. 1969-72 Cougar & Mustang with console

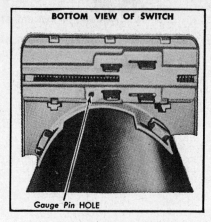

BOTTOM VIEW OF SWITCH

Gauge Pin HOLE

Fig. 5 Neutral safety switch (column shift). 1967 Comet, Fairlane, Falcon

retainer from housing (6 screws).
5. Unfasten switch from lever housing (2 screws). Disconnect wires at plug connector and remove switch.
6. With selector lever in neutral, move lever back and forth until gauge pin (#43 drill) can be fully inserted in gauge pin holes. Fig. 4.
7. Place transmission selector lever firmly against stop of neutral detent position.
8. Slide combination neutral start and back-up light switch forward or rearward as required until switch actuating lever contacts selector lever.
9. Tighten switch screws and remove gauge pin.
10. Complete installation in reverse order of removal.

1967 Comet, Falcon, Fairlane

Column Shift, Fig. 5

1. Disconnect switch wires at plug connector.
2. Remove switch from steering column (2 screws).
3. Reverse procedure to install.
4. With selector lever in neutral, rotate switch and install gauge pin (#43 drill) into gauge pin hole.
5. Tighten switch screws and remove gauge pin.

All 1966 & 1966-68 Mustang, Cougar

Transmission Mounted Switch, Fig. 6

1. Remove downshift linkage rod from transmission downshift lever.
2. Apply penetrating oil to downshift lever shaft and nut; then remove downshift outer lever.
3. Remove switch attaching bolts.
4. Disconnect multiple wire connector and remove switch from transmission.
5. Install new switch.
6. With transmission manual lever in neutral, rotate switch and install gauge pin (#43 drill) into gauge pin holes.
7. Tighten switch attaching bolts and remove gauge pin.
8. Complete the installation in reverse order of removal.

TURN SIGNAL SWITCH, REPLACE
1971-72

1. Remove retaining screw from underside of steering wheel spokes and lift off pad horn switch/trim cover and medallion as an assembly.
2. Disconnect horn switch wires from terminals.
3. Remove steering wheel retaining nut and remove steering wheel with suitable puller.
4. Remove turn signal switch lever by unscrewing it from steering column.
5. Remove shroud from under steering column.
6. Disconnect steering column wiring connector plugs and remove screws that secure switch to column.
7. On tilt column, remove wires and terminals from column plug. *NOTE: Record color code and position of wires before removing. A hole provided in the flange casting on fixed columns makes it unnecessary to separate wires from plug as the plug with wires can be guided through hole.*
8. Remove plastic cover sleeve from wiring harness and remove switch from top of column.

1968-70

The emergency warning flasher switch and the turn signal flasher switch are integral parts of the same switch assembly. To remove, proceed as follows:
1. Disconnect battery ground cable.
2. Remove steering wheel hub.
3. Remove horn button (3 screws).
4. Remove steering wheel.
5. Remove turn signal switch lever and emergency flasher control knob. If so equipped, disconnect set speed switch wiring connector.
6. Remove steering column upper collar (2 screws).
7. Disconnect turn signal switch wiring multiple connector near bottom of steering column. It may be necessary to lower hand brake control and left air vent control on some Mustang and Cougar models to provide access to turn signal wiring connector.
8. Remove wires and terminals from connector blocks. This can be done by depressing the tab on the wire terminal with an awl or with an empty ball point pen refill cartridge, then pull wire and terminal from connector block. *Record color code and location of each wire before removing it from connector block.*
9. Tape wires together and attach a piece of heavy cord to the wires to help pull them through steering column during installation.
10. Remove plastic cover from over wires.
11. Push lower steering column collar down. Remove wiring retainer clip.
12. Remove switch from steering column (2 screws) and pull switch and wiring out of column.
13. Reverse procedure to install.

SERVICE BULLETIN

Before judging the turn signal switch

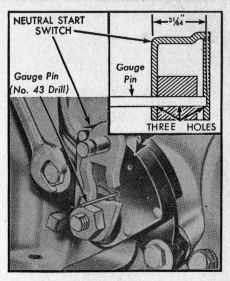

NEUTRAL START SWITCH

Gauge Pin (No. 43 Drill)

Gauge Pin

THREE HOLES

Fig. 6 Neutral safety switch, 1966 and 1967-68 Cougar, Mustang

to be defective on 1966-67 models, it is suggested that the following areas be checked and repaired to make certain that they are not causing the problem:
1. The steering shaft should be centered in the column so that the steering wheel hub cancelling fingers are in proper relation to the switch cancelling mechanism. This is done by loosening the column attachment to the dash panel and shifting the tube in relation to the shaft.
2. Make sure that the ignition switch is not sticking between the "Start" and normal engine "On" position, thereby adversely affecting the electrical circuit.
3. Excessive Loctite on the threads on the turn signal lever may be contacting the turn signal switch mechanism, causing a binding condition.
4. The fingers on the steering wheel hub cancelling cam may be bent so that the proper contact with the cancelling mechanism cannot be accomplished.

1967

1. Disconnect ground cable at battery.
2. Remove steering wheel hub.
3. Remove horn button (3 screws). Springs will fall out.
4. Remove steering wheel.
5. Remove turn signal switch lever and emergency flasher control knob.
6. Remove steering column upper collar (2 screws).
7. Disconnect multiple connector near bottom of steering column.
8. Remove wires and terminals from connector blocks. This can be done by depressing tab on wire terminal with an awl or with an empty ball point pen re-fill cartridge; then pull wire and terminal from connector block. *Record color code of each wire before removing from connector block.*
9. Tape wires together and attach a piece of heavy cord to them to help pull wires through steering column during installation.

10. Remove plastic cover from over wires.
11. Push lower steering column down and remove wiring retainer clip.
12. Unfasten switch (2 screws) and pull switch and wire assembly out of column.
13. Reverse procedure to install.

1966

1. Disconnect battery ground cable.
2. Remove steering wheel.
3. Disconnect two wire connector blocks at dash panel above steering column.
4. Remove wires and terminals from connector blocks.

NOTE: Step 4 can be done by depressing tab on wire terminal with an awl. Then pull wire and terminal from connector block. Be sure to record the color code and location of each wire before removing it from connector block. Tape wires together and attach a piece of heavy cord to them to help pull wires through steering column during installation.

---

5. Remove turn signal lever.
6. Remove three screws and remove bearing retainer, turn signal switch and wires from steering column. Disconnect cord from wires.
7. To install, tape ends of wires together and attach cord to wires.
8. Pull wires down through steering column with the cord, and position switch to steering column hub.
9. Complete the installation by reversing the removal procedure.

HORN SOUNDER & STEERING WHEEL

1969-72 Rim-Blow Type

The rubber insert and copper strip assembly is not replaceable. Therefore if a new insert is required the entire steering wheel will have to be replaced.

1. Unfasten and remove pad from steering wheel (3 screws).
2. Remove the medallion from the pad.
3. After removing retaining nut the steering wheel can be removed with a puller.

1968-72 Except Rim-Blow Type

1. Disconnect battery ground cable.
2. Remove steering wheel hub.
3. Remove horn button (3 screws); springs will fall out.
4. Remove steering wheel.

1966-68

The horn button or ring can be removed by pressing down evenly and turning button counterclockwise until it lifts out.

Mark steering shaft and wheel hub before removing wheel so that the relationship between the wheel and steering gear is maintained when reinstalled.

Then remove the nut from the steering shaft and use a puller to remove the wheel.

INSTRUMENT CLUSTER
1972 Torino & Montego

Standard Cluster

1. Disconnect battery ground cable and remove steering column shroud.
2. Remove three upper and four lower retaining screws from instrument cluster trim cover and remove the cover.
3. Remove two upper and two lower screws retaining instrument cluster to panel.
4. Pull cluster away from panel and disconnect speedo cable.
5. Disconnect cluster feed plug from printed circuit.
6. Remove "Belts and Park" light sockets from receptacles, if so equipped.
7. Remove cluster.

Performance Cluster

1. Disconnect battery ground cable.
2. Remove three upper and four lower retaining screws from cluster trim cover and remove the cover.
3. Remove two upper and two lower screws retaining cluster to the panel.
4. Pull cluster away from panel and disconnect speedo cable.
5. Disconnect cluster feed plug from receptacle in printed circuit.
6. Disconnect clock and tachometer wire loom at connector.
7. Remove cluster.

1971-72 Mustang

1. Disconnect battery ground cable.
2. Remove instrument panel end finish panel and the cluster opening finish panel.
3. Remove four cluster attaching screws and pull cluster away from instrument panel.
4. Disconnect speedometer cable and wiring.

1971-72 Cougar

1. Disconnect battery ground cable.
2. Remove instrument panel pad.
3. Remove four screws attaching cluster to instrument panel.
4. Disconnect speedometer cable and wiring and remove cluster.

1969-70 Mustang & Cougar

1. Disconnect battery ground cable.
2. Remove instrument panel pad for access to cluster mounting screws.
3. Remove six screws retaining cluster to panel and withdraw cluster slightly.
4. Disconnect plug to printed circuit and tachometer if so equipped.
5. Disconnect speedometer cable by pressing on knurled surface of plastic connector and pulling cable away from head.
6. The cluster can now be removed from the panel.
7. Reverse the foregoing to install.

1968 Mustang & Cougar

Instrument cluster components are accessible by removing the cluster as an assembly. Procedure is as follows:

1. Disconnect battery ground cable.
2. On Cougars only, remove instrument panel front pad.
3. Unfasten heater control from instrument panel (4 screws) and position control outward.
4. Reaching through heater control opening, disconnect speedometer cable.
5. Remove three ash tray screws. Disconnect cigar lighter element wiring connector and remove ash tray.
6. Reaching through ash tray opening, remove nut retaining inboard end of instrument cluster to instrument panel.
7. Unfasten cluster from instrument panel (7 screws on Cougar, 5 on Mustang).
8. Position cluster outward, disconnect two multiple connectors and remove cluster assembly.
9. Reverse procedure to install.

1968-71 Fairlane/Torino Late 1970 Falcon

1. Disconnect battery ground cable.
2. Remove instrument panel cover.
3. Remove right instrument panel shield.
4. Unfasten cluster (5 screws) and position cluster out.
5. Disconnect speedometer cable, tachometer (if equipped) and multiple plug from printed circuit and remove cluster. Cluster components are now accessible for service.

1968-69 & Early 1970 Falcon

1. Disconnect battery ground cable.
2. Remove instrument panel pad.
3. Unfasten cluster from instrument panel (5 screws) and position cluster out.
4. Disconnect speedometer cable, heater control cables and heater bulb. Also disconnect heater switch plug and multiple plug to printed circuit. Remove clamp retaining heater cables and remove cluster. Cluster components are now accessible for service.

1970-72 Maverick & 1971-72 Comet

1. Disconnect battery ground cable.
2. From under instrument panel, disconnect speedometer cable.
3. Remove two retaining screws at the top of the cluster and swing it down from the panel.
4. Disconnect electrical connections and remove cluster.

1970-71 Montego

1. Disconnect battery ground cable.
2. Remove heater controls, left finish panels and instrument panel pad.
3. From the front of the cluster, remove four cluster-to-panel retaining screws and position cluster part way out of panel.
4. Disconnect speedometer cable and cluster feed plug and clock wire and remove cluster.

1970-71 Cyclone Spoiler

In addition to the main instrument cluster, the Cyclone Spoiler is equipped with an auxiliary cluster mounted to the right of the panel.

1. Disconnect battery ground cable and remove panel pad.
2. From the inner side of the pad assembly, remove cluster-to-pad retaining nuts and remove cluster.

1968-69 Montego

1. Disconnect battery ground cable.
2. Remove instrument panel pad.
3. Unfasten cluster from instrument panel (8 screws). Position cluster out and disconnect speedometer cable. Also disconnect multiple plug to cluster, multiple plug to convenience control lights (if equipped), heater control cables and switch.
4. Disconnect clock (if equipped) and remove cluster. Cluster components are now accessible for service.

1966-67 Comet & Falcon; 1966 Mustang; 1967 Fairlane

1. Disconnect ground cable at battery.
2. Disconnect cable for speedometer.
3. Unfasten cluster from panel and tilt cluster forward.
4. Disconnect wiring and bulb sockets and remove cluster to workbench for service required.

1967 Cougar & Mustang

1. Disconnect ground cable at battery.
2. Remove instrument panel front pad (Cougar).
3. Unfasten (4 screws) heater control from instrument panel and position control outward.
4. Reaching through heater control opening, disconnect speedometer cable.
5. Remove ash tray (3 screws). Disconnect cigar lighter element.
6. Reaching through ash tray opening, remove nut that retains inboard end of cluster to instrument panel.
7. Separate cluster from panel (7 screws on Cougar, 6 on Mustang).
8. Position cluster outward, disconnect two multiple connectors and remove instrument cluster. All components are now accessible for service.

1966 Fairlane

1. Disconnect battery ground cable.
2. Remove radio knobs and nuts.
3. Disconnect speedometer cable.
4. Remove screws from cluster and position it outward.
5. Disconnect bulbs, constant voltage regulator and ground wire, clock and fuel gauge.
6. Remove cluster to workbench for service required.

W/S WIPER MOTOR
1972 Torino & Montego

Procedure for removal is the same as for 1971 Ford & Mercury Full Size Models and can be found in that car chapter.

1971 Montego & 1971-72 Mustang & Cougar

1. Disconnect battery ground cable.
2. Disconnect wiper motor wiring connector.
3. Remove cowl top left vent screen.
4. Remove wiper link retaining clip from wiper motor arm.
5. Remove three motor retaining bolts and remove wiper and bracket.

1970-72 Maverick & 1971-72 Comet

1. Remove instrument cluster.
2. On air conditioned units, remove center connector and duct assembly.
3. Working through cluster opening, disconnect two pivot shaft links from motor drive arm by removing retaining clip.
4. Disconnect wiring and remove mounting bolts and remove motor through cluster opening.

1969-70 Cougar & Mustang

1. Remove wiper arm and blades.
2. Disconnect washer hose at "T" fitting (left side) on the cowl grille.
3. Remove cowl top grille.
4. Disconnect motor ground wire at forward edge of plenum chamber.
5. Disconnect motor harness at plug and push it back into plenum chamber.
6. Disconnect linkage drive arm from motor output arm crankpin by removing clip.
7. Remove three bolts that retain motor to bracket and rotate motor output arm 180° and remove the motor.

NOTE: Before installing motor, rotate arm 180° and before connecting linkage to motor, turn on ignition to ACC position to allow motor to go into park position.

1967-70 Montego, Comet, Fairlane, Falcon & 1970-71 Torino

1. Disconnect wiper motor wiring connector.
2. Remove wiper arms and blades.
3. Remove cowl top grille panel.
4. Remove wiper link clip from motor arm.
5. Unfasten and remove wiper motor and mounting bracket (4 bolts).
6. Reverse procedure to install.

1967-68 Cougar & Mustang

1. Disconnect ground cable at battery.
2. Remove courtesy light. If vehicle is equipped with a hang-on air conditioner, lower air conditioner to floor.
3. Disconnect wiper motor plug connector.
4. Remove nut retaining pivot arm and wiper arms to motor.
5. Unfasten and remove motor from its mounting bracket.
6. Reverse procedure to install.

1966 Mustang, Comet & Falcon

1. Disconnect harness connector from wiper motor.
2. Unfasten motor from dash panel (3 bolts).
3. Lower assembly and disconnect wiper links at motor. Then remove motor and bracket.

1966-67 Fairlane

1. Disconnect wiper links drive arm from wiper motor drive shaft (under instrument panel).
2. Disconnect wires from motor.
3. Remove motor mounting bolts and remove motor.

W/S WIPER TRANSMISSION
1972 Torino & Montego

1. Disconnect battery ground cable.
2. Remove wiper arm and blade assemblies.
3. Remove cowl screen. Screen snaps into cowl and the arm stop is integral with the screen.
4. Disconnect linkage drive arm from motor by removing retaining clip.
5. Remove pivot shaft retaining bolts and remove linkage and pivot shaft assemblies.

1971 Montego & 1971-72 Mustang & Cougar

1. Disconnect battery ground cable.
2. Remove wiper arm and blade assemblies from pivot shafts.
3. Remove cowl top left vent screen (four retaining drive pins).
4. Remove drive arm to pivot retaining clip.
5. Remove three retaining screws from each pivot and remove pivot shaft and link assembly.

1970-72 Maverick & 1971-72 Comet

Left Side:

1. Remove instrument cluster.
2. Remove wiper arm and blade.
3. Working through cluster opening, disconnect both pivot shaft links from motor drive arm by removing retaining clip.
4. Remove three pivot shaft assembly retaining bolts and remove assembly through cluster opening.

Right Side:

1. Disconnect battery ground cable and remove wiper blade and arm.
2. On air conditioned units, remove right duct assembly.
3. From under the instrument panel, disconnect first left then right pivot shaft link from motor drive arm.
4. Reaching between utility shelf and instrument panel, remove pivot shaft retaining bolts and lower assembly out from under panel.

1969-70 Cougar & Mustang

1. Remove arm and blade assemblies from pivot shafts.
2. Disconnect washer hose at "T" fitting on cowl grille.
3. Remove cowl top grille.
4. Disconnect linkage drive arm from motor output arm crankpin by removing clip.
5. Disconnect right link from right arm and pivot shaft and remove the arm and pivot shaft assembly.
6. Unfasten and remove the left arm and pivot shaft and lift out to the right: the pivot shaft and arm, left link and linkage drive arm as one assembly.

NOTE: When installing the linkage, install the left pivot shaft and linkage first.

1967-70 Montego, Comet, Fairlane, Falcon & 1970-71 Torino

1. Remove wiper arms and blades.
2. Remove cowl top grille panel.
3. Remove drive arm to pivot clip and remove pivot shaft and link assembly.
4. Reverse procedure to install.

1967-68 Cougar & Mustang

Left Side

1. Disconnect ground cable from battery.
2. Remove wiper arms and blades.
3. Unfasten heater control from instrument panel and position heater control outward.
4. Remove clip retaining link to motor drive.
5. Working through heater control opening, remove three retaining bolts and remove pivot and link out through heater control opening.
6. Reverse procedure to install, using a new gasket on pivot.

Right Side

Procedure is the same as left side except that glove box liner must be removed instead of heater control. Then work through the glove box opening to get at the pivot and link assembly.

1966 Electric Wiper

1. Remove wiper blades and arms.
2. Remove pivot shaft nut, bezel and gasket.
3. Disconnect wiper link from motor and remove link and pivot shaft.
4. To install reverse removal procedure.

W/S WIPER SWITCH

1971-72 Montego, Mustang & Cougar

1. Disconnect battery ground cable.
2. Remove wiper switch knob, bezel nut and bezel.
3. Pull out switch from under panel and disconnect plug connector from switch.

1970-72 Maverick & 1971-72 Comet

1. On air conditioned units, remove left AC duct.
2. Release control knob retaining spring by pressing in through slot in knob and pull knob from shaft.
3. Remove switch retaining nut and lower switch from under instrument panel.
4. Disconnect switch wiring and remove switch.

1968-72 Fairlane/Torino Late 1970 Falcon

1. Disconnect battery ground cable.
2. Remove switch control knob and bezel nut.
3. Unplug and remove switch.
4. Reverse procedure to install.

1967 Fairlane

1. Disconnect ground cable from battery.
2. Remove wiper switch control knobs.
3. From lower edge of instrument cluster, unfasten switch from panel (3 screws).
4. Disconnect switch wiring connectors from switch and remove switch.
5. Remove retaining screw and plastic bar and separate washer switch from wiper switch.
6. Reverse procedure to install.

1967-69 & Early 1970 Falcon

1. Disconnect ground cable from battery.
2. Remove switch knobs and unplug connectors at switch.
3. Unfasten (2 screws) and remove switch from under instrument panel.
4. Separate washer switch from wiper switch (2 screws).
5. Reverse procedure to install.

1967-70 Montego, Comet

Standard Wiper

1. Disconnect battery ground cable.
2. Remove switch knob, nut and bezel.
3. Pull switch out from instrument panel.
4. Disconnect plug connector from switch and remove switch.
5. Reverse procedure to install.

Intermittent Wipers

1. Disconnect ground cable from battery.
2. Remove set screws and remove control knob.
3. Remove bezel nut and bezel.
4. Lower switch assembly.
5. Remove three vacuum hoses from switch, disconnect plug connector and remove switch.
6. Reverse procedure to install, using color code provided on switch and hoses.

1967-70 Cougar & Mustang

1. Disconnect ground cable from battery.
2. Remove instrument cluster.
3. Remove switch from cluster (2 screws).
4. Reverse procedure to install.

1966 Comet, Falcon, Mustang

1. Disconnect battery ground cable.
2. Remove switch knob and bezel.
3. Pull switch from under instrument panel. Disconnect plug and remove switch.
4. Reverse procedure to install.

1966 Fairlane

1. Disconnect battery ground cable.
2. Remove both control knobs and disconnect washer.
3. From lower edge of cluster remove retaining screws from switches.
4. Disconnect electrical leads and remove switch assembly from instrument panel.
5. Remove screw and separate wiper and washer switches from each other including plastic bar between switches.
6. Assemble wiper and washer switches to each other including plastic bar so that when washer switch is turned on wipers will start.
7. Reverse procedure to install.

RADIO, REPLACE

NOTE: When installing radio, be sure to adjust antenna trimmer for peak performance.

1969-72 Cougar, Mustang, Maverick & 1971-72 Comet

1. Disconnect battery ground cable.
2. Pull control knobs, discs and sleeve from radio shafts.
3. Remove radio applique panel from dash.
4. Remove right and left finish panels.
5. Remove two mounting plate attaching screws.
6. Pull radio out of panel and disconnect wires.
7. Remove mounting plate and rear support from radio.
8. Reverse procedure to install.

1968-72 Fairlane, Falcon, Montego

1. Disconnect battery ground cable.
2. Pull off radio control knobs.
3. Remove radio support to instrument panel attaching screw.
4. Remove bezel nuts from radio control shafts, then lower radio and disconnect speaker, power and antenna wire from radio.
5. Reverse procedure to install.

1968 Mustang & Cougar

Without Console: Same as 1967.

With Console

1. Remove battery ground cable.
2. Unfasten right and left supports from support bracket (2 screws).
3. Remove console assembly.
4. Disconnect radio wiring and antenna lead.
5. Pull off radio control knobs.
6. Remove nuts from radio shafts and remove radio.
7. Reverse procedure to install.

1966 Mustang, 1966 Comet, 1966-67 Fairlane, Falcon

1. Disconnect battery ground cable.
2. Pull off radio knobs and remove nuts securing radio to instrument panel.
3. Disconnect antenna lead at right side of radio (at back of AM-FM radio).
4. Disconnect speaker lead.
5. Disconnect radio lead wire and dial light wire from quick disconnect.
6. Remove radio support bracket.
7. Remove radio from under instrument panel.
8. Reverse procedure to install.

1967 Cougar & Mustang

Without Console

1. Disconnect ground cable at battery.
2. Remove rear support bracket nut.
3. Remove four screws that attach bezel and radio to instrument panel.
4. Move radio rearward away from instrument panel. Disconnect antenna, speaker and power leads, and remove radio from instrument panel.
5. Reverse procedure to install.

With Console

1. Disconnect battery ground cable.
2. Remove two bolts retaining rear support bracket to instrument panel.
3. Pull off radio control knobs.
4. Remove two screws at top of retaining bezel to instrument panel.
5. Remove four nuts retaining bezel to console. Nuts are located inside console at lower and upper corners.
6. Position radio and bezel assembly away from instrument panel and disconnect wire leads.
7. Remove radio from vehicle.
8. Remove bezel retaining nuts from right and left control and remove bezel.

1967-68 Montego & Comet

1. Disconnect ground cable at battery.
2. Remove glove box.
3. Remove radio control knobs.
4. Remove radio rear support bracket retaining nut.
5. Remove radio control shaft to instrument panel retaining nuts.
6. Disconnect antenna lead-in cable, radio feed and speaker wires.
7. On A/C equipped vehicles, disconnect and remove right-hand register duct from air distribution chamber.
8. Move radio rearward and through glove box opening.

HEATER CORE REMOVAL

1972 Torino & Montego

Less Air Conditioning

Removal of the core is done the same as for previous models and is described further on.

With Air Conditioning

1. Drain engine coolant and disconnect heater hoses from core.
2. Remove glove box.

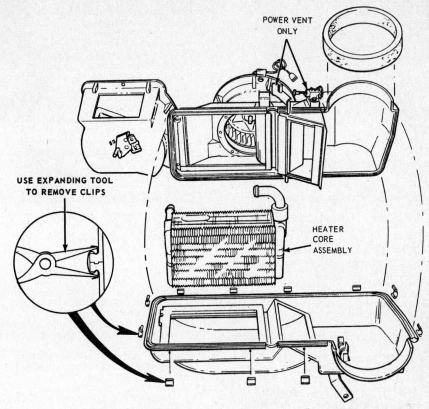

Fig. 7 Heater core removal. 1969-70 Cougar, Maverick & Mustang without air conditioner

3. Remove heater air outlet register from plenum assembly (2 snap clips).
4. Remove temperature control cable assembly mounting screw, and disconnect the end of the cable from the blend door crank arm (1 spring nut).
5. Remove the blue and red vacuum hoses from the high-low door vacuum motor; the yellow hose from the panel-defrost door motor, and the brown hose at the inline tee connector to the temperature by-pass door motor.
6. Disconnect wiring connector from resistor.
7. Remove ten screws from around flange of plenum case and remove rear case half of the plenum.
8. Remove mounting nut from heater core tube support bracket.
9. Remove heater core.

NOTE: During installation of heater core, be sure to apply body sealer around the case flanges to provide a positive seal. Also make sure core mounting gasket is properly installed.

1971-72 Mustang & Cougar

1. Drain coolant and remove heater hoses from core.
2. Remove glove box and right vent air duct assembly.
3. Disconnect control cables from heater case.
4. Remove heater case assembly (4 heater case-to-dash panel mounting stud nuts).

5. Remove heater core cover and pad and remove core from case.

1969-70 Cougar, Mustang & 1970-72 Maverick & Comet

Less Air Conditioning

1. Disconnect battery ground cable and drain cooling system.
2. Remove instrument panel pad.
3. Remove glove box liner and door.
4. Remove air distribution duct from heater.
5. Disconnect control cables from heater.
6. Disconnect wires from blower motor resistor.
7. Remove right courtesy light from underside of dash, if so equipped.
8. Remove heater support to dash panel screw.
9. Disconnect vacuum hoses and remove power vent air duct.
10. Disconnect blower motor ground wire in engine compartment.
11. Disconnect heater hoses from heater at dash.
12. In engine compartment, remove heater retaining nuts.
13. Remove instrument panel-to-cowl panel attaching screws.
14. Remove instrument panel right side brace.
15. Pull heater assembly and right side of instrument panel rearward and remove heater assembly.
16. Remove air inlet seal from heater.
17. Separate halves of heater and remove core, Fig. 7.

With Air Conditioning

1. Disconnect battery ground cable and remove air cleaner.
2. Connect gauge set to compressor valves and isolate compressor.
3. Drain cooling system and remove heat shield from expansion valve.
4. Disconnect low pressure hose and service valve from compressor.
5. Disconnect high pressure hose at quick disconnect.
6. Remove straps retaining refrigerant hoses to the dash-to-fender apron supports.
7. Disconnect heater hoses from heater core.
8. Remove upper and lower seal retainers and remove hose seal.
9. From engine side of dash, remove evaporator housing mounting nuts and blower housing mounting nut.
10. Remove instrument panel pad.
11. Remove instrument cluster.
12. Disconnect vacuum hoses from re-heat door and outside recirc door vacuum motors.
13. Disconnect vacuum hoses from water valve vacuum switch.
14. Disconnect control cable from temperature blend door.
15. Disconnect wires from thermostat switch.
16. Remove right and left air ducts from defrost plenum chamber.
17. Remove defrost plenum chamber.
18. Remove instrument panel right side brace.
19. Remove evaporator housing upper rear support bracket-to-cowl screw.
20. Remove blower housing-to-cowl screws.
21. Move blower housing to left away from evaporator housing.
22. Cover the carpet and pull drain tube from hole in floor.
23. Remove instrument panel-to-cowl screws from right side.
24. Remove instrument panel finish cover from around steering column.
25. Unfasten instrument panel from steering column support.
26. Remove instrument panel-to-cowl screws from left side.
27. Position instrument panel back and remove evaporator housing.
28. Separate halves of evaporator housing.
29. Remove water valve vacuum switch.
30. Remove temperature blend door shaft, frames and door from lower half of evaporator housing.
31. Remove heater core from evaporator lower housing and remove pads from core.
32. Reverse procedure to install.

1967-68 Cougar & Mustang

1. Remove battery ground cable and drain cooling system.
2. Disconnect heater hoses at engine.
3. Loosen screws at choke housing and position hose out.
4. Remove nuts retaining heater to dash.
5. Remove screw retaining ground wire at dash and disconnect two wires.
6. Remove glove box liner.
7. Disconnect defroster hoses, temperature control cable, defroster cable and heat control cable.
8. Remove screw retaining heater to air intake. Lower heater to floor, pulling hoses through dash.
9. Remove both hoses at heater core, take rubber boot from air intake and remove clips retaining both halves of heater together.
10. Separate both halves of heater and remove heater core.

1967-70 Fairlane, Falcon, Comet, Montego
1971 Montego & Torino

1. Drain cooling system and disconnect both heater hoses at dash.
2. Unfasten heater from dash.
3. Disconnect temperature and de-froster cables at heater.
4. Disconnect wires from resistor, and blower motor wires and clip retaining heater to defroster nozzle.
5. Remove glove box.
6. Remove bolt and nut retaining right air duct control to instrument panel.
7. Remove nuts retaining right air duct and remove duct.
8. Take heater assembly to bench. Then remove heater core cover and pad and lift out core.

1966 Mustang

1. Drain cooling system.
2. Remove glove box.
3. Disconnect three control cables.
4. Disconnect defroster hoses at pelnum chamber.
5. Disconnect heater hoses at water pump and carburetor heater.
6. Remove heater hoses from clips.
7. On V8's, remove hose from choke clip.
8. Disconnect wires at heater motor and remove ground wire-to-dash retaining screw.
9. Remove heater and motor retaining nuts from dash.
10. Disconnect fresh air inlet rubber boot, pull heater away from dash and lay assembly on the floor.
11. Separate heater housing halves, then lift out heater core. On Console models, it may be necessary to remove heater from car.

1966 Comet, Falcon, Fairlane

The heater core is mounted in the heater case in a diagonal position in the center of the case and is serviced through an opening in the back plate. With the heater assembly out of the vehicle, simply remove four screws from the cover plate and pull the core from the housing. The core is mounted in the heater housing with rubber pads on each end to insure a snug fit.

Engine Section

ENGINE, REPLACE
1966-72 Six-Cylinder

NOTE: The engine is removed from the chassis, leaving the transmission in place. First disconnect and/or remove as required wires, tubes, hoses and linkage attached to engine. Then do the following:

1. Remove hood, radiator, fan and pulley.

2. Remove starting motor.
3. On cars with manual shift transmission, remove clutch equalizer shaft and arm bracket.
4. Remove flywheel or converter housing-to-engine upper bolts through access holes in underbody.
5. Disconnect engine right and left mount at underbody bracket.
6. Remove flywheel or converter housing cover.
7. Remove flywheel or converter housing-to-engine lower bolts.
8. Support transmission and flywheel or converter housing with a jack.
9. Attach a lifting rig to engine and remove it from vehicle.

1966-72 V8-390, 427, 428, 429

NOTE: The engine is removed from the vehicle, leaving the transmission in place. First disconnect and/or remove as required wires, tubes, hose and linkage attached to engine. Then do the following:

1. Drain cooling system and crankcase.
2. Remove hood, radiator and ignition coil.
3. If air conditioned, unfasten air compressor from its mounting and position it out of the way, leaving refrigerant lines attached.
4. Unfasten and wire power steering pump to hood left hinge in a posi-

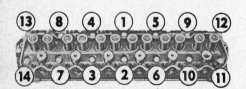

Fig. 1 Cylinder head tightening sequence. Six cylinder

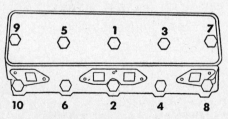

Fig. 2 Cylinder head tightening. V8 engines

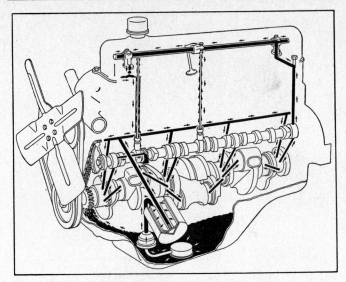

Engine oiling system for 6 cylinder engines

Engine oiling system. V8-289, 302, 351, 400

tion that will prevent oil from draining out.
5. Raise front of car.
6. Remove No. 2 crossmember-to-underbody brace on right side to provide clearance for starter removal. Remove starter and dust seal and transmission fluid filler tube bracket.
7. Remove engine intermediate support bracket-to-crossmember retaining nut on right and left engine front supports.
8. Remove converter housing cover.
9. Remove flywheel-to-converter nuts.
10. Secure converter to housing.
11. Remove converter housing-to-engine lower bolts.
12. Lower car and support transmission.
13. Remove converter housing upper bolts.
14. Remove front fender-to-upper dash braces.
15. Lift engine out of chassis.

1966-72 V8-289, 302, 351, 400

NOTE: The engine is removed from the vehicle, leaving the transmission in place. First disconnect and/or remove as required wires, tubes, hose and linkage attached to engine. Then do the following:

1. Drain cooling system and crankcase.
2. Remove oil filter, hood, radiator, fan and pulley.
3. Remove air cleaner and intake duct.
4. If air conditioned, unfasten and position air compressor out of the way.
5. Remove and position power steering pump to one side.
6. If equipped with Thermactor Exhaust Emission Control System, remove air pump air filter if it is not connected to engine.
7. Remove flywheel-to-converter housing upper bolts.
8. Raise front of car and remove starter and dust seal.
9. Disconnect engine support insulators at brackets on frame underbody.
10. Remove remaining flywheel or con-

verter housing-to-engine bolts.
11. Lower car, then support transmission.
12. Attach a lifting rig to engine and remove from vehicle.

CYLINDER HEAD, REPLACE

Tighten cylinder head bolts a little at a time in three steps in the sequence shown in the illustrations. Final tightening should be to the torque specifications listed in the *Engine Tightening* table. After tightening the bolts to specifications, *they should not be disturbed.*

1966-72 Six-Cylinder

1. Drain cooling system and remove air cleaner.
2. Unfasten exhaust pipe from manifold and pull it down.
3. Disconnect accelerator rod from carburetor.
4. Disconnect fuel inlet line at fuel filter hose, and distributor vacuum line at carburetor.
5. Disconnect coolant lines at carburetor spacer. Remove radiator upper hose at outlet housing.
6. Disconnect distributor vacuum line at distributor. Disconnect carburetor fuel inlet line at fuel pump. Remove lines as an assembly.
7. Disconnect spark plug wires at plugs and temperature sending unit wire at sending unit.
8. Remove crankcase ventilation system. Remove hoses from Thermactor system as necessary for accessability.
9. Remove valve rocker arm cover.
10. Remove rocker arm shaft assembly.
11. Remove valve push rods.

12. Remove remaining cylinder head bolts and lift off head.
13. Reverse procedure to install and tighten head bolts in the sequence shown in Fig. 1.

1966-72 V8-289, 302, 351, 400

1. Remove intake manifold and carburetor as an assembly.
2. Disconnect battery ground cable at cylinder head.
3. If left head is being removed, remove air compressor (if equipped). Also remove and wire power steering pump out of the way. If equipped with Thermactor System, disconnect hose from air manifold on left cylinder head.
4. If right head is to be removed, remove alternator mounting bracket bolt and spacer, ignition coil and air cleaner inlet duct.
5. If right head is to be removed on an engine with Thermactor System, remove air pump from bracket. Disconnect hose from air manifold.
6. Disconnect exhaust manifolds at exhaust pipes.

NOTE: On V8-351, separate the exhaust manifolds from the heads first in order to gain access to the lower row of cylinder head attaching bolts.

7. Remove rocker arm covers. If equipped with Thermactor System, remove check valve from air manifold.
8. Loosen rocker arm nuts so rocker arms can be rotated to one side. Remove push rods.
9. Remove head bolts and lift head off block.
10. Reverse removal procedure to install and tighten head bolts in the sequence shown in Fig. 2.

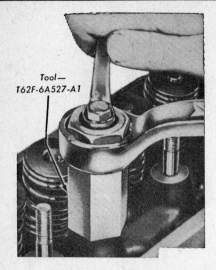

Fig. 3   Rocker arm stud removal. V8-289, 302. Threaded studs on High Performance 8-289 & H.O. V8-302

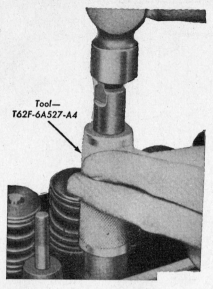

Fig. 4   Rocker arm stud installation. V8-289, 302. Threaded studs on High Performance 8-289 & H.O. V8-302

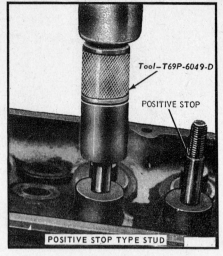

POSITIVE STOP TYPE STUD

Fig. 4A   Positive stud rocker stud installation. V8-351

1966-72 V8-390, 427, 428, 429

1. If equipped with Thermactor System, disconnect air hoses as necessary for accessability, and position them out of the way.
2. Remove intake manifold and carburetor as an assembly.
3. Remove rocker arms and push rods. Keep all parts in sequence so they can be installed in the same locations.
4. Disconnect exhaust manifolds at exhaust pipes.
5. If left head is being removed, remove ignition coil and engine identification tag, and remove power steering pump mounting bolt from right cylinder head.
6. Remove head bolts and take off head.
7. Reverse procedure to install and tighten head bolts in the sequence shown in Fig. 2.

VALVE ARRANGEMENT
Front to Rear

Sixes	E-I-I-E-I-E-E-I-E-I-E
8-289, 302 Right	I-E-I-E-I-E-I-E
8-289, 302 Left	E-I-E-I-E-I-E-I
8-351, 400 Right	I-E-I-E-I-E-I-E
8-351, 400 Left	E-I-E-I-E-I-E-I
V8-390, 427, 428	E-I-E-I-I-E-I-E
V8-429 Right	I-E-I-E-I-E-I-E
V8-429 Left	E-I-E-I-E-I-E-I

VALVE LIFT SPECS.

Engine	Year	Intake	Exhaust
6-170	1966	.348	.348
	1967	.368	.368
	1968-72	.348	.348
6-200	1966-72	.348	.348
6-250	1969-72	.368	.368
6-250[6]	1972	.380	.348
8-289	1966-67	.3684	.380
8-289[3]	1966	.4574	.4574
8-289	1968	.368	.381
8-302	1968-72	.368	.381
8-302 "H.O."	1969-71	.477	.477
8-351[4]	1969-71	.418	.448
8-351[5][1]	1970-71	.407	.407
8-351[5][1]	1972	.400	.400
8-351[5][2]	1970-71	.427	.427
8-351[5][2]	1971	.427	.453
8-351[5][2]	1972	.480	.488
8-390[3]	1966	.4809	.4809
8-390	1966	.440	.440
8-390[1]	1967	.428	.431
8-390[2]	1967	.4809	.4809
8-390[1]	1968	.427	.430
8-390[2]	1968	.440	.440
8-390[2]	1969	.481	.490
8-400	1972	.422	.427
8-427	1968-69	.481	.490
8-428	1969-70	.481	.490
8-429 "CJ"	1970-71	.515	.515
8-429 "SCJ"	1970-71	.500	.500
8-429 "BOSS"	1970	.478	.505
8-429	1972	.442	.486

[1]—Two bar. carb.   [2]—Four bar. carb.
[3]—Hi Perf. engine.
[4]—Windsor engine.
[5]—Cleveland engine.
[6]—California engine

VALVE TIMING
Intake Opens Before TDC

Engine	Year	Degrees
6-170	1966	9
	1967	7
	1968-72	9
6-200	1966-67	7
	1967-72	9
6-250	1969-72	10
	1972[6]	16
8-289	1966[4]	30
	1966-68	16
8-302	1968-72	16
8-302 "H.O."	1969	40
8-302 "BOSS"	1970-71	34
8-351[5]	1969-71	11
8-351[3][1]	1970-72	12
8-351[2][1]	1970	14
8-351[2][1]	1971-72	18
8-390	1966[4]	18
	1966-69	16
8-400	1972	17
8-427	1968-69	18
8-428	1969-70	18
8-429	1972	8
8-429 "CJ"	1970-71	32
8-429 "SCJ"	1970-71	40.5
8-429 "BOSS"	1970	40

[1]—Cleveland engine.
[2]—Four bar. carb.   [3]—Two bar. carb.
[4]—Hi Perf. engine.
[5]—Windsor engine.
[6]—California engine.

VALVES, ADJUST
Six Cylinder

The procedure used to check the valve clearance is to rotate the crankshaft with an auxiliary starter switch until the No. 1 piston is near TDC at the end of the compression stroke. At this point the following valves can be checked:

No. 1 Intake	No. 3 Exhaust
No. 1 Exhaust	No. 4 Intake
No. 2 Intake	No. 5 Exhaust

After the clearance of these valves have been checked, rotate the crankshaft until the No. 6 piston is on TDC at the end of its compression stroke (1 revolution of the crankshaft) and check the following valves:

No. 2 Exhaust	No. 5 Intake
No. 3 Intake	No. 6 Intake
No. 4 Exhaust	No. 6 Exhaust

Hydraulic Lifters With Adjustable Rocker Arms, 1966

Turn the rocker arm adjusting screw clockwise to remove all lash between push rod and rocker arm. This may be determined by rotating and/or moving the push rod with the fingers as the adjusting screw is tightened. Then tighten the adjusting screw the additional number of turns listed in the *Valve Specifications* table. This will place the hydraulic lifter at the approximate center of its travel.

NOTE: If the torque required to tighten the self-locking adjusting screw is less than 3 ft-lbs, install a new standard or a .002" oversize screw. If unable to obtain a minimum torque of 7 ft-lbs with the oversize screw, replace the rocker arm and adjusting screw assembly.

SERVICE BULLETIN

Non-Adjustable Rocker Arm:

All 6-200 engines built after 3/29/65 incorporate a new, non-adjustable rocker arm which has a spherical socket instead of an adjusting screw. In conjunction with this change, the push rod is revised to have a ball on both the upper and lower ends. The service procedure required for this revision is as follows:
1. Position cylinder to be checked at T.D.C.
2. Apply pressure on the push rod end of the rocker arm until the tappet plunger is completely bottomed.
3. Hold rocker arm in this position and check the clearance between rocker arm and valve stem.
4. If the clearance is not within limits, install the appropriate undersize or oversize push rod, which are available in .060" undersize and .060" oversize.

Mechanical Valve Lifters

Before the final lash adjustment is made, operate the engine for 30 minutes at a fast idle to stabilize engine temperatures. To set the lash accurately, use only a step-type feeler gauge. For example, to obtain the correct setting if the clearance is .019", the .018" portion of the gauge should slip between valve tip and rocker arm but the "no go" end (.020") should not.

V8-6, 289, Early 302 w/Hydraulic Lifters

1. Turn crankshaft to position No. 1 piston at TDC of the compression stroke. With the piston in this position, adjust the following valves to obtain the clearances listed in the

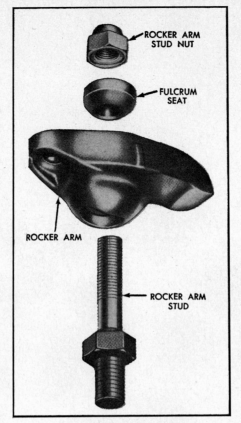

Fig. 5   Valve rocker arm and stud. High Performance V8-289 & H.O. V8-302

Valve Specifications table.

No. 1 Intake	No. 4 Exhaust
No. 1 Exhaust	No. 5 Exhaust
No. 2 Exhaust	No. 7 Intake
No. 3 Intake	No. 8 Intake

2. Turn crankshaft to position No. 6 piston on TDC of the compression stroke, and adjust the following valve clearances, using the same procedure as in Step 1.

No. 2 Intake	No. 6 Intake
No. 3 Exhaust	No. 6 Exhaust
No. 4 Intake	No. 7 Exhaust
No. 5 Intake	No. 8 Exhaust

V8-302 "BOSS", V8-429 "SCJ"

The valves in these engines use mechanical lifters which are adjusted in the conventional manner to the clearance listed in the *Valve Specifications* table.

Late V8-302 w/Hydraulic Lifters, V8-351 "Windsor" Engine

These engines incorporate a positive stop rocker arm stud and nut. Thread nut onto stud until it contacts the stud then tighten nut to 18-22 ft-lbs.

V8-351 "Cleveland" Engine V8-390, 400, 427, 428, 429 "CJ"

For these engines, a .060" longer or a .060" shorter push rod is available to provide a means of compensating for dimensional changes in the valve train.

To check the clearance, bring the piston of the cylinder being checked on top dead center of the compression stroke. Then with hydraulic lifter collapsed, check the clearance between valve stem and rocker arm. If the clearance is less than the minimum, the .060" shorter push rod should be used. If clearance is more than the maximum the .060" longer push rod should be used.

V8-429 "BOSS"

The valve clearance should be set only with the engine cold.
1. Remove rocker arm covers and position No. 1 piston at TDC of its compression stroke.
2. Torque rocker arm shaft nuts for No. 1 cylinder to specifications then adjust valve lash.
3. Rotate crankshaft 90° to bring No. 5 piston to TDC and repeat adjustment for that cylinder.
4. Proceed through the firing order (1-5-4-2-6-3-7-8) until all valves have been adjusted.

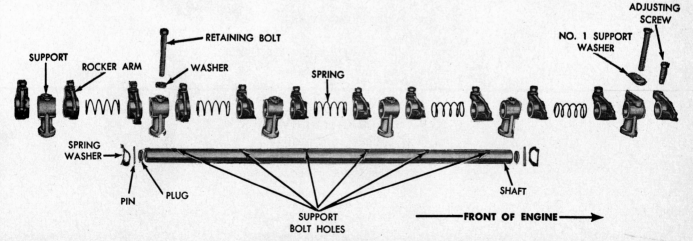

Fig. 6   Rocker arm shaft assembly. Six cylinder engines

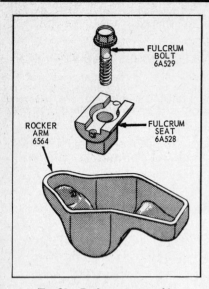

Fig. 6A   Rocker arm assembly.
V8-351 "Cleveland" engine

ROCKER ARM STUD
V8-289, 302

If necessary to replace a rocker arm stud, a rocker arm stud kit is available and contains a stud remover, Fig. 3, a stud installer, Fig. 4, and two reamers, one .003" and the other .015".

Rocker arm studs that are broken or have damaged threads may be replaced with standard studs. Loose studs in the head may be replaced with .003" or .015" oversize studs which are available for service. *The standard studs have no identification marks, whereas the .003" oversize stud has a groove around the pilot end of the stud. The .015" oversize stud has a step produced by the increased diameter of the stud approximately* $1^5/_{32}$" *from the pilot end.*

When going from a standard size stud to a .015" oversize stud, always use a .003" reamer before finish reaming with a .015" reamer.

If a stud is broken off flush with the stud boss, use an easy-out to remove the broken stud, following the instructions of the tool manufacturer.

Late V8-302 w/Hydraulic Lifters & V8-351 "Windsor" Engine

A new type positive stop rocker arm

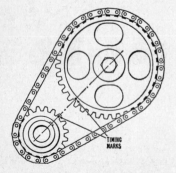

Fig. 9   Timing marks aligned for correct valve timing. Six cylinder engines

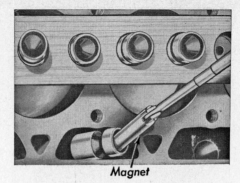

Fig. 7   Removing valve lifter with magnetic rod

stud and nut eliminates the need of adjusting valve lash.

Installation

1. Position the piston of the cylinder being worked on at TDC compression stroke.
2. Locate stud properly with tool T69P-6049D, Fig. 4A. Make sure tool bottoms on the head.
3. Lubricate rocker arm components and place rocker arm and fulcrum on the stud.
4. Thread nut onto the stud until it contacts the shoulder, then tighten nut to 18-22 ft lbs.

High Performance V8-289, 302 V8-429 Except "BOSS"

Threaded rocker arm studs are used in these engines, Fig. 5. To remove stud, remove rocker arm cover, lock nut, if used, stud nut, fulcrum seat and rocker arm. Unscrew stud from cylinder head.

Installation:

1. Apply water resistant sealer to threads.
2. Install push rod guide if used, stud and torque 60-70 ft-lbs. for V8-289, 85 ft-lbs. for V8-302, and 65-75 for V8-429.
3. Lubricate and install rocker arm, fulcrum and stud nut.
4. With engine warmed up, adjust valve lash and install lock nut where used.

VALVE GUIDES

Valve guides consist of holes bored in the cylinder head. For service the guide holes can be reamed oversize to accommodate valves with oversize stems of .003, .015 and .030".

ROCKER ARM SERVICE
6 Cylinder Engines

1. To disassemble, remove pin and spring washer from each end of rocker shaft, Fig. 6.
2. Slide rocker arms, springs and supports off the shaft, being sure to identify location of parts for reassembly.
3. If it is necessary to remove the plugs from the shaft ends, drill or pierce

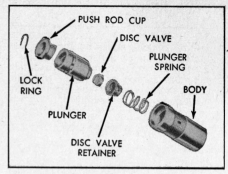

Fig. 8   Hydraulic valve lifter

the plug on one end. Then use a steel rod to knock out the plug on the opposite end. Working from the open end, knock out the remaining plug.

Assemble

1. Lubricate all parts with engine oil. Apply Lubriplate to the rocker arm pads.
2. If plugs were removed from shaft ends, use a blunt tool or large diameter pin punch and install a plug (cup side out) in each end of shaft.
3. Install spring washer and pin on one end of shaft.
4. Install rocker arms, supports and springs in order shown in Fig. 6. *Be sure oil holes in shaft are facing downward.*
5. Complete the assembly by installing remaining spring washer and pin.

V8-351 "Cleveland" Engine

These engines use stamped steel rocker arms retained by a fulcrum seat, Fig. 6A. The fulcrum seat bolts directly to the cylinder head and guides the rocker arm.

V8-390, 427, 428, 429 Except "BOSS"

See Ford-Mercury chapter.

V8-429 "BOSS"

Each rocker arm is mounted on its own

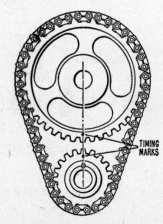

Fig. 10   Timing marks aligned for correct valve timing. V8 engines

shaft which in turn is mounted on a pedestal on the cylinder head. All valves and shafts are independent of each other.

VALVE LIFTERS, REPLACE

6 Cylinder Engines

When necessary to replace valve lifters, remove cylinder head and related parts as outlined previously. Then, using a magnet rod, Fig. 7, remove and install one lifter at a time to be sure they are placed in their original bores.

When installing, apply Lubriplate to each lifter foot and coat the remainder of lifter with oil before installation.

V8 Engines

1. Remove intake manifold.
2. Remove rocker arm covers. On engines with stud-mounted rocker arms, loosen stud nuts and rotate rocker arms to one side. On other engines, remove rocker arms and shafts.
3. Remove push rods in sequence so they can be installed in their original bores.
4. Using a magnet rod, Fig. 7, remove the lifters and place them in a numbered rack so they can be installed in their original bores. *If the lifters are stuck in their bores by excessive varnish, etc., it may be necessary to use a plier-type tool to remove them. Rotate the lifter back and forth to loosen it from the gum or varnish.*
5. The internal parts of each lifter are matched sets. Do not intermix parts. Keep the assemblies intact until they are to be cleaned, Fig. 8.

TIMING CASE COVER

NOTE: On all except V8-351 "Cleveland" engine; if necessary to replace cover oil seal, the cover and oil pan must be removed.

6 Cylinder Engines

1. Drain cooling system and crankcase.

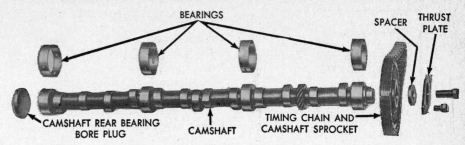

BEARINGS · SPACER · THRUST PLATE

CAMSHAFT REAR BEARING BORE PLUG · CAMSHAFT · TIMING CHAIN AND CAMSHAFT SPROCKET

Fig. 11 Camshaft and related parts. Six cylinder engines

2. Remove radiator, fan and pulley.
3. Use puller to remove damper.
4. Remove front cover and gasket.
5. Remove crankshaft oil slinger.
6. Drive seal out of cover with a pin punch and clean out recess in cover.
7. Coat a new seal with grease and drive it in until fully seated in recess. Check seal after installation to be sure spring is properly positioned in seal.
8. Reverse removal procedure to install.

V8 Engines

1967 V8-390 Engine Note

Formerly, the fuel pump was removed and positioned to one side with the tank fuel line attached. If equipped with power steering, disconnect the fuel tank line at the pump and plug the line. Then remove the fuel pump from the engine compartment.

1. To remove cover, drain cooling system and crankcase. Remove air cleaner and disconnect battery ground cable.
2. Remove water hose as necessary.
3. Remove generator support bolt at water pump, and loosen generator mounting bolts.
4. Remove fan, spacer and pulley.
5. Remove power steering drive belt (if equipped). If air conditioned, remove compressor drive belt.
6. Remove crankshaft pulley and adapter.
7. Remove fuel pump and lay it to one side with flexible fuel line attached.

8. Remove oil level dipstick tube bracket and oil filler tube bracket.
9. Remove oil pan-to-front cover bolts.
10. Remove cover and water pump as an assembly.
11. Drive out cover seal with a pin punch. Clean out recess in cover.
12. Coat a new seal with grease and drive seal in until it is fully seated in recess. Check seal after installation to be sure spring is properly positioned in seal.
13. Reverse removal procedure to install cover.

TIMING CHAIN

After removing the cover as outlined above, remove the crankshaft front oil slinger. Crank the engine until the timing marks are aligned as shown in Figs. 9 and 10. Remove camshaft sprocket retaining bolt and washer. Slide both sprockets and chain forward and remove them as an assembly.

Reverse the order of the foregoing procedure to install the chain and sprockets, being sure the timing marks are aligned.

CAMSHAFT, REPLACE

1967 V8-390 Engine Note

Follow the procedure outlined below for removing the camshaft. In addition, remove the through bolts from the insulator bracket-to-frame bracket on both engine front supports. Use a floor jack to raise the engine just enough for the camshaft to clear the center grille support.

To remove camshaft, remove cylinder head and related parts, radiator, oil pan, distributor, timing chain cover and valve lifters.

Remove timing chain and sprockets, camshaft thrust plate, and pull camshaft out of engine. If thrust plate shows signs of wear, install a new one, Figs. 11, 12.

SERVICE NOTE: On Mustang models, in addition to the above, it is necessary to remove the front bumper and grille center support bracket. Also remove the bolts from the left side of upper and lower stone shields. If necessary, loosen the bolts on the right side of the stone shields and raise the stone shields out of the way to remove the camshaft.

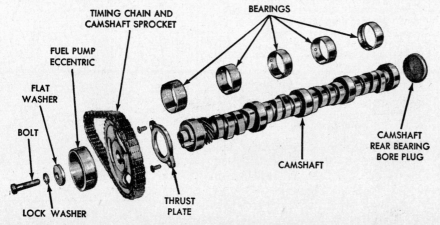

TIMING CHAIN AND CAMSHAFT SPROCKET · BEARINGS · FUEL PUMP ECCENTRIC · FLAT WASHER · BOLT · CAMSHAFT · CAMSHAFT REAR BEARING BORE PLUG · LOCK WASHER · THRUST PLATE

Fig. 12 Camshaft and related parts. V8 engines

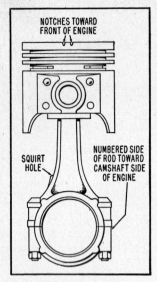

Fig. 13   Piston and rod assembly.
Six cylinder engines

PISTON & ROD ASSEMBLY

When installed, piston and rod assembly should have the notch or arrow in piston head toward front of engine with connecting rod numbers positioned as shown in Figs. 13 and 14.

SERVICE NOTE: On V8-289 engine with four-barrel carburetor two types of connecting rod bolts have been used. These bolts must be installed as shown in Fig. 16 to be properly seated and eliminate the possibility of bolt loosening and eventual failure.

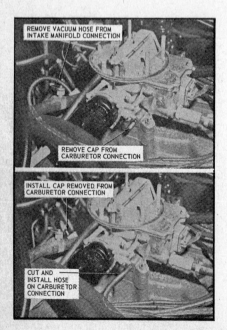

Fig. 15   Procedure for correcting front main bearing knock on 1967 V8-289

PISTONS, PINS & RINGS

Pistons and rings are furnished in standard sizes and oversizes of .020, .030 and .040". On 6-200 and V8-289 engines, .060" oversizes are also available.
Oversize pins are not furnished.

SERVICE BULLETIN

PISTON & PIN REPLACEMENT: When servicing engines using press fit piston pins, the piston and pin must be replaced as an assembly if either does not meet specifications. These components are not serviced separately for the principle reason that excess clearances are usually caused by piston wear rather than pin wear. Elimination of excess clearance by using oversize pins may result in fracture of the connecting rod.

MAIN & ROD BEARINGS

NOTE: Some High Output engines are equipped with an oil baffle tray connected to the main bearing caps. This baffle must be removed to service main and rod bearings.

Front Main Bearing Knock

1967 V8-289 Engines: This problem occurs at 800-1600 rpm under load, and is caused by a high degree of spark advance at idle provided by attachment of the distributor vacuum line to full manifold vacuum; also excessive front main bearing clearance.

To correct the trouble, it is recommended that the distributor vacuum hose be removed from the intake manifold take-off connection and attached to the connection at the base of the carburetor, Fig. 15. Reduce the length of the vacuum hose to provide direct routing to the carburetor connection, free from sharp bends or kinks. The cap removed from the carburetor fitting should be used to close the vacated connection on the manifold.

If the engine knock is not reduced to an acceptable level, then a new front main bearing must be select fitted, utilizing the available .001" or .002" undersize bearing in any combination to provide a desired operating clearance of .0005" to .0015".

Undersize main and rod bearings are furnished in standard and undersizes of

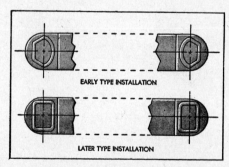

Fig. 16   Connecting rod bolt installation. V8-289 with four barrel carburetor

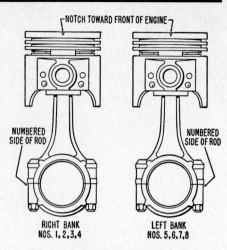

Fig. 14   Piston and rod assembly. V8s

.002, .010, .020 and .030".

SERVICE BULLETIN

UNDERSIZE CRANKSHAFTS: Crankshafts with .010" undersize rod and/or main journals are now authorized for use in all 1966-67 engines beginning 3-12-65. All assemblies containing undersize crankshafts are identified on the cylinder block date stamp pad with a letter M for .010" undersize main journals and/or a letter P for undersize crankpin (rod) journals. These crankshafts can appear in both production and service engines, and short block assemblies. Bearing clearances will remain the same as for standard crankshafts. All rod and/or main journals will be ground undersize if any one of the rod

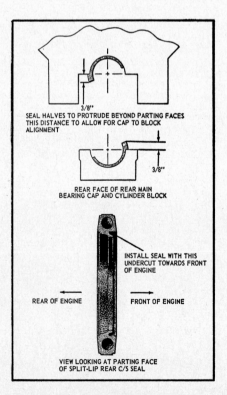

Fig. 17   New split-lip crankshaft rear seal installation

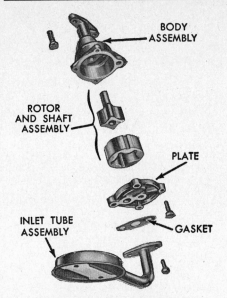

Fig. 18 Oil pump assembly. Six cylinder engines

and/or main journals are undersize. This avoids mixing of standard and undersize bearings in the same engine. Three possible combinations can exist on crankshafts with undersize bearing journals:

1. All rod journals .010″ undersize with standard main bearing journals.
2. All rod journals standard with .010″ undersize main bearing journals.
3. Both rod and main bearing journals .010″ undersize.

CRANKSHAFT OIL SEAL
Braided Type

To replace both upper and lower halves, engine and crankshaft must be removed. To replace lower half only, proceed as follows:

1. Remove oil pan and rear main bearing cap.
2. Remove seal and clean groove and cap and block mating surfaces. Preform new seal to approximate radius of cap.
3. Insert seal in cap, seating the center first and allowing seal to extend equally at both ends.
4. Using seating tool, firmly seat seal in groove and cut off ends flush with cap.
5. Apply sealer to cap at rear of the top mating surfaces. Do not apply sealer forward of the oil slinger groove.
6. Install cap and torque to specification.

Split Lip Type

1. Remove oil pan.
2. Remove rear bearing cap.
3. Loosen remaining bearing caps, allowing crankshaft to drop down about 1/32″.
4. Remove old seals from both cylinder block and rear main bearing cap. Use a brass rod to drift upper half of seal from cylinder block groove.

Rotate crankshaft while drifting to facilitate removal.

5. Carefully clean seal groove in block with a brush and solvent. Also clean seal groove in bearing cap. Remove the oil seal retaining pin from the bearing cap if so equipped. *The pin is not used with the split-lip seal.*
6. Dip seal halves in clean engine oil.
7. Carefully install upper seal half in its groove with undercut side of seal toward front of engine, Fig. 17, by rotating it on shaft journal of crankshaft until approximately 3/8″ protrudes below the parting surface. *Be sure no rubber has been shaved from outside diameter of seal by bottom edge of groove.*
8. Retighten main bearing caps and torque to specifications.
9. Install lower seal in main bearing cap with undercut side of seal toward front of engine, and allow seal to protrude about 3/8″ above parting surface to mate with upper seal upon cap installation.
10. Apply suitable sealer to parting faces of cap and block. Install cap and torque to specifications.

NOTE: If difficulty is encountered in installing the upper half of the seal in position, lightly lap (sandpaper) the side of the seal opposite the lip side using a medium grit paper. After sanding, the seal must be washed in solvent, then dipped in clean engine oil prior to installation.

OIL PAN, REPLACE
1967-72 V8-390, 427, 428, 429

1. If equipped with air conditioning, remove fan shroud from radiator and position it over fan.
2. Disconnect stabilizer bar and pull ends down.

NOTE: To allow for clearance for removal of oil pan, remove engine front support insulator-to-intermediate support bracket nuts. Install a block of wood on a floor jack and position the jack under the front leading edge of the oil pan. Raise the engine about 1 1/4″ and insert a 1″ block of wood between insulators and frame crossmember; then remove floor jack.

3. Unfasten and lower oil pan to crossmember.
4. Crank engine to obtain necessary clearance between crankshaft counterweight and rear of oil pan. Remove upper bolt and loosen lower bolt on inlet tube.
5. Position inlet tube out of the way and remove oil pan.
6. Reverse procedure to install.

1967-72 Sixes

1. Remove oil level dipstick and flywheel housing inspection cover.
2. On a Mustang, disconnect stabilizer bar and pull it downward out of the way. Remove one bolt and loosen the other on the No. 2 crossmember and lower it out of the way.
3. Remove oil pan and gasket.

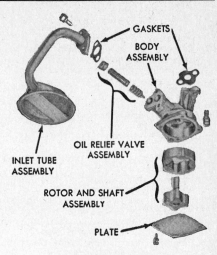

Fig. 19 Oil pump assembly. V8-289, 302

4. Reverse procedure to install.

1970-72 Mustang & Cougar V8-351 "Cleveland" Engine

1. Remove oil dipstick and drain crankcase.
2. Remove starter.
3. Remove sway bar retaining bolts and No. 2 crossmember (under engine)-to-chassis bolts.
4. Remove oil pan bolts, turn crankshaft for maximum clearance and remove oil pan.

1970-72 Fairlane & Montego V8-351 "Cleveland" Engine

1. Remove dipstick, remove fan shroud retaining bolts and position shroud over fan.
2. Raise car and drain crankcase.
3. Remove starter.
4. Disconnect and lower sway bar.
5. Remove front engine support through bolts, raise engine and place wood blocks between supports and brackets.
6. Remove oil pan bolts and lower oil pan.

1967-72 V8-289, 302, 351 "Windsor" Engine

1. Drain crankcase and remove oil level dipstick.
2. Lower stabilizer bar. On a Mustang the idler arm will also have to be lowered.
3. Remove oil pan bolts and crank engine as required to obtain clearance for removal of pan.

1966 V8-390

1. Drain crankcase and remove oil level dipstick.
2. Remove oil pan screws and lower pan to crossmember. Position crankshaft so that counterweight will clear pan.
3. Remove oil pump retaining bolts and place pump, inlet tube screen and intermediate drive shaft in oil pan.
4. Remove oil pan and pump.

All 1966 Sixes

1. Drain engine oil.
2. Remove oil level dipstick and flywheel housing lower cover.
3. On a Mustang, remove stabilizer bar.
4. Unfasten and remove oil pan.

OIL PUMP REPLACE
6 Cylinder Engines

1. Remove oil pan and related parts as directed above.
2. Unfasten and remove pump, gasket and intermediate drive shaft.
3. Prime pump by filling either the inlet or outlet port with engine oil. Rotate pump shaft to distribute oil within pump body.
4. Position intermediate drive shaft into distributor socket.
5. Position new gasket on pump housing. Insert intermediate drive shaft into oil pump.
6. Install pump and shaft as an assembly.
7. Install oil pan.

V8-289, 302, 351, 400

1. Remove oil pan as outlined above.
2. Remove pump inlet tube and screen.
3. Remove pump retaining bolts and remove pump, gasket and intermediate shaft.
4. To install, position intermediate drive shaft into distributor socket. With shaft seated in socket, stop on shaft should touch roof of crankcase. Remove shaft and position stop as necessary.
5. With new gasket on pump housing

and stop properly positioned, insert intermediate shaft into oil pump. Install pump and shaft as a unit. *Do not force pump into position if it will not seat readily. The drive shaft hex may be misaligned with distributor shaft. To align, rotate shaft into new position.*

V8-390, 427, 428, 429

1. Remove oil pan as outlined above.
2. Remove oil pump screws, oil pump and intermediate shaft.
3. Remove inlet tube and screen from pump and discard gasket.
4. Prime pump by filling either inlet or outlet port with engine oil. Rotate pump shaft to distribute oil within pump body.
5. Position new gasket on pump housing.
6. Insert intermediate drive shaft into oil pump.
7. Install pump and shaft as a unit.
8. Complete installation in reverse order of removal.

OIL PUMP REPAIRS
V8-390, 427, 428, 429

See Ford-Mercury Full Size Car chapter for an illustration and service procedure for the oil pump used on this engine.

V8-289, 302 & All Sixes

Referring to Figs. 18 and 19, disassemble pump. To remove the oil pressure relief valve, insert a self-threading sheet metal screw of the proper diameter into the oil pressure relief valve chamber cap

and pull cap out of chamber. Remove spring and plunger.

The inner rotor and shaft and the outer race are serviced as an assembly. One part should not be replaced without replacing the other.

Install the pump cover and tighten to 6-9 ft. lbs. torque.

WATER PUMP, REPLACE

Drain cooling system and disconnect radiator lower hose and heater hose at water pump. Remove drive belt, fan and pulley (also spacer on V8's). Unfasten and remove pump.

FUEL PUMP, REPLACE

1. Remove all gasket material from pump and block gasket surfaces. Apply sealer to both sides of new gasket.
2. Position gasket on pump flange and hold pump in position against its mounting surface. Make sure rocker arm is riding on camshaft eccentric.
3. Press pump tight against its mounting. Install retaining screws and tighten them alternately.
4. Connect fuel lines. Then operate engine and check for leaks.

NOTE: Before installing the pump, it is good practice to crank the engine so that the nose of the camshaft eccentric is out of the way of the fuel pump rocker arm when the pump is installed. In this way there will be the least amount of tension on the rocker arm, thereby easing installation of the pump.

Clutch and Transmission Section

NOTE: 1972 linkage adjustment information is in this section. Repair procedures on both automatic and manual shift transmissions are covered elsewhere in this manual. Procedures for removing automatic transmissions as well as linkage adjustments on 1966-71 models are included in the automatic transmission chapters. See Chapter Index.

CLUTCH PEDAL, ADJUST
1966-72

1. Disconnect clutch return spring from release lever.
2. Loosen release lever rod lock nut.
3. Move release lever rearward until release bearing lightly contacts clutch pressure plate release fingers.
4. Adjust adapter length until adapter seats in release lever pocket.
5. Insert the proper feeler gauge (see below) against back face of rod adapter, then tighten lock nut finger tight against feeler gauge.
1972	.194″
1968-71 except 8-390 engine	.136″
1968-71 8-390 engine	.178″
1966-67 Sixes	.178″
1966-67 V8s	.128″

6. Remove feeler gauge. Hold lock nut in position and tighten adapter against nut.

7. Install release spring and check for free travel of pedal which is 7/8″ to 1 1/8″.

SERVICE BULLETIN

CLUTCH ROD INTERFERENCE: High clutch pedal effort and/or binding on acceleration may exist on some 1969 Cougar and Montego V8-351 with 3 or 4 speed manual transmission due to the clutch release rod contacting the flywheel housing during acceleration. If evidence of this condition exists, grind off flywheel housing cover flush with clutch housing.

CLUTCH, REPLACE

1. Remove transmission as outlined further on.
2. Remove release lever retracting spring. Then slide release bearing and hub off release lever.
3. Remove inspection cover on 6-170 engine and flywheel housing on either engine.
4. Loosen clutch cover attaching bolts a little at a time until spring tension is relieved. *If the same cover and pressure plate is to be installed, mark the cover and flywheel so that the pressure plate can be installed in the same position.*
5. Remove cover, pressure plate and clutch disc.
6. Remove clutch release lever from housing.

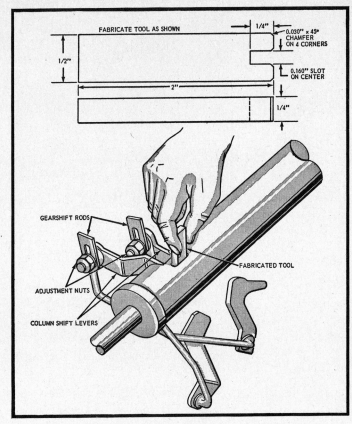

Fig. 1 Three speed shift linkage. 1966-67 Comet, Falcon, Fairlane, and Montego

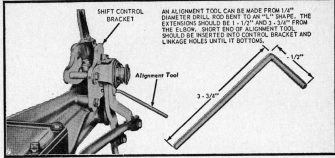

Fig. 2 Gearshift linkage. 1966-68 Cougar and Mustang three speed unit

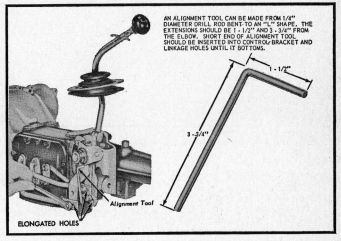

Fig. 3 Dagenham four speed shift linkage. 1966 Mustang

7. Reverse removal procedure to install the clutch and adjust the pedal as outlined previously.

THREE SPEED TRANS. REPLACE

1966-72

1. Disconnect drive shaft from rear U-joint flange.
2. Slide front of drive shaft out of extension housing. Plug extension housing opening to prevent lubricant leakage.
3. Pull speedometer cable out of extension housing.
4. Disconnect shift rods from shift levers on transmission.
5. If car has a floor shift, unfasten shift selector from extension housing (3 bolts) and allow assembly to hang by shift lever.
6. Remove two nuts attaching transmission rear support to crossmember.
7. Raise engine enough to remove weight from crossmember. Then remove crossmember.
8. Support transmission with a jack and unfasten it from flywheel housing (4 bolts).
9. Move transmission and jack rearward until input shaft is clear of flywheel housing.
10. Reverse procedure to install.

FOUR SPEED TRANS. REPLACE

1966 Dagenham Unit

1. Remove starting motor.
2. Remove drive shaft.
3. Remove back-up light switch from shift linkage control bracket.
4. Remove clutch release rod. Remove linkage return spring from clutch release lever.
5. Disconnect parking brake front cable from equalizer bar, and speedometer cable from extension housing.
6. Loosen shift linkage adjustment nuts.
7. Disconnect shift rods from shift levers.
8. Unfasten shift linkage control bracket from extension housing and allow assembly to hang by shift lever.
9. Support engine with a transmission jack and remove extension housing-to-engine rear support nuts.
10. Raise rear of engine and remove transmission crossmember from underbody.
11. Support transmission and unfasten flywheel housing from engine and engine rear plate.
12. Remove transmission from vehicle.
13. Reverse procedure to install.

1966-72 Ford Design

1. Remove drive shaft.

2. Disconnect speedometer cable from extension housing.
3. Detach shift rods from shift levers.
4. Unfasten shift linkage control bracket from extension housing and allow assembly to hang by shift lever.
5. Support engine with a jack and remove transmission rear support crossmember.
6. Support transmission with a jack and unfasten it from flywheel housing.
7. Remove transmission from vehicle.
8. Reverse procedure to install.

GEARSHIFT LINKAGE

NOTE: *If the transmission shifts hard or will not engage, the gearshift levers may need adjusting at the cross-over. Move the shift lever through all positions to see that the cross-over operation is smooth. If not, adjust as follows:*

1972 Torino & Montego Column Shift

1. Working inside car, loosen clamp nut holding gearshift tube and shaft.
2. Loosen shift rod adjusting nuts at transmission.
3. Remove plastic covers over gearshift lever assembly and insert ¼" rod.

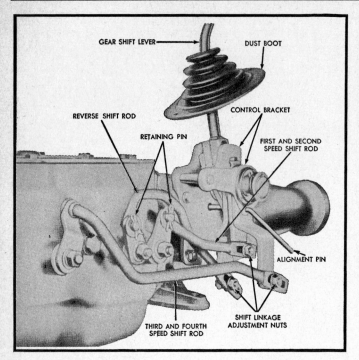

Fig. 4 Ford four speed shift linkage. 1966-68 V8s

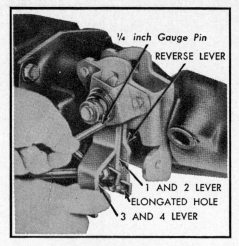

Fig. 5 Warner four speed shift linkage. 1966 V8s

4. Set gearshift lever in Neutral in the 2-3 plane and torque clamp nut inside car to 12-18 ft. lbs.
5. Set transmission levers in Neutral and insert ¼" rod in locator holes in lower end of steering column.
6. Torque shift rod adjusting nuts using care to prevent motion between the rods and the studs on transmission levers.
7. Remove alignment pins and install covers.
8. Check operation to assure smooth crossover.

1968-71 Column Shift

1. Place shift lever in neutral.
2. Loosen two gearshift rod adjustment nuts.
3. See that transmission shift levers are in neutral position.
4. Insert a ³/₁₆" diameter rod through holes in both levers and both holes in lower casting. It may be necessary to align levers to insert tool.
5. Tighten shift rod adjustment nuts.
6. Remove alignment tool and check operation of shift levers.

1966-67 Comet, Falcon & Fairlane, 3 Speed

1. Place shift lever in neutral.
2. Loosen two shift rod adjusting nuts.
3. Insert the fabricated tool shown in Fig. 1 in slot provided in lower steering column. If necessary, align levers to insert tool.
4. Tighten shift rod adjusting nuts.
5. Remove tool from slot in column.
6. Start engine and shift selector lever to each position to make sure it operates freely.

1968-72 3 Speed Floor Shift

NOTE: 1970-72 floor shift linkages incorporate a transmission lock rod. This rod must be adjusted AFTER the shift linkage has been adjusted. With shift lever in Neutral and lock rod adjustment nut loose, align hole in steering column socket casting with alignment mark and insert a .180" dia. rod. The casting must not rotate with the rod in this position. Tighten lock rod adjustment nut.

1. Loosen three shift linkage adjusting nuts. Install a ¼" diameter alignment pin through control bracket and levers, Fig. 2.
2. Tighten three linkage adjusting nuts and remove alignment pin.
3. Check gearshift lever for smooth crossover.

1966 4 Speed Mustang Six

1. Place shift lever in neutral and raise car on a hoist.
2. Insert the tool shown in Fig. 3 into alignment hole as shown. If rod will not enter, check for bellied or bent rods. If shift rods are the correct shape, check for loose lever lock nuts at rod ends.
3. Reset linkage by loosening three rod retaining lock nuts and moving levers until alignment tool will enter alignment holes.

NOTE: Make sure transmission shift levers are in neutral and reverse shift lever is in neutral detent. If there is any doubt about location of neutral position, disconnect shift rods at lock nut and rotate each forward speed shift lever through its three positions until center (neutral) detent is positively located. Move reverse shift lever

forward until positive engagement of detent is felt.

4. Install shift rods and tighten lock nuts to 15-20 ft-lbs.
5. Remove aligning tool and check operation in all positions.

1966-68 V8s 4 Speed

1. Referring to Figs. 4 and 5, loosen three shift linkage adjusting nuts. Install a ¼" diameter aligning pin through control bracket and levers as shown.

NOTE: An alignment tool can be made from ¼" rod bent to an "L" shape. The extensions should be 1½" and 3¾" from the elbow. Short end of alignment tool should be inserted into control bracket and linkage holes until it bottoms.

2. Tighten three linkage adjusting nuts, remove the aligning tool and check operation of linkage in all positions.

1969-72 4 Speed

1. Loosen shift linkage adjustment nuts. Install a ¼" dia. rod through control bracket and lever holes.
2. Disconnect reverse gear shift rod from shift lever.
3. Shift transmission into reverse.
4. Tighten 1-2 and 3-4 shift rod nuts.
5. Connect reverse shift rod to lever, shift reverse lever to neutral position and tighten nut.
6. Remove alignment tool and check operation.
7. On 1970-71 units, adjust transmission lock rod as outlined for 1970-71 three speed units.

1972 AUTO. TRANS. LINKAGE, ADJUST

NOTE: All 1972 vehicles, except Torino and Montego, use the same procedure as previous models and can be found in the front of this book. The procedure for 1972 Torino and Montego follows.

1972 Torino & Montego

1. Place selector in D tight against stop.

2. Remove nut at lower end of cable.
3. Shift manual lever at transmission into "D", second position from back of transmission.
4. Place cable end on transmission lever

stud, using care to align flats.
5. Start attaching nut, make sure selector lever has not moved from "D" position, then tighten nut to 10-15 ft. lbs.
6. Check operation in all lever positions.

Rear Axle, Propeller Shaft & Brakes

REAR AXLES

Figs. 1 and 2 illustrate the rear axle assemblies used on these cars. When necessary to overhaul either of these units, refer to the *Rear Axle Specifications* table in this chapter.

Integral Carrier Type, Fig. 1

In these axles, Fig. 1, the rear axle housing and differential carrier are cast into an integral assembly. The drive pinion assembly is mounted on two opposed tapered roller bearings. Spacers are used and are located between the front and rear bearing cones. Ring gear and pinion tooth contact is adjusted by shims between the rear bearing cone and pinion gear.

The differential carrier assembly is mounted on two opposed tapered roller bearings. The bearings are retained in the housing by removable caps. Differential bearing preload and drive gear backlash is adjusted by threaded ring nuts or sleeves located behind each differential bearing cup.

All service operations on the differential case assembly and the drive pinion assembly can be performed with the housing in the vehicle. The axle shafts and bearings can be pulled out of the housing ends. The differential assembly and then the drive pinion can be removed from the housing after the cover is removed from the rear face of the carrier casting.

Service Bulletin

All Ford Built Rear Axles: Recent manufacturing changes have eliminated the need for marking rear axle drive pinions for individual variations from nominal shim thicknesses. In the past, these pinion markings, with the aid of a shim selection table, were used as a guide to select correct shim thicknesses when a gear set or carrier assembly replacement was performed.

With the elimination of pinion markings, use of the shim selection table is no longer possible and the methods outlined below must be used.

1. Measure the thickness of the original pinion depth shim removed from the axle. Use the same thickness upon installation of the replacement carrier or drive pinion. If any further shim change is necessary, it will be indicated in the tooth pattern check.
2. If the original shim is lost, substitute a nominal shim for the original and use the tooth pattern check to determine if further shim changes are required.

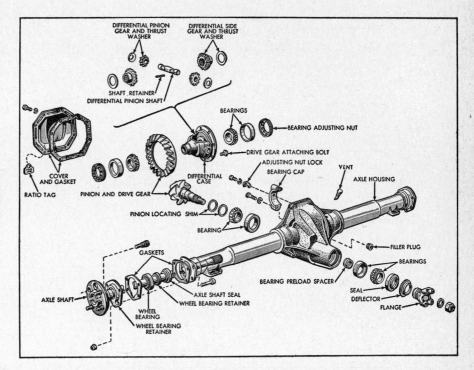

Fig. 1   Disassembled view of integral carrier type rear axle assembly

Removable Carrier Type

In these axles, Fig. 2, the drive pinion is straddle-mounted by two opposed tapered roller bearings which support the pinion shaft in front of the drive pinion gear, and a straight roller bearing that supports the pinion shaft at the rear of the pinion gear. The drive pinion is assembled in a pinion retainer that is bolted to the differential carrier. The tapered roller bearings are preloaded by a collapsible spacer between the bearings. The pinion is positioned by a shim or shims located between the drive pinion retainer and the differential carrier.

The differential is supported in the carrier by two tapered roller side bearings. These bearings are preloaded by two threaded ring nuts or sleeves between the bearings and the pedestals. The differential assembly is positioned for proper ring gear and pinion backlash by varying the adjustment of these ring nuts. The differential case houses two side gears in mesh with two pinions mounted on a pinion shaft which held in place by a pin. The side gears and pinions are backed by thrust washers.

The axle shafts are of unequal length, the left shaft being shorter than the right.

The axle shafts are mounted in sealed ball bearings which are pressed on the shafts.

Axle Shaft, Replace

1. Remove wheel assembly.
2. Remove brake drum from flange.
3. Working through hole provided in axle shaft flange, Fig. 3, remove nuts that secure wheel bearing retainer.
4. Pull axle shaft out of housing. If bearing is a tight fit in axle housing use a slide hammer-type puller, Fig. 4. *Brake carrier plate must not be dislodged. Install one nut to hold the plate in place after axle shaft is removed.*
5. If the axle shaft bearing is to be replaced, loosen the inner retainer by nicking it deeply with a chisel in several places, Fig. 5. The bearing will then slide off easily.
6. Press bearing from axle shaft.
7. Inspect machined surface of axle shaft and housing for rough spots that would affect sealing action of the oil seal. Carefully remove any burrs or rough spots.
8. Press new bearing on shaft until it seats firmly against shoulder on shaft.

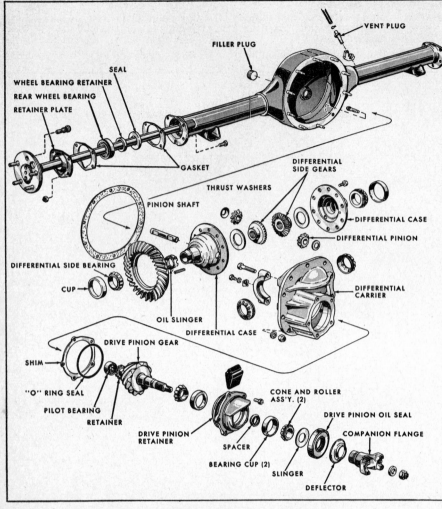

Fig. 2   Rear axle assembly with removable carrier

Fig. 3   Removing nuts from wheel bearing retainer

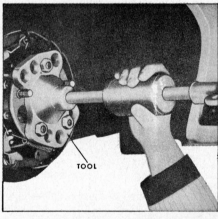

Fig. 4   Removing axle shaft with slide hammer-type puller

9. Press inner bearing retainer on shaft until it seats firmly against bearing.

10. If oil seal is to be replaced, use a hook-type tool to pull it out of housing, Fig. 6. Wipe a small amount of oil resistant sealer on outer edge of seal before it is installed, Fig. 7.

Installation

1. Place a new gasket on each side of brake carrier plate and slide axle shaft into housing. Start the splines into the differential side gear and push the shaft in until bearing bottoms in housing.

2. Install retainer and tighten nuts to 30-40 ft. lbs.

3. Install brake drum and wheel.

PROPELLER SHAFT
Remove & Replace

1. Disconnect rear U-joint from drive pinion flange.

2. Pull drive shaft toward rear of car until front U-joint yoke clears transmission extension housing and output shaft.

3. Install a suitable tool, such as a seal driver, in seal to prevent lube from leaking from transmission.

4. Before installing, check U-joints for

Fig. 5   Splitting bearing inner retainer for bearing removal

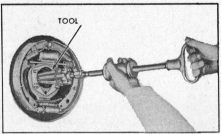

Fig. 6   Using hook-type tool to remove oil seal

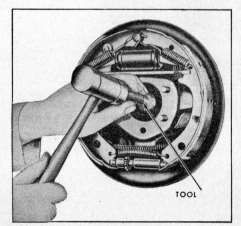

Fig. 7   Using special driver to install oil seal

freedom of movement. If a bind has resulted from misalignment after overhauling the U-joints, tap the ears of the drive shaft sharply to relieve the bind.

5. If rubber seal installed on end of transmission extension housing is damaged, install a new seal.

6. On a manual shift transmission, lubricate yoke spline with conventional transmission grease. On an automatic transmission, lubricate yoke spline with special spline grease. *This spline is sealed so that transmission fluid does not "wash" away spline lubricant.*

7. Install yoke on transmission output shaft.

8. Install U-bolts and nuts which attach U-joint to pinion flange. Tighten U-bolts evenly to prevent binding U-joint bearings.

BRAKE ADJUSTMENTS

SERVICE BULLETIN

REVISED BRAKE ADJUSTMENT PROCEDURE: Mid-year 1965 production (and later) models use a new front and rear brake backing plate which omits the adjusting slot for manual brake adjustment. The backing plates have a partially stamped knock-out slot for use ONLY when the brake drums cannot be removed in a normal manner. The open slot is then covered with a rubber plug as used in the past to prevent contamination of the brakes.

When servicing a vehicle requiring a brake adjustment, the metal knock-out

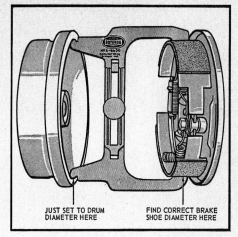

JUST SET TO DRUM DIAMETER HERE

FIND CORRECT BRAKE SHOE DIAMETER HERE

Fig. 8 Revised brake adjustment

plugs should NOT be removed. Rather the drums should be removed and brakes inspected for a malfunction.

Although the brakes are self-adjusting, an initial adjustment will be necessary after a brake repair, such as relining or replacement. The initial adjustment can be obtained by the new procedure which follows:

1. Use the brake shoe adjustment gauge shown in Fig. 8 to obtain the drum inside diameter as shown. Tighten the adjusting knob on the gauge to hold this setting.

2. Place the opposite side of the gauge over the brake shoes and adjust the shoes by turning the adjuster screw

until the gauge just slides over the linings. Rotate the gauge around the lining surface to assure proper lining diameter adjustment and clearance.

3. Install brake drum and wheel. Final adjustment is accomplished by making several firm reverse stops, using the brake pedal.

Self-Adjusting Brakes

These brakes, Figs. 9 and 10, have self-adjusting shoe mechanisms that assure correct lining-to-drum clearances at all times. The automatic adjusters operate only when the brakes are applied as the car is moving rearward or when the car comes to an uphill stop.

Although the brakes are self-adjusting, an initial adjustment in necessary after the brake shoes have been relined or replaced, or when the length of the star wheel adjuster has been changed during some other service operation.

Frequent usage of an automatic transmission forward range to halt reverse vehicle motion may prevent the automatic adjusters from functioning, thereby inducing low pedal heights. Should low pedal heights be encountered, it is recommended that numerous forward and reverse stops be made until satisfactory pedal height is obtained.

NOTE

If a low pedal condition cannot be corrected by making numerous reverse stops (provided the hydraulic system is free of air) it indicates that the self-adjusting

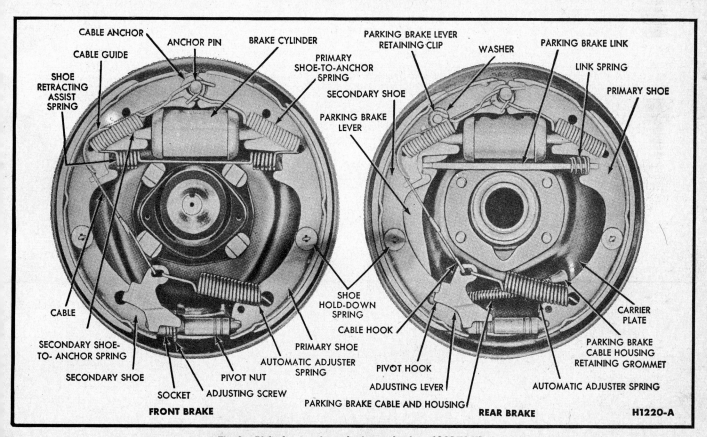

CABLE ANCHOR

CABLE GUIDE

ANCHOR PIN

BRAKE CYLINDER

PARKING BRAKE LEVER RETAINING CLIP

WASHER

PARKING BRAKE LINK

LINK SPRING

SHOE RETRACTING ASSIST SPRING

PRIMARY SHOE-TO-ANCHOR SPRING

SECONDARY SHOE

PARKING BRAKE LEVER

PRIMARY SHOE

CABLE

SECONDARY SHOE-TO-ANCHOR SPRING

SECONDARY SHOE

SOCKET

PIVOT NUT

ADJUSTING SCREW

AUTOMATIC ADJUSTER SPRING

PRIMARY SHOE

SHOE HOLD-DOWN SPRING

CABLE HOOK

PIVOT HOOK

ADJUSTING LEVER

PARKING BRAKE CABLE AND HOUSING

CARRIER PLATE

PARKING BRAKE CABLE HOUSING RETAINING GROMMET

AUTOMATIC ADJUSTER SPRING

FRONT BRAKE

REAR BRAKE

H1220-A

Fig. 9 Right front and rear brake mechanism. 1966-72 V8s

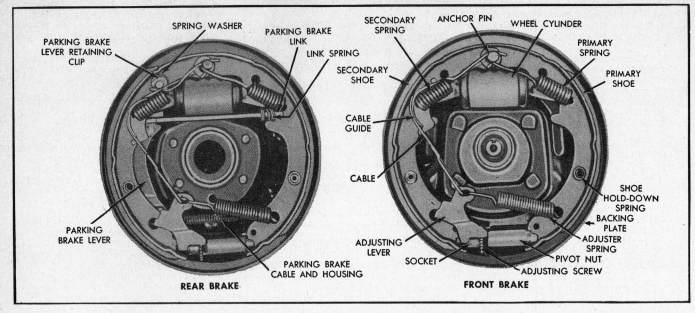

Fig. 10   Right front and rear brakes.   1966-72 Six-Cylinder models

mechanism is not functioning. Therefore, it will be necessary to remove the brake drum, clean, free up and lubricate the adjusting mechanism. Then adjust the brake, being sure the parking brake is fully released.

Adjustment

1. Remove adjusting hole cover from the brake backing plate and, from the backing plate side, turn the adjusting screw upward with a screwdriver or other suitable tool to expand the shoes until a slight drag is felt when the drum is rotated.
2. Remove the drum.
3. While holding the adjusting lever out of engagement with the adjusting screw, Fig. 11, back off the adjusting screw about ¾ turn with the fingers.

NOTE—If finger movement will not turn the screw, free it up. If this is not done, the adjusting lever will not turn during subsequent vehicle operation. Lubricate the screw with oil and coat with wheel bearing grease. Any other adjustment procedure may cause damage to the adjusting screw with consequent self-adjuster problems.

4. Install wheel and drum, and adjusting hole cover. Adjust brakes on remaining wheels in the same manner.
5. If pedal height is not satisfactory, drive the vehicle and make sufficient reverse stops until proper pedal height is obtained.

PARKING BRAKE, ADJUST

1968 Cougar & Mustang

1. Fully release parking brake.

2. Pull brake handle out to third notch from fully released position.
3. Raise vehicle and remove wheel cover.
4. Turn locking adjustment nut forward against cable guide on equalizer until there is 100 ft-lbs breakaway torque at rear wheel when turning rear wheels in direction of forward rotation with a torque wrench. This torque measurement must be made relative to the centerline of the wheel.
5. Release parking brake and make sure brake shoes return to fully released position and no drag is felt when turning rear wheels.

1968 Falcon, Fairlane, Montego; 1969-72 All

1. Fully release parking brake pedal.

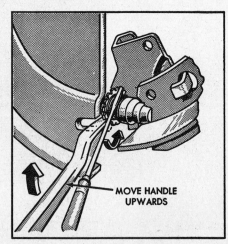

Fig. 11   Backing off brake adjustment by disengaging adjusting lever with screwdriver

2. Push parking brake pedal to first notch from fully released position.
3. Raise vehicle. Loosen equalizer lock nut and turn nut forward against cable guide on equalizer until there is 75-100 pounds tension on left rear cable or 100 ft-lbs breakaway torque when turning rear wheels in the direction of forward rotation with a torque wrench. The torque measurement must be made relative to the centerline of the wheel. Tighten lock nut.
4. Release parking brake and make sure there is no drag when turning rear wheels.

1967 Cougar & Mustang

1. Set parking brake handle at third ratchet bar notch.
2. Raise car and turn equalizer lever adjusting nut until a moderate drag is felt when turning rear wheels by hand.
3. Release parking brake and make sure that brake shoes return to fully released position.

1967 Comet, Falcon, Fairlane

With parking brake control in released position, use a spring scale to adjust cables at the parking brake clevis to obtain 22 to 27 lbs. tension in rear cables.

1966 Comet, Falcon & Fairlane

1. Fully release parking brake pedal.
2. Depress pedal one notch from its normal released position.
3. Raise car.
4. Loosen equalizer lock nut and turn adjusting nut forward against equalizer until a moderate drag is felt when turning rear wheels. Tighten lock nut.
5. Release parking brake and make sure brake shoes return to fully released position.

1966 Mustang

1. Fully release parking brake.
2. From fully released position, pull brake handle out three notches.
3. Raise the car.
4. On a Falcon, Comet or Fairlane, turn lock nut in front of equalizer several turns forward.
5. On all cars, turn adjusting nut forward against equalizer until a moderate drag is felt when turning rear wheels in direction of forward rotation.
6. When cables are properly adjusted on a Falcon, Comet or Fairlane, tighten lock nut against equalizer.
7. Release parking brake and make sure that brake shoes return to fully released position and no drag is felt when turning rear wheels.

MASTER CYLINDER, REPLACE

1967-72 Dual Cylinder

1. Working from inside vehicle below instrument panel, disconnect master cylinder push rod from brake pedal.

2. Disconnect stop light switch wires, remove hairpin retainer and slide stop light switch off brake pedal pin just far enough to clear end of pin. Then lift switch straight upward from pin.
3. Slide master cylinder push rod with nylon washers and bushings from brake pedal pin.
4. Remove brake tubes from outlet ports of master cylinder.
5. Remove lock nuts that secure master cylinder to dash panel and lift cylinder forward and upward from vehicle.
6. Reverse procedure to install.

1966

1. Remove rubber boot from rear end of master cylinder in passenger compartment.
2. Disconnect brake line from cylinder and stop light wires from switch.
3. Unfasten master cylinder from dash panel and lift cylinder out and away from push rod. Remove boot from push rod.
4. Reverse above procedure to install.
5. Fill reservoir to within $3/8''$ of the top with heavy duty brake fluid.

Then bleed hydraulic system as given in the *Hydraulic Brake System* chapter.

POWER BRAKE UNIT, REPLACE

1966-72 Comet, Cougar, Montego, Mustang & Fairlane

1. Working under instrument panel, disconnect stop light switch wires at connector.
2. Remove hairpin type retainer. Slide stop light switch off brake pedal pin just far enough for the switch outer hole to clear the pin, then lower switch away from pin.
3. Slide master cylinder push rod link and nylon washers and bushing off brake pedal pin.
4. Disconnect brake line from master cylinder.
5. Disconnect vacuum hose from booster at check valve.
6. Unfasten and remove booster and bracket assembly from dash panel, sliding push rod link out from engine side of dash panel.

Front End & Steering Section

FRONT SUSPENSION

1972 Torino & Montego

The front suspension has been redesigned with the coil spring mounted on the lower arm rather than on the upper arm as previous. All service and adjustment procedures can be found in the Ford and Mercury Full Size Model chapter in this book.

1972 Except Torino & Montego 1966-71 All

Referring to Fig. 1, each front wheel rotates on a spindle. The upper and lower ends of the spindle are attached to ball joints that are mounted to an upper and lower control arm. The upper arm pivots on a bushing and shaft assembly that is bolted to the underbody. The lower arm pivots on a bolt that is located in an underbody bracket.

A coil spring seats between the upper arm and the top of the spring housing. A double-acting shock absorber is bolted to the arm and the top of the spring housing.

Struts, which are connected between the lower control arms and the underbody, prevent the arms from moving fore and aft.

LUBRICATION

1966-72

These cars are equipped with an ex-

tended chassis lubrication feature which is made possible by a new type of special lubricant combined with special seals and bearing materials which extends the lubrication period to 36,000 miles.

SERVICE BULLETIN

Some uninformed service people recommended that conventional grease fittings be installed and that the car be lubricated every 1000 miles. This is completely unnecessary and, in fact, may cause damage to the special seals used in the lubrication points.

The use of conventional lubricants not only can do damage to the special seals but is incompatible with the special lubricant. Moreover, after the special sealing plugs have been replaced by conventional grease fittings, dirt and water can enter and cause excessive wear, rendering the units unfit for further service.

SERVICE BULLETIN

BALL JOINT LUBRICATION: The ball joint seals have been redesigned to provide improved sealing and longer life. The new seals can be damaged and sealing characteristics destroyed if excessive lubricant is used. Specifications call for the addition of only 10 grams (one level teaspoonful) of lubricant to the ball joint at each 36,000 mile interval. The initial application of 10 grams of lubricant insures forcing grease into the bearing area and still allows for three subsequent lubrications of 10 grams each without bal-

looning the seals and resultant premature failure.

For the above reasons the ball joint seals on new vehicles might appear to be collapsed and give the mistaken impression that additional lubricant is required. This is not the case and under no circumstances should more than 10 grams of grease be added to the ball joint at the 36,000 mile intervals.

SERVICE BULLETIN

STEERING LINKAGE LUBRICATION:

The steering linkage should be greased at 36,000 mile intervals. Normal breathing of the socket joints permits moisture condensation within the joint. Moisture inside the joint will cause no appreciable damage and the joint will function normally. However, if the moisture is concentrated in the bearing grease grooves and is frozen at the time of lubrication, grease cannot flow and pressure greasing may damage the joint.

Do not attempt to grease the steering linkage on these models if it has set in temperatures lower than 20 deg. above zero F. The car should be allowed to warm up in a heated garage for 30 minutes or until the joints accept lubrication.

IMPORTANT: A torch must not be used to heat joints because this quantity of heat will melt the nylon bearing within the joint.

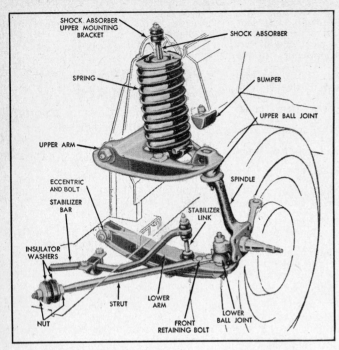

Fig. 1 Front suspension. 1972 except Torino and Montego. 1966-71 Comet, Falcon and Fairlane and 1967-71 Cougar, Montego and Mustang (Typical of earlier models)

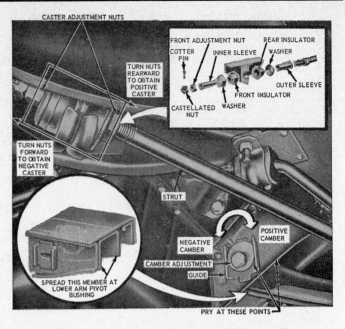

Fig. 2 Caster and camber adjustments. 1972 except Torino and Montego. 1967-71 and 1966 Comet, Falcon, Fairlane

WHEEL ALIGNMENT
1966 Comet, Falcon, Fairlane, 1967-71 & 1972 Except Torino & Montego

As shown in Fig. 2, caster is controlled by the front suspension strut. To obtain positive caster, loosen the strut rear nut and tighten the strut front nut against the bushing. To obtain negative caster, loosen the strut front nut and tighten the strut rear nut against the bushing.

Camber is controlled by the eccentric cam located at the lower arm attachment to the side rail. To adjust camber, loosen the camber adjustment bolt nut at the rear of the body bracket. Spread the body bracket at the camber adjustment bolt area just enough to permit lateral travel of the arm when the adjustment bolt is turned. Rotate the bolt and eccentric clockwise from the high position to increase camber or counterclockwise to decrease it.

1966 Mustang

Caster and camber can be adjusted by removing or installing shims between the inner shaft of the front suspension upper arm and the underbody, Fig. 3. Both adjustments can be made at the same time by loosening the nuts on the two bolts that fasten the shaft to the underbody. After the adjustments are made, torque the nuts to 65-90 ft. lbs.

Adjusting shims are available in thicknesses of 1/32" and 1/8". The 1/32" shims should be placed against the fender housing sheet metal or between the 1/8" shims.

CASTER ADJUST

The removal of shims at the front bolt or the installation of shims at the rear bolt will decrease caster angle. The removal of shims at the rear bolt or the installation of shims at the front bolt will increase caster angle. A 1/32" change of shim thickness will change the caster angle approximately 1/2 degree. The difference between the shim pack thickness at the two bolts should not exceed 1/16".

CAMBER ADJUST

The removal of equal shims at both bolts will decrease camber angle. The installation of equal shims at both bolts will increase camber angle. A 1/16" change of shim thickness at both bolts will change camber angle 1/3°. The total shim pack thickness at each bolt should not exceed 9/16".

TOE-IN, ADJUST

Check the steering wheel spoke position when the front wheels are in the straight-ahead position. If the spokes are not in the normal position, they can be adjusted while toe-in is being adjusted.

1. Loosen clamp bolts on each tie rod end sleeve.
2. Adjust toe-in. If steering wheel spokes are in their normal position, lengthen or shorten both rods equally to obtain correct toe-in. If spokes are not in normal position, make necessary rod adjustments to obtain correct toe-in and steering wheel spoke alignment.

WHEEL BEARINGS, ADJUST
1966-72

1. With wheel and drum rotating, torque adjusting nut to 17 to 25 ft-lbs to seat the bearing.
2. Back off adjusting nut 1/2 turn.
3. Then retighten it to finger tight and install nut lock and cotter pin.

WHEEL BEARINGS, REPLACE
(Disc Brakes)

1. Raise car and remove front wheels.
2. Remove caliper mounting bolts.

NOTE: It is not necessary to discon-

ADJUSTING SHIMS

Fig. 3 Caster and camber adjustment. 1966 Mustang

nect the brake lines for this operation.

3. Slide caliper off of disc, inserting a clean spacer between the shoes to hold them in their bores after the caliper is removed. Position caliper out of the way.

NOTE: Do not allow caliper to hang by brake hose.

4. Remove hub and disc assembly. Grease retainer and inner bearing can now be removed.

CHECKING BALL JOINTS FOR WEAR
Upper Ball Joint

Exc. 1972 Torino & Montego

1. Raise car on frame contact hoist or by floor jacks placed beneath underbody until wheel falls to full down position as shown in Fig. 5. This will unload upper ball joint.
2. With front wheel bearings properly adjusted, attach a dial indicator to the upper control arm and position the indicator so that its plunger rests against the inner side of the wheel rim adjacent to the upper arm ball joint.
3. Grasp tire at top and bottom and slowly move it in and out, Fig. 5. Reading on dial will indicate the amount of radial play. If reading exceeds ¼", replace the upper ball joint.

Lower Ball Joint

Exc. 1972 Torino & Montego

1. With car jacked up as directed above, grasp the lower edge of the tire and move it in and out.
2. As wheel is being moved in and out, observe lower end of spindle and lower arm.
3. Any movement between lower end of spindle and lower arm indicates ball joint wear and loss of preload. If such movement is observed, replace lower arm and/or ball joint.

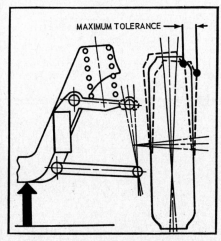

Fig. 5   Measuring upper ball joint for radial play, which should not exceed ¼"

MAXIMUM TOLERANCE

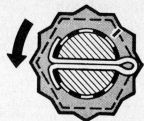

WITH DRUM AND WHEEL ROTATING, TORQUE THE ADJUSTING NUT TO 15-20 ft. lbs.

INSTALL LOCK ON NUT SO THAT CASTELLATIONS ARE ALIGNED WITH COTTER PIN HOLE.

BACK OFF NUT AND NUT LOCK ONE CASTELLATION INSTALL COTTER PIN.

Fig. 4   Front wheel bearing adjustment

NOTE: During the foregoing check, the upper ball joint will be unloaded and may move. Disregard all such movement of the upper ball joint. Also, do not mistake loose wheel bearings for a worn ball joint.

BALL JOINT, REPLACE

Exc. 1972 Torino & Montego

The ball joints are riveted to the upper and lower control arms. The upper ball joint can be replaced by removing the rivets and retaining the new ball joint to the upper control arm with bolts, nuts and washers furnished with the ball joint repair kit. The lower ball joints are furnished as an assembly with the lower control arm. When removing an upper ball joint, use a suitable pressing tool to loosen the ball joint from the spindle.

SHOCK ABSORBER, REPLACE

Exc. 1972 Torino & Montego

1. Raise hood and remove upper mounting bracket-to-spring tower retaining nuts.
2. Raise front of car and place safety stands under lower control arms.
3. Remove shock absorber lower retaining nuts and washers.
4. Lift shock absorber from spring tower.
5. Reverse procedure to install.

COIL SPRING, REPLACE
1966 Mustang

1. Raise front of car, position safety stands under frame and lower car slightly.
2. Remove wheel and shock absorber.
3. On V8s, remove carburetor air cleaner to gain access for spring compressor tool. Then compress until spring clears upper control arm.
4. Remove upper control arm shaft retaining nuts from arm, shaft and retaining bolts from underbody. *Measure and note total shim thickness at each inner shaft retaining bolt.*
5. Swing upper arm and shaft 180-deg. out to provide clearance for spring removal.

6. Remove spring compressor tool and take out spring, Fig. 6.
7. Reverse procedure to install.

1967-71 & 1972 Except Torino & Montego

1. Remove shock absorber and upper mounting bracket as an assembly.
2. Raise car on hoist and install safety stands.
3. Remove wheel, hub and drum.
4. Install a suitable spring compressor and compress spring.
5. Remove two upper-arm-to-spring tower retaining nuts and swing upper arm outward from spring.
6. Release spring compressor. Then remove spring, Fig. 6.
7. Reverse procedure to install.

STEERING GEAR, REPLACE

SERVICE BULLETIN

On some early 1966 vehicles the bottom face of the steering gear in the sector shaft seal area may not be machined. This will in no way affect the function or operation of the steering gear. It will, however, cause a reduction in clearance between the pitman arm and the steer-

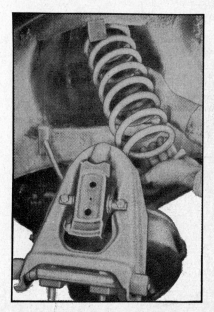

Fig. 6   Removing and installing spring

ing gear housing. It may be necessary to provide extra clearance to insert a pitman arm puller for pitman arm removal. This can be accomplished by turning the wheels completely to either stop and loosening the mesh-load adjusting screw inward until an increase in load is felt. This will allow the additional clearance for the puller.

CAUTION: Do not turn steering wheel across the center position while the adjusting screw is turned in as damage to the worm gear or ball nut may result. When the pitman arm is removed, immediately turn the mesh-load adjusting screw outward to reduce the load.

1971-72 Mustang & Cougar

These models use an integral power steering gear which replaces the linkage power steering used previously. Remove the gear assembly as follows:

1. Disconnect pressure and return lines from gear and plug openings to prevent entry of dirt.
2. Remove two bolts that secure flex coupling to the gear and to the column.
3. Raise vehicle and remove pitman arm with suitable puller.
4. If vehicle is equipped with snychro-mesh transmission, remove clutch release lever retracting spring to provide clearance to remove gear.
5. Support gear and remove three gear attaching bolts.

1968-72 With 6-200, 250 Engines

1. Remove bolt that secures flex coupling to steering shaft.
2. Remove Pitman arm with a suitable puller.
3. Remove two fuel line-to-chassis clips and position fuel line out of the way.
4. Unfasten and remove steering gear.

1968-72 With 289, 302, 351, 400 Engines

1. Remove bolt that secures flex coupling to steering shaft.
2. Remove Pitman arm with a suitable puller.
3. Remove two bolts that attach left front mount to block.
4. Raise engine ½" off mount and block in this position.
5. Unfasten and remove steering gear.

1968-72 With 390, 427, 428, 429 Engines

1. Remove two bolts that secure flex coupling to steering shaft and to steering gear.
2. Remove power cylinder bracket-to-chassis attaching bolts.
3. Remove Pitman arm with a suitable puller.
4. Disconnect and lower exhaust pipes from exhaust manifolds.
5. Unfasten steering gear. Lower gear enough to slide flex coupling off gear input shaft, then remove gear from vehicle.

1966 Mustang

1. Disconnect horn wire and turn signal wires under instrument panel. With automatic transmission, also disconnect neutral switch wires.
2. Remove steering wheel.
3. Remove steering column clamp.
4. Pull rubber seal up on steering column and move dash panel insulation out of the way.
5. Remove steering column cover plates.
6. Slide steering column from steering gear through opening in dash panel.
7. Raise car and remove clutch equalizer and bracket assembly from frame side rail and engine (if equipped).
8. On power steering cars, remove power cylinder rod from bracket to obtain clearance for removal of pitman arm.
9. Remove exhaust pipe from manifold if necessary to obtain clearance.
10. Remove pitman arm with a suitable puller.
11. Remove steering gear retaining bolts.
12. Lower car and disconnect wires from left bank spark plugs to prevent damage to them.
13. On vehicles with column shift, disconnect shift rods from transmission levers.
14. Remove brake booster if necessary.
15. Remove support rod from cowl-to-spring tower.
16. Loosen air cleaner to obtain clearance if required.
17. Lift steering gear assembly from engine compartment.
18. Reverse procedure to install.

1966-67 Comet, Falcon & Fairlane, 1967 Cougar & Mustang Less Power Steering & 390 Engine

1. Disconnect turn signal and horn wires at steering column connectors.
2. Remove steering wheel.
3. Remove column retainer from column and dash panel.
4. Remove steering column-to-instrument panel support bolts.
5. Remove upper bearing centering sleeve and spring from shaft.
6. Disconnect shift linkage from column shift arms.
7. Remove pitman arm with a suitable puller.
8. Remove clutch release arm return spring bracket (standard transmission cars).
9. Unfasten steering gear from frame and remove gear from car.
10. Reverse procedure to install.

1966 Comet & Fairlane with Power Steering

1. Remove two bolts retaining flex coupling to steering shaft.
2. Unfasten and separate power cylinder bracket from frame side rail and allow cylinder and bracket to hang.
3. Remove pitman arm with a suitable puller.
4. On standard transmission jobs, remove clutch release arm return spring bracket.
5. Unfasten and remove gear from car.
6. Reverse procedure to install.

1967 Comet & Fairlane, Cougar & Mustang with 390 Engine & Std. Steering

1. Remove pitman arm.
2. Remove steering gear-to-frame bolts, and disconnect shift rods from shift levers.
3. Disconnect horn and turn signal wires at steering column multiple connectors.
4. Remove steering wheel.
5. Remove steering column opening retainer and slide seal up on column.
6. Unfasten and lift steering column from steering shaft.
7. Disconnect master cylinder brake line from junction block.
8. Remove master cylinder and brake line from dash panel.
9. Disconnect spark plug wires from left bank and remove rocker arm cover.
10. Unfasten and remove gear housing cover from steering gear.
11. Remove gear from car by first placing gear sector shaft against fender apron. Then pull gear up and over spring tower to remove from car.
12. Reverse procedure to install.

SERVICE BULLETIN

LICKS STEERING PROBLEM: Improper steering recovery on a car with a 289 cu. in. engine and power steering can be due to the idler-arm bushing slipping inside the arm. If the steering does not return to the straight-ahead position after a turn and the car leads in the direction of the turn, the following method can be used to determine whether a loose idler arm bushing is the cause.

With the car on a hoist, set the steering wheel in the straight-ahead position, and mark the wheel hub and column as a reference. Then mark a straight line on the idler arm and bushing to establish their positions. Lower the car, start the engine, and turn the front wheels to the right until the idler arm hits the stop. Turn the wheels back to center to align the wheel hub and column markings, and check to see whether the marks on the idler arm and bushing line up.

If they are not aligned, the bushing is slipping and must be replaced.

POWER STEERING
Pump Pressure

The normal oil pressure against either steering stop with engine idling is 750 to 900 psi.

Control Valve Removal

1. Disconnect fluid fittings at control valve and drain fluid from lines by turning wheels to left and right several times.
2. Loosen clamp at right-hand end of sleeve. Remove roll pin from steering arm-to-idler arm rod through slot in sleeve.
3. Remove ball stud from sector shaft.
4. Turn wheels fully to left and unthread control valve from idler arm rod.

FORD PINTO

OLD CAR SPECIFICATIONS: For 1946-65 Tune Up and Wheel Alignment Specifications see back of book.

*This material covered only in the "Service Trade Edition" of this manual.

INDEX OF SERVICE OPERATIONS

FORD PINTO

1971-72

ENGINE & SERIAL NUMBER LOCATION: Vehicle warranty plate on rear face of left front door.

ENGINE IDENTIFICATION: Engine code is last letter in serial number on vehicle warranty plate.

Year	Engine	Engine Code
1971-72	4-98①	W
	4-122②	X

①—1600 cc engine.
②—2000 cc engine.

GENERAL ENGINE SPECIFICATIONS

Year	Engine	Carburetor	Bore and Stroke	Piston Displacement, Cubic Inches	Compression Ratio	Maximum Brake H.P. @ R.P.M.	Maximum Torque Lbs. Ft. @ R.P.M.	Normal Oil Pressure Pounds
1971	4-98①	1 Barrel	3.45 x 2.60	98①	8.4	75 @ 5000	96 @ 3000	35
	4-122②	2 Barrel	3.57 x 3.03	122②	9.0	100 @ 5600	120 @ 3600	50
1972	4-98①③	1 Barrel	3.188 x 3.056	98①	8.0	54 @ 4600	80 @ 2400	35–60
	4-122②③	2 Barrel	3.57 x 3.03	122②	8.2	86 @ 5400	103 @ 3200	35–60

①—1600 cc engine.　　②—2000 cc engine.　　③—Net Rating—as installed in vehicle.

TUNE-UP SPECIFICATIONS

OLD CAR SPECIFICATIONS: For 1946-65 Tune-Up Specifications see back of book.

★ When using a timing light, disconnect vacuum hose or tube at distributor and plug opening in hose or tube so idle speed will not be affected

Year	Engine	Spark Plug Type	Spark Plug Gap Inch	Distributor Point Gap Inch	Distributor Dwell Angle Deg.	Firing Order	Ignition Timing★ BTDC ①	Ignition Timing★ Mark	Hot Idle Speed③ Std. Trans.	Hot Idle Speed③ Auto. Trans. ②	Fuel Pump Press. Lbs.
1971	4-98	AGR-22	.030	.025	38–42	Fig. A	12°	Fig. C	800/500	—	3½–4½
	4-122	BRF-32	.025	.025	38–42	Fig. B	6°	Fig. D	750	650D	3½–4½
1972	4-98	AGR-22	.030	.025	36–40	Fig. A	12°	Fig. C	900/600	—	3½–4½
	4-122	BRF-42	.034	.025	36–40	Fig. B	6°④	Fig. D	750/500	650/500	3½–4½

①—BTDC: Before top dead center.
②—D: Drive.
③—Headlamps on Hi Beam—Air Conditioner OFF. Where two speeds are listed, lower speed indicates solenoid disconnected.
④—California vehicles with Auto. Trans. 9°.

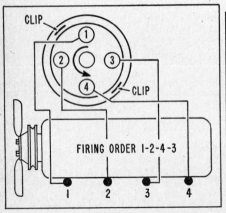

Fig. A

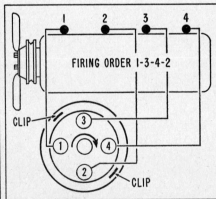

Fig. B

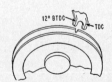

Fig. C

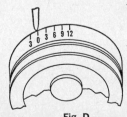

Fig. D

DISTRIBUTOR SPECIFICATIONS

★If advance is checked on vehicle, double R.P.M. and degrees advance to get crankshaft figures.

Year	Engine	Distributor Basic Part No. 12100	Breaker Gap	Dwell Angle Deg.	Breaker Arm Spring Tension	Centrifugal Advance Degrees @ R.P.M. of Distributor★ Advance Starts	Full Advance	Vacuum Advance Inches of Vacuum To Start Plunger	Max. Adv. Dist. Deg. @ Vacuum	Vacuum Retard. Max. Ret. Dist. Deg. @ Vacuum
1971	4-98①	D1FZ-B	.025	38—40	17—21	½ @ 400	14 @ 2500	5	8 @ 25	7 @ 20
	4-122②	D1FZ-A	.025	48—52	17—21	½ @ 350	11¾ @ 2500	5	7½ @ 25	4 @ 20
		D1FZ-C	.025	48—52	17—21	½ @ 350	12½ @ 2500	5	10 @ 25	4 @ 20
1972	4-98①	721F-YA	.025	36—40	17—21	½ @ 500	12 @ 2000	5	8 @ 20	7 @ 20
		721F-TA	.025	36—40	17—21	½ @ 500	12 @ 2000	5	8 @ 20	7 @ 20
	4-122②	72HF-DC	.025	36—40	17—21	½ @ 500	14 @ 2000	5	7½ @ 20	—
		72HF-FA	.025	36—40	17—21	½ @ 500	14 @ 2000	5	7½ @ 20	4 @ 20
		72HF-SC	.025	36—40	17—21	½ @ 500	15½ @ 2000	5	7½ @ 20	—

①—1600 cc engine. ②—2000 cc engine.

ALTERNATOR & REGULATOR SPECIFICATIONS

Year	Make or Model	Current Rating Amperes	Volts	Field Current @ 75°F. Amperes	Volts	Voltage Regulator Make	Voltage @ 75°F.	Contact Gap	Armature Air Gap	Field Relay Armature Air Gap	Closing Voltage @ 75°F.
1971-72	D0ZF-B	38	15	2.4	12	Autolite	13.5-15.3	—	—	—	2.0-4.2
	D0AF-G	42	15	2.9	12	Autolite	13.5-15.3	—	—	—	2.0-4.2

STARTING MOTOR SPECIFICATIONS

Year	Engine Model	Part No.	Brush Spring Tension, Ounces	No Load Test Amperes	Volts	R.P.M.	Torque Test Amperes	Volts	Torque Lbs. Ft.
1971-72	All	D1ZF-AA	40 Min.	70	—	—	460	5	9

VALVE SPECIFICATIONS

Year	Engine	Valve Lash Int.	Exh.	Valve Angles Seat	Face	Valve Spring Installed Height	Valve Spring Pressure Lbs. @ In.	Stem Clearance Intake	Exhaust	Stem Diameter, Standard Intake	Exhaust
1971	4-98	.010H	.017H	45	45	1.263	118 @ .957	.0008-.0030	.0017-.0039	.3100	.3100
	4-122	.008①	.010①	45	45	1.417	144 @ 1.059	.0015-.0025	.0015-.0025	.3149	.3149
1972	4-98	.010H	.017H	44	45	1.263	122 @ .953	.0008-.0027	.0017-.0036	.3102	.3093
	4-122	.008①	.010①	44	45	1.418	176 @ 1.02	.0008-.0025	.0018-.0035	.3162	.3152

①—Set Hot or Cold.

ENGINE TIGHTENING SPECIFICATIONS

★Torque specifications are for clean and lightly lubricated threads only. Dry or dirty threads produce increased friction which prevents accurate measurement of tightness.

Year	Engine	Spark Plugs Ft. Lbs.	Cylinder Head Bolts Ft. Lbs.	Intake Manifold Ft. Lbs.	Exhaust Manifold Ft. Lbs.	Rocker Arm Shaft Bracket Ft. Lbs.	Rocker Arm Cover Ft. Lbs.	Connecting Rod Cap Bolts Ft. Lbs.	Main Bearing Cap Bolts Ft. Lbs.	Flywheel to Crankshaft Ft. Lbs.	Vibration Damper or Pulley Ft. Lbs.
1971–72	4-98	22–28	65–70	①	②	25–30	2½–3½	30–35	65–70	50–55	24–28
	4-122	14–20	39–43	12–15	12–15	③	4–6	29–34	65–75	47–51	39–43

①—Studs 9-12 ft.-lbs., nuts 12-15 ft.-lbs., bolts 12-15 ft.-lbs.
②—Studs 9-12 ft.-lbs., nuts 15-18 ft.-lbs.
③—Rocker arm ball stud nut 32–36 ft.-lbs.

PISTONS, PINS, RINGS, CRANKSHAFT & BEARINGS

Year	Engine	Piston Clearance	Ring End Gap①		Wrist-pin Diameter	Rod Bearings		Main Bearings		Thrust on Bear. No.	Shaft End Play
			Comp.	Oil		Shaft Diameter	Bearing Clearance	Shaft Diameter	Bearing Clearance		
1971–72	4-98	.0012–.0014	.009	.009	.8119	1.9372	.004–.010	2.1257	.0004–.0024	3	.003–.011
	4-122	.0017–.0025	.0189	.016	.9475	2.0472	.004–.008	2.2441	.0006–.0019	3	.004–.008

①—Fit rings in tapered bores for clearance listed in tightest portion of ring travel.

WHEEL ALIGNMENT SPECIFICATIONS

OLD CAR SPECIFICATIONS: For 1946-65 Wheel Alignment Specifications see back of book.

Year	Model	Caster Angle, Degrees		Camber Angle, Degrees				Toe-In. Inch	Toe-Out on Turns, Deg.	
		Limits	Desired	Limits		Desired			Outer Wheel	Inner Wheel
				Left	Right	Left	Right			
1971–72	All	+1 to +2	+1½	0 to +1½	0 to +1½	+¾	+¾	3/16	18.95	20

REAR AXLE SPECIFICATIONS

Year	Model	Carrier Type	Ring Gear & Pinion Backlash Inch	Nominal Pinion Locating Shim, Inch	Pinion Bearing Preload				Differential Bearing Preload	Pinion Nut Torque Ft.-Lbs. 8
					New Bearings With Seal Inch-Lbs.	Used Bearings With Seal Inch-Lbs.	New Bearings Less Seal Inch-Lbs.	Used Bearings Less Seal Inch-Lbs.		
1971–72	All	Integral	.008–.012	.030	17–32	6–12	—	—	.003–.005	140

COOLING SYSTEM & CAPACITY DATA

Year	Model or Engine	Cooling Capacity, Qts.			Radiator Cap Relief Pressure, Lbs.		Thermo. Opening Temp.	Fuel Tank Gals.	Engine Oil Refill Qts. ①	Transmission Oil			Rear Axle Oil Pints
		No Heater	With Heater	With A/C	With A/C	No A/C				3 Speed Pints	4 Speed Pints	Auto. Trans. Qts.	
1971–72	4-98	—	6¾	6¾	12–15	12–15	188	11	3½	—	2½	—	2.2
	4-122	—	7½	7½	12–15	12–15	188	11	5	—	2½	8	2.2

①—Includes 1 qt. for filter.

BRAKE SPECIFICATIONS

Year	Model	Brake Drum Inside Diameter	Wheel Cylinder Bore Diameter			Master Cylinder Bore Diameter		
			Front Disc Brakes	Front Drum Brakes	Rear Brakes	With Disc Brakes	With Drum Brakes	With Power Brakes
1971–72	All	9.0	2.125	1.00	.7187	.9375	.9375	—

Electrical Section

DISTRIBUTOR, REPLACE

1600 cc Engine

1. Remove distributor cap and disconnect vacuum lines from distributor.
2. Scribe a mark on distributor body and the engine block indicating the position of the body in the block, and scribe another mark on the distributor body showing position of rotor.
3. Remove hold down bolt and remove distributor.

2000 cc Engine

1. Remove distributor cap and disconnect vacuum lines from distributor.
2. Rotate the engine until the timing notch in the pulley is at the specified BTC mark. Check that No. 1 cylinder is on compression stroke by removing oil filler cap. The cam lobe should be visible through the opening. The distributor rotor should now be pointing at the No. 1 cylinder mark on the distributor body.
3. Remove hold down bolt and remove distributor.

NOTE: *The hex shaft that drives the oil pump may stick in the distributor and be withdrawn from the pump.*

STARTER, REPLACE

1. Raise vehicle on hoist.
2. Disconnect starter cable from starter terminal.
3. Remove starter attaching bolts. Then move starter forward over the steering linkage and remove starter.

IGNITION SWITCH, REPLACE

1. Remove shrouding from steering column and detach and lower steering column from brake support bracket.
2. Disconnect battery ground cable.
3. Disconnect switch wiring at plug.
4. Remove two nuts that retain switch to column.
5. Remove the pin that connects switch plunger directly to actuator and remove the switch.
6. To install switch, both the locking mechanism at top of column and the switch must be in LOCK position for correct adjustment.
7. Move shift lever into Park (with automatic transmission) or Reverse (with manual transmission), turn the key to LOCK position and remove the key.

NOTE: *New switches, when received, are already pinned in LOCK position by a plastic shipping pin inserted in a locking hole on top of switch.*

8. Position the hole in the end of switch plunger to the hole in the actuator and install the connecting pin.
9. Position switch on column and install retaining nuts, but do not tighten them.
10. Move switch up and down along column to locate the mid-position of rod lash and then tighten nuts.
11. Remove the plastic or substitute locking pin, connect battery and check switch for proper start in PARK or NEUTRAL.

LIGHT SWITCH, REPLACE

1. Disconnect battery ground cable.
2. Remove instrument cluster as described further on.
3. Remove headlight switch knob and shaft assembly and retaining nut.
4. Disconnect connector plug from switch and remove switch from cluster opening.

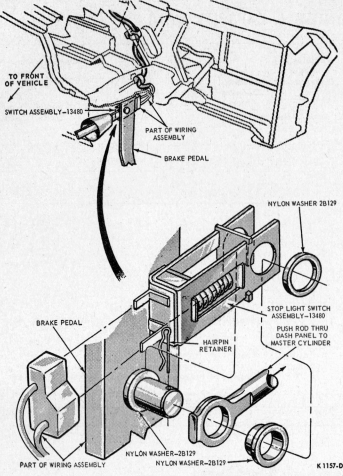

Fig. 1 Stoplight switch installation

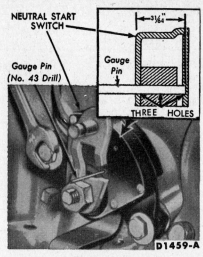

Fig. 2 Neutral safety switch adjustment

STOP LIGHT SWITCH REPLACE

1. Disconnect wires at connector.
2. Remove hairpin retainer, slide switch, push rod and nylon washers and bushing away from the pedal and remove the switch, Fig. 1.

NEUTRAL SAFETY SWITCH, REPLACE

1. Remove downshift linkage rod from transmission downshift lever.
2. Remove downshift outer lever retaining nut and lever.
3. Remove two switch attaching bolts.
4. Disconnect wire connector and remove switch.

Installation

1. Install switch on transmission and replace attaching bolts.
2. With transmission manual lever in neutral, rotate switch and install gauge pin (No. 43 drill) into gauge pin hole, Fig. 2.
3. Tighten switch attaching bolts and remove gauge pin.
4. Install outer downshift lever and attaching nut.

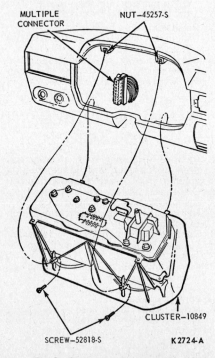

Fig. 3 Instrument cluster removal

5. Install downshift linkage rod to downshift lever.
6. Install switch wire connector and check operation of switch. The engine should start only with lever in Neutral or Park.

TURN SIGNAL SWITCH, REPLACE

1. Disconnect battery ground cable.
2. Remove horn button by pressing down and turning counterclockwise.
3. Remove steering wheel.
4. Remove turn signal switch lever by unscrewing it from column.
5. Snap off lower column shroud.
6. Remove two screws attaching upper column shroud and remove.
7. Disconnect main wiring harness from steering column connector.
8. Remove steering column wiring connector from metal retainer.
9. Remove plastic clip holding ignition and turn signal wire harnesses together to metal retainer.
10. Remove buzzer terminal from hard shell connector.
11. Remove one screw from buzzer terminal at column and three screws holding signal switch to casting.
12. Pull switch and wiring up out of column.

HORN SOUNDER

The horn button can be removed by depressing it and turning it counterclockwise.

INSTRUMENT CLUSTER

1. Disconnect battery ground cable.
2. From under instrument panel, disconnect speedometer cable.
3. Remove two retaining screws at top of cluster and swing cluster down away from panel, Fig. 3.

W/S WIPER MOTOR

1. Loosen two nuts and disconnect wiper pivot shaft and link from the motor drive arm ball.
2. Remove three motor attaching screws and lower motor away from under the left side of the instrument panel.
3. Disconnect wiper motor wires and remove motor.

W/S WIPER TRANSMISSION

1. Remove wiper arms and blades from pivot shafts.
2. Loosen two nuts retaining wiper pivot shaft and link assembly to the motor drive arm ball.
3. Remove three screws attaching each pivot shaft and remove assembly from under left side of instrument panel.

W/S WIPER SWITCH

1. Remove instrument cluster as outlined previously.
2. Insert a thin bladed screwdriver into the slot in the switch knob and depress the spring. Then pull the knob from the switch shaft.
3. Remove wiper switch bezel nut. Then unplug wires and remove switch.

RADIO, REPLACE

NOTE: When installing radio, be sure to adjust antenna trimmer for peak performance.

1. Disconnect battery ground cable.
2. Remove rear support-to-radio attaching bolt.
3. Remove four screws attaching the bezel to the instrument panel opening.
4. Pull radio out from instrument panel and disconnect speaker, power and antenna wires and remove radio.

HEATER CORE REMOVAL

Less Air Conditioning

1. Drain coolant and disconnect battery.
2. Disconnect blower motor wire at engine side of dash.
3. Disconnect heater hoses at engine block.
4. Remove four heater assembly-to-dash mounting nuts from the engine side of the dash.
5. Remove the glove box.
6. Disconnect control cables from heater. Remove mounting bracket clips and disconnect cables from door crank arms.
7. Working inside car, remove snap rivet that attaches the forward side of the defroster air duct to the plenum chamber. Move the air duct back into the defroster nozzle to disengage it from the tabs on the plenum cham-

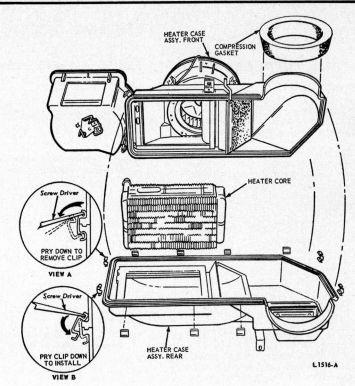

Fig. 4 Heater core removal

ber. Now, tilt the forward edge of the duct up and forward to disengage it from the nozzle and remove it from the left side of the heater assembly.
8. Remove heater case-to-instrument panel support bracket mounting screw and remove the heater case. At the same time, pull the two heater hoses in through the dash panel. Then disconnect the hoses from the heater core in the case.
9. Remove compression gasket from cowl air inlet.
10. Remove eleven clips from around the front and rear case flanges and separate the front and rear halves of the case, Fig. 4.
11. Lift heater core from front half of case.

With Air Conditioning

1. Drain engine coolant, discharge refrigerant from A/C system and disconnect battery.
2. Disconnect heater hoses from heater core tubes.
3. Disconnect expansion valve from evaporator core tubes and apply tape over each core tube to keep out foreign material.
4. Remove three evaporator housing-to-dash panel mounting stud nuts.
5. Remove glove box and right air duct.
6. Disconnect blue vacuum hose from door motor and remove A/C defrost plenum chamber.
7. Disconnect red and yellow vacuum hoses from left door motor and the white hose from the right door motor.
8. Disconnect vacuum harness multiple connector from vacuum selector valve on the control assembly.
9. Disconnect temperature control cable from door crank arm on the evaporator housing, and disconnect purple and green vacuum hoses from the adjacent water valve vacuum switch.
10. Remove screw that retains evaporator housing to cowl upper support and remove the A/C assembly rearward and away from dash panel in order to clear mounting studs.
11. Remove tape from red and yellow vacuum hoses on top of blower housing. Disengage the green, white and purple vacuum hoses from clip on top of evaporator housing.
12. Disconnect wire connectors from A/C thermostat switch on evaporator housing and from resistor on blower housing. Disconnect blower ground wire.
13. Lower evaporator and blower housing and remove from vehicle.
14. Remove rubber dash panel seal from evaporator housing.
15. Remove eleven clips that hold two halves of housing together.
16. Remove A/C thermostat switch from upper housing.
17. Remove evaporator core from upper housing.
18. Remove temperature blend door upper frame.
19. Remove retaining clip from temperature door crank arm, slide crank arm out of door and lower housing and remove the door.
20. Remove temperature blend door lower frame.
21. Remove heater core from lower housing.

Engine Section

ENGINE, REPLACE

1600 cc Engine

1. Remove hood and disconnect battery lead and ground wire.
2. Drain coolant, disconnect radiator hoses at the engine and remove the radiator.
3. Disconnect hot air pipe at air cleaner and remove air cleaner.
4. Disconnect heater hoses from water pump and intake manifold.
5. Disconnect accelerator linkage from carburetor.
6. Disconnect temperature gauge and oil pressure gauge sender unit leads and alternator leads.
7. Disconnect exhaust pipe from manifold and remove hot air pipes from manifold, where applicable.
8. Disconnect fuel intake pipe from pump.
9. Disconnect distributor leads from coil, leads from spark plugs and remove distributor cap.
10. Jack up front of car and support with stands.
11. Remove starter motor, clutch housing lower bolts and remove the cover.
12. Remove stands and jack from under car.
13. Remove clutch housing to engine bolts.
14. Install suitable lifting bracket to engine and support engine with hoist.
15. Disconnect engine mounts from crossmember.
16. Support transmission and pull engine forward off main drive gear and lift from engine compartment.

2000 cc Engine

1. Drain coolant from radiator and oil from crankcase.
2. Raise hood and secure in vertical position.
3. Remove air cleaner and exhaust manifold shroud.
4. Disconnect battery ground cable.
5. Remove radiator hoses and remove radiator and fan.
6. Disconnect heater hoses from water pump and carburetor choke fitting.
7. Disconnect wires from alternator and starter and disconnect accelerator cable from carburetor. On A/C vehicles, remove compressor from bracket and position it out of way with lines attached.
8. Disconnect flex fuel line from tank line and plug tank line.
9. Disconnect primary wire at coil and disconnect oil pressure and temperature sending unit wires at sending units.
10. Remove starter and raise vehicle to remove the flywheel or converter housing upper attaching bolts.
11. Disconnect inlet pipe at exhaust manifold. Disconnect engine mounts at underbody bracket and remove flywheel or converter housing cover.
12. On vehicle with manual shift, remove flywheel housing lower attaching bolts.
13. On vehicle with automatic transmission, disconnect converter from

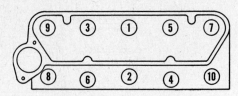

Fig. 1   Cylinder head tightening sequence. 1600 cc engine

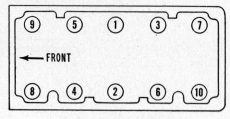

Fig. 2   Cylinder head tightening sequence. 2000 cc engine

flywheel and remove converter housing lower attaching bolts.
14. Lower vehicle and support transmission and flywheel or converter housing with a jack.
15. Attach engine lifting hooks to brackets and carefully lift engine out of engine compartment.

CYLINDER HEAD, REPLACE

1600 cc Engine

1. Disconnect hoses at air cleaner and remove air cleaner.
2. Disconnect fuel lines at pump and carburetor.
3. Drain coolant and disconnect spark plug leads.
4. Disconnect heater and vacuum hoses at intake manifold and at choke housing.
5. Disconnect lead from temperature gauge sender unit.
6. Detach exhaust pipe and move clear of cylinder head.
7. Disconnect throttle linkage and distributor vacuum pipe from carburetor.
8. Remove thermostat housing, pull to one side and remove thermostat.
9. Remove rocker cover and gasket.
10. Remove rocker arm shaft bolts evenly and lift off rocker shaft assembly.
11. Lift out push rods and keep them in their correct order for installation.
12. Remove cylinder head bolts and lift off cylinder head.
13. Reverse procedure to install and tighten bolts in sequence shown in Fig. 1.

2000 cc Engine

1. Drain cooling system and remove air cleaner and rocker arm cover.

2. Remove exhaust manifold and remove intake manifold, carburetor and decel valve as an assembly.
3. Remove camshaft drive belt cover.
4. Loosen drive belt tensioner and remove drive belt.
5. Remove water outlet elbow from head.
6. Remove cylinder head attaching bolts.
7. Lift head and camshaft assembly from engine.
8. Reverse procedure to install and tighten bolts in sequence shown in Fig. 2.

VALVE ARRANGEMENT

Front to Rear

1600 cc Engine .... E-I-I-E-E-I-I-E
2000 cc Engine .... E-I-E-I-E-I-E-I

VALVE LIFT SPECS.

Engine	Year	Intake	Exhaust
1600 cc	1971	.2967	.3199
	1972	.3247	.3351
2000 cc	1971-72	.3993	.3993

VALVE TIMING

Intake Opens Before TDC

Engine	Year	Degrees
1600 cc	1971-72	17
2000 cc	1971	18
	1972	24

VALVES, ADJUST

1600 cc Engine

1. Start engine and allow it to idle for 20 minutes.
2. Turn engine off and remove air cleaner and wires from spark plugs.
3. Pull rubber grommet from bracket on rocker cover and lay wires over heater hose.
4. Remove screw retaining throttle cable to rocker cover.
5. Disconnect throttle cable link from ball stud and move cable out of way.
6. Pry linkage out of carburetor arm.
7. Unfasten and remove rocker cover being careful not to lose throttle rod retaining spring.
8. Rotate crankshaft clockwise by hand until number 1 valve is completely depressed and adjust valves 3 and 8. Valves are numbered from 1 to 8 (front to rear). Consult Fig. 3 and continue through the sequence shown until all valves are adjusted.

2000 cc Engine

1. If there is a clamp between heat shroud pipe and air cleaner duct and valve assembly, loosen the clamp.
2. Disconnect crankcase ventilation hose and carbon cannister hose at air cleaner.
3. Remove wing nuts and unsnap wire clips on air cleaner cover and lift air

4. Remove screws (11 mm) from rocker cover.
5. Remove spark plug wires from retainer and move out of way.
6. Remove rocker cover.
7. Rotate the crankshaft clockwise by hand until the high point of the number 1 cam lobe is pointing down. Check clearances on valves 6 and 7. Consult Fig. 4 and continue on through sequence until all valves are adjusted.

VALVE GUIDES

Valve guides consist of holes bored in the cylinder head. For service the guides can be reamed oversize to accommodate valves with oversize stems of .003, .015 and .030".

ROCKER ARM SERVICE

1600 cc Engine

1. Remove rocker arm cover.
2. Remove rocker shaft attaching bolts and lift off rocker shaft assembly.
3. Remove cotter pin from one end of shaft and slip flat washer, crimped washer and second flat washer off the shaft. The rocker arm shaft supports, rocker arms and springs can now be removed.
4. Remove plugs from shaft ends by drilling a hole in one plug. Insert a long rod through the drill plug and knock the opposite plug out of the shaft. Remove drilled plug in same manner.
5. To assemble, refit new plugs in ends of shaft. *The bolt hole in the rocker arm shaft support must be on the same side as the adjusting screw in the rocker arm. The rocker arms are right and left handed, the rocker pads being inclined towards the supports.* Install cotter pins with heads upwards and bend over the legs to secure.

1600 cc Engine – Set Hot

Valve Depressed	Valves to Adjust to .010	.017
no. 1	no. 3	no. 8
no. 2	no. 7	no. 5
no. 3	no. 6	no. 1
no. 5	no. 2	no. 4

Fig. 3   Valve adjustment table. 1600 cc engine

2000 cc Engine – Set at Any Temperature

Valve Depressed	Valves to Adjust to .008	.010
no. 1	no. 6	no. 7
no. 2	no. 8	no. 3
no. 3	no. 2	no. 5
no. 6	no. 4	no. 1

Fig. 4   Valve adjustment table. 2000 cc engine

2000 cc Engine

1. Remove air cleaner.
2. Remove rocker arm cover.
3. Rotate crankshaft as required to place the low side of the camshaft lobe next to the rocker arm that is being replaced.
4. Remove the rocker arm retaining spring.
5. Depress the valve spring with Tool T71P6565-A just enough to remove the rocker arm.

VALVES, GRIND

NOTE: The intake valves on the 1600 cc engine have aluminized faces. Under no conditions should the faces of aluminized valves be ground or lapped in as this will remove the coating and reduce the valves' wear and heat resistant properties. If valve faces are worn or pitted it will be necessary to install new valves and to resurface the valve seats or alternatively lap the seats using dummy valves. The exhaust valves may be lapped in or the faces ground as required.

VALVE LIFTERS, REPLACE

1600 cc Engine—The chilled cast iron tappets can only be removed from the engine after the camshaft has been removed. See "Camshaft, Replace" further on in this section.

TIMING CASE COVER

1600 cc Engine

1. Drain coolant and disconnect radiator hoses at engine.
2. Remove radiator assembly.
3. Remove fan belt and then remove fan and water pump pulley.
4. Remove water pump.
5. Remove crankshaft pulley with suitable puller.
6. Remove the front cover. When replacing cover, install a new oil seal as this seal can only be replaced with the cover removed.

2000 cc Engine

It is not necessary to remove the front cover to replace the crankshaft oil seal. Proceed as follows:
1. Remove alternator belt.
2. Remove crankshaft pulley bolt and slide pulley off shaft.
3. Remove camshaft drive belt and slide sprocket and belt guide off the crankshaft. If sprocket cannot be slid off shaft use a puller.
4. Install tool T71P-6150A over end of crankshaft and remove seal, Fig. 5.
5. Install a new seal with tool T71P-6150B, Fig. 6.

TIMING CHAIN/BELT

1600 cc Engine

The timing chain can be replaced after removing the front cover as follows:
1. Remove the crankshaft oil slinger.
2. Remove the camshaft sprocket and disconnect timing chain. When replacing chain, be sure to align marks when the sprocket is fitted, Fig. 7.

2000 cc Engine

1. Place crankshaft on TDC.
2. Remove the three camshaft drive belt cover screws and remove cover.
3. Loosen camshaft drive belt tensioner adjustment bolt, Fig. 8 and force the tensioner toward the exhaust manifold side of engine to relax belt tension, then tighten the bolt.
4. Lift the belt off the sprockets.

NOTE: Do not rotate the crankshaft or the camshaft after the belt is removed. Rotating either one will impair valve timing.

5. To install, make sure timing marks are aligned as in Fig. 8 and place the belt over the sprockets.
6. Loosen the tensioner adjustment bolt to place tension on the belt.

SEAL

Tool T71P-6150-A

A3423-A

Fig. 5   Removing crankshaft oil seal. 2000 cc engine

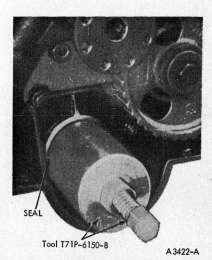

SEAL

Tool T71P-6150-B

A3422-A

Fig. 6   Installing crankshaft oil seal. 2000 cc engine

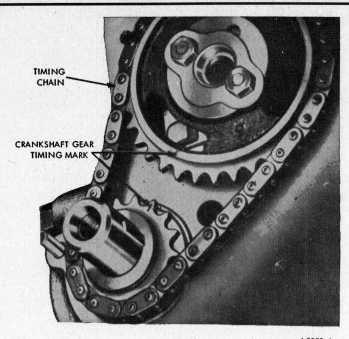

Fig. 7 Valve timing marks. 1600 cc engine

7. Rotate the crankshaft two complete turns to place the timing marks in the proper position and to remove all slack from the belt. Torque the adjustment bolt and the pivot bolt.
8. Position camshaft drive belt cover and install screws.
9. Start engine and check ignition timing and adjust as required.

CAMSHAFT, REPLACE

1600 cc Engine

1. Remove engine as previously described.
2. With engine mounted on a stand, disconnect fuel line at pump.
3. Loosen alternator belt and remove belt.

4. Remove fan and water pump pulley.
5. Remove oil and fuel pumps from cylinder block.
6. Remove distributor.
7. Remove rocker arm cover and remove rocker arm shaft assembly.
8. Withdraw push rods from block and keep them in order for installation.
9. Invert engine on stand and remove the oil pan.
10. Remove dipstick, crankshaft pulley, front cover and oil slinger.
11. Remove timing chain tensioner and remove camshaft sprocket and chain.
12. With engine inverted, remove camshaft thrust plate and withdraw camshaft.

2000 cc Engine

After removal of cylinder head, proceed as follows:
1. Remove rocker arms.
2. Remove camshaft gear bolt and washer, and slide the gear and the belt guide plate off the shaft.
3. Remove camshaft thrust plate from rear of head and carefully slide camshaft from the rear of the head.

PISTON & ROD, ASSEMBLE

1600 cc Engine

Assemble the rod to the piston with the Front mark on the rod on the same side of the assembly as the arrow in the piston crown.

2000 cc Engine

Assemble the piston to the rod with the oil squirt hole in the rod positioned to the right side of the engine. The arrow on the piston must face forward.

PISTONS, PINS & RINGS

1600 cc Engine

Oversize pistons and rings are available in .0015, .0025 and .0030". Oversize pins are not available.

2000 cc Engine

Oversize pistons and rings are available in .0020 and .0040". Oversize pins are not available.

MAIN & ROD BEARINGS

Undersize main bearings are available in .010, .020 and .030". Rod bearing undersizes are available in .010, .020, .030 and .040" on the 1600 cc engine. Only .010 and .020" undersizes are available on the 2000 cc engine.

CRANKSHAFT OIL SEAL

1600 cc Engine

With the engine removed and mounted on a work stand, proceed as follows:
1. Remove the pressure plate bolts evenly and remove the pressure plate and clutch disc.
2. Remove the flywheel.

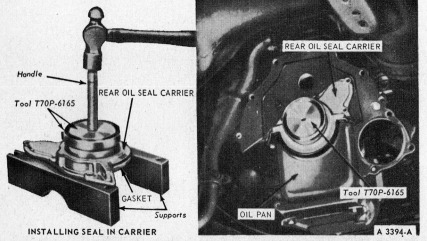

Fig. 9 Installing crankshaft rear oil seal. 1600 cc engine

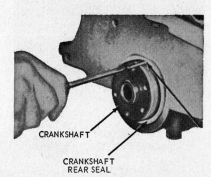

Fig. 10 Removing crankshaft rear oil seal. 2000 cc engine

6. Remove three bolts and remove starter motor.
7. Remove left bottom bolt from lower rear cover and remove cover.
8. Unfasten and remove the oil pan.

2000 cc Engine

1. Drain crankcase and remove oil dipstick and flywheel inspection cover.
2. Disconnect steering cable from rack and pinion.
3. Disconnect rack and pinion from crossmember and move it forward to provide clearance.
4. Unfasten and remove the oil pan.

OIL PUMP, REPLACE

The oil pump used on the 1600 cc engine may be one of two different types, an eccentric bi-rotor or a sliding vane type, Figs. 12 and 13. The pumps are directly interchangeable, differing only in internal design.

The oil pump on 2000 cc, Fig. 14, engines is easily removed after removal of the pan. It is not necessary to remove the pan on 1600 cc engines.

OIL PUMP REPAIRS

1600 cc Engine

1. On the bi-rotor type pump, remove filter body and element and extract sealing ring from the groove.
2. Remove end plate and withdraw O ring from groove in body.
3. Check clearance between lobes of inner and outer rotors. This should not exceed .006″. Rotors are supplied only in a matched pair.
4. Check clearance between outer rotor and the housing. This should not exceed .010″.
5. Place a straightedge across face of pump body. Clearance between face of rotors and straightedge should not exceed .005″.
6. If necessary to replace rotor or drive shaft, remove outer rotor and then drive out retaining pin securing the skew gear to drive shaft and pull off the gear.
7. Withdraw inner rotor and drive shaft

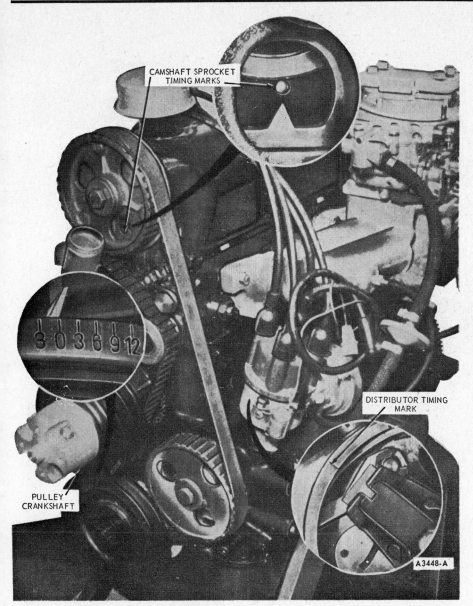

Fig. 8   Timing marks. 2000 cc engine

3. Remove the oil pan and gaskets.
4. Remove the rear oil seal carrier and use tool T70P-6165 to remove and install a new seal, Fig. 9.

2000 cc Engine

1. Remove transmission, clutch and flywheel or the automatic transmission, converter and flywheel.
2. Remove crankshaft rear seal with a sheet metal screw as shown in Fig. 10.
3. Install new seal with tool T71P-6701A as shown in Fig. 11.

OIL PAN, REPLACE

1600 cc Engine

1. Drain crankcase and remove oil dipstick.
2. Disconnect battery ground cable.
3. Disconnect throttle linkage from carburetor.
4. Disconnect steering cable from rack and pinion.
5. Disconnect rack and pinion from crossmember and move it forward to provide clearance for oil pan.

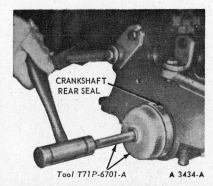

Fig. 11   Installing crankshaft rear oil seal. 2000 cc engine

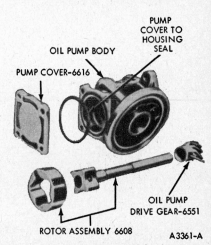

Fig. 12   Eccentric Bi-Rotor type oil pump. 1600 cc engine

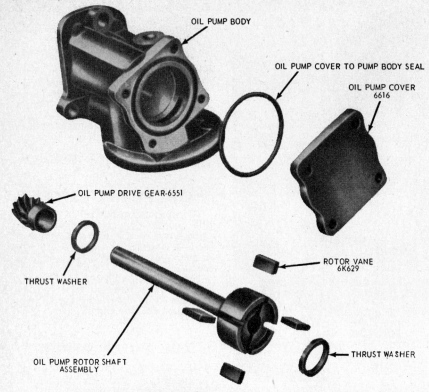

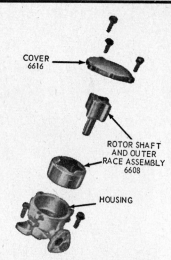

OIL PUMP BODY

OIL PUMP COVER TO PUMP BODY SEAL

OIL PUMP COVER
6616

OIL PUMP DRIVE GEAR-6551

THRUST WASHER

ROTOR VANE
6K629

OIL PUMP ROTOR SHAFT
ASSEMBLY

THRUST WASHER

COVER
6616

ROTOR SHAFT
AND OUTER
RACE ASSEMBLY
6608

HOUSING

Fig. 14   Oil pump assembly. 2000 cc engine

Fig. 13   Sliding vane type oil pump. 1600 cc engine

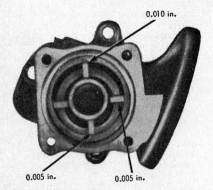

0.010 in.

0.005 in.   0.005 in.

Fig. 16   Checking vane and rotor clearances. 1600 cc engine vane pump

On the sliding vane type pump, if clearances exceed those shown in Figs. 15 and 16, it will be necessary to rebuild or replace the pump.

WATER PUMP, REPLACE

1. Drain cooling system and disconnect heater hose and radiator lower hose from the pump.
2. Loosen alternator and remove the belt.
3. Remove the fan, spacer and pulley.
4. On 2000 cc engine, remove the camshaft drive belt cover.
5. Unfasten and remove the pump.

FUEL PUMP, REPLACE

1. Disconnect inlet and outlet lines at pump.
2. Unfasten and remove the fuel pump.
3. On 2000 cc engine, remove the actuator rod.

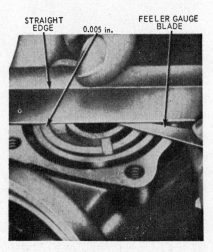

STRAIGHT
EDGE   0.005 in.   FEELER GAUGE
BLADE

Fig. 15   Checking vane and rotor end-float. 1600 cc engine vane pump

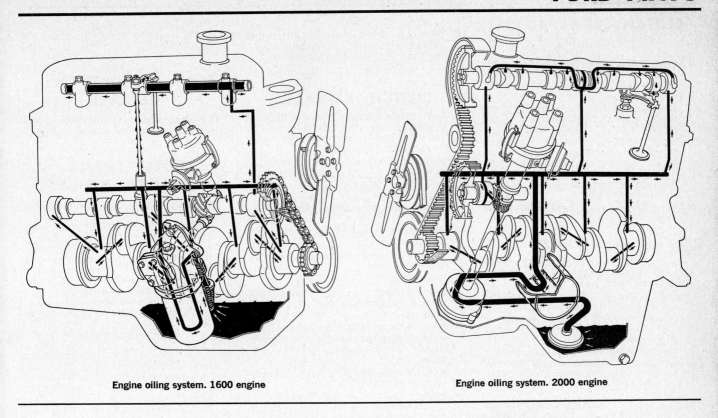

Engine oiling system. 1600 engine

Engine oiling system. 2000 engine

Clutch & Transmission Section

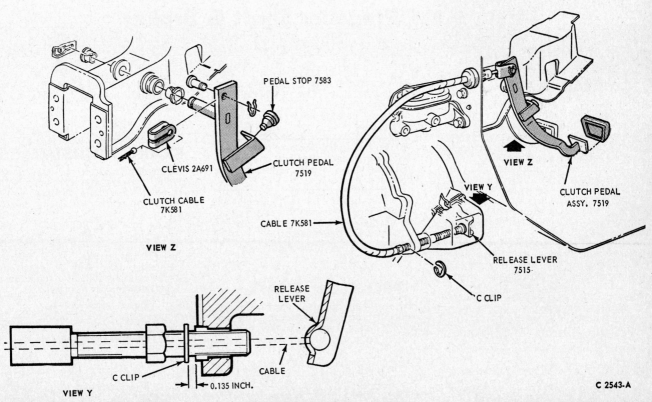

PEDAL STOP 7583

CLEVIS 2A691

CLUTCH PEDAL 7519

CLUTCH CABLE 7K581

VIEW Z

CABLE 7K581

VIEW Y

VIEW Z

CLUTCH PEDAL ASSY. 7519

RELEASE LEVER 7515

C CLIP

RELEASE LEVER

CABLE

C CLIP

0.135 INCH.

VIEW Y

C 2543-A

Fig. A   Clutch linkage. Early 1971

CLUTCH PEDAL, ADJUST

Early 1971

1. From under car, pull the flexible cable toward front of car until "C" clip can be removed from cable. Remove the clip.
2. Continue to pull cable toward front of car until all free movement of the release bearing is eliminated.
3. While holding cable in zero free movement position, place a .135" spacer against flywheel boss on the engine side and install the "C" clip into closest possible groove next to the spacer, Fig. 1.
4. Remove the spacer and release the cable.

Late 1971; 1972

The C clip has been eliminated from the cable and is replaced by a locknut. To adjust, proceed as follows:
1. From under car, loosen cable locknuts and adjusting nut at flywheel housing.
2. Pull cable toward front of car until all free movement of the release lever is eliminated.
3. Holding cable in this position, place a 1/4" spacer block against the flywheel housing boss (on engine side). Run adjusting nut against the spacer finger tight.
4. Tighten the front locknut against the adjusting nut, being careful not to disturb the adjustment. Torque locknut to 40-60 ft. lbs.
5. With spacer still in place, tighten the rear locknut against the flywheel housing boss. Remove the spacer.

CLUTCH, REPLACE

1. From inside the car, remove shift lever by bending the locking tabs, removing the "C" clip and unscrewing the lever from transmission housing.
2. Raise vehicle on a hoist.
3. Disconnect drive shaft from U joint flange and slide drive shaft off transmission output shaft. Insert tool over output shaft to prevent loss of lubricant.
4. Disconnect speedometer cable from extension housing.
5. Disconnect lower end of clutch cable at release lever.
6. Remove starter motor.
7. Remove bolts securing engine rear plate to front lower part of flywheel housing.
8. Remove bolt attaching engine rear support. Also remove crossmember attaching bolts and remove the crossmember.
9. Remove bolts attaching flywheel housing to engine block.
10. Move transmission and flywheel assembly rearward until housing clears the clutch pressure plate. Lower transmission and remove.
11. Unfasten and remove the pressure plate, marking same to assure correct assembly.

FOUR SPEED TRANS., REPLACE

The transmission is removed as described under "Clutch Replace".

AUTO. TRANS. LINKAGE, ADJUST

The downshift linkage is adjusted as follows:
1. Disconnect downshift rod return spring. Hold throttle shaft lever in wide open position. Hold downshift rod against the through detent stop.
2. Adjust downshift screw to provide .050-.070" clearance between screw tip and throttle shaft lever tab.
3. Connect downshift lever spring.
To adjust the manual linkage, proceed as follows:
1. Position transmission selector lever in "D".
2. Raise vehicle and loosen manual lever shift rod retaining nut. Move transmission manual lever to "D" position, fourth detent from position back of transmission.
3. With selector lever and manual lever in "D" positions, tighten attaching nut to 10-20 ft. lbs.

Rear Axle, Propeller Shaft & Brakes

REAR AXLE

The rear axle, Fig. 1, is an integral design hypoid with the centerline of the pinion set below the centerline of the ring gear. The semi-floating axle shafts are retained in the housing by ball bearings and bearing retainers at axle ends.

The differential is mounted on two opposed tapered roller bearings which are retained in the housing by removable caps. Differential bearing preload and drive gear backlash is adjusted by nuts located behind each differential bearing cup.

The drive pinion assembly is mounted on two opposed tapered roller bearings. Pinion bearing preload is adjusted by a collapsible spacer on the pinion shaft. Pinion and ring gear tooth contact is adjusted by shims between the rear bearing cone and pinion gear.

Axle Shaft, Bearing & Oil Seal

1. Remove wheel and tire from brake drum.
2. Remove Tinnerman nuts that secure brake drum to axle flange and remove brake drum.
3. Working through hole in each axle flange, remove nuts that secure wheel bearing retainer plate. Then pull the axle shaft assembly out of the housing being careful not to cut or rough up the seal.

NOTE: *The brake backing plate must not be dislodged. Replace one nut to hold the plate in place after shaft is removed.*

4. If wheel bearing is to be replaced, loosen inner retainer ring by nicking it deeply with a chisel in several places. It will then slide off.
5. Remove bearing from shaft.

PROPELLER SHAFT

1. To maintain balance, mark relationship of rear drive shaft yoke and the drive pinion flange of the axle if alignment marks are not visible.
2. Disconnect rear U-joint from companion flange, Fig. 2. Wrap tape around loose bearing caps to prevent them from falling off spider. Pull drive shaft toward rear of car until slip yoke clears transmission extension housing and the seal. Install tool in extension housing to prevent lubricant leakage.

BRAKE ADJUSTMENTS

The hydraulic drum brakes are self-adjusting and require a manual adjustment only after brake shoes have been replaced. The adjustment is made as follows:
1. Using tool HRE 8650, Fig. 3, determine inside diameter of brake drum.
2. Reverse tool and adjust brake shoes to fit the gauge. Hold automatic adjusting lever out of engagement while rotating adjusting screw, to prevent burring slots in screw.

PARKING BRAKE, ADJUST

1. Release parking brake.
2. Place transmission in Neutral and raise vehicle until rear wheels clear floor.

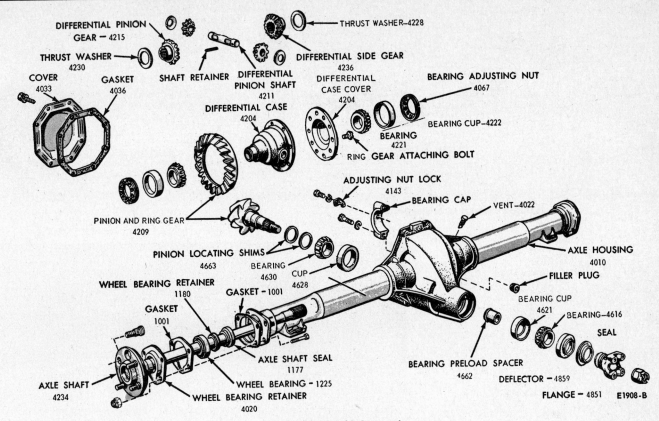

Fig. 1 Disassembled rear axle

3. Tighten adjusting nut on equalizer rod at the control, Fig. 4, to cause the rear wheel brakes to drag.
4. Loosen adjusting nut until rear brakes are just free.

MASTER CYLINDER, REPLACE

1. Disconnect stoplight switch wires at connector. Remove spring retainer and slide stop light switch off brake pedal pin just far enough to clear end of pin, then lift switch straight upward from the pin.
2. Slide master cylinder push rod and nylon washers and bushings off brake pedal pin.
3. Remove brake tube from master cylinder ports.
4. Unfasten and remove master cylinder forward and upward from vehicle.

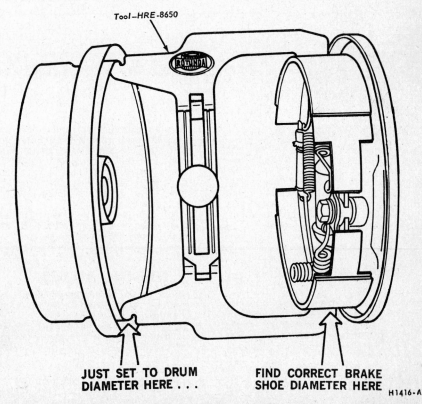

Fig. 3 Self-adjusting brake adjustment

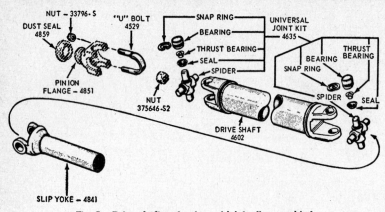

Fig. 2 Drive shaft and universal joints disassembled

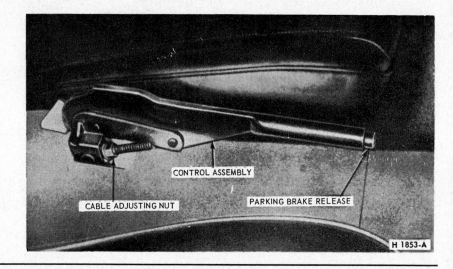

Fig. 4 Parking brake adjustment ▶

Front End & Steering Section

FRONT SUSPENSION

The upper and lower ends of the spindle are attached to upper and lower ball joints which are mounted in upper and lower arms. The upper arm pivots on a bushing and shaft assembly which is bolted to the frame. The lower arm pivots on a bolt in the front crossmember, Fig. 1.

WHEEL ALIGNMENT

Caster and Camber

1. Working inside front wheel housing, install tool T71P-3000A, one at each end of the upper arm inner shaft. Turn the special tool bolts inward until the bolt ends contact the body metal, Fig. 2.
2. Loosen the two upper arm inner shaft-to-body bolts. The upper shaft will move inboard until stopped by the tool bolt ends solidly contacting the body metal.
3. Turn the special tool bolts inward or outward until caster and camber are within specifications. Tightening these bolts on the special tool force the arm outward; while loosening the bolts on the tools permits the arm and inner shaft to move inboard due to weight force.
4. When properly adjusted, tighten shaft-to-body bolts to 75-105 ft. lbs. and remove the special tools.

TOE-IN, ADJUST

1. Check to see that steering shaft and steering wheel marks are in alignment and in the top position.
2. Loosen clamp screw on the tie rod bellows and free the seal on the rod to prevent twisting of the bellows, Fig. 3.
3. Loosen tie rod jam nut.
4. Use suitable pliers to turn the tie rod inner end to correct the adjustment to specifications. Do not use pliers on tie rod threads. Turning to reduce number of threads showing will increase toe-in. Turning in the opposite direction will reduce toe-in.

WHEEL BEARINGS, ADJUST

1. Raise vehicle until wheel and tire clear floor.
2. Remove wheel cover and dust cap from hub.
3. Remove cotter pin and lock nut.
4. While rotating wheel assembly, torque the adjusting nut to 17-25 ft. lbs. to seat the bearings.
5. Using a 1⅛" box wrench, back off the adjusting nut one half turn. Retighten the nut to 10-15 in. lbs. with a torque wrench or finger tight.
6. Locate the nut lock on the adjusting nut so the castellations on the lock are aligned with the cotter pin hole in the spindle.
7. Install new cotter pin and replace dust cap and wheel cover.

WHEEL BEARINGS, REPLACE
(Disc Brakes)

1. Raise car and remove front wheels.
2. Use a ¾" wrench to loosen the large bolt at top of caliper assembly and washer at the front of the caliper. Loosen it until it can be turned with the fingers.
3. Remove the smaller bolt at bottom of caliper with a ⅝" wrench.
4. Insert a strong piece of wire carefully through the upper opening in the caliper and fasten it. Position the free end of the wire over the suspension upper arm.
5. When removing caliper from disc the brake pads must be held apart. Do this by inserting a piece of wood or cardboard. While holding the caliper, remove the large bolt in front. Now carefully slide the caliper back and slightly upward to remove it. While doing this, insert the wood or cardboard between the brake pads.
6. Carefully move caliper back to suspension upper arm and fasten loose end of wire so caliper will not drop.
7. Dust cap can now be removed from hub. Remove nut lock, etc. and rock disc to ease out washer and outer bearing. Disc can now be removed to service grease seal or inner bearing.

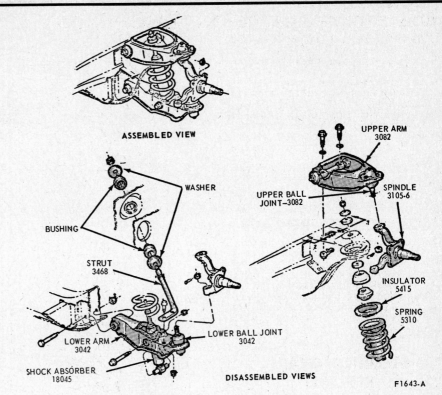

ASSEMBLED VIEW

DISASSEMBLED VIEWS

F1643-A

Fig. 1   Front suspension assembly

CHECKING BALL JOINTS FOR WEAR
Upper Ball Joint

1. Raise car and place floor jacks beneath lower arms.
2. Ask an assistant to grasp lower edge of tire and move wheel in and out.
3. As the wheel is being moved, notice any movement between the upper end of the spindle and the upper arm. If movement is present, replace the ball joint.

Lower Ball Joint

1. Raise vehicle and place jacks under lower arms as shown in Fig. 4.
2. Be sure wheel bearings are properly adjusted.
3. Attach a dial indicator to lower arm and position indicator so that plunger rests against inner side of wheel rim near lower ball joint.
4. Grasp tire at top and bottom and slowly move tire in and out. If the reading exceeds .250", replace the joint.

SHOCK ABSORBER, REPLACE

1. Unfasten the upper end of the shock.
2. Raise vehicle and install safety stands.
3. Unfasten lower end of shock. It may be necessary to use a pry bar to free "T" shaped end of the shock from the lower end.

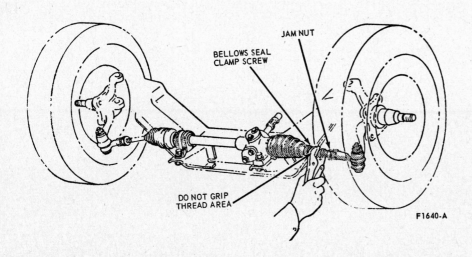

Fig. 3   Toe-in adjustment

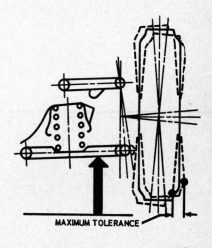

F1435-A

Fig. 4   Measuring lower ball joint play

COIL SPRING, REPLACE

1. Raise vehicle and support front end with safety stands.
2. Place a jack under lower arm to support it.
3. Disconnect lower end of shock.
4. Remove bolts that attach strut to lower arm.
5. Remove nut that retains shock to crossmember and remove the shock.
6. Remove nut and bolt that secures inner end of lower arm to crossmember.
7. Carefully lower jack to relieve pressure from spring and remove spring.

BALL JOINTS, REPLACE

The ball joints are riveted to the control arms. The ball joints can be replaced on the car by removing the rivets and replacing them with new attaching bolts, nuts and washers furnished with the kit.

When removing a ball joint, use a suitable pressing tool to force the ball joint out of the spindle.

STEERING GEAR, REPLACE

1. Position steering wheel in straight ahead position and raise vehicle on a hoist.
2. Remove bolts retaining the flexible coupling to the pinion shaft, Fig. 5.
3. Remove four nuts and bolts securing the steering gear to the mounting pads on the crossmember.
4. Remove the U-clamp.
5. Remove cotterpins and loosen nuts securing connecting rod ends to the spindle arms.
6. Use ball joint separator (tool 3290C) to separate the connecting rod ends from the spindle arms.
7. Remove nuts from connecting rods and remove gear from vehicle left side.

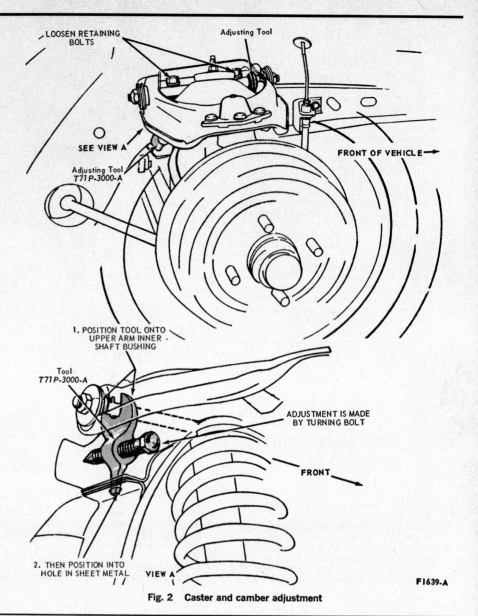

LOOSEN RETAINING BOLTS

Adjusting Tool

SEE VIEW A

FRONT OF VEHICLE ➡

Adjusting Tool T71P-3000-A

1. POSITION TOOL ONTO UPPER ARM INNER SHAFT BUSHING

Tool T71P-3000-A

ADJUSTMENT IS MADE BY TURNING BOLT

FRONT

2. THEN POSITION INTO HOLE IN SHEET METAL

VIEW A

F1639-A

Fig. 2 Caster and camber adjustment

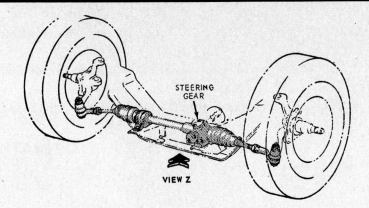

Fig. 5 Steering gear installation

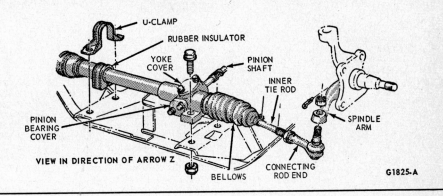

FORD THUNDERBIRD

OLD CAR SPECIFICATIONS: For 1946-65 Tune Up and Wheel Alignment Specifications see back of book.

*This material covered only in the "Service Trade Edition" of this manual.

Service procedures on the V8-400 are covered in the Ford & Mercury car chapters.

INDEX OF SERVICE OPERATIONS

ENGINE & SERIAL NUMBER LOCATION

Vehicle Warranty Plate On Left Front Door Pillar.

1966

1967

1968

ENGINE IDENTIFICATION

*Serial number on vehicle Warranty Plate.

Year	Engine	Engine Code
1966–67	V8-390	Z
	V8-428	Q
1968	V8-390	Z
	V8-429	N
1969–72	V8-429	N
1972	V8-400	S

1969

1970

1971

1972

GENERAL ENGINE SPECIFICATIONS

Year	Engine	Carburetor	Bore and Stroke	Piston Displacement, Cubic Inches	Compression Ratio	Maximum Brake H.P. @ R.P.M.	Maximum Torque Lbs. Ft. @ R.P.M.	Normal Oil Pressure Pounds
1966–67	315 Horsepower............V8-390	4 Barrel	4.0500 x 3.784	390	10.50	315 @ 4600	427 @ 2800	35–55
	345 Horsepower............V8-428	4 Barrel	4.1300 x 3.984	428	10.50	345 @ 4600	462 @ 2800	35–55
1968	315 Horsepower............V8-390	4 Barrel	4.05 x 3.78	390	10.50	315 @ 4600	427 @ 2800	35–55
1968–70	360 Horsepower............V8-429	4 Barrel	4.36 x 3.59	429	11.00	360 @ 4600	476 @ 2800	35–60
1971	360 Horsepower............V8-429	4 Barrel	4.36 x 3.59	429	10.30	360 @ 4600	480 @ 2800	35–75
1972	212 Horsepower①...........V8-400	2 Barrel	4.00 x 4.00	400	—	—	—	—
	212 Horsepower①...........V8-429	4 Barrel	4.36 x 3.59	429	8.50	212 @ 4400	327 @ 2600	35–75

①—Ratings are NET—as installed in the vehicle.

TUNE UP SPECIFICATIONS

OLD CAR SPECIFICATIONS: For 1955-65 Tune Up Specifications see back of book.

★When using a timing light, disconnect vacuum hose or tube at distributor and plug opening in hose or tube so idle speed will not be affected.

Year	Engine	Spark Plug		Distributor		Firing Order	Ignition Timing★		Hot Idle Speed		Comp. Press. Lbs. ③	Fuel Pump Press. Lbs.
		Type	Gap Inch	Point Gap Inch	Dwell Angle Deg.		BTDC ①	Mark	M/S Trans.	Auto. Trans. ②		
1966	Std. Ignition⑧	BF-42	.034	.017	26–31	Fig. A	10°⑤	Fig. D	—	475D⑦	190	4½–6½
	Std. Ignition⑨	BF-42	.034	.017	26–31	Fig. A	6°⑤	Fig. D	—	525D⑦	190	4½–6½
	Transistor Ign.⑧	BF-42	.034	.020	22–24	Fig. A	10°⑤	Fig. D	—	475D⑦	190	4½–6½
	Transistor Ign.⑨	BF-42	.034	.020	22–24	Fig. A	6°⑤	Fig. D	—	525D⑦	190	4½–6½
1967	Standard⑧	BF-32	.034	.017	26–31	Fig. A	10°⑤	Fig. D	—	475D⑦	190	4½–6½
	With Thermactor⑨	BF-32	.034	.017	26–31	Fig. A	6°⑤	Fig. D	—	550D⑦	190	4½–6½
1968	8-390	BF-42	.034	.017	26–31	Fig. A	6°⑤	Fig. B	—	550D④	190	4½–6½
1968–69	8-429	BF-42	.034	.017	26–31	Fig. A	6°⑤	Fig. B	—	550D④	190	4½–6½
1970–71	8-429	BRF-42	.034	.017	26–31	Fig. A	4°	Fig. B	—	600D⑩	190	5
1972	8-400	ARF-42	.034	.017	26–30	Fig. C	6°	Fig. B	—	625D⑩	190	5
	8-429	BRF-42	.034	.017	26–30	Fig. A	10°	Fig. B	—	600D⑩	190	5

①—BTDC: Before top dead center.
②—D: Drive. N: Neutral.
③—Plus or minus 20 lbs.
④—With headlights and A/C on.

⑤—Whenever idle speed or ignition timing is adjusted, vacuum line to brake release mechanism must be disconnected and plugged to prevent parking brake from releasing when selector is moved to Drive.

⑥—Either Fig. C or D.
⑦—If air conditioned, turn A/C switch to "Full On" position.
⑧—Without Thermactor System.
⑨—With Thermactor System.
⑩—With headlamp on Hi Beam—Air Conditioning OFF.

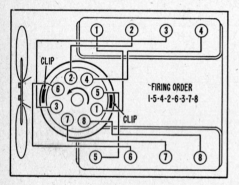

Fig. A

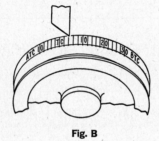

Fig. B

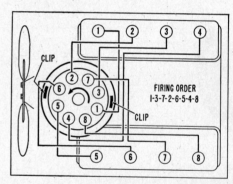

Fig. C

Fig. D

VALVE SPECIFICATIONS

Year	Engine Model	Valve Lash		Valve Angles		Valve Spring Installed Height	Valve Spring Pressure Lbs. @ In.	Stem Clearance		Stem Diameter	
		Int.	Exh.	Seat	Face			Intake	Exhaust	Intake	Exhaust
1966	V8-390, 428	.050–.150①		45	44	1¹³⁄₁₆	80 @ 1.82	.001–.0024	.001–.0024	.3711–.3718	.3711–.3718
1967	All	.100–.200①		45	44	1¹³⁄₁₆	85 @ 1.82	.001–.0024	.001–.0024	.3711–.3718	.3711–.3718
1968	8-390	.100–.200①		45	44	1¹³⁄₁₆	72 @ 1.82	.0010–.0024	.0015–.0032	.3711–.3718	.3706–.3713
1968–70	8-429	.075–.125②		45	44	1¹³⁄₁₆	80 @ 1.81	.0010–.0027	.0010–.0027	.3416–.3423	.3416–.3423
1971	8-429	.105–.205②		45	45	1¹³⁄₁₆	80 @ 1.81	.0010–.0027	.0010–.0027	.3416–.3423	.3416–.3423
1972	8-400	.100–.200②		45	45	1¹³⁄₁₆	80 @ 1.81	.0010–.0027	.0015–.0032	.3416–.3423	.3411–.3418
	8-429	.075–.175②		45	45	1¹³⁄₁₆	80 @ 1.81	.0010–.0027	.0010–.0027	.3416–.3423	.3416–.3423

①—Clearance specified is obtained at valve stem with lifter collapsed. See "Valves, Adjust" text.
②—1968 One turn down after contact. 1969–72 Non adjustable.

PISTONS, PINS, RINGS, CRANKSHAFT & BEARINGS

Year	Engine Model	Piston Clearance	Ring End Gap①		Wrist-pin Diameter	Rod Bearings		Main Bearings		Thrust on Bear. No.	Shaft End Play
			Comp.	Oil		Shaft Diameter	Bearing Clearance	Shaft Diameter	Bearing Clearance		
1966–67	8-390, 428	.0015–.0023	.010	.015	.9752	2.4380–2.4388	.0008–.0026	2.7484–2.7492	.0005–.0025	3	.004–.010
1968	8-390	.0015–.0023	.010	.015	.9752	2.4380–2.4388	.0008–.0026	2.7484–2.7492	.0005–.0025	3	.004–.010
1968–72	8-429	.0014–.0022	.010	.015	1.0410	2.4992–.25000	.0010–.0015	2.9994–3.0002	.0005–.0015	3	.004–.008
1972	8-400	.0014–.0022	.010	.015	.9752	2.3103–2.3111	.0008–.0026	2.9994–3.0002	.0009–.0026	3	.004–.010

①—Fit rings in tapered boxes for clearance listed in tightest portion of ring travel.

REAR AXLE SPECIFICATIONS

Year	Model	Carrier Type	Ring Gear & Pinion Backlash Inch	Nominal Pinion Locating Shim, Inch	Pinion Bearing Preload				Differential Bearing Preload	Pinion Nut Torque Ft.-Lbs.
					New Bearings With Seal Inch-Lbs.	Used Bearings With Seal Inch-Lbs.	New Bearings Less Seal Inch-Lbs.	Used Bearings Less Seal Inch-Lbs.		
1966	All	Removable	.008–.012	.020	17–32③	10–14③	—	—	.008–.012④	②⑤
1967–72	All	Removable	.008–.012	.015	22–32⑥	8–14⑥	—	—	.008–.012④	②⑤

①—Threaded adjusters—notches tight by right-hand adjuster.
②—If torque is not possible, install new spacer.
③—With collapsible spacer. With solid spacer 12½–32½ inch-lbs. without seal; 17–32 inch-lbs. with seal in place.
④—Case spread with new bearings. With used bearings .005–.008".
⑤—With 9" ring gear 175 ft.-lbs. With 9⅜" ring gear 200 ft.-lbs.
⑥—With collapsible spacer. With solid spacer 15–35 inch-lbs. with seal in place.

ENGINE TIGHTENING SPECIFICATIONS

★Torque specifications are for clean and lightly lubricated threads only. Dry or dirty threads produce increased friction which prevents accurate measurement of tightness.

Year	Engine	Spark Plugs Ft. Lbs.	Cylinder Head Bolts Ft. Lbs.	Intake Manifold Ft. Lbs.	Exhaust Manifold Ft. Lbs.	Rocker Arm Shaft Bracket Ft. Lbs.	Rocker Arm Cover Ft. Lbs.	Connecting Rod Cap Bolts Ft. Lbs.	Main Bearing Cap Bolts Ft. Lbs.	Flywheel to Crankshaft Ft. Lbs.	Vibration Damper or Pulley Ft. Lbs.
1966–68	V8-390	15–20	80–90	32–35	18–24	40–45	4–7	40–45	95–105	75–85	70–90
1966–67	V8-428	15–20	80–90	32–35	18–24	40–45	4–7	40–45	95–105	75–85	70–90
1968	V8-429	15–20	130–140	25–30	28–33	65–75①	2½–4	40–45	95–105	75–85	75–90
1969–72	V8-429	15–20	130–140	25–30	28–33	65–75①	5–6	40–45	95–105	75–85	75–90
1972	V8-400	10–15	95–105	②	12–16	—	3–5	40–45	95–105	—	70–90

①—Rocker arm stud to cylinder head. ②—¼" bolt 6–9; 5/16" bolt 21–25; ⅜" bolt 27–33.

DISTRIBUTOR SPECIFICATIONS

★NOTE: If advance is checked on vehicle, double the R.P.M. and degrees advance to get crankshaft figures.

Year	Model	Basic Distributor Part No.① 12127	Breaker Gap	Cam Angle	Breaker Arm Spring Tension	Centrifugal Advance Degrees @ R.P.M. of Distributor★		Vacuum Advance		Dist. Retard
						Advance Starts	Full Advance	Inches of Vacuum To Start Plunger	Max. Adv. Dist. Deg. @ Vacuum	Max. Ret. Dist. Deg. @ Vacuum
1966	8-390 Standard	C6AF-D	.017	26–31	17–21	2 @ 500	10 @ 2000	6	12 @ 18	—
	8-390, 428 Thermactor③	C6AF-L	.017	26–31	17–21	2 @ 500	12 @ 2000	6	10 @ 15	—
	8-428 Standard	C6AF-E	.017	26–31	17–21	2 @ 500	10 @ 2000	6	10 @ 15	—
	8-428 Std. Transistor	C6SF-B	.020	22–24	17–21	2 @ 500	10 @ 2000	6	10 @ 15	—
	8-428 Transistor③	C6SF-D	.020	22–24	17–21	2 @ 500	12 @ 2000	6	10 @ 15	—
1967	8-390②	C7SF-A	.017	26–31	17–21	½ @ 300	10 @ 2000	5	12 @ 20	—
	8-390, 428③	C7SF-B	.017	26–31	17–21	½ @ 300	12 @ 2000	5	12 @ 20	—
	8-428②	C7AF-J	.017	26–31	17–21	½ @ 300	10 @ 2000	5	12 @ 20	—
1968	8-390	C7AF-AC	.017	26–31	17–21	½ @ 350	14 @ 2000	5	12½ @ 25	—
1968–69	8-429	C8VF-A	.017	26–31	17–21	½ @ 350	14 @ 2000	5	12 @ 25	—
1970–71	8-429	D0AF-Z	.017	26–31	17–21	½ @ 350	14 @ 2950	5	11 @ 25	—
1971	8-429	D1SF-BA	.017	26–31	17–21	½ @ 350	13 @ 2500	5	11 @ 25	—
1972	8-400	D2AF-RA	.017	26–30	17–21	½ @ 500	12 @ 2000	5	13½ @ 20	4 @ 20
	8-400	D2AF-SA	.017	26–30	17–21	½ @ 500	12 @ 2000	5	13½ @ 20	4 @ 20
	8-429	D2MF-EA	.017	26–30	17–21	½ @ 500	9½ @ 2000	5	11½ @ 20	4 @ 20
	8-429	D2MF-FA	.017	26–30	17–21	½ @ 500	9½ @ 2000	5	11½ @ 20	4 @ 20

①—Stamped on distributor housing plate. ②—Without Thermactor System. ③—With Thermactor System.

STARTING MOTOR SPECIFICATIONS

Year and Model	Part No. (11001)	Rotation ①	Brush Spring Tension, Ounces	No Load Test			Torque Test		
				Amperes	Volts	R.P.M.	Amperes	Volts	Torque Ft. Lbs.
1966–67		C	40	70	12		670	5	15½
1968 V8-390	C7AF-E	C	40	70	12	11000	700	4	15½
1968 V8-429	C8VF-A	C	40	70	12	11000	600	4	15.3
1969–72 V8-429	C8VY-C	C	40	70	12	10000	700	5	15.5

①—As viewed from the drive end.   C—Clockwise.

ALTERNATOR & REGULATOR SPECIFICATIONS

Year	Make	Current Rating①		Field Current @ 75°F.		Voltage Regulator②				Field Relay	
		Amperes	Volts	Amperes	Volts	Make	Voltage @ 75°F.	Contact Gap	Armature Air Gap	Armature Air Gap	Closing Voltage @ 75°F.
1966–67	Autolite	42	15	2.8–3.3	12	Autolite	14.1–14.9	.017–.022	.049–.056	.015–.022	2.5–4.0
	Autolite	45	15	2.8–3.3	12	Autolite	14.1–14.9	.017–.022	.049–.056	.015–.022	2.5–4.0
	Autolite	55	15	2.8–3.3	12	Autolite	14.1–14.9	.017–.022	.049–.056	.015–.022	2.5–4.0
1968	Autolite	55	15	2.8–3.3	12	Autolite	13.5–15.3	③	③	③	2.0–4.2
1969–72	Autolite	55	15	2.8–3.3	12	Autolite④	③	③	③	③	2.0–4.2

①—Stamped on housing.   ②—Stamped on cover.   ③—Not adjustable.   ④—Integral regulator solid state.

WHEEL ALIGNMENT SPECIFICATIONS

OLD CAR SPECIFICATIONS: For 1955-65 Wheel Alignment Specifications see back of book.

Year	Model	Caster Angle, Degrees		Camber Angle, Degrees				Toe-In. Inch	Toe-Out on Turns, Deg.	
		Limits	Desired	Limits		Desired			Outer Wheel	Inner Wheel
				Left	Right	Left	Right			
1966	All	−¾ to −2¼	−1½	0 to +1	0 to +1	+½	+½	3/16	19½	20
1967	All	0 to +1	+½	+½ to +1½	+½ to +1½	+1	+1	3/16	18⅛	20
1968–69	All	0 to +2	+1	−¼ to +1¼	−¼ to +1¼	+½	+½	3/16	18¼	20
1970	All	0 to +2	+1	−¼ to +1¼	−¼ to +1¼	+½	+½	3/16	19¼	20
1971	All	−1 to +3	+1	−½ to +1½	−½ to +1½	+½	+½	3/16	19¼	20
1972	All	−1 to +3	+1	+¼ to +1¾	−¼ to +1¾	+¾	+¾	3/16	—	—

FORD THUNDERBIRD

BRAKE SPECIFICATIONS

Year	Model	Brake Drum Inside Diameter	Wheel Cylinder Bore Diameter			Master Cylinder Bore Diameter		
			Front Disc Brakes	Front Drum Brakes	Rear Brakes	With Disc Brakes	With Drum Brakes	With Power Brakes
1966	All	11.03	1^{15}⁄₁₆	—	^{15}⁄₁₆	^{15}⁄₁₆	^{15}⁄₁₆	^{15}⁄₁₆
1967	All	11.03	1^{15}⁄₁₆	—	^{15}⁄₁₆	1.00	1.00	1.00
1968–71	All	11.03	2¾	—	^{15}⁄₁₆	1.00	1.00	1.00
1972	All	11.03	3.100	—	1.00	1.00	—	1.00

COOLING SYSTEM & CAPACITY DATA

Year	Model or Engine	Cooling Capacity, Qts.			Radiator Cap Relief Pressure, Lbs.		Thermo. Opening Temp. ①	Fuel Tank Gals.	Engine Oil Refill Qts. ②	Transmission Oil			Rear Axle Oil Pints
		No Heater	With Heater	With A/C	With A/C	No A/C				3 Speed Pints	4 Speed Pints	Auto. Trans. Qts. ④	
1966	All	19½	20½	20½	12–15	12–15	195	22	4	—	—	③	5
1967	All	19	20	20	12–15	12–15	195	22	4	—	—	13	5
1968	V8-390	19½	20½	20½	12–15	12–15	195	24	4	—	—	13	5
	V8-429	18	19	19	12–15	12–15	195	24	4	—	—	13	5
1969	V8-429	19½	20½	20½	12–15	12–15	195	24	4	—	—	12¾	5
1970	V8-429	17½	18½	18½	12–15	12–15	188	⑤	4	—	—	12¾	5
1971	V8-429	18½	19½	19½	12–15	12–15	188	23	4	—	—	12¾	5
1972	V8-400	16¾	17¾	18½	12–15	12–15	188	22½	4	—	—	12¾	5
	V8-429	17¾	18¾	19½	12–15	12–15	188	22½	4	—	—	12¾	5

①—With alcohol-type anti-freeze, use a 160-deg. unit.
②—Add one quart with filter change.
③—C6 13 qts., others, 10 qts.
④—Approximate. Make final check with dipstick.
⑤—California vehicles 22½; all others 24.

Electrical Section

DISTRIBUTOR, REPLACE
Removal

1. To remove the distributor, disconnect the primary wire and vacuum control pipe. On some models the work may be made easier if the accelerator pull back spring is disconnected.
2. Remove distributor cap.
3. Scribe a mark on the distributor body indicating the position of the rotor, and scribe another mark on the body and engine block indicating position of distributor body in block. These marks can be used as guides when installing distributor in a correctly timed engine.
4. Remove hold down screw and screws and lift distributor out of block. *Do not crank engine while distributor is removed or the initial timing operation will have to be performed.*

Installation

If the crankshaft has not been disturbed, install the distributor, using the scribed marks previously made on the distributor body and engine block as guides.

If the crankshaft has been rotated while the distributor was removed from the engine, it will be necessary to retime the engine. Crank the engine to bring No. 1 piston on top dead center of its compression stroke. Align the timing mark on the vibration damper or pulley with the timing pointer (see *Tune Up* chart). Install the distributor so that the rotor points to the No. 1 spark plug wire terminal in the distributor cap.

NOTE: Make sure the oil pump intermediate shaft properly engages the distributor shaft. It may be necessary to crank the engine with the starter, after the distributor drive gear is properly engaged, in order to engage the oil pump intermediate shaft.

STARTER, REPLACE
1970-72

The starter does not use an auxiliary starter relay as did previous models therefore when replacing starter be sure to disconnect battery ground cable. Removal is otherwise the same as previous models.

1968-69

To provide working clearance, it may be necessary to turn wheels fully to the right and to disconnect the steering idler arm from the frame.

When installing the starter, be sure all mating surfaces are clean to insure a good electrical ground. To maintain proper alignment, hold the starter squarely against the mounting plate and fully inserted into the mounting hole while tightening the mounting bolts.

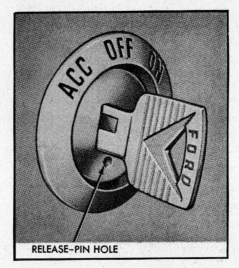

Fig. 1 Ignition switch and lock. 1966-67

1966-67

1. On 1966 models, remove brace on right side that connects No. 2 crossmember to side rail. On all models, disconnect cable at starter terminal, unfasten and remove starter.
2. Position starter to flywheel housing and start mounting bolts. Snug all bolts, then torque them to 12-15 ft-lbs, tightening the middle bolt first.
3. Connect starter cable.

IGNITION SWITCH, REPLACE
1972

The ignition switch is mounted on the steering column and is controlled by the lock cylinder through an actuator in the locking mechanism. The switch is connected to the actuator by an actuator rod. The two multiple connector plugs are secured to the switch by snap type retainers. To remove switch, proceed as follows:
1. Disconnect battery ground cable.

Fig. 2 Light switch. 1966-69

2. Remove screws holding instrument panel cluster.
3. Press locking tabs and remove blade type connector on top of switch.
4. Remove two mounting nuts from switch and lift up on switch enough to unhook the switch rod.
5. Remove the switch.

1970-71

1. To gain access, remove shrouding from steering column and detach and lower the steering column from the brake support bracket.
2. Disconnect battery cable.
3. Disconnect switch wiring at multiple plug.
4. Remove nuts that retain switch to column.
5. Detach switch plunger from actuator rod and remove switch.
6. When installing switch, both the switch and the locking mechanism at top of column must be in the "LOCK" position. New replacement switches are already pinned in the "LOCK" position when received by a plastic shipping pin inserted in a locking hole on top of switch.

1968-69

1. Disconnect battery ground cable.
2. Remove ignition switch lower finish panel.
3. Depress tabs securing connector to rear of switch and pull connector from switch.
4. Remove the bezel nut and remove the switch.

1967

1. Disconnect ground strap at battery.
2. Turn ignition key to accessory position. Slightly depress pin in pin hole on front of lock tumbler, Fig. 1. Turn key counterclockwise and pull key and lock cylinder out of switch.
3. Remove bezel, push switch back part way and remove accessory wire retaining nut.
4. Pull off rubber-covered multiple connector and one push-on connector and remove switch.
5. Reverse procedure to install.

1966

1. Disconnect a battery cable.
2. Turn ignition key to accessory position. With a paper clip, slightly depress pin, Fig. 1, turn key counterclockwise and pull key and lock cylinder out of switch. If only lock cylinder is to be replaced, proceed to Step 9.
3. Remove lower instrument panel shield (5 screws).
4. Press in on rear of switch and rotate it counterclockwise $\frac{1}{8}$ turn (as viewed from terminal end). Remove bezel and switch.
5. Remove lock nut and retaining nut

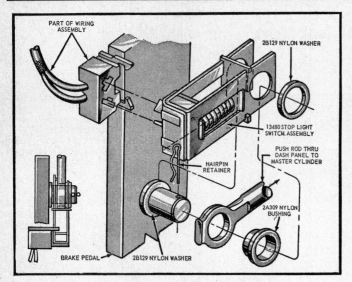

Fig. 3   Mechanical stop light switch. 1966-72

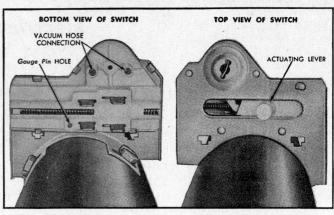

Fig. 4   Neutral start switch showing parking brake
vacuum connections. 1967 with C6 transmission

and pull connector from switch.

6. If a new switch as well as lock cylinder is to be installed, insert a screwdriver into lock opening of switch and turn slot in switch to full counterclockwise position.
7. Install connector to switch with retaining and lock nuts.
8. Position switch in instrument panel with light bulb and retainer. Position bezel in instrument panel. Rotate switch ⅛ turn to lock it in bezel.
9. If a new lock cylinder is to be installed, insert key in cylinder and turn it to accessory position. Place lock and key in switch. Depress pin slightly and turn counterclockwise. Push lock cylinder into switch and turn key to check operation of lock cylinder.
10. Install lower instrument panel shield. Connect battery cable and check operation of switch.

LIGHT SWITCH, REPLACE

1972

1. Disconnect battery ground cable.
2. Remove instrument cluster trim panel.
3. Remove switch mounting plate.
4. Remove bezel nut and disconnect multiple connector.
5. Remove vacuum lines, if so equipped.

1968-71

1. Disconnect battery ground cable.
2. Remove three screws attaching air control assembly to the lower left side of instrument panel and lower the assembly.
3. Remove control knob and shaft by pressing release button on switch housing with knob in full "ON" position. Pull knob and shaft out of switch.
4. Remove retaining bezel nut and remove switch from instrument panel through the air control assembly opening.
5. Reverse procedure to install.

1967

1. Remove control knob and shaft by pressing release button on switch housing with knob in full "ON" position. Pull knob and shaft out of switch.
2. Remove retaining nut and switch from instrument panel.
3. Reverse procedure to install.

1966

1. Remove control knob and shaft by pressing knob release button on switch housing, Fig. 2, with knob in full "On position. Pull knob out of switch.
2. Unscrew mounting nut, remove switch and disconnect wiring connector.
3. To install, attach wiring connector, insert switch in panel and install mounting nut.
4. Install knob and shaft assembly by

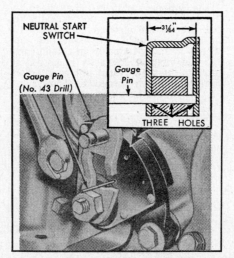

Fig. 5   Neutral start switch on transmission. 1966 with C6 transmission

inserting it all the way into switch until a distinct click is heard. In some instances it may be necessary to rotate shaft slightly until it engages switch contact carrier.

STOP LIGHT SWITCH, REPLACE

1966-72

1. Disconnect wires at connector.
2. Remove hairpin retainer. Slide stop light switch, push rod and nylon washers and bushing away from pedal, and remove switch, Fig. 3.
3. Position switch, push rod, bushing and washers on brake pedal pin in the order shown, and install hairpin retainer.
4. Connect wires and install wires in clip.

NEUTRAL SAFETY SWITCH

1970-72

The neutral start switch has been eliminated from all column shift vehicles. A series of steps have been designed into the steering column selector lever hub casting which eliminates the need for a switch.

1969

Adjustment Procedure

1. Loosen retaining screws and with selector lever held lightly against the Neutral stop, rotate switch until a start is obtained. Tighten attaching screws to 20 in-lbs.
2. With the switch properly adjusted, place selector lever in the "1" position and push the Park reset button to the left until it stops. *The Park reset must be performed whenever the switch has been adjusted.*

1968

To adjust the switch it must be removed from the column. Put the selector lever in neutral and set the parking brake. Then disconnect the electrical and va-

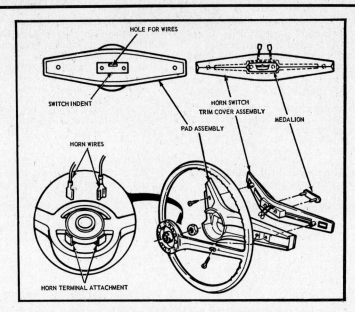

HOLE FOR WIRES

SWITCH INDENT

HORN SWITCH
TRIM COVER ASSEMBLY

PAD ASSEMBLY

MEDALION

HORN WIRES

HORN TERMINAL ATTACHMENT

Fig. 6   Steering wheel and horn switch. 1970-71

cuum connections and remove the two fastening screws to allow the switch to be lifted straight up and out.

Adjustment Procedure

1. Hold the switch with the wire terminal facing you. Move the actuator all the way to the left, but do not force as the switch will be damaged internally.
2. Insert a 3/32" drill shank in the hole in the tapered round boss facing you.
3. Gently but firmly move the actuator lever back to the right until it stops. This will move the Park circuit to its position of minimum travel, which must be done if the switch is to function properly upon installation.
4. Pull out the drill gauge and fit it into the hole on the top surface of the switch case to engage the switch internal carrier in the neutral position.
5. Reinsert the drill gauge.
6. With the transmission selector lever held against the stop in the neutral detent position, set the switch in place on the column and fasten it with the two screws.
7. Connect the electrical connector and any vacuum hose, and be sure to remove the drill gauge before operating the selector lever.

1966 Cruiseomatic, 1967 C6

Column Shift, Fig. 4

1. With manual linkage properly adjusted, check starter engagement circuit in all selector lever positions. The circuit must be open in all drive positions and closed only in Park and Neutral.
2. To adjust, loosen switch mounting screws. Place transmission selector lever firmly against stop of neutral detent position.
3. Rotate switch actuating lever until gauge pin (#43 drill) can be inserted in gauge pin holes.
4. Tighten switch retaining screws and remove gauge pin.

1966 with C6 Trans.

1. With manual linkage properly adjusted, check starter engagement circuit in all selector lever positions. The circuit must be open in all drive positions and be closed only in park and neutral.
2. To adjust switch, loosen retaining screws that locate switch on steering column.
3. Place selector lever firmly against stop of neutral detent position.
4. Rotate switch actuating lever until a #43 drill can be inserted in the gauge pin holes, Fig. 5.
5. Tighten two switch retaining screws and remove drill gauge.
6. Check operation of switch in each selector position. The starter should operate only when the lever is in P or N positions.

HORN SOUNDER
1970-72

A two spoke steering wheel with a pressure sensitive horn switch built into the trim cover is used, Fig. 6. If the switch needs to be replaced, the entire horn switch/trim cover assembly will have to be replaced.

1969 Rim-Blow Type

The rubber insert and copper strip is not replaceable. If a new insert assembly is required, the entire steering wheel will have to be replaced.

1. Remove pad from steering wheel.
2. Remove medallion from pad.
3. After removing the retaining nut, the steering wheel can be removed with a suitable puller.

1966-69 Except Rim-Blow Type

1. Disconnect battery ground cable.
2. Remove center medallion from wheel.

3. Remove three screws from center of wheel and remove horn buttons.
4. Reverse procedure to install.

TURN SIGNAL SWITCH, REPLACE
1971-72

1. Remove retaining screw from underside of steering wheel spoke and lift off the pad horn switch/trim cover and medallion as an assembly. Disconnect horn switch wires from terminals.
2. Remove steering wheel retaining nut and steering wheel.
3. Remove turn signal switch lever by unscrewing it from column.
4. Remove shroud from under steering column.
5. Disconnect steering column wiring connector plugs and remove screws that secure switch assembly to column.
6. On vehicles with tilt column, remove wires and terminals from steering column connector plug.

NOTE: *Record the color code and location of each wire before removing it from connector. A hole provided in the flange casting on fixed columns makes it unnecessary to separate the wires from the connector. The plug with wires installed can be guided through the hole.*

7. Remove plastic cover sleeve from wiring harness and remove the switch and wires from top of column.
8. Reverse procedure to install.

1968-70

Fixed Column

The combination turn signal and hazard warning switch for cars with fixed steering columns has been redesigned in that the warning switch knob is an integral part of the switch and is no longer replaceable. Electric wiring is bonded for ease of installation.

1. Disconnect battery and remove steering wheel.
2. Remove protective wire cover that runs along bottom of steering column tube and disconnect electrical plug, noting the color codes and location.
3. If equipped with speed control, remove the sleeve around the wiring and pull the first three speed control wires out of the column.
4. Remove turn signal lever, then remove three screws holding the switch to the column and lift switch from column.
5. Reverse procedure to install.

1967-70

Tilt Column

1. Disconnect ground cable at battery.
2. Remove steering wheel.
3. Unscrew turn indicator lever.
4. Remove emergency flasher control knob.
5. Remove upper tilt mechanism cover

FORD THUNDERBIRD

(2 screws).

6. Remove five screws from lower finish panel under steering column and remove plate.
7. Disconnect multiple connector beneath instrument panel and at base of steering column.
8. Disconnect connector block from bullet connectors by depressing tabs one at a time and remove plastic cover over wires.
9. Position lower collar down and remove plastic clip from side of steering column.
10. Remove two screws from switch and remove switch and wires from column.
11. Reverse procedure to install.

1966

1. Remove steering wheel.
2. Unscrew signal lever.
3. Remove switch mounting bracket screw, then remove switch and bracket.
4. Remove conical tension spring and switch actuating arm.
5. Disconnect switch wires from bullet connectors. Remove wire protector from side of steering column.
6. Remove switch-to-mounting bracket screws, and remove switch and wires.

NOTE: When installing the new switch, make certain that canceling cam on steering wheel makes contact with canceling pawls on switch. The clearance between steering wheel hub and steering shaft housing flange should not be more than 1/16″ for proper switch canceling. Reposition steering shaft housing if necessary.

INSTRUMENT CLUSTER
1972

1. Disconnect battery ground cable.
2. Remove screw retaining lower cluster applique cover below steering column.
3. Squeeze the lower half of the column shroud together and separate the lower half from the upper.
4. Remove upper half of shroud from column.
5. Remove screw attaching PRNDL control cable wire to the column.
6. Remove heated backlite control knob.
7. Reach under instrument panel and depress the button on side of headlight switch while withdrawing switch control knob and shaft assembly.
8. Reach under panel and disconnect speedo cable.
9. Remove threaded headlight switch bezel.
10. Remove windshield wiper/washer control knob and bezel.
11. Remove cigar lighter from its receptacle.
12. Remove four screws retaining cluster front cover.
13. Insert a right angle standard tip screwdriver along edges of the finish panel withdrawing studs in sequence gradually around the periphery of the panel.
14. Remove four screws retaining cluster to panel.

15. Pull cluster away from panel; disconnect cluster feed plug from its receptacle in the printed circuit.
16. Tilt cluster out, top first, and move the cluster toward center of car.

1968-71

The instrument cluster is a new design. The face covering gives the illusion of five integrated housings. Actually, only the four to the left form the main cluster; the right housing is attached to the main instrument panel. The housings cannot be removed individually until the cluster cover, lens and mask have been removed.

1967 Fuel & Oil Gauge

1. Loosen set screw at bottom of gauge pod.
2. Remove screw from upper inner surface of pod.
3. Pull gauge and pod assembly straight out from instrument cluster.
4. Separate housing from lens and bezel (3 screws).
5. Remove four nuts and insulators and remove gauge unit.
6. Reverse procedure to install.

1967 Ammeter & Temperature Gauge

1. Loosen set screw on underside of gauge housing and remove screw from upper part of housing.
2. Pull gauge assembly from instrument cluster.
3. Separate face from back (3 screws).
4. Remove gauge unit (4 nuts).
5. Reverse procedure to install.

1967 Speedometer

1. Loosen set screw at bottom of speedometer pod.
2. Remove screw from upper inner surface of pod.
3. Pull speedometer and pod assembly straight and away from instrument panel.
4. Remove speedometer from front housing (3 screws).
5. Remove speedometer from rear housing (2 screws).
6. Reverse procedure to install.

1966

The fuel gauge, oil pressure gauge and temperature gauge can be replaced without removing the instrument cluster. To replace the speedometer, constant voltage regulator or charge indicator gauge it is necessary to remove the cluster.
1. Disconnect battery ground cable.
2. Remove light switch and radio knobs.
3. Remove instrument panel (2 pieces).
4. Remove light switch screws and push switch toward front of car.
5. Remove console panel finish molding cap, then remove left lower half of cluster housing (5 screws).
6. Remove clock housing screws and rotate clock housing upward and rearward to expose the two tab screws retaining instrument panel upper molding. Remove these screws.
7. Remove five screws under cluster. Pull molding away from instrument panel for access to cluster screws.

8. Remove four instrument indicator cover screws and remove covers.
9. Through indicator openings, remove four screws retaining lower cluster to upper cluster. Position four instrument covers on instruments to prevent damage. Install retaining screw on charge indicator cover.
10. Remove four screws retaining speedometer cluster to instrument panel at top of cluster, and position speedometer cluster out from instrument panel.
11. Disconnect light bulbs from across top of speedometer. Remove wiring harness from plastic clips, disconnect speedometer cable and constant voltage regulator wires and remove speedometer cluster.
12. Unfasten and remove speedometer housing. Then separate speedometer from housing cover.
13. Reverse procedure to install.

W/S WIPER MOTOR, REPLACE
1972

1. Disconnect battery ground cable.
2. Remove wiper arm and blade assemblies.
3. Remove left cowl screen for access through cowl opening.
4. Disconnect linkage drive arm from motor output arm crankpin by removing the retaining clip.
5. From engine side of dash, disconnect wire connectors from motor.
6. Remove bolts that retain motor to dash and remove motor. If output arm catches on dash during removal, handturn the arm clockwise so it will clear.

1971

1. Remove wiper arm and blade assemblies.
2. Remove air cleaner.
3. Remove retaining screws and remove cowl top panel. Disconnect washer hose.
4. Remove the clip retaining the left wiper link to the motor and disconnect the link.
5. Disconnect both hydraulic lines from motor. Be careful not to burn hands with hot hydraulic fluid.
6. Remove the three bolts retaining motor to cowl. Disconnect wiper control cable and remove motor through left cowl opening.

1970

1. Disconnect battery ground cable.
2. Disconnect washer hose, remove three retaining bolts and pull the cowl top grille out from under two slips.
3. Disconnect connector plug (two plugs with intermittent wiper) from wiring harness at engine side of dash. Push wiring and plugs along with grommet through opening in dash panel.
4. Remove four motor-to-cowl retaining bolts. Lift motor out and at same time pull wiper arm and blade assembly to the left for access to the

motor crank pin clip. Remove the clip and disconnect the drive link from the motor crank pin.

5. Remove three retaining bolts and separate motor from the mounting plate and cover and wiring harness assembly.

1967-69

Procedure remains the same as 1966 models except that the cowl top panel is retained with eight screws and the two rear hood panel bumpers instead of 14 retaining screws. The wiper motor is attached to the upper cowl panel with three screws instead of two.

1966

1. Remove wiper arm and blades.
2. Remove pivot shaft bezel.
3. Remove air cleaner.
4. Remove cowl top panel (14 screws).
5. Remove seal plate from dash panel (2 screws).
6. Remove two clips retaining wiper links to motor. Rotate link to remove left clip.
7. Disconnect hydraulic line under hood.
8. Disconnect hydraulic line in cowl from motor.
9. Unfasten motor from mounting bracket (2 bolts). Disconnect control cable and remove motor.

W/S WIPER SWITCH, REPLACE

1972

1. Remove instrument cluster finish panel.
2. Remove wiper switch mounting plate.
3. Disconnect cigar lighter and wiper switch wires.
4. Remove switch bezel nut and remove switch.

1970-71

1. Disconnect battery ground cable.
2. Remove five screws retaining upper edge of instrument cluster pad and retainer assembly to the instrument panel pad and remove the pad and retainer assembly from the face of the cluster.
3. Remove the three screws retaining the rear vent and wiper control pod and pull the pod from the instrument panel. On 1971 models, note positions of vacuum hoses for reference during installation. Disconnect vacuum hoses and electrical connector and remove illumination bulbs.
4. On 1971 models, remove clip retaining the control cable to the control and remove the control assembly.
5. Remove control knobs and remove the two screws retaining switch and remove the switch.

1968-69

1. Disconnect battery ground cable.
2. Remove five screws attaching the top of the cluster bezel to the instrument panel. Loosen five screws at-

taching bottom of the bezel to the instrument panel pad retainer and remove the bezel.

3. Remove three screws attaching the wiper and rear vent control to the instrument panel.
4. Disconnect vacuum hoses, lights and push on connector; remove the cable retaining clip; and remove the control assembly from the cluster.
5. Remove the knobs from control assembly.
6. Remove two wiper control attaching screws and remove control.
7. Reverse procedure to install.

1967

Procedure remains the same as 1966 models except for the differences stated under *W/S Wiper Motor, Replace*

1966

1. Disconnect battery cable.
2. Remove wiper, washer and right-and left-hand air vent control knobs.
3. Unfasten and lower clock housing. Then disconnect two courtesy light wires (4 screws).
4. Unfasten wiper control from control plate (2 screws).
5. Remove wiper arms and blades.
6. Remove wiper pivot shaft bezel and nuts.
7. Remove cowl top panel (14 screws).
8. Disconnect control cable from motor.
9. From passenger compartment, pull cable through dash panel and remove wiper control and cable assembly.
10. Reverse above procedure to install. However, before connecting courtesy light wires, be sure to position one wire over wiper control cable and the other wire over air vent control cable.

W/S WIPER TRANSMISSION, REPLACE

1972

1. Disconnect battery ground cable and remove wiper arm and blade assemblies.
2. Remove cowl screen and left arm and blade stop.
3. Disconnect linkage drive arm from motor by removing retaining clip.
4. Remove pivot shaft retaining bolts and remove linkage and pivot shaft assemblies.

NOTE: When installing, be sure to force the linkage connecting clip into the locked position.

1971

1. Remove wiper arm and blade assemblies. Be sure to release tension arm retaining clip from the tension arm retaining stud on the left pivot assembly.
2. Remove retaining screws and remove the cowl vent grille. Disconnect windshield washer hoses.
3. Remove clip retaining the link assembly to the motor. Remove screws

retaining pivot shaft and link assembly to the cowl and remove the pivot shaft and link assembly.

1970

1. Disconnect battery ground cable.
2. Disconnect washer hose and remove cowl vent top panel.
3. Disconnect drive link from motor.
4. Remove retaining clip and disconnect both links from right pivot shaft.
5. Remove three screws from the drive pivot plate at the right end of the cowl panel and withdraw the drive pivot plate and the two drive links as an assembly.
6. Remove the right pivot shaft assembly (three screws).
7. Remove the three left pivot shaft screws and withdraw the left pivot shaft and link as an assembly.

1967-69

Procedure remains the same as 1966 models except for the differences stated under *W/S Wiper Motor, Replace*.

1966

1. Remove wiper arms and blades.
2. Remove wiper pivot shaft bezel and nuts.
3. Remove cowl top panel (14 screws).
4. Remove clip retaining link to motor. Rotate link to remove left clips.
5. Remove one nut and two bolts retaining pivot shaft and link to cowl and remove.
6. Reverse above procedure to install.

RADIO, REPLACE

NOTE: When installing radio, be sure to adjust antenna trimmer for peak performance.

1972

1. Disconnect battery ground cable.
2. Pull radio knobs off shafts.
3. Remove nut from radio control shafts.
4. Remove radio rear support attaching screw at instrument panel.
5. Disconnect power and speaker wires at connectors.
6. Disconnect antenna lead and remove radio.

1970-71

1. Disconnect battery ground cable.
2. Pull knobs off radio control shafts and remove cover plate located below steering column.
3. Remove the nut from the right radio control shaft.
4. Remove six screws and remove the trim applique from in front of radio.
5. Remove nut and washer from right radio control shaft.
6. Remove the screw attaching front left side of radio to instrument panel.
7. Remove radio rear support attaching screw.
8. Disconnect radio power wires at connectors.
9. Disconnect antenna lead-in cable and remove radio.

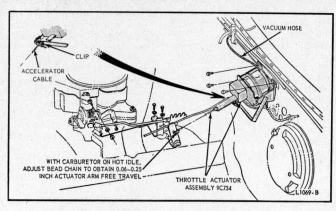

Fig. 7 Throttle actuator assembly. 1970-71

NOTE: When installing, apply body sealer between front and rear case halves and make sure core mounting gasket is properly installed.

1970-71

1. Remove hood and air cleaner and drain engine coolant.
2. Disconnect wiper hydraulic lines.
3. Disconnect heater hoses at heater core.
4. Disconnect vacuum hose at top of housing and remove oil pressure sender unit from back of engine.
5. Remove transmission dip stick and tube assembly.
6. Disconnect multiple connector leading to icing switch.
7. Remove evaporator housing front cover.
8. Remove heater core housing cover.
9. Remove heater core retaining bracket and remove the core.
10. Reverse the procedure to install.

1967-69

1. Remove hood and carburetor air cleaner.
2. Disconnect vacuum supply hose on top of heater case and pull it away from case mounting studs and disconnect hydraulic lines at wiper motor.
3. Remove transmission dipstick and tube.
4. Disconnect multiple connector leading to thermostat switch inside heater case cover and to resistor on front of cover.
5. Remove five nuts and two screws from heater core case cover and take off cover.
6. Slide heater core from case.

1966

1. Remove molding from right instrument panel and from right side of console.
2. Remove three screws and two bolts from lower right instrument panel and remove panel.

1968-69

1. Disconnect battery ground cable.
2. Pull knobs off radio control shafts.
3. Remove cover plate located below steering column.
4. Remove six screws and remove trim applique from in front of radio.
5. Remove nut and washer from right radio control shaft.
6. Remove screw attaching the front left side of radio to instrument panel.
7. Remove radio rear support attaching screw.
8. Disconnect radio power wires and speaker leads at connectors.
9. Disconnect antenna lead in cable and remove radio.
10. Reverse procedure to install.

1967

1. Disconnect ground strap from battery.
2. Remove inspection hole cover plate below steering column.
3. It may be necessary to remove vacuum motor on inboard side of tilt swing column to provide clearance for radio. If so, position wheel in any position but PARK, and remove vacuum motor.
4. Remove two knobs and discs from radio.
5. Remove sleeve or fader control and two hex nuts on radio shafts.
6. Remove radio rear support bracket.
7. Slide radio forward and down toward inspection hole.
8. Disconnect multiple connector and antenna lead-in cable and remove radio.
9. Reverse procedure to install.

1966

1. Pry off right and left side console mouldings and remove retainers.
2. Pry off right and left side instrument panel chrome mouldings.
3. Remove six screws and two bolts retaining lower right and left side finish mouldings to instrument panel and pull finish panels away from instrument panel.
4. Remove right and left side console finish panels.
5. Unfasten lower end of radio from support brackets (2 screws).
6. Remove radio knobs and bezel nuts.

7. Disconnect antenna and speaker connectors and remove radio.

HEATER CORE REMOVAL
1972

1. Drain coolant and disconnect heater hoses from core.
2. Remove glove box.
3. Remove heater air outlet register from plenum assembly (2 snap clips).
4. Remove temperature control cable assembly mounting screw and disconnect end of cable from blend door crank arm (1 spring nut).
5. Remove the blue and red vacuum hoses from the high-low door vacuum motor; the yellow hose from the panel-defrost door motor, and the brown hose at the inline tee connector to the temperature by-pass door motor.
6. Disconnect wiring connector from resistor.
7. Remove ten screws from around flange of plenum case and remove the rear case half of the plenum.
8. Remove mounting nut from heater core tube support bracket.
9. Remove core.

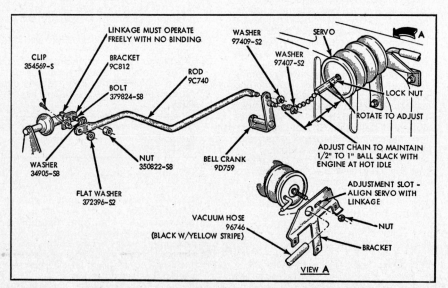

Fig. 8 Servo assembly and accelerator linkage. 1967-69

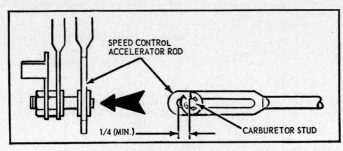

Fig. 9   Accelerator linkage adjustment. 1966

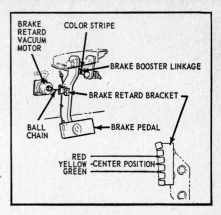

Fig. 10   Brake retard ball chain adjustment. 1966

3. Disconnect heater resistor plug and remove seven screws from recirculating air grille and take off grille.
4. Remove two screws from front of heater core cover and loosen seven nuts from engine side of dash that secure heater assembly.
5. Pull heater away from dash, disconnect cable and push fresh air duct out of the way to reach rear screws of heater core housing.
6. Remove two screws from rear of housing and take out core.

SPEED CONTROLS

1972

Adjust the bead chain to obtain .06-.25" actuator arm free travel when the engine is at hot idle. The adjustment should be made to take as much slack as possible out of the chain without restricting the carburetor lever from returning to idle. On vehicles with a solenoid anti-diesel valve, perform this adjustment with the ignition switch in the ON position.

1970-71

Linkage Adjustment

Adjust the bead chain to obtain .06-.25" actuator arm free travel when the engine is at hot idle, Fig. 7.

1967-69

Bead Chain Adjustment

This is the only adjustment required for proper functioning of the system and assure a normal engine idle.

Adjust the chain to maintain ½" to 1" ball slack with engine at hot idle, Fig. 8.

1966

Accelerator Linkage Adjust

Improper accelerator linkage adjustment can result in engine not returning to normal idle, the system not controlling at high speeds, or a lag in response to speed changes.
1. Remove air cleaner.
2. Check adjustment of throttle linkage to be sure it is correct.
3. Place linkage against hot idle adjusting screw with engine stopped.
4. Loosen adjusting nuts on vacuum bellows.
5. With vacuum bellows in released

position, move adjusting nuts until there is about ¼ inch clearance between carburetor stud and end of slot in accelerator, Fig. 9.
6. Tighten adjusting nuts and install air cleaner.

Brake Retard Ball Chain, Adjust

The brake retard bracket has five notches in which to attach the ball chain. To obtain proper deceleration, the ball chain must be installed in the bracket as per color coding, Fig. 10. The color coding is visible by looking up under the instrument panel. The color coding compensates for differences in building of the cars.

NOTE: The amount of deceleration provided by the brake retard system may be further adjusted to the individual driver's preference by lowering the ball chain one notch to increase the rate of deceleration. Raising the ball chain one notch will decrease the rate of deceleration.

Engine Section

Service procedures on the V8-400 are covered in the Ford & Mercury car chapters

ENGINE, REPLACE

Because of engine compartment tolerances, the engine should not be removed and installed with the transmission attached.
1. Drain cooling system and crankcase.
2. Remove radiator and air cleaner.
3. Remove hood.
4. Remove fuel and vacuum lines and all hoses, wires and linkage attached to engine.
5. Disconnect exhaust pipe from manifolds.
6. Remove starter and automatic transmission filler tube (if equipped).
7. Remove converter or flywheel housing lower cover.
8. Remove clutch release linkage (if equipped).
9. Support transmission with jack.
10. Unfasten converter or flywheel housing from engine.
11. Remove engine mounting bolts and lift engine out of chassis.

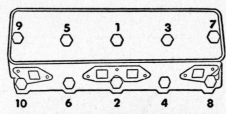

Fig. 1   Cylinder head tightening sequence

CYLINDER HEAD REPLACE

NOTES

Before installing cylinder head, wipe off engine block gasket surface and be certain no foreign material has fallen into cylinder bores, bolt holes or in the valve lifter area. It is good practice to clean out bolt holes with compressed air.

Some cylinder head gaskets are coated

with a special lacquer to provide a good seal once the parts have warmed up. Do not use any additional sealer on such gaskets. If the gasket does not have this lacquer coating, apply suitable sealer to both sides.

Tighten cylinder head bolts at little at a time in three steps in the sequence shown in the illustrations. Final tightening should be to the torque specifications listed in the *Engine Tightening* table. After the bolts have been torqued to specifications, *they should not be disturbed.*

In instances where cylinder head gasket leakage is hard to control, aluminum paint can be applied to the gasket as a sealer.

Spray one coat of the aluminum paint on both sides of the gasket and allow the paint to dry. Then spray a second coat on both sides and, while the paint is still wet, install the gasket. Torque the head and manifold bolts to specifications to complete the job.

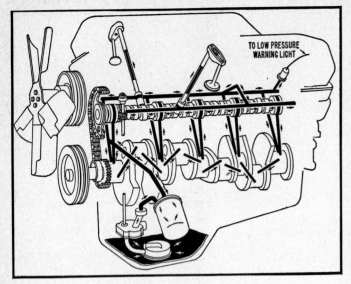

Engine lubrication system. V8-390, 428

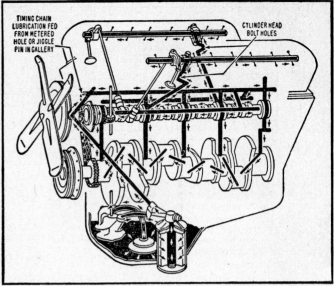

Engine lubrication system. V8-429

1966-72

1. Remove intake manifold, carburetor and radiator supply tank as a unit.
2. Disconnect exhaust pipes from manifolds. It may also be necessary to unbolt and lay aside the power steering pump, air conditioning compressor and mounting bracket. On 1968-72 models, remove air conditioning evaporator housing and capillary tube as an assembly from dash panel.
3. Remove bolts and lift off head.
4. Install cylinder heads in reverse order of removal and tighten bolts in the sequence shown in Fig. 1.

NOTE

The cylinder head gaskets are marked "Top" or "Front" stamped near the front end of the gasket. The gasket is properly installed when the word is at the forward end of the engine and water passage holes line up. This results in the sealing beads on the right head gasket being inverted with respect to the left head gasket.

spring washers. Slide rocker arms, springs and supports off shaft, being sure to identify all parts so they can be assembled in the same position.

If it is necessary to remove the plugs from each end of the shaft, drill or pierce one plug, then insert a steel rod through the plug and knock out the plug on the opposite end. Working from the open end, knock out the remaining plug.

Assemble the rocker arms and related parts, Fig. 2.

VALVE LIFT SPECS.

Engine	Year	Intake	Exhaust
8-390	1966-67	.437	.437
	1968	.440	.440
8-400	1972	.422	.427
8-428	1966-67	.437	.437
8-429	1968-72	.443	.486

VALVE TIMING
Intake Opens Before TDC

Engine	Year	Degrees
8-390	1966-67	16
	1968	18
8-400	1972	17
8-428	1966-67	16
8-429	1968-71	16
	1972	8

VALVE ARRANGEMENT
Front to Rear

V8-390, 428 .... E-I-E-I-I-E-I-E
V8-400, 429 Right Bank .... I-E-I-E-I-E-I-E
V8-400, 429 Left Bank .... E-I-E-I-E-I-E-I

VALVES, ADJUST
1969-72, V8-429

A positive stop rocker arm stud and nut is used to eliminate the need of adjusting

ROCKER ARM STUDS
V8-429

Rocker arm studs are screwed into threaded bores in the cylinder head bosses. To install, apply water resistant sealer to stud threads that screw into cylinder head. Install stud and torque to 65-75 ft-lbs. Apply Lubriplate to top of valve stem and at push rod guide in cylinder head. Install rocker arm, fulcrum and stud nut.

ROCKER ARM SERVICE
V8-390, 428

To disassemble the rocker arms, remove cotter pins from each end of the shaft and remove the flat washers and

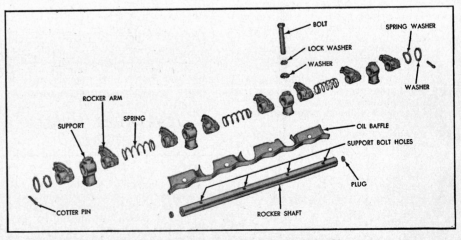

Fig. 2 Valve rocker shaft assembly. V8-390, 428

valve lash.

It is very important that the correct push rod be used and all components be installed and torqued as follows.

1. Position the piston of the cylinder being worked on at TDC of its compression stroke.
2. Install rocker arm stud and torque to 65-75 ft-lbs.
3. Lubricate and install rocker arm and fulcrum.
4. Thread nut onto stud until it contacts stud shoulder. Torque to 18-22 in-lbs.

1968 V8-429

Rotate crankshaft until No. 1 piston is on TDC at the end of compression stroke. Loosen rocker arm stud nut until there is end clearance in the push rod. This may be determined by moving the push rod with the fingers as the stud nut is tightened. When the push rod-to-rocker arm clearance has been eliminated, tighten the stud nut an additional 1 turn to place the hydraulic lifter in the desired operating range.

Repeat this procedure for the remaining set of valves in the firing order sequence, which is 1-5-4-2-6-3-7-8.

V8-390, 428

For these engines a .060" shorter push rod (color coded white) or a .060" longer push rod (color coded yellow) are available for service to provide a means of compensating for dimensional changes in the valve mechanism. Valve stem-to-rocker arm clearance should be as listed in the *Valve Specifications* table, with the hydraulic lifter completely collapsed. Repeated valve grind jobs will decrease this clearance to the point that if not compensated for the lifters will cease to function.

To check the clearance, bring the piston of the cylinder being checked on top dead center of the compression stroke. Then with hydraulic lifter collapsed, check the clearance between valve stem and rocker arm. If the clearance is less than the minimum, the .060" shorter push rod should be used. If clearance is more than the maximum, the .060" longer push rod should be used. (See *Valve Specifications* table).

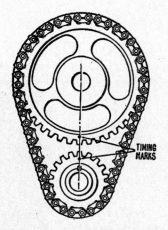

Fig. 4   Valve timing marks. V8-390, 428, 429

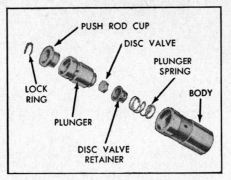

Fig. 3   Hydraulic valve lifter (typical)

VALVE GUIDES

Valve guides in these engines are an integral part of the head and, therefore, cannot be removed. For service, guides can be reamed oversize to accommodate one of three service valves with oversize stems (.003", .015" and .030").

Check the valve stem clearance of each valve (after cleaning) in its respective valve guide. If the clearance exceeds the service limits of .004" on the intake or .005" on the exhaust, ream the valve guides to accommodate the next oversize diameter valve.

HYDRAULIC VALVE LIFTERS

The internal parts of each hydraulic valve lifter assembly are a matched set. If these are mixed, improper valve operation may result. Therefore, disassemble, inspect and test each assembly separately to prevent mixing the parts, Fig. 3.

TIMING CASE COVER

NOTE: If it becomes necessary to replace the oil seal in the timing case cover the cover must be removed.

1969-71, V8-429

1. Drain cooling system and crankcase.
2. Remove fan and shroud.
3. Remove radiator.
4. Remove drive belts and water pump pulley. Remove compressor support if so equipped.
5. Remove bolt and washer attaching crankshaft damper. Remove damper with suitable puller. Remove Woodruff key from crankshaft.
6. Remove power steering pump.
7. Remove fuel pump.
8. Remove front cover to cylinder block bolts. Cut the oil pan seal flush with cylinder block face prior to separating cover from cylinder block. Remove front cover and water pump as a unit.

1968 V8-429

1. Drain cooling system and crankcase.
2. Remove fan assembly. If air conditioned, remove bolts retaining fan assembly to water pump shaft. Remove

screws retaining radiator shroud to radiator. Remove fan assembly and radiator shroud.
3. Disconnect radiator hoses at engine and oil cooler lines at radiator.
4. Remove radiator upper support and remove radiator.
5. Unfasten power steering pump brackets from engine and position pump and brackets out of way.
6. Loosen alternator adjusting bolt and if air conditioned loosen compressor idler pulley. Remove drive belts and water pump pulley.
7. Unfasten alternator brackets from engine and position alternator and bracket out of way.
8. Disconnect heater hose at water pump and loosen bypass hose clamp at intake manifold.
9. Remove vibration damper and sleeve from crankshaft.
10. Disconnect fuel lines at pump and remove fuel pump. Plug pump inlet line.
11. Remove bolts retaining front cover to block and remove front cover and water pump as an assembly. If new front cover is to be installed, remove water pump and install on new front cover.
12. Remove oil pan and oil pump as described further on.
13. Reverse above procedure to install.

1966-68 V8-390, 428

1. Drain cooling system and crankcase.
2. Disconnect battery ground cable.
3. Remove fuel pump, leaving it attached to flexible fuel line.
4. Remove oil pan.
5. Remove radiator.
6. If air conditioned, unfasten and move condenser forward. *Do not disconnect refrigerant lines.* Remove condenser drive belt.
7. If equipped with Thermactor, remove air pump drive belt.
8. Wire power steering pump to left side of car in a position that will prevent oil from draining out.
9. Remove water pump.
10. Remove vibration damper, crankshaft sleeve and front cover.
11. Reverse procedure to install.

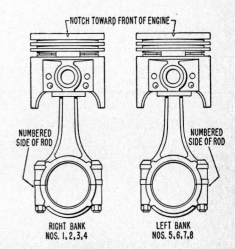

Fig. 5   Piston and rod assembly

TIMING CHAIN

1966-72

1. To remove the chain, first take off the front cover as outlined previously.
2. Crank engine until timing mark on camshaft sprocket is adjacent to timing mark on crankshaft sprocket, Fig. 4.
3. Remove camshaft sprocket cap screw and fuel pump eccentric.
4. Slide both sprockets and chain forward and remove as an assembly.
5. Reverse foregoing procedure to install the chain, being sure to align the timing marks as shown.

CAMSHAFT, REPLACE

1968-72, V8-429

1. Remove timing cover, chain and sprockets as outlined previously.
2. Remove intake manifold and carburetor as an assembly.
3. Remove rocker arm covers. Back off rocker arm stud nuts, turn rocker arms sideways and remove push rods in sequence.
4. Remove valve lifters.
5. If air conditioned, discharge refrigeration system. Disconnect line to evaporator at receiver dryer. Unfasten condenser from radiator support and position out of way.
6. Remove camshaft thrust plate retaining bolts and carefully remove camshaft from engine.
7. Reverse above procedure to install.

1966-68 V8-390, 428

1. Remove front cover as outlined above.
2. Remove valve rocker arm assemblies.
3. Remove distributor cap and spark plug wires as an assembly.
4. Remove distributor.
5. Remove push rods.
6. Remove valve lifters. *In some cases it may be necessary to transfer the lifter over to an adjoining push rod opening in order to remove it.*
7. Remove oil pan and pump screen.
8. Remove timing chain and sprockets.
9. Remove camshaft thrust plate and spacer, then remove camshaft from engine.
10. Reverse above procedure to install.

CAMSHAFT BEARINGS

When necessary to replace camshaft bearings, the engine will have to be removed from the vehicle and the plug at the rear of the cylinder block will have to be removed in order to utilize the special camshaft bearing removing and installing tools required to do this job. If properly installed, camshaft bearings require no reaming—nor should this type bearing be reamed or altered in any manner in an attempt to fit bearings.

PISTON & ROD, ASSEMBLE

All V8's

Assemble the pistons to the rods as shown in Fig. 5.

PISTONS, PINS & RINGS

Pistons are available in oversizes of .003, .020, .030, .040 and .060".
Piston pins are available in oversizes of .001 and .002".
Rings are available in oversizes of .002, .010, .020, .030 and .040".

MAIN & ROD BEARINGS

Main and rod bearings are available in undersizes of .002, .010, .020 and .030".

OIL PAN, REPLACE

1968-72, V8-429

1. Disconnect radiator shroud from radiator if so equipped and position over fan.
2. Raise car on a hoist and drain crankcase.
3. Disconnect engine front support insulators from underbody crossmember. Place floor jack under front edge of oil pan, with block of wood between jack and oil pan. Raise engine just enough to insert 1¼" blocks of wood between insulators and underbody side members. Remove floor jack.
4. Disconnect starter cable, unfasten and remove starter.
5. Remove end attachments of stabilizer bar and rotate ends of bar down to raise center of bar. Remove oil filter.
6. Unbolt and remove oil pan ahead of underbody crossmember.
7. Reverse above procedure to install.

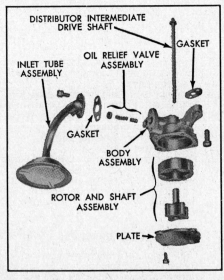

DISTRIBUTOR INTERMEDIATE DRIVE SHAFT

GASKET

INLET TUBE ASSEMBLY

OIL RELIEF VALVE ASSEMBLY

GASKET

BODY ASSEMBLY

ROTOR AND SHAFT ASSEMBLY

PLATE

Fig 6   Rotor type oil pump

1966-68 V8-390, 428

1. Drain crankcase and remove oil lever dipstick.
2. Remove pan screws and lower pan to crossmember.
3. Position crankshaft so that counterweight will clear oil pan.
4. Unfasten and place oil pump, screen and intermediate drive shaft in pan.
5. Remove oil pan and pump.

NOTE: *When installing, place pump in pan and position pan on crossmember. Do not attempt to force oil pump into position if it will not seat readily. The drive shaft hex may be misaligned with distributor shaft. To align, rotate intermediate shaft into a new position if necessary.*

OIL PUMP REPAIRS

Rotor Type Pump, Fig. 6

1. With all parts clean and dry, check the inside of the pump housing and the outer race and rotor for damage or excessive wear.
2. Check the mating surface of the pump cover for wear. If this surface is worn, scored or grooved, replace the cover.
3. Measure the clearance between the outer race and housing. This clearance should be .006-.009".
4. With the rotor assembly installed in the housing, place a straight edge over the rotor assembly and housing. Measure the clearance between the straight edge and the rotor and outer race. Recommended limits are .001-.0035". *The outer race, shaft and rotor are furnished only as an assembly.*
5. Check the drive shaft-to-housing bearing clearance by measuring the O.D. of the shaft and the I.D. of the housing bearing. The recommended clearance limits are .0015-.0029".
6. Inspect the relief valve spring for a collapsed or worn condition.
7. Check the relief valve piston for scores and free operation in the bore. The specified piston clearance is .0015-.0029".

WATER PUMP, REPLACE

1968-72, V8-429

Refer to procedure for removing timing cover mentioned previously.

1966-68 V8-390, 428

1. Drain cooling system.
2. If equipped, remove power steering drive belt and wire pump to left side of car in a position that will prevent oil from draining out.
3. If air conditioned, remove compressor drive belt.
4. Unfasten and move alternator or generator inward and remove fan belt.
5. Remove fan and pulley.
6. If equipped with fan drive clutch, re-

move clutch and fan.
7. Remove water pump pulley.
8. Disconnect hoses at water pump.
9. Remove pump for engine.

FUEL PUMP, REPLACE

1. Remove all gasket material from the pump and block gasket surfaces.

Apply sealer to both sides of new gasket.
2. Position gasket on pump flange and hold pump in position against its mounting surface. Make sure rocker arm is riding on camshaft eccentric.
3. Press pump tight against its mounting. Install retaining screws and tighten them alternately.
4. Connect fuel lines. Then operate engine and check for leaks.

SERVICE NOTE: Before installing the pump, it is good practice to crank the engine so that the nose of the camshaft eccentric is out of the way of the fuel pump rocker arm when the pump is installed. In this way there will be the least amount of tension on the rocker arm, thereby easing the installation of the pump.

Transmission Section

> NOTE: 1972 linkage adjustment information is in this section. Repair procedures on both automatic and manual shift transmissions are covered elsewhere in this manual. Procedures for removing automatic transmissions as well as linkage adjustments on 1966-71 models are included in the automatic transmission chapters. See Chapter Index.

1972 AUTO TRANS. LINKAGE, ADJUST

1. Place selector lever in D position tight against its stop.
2. Remove nut securing cable to transmission manual lever stud.
3. Shift manual lever at transmission into D position, second detent from back of transmission.
4. Place cable end on transmission manual lever stud, using care to align flats on stud with flats on cable. Start attaching nut.
5. Make sure that selector lever has not moved from D stop; then tighten nut at transmission stud to 10-15 ft. lbs.
6. Check operation for all selector positions.

Rear Axle, Propeller Shaft & Brakes

REAR AXLES

Fig. 1 illustrates the rear axle assembly used on these cars. When necessary to overhaul the unit, refer to the *Rear Axle Specifications* table in this chapter.

Description

In these axles, Fig. 1, the drive pinion is straddle-mounted by two opposed tapered roller bearings which support the pinion shaft in front of the drive pinon gear, and straight roller bearing that supports the pinion shaft at the rear of the pinion gear. The drive pinion is assembled in a pinion retainer that is bolted to the differential carrier. The tapered roller bearings are preloaded by a collapsible spacer between the bearings. The pinion is positioned by a shim or shims located between the drive pinion retainer and the differential carrier.

The differential is supported in the carrier by two tapered roller side bearings. These bearings are preloaded by two threaded ring nuts or sleeves between the bearings and pedestals. The differential

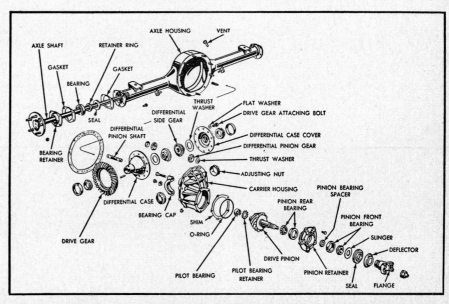

Fig. 1   Rear axle disassembled

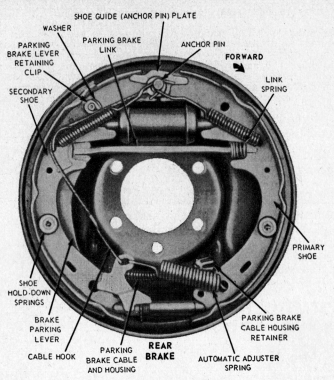

Fig. 2 Rear brake on 1966-72

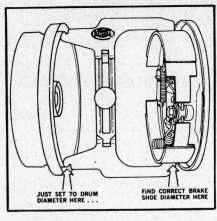

Fig. 3 Brake adjustment with gauge

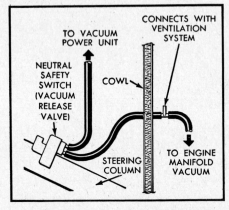

Fig. 4 Vacuum connections for automatic parking brake release. 1966-72

assembly is positioned for proper ring gear and pinion backlash by varying the adjustment of these ring nuts. The differential case houses two side gears in mesh with two pinions mounted on a pinion shaft which is held in place by a pin. The side gears and pinions are backed by thrust washers. With high performance engines, an optional rear axle having a four-pinion differential is also used.

The axle shafts are of unequal length, the left shaft being shorter than the right. The axle shafts are mounted in sealed ball bearings that are pressed on the shafts.

Diff. Carrier Assy.

Service Bulletin

All Ford Built Rear Axles: Recent manufacturing changes have eliminated the need for marking rear axle drive pinions for individual variations from nominal shim thicknesses. In the past, these pinion markings, with the aid of a shim selection table, were used as a guide to select correct shim thicknesses when a gear set or carrier assembly replacement was performed.

With the elimination of pinion markings, use of the shim selection table is no longer possible and the methods outlined below must be used.

1. Measure the thickness of the original pinion depth shim removed from the axle. Use the same thickness upon installation of the replacement carrier or drive pinion. If any further shim change is necessary, it will be indicated in the tooth pattern check.
2. If the original shim is lost, substitute a nominal shim for the original and use the tooth pattern check to de-

termine if further shim changes are required.

Remove & Replace

In servicing the rear axles it is not necessary to remove the rear axle assembly for any normal repairs. The axle shafts and carrier assembly can easily be removed from the vehicle, leaving the axle housing in place.

1. Place a drain pan under the carrier and housing to catch the old grease when the carrier is separated from the housing.
2. Use a wire brush to clean dirt from the area around the carrier and housing mating surfaces. Then wipe the area clean with a cloth dampened in solvent.
3. Remove axle shafts and drive shaft as explained below.
4. Unfasten carrier from housing and lift out carrier.
5. Reverse removal procedure to install, using a new gasket between the carrier and housing.

AXLE SHAFTS
Removal

1. Remove wheel assembly.
2. Remove brake drum from flange.
3. Working through hole provided in axle shaft flange, remove nuts that secure bearing retainer.
4. Pull axle shaft out of housing. If bearing is a tight fit in axle housing, use a slide hammer-type puller. *Brake carrier plate must not be dislodged. Install one nut to hold plate in place after axle shaft is removed.*

5. If axle shaft bearing is to be replaced, loosen inner retainer by nicking it deeply with a chisel in several places. On 1969-72 models, a $\frac{1}{4}$" hole must be drilled *not more than* $\frac{5}{16}$" *deep* in the retaining ring surface before using chisel. The bearing will then slide off easily.
6. Press bearing from axle shaft.
7. Inspect machined surfaces of axle shaft and housing for rough spots that would affect the sealing action of the oil seal. Carefully remove any burrs or rough spots.
8. Press new bearing on shaft until it seats firmly against shoulder on shaft.
9. Press inner bearing retainer on shaft until it seats firmly against bearing.
10. If oil seal is to be replaced, use a hook-type tool to pull it out of the housing. Wipe a small amount of oil resistant sealer on outer edge of seal before it is installed.

Installation

1. Place a new gasket on each side of brake carrier plate and slide axle shaft into housing. Start the splines into the differential side gear and push the shaft in until bearing bottoms in housing.
2. Install retainer and tighten nuts to

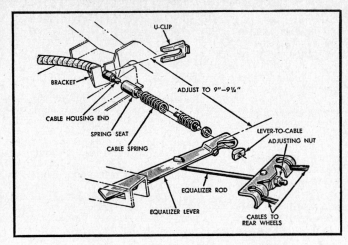

Fig. 5 Parking brake adjustments. 1966-67

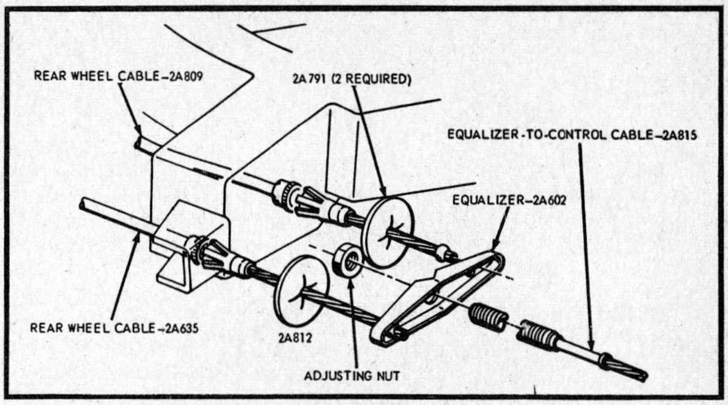

Fig. 6 Parking brake linkage. 1968-72

30-40 ft. lbs.
3. Install brake drum and wheel.

PROPELLER SHAFT
Remove & Replace

1. Disconnect rear U-joint from drive pinion flange.
2. Pull drive shaft toward rear of car until front U-joint yoke clears transmission extension housing and output shaft.
3. Install a suitable tool, such as a seal driver, in seal to prevent lube from leaking from transmission.
4. Before installing, check U-joints for freedom of movement. If a bind has resulted from misalignment after overhauling the U-joints, tap the ears of the drive shaft sharply to relieve the bind.
5. If rubber seal installed on end of transmission extension housing is damaged, install a new seal.
6. On an automatic transmission, lubricate yoke spline with special spline lubricant. *This spline is sealed so that transmission fluid does not "wash" away spline lubricant.*
7. Install yoke on transmission output shaft.
8. Install U-bolts and nuts which attach U-joint to pinion flange. Tighten U-bolts evenly to prevent binding U-joint bearings.

BRAKE ADJUSTMENTS
1970-72

A new self centering pressure differential valve is used which no longer requires bleeding at the opposite end of the car to cause the brake warning light to go out. This is now accomplished as follows:
1. Turn on ignition switch.
2. Depress the brake pedal. This will automatically center the plunger in the switch causing the light to go out.

Self-Adjusting Brakes

These brakes, Fig. 2, have self-adjusting shoe mechanisms that assure correct lining-to-drum clearances at all times. The automatic adjusters operate only when the brakes are applied when the car is moving rearward or when it comes to an uphill stop.

Although the brakes are self-adjusting, an initial adjustment is necessary when the brake shoes have been relined or replaced, or when the length of the star wheel adjuster has been changed during some other service operation.

Frequent usage of an automatic transmission forward range to halt reverse vehicle motion may prevent the automatic adjusters from functioning, thereby inducing low pedal heights. Should low pedal heights be encountered, it is recommended that numerous forward and reverse stops be made until satisfactory pedal height is obtained.

Service Note

If a low pedal height condition cannot be corrected by making numerous reverse stops (provided the hydraulic system is free of air) it indicates that the self-adjusting mechanism is not functioning. Therefore, it will be necessary to remove the brake drum, clean, free up and lubricate the adjusting mechanism. Then adjust the brakes as follows, being sure the parking brake is fully released.

Adjustment

1. Remove adjusting hole cover from brake backing plate and, from the backing plate side, turn the adjusting screw upward with a screwdriver or other suitable tool to expand the shoes until a slight drag is felt when the drum is rotated.
2. Remove the drum.
3. While holding the adjusting lever out of engagement with the adjusting screw, back off the adjusting screw ¾ turn with the fingers.

NOTE—*If finger movement will not turn the screw, free it up. If this is not done, the adjusting lever will not turn the screw during subsequent vehicle operation. Lubricate the screw with oil and coat with wheel bearing grease. Any other adjustment procedure may cause damage to the adjusting screw with consequent self-adjuster problems.*

4. Install wheel and drum, and adjusting hole cover. Adjust brakes on remaining wheels in the same manner.
5. If pedal height is not satisfactory, drive the vehicle and make sufficient reverse stops until proper pedal height is obtained.

Revised Brake Adjustment

The adjustment is made with the drums removed, using the brake gauge shown in Fig. 3. With the gauge, determine the inside diameter of the drum braking surface. Reverse the tool as shown and adjust the brake shoe diameter to fit the gauge. Hold the automatic adjusting lever out of engagement while rotating the adjusting screw to prevent burring the screw slots. Rotate the gauge around the brake shoes to be sure of the setting. After the brake drums and wheels have been installed, complete the adjustment by applying the brakes several times while backing the vehicle.

PARKING BRAKE, ADJUST
1966-72 Vacuum Release Unit

The vacuum power unit, Fig. 4, will release the parking brake automatically when the transmission selector lever is moved into any driving position with the engine running. The brakes will not release automatically, however, when the selector lever is in neutral or park position with the engine running, or in any other position with the engine off.

The lower end of the release handle extends out for alternate manual release in the event of vacuum power failure or for optional manual release at any time.

1970-72

1. Make sure parking brake is released.
2. Place transmission in neutral and raise the vehicle.
3. Tighten the adjusting nut against the cable equalizer to cause rear brakes to drag.

4. Then loosen the adjusting nut until the rear wheels are fully released. There should be no drag.
5. Lower vehicle and check operation.

1968-69

1. Check the parking cables when the brakes are fully released. If the cables are loose, adjust as follows:
2. Fully release parking brake pedal by pushing down the manual release lever.
3. Depress the parking brake pedal approximately 1¼".
4. Raise the vehicle. With the transmission in neutral, turn the adjusting nut forward against the equalizer, Fig. 6, until a moderate drag is felt when turning the rear wheels (approximately 100 lbs. of force at the outside diameter of the tire is required to turn the rear wheels).
5. Release the parking brake and check to be sure the brake shoes return to the fully released position.
6. Depress the parking brake pedal until it is fully engaged.
7. Release the parking brake again and check as in step 5.
8. If the rear brakes do not fully release, check the cables for kinks or binds and free as required.

1966-67

1. Check the parking brake cables when the service brakes are fully released. If cables are loose, adjust as follows:
2. Fully release parking brake pedal by pushing down manual release lever.
3. Raise car. Adjust equalizer lever against cable spring on pedal cable to the dimension shown in Fig. 5.
4. Loosen adjusting nut on equalizer rod, then turn lock nut in front of equalizer several turns forward.
5. Depress pedal 1¾" from its normal release position.
6. While turning rear wheels in rearward direction, turn adjusting nut against equalizer until a moderate drag is felt.
7. When cables are properly adjusted, tighten both nuts against equalizer.
8. Release parking brake and check to make sure brake shoes return to fully released position.
9. Depress parking brake pedal 2". Under normal conditions this will satisfactorily hold the car.
10. Release pedal again, then depress pedal ½"; the brakes should not drag.

POWER BRAKE UNIT, REPLACE

1966-72

1. Disconnect vacuum hose from booster.
2. Remove three bolts and loosen one to allow brace between cowl and spring tower to be positioned inboard to obtain clearance.
3. Remove master cylinder from booster. It is not necessary to disconnect brake lines.
4. Working under instrument panel, disconnect booster push rod link from brake pedal as follows: 1) disconnect stop light switch wires at connector and remove hairpin clip, 2) slide stop light switch off pedal just far enough for switch outer hole to clear pin, then tilt switch straight upward from pin, 3) slide master cylinder push rod and nylon washer and bushing from brake pedal pin.
5. Unfasten and remove booster from dash panel, sliding push rod link out from engine side of dash panel.
6. Remove dust seal from push rod link and place it in slot of dash panel for installation.
7. Reverse procedure to install.

Front End & Steering Section

FRONT SUSPENSION

1966

This suspension, Fig. 1, has the coil springs mounted on the upper control arm at the lower end and a spring guide at the upper end. Ball joints connect the steering knuckle to the upper and lower control arms.

1967-72

The construction of these units differs from earlier models in that the lower control arm pivots on a bolt in the front crossmember. The struts, which are connected between the lower control arms and frame crossmember, prevent the control arms for moving forward or backward. Service is the same as that for 1967 Ford full size models.

LUBRICATION

Lubrication should be performed at 36,000-mile intervals at which time the special plugs should be removed and specially formulated grease applied with a hand-operated gun. This extended lubrication interval is made possible by a special type chassis lubricant combined with special seals and bearing materials. Under no circumstances should the special plugs be removed and fittings installed to accommodate conventional type grease as damage to the special seals may result.

WHEEL ALIGNMENT

1966

Camber—Adjust camber by removing or installing shims between pivot bracket of lower control arm and mounting bracket underbody in engine compartment, Fig. 2.

Removal of shims will increase camber; installing shims will decrease camber. A 1/16" shim change will change camber angle 1/3°.

Caster—Adjustment is made by repositioning strut on lower control arm as shown in Fig. 2. Adjust caster by loosening rear retaining bolts and lift strut so that strut serrations will be free from serrations on lower arm.

Lengthen distance of "Dimension A", Fig. 2 to decrease caster and shorten distance to increase caster angle. Tighten rearward nuts that retain strut to lower control arm and recheck caster and camber.

1967-72

Wheel alignment is adjusted in the same manner as described for 1967 Ford Full Size models.

TOE-IN, ADJUST

Turn both tie rod adjusting sleeves an equal amount until toe-in is correct.

WHEEL BEARINGS, ADJUST

1966-72

1. While rotating wheel assembly, torque adjusting nut to 15-20 ft.-lbs. to seat bearings.
2. Locate nut lock on adjusting nut so that slots on nut lock are aligned with cotter pin hole in spindle.
3. Back off both adjusting nut and nut lock together until next slot on nut lock aligns with cotter pin hole in spindle.
4. Secure cotter pin and check for free rotation of wheel.

WHEEL BEARINGS, REPLACE

(Disc Brakes)

1. Raise car and remove front wheels.
2. Remove caliper mounting bolts.

NOTE: It is not necessary to disconnect brake lines for this operation.

3. Slide caliper off of disc, inserting a spacer between the shoes to hold pistons in their bores after the caliper is removed. Position caliper assembly out of the way.

NOTE: Do not allow caliper to hang

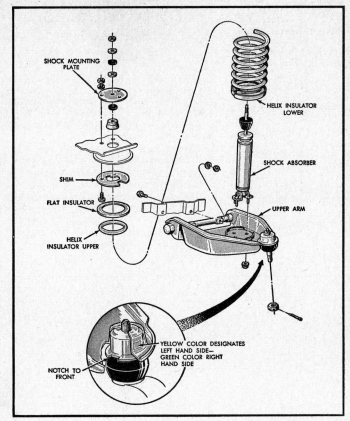

Fig. 1 Front suspension details. 1966

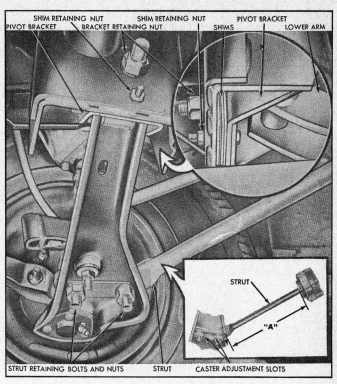

Fig. 2 Camber and caster adjustments. 1966

by the brake line.

4. Remove hub and disc assembly. Grease retainer and inner bearing can now be removed.

CHECKING BALL JOINTS FOR WEAR

If loose ball joints are suspected, first be sure the front wheel bearings are properly adjusted and that the control arms are tight. Then check ball joints as follows:

Referring to Fig. 3, raise wheel with a jack placed under the suspension as shown. Then test by moving the wheel up and down to axial play, and rocking it at the top and bottom to measure radial pay.

On 1966 models, the upper ball joint should be replaced if radial play exceeds .250" and axial play exceeds .060". Lower ball joint should be replaced if there is any noticeable looseness at the joint.

On 1967-72 models, the upper ball joint should be replaced if there is any noticeable looseness at the joint. Lower ball joint should be replaced if radial play exceeds .250", and if there is any noticeable axial play at the joint.

BALL JOINTS, REPLACE

The upper and lower ball joints are riveted to the control arms. On later models, the upper ball joint is pressed

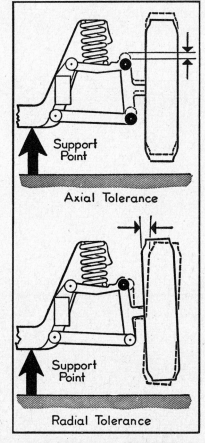

Fig. 3 Checking ball joints for wear. 1966

into the upper control arm whereas the lower ball joint is riveted to the lower control arm.

When replacing a riveted ball joint, remove the rivets and retain the ball joint to its control arm with the bolts, nuts and washers furnished with the ball joint kit. Also, use a suitable pressing tool to force the ball joint studs out of the spindle.

SHOCK ABSORBER, REPLACE

1967-72

To remove a shock absorber, unfasten it from the frame at its upper end. Remove the two cap screws that retain the shock absorber mounting plate to the lower control arm and lower the shock absorber unit.

To install, reverse the removal procedure and tighten the two lower cap screws to 13-18 lbs. ft. torque.

1966

When installing, position the shock absorber and upper mounting plate in place and install mounting plate bolts and dash panel brace nuts. Lower car slightly with safety stands under lower control arm. This will raise upper arm enough to position lower shock absorber stud through hole at bottom of spring lower seat. Secure shock absorber to spring seat by installing insulator, washer and retaining nut.

COIL SPRING, REPLACE
1966

1. With safety stand under lower control arm, remove wheel, shock absorber and upper control arm bumper and bracket.
2. Raise car slightly in order to lower upper control arm.
3. Insert a lock bar through top of spring and position bar on 7th coil from bottom and compress spring until top coils are drawn out of spring upper seat.
4. Remove 4 bolts attaching lower spring seat to upper arm and remove spring and lower seat as an assembly.
5. If a new spring is being installed, tape rubber insulator to upper end of spring in 3 places. Fasten spring seat to spring and install spring in reverse order of removal.

1967-72

1. Disconnect stabilizer at lower control arm.
2. Disconnect lower end of shock absorber and push it up to the retracted position.
3. Loosen lower ball joint stud nut one or two turns. Tap spindle at lower ball joint area to loosen stud from spindle.
4. Place a floor jack under lower arm at a 60° angle away from wheel and toward center of car. Hook saddle of jack under outer edge of spring seat.
5. Remove nut from lower ball stud and slowly lower arm until spring is extended.
6. Apply foot pressure to lower arm to push arm inward so that spring can be removed.
7. Reverse procedure to install.

POWER STEERING, REPLACE
1966-72

1. Disconnect pressure and return lines from steering gear. Cap each line and plug each port to prevent entry of dirt.
2. Remove bolt that secures flex joint to steering gear.
3. Loosen bolt that attaches flex joint to steering shaft.
4. With a pry bar, carefully loosen flex joint from steering shaft.
5. Remove two bolts that secure left strut to underside of car and remove strut.
6. Use a puller to remove pitman arm.
7. Unfasten (3 bolts) and remove gear.
8. Reverse procedure to install.

LINCOLN CONTINENTAL

*This material covered only in the "Service Trade Edition" of this manual.

INDEX OF SERVICE OPERATIONS

LINCOLN CONTINENTAL

SERIAL & ENGINE NUMBER LOCATION
Vehicle Warranty Plate on Left Front Door Pillar

1966

1967

1968

1969 Continental

ENGINE IDENTIFICATION
*Serial number on vehicle Warranty Plate.

Engine code for 1966–72 is the last letter in the serial number.

Year	Engine	Engine Code*
1966–67	V8-462	G
1968–69	V8-460	A
	V8-462	G
1971–72	V8-460	A

1969-71 Mark III

1970 Continental

1971 Continental

1972 Continental

1972 Mark IV

GENERAL ENGINE SPECIFICATIONS

Year	Engine	Car-buretor	Bore and Stroke	Piston Displacement, Cubic Inches	Compression Ratio	Maximum Brake H.P. @ R.P.M.	Maximum Torque Lbs. Ft. @ R.P.M.	Normal Oil Pressure Pounds
1966–68	340 Horsepower............V8-462	4 Barrel	4.3800 x 3.830	462	10.25	340 @ 4600	485 @ 2800	35–55
1968–70	365 Horsepower............V8-460	4 Barrel	4.3600 x 3.850	460	10.5	365 @ 4600	500 @ 2800	35–60
1971	365 Horsepower............V8-460	4 Barrel	4.3600 x 3.850	460	10.2	365 @ 4600	500 @ 2800	35–60
1972	212 Horsepower①..........V8-460	4 Barrel	4.3600 x 3.850	460	8.50	212 @ 4400	342 @ 2800	35–60
	224 Horsepower①..........V8-460	4 Barrel	4.3600 x 3.850	460	8.50	224 @ 4400	357 @ 2800	35–60

①—Ratings are NET—as installed in the vehicle.

TUNE UP SPECIFICATIONS

OLD CAR SPECIFICATIONS: For 1946-65 Tune Up Specifications see back of book.

★When using a timing light, disconnect vacuum hose or tube at distributor and plug opening in hose or tube so idle speed will not be affected.

Year	Engine	Spark Plug		Distributor		Firing Order	Ignition Timing ★		Hot Idle Speed⑪		Comp. Press. Lbs. ③	Fuel Pump Press. Lbs.
		Type Autolite	Gap Inch	Point Gap Inch	Dwell Angle Deg.		BTDC ①	Mark	Std. Trans.	Auto. Trans. ②		
1966-67	V8-462	BTF-42	.034	.017	26-31	Fig. C	10°⑩	Fig. B	None	475D⑩	180	4½-6½
	V8-462⑤	BTF-42	.034	.017	26-31	Fig. C	10°⑩	Fig. B	None	500D⑥	180	4½-6½
1968	V8-462④	BTF-42	.034	.017	26-31	Fig. C	10°⑩	Fig. B	—	500D⑥	180	4½-6½
1968-69	V8-460④	BRF-42	.034	.017	26-31	Fig. C	10°⑩	Fig. B	—	550D⑥	190	5
1970	V8-460	BRF-42	.034	.017	26-31	Fig. C	10°⑩	Fig. A	—	600D⑫	190	5
1971	V8-460	BRF-42	.034	.017	26-31	Fig. C	5°⑩	Fig. A	—	600D⑫	190	5
1972	V8-460 Exc. Calif.	BF-42	.034	.017	26-30	Fig. C	10°⑩	Fig. A	—	625D⑫	190	5
	V8-460 Calif.	BF-42	.034	.017	26-30	Fig. C	6°⑩	Fig. A	—	625D⑫	190	5

①—BTDC-Before top dead center.
②—D-Drive. N-Neutral.
③—Plus or minus 20 lbs.
④—With IMCO system.
⑤—With Thermactor exhaust emission control system.
⑥—With headlights on and A/C "Full On".
⑦—Transistor ignition .030".
⑧—Transistor ignition .020".
⑨—Transistor ignition 22-24°.
⑩—Whenever idle speed or ignition timing is adjusted, vacuum line to brake release mechanism must be disconnected and plugged to prevent parking brake from releasing when selector is moved to Drive.
⑪—If air conditioned, turn A/C switch to "Full On" position.
⑫—Headlamps on Hi Beam—Air Conditioner OFF.

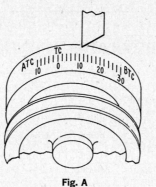

Fig. A

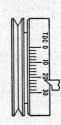

Fig. B

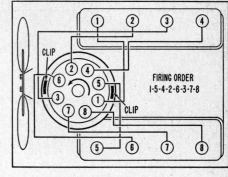

FIRING ORDER 1-5-4-2-6-3-7-8

Fig. C

VALVE SPECIFICATIONS

Year	Engine Model	Valve Lash		Valve Angles		Valve Spring Installed Height	Valve Spring Pressure Lbs. @ In.	Stem Clearance		Stem Diameter	
		Int.	Exh.	Seat	Face			Intake	Exhaust	Intake	Exhaust
1966	V8-462	.050-.150①		45	44	1⅝	70 @ 1.65	.0008-.0018	.002-.003	.3712-.3722	.3701-.3709
1967-68	V8-462	.083-.183①		45	44	1⅝	70 @ 1.65	.0008-.0025	.001-.0027	.3710-.3717	.3708-.3715
1968-72	V8-460	.075-.175②		45	44	1¹³⁄₁₆	80 @ 1.810	.0010-.0027	.0010-.0027	.3416-.3423	.3416-.3423

①—With rocker arm rotated to collapse lifter, the clearance listed should exist between end of valve stem and rocker arm. See text for details.
②—Valve lifter adjustment is 1 turn down after contact. Check as in note①.

DISTRIBUTOR SPECIFICATIONS

★ NOTE: If advance is checked on vehicle, double the R.P.M. and degrees advance to get crankshaft figures.

Year	Model	Basic Distributor Part No.① 12127	Breaker Gap	Dwell Angle Deg.	Breaker Arm Spring Tension	Centrifugal Advance Degrees @ R.P.M. of Distributor★		Vacuum Advance		Dist. Retard
						Advance Starts	Full Advance	Inches of Vacuum To Start Plunger	Max. Adv. Dist. Deg. @ Vacuum	Max. Ret. Dist. Deg. @ Vacuum
1966	Conventional	C6VF-A	.017	26–31	17–21	2 @ 450	7 @ 2000	6	9 @ 15	—
	Transistor	C6VF-B	.020	22–24	17–21	2 @ 450	7 @ 2000	6	9 @ 15	—
1967	All	C7VF-A	.017	26–31	17–21	½ @ 300	7 @ 2000	5	12 @ 20	—
1968	V8-462	C8VF-F	.017	26–31	17–21	½ @ 350	11 @ 2000	5	12 @ 25	—
1968–69	V8-460	C8VF-G	.017	26–31	17–21	½ @ 350	11 @ 2000	5	12 @ 25	—
1970	V8-460	D0VF-B	.017	26–31	17–21	½ @ 350	11 @ 2575	5	12 @ 25	—
1971	V8-460	D1VF-AA	.017	26–31	17–21	½ @ 350	13 @ 2500	5	8½ @ 25	—
1972	V8-460	D2VF-AA	.017	26–30	17–21	½ @ 500	10½ @ 2000	5	11½ @ 20	—
	V8-460	D2VF-BA	.017	26–30	17–21	½ @ 500	11½ @ 2000	5	12 @ 20	—

①—Stamped on distributor housing plate.

ALTERNATOR & REGULATOR SPECIFICATIONS

Year	Make	Current Rating①		Field Current @ 75°F.		Voltage Regulator②				Field Relay	
		Amperes	Volts	Amperes	Volts	Make	Voltage @ 75°F.	Contact Gap	Armature Air Gap	Armature Air Gap	Closing Voltage @ 75°F.
1966–67	Autolite	60	15	2.8–3.3	12	Autolite	14.1–14.9	.017–.022	.049–.056	.010–.018	2.5–4.0
1968	Autolite	55	15	2.8–3.3	12	Autolite	13.5–15.3	③	③	③	2.0–4.2
1969–72	Autolite	55	15	2.8–3.3	12	Autolite④	—	③	③	—	—

①—Stamped on housing.　②—Stamped on cover.　③—Not adjustable.　④—Integral regulator solid state.

ENGINE TIGHTENING SPECIFICATIONS*

★Torque specifications are for clean and lightly lubricated threads only. Dry or dirty threads produce increased friction which prevents accurate measurement of tightness.

Year	Spark Plugs Ft. Lbs.	Cylinder Head Bolts Ft. Lbs.	Intake Manifold Ft. Lbs.	Exhaust Manifold Ft. Lbs.	Rocker Arm Shaft Bracket Ft. Lbs.	Rocker Arm Cover Ft. Lbs.	Connecting Rod Cap Bolts Ft. Lbs.	Main Bearing Cap Bolts Ft. Lbs.	Flywheel to Crankshaft Ft. Lbs.	Vibration Damper or Pulley Ft. Lbs.
1966–68 V8-462	15–20	135–145	20–25	15–21	45–50	2½–4	40–45	95–105	75–85	75–90
1968 V8-460	15–20	130–140	25–30	28–33	65–75①	2½–4	40–45	95–105	75–85	75–90
1969–72 V8-460	15–20	130–140	25–30	28–33	65–75①	5–6	40–45	95–105	75–85	75–90

①—Rocker arm stud.

STARTING MOTOR SPECIFICATIONS

Year	Car Model	Starter Model	Brush Spring Tension Ounces	No Load Test			Torque Test		
				Amperes	Volts	R.P.M.	Amperes	Volts	Torque Lbs. Ft.
1966–67	All	Ford	40	70	12		670	5.0	15½
1968	All	C8VF-11001-A	40	70	12	11000	700	5.0	15½
1969–72	All	C8VY-11002-C	40	70	12	10000	700	5.0	15½

PISTONS, PINS, RINGS, CRANKSHAFT & BEARINGS

Year	Model	Piston Clearance	Ring End Gap①		Wrist-pin Diameter	Rod Bearings		Main Bearings			
			Comp.	Oil		Shaft Diameter	Bearing Clearance	Shaft Diameter	Bearing Clearance	Thrust on Bear. No.	Shaft End Play
1966–68	V8-462	.0015–.0021	.010	.015	.9750	2.5992–2.6001	.0007–.002	2.8994–2.9003	.0008–.0024	3	.004–.008
1968–72	V8-460	.0014–.0022	.010	.015	1.040	2.4992–2.5000	.0008–.0015	2.9994–3.0002	.0005–.0015	3	.004–.008

①—Fit rings in tapered bores for clearance listed in tightest portion of ring travel.

BRAKE SPECIFICATIONS

Year	Model	Brake Drum Inside Diameter	Wheel Cylinder Bore Diameter			Master Cylinder Bore Diameter		
			Front Disc Brakes	Front Drum Brakes	Rear Brakes	With Disc Brakes	With Drum Brakes	With Power Brakes
1966	All	11.030	1.938	—	15/16	1	1	1
1967–69	Lincoln	11.090	1.938	—	15/16	1	1	1
1969–70	Mark III	11.030	2.755	—	15/16	1	—	1
1970	Lincoln	11.090	2.755	—	15/16	1	—	1
1971	All	11.030	2.755	—	15/16	1	—	1
1972	Lincoln	11.030	3.100	—	.938	1	—	1
	Mark IV	11.030	3.100	—	1.000	1	—	1

REAR AXLE SPECIFICATIONS

Year	Model	Carrier Type	Ring Gear & Pinion Backlash Inch	Nominal Pinion Locating Shim, Inch	Pinion Bearing Preload				Differential Bearing Preload	Pinion Nut Torque Ft.-Lbs.
					New Bearings With Seal Inch-Lbs.	Used Bearings With Seal Inch-Lbs.	New Bearings Less Seal Inch-Lbs.	Used Bearings Less Seal Inch-Lbs.		
1966	All	Removable	.008–.012	.015	17–32	—	12½–32½	—	.008–.012②	200①
1967–72	All	Removable	.008–.012	.015	15–35	—	12½–32½	—	.008–.012②	200①

①—If torque cannot be obtained, install new spacer.
②—Case spread with new bearings; with used bearings .005–.008".

LINCOLN CONTINENTAL

WHEEL ALIGNMENT SPECIFICATIONS

OLD CAR SPECIFICATIONS: For 1946-65 Wheel Alignment Specifications see back of book.

Year	Model	Caster Angle, Degrees		Camber Angle, Degrees				Toe-In. Inch	Toe-Out on Turns, Deg.①	
		Limits	Desired	Limits		Desired			Outer Wheel	Inner Wheel
				Left	Right	Left	Right			
1966	All	−½ to −2½	−1½	−¼ to +1¼	−¼ to +1¼	+½	+½	⅛	17¾	20
1967	All	−¾ to −2¼	−1½	0 to +1	0 to +1	+½	+½	⅛	17¾	20
1968–69	Lincoln	−½ to −2½	−1½	−¼ to +1¼	−¼ to +1¼	+½	+½	⅛	17¾	20
1969–70	Mark III	0 to +2	+1	−¼ to +1¼	−¼ to +1¼	+½	+½	3/16	19¼	20
1971–72	Lincoln	−½ to +3½	+1½	−½ to +1½	−½ to +1½	+½	+½	⅛	18¾	20
1971	Mark III	−1 to +3	+1	−½ to +1½	−½ to +1½	+½	+½	3/16	—	—
1972	Mark IV	−1 to +3	+1	−¼ to +1¾	−¼ to +1¾	+¾	+¾	3/16	—	—

①—Incorrect toe-out, when other adjustments are correct, indicates
bent steering arms.

COOLING SYSTEM & CAPACITY DATA

Year	Model or Engine	Cooling Capacity, Qts.			Radiator Cap Relief Pressure, Lbs.		Thermo. Opening Temp. ①	Fuel Tank Gals.	Engine Oil Refill Qts. ②	Transmission Oil			Rear Axle Oil Pints
		No Heater	With Heater	With A/C	With A/C	No A/C				3 Speed Pints	4 Speed Pints	Auto. Trans. Qts. ③	
1966	All	—	23½	23½	12–15	12–15	185	25	5	—	—	13	5½
1967	All	—	23	23	12–15	12–15	185	25	5	—	—	13½	5
1968–69	V8-462	22½	23½	23½	12–15	12–15	185	25½	4	—	—	13½	5
	V8-460	—	22	22	12–15	12–15	185	25½	4	—	—	13½	5
1970	Lincoln	—	20½	—	12–15	12–15	188	24④	4	—	—	13	5
	Mark III	—	20½	—	12–15	12–15	188	24④	4	—	—	12¾	5
1971	Lincoln	—	19½	19½	12–15	12–15	188	23	4	—	—	13	5
	Mark III	—	19½	19½	12–15	12–15	188	23	4	—	—	12¾	5
1972	Lincoln	—	19½	19½	12–15	12–15	188	22	4	—	—	13	5
	Mark IV	—	19½	19½	12–15	12–15	188	23	4	—	—	12¾	5

①—With alcohol type anti-freeze, use a 160° unit.   ③—Approximate.   Make final check with dipstick.
②—Add one quart with filter change.   ④—California vehicles 22½.

Electrical Section

DISTRIBUTOR, REPLACE

1. Disconnect distributor primary wire from coil terminal and remove distributor cap.
2. Unscrew vacuum line connection from vacuum advance unit.
3. Remove tachometer drive cable retaining screw and clip and pull cable and driven gear from distributor housing on models so equipped.
4. Unscrew distributor clamp bolt and remove lock washer and clip.
5. As the distributor is lifted from engine the shaft and rotor will turn counterclockwise part of a revolution. Lift distributor only far enough to disengage the gear.
6. When rotor stops turning, scribe a mark on the manifold or on engine casting to indicate the rotor position, then remove the distributor. *Do not crank the engine after the distributor is removed, otherwise the distributor will have to be initially timed to the engine.*
7. Install the distributor in the reverse order of its removal. Then start the engine, check the oil pressure and adjust the ignition timing.

STARTER, REPLACE
1968-72

1. Raise vehicle and disconnect cable at starter terminal. On Mark III models, turn the front wheels fully to the right and remove the two bolts attaching the idler arm to the frame.

1966-67

1. Raise vehicle and disconnect cable at starter terminal.
2. Unfasten and remove starter.
3. Position starter to flywheel housing and start mounting bolts.
4. Snug all bolts while holding starter squarely against its mounting surface.

IGNITION SWITCH, REPLACE

1972 Mark IV

The ignition switch is mounted on the steering column and is controlled by the lock cylinder through an actuator in the locking mechanism. The switch is connected to the actuator by an actuator rod. The multiple connector plugs are secured to the switch by snap type retainers. To remove switch, proceed as follows:
1. Disconnect battery ground cable.
2. Remove screws holding instrument panel cluster.
3. Press locking tabs and remove blade type connector on top of switch.
4. Remove mounting nuts for switch and lift up on switch enough to unhook the switch rod.
5. Remove the switch.

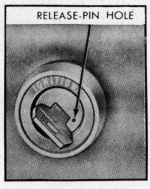

Fig. 1 Ignition lock cylinder release pin hole

1972 Continental & 1970-71 All

1. Remove shrouding from steering column and detach and lower steering column from brake support bracket.
2. Disconnect battery cable.
3. Disconnect switch wiring at multiple plug.
4. Remove two nuts that retain switch to column.
5. Detach switch plunger from actuator rod and remove the switch.
6. When installing switch, both the locking mechanism at the top of the column and the switch must be in the "LOCK" position for correct adjustment. New replacement switches are already pinned in "LOCK" position by a plastic pin inserted in a locking hole.

1969 Mark III

1. Disconnect battery ground cable.
2. Insert wire pin in hole in ignition switch and turn key to accessory position while pressing pin. Lock cylinder can now be removed.
3. Remove bezel nut and lower switch from instrument panel.
4. Depress tabs securing multiple connector to switch and pull connector off switch.
5. Reverse procedure to install.

1966-69 Continental

1. Disconnect battery ground cable.

Fig. 2 Light switch. 1966-69

2. Remove 8 screws from lower control housing and drop housing.
3. Remove nut retaining wiring connector at ignition switch and remove connector.
4. Unscrew bezel and remove switch.
5. Insert key into switch and turn it to left. Insert a paper clip into hole below key slot and pull out tumbler, Fig. 1.
6. Reverse procedure to install.

LIGHT SWITCH, REPLACE
1972 Mark IV

1. Disconnect battery ground cable.
2. Remove instrument cluster trim panel.
3. Remove the headlight switch mounting plate.
4. Remove bezel nut and disconnect multiple connector.
5. Remove vacuum lines, if so equipped.
6. Remove the switch.

1970-72 Continental;
1969-71 Mark III

1. Disconnect battery ground cable.
2. Remove control knob and shaft by pressing knob release button and pulling it out of switch housing, Fig. 2.
3. Remove bezel nut and lower switch assembly.
4. Disconnect multiple plug and vacuum hoses at switch body and remove switch.
5. Reverse procedure to install.

1966-69 Continental

1. Disconnect battery ground cable.
2. Remove 8 screws from lower control housing and drop housing.
3. Remove control knob and shaft by pressing knob release button and pulling it out of switch housing, Fig. 2.
4. Disconnect wiring connector to switch.
5. Remove bezel nut and remove switch.
6. Reverse procedure to install.

STOP LIGHT SWITCH, REPLACE
1966-72

1. Disconnect wires at switch connector.
2. Remove hairpin retainer, slide switch, push rod and nylon washers and bushing away from brake pedal, and remove switch, Fig. 3.
3. Reverse above procedure to install.

NEUTRAL SAFETY SWITCH
1970-72

The neutral safety switch has been

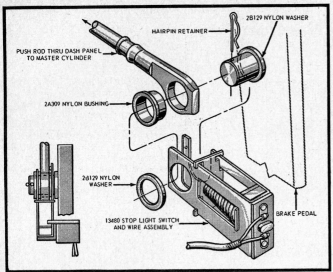

Fig. 3   Stop light switch. 1966-72

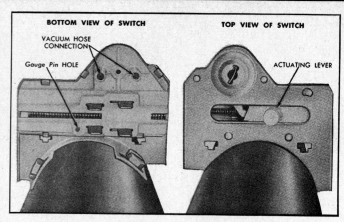

Fig. 4   Neutral safety switch showing parking brake vacuum connections. 1967

eliminated and is replaced by a series of steps designed into the steering column selector lever hub casting.

1969 Continental

The neutral start switch is mounted on the top of the steering column jacket just below the collapsible section of the column jacket.

Adjustment

1. With transmission lever against the stop in Neutral, loosen retaining screws and rotate switch until a start is obtained.
2. Tighten screws to 20 in-lbs.
3. Place selector in the "1" position and push the Park reset button counterclockwise until it stops. *The Park reset must be performed whenever the switch has been adjusted.*

1969 Mark III & 1968 All

The neutral start switch is mounted on the top of the steering column jacket just below the collapsible section of the column jacket.

To adjust the switch it must be removed from the column. Put the selector lever in neutral and set the parking brake. Then disconnect the electrical and vacuum connections, remove the two fastening screws and lift the switch straight up and out.

Adjustment

1. Hold the switch with the wire terminal facing you. Move the actuator lever all the way to the left but do not force as the switch will be damaged internally.
2. Insert a 3/32" drill shank in the hole in the tapered round boss.
3. Gently move the actuator lever to the right until it stops. This will move the Park circuit to its position of minimum travel, which must be done if the switch is to function properly upon installation.
4. Pull out the drill gauge and fit it in the hole on the top surface of the switch case to engage the switch

internal carrier in the neutral position. Then reinsert the drill gauge.
5. With the selector lever held against the stop in the neutral detent position, set the switch in place on the column and fasten it with the two mounting screws.
6. Connect the electrical connector and any vacuum hose, and be sure to remove the drill gauge before operating the selector lever.

1967

Column Shift, Fig. 4

1. With manual linkage properly adjusted, check starter engagement circuit in all transmission selector lever positions. The circuit must be open in all drive positions and closed only in Park and Neutral.
2. To adjust, loosen switch retaining screws on steering column.
3. Place transmission selector lever firmly against stop of neutral detent position.
4. Rotate switch actuating lever until gauge pin (43 drill) can be inserted in gauge pin holes.
5. Tighten switch retaining screws and remove gauge pin.

1966

1. Disconnect wiring from switch and remove switch from steering column.
2. Install switch on steering column.
3. Place transmission selector lever firmly against stop of neutral detent position.
4. Move switch actuating post until the shank end of a No. 43 drill can be inserted into switch carrier and case.
5. With steering column selector lever held against the stop in "N" position, rotate switch on column until switch actuating post contacts actuating lever.
6. Tighten switch screws and remove gauge drill. Starter should engage only in neutral and park positions.

TURN SIGNAL SWITCH, REPLACE

1971-72

1. Remove retaining screw from underside of steering wheel spoke and lift off the pad horn switch/trim cover and medallion as an assembly.
2. Disconnect horn switch wires from terminals.
3. Remove steering wheel retaining nut and remove steering wheel using suitable puller.
4. Remove turn signal switch lever by unscrewing it from steering column.
5. Remove shroud from under steering column.
6. Disconnect steering column wiring connector plugs and remove the screws that secure switch assembly to the column.
7. On vehicles with tilt column, remove wires and terminals from steering column wiring connector plug.

NOTE: *Record the color code and location of each wire before removing it from connector. A hole provided in the flange on fixed columns makes it unnecessary to separate the wires from the connector plug. The plug with wires installed can be guided through the hole.*

8. Remove the plastic cover sleeve from the wiring harness and remove the switch and wires from the top of the column.

1968-70

1. Disconnect battery and remove steering wheel.
2. Remove protective wire cover that runs along bottom of steering column tube and disconnect electrical plug, noting color codes and location. If equipped with tilt steering column, tape wire ends together and attach a piece of heavy cord to the wires to help pull them through the column during installation.
3. If equipped with speed control, remove the sleeve around the wiring and pull the first three speed control wires out of the column.
4. Unscrew turn signal lever. If equipped

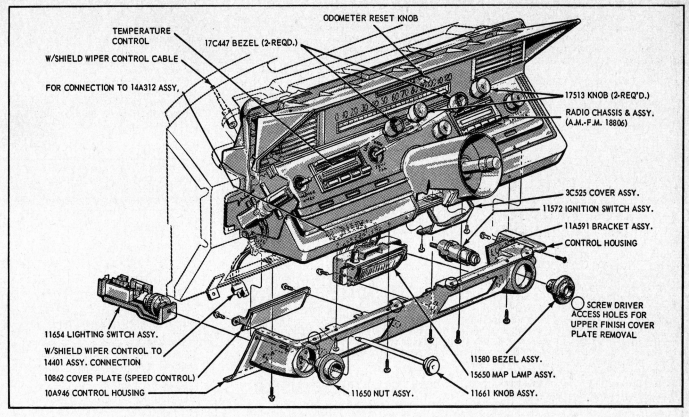

Fig. 5 Instrument cluster and controls. 1966-67. Typical of 1968-69 Continental

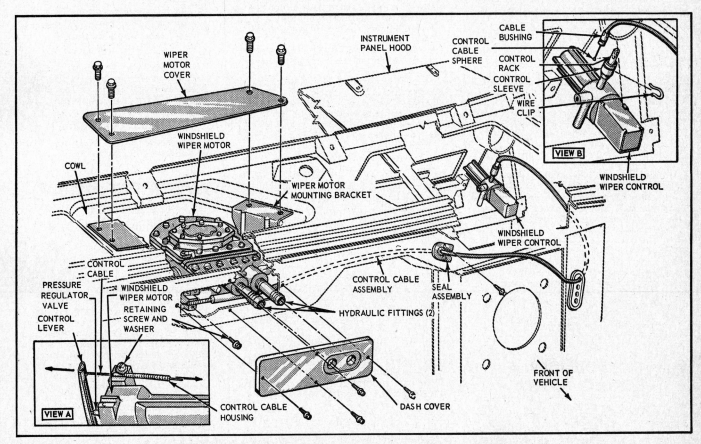

Fig. 6 Windshield wiper control and motor installation. 1966-69

with speed control, first separate the wire to the set-speed switch.

5. If equipped with tilt column, remove upper collar and push lower collar down. Remove wiring retaining clip.
6. Remove switch retaining screws and remove switch.
7. Reverse procedure to install.

1967

1. Remove steering wheel.
2. Remove turn signal lever and flasher control knob from column.
3. Remove horn wire and turn signal switch attaching screws. Lift switch and horn wire from flange.
4. Reverse procedure to install.

SERVICE BULLETIN

1966-67: TURN SIGNAL MALFUNCTION: Before judging the turn signal switch to be the cause of a malfunction and replacing it as defective, first check the following areas to make certain they are not causing the trouble.

1. The steering shaft should be centered in the column so that the steering wheel hub canceling fingers are in proper relation to the switch canceling mechanism. This can be accomplished by loosening the column attachment to the dash panel and shifting tube in relation to shaft.
2. Make sure the ignition switch is not sticking between the "Start" and "On" position, thereby adversely affecting the electrical circuit.
3. Excessive "Loctite" on the threads of the turn signal lever may be contacting the turn signal switch mechanism causing a bind.
4. The fingers on the steering wheel hub canceling cam may be bent so that the proper contact with the canceling mechanism cannot be accomplished.

1966

1. Disconnect battery ground cable.
2. Remove steering wheel.
3. Unscrew turn signal lever.
4. Remove switch and bracket from steering column.
5. Remove conical tension spring and switch actuating arm.
6. Disconnect switch wires from bullet connectors. Remove access plate at steering column, and remove switch and wires.

NOTE: When installing new switch, make certain that canceling cam on steering wheel makes contact with canceling pawls on switch. Clearance between steering wheel hub and steering shaft housing flange should not be more than $1/16''$ for proper switch canceling. Reposition steering shaft housing if necessary.

HORN SOUNDER & STEERING WHEEL

1969-71 Mark III

1. Disconnect battery ground cable.
2. Remove the medallion from steering wheel spoke pad by gently prying

out with a knife blade. Working from the underside of the spoke, remove the two screws that secure the crash pad. Remove pad.
3. Disconnect two horn wires at horn switch assembly. Remove steering wheel nut and, using a suitable puller, remove steering wheel.

NOTE: Do not use hammer or knock-off type puller. Striking the puller or shaft may cause damage to the bearings or collapsible column.

1967-71 Continental

1. Turn hub cap counterclockwise and lift it from steering wheel.
2. Remove hub mounting plate from top of wheel.
3. Remove nut and pull off wheel.

1966

1. Disconnect battery ground cable.
2. Remove center steering wheel cover.
3. Remove two screws in center of steering wheel and one screw retaining the three horn wires.
4. Remove three screws under steering wheel and remove horn buttons.
5. Reverse procedure to install.

INSTRUMENT CLUSTER

1972 Mark IV

1. Disconnect battery ground cable.
2. Remove three screws attaching upper access cover to instrument panel pad.
3. Remove one screw retaining lower cluster applique cover below steering column.
4. Squeeze lower half of steering column shroud together and separate lower half from upper.
5. Remove upper half of shroud from column.
6. Remove one screw attaching PRNDL control cable to steering column.
7. Remove headed backlite control knob.
8. Reach under panel and depress the button on side of headlight switch while withdrawing switch control knob and shaft. Remove headlight switch bezel.
9. Reach under panel and disconnect speedo cable.
10. Remove wiper/washer control knob.
11. Remove threaded wiper/washer bezel.
12. Remove cigar lighter from its receptacle.
13. Remove four screws retaining cluster front cover.
14. Insert a right angle standard tip screwdriver along edges of finish panel withdrawing studs in sequence gradually around periphery of panel.
15. Remove two screws from cluster light baffle at cluster top.
16. Remove four screws retaining cluster to instrument panel.
17. Pull cluster away from panel and disconnect printed circuit feed plug.
18. Tilt cluster out, bottom first, and move cluster toward center of vehicle.

1970-72 Continental

1. Remove the instrument panel pad. The cluster trim cover does not have

to be removed if only the cluster is being removed.
2. Reach under instrument panel and disconnect cluster printed circuit plug.
3. From the passenger side, remove the cluster-to-cluster housing retaining screws and swing the cluster away from housing.
4. From the underside of the cluster, unhook the pointer control cable from the PRNDL pointer lever.
5. Remove the cable retaining clip from cluster and remove the cluster.

NOTE: When replacing the cluster be sure to connect the control wire to the PRNDL pointer and attach the cable to the cluster with the retainer.

1969-71 Mark III

1. Disconnect battery ground cable.
2. Remove screws retaining upper edge of instrument cluster pad and retainer assembly to panel pad. Remove pad and retainer from face of cluster.
3. Remove clock knob and instrument cluster mask retainers and remove mask.
4. Remove three speedometer to cluster screws and pull speedometer from cluster. Disconnect two speedometer cable to cluster screws and clamps, release the tab of the plastic retainer and remove it from the cable. If equipped with speed control, the speedometer cable may be disconnected at the speed control unit instead.
5. Remove eight cluster to panel retaining screws and three screws retaining rear vent and wiper control pod. Pull cluster and pod out of the panel.
6. Disconnect the multiple connector and the low fuel warning and dual brake warning lights at the printed circuit and remove the cluster.

1966-69 Continental

Fig. 5 illustrates the assembly layout of the instrument cluster and controls.

W/S WIPER MOTOR, REPLACE

1971 Continental; 1972 All

1. Disconnect battery ground cable.
2. Remove wiper arm and blade assemblies.
3. Remove left cowl screen for access through cowl opening.
4. Disconnect linkage drive arm from motor output arm crankpin by removing the retaining clip.
5. From engine side of dash, disconnect wire connectors from motor.
6. Remove bolts that retain motor to dash and remove the motor. If the output arm catches on dash during removal, handturn the arm clockwise so it will clear the opening in dash.

NOTE: *Before installing motor be sure the output arm is in the Park position.*

1971 Mark III

1. Remove wiper arm and blade assemblies.
2. Remove the air cleaner.
3. Remove retaining screws and remove the cowl top panel. Disconnect washer hose.
4. Remove clip retaining left wiper link to motor and disconnect the link.
5. Disconnect hydraulic lines from motor being careful not to burn hands with hot hydraulic fluid.
6. Remove three bolts retaining motor to cowl and disconnect wiper control cable and remove through left cowl opening.

1970 Continental

For 1970, the hydraulic motor is replaced by a depressed park type electric motor. The motor is mounted on the engine side of the cowl panel under the left front fender. To remove, proceed as follows:

1. Disconnect battery ground cable.
2. Remove wiper arms and blades.
3. Remove cowl top grille and disconnect linkage drive arm from motor output crankpin.
4. Disconnect wires from the motor.
5. From engine side of dash, remove bolts retaining motor. If the output arm catches on the dash during removal, handturn the arm clockwise so it will clear the opening in the dash.

Late 1970 Mark III

All vehicles built after 9-22-69 will again use the hydraulic wiper system which was used on previous models. The major difference is the elimination of the surge chamber. Service is similar to 1969 models.

Early 1970 Mark III

The hydraulic motor used previously is replaced by an oscillating type, two speed electric motor. Removal is as follows:

1. Disconnect battery ground cable and washer hose.
2. Remove the cowl vent top panel.
3. Remove four bolts that retain the plastic cover and motor to the cowl panel.
4. Remove the plastic cover.
5. Disconnect the drive link from the motor arm.
6. Disconnect motor wiring at connector and remove the motor.

1969 Mark III

1. Remove wiper arm and blade assemblies.
2. Remove the air cleaner.
3. Remove retaining screws and remove cowl top panel. Disconnect washer hose.
4. Remove clip retaining left wiper link to motor and disconnect the link.
5. Disconnect hydraulic lines, being careful not to burn hands with hot hydraulic fluid.
6. Remove three bolts retaining motor to cowl. Disconnect wiper control cable and remove motor through left cowl opening.

1966-69 Continental

1. Referring to Fig. 6, remove wiper arms and blades.
2. Remove cowl top grille, wiper nozzles and weatherstrip (6 screws).
3. Disconnect two hydraulic lines at wiper motor, *using care as oil may be hot.*

1966-69 NOTE

The windshield wiper is hydraulically operated. Hydraulic power for the motor is obtained from the power steering unit. Hydraulic fluid flows from the pump, through the steering gear to the wiper motor, and then to the fluid reservoir. During wiper operation, a part of the fluid is by-passed through the motor by a valve on the motor.

W/S WIPER TRANSMISSION

1972 Mark IV

1. Disconnect battery ground cable and remove wiper arm and blades.
2. Remove cowl screen and left arm and blade stop.
3. Disconnect linkage drive arm from the motor by removing retaining clip.
4. Remove pivot shaft retaining bolts and remove linkage and pivot shaft.

NOTE: When installing pivot shaft assemblies, be sure to force the linkage connecting clip into the locked position.

1971 Mark III

1. Remove wiper arm and blade assemblies. Be sure to release the tension arm retaining clip from the tension arm retaining stud on the left pivot assembly.
2. Remove retaining screws and remove the cowl vent grille. Disconnect washer hoses.
3. Remove clip retaining link assembly to the motor. Remove screws retaining pivot shaft and link assembly to the cowl and remove the pivot shaft and link assembly.

1970-72 Continental

1. Disconnect battery ground cable.
2. Remove wiper arm and blade assemblies.
3. Remove cowl screens for access to linkage.
4. Disconnect left linkage arm from the drive arm by removing the clip.
5. Remove three bolts retaining left pivot shaft assembly to the cowl and remove the left arm and pivot shaft assembly through cowl opening.
6. Disconnect linkage drive arm from motor crankpin by removing the clip.
7. Remove three bolts that connect the drive arm pivot assembly to the cowl and remove the pivot shaft drive arm and right arm as an assembly.

1970 Mark III

1. Disconnect battery ground cable.
2. Disconnect washer hose and remove cowl vent top panel.
3. Disconnect drive link from motor arm and disconnect both links from the right pivot shaft assembly.
4. Remove three screws from the drive pivot plate at the right end of the cowl panel and withdraw the drive pivot plate and the two drive links as an assembly.
5. Remove the right pivot shaft (three screws).
6. Remove the three left pivot shaft screws and withdraw the left pivot shaft and link as an assembly.

1969 Mark III

1. Remove wiper arm and blade assemblies, being sure to release the tension arm retaining clip from the stud on the left pivot assembly.
2. Remove cowl top panel and disconnect washer hose.
3. Remove link retaining clip and pivot shaft assembly to cowl screws. Remove pivot shaft and link assembly.
4. Reverse procedure to install.

1966-69 Continental

1. Remove wiper arms and blades.
2. Remove cowl grille (6 screws) and disconnect washer hoses and weatherstrip.
3. Remove drive arm clip.
4. Remove three bolts at each pivot.
5. Remove pivots from connecting linkage and lift assembly out through left side of cowl.
6. Reverse procedure to install.

W/S WIPER SWITCH

1972 Mark IV

1. Disconnect battery ground cable.
2. Remove instrument cluster finish panel.
3. Remove switch mounting plate and disconnect cigar lighter and wiper switch wires.
4. Remove switch bezel nut and remove switch.

1970-72 Continental

1. Disconnect battery ground cable.
2. Pull the knob and remove retaining nut and gasket from switch shaft.
3. Lower switch from behind instrument panel and disconnect the multiple connector.

1969-71 Mark III

1. Disconnect battery ground cable.
2. Remove five retaining screws and remove instrument cluster pad and retainer from face of cluster.
3. Remove three retaining screws and pull wiper control pod from panel. Disconnect vacuum hoses and electrical connector and remove bulbs. Remove control cable retaining clip and remove control assembly.
4. Remove control knobs, two retaining screws and remove control unit.

1966-69 Continental

1. Disconnect battery ground cable.
2. Remove eight screws from lower control housing and drop housing.
3. Remove knob and bezel.
4. Remove nut on control shaft and lower the control.
5. Turn wiper control knob counterclockwise to the stop.
6. Remove wire clip, Fig. 6. Slide cable bushing up and out of control sleeve (view B). Remove control cable sphere from control rack.
7. Disconnect plug connector from wiring harness. Disconnect two vacuum hoses and remove wiper control.
8. Reverse procedure to install.

RADIO REMOVAL

NOTE: When installing radio, be sure to adjust antenna trimmer for peak performance.

1972 Mark IV

1. Disconnect battery ground cable.
2. Pull radio control knobs off shafts.
3. Remove nut from both radio shafts.
4. Remove radio rear support attaching screw at instrument panel.
5. Disconnect radio power and speaker wires at connectors.
6. Disconnect antenna and remove radio.

1970-71 Continental

1. Disconnect battery ground cable.
2. Remove map light assembly.
3. Remove right and left inspection covers.
4. Remove lower instrument panel pad.
5. Remove the glove box. Open ash tray and let it hang open.
6. Remove glove box switch.
7. Through glove box opening remove two nuts retaining radio finish panel to the instrument panel.
8. Remove radio knobs.
9. Remove two screws at top of finish panel. Position panel out and disconnect cigar lighter and light from the right panel.
10. Through the glove box opening remove the nut from the lower right corner of the center finish panel.
11. Remove radio top support nut and the three mounting screws. Pull radio out, disconnect power leads and antenna cable and remove radio.

1969-71 Mark III

1. Disconnect battery ground cable.
2. Pull off control knobs.
3. Remove cover plate below steering column, and the nut from right radio control shaft.
4. Remove six screws and remove trim from front of radio.
5. Remove nut and washer from right control shaft, and screw attaching front left side of radio to instrument panel.
6. Remove rear support attaching screw, disconnect wires and remove radio.
7. Reverse procedure to install.

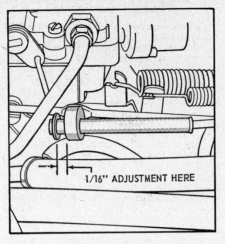

Fig. 7   Control cable adjustment. 1967-69

1966-69 Continental

1. Disconnect battery ground cable.
2. Remove eight screws in lower control housing and lower the housing.
3. Disconnect lead from speakers.
4. Disconnect power antenna lead.
5. Disconnect lead from foot-operated switch for AM/FM radios (if equipped).
6. Disconnect one two-way disconnect for pilot light and radio power.

7. Remove two knobs and bezels on selector shafts.
8. Remove two nuts and retainers on selector shafts.
9. Remove two screws attaching radio bracket to lower reinforcement on instrument panel.
10. Remove two nuts from selector shafts.
11. Disconnect antenna lead and remove radio.

SPEED CONTROLS
1972

Adjust the bead chain to obtain .06-.25" actuator arm free travel when engine is at hot idle. The adjustment should be made to take as much slack as possible out of the bead chain without restricting the carburetor lever from returning to idle. On vehicles with solenoid anti-diesel valve, perform the adjustment with the ignition switch in the ON position.

1970-71

A mercury cut-off switch has been mounted in the speed control regulator. The cut-off switch makes certain that the speed control is shut off when the vehicle is suddenly stopped. When installing a regulator, use a level to make certain the mercury will operate properly. It may be necessary to place washers under one of the mounting studs to make it level.

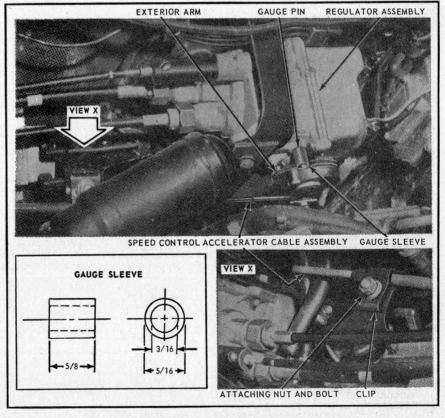

Fig. 8   Accelerator linkage adjustment for Slide Switch type Speedostat. 1966

Linkage Adjustment

Adjust the servo chain to obtain a ½ to 1 ball slack when the engine is at hot idle.

1969 Mark III

Linkage Adjustment

Adjust the servo chain to obtain a ½ to 1 ball link slack when the engine is at hot idle.

1967-69 Continental

Control Cable, Adjust

With the carburetor set at hot idle, adjust the Bowden cable to provide a 1/16" clearance between the Bowden cable end "C" washer and the accelerator linkage sleeve, Fig. 7.

1966 Speedostat

Control Cable Adjustment, 1966-67

The cable requires no adjustment; it simply snaps into the nylon retainer in the regulator assembly.

Accelerator Linkage

1. Adjust throttle rod.
2. Start engine and operate at slow idle with transmission lever in "Park".
3. Separate linkage from exterior arm.
4. Adjust trunnion so that when it is installed through exterior arm, the stop stud will be aligned with locating notch and throttle valves will be closed.
5. Install washer on trunnion and secure with cotter pin.

NOTE: Due to the angle at which the trunnion enters hole in exterior arm, it is necessary to rotate the exterior arm slightly forward when inserting the trunnion. Repeat this operation until proper alignment is obtained. Be careful not to turn trunnion too far back or throttle valves will unseat and cause an incorrect adjustment. Insert the gauge shown in Fig. 8 (or small diameter pipe) over stop stud to check alignment.

Brake Release Switch

1. Turn on ignition but do not start engine.
2. Momentarily move slide switch to AUTO position until red indicator light glows.
3. Using a test lamp, ground one lead and touch the other lead to terminal No. 4, Fig. 9.
4. Loosen mounting screw securing release switch to brake pedal mounting bracket.
5. Adjust release switch so that lamp will go out when brake pedal is depressed and light again when the pedal is released. If the lamp lights, the brake release relay (on left fender) is defective and must be replaced. If the lamp does not light, the wiring to the relay is defective. If the stop lights do not light, the brake stop light switch is defective.

Fig. 9   Electrical connections on Slide Switch type Speedostat. 1966

HEATER CORE REMOVAL
1970-72 Continental

1. Drain the engine coolant.
2. Disconnect vacuum junction valve from dash panel and move valve and hoses away from case.
3. Disconnect speed control from dash, if so equipped, and move it away.
4. Disconnect multiple connector from blower resistor and the harness from the clip on the case.
5. Disconnect heater hoses from the case and the hose support clamp from the case. Move the hoses and the water valve away from the case.
6. Remove case cover-to-case flange screws and the wire harness clip.
7. Remove six case cover-to-back plate stud nuts.
8. Remove one upper case-to-dash panel mounting screw.
9. Remove two case-to-dash panel mounting stud nuts, one on the inboard mounting flange and one below the case on the lower flange.
10. Carefully move the heater core cover assembly forward to clear the mounting studs and lift it up and out of the car.
11. Remove the spring clips from the core tubes on the front of the core cover.
12. Remove three core end plate mounting screws and remove the plate. The heater core and gasket can now be removed from the cover.

1969-72 Mark III

1. Remove hood and air cleaner and drain radiator.
2. Disconnect wiper motor hydraulic lines, vacuum supply hose, icing switch multiple connector and heater hoses.
3. Remove oil pressure sending unit and transmission dip stick and tube.
4. Remove evaporator housing front cover and heater core housing cover.
5. Remove heater core retaining bracket and heater core.

1966-69 Continental

1. Remove air cleaner and harness clamp on top evaporator-heater case in engine compartment.
2. Take off actuator for temperature blending door, adjacent to evaporator-heater case.
3. Remove retaining screws and heater core cover plate and lift out core.

Engine Section

ENGINE, REPLACE

In addition to the usual items such as fuel lines, linkage and radiator hoses, the following operations must be performed:

1. Remove hood, radiator and air cleaner.
2. Remove power steering pump and starter.
3. Disconnect exhaust pipes from manifolds. On Mark III, disconnect idler arm at frame bracket.
4. Support transmission with a suitable jack.
5. Unfasten engine mountings and attach lifting rig to engine.
6. Remove bell housing to engine attaching bolts and carefully lift engine out of chassis. *Be sure to support transmission with front end tilted up to prevent converter from falling out.*

CYLINDER HEADS
1968-72 V8-460

1. Remove intake manifold and carburetor as an assembly.
2. Disconnect resonator inlet pipe at exhaust manifold.
3. Loosen air conditioner compressor belt if so equipped.
4. Loosen alternator retaining bolts and remove bolt retaining alternator bracket to right head.
5. If air conditioned, isolate compressor at service valves and hoses from compressor. Remove nuts retaining compressor bracket to water pump. Remove bolts retaining compressor to upper mounting bracket and lay compressor out of way. Remove compressor upper bracket from head.
6. If not air conditioned, remove bolts retaining power steering reservoir bracket to left head and position reservoir out of way.
7. Remove rocker arm covers. Loosen rocker arm stud nuts and turn rocker arms to side. Remove push rods in sequence so they can be installed in their positions.
8. Remove head retaining bolts and lift head with exhaust manifold.
9. Reverse procedure to install.

1966-68 V8-462

NOTE: *Due to engine compartment clearance factors it is necessary to remove the exhaust manifold and cylinder head as a unit from each cylinder bank.*

1. Remove battery ground cable.
2. Disconnect exhaust pipes from exhaust manifolds.
3. Remove intake manifold and push rod cover.
4. Remove rocker arm cover.
5. If air conditioned, disconnect compressor mounting bracket at cylinder head.

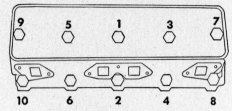

Fig. 1 Cylinder head tightening

6. To remove right-bank head, disconnect transmission oil filler pipe bracket at exhaust manifold.
7. Remove horns and bracket assembly from fender apron (if so mounted).
8. Remove cylinder head bolts and lift head with exhaust manifold attached off two locating dowels on each bank of cylinder block.
9. Reverse removal procedure to install the head and tighten bolts in the sequence shown in Fig. 1 and to the proper torque specifications.

VALVE CLEARANCE
1969-71 V8-460

A positive stop rocker arm stud and nut eliminates the need of adjusting the valve lash. It is very important that the correct push rod be used and all components be installed and torqued as follows:

1. Position the piston of the cylinder being worked on at TDC of the compression stroke.
2. Install positive stop stud and torque to 65-75 ft.-lbs.
3. Lubricate and install the rocker arm and fulcrum on the stud. Thread nut onto stud until it contacts the shoulder then tighten it to 18-22 ft-lbs.

1968 V8-460

1. Rotate the crankshaft until No. 1 piston is at TDC on the compression stroke. Adjust both valves for No. 1 cylinder by turning the rocker arm stud nut until all clearance has been eliminated then tighten stud nut one additional turn to place the lifter in the correct operating range.
2. Repeat this procedure for the remaining sets of valves, turning the crankshaft ¼ turn at a time and adjust the valves in firing order sequence, which is 1-5-4-2-6-3-7-8.

An alternate method is to remove the distributor cap and, watching for the distributor points to open, adjust each set of valves in order as the breaker points reach the high spot of the distributor cam.

1966-68 V8-462

A .060" shorter push rod (color coded white) or a .060" longer push rod (color coded yellow) are available for service to provide a means of compensating for dimensional changes in the valve mechanism. Valve stem-to-rocker arm clearance should be within the specification limits given in the *Valve Specifications* table with the hydraulic valve lifter completely collapsed and the lifter on the base circle of the camshaft. Repeated valve grinding operations will decrease this clearance to the point that the hydraulic valve lifter will cease to function. To determine whether a shorter or longer push rod is necessary, make the following check:

1. Disconnect coil high tension cable and ground it against the engine.
2. Disconnect starter relay leads and install an auxiliary starter switch.

NOTE: To crank an engine equipped with transistor ignition, disconnect the cold start relay and connect the auxiliary starter switch to the "S" terminal and battery terminal on the starter solenoid. Be sure the ignition switch is turned OFF when using the auxiliary starter switch.

3. With the piston of the cylinder on which the valve is being checked on top center of its compression stroke, apply pressure on the rocker arm to bleed the hydraulic lifter until the plunger is completely bottomed. Hold the lifter in fully collapsed position and check the clearance between valve stem and rocker arm.
4. Check the clearance with a .050" and a .150" feeler gauges. If the .050" gauge enters, a standard push rod may be used. If it does not enter, replace the standard push rod with a .060" shorter service rod.
5. If the .150" gauge enters, the operating range of the lifter is excessive. This indicates that the incorrect push rod has been installed or severe wear has occurred at the push rod ends, rocker arm or valve stem. In this case it will be necessary to determine the area of discrepancy and the incorrect or defective part or parts should be replaced.
6. If all the valve train components except the push rod are within limits, install a .060" longer push rod.

VALVE ARRANGEMENT
Front to Rear

Right Bank .... I-E-I-E-I-E-I-E
Left Bank .... E-I-E-I-E-I-E-I

VALVE LIFT SPECS.

Engine	Year	Intake	Exhaust
V8-462	1966-67	.442	.442
	1968	.441	.441
V8-460	1968	.443	.443
	1969-72	.443	.486

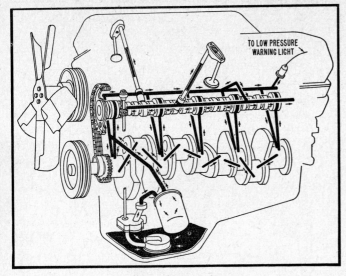

Engine lubrication. V8-460

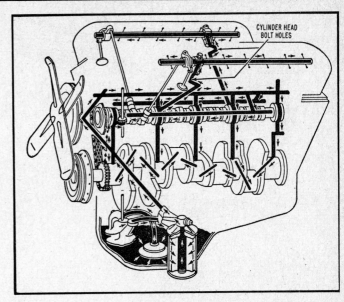

Engine lubrication. V8-462

VALVE TIMING
Intake Opens Before TDC

Engine	Year	Degrees
V8-462	1966-68	20
V8-460	1968-71	16
	1972	8

ROCKER ARM STUDS
V8-460

Rocker arm studs are screwed into threaded bores in the cylinder head bosses. To install, apply water resistant sealer to stud threads that screw into cylinder head. Install stud and torque to 65-75 ft-lbs. Apply Lubriplate to top of valve stem and at push rod guide in cylinder head. Install rocker arm, fulcrum and stud nut.

ROCKER ARMS & SHAFTS
V8-462

Dress up minor surface defects on rock-er arm shaft and in rocker arm bore with a hone. If the pad on the valve end of the rocker arm is grooved, replace the rocker arm. *Do not attempt to smooth this surface by grinding.*

Make certain that the push rods are installed in the valve lifters from which they were removed. If the valves have been reground, check the valve clearance as outlined previously and, if necessary, install longer or shorter service push rods to establish the required valve clearance. Figs. 2 and 3.

VALVE GUIDES

Valve guides in these engines are an integral part of the head and, therefore, cannot be removed. For service, guides can be reamed oversize to accommodate one of three service valves with oversize stems (.003", .015" and .030").

Check the valve stem clearance of each valve (after cleaning) in its respective valve guide. If the clearance exceeds the service limits of .004" on the intake or .005" on the exhaust, ream the valve guides to accommodate the next oversize diameter valve.

HYDRAULIC VALVE LIFTERS

The internal parts of each hydraulic valve lifter assembly are a matched set. If these are mixed, improper valve operation may result. Therefore, disassemble, inspect and test each assembly separately to prevent mixing the parts.

Fig. 4, illustrates the type of hydraulic lifter used. See the *Trouble Shooting Chapter* under the heading *Engine Noises* for causes of hydraulic valve lifter noise.

TIMING CASE COVER

NOTE: If necessary to replace the cover oil seal the cover must first be removed.

V8-460

1. Drain cooling system and crankcase.

Fig. 3 Rocker arm shaft installation identification mark

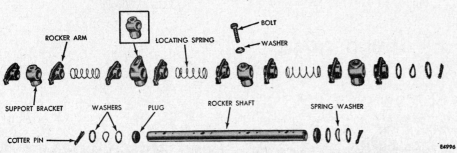

Fig. 2 Rocker arm assembly. V8-462

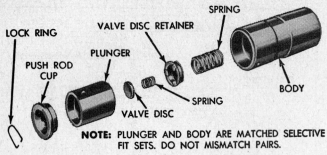

Fig. 4 Hydraulic valve lifter disassembled (typical)

NOTE: PLUNGER AND BODY ARE MATCHED SELECTIVE FIT SETS. DO NOT MISMATCH PAIRS.

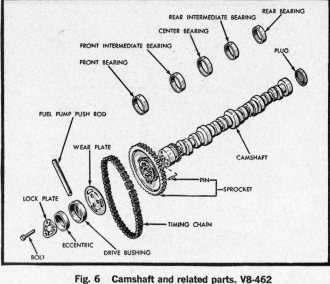

Fig. 6 Camshaft and related parts. V8-462

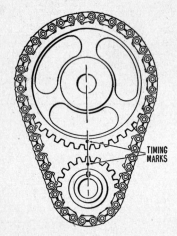

Fig. 5 Valve timing marks

2. Remove fan and radiator.
3. Remove drive belts and water pump pulley. Remove compressor support if so equipped.
4. Remove bolt and washer retaining crankshaft damper and, using a suitable puller, remove damper. Remove Woodruff key from crankshaft.
5. Remove power steering pump.
6. Loosen by-pass hose and remove heater return tube at water pump.

7. Remove fuel pump.
8. Remove front cover to cylinder block bolts. Cut oil pan seal flush with cylinder block face prior to separating cover from the cylinder block. Remove front cover and water pump as a unit.

V8-462

1. Drain cooling system and disconnect water hoses. Remove radiator supply tank, thermostat and gasket.
2. Disconnect wires from coil, engine ground strap and battery ground cable at water pump.
3. Remove fan shield from radiator.
4. On air conditioned cars, loosen bracket bolts and push compressor inward toward engine and remove drive belt. Remove fan blade, fan and compressor drive pulley as a unit.
5. Remove generator splash shield and drive belts. Remove fan, spacer and mounting bolts from water pump as a unit.
6. Remove water pump.
7. Remove vibration damper.
8. Remove power steering pump.
9. Remove fuel pump. Then remove cup-type plug from top of cylinder front cover with a long punch.
10. Raise front of car and unfasten front cover from oil pan and cylinder block. Remove front cover. *If oil pan gasket is damaged during removal of front cover, it will be necessary to replace the gasket before installing front cover.*

TIMING CHAIN

1. To remove the chain, first take off the timing chain cover as outlined previously.
2. Crank the engine until the timing mark on the camshaft sprocket is adjacent to the timing mark on the crankshaft sprocket, Fig. 5.
3. Remove cap screws, lock plate and fuel pump eccentric from front of camshaft.

4. Place a screwdriver behind the camshaft sprocket and carefully pry the sprocket and chain off the camshaft.
5. Reverse the foregoing procedure to install the chain, being sure to align the timing marks as shown in Fig. 5.

CAMSHAFT, REPLACE

If it is necessary to replace the camshaft only it may be accomplished without removing the engine from the chassis. But if the camshaft bearings are to be replaced the engine will have to be removed. To remove the camshaft, proceed as follows:

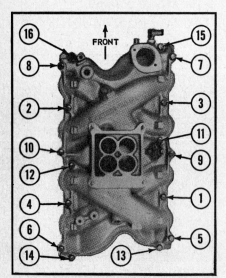

Intake manifold tightening sequence. V8-460

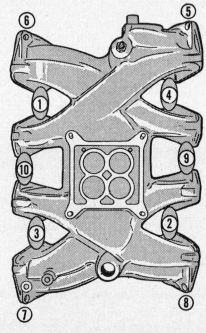

Intake manifold tightening sequence. V8-462

V8-460

1. Drain crankcase and remove oil pan.
2. Remove timing cover, chain and sprockets as outlined previously.
3. Remove intake manifold and carburetor as an assembly.
4. Remove rocker arm covers. Back off all rocker arm stud nuts, turn rocker arms sideways and remove push rods in sequence.
5. Remove valve lifters.
6. If air conditioned, unbolt and lay condenser on left fender. Secure in this position.
7. Remove grille center support.
8. Remove camshaft thrust plate bolts and carefully remove camshaft from front of engine.
9. Reverse above procedure to install.

V8-462

1. Remove the timing chain cover and chain as outlined previously.
2. Remove intake manifold.
3. Remove valve lifter cover.
4. Remove the hydraulic valve lifters and place them in a rack so they may be reinstalled in their respective bores. It may be necessary to remove the carbon from the top of the lifter bore before the lifters can be removed.
5. Remove grille.
6. Carefully slide camshaft out of engine, Fig. 6.

PISTON & ROD, ASSEMBLE

If the old pistons are serviceable, make certain that they are installed on the rods from which they were removed. The assembly must be made as shown in Fig. 7.

PISTONS, RINGS & PINS

Pistons are available in standard size and oversizes .020 and .030".
Rings are available in standard size and oversizes of .020, .030 and .040".
Pins are available in standard size only.

MAIN & ROD BEARINGS

Main and rod bearings are available in standard size and undersizes of .002, .010, .020 and .030".

OIL PAN, REPLACE
V8-460

1. Disconnect radiator shroud from radiator.
2. Raise vehicle on hoist and drain crankcase.
3. Disconnect idler arm from underbody.
4. Loosen starter retaining bolts.
5. Remove cylinder block to converter housing supports.

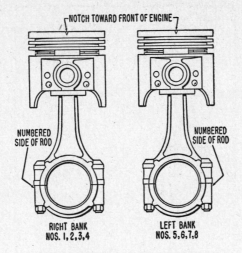

NOTCH TOWARD FRONT OF ENGINE

NUMBERED SIDE OF ROD — NUMBERED SIDE OF ROD

RIGHT BANK NOS. 1, 2, 3, 4   LEFT BANK NOS. 5, 6, 7, 8

Fig. 7 Piston and rod assembly

6. Disconnect engine front support insulators from underbody crossmember. Place floor jack under front of oil pan, with block of wood between jack and oil pan. Raise engine just enough to insert 1" blocks of wood between insulators and underbody side members. Remove floor jack.
7. Remove end attachments of front stabilizer and rotate ends of bar down to raise center of bar. Remove oil filter.
8. Remove oil pan bolts and lower pan to underbody crossmember. Remove splash shield from right side of pan.
9. Disconnect pressure line at power steering pump. Remove bolts retaining pump to front cover and rotate pump to clear oil pan. Remove oil pan.
10. Reverse procedure to install oil pan.

V8-462

1. Raise hood and oil level dipstick.
2. Revolve engine to position No. 1 piston 15°BTDC for oil pan clearance purposes (refer to timing marks on vibration damper).
3. Set parking brake and raise car.
4. Drain oil pan.
5. To allow clearance for oil pan removal, remove engine front support retaining nut. Place a block of wood on a floor jack and position jack under front leading edge of oil pan. Raise engine about 1" and insert a ½" block of wood between support insulators and underbody engine support pad. Then remove floor jack.
6. If necessary, unfasten and pull stabilizer arms downward to gain additional clearance.
7. Remove engine mounting bolts. Free oil pan from block. Remove two mounting bolts securing oil pump pick-up tube and screen assembly to oil pump, and allow pump to drop into oil pan. Then remove oil pan.

OIL PUMP

To remove the pump, drop the oil pan as outlined above. Then remove the two bolts that attach the pump to the crankcase and remove pump, gasket and the intermediate shaft.

To disassemble, remove the pump cover plate, Fig. 9, and lift out the rotor and shaft. Scrape the stake marks that hold the relief valve in the pump housing until the retainer can be removed. Then remove the retainer, spring and relief valve from the pump housing. Inspect the pump as follows:
1. With all parts clean and dry, check the inside of the pump housing and the outer race and rotor for damage or excessive wear.
2. Check the mating surface of the

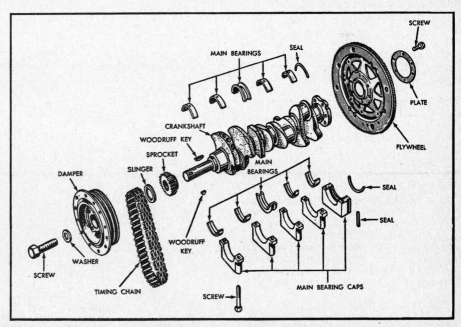

Fig. 8 Crankshaft and related parts

pump cover for wear. If this surface is worn, scored or grooved, replace the cover.

3. Measure the clearance between the outer race and housing. This clearance should be .006-.012".

4. With the rotor assembly installed in the housing, place a straight edge over the rotor assembly and housing. Measure the clearance between the straight edge and the rotor and outer race. Recommended limits are .0015-.004".

5. Check the drive shaft-to-housing bearing clearance by measuring the O.D. of the shaft and the I.D. of the housing bearing. The recommended clearance limits are .0015-.0029".

6. Inspect the relief valve spring for a collapsed or worn condition.

7. Check the relief valve piston for scores and free operation in the bore.

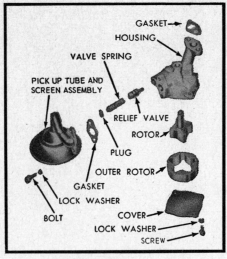

Fig. 9   Oil pump assembly

WATER PUMP, REPLACE
V8-460

1. Drain cooling system.
2. Remove shroud and fan.
3. Remove drive belts and water pump pulley.
4. Remove bolts attaching compressor bracket to water pump if so equipped.
5. Loosen alternator bracket and remove bolts attaching bracket to water pump.
6. Disconnect lower radiator hose, heater return tube and bypass hose at water pump.
7. Remove remaining water pump bolts and remove water pump.

V8-462

1. Disconnect battery cable.
2. On air conditioned cars, remove fan shield, power booster clutch, fan and compressor drive pulley.
3. With standard cooling system, remove fan shield, fan and spacer.
4. Remove radiator supply tank.
5. Loosen clamp securing by-pass hose to water pump.
6. Remove generator splash shield.
7. Remove drive belts.
8. Remove hose from pump.
9. Remove pump mounting bolts. Then after positioning oil dipstick tube

bracket and power steering pump bracket to allow removal of water pump, remove water pump.

FUEL PUMP, REPLACE
Removal

1. Remove hose clamps and fuel line hoses from pump inlet and vapor discharge connections. Disconnect fuel filter from fuel line.
2. Loosen but do not remove pump attaching capscrews. Crank engine until fuel pump eccentric on camshaft is in a position which applies the least tension on fuel pump rocker arm. Then remove capscrews and pump.
3. If replacement of fuel pump push rod is required, remove access cover from cylinder front cover and remove push rod.

Installation

1. Remove old gasket material from pump mounting pad and pump flange.
2. Install adapter and vapor discharge valve in new pump. Install heat shield and tighten retaining nuts. If pump push rod was removed, install it on eccentric sleeve and install access cover to cylinder front cover.
3. Apply sealer to both sides of new gasket. Position gasket on pump flange and hold pump in position on cylinder front cover. Make sure rocker arm is riding on push rod.
4. Press pump tight against cylinder front cover. Install and tighten retaining screws.
5. Connect fuel lines. Then operate engine and check for leaks.

Transmission, Rear Axle, Propeller Shaft & Brakes

1972 AUTO. TRANS. LINKAGE ADJUST
1972 Mark IV

1. Place selector lever in D position tight against the stop.
2. Remove nut from transmission end of cable and remove cable from lever stud.
3. Shift manual lever at transmission into D position, second detent from back.
4. Place cable end on transmission manual lever stud, using care to align flats on the stud with the flats on the cable. Start attaching nut.
5. Make sure selector lever has not moved from D stop; then tighten nut to 10-15 ft. lbs.
6. Check operation for all lever positions.

1972 Continental

The control linkage adjustment proce-

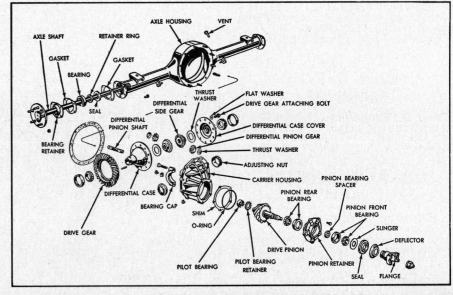

Fig. 1   Rear axle assembly. 1966-72

Fig. 2 Removing nuts from
rear bearing retainer

Fig. 3 Removing axle shaft with
slide hammer-type puller

Fig. 4 Splitting bearing inner retainer
for bearing removal

dures are the same as described for the 1971 models in the front of this manual.

REAR AXLES

Fig. 1 illustrates the rear axle assemblies used on these cars. When necessary to overhaul either of these units, refer to the *Rear Axle Specifications* table in this chapter.

1966-72 Removable Housing Type

In these axles, Fig. 1, the drive pinion is straddle-mounted by two opposed tapered roller bearings which support the pinion shaft in front of the drive pinion gear, and straight roller bearing that supports the pinion shaft at the rear of the pinion gear. The drive pinion is assembled in a pinion retainer that is bolted to the differential carrier. The tapered roller bearings are preloaded by a collapsible spacer between the bearings. The pinion is positioned by a shim or shims located between the drive pinion retainer and the differential carrier.

The differential is supported in the carrier by two tapered roller side bearings. These bearings are preloaded by two threaded ring nuts or sleeves between the bearings and pedestals. The differential assembly is positioned for proper ring gear and pinion backlash by varying the adjustment of these ring nuts. The differential case houses two side gears in mesh with two pinions mounted on a pinion shaft which is held in place by a

pin. The side gears and pinions are backed by thrust washers. With high performance engines, an optional rear axle having a four-pinion differential is also used.

The axle shafts are of unequal length, the left shaft being shorter than the right. The axle shafts are mounted in sealed ball bearings that are pressed on the shafts.

Service Bulletin

All Ford Built Rear Axles: Recent manufacturing changes have eliminated the need for marking rear axle drive pinions for individual variations from nominal shim thicknesses. In the past, these pinion markings, with the aid of a shim selection table, were used as a guide to select correct shim thicknesses when a gear set or carrier assembly replacement was performed.

With the elimination of pinion markings, use of the shim selection table is no longer possible and the methods outlined below must be used.

1. Measure the thickness of the original pinion depth shim removed from the axle. Use the same thickness upon installation of the replacement carrier or drive pinion. If any further shim change is necessary, it will be indicated in the tooth pattern check.
2. If the original shim is lost, substitute a nominal shim for the original and use the tooth pattern check to determine if further shim changes are required.

DIFFERENTIAL CARRIER, REPLACE

1966-72 Rear Axles

In servicing the rear axles shown in Fig. 1, it is not necessary to remove the rear axle assembly for any normal repairs. The axle shafts and carrier assembly can easily be removed from the vehicle, leaving the axle housing in place.

1. Place a drain pan under the carrier and housing to catch the old grease when the carrier is separated from the housing.
2. Use a wire brush to clean dirt from

the area around the carrier and housing mating surfaces. Then wipe the area clean with a cloth dampened in solvent.
3. Remove axle shafts and drive shaft as explained below.
4. Unfasten carrier from housing and lift out carrier.
5. Reverse removal procedure to install, using a new gasket between the carrier and housing.

AXLE SHAFTS

1. Remove wheel assembly.
2. Remove brake drum from flange.
3. Working through hole provided in axle shaft flange, Fig. 2, remove nuts that secure wheel bearing retainer.
4. Pull axle shaft out of housing with a slide hammer-type puller, Fig. 3. *Brake carrier plate must not be dislodged. Install one nut to hold the plate in place after axle shaft is removed.*
5. If axle shaft bearing is to be replaced, loosen inner retainer by nicking it deeply with a chisel in several places, Fig. 4. The bearing will then slide off easily.
6. Press bearing from axle shaft.

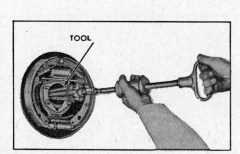

Fig. 5 Using hook-type tool
to remove oil seal

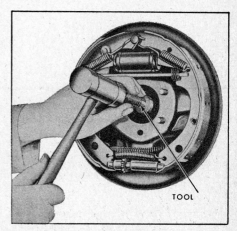

Fig. 6 Using special driver
to install oil seal

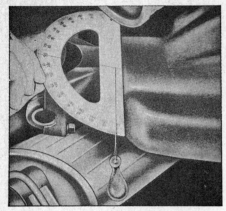

Fig. 7 Checking pinion nose angle. To make this tool, obtain a common protractor and drill a small hole at the exact center of the base line (0°). Attach a string and weight as shown

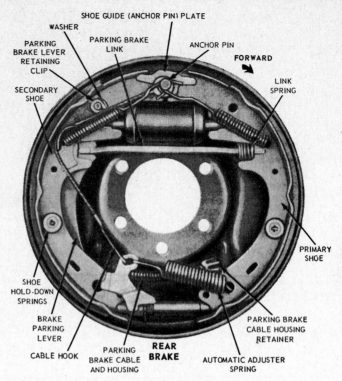

Fig. 8 Rear only on 1966-72

7. Inspect machined surface of axle shaft and housing for rough spots that would affect the sealing action of the oil seal. Carefully remove any burrs or rough spots.
8. Press new bearing on shaft until it seats firmly against shoulder on shaft.
9. Press inner bearing retainer on shaft until it seats firmly against bearing.
10. If oil seal is to be replaced, use a hook-type tool to pull it out of the housing, Fig. 5. Wipe a small amount of oil resistant sealer on outer edge of seal before it is installed, Fig. 6.

Installation

1. Place a new gasket on each side of brake carrier plate and slide axle shaft into housing. Start splines into differential side gear and push the shaft in until bearing bottoms in housing.
2. Install retainer and tighten nuts to 30-40 ft. lbs.
3. Install brake drum and wheel.

PROPELLER SHAFT

To maintain proper drive line balance, mark the drive shaft, universal joints, slip yoke and companion flange before removing the shaft assembly so it can be reinstalled in its original position.
1. Remove cap-screws attaching slip yoke to front U-joint.
2. Push slip yoke forward on transmission output shaft and lower front of drive shaft.
3. Remove nuts, lockwashers and U-bolts attaching rear U-joint to differential drive pinion flange.
4. Remove shaft assembly.
5. Reverse removal procedure to install the assembly, and torque capscrews and U-bolts to 15-18 ft. lbs.

PROPELLER SHAFT BALANCE

If detailed parts of the drive shaft assembly have been replaced and shaft vibration is encountered after installation, disconnect the shaft at the slip yoke. Rotate the slip yoke and transmission output shaft 180°; then reconnect the shaft to the yoke. If vibration persists, disconnect the shaft at the rear axle flange and rotate the flange and drive pinion 180° and reconnect shaft to flange.

DRIVE LINE ANGLE CHECK

Vibration or "shudder" which is noticeable either on fast acceleration or when coasting (using engine for a brake) may be caused by rear axle housing being loose on rear springs or by excessive drive line angles. If the rear axle U-bolts are loose, torque the nuts to 50-60 ft. lbs.

Drive line angles may be corrected by tilting the rear axle pinion nose up or down as required. Tapered shims (wedges) are available in three angles: $\frac{1}{2}$, 1 and $1\frac{1}{2}$ degrees with no more than one wedge to be used on a side.

To determine if shimming or a change of shimming is required, check the pinion nose angle as related to the rear riding height of the car. After checking and recording riding height, check the pinion nose angle as follows:
1. Measure pinion nose angle as shown in Fig. 7.
2. Compare riding height measurement and pinion nose angle with those shown in the following chart:

Fig. 9 Backing off brake adjustment by disengaging adjuster lever with screwdriver

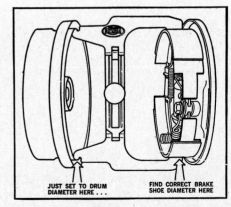

Fig. 10 Brake adjustment with gauge

Riding Height	Pinion Nose Angle*
6"	4° Down
7"	3½° Down
8"	3° Down
9"	2½° Down

*Plus or minus ¼°

3. If nose angle does not compare to related riding height, remove U-bolt nuts and install appropriate wedges between each spring insulator upper retainer and axle housing mounting pad.
4. Install and torque U-bolt nuts to 50-60 ft. lbs. Make sure lower insulator retainer contacts upper retainer.

BRAKE ADJUSTMENTS

NOTE: For 1970-72 a new self centering pressure differential valve is used which no longer requires bleeding at the opposite end of the car to cause the brake warning light to go out. To center the new valve, after any brake repair or bleeding, it is only necessary to turn the ignition switch on and depress the brake pedal. This action will center the piston and the light will go out.

These brakes, Fig. 8, have self-adjusting shoe mechanisms that assure correct lining-to-drum clearances at all times. The automatic adjusters operate only when the brakes are applied when the car is moving rearward or when the car comes to an uphill stop.

Although the brakes are self-adjusting, an initial adjustment is necessary when the brake shoes have been relined or replaced, or when the length of the star wheel adjuster has been changed during some other service operation.

Frequent usage of an automatic transmission forward range to halt reverse vehicle motion may prevent the automatic adjusters from functioning, thereby inducing low pedal heights. Should low pedal heights be encountered, it is recommended that numerous forward and reverse stops be made until satisfactory pedal height is obtained.

NOTE

If a low pedal height condition cannot be corrected by making numerous reverse stops (provided the hydraulic system is free of air) it indicates that the automatic adjusting mechanism is not functioning. Therefore, it will be necessary to remove the brake drum, clean, free up and lubricate the adjusting mechanism. Then adjust the brakes, being sure the parking brake is fully released.

Adjustment

1. Remove adjusting hole cover from brake backing plate and, from the backing plate side, turn adjusting screw upward with a screwdriver or other suitable tool to expand the shoes until a slight drag is felt when the drum is rotated.
2. Remove the drum.
3. While holding the adjusting lever out of engagement with the adjusting screw, Fig. 9, back off the ad-

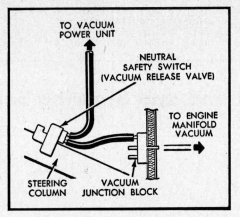

Fig. 11 Vacuum connections for automatic parking brake release. 1966-72

justing screw ¾ turn with the fingers.

NOTE: *If finger movement will not turn the screw, free it up. If this is not done, the adjusting lever will not turn the screw during subsequent vehicle operation. Lubricate the screw with oil and coat with wheel bearing grease. Any other adjustment procedure may cause damage to the adjusting screw with consequent self-adjuster problems.*

4. Install wheel and drum, and adjusting hole cover. Adjust brakes on remaining wheels in the same manner.
5. If pedal height is not satisfactory, drive the vehicle and make sufficient reverse stops until proper pedal height is obtained.

SERVICE BULLETIN

REVISED BRAKE ADJUSTMENT PROCEDURE: Mid-year 1965 production and later models use a new front and rear brake backing plate which omits the adjusting slot for manual brake adjustment. The backing plates have a partially stamped knock-out slot for use ONLY when the brake drums cannot be removed in a normal manner. The open slot is then covered with a rubber plug as used in the past to prevent contamination of the brakes.

When servicing a vehicle requiring a brake adjustment, the metal knock-out plugs should NOT be removed. Rather the drums should be removed and brakes inspected for a malfunction.

Although the brakes are self-adjusting, an initial adjustment will be necessary after a brake repair, such as relining or replacement. The initial adjustment can be obtained by the new procedure which follows:

1. Use the brake shoe adjustment gauge shown in Fig. 10 to obtain the drum inside diameter as shown. Tighten the adjusting knob on the gauge to hold this setting.
2. Place the opposite side of the gauge over the brake shoes and adjust the shoes by turning the adjuster screw until the gauge just slides over the linings. Rotate the gauge around the lining surface to assure proper lin-

ing diameter adjustment and clearance.
3. Install brake drum and wheel. Final adjustment is accomplished by making several firm reverse stops, using the brake pedal.

PARKING BRAKES, ADJUST

1970-72

1. Make sure the parking brake is fully released.
2. Place transmission in neutral and raise the vehicle.
3. Tighten the adjusting nut against the cable equalizer to cause rear wheel brake drag. Then loosen the adjusting nut until the rear brakes are fully released. There should be no brake drag.
4. Lower the vehicle and check operation.

1966-69

1. Fully release parking brake.
2. Loosen adjusting nut on equalizer rod, then turn lock nut in front of equalizer several turns forward.
3. Depress parking brake slowly until initial locking position is obtained.
4. Turn adjusting nut forward against equalizer until about 100 lbs. of force at the outside diameter of the tire is required to turn the rear wheels.
5. Tighten lock nut against equalizer.
6. Release parking brake and check to make sure that there is no drag when rear wheels are turned.

1966-72 Vacuum Release Unit

The vacuum power unit, Fig. 11, will release the parking brake automatically when the transmission selector lever is moved into any driving position with the engine running. The brakes will not release automatically, however, when the selector lever is in neutral or park position with the engine running, or in any other position with the engine off.

The lower end of the release handle extends out for alternate manual release in the event of vacuum power failure or for optional manual release at any time.

POWER BRAKE UNIT, REPLACE

1966-72

1. Disconnect battery.
2. Disconnect outlet lines from master cylinder.
3. Unfasten and remove master cylinder.
4. Disconnect vacuum hose at booster.
5. Disconnect power steering return line from steering gear to obtain necessary clearance. Install plug in line to keep out dirt.
6. Remove cowl-to-fender brace, and the belt that holds compressor and power steering hoses to bracket.
7. Working inside car below instrument panel, disconnect booster push rod from brake pedal as follows: Dis-

connect stop light switch wires at connector. Remove C-clamp retainer. Slide stop light switch off brake pedal pin just far enough for switch outer hole to clear pin. Then lift switch straight upward from pin.
8. Slide master cylinder push rod link, nylon washers and bushing off brake pedal pin.
9. Unfasten and remove booster unit from dash panel.
10. Reverse procedure to install.

Front End and Steering Section

FRONT SUSPENSION
1969 Mark III & 1970-72 All

Referring to Fig. 1, each wheel rotates on a spindle. The upper and lower ends of the spindle are attached to upper and lower ball joints that are mounted to an upper and lower control arm. The upper control arm pivots on a shaft assembly that is bolted to the frame. The lower control arm pivots on a bolt in the front crossmember. The struts, which are connected between the lower control arms and frame crossmember, prevent the control arms from moving forward or backward.

1966-69 Continental

The front wheel suspension is a ball joint type utilizing coil springs and double acting shock absorbers. Fore and aft movement of each front wheel is controlled by a non-adjustable type stabilizing strut connected to the suspension lower control arm and to a point forward on the front crossmember, Fig. 2. A single rubber-cored bushing is used at the inner end of the lower control arm. Caster and camber are adjusted without the use of shims but rather by movement of the serrated upper control arm shaft.

LUBRICATION

1966-72 STEERING LINKAGE: The steering linkage should be lubricated at 36,-000 mile intervals. Normal breathing of socket joints permits moisture condensation within the joint. Moisture inside the joint assembly will cause no appreciable damage and the joint will function normally. However, if the moisture is concentrated in the bearing grease grooves and is frozen at the time of attempted lubrication, grease cannot flow and pressure greasing may damage the joint assembly.

Do not attempt to lubricate the steering linkage if it has set in temperatures lower than 20 deg. above zero F. The vehicle should be allowed to warm up in a heated garage for 30 minutes or until the joints accept lubrication.

IMPORTANT: A torch must not be used to heat joints because this quantity of heat will melt the nylon bearing within the joint.

Ball Joint Lubrication

Ball joints should be lubricated with special grease formulated just for this purpose every 36,000 miles on 1966-69. Lubrication points are fitted with screw plugs. The plugs should be removed, grease fittings installed and, after applying the grease, remove the fittings and reinstall the plugs.

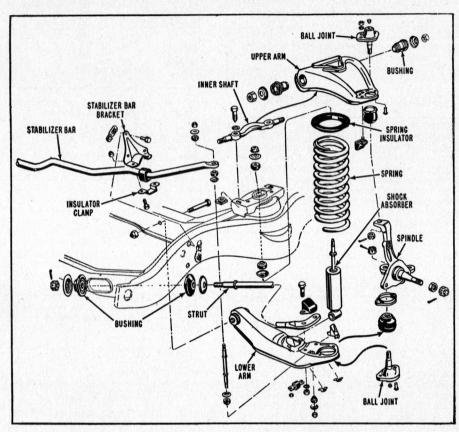

Fig. 1   Front suspension. 1969 Mark III & 1970-72 All

WHEEL ALIGNMENT

SERVICE BULLETIN

WHEEL BALANCING DIFFERS: On cars with disc brakes, dynamic balancing of the wheel-and-tire assembly on the car should not be attempted without first pulling back the shoe and lining assemblies from the rotor. If this is not done, brake drag may burn out the motor on the wheel spinner.

The drag can be eliminated by removing the wheel, taking out the two bolts holding the caliper splash shield, and detaching the shield. Then push the pistons into their cylinder bores by applying steady pressure on the shoes on each side of the rotor for at least a minute. If necessary, use waterpump pliers to apply the pressure.

After the pistons have been retracted, reinstall the splash shield and wheel. The wheel-and-tire assembly can then be dynamically balanced in the usual way. After the balancing job has been completed, be sure to pump the brake pedal several times until the shoes are seated and a firm brake pedal is obtained.

1969 Mark III & 1970-72 All

Caster and camber can be adjusted by loosening the bolts that attach the upper suspension arm to the shaft at the frame side rail, and moving the arm assembly in or out in the elongated bolt holes, Fig. 3. Since any movement of the arm affects both caster and camber, both factors should be balanced against one another when making the adjustment.

Caster, Adjust
1. To adjust caster, install the adjusting tool as shown in Fig. 3.
2. Loosen both upper arm inner shaft retaining bolts and move either front or rear of the shaft in or out as necessary to increase or decrease caster angle. Then tighten bolt to retain adjustment.

Camber, Adjust
1. Loosen both upper arm inner retain-

ing bolts and move both front and rear ends of shaft inward or outward as necessary to increase or decrease camber angle.

2. Tighten bolts and recheck caster and readjust if necessary.

1966-69 Continental

Caster, Adjust

1. Raise hood and unsnap clips retaining top of rubber bushing shield to fender apron.
2. Loosen bolts that secure upper control arm shaft to frame and, with a pry bar, move shaft in or out as required. A movement of approximately $3/32''$ at either front or rear bolt location will change caster $1/2°$. Inboard movement of the front bolt, or outboard movement of rear bolt, will change caster in negative direction. Outboard movement of front bolt or inboard movement of rear bolt will change caster in positive direction.
3. When adjustment is correct, torque shaft retaining bolts to 100-125 ft. lbs.

Camber, Adjust

1. Raise hood and unsnap clips retaining top of bushing rubber shield to fender apron.
2. Loosen bolts that secure upper control arm shaft to frame and, with a pry bar, move shaft in or out as required. A movement of approximately $3/64''$ of the entire shaft will change camber $1/4°$. Inboard movement will change camber in negative direction. Outboard movement will change camber in positive direction.
3. When adjustment is correct, torque shaft retaining bolts to 100-125 ft. lbs.

Toe-In, Adjust

Position the front wheels in their straight-ahead position. Then turn both tie rod adjusting sleeves an equal amount until the desired toe-in setting is obtained.

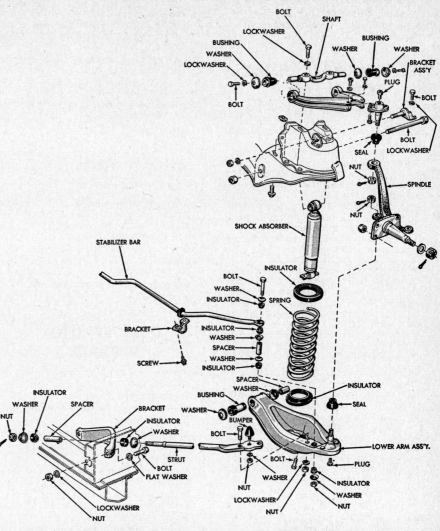

Fig. 2   Front suspension. 1966-69 Continental

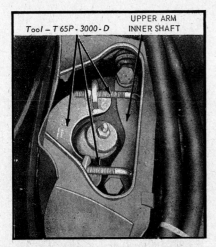

Fig. 3   Caster and camber adjusting tool. 1969 Mark III & 1970-72 All

WHEEL BEARINGS, ADJUST

With wheel rotating, torque spindle nut to 15-20 ft. lbs. Locate nut-lock on spindle nut so that cotter pin castellations are aligned with cotter pin hole in spindle. Back off spindle nut and nut-lock together until next castellation on nut-lock aligns with cotter pin hole in spindle, and install cotter pin.

WHEEL BEARINGS, REPLACE

(Disc Brakes)

1. Raise car and remove front wheels.
2. Remove caliper mounting bolts.

NOTE: It is not necessary to disconnect the brake line for this operation.

3. Slide caliper off of the disc, inserting a spacer between the shoes to hold them in their bores after the caliper is removed. Position caliper assembly out of the way.

NOTE: Do not allow caliper to hang by brake hose.

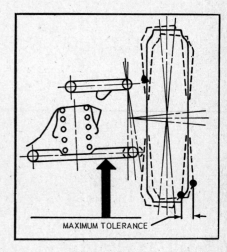

Fig. 4   Checking ball joints for wear

4. Remove hub and disc. Grease retainer and inner bearing can now be removed.

CHECKING BALL JOINTS FOR WEAR

Upper Ball Joint

1. Raise car on floor jacks placed beneath lower control arms.
2. Grasp lower edge of tire and move wheel in and out.
3. As wheel is being moved in and out, observe upper end of spindle and upper arm.
4. Any movement between upper end of spindle and upper arm indicates ball joint wear and loss of preload. If such movement is observed, replace upper ball joint.

NOTE: During the foregoing check, the lower ball joint will be unloaded and may move. Disregard all such movement of the lower joint. Also, do not mistake loose wheel bearings for a worn ball joint.

Lower Ball Joint

1. Raise car on jacks placed under lower control arms as shown in Fig. 4.
2. With a dial indicator attached to the lower arm, position indicator so that the plunger rests against inner side of wheel rim adjacent to lower ball joint.
3. Grasp tire at top and bottom and slowly move tire in and out. Note reading on dial, which is the radial play. If the reading exceeds ¼", replace lower ball joint.

BALL JOINTS, REPLACE

The upper ball joints on Continental models are bolted to the upper control arm, while on the Mark III, the ball joints are riveted to the arm. The lower ball joints are riveted to the lower control arm on all models.

When replacing a riveted joint, remove the rivets and retain the new joint in its control arm with the bolts, nuts and washers furnished with the ball joint kit.

Use a suitable pressing tool to force the ball joint from the spindle.

SHOCK ABSORBER, REPLACE

1. Remove stud nut at upper eye of shock absorber. Remove upper eye stud bracket to crossmember bolt and remove stud bracket.
2. Unfasten shock absorber from lower control arm. Then lower and remove shock absorber.
3. Reverse above procedure to install.

COIL SPRING, REPLACE

1. Raise and support car as for replacing lower ball joint.
2. Remove brake assembly.
3. Remove shock absorber and drag strut from lower arm.
4. Disconnect stabilizer from lower arm.
5. Loosen nut from ball joint stud two turns.
6. Place jack under outer end of lower arm and raise arm several inches.
7. Install a suitable spring compressor inside spring with jaws of tool toward center of car.
8. Remove nut from ball joint stud. Lower jack until spindle and spring are free, then remove spring and insulators.
9. Reverse above procedure to install.

POWER STEERING UNIT, REPLACE

1969-72 Mark III; IV

1. Disconnect lines from steering gear and plug lines and ports to prevent entry of dirt.
2. Remove the two bolts securing flex coupling to steering gear and to column.
3. Raise vehicle and remove sector shaft nut and pitman arm.
4. Support steering gear and remove three attaching bolts. Work steering gear free of coupling and remove it from vehicle.

1966-72 Continental

1. Disconnect pressure and return lines from steering gear. Cap each line and plug each port to prevent entry of dirt.
2. Disconnect ground strap from gear housing.
3. Remove bolt that attaches flex coupling to steering gear.
4. Unfasten brace attached to torque box and frame side rail and swing brace to one side.
5. Use a puller to remove pitman arm.
6. Remove muffler inlet pipe.
7. Disconnect linkage rod from equalizer shaft. Remove equalizer stud from side rail. Move equalizer shaft up and out of the way, being careful not to lose stud or bushings.
8. Remove bolt from lower end of fender splash shield. Move shield to one side to gain access to steering gear.
9. Support gear and remove mounting bolts. Move gear downward to free it from flex joint, then rotate it counterclockwise to provide clearance between side rail and engine.

OLDSMOBILE
All Intermediate & Full Size Models

TORONADO: Service procedures that apply to the Toronado only will be found in the special Toronado supplement starting on page 2-491.

For service procedures on 6-250 see the Chevrolet Chapter.

OLD CAR SPECIFICATIONS: For 1946-65 Tune Up and Wheel Alignment Specifications see back of book.

NOTE: Material marked "F.S.C." means Oldsmobile Full Size Car, or Senior Models

*This material covered only in the "Service Trade Edition" of this manual.

INDEX OF SERVICE OPERATIONS

OLDSMOBILE — All Intermediate & Full Size Models

VEHICLE IDENTIFICATION PLATE: 1966-67 on left front door pillar. 1968-72 on left upper dash.

ENGINE NUMBER LOCATION

1966-67 V8-330, 425: Stamped on machined pad at front of right cylinder head.

1966-71 6-250: Right side of engine block directly to rear of distributor.
1968-72 V8s: Stamped on oil fill tube.

ENGINE IDENTIFCATION CODE

YEAR	ENGINE	ENGINE PREFIX
1966	6-250	F or T
	V8-330	V or X
	V8-400	V
	V8-425 2 Bar. Carb.	M
	V8-425 4 Bar. Carb.	N
	V8-425 Toronado	T
1967	6-250	F
	V8-330, F-85	W
	4-4-2, V8-400	V
	Delmont 88, V8-330	X
	V8-425 2 Bar. Carb.	P
	V8-425 4 Bar. Carb.	R
	Toronado (Suffix T)	R
1968	6-250	VA-B-E-F
	V8-350 2 Bar. Carb.	TB-D-L
	V8-350 4 Bar. Carb.	TN
	V8-350 2 Bar. Carb.	QA-B-I-J
	V8-350 4 Bar. Carb.	QN-P-V-X
	V8-400 2 Bar. Carb.	QH
	V8-400 4 Bar. Carb.	QR-S-T-U-W
	V8-455 2 Bar. Carb.	VA-B-C-D-J

YEAR	ENGINE	ENGINE PREFIX
	V8-455 4 Bar. Carb.	UN-O
	V8-455 Toronado	US-T-W-V
1969	6-250	VA-B-E-F
	V8-350 2 Bar. Carb.	QI-A-B
	V8-350 4 Bar. Carb.	QV-N-P
	V8-350 2 Bar. Carb.	TL-B-D
	V8-350 4 Bar. Carb.	QX
	V8-400 4 Bar. Carb.	QW-R-S
	V8-400 4 Bar. Carb.	QU-T
	V8-455 2 Bar. Carb.	UJ-C-D
	V8-455 4 Bar. Carb.	UN-O
	V8-455 4 Bar. Carb.	UL
	V8-455 4 Bar. Carb.	US-T-V
	V8-455 4 Bar. Carb.	UW
1970	6-250	VB-F
	V8-350 2 Bar. Carb.	QI-A-J
	V8-350 2 Bar. Carb.	TL-D-C
	V8-350 4 Bar. Carb.	QV-N-P
	V8-350 4 Bar. Carb.	QX-D
	V8-455 2 Bar. Carb.	UJ-C-D
	V8-455 2 Bar. Carb.	TY-X
	V8-455 4 Bar. Carb.	TU-W-V
	V8-455 4 Bar. Carb.	TQ-P

YEAR	ENGINE	ENGINE PREFIX
	V8-455 4 Bar. Carb.	UN-O
	V8-455 4 Bar. Carb.	TS-T
	V8-455 4 Bar. Carb.	UL
	V8-455 4 Bar. Carb.	US-T-W-V
1971	6-250	VB-F
	V8-350 2 Bar. Carb.	QI-A-J
	V8-350 2 Bar. Carb	TE-D-C
	V8-350 4 Bar. Carb.	QB-O-N-P
	V8-455 2 Bar. Carb.	UC-D-E
	V8-455 4 Bar. Carb.	TQ-P
	V8-455 4 Bar. Carb.	TU-N
	V8-455 4 Bar. Carb.	TS-B-T-L
	V8-455 4 Bar. Carb.	TW-V-A
	V8-455 4 Bar. Carb.	UN-O-S-T
1972	V8-350 2 Bar. Carb.	QA-B-C
	V8-350 2 Bar. Carb.	QN-O
	V8-350 4 Bar. Carb.	QD-E
	V8-350 4 Bar. Carb.	QJ-K-P-Q
	V8-455	UA-B-S-T
	V8-455	UL-N-O
	V8-455	UD-E-U-V

GRILLE IDENTIFICATION

1966 F-85, Cutlass, Vista Cruiser

1966 "4-4-2"

1966 Dynamic, Delta & Jetstar 88

1966 Starfire

1966 "98"

1966 Toronado

1967 F-85, Cutlass, Vista Cruiser

1967 "4-4-2"

1967 Delta 88

GRILLE IDENTIFICATION—Continued

1967 Delmont

1967 98

1967 Toronado

1968 F-85, Cutlass, Vista Cruiser

1968 "4-4-2"

1968 Delmont & Delta 88

1968 98

1968 Toronado

1969 F-85, Cutlass, Vista Cruiser

1969 "4-4-2"

1969 Delta 88, Royale

1969 98

1969 Toronado

1970 F-85, Cutlass, Vista Cruiser

1970 Cutlass Supreme

1970 "4-4-2"

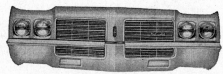

1970 Delta 88

1970 Delta Royale

1970 98

1970 Toronado

1971 F-85, Cutlass

1971 Cutlass Supreme

1971 Cutlass "S"

1971 "4-4-2"

GRILLE IDENTIFICATION—Continued

1971 Delta Royale

1971 98

1971 Toronado

1972 Cutlass "S"

1972 Delta 88 & Royale

1972 98

1972 Toronado

GENERAL ENGINE SPECIFICATIONS

Year	Engine	Car-buretor	Bore and Stroke	Piston Displacement, Cubic Inches	Compression Ratio	Maximum Brake H.P. @ R.P.M.	Maximum Torque Lbs. Ft. @ R.P.M.	Normal Oil Pressure Pounds
1966	155 Horsepower............③6-250	1 Barrel	3.875 x 3.53	250	8.50	155 @ 4200	240 @ 2000	30–45
	250 Horsepower............V8-330	2 Barrel	3.9385 x 3.385	330	9.00	250 @ 4800	335 @ 2800	35–45
	260 Horsepower............V8-330	2 Barrel	3.9385 x 3.385	330	10.25	260 @ 4800	355 @ 2800	35–45
	310 Horsepower............V8-330	4 Barrel	3.9385 x 3.385	330	9.00	310 @ 5200	360 @ 3600	35–45
	320 Horsepower............V8-330	4 Barrel	3.9385 x 3.385	330	10.25	320 @ 5200	360 @ 3600	35–45
	350 Horsepower "442".......V8-400	4 Barrel	4.0000 x 3.975	400	10.50	350 @ 5000	440 @ 3600	35–45
	300 Horsepower............V8-425	2 Barrel	4.126 x 3.975	425	9.00	300 @ 4400	430 @ 2400	35–45
	310 Horsepower............V8-425	2 Barrel	4.126 x 3.975	425	10.25	310 @ 4400	450 @ 2400	35–45
	365 Horsepower............V8-400	3 Carbs.	4.000 x 3.985	400	10.50	365 @ 5000	—	35–45
	365 Horsepower............V8-425	4 Barrel	4.126 x 3.975	425	10.25	365 @ 4800	470 @ 3200	35–45
	375 Horsepower............V8-425	4 Barrel	4.126 x 3.975	425	10.50	375 @ 4800	480 @ 3200	35–45
	385 H.P. Toronado..........V8-425	4 Barrel	4.126 x 3.975	425	10.50	385 @ 4800	475 @ 3200	35–45
1967	155 Horsepower.............③6-250	1 Barrel	3.875 x 3.53	250	8.50	155 @ 4200	240 @ 2000	30–45
	250 Horsepower............V8-330	2 Barrel	3.9375 x 3.385	330	9.00	250 @ 4800	335 @ 2800	35–45
	260 Horsepower............V8-330	2 Barrel	3.9375 x 3.385	330	10.25	260 @ 4800	355 @ 2800	35–45
	300 Horsepower............V8-400	2 Barrel	4.000 x 3.975	400	10.50	300 @ 4600	425 @ 3000	35–50
	300 Horsepower............V8-425	2 Barrel	4.125 x 3.975	425	9.00	300 @ 4400	430 @ 2400	30–45
	310 Horsepower............V8-330	4 Barrel	3.9375 x 3.385	330	9.00	310 @ 5200	340 @ 3600	35–45
	310 Horsepower............V8-425	2 Barrel	4.125 x 3.975	425	10.25	310 @ 4400	450 @ 2400	30–45
	320 Horsepower............V8-330	4 Barrel	3.9375 x 3.385	330	10.25	320 @ 5200	335 @ 3600	35–45
	350 Horsepower............V8-400	4 Barrel	4.000 x 3.975	400	10.50	350 @ 5000	440 @ 3600	35–50
	365 Horsepower............V8-425	4 Barrel	4.125 x 3.975	425	10.25	365 @ 4800	470 @ 3200	30–45
	375 Horsepower............V8-425	4 Barrel	4.125 x 3.975	425	10.50	375 @ 4800	470 @ 3200	30–45
	385 H.P. Toronado..........V8-425	4 Barrel	4.125 x 3.975	425	10.50	385 @ 4800	475 @ 3200	30–45

Continued

GENERAL ENGINE SPECIFICATIONS—Continued

Year	Engine	Carburetor	Bore and Stroke	Piston Displacement, Cubic Inches	Compression Ratio	Maximum Brake H.P. @ R.P.M.	Maximum Torque Lbs. Ft. @ R.P.M.	Normal Oil Pressure Pounds
1968	155 Horsepower............②6-250	1 Barrel	3.875 x 3.53	250	8.50	155 @ 4200	240 @ 2000	30—45
	250 Horsepower............V8-350	2 Barrel	4.057 x 3.385	350	9.00	250 @ 4400	355 @ 2600	35—45
	290 Horsepower............V8-400	2 Barrel	3.870 x 4.25	400	9.00	290 @ 4600	425 @ 2400	30—45
	300 Horsepower............V8-350	4 Barrel	4.057 x 3.385	350	10.25	300 @ 4800	390 @ 3600	35—45
	310 Horsepower............V8-350	4 Barrel	4.057 x 3.385	350	10.25	310 @ 4800	390 @ 3200	35—45
	310 Horsepower............V8-455	2 Barrel	4.126 x 4.25	455	9.00	310 @ 4200	490 @ 2400	30—45
	320 Horsepower............V8-455	2 Barrel	4.126 x 4.25	455	10.25	320 @ 4200	500 @ 2400	30—45
	350 Horsepower............V8-400	4 Barrel	3.870 x 4.25	400	10.50	350 @ 4800	440 @ 3200	30—45
	360 Horsepower............V8-400	4 Barrel	3.870 x 4.25	400	10.50	360 @ 5400	440 @ 3600	30—45
	365 Horsepower............V8-455	4 Barrel	4.126 x 4.25	455	10.25	365 @ 4600	510 @ 3000	30—45
	375 Horsepower............V8-455	4 Barrel	4.126 x 4.25	455	10.25	375 @ 4600	510 @ 3000	30—45
	400 Horsepower............V8-455	4 Barrel	4.126 x 4.25	455	10.25	400 @ 4800	500 @ 3200	30—45
1969	155 Horsepower............②6-250	1 Barrel	3.875 x 3.53	250	8.50	155 @ 4200	240 @ 2000	30—45
	250 Horsepower............V8-350	2 Barrel	4.057 x 3.385	350	9.00	250 @ 4400	355 @ 2600	30—45
	310 Horsepower............V8-350	4 Barrel	4.057 x 3.385	350	10.25	310 @ 4800	390 @ 3200	30—45
	310 Horsepower............V8-455	2 Barrel	4.125 x 4.250	455	9.00	310 @ 4200	490 @ 2400	30—45
	325 Horsepower............V8-350	4 Barrel	4.057 x 3.385	350	10.50	325 @ 5400	360 @ 3600	30—45
	325 Horsepower............V8-400	4 Barrel	3.870 x 4.250	400	10.50	325 @ 4600	440 @ 3000	35—50
	350 Horsepower............V8-400	4 Barrel	3.870 x 4.250	400	10.50	350 @ 4800	440 @ 3200	35—50
	360 Horsepower............V8-400	4 Barrel	3.870 x 4.250	400	10.50	360 @ 5400	440 @ 3600	35—50
	365 Horsepower............V8-455	4 Barrel	4.125 x 4.250	455	10.25	365 @ 4600	510 @ 3000	30—45
	375 Horsepower............V8-455	4 Barrel	4.125 x 4.250	455	10.25	375 @ 4600	510 @ 3000	30—45
	390 Horsepower............V8-455	4 Barrel	4.125 x 4.250	455	10.25	390 @ 5000	500 @ 3200	30—45
	400 Horsepower............V8-455	4 Barrel	4.125 x 4.250	455	10.25	400 @ 4800	500 @ 3200	30—45
1970	155 Horsepower............②6-250	1 Barrel	3.875 x 3.53	250	8.50	155 @ 4200	240 @ 2000	30—45
	250 Horsepower............V8-350	2 Barrel	4.057 x 3.385	350	9.00	250 @ 4400	355 @ 2600	30—45
	310 Horsepower............V8-350	4 Barrel	4.057 x 3.385	350	10.25	310 @ 4800	390 @ 3200	30—45
	310 Horsepower............V8-455	2 Barrel	4.125 x 4.250	455	9.00	310 @ 4200	490 @ 2400	30—45
	320 Horsepower............V8-455	2 Barrel	4.125 x 4.250	455	10.25	320 @ 4200	500 @ 2400	30—45
	325 Horsepower............V8-350	4 Barrel	4.057 x 3.385	350	10.50	325 @ 5400	360 @ 3600	30—45
	365 Horsepower............V8-455	4 Barrel	4.125 x 4.250	455	10.50	365 @ 5000	500 @ 3200	30—45
	370 Horsepower............V8-455	4 Barrel	4.125 x 4.250	455	10.50	370 @ 5200	500 @ 3600	30—45
	375 Horsepower............V8-455	4 Barrel	4.125 x 4.250	455	10.25	375 @ 4600	510 @ 3000	30—45
	390 Horsepower............V8-455	4 Barrel	4.125 x 4.250	455	10.25	390 @ 5000	500 @ 3200	30—45
	400 Horsepower............V8-455	4 Barrel	4.125 x 4.250	455	10.25	400 @ 3200	500 @ 3200	30—45
1971	110 Horsepower③............②6-250	1 Barrel	3.875 x 3.53	250	8.10	110 @ 3800	185 @ 1600	30—45
	155 Horsepower③............V8-350	2 Barrel	4.057 x 3.385	350	8.10	155 @ 4000	275 @ 2400	30—45
	180 Horsepower③............V8-350	4 Barrel	4.057 x 3.385	350	8.10	180 @ 4000	275 @ 2400	30—45
	185 Horsepower③............V8-455	2 Barrel	4.125 x 4.250	455	8.10	185 @ 3600	355 @ 2000	30—45
	225 Horsepower③............V8-455	4 Barrel	4.125 x 4.250	455	8.10	225 @ 3600	360 @ 2600	30—45
	260 Horsepower③............V8-455	4 Barrel	4.125 x 4.250	455	8.10	260 @ 4400	370 @ 3200	30—45
	265 Horsepower③............V8-455	4 Barrel	4.125 x 4.250	455	8.10	265 @ 4200	375 @ 2800	30—45
1972	160 Horsepower③............V8-350	2 Barrel	4.057 x 3.385	350	8.50	160 @ 4000	275 @ 2400	30—45
	175 Horsepower③............V8-350	2 Barrel	4.057 x 3.385	350	8.50	175 @ 4000	295 @ 2600	30—45
	180 Horsepower③............V8-350	4 Barrel	4.057 x 3.385	350	8.50	180 @ 4000	275 @ 2800	30—45
	200 Horsepower③............V8-350	4 Barrel	4.057 x 3.385	350	8.50	200 @ 4400	300 @ 3200	30—45
	225 Horsepower③............V8-455	4 Barrel	4.125 x 4.250	455	8.50	225 @ 3600	360 @ 2600	30—45
	250 Horsepower③............V8-455	4 Barrel	4.125 x 4.250	455	8.50	250 @ 4200	370 @ 2800	30—45
	265 Horsepower③............V8-455	4 Barrel	4.125 x 4.250	455	8.50	265 @ 4200	375 @ 2800	30—45
	270 Horsepower③............V8-455	4 Barrel	4.125 x 4.250	455	8.50	270 @ 4400	370 @ 3200	30—45
	300 Horsepower③............V8-455	4 Barrel	4.125 x 4.250	455	8.50	300 @ 4700	410 @ 3200	30—45

②—See Chevrolet Chapter for service procedure on this engine.

③—All horsepower and torque ratings are net.

OLDSMOBILE — All Intermediate & Full Size Models

TUNE UP SPECIFICATIONS

OLD CAR SPECIFICATIONS: For 1946-65 Wheel Alignment Specifications see back of book.

★When using a timing light, disconnect vacuum tube or hose at distributor and plug opening in hose or tube so idle speed will not be affected. Timing should be set at 850 rpm on V8s.

Year	Engine	Spark Plug Type AC	Gap Inch	Distributor Point Gap Inch	Dwell Angle Deg.	Firing Order	Ignition Timing★ BTDC [1]	Mark	Hot Idle Speed [7] Std. Trans.	Auto. Trans. [2]	Comp. Press. Lbs. [3]	Fuel Pump Press. Lbs.
1966	6-250[8][14]	46N	.035	.019	31-34	Fig. N	6°	Fig. M	500[7]	500D[7]	130	4-5
	6-250[10][14]	46N	.035	.019	31-34	Fig. N	6°	Fig. M	600[7]	600D[7]	130	4-5
	8-330[5][8]	45S	.030	[4]	30	Fig. F	7½°[9]	Fig. H	600[7]	500D[7]	150	7¾-9
	8-330[5][10]	45S	.030	[4]	30	Fig. F	7½°[9]	Fig. H	600[7]	600D[7]	150	7¾-9
	8-330[10][8]	44S	.030	[4]	30	Fig. F	7½°[9]	Fig. H	600[7]	500D[7]	180	7¾-9
	8-330[6][10]	44S	.030	[4]	30	Fig. F	7½°[9]	Fig. H	600[7]	600D[7]	180	7¾-9
	8-400[8]	44S	.030	[4]	30	Fig. F	7½°[9]	Fig. H	600[7]	550D[7]	180	7¾-9
	8-400[10]	44S	.030	[4]	30	Fig. F	7½°[9]	Fig. H	600[7]	600D[7]	180	7¾-9
	8-425 2 Bar. Carb.[5][8]	45S	.030	[4]	30	Fig. F	7½°[9]	Fig. H	550[7]	500D[7]	150	7¾-9
	8-425 2 Bar. Carb.[5][10]	45S	.030	[4]	30	Fig. F	7½°[9]	Fig. H	500[7]	500D[7]	150	7¾-9
	8-425 2 Bar. Carb.[6][8]	44S	.030	[4]	30	Fig. F	5°[9]	Fig. H	550[7]	500D[7]	180	7¾-9
	8-425 2 Bar. Carb.[6][10]	44S	.030	[4]	30	Fig. F	5°[9]	Fig. H	500[7]	500D[7]	180	7¾-9
	8-425 4 Bar. Carb.[8]	44S	.030	[4]	30	Fig. F	7½°[9]	Fig. H	550[7]	500D[7]	180	7¾-9
	8-425 4 Bar. Carb.[10]	44S	.030	[4]	30	Fig. F	7½°[9]	Fig. H	500[7]	500D[7]	180	7¾-9
1967	6-250[8][14]	46N	.035	.019	31-34	Fig. N	4°	Fig. M	500	500D[7]	130	3½-4½
	6-250[10][14]	46N	.035	.019	31-34	Fig. N	4°	Fig. M	700	500D[7]	130	3½-4½
	8-330, 250 H.P.[8]	45S	.030	[4]	30	Fig. F	7½°[9]	Fig. H	600[11]	575D[11]	150	7¾-9
	8-330, 250 H.P.[10]	45S	.030	[4]	30	Fig. F	7½°[9]	Fig. H	650[11]	600D[11]	150	7¾-9
	8-330, 260 H.P.[8]	44S	.030	[4]	30	Fig. F	7½°[9]	Fig. H	600[11]	575D[11]	150	7¾-9
	8-330, 260 H.P.[10]	44S	.030	[4]	30	Fig. F	7½°[9]	Fig. H	650[11]	600D[11]	150	7¾-9
	8-330 4 Bar. Carb.[8]	44S	.030	[4]	30	Fig. F	7½°[9]	Fig. H	600[11]	575D[11]	180	7¾-9
	8-330 4 Bar. Carb.[10]	44S	.030	[4]	30	Fig. F	7½°[9]	Fig. H	650[11]	600D[11]	180	7¾-9
	8-400[8]	44S	.030	[4]	30	Fig. F	7½°[9]	Fig. H	600[11]	600D[11]	180	7¾-9
	8-400[10]	44S	.030	[4]	30	Fig. F	7½°[9]	Fig. H	600[11]	600D[11]	180	7¾-9
	8-425 2 Bar. Carb.[8]	44S	.030	[4]	30	Fig. F	5°[9]	Fig. H	575[12]	575D[12]	150	7¾-9
	8-425 2 Bar. Carb.[10]	44S	.030	[4]	30	Fig. F	5°[9]	Fig. H	600[12]	575D[12]	150	7¾-9
	8-425 4 Bar. Carb.[8]	44S	.030	[4]	30	Fig. F	7½°[9]	Fig. H	575[12]	575D[12]	180	7¾-9
	8-425 4 Bar. Carb.[10]	44S	.030	[4]	30	Fig. F	7½°[9]	Fig. H	600[12]	575D[12]	180	7¾-9
1968	6-250 Std. Trans.	46N	.035	.019	31-34	Fig. N	TDC	Fig. M	500[11]	—	130	3½-4½
	6-250 Auto. Tr.[14]	46N	.035	.019	31-34	Fig. N	4°	Fig. M	—	550D[11]	130	3½-4½
	8-350, 250 H.P.	45S	.030	.016	30	Fig. F	5°[11]	Fig. H	650[11]	550D[11]	150	5½-7
	8-350, 300 H.P.	44S	.030	.016	30	Fig. F	7½°[9]	Fig. H	700[11]	500D[11]	180	5½-7
	8-350, 310 H.P.	44S	.030	.016	30	Fig. F	7½°[9]	Fig. H	700[11]	500D[11]	180	5½-7
	8-400, 290 H.P.	45S	.030	.016	30	Fig. F	5°[9]	Fig. H	650[11]	550D[11]	150	5½-7
	8-400, 350 H.P.	44S	.030	.016	30	Fig. F	7½°[9]	Fig. H	700[11]	500D[11]	180	5½-7
	8-400	44S	.030	.016	30	Fig. F	2½°[9]	Fig. H	650[11]	550D[11]	180	5½-7
	8-400, 4-4-2[10]	44S	.030	.016	30	Fig. F	10°[12]	Fig. H	700[11]	500D[11]	180	5½-7
	8-455, 310 H.P.	45S	.030	.016	30	Fig. F	5°[9]	Fig. H	650[11]	550D[11]	150	5½-7
	8-455, 320 H.P.	44S	.030	.016	30	Fig. F	7½°[9]	Fig. H	700[11]	500D[11]	180	5½-7
	8-455, 4 B. Carb.	44S	.030	.016	30	Fig. F	7½°[9]	Fig. H	700[11]	500D[11]	180	5½-7
	Toronado[10]	44S	.030	.016	30	Fig. F	10°[12]	Fig. H	—	500D[11]	180	5½-7
1969	6-250 Std. Trans.[14]	R46N	.035	.019	31-34	Fig. N	TDC	Fig. M	775[11]	—	130	3½-4½
	6-250 Auto. Trans.[14]	R46N	.035	.019	31-34	Fig. N	4°	Fig. M	—	625D[11]	130	3½-4½
	8-350, 250 H.P.	R46S	.030	.016	30	Fig. F	6°	Fig. A	675[11]	600D[11]	150	5½-7
	8-350, 310 H.P.	R45S	.030	.016	30	Fig. F	8°	Fig. A	675[11]	575D[11]	180	5½-7
	8-350, 325 H.P.	R43S	.030	.016	30	Fig. F	12°	Fig. A	675[11]	575D[11]	180	5½-7
	8-400, 325 H.P.	R44S	.030	.016	30	Fig. F	8°[9][15]	Fig. A	—	575D[11]	180	5½-7
	8-400, 350 H.P.	R44S	.030	.016	30	Fig. F	2°[9]	Fig. A	750[11]	—	180	5½-7
	8-400, 360 H.P.	R43S	.030	.016	30	Fig. F	14°[12]	Fig. A	750[11]	650D[11]	180	5½-7
	8-455, 310 H.P.	R45S	.030	.016	30	Fig. F	6°[9]	Fig. A	675[11]	600D[11]	150	5½-7
	8-455, 365 H.P.	R44S	.030	.016	30	Fig. F	8°[9]	Fig. A	—	575D[11]	180	5-7½

Continued

TUNE UP SPECIFICATIONS—Continued

OLD CAR SPECIFICATIONS: For 1946-65 Tune Up Specifications see back of book.

★When using a timing light, disconnect vacuum tube or hose at distributor and plug opening in hose or tube so idle speed will not be affected. Timing should be set at 850 rpm on V8s.

| Year | Engine | Spark Plug | | Distributor | | Firing Order | Ignition Timing★ | | Hot Idle Speed⑦ | | Comp. Press. Lbs. ③ | Fuel Pump Press. Lbs. |
		Type AC	Gap Inch	Point Gap Inch	Dwell Angle Deg.		BTDC ①	Mark	Std. Trans.	Auto. Trans. ②		
1969	8-455, 375 H.P.	R44S	.030	.016	30	Fig. F	8°⑨	Fig. A	—	575D⑪	180	5½–7
	8-455 400 H.P.	R44S	.030	.016	30	Fig. F	10°⑨	Fig. A	—	575D⑪	180	5½–7
1970	6-250 Std. Trans.⑭	R46T	.035	.019	31–34	Fig. N	TDC	Fig. M	750	—	130	3½–4½
	6-250 Auto. Trans.⑭	R46T	.035	.019	31–34	Fig. N	4°	Fig. M	—	600D	130	3½–4½
	8-350, 250 H.P.⑱	R46S	.030	.016	30	Fig. F	10°⑯	Fig. A	750	575D	⑰	5½–7
	8-350, 250 H.P.⑲	R46S	.030	.016	30	Fig. F	8°⑯	Fig. A	675	575D	⑰	5½–7
	8-350, 310 H.P.	R45S	.030	.016	30	Fig. F	10°⑯	Fig. A	650	575D	⑰	5½–7
	8-350, 325 H.P.	R43S	.030	.016	30	Fig. F	14°⑯	Fig. A	750	625D	⑰	5½–7
	8-455, 310 H.P.	R46S	.030	.016	30	Fig. F	8°⑯	Fig. A	675	575D	⑰	5½–7
	8-455, 320 H.P.	R45S	.030	.016	30	Fig. F	8°⑯	Fig. A	—	575D	⑰	5½–7
	8-455, 365 H.P.	R44S	.030	.016	30	Fig. F	8°⑨	Fig. A	750	650D	⑰	5½–7
	8-455, 370 H.P.	R44S	.030	.016	30	Fig. F	8°⑨	Fig. A	750	650D	⑰	5½–7
	8-455, 375 H.P.	R44S	.030	.016	30	Fig. F	12°⑯	Fig. A	750	600D	⑰	5½–7
	8-455, 390 H.P.	R45S	.030	.016	30	Fig. F	8°⑯	Fig. A	—	600D	⑰	5½–7
	8-455, 390 H.P.⑳	R44S	.030	.016	30	Fig. F	12°⑯	Fig. A	—	600D	⑰	5½–7
	8-455, 400 H.P.	R44S	.030	.016	30	Fig. F	12°⑯	Fig. A	—	600D	⑰	5½–7
1971	6-250⑭	R46TS	.035	.019	33	Fig. N	4°	Fig. M	550	500D	⑰	3½–4½
	8-350, 155 H.P.	R46S	.040	.016	30	Fig. F	10°⑯	Fig. A	750	600D	⑰	5½–7
	8-350, 180 H.P. S.Tr.	R45S	.040	.016	30	Fig. F	10°⑯	Fig. A	750	—	⑰	5½–7
	8-350, 180 H.P. A.Tr.	R46S	.040	.016	30	Fig. F	12°⑯	Fig. A	—	600D	⑰	5½–7
	8-455, 185 H.P.	R46S	.040	.016	30	Fig. F	8°⑯	Fig. A	750	600D	⑰	5½–7
	8-455, 225 H.P.	R46S	.040	.016	30	Fig. F	8°⑯	Fig. A	—	600D	⑰	5½–7
	8-455, 260 H.P.	R45S	.040	.016	30	Fig. F	10°⑯	Fig. A	750	600D	⑰	5½–7
	8-455, 260 H.P.⑳ S.Tr.	R45S	.040	.016	30	Fig. F	12°⑯	Fig. A	750	—	⑰	5½–7
	8-455, 260 H.P.⑳ A.Tr.	R45S	.040	.016	30	Fig. F	10°⑯	Fig. A	—	600D	⑰	5½–7
	8-455, 265 H.P.	R46S	.040	.016	30	Fig. F	10°⑯	Fig. A	—	600D	⑰	5½–7
1972	8-350 2 Bar. Carb.	R46S	.040	.016	30	Fig. F	8°⑯	Fig. A	750	650D	⑰	5½–7
	8-350 4 B. Carb. St. Tr.	R45S	.040	.016	30	Fig. F	8°⑯	Fig. A	750	—	⑰	5½–7
	8-350 4 B. Carb. A. Tr.	R46S	.040	.016	30	Fig. F	12°⑯	Fig. A	—	600D	⑰	5½–7
	8-455 250, 270 H.P.	R46S	.040	.016	30	Fig. F	8°⑯	Fig. A	—	600D	⑰	5½–7
	8-455 300 H.P.	R45S	.040	.016	30	Fig. F	10°	Fig. A	1000	650D	⑰	5½–7
	8-455 Others—St. Tr.	R45S	.040	.016	30	Fig. F	10°⑯	Fig. A	750	—	⑰	5½–7
	8-455 Others—A. Tr.	R46S	.040	.016	30	Fig. F	8°⑯	Fig. A	—	650D	⑰	5½–7

①—BTDC: Before top dead center.
②—D: Drive. N: Neutral. Add 50 R.P.M. to slow idle speed for air conditioned cars with A/C off.
③—Plus or minus 20 lbs.
④—Turn adjusting screw in (clockwise) until engine misfires, then back off screw ½ turn.
⑤—Low compression engine.
⑥—High compression engine.
⑦—With A/C "ON".
⑧—Without A. I. R. System.
⑨—At 850 R.P.M.
⑩—With A. I. R. System.
⑪—With A/C "OFF" and idle compensator held closed.
⑫—At 1250 R.P.M.
⑭—See Chevrolet Chapter for service procedures on this engine.
⑮—Vista-Cruiser 10°.
⑯—At 1100 R.P.M.
⑰—Lowest cylinder 80% of highest cylinder with none lower than 100 lbs.
⑱—Intermediate cars.
⑲—Full size cars.
⑳—Air Induction.

Continued

TUNE UP NOTES—Continued

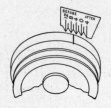

Fig. A

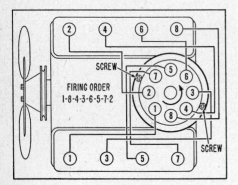

Fig. F

FIRING ORDER 1-8-4-3-6-5-7-2

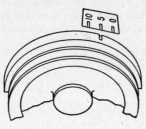

Fig. H

Fig. M

10° 5° 0°

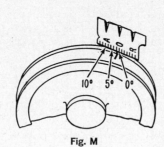

Fig. N

FIRING ORDER 1-5-3-6-2-4

ENGINE TIGHTENING SPECIFICATIONS ★

★Torque specifications are for clean and lightly lubricated threads only. Dry or dirty threads produce increased friction which prevents accurate measurement of tightness.

Year	Engine Model	Spark Plugs Ft. Lbs.	Cylinder Head Bolts Ft. Lbs.	Intake Manifold Ft. Lbs.	Exhaust Manifold Ft. Lbs.	Rocker Arm Shaft Bracket Ft. Lbs.	Rocker Arm Cover Ft. Lbs.	Connecting Rod Cap Bolts Ft. Lbs.	Main Bearing Cap Bolts Ft. Lbs.	Flywheel to Crankshaft Ft. Lbs.	Vibration Damper or Pulley Ft. Lbs.
1966	6-250④	25	95	⑤	⑤	—	55⑥	35	65	60	—
	V8-330	35	80	35⑦	25	35⑩	7	42	①	—	50
	400, 425	35	80	35⑦	25	35⑩	7	42	①	—	50
1967	6-250④	25	95	⑤	⑤	—	55⑥	35	65	60	—
	V8-330	35	80	35⑦	25	25③	7	42	①	—	50
	400, 425	35	80	35⑦	25	25③	7	42	①	—	50
1968–71	6-250④	25	95	⑤	⑤	—	55⑥	35	65	60	—
	V8-350	25-35	80	25-35⑦	20-25	25③	7	42	60-80⑧	⑨	160
	V8-400	25-35	80	25-35⑦	20-25	25③	7	42	90-120	⑨	160
	V8-455	25-35	80	25-35⑦	20-25	25③	7	42	90-120	⑨	160

①—Rear bearing cap 120, all others 80.
③—Rocker arm pivot bolt to head.
④—See Chevrolet Chapter for service procedures on this engine.
⑤—Outer clamp 20 ft.-lbs., all others 30 ft.-lbs.
⑥—Inch pounds.
⑦—Clean and dip entire bolt in engine oil before tightening.
⑧—Rear 90–120 ft.-lbs.
⑨—Auto. trans. 50–65, std. trans. 85–95.
⑩—Rocker arm stud to head.

DISTRIBUTOR SPECIFICATIONS

★Note: If advance is checked on the vehicle, double the R.P.M. and degrees advance to get crankshaft figures.

Year	Model	Distributor Part No.①	Breaker Gap	Dwell Angle Deg.	Breaker Arm Spring Tension	Centrifugal Advance Degrees @ R.P.M. of Distributor★		Vacuum Advance		Dist. Retard
						Advance Starts	Full Advance	Inches of Vacuum To Start Plunger	Max. Adv. Dist. Deg. @ Vacuum	Max. Ret. Dist. Deg. @ Vacuum
1966	6-250	1110351	.020	31-34	19-23	1 @ 500	14 @ 1400	5-7	10 @ 14	—
	8-330 High Comp.	1111048	③	30	19-23	1 @ 400	15 @ 2000	6-8	9 @ 17	—
	8-330 Low Comp.	1111029	③	30	19-23	1 @ 400	13 @ 2125	6-8	9 @ 17	—
	8-400	1111042	③	30	19-23	1 @ 400	11 @ 2000	6-8	9 @ 17	—
	8-425 2 Bar. Carb.	1111042	③	30	19-23	1 @ 400	11 @ 2000	6-8	9 @ 17	—
	8-425 4 Bar. Carb.	1111151	③	30	19-23	1 @ 600	9 @ 2100	8-10	9 @ 17	—
	8-425 Low Comp.	1111089	③	30	19-23	1 @ 400	14 @ 2000	6-8	9 @ 17	—
1967	6-250	1110351	.019	31-34	19-23	1 @ 500	14 @ 1400	5-7	10 @ 14	—
	8-330 2 Bar. Carb.	1111029	③	30	19-23	1 @ 400	13 @ 2125	6-8	9 @ 17	—
	8-400	1111042	③	30	19-23	1 @ 400	11 @ 2000	6-8	9 @ 17	—
	8-330 4 Bar. Carb.	1111048	③	30	19-23	1 @ 400	15 @ 2000	6-8	9 @ 17	—
	8-425 2 Bar. Carb.	1111089	③	30	19-23	1 @ 400	14 @ 2000	6-8	9 @ 17	—
	8-425 4 Bar. Carb.	1111151	③	30	19-23	1 @ 600	9 @ 2100	8-10	9 @ 17	—
	8-425 4 Bar. Carb.	1111179④	—	—	19-23	1 @ 600	9 @ 2100	8-10	9 @ 17	
	8-425 2 Bar. Carb.	1111188	③	30	19-23	1 @ 325	11 @ 2000	6-8	11 @ 22	—
	8-425 2 Bar. Carb.	1111189④	—	—	19-23	1 @ 400	14 @ 2000	6-8	9 @ 17	
1968	6-250	1110351	.019	31-34	19-23	1 @ 450	14 @ 1400	5-7	10 @ 14½	—
	8-350 2 Bar. Carb.	1111286	.016	30	19-23	1 @ 375	15 @ 2000	8-10	12 @ 20½	—
	8-350 4 Bar. Carb.	1111299	.016	30	19-23	1 @ 325	11 @ 2000	6-8	9 @ 18½	—
	8-400 2 Bar. Carb.	1111466	.016	30	19-23	1 @ 500	13 @ 2000	6-8	12 @ 17½	—
	8-400 4 Bar. Carb.	1111468	.016	30	19-23	1 @ 400	11 @ 1900	10-12	8 @ 18	—
	8-400 4 Bar. Carb.	1111287	.016	30	19-23	1 @ 425	11 @ 2000	8-10	12 @ 20½	—
	8-455 2 Bar. Carb.	1111288	.016	30	19-23	1 @ 300	14 @ 2000	6-8	12 @ 17½	—
	8-455 4 Bar. Carb.	1111289	.016	30	19-23	1 @ 500	7 @ 1500	6-8	12 @ 20½	—
	Toronado	1111292④	—	—	19-23	1 @ 500	7 @ 1500	6-8	12 @ 20½	—
	8-455 4 Bar. Carb.	1111469	.016	30	19-23	1 @ 500	11 @ 1800	8-10	12 @ 20½	—
1969	6-250	1110463	.019	32	19-23	1 @ 450	17 @ 2100	6	13 @ 16	—
	6-250	1110464	.019	32	19-23	1 @ 510	15 @ 2100	6	13 @ 16	—
	8-350 2 Bar. Carb.	1111961	.016	30	19-23	1 @ 220	17 @ 2000	9	13¾ @ 25	—
	8-350 4 Bar. Carb.	1111930	.016	30	19-23	1 @ 325	12 @ 2000	8	10¾ @ 23	—
	8-400⑤	1111932	.016	30	19-23	1 @ 425	12 @ 2000	9	12¾ @ 20½	—
	8-400⑥	1111933	.016	30	19-23	1 @ 325	11 @ 1900	11	9 @ 17¾	—
	8-455 2 Bar. Carb.	1111934	.016	30	19-23	1 @ 300	15 @ 2000	7	13¼ @ 26½	—
	8-455 4 Bar. Carb.	1111935	.016	30	19-23	1 @ 500	8 @ 1500	9	13¾ @ 25	—
	8-455 "GT" 4 Bar. Carb.	1111936	.016	30	19-23	1 @ 450	11 @ 1800	9	13¾ @ 25	
1970	6-250⑤	1110463	.019	31-34	19-23	1 @ 450	17 @ 2100	6	13 @ 16	—
	6-250⑥	1110464	.019	31-34	19-23	1 @ 510	15 @ 2100	6	13 @ 16	—
	V8-350 4 Bar. Carb.	1111975	.016	30	19-23	1 @ 400	12 @ 2000	9	10 @ 18½	—
	V8-350 2 Bar. Carb.	1111976	.016	30	19-23	1 @ 405	16 @ 2000	9	12 @ 20½	—
	V8-455 4 Bar. Carb.	1111977	.016	30	19-23	1 @ 500	12 @ 2000	12	8.7 @ 19	—
	V8-455 4 Bar. Carb.	1111979	.016	30	19-23	1 @ 375	16 @ 1500	12	8.7 @ 19	—
	V8-455 2 Bar. Carb.	1111980	.016	30	19-23	1 @ 400	15 @ 2000	9	12 @ 20½	—
	V8-455 4 Bar. Carb.	1111981	.016	30	19-23	1 @ 700	8 @ 1500	12	8.7 @ 19	—
	V8-455 4 Bar. Carb.	1111982	.016	30	19-23	1 @ 550	11 @ 1800	9	8.7 @ 18½	—
1971	6-250	1110489	.019	31-34	19-23	1 @ 635	13 @ 2050	8	10½ @ 18	—
	V8-350	1112079	.016	30	19-23	1 @ 385	18 @ 2050	7	13 @ 17½	—
	V8-350	1112085	.016	30	19-23	1 @ 400	16 @ 2000	6	13 @ 17½	—
	V8-455	1112033	.016	30	19-23	1 @ 540	11 @ 1800	8	12½ @ 20½	—
	V8-455	1112034	.016	30	19-23	1 @ 450	14 @ 1500	6	13 @ 17½	—
	V8-455	1112036	.016	30	19-23	½ @ 500	12 @ 2000	6	13 @ 17½	—
	V8-455	1112078	.016	30	19-23	1 @ 500	9 @ 1950	9	—	—

Continued

DISTRIBUTOR SPECIFICATIONS—Continued

★NOTE: If advance is checked on the vehicle, double the R.P.M. and degrees advance to get crankshaft figures.

Year	Model	Distributor Part No.①	Breaker Gap	Dwell Angle Deg.	Breaker Arm Spring Tension	Centrifugal Advance Degrees @ R.P.M. of Distributor★		Vacuum Advance		Dist. Retard
						Advance Starts	Full Advance	Inches of Vacuum To Start Plunger	Max. Adv. Dist. Deg. @ Vacuum	Max. Ret. Dist. Deg. @ Vacuum
1972	V8-350	1112106	.016	30	19–23	1 @ 485	16 @ 2000	6	13 @ 17½	—
	V8-350	1112085	.016	30	19–23	1 @ 400	16 @ 2000	6	13 @ 17½	—
	V8-455	1112033	.016	30	19–23	1 @ 540	11 @ 1800	8	12½ @ 20½	—
	V8-455	1112034	.016	30	19–23	1 @ 450	14 @ 1500	6	13 @ 17½	—
	V8-455	1112036	.016	30	19–23	½ @ 500	12 @ 2000	6	13 @ 17½	—
	V8-455	1112172	.016	30	19–23	1 @ 575	9 @ 1700	8	12½ @ 20½	—

①—Stamped on distributor housing plate.
③—Turn adjusting screw to the right until engine misfires. Then turn screw to the left ½ turn.
④—Delco-Remy transistor ignition.
⑤—Std. Trans. (Less Air Induction).
⑥—Auto. Trans. & all with Air Induction.

VALVE SPECIFICATIONS

Year	Model	Valve Lash		Valve Angles		Valve Spring Installed Height	Valve Spring Pressure Lbs. @ In.	Stem Clearance		Stem Diameter	
		Int.	Exh.	Seat	Face			Intake	Exhaust	Intake	Exhaust
1966–67	6-250⑧	1 Turn③		46	45	1²¹⁄₃₂	180 @ 1.27	.001–.0027	.0015–.0032	.3404–.3417	.3410–.3417
	V8-330	Hydraulic⑥		45	45	1.67	180 @ 1.27	.001–.0027	.0015–.0032	.3425–.3432	.3420–.3427
	V8-400, 425	Hydraulic⑥		④	④	1.67	180 @ 1.27	.001–.003	.001–.003	.3442–.3452	.3442–.3452
1968–69	6-250⑧	1 Turn③		46	45	1.66	186 @ 1.27	.001–.0027	.001–.0027	.3410–.3417	.3410–.3417
	V8-350	Hydraulic⑥		45	46	1.67	187 @ 1.27	.001–.0027	.0015–.0032	.3425–.3432	.3420–.3427
	V8-400 4 B. C.	Hydraulic⑥		④	⑤	1.67	187 @ 1.27	.001–.0027	.0015–.0032	.3425–.3432	.3420–.3427
	V8-400 2 B. C.	Hydraulic⑥		45	46	1.67	187 @ 1.27	.001–.0027	.0015–.0032	.3425–.3432	.3420–.3427
	V8-455	Hydraulic⑥		45	46	1.67	187 @ 1.27	.001–.0027	.0015–.0032	.3425–.3432	.3420–.3427
	Toronado	Hydraulic⑥		⑤	④	1.67	187 @ 1.27	.001–.0027	.0015–.0032	.3425–.3432	.3420–.3427
1970	6-250⑧	1 Turn③		46	45	1.66	186 @ 1.27	.001–.0027	.001–.0027	.3410–.3417	.3410–.3417
	V8-350	Hydraulic⑥		④	⑤	1.67	187 @ 1.27	.001–.0027	.0015–.0032	.3425–.3432	.3420–.3427
	V8-455⑨	Hydraulic⑥		45	46	1.67	187 @ 1.27	.001–.0027	.0015–.0032	.3425–.3432	.3420–.3427
	V8-455⑩	Hydraulic⑥		④	⑤	1.67	187 @ 1.27	.001–.0027	.0015–.0032	.3425–.3432	.3420–.3427
	Toronado	Hydraulic⑥		④	⑤	1.67	187 @ 1.27	.001–.0027	.0015–.0032	.3425–.3432	.3420–.3427
1971	6-250⑧	1 Turn③		46	45	1.66	186 @ 1.27	.001–.0027	.001–.0027	.3410–.3417	.3410–.3417
	V8-350	Hydraulic⑥		45	46	1.67	187 @ 1.27	.001–.0027	.0015–.0032	.3425–.3432	.3420–.3427
	V8-455⑨	Hydraulic⑥		45	46	1.67	187 @ 1.27	.001–.0027	.0015–.0032	.3425–.3432	.3420–.3427
	V8-455⑩	Hydraulic⑥		④	⑤	1.67	187 @ 1.27	.001–.0027	.0015–.0032	.3425–.3432	.3420–.3427
1972	V8-350①	Hydraulic⑥		⑪	⑫	1.67	187 @ 1.27	.001–.0027	.0015–.0032	.3425–.3432	.3420–.3427
	V8-350⑦	Hydraulic⑥		45	46	1.67	198 @ 1.23	.001–.0027	.0015–.0032	.3425–.3432	.3420–.3427
	V8-455 "98"	Hydraulic⑥		⑪	⑫	1.67	187 @ 1.27	.001–.0027	.0015–.0032	.3425–.3432	.3420–.3427
	V8-455 Toronado	Hydraulic⑥		45	46	1.67	196 @ 1.23	.001–.0027	.0015–.0032	.3425–.3432	.3420–.3427
	V8-455 Others	Hydraulic⑥		④	⑤	1.67	206 @ 1.19	.001–.0027	.0015–.0032	.3425–.3432	.3420–.3427

①—Except California.
②—Plus or minus .0005". Guide tapers to bottom with larger dimension at top.
③—Tighten rocker arm adjusting screw to eliminate all push rod end clearance. Then tighten screw the number of turns listed.
④—Intake 30°, exhaust 45°.
⑤—Intake 30°, exhaust 46°.
⑥—No adjustment.
⑦—California.
⑧—See Chevrolet Chapter for service procedures on this engine.
⑨—Except "4-4-2" models.
⑩—"4-4-2" models.
⑪—Intake 45°, exhaust 30°.
⑫—Intake 46°, exhaust 30°.

PISTONS, PINS, RINGS, CRANKSHAFT & BEARINGS

Year	Model	Piston Clearance	Ring End Gap[1]		Wrist-pin Diameter	Rod Bearings		Main Bearings			
			Comp.	Oil		Shaft Diameter	Bearing Clearance	Shaft Diameter	Bearing Clearance	Thrust on Bear. No.	Shaft End Play
1966–67	6-250[8]	.0005–.0016	.010	.015	.9271	1.999–2.000	.0007–.0027	2.2983–2.2993	.0003–.0009	7	.002–.006
	V8-330	.0007–.0012	.010	.015	.9805	2.1239–2.1248	.0015–.003	2.4985–2.4995	.0015–.0031	3	.004–.008
	V8-400, 425	.0007–.0012	.013	.015	.9805	2.4988–2.5003	.0008–.0018	2.9993–3.0003	.0015–.0031[2]	3	.004–.008
1968	6-250[8]	.0005–.0016	.010	.015	.9271	1.999–2.000	.0007–.0027	2.2983–2.2988	.0003–.0029	7	.002–.006
	V8-350	.0007–.0012	.010	.015	.9805	2.1238–2.1248	.0009–.0031	2.4985–2.4995	.0005–.0021[5]	3	.004–.008
	V8-400	.0007–.0012	.010	.015	.9805	2.4988–2.4998	.0004–.0033	2.9993–3.0003	.0005–.0021[6]	3	.004–.008
	V8-455	.0007–.0012	.013	.015	.9805	2.4988–2.4998	.0004–.0033	2.9993–3.0003	.0005–.0021[6]	3	.004–.008
1969–70	6-250[8]	.0005–.0016	.010	.015	.9271	1.999–2.000	.0007–.0027	2.2983–2.2988	.0003–.0029	7	.002–.006
	V8-350	.001–.002	.010	.015	.9805	2.1238–2.1248	.0004–.0033	[3]	.0005–.0021[5]	3	.004–.008
	V8-400 (1969)	.001–.002	.010	.015	.9805	2.4988–2.4998	.0004–.0033	2.9993–3.0003	.0005–.0021[6]	3	.004–.008
	V8-455	.001–.002	.013	.015	.9805	2.4988–2.4998	.0004–.0033	2.9993–3.0003	.0005–.0021[6]	3	.004–.008
1971	6-250[8]	.0005–.0016	.010	.015	.9271	1.999–2.000	.0007–.0027	2.2983–2.2988	.0003–.0029	7	.002–.006
	V8-350	.001–.002	.010	.015	.9805	2.1238–2.1248	.0004–.0033	[3]	.0005–.0021[6]	3	.004–.008
	V8-455	.001–.002	.013	.015	.9805	2.4988–2.4998	.002–.011	2.9993–3.0003	.0005–.0021[6]	3	.004–.008
1972	V8-350	.001–.002	.010	.015	.9805	2.1238–2.1248	.0004–.0033	[3]	.0005–.0021[5]	3	.004–.008
	V8-455	.001–.002	.013	.015	.9805	2.4988–2.4998	.002–.011	2.9993–3.0003	.0005–.0021[6]	3	.004–.008

[1]—Fit rings in tapered bores for clearance listed in tightest portion of ring travel.
[2]—Rear bearing .002–.0034".
[3]—No. 1: 2.4988–2.4998; Nos. 2, 3, 4, 5: 2.4985–2.4995.
[6]—Rear .0015–.0031.
[5]—Rear .002–.0034.
[8]—See Chevrolet Chapter for service procedures on this engine.

STARTING MOTOR SPECIFICATIONS

Year	Model	Starter Number	Brush Spring Tension Oz.[1]	Free Speed Test			Resistance Test[3]	
				Amps.	Volts	R.P.M.	Amps.	Volts
1966	V8-330	1107298	35	65–100[2]	10.6	3600–5100	300–360	3.5
	V8-330	1107330	35	70–105[2]	10.6	3800–6200	480–540[2]	3.0
	V8-400, 425	1107374	35	65–100[2]	10.6	3600–5100	300–360	3.5
1967	8-330	1107298	35	65–100[2]	10.6	3600–5100	300–360	3.5
	8-330, 400, 425	1107330	35	70–105[2]	10.6	3800–6200	480–540[2]	3.0
	8-425	1107354	35	70–105[2]	10.6	3800–6200	480–540[2]	3.0
	6-250	1107399	35	49–76	10.6	6200–9400	270–310	4.3
1968–69	8-455 "98"	1108333	35	70–99[2]	10.6	7800–12000	—	—
	8-350, 400, 455	1108348	35	70–105[2]	10.6	3800–6200	480–540[2]	3.0
	8-350 2 B. Carb.	1108349	35	65–100[2]	10.6	3600–5100	300–360	3.5
	Toronado	1108352	35	70–105[2]	10.6	3800–6200	480–540[2]	3.0
	6-250	1108365	35	49–87[2]	10.6	6200–10700	—	—
1970–71	6-250	1108365	35	49–87[2]	10.6	6200–10700	—	—
	8-350	1108386	35	55–80[2]	9	3500–6000	—	—
	8-350, 455	1108387	35	45–80[2]	9	4000–6500	—	—
	8-455	1108389	35	65–95[2]	9	7500–10500	—	—
	Toronado	1108352	35	70–105[2]	10.6	3800–6200	480–540[2]	3.0
1972	8-350	1108386	35	55–80[2]	9	3500–6000	—	—
	8-455	1108387	35	45–80[2]	9	4000–6500	—	—
	Toronado	1108352	35	70–105[2]	10.6	3800–6200	480–540[2]	3.0

[1]—Minimum.　　[2]—Includes solenoid.
[3]—Check capacity of motor by using a 500 ampere meter and a carbon pile rheostat to control voltage. Apply volts listed across motor with armature locked. Current should be as listed.

OLDSMOBILE — All Intermediate & Full Size Models

REAR AXLE SPECIFICATIONS

Year	Model	Carrier Type	Ring Gear & Pinion Backlash		Pinion Bearing Preload			Differential Bearing Preload		
			Method	Adjustment	Method	New Bearings Inch-Lbs.	Used Bearings Inch-Lbs.	Method	New Bearings Inch-Lbs.	Used Bearings Inch-Lbs.
1966–67	Toronado	Removable	Shims	.006–.008	Shims	2–3	2–3	Shims	15–20①	5–7①
	All Others	Integral	Shims	.007–.009	Spacer	24–35	15–25	Shims	20–30	10–20
1968–72	Toronado	Removable	Shims	.005–.009	Shims	2–3	2–3	Shims	15–20①	5–7①
	Ser. 31-42	Integral	Shims	.005–.008	②	20–30	5–15	Shims	.010	.010
	Others	Integral	Shims	.007–.009	Spacer	24–35	15–25	Shims	20–30	10–20

①—Over pinion bearing preload.　　　　②—Tighten pinion shaft nut with inch-pound torque wrench.

ALTERNATOR & REGULATOR SPECIFICATIONS

Year	Alternator					Regulator							
		Rated Hot Output Amps.	Field Current 12 Volts @ 80° F.	Output @ 14 Volts			Field Relay			Voltage Regulator		
	Model			2000 R.P.M. Amps.	5000 R.P.M. Amps.	Model	Air Gap In.	Point Gap In.	Closing Voltage	Air Gap In.	Point Gap In.	Voltage @ 125° F.
1966	1100686	55	2.2–2.6	32	50	1119515	.015	.030	6.3–8.3	.060	.014	13.5–14.4
	1100694	55	2.2–2.6	32	50	1119515	.015	.030	6.3–8.3	.060	.014	13.5–14.4
	1100696	42	2.2–2.6	28	40	1119515	.015	.030	6.3–8.3	.060	.014	13.5–14.4
	1100699	42	2.2–2.6	28	40	1119515	.015	.030	6.3–8.3	.060	.014	13.5–14.4
	1100700	55	2.2–2.6	32	50	1119515	.015	.030	6.3–8.3	.060	.014	13.5–14.4
	1100704	37	2.2–2.6	25	35	1119515	.015	.030	6.3–8.3	.060	.014	13.5–14.4
	1100705	37	2.2–2.6	25	35	1119515	.015	.030	6.3–8.3	.060	.014	13.5–14.4
1967–69	1100734	42	2.2–2.6	28	40	1119515	.015	.030	6.3–8.3	.060	.014	13.5–14.4
	1100767	37	2.2–2.6	25	35	1119515	.015	.030	6.3–8.3	.060	.014	13.5–14.4
	1100777	55	2.2–2.6	32	50	1119515	.015	.030	6.3–8.3	.060	.014	13.5–14.4
1969	1100853	37	4.0–4.5	—	32	—	—	—	—	—	—	—
1970	1100777	55	2.2–2.6	32	50	1119515	.015	.030	6.3–8.3	.060	.014	13.5–14.4
	1100878	42	2.2–2.6	28	40	1119515	.015	.030	6.3–8.3	.060	.014	13.5–14.4
	1100879	37	2.2–2.6	25	35	1119515	.015	.030	6.3–8.3	.060	.014	13.5–14.4
	1100880	37	4.0–4.5	—	32	—	—	—	—	—	—	—
	1100886	63	2.8–3.2	35	59	1119515	.015	.030	6.3–8.3	.060	.014	13.5–14.4
	1100888	37	2.2–2.6	25	35	1119515	.015	.030	6.3–8.3	.060	.014	13.5–14.4
	1100890	55	4.0–4.5	—	50	—	—	—	—	—	—	—
	1100891	55	2.2–2.6	32	50	1119515	.015	.030	6.3–8.3	.060	.014	13.5–14.4
	1100892	55	2.2–2.6	32	50	1119515	.015	.030	6.3–8.3	.060	.014	13.5–14.4
	1100893	55	2.2–2.6	32	50	1119515	.015	.030	6.3–8.3	.060	.014	13.5–14.4
	1100907	61	2.2–2.6	33	58	1119515	.015	.030	6.3–8.3	.060	.014	13.5–14.4
1971	1100553	63	4.0–4.5	—	—	1119519	—	—	—	—	—	13.5–14.4
	1100566	37	2.2–2.6	—	—	1119515	—	—	—	—	—	13.5–14.4
	1100567	42	2.2–2.6	—	—	1119515	—	—	—	—	—	13.5–14.4
	1100568	55	2.2–2.6	—	—	1119515	—	—	—	—	—	13.5–14.4
	1100569	55	2.2–2.6	—	—	1119515	—	—	—	—	—	13.5–14.4
	1·100570	61	2.2–2.6	—	—	1119515	—	—	—	—	—	13.5–14.4
	1100888	37	2.2–2.6	—	—	1119515	—	—	—	—	—	13.5–14.4
	1100934	37	4.0–4.5	—	—	—	—	—	—	—	—	—
	1100935	55	4.0–4.5	—	—	—	—	—	—	—	—	—

Continued

ALTERNATOR & REGULATOR SPECIFICATIONS—Continued

| Year | Model | Rated Hot Output Amps. | Field Current 12 Volts @ 80° F. | Output @ 14 Volts | | Model | Field Relay | | | Voltage Regulator | | |
				2000 R.P.M. Amps.	5000 R.P.M. Amps.		Air Gap In.	Point Gap In.	Closing Voltage	Air Gap In.	Point Gap In.	Voltage @ 125° F.
1972	1100573	42	4.0–4.5	—	—	—	—	—	—	—	—	—
	1100597	61	4.0–4.5	—	—	—	—	—	—	—	—	—
	1102435	42	2.2–2.6	—	—	1119515	—	—	—	—	—	13.5–14.4
	1102437	55	2.2–2.6	—	—	1119515	—	—	—	—	—	13.5–14.4
	1102439	55	2.2–2.6	—	—	1119515	—	—	—	—	—	13.5–14.4
	1102440	37	2.2–2.6	—	—	1119515	—	—	—	—	—	13.5–14.4
	1102463	61	2.2–2.6	—	—	1119515	—	—	—	—	—	13.5–14.4

WHEEL ALIGNMENT SPECIFICATIONS

OLD CAR SPECIFICATIONS: For 1946-65 Wheel Alignment Specifications see back of book.

| Year | Model | Caster Angle, Degrees | | Camber Angle, Degrees | | | | Toe-In. Inch | Toe-Out on Turns, Deg.① | |
| | | Limits | Desired | Limits | | Desired | | | Outer Wheel | Inner Wheel |
				Left	Right	Left	Right			
1966–67	Intermediates	− ½ to −2	−1¼	− ¼ to + ½	− ¼ to + ½	+ ⅛	+ ⅛	⅛–³⁄₁₆	18.6	20
	F.S.C.②③	− ½ to −1 ½	−1	− ¼ to + ½	− ¼ to + ½	+ ⅛	+ ⅛	⅛–³⁄₁₆	18.3	20
	F.S.C.②④	− ½ to −1 ½	−1	− ¼ to + ½	− ¼ to + ½	+ ⅛	+ ⅛	⅛–³⁄₁₆	17.7	20
	Toronado	−1 ½ to −2 ½	−2	− ¼ to + ½	− ¼ to + ½	+ ⅛	+ ⅛	0–¹⁄₁₆	18.2	20
1968–69	Intermediates	− ½ to −2	−1¼	− ¼ to + ½	− ¼ to + ½	+ ⅛	+ ⅛	⅛–³⁄₁₆	18.6	20
	F.S.C.②③	− ½ to −1 ½	−1¼	− ¼ to + ½	− ¼ to + ½	+ ⅛	+ ⅛	⅛–³⁄₁₆	18.3	20
	F.S.C.②④	− ½ to −1 ½	− ¾	− ¼ to + ½	− ¼ to + ½	+ ⅛	+ ⅛	⅛–³⁄₁₆	18.7	20
	Toronado	−1 ½ to −2 ½	−2	− ½ to + ¼	− ½ to + ¼	+ ⅛	+ ⅛	0–¹⁄₁₆	18.1	20
1970	Intermediates	− ½ to −2	−1¼	− ¼ to + ½	− ¼ to + ½	+ ⅛	+ ⅛	⅛–³⁄₁₆	18.6	20
	F.S.C.②③	− ½ to −1 ½	−1¼	− ¼ to + ½	− ¼ to + ½	+ ⅛	+ ⅛	⅛–³⁄₁₆	18.3	20
	F.S.C.②④	− ½ to −1 ½	− ¾	− ¼ to + ½	− ¼ to + ½	+ ⅛	+ ⅛	⅛–³⁄₁₆	17.7	20
	Toronado	−1 ½ to −2 ½	−2	− ¼ to + ½	− ½ to + ½	+ ⅛	+ ⅛	0–¹⁄₁₆	18.2	20
1971	Intermediates	− ¼ to −2¼	−1¼	− ½ to +1	−1 to + ½	+ ¼	− ¼	0	—	—
	F.S.C.②	0 to +2	+1	− ½ to +1	−1 to + ½	+ ¼	− ¼	0	—	—
	Toronado	−1¼ to −3¼	−2¼	− ½ to +1	−1 to + ½	+ ¼	− ¼	0	—	—
1972	Intermediates	− ¼ to −2¼	−1¼	− ½ to +1	−1 to + ½	+ ¼	− ¼	0	—	—
	F.S.C.②	0 to +2	+1	− ½ to +1	−1 to + ½	+ ¼	− ¼	0	—	—
	Toronado	−1 to −3	−2	− ½ to +1	−1 to + ½	+ ¼	− ¼	0	—	—

①—Incorrect toe-out, when other adjustments are correct, indicates bent steering arms.
②—F.S.C.-Full size car. ③—Manual Steering. ④—Power Steering.

BRAKE SPECIFICATIONS

Year	Model	Brake Drum Inside Diameter	Wheel Cylinder Bore Diameter			Master Cylinder Bore Diameter		
			Disc Brake	Front Drum Brake	Rear Drum Brake	Disc Brakes	Drum Brakes	Power Brakes
1966	Intermediate Cars	9½	—	1 1/16	15/16	—	1	1
	Intermediate Wagons	9½	—	1 1/16	1	—	1	1
	Jetstar 88	9½	—	1 1/16	15/16	—	⅞	⅞
	Full Size Models	11	—	1⅛	1	—	1	1
	Toronado 1966	11	—	1⅛	⅞	—	⅞	⅞
1967	Intermediate Cars	9½	2.06	1 1/16	⅞	1⅛	1	1
	Intermediate Wagons	9½	2.06	1 1/16	1	1⅛	1	1
	Full Size Models	11	1.94	1⅛	1	1⅛	1	1
	Toronado	11	2.06	—	1.88	1	—	1
1968	F-85, Cutlass, 4-4-2	9½	2.06	1⅛	15/16 ①	—	1	1
	Vista Cruiser	9½	2.06	1.06	1 ①	—	1	1
	Delmont, Delta, 98	11	1.94	1 3/16	1	—	1	1
	Toronado	11	2.06	1⅛	⅞	—	1	1
1969	Intermediate Cars	9½	2 15/16	1⅛	15/16 ①	1⅛	1	1
	Intermediate Wagons	9½	2 15/16	1⅛	15/16 ①	1⅛	1	1
	Delta, 98	11	2 15/16	1 3/16	1	1	1	1
	Toronado	11	2 15/16	1⅛	⅞	1 1/16	1	1
1970	Intermediate Cars	9½	2 15/16	1⅛	⅞	1⅛	1	②
	Intermediate Wagons	9½	2 15/16	1⅝	1	1⅛	1	②
	Delta, 98	11	2 15/16	1 3/16	15/16	1⅛	1	②
	Toronado	11	2 15/16	—	15/16	1⅛	—	1⅛
1971–72	Intermediate Cars	9½	2 15/16	1⅛	⅞	1⅛	1	1
	Intermediate Wagons	9½	2 15/16	—	1	1⅛	—	1
	Delta, 98	11	2 15/16	—	15/16	1⅛	—	1
	Custom Cruiser	12	2 15/16	—	1	1⅛	—	1
	Toronado	11	2 15/16	—	15/16	1⅛	—	1

① —13/16" with front disc brakes.   ② —With drum brakes 1"; with disc brakes 1⅛".

COOLING SYSTEM & CAPACITY DATA

Year	Model or Engine	Cooling Capacity, Qts.			Radiator Cap Relief Pressure, Lbs.		Thermo. Opening Temp. ①	Fuel Tank Gals.	Engine Oil Refill Qts. ②	Transmission Oil			Rear Axle Oil Pints
		No Heater	With Heater	With A/C	With A/C	No A/C				3 Speed Pints	4 Speed Pints	Auto. Trans. Qts. ⑫	
1966	6-250	11	11¾	11¾	15	15	180	20	4	3½	—	④	3
	F85 V8	16	16¼	16¾	15	15	180	20	4	⑦	2¼	④	3
	Jetstar 88	16	16½	17	15	15	180	25	4	5	2¼	⑥	3
	4-4-2	17	17¼	17¾	15	15	180	20	4	⑦	2¼	④	3
	Senior Models	17	17½	18	15	15	180	25	4	5	2¼	⑤	4¾
	Toronado	16½	17½	18	15	15	180	24	5	—	—	⑧	4½
1967	6-250	11	11¾	11¾	15	15	180	20	4	3½	—	④	3¾
	F-85 V8	15	15¼	15¾	15	15	180	20	4	3½	2¼	④	3¾
	4-4-2	17	17¼	17¾	15	15	180	20	4	5	2¼	⑥	3¾
	Delmont V8-330	15½	16½	17	15	15	180	25	4	5	2¼	⑥	3¾
	Senior Models	16½	17½	18	15	15	180	25	4	5	2¼	⑤	5½
	Toronado	16½	17½	18	15	15	180	24	5	—	—	⑧	4½

Continued

COOLING SYSTEM & CAPACITY DATA—Continued

Year	Model or Engine	Cooling Capacity, Qts.			Radiator Cap Relief Pressure, Lbs.		Thermo. Opening Temp. [1]	Fuel Tank Gals.	Engine Oil Refill Qts. [2]	Transmission Oil			Rear Axle Oil Pints
		No Heater	With Heater	With A/C	With A/C	No A/C				3 Speed Pints	4 Speed Pints	Auto. Trans. Qts. [12]	
1968	6-250	11.5	12.2	12.2	15	15	195	20	4	3½	—	[9]	3.69
	8-350	14.5	15.2	15.7	15	15	195	20	4	3½	—	[9]	3.69
	8-400, 4-4-2	15.5	16.2	17.2	15	15	195	20	4	4.90	—	[10]	3.69
	Delmont	—	17.5	18	15	15	195	20	4	4.90	—	[9]	3.69
	Delta, 98	—	17.5	18	15	15	195	25	4	4.90	—	[10]	5.32
	Toronado	—	18	18.5	15	15	195	24	5	—	—	[11]	4.50
1969	6-250	11.5	12.2	12.2	15	15	195	20	4	3½	—	[10]	3.69
	8-350	14.5	15.2	15.7	15	15	195	20[13]	4	3½	4.90	[10]	3.69
	8-400, 4-4-2	15.5	16.2	17.2	15	15	195	20	4	3½	4.90	[15]	3.69
	Delta, 98	—	17.5	18	15	15	195	25	4	4.9	—	[10]	5.32[14]
	Toronado	—	18	18.5	15	15	195	24	5	—	—	[15]	4
1970	6-250	11	12	12.0	15	15	195	20	4	3½	—	[3]	3¾
	8-350[16]	14	15	15.5	15	15	195	20[13]	4	3½	2¼	[3]	3¾
	8-350[17]	15.5	16.5	16.5	15	15	195	25	4	3½	2¼	[10]	3¾
	8-455[16]	15	16	16.5	15	15	195	20[13]	4	3½	2¼	[10]	3¾
	8-455[17]	—	17.5	18	15	15	195	25	4	4½	2¼	[10]	5⅓
	Toronado	—	18	18.5	15	15	195	24	5	—	—	[10]	4
1971	6-250	12	13	13	15	15	195	19[18]	4	3½	—	[3]	4¼
	8-350[16]	15	16	17	15	15	195	19[18]	4	[19]	2¼	[10]	4¼
	8-350[17]	15	16	17	15	15	195	24	4	3½	—	[10]	[20]
	8-455[16]	16	17	18	15	15	195	19	4	[19]	2¼	[10]	4¼
	8-455[17]	—	17	18	15	15	195	24	4	3½	—	[10]	[20]
	Toronado	—	18	19	15	15	195	24	5	—	—	[10]	4
1972	8-350[16]	—	15.2	15.7	15	15	195	19[13]	4	3½	3½	[10]	[20]
	8-350[17]	—	16.2	16.7	15	15	195	24	4	—	—	[10]	4¼
	8-455[16]	—	15.2	15.7	15	15	195	19[13]	4	3½	3½	[10]	4¼
	8-455[17]	—	17	17.5	15	15	195	24	4	—	—	[10]	5½
	Toronado	—	19.5	20	15	15	195	25	5	—	—	[10]	4

[1]—For alcohol type anti-freeze use a 160° unit.
[2]—Add one quart with filter change.
[3]—Oil pan only 2 qts. After overhaul 10 qts.
[4]—Oil pan only 3 qts. After overhaul 9 qts.
[5]—Oil pan only 4 qts. After overhaul 9 qts.
[6]—For Jetaway see Note [4]; for Turbo-Hydramatic, Note [5].
[7]—Standard unit 3½, heavy duty 5.
[8]—Oil pan only 5 qts. After overhaul 10½ qts.
[9]—Oil pan only 2 qts. After overhaul 8 qts.
[10]—Oil pan only 3 qts. After overhaul 10 qts.
[11]—Refill 5½ qts.
[12]—Approximate; make final check with dipstick.
[13]—Vista-Cruiser 23 gallons.
[14]—With Jetaway, 3.69 pts.
[15]—Refill 4 qts.
[16]—Intermediate cars.
[17]—Full size cars.
[18]—Vista-Cruiser 22 gallons.
[19]—Standard unit 3½, heavy duty 4½.
[20]—With 10 bolt cover 4¼; with 12 bolt cover 5½.

Electrical Section

DISTRIBUTOR, REPLACE

1. Disconnect primary wire from distributor and disconnect pipe from vacuum control unit.
2. Remove distributor cap.
3. Crank engine until distributor rotor is in position to fire No. 1 cylinder and the timing mark (see *Tune Up Chart*) is aligned with the timing indicator.
4. Remove distributor clamp and lift the distributor out of the crankcase.

Installation, All Models

1. Check to make sure that the timing mark is aligned with the timing indicator with No. 1 piston on the compression stroke in position to fire.
2. Place a new seal or gasket on distributor housing.
3. Rotate distributor cam until rotor is in position to fire No. 1 cylinder.
4. Rotate oil pump shaft with screwdriver to align slot in shaft with tongue on lower end of distributor shaft.
5. Install distributor in crankcase.
6. Install distributor clamp and bolt with lockwasher, leaving bolt just loose enough to permit movement of distributor.
7. Rotate distributor housing until breaker points just start to open and tighten clamp bolt. This will permit starting engine for setting timing.
8. Connect pipe to vacuum control and primary wire to terminal stud.
9. Install distributor cap. If spark plug wires are disconnected from cap make certain that wires are connected in accordance with firing orders.
10. Check and set ignition timing.

STARTER, REPLACE
1966-69 V8-400

1. Disconnect battery and hoist car.
2. Disconnect clutch return spring at clutch release yoke.
3. Disconnect exhaust pipe from left exhaust manifold.
4. Loosen upper and remove lower starter-to-engine brace bolt.
5. Remove two starter-to-block bolts.
6. Move starter forward and downward, then disconnect wires from three starter terminals.
7. Rotate starter counterclockwise while pulling forward and downward on front of starter and remove starter. *On 4-4-2 with automatic transmission, adequate clearance can be obtained by removing flywheel housing cover.*

1966-72 Except V8-400

1. Disconnect battery.
2. Noting position of wires, disconnect starter wiring.
3. With manual shift transmission, remove flywheel housing cover (4 screws).
4. Remove upper support attaching

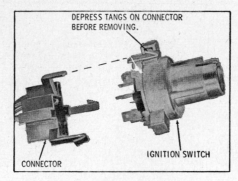

Fig. 1   Ignition switch 1966-68

bolt.
5. Remove starter (2 bolts).

NOTE: If equipped with dual exhaust, the left-hand exhaust pipe may have to be disconnected to provide clearance.

IGNITION SWITCH
1969-72

1. Disconnect battery ground cable.
2. Turn ignition lock to "Accessory" (Run on 1970-71) position.
3. Remove cover attaching bolts, loosen toe pan clamp bolts and remove trim cap from lower part of panel.
4. Remove bracket retaining nuts and lower steering column to the seat.
5. Disconnect and remove switch.
6. Be sure lock is still in "Accessory" (Run on 1970-72) position and insert a .090" pin through positioning hole in switch, install switch onto actuator and column and remove pin. Connect wiring and reinstall column.

1967-68 Except Toronado

1. Disconnect battery ground cable.
2. Insert key into ignition switch and press while turning fully counterclockwise. While holding key in counter-

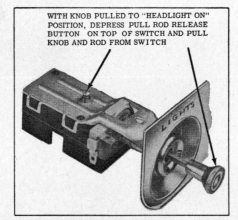

Fig. 2   Light switch with release button

clockwise position, depress lock cylinder retainer with a paper clip through small hole in face of lock cylinder.
3. Remove key and lock cylinder.
4. Remove switch escutcheon.
5. After removing switch from instrument panel, remove connector by depressing tangs.
6. Reverse procedure to install.

1967-68 Toronado

1. Disconnect battery ground cable.
2. Turn switch to ACC position.
3. Insert paper clip into small hole in front side of switch, while turning key counterclockwise the lock will pop out.
4. Remove switch escutcheon.
5. Remove switch from back side of control panel and remove wiring connector.
6. Reverse procedure to install.

1966 Toronado

1. Remove control panel.
2. Turn switch to ACC position.
3. Insert paper clip through small hole in front side of switch and depress. While turning key counterclockwise the lock will pop out.
4. Remove escutcheon and remove switch from back side of instrument panel and remove wiring connector.

1966 Except Toronado

1. Disconnect battery.
2. Insert key into switch and turn fully clockwise.
3. While holding key in clockwise position, depress lock cylinder retainer with a paper clip through small hole in face of lock cylinder.
4. Remove key and lock cylinder.
5. Remove switch escutcheon.
6. After removing switch from panel, connector can be removed as shown in Fig. 1.

LIGHT SWITCH, REPLACE
1968-72

1. On 1968-69 intermediate models with A/C, remove left-hand outlet duct.
2. Disconnect multiiple connector from switch.
3. Pull knob out to headlight ON position, then depress spring-loaded button on switch body and pull knob out of switch assembly.
4. Remove switch escutcheon.
5. Remove switch from rear of panel.
6. On 1968-69 Toronado, disconnect vacuum hoses and note color coding of each.

1966-67 Toronado

1. Remove lower left-hand trim panel.
2. Remove knob by first pulling knob out to HEADLIGHT position, then depress

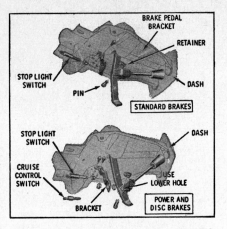

Fig. 3   Brake switch installation. 1967-72

spring-loaded button on switch body and pull knob out of switch.
3. Remove escutcheon nut.
4. Remove switch from rear of panel.
5. Disconnect wiring and vacuum hoses, being sure to note color coding of each hose.

1966-67 Except Toronado

1. Disconnect wiring from switch.
2. If switch is of the type shown in Fig. 2, remove the knob and shaft (rod) as directed in the illustration. If switch has no release button, remove knob.
3. Remove nut and switch escutcheon.
4. Remove switch from instrument panel.
5. Reverse above procedure to install.

STOP LIGHT SWITCH

NOTE: The stop light switch must be checked whenever the brake pedal height has been changed. Adjustment is made on the brake pedal arm. To obtain proper operation of the stop lights, refer to Fig. 4.

1967-72

The stop light switch is attached to the brake pedal bracket and is actuated by

the brake pedal arm, Fig. 3. When installing the switch, insert switch into tubular clip until switch body seats on tube clip. Pull brake pedal rearward until it contacts brake pedal stop. This moves the switch in the tubular clip providing proper adjustment.

1966

1. Referring to Fig. 4, and with brake pedal height correctly adjusted, insert switch into tubular clip until switch body seats in tube clip.
2. Pull brake pedal rearward until it contacts pedal stop. This moves switch in tubular clip, providing proper adjustment.

CLUTCH START SWITCH
1969-72

All cars equipped with a manual transmission use a clutch start switch which is mounted on the pedal bracket. The switch closes when the clutch is depressed and completes solenoid connection. When installing switch, no adjustment is necessary.

NEUTRAL START & BACK-UP LIGHT SWITCH

The neutral safety switch is mounted on the steering column or inside the console on floor shift models with automatic transmission.

Checking

1. Apply parking brake firmly.
2. Position selector lever into "D" range and turn ignition switch to "Start".
3. While holding switch on "Start", slowly move selector lever toward "N" position until engine cranks and starts.
4. Without moving selector lever after engine starts, depress accelerator pedal slightly to determine whether or not transmission is in gear. If switch is properly adjusted, transmis-

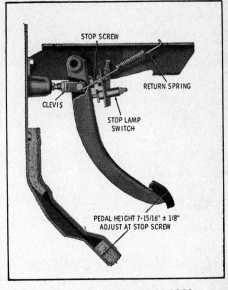

Fig. 4   Stop light switch. 1966

sion will not be in gear.

NOTE: If equipped with back-up lights, lights should operate with ignition on and selector lever in reverse.

All 1966-67
Adjustment

1. Remove console if so equipped.
2. Remove switch attaching screws.
3. With ignition off, position selector lever in "D".
4. Align slot in contact support with hole in bracket and insert a .090" pin, Figs. 5 and 8.
5. Position contact support drive slot over shifter tube drive tang and install mounting screws.

1968-70
Adjustment (Except Console)

1. Place transmission in drive detent with switch installed and drive lug engaged in shift tube.
2. Adjust switch so gauge pin hole will align between contact support and

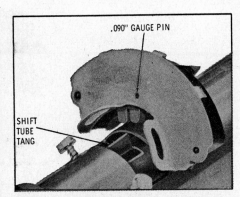

Fig. 5   Neutral safety switch adjustment. All 1966-72 column type

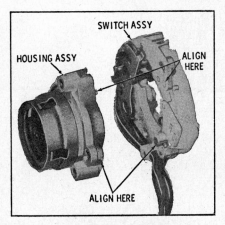

Fig. 6   Aligning turn signal switch with housing. 1967-68

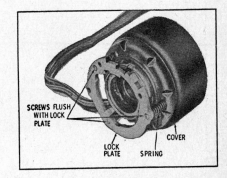

Fig. 7   Installing wave and thrust washer. 1967-68

switch bracket permitting insertion of gauge pin, Fig. 5.

Adjustment (Console Type)
1. Remove console.
2. On 1968-69 units, place shift lever against neutral stop. On 1970, place lever in Park.
3. On 1968-69 units, adjust switch to dimension shown in Fig. 9. On 1970, dimension is $2\frac{1}{16}$".

1971-72
1. Place selector lever in "Neutral".
2. Install .090" gauge pin into outer hole in switch cover.
3. Rotate switch until pin goes into alignment hole in the inner plastic slide.
4. Tighten switch to column screws and remove gauge pin.

TURN SIGNAL SWITCH
1969-72
1. Disconnect battery ground cable.
2. Remove steering wheel.
3. Remove cover screws and cover.
4. Using suitable compressor, depress lock plate far enough to remove the "C" ring from shaft.

NOTE: On Tilt & Travel, compressor must be positioned on large lips of cancelling cam.

5. Remove lock plate, cancelling cam, spring and signal lever.
6. Depress hazard warning knob then unscrew knob and remove.
7. Position lever in right turn position and remove three switch attaching screws.
8. Remove panel lower trim cap, disconnect switch harness and remove bolts attaching bracket to column jacket.

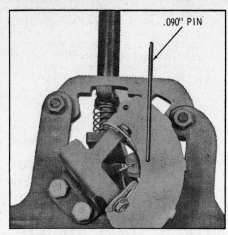

.090" PIN

Fig. 8 Neutral safety switch adjustment. 1966-67 console type

9. Disconnect shift indicator if equipped.
10. Remove two nuts holding column in position, remove bracket and wire protector while holding column in position then loosely install bracket to hold column in place.
11. Tape switch wires at connector keeping wires flat, then carefully remove wires and switch.

1967-68
1. Remove steering wheel, cancelling cam and spring from upper steering shaft.
2. Remove turn signal lever.
3. Unscrew hazard switch knob.
4. Remove "C" ring from upper steering shaft by turning counterclockwise. *Do not pry against switch parts.*
5. Slide thrust washer and wave washer off steering shaft.
6. Loosen three turn signal switch screws five turns each. Rotate cover assembly counterclockwise and

pull it straight off top of jacket. Using side cutters, cut turn signal wiring harness at bottom of cover. Bend harness over bowl to aid in installation.
7. Lock plate and cover should be marked (use colored pencil) for easier reassembly.
8. Remove three previously loosened screws from lock plate, being careful not to lose springs.
9. Turn signal switch can now be removed.
10. Reverse procedure to install, noting details illustrated in Figs. 6, 7.

1966
1. Remove steering wheel, cancelling cam, signal lever and three signal control attaching screws.
2. Disconnect steering column wiring harness plug from main wiring harness.
3. Lift turn signal control out of housing and disconnect wiring plug and horn contact wire from turn signal control.

NOTE: On cars equipped with manual shift transmission, wiring harness is part of turn signal control.

4. On cars with automatic transmission, the bearing, actuator and turn signal contacts can be disassembled, Fig. 15.
5. Reverse removal procedure to install. Before tightening the three attaching screws, rotate housing until it locks to steering column.

HORN SOUNDER & STEERING WHEEL
1967-72 Toronado
1. On 1969-72 pull down and out on pad and remove pad. On 1967-68 pry emblem up to disengage locking tang.
2. Remove wheel nut and use a suitable puller to remove wheel. Horn contact parts are now accessible.
3. With marks on steering wheel hub and steering shaft aligned, install wheel, flat washer and nut.

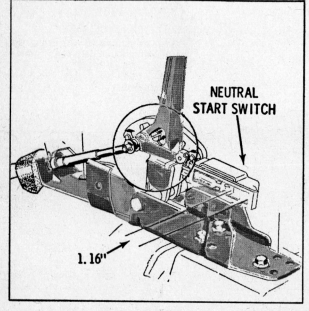

NEUTRAL START SWITCH

1.16"

Fig. 9 Neutral start switch (console type)

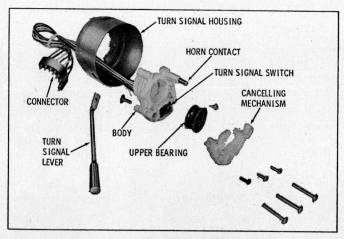

TURN SIGNAL HOUSING
HORN CONTACT
TURN SIGNAL SWITCH
CANCELLING MECHANISM
CONNECTOR
TURN SIGNAL LEVER
BODY
UPPER BEARING

Fig. 10 Turn signal switch. 1966

4. Align tangs of emblem with contact hole in wheel and push in to lock.

1967-70 Except Toronado

1. On standard wheel pull horn cap and retainer from wheel.
2. Deluxe wheel; 1969 pull down and out on pad and remove pad. 1967-68 pry emblem up to disengage locking tabs.
3. Service horn contacts as required.
4. Remove nut and washer and use a suitable puller to remove wheel.
5. Reverse procedure to install.

1966 Toronado

1. Turn emblem counterclockwise to disengage locking tang.
2. Remove wheel attaching nut and use a suitable puller to remove wheel.
3. When installing, align point of emblem with horn contact hole in wheel. Turn emblem clockwise to lock it in place.

1966 Except Toronado

1. Disconnect turn signal connector.
2. On Standard wheel pull lens and bezel from wheel. On deluxe wheel, pry cap and emblem assembly from shroud. On F85 models rotate cap clockwise to disengage locking tab.
3. Remove wheel nut and use a suitable puller to remove wheel.

1966

1. Disconnect turn signal connector.
2. On standard wheel pull lens and bezel from wheel. On deluxe wheel pry cap and emblem assembly from shroud. On F85 models rotate cap clockwise to disengage locking tab.
3. Remove wheel attaching nut and use a suitable puller to remove wheel.

INSTRUMENT CLUSTER

1971-72 Senior Cars

1. Disconnect battery ground cable.
2. Remove steering column trim cover and left trim panel.
3. Remove shift indicator needle.
4. Disconnect speedo cable at speedo. If equipped with Cruise Control, disconnect cable at regulator and push about 6" of cable through toe pan.
5. Turn ignition to RUN position and place shift lever in Drive.
6. Remove two screws from sides of cluster.
7. Remove two screws (outboard) from top of cluster.
8. Pull out on cluster until wiring connector can be disconnected.
9. Pull cluster from dash.

1969-70 Senior Cars (Except Toronado)

1. Disconnect negative battery cable.
2. Disconnect printed circuit multiple connector.
3. Disconnect speedometer cable.
4. Remove pad and bezel assembly.
5. Remove three screws attaching cluster housing to instrument panel and remove cluster.

1970-72 Intermediate Cars

Fuel Gauge Cluster
1. Disconnect battery cable.
2. Remove instrument trim panel.
3. Remove three cluster attaching screws, pull cluster out and disconnect wiring. Remove cluster.
4. When installing cluster, be sure that two of the attaching screws go through ground straps.

Speedometer Cluster
1. Disconnect battery cable.
2. With auto. trans. column shift, remove lower trim panel then disconnect shift indicator clip on shift bowl.
3. Remove instrument trim panel.
4. Disconnect speedometer cable.
5. Remove three cluster attaching screws and pull cluster out carefully so that shift indicator needle is not damaged.
6. Disconnect wiring and remove cluster.

1968-69 Intermediate Cars

Fuel Gauge Cluster
1. If air conditioned, remove left-hand air outlet duct.
2. Disconnect battery ground cable.
3. Disconnect printed circuit multiple connector.
4. Separate cluster from control panel (2 screws) and remove cluster through front of pad.

Speedometer Cluster
1. If air conditioned, remove left-hand air outlet duct.
2. Disconnect battery ground cable.
3. Disconnect multiple wiring connector from printed circuit.
4. If column shift with automatic transmission, disconnect shift indicator link.
5. Separate cluster from control panel (2 screws) and remove cluster through front of pad.

1968-70 Toronado

1. Disconnect battery ground cable.
2. Disconnect Cruise Control cable at regulator (if equipped).
3. Disconnect speedometer cable at transmission.
4. Remove screws from right-hand lower pad and filler.
5. Unfasten steering column clamp (2 nuts) and retain wedge for use when installing.
6. If equipped with tilt and travel, tilt down to lowest position and let steering wheel rest on seat cushion. With a standard column, use a 4" x 4" block of wood between steering wheel and seat. This will prevent accidental disconnecting of hoses and wiring when tilting control panel out to perform service repairs.
7. Loosen two control housing bracket bolts about 1/4".
8. Disconnect radio lead-in.
9. Remove two control housing upper screws and tilt control panel outward from the top.
10. Disconnect printed circuit connectors.
11. Remove radio if speedometer is to be removed.
12. Separate cover from cluster (8 screws).
13. Cluster components are now accessible for service.

1966-67 Intermediate Cars

Speedometer
1. Remove speedometer cable.
2. Remove cluster housing.
3. Remove speedometer (3 screws).
4. Reverse procedure to install.

Fuel Gauge
1. Disconnect battery.
2. Remove cluster housing.
3. Remove fuel gauge (3 bolts).
4. Reverse procedure to install. *Electric connector links must be positioned under each attaching bolt when gauge is installed.*

1967-68 Senior Cars (Except Toronado)

Fuel Gauge & Tell Tale
1. Disconnect battery ground cable.
2. Remove phillips screw from front of bezel.
3. Disconnect fuel gauge cluster connector.
4. Remove rear retaining nuts.
5. Remove fuel gauge and bezel from front.
6. Reverse procedure to install.

Speedometer Cluster
1. Disconnect battery ground cable.
2. Disconnect speedometer cable and printed circuit plug.
3. Remove phillips screw from front of bezel.
4. Remove rear retaining nuts.
5. Remove speedometer cluster from front.
6. Reverse procedure to install.

1966-67 Toronado

1. Disconnect battery.
2. If equipped with Cruise Control, disconnect cable at regulator.
3. Remove screws from right and left side trim panels.
4. Remove transmission indicator needle.
5. Remove nuts and clamps from column-to-upper reinforcement. Column may rest on front seat cushion.
6. Loosen lower bracket bolts (one each side) about 1/4".
7. Disconnect speedometer cable and radio lead-in wire.
8. Remove two panel-to-pad bolts.
9. If A/C equipped, disconnect outlet hose.

NOTE: At this point all components of the control panel can be removed for any service required.

10. If the panel must be removed completely, disconnect main wiring harness from components. Remove the two loosened bracket bolts, then remove the panel.

1966 Senior Cars (Except Toronado)

Speedometer Cluster
1. Disconnect battery.
2. If equipped with air conditioning, remove manifold and left-hand hose.
3. Disconnect speedometer cable and printed circuit plug.

4. Unfasten (2 nuts) and remove cluster.

Fuel Gauge & Telltale
1. Disconnect battery.
2. If equipped with Cruise Control, it may be necessary to loosen control switch mounting bracket to gain access.
3. If equipped with air conditioning, remove left-hand hose.
4. Disconnect printed circuit plug.
5. Unfasten (2 screws) and remove gauge.

1966 F-85

1. Disconnect speedometer cable, printed circuit connector plug and clock wiring.
2. Remove three cluster attaching nuts and remove cluster.
3. Service instruments as required and install cluster in reverse order of removal.

W/S WIPER MOTOR, REPLACE

1971-72

1. Raise hood and remove cowl screen or grille.
2. Reach through cowl opening and loosen transmission drive link attaching nuts to motor crankarm.
3. Disconnect wiring and washer hoses.
4. Disconnect transmission drive link from motor arm.
5. Remove motor attaching screws.
6. Remove motor while guiding crankarm through opening.

1968-70 Intermediate Cars

1. Disconnect wiring and washer hoses.
2. Remove wiper blade and arm as follows:
   Rectangular Motor-Lift up on arm and carefully pry arm up off transmission.
   Round Motor-Refer to Fig. 11.
3. Remove the motor attaching screws.
4. Lift rear edge of vent screen and loosen nuts attaching transmission to motor crank arm. Loosen bolts only until the crankarm will slide out of transmission socket.

1968-70 Full Size Cars

1. Disconnect wiring and washer hoses.
2. Remove three motor attaching screws.
3. Remove access hole plug.
4. Reaching through access hole, loosen two transmission crank arm nuts.
5. Hold motor with one hand and with the other move wiper arm halfway through its travel to center crank arm in dash hole.
6. Remove motor while guiding crank arm through hole.

1966-67 Intermediate Cars

1. Disconnect wiring and washer hoses.
2. Remove three wiper attaching screws.
3. Depending upon the optional equip-

PRESS DOWN ON COIL SPRING WITH SCREWDRIVER AND PUSH WIPER ARM OUT OF BLADE.

COIL SPRING

REMOVING WIPER BLADE

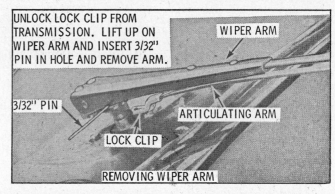

UNLOCK LOCK CLIP FROM TRANSMISSION. LIFT UP ON WIPER ARM AND INSERT 3/32" PIN IN HOLE AND REMOVE ARM.

WIPER ARM

3/32" PIN

ARTICULATING ARM

LOCK CLIP

REMOVING WIPER ARM

Fig. 11   Removing wiper blade and arm from round motor

ment installed, it may be possible to pull the motor back through the dash panel far enough to remove the crank arm-to-transmission clip; if not, it will be necessary to remove the cowl vent grille.
4. Reverse procedure to install. If cowl vent grille was not removed, install crank arm-to-transmission clip before mounting wiper to dash.

1966-67 Senior Cars

1. Disconnect wiring and hoses.
2. Remove access hole cover in upper cowl area.
3. Loosen (do not remove) the two transmission-to-crank arm attaching nuts until transmission ball socket will drop off from crank arm ball.
4. Reverse procedure to install.

W/S WIPER TRANSMISSION, REPLACE
1968-72

Rectangular Motor
1. Remove wiper arms and blades.
2. Raise hood and remove cowl vent screen or grille.
3. Disconnect wiring from motor.
4. Loosen, do not remove, transmission drive link to motor crankarm attaching nuts and disconnect drive link from crankarm.
5. Remove right and left transmission to body attaching screws and guide transmission and linkage out through cowl opening.

Round Motor
1. Raise hood and remove cowl vent screen.
2. On Intermediate models, remove right and left wiper arm and blade assemblies. On Full Size cars, remove arm and blade only from transmission to be removed.
3. Loosen, do not remove, attaching nuts securing transmission drive link to motor crankarm.

NOTE: On Full Size cars, if only the left transmission is to be removed, it will not be necessary to lossen attaching nuts securing the right transmission drive link to the motor.

4. Disconnect drive link from motor crankarm.
5. On Intermediate models, remove right and left transmission to body attaching screws. On Full Size cars, remove the attaching screws securing only the transmission to be removed.
6. Remove transmission and linkage by guiding it through opening.

1966-67

1. Remove cowl vent grille attaching screws.
2. Detach transmission drive linkage retainer from wiper motor crank arm.
3. Remove attaching screws and remove transmission.
4. Remove transmission and linkage arms from cowl.
5. Reverse above procedure to install.

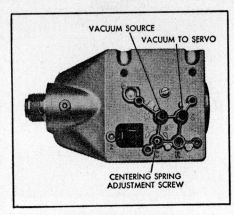

Fig. 12 Centering spring adjustment. 1968-70

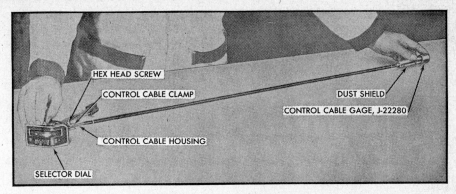

Fig. 13 Control cable adjustment for Slide Switch Speedostat

W/S WIPER SWITCH

1971-72 Full Size Cars

1. Remove control panel.
2. Remove wiring connector from switch.
3. Pull wiper knob from front of switch.
4. Remove switch attaching screws and remove switch.

1971-72 Intermediate Cars

1. Disconnect battery ground cable.
2. Remove instrument trim panel.
3. Remove three fuel gauge cluster attaching screws and pull out cluster so cluster wiring can be disconnected. Remove cluster.
4. Disconnect washer/wiper connector from switch.
5. Remove knob from switch.
6. Remove switch attaching screws and remove switch.

1968-70 Except Toronado

1. On intermediate models with air conditioning, remove left-hand air outlet duct.
2. Pull wiper knob from switch.
3. Remove switch escutcheon.
4. Remove wiper and washer switch from rear of control panel.
5. Disconnect switch wiring.

1968-70 Toronado

1. Disconnect battery ground cable.
2. Disconnect wiring at switch.
3. Unfasten and remove switch from rear of control panel.

1966-67

Disconnect wires or plug connector from switch. Unfasten switch from its mounting and remove it from the car.

RADIO REMOVAL

NOTE: When installing radio, be sure to adjust antenna trimmer for peak performance.

1971-72 Senior Cars

1. Loosen ground strap at lower valance panel support.
2. Remove radio support bracket nut at rear of radio.
3. Disconnect three flood lamps from bezel for clearance.
4. Remove four screws that hold bezel in instrument panel.
5. Pull bezel forward as far as possible.
6. Disconnect electrical connectors at rear of radio.
7. Remove radio knobs, attaching nuts and escutcheons.
8. Remove radio from rear of bezel.

1971-72 Intermediate Cars & 1969-70 Except Toronado

1. If Air Conditioned, remove manifold.
2. Disconnect all wiring and antenna.
3. Remove knobs and attaching nuts from front of dash.
4. Remove attaching bolt (bracket to control panel) and remove radio from rear of panel.

1968-70 Toronado

1. Remove control knobs and nuts from front of dash.
2. Remove control panel.
3. Disconnect radio feed wire.
4. Disconnect dial lamp.
5. Remove attaching nut from support to radio.
6. Remove radio from rear of control panel.

1967-68 Except Toronado

1. Disconnect battery ground cable.
2. Remove radio knobs, washers and rear seat speaker control.
3. Remove radio attaching nuts and escutcheons.
4. Disconnect all wiring and antenna lead-in.
5. Remove lower radio support bracket screw.
6. Remove radio from rear of panel.
7. Reverse procedure to install.

1966-67 Toronado

1. Disconnect battery.
2. Remove both lower cluster panels.

3. Remove steering column attaching nuts and lower bracket.
4. Remove shift indicator needle.
5. Disconnect speedometer cable.
6. Remove attaching nuts from cluster lower brackets, leaving brackets attached to instrument panel.
7. Remove two upper instrument panel screws and lay cluster on steering column.
8. Remove radio knobs, washers and rear seat speaker control.
9. Remove radio attaching nuts and escutcheons.
10. Disconnect all wiring and antenna lead-in.
11. Remove lower radio support bracket nut, then remove radio from panel.

1966 Except Toronado

1. Disconnect battery. If equipped with air conditioning, remove manifold.
2. Remove defroster manifold.
3. Remove radio knobs and rear seat speaker control.
4. Remove radio attaching nuts, and lower radio support bracket attaching screw.
5. Remove radio from rear of panel.

HEATER CORE REMOVAL

1971-72 Full Size Cars

1. Disconnect battery ground cable.
2. Drain radiator below heater level, disconnect heater hoses.
3. Remove four heater case attaching nuts to dash panel.
4. Disconnect temperature cable, defroster cable and vacuum hose from heater case.
5. Remove defroster duct to case attaching screw.
6. Disconnect right half of right trim panel.
7. Remove heater case from inside car.
8. Remove heater core from case.

1966-70 Toronado

1. Disconnect blower wiring, vacuum hoses and cables.
2. Drain coolant and remove heater hoses.

Fig. 14 Accelerator linkage adjustment for Slide Switch type Speedostat

3. Remove attaching screws and remove heater assembly from cowl.
4. Remove core from heater assembly.

1966-70 Full Size Cars

1. Remove glove box and disconnect wiring, vacuum lines and defroster hoses from heater case.
2. Remove blower attaching screws and nuts.
3. From inside car, remove heater assembly and take out core.

1966-72 Intermediate Models

1. In engine compartment, remove five attaching nuts from blower. The lower outboard nut is removed by drilling a 3/4" hole through fender filler panel at dimple or, if no dimple is provided, disconnect the right fender at the bottom and block it away from the body. Remove nut through this opening.
2. Disconnect resistor wiring and three control cables.
3. Remove heater case assembly from under dash. Exposed core can now be removed.

SPEED CONTROLS
1971-72

Vacuum Brake Release Switch, Adjust

The vacuum valve should be pushed all the way into the retaining clip. Pulling the brake pedal up to the stop will automatically adjust the valve.

Servo Rod, Adjust

Adjust servo rod length so that bellcrank clearance is .020-.040" when carburetor is at slow idle.

1968-70

Brake Release Switch, Adjust

1. Disconnect multiple connector at regulator.
2. Turn ignition switch to accessory position.
3. Using a test lamp, ground one test lamp lead and touch the other to terminal No. 2 in harness connector.
4. Adjust switch so that lamp will light when brake pedal is fully released and will go out when brake pedal is depressed about 1/4 inch.
5. If switch cannot be adjusted, it is defective and should be replaced. Install new switch and repeat Step 4.
6. Remove test lamp, turn off ignition key and plug connector to regulator.

Chain Linkage, Adjust

Chain linkage should never be taut. To adjust, start engine set carburetor at hot idle with anti-stall plunger backed off so as not to affect engine idle speed. Hook chain to accelerator linkage, pull taut, then loosen by length of one ball and install chain clip. *When pulling chain taut, do not pull so far as to cause throttle to open.*

Centering Spring, Adjust

1. If speed control system holds speed three or more mph higher than selected speed, turn centering spring adjusting screw (C) toward (S) 1/32" or less, Fig. 12.
2. If speed control system holds speed three or more mph below selected speed, turn centering spring adjusting screw (C) toward (F) 1/32" or less. *Do not move adjustment screw (R).*

1966-67 Speedostat
Control Cable Adjustment, 1966-67

The cable is preset at the factory and should not require adjustment unless a new cable is installed. This adjustment must be performed off the car as follows:

1. Remove the selector assembly.
2. Rotate selector dial to low speed position until it is positioned against its stop but do not force beyond its stop.
3. Position assembly flat on workbench and make certain there are no kinks in cable.
4. Loosen hex head set screw at cable clamp on selector control.
5. Pull cable housing until it is approximately half-way out of cable clamp. Position control cable gauge shown in Fig. 13 in end of dust shield. Hold dust shield and gauge and push toward selector control assembly until gauge bottoms. While holding in this position, tighten set screw at cable clamp.

NOTE: The gauge shown in Fig. 13 is used on Cadillac and Oldsmobile; use the

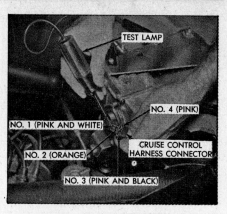

Fig. 15 Electrical connections on Slide Switch type Speedostat

gauge end marked .220" for Oldsmobile and the other end for Cadillac.

Accelerator Linkage

1. Adjust throttle rod.
2. Start engine and operate at slow idle with transmission lever in "Park".
3. Separate linkage from exterior arm.
4. Adjust trunnion so that when it is installed through exterior arm, the stop stud will be aligned with locating notch and throttle valves will be closed.
5. Install washer on trunnion and secure with cotter pin.

NOTE: Due to the angle at which the trunnion enters hole in exterior arm, it is necessary to rotate the exterior arm slightly forward when inserting the trunnion. Repeat this operation until proper alignment is obtained. Be careful not to turn trunnion too far back or throttle valves will unseat and cause an incorrect adjustment. Insert the gauge shown in Fig. 14 (or small diameter pipe) over stop stud to check alignment.

Brake Release Switch

1. Turn on ignition but do not start engine.
2. Momentarily move slide switch to AUTO position until red indicator light glows.
3. Using a test lamp, ground one lead and touch the other lead to terminal No. 4, Fig. 15.
4. Loosen mounting screw securing release switch to brake pedal mounting bracket.
5. Adjust release switch so that lamp will light when brake pedal is fully released, and will go out when brake pedal is depressed about 1/4 inch. Tighten switch mounting screw. If switch cannot be adjusted, it is defective and should be replaced.

Engine Section

IMPORTANT: See the Toronado supplement for procedures on removing the engine and transmission, and method of servicing the front suspension, drive axles and final drive (differential) immediately following this chapter.

See Chevrolet Chapter for Service Procedures on 6-250 Engine.

NOTE: Material marked "F.S.C." means Olds Full Size Car or Senior Models

RAISING ENGINE
1966-72 V8s

1. Mark hood hinge before removing to aid in proper alignment upon reassembly.
2. Drain radiator and disconnect battery.
3. Disconnect radiator hoses, heater hoses, vacuum hoses, power steering pump hoses (if necessary), starter cable at junction block, engine-to-body ground strap, fuel hose from fuel line, wiring and accelerator linkage.
4. Remove fan blade and pulley, coil and upper radiator support.
5. Raise car.
6. Disconnect exhaust pipes at manifolds.
7. Remove torque converter cover and install a suitable holding tool to keep converter from falling out when engine is removed.
8. Remove engine mounting bolts and support engine.
9. Lift engine and secure transmission chain support to frame or support transmission with a jack.
10. Unfasten converter from flywheel (3 bolts) and transmission from engine (6 bolts).
11. Lower car and remove engine.
12. Reverse procedure to install.

NOTE

On V8 engines, whenever installation of a front engine mounting becomes necessary, the cap screws fastening the mounting to the frame or bracket should first be screwed finger tight, then tightened alternately, one at a time. *Do not tighten one cap screw in position independently of the other.* This is extremely important since the lower portion of the assembly would not seat evenly in the upper portion. The front mounting must be properly positioned and tightened, otherwise the mounting will not properly function as an insulator.

CYLINDER HEAD, REPLACE

Some cylinder head gaskets are coated with a special lacquer to provide a good seal once the parts have warmed up. Do not use any additional sealer on such gaskets. If the gasket does not have this lacquer coating, apply suitable sealer to both sides.

Tighten cylinder head bolts a little at a time in three steps in the sequence shown in the illustrations. Final tighten-

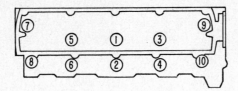

Fig. 1 Cylinder head tightening sequence. V8-330, 350, 400, 425, 455

ing should be to the torque specifications listed in the *Engine Tightening* table.

V8-330, 350, 400, 425, 455

1. Drain radiator and cylinder block.
2. Disconnect spark plug wires and remove intake manifold.
3. Disconnect exhaust crossover pipe for left side and/or crossover pipe and exhaust pipe for right side.
4. Remove valve cover (loosen or remove any accessory brackets that interfere).
5. Remove ground strap from right cylinder head.
6. On 1966-68 engines, unfasten and remove cylinder head with exhaust manifold and rocker arms attached.

7. On 1969-72 engines, remove exhaust manifold, rocker arms and push rods from head to be removed.
8. Reverse removal procedure to install head, and tighten bolts in the sequence shown in Fig. 1.

VALVE ARRANGEMENT
Front to Rear

6-250 . . . . E-I-I-E-I-I-E-I-I-E
V8-330, 350, 400, 425, 455 I-E-I-E-E-I-E-I

VALVE LIFT SPECS.

Engine	Year	Intake	Exhaust
6-250	1966-71	.388	.388
V8-330	1966-67[2]	.387	.388
	1966-67[1]	.430	.432
V8-350	1968-70	.435	.435
	1971-72[2][5]	.400	.400
	1971-72[4]	.472	.472
	1972[10]	.440	.440
V8-400	1967[2]	.435	.435
	1966-69[4]	.472	.472
	1966-69[5]	.430	.432
V8-425	1966[6]	.430	.432
	1966[7]	.472	.461
	1966[8]	.431	.433

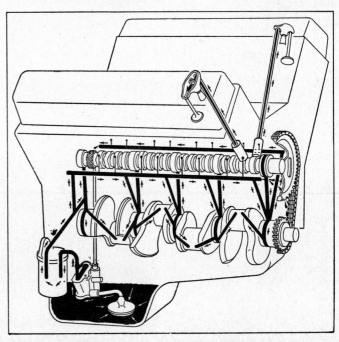

Engine lubrication. V8-330, 350, 400, 425, 455

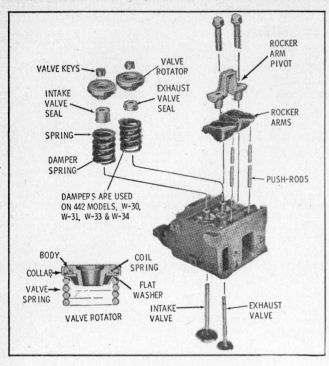

Fig. 2　Cylinder head exploded. 1970-72 V8

HOLD ROCKER ARM STUD WITH WRENCH WHEN REMOVING ROCKER ARM NUT

Fig. 3　Removing rocker arm. V8-330, 350, 400, 425, 455

ROCKER ARMS

1970-72 NOTE

Valve rotators are used in place of the valve spring retainer used previously, Fig. 2. The rotator operates on a sprag clutch principle utilizing the collapsing action of a coiled spring to give rotation to the rotator body which turns the valve.

V8-330, 350, 400, 425, 455

1. To remove rocker arm assemblies, first remove valve cover.
2. Hold stud to prevent it from turning and remove rocker arm stud nuts, washer, lock plates, pivots and rocker arms, Fig. 3.

NOTE: Remove each set (one set per cylinder) as a unit.

Installation

1. Torque studs to 35 ft-lbs. Later engines use pivots and the pivot bolts are torqued to 25 ft-lbs.
2. Position a set of rocker arms (for one cylinder) on proper studs.
3. Install pivots and lock plates, being sure tangs on lock plates seat properly in the pivots. Coat wear points with lubricant.

	1967	.430	.432	V8-330	1966-67[1]	12
	1967[3]	.472	.461		1966-67[2]	21
V8-455	1968-70[5]	.435	.435	V8-350	1968-70	16
	1971[2]	.435	.435		1971[5][6]	14
	1971[1]	.435	.435		1971[7]	30
	1971[9]	.472	.472		1972[5][7]	16
	1972	.435	.435		1972[6]	30
					1972[8]	22

[1]—4 bar. carb.　[2]—2 bar. carb.
[3]—Starfire.
[4]—4 bar. carb., std. trans.
[5]—4 bar. carb., auto. trans.
[6]—310, 365 H.P.　[7]—375 H.P.
[8]—385 H.P.
[9]—"4-4-2".
[10]—California

V8-400	1966-69[1]	30
	1966-69[2]	21
V8-425	1966-67	21
	1966[3]	24
V8-455	1968-70[4]	20
	1971-72	20
	1971 Toronado	22
	1971 "4-4-2"[1]	30
	1971 "4-4-2"[2]	24

[1]—Std. trans.　[2]—Auto. trans.
[3]—Starfire.
[4]—GT & 400 H.P.—24.
[5]—2 bar. carb.
[6]—4 bar. carb., std. trans.
[7]—4 bar. carb., auto. trans.
[8]—California

VALVE TIMING
Intake Opens Before TDC

Engine	Year	Degrees
6-250	1966	12
	1967	62
	1968-71	16

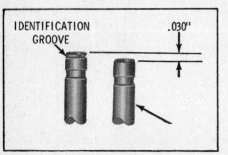

Fig. 4　Valves in 1966-68. Starfire and V8-400 engines are .030" longer than other V8 valves

Fig. 5　Measuring valve stem height. V8-330, 350, 400, 425, 455

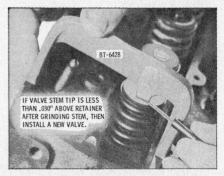

Fig. 6　Measuring valve retaining height. V8-330, 350, 400, 425, 455

Fig. 7 Valve guide bore marking.
V8-330, 350, 400, 425, 455

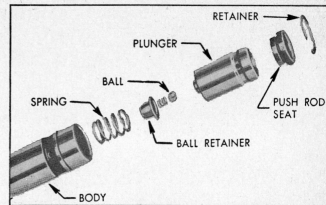

Fig. 8
Hydraulic valve
lifter (typical)

4. Install flat washers and nuts, being sure both valve lifters are in closed valve position when nuts are tightened.

CAUTION: Never exceed specified torque of 25 ft-lbs on nuts. Check to be sure clearance exists between push rod and push rod hole in cylinder head. If no clearance exists, lock plate must be replaced.

5. Reverse removal procedure to install cover, noting data in Fig. 9.

VALVES, REMOVE

1966-69 V8 NOTE

Valves in Starfire and V8-400 engines are .030" longer than other V8 valves, Fig. 4.

Whenever a new valve is installed or after grinding valves, it will be necessary to measure valve stem height using the Special Tool shown in Figs. 5 and 6.

Lacking this tool the only alternative is to lay flat feeler gauges on the retainer and check the distance between the retainer and valve stem tip. As shown in Fig. 6, if the valve stem tip is less than .030" above the retainer after grinding the stem, install a new valve.

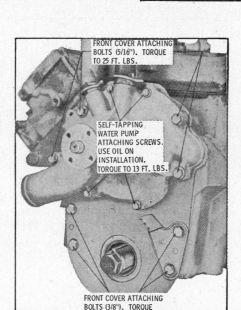

Fig. 9 Engine front cover bolts.
V8-330, 350, 400, 425, 455

VALVE LIFTERS

Valve lifters in production engines may be one of four sizes: standard, .001, .002 or .003 in. oversize. It is important when replacing one or more lifters that the proper size lifter be ordered. An identification numeral is etched on all lifter bodies except standard. The cylinder block is marked for lifter size on the rail under the push rod cover. Valve lifters .005 in. oversize are available for service replacement.

Plungers are not interchangeable because they are selectively fitted to the bodies at the factory.

If plunger and body appear satisfactory blow off with air to remove all particles of dirt. Install the plunger in the body without other parts and check for free movement. A simple test is to be sure that the plunger will drop of its own weight in the body, Fig. 8.

TIMING CASE COVER

NOTE: When it becomes necessary to

VALVE GUIDES
V8-330, 350, 400, 425, 455

Valve stem guides are not replaceable, due to being cast in place. If valve guide bores are worn excessively, they can be reamed oversize.

If a standard valve guide bore is being reamed, use a .003" or .005" oversize reamer. For the .010" oversize valve guide bore, use a .013" oversize reamer. If too large a reamer is used and the spiraling is removed, it is possible that the valve will not receive the proper lubrication.

NOTE: Occasionally a valve guide will be oversize as manufactured. These are marked on the cylinder head as shown in Fig. 7. If no markings are present, the guide bores are standard. If oversize markings are present, any valve replacement will require an oversize valve. Service valves are available in standard diameters as well as .003", .005", .010" and .013" oversize.

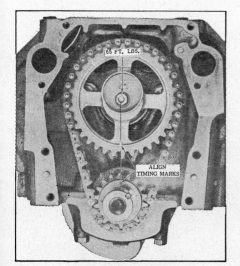

Fig. 10 Timing chain position.
V8-330, 350, 400, 425, 455

Fig. 11 Fuel pump eccentric.
V8-330, 350, 400, 425, 455

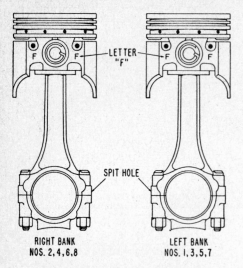

Fig. 12 Assembly of piston to rod. V8 except 1967-72 V8-400, 455

replace the cover oil seal, the cover need not be removed.

V8-330, 350, 400, 425, 455

1. Drain cooling system and disconnect heater hose, by-pass hose and both radiator hoses.
2. Remove all belts, fan and pulley, crankshaft pulley and pulley hub.
3. Remove oil pan.
4. Unfasten and remove cover, timing pointer and water pump assembly.

TIMING CHAIN
V8-330, 350, 400, 425, 455

1. After removing front cover, remove fuel pump eccentric, oil slinger, crankshaft sprocket, chain and camshaft sprocket.
2. Install camshaft sprocket, crankshaft sprocket and timing chain together, aligning timing marks as shown in Fig. 10.
3. Install fuel pump eccentric with flat side rearward, Fig. 11. Then install oil slinger and replace front cover.

CAMSHAFT, REPLACE
V8-330, 350, 400, 425, 455

1. Remove grille and radiator.
2. If air conditioned it will be necessary to remove condenser.
3. Remove fuel pump and front cover.
4. Remove oil slinger, timing chain and sprockets.
5. Remove distributor, intake manifold, rocker arm assemblies, push rods and valve lifters.
6. Slide camshaft out of engine.

NOTE: *To insure proper camshaft installation, and to provide initial lubrication, it is extremely important that the camshaft be coated with GM Concentrate (Part No. 582099).*

PISTON & ROD, ASSEMBLE

Lubricate the piston pin hole and piston pin to facilitate installation of pin, then position the connecting rod with its respective piston as shown in Figs. 12 and 13.

PISTONS, RINGS & PINS
Senior Cars

Pistons are available in standard sizes and oversizes of .010, .020 and .030".

Rings are available in standard sizes and oversizes of .010 and .030" on 1966-72.

F-85 Cars

Pistons are available in standard sizes and oversizes of .010 and .030" on 1966-72 V8.

Rings are available in standard sizes and oversizes of .010 and .030" on 1966-72 V8.

Pins are available in standard size only.

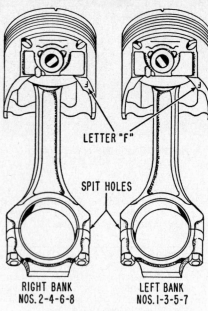

Fig. 13 Assembly of piston to rod. 1969-72 V8-400, 455

MAIN & ROD BEARINGS
Senior Cars

Main bearings are available in standard sizes and undersizes of .0005, .001, .0015, .002, .010 and .020".

Rod bearings are available in standard sizes and undersizes of .002, .010 and .020". On V8-330 a .012" undersize is also available.

F-85 Cars

On 1966-68 V8 undersizes of .0005, .001, .0015, .002, .010 and .020" are available.

On 1966-68 V8, the undersizes available are .002, .010, .012 and .020".

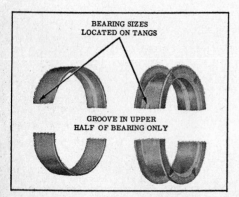

Fig. 14 Main bearing size location. V8-330, 350, 400, 425, 455

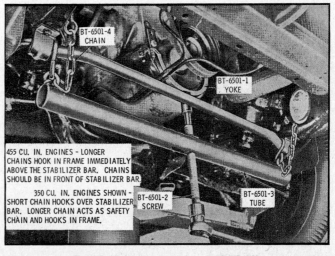

Fig. 15 Engine support bar. F-85 V8-455

NOTE

Main bearing clearances not within specifications must be corrected by the use of selective upper and lower shells. Fig. 14 illustrates the undersize identification marking on the bearing tang.

OIL PAN

1966-72 V8 (Except F-85 V8-400 & 455)

1. Remove oil level dipstick.
2. Raise car and drain oil.
3. On F-85 models, disconnect exhaust pipe from right exhaust manifold.
4. On Olds F.S.C models, lower steering relay rod by disconnecting idler arm or pitman arm.
5. Disconnect engine mounts and raise front of engine as far as possible.

CAUTION: Be sure distributor does not contact cowl and fan blades do not contact fan shroud.

6. Bring No. 1 piston up on top center.
7. Remove crossover pipe and starter.
8. Unfasten and remove oil pan.

V8-400

1. Disconnect battery ground cable.
2. Remove upper radiator baffle.
3. Remove drive shaft, transmission crossmember, transmission and flywheel.
4. Disconnect left exhaust pipe and starter.
5. Disconnect right-hand engine mount.

NOTE: It is necessary to raise both the front and rear of engine and tilt it to the left, using the left engine mount as a pivot.

6. Use a suitable support bar and insert a 1" block between tool and right rear corner of oil pan to obtain additional lift on right side.
7. Raise front of engine.

NOTE: Remove lower two right-hand engine cover bolts to permit the lifting tool to clear water pump outlet. Do not bolt tool to block since engine must rock when being raised. Tool No. BT-6501-3 is available for this operation. Position fork of tool to lift pulley hub.

8. Raise right side of engine about 2½" and insert a block between upper and lower right-hand mounts.
9. Remove support bar tool from rear of engine.
10. Unfasten and remove pan.

NOTE: Before removing pan, have No. 1 and 2 connecting rod journals at the 4 or 7 o'clock position as viewed from front of engine.

11. Reverse procedure to install.

F-85 V8-455

1. Disconnect battery ground cable.
2. Disconnect fan shroud.
3. Raise car and drain oil.
4. Remove drive shaft and disconnect exhaust pipe and starter.
5. Install engine support bar, Fig. 15, and remove inspection cover. Disconnect modulator line, speedometer cable, oil cooler lines, solenoid wire and linkage.
6. Remove transmission crossmember, transmission and flywheel.
7. Remove right engine mount, raise engine 2" and install wedge block.
8. Loosen left engine mount-to-block bolts enough to permit removal of oil pan bolts.
9. Remove oil pan.

OIL PUMP REPAIRS

V8-330, 350, 400, 425, 455

1. Remove oil pan and pump baffle. Remove attaching screws and remove pump and drive shaft extension.
2. To service the pump, refer to Fig. 16.
3. To install, insert the drive shaft extension through the opening in the block until the shaft mates into the distributor drive gear. Position pump onto rear main bearing cap and torque the attaching bolts to 24-34 ft-lbs.
4. Install oil pump baffle and pan.

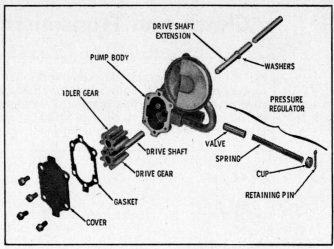

Fig. 16   Oil pump disassembled. V8-330, 350, 400, 425, 455

WATER PUMP, REPLACE

V8-330, 350, 400, 425, 455

1. Drain cooling system and remove heater and lower hoses from pump.
2. Loosen pulley belts and remove fan and pulley. On air conditioned cars, remove clutch fan assembly and pulley.
3. Unfasten and remove pump from front cover.

FUEL PUMP, REPLACE

1. Remove all gasket material from the pump and block gasket surfaces. Apply sealer to both sides of new gasket.
2. Position gasket on pump flange and hold pump in position against its mounting surface. Make sure rocker arm is riding on camshaft eccentric.
3. Press pump tight against its mounting. Install retaining screws and tighten them alternately.
4. Connect fuel lines. Then operate engine and check for leaks.

SERVICE NOTE: Before installing the pump, it is good practice to crank the engine so that the nose of the camshaft eccentric is out of the way of the fuel pump rocker arm when the pump is installed. In this way there will be the least amount of tension on the rocker arm, thereby easing the installation of the pump.

Clutch and Transmission Section

> NOTE: 1972 linkage adjustment information is in this section. Repair procedures on both automatic and manual shift transmissions are covered elsewhere in this manual. Procedures for removing automatic transmission as well as linkage adjustments on 1966-71 models are included in the automatic transmission chapters. See Chapter Index.

CLUTCH PEDAL, ADJUST
1966-72

1. To adjust clutch pedal free travel, loosen lock nut on adjusting rod and remove swivel retainer.
2. Adjust swivel to obtain a free pedal play of ¾" to 1".
3. Install swivel retainer, tighten lock nut and recheck adjustment.

CLUTCH, REPLACE
1971-72 Two Plate Clutch

1. Support engine and remove transmission.
2. Remove flywheel housing leaving starter attached to engine. Release yoke and ball stud will remain with housing.

> NOTE: Before removing clutch assembly, note location of "O" marks on edges of clutch cover, front pressure plate and flywheel. If marks are not visible, scribe or prick punch the parts so they can be reassembled in same position.

3. Remove clutch cover to flywheel attaching bolts and remove the cover assembly with the front pressure plate attached, Fig. 1. The front driven plate can now be removed. Observe the driven plate before removing to be sure which side of the driven plate is the flywheel side.

4. With the clutch assembly on the bench, pressure plate side up, remove the three cover straps to front pressure plate attaching bolts and remove the front pressure plate and the driven plate.

> NOTE: Before lifting the front pressure plate and driven plate from the cover, observe which side of the pressure plate goes towards the flywheel. It is possible to assemble both parts reversed. A washer or shim (.027") is used between each strap and the front pressure plate.

5. Reverse removal procedure to install referring to Fig. 2.

1966-72 Exc. Two Plate Clutch

1. Remove transmission.
2. Disconnect clutch release spring and clutch rod.
3. Remove clutch release bearing.
4. Remove flywheel housing, leaving starter attached to engine. Release yoke and ball stud will remain in housing.
5. Scribe mark on clutch cover to flywheel for correct assembly.
6. Unfasten and remove clutch cover and disc.
7. Reverse removal procedure to install clutch and adjust clutch pedal free play.

THREE SPEED MANUAL TRANS., REPLACE
1966-72

1. Disconnect throttle linkage from cowl bracket to prevent damage.
2. Raise car and remove drive shaft.
3. Disconnect shift rods from shift levers.
4. Support rear of engine.
5. Remove cross support bar-to-rear transmission mount attaching bolts.
6. Disconnect parking brake cables from cross support and remove cross support bar.
7. If equipped with dual exhaust it may be necessary to disconnect left-hand exhaust pipe at exhaust manifold to provide clearance.
8. Disconnect speedometer cable.
9. Remove transmission upper attaching bolts and install aligning studs in the bolt holes.
10. Remove lower bolts and remove transmission.
11. Reverse procedure to install.

3 SPEED SHIFT LINKAGE, ADJUST
1966-72

On 1969-72 models, detent must be ad-

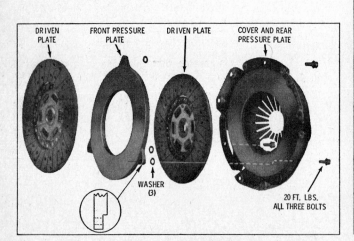

Fig. 1   Exploded view of two-plate clutch

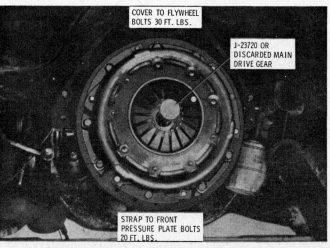

Fig. 2   Two-plate clutch installation

justed as follows. Place transmission in Reverse, loosen shift rods at transmission. Push up on reverse rod until detent in column is felt and tighten bolt for 1st-Reverse rod to 20 ft. lbs. Continue adjustment as follows:

1. Place transmission in Neutral.
2. Loosen swivel nuts on shift rods at transmission.
3. Use a suitable rod as an aligning tool and position it in the slot provided in mast jacket so alignment rod enters holes in low-reverse lever and the interlock pawl.
4. With transmission levers in neutral, tighten swivel nuts to 23 ft-lbs.
5. Remove aligning rod. Make sure neutral positions between low-reverse and second-third are exactly in line. If not, readjust one rod to bring them in line.
6. Check shift operation with engine stopped. Start engine and recheck.
7. On 1969-72 models, place transmission in Reverse and ignition in "Lock" position. Check to be sure key can be removed, steering wheel will not turn and transmission will not shift out of Reverse.

1966-72 3 SPEED HEAVY DUTY TRANS., REPLACE

1. Disconnect throttle linkage from cowl bracket to prevent damage.
2. Raise car and remove drive shaft.
3. Disconnect shift rods from shift levers (column shift).
4. With floor shift, remove shift lever knob and disconnect back-up lamp wiring (if equipped).
5. Disconnect equalizer shaft at side of transmission.
6. Support rear of engine.
7. Disconnect parking brake cable.
8. Remove cross support bar.
9. It may be necessary to disconnect left exhaust pipe from exhaust manifold to provide clearance if equipped with dual exhaust.
10. Remove transmission upper bolts

and install aligning studs in the bolt holes.
11. Remove lower bolts and slide transmission out of car.
12. Reverse procedure to install.

Shift Linkage, Adjust

On 1969-72 models, detent must be adjusted as follows: Place transmission in Reverse and loosen swivel bolt on back drive rod at equalizer. Push up lightly on back drive rod until stop is felt and tighten bolt to 20 ft. lbs. Continue adjustment.

1. Position transmission in neutral.
2. Loosen clamp screws on shift rods.
3. Use a suitable aligning rod and position it in slot provided in mast jacket so that it enters holes in low-reverse lever and the interlock pawl.
4. With floor shift, a 1/4" diameter pin is inserted through shift lever bracket and levers.
5. With transmission levers in neutral, tighten clamp screws to 23 ft-lbs. On 1969-72 models, place transmission in Reverse and ignition in "Lock" position. Check to be sure key can be removed, steering wheel will not turn and transmission will not shift out of Reverse.
6. Remove alignment rod. Make sure neutral positions between low-reverse and second-third are exactly in line. If not, readjust one rod to bring them in line.

4 SPEED TRANS., REPLACE
1966-72

1. Remove propeller shaft and disconnect shift rods from shift levers at transmission.
2. Disconnect back-up lamp switch wires (if equipped).
3. Support engine at rear.

NOTE: On models with dual exhaust

it may be necessary to disconnect left-hand exhaust pipe from manifold to provide clearance.

4. On F-85 models, disconnect speedometer cable.
5. Disconnect parking brake cables from crossmember, then remove crossmember.
6. Remove three bolts that retain shift lever assembly to extension housing. If shift lever assembly removal is not required, it may be left hanging in floor seal.
7. Unfasten transmission and remove from car.

4 SPEED SHIFT LINKAGE, ADJUST
1966-72

1. On 1969-72, place transmission in Reverse and loosen swivel bolt on back drive rod at equalizer. Push up lightly on back drive rod until stop is felt and tighten bolt to 20 ft. lbs.
2. All models: Place transmission in Neutral and loosen shift rods.
3. Using a suitable rod, align levers in Neutral.
4. Adjust swivels to obtain a "free pin" fit at levers. Tighten swivel bolts to 20 ft. lbs.
5. On 1969-72 models, place transmission in Reverse and ignition in "Lock" position. Check to be sure key can be removed, steering wheel will not turn and transmission will not shift out of Reverse.

1972 AUTO. TRANS. LINKAGE, ADJUST

Adjustment procedures for the 1972 models are essentially the same as those for the 1971 units as outlined in the front of this manual.

Rear Axle, Propeller Shaft & Brakes

NOTE: Material marked F.S.C. means Full Size Car or Senior Models

REAR AXLE

Figs. 1 and 2 illustrate the rear axle assemblies used on conventional models. When necessary to overhaul any of these units, refer to the *Rear Axle Specifications* table in this chapter.

Integral Carrier
1966-67 & 1968-72 Type "O"

As shown in Fig. 1, the drive pinion is mounted on two tapered roller bearings that are preloaded by two selected spacers. The drive pinion is positioned by shims located between a shoulder on the pinion and the rear bearing. The front

bearing is held in place by a large nut.

The differential is supported in the carrier by two tapered roller side bearings. These are preloaded by inserting shims between the bearings and the pedestals. The differential assembly is positioned for ring gear and pinion backlash by varying these shims.

Major service work on the differential carrier assembly may be performed with the unit in the car provided a drive-on or twin-post hoist is available. If neither of these hoists are available, the rear axle assembly should be removed from the vehicle. The reason for this is that the axle tubes are pressed into the differential carrier housing and welded.

1968-69 Type "C"

In these rear axles, Fig. 2, the rear axle housing and differential carrier are cast into an integral assembly. The drive pinion assembly is mounted in two opposed tapered roller bearings. The pinion bearings are preloaded by a spacer behind the front bearing. The pinion is positioned by a washer between the head of the pinion and the rear bearing.

The differential is supported in the carrier by two tapered roller side bearings. These bearings are preloaded by spacers located between the bearings and carrier housing. The differential assembly is positioned for proper ring gear and pinion backlash by varying these spacers. The differential case houses two side gears in mesh with two pinions mounted on a pinion shaft which is held in place by a lock pin. The side gears and pinions are backed by thrust washers.

Remove & Replace

Construction of the axle assembly is such that service operations may be performed with the housing installed in the vehicle or with the housing removed and installed in a holding fixture. The following procedure is necessary only when the housing requires replacement.

1. Hoist car and remove rear wheels, drums and axle shafts.
2. Disconnect brake line from wheel cylinders.
3. Unfasten and support backing plates with wire hooks to frame kickup.
4. Disconnect shocks at housing.
5. Position jack stands under frame rear torque boxes, then lower axle housing to stands.
6. Remove springs.
7. Remove propeller shaft and support front of axle housing at companion flange to prevent assembly from rotating when the control arms are disconnected.
8. Remove control arm bolts at axle housing.
9. Remove support at companion flange and lower axle housing.
10. Remove assembly to bench and transfer parts to new axle housing.
11. Reverse procedure to install.

AXLE SHAFT, REPLACE
1968-69 Type "C"

1. Raise vehicle and remove wheel and

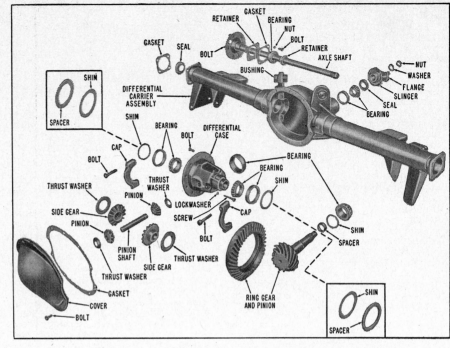

Fig. 1 Integral carrier type rear axle. 1966-67 and 1968-72 Type "O" axle

brake drum.
2. Clean all dirt from area of carrier cover.
3. Drain lubricant from carrier by removing cover.
4. Remove differential pinion shaft lock screw and shaft.
5. Push flanged end of axle shaft toward center of vehicle and remove "C" lock from button end of shaft.
6. Remove axle shaft from housing,

being careful not to damage oil seal.
7. Reverse procedure to install.

All 1966-67, 1968-70 Series 31 to 86, Type "O"

Removal

1. Remove wheel and brake drum.
2. Remove axle bearing retainer (4 nuts).
3. Pull axle shaft from housing. If bearing is a tight fit in housing, use a slide hammer-type puller. Do not drag shaft over seal as this may damage seal.
4. Attach one axle bearing retainer nut to hold brake backing plate in position.
5. Before installing axle shaft, examine oil seal. The seals have feathered edges which form a tight seal around

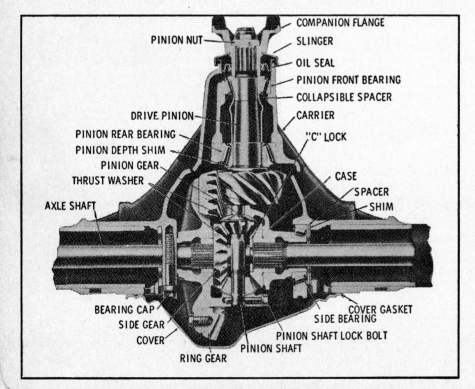

Fig. 2 Integral carrier type differential. 1968-69 Type "C" axle

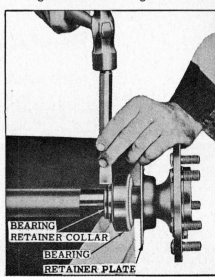

Fig. 3 Removing axle shaft bearing retainer

the shaft. If these edges are damaged in any way, seal must be replaced. Examine seal surface on shaft; if it is not smooth, dress it down with very fine emery cloth.

6. Reverse removal procedure to install axle shaft, being sure to grease outside of axle bearing, seal surface on axle shaft and bore of axle housing with differential lubricant. Place new gasket and bearing retainer over studs, install nuts and tighten them 45 to 60 ft. lbs.

Installation

Bearings should be replaced if found to be rough or have greater than .020" end play. Remove bearing only when new bearing is to be installed; once removed it must not be reused.

1. With axle shaft removed from housing, split bearing retainer with a chisel, Fig. 3.
2. Press bearing off shaft.
3. Press new bearing on shaft up against shoulder on shaft.
4. Press retainer on shaft up against bearing.
5. Reverse removal procedure to install axle shaft.

PROPELLER SHAFT
1966-70

The rear yoke of the Jetaway equipped cars is bonded in rubber to the inside of the propeller shaft tube and cannot be removed for service. The shaft for the manual shift transmission models is one piece, Fig. 4.

1. To remove, remove nuts holding U-bolts at differential companion flange.
2. If U-joint bearings are not retained by a metal retaining strap, use a piece of wire or tape to hold bearings on U-joint cross.
3. Lower rear of shaft and slide rearward.
4. Reverse removal procedure to install the shaft. First, however, apply one ounce of seal lubricant to the splines of the slip yoke on Jetaway and Jetstar 88.

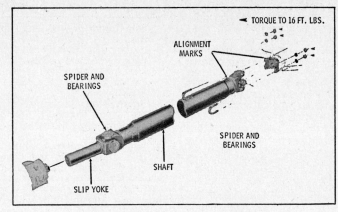

Fig. 4   Propeller shaft installation. 1966-70

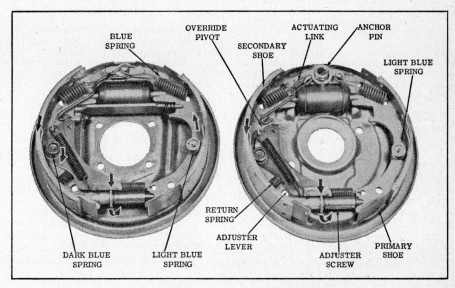

Fig. 5   Right rear and front brake. All 1966-72

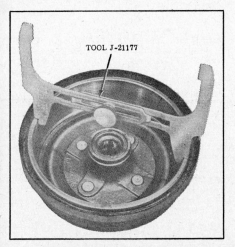

Fig. 6   Brake shoe gauge measuring inside diameter of brake drum. 1966-72

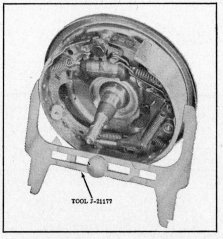

Fig. 7   Brake shoe gauge measuring outside diameter of brake shoes. 1966-72

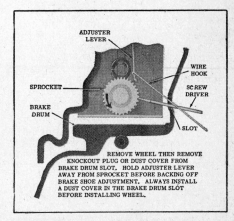

Fig. 8   Backing off brake shoe adjustment

BRAKE ADJUSTMENTS
1966-72

These brakes, Fig. 5, have self adjusting shoe mechanisms that assure correct lining-to-drum clearances at all times. The automatic adjusters operate only when the brakes are applied as the car is moving rearward or when the car comes to an uphill stop.

Although the brakes are self-adjusting, an initial adjustment is necessary after the brake shoes have been relined or replaced, or when the length of the star wheel adjuster has been changed during some other service operation.

Frequent usage of an automatic transmission forward range to halt reverse vehicle motion may prevent the automatic adjusters from functioning, thereby inducing low pedal heights. Should low pedal heights be encountered, it is recommended that numerous forward and reverse stops be made until satisfactory pedal height is obtained.

NOTE

If a low pedal height condition cannot be corrected by making numerous reverse stops (provided the hydraulic system is free of air) it indicates that the self-adjusting mechanism is not functioning. Therefore, it will be necessary to remove the brake drum, clean, free up and lubricate the adjusting mechanism. Then adjust the brakes as follows, being sure the parking brake is fully released.

Adjustment

NOTE: Inasmuch as there is no way to adjust these brakes with the drums installed, the following procedure is mandatory after new linings are installed or if it becomes necessary to change the length of the brake shoe adjusting screw.

1. With brake drums removed, position the caliper shown in Fig. 6 to the inside diameter of the drum and tighten the clamp screw.
2. Next position brake shoe end of the caliper tool over the brake shoes as shown in Fig. 7.
3. Rotate the gauge slightly around the shoes to insure that the gauge contacts the linings at the largest diameter.
4. Adjust brake shoes until the gauge is a snug fit on the linings at the point of largest lining diameter.

NOTE: If it is necessary to back off the brake shoe adjustment, it will be necessary to hold the adjuster lever away from the adjuster screw, Fig. 8.

PARKING BRAKE, ADJUST
1966-72

With parking brake fully released, adjust rear cables by first tightening the brake equalizer adjusting nut until a heavy resistance is felt when rotating rear wheels forward. Then loosen equalizer adjusting nut 7 full turns.

POWER BRAKE UNIT, REPLACE
1967-72

1. Disconnect vacuum hose from vacuum cylinder and cover openings to prevent entrance of dirt.
2. Disconnect pipes from master cylinder outlets and cover openings in master cylinder and end of pipes to prevent entrance of dirt.
3. Loosen inboard master cylinder attaching nut to disengage metering valve (disc brakes only).
4. Disconnect air valve rod from brake pedal.
5. Unfasten and remove power brake unit.
6. Reverse procedure to install.

1966

1. Disconnect hydraulic line. Plug or tape line to prevent dirt from entering hydraulic system.
2. Disconnect vacuum line from vacuum check valve.
3. Disconnect operating rod from brake pedal.
4. Unfasten (4 nuts) and remove power unit from cowl.
5. Reverse removal sequence to install and torque attaching nuts to 20-27 ft-lbs.

BRAKE MASTER CYLINDER, REPLACE
1966-72

The standard brake master cylinder on Olds F.S.C. can be removed without disconnecting the push rod and clevis. On all cars equipped with power brakes, the master cylinder can be removed without removing the vacuum cylinder from the car.

1. Be sure area around master cylinder is clean, then disconnect the hydraulic lines at master cylinder. Plug or tape end of line to prevent entrance of dirt or loss of brake fluid.
2. On F-85 models, remove push rod-to-brake pedal clevis pin.
3. On all models, unfasten (4 bolts) and remove master cylinder.

Front End and Steering Section

NOTE: Material marked F.S.C. means Full Size Car or Senior Models

FRONT SUSPENSION

As shown in Figs. 1 and 2, the front suspension is of the conventional "A" frame design with ball joints. Double acting shock absorbers are mounted within the coil springs. Caster and camber are controlled by shims.

LUBRICATION

An extended lubrication period of every six months or 12,000 miles is prescribed, whichever occurs first. The ball joints, are fitted with plugs which must be removed and grease fittings installed. After applying the approved type of grease, remove the fittings and reinstall the plugs.

IMPORTANT: On Intermediates, if ball joints are noisy, the plugs must be removed and approximately one teaspoonful of specified grease applied directly to the plug hole with a hand-operated, ball type nozzle grease gun. Do not install grease fittings or attempt to fill with a pressure gun. Either method will result in overfill or mixing of greases which may harm the part.

Before using a new grease gun of this type, first count the number of turns or pumps required to obtain approximately one teaspoonful of grease.

WHEEL ALIGNMENT
1966-72 Full Size Cars

Camber and caster are adjusted by shims placed between the upper pivot shafts and the frame. In order to remove or install shims, *do not remove weight from front wheels.* Loosen pivot shaft-to-frame bolts. To gain access to these bolts, loosen top and rear fasteners on fender filler plate aprons.

To decrease positive caster, add shim at the front bolt. To increase positive caster, remove shim at the front bolt. To increase camber, remove shims at both front and rear bolt. To decrease camber, add shims at both bolts.

By adding or subtracting an equal amount of shims from both front and rear bolts, camber will change without affecting caster adjustment. When changing shims, refer to Fig. 3.

1966-72 Intermediates

Caster and camber is adjusted by shimming at the upper control arm shaft

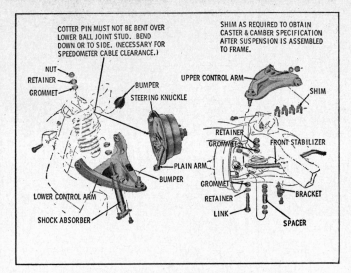

Fig. 1   Front suspension. 1966-72 Full Size Car

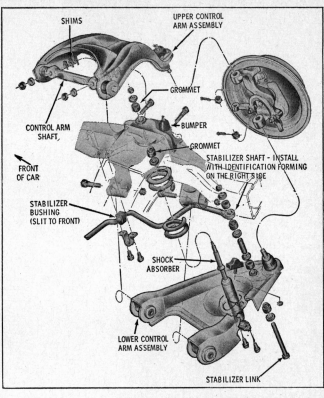

Fig. 2   Front suspension. 1966-72 Intermediate Models

attaching points. See Fig. 4.

Adding shims at the front locations will change caster toward negative with practically no change in camber. Adding shims at the rear locations will change caster toward positive and camber toward negative. Adding equal shims at both front and rear locations will not change caster but will change camber toward negative.

To adjust, loosen both front and rear bolts to free shims for removal or addition.

TOE-IN, ADJUST

To adjust the toe-in, loosen the clamps at both ends of the adjustable tubes at each tie rod. Then turn the tubes an equal amount until the toe-in is correct. Turning the tubes in the direction the wheels revolve when the car moves forward decreases the toe-in and vice-versa. When the adjustment is complete, tighten all clamp screws.

The steering knuckle and steering arm "rock" or tilt as front wheel rises and falls. Therefore, it is vitally important to position the bottom face of the tie rod end parallel with the machined surface at the outer end of the steering arm when tie rod length is adjusted. Severe damage and possible failure can result unless this precaution is taken. The tie rod sleeve

clamps must be straight down to provide clearance.

WHEEL BEARINGS, ADJUST

1966-72 Full Size Cars (Except Jetstar 88)

1. While rotating hub and drum assembly at least three times the speed of nut rotation, tighten nut to 30 ft-lbs to insure all parts are properly seated.
2. Back off nut ½ turn.
3. Retighten nut finger tight and install retaining ring or cotter key if possible. If unable to install retaining ring or cotter key, back off nut (not to exceed 1/24 of a turn) until tabs on clip align with serrations in nut.

1966 F-85 & Jetstar 88

1. While rotating hub and drum assembly at least three times the speed of nut rotation, tighten nut with a torque wrench 25-30 ft-lbs to insure that all parts are properly seated and threads are free.
2. Back off nut ½ turn, then retighten nut finger tight.
3. If unable to install cotter pin (or retainer on Jetstar 88) at finger tight position, back off to first notch and install cotter pin (or retainer).

WHEEL BEARINGS, REPLACE

(Disc Brakes) 1967-72

1. Raise car and remove front wheels.
2. Remove brake pads and caliper assembly but do not disconnect brake line. Suspend caliper from a wire loop or hook to avoid strain on the brake hose.
3. Remove grease cap, cotter pin and nut. Pull off hub and disc assembly. Grease retainer and inner bearing can now be removed.

CHECKING BALL JOINTS FOR WEAR

If loose ball joints are suspected, first be sure the front wheel bearings are

Shim Thickness	One shim added to or subtracted from BOTH BOLTS will change CAMBER	One shim added to or subtracted from FRONT BOLT ONLY will change CASTER
.020"	1/8°	3/16°
.030"	3/16°	1/4°
.060"	3/8°	1/2°
120"	3/4°	1°

Fig. 4   Wheel alignment shim data. 1966-72 Inter.

Shim Thickness	One shim added to or subtracted from BOTH BOLTS will change camber	One shim added to or subtracted from FRONT BOLT ONLY will change caster
.030"	1/8°	1/8°
.060"	5/16°	7/16°
.120"	5/8°	7/8°

Fig. 3   Wheel alignment shim date. 1966-72 Olds F.S.C.

properly adjusted and that the control arms are tight. Then check ball joints for wear as follows:

Referring to Fig. 5, raise wheel with a jack placed under the lower control arm as shown. Then test by moving the wheel up and down to check axial play, and rocking it at the top and bottom to measure radial play.

1. Upper ball joint should be replaced if there is any noticeable looseness at the joint.
2. Lower ball joint should be replaced if radial play exceeds .125".
3. Lower ball joint should be replaced if axial play between lower control arm and spindle exceeds .125".

BALL JOINTS, REPLACE

On some models the ball joints are riveted to the control arms. All service ball joints, however, are provided with bolt, nut and washer assemblies for replacement purposes.

Some ball joints are pressed into the control arms, in which case they may be pressed out and new ones installed.

SHOCK ABSORBER REPLACE
Senior Models

1. Remove upper pivot bolt from shock absorber.
2. Remove two capscrews and washers attaching shock absorber to lower control arm and remove shock absorber.
3. Reverse above procedure to install.

Intermediate Models

1. Remove upper attaching nut, retainer and grommet from shock absorber.
2. Remove two bolts and washers attaching shock absorber to lower control arm and remove shock absorber.
3. To install, position grommet and retainer over shock and slide shock up through spring and frame. Install and tighten attaching nut and lower capscrews.

COIL SPRING, REPLACE
1970-72 Intermediate Models

1. Raise front of car and support frame with floor stands.
2. Remove wheel and disconnect speedometer cable from steering knuckle (if equipped).

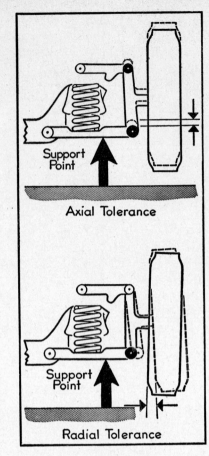

Fig. 5   Checking ball joints for wear

3. Disconnect stabilizer link and speedometer cable clamp from lower control arm.
4. Loosen lower control arm shaft bushing bolts.
5. Remove shock absorber.
6. Position floor jack under lower control arm between spring seat and ball joint. Raise jack until it supports lower control arm.
7. Using suitable compressor, compress spring slightly and disconnect lower ball joint from steering knuckle.
8. Slowly lower floor jack until spring is fully extended and remove spring.

IMPORTANT: Left and right coil springs should not be interchanged. Spring part number is stamped on outer side of end coil.

INSTALLATION: Reverse removal procedure to install spring. However, first tape spring insulator to top of spring at least six places. Top of spring may be identified by flat coil which will allow insulator to seat squarely on top coil.

While holding spring and insulator against pilot in frame crossmember, tilt spring so it will pivot in lower control arm. Rotate spring so end of bottom coil will index with edge of hole in control arm spring seat. Coil should not cover any portion of hole.

1966-69 All & 1970-72 Senior Models

1. Raise car and support frame with floor stands.
2. Remove wheel and tire and disconnect stabilizer link.
3. Remove shock absorber.
4. Using a suitable compressor, compress spring slightly to permit removal of lower control arm bushing bolts. Leave ball joints connected to control arm.
5. Control arm can now be lowered at the inner end to permit removal of spring.
6. Reverse procedure to install taking care to torque the control arm bushing bolts only with the weight of the car on the wheels.

MANUAL STEERING GEAR, REPLACE

1. Remove two flex coupling flange nuts.
2. Hoist and support car with stands under outer ends of lower control arms.
3. Remove nut and use a puller to remove pitman arm.
4. Remove gear-to frame bolts.
5. Position steering linkage and speedometer cable (if equipped) out of the way and withdraw gear assembly from under car.
6. Reverse procedure to install unit.

POWER STEERING
Steering Gear, Replace

1. Remove coupling flange hub bolt.
2. Disconnect hoses from pump and cap pump and hose fittings.
3. Remove pitman arm nut and, using a suitable puller, remove pitman arm.
4. Remove gear-to-frame bolts. Permit lower shaft to slide free of coupling flange, then remove gear with hoses attached.

TORONADO SUPPLEMENT

Items covered in this section apply to the Toronado only. For service procedures and specifications not covered here, refer to the conventional Oldsmobile section of this chapter.

Engine & Transmission Section

ENGINE, REPLACE

1. Drain radiator and remove hood, marking hinge as a guide for reassembly.
2. Disconnect battery, radiator hoses, cooler lines, heater hoses, vacuum hoses, power steering pump hoses, engine-to-body ground strap, fuel hose from fuel line, wiring and accelerator cable.
3. Remove coil, throttle control switch bracket, radiator support and radiator.
4. Raise car and disconnect exhaust pipes at manifold.
5. Remove starter.
6. Remove torque converter cover and three bolts securing converter to flywheel.
7. Attach a tool of the type shown in Fig. 1 to support final drive assembly.
8. Remove two bolts from right output shaft support bracket and one through bolt attaching final drive to engine block on left side.
9. Remove engine mount-to-crossmember nuts.
10. Lower car and support engine with a fixture of the type shown in Fig. 2.
11. Remove six transmission-to-engine bolts and lift engine from car.

NOTE: If car is to be moved, install a converter holding tool of the type shown in Fig. 1.

Installation

1. Lower engine into position.
2. Locate engine dowels into transmission and position mount studs into front crossmember.
3. Secure engine to transmission (6 bolts).
4. Remove engine lifting rig and raise car.
5. Secure torque converter to flywheel.
6. Install engine mount nuts.
7. Install torque converter cover and starter.
8. Install two bolts attaching right output shaft support bracket and one through bolt attaching final drive to engine block on left side.
9. Remove final drive supporting tool.
10. Connect exhaust pipes and lower car.
11. Install remaining parts removed in reverse order of removal.

ENGINE FRONT COVER

With Engine & Oil Pan Removed

1. Disconnect by-pass hose from water pump.
2. Remove cover-to-block bolts and remove cover, timing pointer and water pump.
3. Install cover and torque as shown in Fig. 2.

Oil Pan

1. Remove engine as outlined.
2. Remove dipstick, drain oil and remove mount from front cover.
3. Unfasten and remove oil pan.
4. Apply sealer to both sides of pan gaskets (cork) and install on block.
5. Install front and rear rubber seals.
6. Wipe lube on seal area and install pan. Torque $5/16''$ bolts to 15 ft-lbs and $1/4''$ bolts to 10 ft-lbs.
7. Install mount on front cover and install engine.

TRANSMISSION

Less Final Drive

Removal

1. Disconnect battery, oil cooler lines at transmission and speedometer cable at governor.
2. Install engine support rig of the type shown in Fig. 3.
3. Remove nut "D" and bolts "A", "B" and "C", Fig. 4. A special wrench must be used on nut "D".
4. Remove bolts indicated in Fig. 5.
5. Remove flywheel cover plate bolts.
6. Hoist car and remove starter.
7. Rotate flywheel until all bolts are removed.
8. Disconnect vacuum modulator line

NOTE: REVISE CONVERTER HOLDING TOOL J-21654. DRILL A 3/8" HOLE 15-5/8" FROM ONE EXISTING HOLE.

FINAL DRIVE SUPPORT BT-6322

Fig. 1   Final drive supporting tool

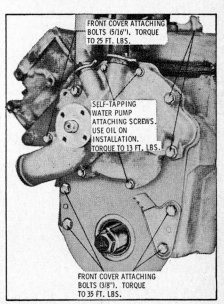

FRONT COVER ATTACHING BOLTS (5/16"). TORQUE TO 25 FT. LBS.

SELF-TAPPING WATER PUMP ATTACHING SCREWS. USE OIL ON INSTALLATION. TORQUE TO 13 FT. LBS.

FRONT COVER ATTACHING BOLTS (3/8"). TORQUE TO 35 FT. LBS.

Fig. 2   Engine front cover bolts

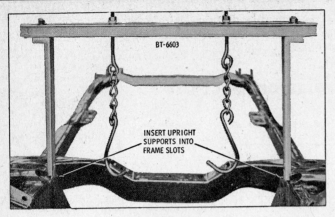

Fig. 3   Installing support bars

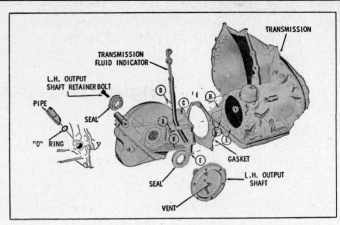

Fig. 4   Transmission attachment

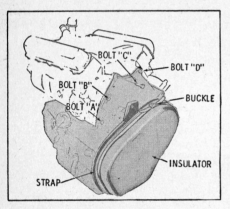

Fig. 5   Transmission-to-engine attachment

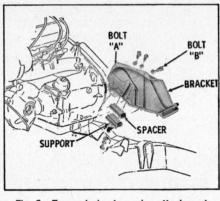

Fig. 6   Transmission-to-engine attachment

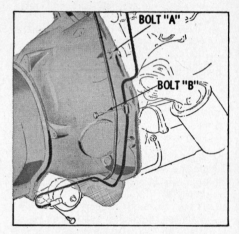

Fig. 7   Engine mount attachment

and stator wiring.
9. Install transmission lift.
10. Remove shift linkage.
11. Remove bolts "E", "F" and "G" and nut "H", Fig. 4.

NOTE: When last three transmission-to-final drive bolts are removed a quantity of oil will be lost.

12. Remove bolts indicated in Fig. 6.
13. Remove bolts indicated in Fig. 7. Then remove the four bracket-to-engine mount bolts.
14. Slide transmission rearward and down. Engine mount bracket will follow transmission down. Install converter holding tool, Fig. 1.
15. After transmission is removed from car, the link assembly cover insulator can be removed or installed.

Installation

When installing the transmission, the motor mount bracket must be positioned loosely on the link assembly cover until the transmission is in place; then reverse removal procedure. Torque bolts to ft-lbs as follows:

Engine-to-converter housing 25
Engine bracket-to-transmission 55
Engine bracket-to-rubber mount 55
Oil cooler lines to transmission 25
Final drive-to-transmission 25
Converter-to-flywheel 30
Flywheel housing cover 5
Starter-to-transmission 30
Adjust shift linkage as directed in Fig. 8.

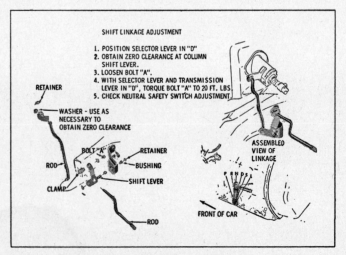

SHIFT LINKAGE ADJUSTMENT

1. POSITION SELECTOR LEVER IN "D"
2. OBTAIN ZERO CLEARANCE AT COLUMN SHIFT LEVER.
3. LOOSEN BOLT "A".
4. WITH SELECTOR LEVER AND TRANSMISSION LEVER IN "D", TORQUE BOLT "A" TO 20 FT. LBS.
5. CHECK NEUTRAL SAFETY SWITCH ADJUSTMENT

Fig. 8   Shift linkage adjustment

Drive Axles & Final Drive Section

DRIVE AXLES
Description

Drive axles are a complete flexible assembly and consist of an axle shaft and an inner and outer constant velocity joint, Fig. 1 & 1A. The right axle shaft has a torsional damper mounted in the center. The inner constant velocity joint has complete flexibility plus inward and outward movement. The outer constant velocity joint has complete flexibility only.

NOTE: Whenever any operations call for disconnecting, connecting, removal or installation of the drive axles, care must be used to prevent damage to constant velocity joint seals. Seals may be wrapped with floor mat rubber or old inner tube, etc. Make sure rubber protective covers that are used are removed before car is started or driven.

DRIVE AXLE, REPLACE
Right Side Unit

Removal
1. Hoist car under lower control arms.
2. Remove axle nut, Fig. 3.
3. Remove oil filter element.
4. Remove inner constant velocity (C. V.) joint attaching bolts.
5. Push inner C.V. joint outward enough to disengage from R.H. final drive output shaft and move rearward.
6. Remove R.H. output shaft bracket bolts to engine and final drive.
7. Remove R.H. final drive output shaft.
8. Remove drive axle assembly.

NOTE: Care must be used to see that C.V. joints do not turn to full extremes and that seals are not damaged against shock absorber or stabilizer bar.

Installation
1. Place R.H. drive axle into lower control arm and enter outer race splines into knuckle.
2. Lubricate final drive output shaft seal with approved seal grease.
3. Install R.H. output shaft into final drive and attach support bolts to engine and brace. Torque to 50 ft-lbs.
4. Move R.H. drive axle toward front of car and align with R.H. output shaft. Install attaching bolts and torque to 65 ft-lbs.
5. Install oil filter element.
6. Install washer and nut on drive axle. Torque to 60 ft-lbs and insert cotter pin.

Left Side Unit

Removal
1. Hoist car under lower control arms.
2. Remove wheel and drum.
3. Remove drive axle nut.
4. Position access slot in hub so that

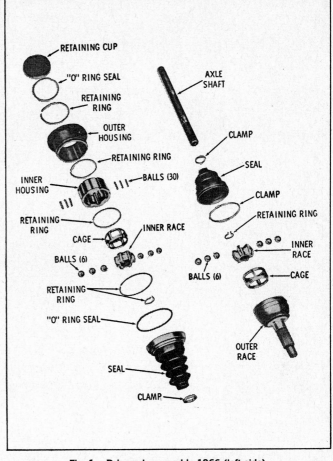

Fig. 1 Drive axle assembly 1966 (left side)

each attaching bolt (4) can be removed, Fig. 4. It will be necessary to push aside adjuster lever to remove one of the bolts.
5. Remove hub assembly, Fig. 4. It will be neceseary to push aside adjuster lever for clearance.
6. Remove tie-rod end nut.
7. Using a hammer and brass drift, drive on knuckle until tie-rod end stud is free.
8. Remove bolts from drive axle and L.H. output shaft, Fig. 5.
9. Remove upper control arm ball joint nut. Using hammer and brass drift, drive on knuckle until upper ball joint stud is free, Fig. 6.
10. Remove ball joint, Fig. 7, being careful not to damage drive axle seal.
11. Remove knuckle and support so that brake hose is not damaged.
12. Carefully guide drive axle out.

NOTE: Care must be used to see that C.V. joints do not turn to full extremes and that seals are not damaged against shock absorber or stabilizer bar.

Installation
1. Guide L.H. drive axle onto lower con-

trol arm in position on block, Fig. 5.
2. Insert lower ball joint stud into knuckle and attach nut (do not tighten).
3. Center L.H. drive axle in opening of knuckle and insert upper ball joint stud.
4. Place brake hose clip over upper ball joint stud and install nut (do not tighten).
5. Insert tie-rod end stud into knuckle and attach nut. Torque to 45 ft-lbs and insert cotter pin.
6. Lubricate hub bearing OD with E.P. grease and install. Torque to 65 ft-lbs.
7. Align inner C.V. joint with output shaft and install attaching nuts. Torque to 65 ft-lbs.
8. Torque upper and lower ball joint nuts to 40 ft-lbs and insert cotter pins.

NOTE: Upper ball joint cotter pin must be crimped toward upper control arm to prevent interference with outer C.V. joint seal.

9. Install drive axle washer and nut. Torque to 60 ft-lbs and install cotter

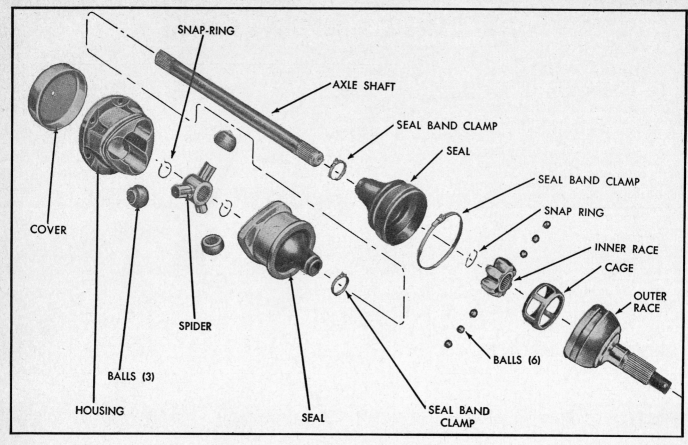

Fig. 1A   Drive axle assembly. 1967-72

pin.
10. Install drum and wheel.
11. Lower car and check wheel alignment.

C.V. JOINT SERVICE

NOTE: The C.V. joints are to be replaced as a unit and are only disassembled for repacking and replacement of seals.

Outer C.V. Joint 1966-72

Disassemble

1. Insert axle in vise, clamping on mid-portion only.
2. Remove inner and outer seal clamps, Fig. 8.
3. Slide seal down axle shaft to gain access to C.V. joint.

4. Referring to Fig. 9, spread retaining ring until C.V. joint can be removed from axle spline.
5. Remove retaining ring, Fig. 10.
6. Slide seal from axle shaft.
7. Remove grease from C.V. joint.
8. Holding C.V. joint with one hand, tilt cage and inner race so that one ball can be removed. Continue until all six balls are removed, Fig. 11.
9. Turn cage 90° and with large slot in cage aligned with land in inner race, lift out, Fig. 12.

10. Turn inner race 90° in line with large hole in case, lift land on inner race up through large hole in cage and turn up and out to separate parts, Fig. 13.

Inspection

Wash all metal parts in cleaning solvent and dry with compressed air. Rubber seal should be replaced whenever joint is disassembled for service. Inspect all metal parts for nicks, cracks, breaks or scores. If any defects are found the joint

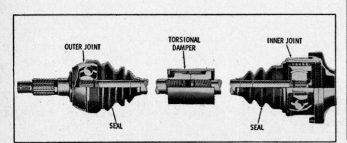

Fig. 2   Drive axle disassembled (right side)

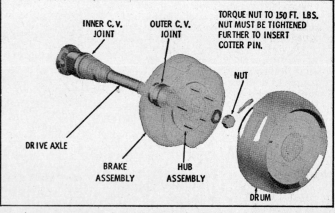

Fig. 3   Drive axle installed

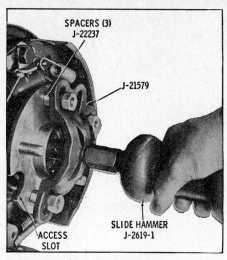

Fig. 4   Removing hub

Fig. 5   Installing support block

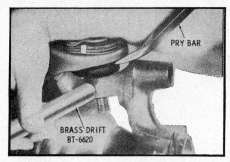

Fig. 6   Removing upper ball joint

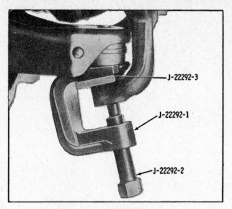

Fig. 7   Removing lower ball joint

Fig. 8   Cutting seal clip

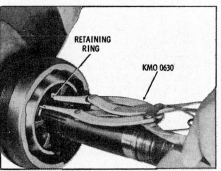

Fig. 9   Removing retaining ring

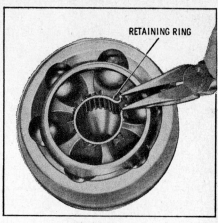

Fig. 10   Removing or installing retaining ring

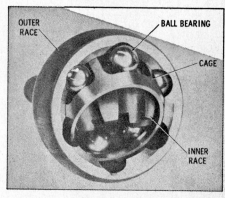

Fig. 11   Removing balls from outer race

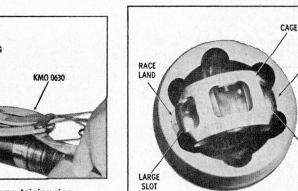

Fig. 12   Positioning cage for removal

assembly will have to be replaced as a unit.

Reassemble

1. Insert land of inner race into large hole in cage and pivot to install in cage, Fig. 13.
2. Align inner race as shown in Fig. 12 and pivot inner race 90° to align in outer race as shown in Fig. 14.
3. Insert balls one at a time until all six are installed. Inner race and cage will have to be tilted as shown

in Fig. 14 so that each ball can be inserted.
4. Pack joint full of approved lubricant. Pack inside of seal with approved lubricant until folds of seal are full.
5. Place small keystone clamp on axle shaft.
6. Install seal on axle shaft.
7. Install retaining ring into inner race, Fig. 10.
8. Insert axle shaft into splines of outer C.V. joint until retaining ring secures shaft.
9. Position seal in slot of outer race.
10. Install large keystone clamp over seal and secure, Fig. 15. Then install small keystone clamp over seal and se-

cure, Fig. 16.

Inner C.V. Joint 1966

Disassemble

1. Clamp mid-portion of axle shaft in vise.
2. Remove small seal clamp.
3. Remove large end of seal from C.V. joint by prying out peened spots and driving off C.V. joint with hammer and chisel, Fig. 17.
4. Slide seal down shaft until C.V. joint is disassembled. Remove O-ring from

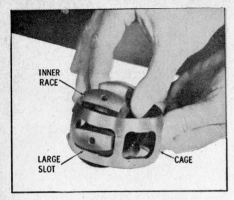

Fig. 13 Removing inner race from ball cage

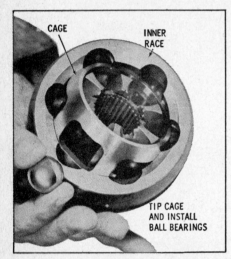

Fig. 14 Installing balls in outer race

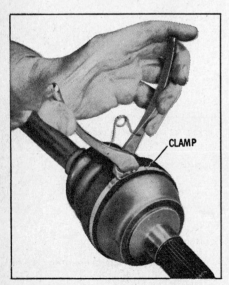

Fig. 15 Installing keystone clamp (large)

outer housing, Fig. 18.
5. Wipe all excess grease from C.V. joint.
6. Remove axle shaft retaining ring, Fig. 18.
7. Remove retaining ring from interior of ball spline outer housing, Fig. 18.
8. Remove ball spline outer housing from ball spline inner housing, being careful not to drop or lose balls (five in a line with six rows).
9. Follow disassembly of outer C.V. joint from Steps 4 thru 9 for inner C.V. joint.
10. Remove grease from inside of ball spline outer housing.
11. Using wood block, carefully drive along outer edges from inside of ball spline outer housing and remove retaining cup.
12. Remove O-ring from interior of ball spline outer housing, Fig. 19.
13. Remove retaining ring from interior of ball spline outer housing.
14. Remove O-ring from exterior of ball spline outer housing.
15. Remove two retaining rings from ball spline inner housing, Fig. 20.

Inspection

Wash all metal parts in cleaning solvent and blow dry with compressed air. Inspect all parts for damage. If any defects are found, replace C.V. joint as a unit.

Reassemble

1. Install two retaining rings on inner spline housing, Fig. 20.
2. Install retaining ring in groove of outer spline housing, Fig. 19.
3. Install O-ring into inner groove of outer spline housing. Lubricate O-ring with approved seal lube.
4. Install cover into outer spline housing, Fig. 21. Care must be used not to damage O-ring.
5. Insert land of inner race into large hole in case and pivot to install in cage, Fig. 22.
6. Align inner race and cage and install into inner spline housing, Fig. 20.
7. Insert balls in inner spline housing one at a time until all six balls are in, Fig. 23. Inner race and cage will have to be tilted as shown so that each ball can be inserted.
8. Install inner spline housing into outer spline housing, Fig. 24. Raise inner spline housing and install five balls into each spline (six splines, 30 balls).
9. Lower inner spline housing into outer spline housing and install retaining ring into groove at top of outer spline housing.
10. Install retaining ring into inner race, Fig. 25.
11. Pack C.V. joint full of approved lubricant. Pack inside of seal until folds of seal are full.
12. Install seal onto axle shaft.
13. Install O-ring on outer spline housing. Insert axle shaft into splines of inner race until retaining ring secures shaft.
14. Insert drive axle in a press, Fig. 26, and peen seal in six places equally spaced around seal.
15. Remove axle from press. Position seal in groove in axle shaft and pull outward on shaft until inner C.V. joint is fully extended. *C.V. joint is*

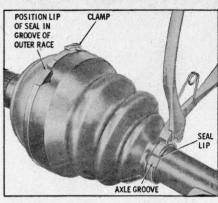

Fig. 16 Installing keystone clamp (small)

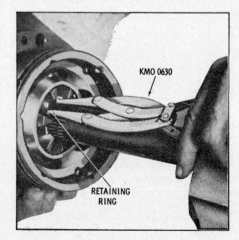

Fig. 17 Removing or installing inner C.V. joint seal. 1966

Fig. 18 Removing joint from axle. 1966

fully extended before installing keystone seal clamp to prevent a vacuum collapsing seal bellows.
16. Install keystone clamp and secure, Fig. 27.

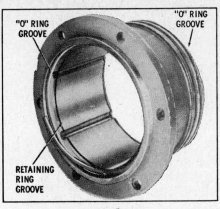

Fig. 19   Outer spline housing. 1966

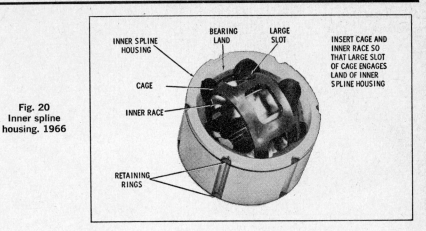

Fig. 20
Inner spline
housing. 1966

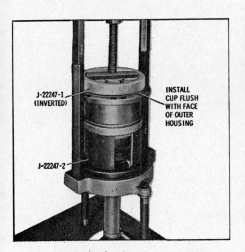

Fig. 21   Installing cover. 1966

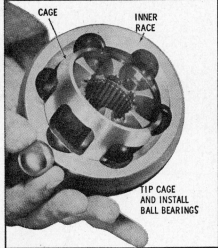

Fig. 23   Installing balls in inner race. 1966

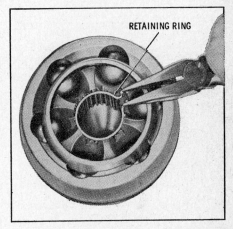

Fig. 25   Installing retaining ring. 1966

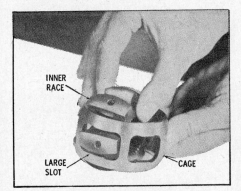

Fig. 22   Installing inner race
into ball cage. 1966

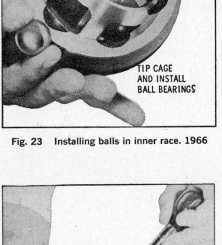

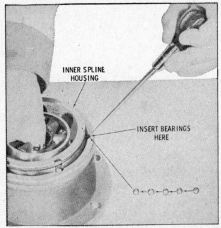

Fig. 24   Installing balls, inner-to-outer
spline housing. 1966

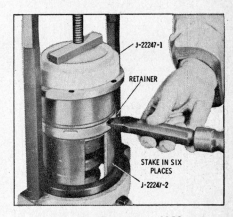

Fig. 26   Staking seal. 1966

Inner C.V. Joint 1967-72

1. Clamp mid portion of axle shaft in vise and remove small seal clamp.
2. Remove large end of seal from C.V. joint by prying out peened spots and driving off with hammer and chisel, Fig. 28.
3. Carefully slide seal down axle shaft.
4. Carefully lift housing from spider assembly and remove "O" ring from housing outer surface.

NOTE: Place a rubber band over ends

of spider to retain the three balls and needle bearings.

5. Remove retaining ring from end of axle.
6. Remove spider assembly from axle.

7. Remove inner retaining ring, seal and cover, Fig. 29.
8. Remove balls from spider, being careful not to lose any needles.
9. Reverse procedure to assemble, being sure to stake housing in six evenly spaced places after reassembly.

FINAL DRIVE, 1968-72
Description, Fig. 30

The final drive assembly, mounted and splined directly to the automatic trans-

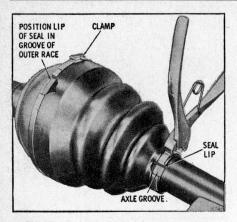

Fig. 27   Installing keystone clamps. 1966

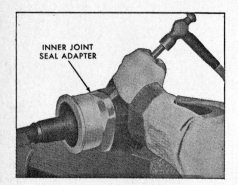

Fig. 28   Removing inner C.V. joint seal. 1967-72

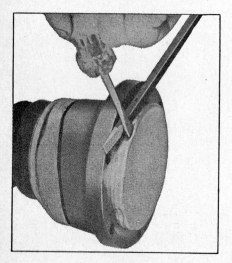

Fig. 29   Removing housing cover. 1967-72

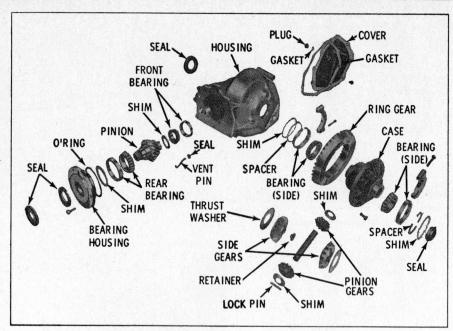

Fig. 30   Final drive disassembled. 1968-72

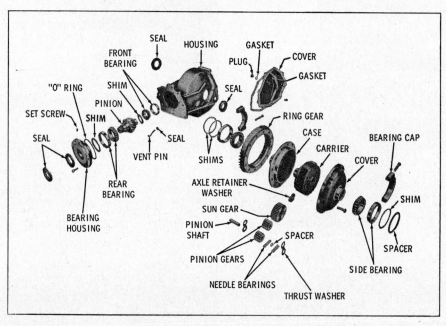

Fig. 31   Final drive disassembled. 1966-67

mission, consists of a pinion drive gear, a ring gear (bolted to the case), case assembly with two side gears and two pinion gears that are retained to the case with a pinion shaft. A lock pin is used instead of a bolt to lock the pinion shaft to the case. There are thrust washers used behind the side gears and shims behind the pinion gears the same as in a conventional differential. The left side gear is different than the right side gear in

that it has a threaded retainer plate to which the left output shaft bolts. The two side bearings are the same and the preload shims are identical for the right and left side. The carrier is identical in external appearance and mounts to the transmission the same as in the past models.

The output shafts remain identical in external appearance as in the past. The left output shaft has the retainer bolt going through the shaft to the side gear.

FINAL DRIVE, 1966-67
Description, Fig. 31

The final drive assembly, mounted and splined to the automatic transmission, consists of a pinion drive gear, a ring gear and a planetary gear train.

The planetary gear train consists of a planet pinion carrier with three pairs of planet pinions, a sun gear and an internal gear and performs the same func-

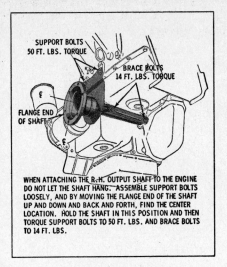

Fig. 32 Aligning right output shaft

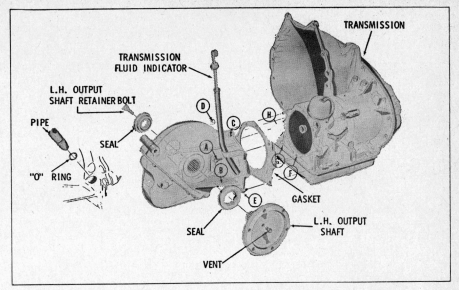

Fig. 34 Final drive attachment. 1966-72

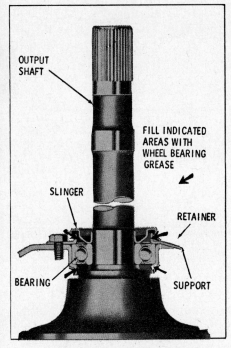

Fig. 33 Output shaft assembled (right side)

tion as the side gears and pinion gears in a conventional differential.

Torque from the final drive is transmitted to a right and left output shaft which connect to drive axles. The right output shaft is splined to the sun gear while the left output shaft is splined to the planet pinion carrier.

OUTPUT SHAFT & SEALS

R.H. Shaft, Bearing & Seal

Removal

1. Disconnect battery. Hoist car.
2. Remove engine oil filter element.
3. Disconnect R.H. drive axle.

4. Disconnect support from engine and brace.
5. Remove output shaft assembly.

Installation Figs. 32 and 33

1. If removed, assemble bearing and related parts. Position assembly in a press and install bearing until seated against shoulder on shaft. Pack area between bearing and retainer with wheel bearing grease, then install slinger. Install seal if removed.
2. Install remaining parts removed in reverse order of removal.

L.H. Output Shaft, Bearing & Seal

NOTE: The L.H. output shaft can normally be removed only after removing the final drive assembly from the car. However, if the L.H. drive axle has been removed for any reason, the output shaft and seal can be removed as follows:

1. Remove R.H. output shaft as outlined above.
2. Remove L.H. output shaft retaining bolt and remove shaft.
3. Apply approved lubricant to the seal, then insert output shaft into final drive, indexing splines of shaft with splines on final drive.
4. Install and torque L.H. output shaft retaining bolt to 45 ft-lbs.
5. Install R.H. output shaft in reverse order of removal.

FINAL DRIVE, REPLACE

1. Disconnect battery and raise hood.
2. Remove bolts "A", "B", "C" and nut "D", Fig. 34. Nut "D" must be removed with a special wrench. It may be necessary to remove transmission filler tube to obtain clearance.
3. Hoist car. If a two-post lift is used the car must be supported with floor stands at the front frame rails and the front post lowered.
4. Disconnect both drive axles from

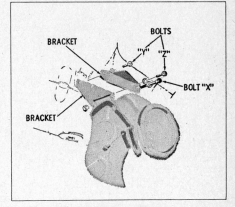

Fig. 35 Disconnecting final drive from engine

output shafts.
5. Remove engine oil filter element.
6. Disconnect brace from final drive, then disconnect R.H. output shaft from engine. Remove output shaft from final drive.
7. Referring to Fig. 35, remove bolt "X" and loosen bolts "Y" and "Z".
8. Remove final drive cover and allow lubricant to drain.
9. Position transmission lift with adapter for final drive. Install an anchor bolt through final drive housing and lift pad.
10. Referring to Fig. 34, remove bolts "E", "F", "G" and nut "H".
11. Move transmission lift toward front of car to disengage final drive splines from transmission. Provide a container to catch transmission fluid.
12. Lower transmission lift and remove final drive from lift.
13. Using a $\frac{9}{16}$" socket, remove L.H. output shaft retaining bolt and pull shaft from final drive.
14. Reverse procedure to install.

Front Suspension & Steering Section

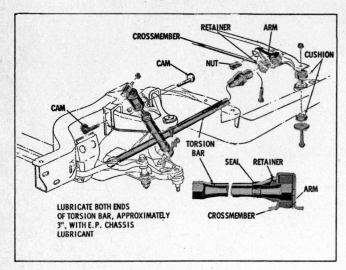

Fig. 1 Front suspension

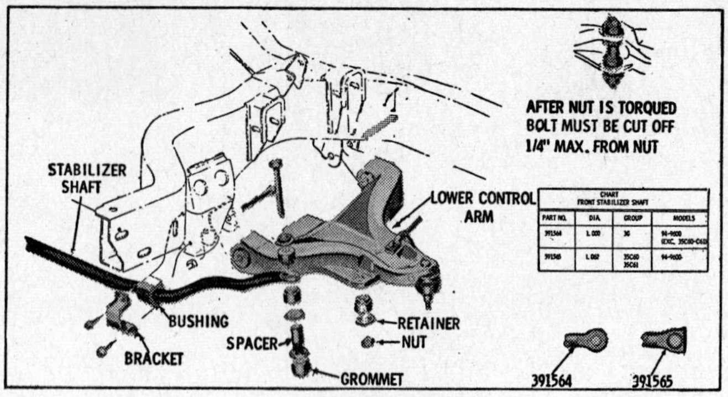

LUBRICATE BOTH ENDS OF TORSION BAR, APPROXIMATELY 3", WITH E.P. CHASSIS LUBRICANT

Fig. 2 Front suspension

AFTER NUT IS TORQUED BOLT MUST BE CUT OFF 1/4" MAX. FROM NUT

CHART FRONT STABILIZER SHAFT			
PART NO.	DIA.	GROUP	MODELS
391564	1.020	30	54-9600 EXC. 39C80-C68
391565	1.062	39C80 39C68	54-9600

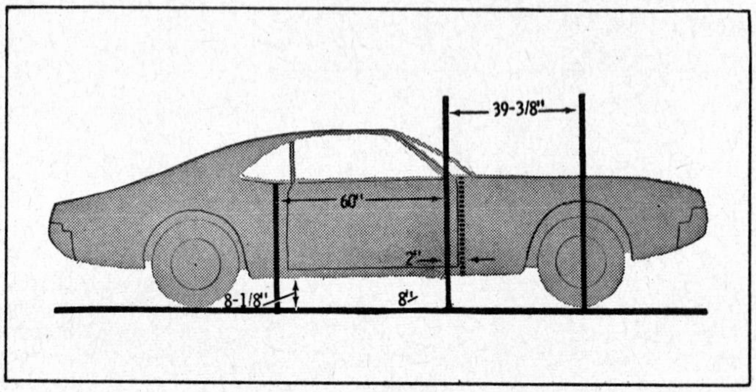

Fig. 3 Riding heights

FRONT SUSPENSION

The front suspension consists of control arms, stabilizer bar, shock absorbers and a right and left torsion bar, Figs. 1 and 2. Torsion bars are used instead of conventional coil springs. The front end of the torsion bar is attached to the lower control arm. The rear of the torsion bar is mounted into an adjustable arm at the torsion bar cross member. The riding height of the car is controlled by this adjustment.

LUBRICATION

The steering linkage should be lubricated every 12 months or 12,000 miles, whichever occurs first, using a commercially available multi-purpose grease.

Ball joints should be lubricated and inspected at 36,000 miles (no time limit) and every 12 months or 12,000 miles thereafter, using a commercially available multi-purpose lubricant.

WHEEL ALIGNMENT

NOTE: When checking wheel alignment the car must be on a level surface, gas tank full or a compensating weight added, front seat all the way to the rear, and tires (front and rear) inflated to 24 psi. All doors must be closed and no passengers or additional weight should be in the car or trunk.

1. Check rocker panel to ground dimensions, Fig. 3. Front to rear must be within 1" and side-to-side within 5/8" of the dimensions shown.
2. Raise car and check wheel runout. Set in center of runout and lower car.
3. Loosen nuts on inboard side of upper control arm cam bolts, Fig. 4.

4. Check camber and adjust if necessary with the rear cam bolt. Camber reading on the right and left wheel should be within $\frac{1}{2}°$ of each other.
5. Take a caster reading. If necessary to adjust, turn wheel to straight ahead position. Use camber reading scale for making this adjustment.
   a. Turn rear bolt so camber reading is $\frac{1}{4}°$ more than the original setting for every one degree of caster change needed for a correct reading. Turn to plus side of camber if caster is negative and to negative camber if caster is positive.
   b. Turn front cam bolt so camber will return to its original proper setting that was made on the camber adjustment.
   c. Recheck caster reading.

NOTE: If a problem exists where you should run out of cam to gain the correct reading, first turn front cam bolt so high part of cam is pointing up. Then turn rear cam bolt so high part of cam is pointing down. This is a location to start from and a correct setting can be obtained with the foregoing procedure. Torque upper control arm cam nuts to 75 ft-lbs. Hold head of bolt securely as any movement of the cam will affect your final setting, which will necessitate a recheck of the camber and caster adjustment.

TOE-IN, ADJUST

1. Center steering wheel.
2. Loosen tie-rod nuts and adjust to proper setting.
3. Tighten tie-rod nuts to 20 ft-lbs. Position tie-rod clamps so opening of clamp is facing up. This is necessary as interference and a possible tie up of front end linkage could occur if clamps snag anything while turning.

TORSION BAR
Removal

1. Hoist car and place floor stands under front frame horns.
2. Slide seat at rear of torsion bar forward.
3. Use a tool of the type shown in Fig. 5.
4. Turn torsion bar adjusting bolt counterclockwise, counting the number of turns necessary to remove. Record this number for installing.
5. Remove adjusting bolt and nut.
6. Turn center screw of tool until torsion bar is completely relaxed.
7. Place block of wood on hoist (6"x6"x8") and raise under lower control arm until drive axle is horizontal.
8. Remove stabilizer bolt and related parts. Discard bolt.

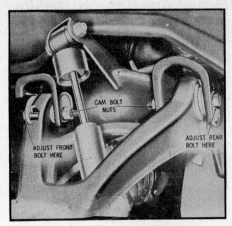

Fig. 4   Front wheel alignment cams

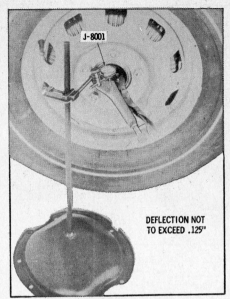

DEFLECTION NOT TO EXCEED .125"

Fig. 6   Ball joint vertical check

OUTER RACE

SEAL

PRY BETWEEN LOWER CONTROL ARM AND OUTER RACE

Fig. 7   Pry bar installation

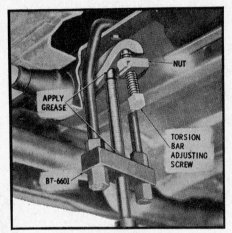

NUT

APPLY GREASE

TORSION BAR ADJUSTING SCREW

BT-6601

Fig. 5   Removing torsion bar

9. Place a daub of paint on bottom side of torsion bar.
10. Slide torsion bar forward until it bottoms in lower control arm (adjusting arm will drop out). *Do not mar, scratch or in any way damage torsion bar as replacement will be necessary if such conditions exist.*
11. Remove crossmember bolt from side torsion bar is being replaced.
12. Remove center bolt from tool.
13. Raise crossmember and twist rearward until torsion bar clears member.
14. Slowly raise lower control arm until maximum height is attained.
15. Raise center crossmember until contact is made with floor pan.
16. Pull rearward on torsion bar with HANDS ONLY until bar is out of lower control arm. *It may be necessary to use air blowing into nut of lower control arm to relieve vacuum caused by grease.*

Installation

NOTE: Check rubber seal for damage; replace if necessary. Check retainer for excessive wear and replace if necessary. A new retainer is required on replacement of torsion bar. Stake as shown in Fig. 1.

1. Grease both ends of torsion bar for about 3" with E.P. chassis lube.
2. With daub of paint in same location as when removed, insert bar into lower control arm nut and push forward until bar bottoms.
3. Pry crossmember back and align bar with hole in crossmember.
4. Lower crossmember and install center bolt in tool, Fig. 5.
5. Lower front lower control arm until drive axle is horizontal.
6. Install torsion bar arm and pull bar rearward until fully seated in arm.
7. Install crossmember bolt through rubber mounting and torque to 40 ft-lbs.
8. Lower front lower control arm and remove wood block.
9. Install new bolt in stabilizer bar to lower control arm. Torque to 14 ft-lbs. *Cut off bottom of bolt so that 1/4" is remaining below nut.*
10. Using the tool shown in Fig. 5 or its equivalent, tighten torsion bar arm to install lock plate under arm and through crossmember.
11. Grease threads of torsion bar adjuster with chassis lube and turn into nut the same number of turns required to remove.
12. Remove tool. Lower car to floor.
13. Check riding height, Fig. 3. Correct by turning torsion bar adjusting bolt as required.

BALL JOINT CHECKS
Vertical Check

1. Raise car and place jack stands under both lower control arms as near as possible to lower ball joints.
2. Install dial indicator, Fig. 6.
3. Place a pry bar as shown in Fig. 7 and push down on bar. Use care to see that drive axle seal is not damaged. Reading must not exceed .125".

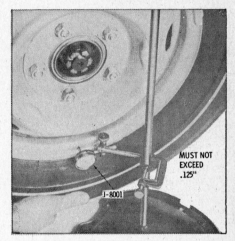

MUST NOT EXCEED .125"

J-8001

Fig. 8   Ball joint horizontal check

Horizontal Check

1. With car placed on floor stands, install dial indicator, Fig. 8.
2. Grasp front wheel and rock top and bottom of tire. Read dial gauge, then reverse the push-pull procedure.
3. Horizontal deflection on dial gauge should not exceed .125" at wheel rim. This procedure checks both upper and lower ball joints.

BALL JOINTS, REPLACE
Lower Ball Joint

1. Remove knuckle.
2. Hacksaw three rivet heads off.
3. Using a 7/32" drill, drill side rivets 3/16" deep.
4. Drive center rivet until joint is out of control arm.
5. Install service ball joint into control arm and torque bolts and nuts as shown in Fig. 9.
6. Replace knuckle.

Upper Ball Joint

1. Raise car and support on floor stands.
2. Remove wheel and drum.

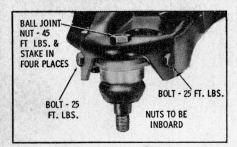

Fig. 9   Installing service ball joint

3. Remove hub assembly, Fig. 10.
4. Remove upper ball joint nut and brake line hose clip from ball joint.
5. Remove anchor bolt.
6. Lift brake plate outward over end of axle shaft and support so brake hose is not damaged.
7. Place support block as shown, Fig. 11.
8. Using a brass drift and hammer loosen and remove ball joint.
9. Install new ball joint and replace parts in reverse order of removal.

WHEEL BEARINGS, REPLACE
(Disc Brakes)

1. Raise car and remove front wheel.
2. Remove drum.

NOTE: For disc brakes remove two bolts securing caliper to steering knuckle and remove caliper.

3. Remove drive axle pin, nut and washer.
4. Position access slot in hub so that each of the attaching bolts can be removed.

NOTE: On disc brakes the attaching bolts are removed from behind the

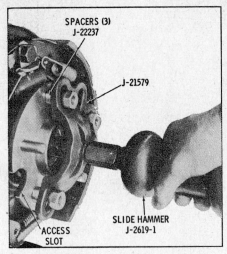

Fig. 10   Removing hub assembly

splash shield.

5. Using slide hammer puller, remove hub, Fig. 10.
6. Remove bearing from hub with puller, Fig. 13.
7. Press new bearing into hub.

SHOCK ABSORBER, REPLACE

1. Remove upper shock attaching bolt.
2. Remove lower attaching nut and guide shock through upper control arm.
3. Reverse procedure to install.

STEERING GEAR, REPLACE

1. Referring to Fig. 12, remove coupling flange hub bolt.
2. Disconnect hoses from power steering pump and cap pump and hose fittings. On cars equipped with a cooler disconnect return hose from cooler inlet pipe.

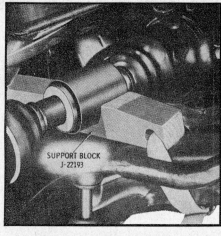

Fig. 11   Drive axle support block

3. Hoist car and pull off pitman arm.
4. Unfasten gear from frame, permit lower shaft to slide free of coupling flange, then remove gear with hoses attached.

NOTE: Before installing steering gear, apply a sodium soap fibre grease to gear mounting pads to prevent squeaks between gear housing and frame. Make sure alignment pin on gear housing enters hole provided in frame side rail. Make sure there is a minimum of .040" clearance between coupling hub and steering gear upper seal.

Install coupling hub bolt and torque to 18 ft-lbs. Before tightening steering gear attaching bolts, shift gear as necessary to place it in the same plane as the steering shaft so that the flexible coupling is not distorted. Tighten gear-to-frame bolts to 70 ft-lbs. and pitman shaft nut to 220 ft-lbs.

5. After hoses are connected to pump, add power steering fluid as necessary to bring the fluid level to the full mark. Run engine at idle for 30 seconds, then run at a fast idle for a minute before turning steering wheel. With engine running, turn steering wheel through its full travel two or three times to bleed air from system. Recheck oil level and add oil if necessary.

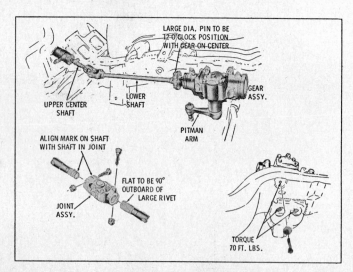

Fig. 12   Steering gear and shaft

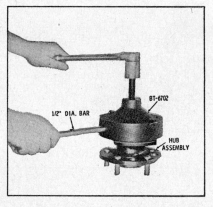

Fig. 13   Removing front wheel bearing. Toronado

PONTIAC
All Intermediate & Full Size Models

OLD CAR SPECIFICATIONS: For 1946-65 Tune Up and Wheel Alignment Specifications see back of book.

Specifications for the 6-250 & V8-307 engines are tabulated on the pages immediately following this index. For service procedure see Chevrolet Chapter.

*This material covered only in the "Service Trade Edition" of this manual.

INDEX OF SERVICE OPERATIONS

PONTIAC — All Intermediate & Full Size Models

SERIAL NUMBER LOCATION
1966-67: On left front door hinge pillar.
1968-72: On plate fastened to upper left instrument
panel area, visible through windshield.

ENGINE IDENTIFICATION

The V8 engine code is located beneath the production engine number on a machined pad on the right-hand bank of the engine block.

The 6-cylinder engine code is stamped on the cylinder head-to-block contact surface behind oil filler pipe.

1966

CODE	TRANS.	ENGINE
ZK	④	6-230①
ZD	④	6-230②
ZS	④	6-230①
WP	④	V8-326①
WX	④	V8-326①
WR	④	V8-326②
WV	④	V8-389①
WW	④	V8-389①
WS	④	V8-389③
WT	④	V8-389②
ZN	⑥	6-230①
ZE	⑥	6-230①
ZM	⑥	6-230①
YN	⑥	V8-326①
YP	⑥	V8-326②
XF	⑥	V8-326①
XG	⑥	V8-326②
XE	⑥	V8-389②
YR	⑥	V8-389①
YS	⑥	V8-389③
WA	④	V8-389①
WE	④	V8-389②
WG	④	V8-421②
WK	④	V8-421③
WH	④	V8-421③
WJ	④	V8-421③
YA	⑥	V8-389①
YU	⑥	V8-389①
YC	⑥	V8-389①
YD⑦	⑥	V8-389①
YV⑦	⑥	V8-389①
YW	⑥	V8-389③
YE	⑥	V8-389②
YF⑦	⑥	V8-389②
YX⑦	⑥	V8-389②
YT	⑥	V8-421①
YH	⑥	V8-421①
YM⑫	⑥	V8-421③
YJ	⑥	V8-421③
YK	⑥	V8-421③

1967

CODE	TRANS.	ENGINE
ZD	④	6-230②
ZE	⑥	6-230②
ZF	④	6-230②
ZG	⑥	6-230②
ZK	④	6-230①
ZL	⑥	6-230①
ZM	④	6-230①
ZN	⑥	6-230①
ZR	④	6-230②
ZS	⑥	6-230②
WP	④	V8-326①
WR	④	V8-326②
WX	④	V8-326①
XF	⑥	V8-326①
XG	⑥	V8-326②
XR	④	V8-326②

CODE	TRANS.	ENGINE
YN	⑥	V8-326①
YP	⑥	V8-326②
WS	④	V8-400②
WT	④	V8-400②
WV	④	V8-400②
WW	④	V8-400②
XL	⑥	V8-400①
XM	⑥	V8-400②
XS	④	V8-400②
YR	⑥	V8-400②
YS	⑥	V8-400②
YZ	⑥	V8-400②
XP	⑥	V8-400②
WA	④	V8-400①
WB	④	V8-400①
WD	④	V8-400①
WE	④	V8-400①
XB	⑥	V8-400①
XC	⑥	V8-400①
XH	⑥	V8-400②
XJ	⑥	V8-400②
XY	⑥	V8-400②
XZ	⑥	V8-400②
YA	⑥	V8-400①
YB	⑥	V8-400①
YC	⑥	V8-400①
YD	⑥	V8-400①
YE	⑥	V8-400①
YF	⑥	V8-400①
WG	All	V8-428②
WJ	④	V8-428②
Y3	⑥	V8-428②
Y2	⑥	V8-428②
XK	⑥	V8-428②
YH	⑥	V8-428②
YK	⑥	V8-428②
YY	④	V8-428②

1968

CODE	TRANS.	ENGINE
ZK	④	6-250①
ZD	④	6-250②
ZN	⑥	6-250①
ZE	⑥	6-250②
YZ	⑥	V8-400②
WS	④	V8-400②
XS	④	V8-400②
WT	④	V8-400②
YS	⑥	V8-400②
XP	⑥	V8-400②
XM	⑥	V8-400②
WP	④	V8-350②
WR	④	V8-350②
YN	⑥	V8-350①
YP	⑥	V8-350②
WC	④	V8-350②
WD	④	V8-350①
YJ	⑥	V8-350①
WK	④	V8-350②
YM	⑥	V8-350②

CODE	TRANS.	ENGINE
XN	⑥	V8-400②
WQ	④	V8-400②
WI	④	V8-400②
WZ	④	V8-400②
YW	⑥	V8-400②
YZ	⑥	V8-400②
YT	⑥	V8-400②
WA	④	V8-400①
WB	④	V8-400①
YA	⑥	V8-400①
YC	⑥	V8-400①
XZ	⑥	V8-400②
XH	⑥	V8-400②
YE	⑥	V8-400②
WG	④	V8-428②
YH	⑥	V8-428②
WJ	④	V8-428②
YK	⑥	V8-428②

1969

CODE	TRANS.	ENGINE
ZC	④	6-250①
ZF	⑥	6-250①
ZH	④	6-250②
ZL	⑥	6-250②
WM	④	V8-350②
WN	④	V8-350②
WU	④	V8-350②
WV	④	V8-350②
XB	⑥	V8-350②
XC	⑥	V8-350②
XS	⑥	V8-350②
XU	⑥	V8-350②
WC	④	V8-350②
WP	④	V8-350②
XL	⑥	V8-350②
XR	⑥	V8-350②
YE	⑥	V8-350②
YN	⑥	V8-350②
YJ	⑥	V8-350②
WH	④	V8-400②
WQ	④	V8-400②
WS	④	V8-400②
WT	④	V8-400②
WZ	④	V8-400②
WW	④	V8-400②
XM	⑥	V8-400②
XN	⑥	V8-400②
XP	⑥	V8-400②
XX	⑥	V8-400①
YS	⑥	V8-400②
YT	⑥	V8-400②
YW	⑥	V8-400②
YZ	⑥	V8-400②
WD	④	V8-400②
WA	④	V8-400①
WB	④	V8-400①
WE	④	V8-400①

Continued

ENGINE IDENTIFICATION—Continued

CODE	TRANS.	ENGINE
YA	⑥	V8-400①
YB	⑥	V8-400①
YC	⑥	V8-400①
YD	⑥	V8-400①
WX	④	V8-400①
XH	⑥	V8-400②
XZ	⑥	V8-400②
YF	⑥	V8-400①
WG	⑥	V8-428②
WJ	④	V8-428②
WF	④	V8-428②
WL	④	V8-428②
XE	⑥	V8-428②
XK	⑥	V8-428②
XJ	⑥	V8-428②
XF	⑥	V8-428②
XG	⑥	V8-428②
YL	⑥	V8-428②
YH	⑥	V8-428②
YK	⑥	V8-428②

1970

CODE	TRANS.	ENGINE
CG	⑥	6-250
RF	④	6-250
ZB	④	6-250
ZG	⑥	6-250
W7	④	V8-350①
X7	⑥	V8-350①
WU	④	V8-350①
YU	⑥	V8-350①
WE	④	V8-400①
YB	⑥	V8-400①
YD	⑥	V8-400①
XZ	⑥	V8-400②
XV	⑥	V8-400②
YZ	⑥	V8-400②

CODE	TRANS.	ENGINE
XX	⑥	V8-400①
XP	⑥	V8-400②
WS	④	V8-400②
WW	④	V8-400②
WT	④	V8-400②
WS	⑤	V8-400②
XH	⑥	V8-400②
YB	⑥	V8-400①
WX	④	V8-400②
YS	⑥	V8-400②
WH	⑤	V8-400②
XN		V8-400②
WG	④	V8-455②
YH	⑥	V8-455②
XF	⑥	V8-455②
WA	④	V8-455②
YA	⑥	V8-455②

1971

CODE	TRANS.	ENGINE
ZB	④	6-250
ZG	⑥	6-250
CAA	④	6-250
CAB	⑥	6-250
CCA	④	V8-307①
CCC	⑥	V8-307①
WN	④	V8-350①
YP	⑥	V8-350①
WP	⑥	V8-350①
YN	⑥	V8-350①
WR	④	V8-350①
WU	⑤	V8-350①
YU	⑥	V8-350①
YX	⑥	V8-400①
WX	④	V8-400①
XR	⑥	V8-350①
WT	④	V8-400②
WK	⑤	V8-400②

CODE	TRANS.	ENGINE
WS	④	V8-400①
XX	⑥	V8-400①
YS	⑥	V8-400②
WL	④	V8-455②
WC	⑤	V8-455②
WJ	④	V8-455②
YC	⑥	V8-455①
WG	⑥	V8-455①
YG	⑥	V8-455②
YE	⑥	V8-455②
YA	⑥	V8-455②

1972

CODE	TRANS.	ENGINE
W6	④	6-250
Y6	⑥	6-250
CBG	④	6-250
CBJ	⑥	6-250
CBA	④	6-250
CBC	⑥	6-250
CKG	④	V8-307
CKH	⑥	V8-307
CAY	④	V8-307
CAZ	⑥	V8-307
YV	⑥	V8-350
YR	⑥	V8-350
WR	④	V8-350
YX	⑥	V8-400①
WS	④	V8-400②
WK	⑥	V8-400②
YS	⑥	V8-400①
ZX	⑥	V8-400①
YH	⑥	V8-455②
YC	⑥	V8-455②
YA	⑥	V8-455②
WM	⑥	V8-455②
YB	⑥	V8-455②
ZH	⑥	V8-455①

①—Two barrel carburetor.
②—Four barrel carburetor.
③—Three 2 barrel carbs.
④—Manual trans.
⑤—Four speed manual trans.
⑥—Automatic trans.
⑦—Air conditioned.
⑨—One barrel carburetor.
⑫—Police.
⑬—Two 4 barrel carbs.

GRILLE IDENTIFICATION

1966 Tempest Except GTO

1966 GTO

1966 Catalina & Star Chief

1966 2+2

1966 Grand Prix

1966 Bonneville

1967 Tempest Except GTO

1967 GTO

1967 Firebird

Continued

PONTIAC—All Intermediate & Full Size Models

GRILLE IDENTIFICATION—Continued

1967 Pontiac Except Grand Prix

1967 Grand Prix

1968 Tempest Custom and LeMans

1968 GTO

1968 Firebird

1968 Catalina, Bonneville, Executive

1968 Grand Prix

1969 Tempest, Custom and LeMans

1969 GTO

1969 Firebird

1969 Catalina, Executive, Ventura

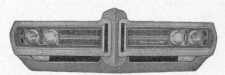

1969 Bonneville

1969 Grand Prix

1970 GTO

1970 Tempest and LeMans

1970-71 Firebird

1970 Catalina, Executive

1970 Bonneville

1970 Grand Prix

1971 T-37 and LeMans

1971 GTO

1971 Catalina

1971 Grand Prix

1971 Bonneville

GRILLE IDENTIFICATION—Continued

1971 Grandville

1971-72 Ventura II

1972 LeMans

1972 Catalina

1972 Grand Prix

1972 Bonneville

1972 Grandville

GENERAL ENGINE SPECIFICATIONS

Year	Engine	Carburetor	Bore and Stroke	Piston Displacement, Cubic Inches	Compression Ratio	Maximum Brake H.P. @ R.P.M.	Maximum Torque Lbs. Ft. @ R.P.M.	Normal Oil Pressure Pounds
1966	165 Horsepower.............6-230	1 Barrel	3.8750 x 3.25	230	9.00	165 @ 4700	216 @ 2600	26–36
	207 Horsepower.............6-230	4 Barrel	3.8750 x 3.25	230	10.50	207 @ 5200	228 @ 3800	26–36
	250 Horsepower.............V8-326	2 Barrel	3.7187 x 3.75	326	9.20	250 @ 4600	333 @ 2800	30–45
	256 Horsepower.............V8-389	2 Barrel	4.0625 x 3.75	389	8.60	256 @ 4600	388 @ 2400	30–40
	285 Horsepower.............V8-326	4 Barrel	3.7187 x 3.75	326	10.50	285 @ 5000	359 @ 3200	30–45
	290 Horsepower.............V8-389	2 Barrel	4.0625 x 3.75	389	10.50	290 @ 4600	418 @ 2400	30–40
	325 Horsepower.............V8-389	4 Barrel	4.0625 x 3.75	389	10.50	325 @ 4800	429 @ 2800	30–40
	333 Horsepower.............V8-389	4 Barrel	4.0625 x 3.75	389	10.50	333 @ 5000	429 @ 3200	30–40
	335 Horsepower.............V8-389	4 Barrel	4.0625 x 3.75	389	10.75	335 @ 5000	431 @ 3200	30–40
	338 Horsepower.............V8-421	4 Barrel	4.0937 x 4.00	421	10.50	338 @ 4600	459 @ 2800	30–40
	356 Horsepower.............V8-421	3 Carbs.	4.0937 x 4.00	421	10.75	356 @ 4800	459 @ 3200	30–40
	360 Horsepower.............V8-389	3 Carbs.	4.0625 x 3.75	389	10.75	360 @ 5200	424 @ 3600	30–40
	376 Horsepower.............V8-421	3 Carbs.	4.0937 x 4.00	421	10.75	376 @ 5000	461 @ 3600	30–40
1967	165 Horsepower.............6-230	1 Barrel	3.8750 x 3.25	230	9.00	165 @ 4700	216 @ 2600	26–36
	215 Horsepower.............6-230	4 Barrel	3.8750 x 3.25	230	10.50	215 @ 5200	240 @ 3800	26–36
	250 Horsepower.............V8-326	2 Barrel	3.7187 x 3.75	326	9.20	250 @ 4600	333 @ 2800	30–45
	255 Horsepower.............V8-400	2 Barrel	4.1200 x 3.75	400	8.60	255 @ 4400	397 @ 2400	30–40
	265 Horsepower.............V8-400	2 Barrel	4.1200 x 3.75	400	8.60	265 @ 4600	397 @ 2400	30–40
	285 Horsepower.............V8-326	4 Barrel	3.7187 x 3.75	326	10.50	285 @ 5000	359 @ 3200	30–45
	290 Horsepower.............V8-400	2 Barrel	4.1200 x 3.75	400	10.50	290 @ 3600	428 @ 2500	30–40
	325 Horsepower.............V8-400	4 Barrel	4.1200 x 3.75	400	10.50	325 @ 4800	445 @ 2900	30–40
	333 Horsepower.............V8-400	4 Barrel	4.1200 x 3.75	400	10.50	333 @ 5000	445 @ 3000	30–40
	335 Horsepower.............V8-400	4 Barrel	4.1200 x 3.75	400	10.75	335 @ 5000	441 @ 3400	30–40

Continued

PONTIAC — All Intermediate & Full Size Models

GENERAL ENGINE SPECIFICATIONS—Continued

Year	Engine	Car-buretor	Bore and Stroke	Piston Dis-place-ment, Cubic Inches	Com-pres-sion Ratio	Maximum Brake H.P. @ R.P.M.	Maximum Torque Lbs. Ft. @ R.P.M.	Normal Oil Pressure Pounds
1967	350 Horsepower..............V8-400	4 Barrel	4.1200 x 3.75	400	10.50	350 @ 5000	440 @ 3200	30—40
	360 H.P. Hi Perf..............V8-400	4 Barrel	4.1200 x 3.75	400	10.75	360 @ 5100	438 @ 3600	30—40
	360 H.P. Ram Air Eng........V8-400	4 Barrel	4.1200 x 3.75	400	10.75	360 @ 5400	438 @ 3800	30—40
	360 Horsepower..............V8-428	4 Barrel	4.1200 x 4.00	428	10.50	360 @ 4600	472 @ 3200	30—40
	376 Horsepower..............V8-428	4 Barrel	4.1200 x 4.00	428	10.75	376 @ 5100	462 @ 3400	30—40
1968	175 Horsepower..............6-250	1 Barrel	3.8750 x 3.52	250	9.00	175 @ 4800	240 @ 2600	26—36
	215 Horsepower..............6-250	4 Barrel	3.8750 x 3.52	250	10.50	215 @ 5200	255 @ 3800	26—36
	265 Horsepower..............V8-350	2 Barrel	3.8750 x 3.75	350	9.20	265 @ 4600	355 @ 2800	30—40
	265 Horsepower..............V8-400	2 Barrel	4.1200 x 3.75	400	8.60	265 @ 4600	397 @ 2400	30—40
	290 Horsepower..............V8-400	2 Barrel	4.1200 x 3.75	400	10.50	290 @ 4600	428 @ 2500	30—40
	320 Horsepower..............V8-350	4 Barrel	3.8750 x 3.75	350	10.50	320 @ 5100	380 @ 3200	30—40
	330 Horsepower..............V8-400	4 Barrel	4.1200 x 3.75	400	10.75	330 @ 4800	430 @ 3300	30—40
	335 Horsepower..............V8-400	4 Barrel	4.1200 x 3.75	400	10.75	335 @ 5000	430 @ 3400	30—40
	340 Horsepower..............V8-400	4 Barrel	4.1200 x 3.75	400	10.50	340 @ 4800	445 @ 2900	30—40
	350 Horsepower..............V8-400	4 Barrel	4.1200 x 3.75	400	10.50	350 @ 5000	445 @ 3000	30—40
	360 Horsepower..............V8-400	4 Barrel	4.1200 x 3.75	400	10.75	360 @ 5100	445 @ 3600	30—40
	375 Horsepower..............V8-428	4 Barrel	4.1200 x 4.00	428	10.50	375 @ 4800	472 @ 3200	30—40
	390 Horsepower..............V8-428	4 Barrel	4.1200 x 4.00	428	10.75	390 @ 5200	465 @ 3400	30—40
1969	175 Horsepower..............6-250	1 Barrel	3.8750 x 3.52	250	9.00	175 @ 4800	240 @ 2600	26—36
	215 Horsepower..............6-250	4 Barrel	3.8750 x 3.52	250	10.50	215 @ 5200	255 @ 3800	26—36
	230 Horsepower..............6-250	4 Barrel	3.8750 x 3.52	250	10.50	230 @ 5400	260 @ 3600	26—36
	265 Horsepower..............V8-350	2 Barrel	3.8750 x 3.75	350	9.20	265 @ 4600	355 @ 2800	30—40
	325 Horsepower..............V8-350	4 Barrel	3.8750 x 3.75	350	10.50	325 @ 5100	380 @ 3200	55—60
	330 Horsepower..............V8-350	4 Barrel	3.8750 x 3.75	350	10.50	330 @ 5100	380 @ 3200	55—60
	265 Horsepower..............V8-400	2 Barrel	4.1200 x 3.75	400	8.60	265 @ 4600	397 @ 2400	30—40
	290 Horsepower..............V8-400	2 Barrel	4.1200 x 3.75	400	10.50	290 @ 4600	428 @ 2500	30—40
	330 Horsepower..............V8-400	4 Barrel	4.1200 x 3.75	400	10.75	330 @ 4800	430 @ 3300	30—40
	335 Horsepower..............V8-400	4 Barrel	4.1200 x 3.75	400	10.75	335 @ 5000	430 @ 3400	30—40
	345 Horsepower..............V8-400	4 Barrel	4.1200 x 3.75	400	10.75	345 @ 5400	430 @ 3700	30—40
	350 Horsepower..............V8-400	4 Barrel	4.1200 x 3.75	400	10.50	350 @ 5000	445 @ 3000	55—60
	350 Horsepower..............V8-400	4 Barrel	4.1200 x 3.75	400	10.75	350 @ 5000	445 @ 3000	55—60
	366 Horsepower..............V8-400	4 Barrel	4.1200 x 3.75	400	10.75	366 @ 5100	445 @ 3600	30—40
	370 Horsepower..............V8-400	4 Barrel	4.1200 x 3.75	400	10.75	370 @ 5500	445 @ 3900	30—40
	360 Horsepower..............V8-428	4 Barrel	4.1200 x 4.00	428	10.50	360 @ 4600	472 @ 3200	30—40
	370 Horsepower..............V8-428	4 Barrel	4.1200 x 4.00	428	10.50	370 @ 4800	472 @ 3200	55—60
	390 Horsepower..............V8-428	4 Barrel	4.1200 x 4.00	428	10.75	390 @ 5200	465 @ 3400	55—60
1970	155 Horsepower..............①6-250	1 Barrel	3.875 x 3.53	250	8.50	155 @ 4200	235 @ 1600	30—45
	255 Horsepower..............V8-350	2 Barrel	3.8750 x 3.75	350	8.80	255 @ 4600	355 @ 2800	30—40
	265 Horsepower..............V8-400	2 Barrel	4.1200 x 3.75	400	8.80	265 @ 4600	397 @ 2400	30—40
	290 Horsepower..............V8-400	2 Barrel	4.1200 x 3.75	400	10.00	290 @ 4600	428 @ 2500	30—40
	330 Horsepower..............V8-400	4 Barrel	4.1200 x 3.75	400	10.00	330 @ 4800	445 @ 2900	30—40
	350 Horsepower..............V8-400	4 Barrel	4.1200 x 3.75	400	10.25	350 @ 5000	445 @ 3000	55—60
	366 Horsepower..............V8-400	4 Barrel	4.1200 x 3.75	400	10.50	366 @ 5100	445 @ 3600	30—40
	370 Horsepower..............V8-400	4 Barrel	4.1200 x 3.75	400	10.50	370 @ 5500	445 @ 3900	30—40
	360 Horsepower..............V8-455	4 Barrel	4.1510 x 4.21	455	10.00	360 @ 4300	500 @ 2700	30—40
	370 Horsepower..............V8-455	4 Barrel	4.1510 x 4.21	455	10.25	370 @ 4600	500 @ 3100	30—40
1971	145 Horsepower..............①6-250	1 Barrel	3.875 x 3.53	250	8.50	145 @ 4200	230 @ 1600	30—45
	200 Horsepower..............②V8-307	2 Barrel	3.875 x 3.25	307	8.50	200 @ 4600	300 @ 2400	30—45
	250 Horsepower..............8-350	2 Barrel	3.8750 x 3.75	350	8.0	250 @ 4400	350 @ 2400	30—40
	265 Horsepower..............8-400	2 Barrel	4.1200 x 3.75	400	8.2	265 @ 4400	400 @ 2400	30—40
	300 Horsepower..............8-400	4 Barrel	4.1200 x 3.75	400	8.2	300 @ 4800	400 @ 3600	30—40
	280 Horsepower..............8-455	2 Barrel	4.1510 x 4.21	455	8.2	280 @ 4400	455 @ 2000	30—40
	325 Horsepower..............8-455	4 Barrel	4.1510 x 4.21	455	8.2	325 @ 4400	455 @ 3200	30—40
	335 Horsepower..............8-455	4 Barrel	4.1510 x 4.21	455	8.4	335 @ 4800	480 @ 3600	30—40

Continued

GENERAL ENGINE SPECIFICATIONS—Continued

Year	Engine	Carburetor	Bore and Stroke	Piston Displacement, Cubic Inches	Compression Ratio	Maximum Brake H.P. @ R.P.M.	Maximum Torque Lbs. Ft. @ R.P.M.	Normal Oil Pressure Pounds
1972	110 Horsepower③..........①6-250	1 Barrel	3.875 x 3.53	250	8.50	110 @ 3800	185 @ 1600	30–45
	130 Horsepower③..........②8-307	2 Barrel	3.875 x 3.25	307	8.50	130 @ 4400	230 @ 2400	30–45
	160 Horsepower③..........8-350	2 Barrel	3.875 x 3.75	350	8.00	160 @ 4400	270 @ 2000	30–40
	175 Horsepower③..........8-350	2 Barrel	3.875 x 3.75	350	8.00	175 @ 4400	275 @ 2000	30–40
	175 Horsepower③..........8-400	2 Barrel	4.1200 x 3.75	400	8.2	175 @ 4000	310 @ 2400	30–40
	200 Horsepower③..........8-400	2 Barrel	4.1200 x 3.75	400	8.2	200 @ 4000	325 @ 2400	30–40
	200 Horsepower③..........8-400	4 Barrel	4.1200 x 3.75	400	8.2	200 @ 4000	295 @ 2800	30–40
	250 Horsepower③..........8-400	4 Barrel	4.1200 x 3.75	400	8.2	250 @ 4400	325 @ 3200	30–40
	185 Horsepower③..........8-455	2 Barrel	4.1510 x 4.21	455	8.2	185 @ 4000	350 @ 2000	30–40
	200 Horsepower③..........8-455	2 Barrel	4.1510 x 4.21	455	8.2	200 @ 4000	370 @ 2000	30–40
	220 Horsepower③..........8-455	4 Barrel	4.1510 x 4.21	455	8.2	220 @ 3600	350 @ 2400	30–40
	230 Horsepower③..........8-455	4 Barrel	4.1510 x 4.21	455	8.2	230 @ 4400	360 @ 2800	30–40
	250 Horsepower③..........8-455	4 Barrel	4.1510 x 4.21	455	8.2	250 @ 3600	370 @ 2400	30–40
	250 Horsepower③..........8-455	4 Barrel	4.1510 x 4.21	455	8.2	250 @ 3600	375 @ 2400	30–40
	300 Horsepower③..........8-455	4 Barrel	4.1510 x 4.21	455	8.4	300 @ 4000	415 @ 3200	30–40

①—For service on this engine, see Six Cylinder in Chevrolet Chapter.
②—For service on this engine, see Eight Cylinder in Chevrolet Chapter.
③—Ratings are NET—as installed in the vehicle.

TUNE UP SPECIFICATIONS

OLD CAR SPECIFICATIONS: For 1946-65 Tune Up Specifications see back of book.

★When using a timing light, disconnect vacuum hose or tube at distributor and plug opening in hose or tube so idle speed will not be affected.

●When checking compression, lowest cylinder to be within 80% of the highest.

Year	Engine	Spark Plug Type AC	Spark Plug Gap Inch	Distributor Point Gap Inch	Distributor Dwell Angle Deg.	Firing Order	Ignition Timing★ BTDC ①	Ignition Timing★ Mark	Hot Idle Speed③ Std. Trans.	Hot Idle Speed③ Auto. Trans. ③	Fuel Pump Press. Lbs.
1966	6-230 Engine	44S	.035	.016	31–34	Fig. H	5°	Fig. F	600④	500D④	4–5½
	6-230 With A.I.R.⑤	44S	.035	.016	31–34	Fig. H	5 ATC	Fig. F	700⑦	600D⑦	4–5½
	V8s	45S	.035	⑥	30	Fig. D	6°	Fig. G	600④	500D④	5–6½
	V8s With A.I.R.⑤⑨	45S	.035	⑥	30	Fig. D	4 ATC	Fig. G	700⑦	600D⑦	5–6½
	Tri-Carb.	44S	.035	⑥	30	Fig. D	6°	Fig. G	600④	500D⑦	5–6½
	Tri-Carb.⑤	44S	.035	⑥	30	Fig. D	6°	Fig. G	700⑦	600D⑦	5–6½
1967	6-230 Engine	44N	.035	.016	31–34	Fig. H	5°	Fig. F	600④	500D④	5–5½
	6-230 With A.I.R.⑤	44N	.035	.016	31–34	Fig. H	TDC	Fig. F	700⑦	600D⑦	4–5½
	8-326, 400 2 B.C.	45S	.035	⑥	30	Fig. D	6°	Fig. G	600④	500D④	5–6½
	8-326, 400 2 B.C.⑤	45S	.035	⑥	30	Fig. D	6°	Fig. G	700⑧	600D⑧	5–6½
	8-326, 400 4 B.C.	45S	.035	⑥	30	Fig. D	6°	Fig. G	600④	500D④	5–6½
	8-326, 400 4 B.C.⑤	45S	.035	⑥	30	Fig. D	6°	Fig. G	700⑦	600D⑧	5–6½
	8-400 Hi Perf.	44S	.035	⑥	30	Fig. D	6°	Fig. G	700⑦	600D④	5–6½
	8-428	44S	.035	⑥	30	Fig. D	6°	Fig. G	700④	650D④	5–6½
	8-428 With A.I.R.	44S	.035	⑥	30	Fig. D	6°	Fig. G	700⑦	650D⑦	5–6½
1968	6-250 1 Bar. Carb.	44N	.035	.016	31–34	Fig. H	TDC	Fig. F	700/500⑦	600/500⑦	4–5½
	6-250 4 Bar. Carb.	44N	.035	.016	31–34	Fig. H	5°	Fig. F	800/600⑦	600/500⑦	4–5½
	8-350	45S	.035	.016	28–32	Fig. D	9°	Fig. C	650/500⑦	650/500⑦	5–6½

Continued

TUNE UP SPECIFICATIONS—Continued

OLD CAR SPECIFICATIONS: For 1946-65 Tune Up Specifications see back of book.

★When using a timing light, disconnect vacuum hose or tube at distributor and plug opening in hose or tube so idle speed will not be affected.

●When checking compression, lowest cylinder to be within 80% of the highest.

| Year | Engine | Spark Plug | | Distributor | | Firing Order | Ignition Timing★ | | Hot Idle Speed | | Fuel Pump Press. Lbs. |
		Type	Gap Inch	Point Gap Inch	Dwell Angle Deg.		BTDC ①	Mark	Std. Trans.	Auto. Trans. ①	
1968	Firebird 400	44S	.035	.016	28–32	Fig. D	9°	Fig. C	850/600⑦	650/500⑦	5–6½
	Firebird 400 H.O.	44S	.035	.016	28–32	Fig. D	9°	Fig. C	850/600⑦	650/500⑦	5–6½
	Firebird Ram Air	44S	.035	.016	28–32	Fig. D	9°	Fig. C	1000/650⑦	650/500⑦	5–6½
	Pontiac 400, 2 B.C.	45S	.035	.016	28–32	Fig. D	9°	Fig. C	800/500⑦	600/500⑦	5–6½
	Pontiac 400, B.C.	45S	.035	.016	28–32	Fig. D	9°	Fig. C	850/650⑦	600/500⑦	5–6½
	8-428	44S	.035	.016	28–32	Fig. D	9°	Fig. C	650/500⑦	650/500⑦	5–6½
1969	6-250 1 Bar. Carb.	R44NS	.035	.016	31–34	Fig. H	TDC	Fig. F	700/500	600/500D①	4–5½
	6-250 4 Bar. Carb.	R44NS	.035	.016	31–34	Fig. H	5°	Fig. F	850/600	600/500D①	4–5½
	8-350 2 Bar. Carb.	R45S	.035	.016	30	Fig. D	9°	Fig. C	850	650D⑦	5–6½
	8-350 4 Bar. Carb.	R45S	.035	.016	30	Fig. D	9°	Fig. C	1000	650D⑦	5–6½
	8-400 2 Bar. Carb.	R45S	.035	.016	30	Fig. D	9°	Fig. C	850	650D⑦	5–6½
	8-400 4 Bar. Carb.	⑪	.035	.016	30	Fig. D	9°	Fig. C	1000	650D⑦	5–6½
	8-400 Ram Air	⑪	.035	.016	30	Fig. D	15°	Fig. C	1000/650	650/500D①	5–6½
	8-428	R44S	.035	.016	30	Fig. D	9°	Fig. C	1000	650D⑦	5–6½
1970	6-250⑩ Std. Tr.	R46T	.035	.019	31–34	Fig. E	TDC	Fig. J	750/400	—	4–5
	6-250⑩ Auto. Tr.	R46T	.035	.019	31–34	Fig. E	4°	Fig. J	—	600/400D	4–5
	8-350 2 Bar. Carb.	R46S	.035	.016	30	Fig. D	9°	Fig. C	800	650D	5–6½⑬
	8-400 2 Bar. Carb.	R46S	.035	.016	30	Fig. D	9°	Fig. C	800	650D	5–6½⑬
	8-400 4 Bar. Carb.	R45S	.035	.016	30	Fig. D	9°	Fig. C	950	650D	5–6½⑬
	8-400 Ram Air	R44S	.035	.016	30	Fig. D	15°	Fig. C	1000/650	750/500D	5–6½⑬
	8-455	R45S⑫	.035	.016	30	Fig. D	9°	Fig. C	950	650D	5–6½⑬
1971	6-250⑩	R46TS	.035	.019	32½	Fig. E	4°	Fig. K	850/550	650/500D	4–5
	8-307⑭ Std. Tr.	R45TS	.035	.019	30	Fig. M	4°	Fig. J	550	—	5–6½
	8-307⑭ Auto. Tr.	R45TS	.035	.019	30	Fig. M	8°	Fig. J	—	550D	5–6½
	8-350 2 Bar. Carb.	R47S	.035	.016	30	Fig. D	12°	Fig. L	800	600D	5–6½⑬
	8-400 2 Bar. Carb.	R47S	.035	.016	30	Fig. D	8°	Fig. L	—	600D	5–6½⑬
	8-400 4 Bar. Carb.	R46S	.035	.016	30	Fig. D	12°	Fig. L	1000/600	700D	5–6½⑬
	8-455	R46S	.035	.016	30	Fig. D	12°	Fig. L	—	650D	5–6½⑬
	8-455 H.O.	R46S	.035	.016	03	Fig. D	12°	Fig. L	1000/600	700D	5–6½⑬
1972	6-250⑩	R46T	.035	.019	32½	Fig. E	4°	Fig. K	850/450	650/450D	4–5
	8-307⑭ Std. Tr.	R44T	.035	.016	30	Fig. M	4°	Fig. J	900/450	—	5–6½
	8-307⑭ Auto. Tr.	R44T	.035	.016	30	Fig. M	8°	Fig. J	—	600/450D	5–6½
	8-350	R46TS	.035	.016	30	Fig. D	8°	Fig. L	800	—	5–6½
	8-350	R46TS	.035	.016	30	Fig. D	10°	Fig. L	—	625D	5–6½
	8-400 2 Bar. Carb.	R46TS	.035	.016	30	Fig. D	10°	Fig. L	—	625D	5–6½
	8-400 4 Bar. Carb.	R45TS	.035	.016	30	Fig. D	10°	Fig. L	1000/600	700/500D	5–6½
	8-455 2 Bar. Carb.	R45TS	.035	.016	30	Fig. D	10°	Fig. L	—	625D	5–6½
	8-455 4 Bar. Carb.	R45TS	.035	.016	30	Fig. D	10°	Fig. L	—	650/500D	5–6½
	8-455 H.O. Std. Tr.	R45TS	.035	.016	30	Fig. D	8°	Fig. L	1000/600	—	5–6½
	8-455 H.O. Auto. Tr.	R45TS	.035	.016	30	Fig. D	10°	Fig. L	—	700/500D	5–6½

①—BTDC: Before top dead center.

②—D: Drive. N: Neutral.

③—Where two figures are given, the higher is with solenoid active.

④—If air conditioned, turn A/C switch to "Full On" position.

⑤—With Air Injection Reactor Emission System (A.I.R.).

⑥—Turn adjusting screw in (clockwise) until engine misfires. Then back off screw ½ turn.

⑦—With A/C off.

⑧—100 R.P.M. higher with A/C off.

⑨—Tempest with manual transmission.

⑩—For service on this engine, see Six Cylinder in Chevrolet Chapter.

⑪—GTO uses R44S; all others use R45S.

⑫—Use R44S on Ram Air option.

⑬—With A/C and all 4 barrel carb. 6½–8.

⑭—For service on this engine, see Chevrolet Chapter.

Continued

TUNE UP SPECIFICATIONS—Continued

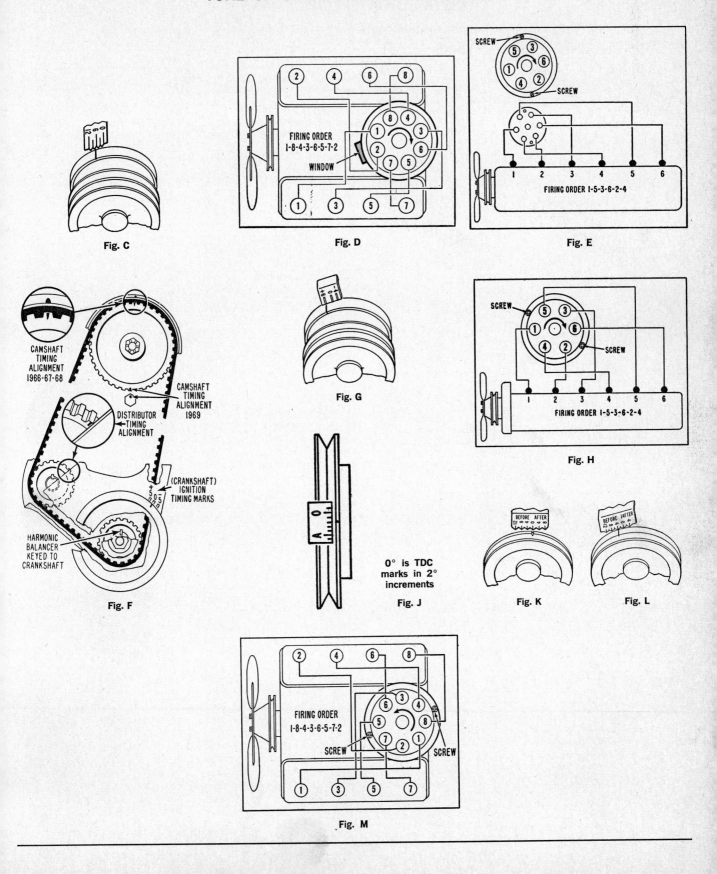

Fig. C

Fig. D

FIRING ORDER 1-8-4-3-6-5-7-2

WINDOW

Fig. E

SCREW

SCREW

FIRING ORDER 1-5-3-6-2-4

CAMSHAFT TIMING ALIGNMENT 1966-67-68

CAMSHAFT TIMING ALIGNMENT 1969

DISTRIBUTOR TIMING ALIGNMENT

(CRANKSHAFT) IGNITION TIMING MARKS

HARMONIC BALANCER KEYED TO CRANKSHAFT

Fig. F

Fig. G

Fig. H

SCREW

SCREW

FIRING ORDER 1-5-3-6-2-4

0° is TDC marks in 2° increments

Fig. J

BEFORE AFTER

Fig. K

BEFORE AFTER

Fig. L

Fig. M

FIRING ORDER 1-8-4-3-6-5-7-2

SCREW

SCREW

DISTRIBUTOR SPECIFICATIONS

★NOTE: If advance is checked on the vehicle, double the R.P.M. and advance degrees to get crankshaft figures.

Year	Model	Distributor Part No.①	Breaker Gap	Dwell Angle Deg.	Breaker Arm Spring Tension	Centrifugal Advance Degrees @ R.P.M. of Distributor★		Vacuum Advance		Dist. Retard
						Advance Starts	Full Advance	Inches of Vacuum To Start Plunger	Max. Adv. Dist. Deg. @ Vacuum	Max. Ret. Dist. Deg. @ Vacuum
1966	6-230	1110341	.016	31–34	19–23	1 @ 475	11 @ 2400	4–6	10 @ 12	—
	6-230	1110343	.016	31–34	19–23	3 @ 500	16 @ 2400	4–6	10 @ 12	—
	6-230④	1110344	.016	31–34	19–23	3 @ 500	12 @ 3000	4–6	10 @ 12	—
	V8-326⑤	1111077	.016	30	19–23	1 @ 400	14 @ 2300	6–8	10 @ 14	—
	V8-326, 389⑤	1111103	.016	30	19–23	2 @ 500	16 @ 2300	8–10	10 @ 16	—
	V8-326④	1111079	.016	30	19–23	1 @ 400	12 @ 2300	8–10	10 @ 16	—
	V8-326 Tr. Ign.	1111081	—	—	—	1 @ 400	13 @ 3000	8–10	10 @ 16	—
	V8-389, 421④	1111078	.016	30	19–23	1 @ 480	11 @ 2300	8–10	10 @ 16	—
	V8-389, 421 3 Carbs.	1111054	.016	30	19–23	2 @ 450	11 @ 2300	8–10	10 @ 16	—
	V8-389 Tr. Ign.	1111080	—	—	—	1 @ 480	11 @ 3000	8–10	10 @ 16	—
	V8-389 Tr. Ign.	1111047	—	—	—	1 @ 400	11 @ 3000	8–10	10 @ 16	—
1967	6-230	1110391	.016	31–34	18–23	2 @ 500	14 @ 2800	4–6	7 @ 10	—
	6-230	1110396	.016	31–34	18–23	2 @ 500	17 @ 1900	4–6	7 @ 10	—
	6-230④	1110397	.016	31–34	18–23	3 @ 500	20 @ 2000	4–6	7 @ 10	—
	V8-326⑤	1111164	③	30	18–23	1 @ 450	14 @ 2300	6–8	10 @ 14	—
	V8-326④	1111165	③	30	18–23	1 @ 500	12 @ 2400	8–10	10 @ 16	—
	V8-326⑤	1111199	③	30	18–23	1 @ 450	14 @ 2300	6–8	10 @ 14	—
	V8-326④	1111238	③	30	18–23	1 @ 500	12 @ 2400	8–10	10 @ 16	—
	V8-400, 428	1111237	③	30	18–23	1 @ 500	14 @ 2200	8–10	10 @ 16	—
	V8-400⑤ Low Comp.	1111242	③	30	18–23	1 @ 500	10 @ 2300	6–8	10 @ 14	—
	V8-400, 428④	1111250	③	30	18–23	1 @ 500	14 @ 2300	8–10	10 @ 16	—
	V8-400, 428④	1111252	③	30	18–23	1 @ 500	14 @ 2200	8–10	10 @ 16	—
	V8-400 Regular Fuel	1111261	③	30	18–23	1 @ 500	10 @ 2300	6–8	10 @ 14	—
	Grand Prix	1111243	③	30	19–23	1 @ 450	14 @ 2300	8–10	10 @ 16	—
	V8-400④	1111244	③	30	19–23	1 @ 450	14 @ 2300	8–10	10 @ 16	—
	V8-400 Premium Fuel	1111253	③	30	19–23	1 @ 500	10 @ 2300	10–12	10 @ 18	—
	V8-400④	1111254	③	30	19–23	1 @ 500	10 @ 2300	10–12	10 @ 18	—
	V8-428	1111183	③	30	18–23	1 @ 500	14 @ 2200	8–10	10 @ 16	—
	Breakerless Dist.	1110386	—	—	—	2 @ 500	10 @ 2400	4–6	7 @ 10	—
	Breakerless Dist.	1111166	—	—	—	1 @ 450	12 @ 2400	8–10	10 @ 16	—
	Breakerless Dist.	1111180	—	—	—	1 @ 500	15 @ 3000	8–10	10 @ 16	—
	Breakerless Dist.	1111245	—	—	—	1 @ 450	15 @ 3000	8–10	10 @ 16	—
	Breakerless Dist.	1111251	—	—	—	1 @ 500	15 @ 3000	8–10	10 @ 16	—
	Breakerless Dist.	1111255	—	—	—	1 @ 500	11 @ 3000	10–12	10 @ 18	—
1968	6-250, 1 Bar. Carb.	1110430	.016	31–34	19–23	0 @ 450	14 @ 2200	4–6	7 @ 10	—
	6-250 Std. Trans.④	1110431	.016	31–34	19–23	0 @ 450	14 @ 2500	4–6	7 @ 10	—
	6-250 Auto. Tr.④	1110449	.016	31–34	19–23	0 @ 450	14 @ 2500	4–6	7 @ 10	—
	8-350, 2 Bar. Carb.	1111281	.016	28–32	19–23	0 @ 400	12 @ 2400	8–10	10 @ 16	—
	8-350 Auto. Tr.④	1111282	.016	28–32	19–23	0 @ 400	9 @ 2500	8–10	10 @ 16	—
	8-350 Std. Trans.④	1111447	.016	28–32	19–23	0 @ 550	9 @ 2400	8–10	10 @ 16	—
	8-400 Std. Trans.④	1111449	.016	28–32	19–23	0 @ 550	10 @ 2300	8–10	10 @ 18	—
	8-400 Auto. Trans.④	1111270	.016	28–32	19–23	0 @ 400	10 @ 2300	10–12	10 @ 16	—
	8-400 2 Bar. Carb.	1111272	.016	28–32	19–23	0 @ 400	16 @ 2275	8–10	10 @ 16	—
	8-400 Auto. Tr.④	1111300	.016	28–32	19–23	0 @ 400	10 @ 2300	10–12	10 @ 18	—
	8-400 Std. Trans.	1111448	.016	28–32	19–23	0 @ 550	10 @ 2300	10–12	10 @ 18	—
	8-428 Auto. Tr.	1111270	.016	28–32	19–23	0 @ 400	10 @ 2300	10–12	10 @ 16	—
	8-428 Std. Trans.	1111449	.016	28–32	19–23	0 @ 550	10 @ 2300	8–10	10 @ 18	—
	8-428 Auto. Tr.	1111435	.016	28–32	19–23	0 @ 400	11 @ 2300	10–12	10 @ 18	—
	8-428 Std. Trans.	1111450	.016	28–32	19–23	0 @ 550	11 @ 2300	8–10	10 @ 18	—
1969	6-250, 4 Bar. Carb.	1110474	.016	31–34	19–23	1 @ 500	14 @ 2550	5–7	7½ @ 11½	—
	6-250, 1 Bar. Carb.	1110475	.016	31–34	19–23	1 @ 450	15 @ 2200	5–7	7½ @ 11½	—
	8-350 Auto. Tr.⑤	1111942	.016	30	19–23	1 @ 400	13 @ 2400	6–8	10 @ 15	—

Continued

DISTRIBUTOR SPECIFICATIONS—Continued

★NOTE: If advance is checked on the vehicle, double the R.P.M. and advance degrees to get crankshaft figures.

Year	Model	Distributor Part No.①	Breaker Gap	Dwell Angle Deg.	Breaker Arm Spring Tension	Centrifugal Advance Degrees @ R.P.M. of Distributor★		Vacuum Advance		Dist. Retard
						Advance Starts	Full Advance	Inches of Vacuum To Start Plunger	Max. Adv. Dist. Deg. @ Vacuum	Max. Ret. Dist. Deg. @ Vacuum
1969	8-350 Std. Tr.⑥	1111960	.016	30	19-23	1 @ 550	12 @ 2300	8-10	10 @ 19	—
	8-350 Auto. Tr.④	1111965	.016	30	28-31	1 @ 425	10 @ 2550	8-10	10 @ 17	—
	8-350 Std. Tr.④	1111966	.016	30	28-31	1 @ 550	10 @ 2500	8-10	10 @ 17	—
	8-400 Auto. Tr.⑤	1111940	.016	30	19-23	1 @ 400	17 @ 2275	8-10	10 @ 17	—
	8-400 Std. Tr.	1111952	.016	30	28-31	1 @ 550	11 @ 2300	8-10	10 @ 17	—
	8-400 Auto. Tr.④	1111253	.016	30	19-23	1 @ 400	11 @ 2300	10-12	10 @ 19	—
	8-400 Auto. Tr.④	1111946	.016	30	28-31	1 @ 400	11 @ 2300	8-10	10 @ 17	—
	8-400 Ram Air	1111941	.016	30	28-31	1 @ 600	15 @ 3050	8-10	10 @ 17	—
	8-428 H.O. Auto. Tr.	1111946	.016	30	28-31	1 @ 400	11 @ 2300	8-10	10 @ 18	—
	8-428 H.O. Std. Tr.	1111952	.016	30	28-31	1 @ 550	11 @ 2300	8-10	10 @ 19	—
	8-428 Auto. Tr.	1111959	.016	30	19-23	1 @ 400	12 @ 2300	8-10	10 @ 17	—
1970	6-250, Std. Tr.	1110463	.019	31-34	19-23	0 @ 450	17 @ 2100	7	11½ @ 16	—
	6-250, Auto. Tr.	1110464	.019	31-34	19-23	0 @ 450	15 @ 2100	7	11½ @ 16	—
	8-350	1112008	.016	30	19-23	1 @ 550	14 @ 2350	7	10 @ 14	—
	8-400, Std. Tr.	1111176	.016	30	28-32	1 @ 550	14 @ 2350	9	10 @ 16	—
	8-400, Auto. Tr.	1111148	.016	30	28-32	1 @ 400	14 @ 2300	9	10 @ 16	—
	8-400⑥	1112007	.016	30	19-23	1 @ 400	9 @ 2200	9	10 @ 16	—
	8-400 Ram Air⑦	1112010	.016	30	28-32	1 @ 550	12 @ 2300	9	10 @ 16	—
	8-400 Ram Air⑧	1112009	.016	30	28-32	1 @ 400	12 @ 2300	9	10 @ 16	—
	8-400 Ram Air IV	1112011	.016	30	28-32	1 @ 600	15 @ 3050	9	10 @ 16	—
	8-455 Std. Tr. & H.O.	1112012	.016	30	28-32	1 @ 400	9 @ 2200	9	10 @ 16	—
	8-455 Auto Tr. exc. H.O.	1111105	.016	30	28-32	1 @ 400	9 @ 2200	9	10 @ 16	—
1971	6-250	1110489	.019	32½	—	1 @ 650	12 @ 2050	7-9	11½ @ 17	—
	8-307 Std. Tr.	1112005	.019	29-31	19-23	1 @ 600	12 @ 2150	8	10 @ 17	—
	8-307 Auto. Tr.	1112039	.019·	29-31	19-23	1 @ 650	11 @ 2100	8	10 @ 17	—
	8-350 2 Bar. Carb.	1112090	.016	30	—	1 @ 800	9 @ 2300	6-8	10 @ 14¾	—
	8-350 Std. Tr.	1112083	.016	30	—	1 @ 600	11 @ 2300	6-8	10 @ 14¾	—
	8-350 Auto. Tr.	1112069	.016	30	—	1 @ 800	11 @ 2300	6-8	10 @ 14¾	—
	8-400 2 Bar. Carb.	1112089	.016	30	—	1 @ 800	12 @ 2300	6-8	10 @ 14¾	—
	8-400 2 Bar. Carb.	1112068	.016	30	—	1 @ 800	14 @ 2300	6-8	10 @ 14¾	—
	8-400 4 Bar. Carb.	1112070	.016	30	—	1 @ 575	11 @ 2300	6-8	10 @ 14¾	—
	8-455 4 Bar. Carb.	1112035	.016	30	—	1 @ 650	11 @ 2300	8-10	10 @ 17	—
	8-455 2 Bar. Carb.	1112071	.016	30	—	1 @ 800	12 @ 2300	8-10	10 @ 10	—
	8-455 4 Bar. Carb.	1112072	.016	30	—	1 @ 825	11 @ 2300	8-10	10 @ 17	—
	8-455 H.O.	1112073	.016	30	—	1 @ 500	13 @ 2225	6-8	10 @ 14¾	—
1972	6-250	1110489	.019	32½	19-23	1 @ 650	12 @ 2050	7-9	11½ @ 17	—
	8-307 Std. Tr.	1112005	.016	30	19-23	1 @ 600	12 @ 2150	8	10 @ 17	—
	8-307 Auto. Tr.	1112039	.016	30	19-23	1 @ 650	11 @ 2100	8	10 @ 17	—
	8-350 Std. Tr.	1112140	.016	30	19-23	½ @ 800	12 @ 2300	6-8	10 @ 15	—
	8-350 Auto. Tr.	1112118	.016	30	19-23	½ @ 800	10 @ 2300	6-8	10 @ 15	—
	8-400 2 Bar. Carb.	1112119	.016	30	19-23	½ @ 800	13 @ 2300	8-10	10 @ 17	—
	8-400 4 Bar. Carb.	1112121	.016	30	28-32	½ @ 700	13 @ 2300	6-8	10 @ 15	—
	8-455 2 Bar. Carb.	1112122	.016	30	19-23	½ @ 800	13 @ 2300	8-10	10 @ 17	—
	8-455 4 Bar. Carb.	1112145	.016	30	28-32	½ @ 700	11 @ 2300	8-10	10 @ 17	—
	8-455 4 Bar. Carb.	1112127	—	30	—	½ @ 700	11 @ 2300	8-10	10 @ 17	—
	8-455 H.O.	1112133	—	30	—	½ @ 550	15 @ 2300	6-8	10 @ 15	—

①—Stamped on distributor housing plate.
②—Turn adjusting screw to the right until engine misfires, then turn screw ½ turn to the left.
④—With four barrel carburetor.
⑤—With two barrel carburetor.
⑥—Regular fuel.
⑦—Std. trans.
⑧—Auto. trans.

PONTIAC — All Intermediate & Full Size Models

VALVE SPECIFICATIONS

Year	Model	Valve Lash		Valve Angles		Valve Spring Installed Height	Valve Spring Pressure Lbs. @ In.	Stem Clearance		Stem Diameter	
		Int.	Exh.	Seat	Face			Intake	Exhaust	Intake	Exhaust
1966	6-230	Hydraulic(7)	(3)	(8)	(8)	1.583	192 @ 1.18	.0021–.0038	.0026–.0043	.3407–.3414	.3402–.3409
	V8-326, 389 Std.	Hydraulic(7)	(3)	(8)	(8)	1.586(4)	106 @ 1.21(4)	.0021–.0038	.0026–.0043	.3407–.3414	.3402–.3409
	V8-389, 421	Hydraulic(7)	(3)	(8)	(8)	1.586(4)	111 @ 1.18(4)	.0021–.0038	.0026–.0043	.3407–.3414	.3402–.3409
1967	6-230 Std. Eng.	Hydraulic(7)	(3)	(8)	(8)	1.583	192 @ 1.83	.0016–.0033	.0021–.0038	.3410–.3417	.3410–.3417
	6-230 Opt. Eng.	Hydraulic(7)	(3)	(8)	(8)	1.586	140 @ 1.34	.0016–.0033	.0021–.0038	.3410–.3417	.3410–.3417
	V8-326, 400 Std.	Hydraulic(7)	(3)	(8)	(8)	1.586(4)	140 @ 1.134(4)	.0016–.0033	.0021–.0038	.3407–.3414	.3402–.3409
	V8-400 GTO	Hydraulic(7)	(3)	(8)	(8)	1.586(4)	140 @ 1.134(4)	.0016–.0033	.0021–.0038	.3407–.3414	.3402–.3409
	V8-400 Ram Air	Hydraulic(7)	(3)	(8)	(8)	1.582(4)	252 @ 1.34(4)	.0016–.0033	.0021–.0038	.3407–.3414	.3402–.3409
	V8-428	Hydraulic(7)	(3)	(8)	(8)	1.586(4)	140 @ 1.134(4)	.0016–.0033	.0021–.0038	.3407–.3414	.3402–.3409
1968	6-250	Hydraulic(7)	(3)	(8)	(8)	1.629	170 @ 1.23	.0016–.0033	.0021–.0038	.3412–.3419	.3407–.3414
	V8-350, 2 B.C.	Hydraulic(7)	(3)	(8)	(8)	1.582(4)	127 @ 1.20	.0016–.0033	.0021–.0038	.3412–.3419	.3407–.3414
	V8-350, 4 B.C.	Hydraulic(7)	(3)	(8)	(8)	1.582(4)	133 @ 1.17	.0016–.0033	.0021–.0038	.3412–.3419	.3407–.3414
	V8-400, 2 B.C.	Hydraulic(7)	(3)	(8)	(8)	1.582(4)	127 @ 1.20	.0016–.0033	.0021–.0038	.3412–.3419	.3407–.3414
	V8-400, 4 B.C.	Hydraulic(7)	(3)	(8)	(8)	1.561(4)	137 @ 1.15	.0016–.0033	.0021–.0038	.3412–.3419	.3407–.3414
	V8-400 Ram Air	Hydraulic(7)	(3)	(8)	(8)	1.712(4)	190 @ 1.30	.0016–.0033	.0021–.0038	.3412–.3419	.3407–.3414
	V8-428	Hydraulic(7)	(3)	(8)	(8)	1.561(4)	137 @ 1.15	.0016–.0033	.0021–.0038	.3412–.3419	.3407–.3414
1969	6-250, 1 B.C.	Hydraulic(7)		46	45	1.629	170 @ 1.23	.0016–.0033	.0021–.0038	.3407–.3414	.3407–.3414
	6-250, 4 B.C.	Hydraulic(7)		46	45	1.629	122 @ 1.10	.0016–.0033	.0021–.0038	.3407–.3414	.3407–.3414
	8-350, 2 B.C.	Hydraulic(7)		45	(8)	1.582(4)	140 @ 1.13	.0016–.0033	.0021–.0038	.3407–.3414	.3407–.3414
	8-350, 4 B.C.	Hydraulic(7)		45	(8)	1.591(4)	140 @ 1.13	.0016–.0033	.0021–.0038	.3407–.3414	.3407–.3414
	8-400, 2 B.C.	Hydraulic(7)		(9)	(10)	1.582(4)	140 @ 1.13	.0016–.0033	.0021–.0038	.3407–.3414	.3407–.3414
	8-400, 4 B.C.	Hydraulic(7)		(9)	(10)	1.561(4)	185 @ 1.29	.0016–.0033	.0021–.0038	.3407–.3414	.3407–.3414
	8-400 Ram Air	Hydraulic(7)		(9)	(10)	1.591(4)	185 @ 1.29	.0016–.0033	.0021–.0038	.3407–.3414	.3407–.3414
	8-428	Hydraulic(7)		(9)	(10)	1.582(4)	140 @ 1.13	.0016–.0033	.0021–.0038	.3407–.3414	.3407–.3414
1970	6-250(5)	1 Turn(2)		46	45	1.66	186 @ 1.27	.0010–.0027	.0010–.0027	.3410–.3417	.3410–.3417
	8-350	Hydraulic(7)		45	44	1.582(4)	130 @ 1.70	.0016–.0033	.0021–.0038	.3412–.3419	.3412–.3419
	8-400, 265 H.P.	Hydraulic(7)		45	44	1.582(4)	(4)(6)	.0016–.0033	.0021–.0038	.3412–.3419	.3407–.3414
	8-400, 290 H.P.	Hydraulic(7)		45	44	1.582(4)	(4)(6)	.0016–.0033	.0021–.0038	.3412–.3419	.3407–.3414
	8-400, 330 H.P.	Hydraulic(7)		45	44	1.582(4)	(4)(11)	.0016–.0033	.0021–.0038	.3412–.3419	.3407–.3414
	8-400, 350 H.P.	Hydraulic(7)		(9)	(13)	1.591(4)	132 @ 1.181	.0016–.0033	.0021–.0038	.3412–.3419	.3407–.3414
	8-400 Ram Air	Hydraulic(7)		(9)	(13)	1.591(4)	132 @ 1.178	.0016–.0033	.0021–.0038	.3412–.3419	.3407–.3414
	8-400 Ram Air IV	Hydraulic(7)		(9)	(13)	1.818(4)	222 @ 1.291	.0016–.0033	.0021–.0038	.3412–.3419	.3407–.3414
	8-455	Hydraulic(7)		(9)	(13)	1.561(4)	(4)(12)	.0016–.0033	.0021–.0038	.3412–.3419	.3407–.3414
1971	6-250(5)	1 Turn(2)		46	45	1.66	186 @ 1.27	.0010–.0027	.0010–.0027	.3410–.3417	.3410–.3417
	8-307(1)	1 Turn(2)		46	45	1.70	200 @ 1.25	.0010–.0027	.0010–.0027	.3410–.3417	.3410–.3417
	8-350	Hydraulic(7)		(9)	(13)	—	—	.0016–.0033	.0021–.0038	.3412–.3419	.3412–.3419
	8-400	Hydraulic(7)		(9)	(13)	—	—	.0016–.0033	.0021–.0038	.3412–.3419	.3407–.3414
	8-400 Ram Air	Hydraulic(7)		(9)	(13)	—	—	.0016–.0033	.0021–.0038	.3412–.3419	.3407–.3414
	8-455	Hydraulic(7)		(9)	(13)	—	—	.0016–.0033	.0021–.0038	.3412–.3419	.3407–.3414
1972	6-250(5)	1 Turn(2)		46	45	1.66	186 @ 1.27	.0010–.0027	.0010–.0027	.3410–.3417	.3410–.3417
	8-307(1)	1 Turn(2)		46	45	1.70	200 @ 1.25	.0010–.0027	.0010–.0027	.3410–.3417	.3410–.3417
	8-350	Hydraulic(7)		(14)	(15)	1.66	186 @ 1.27	.0010–.0027	.0010–.0027	.3410–.3417	.3410–.3417
	8-400 2 Bar. Carb.	Hydraulic(7)		45	44	1.59(4)	126 @ 1.21(4)	.0016–.0033	.0021–.0038	.3412–.3419	.3407–.3414
	8-400 4 Bar. Carb.	Hydraulic(7)		(3)	(8)	1.56(4)	135 @ 1.15(4)	.0016–.0033	.0021–.0038	.3412–.3419	.3407–.3414
	8-455	Hydraulic(7)		(3)	(8)	1.56(4)	137 @ 1.14(4)	.0016–.0033	.0021–.0038	.3412–.3419	.3412–.3419

(1)—For service on this engine, see Chevrolet Chapter.

(2)—With valve fully closed, turn rocker arm nut down until all play in push rod is eliminated, then tighten nut one additional turn.

(3)—Intake 30°, exhaust 45°.

(4)—Outer spring.

(5)—For service on this engine, see Six Cylinder in Chevrolet Chapter.

(6)—Intake 126 @ 1.206, exhaust 134 @ 1.170.

(7)—No adjustment. On V8's, rocker arms are correctly positioned when ball retainer nuts are tightened to 20 ft.-lbs.

(8)—Intake 29°, exhaust 44°.

(9)—Small valve engines, intake and exhaust 45°. Large valve engines, intake 30° and exhaust 45°.

(10)—Small valve engines, intake 46° and exhaust 44°. Large valve engines, intake 29° and exhaust 44°.

(11)—Intake 133 @ 1.172, exhaust 134 @ 1.168.

(12)—Intake 137 @ 1.151, exhaust 137 @ 1.148.

(13)—Small valve engines, intake 44° and exhaust 44°. Large valve engines, intake 29° and exhaust 44°.

(14)—Small valve engines, 46°. Large valve engines, 45°.

(15)—Small valve engines, intake 46° and exhaust 45°. Large valve engines, intake and exhaust 44°.

ALTERNATOR & REGULATOR SPECIFICATIONS

Year	Alternator					Regulator						
				Output @ 14 Volts			Field Relay			Voltage Regulator		
	Model	Rated Hot Output Amps.	Field Current 12 Volts @ 80° F.	2000 R.P.M. Amps.	5000 R.P.M. Amps.	Model	Air Gap In.	Point Gap In.	Closing Voltage	Air Gap In.	Point Gap In.	Voltage @ 125° F.
1966–70	1100699	42	2.2–2.6	28	40	1119515	.015	.030	1.5–3.2	.067	.014	13.5–14.4
	1100700	55	2.2–2.6	32	50	1119515	.015	.030	1.5–3.2	.067	.014	13.5–14.4
	1100702	60	4.0–4.5	36	58	1116368	—	—	—	—	—	13.4–14.1
	1100703	60	4.0–4.5	36	58	1116368	—	—	—	—	—	13.4–14.1
	1100704	37	2.2–2.6	25	35	1119515	.015	.030	1.5–3.2	.067	.014	13.5–14.4
	1100736	37	2.2–2.6	25	35	1119515	.015	.030	1.5–3.2	.067	.014	13.5–14.4
	1100737	55	2.2–2.6	32	50	1119511	—	—	—	.067	.015	13.5–14.4
	1100738	55	2.2–2.6	32	50	1119511	—	—	—	.067	.015	13.5–14.4
	1100739	42	2.2–2.6	28	40	1119511	—	—	—	.067	.015	13.5–14.4
	1100740	60	4.0–4.5	36	58	1116370	—	—	—	—	—	13.7–14.3
	1100745	55	2.2–2.6	32	50	1119515	.015	.030	1.5–3.2	.067	.014	13.5–14.4
	1100747	55	2.2–2.6	32	50	1116370	—	—	—	—	—	13.7–14.3
	1100758	66	4.1–4.5	38	62	1116370	—	—	—	—	—	13.7–14.3
	1100760	55	2.2–2.6	32	50	1119515	.015	.030	1.5–3.2	.067	.014	13.5–14.4
	1100761	37	2.2–2.6	25	35	1119515	.015	.030	1.5–3.2	.067	.014	13.5–14.4
	1100762	37	2.2–2.6	25	35	1119515	.015	.030	1.5–3.2	.067	.014	13.5–14.4
	1100763	66	4.1–4.5	38	62	1116370	—	—	—	—	—	13.7–14.3
	1100800	55	2.2–2.6	—	—	—	—	—	—	—	—	—
	1100801	42	—	—	—	—	—	—	—	—	—	—
	1100830	55	2.2–2.6	32	50	1119515	.015	.030	1.5–3.2	.067	.014	13.5–14.4
	1100832	37	2.2–2.6	25	35	1119515	.015	.030	1.5–3.2	.067	.014	13.5–14.4
	1100905	37	2.2–2.6	25	35	1119515	.015	.030	1.5–3.2	.067	.014	13.5–14.4
1971	1100550	37	4.0–4.5	—	32	—	—	—	—	—	—	—
	1100920	55	4.0–4.5	—	50	—	—	—	—	—	—	—
	1100927	37	4.0–4.5	—	32	—	—	—	—	—	—	—
	1100928	55	4.0–4.5	—	50	—	—	—	—	—	—	—
	1101015	80	4.0–4.5	—	74	—	—	—	—	—	—	—
	1100566	37	2.2–2.6	25	35	1119515	.015	.030	1.5–3.2	.067	.014	13.8–14.8
	1100836	37	2.2–2.6	25	35	1119515	.015	.030	1.5–3.2	.067	.014	13.8–14.8
	1100843	61	2.2–2.6	33	58	1119515	.015	.030	1.5–3.2	.067	.014	13.8–14.8
1972	1100927	37	4.0–4.5	—	32	—	—	—	—	—	—	—
	1100928	55	4.0–4.5	—	50	—	—	—	—	—	—	—
	1101015	80	4.0–4.5	—	74	—	—	—	—	—	—	—
	1100566	37	—	—	35	1119515	.015	.030	1.5–3.2	.067	.014	13.8–14.8
	1102440	37	—	—	32	1119515	.015	.030	1.5–3.2	.067	.014	13.8–14.8
	1102463	61	—	—	55	1119515	.015	.030	1.5–3.2	.067	.014	13.8–14.8

REAR AXLE SPECIFICATIONS

Year	Model	Carrier Type	Ring Gear & Pinion Backlash		Pinion Bearing Preload			Differential Bearing Preload		
			Method	Adjustment	Method	New Bearings Inch-Lbs.	Used Bearings Inch-Lbs.	Method	New Bearings Inch-Lbs.	Used Bearings Inch-Lbs.
1966–72	All	Integral	Shims	.005–.009	③	20–30	14–20	Shims	②	②
1970–72	—	Integral①	Shims	.005–.008	Spacer	20–25	10–15	Shims	②	②
1971–72	Ventura II	Integral①	Shims	.005–.008	Spacer	25	10	Shims	②	②

①—Type C differential (use "C" washers to retain axle shafts).
②—Slip fit plus .008" tight.
③—Tighten pinion shaft nut with inch-pound torque wrench.

STARTING MOTOR SPECIFICATIONS

Year	Model	Starter Number	Brush Spring Tension Oz①	Free Speed Test			Resistance Test③	
				Amps. ①	Volts	R.P.M. ①	Amps. ①	Volts
1966–67	V8s	1107355	35	70–99②	10.6	7800–12000	410–480②	3.0
1966	6-230 Std. Trans.	1107360	35	49–76②	10.6	6200–9400	270–310②	4.3
	6-230 Auto. Trans.	1107363	35	49–76②	10.6	6200–9400	270–310	4.3
	6-230 Prem. Fuel	1107373	35	65–110②	10.6	3600–5100	300–360	3.5
1967–69	6-230, 6-250	1107499	35	49–76②	10.6	6200–9600	270–310	4.3
1968–69	V8s	1107293	—	—	—	—	—	—
	V8s	1107355	35	70–99②	10.6	6800–9400	410–480②	3.0
	6-250 Auto. Trans.	1107594	—	50②	9	5500–10500	—	—
	6-250 Firebird	1108329	—	50②	9	5500–10500	—	—
	V8-400 Firebird	1108335	—	65②	9	7500–10500	—	—
	V8-400 Ram Air Eng.	1108353	—	65②	9	7500–10500	—	—
	V8-350 Firebird	1108328	—	55②	9	3500–6000	—	—
1970	6-250	1108439	—	50②	9	5500–10500	—	—
	V8-350	1108434	—	55②	9	3500–6000	—	—
	V8-400, 455	1108435	—	65②	9	7500–10500	—	—
1971-72	6-250	1108365	35	50②	9	5500–10500	—	—
	V8-307	1108367	35	50–80②	9	5500–10500	—	—
	V8-350	1108445	—	55②	9	3500–6000	—	—
	V8-400, 455	1108446	—	65②	9	7500–10500	—	—
	V8-455	1108436	—	65②	9	7500–10500	—	—

①—Minimum. ②—Includes solenoid.
③—Check capacity of motor by using a 500 ampere meter and a carbon pile rheostat to control voltage. Apply volts listed across motor with armature locked. Current should be as listed.

ENGINE TIGHTENING SPECIFICATIONS★

★Torque specifications are for clean and lightly lubricated threads only. Dry or dirty threads produce increased friction which prevents accurate measurement of tightness.

Year	Model	Spark Plugs Ft. Lbs.	Cylinder Head Bolts Ft. Lbs.	Intake Manifold Ft. Lbs.	Exhaust Manifold Ft. Lbs.	Rocker Arm Ft. Lbs.	Rocker Arm Cover Ft. Lbs.	Connecting Rod Cap Bolts Ft. Lbs.	Main Bearing Cap Bolts Ft. Lbs.	Flywheel to Crankshaft Ft. Lbs.	Vibration Damper or Pulley Ft. Lbs.
1966	6-230	20	93	30	30	—	15	33	100	60	160
	V8's	25	95	40	30	20	5	45	95③	95	160
	326, 389	25	95	40	30	20	5	45	95③	95	160
	421	25	95	40	30	20	5	45	95③	95	160
1967–69	6 Cyl.	20	95	30	30	—	15	33	100	60	160
	V8's	20	95	40	30	20	5	43	100③	95	160
1970–72	6 Cyl.④	15	95	②	25	—	55⑤	35	65	60	—
	V8-307⑦	15	65	30	20⑥	—	45⑤	45	75	60	60
	V8's	25	95	40	30	20	8	43	100③	95	160

②—Outer 20, all others 30.　　　　　④—For service on this engine, see Six Cylinder in Chevrolet Chapter.
③—Rear 120.　　　　　⑤—Inch pounds.
　　　　　⑥—Inside bolts 30 ft. lbs.
　　　　　⑦—For service on this engine, see Chevrolet Chapter.

PISTONS, PINS, RINGS, CRANKSHAFT & BEARINGS

Year	Model	Piston Skirt Clearance	Ring End Gap①		Wrist-pin Diameter	Rod Bearings		Main Bearings			
			Comp.	Oil		Shaft Diameter	Bearing Clearance	Shaft Diameter	Bearing Clearance	Thrust on Bear. No.	Shaft End Play
1966	6-230	.0022–.0028	.010	.015	.9272	2.00	.0007–.0027	2.30	.0003–.0019	7	.002–.006
	V8-326	.0022–.0028	②	.015	.9802	2.25	.0005–.0025	3.00	.0002–.0017	4	.006–.011
	V8-389	.0022–.0028	②	.015	.9802	2.2492–2.2502	.0005–.0025	3.00	.0002–.0017	4	.0035–.0085
	V8-421	.0017–.0013	②	.035	.9802	2.2492–2.2502	.0014–.0025	3.25	.0005–.0020	4	.0035–.0085
1967	6-230	.0022–.0028	.015	.035	.9272	2.00	.0007–.0027	2.30	.0003–.0019	7	.002–.006
	V8-326	.0022–.0028	.019	.035	.9802	2.25	.0005–.0025	3.00	.0002–.0017	4	.0035–.0085
	V8-400	.0022–.0028	③	.035	.9802	2.25	.0005–.0026	3.00	.0002–.0017	4	.0035–.0085
	8-428 Std.	.0017–.0033	③	.035	.9802	2.25	.0005–.0026	3.25	.0002–.0017	4	.0035–.0085
	8-428 H.O.	.0025–.0041	③	.035	.9802	2.25	.0005–.0026	3.25	.0005–.0021	4	.0035–.0085
1968	6-250	.0022–.0028	.015	.035	.9272	2.00	.0007–.0027	2.30	.0003–.0019	7	.002–.006
	V8-350	.0022–.0028	.019	.035	.9802	2.25	.0005–.0025	3.00	.0002–.0017	4	.0035–.0085
	V8-400	.0025–.0031	.019	.035	.9802	2.25	.0005–.0026	3.00	.0002–.0017	4	.0035–.0085
	V8-428	.0030–.0036	③	.035	.9802	2.25	.0005–.0026	3.25	.0005–.0021	4	.0035–.0085
1969	6-250	.0022–.0038	.015	.035	.9272	2.00	.0005–.0028	2.30	.0003–.0020	7	.002–.006
	V8-350	.0025–.0031	.020	.035	.9802	2.25	.0005–.0025	3.00	.0002–.0020	4	.003–.009
	V8-400	.0025–.0031⑤	.020	.035	.9802	2.25	.0005–.0025	3.00	.0002–.0020	4	.003–.009
	V8-428	.0030–.0036	.020	.035	.9802	2.25	.0005–.0025	3.25	.0002–.0020	4	.003–.009
1970–72	6-250④	.0005–.0015	.010	.015	.9272	2.00	.0007–.0027	2.30	.0003–.0029	7	.002–.006
	V8-307⑧	.0005–.0011	.010	.015	.927	2.099–2.100	.0013–.0035	⑨	⑩	5	.002–.006
	V8-350	.0025–.0033	.019	.035	.9802	2.25	.0005–.0025	3.00	.0002–.0017	4	.0035–.0085
	V8-400	.0025–.0033	⑥	.035	.9802	2.25	.0005–.0025	3.00	.0002–.0017	4	.0035–.0085
	V8-455	.0025–.0033	⑦	.035	.9802	2.25	.0005–.0026	3.25	.0005–.0021	4	.0035–.0085

①—Fit rings in tapered bores for clearance listed in tightest portion of ring travel.
②—Top ring .021″, second ring .019″.
③—Top ring .020″, second ring .018″.
④—For service on this engine, see Six Cylinder in Chevrolet Chapter.
⑤—V8-400 Ram Air IV use .0055–.0061″.
⑥—Top ring .019″, second ring .015″.
⑦—Top ring .021″, second ring .015″.
⑧—For service on this engine, see Chevrolet Chapter.
⑨—Front: 2.4502, Rear: 2.4507, others: 2.4505.
⑩—No. 1: .0008–.002; No. 2, 3, 4, .0011–.0023; No. 5: .0017–.0033.

BRAKE SPECIFICATIONS

Year	Model	Brake Drum Inside Diameter	Wheel Cylinder Bore Diameter			Master Cylinder Bore Diameter		
			Disc Brake	Front Drum Brake	Rear Drum Brake	Disc Brakes	Drum Brakes	Power Brakes
1966	Pontiac	11	—	1 3/16	15/16	—	7/8	7/8
	Tempest	9½	—	1 1/8	15/16	—	7/8	7/8
1967	Pontiac	11	2 1/16	1 3/16	15/16	1 1/8	1	1
	Tempest	9½	2 1/16	1 1/8	7/8	1 1/8	1	1
1968	Firebird	9½	2 1/16	1 1/8	7/8	1 1/8	1	1
	Inter. Models	9½	2 1/16	1 1/8	7/8	1 1/8	1	1
	Full Size Models	11	2 1/16	1 1/8	15/16	1 1/8	1	1
1969–72	①	9½	2 15/16	1 1/8	7/8	1 1/8	1	1
	Pontiac	11②	2 15/16	1 1/8	15/16	1 1/8	1	1

①—Intermediates, Ventura II, Firebird and Grand Prix.
②—1971-72 Wagon, 12″.

WHEEL ALIGNMENT SPECIFICATIONS

OLD CAR SPECIFICATIONS: For 1946-65 Wheel Alignment Specifications see back of book.

Year	Model	Caster Angle, Degrees Limits	Caster Desired	Camber Limits Left	Camber Limits Right	Camber Desired Left	Camber Desired Right	Toe-In. Inch	Toe-Out on Turns, Deg. Outer Wheel	Toe-Out Inner Wheel
1966	Tempest Cars	−1 to −2	−1½	−¼ to +¾	−¼ to +¾	+¼	+¼	0-⅛	19	20
	Tempest Wagons	−1½ to −2½	−2	−¼ to +¾	−¼ to +¾	+¼	+¼	0-⅛	19	20
	Pontiac	−1 to −2	−1½	−¼ to +¾	−¼ to +¾	+¼	+¼	0-⅛	19	20
1967	Intermediates	−1 to −2	−1½	−¼ to +¾	−¼ to +¾	+¼	+¼	0-⅛	18.6	20
	Full Size Models	−2 to −1	−1½	+¼ to +½	+¼ to +½	+⅜	+⅜	0-⅛	19.4	20
1968	Firebird	0 to +1	+½	−¼ to +¾	−¼ to +¾	+¼	+¼	⅛-¼	—	20
	Intermediates	−2 to −1	−1½	−¼ to +¾	−¼ to +¾	+¼	+¼	0-⅛	18.6	20
	Full Size Models	−2 to −1	−1½	−¼ to +¾	−¼ to +¾	+¼	+¼	0-⅛	18.4	20
1969–70	Firebird (1969)	0 to +1	+½	0 to +½	0 to +½	+¼	+¼	⅛-¼	18	20
	Firebird (1970)	−½ to +½	Zero	+½ to +1½	+½ to +1½	+1	+1	⅛-³⁄₁₆	18	20
	Intermediates	−1 to −2	−1½①	0 to +½	0 to +½	+¼	+¼	0-⅛	18	20
	Full Size Models	−1 to −2	−1½	0 to +½	0 to +½	+¼	+¼	0-⅛	18	20
1971-72	Firebird	−½ to +½	Zero	+½ to +1½	+½ to +1½	+1	+1	⅛-¼	18	20
	Ventura II	0 to +1	+½	−¼ to +¾	−¼ to +¾	+½	+½	⅛ to ¼	—	20
	②	−1 to −2	−1½	−½ to +½	−½ to +½	Zero	Zero	¹⁄₁₆-³⁄₁₆	18	20
	③	+½ to +1½	+1	+¼ to +1¼	+¼ to +1¼	+¾	+¾	⅛-¼	18	20

①—Station Wagons, −2°.   ②—Intermediates and Grand Prix.   ③—Catalina, Grandville and Bonneville.

COOLING SYSTEM & CAPACITY DATA

Year	Model or Engine	Cooling Capacity No Heater	With Heater	With A/C	Radiator Cap Relief Pressure With A/C	Radiator Cap No A/C	Thermo. Opening Temp.①	Fuel Tank Gals.	Engine Oil Refill Qts.②	Trans. 3 Speed Pints	4 Speed Pints	Auto. Trans. Qts.⑫	Rear Axle Oil Pints
1966	6-230	—	13½	14½	14-17	14-17	190	21½	5	2.8	—	3⑭	3
	V8-326	—	20½	22	14-17	14-17	190	21½	6	2.8	2½	3⑭	3
	V8-389	—	20	21½	14-17	14-17	190	21½	6	2.8	2½	3⑭	3
	Pontiac 2+2	—	19½	19½	14-17	14-17	190	26½	6	2.8	2½	3¾⑧	4½
	All Others	—	20	20	14-17	14-17	190	26½⑦	6	2.8	2½	3¾⑧	4½
1967	6-230	—	12.1	12.7	14-17	14-17	190	21½	5	2.8	—	2½⑧	3
	V8-326	—	18.6	20.2	14-17	14-17	190	21½	6	2.8	2½	2½⑧	3
	V8-400⑪	—	17.8	19.4	14-17	14-17	190	21½	6	2.8	2½	3¾⑧	3
	Grand Prix	—	18.6	18.6	14-17	14-17	190	26½	6	2.8	2½	3¾⑧	4½
	V8-428 Hi Perf.	—	17.2	17.2	14-17	14-17	190	26½	6	2.8	2½	3¾⑧	4½
	Others	—	18	18	14-17	14-17	190	26½⑦	6	2.8	2½	3¾⑧	4½
1968	6-250	—	12.1	12.7	14-17	14-17	190	18½	5	3½	3½	2½⑧	3
	8-350	—	18.6	20.2	14-17	14-17	190	18½	5	2.8	2½	2½⑧	3
	8-350 Fi'bd H.O.	—	18.6	20.2	14-17	14-17	190	18½	5	—	3½	2½⑧	3
	8-400 Firebird	—	17.8	19.4	14-17	14-17	190	18½	5	—	2½	3¾⑧	3
	8-400 Tempest	—	17.8	19.4	14-17	14-17	190	21½	5	3½	3½	3¾⑧	3
	Le Mans V8	—	17.8	19.4	14-17	14-17	190	21½	5	2.8	2½	2½⑧	3
	GTO	—	17.8	19.4	14-17	14-17	190	21½	5	—	2½	3¾⑧	3
	Grand Prix	—	18.6	18.6	14-17	14-17	190	26½⑦	5	5	2½	3¾⑧	4½
	V8-428	—	17.2	17.2	14-17	14-17	190	26½⑦	5	5	2½	3¾⑧	4½
	Others	—	18	18	14-17	14-17	190	26½⑦	5	5	2½	3¾⑧	4½

Continued

COOLING SYSTEM & CAPACITY DATA—Continued

Year	Model or Engine	Cooling Capacity, Qts.			Radiator Cap Relief Pressure, Lbs.		Thermo. Opening Temp. ①	Fuel Tank Gals.	Engine Oil Refill Qts. ②	Transmission Oil			Rear Axle Oil Pints
		No Heater	With Heater	With A/C	With A/C	No A/C				3 Speed Pints	4 Speed Pints	Auto. Trans. Qts. ⑫	
1969	6-250	—	12	12¼	14–17	14–17	190	21½⑮	4½⑯	3½	3½	⑰	3
	8-350 Tempest	—	20	21¼	14–17	14–17	190	21½⑮	5	3½	3½	⑰	3
	8-400 Tempest	—	18¼	19¾	14–17	14–17	190	21½⑮	5	3½	3½	⑰	3
	8-350 Firebird	—	19½	20¼	14–17	14–17	190	18½	5	3½	3½	⑰	3
	8-400 Firebird	—	18½	18¾	14–17	14–17	190	18½	5	3½	3½	⑰	3
	8-400 Pontiac	—	18	18	14–17	14–17	190	26½⑦	5	2.8	—	⑰	4½
	8-428 Pontiac	—	17¼	17¼	14–17	14–17	190	26½⑦	5	2.8	—	⑰	4½
	8-400 Grand Prix	—	18¾	21	14–17	14–17	190	21½	5	2.8	2.5	⑰	3
	8-428 Grand Prix	—	17½	17½	14–17	14–17	190	21½	5	2.8	2.5	⑰	3
1970	6-250	—	11.3	13	14–17	14–17	195	21.5	4	3.5	2½	3¼⑲	3
	V8-350 Tempest	—	19.6	19.6	14–17	14–17	190	21.5	5	⑱	2½	3¼⑲	3
	V8-350 Pontiac	—	19.6	19.6	14–17	14–17	190	26⑦	5	⑱	—	3¼⑲	4½
	V8-400 G.T.O.	—	18.3	18.3	14–17	14–17	190	21.5	5	2.8	2½	3¼⑲	3⑳
	V8-350 Firebird	—	19½	20¼	14–17	14–17	190	19½③	5	④	2½	⑤	3¾
	V8-400 Firebird	—	18½	18¾	14–17	14–17	190	19½③	5	④	2½	⑤	3¾
	V8-400 Pontiac	—	18	18	14–17	14–17	190	26⑦	5	2.8	—	3¼⑲	4½
	V8-400 Gr'd Prix	—	18.7	21.1	14–17	14–17	190	21.5	5	2.8	2½	3¼⑲	3⑳
	V8-455 Gr'd Prix	—	17.5	19.9	14–17	14–17	190	21.5	5	2.8	2½	3¼⑲	3⑳
	V8-455 Pontiac	—	17.2	17.2	14–17	14–17	190	26⑦	5	2.8	—	3¼⑲	4½
1971	6-250 Firebird	—	12	—	14–17	14–17	195	17	4	3.5	3.5	3⑲	4¼
	6-250 Tempest	—	13	12.4	14–17	14–17	195	19⑥	4	3.5	—	3⑲	3
	6-250 Ventura II	—	12.4	—	14–17	14–17	195	16	4	3.5	—	3⑲	3¾
	8-307 Ventura II	14.5	15.5	16.5	14–17	14–17	195	16	4	3.5	—	3⑲	3¾
	8-350 Firebird	—	19.4	20.3	14–17	14–17	195	19	5	3.5	3.5	3⑲	4¼
	8-350 Tempest	—	20.2	20.9	14–17	14–17	195	19⑥	5	3.5㉑	2.5	3⑲	3
	8-350 Pontiac	—	20.2	21	14–17	14–17	195	23.6㉒	5	2.8	—	3⑲	3
	8-400 Firebird	—	18.6	18.7	14–17	14–17	195	17	5	2.8	2.5	3¾⑲	4¼
	8-400 Tempest	—	18.6	20.8	14–17	14–17	195	19⑥	5	2.8	2.5	3¾⑲	3
	8-400 Pontiac	—	18.6	19.6	14–17	14–17	195	23.6㉒	5	2.8	2.5	3¾⑲	3
	8-400 Gr'd Prix	—	18.7	19.7	14–17	14–17	195	23.5	5	2.8	2.5	3¾⑲	3⑳
	8-455 Firebird	—	17.9	18.7	14–17	14–17	195	17	5	2.8	2.5	3¾⑲	4¼
	8-455 Tempest	—	18.6	20.8	14–17	14–17	195	19⑥	5	2.8	2.5	3¾⑲	3
	8-455 Pontiac	—	17.9	19	14–17	14–17	195	23.6㉒	5	—	2.5	3¾⑲	3
	8-455 Gr'd Prix	—	18.7	19.7	14–17	14–17	195	23.5	5	—	2.5	3¾⑲	3⑳
1972	6-250 Ventrua II	—	12	16	14–17	14–17	195	16	4	3	—	6	3¾
	6-250 Firebird	—	12	—	14–17	14–17	195	17	4	3½	—	6	4¼
	6-250 Le Mans	—	13	12.4	14–17	14–17	195	20㉓	4	3½	—	6	5⑳
	8-307 Ventura II	—	15	16	14–17	14–17	195	16	4	3	—	⑤	3¾
	8-350 Ventrua II	—	19.4	20.3	14–17	14–17	195	16	5	—	—	⑤	3¾
	8-350 Firebird	—	19.4	20.3	14–17	14–17	195	17	5	2.8	2.5	6	4¼
	8-350 LeMans	—	20.2	20.9	14–17	14–17	195	20㉓	5	3½	2.5	6	3⑳
	8-400 Pontiac	—	18.6	19.6	14–17	14–17	195	25㉓	5	—	—	7½	5½
	8-400 Firebird	—	18.6	18.7	14–17	14–17	195	17	5	—	2.5	7½	4¼
	8-400 LeMans	—	18.6	20.8	14–17	14–17	196	20㉓	5	2.8	2.5	7½	3⑳
	8-400 Gr'd Prix	—	18.7	19.7	14–17	14–17	195	26	5	—	—	7½	3⑳
	8-455 Pontiac	—	17.9	19.0	14–17	14–17	195	25㉓	5	—	—	7½	5½
	8-455 Firebird	—	17.9	18.9	14–17	14–17	195	17	5	—	2.5	7½	4¼
	8-455 LeMans	—	17.9	18.9	14–17	14–17	195	20㉓	5	—	2.5	7½	3⑳

①—With alcohol-type anti-freeze use a 160° unit.
②—Add one quart with filter change.
③—With Evaporative Control System 17.
④—Saginaw 3.5, Muncie 4.
⑤—Two speed unit; oil pan 3 qts., complete refill 9½ qts. Turbo Hydra Matic 350; oil pan 2½ qts., complete refill 5 qts. Turbo Hydra Matic 400; oil pan 3¾ qts., complete refill 9½ qts.
⑥—Station Wagons 21.5.

⑦—Station Wagons 24 gals.
⑧—Oil pan only. After overhaul 9½ qts.
⑨—Oil pan only. After overhaul 8½ qts.
⑩—Oil pan only. After overhaul 7½ qts.
⑪—Intermediate models.
⑫—Approximate. Make final check with dipstick.
⑬—Oil pan only. After overhaul 10 qts.
⑭—Oil pan only. After overhaul 9¼ qts.
⑮—Station Wagons 20 gals.
⑯—Add ½ qt. with filter change.

⑰—Two speed unit; oil pan 2½ qts. and complete refill 7½ qts. Three speed unit ("J" Prefix); oil pan 3 qts. and complete refill 10 qts. Three speed unit ("P" Prefix); oil pan 3.7 qts. and complete refill 9½ qts.
⑱—Standard unit 3.5 pints, heavy duty 2.8 pints.
⑲—Oil pan only.
⑳—5 pts. with 8¾" ring gear.
㉑—Heavy duty 2.8.
㉒—Station Wagons 22.5.
㉓—Station Wagon 23.

Electrical Section

DISTRIBUTOR, REPLACE

1. Disconnect distributor-to-coil primary wire.
2. Remove distributor cap.
3. Crank engine so rotor is in position to fire No. 1 cylinder and timing mark on vibration damper is indexed with pointer.
4. Remove vacuum line from distributor.
5. Remove distributor clamp.
6. Lift distributor from engine.

Installation

1. Check to see that engine is at firing position for No. 1 cylinder.
2. Install new gasket on block.
3. Install distributor so vacuum unit faces right side of engine and rotor points toward contact in cap for No. 1 cylinder.
4. Install distributor clamp, leaving screw loose enough to allow distributor to be turned for adjustment.
5. Attach vacuum line to distributor.
6. Install wires in distributor cap.
7. Attach distributor primary wire.
8. Adjust point gap, replace cap and set ignition timing.

STARTER, REPLACE

1966-72 Six-Cyl.

1. Disconnect ground cable at battery.
2. Disconnect cable and wiring harness leads from starter solenoid.
3. Unfasten and remove starter.

1966-72 V8s

1. Disconnect cable from battery.
2. Raise front of car and pull battery cable and solenoid wire loom down so they hang free of surrounding parts.
3. Unfasten and remove starter with cable and solenoid wire loom.
4. Remove wires from solenoid and cable from clamp or solenoid bracket.
5. Reverse procedure to install.

IGNITION SWITCH, REPLACE

1969-72

1. Disconnect battery and loosen toe pan screws.
2. Lower steering column from instrument panel.
3. Disconnect switch wires and remove switch.
4. To replace switch move key lock to OFF-LOCK position.
5. Move actuator rod hole in switch to OFF-LOCK position, Fig. 1.
6. Install switch with rod in hole.

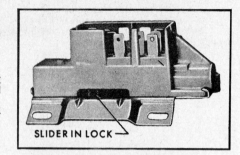

Fig. 1 Ignition switch. 1969-72

1966-68

1. Disconnect a battery cable.
2. Remove lock cylinder (see below).
3. Remove ignition switch ferrule by unscrewing it with a suitable spanner wrench.
4. Remove switch lamp housing brace screw from bottom flange of instrument panel.
5. Remove switch from back of panel and disconnect wires after unlatching special locking terminal.
6. Reverse above procedure to install.

Switch Lock Cylinder

1. Place ignition key in lock and depress lock plunger by inserting a small pin through hole in lock cap.
2. While holding plunger in, turn key about 20-deg. counterclockwise to release lock cylinder and remove cylinder from switch.
3. To install, insert key in cylinder. Then with key and cylinder turned about 20-deg. counterclockwise, insert cylinder in lock and rotate clockwise to lock in place.

FREE UP LOCK: Occasionally an ignition lock may stick, making it difficult to insert key and turn lock. If this occurs, blow a small quantity of powdered graphite into the lock key hole and operate key several times until lock operates freely.

If ignition switch will not free up by the use of the graphite, it must be replaced. To remove a stuck lock use a ⅜" drill and drill out the center of the cylinder. The lock tumblers must be destroyed before the cylinder can be removed.

LIGHT SWITCH, REPLACE

1971-72

1. Depress button on switch and remove knob and shaft.
2. Remove retaining nut.
3. Remove wire connector from switch and remove switch.

1966-70

1. Remove battery cable, pull knob to

"On" position, depress latch button and remove knob and shaft.
2. Remove retaining nut.
3. Remove wire connector and remove switch.
4. On vacuum-operated headlight models, remove vacuum connector.
5. Reverse procedure to install.

STOP LIGHT SWITCH, REPLACE

1966-72

The stop light switch has a slip fit in the mounting sleeve which permits positive adjustment by pulling the brake pedal up firmly against the stop. The pedal arm forces the switch body to slip in the mounting sleeve bushing to position the switch properly.

1. Disconnect wires from switch and remove switch from bracket.
2. Position switch in bracket and push in to maximum distance. Brake pedal arm moves switch to correct distance on rebound. Check if pedal is in full return position by lifting slightly by hand.
3. Connect switch wires by inserting plug on switch.

NEUTRAL SAFETY SWITCH

1969-72

1. To replace switch, position shift tube in drive position.
2. Insert switch drive tang in shifter tube slot and assemble switch to column jacket.
3. To adjust switch, position and hold shift lever in low range while inserting blade of reset gauge J23056-2 into the RESET slot of switch. Be sure the tool is inserted about ⁹/₁₆".
4. Insert blade of gauge J22701-5 into ADJUST slot of switch and move shift lever to park position and remove gauge.
5. Check starter in all ranges.

1966-68

Properly adjusted the switch should turn on the back-up lights in reverse and prevent engine cranking with the selector lever in any position other than Park or Neutral. If the engine cranks in any other position, adjust by loosening the mounting screws and repositioning as required.

If console shift, adjust switch adjusting screw.

On 1967 Pontiac, GTO and Firebird, rivet heads must be removed and rivets punched through into column to remove switch. Replace rivets with ¼ x ⁷/₃₂" self-tapping screws. *Screws must not be larger than ¼" or damage to column may result.*

CLUTCH START SWITCH
1969-72

All cars equipped with a manual transmission use a clutch start switch which is mounted on the pedal bracket. The switch closes when the clutch is depressed and completes solenoid connection. When installing switch, no adjustment is necessary.

TURN SIGNAL SWITCH
1969-72

NOTE: *On tilt column, the column must first be lowered from panel.*

1. Remove steering wheel using puller.

   CAUTION: *Do not hammer on end of shaft as hammering could collapse shaft or loosen plastic injections which maintain column rigidity.*

2. Remove three cover screws and lift cover off shaft.

   NOTE: Screw retainers will be lost if screws are removed completely from cover.

3. Depress lock plate and pry round wire lock ring out of shaft groove.
4. Slide upper bearing preload spring and turn signal cancelling cam off shaft.
5. Slide thrust washer off shaft and remove turn signal lever.
6. Push hazard warning switch in and unscrew knob.
7. Pull turn signal wiring connector out of bracket on jacket and disconnect.
8. Remove three turn signal switch screws and pull switch straight up.

1967-68 Non-Tilt Column

1. Remove steering wheel.

   CAUTION: *Do not hammer on steering shaft as column jacket could be collapsed.*

2. Remove upper bearing preload spring and turn signal cancelling cam off steering shaft.
3. Remove turn signal lever screw and lever. On Tempest and Firebirds with automatic transmission and column shift, remove shift indicator bezel by removing two clips between bezel and inside of switch cover.
4. Push in hazard warning knob and unscrew knob. On 1967, remove turn signal cover, switch retaining screws and switch. On 1968, proceed with disassembly.
5. Remove snap ring from upper steering shaft by sliding sideways out of groove. Do not pry against switch.
6. Slide thrust washer and wave washer off upper steering shaft.
7. Disconnect turn signal switch wiring harness at connector under instrument panel.
8. Remove steering column mounting bracket to provide clearance so that wiring and curved connector can be removed.

9. Pry wiring harness cover off steering column and allow wiring harness to hang free.
10. Position mounting bracket back under instrument panel and install two nuts holding bracket to instrument panel.
11. Loosen three switch mounting screws until cover can be rotated counterclockwise. It may be necessary to push on top of screws to loosen. Rotate cover counterclockwise and pull straight off top of jacket.
12. Remove three mounting screws completely from engagement with the lock plate. Be careful of the three springs which may be lost during this action.
13. Pull switch and housing from cover.
14. Reverse procedure to install.

1967-68 Tilt Column

1. Remove steering wheel.

   CAUTION: *Do not hammer on steering shaft as column jacket could be collapsed.*

2. Remove turn signal cancelling cam and cam spring.
3. Remove tilt release lever and turn signal lever. On Tempest and Firebird with automatic transmission and column shift, remove shift indicator bezel (2 screws each side of bezel).
4. Push in hazard flasher knob, remove knob and turn signal cover. On 1967, disconnect and remove switch and harness. Cut signal harness to allow removal of switch.

   NOTE: *A wire or string attached to wires of harness when pulled through will aid in re-assembly.*

   On 1968, proceed with disassembly.
5. Remove steering column mounting bracket. With mounting bracket removed, pry wiring harness off steering column and allow wiring to hang free.
6. Position mounting bracket back underneath instrument panel and install two nuts attaching bracket to panel.
7. Unplug wiring harness from body harness and disconnect curved connector from wiring harness. Be sure to note exact location of each wire prior to removing from connector body.
8. Remove three turn signal attaching screws and withdraw a wiring harness from steering column.
9. Reverse procedure to install.

1966 Pontiac

Regular Column
1. Remove steering wheel.
2. Remove spring and cam assembly.
3. Unscrew lever from switch.
4. Remove shift lever and spring by removing pivot pin and shim.
5. Disconnect horn wire and turn signal connector.
6. Remove lower trim cover plate.
7. Remove screw which retains washer assembly to column jacket.
8. Remove 3 screws from turn signal housing and lift bearing and turn

signal switch from housing.
9. Rotate turn signal housing counterclockwise and lift off.
10. Remove flat washer.
11. Slide off gearshift lever housing. *On cars with automatic transmission, remove screw and washer that retains tube assembly to shift lever housing.*
12. Remove spacers, washers and sleeve.
13. Reverse procedure to install.

NOTE: After new turn signal switch has been installed to turn signal housing, the wire harness must be inserted through gearshift housing and sleeve before these parts are installed over column assembly.

Tilt Column
1. Remove wiring connector and switch from steering column.
2. Loosen screw and remove control cable from switch.
3. To install, place steering wheel in "pull-down" position.
4. Place switch lever in neutral.
5. Hook control cable wire over actuating pin on switch.
6. Move carrier in switch to neutral position.
7. Lock cable by tightening clamp screw.
8. Locate circuit switch on steering column mast jacket so there is no slack in conduit. Start two mounting screws. *Do not pull on switch so as to extend switch slide screw.*
9. Make certain that lever and switch are still in neutral, then tighten two switch mounting screws.

1966 Tempest

1. Remove steering wheel.
2. Remove spring and cam assembly.
3. Remove lever from switch.
4. Remove lever retaining pin and lever.
5. Disconnect horn wire and turn signal connector.
6. Remove 2 screws from lower trim cover plate.
7. Remove column bracket so wire loom can slide through.
8. Remove wiring cover.
9. Remove 3 screws on upper bearing and turn signal switch.
10. Remove signal and housing, and shift lever housing from steering jacket. *Signal housing will need to be rotated.*
11. Remove turn signal from signal and shift lever housing.
12. Reverse procedure to install.

NOTE: Turn signal control assembly must be in neutral position when installing steering wheel to prevent damage to cancelling cam and control assembly.

HORN SOUNDER & STEERING WHEEL
1966-72

1. Lift ornament out of wheel hub.
2. Remove nut and washer from shaft. On 1966 Tempest, remove spacer bushing.

3. Remove horn bar (deluxe wheel) or extension and switch assembly (standard wheel).
4. Use a suitable puller to remove wheel.
5. Reverse procedure to install, making sure wheel is in straight ahead position.

INSTRUMENT CLUSTER

1971-72 Ventura II

1. Disconnect battery and remove steering column cover trim.
2. Remove three screws retaining heater or A/C control panel to instrument panel carrier.
3. Remove radio control knobs, bezels and nuts.
4. Remove screws at top, bottom and side of carrier securing it to instrument panel pad.
5. Disconnect shift quadrant indicator cable at shaft bowl (if automatic), remove two steering column to panel nuts.
6. Remove toe plate cover and five toe plate to cowl screws, lower column from panel and protect it with shop towels or tape.
7. Remove ground wire screw from under left side of panel pad above kick pad and disconnect speedo cable from under dash.
8. Tilt carrier and cluster rearward, disconnect printed circuit and cluster ground connectors and rest assembly on top of column.
9. Remove screws from cluster to carrier assembly and remove cluster.

1971-72 Catalina, Grandville, Bonneville

1. Disconnect battery and remove upper instrument panel trim plate.
2. Remove transmission shift indicator (if automatic) and speedometer cluster bezel.
3. Remove cluster retaining screws, pull rearward, disconnect speedometer cable and printed circuit connector.

1971-72 T-37, LeMans & GTO

1. Disconnect battery and remove lower A/C duct if equipped.
2. Remove lower instrument panel trim and glove box.
3. Lower steering column.
4. Disconnect speedometer cable and heater cable at heater case.
5. Remove three instrument panel screws at gauges.
6. Remove three right upper instrument panel nuts.
7. Remove lower instrument panel bolts at right and left ends and at steering column.
8. Position crash pad outward on column.
9. Disconnect printed circuit.
10. Remove instrument panel harness retaining screws.
11. Remove cluster retaining screws and remove cluster.

1971-72 Grand Prix

1. Disconnect battery and remove lower A/C duct if equipped.
2. Remove pillar post mouldings and filler plate at windshield.
3. Remove lower instrument panel trim at steering column.
4. Disconnect speedometer cable and radio antenna lead.
5. Lower steering column.
6. Remove upper air outlet vents and instrument panel attaching screws at steering column, console, ends and upper center.
7. Remove lower defroster duct screw at heater case.
8. Position instrument panel pad outward on column.
9. Disconnect printed circuit.
10. Remove wire harness retaining screws and cluster ground screw.
11. Remove cluster mounting screws and cluster.

1970-72 Firebird

1. Disconnect battery cable and upper instrument panel trim plate.
2. Remove lower instrument panel trim and bracket at steering column.
3. Loosen two steering column nuts to lower column.
4. Remove cluster screws, pull rearward, disconnect speedometer cable and printed circuit connector.

1969-70 Grand Prix

1. Disconnect battery and remove glove box.
2. Disconnect speedo cable and wire connectors at headlight switch, wipers, turn signal, ignition switch, printed circuit, heater and air conditioner panel.
3. Remove lower column trim and disconnect air control cable at heater case.
4. Remove screws at instrument locations and instrument panel to column support.
5. Remove screws at outboard lower ends of panel.
6. Remove screws retaining right and left side of instrument panel to body. To do this, remove upper vent nozzles by inserting two thin blade screwdrivers on right and left side of nozzle to disengage retaining clips.
7. Remove upper instrument panel cover plate. Studs are pushed into retainers, pry up carefully to remove.
8. Remove two upper panel retaining screws and upper speaker support bracket screw.
9. Remove console to instrument panel screws.
10. Loosen toe plate screws.
11. Remove column to lower panel retaining nuts and lower column.
12. Pull entire instrument panel rearward on left far enough to gain access to cluster.
13. Remove ground strap screws and panel harness retaining screws.
14. Remove cluster retaining screws and remove cluster.

1969-70 Pontiac

1. Disconnect battery.

2. Remove lower instrument panel cover and remove radio.
3. Remove heater or air conditioning control panel.
4. Disconnect speedometer, printed circuit connector, cigar lighter and instrument panel harness from rear of cluster.
5. Remove four cluster retaining screws.
6. Position ground straps so that cluster may be pulled from studs and removed towards center of car.

1969-70 Tempest

1. Disconnect battery and remove glove box.
2. Disconnect speed cable and wire connectors at light switch, wiper, turn signal, ignition switch, printed circuit, heater and air conditioning control panel.
3. Remove lower column trim and disconnect air control cable at heater case.
4. Remove three screws at instrument locations.
5. Remove two screws at instrument panel to column support, one screw at each outboard lower end of panel and three nuts above glove box (inner).
6. Loosen two right hand toe plate screws and two screws clamping right toe plate to left toe plate.
7. Remove column to instrument panel bracket nuts and lower column.
8. Pull entire instrument panel rearward far enough to gain access to cluster.
9. Remove ground strap screws and two panel harness retaining screws.
10. Remove cluster retaining screws and remove cluster.

1969 Firebird

1. Disconnect battery and remove lower instrument panel cover.
2. Remove ash tray bracket screws and radio retaining nuts and glove box.
3. Disconnect heater control cables and wire connectors.
4. Disconnect speedo cable and remove upper L. H. vent duct connector.
5. Disconnect headlamp switch shaft.
6. Remove screws across top and bottom of instrument plate and nut on right side (stud through steel portion of dash).
7. Drop steering column by loosening toe plate screws and removing lower column support nuts.
8. Protect top of column and pull panel rearward to rest on column.
9. Disconnect printed circuit accessory, wiper and cigar lighter.
10. Remove ground strap, cluster retaining screws and carefully remove cluster.

1968 Tempest

1. Disconnect battery.
2. Remove instrument panel fore pad.
3. Disconnect speedometer cable, main wire and switch connectors.
4. Remove instrument panel trim panel retaining screws and disconnect heater control.
5. Remove mast jacket upper retaining screws, lower column and remove trim panel.

6. Remove cluster retaining screws and take out cluster.
7. Reverse procedure to install.

1967-68 Firebird

1. Disconnect battery ground cable.
2. Remove mast jacket lower support screws at toe pan.
3. Remove mast jacket upper support bolts and allow steering wheel to rest on seat cushion. Both supports must be detached to prevent distortion of mast jacket.
4. Remove screws from face of panel and partially remove cluster from console opening.
5. Reach behind cluster and disconnect speedometer cable, speed warning device (if equipped) and chassis harness connector at rear of panel.
6. Remove cluster from console opening.
7. Reverse procedure to install.

1966 Pontiac Speedometer Cluster

1. Disconnect Safeguard control cable (if equipped).
2. Remove speedometer cluster.
3. Remove cluster face plate and lens by unsnapping face plate from housing.
4. Remove screws on back of cluster at speedometer fitting area.
5. Remove speedometer and instruments carefully.

NOTE: If equipped with Safeguard speedometer, disconnect ground wire at clip terminal and also wire-retaining clip. Carefully note routing of wires before removing ground wire.

6. Remove two screws retaining numeral plate and remove speedometer head.
7. Reverse procedure to install.

1967-68 Pontiac

1. Disconnect battery.
2. Remove instrument panel pad.
3. If equipped with front speaker, disconnect speaker wire.
4. Remove two bolts on each end of instrument panel trim plate.
5. On A/C cars remove lower duct assembly.
6. Remove bolts connecting instrument panel trim plate and lower instrument panel.
7. If equipped with automatic transmission, remove column cover and shift indicator.
8. On models with headlamp doors, it may be necessary to disconnect vacuum lines from headlight switch.
9. On models with upper level ventilation system, remove pipes connecting to nozzle assembly.
10. If radio equipped, remove bolt from radio-to-radio support brace.
11. If equipped with Safeguard speedometer, buzzer must be detached.
12. Disconnect "feeder" of fiber optic system from cigar lighter.
13. If equipped with Multiplex, disconnect unit.
14. Disconnect speedometer.
15. Pull instrument panel plate forward. *Make sure all wires and routing clips are loose enough to allow panel to come forward.*
16. Disconnect wires attaching to instrument cluster.
17. Detach cluster from panel trim plate (4 nuts).
18. Remove cluster.
19. Reverse procedure to install.

1967 Tempest

1. Disconnect battery.
2. Remove 10 screws retaining bezel and cluster assembly to instrument panel.
3. Remove speedometer cable.
4. Disconnect heater control cables.
5. Lower steering column by removing trim plate and loosening nuts on column bracket.
6. Pull cluster and bezel out from instrument panel opening to gain access to wiring and other connections.
7. Starting at top, remove bulbs, wiring and other connections as necessary.
8. Remove screws retaining cluster to bezel and remove cluster.
9. Reverse procedure to install.

1966 Tempest

1. To remove cluster, disconnect battery. Then remove 10 screws retaining bezel and cluster to panel.
2. Remove speedometer cable.
3. Pull cluster and bezel out from panel opening to gain access to wiring.
4. Starting at top, remove bulbs and wiring.
5. Remove four screws retaining cluster to bezel and remove cluster.
6. Service instruments as required and install in reverse order of removal.

W/S WIPER MOTOR, REPLACE
1971-72

1. Raise hood and remove cowl screen or grille.
2. Disconnect wiring and washer hoses.
3. Reaching through opening, loosen transmission drive link to crankarm attaching nuts.
4. Remove drive link from motor crankarm.
5. Remove three motor attaching screws and remove motor while guiding crankarm through opening.

1970 Firebird

1. Remove two cowl screen attaching screws from center of cowl screen.
2. Pry cowl screen up at eight integral clips and remove.

NOTE: Install screw as an alternate method of retention in hole provided in screen adjacent to clips.

3. Reaching through cowl opening, loosen two transmission crankarm attaching nuts.
4. Remove transmission crankarm.
5. Disconnect wiring and washer hoses.
6. Remove three motor attaching screws and remove motor while guiding crankarm through hole.

1969 All; 1970 Exc. Firebird

1. Remove hoses and wires connected to wiper.
2. On Pontiac, remove retainer securing wiper crank to transmission linkage. This can be done by removing plastic plug from left side of upper shroud, above wiper motor.
3. On Tempest and Grand Prix, remove screen and loosen clamp securing wiper crank to linkage.
4. Remove screws securing wiper assembly to dash.
5. On Firebird, carefully pull wiper assembly away from firewall until retainer securing wiper crank to transmission can be removed.
6. Remove wiper motor.

1966-68

1. Remove hoses and wire terminals connected to wiper unit.
2. On Pontiac models, remove retainer securing wiper crank to wiper transmission linkage. This can be done by removing plastic plug from left side of upper shroud, directly above wiper motor.
3. On Tempest Optional System models, remove screen and remove retainer securing wiper crank to wiper transmission linkage.
4. Remove screws securing wiper assembly to firewall.
5. On Tempest and Firebird models, carefully pull wiper assembly away from firewall until retainer securing wiper crank to wiper transmission arm can be removed.
6. On Tempest models, remove arm.
7. Remove wiper motor from firewall.
8. Reverse procedure to install.

W/S WIPER TRANSMISSION, REPLACE
1971-72

With Rectangular Motor

1. Remove wiper arms and blades.
2. Raise hood and remove cowl vent screen or grille.
3. Disconnect wiring from motor.
4. Loosen, do not remove, transmission drive link to motor crankarm attaching nuts and disconnect drive link from crankarm.
5. Remove right and left transmission to body attaching screws and guide transmission and linkage assembly out through opening.

NOTE: When installing, motor must be in Park position.

With Round Motor

1. Raise hood and remove cowl vent screen.
2. On Intermediates, remove right and left wiper arm and blade assemblies. On Full Size cars, remove the arm and blade only from the transmission to be removed.
3. Loosen, do not remove, attaching nuts securing transmission drive link to motor crankarm.

NOTE: On Full Size cars, if only the left transmission is to be removed, it will not be necessary to loosen nuts securing the right assembly.

4. Disconnect transmission drive link from motor crankarm.
5. On Intermediate models, remove right and left transmission to body attaching screws. On Full Size cars, remove the attaching screw securing the transmission to be removed.
6. Remove transmission and linkage assembly by guiding it through opening.

NOTE: When installing, motor must be in Park position.

1966-70

1. Remove wiper arms and blades.
2. Remove fresh air intake screen or grille.
3. Remove wiper transmission screws.
4. On Pontiac models, remove center support screws.
5. On Depressed Park Optional System models, remove retainer securing linkage that attaches to wiper motor crank. On Pontiac models, this can be done by removing plastic plug from left side of upper shroud, directly above wiper motor.
6. On Tempest models, remove retainer securing right wiper transmission to linkage that attaches to wiper motor crank.
7. Remove transmission and linkage.
8. Reverse procedure to install.

W/S WIPER SWITCH

1971-72 Catalina, Grandville & Bonneville

1. Disconnect battery and remove upper and lower instrument panel trim plates.
2. Remove speedometer bezel and cluster.
3. Disconnect headlamp, windshield wiper and accessory switch connectors.
4. Remove instrument panel bezel assembly screws, pull rearward and disconnect vent control cable if equipped.
5. Remove wiper switch from backside of bezel assembly.

1971-72 T-37, LeMans, GTO & Grand Prix

1. Disconnect battery and remove lower A/C duct if equipped.
2. Disconnect wire connector.
3. Remove ground strap screw.
4. Unfasten and remove switch.

1971-72 Ventura II

1. Disconnect battery ground cable.
2. From under dash, disconnect wiring from switch.
3. Remove three screws retaining switch to lower instrument panel and remove switch from panel.

1970-72 Firebird

1. Remove upper and lower instrument panel trim plates.

2. Disconnect wire and unfasten and remove switch.

1969-70 Pontiac, Tempest & Grand Prix

1. Disconnect battery and wire from switch.
2. Remove retaining nuts.
3. Position ground straps and remove switch.

1969 Firebird

1. Disconnect battery.
2. Remove upper vent duct.
3. Remove switch retaining screws and reposition ground straps.
4. Remove switch.

1966-68

1. Loosen Allen screw and remove knob.
2. Remove nut securing shaft and bezel.
3. Remove switch and disconnect terminals.
4. On models with vacuum headlight doors, disconnect vacuum lines.
5. Reverse procedure to install.

RADIO, REPLACE

NOTE: When installing radio, be sure to adjust antenna trimmer for peak performance.

1971-72 Catalina, Grandville & Bonneville

1. Disconnect battery and remove radio knobs and hex nuts.
2. Remove upper and lower instrument panel trim plates and front lower radio bracket.
3. Remove glove box and disconnect all connections to radio.
4. Loosen screw holding radio brace to side of radio and slide radio toward front seat.

1971-72 T-37, LeMans, GTO & Grand Prix

1. Disconnect battery and remove lower A/C duct if equipped.
2. Remove radio control knobs and hex nuts.
3. Remove radio support bracket bolt.
4. Disconnect all leads to radio and remove radio.

1971-72 Ventura II

1. Disconnect battery ground cable.
2. Remove radio knobs, bezels, nuts and side braces screw and disconnect wiring and antenna.
3. Remove radio from under dash.

1970-72 Firebird

1. Disconnect battery.
2. Remove glove box and door and right lower A/C duct if equipped.
3. Remove radio knobs and hex nuts and trim plate.
4. Disconnect all leads to radio.
5. Remove radio bracket and radio from passenger side of instrument panel.

1969 All; 1970 Exc. Firebird

1. Disconnect antenna and wires from radio.
2. Remove knobs, springs, nuts and bezels from control shafts.
3. Remove screws securing radio to dash or to brace and carefully remove radio.

1967-68 Firebird

1. Remove tape player and/or Multiplex Adapter (if equipped).
2. Remove radio knobs, bezels, nuts and radio trim plate.
3. Remove ash tray.
4. Remove four screws from lower edge of instrument panel trim plate (two retain ash tray housing). Remove trim plate by pulling bottom of plate outward to disengage from plastic retainer at top of instrument panel.
5. On A/C cars, remove right and left hand hoses from distribution ducts to instrument panel outlets. Remove center distribution duct and left hand plenum together.
6. Remove ash tray housing.
7. Disconnect all radio leads.
8. Remove radio brace to radio screw.
9. Remove two screws at sides of radio controls and lower radio out left side of instrument panel.
10. Reverse procedure to install.

1967-68 All

1. Remove stereo tape player (if equipped).
2. Remove knobs, springs, nuts and bezels from control bushings.
3. If equipped with A/C, remove three Phillips head screws holding bottom A/C air duct and remove duct.
4. Disconnect stereo multiplex plug from radio (if equipped).
5. Remove antenna lead-in and speaker connector.
6. Remove hex screws holding right side of radio to brace.
7. Disconnect dial light socket and lower radio.
8. Remove Multiplex Adapter (if equipped).
9. Reverse procedure to install.

1966 All

1. Remove knobs and springs and 5/8" hex nuts from control bushings.
2. On Pontiac, remove A/C duct if so equipped. On Tempest with A/C, remove glove box.
3. On all models, remove hex screw from radio mounting bracket.
4. Remove antenna and speaker connectors.
5. Remove dial light socket from radio before "dropping" radio to floor area.
6. Reverse procedure to install.

NOTE: On AM models, remove dial light socket from radio and remove radio through glove box.

On AM-FM models, remove two 5/16" screws from under dash mounted nozzles (passenger and driver side). Remove auxiliary nozzle, air distributor and center air duct. Remove dial socket and lower radio to floor.

HEATER CORE REMOVAL
1971-72 Without Air Cond.

All except Ventura II
1. Drain radiator and disconnect heater hoses from core.
2. Remove retaining nuts from core case studs on engine side of dash.
3. Inside car, remove glove box and door on Firebird and heater outlet from case on Firebird.
4. Remove defroster duct retaining screw from heater case and pull entire heater assembly from firewall.
5. Disconnect control cables and wiring and remove assembly. On Grand Prix, disconnect vacuum hoses.
6. Remove core tube seal and core retaining strips and remove core.

Ventura II
1. Drain radiator and disconnect heater hoses from core.
2. Disconnect battery ground cable.
3. Remove retaining nuts from core case studs on engine side of dash.
4. Inside car, drill out lower right hand heater case stud with 1/4" drill.
5. Pull entire heater core and case assembly from firewall.
6. Disconnect cables and wiring and remove assembly from car.
7. Remove core tube seal and core retaining strips and remove core.

1971-72 With Air Cond.

Catalina, Grandville & Bonneville
1. Drain radiator and disconnect heater hoses from core.
2. Remove three nuts and one screw retaining core and case to dash.
3. Remove glove box and upper and lower instrument panel trim plates.
4. Remove radio.
5. Remove cold air duct and heater outlet duct.
6. Remove defroster duct to heater case screw.
7. Disconnect A/C temperature cable at heater case.
8. Disconnect vacuum hoses from diaphragms on heater case and remove core and case assembly.
9. Remove core from case (three screws).

LeMans & Grand Prix
1. Drain radiator and disconnect heater hoses from core.
2. Remove lower duct and outlet assembly.
3. Remove glove box.
4. Remove defroster duct attaching screw.
5. Remove screws retaining case to dash.
6. Move core and case assembly rearward to free attaching studs from cowl and remove assembly.
7. Disconnect cables and wiring.
8. Mark heater cam and bracket assembly in three places to insure proper installation.
9. Remove heater cam and bracket assembly.
10. Remove front case to rear case attaching screws.
11. Separate front and rear case.
12. Remove screws retaining core attaching bands and remove core.

Firebird
1. Drain radiator.
2. Remove glove box and door.
3. Remove cold air duct (lower right hand duct) and remove left and center lower A/C ducts.
4. Jack right front area of car and place on safety stand.
5. Remove rocker panel trim on right side and remove screws holding forward portion of rocker panel trim attaching bracket.
6. Remove three lower fender bolts at rear of fender.
7. Remove four fender to skirt bolts at rear of wheel opening.
8. Remove two fender skirt bolts near blower motor area.
9. Pry rear portion of fender out at bottom to gain access to hose clamp on lower core hose and disconnect hose.
10. Disconnect water pump to core hose at core.
11. Remove heater case retaining nuts under hood at dash.
12. Remove two heater case retaining bolts (inside car).
13. Remove console, if equipped. If equipped with tape player, remove console with tape player intact. If equipped with tape player and no console, remove tape player.
14. Disconnect temperature cable at heater case.
15. Remove heater outlet duct.
16. Remove lower defroster duct screw at heater case.
17. Remove right kick panel.
18. Remove heater core and case.
19. Disconnect vacuum hoses from heater case.
20. Remove core from case.

Ventura II
1. Disconnect battery and drain coolant.
2. Disconnect upper heater hose from core.
3. Remove right front fender skirt bolts and lower skirt to gain access to lower heater hose clamp. Disconnect lower hose and remove lower right hand heater core and case attaching nut.
4. Remove glove box and door.
5. Remove recirculation vacuum diaphragm at right kick panel.
6. Remove heater outlet (at bottom of heater case).
7. Remove cold air distributor duct from heater case.
8. Remove heater case extension screws and separate extension from case.
9. Disconnect cables and wiring and remove case and core assembly.
10. Separate core from case.

1970
1. Drain radiator and remove heater hoses at their connections beside the air inlet assembly.
2. Remove retaining nuts from core case studs on engine side of dash.
3. On Firebird, remove the glove box and door and the heater outlet from the heater case.
4. Remove defroster duct retaining screw from heater case and pull entire heater assembly from firewall.
5. Remove all cables, wiring and vacuum hoses if used from heater and remove assembly.
6. Remove core tube seal and core assembly retaining strips and remove core.

1969
1. Drain radiator and remove heater hoses at their connections beside air inlet assembly.
2. Remove five nuts from core case studs on engine side of dash.
3. Inside the car, pull entire heater assembly from firewall.
4. Remove cables and all electrical connectors from heater and remove heater. On Grand Prix, remove vacuum hoses.
5. Remove core tube seal and core retaining strips and remove core.

1966-68 Full Size Models
1. Disconnect temperature control cable on top of heater.
2. Disconnect vacuum hose from defroster and air inlet diaphragms.
3. Remove wire connector from resistor on top of air outlet duct by prying it up with a flat-blade screwdriver.
4. Unfasten air inlet duct from heater.
5. Heater core can now be removed.

1968 Firebird
1. Remove nuts from heater core case on engine side of dash.
2. From inside vehicle, pull heater from under dash and remove bowden cables and all electrical connectors.
3. Lift out assembly and remove core tube seal and core retaining springs and lift out heater core.

1966-68 Intermediates Except 1968 Firebird
1. Remove glove box.
2. Remove five nuts retaining heater case to dash.
3. Pull case from dash and disconnect all cables and the wire connector from heater resistor.
4. Heater core is now exposed and easily removed.

SPEED CONTROLS
1969-72 Cruise Control

Brake Release Switch, Adjust

Apply brake pedal and push both switches forward as far as possible. Pull pedal forcibly rearward to adjust switches.

Chain Linkage, Adjust 1970-72

This adjustment is no longer necessary because of the use of cable-connection to the carburetor.

Chain Linkage, Adjust 1969
1. Start engine and set carburetor to hot idle position.
2. Thread bead chain through hole in carburetor lever extension.
3. Adjust bead chain at extension to provide minimum slack and assemble clip to extension by straddling extension.
4. A minimum of two beads must extend outside of clip after adjustment. Cut off excess chain.

Centering Spring, Adjust

If speed control holds speed three or more mph higher than selected speed, turn centering screw (C) clockwise 1/8 turn or less, Fig. 2.

If speed control holds speed three or more mph below selected speed, turn centering adjustment screw (C) counter-clockwise 1/8 turn or less. *Do not move adjustment screw (R).*

1967-68 Cruise Control

Brake Release Switch, Adjust

1. Disconnect multiple connector at regulator.
2. Turn ignition switch to accessory position.
3. Using a test lamp, ground one test lamp lead and touch the other to terminal No. 2 in harness connector.
4. Adjust switch so that lamp will light when brake pedal is fully released and will go out when brake pedal is depressed about 1/4 inch.
5. If switch cannot be adjusted, it is defective and should be replaced. Install new switch and repeat Step 4.
6. Remove test lamp, turn off ignition key and plug connector to regulator.

Chain Linkage, Adjust

Chain linkage should never be taut. To adjust, start engine, set carburetor at hot idle with anti-stall plunger backed off so as not to affect engine idle speed. Hook chain to accelerator linkage, pull taut, then loosen by length of one ball and install chain clip. *When pulling chain taut, do not pull so far as to cause throttle to open.*

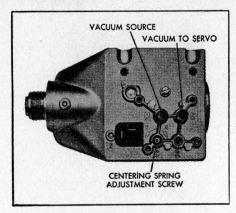

Fig. 2 Centering spring adjustment. 1967-72 Cruise Control

Centering Spring, Adjust

If speed control system holds speed three or more mph higher than selected speed, turn centering adjusting screw (C) toward (S) 1/32″ or less, Fig. 2.

If speed control system holds speed three or more mph below selected speed, turn centering spring adjusting screw (C) toward (F) 1/32″ or less. *Do not move adjustment screw (R).*

1966 Electro Cruise

Power Unit Ball Chain, Adjust

IMPORTANT: Do not lubricate power unit ball chain or its pulley.

1. Loosen jam nut on threaded stud attached to end of ball chain.

2. With carburetor set on slow idle cam, rotate threaded stud so that chain is just taut without advancing idle speed of engine with engine running, then back off one full turn.
3. Tighten jam nut against rivnut on throttle bracket.
4. This adjustment should always be checked whenever carburetor linkage is adjusted.

Brake Release Switch, Adjust

1. Disconnect wiring harness connector from brake release switch.
2. Connect test lamp across switch terminals.

NOTE: If desired, the cruise lamp in the engagement switch may be used as a test lamp by unplugging connector to speed transducer in speedometer and leaving release switch wiring connector on switch. Then turn ignition switch on and press control knob which will cause Cruise light to be on.

3. Loosen screw that retains switch to brake pedal support bracket. Position switch to open the circuit at 1/2 inch brake pedal travel. An open circuit will be indicated by an unlit test lamp. If Cruise lamp is used, an open circuit will be indicated when light goes out.
4. When brake pedal is at released position, the circuit must be closed for the Electro-Cruise to operate.
5. Tighten adjusting screw and recheck switch adjustment by depressing brake pedal several times with test lamp connected.
6. Readjust as necessary and reconnect wiring harness.

Conventional Engine Section

See page 2-532 for the Overhead Camshaft Engine

For service on 6-250 & V8-307 see Chevrolet Chapter

ENGINE, REPLACE
1970-72

1. Disconnect battery cables at battery and drain cooling system.
2. Scribe alignment marks on hood and remove hood from hinges.
3. Disconnect all wiring, ground straps, fuel lines and vacuum hoses from engine.
4. Remove air cleaner and upper radiator shield assembly.
5. Disconnect radiator hoses and heater hoses at engine.
6. Remove fan and disconnect accelerator linkage.
7. If equipped with power steering or air conditioning, remove pump and/or compressor from mountings and set aside. Do not disconnect hoses.
8. On V8, disconnect transmission vacuum modulator line and power brake vacuum line at carburetor and fold back out of way.

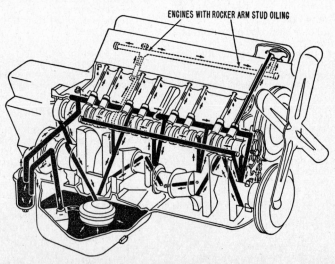

ENGINES WITH ROCKER ARM STUD OILING

Engine oiling system. V8s (except V8-307)

Fig. 1 Installing rocker arm stud without removing cylinder head. 1966-68 engines with push rod oiling

Fig. 2 Slots filed in rocker arm stud

9. Raise vehicle on hoist and drain crankcase.
10. Disconnect exhaust pipe from manifold and remove starter.
11. If equipped with automatic transmission, remove converter cover and three converter retaining bolts and slide converter to rear.
12. With manual transmission, disconnect clutch linkage and remove clutch cross shaft.
13. Remove four lower bell housing bolts.
14. Disconnect transmission filler tube support and starter wire harness shield from cylinder head.
15. Remove two front motor mount to frame bracket bolts.
16. Lower vehicle and using a jack and block of wood, support transmission.
17. Support weight of engine with suitable lifting device.
18. Remove two remaining bell housing bolts.
19. Raise transmission slightly.
20. Position engine forward to free it from transmission and remove from car by tilting front of engine up.

1966-69 Pontiac & 1967-69 Tempest & Firebird V8

1. Scribe alignment marks around hood and remove hood.
2. Disconnect engine wiring harness and engine-to-body ground straps.
3. Remove air cleaner and fan shield.
4. If equipped with manual transmission, remove radiator.
5. With power steering or air conditioning, remove pump and compressor from mounting brackets and set aside. Do not disconnect hoses.
6. Remove engine fan and pulley.
7. Disconnect accelerator control linkage and linkage support bracket.
8. If equipped, disconnect automatic transmission vacuum modulator line and power brake vacuum line at carburetor and fold back out of the way.

NOTE: On Firebird with A/C, remove wiper motor.

9. Raise vehicle and drain crankcase.
10. Disconnect fuel lines and exhaust pipes.
11. Disconnect starter wires.
12. With automatic transmission, remove converter cover, converter retaining bolts and slide converter to rear.
13. With manual transmission, disconnect clutch linkage, remove clutch cross shaft, starter and lower flywheel cover.
14. Remove lower bell housing bolts.
15. Remove front engine mounts at frame.
16. Lower vehicle.
17. Using jack and block of wood, support transmission.
18. Remove remaining bell housing bolts.
19. Raise transmission slightly. Then, using suitable lifting equipment, remove engine.
20. Reverse procedure to install.

1966-69 Six & 1966 Tempest V8

NOTE: The engine and transmission are removed as a unit. First disconnect and/or remove as required wires, tubes, hoses and linkage attached to engine and transmission. Then perform the following:

1. Remove hood, radiator and fan.
2. Remove drive shaft.
3. Remove four lower transmission mounting bolts.
4. Disconnect exhaust pipe from engine.
5. Remove starting motor.
6. Loosen engine front mounting bolts.
7. Remove engine and transmission as a unit, using suitable lifting equipment.

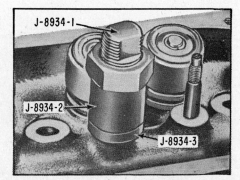

Fig. 3 Tools positioned to remove rocker arm stud

8. Remove engine and transmission as an assembly.

CYLINDER HEAD

NOTE: Pontiac recommends no numerical sequence for tightening cylinder heads. However, they may be tightened by starting at the center bolts and then working alternately from side to side and outward toward the ends.

V8 Engines

1. Remove intake manifold, push rod cover and rocker arm cover.
2. Loosen all rocker arm nuts and move rocker arms off push rods.
3. Remove push rods, keeping them in order so they may be installed in their original locations.
4. Detach exhaust crossover pipe from manifolds.
5. Remove battery ground strap and engine ground strap on left head or engine ground strap.
6. Unfasten and remove head with exhaust manifold attached.

CAUTION: Use extreme care when handling heads as the rocker arm studs are hardened and may crack if struck.

NOTE: If left head is being removed, it will be necessary to raise head off dowel pins, move it forward and "jockey" it in order to clear power steering and power brake equipment if so equipped.

7. Reverse removal procedure to install the heads.

NOTE: On V8-326 engines, bolts are three different lengths. When inserted in proper holes all bolts will project an equal distance from the head. Do not use sealer of any kind on bolt threads.

ROCKER ARM STUDS
1967-72 V8 With Screw in Stud

1. Remove rocker arm cover.
2. Remove rocker arm and nut.
3. Using a deep socket, remove rocker stud.
4. Install new stud and tighten to 50 ft. lbs.

5. Install rocker arm and tighten nut to 20 ft. lbs.
6. Install rocker cover using new gasket.

1966-72 V8 With Push Rod Oiling - Pressed in Stud

NOTE: Engines with push rod oiling are: 1966-72 all, and all 389 Tri-Power engines. On these engines, rocker arm studs can now be replaced without removing the cylinder head. This is accomplished by the use of a new .005" oversize stud and a new reamer (J-22126), which is available from the Service Tool Division of Kent-Moore Organization, Inc., 28635 Mound Road, Warren, Michigan 48092.

1. Disconnect battery cable and drain radiator.
2. Pack oily rags around stud and over engine openings before removing stud.
3. After removing stud as outlined for earlier models, carefully ream stud hole, using the new reamer. This reamer is made with a removable pilot shaft. Stud hole must first be reamed with pilot shaft attached to reamer. Pilot shaft should then be removed and stud hole must be reamed again.
4. Clean stud hole and surrounding area. *If reamer did not clean up completely, it will be necessary to replace cylinder head.*
5. Remove intake manifold and valley cover.
6. Position rocker arm on new .005" stud and place rocker arm installer J-8927 on stud in place of rocker arm ball, Fig. 1.
7. Coat rocker arm stud with white lead and oil and drive stud into cylinder head about half way (7/16").
8. Clamp straight-edge on cylinder head as shown in Fig. 1, and position valve train gauge J-8928 in push rod hole so that it seats properly in rocker arm. *When working on right cylinder head, heater hose connector will have to be removed before straight-edge can be positioned correctly.*
9. With valve seated, drive rocker arm stud into cylinder head until the result outlined in Fig. 1 is obtained.
10. Remove tools and rocker arm. Then install push rod, rocker arm, ball, and tighten rocker arm ball retaining nut. Finally, install parts removed and fill radiator.

VALVE ARRANGEMENT
Front to Rear

Six Cyl. . . . . E-I-I-E-E-I-I-E-E-I-I-E
V8s . . . . E-I-I-E-E-I-I-E

VALVE LIFT SPECS.

Year	Engine	Intake	Exhaust
1966	6-230[7]	.400	.400
	6-230[2]	.438	.438
	8-326	.370	.406
	8-389[2]	.406	.408
	8-389[8]	.409	.409

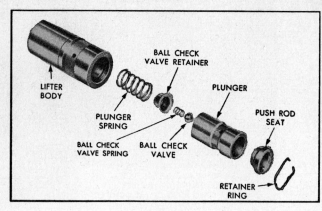

Fig. 4 Hydraulic valve lifter. Some lifters do not have the ball check valve spring shown

Year	Engine	Intake	Exhaust
1967	8-389[1][3]	.370	.406
	8-389[4]	.406	.409
	8-421	.406	.408
	8-421[9]	.409	.409
	6-230[7]	.400	.400
	6-230[2]	.438	.438
	8-326	.375	.410
	8-400[2][5]	.407	.411
	8-400[2][6]	.407	.412
	8-400[9]	.414	.413
	8-400[1]	.375	.410
	8-400[10]	.413	.413
	8-400[2][5][11]	.410	.413
	8-400[2][6][11]	.410	.414
	8-428[2][5]	.410	.413
	8-428[2][6]	.410	.414
1968	6-250[7]	.400	.400
	6-250[2]	.438	.438
	8-350[1]	.376	.412
	8-350[2][5]	.410	.413
	8-350[2][6]	.410	.414
	8-400[1][3]	.376	.412
	8-400[1][4][5]	.410	.414
	8-400[1][4][6]	.376	.412
	8-400[2][5]	.410	.413
	8-428[5]	.414	.413
	8-428[6]	.410	.413
1969	6-250[7]	.400	.400
	6-250[2]	.438	.438
	8-350[1]	.376	.412
	8-350[2][5]	.414	.413
	8-350[2][6]	.410	.413
	8-400[1][3]	.376	.412
	8-400[1][4][5]	.410	.414
	8-400[1][4][6]	.376	.412
	8-400[2][5]	.413	.413
	8-400[2][6]	.410	.413
	8-400[10][5]	.413	.413
	8-400[10][6]	.414	.413
	8-428[5]	.410	.413
	8-428[6]	.410	.414
	8-428[9][5]	.414	.413
	8-428[9][6]	.410	.413
1970	6-250	.388	.388
	8-350	.376	.412
	8-400[1]	.376	.412
	8-400[2]	.410	.414
	8-400[12]	.527	.527
	8-455[5]	.414	.413
	8-455[6]	.410	.413
1971	6-250	.388	.388
	8-350[5]	.376	.412
	8-350[6]	.410	.414
	8-400[1]	.376	.412
	8-400[2]	.410	.413
	8-455[1]	.376	.412
	8-455[2]	.410	.413
	8-455[9]	.414	.413
1972	6-250[13]	.388	.388
	6-250[14]	.388	.405

Engine	Intake	Exhaust
8-307	.390	.409
8-350[15]	.374	.407
8-350[16]	.404	.408
8-400[1][15]	.374	.407
8-400[1][16]	.404	.408
8-400[2]	.403	.406
8-455[1][15]	.404	.408
8-455[1][16]	.403	.406
8-455[2]	.403	.406
8-455[9]	.408	.406

[1]—2 bar. carb. [2]—4 bar. carb.
[3]—Reg. fuel. [4]—Premium fuel.
[5]—Std. trans. [6]—Auto. trans.
[7]—One bar. carb. [8]—Three carbs.
[9]—Hi perf. eng. [10]—Ram air eng.
[11]—Grand Prix and GTO.
[12]—Ram Air IV engine.
[13]—Without Air Injection Pump.
[14]—With Air Injection Pump.
[15]—Exc. California cars.
[16]—California cars.

VALVE TIMING
Intake Opens Before TDC

Engine	Year	Degrees
6-230	1966[7]	12
	1966[2]	20
	1967[7]	7
	1967[2]	14
6-250	1968	14
	1969[7]	14
	1969[2][5]	22
	1969[2][6]	14
	1970-71	16
	1972	25
8-307	1971-72	28
8-326	1966-67	22
8-350	1968-69[1]	22
	1968[2][5]	23
	1968[2][6]	30
	1969[2][5]	31
	1969[2][6]	23
	1970	22
	1971[5]	26
	1971[6]	30
	1972[1][12]	26
	1972[1][13]	30
8-389	1966[2]	23
	1966[8]	31
	1966[1][3]	22
	1966[4]	30
8-400	1967-68[2][5]	23
	1967[2][6]	30
	1967[9]	31
	1967[1]	22
	1967[10]	38
	1967[2][5][11]	23

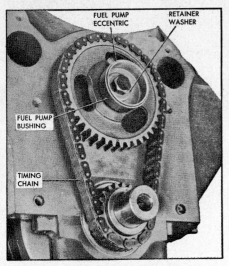

Fig. 5 Front of engine with timing case cover removed. V8 engines

8-455	1970[5]	31
	1970[6]	23
	1970[9]	23
	1971[1]	30
	1971[2]	23
	1971[9]	31
	1972[1][12]	30
	1972[1][13]	23
	1972[2]	23
	1972[9]	31

[1]—2 bar. carb.　　[2]—4 bar. carb.
[3]—Regular fuel.　　[4]—Prem. fuel.
[5]—Std. trans.　　　[6]—Auto. trans.
[7]—1 bar. Carb.　　[8]—3 carbs.
[9]—Hi perf. eng.　　[10]—Ram air eng.
[11]—Grand Prix and GTO.
[12]—Except California cars.
[13]—California cars.

VALVE GUIDES

Valve guides are cast integral with the cylinder head. Valves with oversize stems are available in .001″, .003″ and .005″ larger than standard.

Oversize reamers are required to enlarge valve guide holes to fit the oversize stems. For best results when installing .005″ oversize valve stem use a .003″ oversize reamer first and then ream to .005″ oversize. Always reface the valve and valve seat after reaming valve guide. Valves are marked .001, .003 or .005 with colored ink.

VALVE LIFTERS

Remove intake manifold, push rod cover and rocker arm cover. Loosen rocker arm ball nut and move rocker arm off push rod. Remove push rod.

Remove lifter or lifters. If more than one lifter is to be replaced, be sure to identify them (push rods as well) so they will be installed in the same position, Fig. 4.

TIMING COVER

NOTE: If necessary to replace the cover oil seal it can be accomplished without removing the timing chain cover.

1966-72 V8s

1. Drain cooling system.
2. Loosen alternator adjusting bolts.
3. Remove fan and accessory drive belts.
4. Remove fan and pulley.
5. Disconnect radiator hoses.
6. Remove fuel pump.
7. Remove vibration damper.
8. Remove front four oil pan-to-timing chain cover screws, Fig. 12.
9. Remove cover attaching screws.
10. Pull cover forward to clear studs and remove.

TIMING CHAIN
V8 Engines

1. Remove timing chain cover, making certain O-ring seal and hollow dowels are retained for installation at assembly.

	1967[2][6][11]	30
	1968-70[1][4][6]	22
	1968-70[1][4][5]	30
	1969-70[1][3]	22
	1971[1]	26
	1971[2]	23
	1972[1][12]	26
	1972[1][13]	30
	1972[2]	23
8-421	1966[9]	31
	1966	23
8-428	1967[2][5]	23
	1967[2][6]	30
	1968[5]	31
	1968[6]	23
	1969[5]	23
	1969[6]	30
	1969[9][5]	31
	1969[9][6]	23

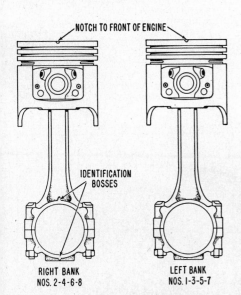

Fig. 7 Piston and rod assembly. 1966-72 V8s (Oil spurt hole toward camshaft)

NOTCH TO FRONT OF ENGINE

IDENTIFICATION BOSSES

RIGHT BANK NOS. 2-4-6-8

LEFT BANK NOS. 1-3-5-7

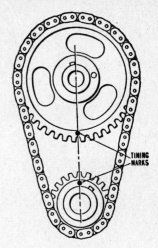

Fig. 6 Valve timing marks. V8 engines

TIMING MARKS

2. Remove fuel pump eccentric, bushing and timing chain cover oil seal, Fig. 5.
3. Align timing marks to simplify proper positioning of sprockets during assembly, Fig. 6.
4. Slide off chain and sprockets.
5. Install new chain and sprockets, making sure timing marks are aligned exactly on a straight line passing through the shaft centers, Fig. 6. Camshaft should extend through sprocket so that hole in fuel pump eccentric will locate on shaft.
6. Install fuel pump eccentric and bushing, indexing tab on eccentric with keyway cutout in sprocket. Install retainer bolt with washer and tighten securely.
7. Making sure hollow dowels are in place in block, place timing chain cover gasket over studs and dowels.
8. Install cover, making sure O-ring seal is in place.

CAMSHAFT
All V8s

The camshaft and camshaft bearings can be replaced with the engine installed in the car or with engine removed and disassembled for overhaul. However, to replace the rear camshaft bearing without removing and completely disassembling the engine, the propeller shaft, transmission and clutch housing must first be removed. The procedure for re-

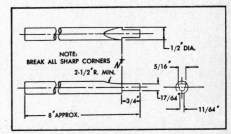

NOTE: BREAK ALL SHARP CORNERS
1/2″ DIA.
2-1/2″ R. MIN.
5/16″
17/64″
3/4″
8″ APPROX.
11/64″

Fig. 8 Rear main bearing oil seal tool. V8-326, 350, 400

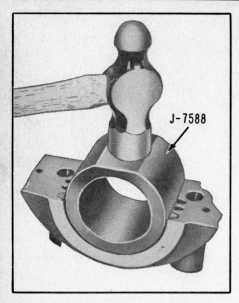

Fig. 9 Installing rear main bearing oil seal. V8-326, 350, 400, 455 engines

moving the camshaft is as follows:
1. Remove radiator, fan and pulleys.
2. On air conditioned cars, remove alternator and its mounting bracket.
3. Remove crankcase ventilator hose or outlet pipe.
4. Remove rocker arm covers.
5. Remove intake manifold. *Make certain "O" ring seal between intake manifold and timing chain cover is retained and installed during assembly.*
6. Remove push rod cover.
7. Loosen rocker arm ball retaining nuts so that rocker arms can be disengaged from push rods and turned sideways.
8. Remove push rods and hydraulic lifters, keeping them in proper sequence so that they may be returned to their original locations.
9. Remove vibration damper.
10. Remove fuel pump.
11. Remove timing chain cover.
12. Remove fuel pump eccentric and fuel pump bushing.
13. Remove chain and sprockets.
14. Remove camshaft thrust plate and carefully pull camshaft from engine. *Clearance for camshaft removal is very limited and, in cases where engine mounts are worn excessively, it may be necessary to raise the front of the engine to permit removal.*

PISTON & ROD, ASSEMBLE

Assemble pistons and rods as indicated in Fig. 7.

PISTONS, PINS & RINGS

Pistons are available in standard sizes and oversizes of .005, .010, .020 and .030" on all four and six cylinder engines as well as 1966-71 V8s.

Piston rings are furnished in standard sizes only.

Piston pins are available in oversizes of .001 and .003" on four cylinder engines and 1966-71 V8s. No oversizes are supplied on 6 cylinder engines.

MAIN & ROD BEARINGS

Main bearings are available in standard sizes and undersizes of .001 and .002".

Rod bearings are available in standard sizes and undersizes of .001 and .002". On 1966 V8-421 engines, undersizes of .0005", .001 and .002" are available.

CRANKSHAFT OIL SEAL
V8-326

1. Remove oil pan and oil pump.
2. Remove rear main bearing cap.
3. Make a tool of brass bar stock to the dimensions shown in Fig. 8 to pack the upper seal as follows:
   a. Insert tool against one end of seal in cylinder block and drive seal gently into groove until tool bottoms.
   b. Remove tool and repeat at other end of seal in block.
4. Clean block and bearing cap parting line thoroughly.
5. Form a new seal in cap, Fig. 9.
6. Remove newly formed seal from cap and cut four pieces about ⅜" long from this seal.
7. Work two ⅜" pieces into each of gaps which have been made at end of seal in block. Without cutting off ends, work these seal pieces in until flush with parting line and no fibers are protruding over metal adjacent to groove.

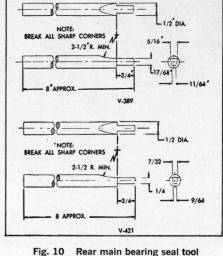

Fig. 10 Rear main bearing seal tool dimensions. Make from brass bar stock. Pontiac V8s

8. Form another new seal in bearing cap.
9. Assemble cap to block and torque to specifications.
10. Remove cap and inspect parting line to be sure that no seal material has been compressed between block and cap. Clean as necessary.
11. Apply a 1/16" bead of sealer from center of seal across to external cork groove.
12. Install and torque bearing cap. Install oil pump and pan.

V8s Except 326

1. Remove oil pan, oil pump and pump drive shaft.
2. Remove oil baffle and cylinder block-to-oil baffle tube.
3. Remove rear main bearing cap.
4. Use tool shown in Fig. 10 made from brass bar stock to pack upper seal as follows:
   a. Insert tool against one end of oil seal in cylinder block and drive seal gently into groove until tool bottoms.
   b. Remove tool and repeat at other end of seal in cylinder block.
5. Clean block and bearing cap parting line thoroughly.

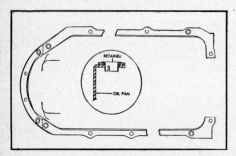

Fig. 11 Installing oil pan gasket retainers. V8-326, 350, 400, 455 engines

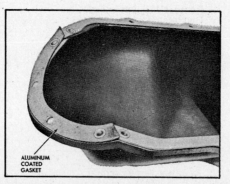

Fig. 12 Front oil pan gasket overlapping side gaskets. V8-326, 350, 400, 455 engines

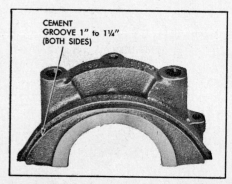

Fig. 13 Rear oil pan gasket positioned in bearing cap. V8-326, 350, 400, 455 engines

6. Form a new seal in cap.
7. Remove newly formed seal from cap and cut four pieces about ⅜″ long from this seal.
8. Work two ⅜″ pieces into each end of the gaps which have been made at the end of seal in cylinder block. Without cutting off the ends, work these seal pieces in until flush with parting line, being sure that no fibers are protruding over the metal adjacent to the groove.
9. Form another new seal in the cap.
10. Assemble the cap to the block and torque to specifications.
11. Remove cap and inspect parting line to insure that no seal material has been compressed between the block and cap.
12. Apply a ¹⁄₁₆″ bead of sealer from the center of the seal to the external cork groove.
13. Reassemble the cap and torque to specifications.

OIL PAN
1971-72 Ventura II

1. Disconnect battery ground cable.
2. If equipped with power steering, remove drive belt and tilt pump upward.
3. Remove two fan shroud screws and position shroud so it will swing up with engine.
4. Raise car and drain oil.
5. Disconnect exhaust pipe to manifold bolts and let exhaust pipes hang down.
6. Remove flywheel dust cover.
7. Remove starter mounting bolts and let starter hang by wires.
8. Remove both frame bracket to engine mount thru bolts.
9. Attach a suitable engine lifting tool to engine.
10. Remove oil pan bolts.
11. Raise engine until pan can be removed.

1970-72 Except Ventura II

NOTE: On 1970 Tempest, T-37 and LeMans models with manual transmission, it will

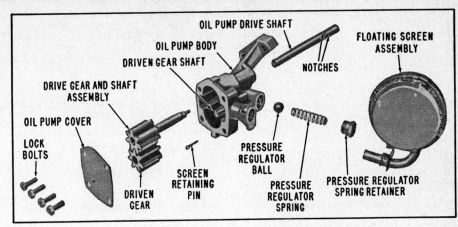

Fig. 14   Exploded view of oil pump. V8-326, 350, 400, 455 engines

be necessary to remove the engine before removing the oil pan. On all other models, proceed as follows:

1. Disconnect battery cable at battery and remove fan.
2. Make sure all hoses and wiring are routed properly to avoid bind when engine is raised.
3. Raise vehicle and drain crankcase.
4. On 1971 Firebird and Grand Prix, disconnect steering idler arm at frame and pitman arm from shaft. On 1970 full size Pontiac, disconnect steering idler arm support from frame.
5. Disconnect exhaust pipes from manifolds.
6. Remove starter assembly (set to one side with wires attached), starter motor bracket and flywheel inspection cover.
7. On 1971 T-37, LeMans and GTO, remove stabilizer shaft to frame bracket attaching bolts to insure free movement of lifting device. It may also be necessary to loosen fuel pump to timing cover bolts for clearance.
8. Attach lifting tool, loosen oil pan bolts and raise engine until oil pan can be removed.

1969 Tempest V8

1. Disconnect battery positive cable.
2. Remove fan blade assembly.
3. Inspect all hoses and wiring for proper routing to avoid excessive binding when engine is raised 4½″.
4. Raise car and drain crankcase.
5. Disconnect idler arm from frame and drop steering linkage.
6. Disconnect exhaust crossover pipe on single exhaust models.
7. Remove starter motor and flywheel cover.
8. Position lifting tool J22603 in place with J22603-8 crossbar in position on lifting tool. Bolt tool to timing cover.
9. Using frame jack, support engine at J22603 and remove motor mount to frame bolts.
10. Raise engine about 4½″ and remove oil pan.

1966-68 Tempest V8 & 1967 Firebird V8

1. Remove engine, clutch and transmission from vehicle as a unit.
2. Remove clutch and transmission from engine.
3. Remove oil pan.
4. Install oil pan gaskets as shown in Figs. 11, 12, 13.
5. Install clutch and transmission to engine, and install the assembly into the vehicle.

1968-69 Firebird V8

1. Disconnect positive battery cable.
2. Disconnect fan shroud from radiator.
3. Remove air cleaner and distributor cap.
4. Make sure all hoses and wiring are free so as not to bind when engine is raised 4½″ and moved forward 1½″.
5. Raise car and drain crankcase.
6. Disconnect idler arm from frame.
7. Disconnect crossover pipe. If equipped with dual exhausts, disconnect exhaust pipes from manifolds.
8. Remove starter and flywheel cover.
9. Attach lifting tool J22603 to engine and place crossbar J22603-8 in position on tool.
10. Using frame jack or transmission jack, support engine at tool J22603 and remove motor mounts from engine.

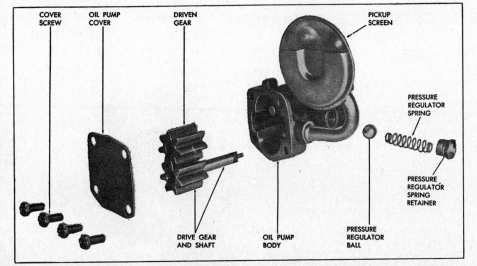

Fig. 15   Oil pump disassembled. V8 Pontiac engines

11. Remove rear transmission to cross-member bolts.
12. Raise engine 4½" and at the same time move engine forward 1½".
13. Remove oil pan.

1966-69 Pontiac

1. Disconnect battery ground cable.
2. Remove fan shield.
3. On A/C cars, remove fan and pulley.
4. Disconnect engine ground cables.
5. On A/C cars, remove compressor from mounting brackets and position to one side.

NOTE: At this time, inspect all water hoses and wiring harnesses for proper routing to avoid excessive bind when engine is raised about 4½".

6. Raise car and drain crankcase.
7. Disconnect steering idler arm from frame.
8. Remove exhaust crossover pipe. If equipped with dual exhausts disconnect exhaust pipes from manifolds.
9. Remove starter and flywheel cover.
10. Remove front engine mount-to-frame bolts.

NOTE: On 1966 models, a special Engine Support Bracket (J-22376) is available which is installed on timing cover with two 5/16" bolts 1" long. With suitable equipment, support engine at this tool, remove left motor mount and loosen right engine mount-to-block bolts. Remove oil pan bolts, raise engine and remove pan.

On 1967-69 models, special Engine Lifting Tool (J-22603) is available. Bolt tool to timing chain cover with bolts provided with tool. Using frame jack or automatic transmission jack, support engine at Tool J-22603 and remove engine mounts. Loosen rear transmission mount. It may be necessary to remove this mount and rest rear of transmission on cross-mem-

ber to obtain necessary clearance. Remove oil pan bolts and raise engine *straight up* until transmission is against floor pan. Remove pan by first rotating clockwise (facing forward) to clear oil pump.

NOTE: If work other than oil pan gasket replacement is to be performed, support engine with suitable blocks of wood and remove engine support.

OIL PUMP

V8-326, 350, 400, 455 Engines

To remove the pump, remove the oil pan as outlined above. Then remove oil pump from engine.

In servicing the pump, refer to Fig. 14.

V8s Except 326, 350, 400, 455

Remove oil pan. While holding pump in place, remove attaching screws. Lower the pump away from the block with one hand while removing the oil pump drive shaft with the other.

Remove oil screen and pressure regulator parts. Detach cover from pump body and take out gears, Fig. 15.

Examine all parts for damage and assemble. Do not attempt to change oil pressure by varying length of pressure regulator spring.

Position drive shaft in distributor and oil pump drive gear. Place pump in position in the block, indexing the drive shaft with pump drive gear shaft. Install attaching screws with lock washers and tighten securely.

Removal and installation of pump does not affect distributor timing since the oil pump and distributor drive gear are mounted on the distributor shaft.

WATER PUMP, REPLACE
V8s Except 326, 350, 400, 455

Water pump is serviced only as an assembly. To remove, drain radiator and engine block. Remove fan belt, fan and pulley. Unfasten pump from block.

Install the pump in the reverse order. When pump is installed, drain hole will be at the bottom.

V8-326, 350, 400, 455 Engines

To remove water pump, which is *serviced only as an assembly,* drain cooling system. Remove fan belt, fan and pulley. Unfasten and remove pump from engine.

When pump is installed on engine, drain hole will be at bottom. Tighten pump attaching nuts to 15 ft. lbs.

FUEL PUMP, REPLACE

1. Remove all gasket material from the pump and block gasket surfaces. Apply sealer on both sides of new gasket.
2. Position gasket on pump flange and hold pump in position against its mounting surface. Make sure rocker arm is riding on camshaft eccentric.
3. Press pump tight against its mounting. Install retaining screws and tighten them alternately.
4. Connect fuel lines. Then operate engine and check for leaks.

SERVICE NOTE: Before installing the pump, it is good practice to crank the engine so that the nose of the camshaft eccentric is out of the way of the fuel pump rocker arm when the pump is installed. In this way there will be the least amount of tension on the rocker arm, thereby easing the installation of the pump.

Overhead Camshaft Engine Section

INDEX OF SERVICE OPERATIONS

ENGINE, REPLACE

1. Disconnect cables at battery.
2. Drain cooling system.
3. Scribe alignment marks on hood around hood hinges and remove hood.
4. Disconnect engine wiring harness and

engine ground straps.
5. Remove air cleaner and fan shield.
6. Disconnect all hoses at engine.
7. With manual transmission, remove radiator.
8. If equipped with power steering or air conditioning, remove pump and compressor from mounting brackets

and set aside (do not disconnect hoses).
9. Remove engine fan and pulley.
10. Disconnect accelerator linkage.
11. Disconnect transmission vacuum modulator line and power brake vacuum line at carburetor and fold back out of the way.

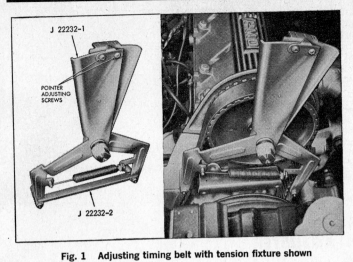

Fig. 1 Adjusting timing belt with tension fixture shown

Fig. 2 Accessory drive housing mounting bolts

12. Raise vehicle and drain crankcase.
13. Disconnect fuel lines at fuel pump, exhaust pipes from manifold and starter wires.
14. If equipped with automatic transmission, remove converter cover and 3 converter retaining bolts and slide converter to rear.
15. If equipped with manual transmission, disconnect clutch linkage and remove clutch shaft. Remove four lower bell housing bolts (two each side).
16. Disconnect transmission filler tube support and starter wire harness shield from cylinder head.
17. Remove two front engine mounts to-frame thru bolts.
18. Lower vehicle.
19. Support transmission with a jack and block of wood.

20. Remove two remaining bell housing bolts, raise transmission slightly and remove engine.
21. Reverse procedure to install. Do not lower engine completely while jack is supporting transmission.

TIMING BELT, ADJUST

1. Remove 3 screws on front of top cover. Lift up cover to disengage side clips. Remove retaining clips from cover.
2. Using the equipment shown in Fig. 1, set the pointer of the fixture on the zero mark. *This calibration must be performed prior to each use of the fixture to insure an accurate belt adjustment.*
3. Remove camshaft sprocket-to-camshaft bolt and install the fixture on the belt with the rollers on the outside (smooth) surface of belt. Thread the fixture mounting bolt into camshaft sprocket bolt location finger tight.
4. Squeeze indicator end (upper) of fixture and quickly release so that fixture assumes released or relaxed position.
5. With the tool installed as directed, adjust accessory drive housing, Fig. 2, up or down as required to obtain a tension adjuster indicator centered in the green range with drive housing mounting bolts torqued to 15 ft-lbs.
6. Remove tension fixture and install sprocket retaining bolt, making sure bolt threads and washer are free of dirt. Install cover.

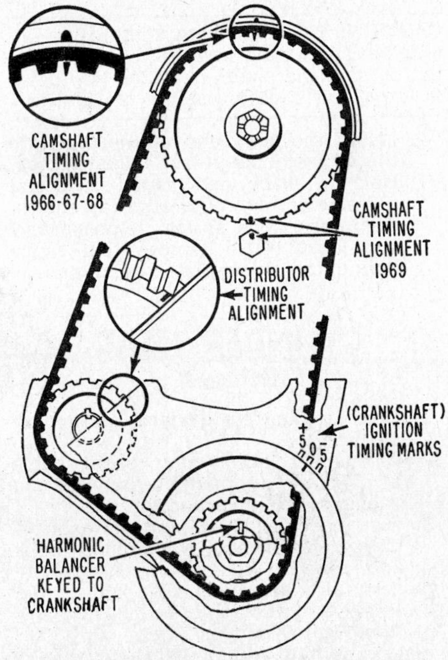

CAMSHAFT SPROCKET OR SEAL

CAUTION: Do not use tools of any type, other than hands, to pry on timing belt during belt removal or replacement or during other service operations.

1. Remove timing belt top front cover. *For ease on reassembly, index three timing marks as shown in Fig. 3.*
2. Loosen accessory drive housing bolts, Fig. 2.

3. Remove belt from camshaft sprocket.
4. Remove sprocket.

NOTE: If necessary to replace camshaft seal, reinstall sprocket bolt. Thread a tool of the type shown, Fig. 4, into camshaft seal. Tighten center bolt on tool until seal is extracted. Install a suitable seal protector and pilot, Fig. 5, on end of camshaft. Slide seal over on tool, then drive it in place, Fig. 6.

5. Install sprocket, indexing pin on sprocket with hole in camshaft.
6. Install sprocket bolt finger tight.

Fig. 4 Removing camshaft seal

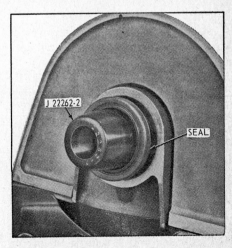

Fig. 5 Seal and protector tool installed

Fig. 3 Valve timing marks

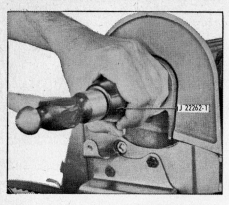

Fig. 6   Installing camshaft seal

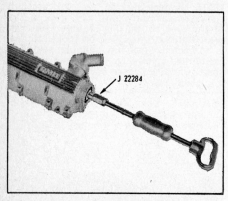

Fig. 7   Removing camshaft

7. Align timing marks and install belt.
8. Adjust timing and belt tension.
9. Torque sprocket bolt to 40 ft-lbs and install top cover.

ROCKER ARM COVER

1. Drain cooling system and disconnect radiator hose at fitting on cover.
2. Remove timing belt top cover.
3. Align timing marks and remove belt from camshaft sprocket.
4. Disconnect necessary fuel and vacuum lines.
5. Unfasten and remove rocker arm cover.
6. Reverse procedure to install.

CAMSHAFT

1. Remove camshaft sprocket and seal.
2. Remove rocker arm cover.
3. Using tools of the type shown in Fig. 7, drive camshaft from rocker cover.

CAUTION: *Do not allow camshaft to damage bearing surfaces of rocker cover.*

4. Remove parts shown from rear of camshaft, Fig. 8.
5. Remove water outlet fitting and thermostat from rocker cover.
6. Clean all parts and inspect for wear or damage. Minor nicks or scratches on edge of bearing surface can be corrected with a suitable scraper or file.

Installation

1. Install camshaft into rocker cover.
2. Install thrust washer, Fig. 9.
3. Install retaining bolt and washer and torque to 40 ft-lbs.
4. Using a tool of the type shown in Fig. 10, drive plug in so it is fully seated.

IMPORTANT: A camshaft bore plug not fully seated could result in excessive camshaft end play which is .003" to .009" when read at the sprocket end with a dial indicator.

5. Replace water outlet fitting and thermostat.

ROCKER ARM OR VALVE LASH ADJUSTER

1. Remove rocker arm cover.
2. Remove rocker arm and hydraulic lash adjuster assembly and store so that each assembly can be installed in its original location.

NOTE: If a new lash adjuster is to be installed, it will be necessary to check the leak-down rate and prime the adjuster before installation.

3. Install retainer clip, Fig. 11.
4. Place each lash adjuster in its original location, and install rocker cover.

Lash Adjuster Service

NOTE: Because of the important part hydraulic lash adjusters play in the operation of the engine, and the close tolerances to which they are manufactured, proper handling and, above all, cleanliness, cannot be overstressed when servicing these parts.

New adjusters are serviced as individual units, packaged with a plastic coating. Leave the coating on until ready to check leak-down rate. It is necessary to remove the oil from the new adjusters prior to checking leak-down rate since special oil is in new adjusters. Fill adjusters with SAE 10 oil before checking leak-down rate. If leak-down test equipment is not available, the supplier should check lash adjusters for you.

Removing Stuck Lash Adjuster

After removing the rocker arm, fill the vent hole adjacent to the stuck lifter with engine oil. Using a length of ³/₁₆" diameter rod approximately 4" in length, insert it into the top of the vent hole and strike the end of the rod with a hammer. The hydraulic effect of the oil on the base of the lash adjuster will then break the adjuster free from the boss in the cylinder head. The use of pliers for this operation is not recommended since lifter damage will result.

VALVE SPRINGS & SEALS

Valve springs and seals can be replaced without removing the cylinder head if tools of the type shown in Fig. 14 are

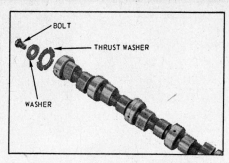

Fig. 8   Camshaft and related parts

Fig. 9   Thrust washer installation

available.
1. Remove rocker arm cover.
2. Remove rocker arm of valve being serviced.
3. Remove spark plug from cylinder of valves to be serviced and install an air hose with an adapter that will screw into the spark plug hole.

CAUTION: When applying compressed air into the spark plug hole to hold the valve up, be sure the piston is all the way down in the cylinder, otherwise the fan will turn.

4. Install the hook end of the tool into the oil feed hole in lash adjuster bore. Hold in place and install fork end of valve spring compressor as shown. Compress valve spring, remove valve cup locks. Then remove tool, valve spring, cup shield and valve stem seal.

CYLINDER HEAD
Removal

1. Drain cooling system and remove air cleaner.
2. Disconnect accelerator pedal cable at bellcrank on manifold and fuel and vacuum lines at carburetor.
3. Disconnect exhaust pipe at manifold flange, then remove manifold bolts and clamps. Remove manifolds and carburetor as an assembly.
4. Remove rocker arm cover.
5. Remove timing belt upper front cover mounting support bracket and rear lower cover.
6. Disconnect spark plug wires.

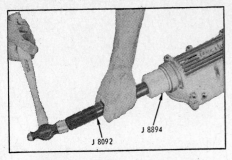

Fig. 10   Installing camshaft bore plug

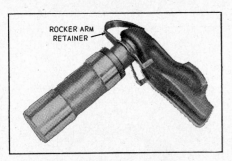

Fig. 11   Rocker arm retainer
and lash adjuster

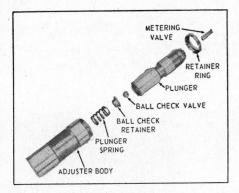

Fig. 12   Hydraulic lash
adjuster disassembled

Fig. 14   Depressing valve spring

7. Remove rocker arms and hydraulic valve lash adjusters. *Store rocker arms and lash adjusters so they can be replaced in exactly the same location.*
8. Remove head bolts and lift off head.

Installation

When installing a new head, transfer all serviceable parts to new head using new seals on intake and exhaust valve stems and new manifold gaskets.

Head bolts are of two different lengths. When inserted in proper holes, all bolts will project an equal distance from head. Do not use sealer of any kind on threads. Pontiac recommends no numerical sequence for tightening cylinder head bolts. Tighten them a little at a time, starting at the center bolts and working alternately from side to side outward to the end bolts.

VALVE SERVICE

Fig. 15 shows the valves and related parts.

Valves with oversize stems are available in .001", .003" and .005" larger than standard. The same valve stem-to-guide clearance listed in the *Valve Specifications* table applies for oversize stems.

Carefully ream the valve guide. For best results when installing a .005" oversize valve stem, use a .003" oversize reamer first, then ream the .005" oversize. Always reface the valve seat after reaming valve guide.

When installing valve springs, place the closed coil end toward the cylinder head.

CRANKCASE COVER SEAL

1. Remove upper timing cover.
2. Align timing marks, Fig. 3.
3. Remove fan and water pump pulley.
4. Remove vibration damper.
5. Remove timing belt lower cover, Fig. 16.
6. Loosen accessory drive mounting bolts to provide slack in timing belt, Fig. 2.
7. Remove timing belt.
8. Remove crankshaft timing belt flange and sprocket, Fig. 17.
9. Pry seal from front of crankcase.
10. Install new seal with lip of seal inward, using a suitable seal driver.
11. Reverse procedure to install, being sure to align the belt timing marks and adjust belt tension, Fig. 1.

FRONT CRANKCASE COVER

1. Remove crankshaft sprocket.
2. Remove 4 front oil pan-to-crankcase cover bolts.
3. Loosen remaining oil pan bolts as necessary to provide clearance between cover and pan. *It may be necessary to jar oil pan to gain necessary clearance.*
4. Remove 5 cover bolts.
5. Remove cover and gasket. Clean gasket surface, using care to see that gasket particles do not fall into oil pan.

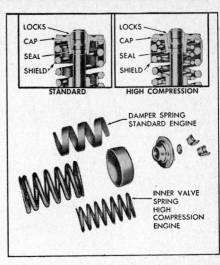

Fig. 15   Valves and related parts

Fig. 16   Lower front timing
belt cover bolts

Fig. 17   Crankshaft sprocket

Fig. 18   Front crankcase
with cover removed

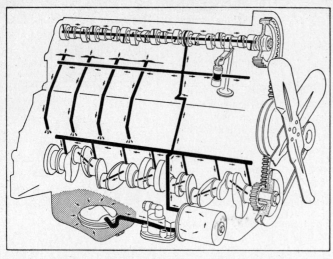

Engine oiling system. OHC Six

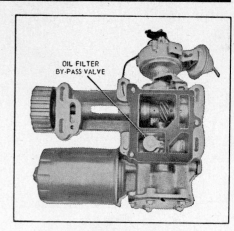

Fig. 19   Oil filter by-pass valve

Fig. 20   Removing eccentric and distributor drive gear retaining pin

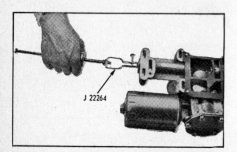

Fig. 21   Removing bearing and seal

6. Reverse procedure to install, Fig. 18.

ACCESSORY DRIVE HOUSING

Oil Pressure Regulator Valve

1. Remove cap, washer and spring from housing.
2. Using a magnet, remove valve from housing.
3. Reverse procedure to install.

Oil Pump

1. Remove pump cover and gasket.
2. Remove two gears.
3. Replace worn parts, install cover with new gasket and torque bolts to 20 ft-lbs.

Housing Assembly

1. Remove timing belt top cover.
2. Align timing marks, Fig. 3.
3. Loosen 6 housing-to-cylinder block bolts, Fig. 2.
4. Remove timing belt from camshaft sprocket and distributor drive.
5. Disconnect fuel lines from fuel pump.
6. Remove distributor cap, vacuum lines and wires from distributor.
7. Remove housing assembly.
8. Reverse procedure to install, using new housing gasket. Be sure to align timing marks and adjust timing belt tension.

Oil Filter By-Pass Valve

1. Remove housing assembly.
2. Remove valve retaining screw, Fig. 19.
3. Remove by-pass valve.
4. Reverse procedure to install.

Sprocket, Seal, Fuel Pump, Distributor Drive

1. Remove housing assembly.
2. Look for and write down location of sprocket timing mark and direction of distributor rotor, then remove distributor.
3. Remove drive gear retaining pin, Fig. 20. Position shaft to allow adequate clearance in housing body for pin removal.
4. Remove shaft and sprocket.
5. If necessary to replace bearing or seal use a slide hammer and tool of the type shown in Fig. 21 to remove seal or bearing and seal together.
6. Reverse procedure to install.

OIL PAN

1. Disconnect battery cable.

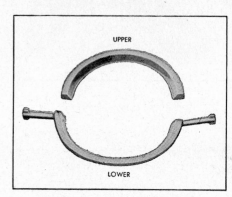

Fig. 22   Rear main bearing oil seal

Fig. 23   Removing rear main bearing cap

2. Remove air cleaner.
3. On air conditioned cars, remove compressor from mounting brackets and position to one side.
4. Inspect all water hose and wiring harness for proper routing to prevent excessive binding when engine is raised about $4\frac{1}{2}$".

NOTE: Before raising vehicle prop hood open at least 6" to insure adequate clearance between timing belt cover and inner hood panel.

5. Remove starter and flywheel cover.
6. Reroute or disconnect any wiring be-

tween bellcrank and floor pan to insure against damage when bell housing contacts floor pan.

7. Loosen transmission insulator-to-crossmember bolts.
8. Remove right and left engine insulator-to-frame bracket thru bolts.
9. Rotate vibration damper until timing mark is at bottom so crankshaft counterweights will be in proper position for oil pan removal.
10. With suitable equipment, raise engine at front until insulators clear frame brackets.
11. Remove oil pan bolts.
12. Raise engine at front. Apply a rearward force on engine-transmission assembly until oil pan clears flywheel housing and remove pan.
13. Reverse procedure to install.

Rear Main Bearing Seal

The rear main bearing oil seal can be replaced (both halves) without removal of crankshaft. Always replace upper and lower seal as a unit, Fig. 22.
1. Remove oil pan.

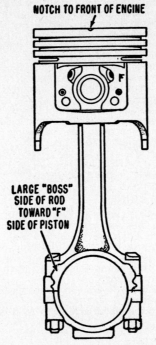

NOTCH TO FRONT OF ENGINE

LARGE "BOSS" SIDE OF ROD TOWARD "F" SIDE OF PISTON

Fig. 24   Piston and rod assembly

2. Use a slide hammer of the type shown in Fig. 23 to remove bearing cap.
3. Pry seal from groove and bearing cap side seals.
4. Clean crankshaft surface.
5. Place new side seals in position and place bearing cap in vise and compress seals into place.
6. Insert new seal well lubricated with engine oil in bearing cap groove. Gradually push with a hammer handle until seal is rolled into place.
7. To replace upper half of seal, use a small hammer and brass pin punch to tap one end of oil seal until it protrudes far enough to be removed with pliers. Push new seal into place.
8. Install bearing cap and oil pan.

PISTONS & CRANKSHAFT BEARINGS

Service on pistons, rings, pins, main and rod bearings are conventional.
Assemble pistons to rods as shown in Fig. 24.

Clutch & Standard Transmission Section

NOTE: 1972 linkage adjustment information is in this section. Repair procedures on both automatic and manual shift transmissions are covered elsewhere in this manual. Procedures for removing automatic transmissions as well as linkage adjustments on 1966-71 models are included in the automatic transmission chapters. See Chapter Index

CLUTCH PEDAL, ADJUST

1966-72 All Models

1. Unhook linkage return spring.

2. With clutch pedal against stop, loosen lock nut enough to allow adjusting rod to be turned out of swivel (V8) or push rod (6-cyl.) and rearward against clutch fork until clutch release bearing contacts pressure plate fingers lightly.

3. Rotate adjustable rod into swivel or push rod 3½ turns and tighten lock nut.

4. Install return spring and check free pedal travel; it should be about 1".

CLUTCH, REPLACE

1966-72 All

1. Disconnect battery-to-starter cable.
2. Remove transmission as outlined below.
3. Remove release bearing through rear opening in clutch housing.
4. Remove pedal return spring, starter, front flywheel housing shield and flywheel housing.
5. Mark clutch cover and flywheel to insure reassembly in the same position as balanced at the factory.
6. Loosen bolts holding clutch cover to flywheel a little at a time until all tension is relieved. Then remove clutch and driven disc.
7. Reverse removal procedure to install the clutch and adjust pedal free travel.

THREE SPEED MANUAL TRANS.

Transmission, Replace 1966-72

1. Disconnect speedometer cable.
2. Disconnect shift rods from transmission.
3. Remove propeller shaft.
4. Support rear of engine and remove transmission mount.
5. Remove 4 crossmember bolts and slide member rearward.
6. Remove 2 upper transmission-to-flywheel housing bolts, insert guide pins.
7. Remove two lower bolts.
8. Remove transmission.
9. Reverse procedure to install.

SHIFT LINKAGE 3 SPEED TRANS.

1970-72

Column Shift

1. Set gearshift lever in Reverse position and lock ignition.
2. Loosen swivel clamp screws at transmission shifter lever (1st & Rev) and at cross shaft assembly.
3. Position front transmission shifter lever (2nd & 3rd) in Neutral position and rear transmission shifter lever (1st & Rev) in Reverse position.
4. Tighten swivel clamp screw at transmission 1st & Rev lever, unlock steering column and shift into Neutral.
5. Align gearshift lower control levers on column in Neutral position and insert a .185" pin through hole in levers.
6. Tighten swivel clamp screw at cross shaft, remove gauge pin and check operation.

Floor Shift

1. With steering column unlocked, position the shaft control lever into Neutral.
2. Loosen swivel clamp nut retaining the gearshift control rod to the idler lever.
3. Loosen trunnion jam nuts on 1st & Rev control rod, loosen jam nuts on 2nd & 3rd control rod and insert a

.250" gauge pin into shifter assembly.
4. Manually position both transmission shifter levers in Neutral and torque jam nuts to 25 ft. lbs.
5. Remove gauge pin from shifter assembly and check operation.
6. Adjust backdrive by shifting into Reverse gear, set gearshift control rod in Lock position and lock the steering column.
7. Push up on gearshift control rod to take up clearance in column lock mechanism and torque adjusting swivel clamp nut to 20 ft. lbs.

1966-69 All

Column Shift

1. Align upper and lower gearshift levers on steering column in neutral position. Where provision has been made, insert a 3/16" gauge pin through holes in levers.
2. Loosen clamp screws at transmission control rods.
3. Position levers on transmission in neutral.
4. Tighten clamp screws to 20 ft-lbs.

Floor Shift

1. Position selector lever in neutral.
2. Loosen trunnion jam nut on transmission control rods.
3. Place transmission lever and bracket assembly in neutral. Where provision has been made, install a 1/4" gauge pin through hole in bracket.
4. Position transmission lever in neutral.
5. Tighten jam nuts to 30 ft-lbs.

6. Remove gauge pin.

4 SP. TRANS., REPLACE
1966-72

Follow procedure outlined for 1966-72 three-speed model.

SHIFT LINKAGE 4 SPEED TRANS.

1. Place selector lever in neutral.
2. Loosen trunnion nuts on transmission control rod.
3. Place transmission lever and bracket assembly in neutral and install a gauge pin through hole and slot provided in bracket.
4. Position lever on transmission in neutral.
5. Tighten trunnion nuts and remove gauge pin.
6. On 1969-72 units, position shift lever in Reverse, set steering column lever in Lock position and lock ignition. Push up on control rod to remove clearance and tighten nut of adjusting swivel to 20 ft.-lbs.

1972 AUTO. TRANS. LINKAGE, ADJUST

Adjustment procedures for the 1972 linkages are essentially the same as those for 1971 units which are outlined in the front of this manual. The 2 speed automatic transmission used in 1970-72 is the Powerglide unit which is also described in the front of this manual.

Rear Axle, Propeller Shaft & Brake Section

REAR AXLES

Figs. 1 and 2 illustrate the rear axle assemblies used on 1966-72 conventional models. When necessary to overhaul either of these units, refer to the *Rear Axle Specifications* table in this chapter.

All 1966-69 & 1970-72 Except Type "C"

In this rear axle, Fig. 1, the rear axle housing and differential carrier are cast into an integral assembly. The drive pinion assembly is mounted in two opposed tapered roller bearings. The pinion bearings are preloaded by a spacer behind the front bearing. The pinion is positioned by a washer between the head of the pinion and the rear bearing.

The differential is supported in the carrier by two tapered roller side bearings. These bearings are preloaded by shims located between the bearings and carrier housing. The differential assembly is positioned for proper ring gear and pinion backlash by varying these shims. The differential case houses two side gears in mesh with two pinions mounted on a pinion shaft which is held in place by a

lock screw. The side gears and pinions are backed by thrust washers.

Diff. Carrier Assy

All 1966-69 & 1970-72 except type "C"

Construction of the axle assembly is such that service operations may be performed with the housing installed in the vehicle or with the housing removed and installed in a holding fixture. The following procedure is necessary only when the housing requires replacement.

1. Raise car and place a floor jack under center of axle housing so it starts to raise rear axle assembly. Place car stands solidly under body members on both sides.
2. Disconnect rear U-joint from drive pinion flange and support propeller shaft out of the way.
3. Remove both axle shafts.
4. Support both brake backing plates out of the way.
5. Disconnect rear brake hose bracket by removing top cover bolt. Remove brake line from housing by bending back tabs.
6. Loosen remaining cover bolts, break loose cover about 1/8" and allow lube

to drain.
7. Disconnect shock absorbers at axle housing. Lower jack under housing until rear springs can be removed.
8. Disconnect upper control arms at axle housing.
9. Disconnect lower control arms at axle housing and remove rear axle assembly from vehicle.
10. Reverse removal procedure to install the unit.

Axle Shaft, Replace

All 1966-69 & 1970-72 except type "C"

NOTE: Design allows for axle shaft end play up to .032" loose. This end play can be checked with the wheel and brake drum removed by measuring the difference between the end of the housing and the axle shaft flange while moving the axle shaft in and out by hand. End play over .032" is excessive. Compensating for all of the end play by inserting a shim inboard of the bearing in the housing is not recommended since it ignores the end play of the bearing itself, and may result in improper seating of the gasket or backing plate against the housing. If

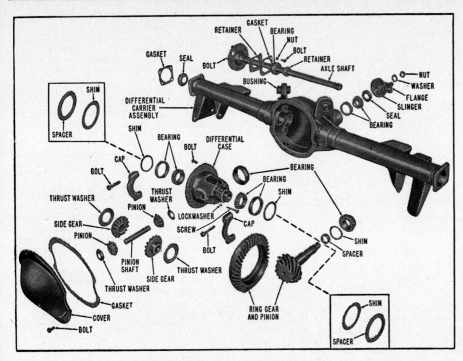

Fig. 1 Rear axle assembly exploded. All 1966-69 and 1970-72 except type "C"

the end play is excessive, the axle shaft and bearing assembly should be removed and the cause of the excessive end play corrected.

1. To remove, take off wheels and brake drums.
2. Remove nuts holding retainer plates and brake backing plates. Pull retainers clear of bolts and reinstall two lower nuts finger tight to hold backing plate in position.
3. Use a slide hammer-type puller to remove axle shaft, Fig. 3.

Axle Shaft Bearing

1. Press axle shaft bearing off shaft.

2. Press new bearing against shoulder on shaft.

CAUTION: Outer retainer plate which retains bearing in housing must be on axle shaft before bearing is installed. A new outer retainer gasket can be installed after bearing. Use care not to wedge outer retainer between bearing and shoulder of shaft. Do not press bearing and inner retainer on in one operation.

3. Press new inner retainer ring against bearing.

Axle Shaft Seal

1. Insert suitable tongs behind seal and

pull straight out to remove seal.
2. Apply sealer to outside diameter of new seal.
3. Position seal over a suitable installer and drive straight into axle housing until tool bottoms on bearing shoulder in housing.

Axle Shaft, Install

1. Apply a coat of wheel bearing grease in bearing recess of housing. Also lightly lubricate the axle shaft with rear axle lube from the sealing surface to about 6" inboard.
2. Install new axle housing-to-brake backing plate gasket.
3. Install brake assembly with backing plate in proper position.
4. With a new outer retainer gasket in proper position, insert axle shaft until splines engage differential. *Do not allow shaft to drag on seal.*
5. Drive axle shaft into position.
6. Place new outer retainer gasket and retainer over studs and install nuts, torqueing them to 45-55 ft-lbs.
7. Install brake drums and wheels.

1970-72 Type "C" Axle

1. Raise and support car leaving the rear wheels and differential suspended.
2. Remove rear wheels and brake drums.
3. Remove differential cover and drain lubricant.
4. Remove pinion shaft lock bolt and pinion shaft.
5. Push axle shaft inward to permit removal of "C" locks then remove axle shaft.
6. Install axle shaft bearing and seal remover and remove the bearing and seal.

PROPELLER SHAFT

1966-72

Two designs of propeller shaft are used, a solid type which is of one piece tubular steel construction, and a "rubber" type which incorporates rubber torsional dampers between two concentric tubes of steel.

Two methods are used to retain the U-joint bearings to the yoke: conventional snap rings are used at the companion flange of the differential: the remaining six U-joint bearings are held in place with nylon rings.

SERVICE NOTE: Because of the elastic properties of the nylon retainers, Fig. 4, it is not possible to drive the bearings out in the conventional manner. They

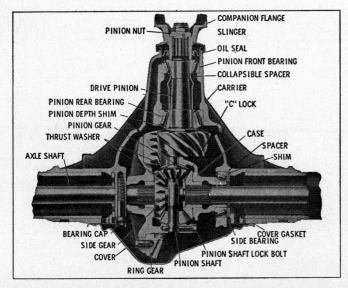

Fig. 2 1970-72 type "C" differential case

Fig. 3 Removing axle shaft with slide hammer-type propeller

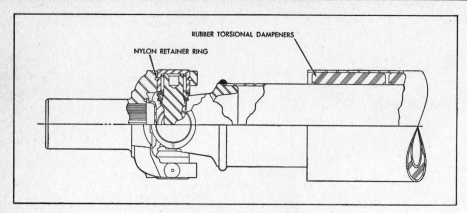

Fig. 4   Insulated propeller shaft. 1966-68 (typical)

must be pressed out, which shears the nylon retainers in half, rendering the bearings and journal unsuitable for further use. Therefore, when reassembling, a new bearing and journal assembly employing the conventional snap ring retainers must be used.

CAUTION: Do not attempt to replace the U-joints of propeller shafts from cars equipped with 421 H.O. engines and axles of 3.42 ratio and over. They are high speed balanced assemblies and replacement of composite U-joint will destroy this balance.

BRAKE ADJUSTMENTS
1966-71 Self-Adjusting Brakes

These brakes, Fig. 5, have self-adjusting shoe mechanisms that assure correct lining-to-drum clearances at all times. The automatic adjusters operate only when the brakes are applied as the car is moving rearward or when the car comes to an uphill stop.

Although the brakes are self-adjusting, an initial adjustment is necessary after the brake shoes have been relined or replaced, or when the length of the star wheel adjuster has been changed during

some other service operation.

Frequent usage of an automatic transmission forward range to halt reverse vehicle motion may prevent the automatic adjusters from functioning, thereby inducing low pedal heights. Should low pedal heights be encountered, it is recommended that numerous forward and reverse stops be made until satisfactory pedal height is obtained.

If a low pedal height condition cannot be corrected by making numerous reverse stops (provided the hydraulic system is free of air) it indicates that the self-adjusting mechanism is not functioning. Therefore, it will be necessary to remove the drum, clean, free up and lubricate the adjusting mechanism. Then adjust the brakes as follows, being sure the parking brake is fully released.

Adjustment

1. Remove adjusting hole cover from brake backing plate and, from backing plate side, turn adjusting screw upward with a screwdriver or other suitable tool to expand the shoes until a slight drag is felt when the drum is rotated.
2. Remove brake drum.
3. While holding adjusting lever out of engagement with the adjusting screw,

Fig. 6, back off the adjusting screw one full turn with the fingers.

NOTE: *If finger movement will not turn the screw, free it up. If this is not done, the adjusting lever will not turn the screw during subsequent vehicle operation. Lubricate the screw with oil and coat with wheel bearing grease. Any other adjustment procedure may cause damage to the adjusting screw with consequent self-adjuster problems.*

PARKING BRAKE, ADJUST

CAUTION: It is very important that parking brake cables are not adjusted too tightly causing brake drag. With automatic brake adjusters, a tight cable causes brake drag and also positions the secondary brake shoe, hence the adjuster lever, so that it continues to adjust to compensate for wear caused by the drag. The result is a cycle of wear and adjustment that can wear out linings very rapidly.

1966-72

1. Jack up both rear wheels.
2. Pull parking brake pedal five to seven notches from fully released position (two notches on Firebird models).
3. Loosen equalizer rear lock nut. Adjust forward nut until a light to moderate drag is felt when rear wheels are rotated.
4. Tighten lock nut. Fully released parking brake and rotate rear wheels to be sure there is no drag.

POWER BRAKE UNIT, REPLACE
1969-72 All Models

1. Disconnect vacuum hose at vacuum check valve. Plug hose and cover valve opening to exclude dust.
2. Disconnect pipe(s) from master cylinder hydraulic port and cover opening and pipe end to exclude dirt.
3. Remove clevis pin from brake pedal

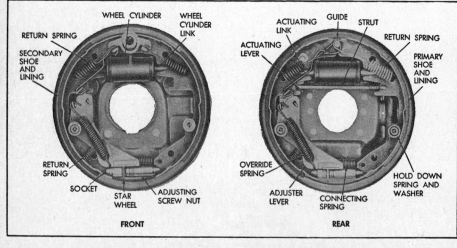

Fig. 5   Right front and rear brake. 1966-72 (typical)

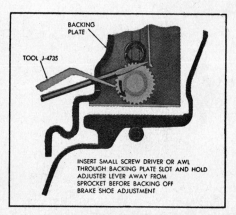

INSERT SMALL SCREW DRIVER OR AWL THROUGH BACKING PLATE SLOT AND HOLD ADJUSTER LEVER AWAY FROM SPROCKET BEFORE BACKING OFF BRAKE SHOE ADJUSTMENT

Fig. 6   Backing off adjusting screw. 1966-72

inside car.

4. Remove nuts from rear half housing and remove power cylinder assembly.

5. Reverse removal procedure to install.

BRAKE MASTER CYLINDER, REPLACE
1966-72

1. Disconnect brake lines from two out-

lets on master cylinder and tape end of lines to prevent entrance of dirt.

2. Disconnect master cylinder push rod from brake pedal.

3. Remove master cylinder from dash.

Front Suspension & Steering Section

FRONT SUSPENSION
1966-72

The front suspension is of the conventional "A" frame design with coil springs and ball joints. The ball joints have a "fixed boot" grease seal for protection against the entry of dirt and water. The steering knuckles and spindles are of integral design and brake cylinders are rigidly attached to the knuckles with the backing plates serving principally as a support for brake shoes and as a protective cover.

On some 1971-72 models, an integral steering knuckle which is a combination steering knuckle, brake caliper support and steering arm is used. On other models, the steering knuckle is of the conventional type with a separate steering arm.

Rubber bushings at the inner ends of the upper control arms pivot on shafts attached to the car frame. Caster and camber adjustments are made with shims at this point, Fig. 1. Direct acting shock absorbers operate within the coil springs.

LUBRICATION

These cars are completely lubricated at the factory with a special long-lasting chassis grease and under normal conditions chassis lubrication will not be required for 12,000 miles or one year whichever comes first. For subsequent lubrications, the specially formulated grease is recommended and is available at Pontiac dealers.

NOTE: If conventional chassis lubrication is used, relubrication at six months or 6000 miles, whichever occurs first, is necessary.

WHEEL ALIGNMENT
1966-72 All Models

Caster and camber adjustments are made by placing shims between the upper pivot shafts and frame, Fig. 2. Both adjustments can be made at the same time. In order to remove or install shims, raise car to remove weight from front wheel, then loosen control arm shaft-to-frame bolts.

1. To decrease positive caster add shims to front bolt.
2. To increase positive caster remove shims from front bolt.
3. To increase camber remove shims from both front and rear bolts.
4. To decrease camber add shims to both front and rear bolts.

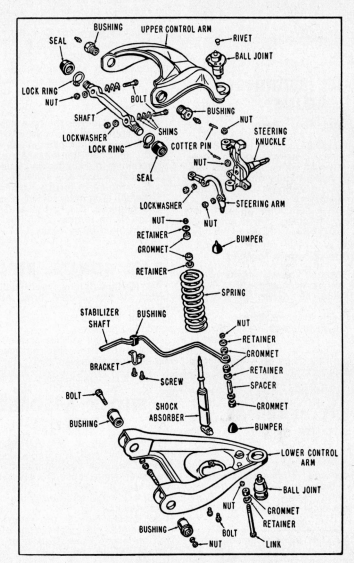

Fig. 1   Disassembled view of front suspension. 1966-72 (typical)

5. Compensate for drift to right due to road camber by setting left angle $\frac{1}{4}°$ greater than right.

NOTE: By adding or subtracting an equal amount of shims from front and rear bolts, camber will be changed without affecting caster.

6. After the correct number of shims have been installed, torque pivot shaft mounting bolts to 55-75 ft-lbs.

TOE-IN, ADJUST

1. With wheels in straight ahead position, loosen tie rod clamp bolts and turn tubes an equal amount until toe-in is according to specifications. Turn right tie rod in direction of forward rotation of wheels to increase toe-in. Turn left tie rod in opposite direction to increase toe-in.

2. Tighten tie rod adjuster sleeve bolts to 14-20 ft-lbs, making sure bolts are to lower rear side of tie rod.

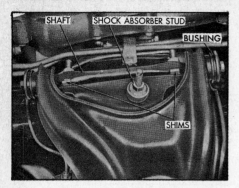

Fig. 2   Caster and camber shim location

WHEEL BEARINGS, ADJUST

Hand Feel Method

1. Tighten spindle nut with an 8" or 10" wrench, using enough arm length leverage to be sure parts are properly seated while rotating wheel.
2. Back off nut finger loose, then tighten finger tight.
3. If hole in spindle lines up with slot in nut, install cotter pin. If not, back off to next slot and install cotter pin.

Torque Wrench Method

1. While rotating wheel tighten nut with a torque wrench to 10-16 ft-lbs to be sure all parts are properly seated.
2. Back off adjusting nut finger free.
3. Tighten adjusting nut to 20-25 *inch-pounds*.
4. Loosen adjusting nut until nearest cotter pin hole lines up with a slot in nut and insert cotter pin.

WHEEL BEARINGS, REPLACE

(Disc Brakes)

1. Raise car and remove front wheels.
2. Remove brake hose support to caliper mounting bracket screw.
3. Remove caliper to mounting bracket bolts.

NOTE: Do not place strain on brake hose.

4. Remove spindle nut, and disc and hub assembly. Grease retainer and inner bearing can now be removed.

CHECKING BALL JOINTS FOR WEAR

Before checking ball joints for wear, make sure the front wheel bearings are properly adjusted and that the control arms are tight.

Referring to Fig. 3, raise wheel with a jack placed under the lower control at

the point shown. Then test by moving the wheel up and down to check axial play, and rocking it at the top and bottom to measure radial play.

1. Upper ball joint should be replaced if there is any noticeable looseness at this joint.
   If the ball joint is the type using a built in rubber pre-load cushion it will be necessary to remove the ball stud from the knuckle. Then replace the ball joint retaining nut on the ball stud. Using a socket and torque wrench, measure amount of torque required to turn the ball stud in its socket. If any torque is required, the ball joint is satisfactory. If no torque is required, the ball joint must be replaced.
2. Lower ball joint should be replaced if radial play exceeds .250".
3. Lower ball joint should be replaced if axial play between lower control arm and spindle exceeds the following:
   1966-72 .050"
   If the ball joint is the type using a built-in rubber pre-load cushion it will be necessary to remove the ball stud from the knuckle. Then replace the ball joint retaining nut on the ball stud. Using a socket and torque wrench, measure the amount of torque required to turn the ball stud in its socket. If any torque is required, the ball joint is satisfactory. If no torque is required, the ball joint must be replaced.

BALL JOINTS, REPLACE

On all models the upper ball joint is riveted to the control arm. All service ball joints, however, are provided with bolt, nut and washer assemblies for replacement purposes.

The lower ball joint is pressed into the control arm. They may be pressed out and new joints pressed in.

SHOCK ABSORBER, REPLACE

Hold the shock absorber upper stem from turning with a suitable wrench and remove the nut and grommet. Unfasten the lower shock absorber pivot from the lower control arm and pull the shock absorber and mounting out at the bottom of the spring housing.

To install, reverse the removal procedure. Tighten the upper retaining nut until it bottoms on the shoulder of the stem. Torque the nut to 4-6 lb. ft. and stake in place.

COIL SPRING, REPLACE

1. Remove shock absorber.
2. Jack up car and place stand jacks under frame side rails.
3. Remove wheel assembly to avoid damage to ball joints during spring operations.
4. Loosen 4 lower control arm cross shaft bushing bolts.
5. Install Special Spring Compressor or its equivalent through shock ab-

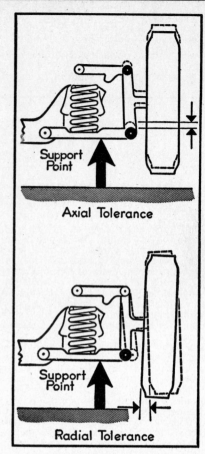

Fig. 3   Checking ball joints for wear

sorber mounting hole in front cross member and through spring. Install plate, thrust washer and nut and tighten so the spring is compressed slightly.

6. Remove nut from lower ball joint. Loosen the stud by hammering on the side of the steering knuckle joint boss, backing up the knuckle with a heavy hammer.
7. Remove upper ball joint stud in similar manner, and hang drum and knuckle assembly so as not to place a strain on brake hose.
8. Unfasten lower control arm inner shaft from frame cross member.
9. Unscrew spring compressor nut and remove spring from vehicle.
10. Installation is made in the reverse order of removal with the aid of the spring compressor. Rotate spring to be certain it fits the helical seats in both the cross member and lower control arm.

STEERING GEAR, REPLACE
1966-72

1. Use puller to remove pitman arm from steering gear shaft.
2. Scribe a mark on worm shaft flange and steering shaft and disconnect lower flange from steering shaft

3. Unfasten gear housing from frame (3 bolts) and remove from car.

POWER STEERING UNIT, REPLACE

1966-72

1. Disconnect pressure and return hoses from gear housing.
2. Raise vehicle and disconnect pitman arm from shaft.
3. Scribe a mark on steering shaft worm shaft flange and disconnect flexible coupling from steering shaft.
4. Remove gear housing-to-frame bolts, noting number and location of gear-to-frame shims (if any). On 1969 Pontiac models a brake hose bracket must be removed prior to removing frame bolts.

NOTE: *Metal-to-metal contact between flanges of stub shaft and steering shaft will transmit and amplify gear noise to driver. Therefore, when installing the gear, align steering column jacket, shaft and steering gear so head of lower coupling bolt has 1/4" clearance from flange on steering shaft. Adjust mast jacket up or down to avoid metal-to-metal contact.*

VOLKSWAGEN

INDEX OF SERVICE OPERATIONS

Type 1—Beetle and Karmann Ghia
Type 3—Fastback and Squareback
Type 4—411, 415, 421, 425, 461, 465

CHASSIS NUMBER LOCATION: Under front hood behind spare tire and on frame tunnel under rear seat.

ENGINE NUMBER LOCATION: On crankcase flange for generator support.

GENERAL ENGINE SPECIFICATIONS

Engine	Application	Number Cylinders Bore & Stroke	Piston Displacement Cubic Inch	Compression Ratio	Horsepower @ R.P.M. S.A.E. Rating	Torque Ft. Lbs. @ R.P.M.	Normal Oil Pressure P.S.I.	Oil Capacity Pints Refill
1300 ①	1966	4-3.301 x 2.716	78.30	7.3	50 @ 4600	69 @ 2600	28	5.3
1500 1 Carb.①	1967-69	4-3.268 x 2.717	91.10	7.8	54 @ 4200	82 @ 2800	28	5.3
1600 1 Carb.①	1970	4-3.37 x 2.717	96.6	7.5	57 @ 4400	82 @ 3000	28	5.3
1600①	1971	4-3.37 x 2.712	96.6	7.5	60 @ 4400	82 @ 3000	28	5.3
1600 2 Carbs.②	1966-67	4-3.37 x 2.717	96.66	7.7	65 @ 4600	87 @ 2800	28	5.3
1600②③	1968	4-3.37 x 2.717	96.66	7.7	65 @ 4600	87 @ 2800	28	5.3
1600②③	1969-71	4-3.37 x 2.717	96.66	7.7	65 @ 4600	87 @ 2800	28	5
1700③④	1971	4-3.543 x 2.598	102.5	8.2	85 @ 5000	99 @ 3500	28	6.3

①—Type 1.
②—Type 3.
③—Fuel Injection.
④—Type 4.

DISTRIBUTOR SPECIFICATIONS

★NOTE: If advance is checked on the vehicle, double the R.P.M. and degrees advance to get crankshaft figures.

Engine	Application	Distributor Make & Number	Breaker Gap	Dwell Angle Degrees	Breaker Arm Spring Tension Ounces	Centrifugal Advance Degrees at R.P.M. of Distributor		Maximum Vacuum Advance Dist. Deg.
						Advance Starts	Full Advance	
1300	1966	VW 113-905-205-K	.016	48–52	16	—	—	14
1500 1 Carb.	1966	Bosch 111-905-205-M	.016	47–53	16	—	—	17½
1500 1 Carb.	1967	VW 113-905-205-L	.016	48–52	16	—	—	14
1500 1 Carb.	1968	Bosch 113-905-205-M	.016	47–53	16	—	—	17½
1500 1 Carb.	1969–70	Bosch 113-905-205T	.016	47–53	16	—	—	17½
1500 1 Carb.	1969	Bosch 113-905-205P	.016	47–53	16	11½ @ 750	16½ @ 1850	6
1500 1 Carb.	1969	Bosch 113-905-205AA	.016	47–53	16	11½ @ 750	16½ @ 1850	6
1600	1966–68	Bosch 311-905-205-F	.016	47–53	16	—	—	11½ to 14
1600	1968	Bosch 311-905-205G	.016	47–53	16	—	—	14
1600	1969	Bosch 311-905-205L	.016	47–53	16	1 @ 550	15 @ 1300	6
1600	1970	Bosch 311-905-205M	.016	47–53	16	1 @ 525	15 @ 1350	6
1600	1970	Bosch 311-905-205AB	.016	47–53	16	1 @ 550	15 @ 1400	6
1700	1971	Bosch 022-905-205H	.016	44–50	16	1 @ 400	14½ @ 1200	7

VOLKSWAGEN

TUNE UP SPECIFICATIONS

★Use of timing light is now recommended. Disconnect and plug vacuum hose at distributor.

Engine	Application	Spark Plugs		Distributor		Firing Order	Ignition Timing★		Engine Idle Speed	Cylinder Head Torque Ft.-Lbs.	Fuel Pump Pressure, Lbs.
		Type	Gap	Breaker Gap	Cam Dwell		Mark	Location			
1300	1966④	Various	.026	.016	①	Fig. A	7½°	Fig. C	550	23	2.8
1500	1967④	Various	.026	.016	①	Fig. A	7½°	Fig. C	550	23	2.8
1500	1968-69③④	Various	.026	.016	①	Fig. A	TDC	Fig. E	850	23	4.3
1600	1966-67⑤	Various	.026	.016	①	Fig. A	7½	Fig. B	550	23	4.3
1600	1968-69②⑤	Various	.026	.016	①	Fig. A	TDC	Fig. D	850	23	2.8
1600	1970-71②⑤	Various	.028	.016	①	Fig. A	TDC	Fig. D	850	23	2.8
1600	1970-71④	Various	.028	.016	①	Fig. A	5° ATDC	—	—	23	4.3
1700	1971②⑥	Various	.028	.016	①	Fig. A	—	—	—	23	—

①—See "Distributor Specifications" table. ③—Equipped with exhaust control system. ⑤—Type 3.
②—Fuel injection. ④—Type 1. ⑥—Type 4.

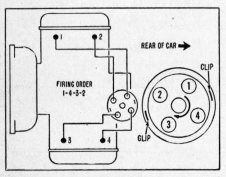

Fig. A

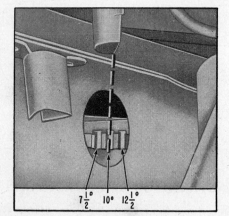

Fig. B

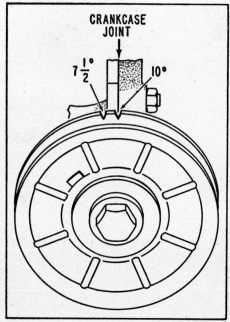

Fig. C

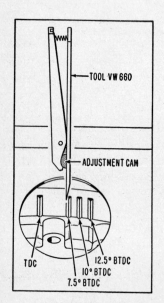

Fig. D

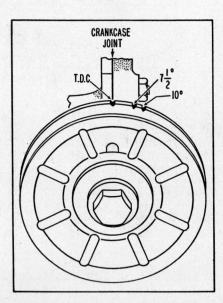

Fig. E

VALVE SPECIFICATIONS

Engine	Valve Lash, Cold		Valve Angles		Valve Springs		Valve Guide Clearance		Valve Stem Diameter	
	Intake	Exhaust	Seat	Face	Installed Height	Lbs. @ Inches Length	Intake	Exhaust	Intake	Exhaust
1300 to 710799	.008	.012	45	④	1.22	125 @ 1.22	.002–.003	.0031–.0041	.3126–.3130	.3114–.3118
1300 from 710800	.004	.004	45	④	1.22	125 @ 1.22	.002–.003	.0031–.0041	.3126–.3130	.3114–.3118
1500 to 672748①	.008	.012	45	④	1.22	132 @ 1.22	.002–.003	.0031–.0041	.3126–.3130	.3114–.3118
1500 from 672749①	.004	.004	45	④	1.22	132 @ 1.22	.002–.003	.0031–.0041	.3126–.3130	.3114–.3118
1500 to 672697② 1966	.008	.012	45	④	1.22	132 @ 1.22	.002–.003	.0031–.0041	.3126–.3130	.3114–.3118
1500 from 672698② 1966	.004	.004	45	④	1.22	132 @ 1.22	.002–.003	.0031–.0041	.3126–.3130	.3114–.3118
1500 1967–69	.004	.004	45	④	1.22	125 @ 1.22	.002–.003	.0031–.0041	.3126–.3130	.3114–.3118
1600	.004	.004	45	④	1.22	132 @ 1.22	.002–.003	.0031–.0041	.3126–.3130	.3114–.3118
1700	.004	.004	⑤	⑥	1.18	172 @ 1.18	.0024–.0028	.0035–.0039	.3126–.3130	.3508–.3512

①—With one carburetor.
②—With two carburetors.
③—Free length.
④—Intake 44°, exhaust 45°.
⑤—Intake 30°, exhaust 45°.
⑥—Intake 29° 30', exhaust 45°.

PISTON, RINGS, PIN, CRANKSHAFT & BEARINGS

Engine	Year	Piston Clearance	Piston Pin Dia.	Ring Gap (Min.)		Crankshaft and Bearings					
				Comp.	Oil	Rod Journal Dia.	Main Journal Dia. 1-2-3	Main Journal Dia. No. 4	Rod & 1-2-3 Main Bearing Clearance	No. 4 Main Bearing Clearance	Crankshaft End Play No. 1 Bearing
1300	1966	.0015–.0020	.866	.012	.010	2.1653	2.1653	1.5748	.001–.004	.002–.004	.0027–.005
1500, 1600	1966–71	.0016–.0023	.866	.012	.010	2.1653	2.1653	1.5748	.0016–.004	.0019–.004	.0027–.005
1700	1971	.0016–.0024	.9448	.014	.010	2.1653	2.3622	1.5748	.0015–.0039	.0019–.0039	.003–.005

①—No. 2 Main bearing (steel) from August 1965 .0011–.0035".

ENGINE TORQUE SPECIFICATIONS

Year	Engine	Cylinder Head Nuts Ft.-Lbs.	Connecting Rod Bolts Ft.-Lbs.	Crankcase Halves		Fly Wheel Gland Nut, Ft.-Lbs.
				12 MM Ft.-Lbs.	8 MM Ft.-Lbs.	
1966	1300	22–23	36	24–26	14	217
1966–69	1500	22–23	36	24–26	14	217
1966–71	1600	23	22–25	25	14	217
1971	1700	23	24	24	14	61①

①—Driveplate to crankshaft.

WHEEL ALIGNMENT SPECIFICATIONS

Series	Year	Front Wheel			Rear Wheel	
		Caster	Camber ①	Toe-In	Camber ①	Spring Plate Inclination ①
Type 1	1966	+2°	+½°	⅛"	3°	17½°
Type 3	1966	+11¼°	+1⅓°	⅛"	3°	②
Type 1	1967–68	+2°	+½°	⅛"	−1½°	③
Type 1	1969–71	+2°	+½°	⅛"	−1½°	21½°
Type 3	1967–71	+11⁵⁄₆°	+1⅓°	⅛"	3°	20½°
Type 4	1971	+1⅙°	+1⅙°	⅛"	—	—

①—Car unloaded.
②—Variant standard wagon 18½°, DeLuxe wagon 21½°.
③—Except Automatic Stickshift 20°, Automatic Stickshift 21½°.

STARTER MOTOR SPECIFICATIONS

Model	Year	Starter Model	Free Speed Test		Load Test @ 1650 R.P.M.			Lock Test		
			Amperes	R.P.M.	Amperes	Volts	Torque, Ft. Lbs.	Amperes	Volts	Torque, Ft.-Lbs.
1300	1966	VW 113911021A	40–80	4500	220	5.0–5.3	4.0	500	3.5–4.0	8.5
1500, 1600	1966–69	Bosch 311911021	40–55	6500	260①	4.6①	4.3①	485	3.5	9.4–10.8
12 Volt	1966–71	Bosch EF(L)12V	38–45	6400+	180②	9②	6.5–8.2②	270	6.0	6.5–8.2

①—At 800–1000 R.P.M. starter speed. ②—At 1100–1400 R.P.M. starter speed.

GENERATOR & REGULATOR SPECIFICATIONS

Series	Application	Generator Unit Number	No Load Voltage	Charging Current No Load	Cut-In Voltage	Rated Output @ 6/12 V.		Regulator Unit Number
						Watts	Gen. R.P.M.	
1300	1966	Bosch 111903021G	7.4–8.1	45	6.2–6.8	180	2500	RS/TAA 180/6/A4
1300	1966	VW 113903021C	7.4–8.1	45	6.4–6.7	180	2400	VW 113903801C
1500, 1600	1966–68	Bosch 311903021C	6.9–7.5	50	5.9–6.5	200	2600	311903801
12 Volt	1966–69	Bosch 14V38A32	13.5–14.5	40	12.5–13.2	450	3700	UAM14V38A
1600 Type 1	1970–71	101-302-085-085	13.5–14.5	45	12.4–13.1	360	3500	0190-350-68

Engine & Clutch Section

ENGINE, REPLACE
Type 1—1300, 1500 & 1600

1. Disconnect battery ground strap.
2. On early models turn off fuel tap. On later models pull fuel hose off and clip it.
3. Remove carburetor air cleaner.
4. Remove engine rear cover plate.
5. Disconnect wires from generator, ignition coil and oil pressure switch.
6. Disconnect accelerator cable from carburetor.
7. Loosen and turn distributor to allow vacuum unit to clear rear cover plate when engine is being removed.
8. Raise vehicle at least three feet off the floor.
9. Disconnect both heater control cables and loosen flexible heater pipes from engine.
10. Disconnect fuel hose from engine.
11. Remove nuts from both engine lower mounting bolts.
12. Pull accelerator cable from guide tube.
13. Place a roller jack under engine.
14. While holding the two upper engine mounting bolts, have an assistant remove the nuts.
15. Raise jack to support engine.
16. Withdraw engine far enough to allow clutch release plate to clear main drive shaft. Then lower jack and tilt rear of engine downward until it can be completely removed.

Type 3—1600

1. Disconnect battery ground strap.
2. Remove air cleaner.
3. Remove cables from generator, coil, oil pressure switch and automatic choke.
4. Detach accelerator cable at connecting link.
5. Remove oil dipstick and take off rubber boot between oil filler and body.
6. Loosen clip on bellows at cooling air intake housing and pull off bellows.
7. Remove rear engine support.
8. Raise and support vehicle on stands.
9. Disconnect flexible pipes between engine and warm air mixing boxes.
10. Disconnect heater flap cables.
11. Take warm air hose from carburetor pre-heater off engine.
12. Pull off fuel hose at front engine cover plate and seal it with a suitable plug.
13. Remove two lower engine mounting nuts.
14. Support engine with roller jack.
15. Hold two upper engine mounting bolts while an assistant removes nuts.
16. Pull engine back slightly until release plate clears main drive shaft.
17. Lower engine, being sure that clutch release plate or main drive shaft are not damaged.

Type 4—1700

1. Disconnect battery ground strap.
2. Remove air cleaner and warm air hoses.
3. Remove dipstick and rubber boot between dipstick tube or oil filler and body.
4. Remove wires from fuel injection components and hang wires up out of the way.
5. Remove coil and bracket.
6. Remove alternator regulator and oil pressure switch wires.
7. Disconnect accelerator cable and vacuum hose on intake air distributor.
8. Remove the three M8 screws from the converter through the access hole.
9. Remove ATF dipstick and rubber boot.
10. Remove the two upper engine mounting nuts.
11. Raise vehicle.
12. Remove muffler shield.
13. Remove heat exchanger.
14. Disconnect cable 30 at starter.
15. Pull off fuel hoses and plug.
16. Remove heater booster exhaust pipe.
17. Pull accelerator cable, vacuum hose and heater air blower cable forward.
18. Remove the nuts from the two engine lower securing studs.
19. Lower vehicle slightly and life engine a little with floor jack.
20. Remove the four screws from the engine carrier.

Note: If the mountings on the body are loosened, the engine/transmission unit must be centralized again.

21. Lower engine to remove (**Important:** Install a retaining plate or take other precautions to keep the converter from falling out).

Fig. 1 Showing cylinder retainer in place when removing cylinder head

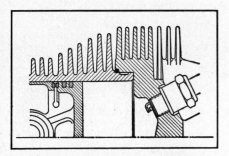

Fig. 2 Showing location of sealing ring (deep black) between cylinder shoulder and cylinder head.

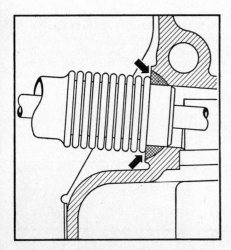

Fig. 3 Oil seals at ends of push rod tubes. All engines

Installation, Types 1 & 3

When installing the engine, use care to prevent damage to the flywheel gland nut needle bearing and clutch release bearing. To facilitate entering the main drive shaft into the clutch plate and gland nut needle bearing, engage a transmission gear train to keep the mainshaft from turning

and rotate the engine by means of the fan belt as required.

When installing the engine, first install the mounting bolts into the transmission case flange. Then press the engine against the flange, being sure it seats properly around the flange before installing the nuts. Tighten the upper nuts finger tight first, then the lower nuts. The final tightening should be done in the same order.

Installation, Type 4

1. Install engine compartment seal to the cover plates with the water deflecting side downward and place a string in the slot.
2. Lift engine until it is about 4″ from the body and push the accelerator cable through the front cover plate.
3. Guide the lower studs into the holes in the transmission case first, then locate engine carrier in the mountings.
4. Bolt the engine carrier to the brackets on the body so that the screws are at the top of the elongated holes. Tighten the nuts to 18 ft.-lbs. and bend lock-plates up.
5. Tighten the two nuts of the additional side engine carrier mounting against one another from above and below.
6. After installing the engine, check that the limiting flange is centered in the rear axle carrier and re-position if necessary.
7. Make sure that the engine carrier is vertical and parallel to the fan housing. If necessary the position can be altered by moving the brackets on the side members.
8. Pull engine compartment seal into correct position with the aid of the string.
9. Tighen the converter securing screws to 22 ft.-lbs.
10. Adjust accelerator cable in the full throttle position.
11. Set ignition timing.

ENGINE, DISASSEMBLE

The following sequence of operations is recommended when disassembling the engine. Reverse the order of procedure to reassemble, and refer to the text which follows for details of the installation of the various components.

Type 1—1300, 1500 & 1600

1. Drain engine oil.
2. Remove hoses between fan housing and heat exchangers.
3. Remove front engine cover plate.
4. Remove rear engine cover plate.
5. Remove muffler.
6. Remove fan belt.
7. Pull off coil-to-distributor cable.
8. Remove fan housing with generator.
9. Remove intake manifold with pre-heating pipe.
10. Remove both head exchangers.
11. Disassemble and remove cylinder deflector plates.
12. Remove crankshaft pulley.
13. Remove cylinder head cover.
14. Remove rocker shafts.

Fig. 4 Centering push rod tubes with tool shown

Fig. 5 When installed, push rod tubes should be stretched, if necessary, to the following lengths (dimension "A"):

1300	1966	7.480-7.520″
1500, 1600	1966-71	7.480-7.520″

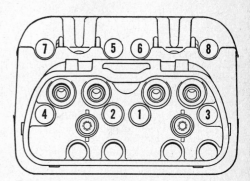

Fig. 6 Initial tightening sequence of cylinder head

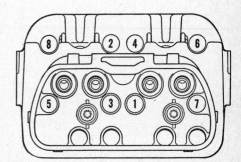

Fig. 7 Final tightening sequence of cylinder head

Fig. 8 Rocker arm mechanism

15. Remove push rods.
16. Remove cylinder heads.
17. Remove push rod tubes.
18. Remove deflector plates below cylinders.
19. Remove cylinders.
20. Remove pistons.
21. Remove oil cooler.
22. Remove oil pump.
23. Remove oil strainer.
24. Remove fuel pump.
25. Remove distributor and drive pinion.
26. Remove clutch and flywheel.
27. Disassemble crankcase.
28. Remove camshaft and crankshaft.

Type 3—1600

1. Drain engine oil.
2. Remove front engine cover plate.
3. Remove muffler.
4. Remove intake manifold and carburetors.
5. Disconnect heat exchangers.
6. Remove generator and belt.
7. Remove cooling air intake housing.
8. Remove crankshaft pulley.
9. Remove rear half of fan housing.
10. Remove fan.
11. Remove front half of fan housing.
12. Remove distributor and fuel pump.
13. Remove distributor drive pinion.
14. Remove oil cooler.
15. Remove rocker shafts.
16. Remove cylinder heads.
17. Remove cylinders and pistons.
18. Remove clutch and flywheel.
19. Remove oil pump and strainer.
20. Disassemble crankcase.
21. Remove camshaft and crankshaft with connecting rods.

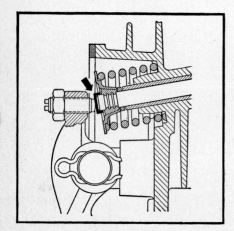

Fig. 10 Cap used on worn valve stems

Type 4—1700

1. Drain engine oil.
2. Remove muffler and heat exchanger.
3. Remove front engine cover plate.
4. Remove intake distributor with intake pipe and injection valves.
5. Remove oil filler neck with oil vent.
6. Remove distributor.
7. Remove rear engine cover plate.
8. Remove impeller.
9. Remove cooling blower housing with alternator.
10. Remove engine mount.
11. Remove cylinder jackets with warm air guides front and rear.
12. Remove oil cooler.
13. Remove oil filter.
14. Remove oil pump.
15. Remove rocker arm shafts with push rods, protective tubes and tappets
16. Remove cylinder heads.
17. Remove cylinders and pistons.
18. Remove drive plate.
19. Disassemble crankcase.
20. Remove camshaft and crankshaft with connecting rods.

CYLINDER HEAD

Each pair of cylinders has one detachable cylinder head. The cylinder head is provided with cooling fins and incorporates shrunk-in valve seat inserts and valve guides. No gasket is used between the joining faces of the cylinder and cylinder head. Gaskets are used, however, between the flanges of the cylinder and cylinder head to prevent leakage of combustion gases.

NOTE: If it is intended to remove cylinder heads only, a suitable cylinder retainer can be made locally to prevent the cylinders from being withdrawn unintentionally and eliminates the danger of dirt entering the crankcase. Fig. 1 shows the retainer bolted to crankcase and positioned between cooling fins.

When installing heads the following points should be observed.
1. Check heads for cracks in combustion chamber and exhaust ports. Cracked heads must be replaced.
2. Check threads for spark plugs. If necessary, install Heli-Coil threaded inserts.
3. There is no gasket between upper edge of cylinder and cylinder head.
4. Fit new sealing ring between cylinder shoulder and cylinder head, Fig. 2.
5. On all engines, when installing cyl-

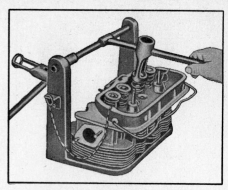

Fig. 9 Cylinder head mounted in valve remover tool (VW-311A)

inder head, make sure that oil seals at ends of push rod tubes are properly seated, Fig. 3.
6. Push rod tubes can best be centered by using a centering tool of the type shown (made locally) when installing cylinder head, Fig. 4.
7. Turn the tubes so that the seam is facing upwards. To ensure perfect sealing, used tubes must be stretched to the correct length before they are installed, Fig. 5. This operation must be carried out carefully to avoid cracking tubes.
8. Coat attaching nuts with graphite paste and screw them down until resistance can be felt. Then make an initial tightening with a torque wrench to 7 ft-lbs in the sequence shown in Fig. 6. The final tightening should be made in the sequence shown in Fig. 7 to the specified torque (see table).

VALVE MECHANISM

The camshaft is carried in three bearings machined in the crankcase. It is driven by the crankshaft by helical gears. The valves are operated by the cams via cam followers, push rods and rocker arms. Each cam operates in turn one of the valves of two opposed cylinders. The exhaust valves are plated with chrome-nickel steel.

Fig. 11 Timing gear marks located for correct valve timing

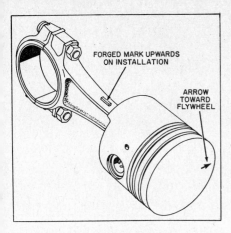

Fig. 12   Correct assembly of piston and connecting rod

Valves, Remove

1. Using a suitable valve spring compressor, Fig. 9, press down on valve spring and remove valve locks and spring caps.
2. Lift off valve springs and take out valves. If the valve lock grooves are burred, remove the burr with a smooth file before attempting to remove the valve from its guide.
3. Place valves in a board with numbered holes to identify their location so that if re-used they can be returned to the original guide holes.

VALVE STEM CAPS: Valves with worn stem ends can be made usable by fitting caps (available from VW) on the stems, Fig. 10. The caps are merely placed on the stems before the rocker arms are fitted and do not need securing.

Valve Springs

Check the tension of all springs on a spring testing tool. If such a tool is not available, check the free length of each spring. Any spring that does not conform to the pressure specifications (see chart) within 10 per cent should be replaced. Likewise, any spring that stands shorter than the specified free length, or is distorted or cocked should be discarded.

Valve Guides

Inasmuch as the valve guides are shrunk (chilled) into position, it is not possible to remove them by pressing them out of the cylinder head in the conventional manner as damage to the cylinder head would most likely result.

Use a reamer or broach to remove carbon deposits from the guides. Then check the clearance between valve stem and guide, using a suitable plug gauge or a thin feeler gauge strip. If the clearance approaches the wear limit of .0063″, replace the cylinder head with a new or factory-reconditioned one.

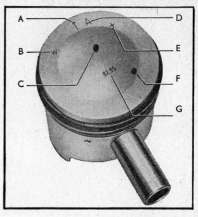

Fig. 13   Piston markings

Camshaft & Timing Gears

1300, 1500, 1600 & 1700 Engines: The camshaft is mounted in the crankcase in three split steel bearings with lead-coated working surfaces. Camshaft end thrust is on the No. 3 bearing which has a shoulder to take the thrust.

When installing these bearings, break the edges of the camshaft bearing bores slightly at the crankcase joint to prevent seizure due to pressure on the bearing shells. Fit the bearings so that the tongues engage in the recesses in the crankcase. Coat all bearings with oil before installing camshaft.

1. To remove, open the crankcase and take out the camshaft and gear assembly.
2. Examine riveted joint between gear and camshaft. Check camshaft bearing points and cam faces for wear. Cam faces must not be scored but must be smooth and square.
3. Check cam journals, cams and gear for damage. Slight damage may be corrected with a silicone-carbide oilstone; do not use a grinder.
4. Carefully clean camshaft of any abrasive material.
5. When installing the camshaft, be sure that the timing gear tooth marked "O" is placed between the two punch-marked teeth on the crankshaft gear, Fig. 11.

SERVICE NOTE: To insure that the timing gears operate quietly, a backlash of .002″ must be present. This check is made by rocking the gears back and forth with both hands while gradually turning the camshaft gear until it has made one complete turn. To obtain the specified backlash, camshafts are available with timing gears of various sizes, the standard size gear being marked with an "O" etched on the inner face of the gear. Other gears are marked −1, +1, +2. The crankshaft gear is available in one size only.

Valves, Adjust

Valve lash should be adjusted only when the engine is cold and at approximate room temperature. To adjust the valves, crank the engine to the left of the fan pulley until both valves of the cylinder being adjusted are fully closed and the timing mark on the pulley is in line with the vertical joint faces of the crankcase.

1. Remove cylinder head cover.
2. Set engine in firing position for No. 1 cylinder.
3. Check valve clearance with a feeler gauge. If adjustment is required, loosen the rocker arm adjusting screw lock nut and turn the adjusting screw until the specified clearance is obtained (see chart) and tighten lock nut.
4. Check and adjust remaining valves in the same manner.

Rocker Arm Mechanism, Fig. 8

1. Take off cylinder head cover, rocker shaft retaining nuts and lift off assembly with stud seals.
2. To install, first slip on the stud seals. Then install the mechanism in the reverse order or removal.
3. Make sure ball end of push rods rest centrally in rocker arm sockets.
4. To make valves rotate during operation, the rocker arm adjusting screws should contact valve stems slightly to the right.
5. Adjust valve lash. Install head cover, using a new gasket cemented to the cover all around. If gasket shows evidence of shrinkage as a result of prolonged storage, place it in lukewarm water before cementing it in place.

Push Rods & Tubes

When installing push rods and their tubes, be sure the tube seams are facing upward. If the old tubes are to be re-used, and to insure perfect sealing between tube and crankcase and/or cylinder head, they should be stretched to the dimension indicated in Fig. 5.

Fig. 14   Checking crankshaft with engine installed. Use bracket (VW-659) and dial gauge

CYLINDERS & PISTONS

The four cylinders are interchangeable and can be replaced separately together with the corresponding piston. The cyl-

Fig. 15   Checking crankshaft end play when engine is removed

inders are provided with fins for efficient cooling.

The pistons are a light metal alloy fitted with three rings, the bottom ring being an oil control ring. Piston pins are full floating and are retained in place by lock rings. Assemble pistons to rods as shown in Fig. 12.

PISTON MARKINGS: The symbols present on pistol heads, Fig. 13, denote the following:

A. Arrow (indented or stamped on) must point towards flywheel when piston is installed.
B. Details of piston pin bore size indented or stamped on (S for black, W for white).
C. Paint spot indicating matching size (blue, pink, green).
D. The letter near arrow corresponds to the index of the part number of the piston. It serves as an identification mark.
E. Details of weight grading ($+$ or $-$) indented or stamped on.
F. Paint spot indicating weight grading (brown $-$ weight, grey $+$ weight).
G. Details of piston size in mm.

Cylinder Inspection

Volkswagen recommends that an inspection of cylinders be carried out by means of a dial gauge for inside diameters and gauge rings corresponding to the cylinder sizes. Cylinders should be measured about $\frac{1}{2}$" below the upper edge.

When measuring the piston in its cylinder, if it is found that the clearance approaches the wear limit of .008", replace the piston and cylinder with another pair of the same size and weight. The piston must not be fitted separately if the corresponding cylinder shows signs of wear. If the cylinder of a damaged piston does not show signs of wear, it is usually sufficient to install a new piston of the same size and weight.

Pistons & Pins

1. Remove pistons from cylinders and mark them so that, if re-used, they can be installed in the original cylinders.

2. Remove piston pin lock ring and push pin out of piston. If pin cannot be pushed out it will be necessary to heat the piston with an electric piston heating tool to expand the piston. The pin may then be pushed out.
3. In all cases where the piston pin is not a light finger push fit in the cold piston, the piston should be heated. The pin should also be heated in order to avoid the rapid cooling of the piston bosses. As the steel pin has less expansion qualities than the aluminum piston when it is heated, the pin can easily be pushed into the piston.

Installation Of Cylinders

1. Before installing cylinders, check the seating surface of the crankcase, cylinder shoulder and gasket; all must be thoroughly clean as distortion of the cylinder may occur if dirt is present.
2. Be sure to use a new gasket between cylinder and crankcase.
3. Apply engine oil to piston and piston pin. Use a suitable compressor to compress piston rings, being sure to stagger the ring end gaps around the piston. The oil ring gap must always be at the top when pistons are in horizontal position in the engine.
4. Oil cylinder walls and slide cylinder over piston. Be sure crankcase studs do not contact cylinder cooling fins.
5. Install deflector plates. To prevent them from rattling, bend the plates as necessary until they bear tightly on the cylinder head studs.
6. When installing push rods and their tubes, be sure the tube seams are facing upward. If the old tubes are to be re-used, and to insure perfect sealing between tube and crankcase and/or cylinder head, they should be stretched to the dimension indicated in Fig. 5.

CRANKSHAFT

The crankshaft is fitted with four main bearings, No. 2 bearing (seen from the clutch) is the split type. No. 1 bearing is lead-coated and controls the crankshaft end thrust. The flywheel is held by a

Fig. 17   Measuring depth of crankshaft seat

Fig. 16   Measuring distance from crankshaft face to outer race of No. 1 main bearing with dial gauge (VW-292)

gland nut and in addition is secured to the crankshaft by four dowel pins. The crankshaft timing gear and distributor drive gear are held in place by woodruff keys. The fan pulley is bolted to the crankshaft. An oil seal is fitted to the clutch side of the crankshaft and an oil thrower and oil return thread to the pulley side.

Crankshaft, Replace

1. Open crankcase as outlined under *Crankcase* and remove crankshaft and camshaft.
2. Crankshaft bore in crankcase must have no sharp edges at the joining faces. Slightly chamfer edges, if necessary.
3. Check dowel pins for tightness.
4. Oil passages in crankshaft must have no sharp edges. Should foreign matter be embedded in main bearings, remove it with a scraper, using care not to remove any metal from the bearing shell itself.
5. Place one-half of No. 2 main bearing in crankcase.
6. Slide on No. 1 main bearing so that the dowel pin hole is toward flywheel.
7. Install crankshaft, making sure dowel pins are correctly seated in main bearings.
8. Note marks on timing gears when installing camshaft, Fig. 11.

Crankshaft, Overhaul

DISASSEMBLE

1. With crankshaft in a holding fixture, remove woodruff key, oil thrower and No. 4 main bearing.
2. Remove retaining ring and take off distributor drive gear, spacer and crankshaft timing gear.
3. Remove No. 3 main bearing.
4. Remove connecting rods.

REASSEMBLE

1. First place Nos. 1, 3 and 4 main bearings in left crankcase half, noting proper position of dowel holes and oil holes which must register with oil passages in crankcase.

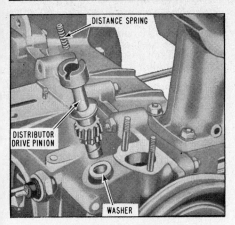

Fig. 18 Installation of distributor drive gear components

Dowel hole in No. 1 main bearing must be towards flywheel.

NOTE: *To facilitate fitting of main bearings on dowels when installing crankshaft, mark bearings at crankcase joining faces with a pencil.*

2. If dowel holes in crankshaft are worn, remove crankshaft and drill new holes 45 degrees away from the old holes and ream them to .315".
3. Slide No. 3 main bearing in position and insert woodruff key for crankshaft gear and distributor drive gear.
4. Heat crankshaft gear in an oil bath and press into position. Slide spacer on crankshaft.
5. Heat distributor drive gear and press it in position.
6. Install retaining ring, using a suitable tapered guide to avoid damage to crankshaft journal. Check gears for proper seating after they have cooled.
7. Clean out oil passages and blow out with compressed air.
8. Slide No. 4 main bearing on crankshaft. Install oil thrower with its concave surface facing crankshaft pulley.
9. Insert woodruff key.
10. Install connecting rods.

Fig. 20 Narrow offset side of slot must face crankshaft pulley

Checking Crankshaft End Play

Crankshaft end play should not exceed .006". End play can be checked with the engine installed or removed.

With the engine installed in the vehicle, mount a dial gauge and bracket, Fig. 14, so the stem of the gauge contacts the crankshaft pulley. Mount the bracket on the rearmost crankcase stud. An end play reading is obtained by rocking the crankshaft back and forth at the pulley hub.

To check the end play with the engine removed, the dial gauge is mounted at the flywheel by one of the engine mounting bolts, Fig. 15.

Adjusting Crankshaft End Play

1. Force the installed crankshaft against the flywheel side of the engine (flywheel removed) to take up the play.
2. Insert dial gauge in flywheel seat, Fig. 16, and measure distance from crankshaft face to outer face of No. 1 main bearing.
3. Next place dial gauge on flywheel joint flange, Fig. 17, and measure depth of crankshaft seat.
4. The thickness of shims to be used is determined by the difference in both readings (including the paper gasket). The thickness of the paper gasket is .0078" and is compressed by .0019" in assembling. This leaves .0059" to be considered when determining thickness of shimming. Three shims of the required thickness are to be installed. Never use more than one paper gasket.

Crankshaft Oil Seal

Oil losses at the flywheel side resulting from a leaky oil seal are frequently mistaken for a leak at the crankcase joining faces. Therefore, it is advisable always to check the crankshaft oil seal first whenever oil losses are noticed at the flywheel side. Replace the seal as follows:

1. Remove flywheel and oil seal.
2. Clean oil seal recess in crankcase and coat it with a thin film of sealing compound. If necessary, slightly chamfer the outer edge with a scraper, and clean recess of metal chips.
3. Install new oil seal, being sure it seats squarely on the bottom of the recess.
4. Install flywheel. Lubricate seal lip contact surface with oil.

CONNECTING RODS

The crankshaft ends of the four connecting rods contain replaceable bearings. The piston pin ends are provided with bronze bushings.

1. Remove crankshaft and place in a holding fixture. Unfasten and remove connecting rods.
2. Inspect piston pin bushing. The correct fit of a new bushing is indicated by a light finger push fit of the pin at room temperature.
3. Check connecting rod alignment.
4. Insert bearing shells in rods and install rods on crankshaft. Be sure identification numbers stamped on rods and caps are both on the same side.
5. After tightening rod bolts to the

Fig. 19 Use a screwdriver to guide washer into place so it will not fall into timing gear chamber

specified torque (see chart), and with bearings well lubricated with engine oil prior to assembly, rods must slide on the crankpin by their own weight. Stake or peen the bolt heads to prevent them from working loose.

CRANKCASE

The crankcase is a light-metal die casting in two parts. The crankcase halves are machined in pairs to very close limits; therefore, replacements must be made in pairs.

DISASSEMBLE

1. Remove oil pressure switch.
2. Remove crankcase nuts. Keep cam followers or right crankcase half in position with suitable retaining springs.
3. Take off right-hand crankcase half, using a rubber hammer to loosen it. To avoid damage do not use metal tools to separate crankcase halves.
4. Remove crankshaft oil seal and camshaft end plug.
5. Remove camshaft, crankshaft, cam followers and bearing shells.

Fig. 21 Modified drive shaft shown at right

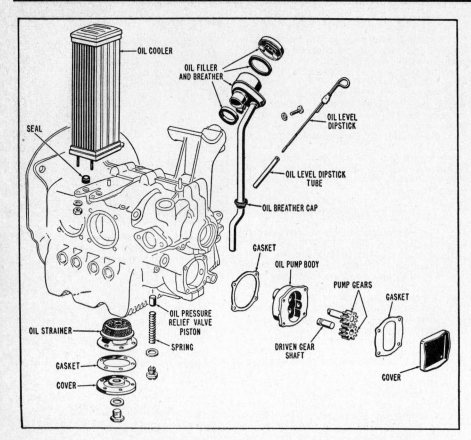

Fig. 22   Disassembled view of oil pump, cooler, strainer and filler (typical)

REASSEMBLE

1. Reverse disassembly procedure to reassemble, noting the following:
2. Examine crankcase for damage or cracks, and check studs for secure seating and oil leaks.
3. Remove all traces of sealing compound from crankcase joining faces. The joining faces must be perfectly clean and free of burrs. The edges of the main bearings should be slightly chamfered to obtain accurate matching of the crankcase halves. Oil passages should be flushed out and cleaned with compressed air.
4. Check oil suction pipe for secure seating and leaks.
5. Install cam followers.
6. Install oil pressure switch.
7. Note position of timing marks on timing gears and make sure crankshaft oil thrower is correctly installed.
8. Oil crankshaft bearing joints and install crankshaft and bearings.
9. Install camshaft, and camshaft end plug, using sealing compound on plug.
10. Install thrust washers and crankshaft oil seal, being sure seal rests squarely on bottom of its recess in crankcase.
11. Evenly spread a thin film of sealing compound on the crankcase joining faces. Be sure that no sealing compound enters oil return passages of crankshaft and camshaft bearings.
12. Keep cam followers of right crankcase half in position with retaining springs.
13. Join the crankcase halves and evenly tighten nuts with a torque wrench. First tighten the 8MM nut beside the stud of No. 1 main bearing; then tighten the 12MM nuts to specifications (see chart).

DISTRIBUTOR DRIVE PINION

REMOVAL

1. Loosen distributor clamp bolt and lift out distributor.

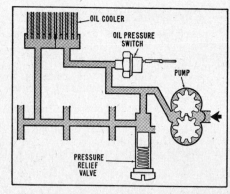

Schematic diagram of engine oil flow

2. Remove distance spring on drive pinion, Fig. 18. Pull drive pinion out by twisting it counter-clockwise.
3. Remove washer under pinion, being careful not to drop it into the crankcase. **Note:** If the engine is in the car the washer can be removed with a magnet. If engine is out of the car, turn engine upside down so that washer can fall out.

INSTALLATION

1. Check fuel pump push rod drive surface on drive pinion and pinion teeth for wear. If badly worn, the gear on the crankshaft must be examined.
2. If washer under pinion is worn, replace with a new one, being careful not to drop it into the crankcase, Fig. 19.
3. Set No. 1 cylinder to the firing point and insert the distributor drive pinion. The offset slot in the top of the pinion must be toward the pulley, Fig. 20.
4. Insert distance spring, install distributor, time ignition and install fuel pump. **NOTE:** On late model cars the thrust surface of the distributor drive shaft in the left crankcase half is machined .196" deeper. Also the distributor drive shaft is modified in that it has a thrust shoulder with a flat machined on one side, Fig. 21, in place of the reduced diameter toothing on the oil pinion. The thrust washer is still used.

CAUTION: This modified distributor drive shaft can only be removed and installed when No. 1 cylinder is at the firing point as the flat on the thrust shoulder is then toward the distributor drive gear. In this position the offset slot in the upper part of the shaft is at right angles to the crankcase joint. Any attempt to remove or install the shaft in another position will damage the distributor drive gear. This modified distributor shaft cannot be installed in the earlier crankcase.

ENGINE OILING SYSTEM

The oil pump, Fig. 22, is located on the gear side of the camshaft, from which it is driven. Oil is drawn from the bottom of the crankcase and forced into the oil passages by way of the oil cooler, Fig. 22. Some of the oil is fed via the main bearings through the drilled passages in the crankshaft to the connecting rod bearings. Oil is also fed to the camshaft bearings, and through the hollow push rods to the rocker arms. Cylinder walls, pistons and piston pins are splash lubricated. In the 1300, 1500 and 1600 engines the oil returns to the bottom of the crankcase where it is filtered by a gauze strainer at the lowest point before re-entering the circulation. In the 1700 engine, there is a replaceable oil filter mounted in the main flow which works in conjunction with the oil strainer.

The oil cooler on the crankcase is positioned in the duct air flow. This enables the oil to maintain its lubricating qualities even at high outside temperatures and at sustained high engine speeds.

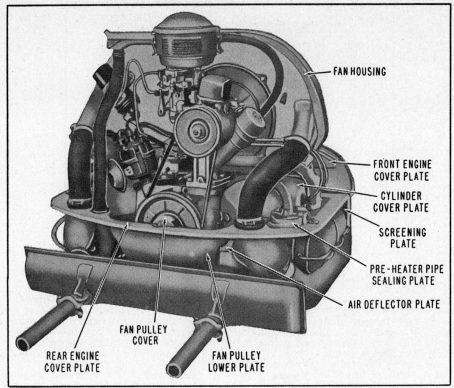

Fig. 23   Exterior view of Type 1—1300, 1500 & 1600 engine

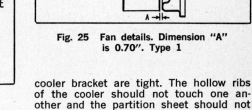

Fig. 25   Fan details. Dimension "A"
is 0.70". Type 1

cooler bracket are tight. The hollow ribs of the cooler should not touch one another and the partition sheet should not be loose. Use new gaskets.

Oil Strainer

1. The oil strainer is removed as indicated in Fig. 22.
2. When installing, check the suction pipe for tight and proper seating.
3. Clean strainer and remove traces of old gasket material.
4. Use new gaskets. Install strainer, making sure that suction pipe is correctly seated in strainer. If necessary, bend strainer as required.
5. Remove traces of old gasket from bottom plate. Straighten bent or distorted bottom plates to insure a proper seal.
6. Do not over-tighten nuts, especially when using thicker gaskets, to avoid bending bottom plates.

NOTE: *The strainer can be provided with a magnet ring which will trap all metal abrasives contained in the oil circulation. The ring is held in the strainer by a spring. When cleaning the strainer, the magnetic ring should be removed.*

Oil Pressure Relief Valve

Check the oil pressure relief valve when defects in the oiling system takes place. If the plunger sticks at top dead center when the oil is thick the oil cooler may be leaking. If the plunger sticks at bottom dead center the oil will flow directly back to the crankcase.

Oil Cooler

When removing the oil cooler with the

engine in the vehicle or from an assembled engine out of the car, the fan housing should be removed first. If the oil cooler is leaking, check the oil pressure relief valve.

When installed, be sure the studs and

Oil Pump

1. With the engine installed, the oil pump can be removed after the engine cover plate, crankshaft pulley and the cover plate below the pulley have been removed.

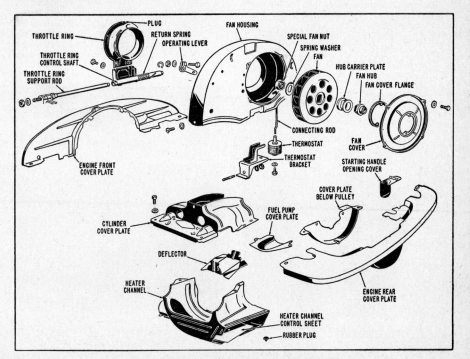

Fig. 24   Disassembled view of cooling system components. Type 1

VOLKSWAGEN

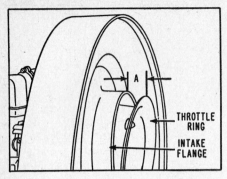

Fig. 26 Distance "A" from outer intake flange to edge of throttle ring is 0.98" to 1.18". Type 1

2. Remove pump cover and gears, Fig. 22.
3. Remove pump body with a puller.
4. Examine gears for wear. Backlash between gears should be .0012-.0031". End play without pressure of cover should be .0026"-.0072", with wear limit being .0079".
5. If idler gear pin cannot be tightened, install a new pump body.

INSTALLATION

1. Install pump body with gasket.
2. Install pump drive shaft and turn it as required to allow tang on shaft to enter slot in camshaft. Then install driven gear.
3. Place a straightedge across pump body and use a feeler gauge between gears and straightedge to check clearance. With gasket removed, this clearance should not exceed .004". If cover is worn from contact with gears, plane it off or replace cover.
4. Use new accredited gaskets without sealing compound and replace cover. When tightening the nuts, make sure the position of the pump body is not disturbed.

COOLING SYSTEM TYPE 1—1300, 1500 & 1600

Fig. 24 is a layout of the components

Fig. 27 Exterior view of 1966-67 Type 3 1600 engine

of the cooling system. The engine is cooled by the fan which is attached to the generator shaft. The fan is driven by the crankshaft by an adjustable belt. The fan sucks in air through an opening in the fan housing, and the air cools the engine by being forced through the fins of the cylinders and cylinder heads.

Air flow is directed by the air deflector plates, some of which are located in the fan housing, the others cover the cylinders. The throttle ring at the air intake opening of the fan housing is thermostatically controlled to ensure that the operating temperature is quickly attained and steadily maintained.

Engine Cover Plates

1. If the deflector plates below the cylinders cannot be seated properly, bend them as required so they bear against the cylinder head studs to prevent them from working loose and causing a rattle.
2. When replacing the cylinder head cover plates, be sure the spark plug rubber caps are in good condition and seat properly. The cylinder cover

plates must fit snugly on the fan housing to prevent loss of cooling air.
3. Before installing the engine front cover plate, check the condition of the weatherstrip and replace if necessary.
4. After the engine has been installed, the rear cover plate weatherstrip lips must straddle the plate. Be sure the washers are installed under the slotted screw heads, and see that the breather pipe grommet bears squarely on the cover plate.

Fan Housing

1. When installing the fan housing, be sure the air deflector plates are not loose and that the fan housing is not damaged in any way.
2. No air must be allowed to blow between the fan housing and cylinder cover plates. Bend plates into correct position, if necessary.
3. When inserting the throttle ring, screw it to the operating shaft holding plate, making certain that the throttle ring is not off center from the intake flange. Connect the return spring and adjust the throttle ring. Install ignition cable rubber holders in fan housing.

Fig. 28 Insert crankshaft pulley so pin engages hole in fan. Type 3

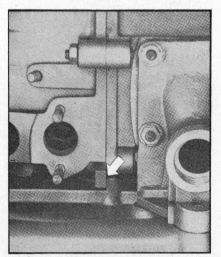

Fig. 29 Arrow indicates where front lug contacts left crankcase half. Type 3

Fig. 30 Belt tension is corrected by varying number of washers between pulley halves. Taking washers out increases tension and vice versa

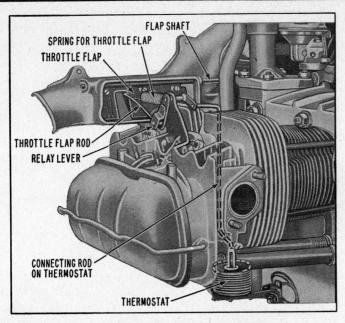

Fig. 31 Automatic cooling control. Type 3

Fan, Replace

REMOVAL

1. Remove screws from fan cover.
2. Take off generator and fan.
3. While holding fan, and assistant may remove special nut.
4. Remove fan, spacer washers and nut.

INSTALLATION

1. With woodruff key seated in shaft keyway, place hub on generator shaft.
2. Insert washers and install fan.
3. Install and torque special nut to 40-47 ft-lbs.
4. Clearance between fan and cover should be 0.70", Fig. 25. To establish this clearance, insert spacer washers as required between carrier plate and hub. If only one washer is used, the other two should be placed between fan and lock washer.
5. Install generator in fan housing and secure with four screws.

Air Intake Control

1. The automatic air intake control should be inspected each spring and fall and adjusted if necessary.
2. If the throttle ring remains open or opens too early, the engine will attain its normal operating temperature too slowly. In some cases excessive fuel consumption and continuous "popping" through the carburetor will result due to prolonged cold operation.
3. If the throttle ring opens too much it may cause fan noise. If it opens too slowly during warm weather the engine will overheat during sustained high load conditions.
4. If the throttle ring remains open while the engine is cold, it may be due to a defective thermostat. To prevent the engine from overheating,

the throttle ring opens automatically should the cooling system become inoperative.

ADJUSTMENT

1. When making the adjustment with the engine installed in the vehicle, first unhook the return spring.
2. Release throttle ring operating lever.
3. Operate engine until upper end of thermostat contacts the support upper stop.
4. Adjust throttle ring to open 0.98" to 1.18", Fig. 26.
5. Tighten operating lever, connect return spring and make sure throttle ring and linkage moves freely in all positions.

Fan Belt, Adjust

1. Proper fan belt tension is attained when a deflection of about 5/8" is present when the belt is pressed firmly with the thumb midway between the pulleys.
2. To adjust, insert a screwdriver in the slot cut into the inner half of the generator pulley and support it against the generator housing upper bolt. Then remove pulley outer half.
3. Install spacer washers between the two pulley halves as required to obtain the correct belt tension. Belt slackness is taken up by removing washers. If belt is too tight, add washers as required.

COOLING SYSTEM TYPE 3—1600

NOTE: The engine must always be removed when performing operations on the fan or crankshaft pulley.

Crankshaft Pulley, Replace

1. Remove muffler and generator.
2. Remove cooling air intake housing.
3. Remove plastic cap on pulley.
4. Remove pulley bolt and pulley.
5. Reverse procedure to install, observing the following point:
6. Use a proper gasket between pulley and fan. Insert pulley so that pin engages hole in fan, Fig. 28. Torque pulley to 94-108 ft-lbs.

Fan, Replace

1. Remove crankshaft pulley, coil, rear fan housing half, and use a suitable puller to remove fan.
2. During installation, check condition of oil return thread on fan hub. Press fan on crankshaft, attach rear fan housing half, install coil and pulley.

Fan Housing, Replace

1. Remove crankshaft pulley, rear fan housing half and fan.
2. Unhook linkage and spring at right-hand air control flap.
3. Remove attaching screws and front fan housing half.
4. Before installing, check front fan housing half for distortion and damage.
5. Slide a suitable centering tool on crankshaft and install front fan housing half, being sure it is sealed correctly in cylinder cover plates.
6. Insert mounting screws and tighten lightly. Turn fan housing halves to the left until lug contacts left crankcase half, Fig. 29.
7. Tighten two lower mounting screws securely.
8. Loosen nuts on breather support until it can be moved.
9. Insert and tighten upper fan housing half mounting screws. Then tighten breather support nuts fully.
10. Remove centering tool and connect linkage and spring to right-hand air control flap.
11. Install fan and rear fan housing half.

Check and Adjust Belt Tension

NOTE: Tension is correct if the belt yields about 1/2" when pressed firmly at its center with thumb. Belt should not show any signs of excessive wear such as frayed edges or cracks. Oily belts can often be made usable by washing in solvent and rinsing in clear water. Petroleum products must not be used for this purpose.

1. To adjust belt tension, remove air intake housing cover.
2. Hold generator pulley with a suitable wrench and remove nut.
3. Remove sleeve and outer pulley half.
4. Arrange spacer washers as required.

NOTE: Tension is corrected by varying the number of washers between pulley halves, Fig. 30. Taking washers out increases tension and vice versa. Install outer half of pulley. All washers not used between pulley halves must be placed between rear half and sleeve so that total number remains the same.

5. Install nut and housing cover.

Cooling Air Control

1. Referring to Fig. 31, remove cylinder cover plates and warm air ducts.
2. Unhook return spring at support plate.
3. Detach throttle flap rod at relay lever.
4. Remove front half of fan housing.
5. Remove throttle flaps screws (6).
6. Remove clip at right-hand end of flap shaft and remove shaft out to the left.
7. Reverse procedure to install, being sure that rubber stop for right-hand flap is in position.

Adjustment

1. Assemble all parts of linkage and lubricate joints with graphite paste.
2. Press flaps into closed position. If flaps do not close evenly, loosen one flap and turn it on shaft.
3. Tighten clamp screw on relay lever.
4. Connect long end of spring to flap and short end to support plate. Spring must be between support plate and bent lug. When spring is connected there should be a gap of about $1/2''$ between lower edge of flap and fan housing.

NOTE: When necessary, the air control linkage can be adjusted with the engine in the vehicle if the right-hand cylinder cover plate is removed.

COOLING SYSTEM
TYPE 4—1700

Fan Housing, Replace

1. Remove the three socket head capscrews and take off belt pulley and fan together, Fig. 31A.
2. Remove spacer.
3. Remove alternator cover plate and alternator.

NOTE: The fan housing can be taken off without removing the alternator.

4. Disconnect cooling air regulating cable from shaft.
5. Remove the four M8 nuts and take front and rear halves of man housing off together.
6. When installing, adjust cooling regulating flaps.
7. Install connecting elbow for alternator in the front half of the fan housing.
8. Adjust belt tension.

Check and Adjust Belt Tension

NOTE: Tension is correct if the belt yields about $1/2''$ when pressed firmly at its center with thumb. Belt should not show any signs of excessive wear such as frayed edges or cracks. Oily belts can often be made usable by washing in solvent and rinsing in clear water. Petroleum products must not be used for this purpose.

1. Remove insert in cover plate.

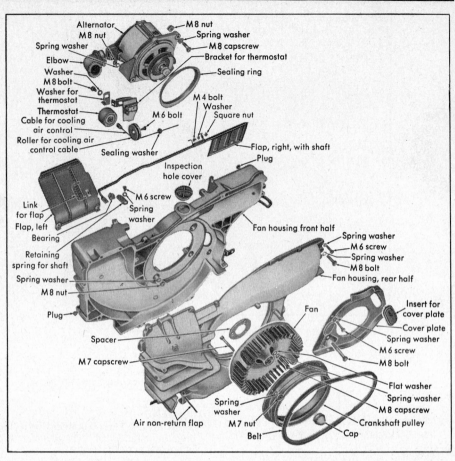

Fig. 31A Disassembled view of cooling components. Type 4—1700

2. Loosen M8 bolt and M8 socket head capscrew.
3. Adjust tension by moving the alternator to left or right.
4. Tighten bolts.

Cooling Air Control

1. To remove, loosen the holding springs

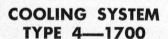

Fig. 31B Aircontrol Adjustment

and the right throttle flap with shaft can be removed, and the left throttle flap can be disconnected.

2. When installing, the return spring should rest with its bent ends against the holding spring lug and behind the cable guide.

Adjustment

1. Assemble all control parts, lubricate joints and pivot points with a moly-based grease, Fig. 31B.
2. Push throttle flaps into closing position and tighten cable control.

NOTE: To check thermostat, heat in water. At 149-158 degrees F the pressure capsule length should be at least 1.81 inches.

INTAKE & EXHAUST
SYSTEMS

Intake Manifold

1. To remove intake manifold and pre-heating pipe (single carburetor engine only), first remove air cleaner.
2. Disconnect accelerator cable.
3. Pull off cable at automatic choke.

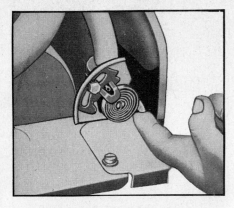

Fig. 32 Checking preheating pipe valve for free movement. Type 3

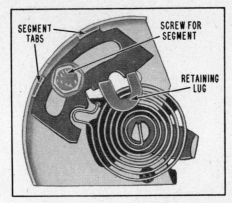

Fig. 33 Preheating pipe valve assembly. Type 3

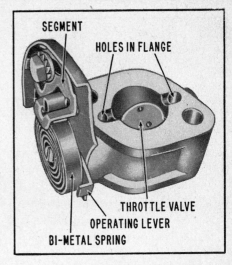

Fig. 34 Details of preheating pipe valve. Type 3

4. Pull fuel and vacuum lines off carburetor.
5. Remove bolts and nuts at cylinder heads and exhaust pipes.
6. Remove intake manifold with preheating pipe.
7. Remove manifold gaskets in cylinder heads.
8. Before installing, see that manifold flanges are clean and smooth and not cracked.
9. Use new manifold gaskets.
10. Make sure when installing manifold that flange holes align correctly with studs and tapped holes. If necessary, straighten manifold. If it has been heated, see that no scale remains in the interior.
11. Check preheating pipe valve for free movement, Fig. 32.

Preheating Pipe Valve Thermostat

The pre-load angle of the thermostat spring need only be checked if a new throttle valve has been installed. This is accomplished as follows:
1. Press bi-metal spring out of retaining lug on segment, Fig. 33.
2. Open throttle valve fully. Looped end of spring must then be located as shown.

3. If spring angle is not correct, loosen screw and move segment until spring loop and recess are correctly positioned.
4. Before tightening screw, be sure that the segment tabs are hard against edge of plate.

Installation

When installing the throttle, check angle of bi-metal spring as directed above. Install throttle so that bi-metal spring is outward, Fig. 34. Fit new gaskets for the preheater pipe.

NOTE: Every 3000 miles see that the throttle valve shaft moves easily. This is done by pulling the operating lever, Fig. 34, up with a suitable hook. If the throttle shaft is stiff in operation, hook the bi-metal spring out of the segment and remove the throttle. Lubricate the shaft bearings through the holes in the flange with one or two drops of oil. If this does

not free the shaft properly, a new throttle valve should be installed. This also applies when the bi-metal spring is damaged.

Warm Air Mixer Thermostat

1. When necessary to install a new thermostat, screw it on to the threaded pin about two turns. Install deflector plate.
2. Place fresh air feed valve in adapter and screw it on tightly.
3. Screw thermostat down until valve contacts mixer housing, Fig. 35.
4. Screw thermostat down a further 1 to $1\frac{1}{2}$ turns to give a preload of approximately $\frac{3}{64}$".
5. Secure thermostat with lock nut.

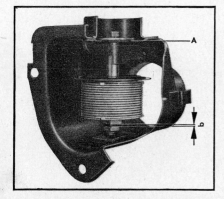

Fig. 35 Warm air mixture thermostat adjustment. Type 3. Valve must contact housing at "A"; preload adjustment at "b" is $\frac{3}{64}$"

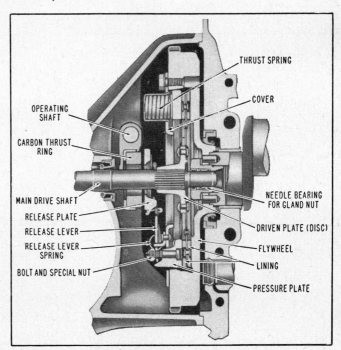

Fig. 36 Sectional view of clutch. Some models use a diaphragm spring type clutch cover and a ball release bearing in place of the carbon thrust ring

Fig. 37   Removing and installing clutch

Fig. 38   Clutch release bearing installed

Fig. 39   Adjusting clutch cable end to establish pedal free play

CLUTCH

The single-plate clutch, Fig. 36, is attached to the flywheel. The driven plate is splined to the main drive shaft. The clutch operating shaft and clutch release bearing are located in the transmission case.

Clutch, Replace

REMOVAL

1. Remove engine.
2. Loosen clutch cover a turn or two at a time so that the spring pressure is released gradually and evenly so as not to distort the clutch cover.
3. With all bolts removed, lift off clutch cover and take out driven plate, Fig. 37.

INSTALLATION

1. Clean clutch contact surface of flywheel and inspect it for wear. If necessary, the flywheel may be reground to a limit of .008" and polished with emery cloth. If damage is too severe for this operation, replace flywheel.
2. Check clutch release bearing for wear and replace the complete bearing if necessary. Note correct position of retaining springs.
3. Pack needle bearing in flywheel gland nut with universal grease.
4. Install driven plate, using a suitable pilot mandrel (VW-219) to be sure it is centered correctly.
5. Note proper position of clutch cover locating lugs in flywheel. Then gradually and evenly tighten clutch cover-to-flywheel bolts.

Release Bearing, Replace

1. Remove engine. Take off release bearing retaining springs and remove release bearing.
2. Inspect carbon thrust ring of release bearing for wear and cracks; if damaged, install a new bearing. The thrust ring should not be replaced separately as it will be damaged when it is pressed into position.
3. Note position of retaining springs, Fig. 38.
4. After engine is installed, adjust clutch pedal free play.

Pedal Free Play, Adjust

1. Release lock nut on threaded cable end, Fig. 39.
2. Adjust clutch clearance by turning the adjusting nut on the cable end to obtain a clutch pedal free play of 0.40" to 0.80".
3. Depress clutch pedal a few times and recheck the adjustment.

Fuel & Electrical Section

CARBURETORS

Type 1—1300, 1500 & 1600

Figs. 1, 2 and 2a illustrate sectional views of the three basic carburetors in use. Fig. 1 has a manually operated choke while Figs. 2 and 2a are provided with automatic chokes.

Idling Adjustment

1. Normal idle speed usually requires that the volume (mixture) control screw be backed out $1\frac{1}{4}$ to $1\frac{1}{2}$ turns from its seated position. When making the adjustment of the automatic choke carburetor, be sure that the idle speed adjusting screw is not resting on one of the steps of the fast idle cam.
2. With engine running at normal operating temperature, turn the idle speed screw in or out to obtain a speed of 550 rpm.
3. Turn volume control screw clockwise until engine speed begins to slow down. Then turn the screw in about $\frac{1}{4}$ turn in the opposite direction. A final adjustment may require that the volume control screw be turned slightly in either direction to get the engine to idle smoothly.
4. The adjustment is correct if the engine continues to run when the throttle is opened and closed quickly or when the clutch pedal is depressed. If the engine stalls the idle mixture is too

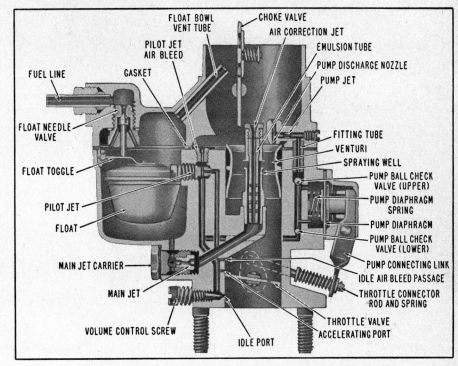

Fig. 1 Solex carburetor 28 PCI with manual choke

lean; turn the volume control screw out slightly (about $\frac{1}{8}$ turn). If the engine stalls when the throttle is closed suddenly, as when applying the brakes, the idling mixture is probably too rich.

5. If the engine idle is rough after the adjustments have been completed, check for damaged intake manifold flange gasket, a cracked or loose intake manifold or an improperly adjusted fuel pump.

Carburetor Service

In servicing the carburetors, refer to Figs. 3 through 8 and note the following:
1. Check needle valve for leaks. Examine needle valve gasket for damage and see that it is properly installed to prevent leaks.
2. On manual choke units, check choke valve spring and choke valve shaft clearance. Make sure that choke poppet valve opens easily and check for perfect sealing.
3. On automatic choke units, check heater element and bimetal spring; if either of the parts is damaged the complete ceramic plate must be replaced.

NOTE: *When installing the ceramic plate with bimetal spring heater element, be sure that the marking on*

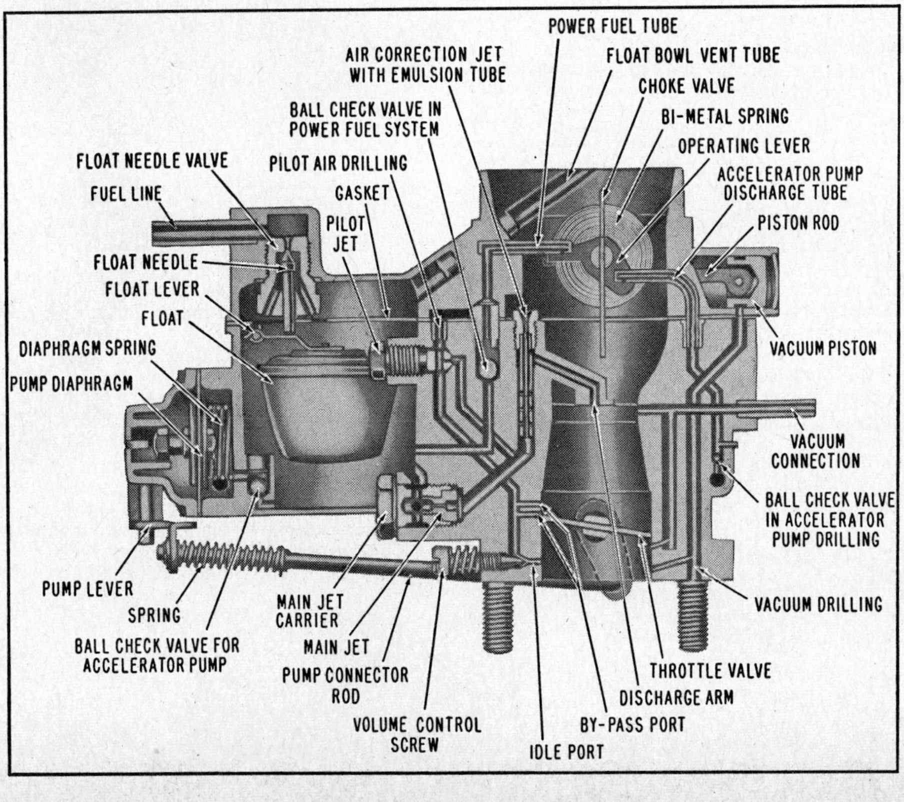

Fig. 2 Solex carburetor 28 and 30 PICT-1 with automatic choke

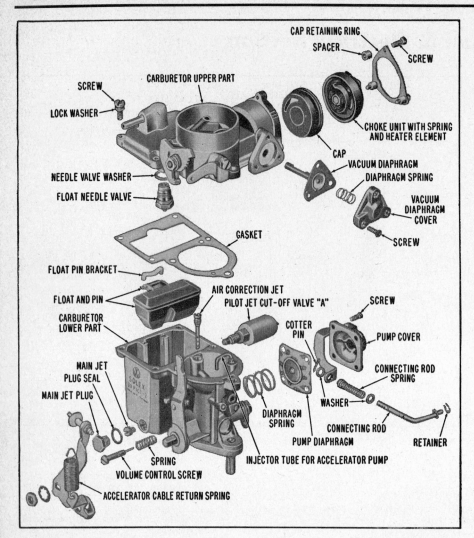

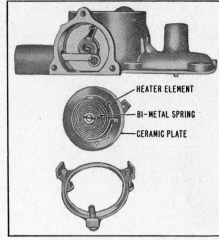

Fig. 4   Automatic choke components.
Solex 28 and 30 PICT-1

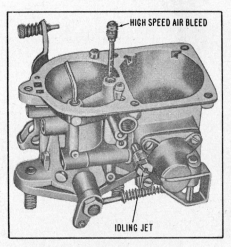

Fig. 5   Carburetor lower body.
Solex 28 and 30 PICT-1

the ceramic plate corresponds with that on the spring housing.

4. On manual choke units, when the air correction jet is installed, a clearance of .020″ should be present between the shoulder of the jet and the spray well face to prevent the face from cracking.
5. On all units, see that the pump diaphragm is not leaking. A "flat spot" when the throttle is opened suddenly is an indication of a leaky diaphragm.
6. Check the float for leaks by dipping it in hot water. Air bubbles will appear if the float is punctured.
7. On manual choke units, install the venturi as indicated in Fig. 8.
8. On all units, be sure the throttle valve shaft is not loose. Excessive looseness causes excessive flow into the carburetor which affects starting and idling operation. If necessary, throttle shaft may be re-bushed to eliminate looseness.
9. Replace volume control screw if its tip is damaged. If the tip has broken off be sure to remove the broken piece from the casting, and see that the screw seat in the casting is not damaged.
10. On manual choke units, the word

"oven" on the float toggle lever must face upward.

1966-67 Type 3—1600 Twin Carburetor System

The twin carburetor system has two carburetors of the type shown in Fig. 9. The carburetors are attached to the cylinder heads with short intake pipes that are connected by a balance pipe. The carburetors are left and right handed and cannot be interchanged; they are operated by rods and ball joints and relay levers.

The carburetors have automatic chokes, accelerator pumps and power fuel systems. The vacuum for the spark advance mechanism is taken from the left-hand carburetor only. Intake air passes through a common air cleaner, via distribution ducts to the carburetors.

Carburetor Service

When checking and assembling the carburetor, note the following points when checking the individual parts:

Upper Body

1. Check float needle valve for leakage and spring-loaded ball for ease of movement. It should not be possible to blow air through the valve when

the needle is pressed lightly on the seat.
2. Check height of injector tube opening with a T-scale as shown, Fig. 10, from upper part of carburetor and adjust if necessary by bending carefully.
3. Check height of power tube fuel opening, Fig. 11, from upper part of carburetor and correct, if necessary, by bending carefully.
4. Check choke valve shaft and vacuum piston for ease of movement.
5. Check heater element and bi-metal coil. If either part is damaged the complete cover must be replaced.

IMPORTANT: The arrangement of the bi-metal coils in the automatic choke covers is different for right and left carburetors, Fig. 12. The hook-shaped ends of the coils face to opposite sides. Covers are marked externally:

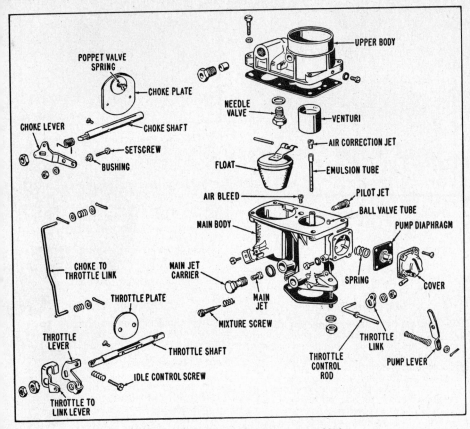

Fig. 3 Solex carburetor 28 PCI disassembled

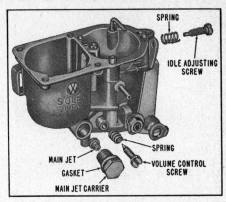

Fig. 6 Carburetor lower body.
Solex 28 and 30 PICT-1

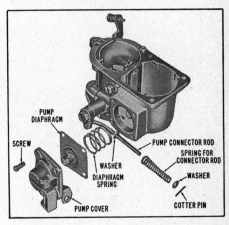

Fig. 7 Details of accelerating pump.
Solex 28 and 30 PICT-1, 2

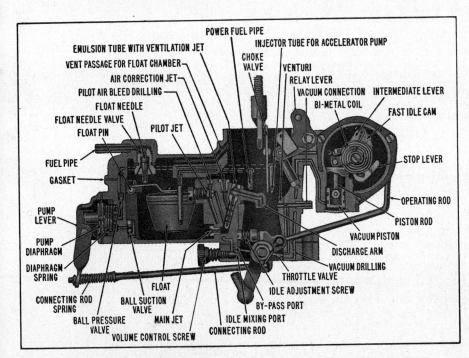

Fig. 9 Solex 32 PDSIT carburetor, two are used on twin carburetor engines

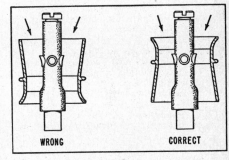

Fig. 8 Install venturi with curved
end up. Solex 28 PCI

"Li" for left unit; "Re" for the right-hand carburetor. When cover is installed the intermediate lever must engage the hook on the bi-metal coil.

6. Install and turn choke cover so that

mark is in line with lug on upper part of carburetor and tighten screws, Fig. 13.

Lower Body

1. When tightening pump cover screws,

press pump lever down so that diaphragm is in pressure stroke position. *Spitting in carburetor on sudden acceleration usually indicates a leaking pump diaphragm.*

2. Place float in hot water and check for leakage. If bubbles appear, float is leaking and must be replaced.

3. Check throttle valve shaft end play. *Excessive play encourages the entry of secondary air and is detrimental to starting and idling.*

4. Check idle mixture screw; the tapered part must not be grooved, damaged or bent.

5. Install venturi in carburetor body so that the cutaway is at the discharge arm.

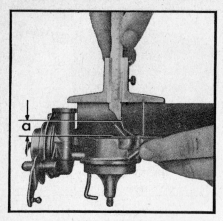

Fig. 10   Checking height of injector tube opening .470" for 1600 models)

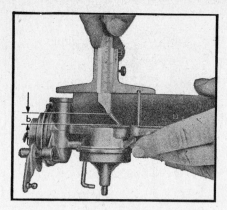

Fig. 11   Checking height of power tube fuel opening (.590" for 1600 models)

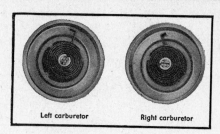

Fig. 12   Arrangement of automatic choke covers

for the unusual internal construction of the carburetor. All the drillings for the individual systems pass up through the carburetor body to the cover and from there down to the various discharge ports in the choke tube.

The carburetor has an automatic choke, an accelerating pump, a power fuel system and a double vacuum drilling for the ignition advance mechanism.

6. The end of the power fuel pipe should be roughly in the center between discharge arm and venturi. Moreover, the choke valve must not contact pipe as it closes.
7. The accelerator pump injector pipe must be positioned so that the fuel is sprayed into the throttle valve gap when throttle is opened. *The pipe position should be corrected as necessary but must be moved sideways only; height must not be altered.*
8. Check length of pull rods with a measuring jig which can be made locally, Fig. 14. Both ball joint locknuts should be sealed with paint afterwards.
9. After installing operating rod for automatic choke stop lever, adjust as follows:
   a. Close choke.
   b. Screw idle adjusting screw out so that throttle valve is closed.
   c. Adjust both nuts on operating rod so that there is a gap of .021-.023" at throttle valve when choke valve is closed, on 1966 1500 and .024-.026" on all 1600, Fig. 15. Gap must be measured with a wire gauge.
   Throttle valve should be pressed in closed position lightly while measuring.
   d. Tighten nuts firmly and lock, be-

ing sure that pull rod and throttle valve lever move easily.

Idle Adjustments

1. Take off right-hand connecting rod.
2. Turn idle adjusting screw until throttle valve is completely closed. Then slowly screw it in until it just contacts throttle valve lever, and give it a further ½ turn inward.
3. Turn in idle mixture screw until its point comes to rest on its seat, then back it out 1½ turns.
4. Warm up engine to operating temperature.
5. Remove oil bath air cleaner.
6. Connect cables for automatic choke cover and coil.
7. Start engine and connect accelerator cable rod at the three-arm lever.
8. Set idle adjusting screws on both carburetors the same amount so that an idling speed of 700 to 750 rpm is obtained.
9. Slowly screw in idle mixture screws on both carburetors until engine begins to slow down. Turn screws out until engine runs smoothly and then turn them out a further ¼ turn.

SINGLE CARBURETOR SYSTEM

Type 1

This carburetor, Fig. 16, is a side-draft Solex unit which is distinguished by the fact that the induction passage is horizontal and below the float chambers. With this design the discharge openings for idling and normal running mixtures are below the level of the fuel which accounts

Carburetor Service

When checking and assembling the carburetor, the following points should be observed:

Float Chamber Cover

1. Check float needle valve for leakage. It should not be possible to blow air through the valve when the needle is pressed lightly to its seat.
2. Examine condition of needle valve gasket and see that gasket seats properly on installation.
3. Check gasket between upper and lower parts of carburetor.

Carburetor Body

1. Check automatic choke bi-metal spring and heater element; if either of these parts is damaged, install a new choke cover.
2. Check operation of spring for fast idle cam lever. Lubricate steps on cam.
3. When installing choke cover, see that hooked end of bi-metal spring engages with operating lever. Turn choke cover so that mark on cover is aligned with lug on choke housing.
4. Dip float in hot water. If bubbles ap-

Fig. 13   Adjust automatic choke by turning choke cover so that mark is in line with lug on carburetor

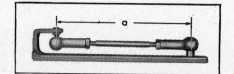

Fig 14   Length of pull rods should be adjusted to approximately 3.89" at "A"

Fig. 15   Adjust length of operating rod so throttle valve opening is .024" to .026" when choke valve is closed on 1600

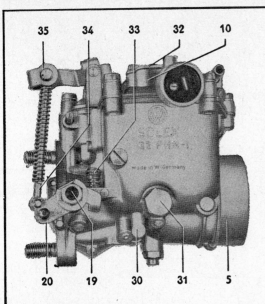

Carburetor, left side

31 - Main jet carrier
32 - Sealing plate for vent chamber
33 - Idle adjustment screw
34 - Connecting rod with spring
35 - Pump lever

Carburetor (right side), Automatic choke

36 - Screws for choke control housing
37 - Ceramic insert with heater element
38 - Bi-metal coil
39 - Gasket for cover

40 - Intermediate spindle
41 - Fast idle cam
42 - Cam return spring
43 - Operating lever
44 - Piston rod
45 - Piston
46 - Stop lever
47 - Stop screw

Fig. 16   Solex PHN-1 carburetor used on 1966 1500 with one carburetor

pear, float is leaking and must be replaced.

5. Check throttle shaft clearance. Excessive clearance encourages the entry of secondary air and has a detrimental effect on starting and idling conditions. If necessary, holes for throttle shaft must be bushed.
6. Examine tapered portion of idle mixture screw and replace if tip is bent or broken.
7. The large hole in accelerator pump cover must be toward carburetor flange.

Accelerator Pump, Adjust

The accelerator pump on the carburetor is set so that when the choke is fully open and the throttle valve is in the idling position, there is a clearance of .024 to .040" between pump lever and plunger.

When trouble is experienced with flat spots which are caused by too small or too large injection quantities, the accelerator pump can be set with the adjusting screw, Fig. 17. Experience has shown that the engine requires a larger amount of fuel at low temperatures and a smaller amount at high temperatures.

If the injection quantity is too small, turn adjusting screw to the left; injection will then commence earlier. If the injection quantity is too large, turn adjusting screw to the right; injection will then commence later. Usually a half to a full turn is sufficient. The setting should always be checked by road testing afterwards.

Throttle Valve Gap, Adjust

When the automatic choke has closed the choke valve, the stop lever rests on the highest step of the fast idle cam. At this position the throttle valve should be opened to a definite angle. This angle corresponds to a throttle valve gap of .031 to .035" and can be measured with a wire feeler gauge, Fig. 18.

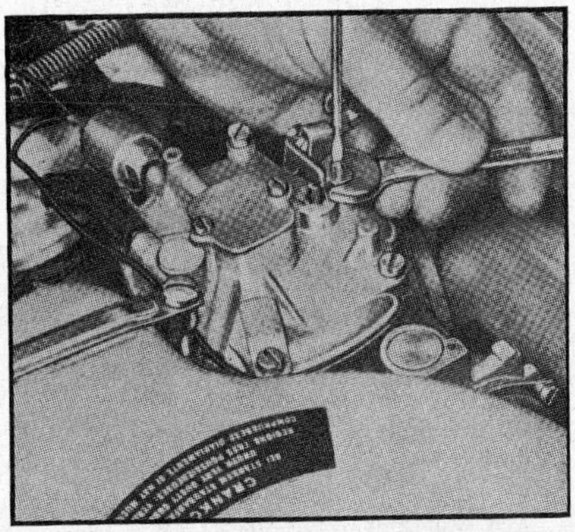

Fig. 17   Adjusting accelerator pump

Fig. 18   Adjusting throttle valve gap

Fig. 19   Adjusting automatic choke (1st step)

Fig. 20   Adjusting automatic choke (2nd step)

If the gap is smaller, the cold engine will start badly and stop again quickly. If the gap is too large, the idling speed will be too high and the engine will run too fast.

Automatic Choke, Adjust

1. Remove carburetor and choke cover.
2. Close choke valve. The stop screw (1), Fig. 19, in the stop lever should be on the highest step of the fast idle cam (2).
3. Turn stop screw until gap at throttle valve is .031 to .035", Fig. 20.
4. Seal stop screw with paint afterwards. *All carburetors are adjusted in this manner. In isolated cases, however, the screw works loose and this alters the opening angle of the throttle valve.*

Idling Adjustment

1. Set engine speed to approximately 550 rpm with idle adjusting screw.
2. Turn idle mixture screw in slowly until engine speed starts to drop. Then turn it to the left until engine runs smoothly. From this position, turn idle mixture screw out about ¼ turn.
3. Regulate engine speed as necessary. The adjustment is correct if the throttle can be opened and snapped closed quickly without stalling when engine is warm and clutch pedal is depressed.

1971

This engine is equipped with a new Solex 34 PICT carburetor which has a

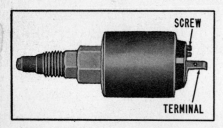

Fig. 22   Electro-Magnetic pilot jet used to prevent engine from "running-on" when ignition is turned off

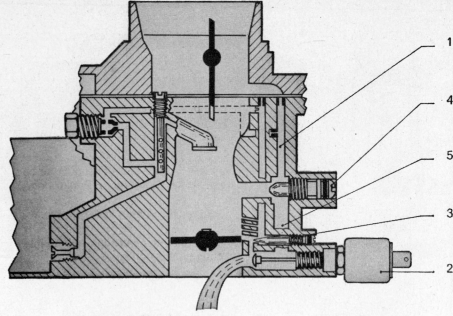

1. By-pass fuel passage
2. By-pass mixture cut-off valve
3. Volume control screw
4. By-pass air screw
5. By-pass air passage

Fig. 21   Cutaway of Solex 34 PICT carburetor

by-pass air drilling through which the air required when idling by-passes the throttle valve. On these carburetors the throttle is completely closed when idling.

Adjustments

Idling adjustments are made at the factory with the volume screw. Thereafter, routine adjustments are made only with the by-pass air screw. Altering the by-pass air screw prevents the mixture from becoming too lean or too rich due to changes in the amount of idling air. It has no influence on the actual composition of the idling mixture, Fig. 21.

EMISSION CONTROL SYSTEM

The control of exhaust emissions is accomplished by the use of special carburetor, distributor and a throttle positioner. The purpose of the throttle positioner is to open the throttle slightly when the vehicle is over-running the engine, thus preventing the intake manifold vacuum from rising as high as it would with a closed throttle. Even on deceleration, the engine receives an adequate charge of combustible mixture and stops the fuel passing into the exhaust unburned. This also prevents backfiring in the muffler.

Idling Adjustment

1. Be sure timing is set to TDC.
2. With engine warm, connect a tachometer and set idling speed by turning the idle screw, Fig. 24.
3. Turn volume control screw, Fig. 24, to right until speed starts to drop. From this position turn volume screw to left until engine runs fastest. If

necessary, regulate engine speed again with the idle screw.

Throttle Positioner Adjustment

Before attempting this adjustment the engine should be thoroughly warmed up and the automatic choke fully open.

1. Connect a tachometer and turn the adjusting screw on the throttle positioner clockwise until the stop washer on the pull rod contacts the throttle positioner housing, Fig. 25. Engine speed should then be between 1700 and 1800 rpm.
2. If speed is higher, lengthen the pull rod. If the speed is lower, shorten the pull rod. Then turn the adjusting screw on the throttle positioner counterclockwise until the idle speed is 850 rpm.
3. Increase the engine speed to 3000 rpm and release the throttle lever. The time taken for the speed to drop from 3000 rpm to 1000 rpm must be between 3 and 4 seconds. If the time taken is shorter, turn the adjusting screw clockwise. If the time taken is longer, turn the adjusting screw counterclockwise.

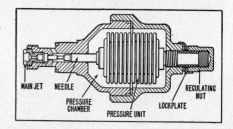

Fig. 23   Main jet with altitude corrector

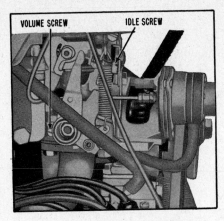

Fig. 24 Adjusting idle speed on Solex 30 PICT-2 carburetor with exhaust control system

ELECTRO-MAGNETIC PILOT JET

On 1500 single carburetor engines, this jet, Fig. 22, is fitted in production. The jet can be service installed on 1300 and twin carburetor engines on which "running-on" cannot be eliminated. The pilot jet is fitted with a cut-off valve that cuts off the supply of fuel as soon as the engine is switched off, thus effectively stopping engine from continuing to run when ignition is turned off.

The needle in the pilot jet is operated electro-magnetically and closes the pilot jet when the ignition is switched off so that fuel can no longer flow through the jet. When the ignition is switched on, the jet needle is withdrawn and the jet cleared.

Service

If "running-on" occurs on an engine that is already fitted with an electro-magnetic pilot jet, the cut-off valve should be checked as follows:

1. Pull cable off terminal.
2. Check if screw is in tight.
3. Switch ignition on and touch terminal with cable end. The needle should move in and out with a ticking noise as the cable makes and breaks contact. *With the cable end off, needle moves toward carburetor and closes jet. With cable end on, needle moves away from carburetor and opens jet.*
4. If the cut-off valve does not work when checked in this manner or if the engine still tends to "run-on", the cut-off valve should be replaced.

NOTE: If the valve fails in operation, the needle can be withdrawn by turning the screw, Fig. 22. Turning the screw as far as it will go to the right closes the needle valve; turning screw all the way to the left opens the needle valve. In the opened position the cut-off valve is switched off and the fuel flow to pilot jet is open continuously. The jet can be screwed off the cut-off valve and blown out.

MAIN JET WITH ALTITUDE CORRECTOR

1500 Single Carburetor Engines

In order to ensure satisfactory mixture formation in the carburetor at high altitudes, the main jet carrier can be replaced by an altitude corrector with a suitable main jet, Fig. 23. (The twin carburetor engine cannot be fitted with this device.)

At one end of the altitude corrector is the main jet through which fuel coming from the float chamber has to flow. At the end opposite to the main jet, the pressure unit is screwed into the housing

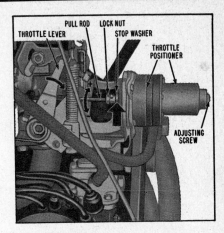

Fig. 25 Adjusting throttle positioner

of the corrector to locate it axially. The other end of the pressure unit carries the needle which moves freely in the passage leading to the main jet. When the pressure unit expands due to the change in atmospheric pressure at high altitudes, the needle throttles the fuel flow to the main jet to suit the changing conditions.

When the vehicle is operated at sea level, the needle in the corrector moves into a position where it has no influence on fuel consumption.

IMPORTANT: When the altitude corrector is assembled, the pressure unit is set with the regulating nut which is secured with a lockplate. This setting must not be altered under any circumstances.

FUEL PUMPS

NOTE: From August 1965 (Engine No. D/F 000 001) a valve that cuts off the flow of fuel when the engine is not running, is fitted in the top half of the fuel pump. On this pump the filter is at the side and can be removed for cleaning by taking out the screw plug. The valve formerly installed in the fuel line has been discontinued. The new pump is marked VW-7. Delivery capacity and pressure remains the same of other pumps.

The fuel pump is actuated mechanically from an eccentric on the distributor drive shaft.

To remove, disconnect fuel lines from pump. Remove nuts from mounting studs at flange and take off pump. Remove push rod, intermediate flange and gasket

DISTRIBUTOR
Breaker Points, Adjust

1. Remove distributor cap and rotor.
2. Crank engine until fiber block on breaker arm rests on highest point on cam lobe.
3. Loosen lock screw of fixed breaker point.
4. On the unit shown in Fig. 27, turn the eccentric adjusting screw until the correct gap of .016" is obtained.
5. On the unit shown in Fig. 27A, insert a screwdriver between the two small pins on the contact breaker plate and in the slot at the end of the fixed

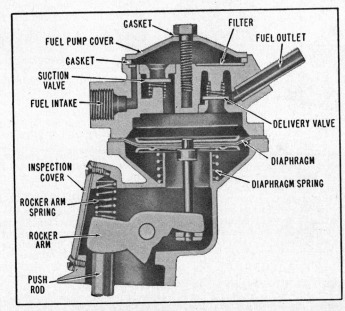

Fig. 26 Solex fuel pump

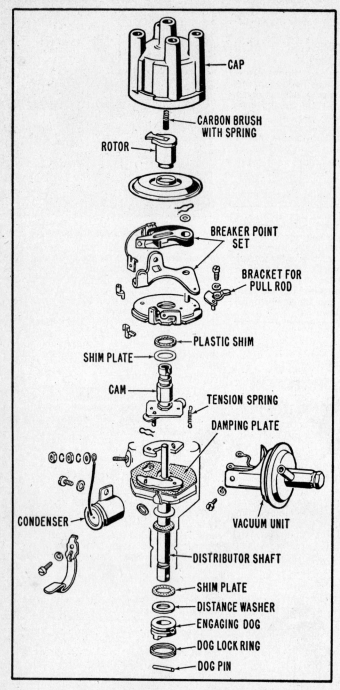

Fig. 27   Bosch distributor with centrifugal and vacuum advance (early models)

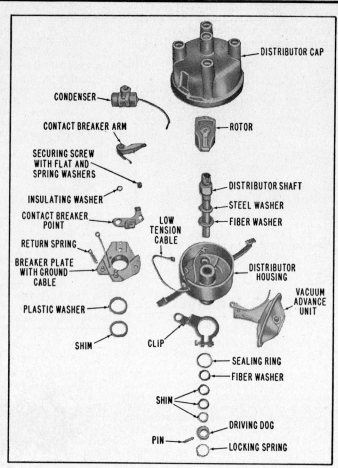

Fig. 27A   Bosch distributor with vacuum advance only (typical)

point. Turn the screwdriver until a clearance of .016″ is obtained.

NOTE: *When the points have been adjusted, the ignition timing must be re-set as an alteration of .004″ in the point gap alters the ignition timing about 3 degrees.*

Ignition Timing

IMPORTANT: When setting the timing on engines with fuel injection or exhaust control system a timing light must be used

and the engine must be warmed. The use of a timing light is also recommended on all other models as this method does provide a more accurate setting. However, the previous method of setting timing on a cold engine by using a test lamp the same voltage as the car may still be used on other than fuel injected or exhaust controlled engines as follows:

Type 3—1600

1. Referring to Fig. 27B, remove air intake housing cover.
2. Turn engine at the generator until the right-hand mark on the crankshaft

pulley is aligned with the setting surface on the fan housing and the rotor arm points to the No. 1 cylinder mark on the edge of the distributor housing.

IMPORTANT: The ignition can only be set when No. 1 cylinder is at top dead center on the compression stroke. The firing point of No. 3 cylinder is then 4 crankshaft degrees later than that of No. 1 cylinder.

3. Loosen clamp screw on distributor retainer.
4. Rotate distributor body clockwise until the breaker points are closed and then slowly counterclockwise until the points just begin to open and the test lamp lights.
5. Tighten distributor retainer clamp screw, reinstall rotor and distributor cap.

Type 1—1300, 1500 & 1600

1. Crank engine until mark on crankshaft pulley (see *Tune Up* table) lines up with the vertical crankcase joining faces and the distributor rotor arm is in No. 1 firing position (see mark on rim of distributor base).
2. Loosen clamp screw of distributor.
3. Connect one lead of a 6-volt test lamp to No. 1 at distributor and the other to ground.
4. Switch on ignition.

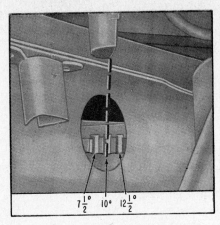

Fig. 27B Ignition timing marks on crankshaft pulley. Type 3—1600

5. Rotate distributor body clockwise until breaker points are closed and then slowly counter-clockwise until points are just about to open and the test lamp lights.
6. Tighten clamp screw on distributor.
7. Install distributor cap and rotor.

Distributor, Replace

1. On early distributors, Fig. 27, disconnect vacuum line from vacuum chamber, and lead from No. 1 terminal at distributor. On later units, Fig. 27A, remove vacuum pipe at distributor and disconnect lead No. 1 at ignition coil.
2. Remove distributor cap.
3. On early units, remove clamp screw at distributor retainer. On later units, remove retaining bracket screw or nut on crankcase.
4. Lift out distributor.
5. Reverse the procedure to install the distributor, noting the following:
6. On Type 1—1300, 1500 & 1600 position No. 1 cylinder at firing point. The slot in the distributor drive pinion must be positioned as shown in Fig. 28, with small offset side of slot toward pulley and ignition mark on pulley aligned with joint in crankcase. On Type 3—1600, refer to Fig. 30 and place No. 1 cylinder at firing point. The slot in the drive pinion must then be at an angle of 60 as shown and the small segment on the head of the drive shaft towards the coil.
7. When inserting the distributor, turn distributor shaft until the rotor points to the mark for No. 1 cylinder on the distributor housing and the distributor shaft engages in the drive shaft slot after being turned slightly back and forth. (See Fig. 29 for Type 1—1300, 1500 & 1600.)
8. Adjust ignition timing.

GENERATOR, REPLACE
Type 1—1300, 1500 & 1600

1. Disconnect cables from regulator.
2. Remove carburetor and fan belt.
3. Disconnect generator mounting strap.

4. Remove throttle ring and screws on both sides of fan housing. Raise housing a few inches.
5. Remove four screws on fan cover and take off generator and fan.
6. When installing, make sure that fan housing seats properly against cylinder cover plates all around. Also note concentric position of throttle ring.

Type 3—1600

1. Remove cables from generator.
2. Remove air intake housing cover and remove drive belt.
3. Unfasten and remove generator.
4. The generator should be installed so that the mark on the housing (notch) is in line with the mark on the clamping strap.
5. The clearance between the belt and the air intake housing must be at least $^{11}/_{64}''$ and the generator pulley properly aligned with the crankshaft pulley.

IMPORTANT: If the markings can no longer be seen or if another generator is installed, the openings in the generator housing and those in the cooling air housing must be aligned so that the generator is properly cooled, Fig. 31. The generator should be turned so that the D+ terminal is at the angle indicated in the illustration.

6. Be sure that the boot for the generator and the rubber gasket on the air intake housing cover are correctly sealed.

STARTER, REPLACE

1. Disconnect negative battery cable.
2. Disconnect battery cable and cables to generator and ignition switch at terminal No. 30 of starting motor.
3. Disconnect control cable to starting switch at terminal No. 50 at starting motor.

Fig. 29 With ignition mark on pulley in line with crankcase joint, rotor points to No. 1 mark on distributor housing. Type 3—1600

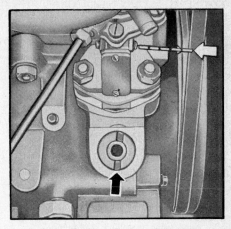

Fig. 28 Note position of offset slot in distributor drive pinion. Type 3—1600

4. Unfasten starter from transmission case and lift it off.
5. When installing lubricate starter shaft bushing with multi-purpose grease. Apply VW Sealing Compound D2 between intermediate bracket and transmission case. Make sure all terminals are tight.

IGNITION SWITCH, REPLACE

1. Disconnect battery ground cable.
2. Remove protective cover behind instrument panel.
3. Disconnect one cable at cable connector, one cable at speedometer and two cables at fuse box and pull all cables through body.
4. Remove two screws and take out ignition switch (steering lock need not be removed).
5. Reverse procedure to install, being sure that lug on switch engages in groove on steering lock.

FUEL INJECTION
Type 3—1600
Type 4—1700

The electronic fuel injection system is shown schematically in Fig. 32, while Fig. 33 is a layout of system components.

CONTROL UNIT

The heart of the system is the electronic control unit. It controls the amount of fuel to be injected according to engine speed, engine load (intake manifold pressure) and engine temperature.

When the ignition is switched on, current is supplied to the control unit via the main relay. The unit also controls the fuel pump to which current is supplied via the pump relay when the engine is running.

The control unit opens the injector valves electronically in pairs (cylinders 1 and 4 and cylinders 2 and 3). The amount of fuel injected depends upon the length of time the injectors are kept open and is metered according to engine requirements. This is possible because the in-

Fig. 30 Showing angle of drive pinion slot when installing distributor. Type 3—1600

FUNCTION OF COMPONENTS

1. The pressure sensor controls the basic fuel quantity by measuring intake manifold pressure.
2. The pressure switch controls the fuel enrichment. It is operated by the differential between the intake manifold and ambient air pressure.
3. The temperature sensor in the crankcase and the temperature sensor on the cylinder head control the fuel mixture enrichment for cold starting and the warm-up period.
4. The trigger contacts in the distributor feed a signal to the control unit when and into which cylinder group fuel is to be injected.
5. The distributor, which was developed especially for the fuel injection engine, houses the normal contact breaker points and the trigger contacts for the cylinders' injectors.

FUEL PUMP OPERATION

The electric fuel pump draws fuel from the tank through a filter and pumps it through a pressure line into the ring main which distributes fuel to the injectors and also pipes excess amounts of fuel back to the return line. Electro-magnetic injectors are connected to the ring main by distributor pipes. A pressure regulator

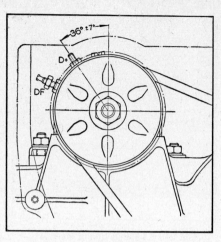

Fig. 31 Generator properly installed. Type 3—1600

at the end of the ring main maintains a constant pressure of 28 psi.

AIR SUPPLY, Fig. 34

Air for the fuel injection system passes through four pipes attached to the intake air distributor. A pressure switch, pressure sensor, air cleaner and ignition distributor all are connected to the intake air distributor.

A throttle valve on the inlet side of the air distributor is connected by a cable

jectors are under a constant fuel pressure.

Duration of injection is determined by the control unit, the information processed there being fed by sensing devices mounted on the engine. The control unit is mounted in the left air duct and is connected by a cable harness to the sender units.

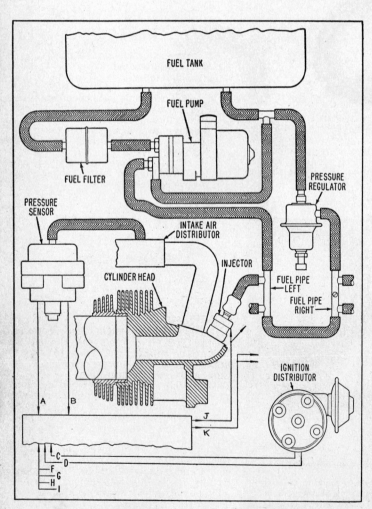

Fig. 32 Schematic drawing of the fuel injection system

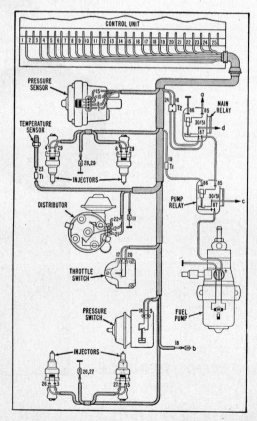

Fig. 33 Diagram of fuel injection system components

to the accelerator pedal. At idling speed, the throttle valve is fully closed and air passes through an idling circuit into the intake air distributor. An idling air screw controls the amount of air for idling.

At engine temperatures below 120 deg. F, more air is required and comes in through a line leading from the air cleaner into the air intake distributor. An auxiliary air regulator in that line varies the amount of air, meeting requirements which change as engine temperature varies.

SIGNAL SYSTEM OPERATION

Referring to the letters indicated in Fig. 32, the signals perform the following functions:

1. Signal for engine loading is from pressure sensor at "A" and "B".
2. Signal for engine speed and triggering is from the distributor contacts at "C" and "D".
3. Signal for warming up and cold starting is from temperature sensor at "F".
4. Signal for cutting off fuel at deceleration is from the throttle switch at "G".
5. Signal for full load enrichment is from the pressure switch at "H".
6. Signal for cold start enrichment is from starter at "I".
7. "J" is to injectors for cylinders 1 and 4.
8. "K" is to injectors for cylinders 2 and 3.

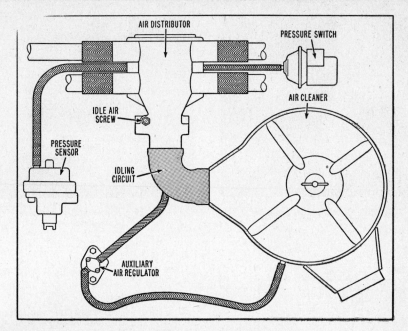

Fig. 34   Air supply for fuel injection system

Fuel Injection Adjustments

Pressure Regulator

1. Remove air cleaner and connect pressure gauge, Fig. 36.
2. Start engine and allow to idle.
3. If necessary to adjust regulator, back off locknut and turn adjusting screw

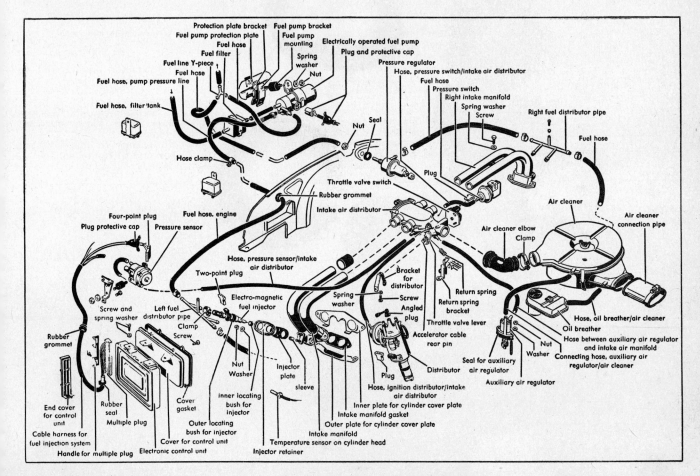

Fig. 35   Fuel injection system's components (Typical)

Fig. 36   Checking fuel pressure

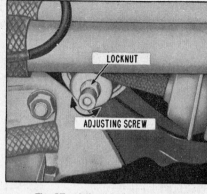

Fig. 37   Adjusting fuel pressure regulator

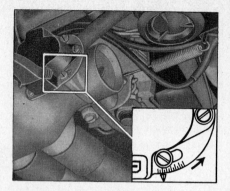

Fig. 38   Adjusting throttle valve switch

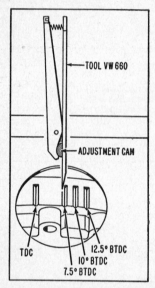

Fig. 39   Timing marks on fuel injected engine

as required to reach a setting of 28 lbs.

Throttle Valve Switch

The throttle valve switch should operate when the throttle valve is opened by 4° from its closed position. Adjust as follows:

1. Close throttle valve completely.
2. Loosen throttle valve switch and turn it until it can be heard to switch.
3. Turn the switch two graduations (4°) in direction of arrow from the mark opposite the cast-on projection at the switching point, Fig. 38.
4. Tighten screws.

Ignition Timing

1. Set breaker gap or dwell angle to specifications.
2. Connect timing light.
3. Loosen clamp screw on distributor bracket so distributor can just be turned by hand.
4. Pull vacuum hose off distributor vacuum unit.
5. Start engine and allow it to idle.
6. Aim timing light at pulley màrk and turn distributor until TDC mark, Fig. 39, aligns with crankcase joint.

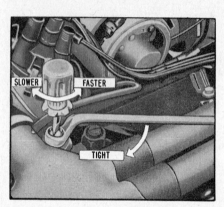

Fig. 40   Adjusting idle speed

7. Tighten distributor bracket and reconnect vacuum hose.

Engine Idle Speed

1. Connect tachometer, start engine and allow it to reach · operating temperature.
2. Back off locknut on idle adjusting screw and set idling speed and retighten locknut, Fig. 40.

Automatic Stickshift Trans-Axle Section

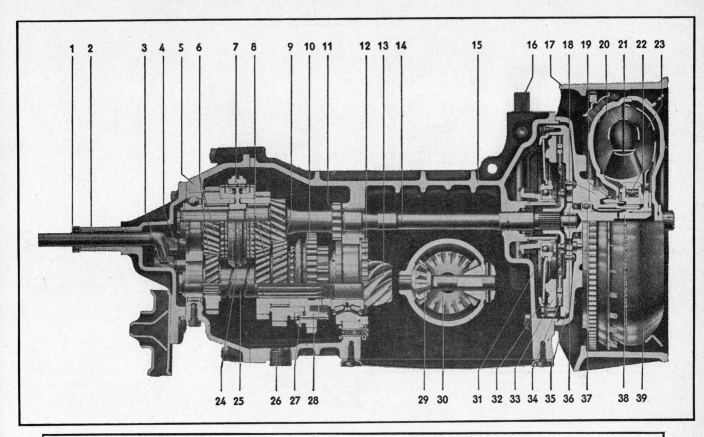

Fig. A1   Automatic Stickshift Trans-Axle

1 - Inner shift lever
2 - Gearshift housing
3 - 1st/reverse shift rod
4 - 2nd/3rd shift rod
5 - Gear carrier
6 - 3rd speed gears
7 - 2nd/3rd gear synchronizer rings
8 - 2nd speed gears
9 - 1st speed gears
10 - Operating sleeve for 1st/reverse gear
11 - Reverse gear drive
12 - Retaining ring for pinion
13 - Pinion

14 - Drive shaft
15 - Transmission case
16 - Shift clutch release shaft
17 - Converter housing
18 - Support tube for one-way clutch
19 - Oil seal for converter
20 - Impeller
21 - Stator
22 - One-way clutch
23 - Turbine
24 - 2nd/3rd gear operating sleeve
25 - 2nd/3rd gear spacer spring
26 - Magnetic oil drain plug

27 - 1st gear synchronizer ring
28 - Synchronizer hub 1st/reverse gear
29 - Differential pinion
30 - Differential side gear
31 - Shift clutch release bearing
32 - Diaphragm spring
33 - Pressure plate
34 - Clutch plate
35 - Carrier plate
36 - Oil seal for converter housing
37 - Bearing for turbine shaft
38 - Turbine shaft
39 - Torque converter

Description

The Automatic Stickshift consists of the torque converter, a fully synchronized three speed transmission and an automatically operated clutch. The power flow passes from the engine via the converter, clutch and gearbox to the final drive, Fig. A1.

The converter performs the functions of the conventional clutch for starting and stopping while the shift clutch serves only for engaging and changing the speed ranges. The converter has an independent oil supply provided by an engine driven pump and a reservoir.

The automatic clutch is operated by a servo which is influenced by intake manifold vacuum. A control valve between intake manifold and servo controls engagement and release of the clutch, Fig. A2. The signal for this is transmitted from an electrical contact in the gear selector lever. When engaging a driving range this contact is closed and the clutch is disengaged. It remains disengaged until the shift is complete and the driver releases the lever, Fig. A3.

A vacuum reservoir insures that one can still shift the lever even though the engine is switched off, or if there is not sufficient vacuum in the intake manifold.

Operation

Starting: To start the engine the selector lever must be moved to "N" (neutral position). A starter lock switch prevents the engine from starting if a driving range is engaged.

Drive Range L: Used only for pulling away on hills with a fully loaded vehicle or when pulling a trailer. Range is from 0-34 mph.

Drive Range 1: Should be used in heavy town traffic, medium hills, in slow moving traffic or when rapid acceleration is needed. Range is from 0-56 mph.

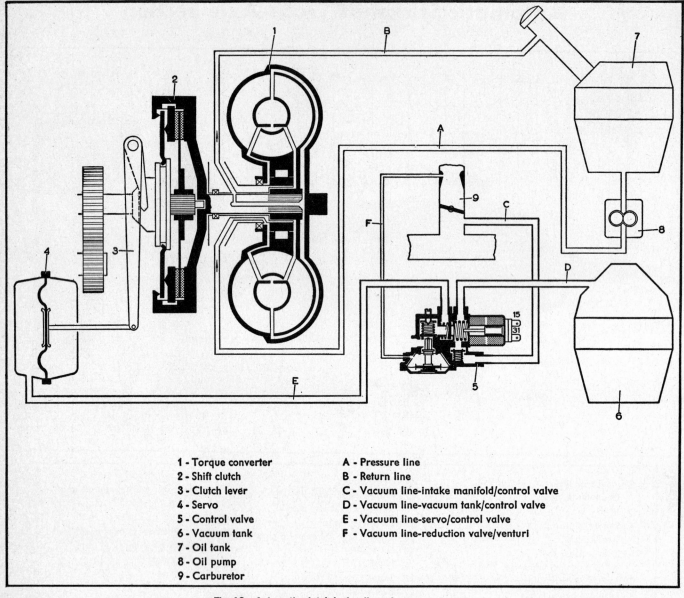

1 - Torque converter
2 - Shift clutch
3 - Clutch lever
4 - Servo
5 - Control valve
6 - Vacuum tank
7 - Oil tank
8 - Oil pump
9 - Carburetor

A - Pressure line
B - Return line
C - Vacuum line-intake manifold/control valve
D - Vacuum line-vacuum tank/control valve
E - Vacuum line-servo/control valve
F - Vacuum line-reduction valve/venturi

Fig. A2   Automatic clutch hydraulic and vacuum systems

Drive Range 2: This is the normal driving range for use on open road at cruising speed and for low to medium speeds in free flowing town traffic. In this range shifting gears is not necessary. Range is from 0 to maximum speed.

Reverse: To engage reverse the selector lever must be depressed while pushing forward.

NOTE: Temperature switches are incorporated which will cause a warning light in the speedometer to light when the converter fluid exceeds permissible temperature. Should this light go on it is an indication to shift the transmission to the next lowest speed range. Higher engine speeds and therefore reduced converter load and faster fluid circulation will lower the temperature and the light will go out.

CONSTANT VELOCITY JOINTS

Description

Vehicles using the Automatic Stickshift are also equipped with a new type rear axle known as a double joint axle.

Both the drive shafts of the new axle have two joints, one on the transmission case and one on the wheel. The joints are all of the constant velocity sliding type, Fig. A4. All movements which take place between joint flange on differential and wheel shafts are compensated for by the constant velocity joints. The grooves in which the balls move inside the joint are arranged in such a way that, together with the torque effective on the shaft, all var-

iations in length are taken up by the joints and the shaft remains in the correct location.

Removal

1. Remove socket head drive shaft bolts, Fig. A5, tilt shafts downwards and remove.
2. Loosen dust seal clips and slide back dust seal.
3. Remove snap ring from ball hub.
4. Drive cap off with a drift. *Do not tilt ball hub more than 20° or the balls may fall out.*
5. Slide outer part with balls on to the ball hub.
6. Support hub and press drive shaft out of ball hub. Remove dished washer.

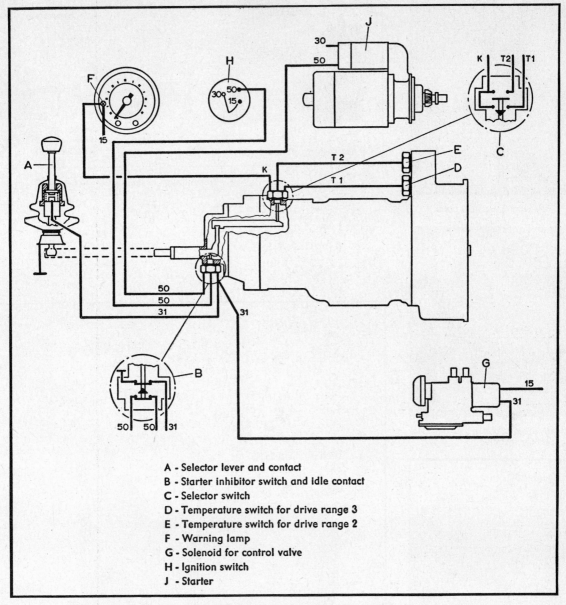

A - Selector lever and contact
B - Starter inhibitor switch and idle contact
C - Selector switch
D - Temperature switch for drive range 3
E - Temperature switch for drive range 2
F - Warning lamp
G - Solenoid for control valve
H - Ignition switch
J - Starter

Fig. A3   Automatic clutch electrical circuit

7. Reverse the removal procedure to install, being sure that the large diameter of the outer part of the joint points to the dust seal.

Rear Wheel Bearing

Removal

1. Loosen castle nut on rear wheel spline.

IMPORTANT: Accidents are liable to be caused if these nuts are loosened or tightened with the vehicle raised on a lift. It is therefore recommended that these nuts be loosened or tightened with the vehicle on the ground.

2. After loosening castle nut, raise vehicle and remove drive shafts and cover constant velocity joints with plastic covers.

3. Remove castle nut and pull brake drum off.

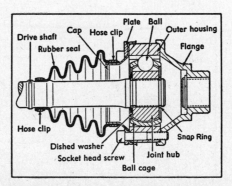

Fig. A4   Constant velocity joint

4. Detach brake line and hand brake cable.
5. Remove backing plate.
6. Mark position of spring plate and diagonal arm at top and bottom with a chisel.
7. Remove lower shock absorber bolt.
8. Remove bolts holding diagonal arm to spring plate and Allen-head bolt securing diagonal arm to bracket and take arm off.

Disassembly

1. Knock rear wheel shaft out with a rubber hammer.
2. Remove spacer ring and roller bearing inner ring.
3. Knock outer ring out with a drift and pry out inner oil seal.
4. Remove snap ring and pull bearing with VW 771.
5. Press rubber bushing out of arm.
6. Press oil seal out of cover.

VOLKSWAGEN

Fig. A5   Removing drive-shaft bolts

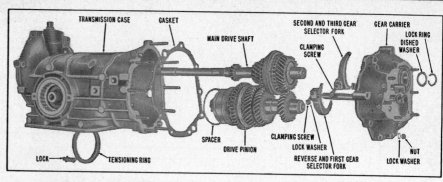

Fig. A7   Transmission assembly exploded

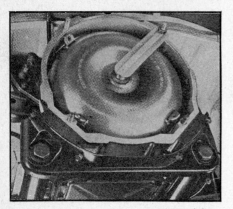

Fig. A6   Torque converter retainer installed

Fig. A8   Removing pinion bearing retaining nut with special wrench

Fig. A10   Removing joint flange caps

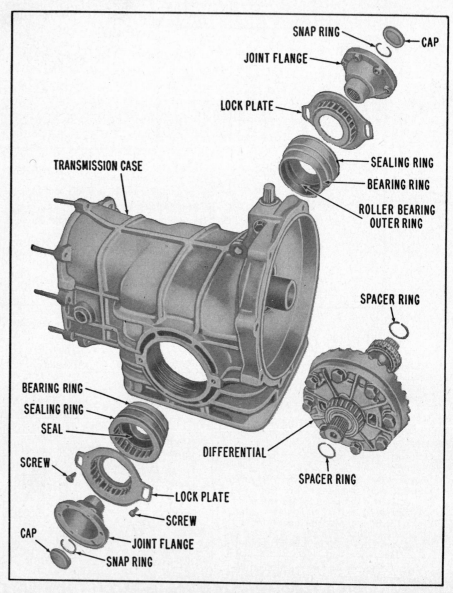

Fig. A9   Rear axle assembly exploded

Fig. A11   Removing joint flanges

Reassembly

Reverse disassembly procedure to assemble the unit.

TRANS-AXLE, REPLACE

1. Disconnect ground strap at battery.
2. Remove engine as outlined in the *Engine and Clutch Section*.
3. Disconnect gearshift rod coupling.
4. Remove drive shaft screws Fig. A5 and remove drive shafts completely.
5. Disconnect oil hoses, thermo switch connections and starter cables.
6. Disconnect clip for vacuum hoses at clutch servo and pull off hose.
7. Push back rubber cap and pull three-pin plug off neutral safety switch on gearshift housing. Remove nuts at front transmission mounting.
8. Attach retainer for torque converter, Fig. A6. (Fabricate strap).
9. Support transmission with a suitable jack, remove screws at rear transmission mounting and withdraw transmission from vehicle.
10. Reverse the removal procedure to install the assembly, noting the following.
    a. Be sure the slot in the plug and lug on the switch are aligned properly.
    b. Clean flanges of rear wheel shafts.

There must be no grease between the contact surfaces of the joints at the flanges.

TRANS-AXLE, OVERHAUL
Transmission Disassembly Sequence Fig. A7

The following sequence of operations is recommended by Volkswagen when disassembling the trans-axle. When reassembling, reverse the procedure and observe the remarks which follow this sequence. Before removing the differential, the transmission gears must be removed.

1. Remove gearshift housing and inner transmission lever.
2. Remove nuts at gear carrier.
3. Remove transmission cover and gasket.
4. Remove lock and back off pinion bearing retaining nut until it just contacts the ring gear, Fig. A8.
5. Press out transmission until retaining nut contacts the case again then alternately loosen the retaining nut and press out transmission until the nut has been completely screwed clear of the bearing. Press out bearing completely with transmission and remove. Note thickness of shim "S3" Fig. A19, for drive pinion adjustment. If no parts directly effecting the drive pinion adjustment are replaced during repairs, the old shims must be inserted again when assembling.
6. Clamp transmission at gear carrier in a vise or install it in selector fork adjustment device (VW492a) and remove selector fork for first and reverse gear.
7. Pull second and third selector shaft out of selector fork.
8. Remove snap ring and dished washer from main drive shaft. *Use caution as the dished washer is pretensioned.*
9. Press out main drive shaft.

Rear Axle Disassembly Sequence Fig. A9

1. Remove transmission and gears.
2. Pierce caps of joint flanges with a screwdriver and remove caps, Fig. A10.

Fig. A12   Removing carrier bearing rings

3. Remove snap ring and carefully pry out joint flanges, Fig. A11.
4. Remove lock plates and carrier bearing rings, Fig. A12.
5. Lift differential and ring gear out of case and remove spacer rings.

Differential Repairs

Disassembly Fig. A13

1. Remove ring gear bolts and press ring gear off housing.
2. Press cover from housing and take out side gear with thrust washer.
3. Press carrier bearing from differential cover and housing.
4. Drive out pin and shaft. Remove differential pinions and side gear.

Reassemble

Reverse the disassembly procedure to assemble the unit, noting the following.

1. When installing differential pinions, use a new roll pin and peen at both ends.
2. Be sure all surfaces between ring gear and cover are clean, and free of burrs and pressure marks.
3. Tighten ring gear bolts diagonally opposite.

IMPORTANT: If ring gear and pinion are

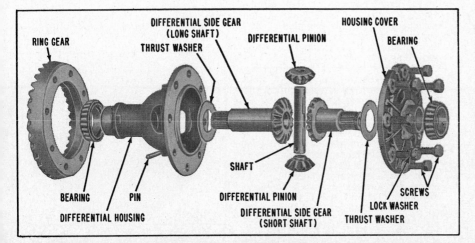

Fig. A13   Differential assembly exploded

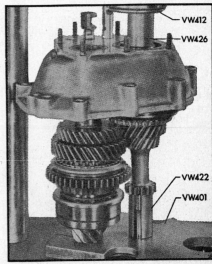

Fig. A14   Pressing main drive shaft and pinion into gear carrier

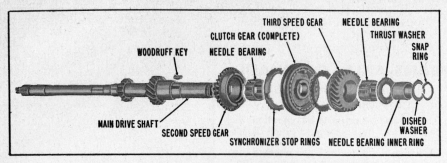

Fig. A15   Main drive shaft parts

Fig. A16 Checking synchronizer
rings for wear

to be replaced, a new selective spacer must be used to reset pinion depth.

Adjusting Drive Pinion & Ring Gear

The ring gear and drive pinion are a matched set and must be replaced as such. If the gear set is not to be replaced, the existing "S3" pinion depth shim Fig. A19 should be retained to preserve the original pinion setting. If, however, the gear set is replaced, the pinion depth must be reset by the use of a new "S3" shim. The size of the new shim can be calculated by comparing the pinion markings "r" plus shim sizes to duplicate the original pinion depth.

The ring gear must be reset whenever work is done on the differential assembly or its original position is disturbed.

The ring gear is adjusted for bearing pre-load and gear backlash through the use of threaded carrier bearing rings. These rings are screwed in or out to change the lateral position of the ring gear once the pinion depth has been established. Ring gear carrier bearing pre-load is established by first screwing the ring on the ring gear side of the housing in until the outer edge is .006" below the measuring surface of the case. The other ring is then installed on the opposite side and turned in until the force required to turn the ring gear reaches 16-20 in. lbs. for new bearings. This is measured by turning the ring gear side of the differential assembly with a torque wrench while tightening the opposite side ring.

The ring gear backlash is then adjusted by loosening one side ring while tightening the opposite side *an equal amount.* This

is critical, as any change in the relationship of the rings to each other will change the preload. Adjust the ring gear until a backlash of .006-.009" is obtained.

IMPORTANT: In view of the foregoing remarks, it can be seen that any major repairs on the rear axle, call for most accurate and precise adjustment. If the necessary tools and equipment designed for this work are not available to do the job, the work should be farmed out to a Volkswagen service station or other establishment having the facilities to do the work properly.

Transmission Installation Sequence

1. Engage selector fork for 2nd and 3rd gears in the operating sleeves.
2. Position pinion, main drive shaft and gear carrier under press Fig. A14 and press onto the main drive shaft. Guide main drive shaft and pinion carefully in order to avoid damage to the splines. Also, be sure that the selector fork for the 2nd and 3rd gear is correctly positioned.
3. Slide spring washer onto the main drive shaft, install new lock ring and press down until it snaps into the groove. Squeeze lock ring with pliers to be sure it bottoms correctly in the groove.
4. Install and adjust shift forks.

NOTE: The shift forks can only be set properly with the aid of setting fixture VW294a. During adjustment, the pinion and main drive shaft must be in the exact position as they will be when installed in the transmission case. To achieve this, the shims "S3" (or pinion depth) must be determined beforehand and placed in the setting fixture as well.

5. Install gear carrier, pinion with shim and drive shaft in setting fixture and secure with four nuts.
6. Screw retaining ring on to double taper roller bearing and hand tighten with "C" wrench VW 183.
7. Push shift rod into 2nd and 3rd gear fork and install clamp screw.
8. Install shift fork for 1st and reverse gears and insert clamp screw.
9. Place 1st and reverse shift rod into the detent groove for 1st and slide the operating sleeve and fork over the synchro teeth until it is against the 1st speed gear. Centralize the fork in the operating sleeve groove and tighten the clamp screw.

NOTE: The shift forks must not rub on the sides of the groove in the sleeve when in neutral or when a gear is engaged.

10. Select both gears and neutral several times while turning transmission and check clearance between fork and sleeve groove in each position. When uniform clearance has been established, at each side of the groove, tighten the clamp screw to 18 lb. ft.
11. Place 2nd and 3rd shift rod into the detent groove for 3rd gear. Adjust as for 1st and reverse and tighten clamp screw to 18 lb. ft.
12. Check interlock mechanism to be sure that when one gear is engaged it is not possible to engage any other gear.
13. Insert transmission and gasket into the transmission case and use a rubber hammer to drive in the pinion and main drive shaft.

NOTE: If the differential and ring gear are still installed in the case as the transmission is being installed the retaining nut of the tapered roller bearing must be inserted and screwed on while the transmission is being driven in.

14. Tighten tensioning nut to 87 lb. ft. with special wrench VW 183. Tighten gear carrier nuts diagonally. Insert retaining nut lock plate and tighten screws.
15. Insert gearshift housing with transmission shift lever and tighten nuts.
16. Install transmission cover with gasket and tighten screws diagonally.

Main Drive Shaft Repairs
Fig. A15

Disassemble

1. Remove thrust washer, 3rd gear,

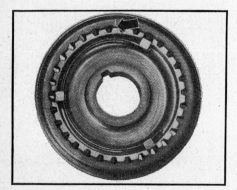

Fig. A17   Etched marks must be aligned
when assembling clutch gear

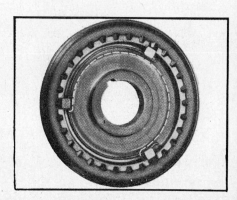

Fig. A18   Springs assembled
over clutch keys

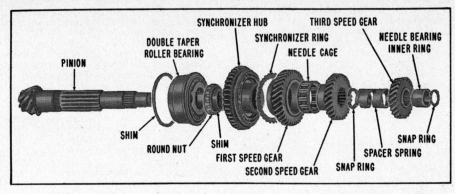

Fig. A19   Drive pinion parts

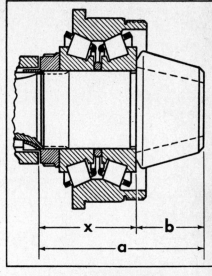

Fig. A20   Drive pinion dimensions

needle bearing and synchronizer stop ring.

2. Press off inner race of needle bearing, clutch gear with operating sleeve and 2nd gear.
3. Remove woodruff key and disassemble synchronizer hub.

Inspection

1. Check gears, particularly clutch toothing, operating sleeve, thrust gear, needle bearings, race rings and woodruff key for wear and damage. Replace if necessary.
2. Press synchronizer stop rings onto gears and measure clearance between gear and ring. Dimension A Fig. A16. If the clearance exceeds .067", the ring must be replaced.

Reassembly

Reverse disassembly procedure to reassemble the unit, noting the following.

1. Install 2nd speed gear, needle bearing and synchronizer stop ring.
2. Install woodruff key.
3. When assembling clutch gear for 2nd and 3rd gears, take care to align the etched marks. Fig. A17. Operating sleeve and clutch gear are matched and must be replaced in pairs only.

NOTE: There is a 1mm deep groove on the operating sleeve which must point towards 3rd gear.

4. Position spring rings on clutch gear assembly so they are angled 120° offset from each other Fig. A18. Be sure to fully engage the spring ends

over the clutch keys.
5. Press clutch gear assembly onto shaft.
6. Heat inner race of needle bearing for 3rd gear to about 200°F before pressing onto shaft.
7. Install needle bearing gear, synchronizer stop ring and thrust washer for 3rd gear.

Drive Pinion Repairs Fig. A19

Disassemble

1. Remove snap ring and press off 3rd speed gear and needle bearing inner ring.
2. Remove spacer spring and 2nd gear snap ring.
3. Remove 2nd speed gear, 1st speed gear with synchronizer ring, needle bearing, synchronizer hub with operating sleeve and shim.
4. Using special wrench VW 293, unscrew round nut.
5. Press off pinion bearing.
6. Remove operating sleeve, clutch keys and spring from synchronizer hub.

Inspection

1. Check pinion, tapered bearing, needle bearing and rings, gears, clutch keys and synchronizer hub for wear or damage.
2. Check synchronizer teeth on gear, synchronizer ring and operating sleeve.
3. Press synchro ring over cone on gear and measure dimension "A" Fig. A16. If clearance exceeds .067", the synchro ring must be replaced.
4. If necessary to replace either 2nd or 3rd speed gear, these must be re-

placed in pairs.

Reassemble

Reverse disassembly procedure to assemble the unit, noting the following.

1. Before being pressed onto the pinion, the inner rings of the double taper roller bearing should be heated to about 200° F.
2. Install new round nut and tighten to 145 lb. ft. in fixture VW 293.
3. Stake locking shoulder of round nut into pinion splines 120° apart using blunt chisel. Inspect the shoulder at this point to be sure it is not cracked or burred.
4. To find thickness of shim for round nut, use this formula A-B + shim = X. Fig. A20. Dimension X is measured from tapered roller bearing *inner* race to shim and includes shim thickness. Select fit shim to make dimension X=1.75" with a tolerance of .002".
5. Assemble pinion up to 2nd speed gear. Install a select fit snap ring to give a clearance of .001-.010" between gear and snap ring with the smaller dimension desired.

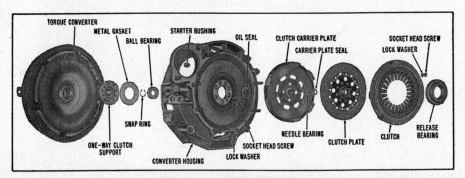

Fig. A21   Shift clutch exploded

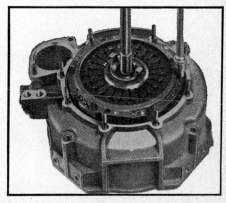

Fig. A22   Centering clutch plate with pilot shaft

6. Fit spacer spring and 3rd speed gear.
7. Heat needle bearing inner ring to 200° F and press it on with 3rd speed gear.
8. Fit snap ring.

Shift Clutch Fig. A21

Removal

1. Pull torque converter off one-way clutch support tube and remove. Seal off hub opening.
2. Remove clutch operating lever. Remove nuts between clutch housing and transmission case. Two are accessible from the differential housing

after the transmission cover has been removed.
3. Pull transmission off the studs of the clutch housing and remove it. Turn the clutch lever shaft so that the jaws disengage from the release bearing. Remove both lower engine mounting bolts.
4. Remove clutch disc and pressure plate.

Installation

1. Coat release bearing guide on transmission case neck and both lugs lightly with lithium grease and insert bearing into clutch.
2. Center clutch plate with a pilot

shaft and tighten clutch bolts evenly. Fig. A22. Use caution to be sure the release bearing is properly located in the diaphragm spring.
3. Insert lower bolts for engine mounting from the front. Check stud sealing rings and replace if necessary.
4. Push transmission onto the converter housing studs. Insert clutch lever shaft behind the lugs of the release bearing and push the release bearing onto the transmission case neck. Tighten nuts evenly.
5. Install clutch operating lever and adjust clutch.
6. Push torque converter onto the one way clutch support tube and insert into the turbine shaft by turning.

4-Speed Trans-Axle Section

DESCRIPTION

The transmission, rear axle and engine are a unit. The rear axle is the swing half-axle type. The rubber cushioned transmission case is secured to the frame at three points and incorporates the transmission, final drive and differential, Fig. 1.

The transmission case is of tubular construction with an integral clutch housing and engine mounting flange at one end and gear carrier and gearshift housing attached at the other end. Two final drive covers with ball-shaped surfaces are provided for mounting the rear axle tubes.

The transmission has four forward speeds and one reverse. Synchromesh is obtained with all forward speeds which are in constant mesh for quiet operation.

The shifting rod in the frame tunnel links the transmission to the gearshift lever. The synchronizers are located on the drive pinion for 1st and 2nd, and on the main drive shaft for 3rd and 4th speeds.

The transmission gears and differential are combined in the transmission case and are both lubricated with the same gear oil. The oil capacity is 5.3 pints.

REAR AXLE, REPLACE

NOTE: If the rear axle is to be disassembled upon its removal from the car, loosen the axle shaft nuts before raising the vehicle.

REMOVAL

1. Disconnect battery ground strap.
2. Raise and support vehicle on jack stands and remove engine as outlined in the *Engine & Clutch Section*.
3. Remove rear wheels.
4. Disconnect brake hoses at rear.

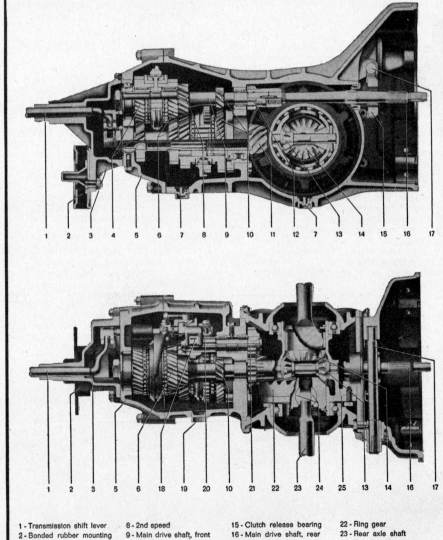

Fig. 1 Transmission and rear axle assembly. The transmission is housed in a one-piece case and is synchronized in all forward gears.

1 - Transmission shift lever	8 - 2nd speed	15 - Clutch release bearing	22 - Ring gear
2 - Bonded rubber mounting	9 - Main drive shaft, front	16 - Main drive shaft, rear	23 - Rear axle shaft
3 - Gearshift housing	10 - 1st speed	17 - Clutch operating shaft	24 - Fulcrum plate
4 - 4th speed	11 - Drive pinion	18 - Reverse sliding gear	25 - Differential housing
5 - Gear carrier	12 - Reverse gear	19 - Oil filler plug	
6 - 3rd speed	13 - Differential pinion	20 - Reverse shaft	
7 - Oil drain plugs	14 - Differential side gear	21 - Reverse drive gear	

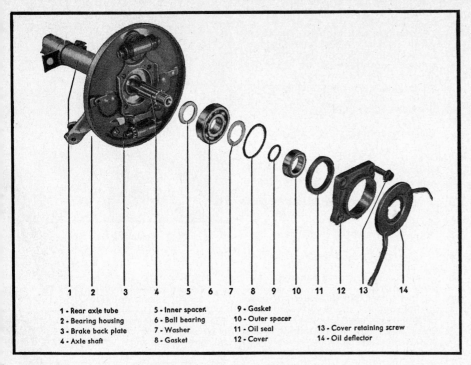

Fig. 2 Rear axle shaft details (typical)

1 - Rear axle tube
2 - Bearing housing
3 - Brake back plate
4 - Axle shaft
5 - Inner spacer
6 - Ball bearing
7 - Washer
8 - Gasket
9 - Gasket
10 - Outer spacer
11 - Oil seal
12 - Cover
13 - Cover retaining screw
14 - Oil deflector

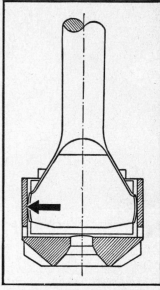

Fig. 4 Clearance between flat end of axle shaft and side gear should be .0012-.004"

5. Disconnect brake cables at emergency brake, remove hand brake and pull cables from conduits.
6. Loosen dust sleeves.
7. Remove shock absorber lower mounting bolts.
8. With a chisel, mark the position of the spring plate in relation to the axle shaft bearing housing in line with the groove in the bearing housing.
9. Remove rear axle shaft bearing housing bolts.
10. Disconnect clutch cable from clutch operating shaft lever. Slide off rubber boot and remove cable and sleeve from bracket on left-hand final drive cover.
11. Unhook accelerator cable from gear carrier.
12. Disconnect cables from starter.
13. Remove inspection cover under rear

seat and remove screw at rear of shifting rod coupling. Move shift lever to withdraw coupling from transmission shift rod.
14. Remove nuts from cushions at front of transmission case.
15. Push a roller jack under vehicle and clamp a suitable cradle (VW-609) to rear axle.
16. Remove two bolts at transmission carrier. Then roll rear axle from under car.

INSTALLATION: Reverse the removal procedure to install the assembly, noting the following:

1. Grease the two transmission carrier mounting bolts and tighten them.
2. Tighten mounting plate nuts at front of transmission case.

IMPORTANT: When installing a new rear axle the nuts that attach transmission carrier to rear rubber cushions should be loosened and tightened after nuts of front rubber cushion have been tightened. This procedure applies also when the transmission carrier has been removed. This tightening sequence is recommended to avoid distortion and premature wear of rubber cushions.

3. When lowering the rear axle, do not allow main drive shaft to strike floor.
4. Be certain that points on the coupling screws are seated in their recesses. Secure each screw with wire.
5. Hook accelerator cable to retainer on gear carrier.
6. Adjust rear wheels and tighten spring plate mounting bolts to 72-87 ft.-lbs.
7. Tighten shock absorber lower mounting bolts.
8. Examine splines in hub of brake drum; if worn or damaged, replace drum.

9. Adjust clutch pedal free play after engine is installed.
10. Torque rear axle nuts to 217 ft.-lbs.
11. Bleed and adjust brake system.

REAR AXLE, OVERHAUL
Disassembly Sequence

The following sequence of operations is recommended by Volkswagen when disassembling the rear axle. When reassembling, however, reverse the procedure and observe the remarks which follow this sequence.

1. Mount rear axle in a suitable fixture (VW-307).
2. Remove drain plugs and drain unit.
3. Remove starting motor.
4. Remove axle shaft nuts and brake drums.
5. Remove brakes and back plates.
6. Remove rear axle tubes and shafts.
7. Remove gearshift housing.
8. Remove differential.

Fig. 3 Location of differential side gear lock ring

Fig. 5 Clearance between fulcrum plates and side gears should be .0014-.0096"

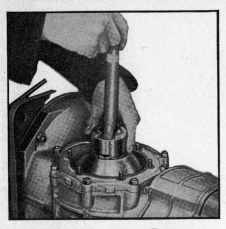

Fig. 6 Installing differential side gear, axle shaft and thrust washer

9. Remove rear main drive shaft.
10. Remove transmission.
11. Remove reverse drive gear and shaft.
12. Remove main drive shaft and drive pinion from gear carrier.
13. Remove selector shafts and detent balls and springs.

Rear Wheel Bearing & Oil Seal

REMOVAL

1. Remove axle shaft nut and brake drum, Fig. 2.
2. Remove screws and take off cover and oil seal.
3. Remove brake backing plate.
4. Remove outer spacer, gasket, washer and cover gasket.
5. Use a suitable puller to remove bearing, and take off inner spacer (VW-241 and VW-202k).

INSTALLATION

1. Use new gaskets.
2. If any signs of unevenness are visible on the lip, the oil seal should be replaced. Press the old seal out of the cover. Lightly coat the new seal with oil and press it into the cover.
3. Check and replace the outer spacer if it is scored, cracked or rusted.
4. To avoid damage to the oil seal lip by friction, the spacer should be lightly coated with oil.

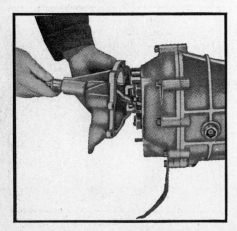

Fig. 8 Installing gearshift housing

5. Install cover so that oil drip nose points downward.
6. Make certain that oil drip tube bears tightly against brake drum to prevent oil from fouling brake shoes.
7. Tighten axle shaft nut to 217 ft-lbs and secure with cotter pin.
8. Check and replenish transmission oil level.
9. Bleed and adjust brakes.

Rear Axle Tubes & Shafts

REMOVAL

1. Remove brake drum, bearing cover, brake backing plate and wheel bearing.
2. Remove nuts and withdraw axle tube and retainer. Take off gasket and plastic packing.
3. Remove differential side gear lock ring, Fig. 3.
4. Remove side gear thrust washer and axle shaft.
5. Remove side gear and fulcrum plates from housing.
6. Drive out lock pin in axle shaft bearing housing.
7. Loosen dust sleeve.
8. Press axle tube from bearing housing. If bearing housing is damaged during pressing operation, replace it with a new one.
9. Remove dust sleeve from axle tube and take off axle tube retainer.

INSTALLATION: Reverse the procedure to assemble, observing the following:

1. Before pressing bearing housing into place, clean and oil all seating surfaces.
2. Clearance between flat end of axle shaft and inner diameter of differential side gear should be .0012-.004", measured across the ball-shaped sides, Fig. 4. If clearance is excessive, replace with a new axle shaft and side gear set. Excessive clearance can lead to rear axle noise.
3. Check axle shaft run-out at ball bearing seat. If found to be in excess of .002", straighten axle shaft cold in a press or install a new one.
4. Check clearance between axle shaft fulcrum plates and differential side gears, Fig. 5. If excessive clearance is present, install oversize fulcrum plates or replace worn parts.
5. Install differential side gear, axle shaft and thrust washer in differential housing and install lock ring, Fig. 6.
6. Axle tube should be installed without end play by selecting a tube retainer gasket of appropriate thickness. Tighten retainer nuts to 14 ft-lbs.
7. Dust sleeve clips should not be tightened until after axle shaft is installed to prevent sleeves from being twisted and subsequently damaged.

Rear Axle Dust Sleeve

NOTE: To avoid removal or disassembly of rear axle when renewing a damaged sleeve, a split type dust seal is available, Fig. 7.

1. To remove damaged sleeve, take off both clips and cut off damaged sleeve. Clean axle tube and retainer.
2. To install, lightly coat joining faces

Fig. 7 Installing split type rear axle dust sleeve

of split type sleeve with sealing compound. The joining faces should point to rear as shown in Fig. 7.

NOTE: Dust sleeve screws and retaining clips should not be over-tightened. Tighten screws and clips with rear axle under load (car wheels on floor).

TRANSMISSION CASE

Transmission Carrier

1. Remove attaching screws and take off carrier.
2. Remove nuts attaching rubber cushions to transmission case and take off cushions.
3. To install, tighten carrier attaching screws *but only after the transmission is installed and front rubber cushion screws are tightened.*

Gearshift Housing

1. Remove gearshift housing rubber cushion. Unfasten and remove gearshift housing and transmission shift lever. Remove gasket and clean joining faces.
2. If shift lever bushings require replacement, ream new bushings (when installed) to .5918-.5925".

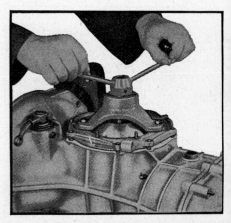

Fig. 9 Removing final drive cover with puller (VW297)

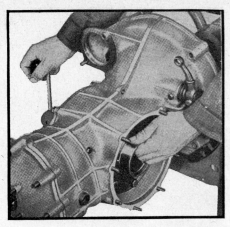

Fig. 10 Pressing out differential

3. Make sure selector shafts are in neutral position when attaching gearshift housing, Fig. 8. Tighten nuts to 14 ft-lbs.
4. Check rubber cushion for damage. If cushion is replaced, rear wheels have to be re-adjusted.

Differential & Transmission

REMOVAL
1. Remove gearshift housing.
2. Pry off lock plates for drive pinion and main drive shaft nuts.
3. Lock transmission by engaging reverse and 3rd gear.
4. Remove drive pinion and main drive gear nuts and take off lock plates. Discard lock plates.
5. Remove gear carrier stud nuts and take off ground strap and accelerator cable retainer.
6. Remove nuts from studs on left-hand final drive cover.
7. Remove final drive cover, Fig. 9. The thrust plate of the tool is positioned on differential housing flange and spindle is attached to axle tube retainer studs.
8. Position spindle and thrust plate of tool shown in Fig. 9 on right-hand final drive cover and press out differential, Fig. 10.

IMPORTANT: When removing differential, make note of thicknesses and arrangement of shims present to facilitate re-assembly.

9. Loosen retaining ring for reverse gear on mainshaft, slide reverse gear rearward and screw main drive shaft apart.
10. Remove reverse gear and retaining ring and withdraw mainshaft toward the rear, taking care not to damage oil seal.
11. Remove right-hand final drive cover.
12. Remove drive pinion bearing retainer.
13. Push transmission out of case, Fig. 11. *In order to facilitate reassembly note quantity and thickness of pinion shims present.*
14. Remove snap ring and reverse drive gear, Fig. 12.
15. Remove woodruff key and pull reverse gear shaft and thrust washer from case.
16. Remove screw securing spacer sleeve for reverse gear shaft needle bearings. Then drive out needle bearings, Fig. 13.
17. Remove screw securing needle bearing on main shaft. Then drive out needle bearing.
18. Press bearing from left and right final drive covers.
19. Remove clutch release bearing and operating shaft.

INSTALLATION: Clean and inspect all parts, replacing any that are damaged. When installing, observe the following remarks:
1. Check clutch operating shaft for free movement, if necessary, apply grease to shaft.
2. Install reverse gear shaft needle bearings and spacer sleeve.
3. Install main shaft needle bearing.
4. Install reverse shaft with thrust washer and drive gear over woodruff key and secure with snap ring.
5. Place drive pinion shims over bearing and screw two 4" studs into bearing retainer to prevent retaining ring from turning when transmission is installed, Fig. 14.
6. Push reverse selector fork and sliding gear onto reverse lever and engage reverse gear.
7. Install transmission into case. If necessary, use a rubber mallet to position pinion correctly in bearing seat. Use a new gear carrier gasket. Tighten bearing retainer screws to 36 ft-lbs, and use new lock plates.
8. Lubricate lip of oil seal before installing rear half of main shaft. Screw both halves of main shaft together. Back them off until reverse gear splines are in line. Make sure that reverse gear snap ring tension is correct.
9. Press bearings into left and right final drive covers.
10. Using a new gasket, install right-hand final drive cover. Tighten nuts to 14 ft-lbs.
11. Install differential in transmission case, being sure that shims are inserted correctly, Fig. 15.
12. Tighten rear carrier stud nuts to 14 ft-lbs.
13. Engage reverse and 3rd speed gear to prevent transmission from turning. Then tighten main shaft nut to 87 ft-lbs. Back nut off and re-tighten

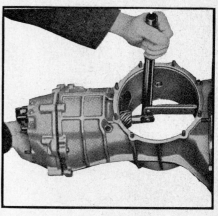

Fig. 11 Pushing transmission out of case with Tool VW296

to 36 ft-lbs and secure with new lock plates.
14. Tighten drive pinion nut to 22 ft-lbs and secure with new lock plate.
15. When attaching gearshift housing, be sure that the three selector shafts are in neutral position.

Gear Carrier

DISASSEMBLE
1. Remove reverse selector fork with sliding gear from reverse lever.
2. Remove shims from drive pinion bearing, noting the thickness of shims present to facilitate reassembly.
3. Mount gear carrier in vise, Fig. 16, and loosen shift fork lock screws. Remove 1-2 selector fork.
4. Pull out 3-4 selector shaft from its fork.
5. Place a rubber band around 1-2 gear operating sleeve and mainshaft.
6. Mount assembly in a press as shown, Fig. 16. Apply force to mainshaft to remove transmission gears from gear carrier. Drive pinion should be guided carefully to avoid tilting which would lead to damage to gears and needle bearings.
7. Remove screw that secures drive pinion needle bearing and press out bearing.

Fig. 12 Removing snap ring and reverse drive gear

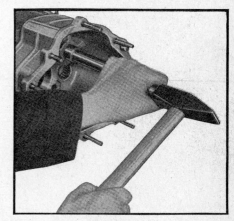

Fig. 13 Driving out reverse gear shaft needle bearings

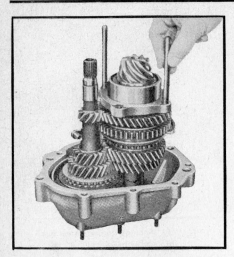

Fig. 14 Showing use of guide studs to prevent retaining ring from turning when installing transmission

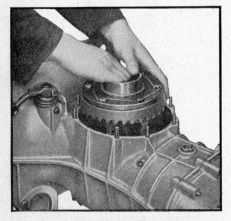

Fig. 15 Installing differential into transmission case. Make sure shims are installed correctly

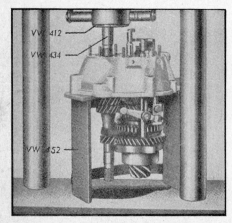

Fig. 16 Pressing transmission gear assembly from gear carrier

8. Press ball bearing from mainshaft.
9. Place gear carrier in vise and remove reverse lever guide screw, Fig. 17.
10. Pull out reverse gear selector shaft and remove reverse lever guide.
11. Pull out 1-2 selector shaft and remove reverse lever from support.
12. Remove 3-4 selector shaft.
13. Remove plungers and detent balls. Then remove springs with screwdriver, Fig. 18.

NOTE: If it becomes necessary to remove the reverse lever support, the dimensions indicated in Fig. 19 should be present. Check the reverse lever for proper position when adjusting selector forks. The lock nut should be tightened to 25 ft-lbs.

REASSEMBLE: Clean all parts and replace those that are damaged. Check the detent springs. Free length of springs are 1", wear limit 0.9". If difficult shifting is experienced, check the force of the springs with the drive pinion and mainshaft removed. The force applied to overcome detent ball grooves in the selector shafts should be 33 to 44 lbs.

1. Insert detent springs through holes in selector shafts. Inasmuch as the top halves of detent spring bores are not bushed, the 1st, 2nd and reverse springs can more easily be installed into the top halves first.
2. Install reverse selector shaft with reverse lever and its guide.
3. Install 1-2 and 3-4 speed selector shafts along with two interlock plungers. Engage a gear to check for correct interlocking. The selector shaft next to the one used must be locked. When engaging 1st and 2nd gears the other two selector shafts should be locked.
4. Install drive pinion needle bearing.
5. Place carrier in a press and press mainshaft ball bearing into position.
6. Check selector forks for wear. If clearance between forks and operating sleeves are beyond the limits of .004-.012", replace worn parts.
7. Position 3rd and 4th gear selector fork before pressing transmission into gear carrier. When pressing, the drive pinion should be lifted slightly and care should be exercised to see that the installed selector fork is not jammed on the selector shaft. Fully insert the shaft into the fork beforehand.

NOTE: When pressing transmission into position, wrap a strong rubber band around the assembly as shown in Fig. 20 to hold the drive pinion and mainshaft together.

8. Install 1-2 selector fork.
9. Attach reverse selector fork with reverse sliding gear on reverse lever.
10. Adjust selector forks.

Selector Forks, Adjust

NOTE: Proper adjustment of the forks can only be accomplished with the special Gear Shift Test Tool VW-294. Since the adjustment of the 1-2 and reverse forks alters in accordance with the adjustment of the drive pinion, the drive pinion adjustment must be made beforehand. Aside from that the drive pinion and

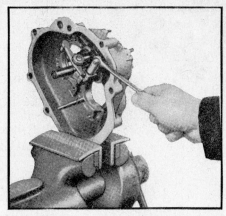

Fig. 17 Removing reverse lever guide screw

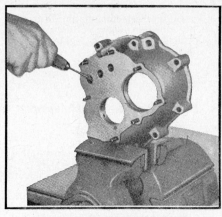

Fig. 18 Removing detent springs with screwdriver

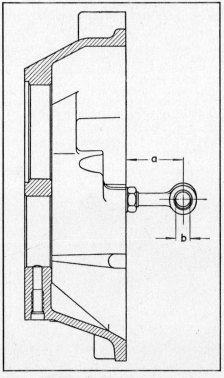

Fig. 19 Correct reverse lever support position. Dimension "A" is 1.520", "B" is 0.40"

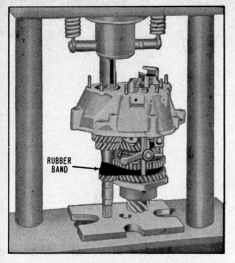

Fig. 20 Pressing transmission gear assembly into gear carrier. Note heavy rubber band around gear assembly to hold drive pinion and mainshaft together

RUBBER BAND

Fig. 21 Gear carrier mounted in Tool VW294

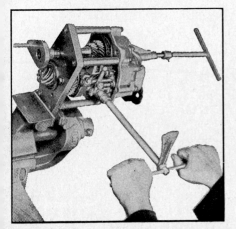

Fig. 22 Gearshift housing mounted in Tool VW 294

mainshaft nuts must be tightened beforehand to the specified torque. The equipment needed is shown in use in Figs. 21 and 22.

1. Place transmission with drive pinion shims and gear carrier gasket on Tool VW-294 and attach gear carrier with four screws, Fig. 21.
2. Tighten drive pinion ball bearing retainer with two screws installed diagonally to 36 ft-lbs.
3. Push crank of tool onto splines of mainshaft so that mainshaft is locked by crank handle. Engage 1st and 2nd gears.
4. Tighten mainshaft nut to 87 ft-lbs. Then loosen nut and re-tighten to 36 ft-lbs.
5. Tighten drive pinion nut to 22 ft-lbs.
6. Attach gearshift housing and shift handle, Fig. 22. By attaching gearshift handle, a proper seating of the mainshaft ball bearing in gear carrier is assured.
7. Set 1-2 and 3-4 selector forks so they are moving freely in operating sleeve, not only in neutral position but also when different gears are engaged.
8. Set reverse gear selector fork so that reverse sliding gear is centered between operating sleeve and mainshaft 2nd gear with 2nd gear engaged, and properly engaged in reverse gear on drive pinion with reverse gear engaged.
9. Selector fork lock screws should be tightened to 18 ft-lbs, using a T-handle torque wrench as shown in Fig. 22. Tighten reverse lever guide screw to 14 ft-lbs.

Mainshaft Oil Seal, Replace

1. Remove engine, clutch release bearing and damaged oil seal, Fig. 23.
2. When installing, lightly coat exterior of new seal with sealing compound. Oil mainshaft and oil seal lip.
3. Slide seal on mainshaft and drive it in position with a suitable driving sleeve (VW-244b). Use care to see that spring around seal lip is securely in place, Fig. 24.

Fig. 23 Removing mainshaft oil seal

Fig. 24 Installing mainshaft oil seal

DRIVE PINION REPAIRS

DISASSEMBLE

1. Press needle bearing inner race and 4th gear off shaft.
2. Remove 4th gear woodruff key and

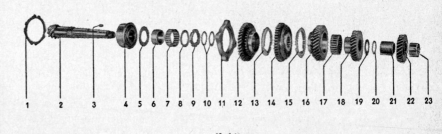

1 - Shim
2 - Drive Pinion
3 - Woodruff key for 4th gear
4 - Ball bearing
5 - Thrust washer for 1st gear
6 - Needle bearing inner race (1st gear)
7 - Needle cage (1st gear)
8 - Thrust washer for needle bearing (1st gear)
9 - Round nut
10 - Shims, end play 1st gear
11 - Ball bearing retainer

12 - 1st gear
13 - Synchronizer stop ring (1st gear)
14 - Clutch gear for 1st and 2nd gears, and reverse gear
15 - Synchronizer stop ring (2nd gear)
16 - 2nd gear
17 - Needle cage (2nd gear)
18 - 3rd gear
19 - Concave washer
20 - Shims for concave washer.
21 - Spacer sleeve
22 - 4th gear
23 - Inner race, needle bearing in gear carrier

Fig. 25 Drive pinion disassembled

Fig. 26 When installed, bearing numbers on both races should be exactly opposite to one another to avoid noisy bearing operation

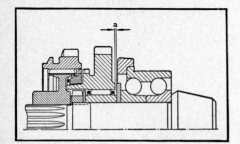

Fig. 27 First gear end play at "A" should be .004-.010"

Fig. 28 Dial gauge and associated tools (VW299) used to check concave washer adjustment

strip pinion of loose parts, Fig. 25.
3. Then press off inner race of needle bearing, 1st gear thrust washer and ball bearing.

INSPECTION

1. Inspect all parts for wear or damage. If drive pinion is to be replaced, a matching ring gear and pinion should be used. Note the matching number on pinion and ring gear.
2. If drive pinion or ball bearing are to be replaced, the pinion and ring gear

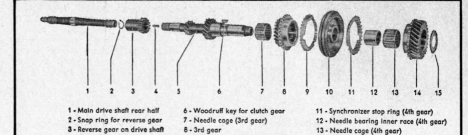

Fig. 29 Main drive shaft disassembled

1 - Main drive shaft rear half
2 - Snap ring for reverse gear
3 - Reverse gear on drive shaft
4 - Stud
5 - Main drive shaft front half
6 - Woodruff key for clutch gear
7 - Needle cage (3rd gear)
8 - 3rd gear
9 - Synchronizer stop ring (3rd gear)
10 - Clutch gear (3rd and 4th speeds)
11 - Synchronizer stop ring (4th gear)
12 - Needle bearing inner race (4th gear)
13 - Needle cage (4th gear)
14 - 4th gear
15 - Thrust washer (4th gear)

must be re-adjusted.
3. Whenever a damaged gear must be replaced, the mating gear must also be replaced. Worn or damaged 1st and 2nd gears require the replacement of the front mainshaft.
4. If a gear will not engage even though clutch is fully released, it may be due to the teeth of the synchronizer stop ring being too much out of line with the splines of the operating sleeve. This condition is caused by worn stop ring slots.
5. Check the clearance between synchronizer stop ring face and clutch teeth of the corresponding gear (normal .043"). If the wear limit of 0.24" is reached the stop ring should be replaced. Premature wear of stop rings is due to clutch in bad condition.

REASSEMBLE: Reverse disassembly procedure to assemble the unit, noting the following remarks:

1. Before pressing onto pinion, inner races of ball bearing and needle bearing inner race of 1st gear should be heated in an oil bath to 194°.
2. Slide one inner bearing race onto pinion. Slide on ball bearing, then second inner race so that bearing numbers on both races are exactly opposite one another, Fig. 26.
3. Slide 1st gear thrust washer and needle bearing inner race onto pinion.
4. Mount assembly in a press and press all parts in position. Tighten round nut to 87 ft-lbs.
5. After 1st and 2nd gears have been installed, measure clearance between thrust washer and 1st gear ("a"), Fig. 27. Shims are available in several thicknesses for selective fitting.
6. Referring to Fig. 25, assemble remaining parts on pinion. When installing the concave washer it should be adjusted with Tool VW-299 (see below).
7. The 4th gear and needle bearing inner race should be heated in an oil bath to 194° before being pressed into position. Then insert woodruff key and slide 4th gear on pinion with its wide shoulder facing spacer sleeve. Finally press 4th gear and needle bearing inner race into position.

Concave Washer, Adjust

The drive pinion concave washer must be adjusted to provide a spring travel of .007" (plus or minus .0004"). This washer exerts a pressure of about 200 lbs on the 3rd gear and the 1-2 clutch gear and also

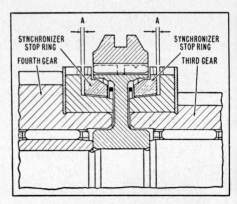

Fig. 30 Check clearance between synchro stop ring face and clutch teeth of corresponding gear at "A"

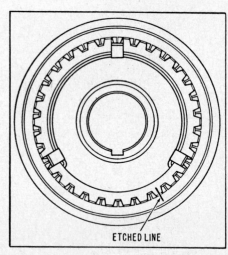

Fig. 31 Assemble 3-4 speed synchronizer with etched line lined up

reduces oscillations of these parts which are fitted to the drive pinion with a minimum backlash of .002". The quiet running of the rear axle will be affected if the clutch gear and 3rd gear are tightly seated and no backlash is present as a result of the concave washer being too tightly adjusted. If the maximum spring travel is exceeded the 2nd gear will tend to jump out. It is important, therefore, that the equipment shown in Fig. 28 be used to correctly determine the shimming required to adjust the concave washer.

MAINSHAFT REPAIRS

DISASSEMBLE, Fig. 29

1. Remove thrust washer, 4th gear, needle cage and stop ring.
2. Remove 4th gear needle bearing inner race, 3-4 clutch gear and 3rd gear by pressing shaft through these parts.
3. Remove needle cage for 3rd gear.
4. Disassemble 3-4 synchronizer.

INSPECTION

1. Check all parts for wear or damage.
2. Suspend front mainshaft between two points and check runout at the contact surface of 3rd gear needle bearing. Runout should not exceed .0006".

IMPORTANT: If front mainshaft has excessive wear or runout it should be replaced. Since the gears may only be replaced in pairs, the gear for 1st and 2nd speeds on drive pinion must also be replaced.

3. Check clearance between stop ring face and clutch teeth of corresponding gear with a feeler gauge. Normal clearance is .043". If wear limit of .024" is reached, replace stop rings.
4. If a gear will not engage, even though clutch fully releases, teeth of stop ring may be too much out of line with splines of operating sleeve. This may be caused by slots in stop ring being worn, Fig. 30.

REASSEMBLE

1. Reverse disassembly procedure to assemble the unit, observing the following:
2. Assemble 3-4 synchronizer unit, being sure etched line on clutch gear and sleeve line up as shown in Fig. 31. To reduce backlash between these parts to a minimum, they are paired and etched for identification. Install shifting plates and position the two snap rings offset to one another, making sure that ends of each ring engage behind the shifting plates.
3. Insert woodruff key for clutch in mainshaft and install 3rd gear synchro stop ring on gear cone.
4. Press 3-4 clutch gear on shaft. The identifying No. 4 on clutch gear must point toward 4th gear. The 3rd gear is lifted slightly and turned until stop ring engages in shifting plates.
5. Press 4th gear needle bearing inner race into position.

DIFFERENTIAL REPAIRS

DISASSEMBLE, Fig. 32

1. Remove lock wire and ring gear screws.
2. Lift off ring gear.
3. Drive out differential pinion shaft

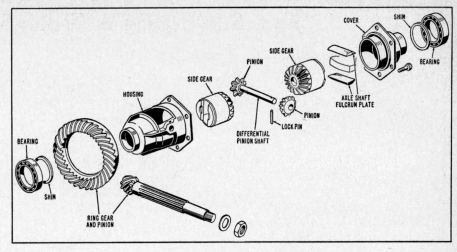

Fig. 32   Rear axle differential

with a drift after having removed the pin and remove pinions.

REASSEMBLE

1. Check concave differential pinion contact surfaces in housing for wear and damage. If necessary, replace differential housing.
2. Peen lock pin for differential shaft when unit is assembled.
3. Check ring gear for wear or damage. If necessary, replace with matched set of ring gear and drive pinion.

IMPORTANT: If differential housing or ring gear and pinion is to be replaced, the transmission must be re-adjusted.

4. Keep contact surfaces of differential housing and ring gear absolutely clean to insure a uniform backlash.
5. Tighten ring gear attaching screws to a torque of 43 ft-lbs.
6. Insert wire so that it imposes a clockwise tension on the screws when twisting its ends.

Adjusting Drive Pinion & Ring Gear

Quiet operation and minimum wear of the final drive depend on the proper adjustment of the ring gear and drive pinion. For this reason, the drive pinion and ring gears are machined in pairs during production, and inspections carried out with special test appliances to ensure correct tooth contact and silent meshing in both turning directions.

Quiet operation is obtained by adjusting the pinion endwise with the ring gear lifted sufficiently out of the fully engaged position (without backlash) to ensure that the backlash is within the prescribed tolerance of .0067" to .0098". The tolerance discrepancy from the standard fitting dimension of the drive pinion is measured and marked on the pinion face. Each gear set is given a matching number and replacement must be made in pairs.

It is usually only necessary to re-adjust the ring gear and drive pinion when doing repairs to the rear axle if parts have had to be replaced which directly affect the adjustment. It is sufficient to re-adjust the ring gear if the differential housing, a final drive cover or a differential bearing have been replaced. However, the ring gear and drive pinion must be re-adjusted if the transmission case, the gear set itself or the drive pinion ball bearing have been replaced.

In making the adjustment, the drive pinion must first be adjusted by installing shims between the ball bearing and the contact surface of the transmission case to ensure that the distance from the ring gear center line to the drive pinion face coincides with the fitting dimension determined at the factory. Then the ring gear is adjusted to give the prescribed backlash and the thickness of the shims for the differential housing determined. It is important, however, to note that both final drive covers must be installed with a pre-load of .0055". After determining the thickness of the shims, a preload of .0028" must be taken into consideration on both sides.

IMPORTANT: In consideration of the foregoing remarks, any major repairs on the rear axle calls for most accurate and precise adjustment of the assembly. Therefore, if the necessary tools and equipment especially designed for this work are not available to do a first rate job, the work should be farmed out to a Volkswagen service station or other establishment who has the facilities to do the work properly.

Rear Suspension & Brake Section

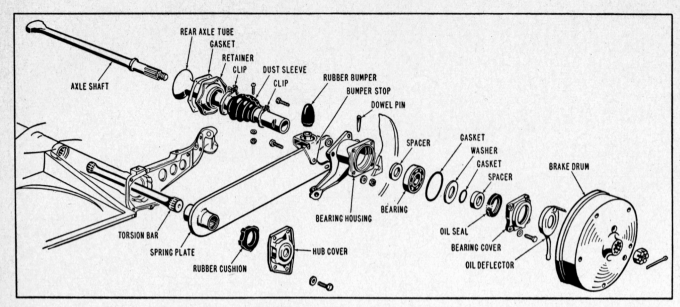

Fig. 1   Rear suspension disassembled (Exc. Double Jointed Rear Axle & Type 4)

REAR SUSPENSION
Exc. Double Jointed Rear Axle & Type 4

The rear wheels are independently sprung. The inner ends of the two torsion bars are anchored in the frame cross member by a splined tube which is welded in position. The outer ends of the torsion bars, which are also provided with splines, carry the spring plates (radius arms) the hubs of which are rubber cushioned.

The rear axle tubes are attached to the rear ends of the spring plates, Fig. 1.

The suspension is adjustable by means of splines. Screwed to the spring plate and axle shaft bearing housing is a rubber bumper which becomes active in the upper deflection range. Double-acting telescopic shock absorbers prevent excessive rebound.

Torsion Bar, Replace

1. Raise car front and rear and support in a horizontal position.
2. Remove rear wheel.
3. Disconnect cables at hand brake lever and pull them slightly towards the rear. Remove hand brake lever.
4. With a chisel, mark position of spring plate in relation to rear axle bearing housing. Mark on spring plate must be dead in line with groove in bearing housing.
5. Remove shock absorber lower mounting bolts.
6. Except Automatic Stickshift models, remove bolts at axle shaft bearing housing. Pull rear axle towards rear until it clears spring plate. On models equipped with the Automatic Stickshift, remove constant velocity joint bolts and remove axle.
7. Remove spring plate hub cover.
8. Remove spring plate and both rubber cushions.

9. Remove five of the foremost fender screws. Pull fender aside and remove torsion bar from frame cross tube.

NOTE: If the torsion bar is broken, push the broken end from the splined center anchor with a steel rod after having removed opposite torsion bar.

INSTALLATION

1. Inspect splined ends of torsion bar and paint for damage. If damaged or if there are signs of rust, install a new bar.
2. Grease torsion bar splines. Install bar and spring plate.

IMPORTANT: Torsion bars are pre-stressed. Left and right bars are not interchangeable and are identified by an arrow on the ouside face showing the direction of torque.

3. Apply graphite on rubber cushions when installing them.
4. Lift spring plate with the aid of Spring Plate Tensioner VW655 until its lower edge is higher than the lower stop

Fig. 1A   1968-71 double jointed axle

in cross tube flange. Then press spring plate in position with Spring Plate Installing Tool VW-656.
5. Install and tighten spring plate hub cover.

NOTE: To facilitate installation of hub cover and to avoid damage to threads, screw two tapered guide pins (about 1.8" long) in two diagonally opposite tapped holes. The cover is then pushed over the guide pins, allowing two of the cover bolts to be installed. Then remove the guide pins and install remaining screws.

6. Clean mating surfaces between spring plate and axle bearing housing.

NOTE: When bolting spring plate and axle bearing housing together, make sure that the mark made on spring plate previously is dead in line with the groove in the axle bearing housing. Tighten bearing housing bolts to 72-87 ft-lbs.

7. Install hand brake lever and adjust hand brake.

Spring Plate, Adjust

It is very important that there be no difference in the inclinations of both spring plates if perfect riding qualities under all conditions of load are to be insured. When adjusting one spring plate the inclination of the other should be checked and adjusted if necessary.

An exact adjustment of the rear suspension is effected by measuring the inclination of the spring plate with the frame in the horizontal position and with spring plate unloaded. The inclination of the unloaded spring plate should be as shown in table below. The adjustment is made as follows:

1. Check horizontal position of vehicle

Fig. 2 Lifting spring plate with Torsion Bar Tensioner VW655

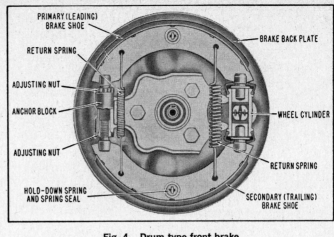

Fig. 4 Drum type front brake

Fig. 3 Protractor VW245a mounted on spring plate

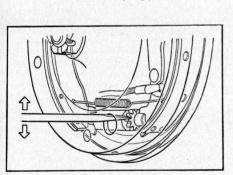

Fig. 6 Adjust wheel brake

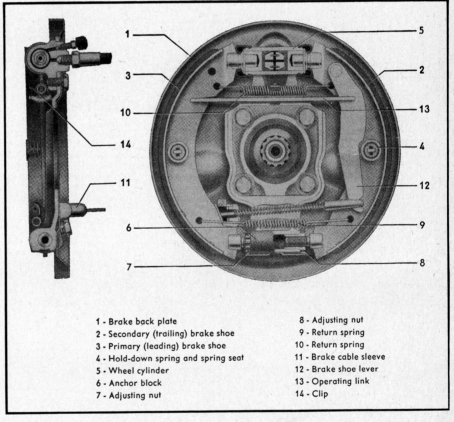

1 - Brake back plate
2 - Secondary (trailing) brake shoe
3 - Primary (leading) brake shoe
4 - Hold-down spring and spring seat
5 - Wheel cylinder
6 - Anchor block
7 - Adjusting nut
8 - Adjusting nut
9 - Return spring
10 - Return spring
11 - Brake cable sleeve
12 - Brake shoe lever
13 - Operating link
14 - Clip

Fig. 5 Rear wheel brake

by placing a protractor (VW245a) on door opening.

2. Insert inner end of torsion bar in center anchor.

3. Press spring plate on outer end of torsion bar, Fig. 2.

4. Place protractor on the unloaded spring plate, Fig. 3. To obtain a correct reading the half axle must be supported.

5. Adjust protractor until bubble is in center position.

NOTE: If the protractor indicates a departure from the prescribed inclination the adjustment is to be corrected. There are more splines on the outer end of the torsion bar than at the inner end, so an exact adjustment is possible.

6. If the inner end of the bar is turned by one spline the adjustment is altered by 9°. If the spring plate is displaced by one spline the adjustment is altered by 8°10′. Thus the inclination of the spring plate can be corrected by 0°50′.

Spring Plate Adjustment "See Wheel Alignment Chart"

Rear Wheel Alignment

The holes provided in the spring plate for attaching it to the axle bearing housing are elongated. A groove is provided on the side of the spring plate and on the axle bearing housing above the top mounting hole. When adjusting the wheels without an alignment gauge these two grooves must be dead in line.

The camber angle of the rear wheels with the vehicle unloaded and correct spring plate adjustment is 3° (plus or minus 30′). Small deviations on both wheels do not influence road-holding ability. However, it is important that the

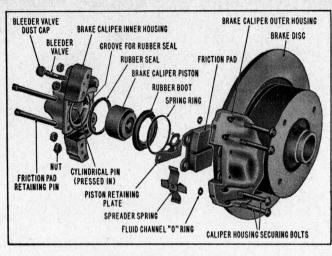

Fig. 7   Disc brake assembly

BLEEDER VALVE DUST CAP
BLEEDER VALVE
BRAKE CALIPER INNER HOUSING
GROOVE FOR RUBBER SEAL
RUBBER SEAL
BRAKE CALIPER PISTON
RUBBER BOOT
SPRING RING
FRICTION PAD
BRAKE CALIPER OUTER HOUSING
BRAKE DISC
NUT
FRICTION PAD RETAINING PIN
CYLINDRICAL PIN (PRESSED IN)
PISTON RETAINING PLATE
SPREADER SPRING
FLUID CHANNEL "O" RING
CALIPER HOUSING SECURING BOLTS

Fig. 8   Pushing pistons into their end positions with special pliers

wheels have the same camber angle, the maximum deviation being 20'. Incorrect camber readings are to be corrected as follows:

1. If camber angle is too wide but equal on both wheels, re-adjust spring plates.
2. If camber angle is too narrow but equal on both wheels, it indicates that spring plates have settled and should be re-adjusted.
3. If camber angle is uneven on both wheels, the spring plates may be unevenly adjusted, in which case they require re-adjustment. Another cause would be if the rubber cushions are improperly seated in the spring plates, in which case apply graphite to the cushions.

REAR SUSPENSION
Double Jointed Rear Axle

On 1968-71 Type 1 with Automatic Stickshift, 1969-71 Type 1 with manual transmission and all 1969-71 Type 3, the rear suspension is of the double jointed type with trailing diagonal control arms.

For description and repair operations, refer to the *Automatic Stickshift* section.

REAR SUSPENSION
Type 4

The rear wheels are independently sprung with coil springs rather than the torsion bars used on all other Volkswagens. The coil springs are mounted between the frame and two trailing wishbones. The shock absorbers are mounted inside the coil springs. The rear axles are of the double jointed type, each having two constant velocity joints.

SERVICE NOTE: Due to the complexity of the operation and the special tools necessary, it is recommended that the vehicle be returned to the dealer for rear axle alignment.

Shock Absorber, Coil Spring or Wishbone, Replace

NOTE: Before loosening the shock absorber mountings with the vehicle raised, always place spacer links (VW 361/2) between wishbone and body to prevent the spring tension from being released suddenly.

1. Remove the socket head screws holding the drive shaft joints, take the shafts out and cover the joints.
2. Disconnect the handbrake cable at the handbrake lever and pull it out.
3. Disconnect brake lines.
4. Remove the stabilizer, if equipped.
5. With the vehicle on the ground or with the links installed, remove the lower shock absorber bolt.
6. If the shock absorber is to be removed, detach the floor covering at the sides of the rear luggage shelf to gain access to the plastic cover in the body. Remove the cover, unscrew the self-locking nut on the shock absorber and remove the shock absorber upwards.
7. Detach spacer links from wishbones

and lift vehicle slowly. Remove coil springs.
8. To take out the wishbones, remove the nuts holding the brackets in the rear axle carrier or the bolts in the bonded rubber bushings. Mark the position of the brackets or the eccentric beforehand.
9. To install, first check the plastic tube on the spring and replace if necessary.
10. Bolt the wishbone brackets to the rear axle carrier but do not fully tighten the nuts.
11. If the wishbones were removed by detaching them from the brackets, insert the bolts and eccentric washers and set eccentrics to the mark made upon removal. Tighten the nuts to the correct torque. Insert the bolts in the outer brackets and tighten nuts.

NOTE: Only tighten the bolts in the bushings with the spacer links installed in order to avoid excessive tension over the entire range of spring movement.

12. Install the coil springs with the close coils downward and lower the vehicle slowly until it rests on the ground. Guide the springs into their correct locations while vehicle is being lowered.

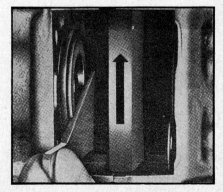

Fig. 10   Checking piston position with piston setting gauge

Fig. 9   Positioning piston with rotating pliers

13. With the vehicle in this position, place the spacer links on the wishbones and install the shock absorbers. Do not re-use the old self-locking nuts.
14. Install stabilizer, if so equipped.
15. Connect hand brake cable and adjust.
16. Connect brake lines and bleed hydraulic brakes.
17. Add a small amount of grease to the constant velocity joints if necessary. Install drive shafts. Be sure to use new screw lock plates.
18. Install remaining parts.
19. Have rear axle alignment checked and reset.

Rear Axle Carrier, R&R

1. Remove engine/transmission assembly.
2. Remove wishbones and brackets.
3. Remove bolts holding cover plates and remove plates.
4. Remove rear axle carrier complete with damping rings and bushings.
5. To install, place two damping rings on the spacer sleeves on body.
6. Install rear axle carrier and lower damping rings and bushings.
7. Install cover plates.
8. Install wishbones with brackets and engine/transmission assembly.
9. Adjust wishbones and engine/transmission assembly.
10. Have rear axle alignment checked and reset.

BRAKES

The brake shoes are self-centering and rest freely in the slots of the wheel cylinder piston push rods and adjusting screws. The hold-down springs, Figs. 4 and 5, assure a constant contact of the shoes with the bosses on the brake backing plate. The brake shoes are adjusted by means of screws and nuts at the anchor block.

Wheel Brakes, Adjust

1. Raise car and release hand brake.
2. Depress brake pedal several times to centralize the shoes in the drums.
3. Turn the wheel forward until the hole in the brake drum is in line with one of the adjusting nuts.
4. Insert a screwdriver through this hole, Fig. 6 and turn the adjusting nut, using the screwdriver as a lever until a slight drag is noted when wheel is turned by hand.
5. Back off adjusting nut 3 to 4 teeth to allow the wheel to turn freely.

NOTE: Repeat the procedure on the other adjusting nut, noting the opposite turning direction of the two nuts.

6. Repeat on the other wheels.

Hand Brake, Adjust

1. Raise rear of car.
2. Fold back hand brake lever rubber boot until brake cable adjusting nuts are accessible.
3. Back off lock nuts and tighten adjusting nuts to the point which will still allow the rear wheels to turn freely when hand brake lever is in release position.
4. Pull hand brake lever up two notches, and make sure both rear wheels have the same braking effect. At the fourth notch, the rear wheels should lock.
5. Tighten lock nuts and fasten rubber boot.

Master Cylinder, Replace

1. Pull rubber plug off master cylinder and allow fluid to drain into a clean container if it is still usable.
2. Disconnect stop light cable.
3. Disconnect brake line and plug opening.
4. Remove piston push rod-to-brake pedal bolt and loosen pedal stop.
5. Remove piston push rod.
6. Unfasten master cylinder (2 nuts) and withdraw master cylinder toward front.
7. Disconnect line between brake fluid reservoir and master cylinder. Unscrew bolt from base of reservoir and remove reservoir.
8. When installing, adjust piston push rod to 2.05″ to 2.09″ measured from convex end to face of nut. Adjust brake pedal free play by shifting stop plate until clearance is 0.04″ between push rod and piston.

DISC BRAKES

The front brakes of types 3 & 4 are of the disc type, Fig. 7, the main parts being the brake disc and caliper which contains the hydraulically operated components of the brake system. A splash shield, attached to the steering knuckle, protects the brake disc inner surface from dirt, stone damage or similar damage. The outer side of the brake disc is protected from damage by the wheel.

Friction Pads

The friction pads must be checked for wear every 6000 miles. Pads that have worn down to the thickness of $5/64″$ must be replaced with new ones.

IMPORTANT: All four friction pads must always be renewed together. It is not permissible to renew single friction pads or both pads of only one wheel. In addition, the spreader springs of both calipers must also be renewed with the friction pads. All necessary parts are furnished in a repair kit.

Removal

1. Remove front wheel.
2. Using a punch, drive out pad upper retaining pin.
3. Remove pad spreader spring.
4. Using a punch, drive out pad lower retaining pin.
5. Pull pads out of caliper, using a suitable hook.

IMPORTANT: If the friction pads are to be reused, they are the appropriate caliper housings must be marked as it is not permissible to change the pads from the outside to the inside and vice versa or from the right to the left wheel.

Installation

1. Oily friction pads and those with deep cracks or which have become detached from the metal plate must be renewed. In this case, all four friction pads must be renewed.
2. If pads are to be reused, remove excess dirt from grooves.
3. Push both pistons into their end positions with the retaining pliers shown in Fig. 8.

IMPORTANT: When doing this, the brake fluid behind the piston in the cylinder is forced back into the fluid reservoir. To prevent the reservoir overflowing, some of the fluid must be removed from the reservoir with a container that is used only for brake fluid. Brake fluid is poisonous and must not be siphoned off with a hose.

4. Clean seating and sliding surfaces of friction pads in brake caliper. To do this, remove piston retaining plates. Never used petroleum products for cleaning. After cleaning, blow out with compressed air.
5. Check rubber boot for damage. Hardened, brittle or cracked boots must be replaced. To replace a rubber boot the brake caliper must be removed.
6. Insert piston retaining plate. The circular part of the plate must be firmly pressed into the piston crown. In addition, the plate must lie below the relieved part of the piston. When the retaining plate is correctly installed, the 20° position of the piston is correct. Corroded or damaged piston retaining plates must be replaced.
7. Correct position of piston, if necessary, with piston rotating pliers, Fig. 9.
8. Check position of piston again, using a piston setting gauge, Fig. 10. The gauge must be held against the lower guide surface in the brake caliper which is counterclockwise to the brake disc rotation (arrow) when driving the vehicle forward.
9. Check brake disc for wear.
10. Insert pads into brake caliper. The pads must be free enough to move to and fro in caliper.
11. Insert pad lower retaining pin into caliper.

IMPORTANT: The retaining pin must not be driven in with a punch smaller in diameter than the pin as the front shoulder can easily be sheared off by the split clamping bushing. It is advisable to drive in the retaining pins with a hammer only and no additional tools.

12. Install new pad spreader spring.
13. Push in pad upper retaining pin after first pressing spreader spring down with thumb.

IMPORTANT: Depress brake pedal several times while vehicle is stationary to enable pistons and pads to assume their correct positions to the brake disc.

VOLKSWAGEN

Front Axle & Steering Gear Section

FRONT AXLE
Type 1

As shown in Fig. 1, this front axle is similar to that used previously. However, the torsion bars consist of ten spring leaves instead of the eight leaves used formerly. Ball joints are used instead of the former kingpins. The ball joints connect the torsion arms to the steering knuckles. They are pressed into the torsion arms and bolted to the steering knuckles. The upper ball joints engage in eccentric bushings with which front wheel camber can be adjusted.

Type 3

As shown in Fig. 2, the front axle is a complete replaceable assembly that can be detached from the frame fork quickly. The axle is mounted on the frame in rubber collars which prevent the transmission of road noises to the body. The wheels are independently suspended so that shocks taken on one wheel are not transferred across the vehicle to the opposite wheel.

The axle beam is of fabricated sheet steel construction that must be replaced as a unit when damaged. It is made up of two shells welded together. Side plates welded on each end reinforce the axle beam and also carry the upper mounting points for the shock absorbers. Bearing tubes are welded inside the axle beam to locate the torsion arms.

The torsion arms are supported in needle bearings at the outer points and plain metal bushings at the inner points. These needle bearings and bushings are replaceable.

Torsion Bars

Springing of the front wheels is provided by a separate, adjustable torsion bar for each wheel. The torsion bars are made of round material with upset ends that are splined. An internally splined bushing is welded into each side plate and the splined ends of the torsion bars are inserted into these bushings and secured with a screw on each side.

Stabilizer

The upper torsion arms are connected by a stabilizer bar that is fitted to improve road holding. The stabilizer bar has square upset ends that fit into the upper torsion arms. The left upper torsion arm is secured by means of an integral hexagon socket setscrew that engages in a countersunk depression in the stabilizer and is locked with a locknut. The right upper torsion arm is secured with an adjusting screw and a clamp screw. The adjusting screw is used to set the torsion arm axial movement.

Ball Joints

The pins in the ball joints have square ends at the bottom so that the pins can be turned to adjust wheel camber.

1971 Super Beetle & Type 4

The suspension system for these models is an all new MacPherson type unit, Fig. 3. At the top, the strut is attached to the body with a ball bearing and a rubber mounting. At the bottom it is bolted to the steering knuckle and a ball joint and held in position by the track control arm. Fig. 4 shows the various parts of the assembly.

WHEEL ALIGNMENT
Camber Angle

Type 1 (Except Super Beetle)

The camber angle cannot be adjusted on vehicles manufactured up to August 1965. Deviations from the prescribed specifications can, therefore, only be caused by wear or distortion of front axle parts. It is not permissible to correct camber by altering the prescribed positions of the washers.

On vehicles manufactured from August 1965, camber angle can be adjusted by an eccentric bushing on the upper ball joint. To do this, loosen hexagon nut on upper ball joint and turn eccentric bushing as required to obtain the proper camber angle as listed in the *Wheel Alignment Specifications* table.

IMPORTANT: The eccentric bushing is provided with a notch which, in the basic position, must face in the normal driving direction. This notch may be moved a maximum of 90° to the left and right of this basic position.

Type 3

The pins in the ball joints have square ends so they can be turned to adjust camber as required. Only the upper ball joints are to be adjusted. This will prevent the wheel steering lock angles from being enlarged.

The ball joints are marked with a notch on the pin end which shows the position of the eccentric. In the basic position, the mark points to the front. The eccentric may only be turned a maximum of 90° to right and left from this position.

Wheel Toe-In

1. First make sure that there is no front wheel run-out, and that the wheel bearings, torsion arm link pins and tie rod ends are not excessively worn.
2. Turn wheels exactly to their straight-ahead position.
3. Force the front wheels apart at the front to take up any slack in the wheel suspension and tie rods.
4. Check the toe-in in the conventional manner. If toe-in does not conform to the specifications called for in the Wheel Alignment chart, adjust as follows:
5. Loosen lock nut at both ends of the adjustable tie rod. Adjust toe-in by turning the tie rod until correct toe-in is obtained and tighten lock nuts.

WHEEL BEARINGS, ADJUST
Type 3

1. Lift front of vehicle.
2. Check that brake drums or discs turn freely. Brake linings must not rub.
3. Pull hub caps off.
4. Remove one wheel bolt and mount at dial gauge in the threaded bolt hole.
5. Set dial gauge so that feeler pin is touching outer hexagon nut or clamp nut.
6. Move wheel in and out firmly. End play should be from .001″ to .005″. If not within this range, adjust as follows:

NOTE: When play is at the upper limit, the wheel has quite a noticeable amount of rock. This is in order and there is no need to re-adjust the bearings. A re-adjustment is necessary only if isolated complaints of front axle noises are received. In such a case, try to adjust the bearings to obtain as near to the low limit as possible (.0012″ to .0024″).

7. Tighten inner nut or clamp nut to not more than 11 ft-lbs. Wheel must be turned while doing this so that bearing rollers contact shoulder of inner bearing race.
8. Slacken off the adjustment until play is between .0012″ and .0048″ when wheel is moved firmly in and out.
9. On drum brakes, hold inner bearing nut and tighten lock nut to 50 ft-lbs.
10. On disc brakes, tighten clamp nut screw to 7 ft-lbs.
11. Check adjustment again and if satisfactory, secure lock nuts or clamp screw nut.

Type 1 (Except Super Beetle)

1. Bend tab of lock plate on spindle and use two wrenches to loosen both nuts. Take off outer nut, discard lock plate and install the nut with a new lock plate.
2. Tighten inner nut until thrust washer at outer bearing can just be moved laterally with a screwdriver. This is the correct adjustment provided there is no bearing end play when checked by rocking the brake drum back and forth.
3. If the foregoing conditions are met, hold the inner nut with a wrench and tighten the outer nut against the lock plate.
4. Secure the adjustment by bending the lock plate tab against nut.

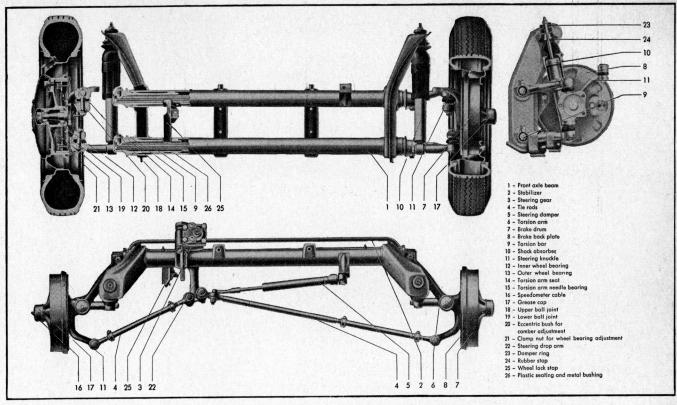

1 – Front axle beam
2 – Stabilizer
3 – Steering gear
4 – Tie rods
5 – Steering damper
6 – Torsion arm
7 – Brake drum
8 – Brake back plate
9 – Torsion bar
10 – Shock absorber
11 – Steering knuckle
12 – Inner wheel bearing
13 – Outer wheel bearing
14 – Torsion arm seal
15 – Torsion arm needle bearing
16 – Speedometer cable
17 – Grease cap
18 – Upper ball joint
19 – Lower ball joint
20 – Eccentric bush for camber adjustment
21 – Clamp nut for wheel bearing adjustment
22 – Steering drop arm
23 – Damper ring
24 – Rubber stop
25 – Wheel lock stop
26 – Plastic seating and metal bushing

Fig. 1   Front axle assembly with ball joints. Type 1 (Exc. Super Beetle)

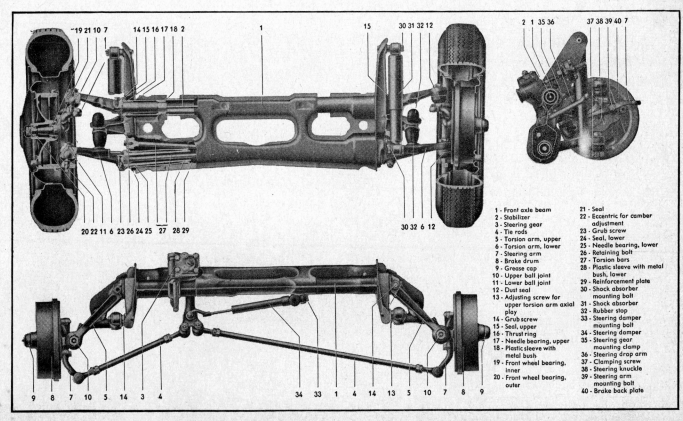

1 - Front axle beam
2 - Stabilizer
3 - Steering gear
4 - Tie rods
5 - Torsion arm, upper
6 - Torsion arm, lower
7 - Steering arm
8 - Brake drum
9 - Grease cap
10 - Upper ball joint
11 - Lower ball joint
12 - Dust seal
13 - Adjusting screw for upper torsion arm axial play
14 - Grub screw
15 - Seal, upper
16 - Thrust ring
17 - Needle bearing, upper
18 - Plastic sleeve with metal bush
19 - Front wheel bearing, inner
20 - Front wheel bearing, outer

21 - Seal
22 - Eccentric for camber adjustment
23 - Grub screw
24 - Seal, lower
25 - Needle bearing, lower
26 - Retaining bolt
27 - Torsion bars
28 - Plastic sleeve with metal bush, lower
29 - Reinforcement plate
30 - Shock absorber mounting bolt
31 - Shock absorber
32 - Rubber stop
33 - Steering damper mounting bolt
34 - Steering damper
35 - Steering gear mounting clamp
36 - Steering drop arm
37 - Clamping screw
38 - Steering knuckle
39 - Steering arm mounting bolt
40 - Brake back plate

Fig. 2   Front axle assembly. Type 3

Fig. 3   Front suspension. 1971 Type 1 Super Beetle

TORSION ARMS & BALL JOINTS

Type 1 (Except Super Beetle)

Torsion Arm Removal

1. Remove steering knuckle complete with brake drum.
2. If lower torsion arm is to be removed, take stabilizer off.
3. Loosen lock nuts on torsion arm pins and screw pins out.
4. Pull torsion arms out of axle tubes.
5. If necessary, take sealing rings out of axle tubes.
6. Clean torsion arms and ball joints.
7. Checking bearing seats on torsion arms for wear.

IMPORTANT: Bent torsion arms or arms with worn bearing surfaces should be replaced complete with ball joints.

8. Seal ball joints with new plastic plugs.

Checking Ball Joints

1. The dust seals must be taken off to check ball joints. It is essential to ensure that no dirt gets into the joints when doing this.
2. To check upper ball joint, press out eccentric bushing.
3. Check dust seals for damage.

NOTE: If the dust seal is damaged and there is a risk of dirt having got into the ball joint, the joint must be

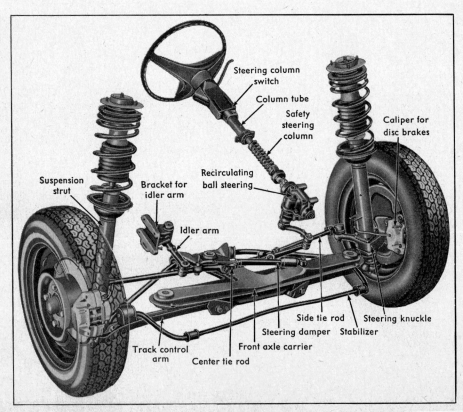

Fig. 3A   Front suspension. 1971 Type 4

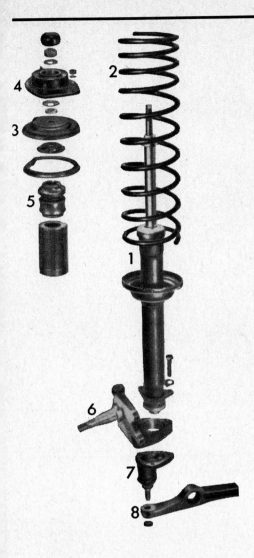

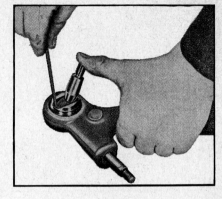

Fig. 5 Checking ball joint for wear with feeler gauge

1. Shock absorber

2. Coil spring

3. Spring plate

4. Strut bearing

5. Hollow rubber spring

6. Steering knuckle

7. Ball joint

8. Track control arm

Fig. 4 Exploded view of MacPherson unit

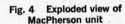

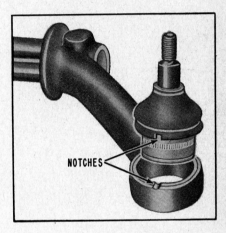

NOTCHES

Fig. 6 Notch in ball joint must line up with notch in torsion arm eye

cleaned thoroughly with a suitable solution. The plastic plug should then be removed, a grease nipple screwed in and lithium grease forced into the joint until all traces of dirt have been removed.

4. Check ball joint with feeler gauge as shown in Fig. 5. Permissible play on new joint should be .02″ with a wear limit of .08″.
5. If ball joints are in order, install dust seals and grease joint as follows:
6. According to the type of joint, secure dust seal to housing with a .04″ diameter wire or with spring ring.
7. Fit dust seal plastic clip on pin end of joint, using a suitable sleeve to aid in the installation. See that the ring does not twist.
8. Lubricate joint with lithium grease by forcing grease into nipple until seal just begins to expand. This point can be detected easily if the seal is squeezed lightly with two fingers. Grease nipple is then screwed out and a new plug is installed.

Replacing Ball Joints

1. Press upper ball joint out of torsion arm. If necessary, press eccentric bushing off ball joint. Press in new ball joint, being sure that notch in

joint is in line with notch in torsion arm eye, Fig. 6.

IMPORTANT: For production reasons, ball joints with a .16″ oversize knurl are occasionally installed in the tor-

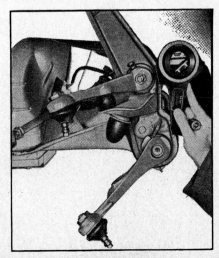

Fig. 7 Protractor (VW 261) positioned on face of anchor plate

sion arms in addition to standard size ball joints. These joints are marked for installation purposes with two grooves at 180° to each other, while the standard joints have only one such groove. Pay attention to these markings when replacing ball joints as the joints have no markings indicating their sizes.

2. To replace lower ball joints, proceed in a similar manner as for upper joints. If the ball comes out of the socket when pressing the ball joint out, the socket can be pressed out of the torsion arm.

NOTE: Old ball joints must not be pressed back in again under any circumstances.

TORSION ARMS & BARS
Type 3

IMPORTANT: Removal and installation of torsion arms and bars should not be attempted without the aid of a special protractor (VW 261) and special mandrel, Fig. 7. The protractor has two spirit levels and, unless it is used to set up the proper angle of 39°10′ of the torsion arm, road hold-

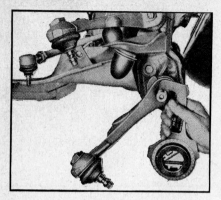

Fig. 8   Mandrel inserted in torsion arm

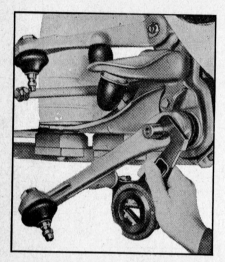

Fig. 9   Protractor swiveled against shock absorber mounting bolt

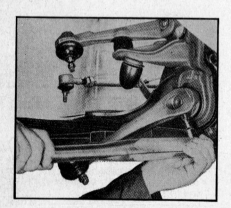

Fig. 10   Tightening torsion arm set screw

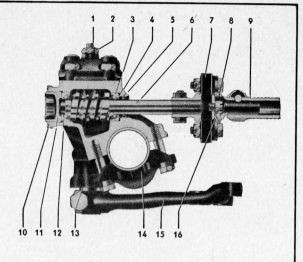

1 - Roller shaft adjusting screw
2 - Lock nut
3 - Upper worm bearing
4 - Adjusting shim for worm
5 - Oil seal for worm
6 - Steering worm
7 - Coupling disc
8 - Flange for coupling disc
9 - Steering column
10 - Lock nut
11 - Worm adjusting screw
12 - Lower worm bearing
13 - Steering roller shaft
14 - Mounting clamp
15 - Drop arm
16 - Ground connection terminal
17 - Steering roller
18 - Roller needle bearings
19 - Roller support pin

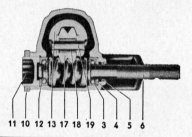

Fig. 11   Steering gear assembly

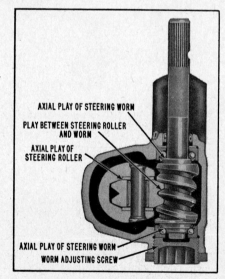

AXIAL PLAY OF STEERING WORM
PLAY BETWEEN STEERING ROLLER AND WORM
AXIAL PLAY OF STEERING ROLLER
AXIAL PLAY OF STEERING WORM
WORM ADJUSTING SCREW

Fig. 12   Steering gear points of adjustment

ing ability of the vehicle during subsequent operation will not be achieved. However, if this equipment is available, proceed as follows:

1. Slide torsion arm onto torsion bar splies and adjust with protractor to 39°10′ + 50′ as follows:
2. Position protractor on face of anchor plate, Fig. 7. Protractor must contact at bearing surface for the upper torsion arm and level with welded in bushing (support bearing for tor-sion bar).
3. Turn spirit level until bubble marked "Achskorper" is exactly in central position.
4. Remove protractor at this setting and insert mandrel in torsion arm, Fig. 8. Do not slide torsion arm fully onto torsion bar because mandrel must also be pushed into torsion arm splines.
5. Swivel protractor from underneath against shock absorber mounting bolt so that it is positioned as close as possible to torsion arm at mounting bolt, Fig. 9.
6. The torsion arm is correctly adjusted when the bubble of the spirit level marked "Traghebel" is exactly in the central position.

NOTE: The different number of splines on the torsion bar ends make it possible to correct the adjustment. There are 29 inner splines and 31 outer splines. The minimum adjustment range of 50′ is achieved by turning the torsion arm by one tooth and the torsion bar also by one tooth but in the opposite direction.

IMPORTANT: It is of the utmost importance for road holding that the adjustment angles of the lower torsion arms correspond as far as possible and are not below the prescribed angle of 39°10′. When adjusting one side, the adjustment angle of the other side must also be checked. If it is not within the tolerance range of 39°10′ + 50″, it must be corrected.

7. Install and tighten torsion arm bolt and torque to 29 ft-lbs.
8. Tighten set screw in lower torsion arm to 22 ft-lbs and secure with lock nut, Fig. 10. This operation must be performed carefully to avoid damage to torsion bars.
9. Install steering knuckle with brake drum, bleed brakes and adjust camber and toe-in.

STEERING GEAR
Steering Wheel

Removal
1. Disconnect battery ground cable.
2. Remove horn lever cover with screwdriver.
3. Disconnect horn ground wire at horn lever.
4. Remove steering wheel nut.
5. On 1200, 1300 & 1967-68 1500, remove spring washer. Then remove wheel with horn lever.
6. On 1966 1500 & all 1600, remove nut, spring washer, steering wheel and horn lever.

Installation
1. On 1200, 1300 and 1967-68 1500, position brass washer with cut-away part exactly to the right when wheels are straight ahead.
2. On 1966 1500 and all 1600, install support ring and brass washer. Milled end of support ring must be toward steering gear and cut-away part of brass washer must be to the right when wheels are in straight ahead position.
3. Locate steering gear in center position and install wheel so that spokes are horizontal. Tongue of cancelling ring must engage recess in brass washer.
4. On 1200, 1300 and 1967-68 1500, install spring washer and nut and tighten to 36 ft-lbs.

NOTE: The distance between turn signal switch and steering wheel hub should be .08" to .10". Distance can be set by moving column on upper coupling flange as required. Connect horn cable to horn lever.

5. On 1966 1500 and all 1600, install spring washer and tighten nut to 36 ft-lbs. Connect horn wire to horn lever.

NOTE: The distance between turn signal switch and wheel hub should be .08" to .12". When the two switch screws are loosened, the column tube and switch can be moved as the holes in the housing are elongated. *The switch must only be moved when in the position to avoid damaging cancelling cams.* If the range of adjustment is inadequate, the steering column must be moved axially in the upper coupling flange.

Steering Gear, Replace

Type 1 (Except Super Beetle)
1. Raise car and remove left front wheel.
2. Detach tie rods from steering drop arm with a suitable puller.
3. Unscrew nut on column clamp.
4. Disconnect cable on coupling contact.
5. Pull column off column flange.
6. Remove steering gear clamp.
7. Remove steering gear.
8. Reverse procedure to install.

Type 3
1. Raise vehicle and remove fuel tank.
2. Remove spare wheel well.
3. Remove both tie rods from drop arm, using a suitable puller.
4. Remove steering damper from drop arm.
5. Remove coupling bolts.
6. Disconnect ground cable.
7. Remove mounting clamp.
8. Take steering gear off axle.
9. Reverse procedure to install.

Steering Gear, Adjust

Gear Installed In Car
1. With wheels on floor and facing straight ahead, move steering wheel lightly to and fro until resistance is felt in both directions. This range at the center position is determined by the steering adjustment as well as by the tie rods and steering coupling. Measured at the steering wheel rim the free play should be 1 inch.
2. If there is excessive play in the center position, there are three adjustments that can be made: axial play of steering worm, play between worm and roller, and axial play of steering roller, Fig. 12.

Axial Play of Worm
The axial play of the worm is determined by turning the worm to and fro at the steering coupling. To do this, the vehicle must be raised. If there is play, it can be eliminated as follows:
1. Turn steering wheel fully to left or right.
2. Loosen locknut on steering worm adjusting screw, Fig. 12.
3. Turn worm to and fro at coupling and at the same time tighten worm adjusting screw until play is no longer detectable.

4. Hold adjusting screw and tighten locknut.
5. Turn steering worm from one extreme to the other. When turning, there should be no unusually tight positions noticeable. If there are any, the adjusting screw is too tight, and must be corrected.

Play Between Worm and Roller
If play in the steering cannot be eliminated by adjusting the worm, the roller-to-worm setting must be adjusted. There should be no play between roller and worm with steering in central position. The worm-to-roller adjustment can be made with the vehicle raised. However, to make the adjustment the vehicle must be on the ground.
1. Turn steering wheel 90° left or right.
2. Loosen roller shaft adjusting screw locknut.
3. Loosen adjusting screw about one turn.
4. Tighten adjusting screw until roller can be felt contacting worm.
5. Hold adjusting screw and tighten locknut 14 to 18 ft-lbs.
6. Check the adjustment with steering wheel turned 90° to each side with vehicle resting on ground. The play must not exceed 1 inch, measured at the rim of the steering wheel. If there is more play on one side, the adjustment of the roller to the worm at the 90° position should be repeated on this side.
7. Check toe-in and adjust if necessary.
8. Road test. If steering does not return to within 45° of the central position after making a turn at 10 to 12 mph, the roller is too tight. The adjustment should then be repeated, otherwise the worm and roller will be damaged.

Roller Axial Play
If the steering gear cannot be properly adjusted by the foregoing adjustments, the gear must be dismantled and axial play of the roller checked.
1. With steering gear disassembled, the axial play of the roller should not exceed .0016".
2. Measure play between roller and washer with a .002" feeler gauge. If feeler gauge can be inserted between roller and washer, the roller shaft should be replaced.
3. Assemble, adjust and install steering gear. Check and adjust toe-in if necessary, and road test vehicle.

Foreign Car Data

Year	Model	Spark Plug Gap, In.	Ignition: Breaker Gap, In.	Ignition: Dwell Angle Deg.	Ignition: Firing Order	Ignition: Timing Mark & Location	Valve Lash: In-take	Valve Lash: Ex-haust	Capacities: Engine Oil Qts.	Capacities: Coolant Qts. W/Heater	Wheel Alignment: Cas-ter	Wheel Alignment: Cam-ber	Wheel Alignment: Toe-in
AUSTIN-HEALEY													
1965–70	MG Midget	.025	.015	....	1342	4° BTC①	.012H	.012H	3	6	3°	1°	1/16–1/8
	MG 13	.025	.015	....	1342	10° BTC①	.015C	.015C	4½	6	7½°	1°	1/16–3/32
1965	3000	.024	.014	....	153624	10° BTC①	.012	.012	7.4	11.4	2°	1°	1/16–1/8
1966–67	3000	.024	.014	....	153624	10° BTC①	.012	.012	8	11	2°	1°	1/16–1/8
1965	Sprite	.025	.015	....	1342	4° BTC①	.012	.012	4	6	3°	1°	0–1/8
1966–69	Sprite	.024	.014	....	1342	4° BTC①	.012	.012	4	6	3°	¾°	0–1/8
1969–70	America	.025	.015	....	1342	3° BTC①	.012	.012	5½	4	②	③	④
1968	1300	.025	.014	....	1342	7° BTC①	.012	.012	4	6	3°	¾°	0–1/8
1969–70	MG 13/GT	.025	.015	..	1342	10° BTC①	.015C	.015C	4½	6	7½°	1°	1/16–3/32
1971	America	.025	.015	57°–63°	1342	Flywheel	.012	.012	6	4	5½°	¾°	④

①—Located at pulley.
②—+5½° ±½°.
③—+¾ ±1°.
④—+1/16" toe-out.

Year	Model	Spark Plug Gap, In.	Breaker Gap, In.	Dwell Angle Deg.	Firing Order	Timing Mark & Location	In-take	Ex-haust	Engine Oil Qts.	Coolant Qts. W/Heater	Cas-ter	Cam-ber	Toe-in
DATSUN													
1965	SPL 310	.030	....	①	1342	16° BTC④	.017H	.017H	4	7	1°30′	1°26′	1/8
1965–67	L 60 & KL 60	.028	....	②	153624	10° BTC④	.016H	.016H	5	....	....		1/8
1965–66	(W) PL 410	.030	....	①	1342	14° BTC④	.014H	.014H	4	6	1°30′	1°30′	1/8
1966–67	L 520	.030	....	①	1342	14° BTC④	.014H	.014H	4	6	1°50′	1°15′	1/8
1966–67	PL 411	.030	....	①	1342	14° BTC④	.014H	.014H	4	6	0°	1°45′	1/8
1967	(W) RL 411	.030	..	①	1342	16° BTC④	.017H	.017H	4	6	0°	1°45′	1/4
1966–70	SPL 311	.030		①	1342	10° BTC④	.017H	.017H	4	9	1°30′	1°26′	1/8
1967–70	SRL 311	.030	....	③	1342	10° BTC④	.008H	.012H	7	9	1°30′	1°25′	1/8
1971	510 Series	.033	.020	49°-55°	1342	10° BTDC④⑤	.010H	.012H	4¼⑥	7¼	+2°	+1°	5/64

①—Dwell angle 50°–55°.
②—Dwell angle 35°–41°.
③—Dwell angle 50°.
④—Location-Pulley.
⑤—Man. trans. @ 700 RPM; auto. trans. @ 575 RPM in drive.
⑥—Add ¾ qt. when replacing oil filter.

Year	Model	Spark Plug Gap, In.	Breaker Gap, In.	Dwell Angle Deg.	Firing Order	Timing Mark & Location	In-take	Ex-haust	Engine Oil Qts.	Coolant Qts. W/Heater	Cas-ter	Cam-ber	Toe-in
FIAT													
1965	600D	.024	.019	50°	1342	10° BTC①	.006C	.006C	3.1	4.7	9°	1°	3/64
1965	1100D	.024	.016	56°	1342	TDC①	.004C	.004C	3.2	5¼	2°	1/3°	5/64
1965	1500	.020	.017	60° ±3°	1342	12° BTC①	.008C	.008C	3.7	6.3	2°20′	1/3°	5/64
1966–67	600D	.024	.019	50°	1342	0°①	.006C	.006C	3.1	4.7	9°	1°	2/25
1966–67	1100D	.024	.016	56°	1342	12° BTC①	.004C	.004C	3.2	5¼	2°	½°	5/64
1966–67	1500	.020	.017	60° ±3°	1342	12° BTC①	.008C	.008C	3.7	6.3	2°20′	1/3°	5/64
1967	1100R	.027	.018	56°	1342	1° BTC①	.004C	.004C	3.5	5	1¾–2½	½°	5/64
1967	124	.026	.018	60°	1342	10° BTC①	.008C	.008C	3.1	4.7	2°5′	0°20′	5/64
1968–70	850 Sedan	.026	.018	57°	1342	10° BTC①	.006C	.006C	3.5	8	9°	2 1/64°	1/4
1968–69	124 Sedan	.026	.018	60° ±2°	1342	0°①	.008C	.008C	4	6.3	2¼°	1/12°	1/4
1970	850 Spider	.024	.017	38°	1342	0° TDC	.006C	.008C	4.2	8°	....	....	....
1970	124 Spider	.024	.017	6° ±3°	1342	5° BTC	.008C	.020C	4.2	8°	....	....	....
1971	850 Sedan	.022	.018	60° ±3°②	1342	10° BTC	.006C	.006C	3.5	8	+10°	+1°10′	½
	850 Sport Coupe	.022	.016	55° ±3°③	1342	0°	.006C	.008C	4.2	8	+10°	+2°	½
	850 Spider, Racer	.022	.016	55° ±3°③	1342	0°	.006C	.008C	4.2	8	+10°	+2°10′	19/32
	124 Sedan, Sta. Wag.	.022	.018	60° ±3°③	1342	0°	.008C	.008C	4	8	+ 3°	+0°35′	5/16
	124 Sport Coupe, Spider	.022	.016	55° ±3°③	1342	5° BTC	.018C	.020C	4.2	8	+ 3°30′	+0°30′	9/32

①—Located at pulley.
②—At 700 RPM.
③—At 850 RPM.

Year	Model	Spark Plug Gap, In.	Breaker Gap, In.	Dwell Angle Deg.	Firing Order	Timing Mark & Location	In-take	Ex-haust	Engine Oil Qts.	Coolant Qts. W/Heater	Cas-ter	Cam-ber	Toe-in
FORD													
1965–67	Anglia 1200	.025	①	②	1243	6° BTC③	.010H	.017H	3.3	6.3	1°30′–3°	30′–2°	1/8–3/16
1965	Zephyr MK-III	.025	.015	57°–63°	1243	8° BTC③	.014C	.014C	3.9	10.2	④	⑤	1/16–3/16
	Zephyr & Zodiac	.025	.015	33°–37°	153624	8° BTC③	.014C	.014C	4.2	12.6	④	⑤	1/16–3/16
1965–67	Cortina 1200	.023	.015	57°–63°	1243	6° BTC③	.010H	.017H	3.3	6.3	⑥	⑦	1/16–3/16
	Cortina 1500	.023	①	②	1243	6° BTC③	.010H	.017H	4.2	7.3	⑥	⑦	1/16–1/8
	Cortina 1500 GT	.023	①	②	1243	10° BTC③	.012H	.022H	4.2	7.3	⑥	⑦	1/16–1/8
	Cortina Lotus	.023	.015	57°–63°	1342	⑧	⑨	⑩	4.2	7.3	⑥	⑦	1/16–1/8

Continued

Year	Model	Spark Plug Gap, In.	Breaker Gap, In.	Dwell Angle Deg.	Firing Order	Timing Mark & Location	Intake	Exhaust	Engine Oil Qts.	Coolant Qts. W/Heater	Caster	Camber	Toe-in

FORD—Continued

Year	Model	Spark Plug Gap	Breaker Gap	Dwell Angle	Firing Order	Timing	Intake	Exhaust	Oil Qts	Coolant	Caster	Camber	Toe-in
1967–69	Cortina 1600	.023	.025	38°–40°	1243	4° BTC(11)	.010H	.017H	4.2	6.9	(13)	(14)	1/8–3/16
	Cortina 1600 GT	.023	.025	38°–40°	1243	4° BTC(12)	.012H	.022H	4.2	6.9	(13)	(14)	1/8–3/16
1970	Cortina 1600	.023	.025	38°–40°	1243	12°	.010H	.017H	4.2	6.1	(13)	(14)	1/8–3/16
	Cortina 1600 GT	.023	.025	38°–40°	1243	0°	.012H	.022H	4.2	6.1	(13)	(14)	1/8–3/16
1971	Capri 1600	.025	.022–.028	38°–40°	1243	(15)	.010H	.017H	3.5	6.2	1/2–1 1/2	1/2–1/2	0–1/4
	Capri 2000	.025	.023–.027	37°–41°	1342	(15)	.008C	.018C	5.0	7.5	....	....	....

①—Lucas distributor .015. Autolite distributor .025.
②—Lucas distributor 57°–63°. Autolite distributor 36°–40°.
③—Located at crank-pulley. All models except Lotus use a pointer with three positions, each representing two degrees. The middle position is 8° BTDC. Lotus models have a notch on the pulley which lines up with a scale showing three positions, each representing ten degrees. The middle position is 10° BTDC.
④—0°19' to + 0°41'.
⑤—1°37' to 2°37'.
⑥—1°12' to 2°42'.
⑦—0°40' to 2°10'.
⑧—Dist. with vacuum advance 7° BTDC (See note ③)
Dist. less vacuum advance 14° BTDC. (See note ③)
⑨—.005-.006C.
⑩—.006-.007C.
⑪—6° if no emission pump is used.
⑫—8° if no emission pump is used.
⑬——0°54' to +0°36'.
⑭—1° to 2°30'.
⑮—Pulley & front cover.

JAGUAR

Year	Model	Spark Plug Gap	Breaker Gap	Dwell Angle	Firing Order	Timing	Intake	Exhaust	Oil Qts	Coolant	Caster	Camber	Toe-in
1965	MK10	.025	.015	33°–37°	153624	10° BTC①	.004	.006	7 1/4	14 3/4	0°±1/2	+1/2±1/2	1/16–1/8
1965–66	3.8 MK11	.025	.015	33°–37°	153624	5° BTC①	.004	.006	6 3/4	13 1/4	0°±1/2	+1/2±1/2	0–1/16
1965–67	4.2 Sedan	.025	.015	33°–37°	153624	10° BTC①	.004	.006	7 1/4	14 3/4	0°±1/2	+1/2±1/2	1/16–1/8
1965–66	3.8 "S"	.025	.015	33°–37°	153624	5° BTC①	.004	.006	7 1/4	13 1/4	0°±1/2	+1/2±1/2	0–1/16
1965–67	E Type 4.2	.025	.015	33°–37°	153624	10° BTC①	.004	.006	9	19 1/4	2°±1/2	+1/4±1/2	1/16–1/8
	420 Sedan	.025	.015	33°–37°	153624	8° BTC①	.004	.006	7 1/4	15 1/4	0°±1/2	+1/2±1/2	0–1/8
	340 Sedan	.025	.015	33°–37°	153624	7° BTC①	.004	.006	6 3/4	13 1/4	0°±1/2	+1/2±1/2	0–1/16
1968–69	E Type	.025	.015	33°–37°	153624	②	.004	.006	9	16	2°±1/2	+1/4±1/2	1/16–1/8
1967	420G SSedan	.025	.015	33°–37°	153624	10° BTC①	.004	.006	7 1/4	14	0°±1/2	+1/2±1/2	1/16–1/8
1970	XKE, XJ Sedan	.025	.015	32°–38°	153624	②	.004	.006	9	16	2°±1/2	1/4±1/2	1/16–1/8
1971	XJ6	.025	.015	32°–38°	153624	Damper	.013	.013	9	10	2 1/4°±1/4	1/2°±1/4	1/16
	XKE	.025	.015	31°–37°	153624	Damper	.013	.013	9	10 1/4	1 3/4°±1/4	1/4°	1/16

①—Located at crank-pulley.
②—5° BTDC static; 10° BTDC @ 1000 RPM.

MERCEDES-BENZ

Year	Model	Spark Plug Gap	Breaker Gap	Dwell Angle	Firing Order	Timing	Intake	Exhaust	Oil Qts	Coolant	Caster	Camber	Toe-in
1965	190Dc①	....	....	....	1342		.006C	.014C	4 1/4	10 3/4	3 1/2°	1/2°	1/16
1965–66	300SE	.021	.017		153624	3° BTC④	.005C	.010C	7	18	4°	1/2°	1/16
1966	220SEB	.021	.014		153624	4° BTC④	.003C	.006C	6	12	2 1/2°–3°	1/2°	1/16
1966	220SB	.030	.014		153624	3° BTC④	.003C	.006C	6	12	2 1/2°–3°	1/2°	1/16
1966	230SL	.030	.012		153624	3° BTC④	.003C	.007C	6.3	11.5	3 1/4	1/2°	1/3
1967–68	230S	.030	.014		153624	2° BTC④	.003C	.006C	5.8	12	3 1/2	1/2°	3/64–7/64
1967–68	230	.030	.014		153624	2° BTC④	.003C	.006C	5.8	14.8	3 1/2	1/2°	3/64–7/64
1967–68	200	.030	.018		1342	2° BTC④	.003C	.007C	4.3	10.8	3 1/2	1/2°	3/64–7/64
1968–71	220/8	.024	.018	45°–49°	1342	5° ATDC④	.003C	.008C	4 1/4	11	+2 1/2②	0°	13/64
1968–69	230, 250/8	.024	.014	28°–32°	153624	0°④	.003C	.007C	5 3/4	11	+2 1/2②	0°	13/64
1968–71	280/8	.021⑤	.014	30°–36°⑥	153624	⑦④	.003C	⑧	5 3/4	12⑨	⑩	0°	⑪
1970–71	250/8	.024	.014	30°–36°	153624	4° ATDC④	.003C③	.008C③	5 3/4	11	+2 1/2②	0°	13/64

①—Diesel engine.
②—With power steer. +3 1/2.
③—1970 sedan—intake .003C; exhaust .007C.
④—Location, Damper or Pulley.
⑤—280 S & SEL .024.
⑥—1968–69—28°–32°.
⑦—1968–69; 280S—@ 4000–4500 RPM, vacuum line disconnected 37° BTDC; 280 SE, SEL, SL 30° BTDC. 1970–71; except 280S, 8° ATDC; 280S, 4° ATDC.
⑧—1968–69 .007C; 1970–71 .008C.
⑨—280S—11 1/2 qts.
⑩—Except 280 SL—w/p. steer. +3 1/2; w/o p. steer. +2 1/2; 280 SL—w/p. steer. +4; w/o p. steer. +3 1/4.
⑪—Except 280 SL—13/64; 280 SL—5/64.

MG

Year	Model	Spark Plug Gap	Breaker Gap	Dwell Angle	Firing Order	Timing	Intake	Exhaust	Oil Qts	Coolant	Caster	Camber	Toe-in
1965–70	MG Midget	.025	.015	....	1342	4° BTC①	.012H	.012H	3	6	3°	1°	1/16–1/8
	MGB	.025	.015	....	1342	10° BTC①	.015C	.015C	4 1/2	6	7 1/2°	1°	1/16–3/32
1965–68	MG 1100	.025	.015	....	1342	5° BTC②	.012C	.012C	5.2	4	6°	1/2°	1/16③
1969–70	MGB/GT	.025	.015	....	1342	10° BTC①	.015C	.015C	4 1/2	6	7 1/2°	1°	1/16–3/32
1969	MGC	.025	.015	....	153624	TDC①	.015	.015	7 1/2	11	5°	0°	0°
1969	MCG/GT	.025	.015	....	153624	TDC①	.015	.015	7 1/2	11	5°	0°	0°
1971	MG Midget	.025	.015	57°–63°	1342	②	.012	.012	4	3 1/2	3°	3/4°	0–1/8
	MGB/MGB. GT	.025	.015	57°–63°	1342	②	.015	.015	5	6	7°	1°	1/16–3/32

①—Located at pulley.　②—Located at flywheel.　③—Toe-out.

Year	Model	Spark Plug Gap, In.	Breaker Gap, In.	Dwell Angle Deg.	Firing Order	Timing Mark & Location	In-take	Ex-haust	Engine Oil Qts.	Coolant Qts. W/Heater	Cas-ter	Cam-ber	Toe-in

OPEL

Year	Model	Spark Plug Gap, In.	Breaker Gap, In.	Dwell Angle Deg.	Firing Order	Timing Mark & Location	In-take	Ex-haust	Engine Oil Qts.	Coolant Qts. W/Heater	Cas-ter	Cam-ber	Toe-in
1965-66	(Exc. Rallye)	.038	.015	....	1342	TDC[5]	.006H[7]	.010H[7]	2½	4½	0-2°	1½-2°	1/16
1967-68	(Exc. Rallye)	.030	.018	....	1342	4° BTC[5]	.012H	.012H	3¼	6	0-1°	0°	1/16
1967-68	Rallye	.030	.018	....	1342	....	.012	.012	3¼	6	0-1²/₅°	2/3°	1/32-1/8
1969	1.1 Litre	.030	.018	48°-52°	1342	[1]	.006	.010	2½	5½	[2]	[3]	1/32-1/8
	1.9 Litre	.030	.018	48°-52°	1342	[6]	.012H	.012H	3	6	[2]	[3]	1/32-1/8
1970	1.1 Litre	.030	.018	48°-52°	1342	[1]	.006	.010	2½	5½	2°	1°±½°	1/32-1/8
	1.9 Litre	.030	.018	48°-52°	1342	[6]	.012H	.012H	3	6	2°	1°±½°	1/32-1/8
1971	1.1 Litre	.030	.018	48°-52°	1342	[8][5]	.006	.010	[9]	5	2°±1°	1°±½°	1/8"
	1.9 Litre	.030	.018	48°-52°	1342	TDC[4][10]	Hydraulic		[11]	6[12]	[13]	1°±½°	[14]

[1]—4°-9° BTDC. (See note [5])
[2]—1-1½°, left & right wheel angles to be within 1° of each other.
[3]—Except GT ¾°; GT ½°.
[4]—Located at flywheel.
[5]—Located at pulley.
[6]—4°-9° BTDC (See note [4])
[7]—On models with pocketed sliding areas .022-.024 feeler gauges must be used.
[8]—At 950 RPM align timing marks (slot).
[9]—3 qts.; w/o filter 2¾ qts.
[10]—At 900 RPM align timing marks.
[11]—3¼ qts.; w/o filter 3 qts.
[12]—1900 series; manual trans. 6 qts.; auto. trans. 1-3/5 gals.
[13]—1900 series 3½°±1°; Opel 2°±1°; GT 3°±1°.
[14]—Exc. 1900 1/8"; 1900 3/16".

PEUGEOT

Year	Model	Spark Plug Gap, In.	Breaker Gap, In.	Dwell Angle Deg.	Firing Order	Timing Mark & Location	In-take	Ex-haust	Engine Oil Qts.	Coolant Qts. W/Heater	Cas-ter	Cam-ber	Toe-in
1965	403, 404	.025	.016	55°-57°	1342	Slot[1]	.004C	.010C	4¼	8½	2°	0°	1/16
1966	403	.025	.016	55°-57°	1342	Slot[1]	.004C	.010C	4½	9½	2°	0°	2°
1966-69	404	.025	.016	55°-57°	1342	Slot[1]	.004C	.010C	4½	8½	2°	0°	1/16
1971	504	.024	.016	57°-59°	1342	[2]	.004	.010	[3]	8.5	2°40'	0°38'	1/8

[1]—The ignition is set statically by inserting a rod in the role in the clutch housing. By turning engine with hand crank, the rod will fall into a slot in the flywheel. At this point, the ignition points will open in the firing position.
[2]—Front timing cover mark on pulley.
[3]—8.44 pints.

PORSCHE/PORSCHE AUDI

Year	Model	Spark Plug Gap, In.	Breaker Gap, In.	Dwell Angle Deg.	Firing Order	Timing Mark & Location	In-take	Ex-haust	Engine Oil Qts.	Coolant Qts. W/Heater	Cas-ter	Cam-ber	Toe-in
1965	356C	[1]	[2]	[3]	1432	[4]	[5]	[6]	[7]	....	[8]	[9]	[10]
1966	911	.014	....	....	162435	TDC[11]	....	....	9½	....	7°45'	[12]	[13]
	912	.024	....	....	1432	3° BTC[11]	....	....	4.2		7°35'	[14]	[15]
1967	911	.014	....	....	162435	TDC	....	....	9½		[16]	[17]	[18]
	911S	.014	....	....	162435	[19]	....	....	9½		[16]	[17]	[18]
	912	.024	....	....	1432	3° BTC[11]	....	....	4.2		[16]	[17]	[18]
1968	911L	[20]	....	....	162435	[21]	....	....	9½		[16]	[22]	[23]
	911	[20]	....	....	162435	[21]	....	....	9½		[16]	[22]	[23]
	912	.026	....	....	1432	3° BTC[11]	....	....	4.2		[16]	[22]	[23]
1969	911E & S	.014	....	....	162435	[21]	....	....	9½		[16]	[22]	[23]
	911T	.024	....	....	162435	[24]	....	....	9½		[16]	[22]	[23]
	912	.026	....	....	1432	3° BTC[11]	....	....	4.2		[16]	[22]	[23]
1970-71	Audi S-90	.024	.016	47°-53°	1342	[25]	.008	.008	[26]	8	10'±20	[27]	0 to —.08"
	Audi 100 LS	.024	.016	47°-53°	1342	[25]	.016	.016	[26]	8	[28]	[29]	0 to —.079"
	911E, S&T	.024	....	35°-41°	162435	[30][11]	.004C	.004C	9.5	....	[16]	[22]	[23]
	914	.028[31]	.016	44°-50°	1432	[32]	.006C	.006C	[33]	....	6°±30'	[34]	[35]
	914/6	.024	.016	37°-43°	162435	[24][36]	.004C	.004C	9.5	....	6°±30'	[34]	[35]

[1]—Exc. Bosch W225T7 .020-.024; Bosch W225T7 .024-.028.
[2]—Dist. #VJS (R) 4R2, 4R4 & 4R5 .014. Dist. #VJS 4L2 Mk. .014. Other Dist. .016.
[3]—Dist. #VJS (R) 4R2, 4R4 & 4R5 60-65°. Dist. #VJS 4L2 Mk. 60-65°. Other Dist. 47-53°.
[4]—1600, 1600S, 1600C 5° BTDC (located at pulley); 1600S-90, 1600SC 3° BTDC (located at pulley).
[5]—1600, 1600C .004; 1600S (exc. following description) .004, from engine No. P-84771 (356B) with light-alloy rocker arm brackets & light-alloy push rods .006; 1600SC (exc. following description) .006, from engine No. 820641 or 811362 (616/16) with "Bi-ral" cylinders & two metal push rods .004.
[6]—1600, 1600C .006; 1600S (exc. following description) .006, from engine No. P-84771 (356B) with light-alloy arm brackets & light-alloy push rods .004; 1600SC (exc. following description) .004, from engine No. 820641 or 811362 (616/16) with "Bi-ral" cylinder & two metal push rods .006.

Continued

Year	Model	Spark Plug Gap, In.	Ignition: Breaker Gap, In.	Ignition: Dwell Angle Deg.	Ignition: Firing Order	Ignition: Timing Mark & Location	Valve Lash: In-take	Valve Lash: Ex-haust	Capacities: Engine Oil Qts.	Capacities: Coolant Qts. W/Heater	Wheel Alignment: Cas-ter	Wheel Alignment: Cam-ber	Wheel Alignment: Toe-in

PORSCHE/PORSCHE AUDI—Continued

⑦—After overhaul 5 qts.; with filter change 4 qts.; less filter change 3 qts.
⑧—5° ± 30′ (unloaded car).
⑨—1600 (Exc. S-90) Front +40°±30′; Rear +30′ to +2°. 1600S-90 Front +40°±30°; Rear +10° to 1°30′.
⑩—Front .040 to .120 in.; Rear 0 ± .040 in.
⑪—Pulley.
⑫—Front +4′; Rear —1°6′.
⑬—Front 15 to 20′; Rear 0° to —2′.
⑭—Front +5′; Rear —1°5′.
⑮—Front 40′; Rear 0′.
⑯—6°45′ ±45′.
⑰—Front 0 ± 20′; Rear —1°15′ ± 20′.
⑱—Front 40′; Rear 0° ± 10′.
⑲—30–31° BTDC @ 6000 RPM (Engine Loaded).
⑳—Bosch W250P21 .014; WG265T2SP .016; Champion N6Y .022.
㉑—30° BTDC @ 6000 RPM (Engine free or loaded).
㉒—Front 0 ± 20′; Rear 50′ ± 20′.
㉓—Front ± 0°; Rear 0° ± 10′.
㉔—35° BTDC @ 6000 RPM (Engine free or loaded).
㉕—27° BTDC @ 2500 RPM; timing chain housing cover.
㉖—8.5 pints.
㉗—Front, 15′ ± 20′; Rear, —30′ ± 15′.
㉘—0°6′ ± 20′.
㉙—Front 0°11′ ± 20′; Rear, —0°30′.
㉚—911 E&S, see note ㉑. 911T, see note ㉔.
㉛—For winter .020.
㉜—27° BTC @ 3500 R.P.M.; red mark on blower wheel notch on blower housing (cap removed).
㉝—3.7 qts.; w/o oil filter 3.2 qts.
㉞—Front, 0′ ± 20′; Rear, —30′ ± 20′.
㉟—Front, + 20′ ± 10′; Rear, 0° + 15′.
㊱—Mark on flywheel notch on engine housing center.

RENAULT

Year	Model	Spark Plug Gap	Breaker Gap	Dwell	Firing Order	Timing	Intake	Exhaust	Oil	Coolant	Caster	Camber	Toe-in
1965	Dauphine "40"	.025	.016	56°	1342	2° BTC①	.006C	.008C	3②	5	10°	0°	⅛–3/16③
1965	R-8	.025	.016	56°	1342	TDC①	.005C	.008C	3②	7	9°	1°40′	1/64
1965	Caravelle 1100	.025	.016	56°	1342	TDC①	.005C	.008C	3②	7	9°	1⅔	1/64
1966–67	Gordini	.025	.016	56°	1342	1° BTC①	.008C	.012C	3②	7½	9°	1°40′	3/64–5/64③
1966–67	R-8	.025	.016	56°	1342	TDC①	.006C	.008C	3②	7½	9°	1°40′	3/64–5/64③
1966–67	Caravelle 1100	.025	.016	56°	1342	TDC①	.006C	.008C	3②	6¼	9°	1°40′	3/64–5/64③
1966–67	Dauphine	.025	.016	56°	1342	TDC①	.006C	.008C	3②	5	10°	1°	⅛–3/16③
1967	Renault 10	.025	.018	56°	1342	TDC①	.006C	.008C	3②	7½	9°±2	1°40′	④
1968	Renault 10	.028	.018	56°	1342	6° ATC①	.006C	.008C	3②	7½	9°±2	1°40′	④
1968	R1190	.028	.016	56°	1342	6° BTC①	.006C	.008C	3②	7½	9°	1⅔°	5/64
1969	Renault 10	.020	.018	56°	1342	TDC①	.006C	.008C	3②	7½	9°±2	1°40′	④
1969	Renault 16	.025	.018	56°	1342	TDC①	.008C	.010C	4½②	7	⑥	0°45′	0 to ⅛″
1970–71	R1190A, 1192	.025	.018	54°–60°	1342	3°ATC⑤	.006	.008	⑦②	7.5	9°±2	1°40′	④⑧
	R1152, 1153	.024	.018	54°–60°	1342	0° ± 1°⑨⑩	.008	.010	4½	7	⑪	0°45′	0 to ⅛″ T.O.⑫

①—Located at crank-pulley.
②—Includes oil filter.
③—Car unloaded.
④—3/64 out to 5/64 in.
⑤—Notch on crankshaft pulley ⅛″ past pointer (with hole) on timing chain cover.
⑥—1°40′ to 2°40′.
⑦—1190A–3; 1192–3.5.
⑧—To be measured with vehicle in half-loaded position.
⑨—1152—notch on flywheel to line-up with "0" mark on clutch housing; 1153—hole on converter plate to line-up with "0" mark on converter housing.
⑩—1153—with timing light; distributor vacuum hose disconnected, engine idling below 800 R.P.M.
⑪—1°40′ to 3°40′.
⑫—With 37MM (1 15/32″) steer. height.

SIMCA

Year	Model	Spark Plug Gap	Breaker Gap	Dwell	Firing Order	Timing	Intake	Exhaust	Oil	Coolant	Caster	Camber	Toe-in
1965	1000	.026	.018–.021		1342	12° BTC①	.013H	.013H	2.6	5.8	9¼°	½°	⅛
1966	All	.024	.018		1342	12° BTC①	.012H	.012H	2.6	5.8	9°	0°	⅛
1967	All	.023	.019		1342	12° BTC①	.011H	.015H	3.1	8	2°–3°	1°–1°45′	⅛
1968	All	.024	.018		1342	12° BTC①	.012H	.012H	2.6	6	2°	¾°	1/12
1969	All	.024	.013		1342	4° BTC①	.012H	.014H	....	....	+1¼	+¼	1/36②
1970–71	All	.024	.013		1342	③	.012H	.014H	....	....	+1¼	+¼	1/36②

①—Located at pulley.
②—Toe-out.
③—Std. Trans. 0°; Auto Trans. 4° BTDC.

TOYOTA

Year	Model	Spark Plug Gap	Breaker Gap	Dwell	Firing Order	Timing	Intake	Exhaust	Oil	Coolant	Caster	Camber	Toe-in
1965–69	Land Cruiser	.032	.018		153624	7° BTDC	.008H	.014H			+1°	+1°	⅛
1965–66	Crown	.032	.018		1243	12° BTDC	.008H	.014H	4	8½	+1°	+1°	5/64
1965	Tiari	.032	.018		1243	8° BTDC	.008H	.014H	4	8½	+1°	+1°	1/32
1965–66	Lite Scout	.032	.018	....	1243	8° BTDC	.008H	.014H	4	10	+1°	+1°	5/64
1966–67	Corona	.032	.018	....	1243	5° BTDC	.008H	.014H	4½	8.4	+½°	+½°	3/64
1967	2000/GT	.032	.018	....	153624	15° BTDC	.138C	.177C	....		+2°	+½°	5/64
1967–69	Crown	.032	.018	....	153624	10° BTDC	.004C	.007C		....	+1°	+1°	3/64
1968–70	Corona	.032	.018		1243	5° BTDC	.008H	.014H	4½	8.4	+½°	+½°	3/64
1968–70	Corolla	.032	.018		1342	5° ATDC	.003C	.007C	4	5	+½°	+½°	5/64
1969–70	Corona Mark II	.030	.018		1342	①	.008H	.014H	4½	7.8	+⅙°	+1¼°	5/64
1971	Corolla	.030	.018	50°–54°	1342	5° ATDC②	.008H⑦	.012H⑦	3③	5.1⑥	1°55′⑧	50′	⅛
	Corona	.029	.018	50°–54°	1342	④	.007C⑤	.013C⑤	4¼③	7.8⑥	·20′±30′	1°20′	¼
	Corona Mark II	.030	.018	50°–54°	1342	④	.007C⑤	.013C⑤	4¼③	7.8⑥	⑨	⑨	5/16
	Crown	.030	.018	38°–44°	153624	TDC②	.007H	.010H	4.8③	10.6	⑩	⑪	3/16

①—Std. Trans. 0° TDC; Auto. Trans. 5° BTDC.
②—@ 650 RPM; located at pulley.
③—Add 1 qt. when replacing oil filter.
④—Exc. Calif., TDC; Calif., 10° BTDC on crank pulley.
⑤—Hot; intake .008; exhaust .014.
⑥—W/O heater.
⑦—Cold; intake .003; exhaust .007.
⑧—KE26, 1°40′.
⑨—Caster; 10′ +45 —15; Camber; 1°15′ ±30′.
⑩—MS 55; 45′ +45 —15′; MS 53; 55′ +45′ —15′.
⑪—MS 53, 55; 25′ ±30′.

Continued

Year	Model	Spark Plug Gap, In.	Ignition				Valve Lash		Capacities		Wheel Alignment		
			Breaker Gap, In.	Dwell Angle Deg.	Firing Order	Timing Mark & Location	In-take	Ex-haust	Engine Oil Qts.	Coolant Qts. W/Heater	Cas-ter	Cam-ber	Toe-in

TRIUMPH

Year	Model	Spark Plug Gap, In.	Breaker Gap, In.	Dwell Angle Deg.	Firing Order	Timing Mark & Location	Intake	Exhaust	Engine Oil Qts.	Coolant Qts. W/Heater	Caster	Camber	Toe-in
1965	1200	.025	.015	....	1342	10° BTC①	.010C	.010C	4.2	5.1	4°	2°	1/16
	TR4	.025	.015	....	1342	4° BTC①	.010C	.010C	6	8.4	②	2°	1/16
	Spitfire 4	③	.015	....	1342	13° BTC①	.010C	.010C	4.2	6.3	4°	2°	1/32
	Sports 6	.025	.015	....	153624	10° BTC①	.010C	.010C	4.2	8.4	4°	2°	1/32
1966–68	TR4	.025	.015	....	1342	4° BTC①	.010C	.010C	6.6	8.4	2°40′	0°	1/16
	1200	.025	.015	....	1342	15° BTC①	.010C	.010C	4.2	....	4°	2°	1/16
	Spitfire 4	.025	.015	....	1342	13° BTC①	.010C	.010C	4.2	5.7	4°	2°	1/16
	2000	.025	.015	....	153624	8° BTC①	.010C	.010C	4	6¾	2½°	¾°	1/16
	Sports 6	.025	.015	....	153624	8° BTC①	.010C	.010C	4	6¾	2½°	¾°	1/16
	GT6	.025	.020	....	153624	13° BTC①	.010C	.010C	4	6¾	4°	2°	1/16
1969–70	TR6	.025	.015	...	153624	4° ATC①	.010	.010	4.7	6.6	1°	④	1/16–1/8
	GT6 +	.025	.020	....	153624	4° ATC①	.010	.010	4.7	6.6	1°	⑤	1/16–1/8
	Spitfire Mk III	.025	.015	....	1342	2° ATC①	.010C	.010C	4.2	4.8	+4°	+2°	0–1/16
1971	TR-6	.025	.015	32°-38°	153624	①	.010	.010	4.8	6.6	2¾°⑥	¼°⑥	1/16
	GT-6X	.025	.015	40°-42°	153624	①	.010	.010	4.8	6.6	4°⑥	2°⑥	1/16
	Spitfire	.025	.015	40°-42°	1342	①	.010	.010	4.8	4.5	4½°⑥	2°⑥	1/16

①—Located on pulley.
②—From Ser. No. CT6343 w/wire wheels & CT6390 w/disc wheels 3°; all others 0°.
③—High compression .026"; low compression .030".
④—+½° ±1°.
⑤—2¾° ±1°.
⑥—Plus or minus ½°.

VOLKSWAGEN

Year	Model	Spark Plug Gap, In.	Breaker Gap, In.	Dwell Angle Deg.	Firing Order	Timing Mark & Location	Intake	Exhaust	Engine Oil Qts.	Coolant Qts. W/Heater	Caster	Camber	Toe-in
1965–70	1200	.026	.016	①	1432	10°②	③	④	2¾	....	+2°	⑤	1/8"
	1300	.026	.016	48–52	1432	7½°②	⑥	⑦	2¾	....	+2°	⑧	1/8"
	1500	.026	.016	⑨	1432	⑩	⑪	⑫	⑬	.....	⑭	⑮	1/8"
	1600	.026	.016	47–53	1432	⑯	.004	.004	⑬	....	+11¼°	⑰	1/8"
1971	Type 1	.028	.016	47°–53°	1432	5°ATDC	.004	.004	2.7	....	....	....	....
	1600	.028	.016	47°–53°	1432	TDC②	.004	.004	2.5	....	+11¼°	⑰	1/8"

①—Bosch Dist. from 8-1964 54-58; VW Dist. 48-52.
②—Located at pulley.
③—To 9205699 .008; From 9205700 .004.
④—To 9205699 .012; From 9205700 .004.
⑤—DeLuxe to 8-1965 Front + ⅔°; Rear 3° (Car Unloaded). Sedan from 8-1965 Front + ½°; Rear 3° (Car Unloaded).
⑥—To 710799 .008; From 710800 .004.
⑦—To 710799 .012; From 710800 .004.
⑧—Front + ½°; Rear 3° (Car Unloaded).
⑨—Exc. VW-113-905-205-H Dist. 47-53. With VW-113-905-205-H Dist. 48-52.
⑩—1965-66 10°; 1967 7½°; 1968 TDC (All Located At Pulley).
⑪—To 672748 (w/1 Carb.) .008. From 672749 (W/1 Carb.) .004. To 672697 (w/2 Carbs.) .008. From 672698 (w/2 Carbs.) .004. 1967-68 All .004.
⑫—To 672748 (w/1 Carb.) .012. From 672749 (w/1 Carb.) .004. To 672697 (w/2 Carbs.) .012. From 672698 (w/2 Carbs.) .004. 1967–68 All .004.
⑬—1965–68 2¾; 1969–70 2½.
⑭—1965–66 +11¼°; 1967–68 +2°.
⑮—1965–66 Front +1⅓°; Rear 3° (Car Unloaded). 1967–70 Front +½°; Rear 3° (Car Unloaded).
⑯—Remove Air Intake Housing Cover. 1965–67 7½°; 1968–70 TDC.
⑰—Front +1⅓°; Rear 3°.

VOLVO

Year	Model	Spark Plug Gap, In.	Breaker Gap, In.	Dwell Angle Deg.	Firing Order	Timing Mark & Location	Intake	Exhaust	Engine Oil Qts.	Coolant Qts. W/Heater	Caster	Camber	Toe-in
1965–68	B14A, 16A & B	.028	.016	47°–50°	1342	③	④	④	②	9	⑤	⑥	1/16
	B18D	.028	.016	60°–63°	1342	⑦	⑧	⑧	3½⑩	9①	⑤	⑥	1/16
	B18B	.028	.016	⑪	1342	⑫	.021C	.021C	3½⑩	9½	⑤	⑥	1/16
1969–71	140, B20B	.028	.016	60°	1342	⑬	.021C	.021C	3½⑩	9①	⑤	⑥	1/16
	164, B30A	.028	.010	40°	153624	⑬	.017C	.017C	5½⑩	13	⑤	⑥	1/16
1969	180S, B20B	.028	.016	60°	1342	⑬	.021C	.021C	3½⑩	9½	⑤	⑥	1/16
1970–71	180E, B20E	.028	.016	60°	1342	⑬	.017C	.017C	3½⑩	9½	⑤	⑥	1/16

①—For 100 H.P. B18D eng. add ½ qt.
②—B14A eng. 3½ qt.; B16A & B 3 qt. (Add ½ qt. with oil change).
③—B14A eng. 3°–5° Static; B16A & B eng. 4–6° Static.
④—B14A & B eng. .020–.022; B16A eng. .016–.018.
⑤—Except following models 0° to +1°; P444, 445, 544, 1100, 2100 ¾° to +¼°.
⑥—Except following models 0 to +½; P444, 445, 544, 1000, 2100 ¼° to +½°.
⑦—17°–19° BTDC @ 1500 RPM.
⑧—90 H.P. eng. .016–.018; 95 & 100 H.P. eng. .020–.022.
⑨—100 H.P. eng. add ½ qt.
⑩—Add ½ qt. with filter change.
⑪—Less smog control 60°–63°; with smog control 60°.
⑫—Less smog control 17°–19° BTDC @ 1500 RPM; with smog control 5° BTDC @ 800 RPM. (If equipped with vacuum line, disconnect while adjusting timing.)
⑬—Smog control 10° BTDC vacuum line disconnected.

1946-65 Tune Up Data & Wheel Alignment

Year	Engine or Car Model	Spark Plug Gap	Distributor Point Gap	Distributor Dwell Angle	Firing Order	Ignition Timing BTDC or Mark	Ignition Timing Mark Location	Valve Lash Intake	Valve Lash Exhaust	Wheel Alignment Caster Degrees	Wheel Alignment Camber Degrees	Wheel Alignment Toe-In Inch
BUICK												
1946–49	All Models	.025	.016	21–30	16258374	"ADV"	Flywheel	.015H①	.015H①	+⅜	+⅜	1/32
1950–52	All Models	.025	.016	21–30	16258374	"ADV"	Flywheel	.015H①	.015H①	+¾	+⅜	3/32
1953	Series 40	.025	.016	21–30	16258374	"ADV"	Flywheel	.015H	.015H	Zero	+⅜	3/32
	All Others	.032	.016	21–30	12784563②	"ADV"	Flywheel	Zero	Zero	Zero	+⅜	3/32
1954	All	.032	.016	21–30	12784563②	5°	Damper	Zero	Zero	−¼	+⅜	1/32
1955	All Models	.032	.016	26–33	12784563②	5°	Damper	Zero	Zero	−⅛	+⅜	0–1/16
1956	All Models	.032	.016	26–33	12784563②	5°	Damper	Zero	Zero	−½	+⅜	1/16–⅛
1957	All Models	.032	③	30	12784563②	5°	Damper	Zero	Zero	−1¾	+½	1/16–⅛
1958	All Models	.032	③	30	12784563②	④	Damper	Zero	Zero	−½	+½	1/16–⅛
1959	364, 401, Std. Tr.	.032	.016③	30	12784563②	5°	Damper	Zero	Zero	−1½	+½	1/16–5/32
	364, 401 Auto. Tr.	.032	.016③	30	12784563②	12°	Damper	Zero	Zero	−1½	+½	1/16–5/32
1960	364, 401 Std. Tr.	.032	.016③	30	12784563②	5°	Damper	Zero	Zero	−2	+½	1/16–5/32
	364, 401 Auto. Tr.	.032	.016③	30	12784563②	12°	Damper	Zero	Zero	−2	+½	1/16–5/32
1961–62	364, 401	.032	.016③	30	12784563②	12°	Damper	Zero	Zero	−2	+⅓	3/16–5/32
	V6-198	.035	.016③	30	165432⑤	5°	Damper	Zero	Zero	−2	−⅝	7/32–5/16
	V8-215	.035	.016③	30	18436572⑥	5°	Damper	Zero	Zero	−2	−⅝	7/32–5/16
1963	401, 425 Std. Tr.	.035	.016③	30	12784563②	5°	Damper	Zero	Zero	−½	+⅓	7/32–5/16
	401, 425 Auto. Tr.	.035	.016③	30	12784563②	12°	Damper	Zero	Zero	−½	+⅓	7/32–5/16
	V6-198	.035	.016③	30	165432⑤	5°	Damper	Zero	Zero	−2	−⅝	7/32–5/16
	V8-215	.035	.016③	30	18436572⑥	5°	Damper	Zero	Zero	−2	−⅝	7/32–5/16
1964	V6-225	.035	.016③	30	165432⑤	5°	Damper	Zero	Zero	−½	+½	7/32–5/16
	V8-300 Special	.035	.016③	30	18436572⑥	2½°	Damper	Zero	Zero	−½	+½	7/32–5/16
	V8-300 LeSabre	.035	.016③	30	18436572⑥	2½°	Damper	Zero	Zero	−½	+¼	7/32–5/16
	V8-401, 425	.035	.016③	30	12784563②	2½°⑦	Damper	Zero	Zero	−½	+¼	7/32–5/16
1965	V6-225	.035	.016③	30	165432⑤	5°	Damper	Zero	Zero	−½	+½	⅛–¼
	V8-300 Special	.035	.016③	30	18436572⑥	2½°	Damper	Zero	Zero	−½	+½	⅛–¼
	V8-300 Le Sabre	.035	.016③	30	18436572⑥	2½°	Damper	Zero	Zero	+1	+½	7/32–5/16
	V8-401, 425	.035	.016③	30	12784563②	2½°⑦	Damper	Zero	Zero	+1	+½	7/32–5/16

①—With mechanical valve lifters. Zero lash with hydraulic lifters.
②—Cylinders numbering (front to rear): Right bank 1-3-5-7, left bank 2-4-6-8.
③—Turn adjusting screw clockwise until engine begins to misfire, then back off screw ½ turn.
④—Std. Trans. 5°, Auto. Trans. 12°.
⑤—Cylinders numbering (Front to rear): Right bank 2-4-6, Left bank 1-3-5.
⑥—Cylinders numbering (Front to rear): Right bank 2-4-6-8, Left bank 1-3-5-7.
⑦—12° for V8-425 with 2 carbs. and automatic transmission.

Year	Engine or Car Model	Spark Plug Gap	Distributor Point Gap	Distributor Dwell Angle	Firing Order	Ignition Timing BTDC or Mark	Ignition Timing Mark Location	Valve Lash Intake	Valve Lash Exhaust	Wheel Alignment Caster Degrees	Wheel Alignment Camber Degrees	Wheel Alignment Toe-In Inch
CADILLAC												
1946–47	All Models	.030	.016	21–30	18736542①	②	Damper	Zero	Zero	−2⅛	Zero	1/16
1948–51	All Models	.035	.016	21–30	18436572①	③	Damper	Zero	Zero	Zero	Zero	3/32
1952–53	All Models	.035	.0125	31	18436572①	③	Damper	Zero	Zero	Zero	Zero	3/32
1954	All Models	.035	.016	31	18436572①	③	Damper	Zero	Zero	Zero	Zero	3/32
1955	All Models	.035	.016	26–33	18436572①	"A"	Damper	Zero	Zero	−½	Zero	3/16–¼
1956–57	All Models	.035	④	30	18436572①	"A"	Damper	Zero	Zero	−½	Zero	3/16–¼
1958	All Models	.035	④	30	18436572①	5°	Damper	.025"Min.⑤	.025"Min.⑤	−½	Zero	3/16–¼⑥
1959–62	All Models	.035	④	30	18436572①	5°	Damper	.025"Min.⑤	.025"Min.⑤	⑦	⑧	3/16–¼⑥
1963–65	All Models	.035	④	30	18726543①	5°	Damper	Zero	Zero	−1	⑨	3/16–¼

①—Cylinder numbering (front to rear): Left bank 1-3-5-7, right bank 2-4-6-8.
②—"IGA" or "IGN" mark.
③—"A" mark for premium fuel, "C" mark for regular fuel.
④—Turn adjusting screw clockwise until engine begins to misfire, then back out screw ½ turn.
⑤—Clearance between valve stem and rocker arm with hydraulic lifters collapsed and lifters on heel of cam.
⑥—Air suspension cars 1/16".
⑦—1959–60 Ser. 60, 62 −½, Ser. 75 −1¼, 1961–62 All −1.
⑧—1959–60 Zero, 1961–62 −¼.
⑨—Left side Zero; right side −¼.

Year	Engine or Car Model	Spark Plug Gap	Distributor Point Gap	Distributor Dwell Angle	Firing Order	Ignition Timing BTDC or Mark	Ignition Timing Mark Location	Valve Lash Intake	Valve Lash Exhaust	Wheel Alignment Caster Degrees	Wheel Alignment Camber Degrees	Wheel Alignment Toe-In Inch
CHEVELLE												
1964	6-194	.035	①	31–34	153624	8°	Damper	1 Turn③	1 Turn③	−1	+¾	1/16–3/16
	6-230	.035	①	31–34	153624	4°	Damper	1 Turn③	1 Turn③	−1	+¾	1/16–3/16
	V8-283	.035	①	28–32	18436572②	4°	Damper	1 Turn③	1 Turn③	−1	+¾	1/16–3/16
	V8-327, 250 H.P.	.035	①	28–32	18436572②	4°	Damper	1 Turn③	1 Turn③	−1	+¾	1/16–3/16
	V8-327, 300 H.P.	.035	①	28–32	18436572②	8°	Damper	1 Turn③	1 Turn③	−1	+¾	1/16–3/16

Continued

Year	Engine or Car Model	Spark Plug Gap	Point Gap	Dwell Angle	Firing Order	BTDC or Mark	Mark Location	Intake	Exhaust	Caster Degrees	Camber Degrees	Toe-In Inch
			Distributor			**Ignition Timing**		**Valve Lash**		**Wheel Alignment**		

CHEVELLE—Continued

Year	Engine or Car Model	Spark Plug Gap	Point Gap	Dwell Angle	Firing Order	BTDC or Mark	Mark Location	Intake	Exhaust	Caster Degrees	Camber Degrees	Toe-In Inch
1965	6-194	.035	①	31–34	153624	8°	Damper	1 Turn③		④	+½	⅛–¼
	6-230	.035	①	31–34	153624	4°	Damper	1 Turn③		④	+½	⅛–¼
	V8-283, 195 H.P.	.035	①	28–32	18436572②	4°	Damper	1 Turn③		④	+½	⅛–¼
	V8-283, 220 H.P.	.035	①	28–32	18436572②	6°	Damper	1 Turn③		④	+½	⅛–¼
	V8-327, 250 H.P.	.035	①	28–32	18436572②	4°	Damper	1 Turn③		④	+½	⅛–¼
	V8-327, 300 H.P.	.035	①	28–32	18436572②	8°	Damper	1 Turn③		④	+½	⅛–¼
	V8-327, 350 H.P.	.035	①	28–32	18436572③	8°	Damper	1 Turn③		④	+½	⅛–¼

①—New points .019″, used .016″.
②—Cylinder numbering (front to rear): Left bank 1-3-5-7, right bank 2-4-6-8.
③—Turn rocker arm adjusting screw down until all lash is removed. Then turn screw down the additional number of turns specified.
④—Super Sport —½; all others —1.

CHEVROLET

Year	Engine or Car Model	Spark Plug Gap	Point Gap	Dwell Angle	Firing Order	BTDC or Mark	Mark Location	Intake	Exhaust	Caster Degrees	Camber Degrees	Toe-In Inch
1946–48	All Models	.040	.022	31–37	153624	Ball	Flywheel	.006H	.013H	Zero	−¼	1/32
1949–52	Std. Trans.	.035	.022	31–37	153624	Ball	Flywheel	.006H	.013H	+½	+½	1/16
1950–52	Powerglide	.035	.022	31–37	153624	Ball	Flywheel	1½ Turns②		+½	+½	1/16
1953	Std. Trans.	.035	.016	38–45	153624	①	Flywheel	.006H	.013H	+½	+½	⅛
	Powerglide	.035	.016	38–45	153624	①	Flywheel	1½ Turns②		+½	+½	⅛
1954	Std. Trans.	.035	.016	38–45	153624	Ball	Flywheel	.006H	.016H	+½	+½	⅛
	Powerglide	.035	.016	38–45	153624	Ball	Flywheel	1½ Turns②		+½	+½	⅛
1955	6 Std. Trans.	.035	③	28–35	153624	Ball	Flywheel	.006H	.013H	Zero	+½	⅛–3/16
	6 Powerglide	.035	③	28–35	153624	Ball	Flywheel	1½ Turns②		Zero	+½	⅛–3/16
	V8 Std. Trans.	.035	③	26–33	18436572④	4°	Damper	.008H	.016H	Zero	+½	⅛–3/16
	V8 Powerglide	.035	③	26–33	18436572④	4°	Damper	1 Turn②		Zero	+½	⅛–3/16
1956–57	Six	.035	③	28–35	153624	Ball	Flywheel	1½ Turns③		+1	+½	⅛–3/16
	V8	.035	③	26–33	18436572④	4°	Damper	1 Turn②		+1	+½	⅛–3/16
1958	Six	.035	③	28–35	153624	Ball	Flywheel	1½ Turns		Zero	+½	1/16–3/16
	V8	.035	③	30	18436572④	4°	Damper	1 Turn		Zero	+½	1/16–3/16
1959	6-235	.035	③	28–35	153624	Ball	Flywheel	1½ Turns		Zero	+½	1/16–3/16
	8-283	.035	③	30	18436572④	4°	Damper	1 Turn		Zero	+½	1/16–3/16
	8-283 Special Cam	.035	③	30	18436572④	4°	Damper	.012H	.018H	Zero	+½	1/16–3/16
	8-348	.035	③	30	18436572④	8°	Damper	1 Turn		Zero	+½	1/16–3/16
1960–61	6-235 Hydraulic	.035	③	28–35	153624	Ball	Flywheel	1½ Turns		Zero	+½	1/16–3/16
	6-235 Mechanical	.035	③	28–35	153624	Ball	Flywheel	.008H	.015H	Zero	+½	1/16–3/16
	8-283 170 H.P.	.035	③	30	18436572④	4°	Damper	1 Turn⑦		Zero	+½	1/16–3/16
	8-283 230 H.P.	.035	③	30	18436572④	4°	Damper	1 Turn⑦		Zero	+½	1/16–3/16
	8-283 Special Cam	.035	③	30	18436572④	4°	Damper	.012H	.018H	Zero	+½	1/16–3/16
	8-348 250 H.P.	.035	③	30	18436572④	8°	Damper	1 Turn⑦		Zero	+½	1/16–3/16
	8-348 280 H.P.	.035	⑤	⑥	18436572④	8°	Damper	1 Turn⑦		Zero	+½	1/16–3/16
	8-348 305 H.P.	.035	③	30	18436572④	8°	Damper	1 Turn⑦		Zero	+½	1/16–3/16
	8-348 320 H.P.	.035	③	30	18436572④	8°	Damper	.008H	.018H	Zero	+½	1/16–3/16
	8-348 335 H.P.	.035	⑤	⑥	18436572④	12°	Damper	.008H	.018H	Zero	+½	1/16–3/16
	8-348 340 H.P. (1961)	.035	③	30	18436572④	8°	Damper	.008H	.018H	Zero	+½	1/16–3/16
	8-348 350 H.P. (1961)	.035	⑤	⑥	18436572④	8°	Damper	.008H	.018H	Zero	+½	1/16–3/16
	8-409 360 H.P. (1961)	.035	③	30	18436572④	12°	Damper	.008H	.018H	Zero	+½	1/16–3/16
1962	6-235	.035	③	28–35	153624	⑧	Flywheel	1 Turn⑦		Zero	+½	⅛
	V8-283	.035	③	30	18436572④	4°	Damper	1 Turn⑦		Zero	+½	⅛
	V8-327	.035	③	30	18436572④	4°	Damper	1 Turn⑦		Zero	+½	⅛
	V8-327 Special Cam	.035	③	30	18436572④	8°	Damper	.008H	.018H	Zero	+½	⅛
	V8-409	.035	⑤	⑥	18436572④	12°	Damper	.008H	.018H	Zero	+½	⅛
1963	6-230	.035	③	31–34	153624	4°	Damper	1 Turn②		Zero	+½	1/16–3/16
	V8-283	.035	③	30	18436572④	4°	Damper	1 Turn②		Zero	+½	1/16–3/16
	V8-327 250 H.P.	.035	③	30	18436572④	4°	Damper	1 Turn②		Zero	+½	1/16–3/16
	V8-327 300 H.P.	.035	③	30	18436572④	8°	Damper	1 Turn②		Zero	+½	1/16–3/16
	V8-409 340 H.P.	.035	③	30	18436572④	6°	Damper	1 Turn②		Zero	+½	1/16–3/16
	V8-409 400 H.P.	.035	③	30	18436572④	12°	Damper	⑨		Zero	+½	1/16–3/16

Continued

CHRYSLER—Continued

Year	Engine or Car Model	Spark Plug Gap	Distributor		Firing Order	Ignition Timing		Valve Lash		Wheel Alignment		
			Point Gap	Dwell Angle		BTDC or Mark	Mark Location	Intake	Exhaust	Caster Degrees	Camber Degrees	Toe-In Inch
1963	V8-409 425 H.P.	.035	③	30	18436572④	12°	Damper	⑨		Zero	+½	1/16-3/16
1964	6-230	.035	③	31-43	153624	4°	Damper	1 Turn②		Zero	+½	1/32-3/32
	V8-283	.035	③	30	18436572④	4°	Damper	1 Turn②		Zero	+½	1/32-3/32
	V8-327, 250 H.P.	.035	③	30	18436572④	4°	Damper	1 Turn②		Zero	+½	1/32-3/32
	V8-327, 300 H.P.	.035	③	30	18436572④	8°	Damper	1 Turn②		Zero	+½	1/32-3/32
	V8-409, 340 H.P.	.035	③	30	18436572④	6°	Damper	1 Turn②		Zero	+½	1/32-3/32
	V8-409, 400 H.P.	.035	③	30	18436572④	12°	Damper	⑨		Zero	+½	1/32-3/32
	V8-409, 425 H.P.	.035	③	30	18436572④	12°	Damper	⑨		Zero	+½	1/32-3/32
1965	6-230	.035	③	31-34	153624	4°	Damper	1 Turn②		+¾	+¼	1/8-1/4
	V8-283, 195 H.P.	.035	③	30	18436572④	4°	Damper	1 Turn②		+¾	+¼	1/8-1/4
	V8-283, 4 Bar. Carb.	.035	③	30	18436572④	4°	Damper	1 Turn②		+¾	+¼	1/8-1/4
	V8-327, 250 H.P.	.035	③	30	18436572④	4°	Damper	1 Turn②		+¾	+¼	1/8-1/4
	V8-327, 300 H.P.	.035	③	30	18436572④	8°	Damper	1 Turn②		+¾	+¼	1/8-1/4
	V8-396, 325 H.P.	.035	③	30	18436572④	4°⑩	Damper	1 Turn②		+¾	+¼	1/8-1/4
	V8-396, 425 H.P.	.035	③	30	18436572④	10°	Damper	.020H	.024H	+¾	+¼	1/8-1/4
	V8-409, 340 H.P.	.035	③	30	18436572④	6°	Damper	1 Turn②		+¾	+¼	1/8-1/4
	V8-409, 400 H.P.	.035	③	30	18436572④	12°	Damper	.018H	.030H	+¾	+¼	1/8-1/4

①—Before Engine No. LAA-283230 and LAQ-117209, set timing 7/32" after timing ball. Starting with these engine numbers, set timing at the ball.

②—Turn rocker arm adjusting screw down until all lash is removed. Then turn screw down the additional number of turns specified.

③—New points .019", used points .016".

④—Cylinder numbering (front to rear): Left bank 1-3-5-7, right bank 2-4-6-8.

⑤—New Points .018", used .015".

⑥—Each set of points 28-30° total both sets 33-35°.

⑦—For long travel lifters 2 turns.

⑧—First short vertical line clockwise from ball in flywheel.

⑨—Early production: intake .012H, exhaust .020H. Engines date stamped TO-1118QA or QB: intake .018H, exhaust .030H.

⑩—Transistorized ignition 6° BTDC.

CHEVY II

Year	Engine or Car Model	Spark Plug Gap	Point Gap	Dwell Angle	Firing Order	BTDC or Mark	Mark Location	Intake	Exhaust	Caster Degrees	Camber Degrees	Toe-In Inch
1962-63	4-153	.035	②	31-34	1342	4°	Damper	1 Turn④		+1	+½	1/4
	6-194	.035	②	31-34	153624	8°	Damper	1 Turn④		+1	+½	1/4
1964	4-153	.035	②	31-34	1342	4°	Damper	1 Turn④		+1	+½	3/16-5/16
	6-194	.035	②	31-34	153624	8°	Damper	1 Turn④		+1	+½	3/16-5/16
	6-230	.035	②	31-34	153624	4°	Damper	1 Turn④		+1	+½	3/16-5/16
	V8-283, 195 H.P.	.035	②	30	18436572③	4°	Damper	1 Turn④		+1	+½	3/16-5/16
	V8-283, 220 H.P.	.035	②	30	18436572③	8°	Damper	1 Turn④		+1	+½	3/16-5/16
1965	4-153	.035	②	31-34	1342	4°	Damper	1 Turn④		+1	+½	1/4-3/8
	6-194	.035	②	31-34	153624	8°	Damper	1 Turn④		+1	+½	1/4-3/8
	6-230	.035	②	31-34	153624	4°	Damper	1 Turn④		+1	+½	1/4-3/8
	V8-283, 195 H.P.	.035	②	30	18436572③	4°	Damper	1 Turn④		+1	+½	1/4-3/8
	V8-283, 220 H.P.	.035	②	30	18436572③	6°	Damper	1 Turn④		+1	+½	1/4-3/8
	V8-327, 250 H.P.	.035	③	30	18436572③	4°	Damper	1 Turn④		+1	+½	1/4-3/8
	V8-327, 300 H.P.	.035	②	30	18436572③	8°	Damper	1 Turn④		+1	+½	1/4-3/8

①—For long travel lifters 2 turns.

②—New points .019", used points .016".

③—Cylinder numbering (front to rear): Left bank 1-3-5-7, right bank 2-4-6-8.

④—Turn rocker arm adjusting screw down until all lash is removed. Then turn screw down the additional number of turns specified.

CHRYSLER

Year	Engine or Car Model	Spark Plug Gap	Point Gap	Dwell Angle	Firing Order	BTDC or Mark	Mark Location	Intake	Exhaust	Caster Degrees	Camber Degrees	Toe-In Inch
1946-48	Six	.025	.020	35-38	153624	②	Damper	.008H	.010H	Zero	+⅜	1/32
	Eight	.025	.017	37-30	16258374	②	Damper	.008H③	.010H③	Zero	+⅜	1/32
1949-50	Six	.035	.020	35-38	153624	"0"	Damper	.008H	.010H	-2	+⅜	1/32
	Eight	.035	.017	27-30	16258374	"0"	Damper	.008H③	.010H③	-2	+⅜	1/32
1951-52	Six	.035	.020	35-38	153624	②	Damper	.008H	.010H	-2	Zero	Zero
	V8	.035	.017	④	18436572⑤	"0"	Damper	Zero	Zero	-2	Zero	Zero
1953-54	Six	.035	.020	35-38	153624	"0"	Damper	.008H	.010H	-2	Zero	Zero
	V8	.035	.017	④	18436572⑤	⑥	Damper	Zero	Zero	-2	Zero	Zero
1955	300	.035	.017	④	18436572⑤	10°	Damper	.015H	.024H	⑨	⑩	0-1/16
	Others	.035	.017	④	18436572⑤	6°	Damper	Zero	Zero	⑨	⑩	0-1/16
1956	Windsor	.035	.017	31	18436572⑤	2°	Damper	Zero	Zero	⑨	⑩	1/8
	New Yorker	.035	.017	⑦	18436572⑤	4°	Damper	Zero	Zero	⑨	⑩	1/8
	300B	.035	.017	31	18436572⑤	8°	Damper	.015H	.024H	⑨	⑩	1/8

Continued

Year	Engine or Car Model	Spark Plug Gap	Distributor		Firing Order	Ignition Timing		Valve Lash		Wheel Alignment		
			Point Gap	Dwell Angle		BTDC or Mark	Mark Location	Intake	Exhaust	Caster Degrees	Camber Degrees	Toe-In Inch
CHRYSLER—Continued												
1957	300C	.035	.017	[8]	18436572[5]	4°	Damper	.015H	.024H	[11]	[12]	3/32-5/32
	New Yorker	.035	.017	[8]	18436572[5]	6°	Damper	Zero	Zero	[11]	[12]	3/32-5/32
	Others	.035	.017	29	18436572[5]	6°	Damper	Zero	Zero	[11]	[12]	3/32-5/32
1958	V8-354	.035	.017	27-32	18436572[5]	[13]	Damper	.060-.210[14]		[15]	[12]	3/32-5/32
	V8-392 New Yorker	.035	.017	[8]	18436572[5]	6°	Damper	.060-.210[14]		[15]	[12]	3/32-5/32
	V8-392 "300D"	.035	.017	[8]	18436572[5]	6°	Damper	.015H	.024H	[15]	[12]	3/32-5/32
1959	V8-383	.035	.017	27-32	18436572[5]	10°	Damper	.060-.210[14]		−3/4	[12]	1/8
	V8-413	.035	.017	[7]	18436572[5]	10°	Damper	.060-.210[14]		−3/4	[12]	1/8
1960	V8-383	.035	.017	27-32	18436572[5]	10°	Damper	.060-.210[14]		[11]	[16]	1/8
	V8-413 New Yorker	.035	.017	27-32	18436572[5]	10°	Damper	.060-.210[14]		[11]	[16]	1/8
	V8-413 "300F" S.T.	.035	.017	[7]	18436572[5]	10°	Damper	.060-.210[14]		[11]	[16]	1/8
	V8-413 "300F" A.T.	.035	.017	[7]	18436572[5]	5°	Damper	.060-.210[14]		[11]	[16]	1/8
1961	V8-361 Newport	.035	.017	27-32	18436572[5]	10°	Damper	.060-.210[14]		[17]	[18]	1/8
	V8-383 Windsor	.035	.017	27-32	18436572[5]	10°	Damper	.060-.210[14]		[17]	[18]	1/8
	V8-413 New Yorker	.035	.017	27-32	18436572[5]	10°	Damper	.060-.210[14]		[17]	[18]	1/8
	V8-413 "300G" S.T.	.035	.017	[7]	18436572[5]	10°	Damper	.060-.210[14]		[17]	[18]	1/8
	V8-413 "300G" A.T.	.035	.017	[7]	18436572[5]	5°	Damper	.060-.210[14]		[17]	[18]	1/8
1962	V8-361 Newport	.035	.017	27-32	18436572[5]	10°	Damper	.060-.210[14]		[17]	[18]	1/8
	V8-383 "300"	.035	.017	27-32	18436572[5]	10°	Damper	.060-.210[14]		[17]	[18]	1/8
	V8-413 New Yorker	.035	.017	27-32	18436572[5]	10°	Damper	.060-.210[14]		[17]	[18]	1/8
	V8-413 "300H"	.035	.017	[7]	18436572[5]	10°	Damper	.015H	.024H	[17]	[18]	1/8
1963	V8-361 Newport	.035	.017	27-32	18436572[5]	10°	Damper	.060-.210[14]		[17]	[18]	1/8
	V8-383 "300"	.035	.017	27-32	18436572[5]	10°	Damper	.060-.210[14]		[17]	[18]	1/8
	V8-413 "300"	.035	.017	[7]	18436572[5]	10°	Damper	.060-.210[14]		[17]	[18]	1/8
	V8-413 New Yorker	.035	.017	28-33	18436572[5]	10°	Damper	.060-.210[14]		[17]	[18]	1/8
	V8-413 "300J"	.035	.017	[7]	18436572[5]	12½°	Damper	.015H	.024H	[17]	[18]	1/8
1964	V8-361 Newport	.035	.017	28-33	18436572[5]	10°	Damper	.060-.210[14]		[17]	[18]	1/8
	V8-383 "300"	.035	.017	28-33	18436572[5]	10°	Damper	.060-.210[14]		[17]	[18]	1/8
	V8-413 "300"	.035	.017	[7]	18436572[5]	10°	Damper	.060-.210[14]		[17]	[18]	1/8
	V8-413 New Yorker	.035	.017	28-33	18436572[5]	10°	Damper	.060-.210[14]		[17]	[18]	1/8
	"300K" 1 Carb.	.035	.017	[7]	18436572[5]	10°	Damper	.060-.210[14]		[17]	[18]	1/8
	"300K" 2 Carbs.	.035	.017	[7]	18436572[5]	12½°	Damper	.017H	.028H	[17]	[18]	1/8
1965	V8-383, 270 H.P.	.035	.017	28-32	18436572[5]	10°	Damper	.060-.210[14]		[17]	[18]	1/8
	V8-383, 315 H.P.	.035	.017	28-32	18436572[5]	10°	Damper	.060-.210[14]		[17]	[18]	1/8
	V8-413, 340 H.P.	.035	.017	28-32	18436572[5]	12½°	Damper	.060-.210[14]		[17]	[18]	1/8
	V8-413, 360 H.P.	.035	.017	[1]	18436572[5]	12½°	Damper	.060-.210[14]		[17]	[18]	1/8

[1]—Each set of points 27-31°; total dwell both sets 36-40°.
[2]—Second line after "0" mark.
[3]—Zero lash for hydraulic valve lifter jobs.
[4]—Each set of points 26-28°, total dwell both sets 32-36°.
[5]—Engine numbering (front to rear): Left bank 1-3-5-7, right bank 2-4-6-8.
[6]—Fourth line after "0" mark.
[7]—Each set of points 27-32°, total dwell both sets 34-40°.
[8]—Each set of points 29-32°, total dwell both sets 36-39°.
[9]—Manual steering −2°, power steering 0°.
[10]—Left side +½°, right side 0°.
[11]—Manual steering −¾°, power steering +¾°.
[12]—Left side +⅜°, right side 0°.
[13]—Windsor 8°, Saratoga 6°.
[14]—With lifter collapsed.
[15]—Manual steering −¾°, Power steering 0°.
[16]—Left side +⅜°, Right side +⅛°.
[17]—Manual Steering −½°, Power Steering +¾°.
[18]—Left side +½°, right side +¼°.

COMET												
1960-61	6 Cyl. Std. Trans.	.034	.025	37-42	153624	4°	Pulley	.016H	.016H	+½	+½	1/4-5/16
	6 Cyl. Auto. Trans.	.034	.025	37-42	153624	10°	Pulley	.016H	.016H	+½	+½	1/4-5/16
1962	6 Cyl. Std. Tr.	.034	.025	37-42	153624	4°	Damper	.016H	.016H	+½	+½	1/4-5/16
	6 Cyl. Auto. Tr.	.034	.025	37-42	153624	10°	Damper	.016H	.016H	+½	+½	1/4-5/16
1963	6-144 Std. Trans.	.034	.025	37-42	153624	8°	Damper	.066-.216[3]		+½	+⅜	1/4-5/16
	6-144 Auto. Trans.	.034	.025	37-42	153624	12°	Damper	.066-.216[2]		+½	+⅜	1/4-5/16
	6-170 Std. Trans.	.034	.025	37-42	153624	6°	Damper	.006-.216[3]		+½	+⅜	1/4-5/16
	6-170 Auto. Trans.	.034	.025	37-42	153624	12°	Damper	.066-.216[3]		+½	+⅜	1/4-5/16
	V8 Std. Trans.	.034	.017	26-31	15426378[1]	6°	Damper	¾ Turn[2]		+½	+⅜	1/4-5/16
	V8 Auto. Trans.	.034	.017	26-31	15426378[1]	10°	Damper	¾ Turn[2]		+½	+⅜	1/4-5/16

Continued

Year	Engine or Car Model	Spark Plug Gap	Distributor Point Gap	Distributor Dwell Angle	Firing Order	Ignition Timing BTDC or Mark	Ignition Timing Mark Location	Valve Lash Intake	Valve Lash Exhaust	Wheel Alignment Caster Degrees	Wheel Alignment Camber Degrees	Wheel Alignment Toe-In Inch

COMET—Continued

Year	Engine or Car Model	Spark Plug Gap	Point Gap	Dwell Angle	Firing Order	BTDC or Mark	Mark Location	Intake	Exhaust	Caster Degrees	Camber Degrees	Toe-In Inch
1964	Six, Std. Trans.	.034	.025	37–42	153624	6°	Damper	.066–.216③		+½	+½	¼–⁵⁄₁₆
	Six, Auto. Trans.	.034	.025	37–42	153624	12°	Damper	.066–.216③		+½	+½	¼–⁵⁄₁₆
	V8, Std. Trans.	.034	.017	26–31	15426378①	6°	Damper	¾ Turn②		+½	+½	¼–⁵⁄₁₆
	V8, Auto. Trans.	.034	.017	26–31	15426378①	10°	Damper	¾ Turn②		+½	+½	¼–⁵⁄₁₆
1965	6-170 Std. Tr.	.034	.025	37–42	153624	6°	Damper	.066–.216③		+¾	+½	¼
	6-170 Auto. Tr.	.034	.025	37–42	153624	12°	Damper	.066–.216③		+¾	+½	¼
	6-200 Std. Tr.	.034	.025	37–42	153624	6°	Damper	.066–.216③④		+¾	+½	¼
	6-200 Auto. Tr.	.034	.025	37–42	153624	12°	Damper	.066–.216③④		+¾	+½	¼
	V8-289	.034	.017	26–31	15426378①	6°	Damper	¾ Turn②		+¾	+½	¼
	V8-289 Hi. Perf.	.030	.020	30–33	15426378①	12°	Damper	.018H	.018H	+¾	+½	¼

①—Engine numbering (front to rear): Right bank 1-2-3-4, left bank 5-6-7-8.
②—Tighten rocker arm adjusting screw to eliminate all push rod end clearance, then tighten screw the number of turns listed.
③—Clearance is obtained at valve stem tip with hydraulic lifter collapsed. If clearance is less than the minimum install an undersize push rod; if clearance is greater than the maximum install an oversize push rod.
④—After 3-29-65, clearance is .067–.200.

CORVAIR

Year	Engine or Car Model	Spark Plug Gap	Point Gap	Dwell Angle	Firing Order	BTDC or Mark	Mark Location	Intake	Exhaust	Caster Degrees	Camber Degrees	Toe-In Inch
1960–61	All	.035	①	31–34	145236⑥	②	Pulley	1 Turn③		④	+1	⑤
1962–63	Turbo-Air, Std. Tr.	.035	①	31–34	145236⑥	4°	Damper	1 Turn③		+1¾	+½	¼–⅜
	Turbo-Air, Auto. Tr.	.035	①	31–34	145236⑥	13°	Damper	1 Turn③		+1¾	+½	¼–⅜
	Monza, Powerglide	.030	①	31–34	145236⑥	13°	Damper	1 Turn③		+1¾	+½	¼–⅜
	Super Turbo-Air	.030	①	31–34	145236⑥	13°	Damper	1 Turn③		+1¾	+½	¼–⅜
	Turbocharged Eng.	.030	①	31–34	145236⑥	24°	Damper	1 Turn③		+1¾	+½	¼–⅜
1964	95 H.P.-Std. Trans.	.035	①	31–34	145236⑥	6°	Damper	1 Turn③		+1¾	Zero	¼–⅜
	95 H.P.-Auto. Trans.	.035	①	31–34	145236⑥	14°	Damper	1 Turn③		+1¾	Zero	¼–⅜
	110 Horsepower	.030	①	31–34	145236⑥	14°	Damper	1 Turn③		+1¾	Zero	¼–⅜
	150 Horsepower	.030	①	31–34	145236⑥	24°	Damper	1 Turn③		+1¾	Zero	¼–⅜
1965	95 H.P.-Std. Trans.	.035	①	31–34	145236⑥	6°	Damper	1 Turn③		+3	+1	¼
	95 H.P.-Auto. Trans.	.035	①	31–34	145236⑥	14°	Damper	1 Turn③		+3	+1	¼
	110 Horsepower	.030	①	31–34	145236⑥	14°	Damper	1 Turn③		+3	+1	¼
	4 Carb. Engine	.030	①	31–34	145236⑥	18°⑦	Damper	1 Turn③		+3	+1	¼
	Turbocharged Eng.	.030	①	31–34	145236⑥	24°	Damper	1 Turn③		+3	+1	¼

①—New points .019″, used .016″.
②—For Dist. No.'s (1110259, 260) 13°. Dist No.'s (1110256-7) 16°. All others 4°.
③—Tighten adjusting screw until all clearance between valve stem and rocker arm has been eliminated. Then tighten screw the additional number of turns listed to center the lifter plunger.
④—1960 +3, 1961 +2.
⑤—1960 ⅛–³⁄₁₆, 1961 ¼–⅜.
⑥—Engine numbering (rear to front): Right bank 1-3-5, left bank 2-4-6.
⑦—With head gasket (Part No. 3891552) set at 14°.

CORVETTE

Year	Engine or Car Model	Spark Plug Gap	Point Gap	Dwell Angle	Firing Order	BTDC or Mark	Mark Location	Intake	Exhaust	Caster Degrees	Camber Degrees	Toe-In Inch
1953–54	All Models	.035	.015	41–47	153624	Ball	Flywheel	.010H	.020H	+½	+½	⅛
1955	Six	.035	.015	41–47	153624	Ball	Flywheel	.006H	.013H	+½	+½	0–⅛
	V8	.035	.019	①	18436572②	4°	Damper	.008H	.018H	+½	+½	0–⅛
1956	All Models	.035	.019	①	18436572②	4°	Damper	.008H	.018H	+½	+½	0–⅛
1957	220 Horsepower	.035	.019	①	18436572②	4°	Damper	1 Turn③		+½	+½	0–⅛
	245 Horsepower	.035	.019	①	18436572②	12°	Damper	1 Turn③		+½	+½	0–⅛
	250 Horsepower	.035	.019	①	18436572②	13°	Damper	1 Turn③		+½	+½	0–⅛
	270 Horsepower	.035	.019	①	18436572②	12°	Damper	1 Turn③		+½	+½	0–⅛
	283 Horsepower	.035	.019	①	18436572②	6°	Damper	.012H	.018H	+½	+½	0–⅛
1958–59	230 Horsepower	.035	④	30	18436572②	4°	Damper	1 Turn③		⑥	⑦	0–⅛
	245 Horsepower	.035	④	30	18436572②	4°	Damper	1 Turn③		⑥	⑦	0–⅛
	250 Horsepower	.035	④	30	18436572②	4°	Damper	1 Turn③		⑥	⑦	0–⅛
	270 Horsepower	.035	⑤	①	18436572②	7°	Damper	.012H	.018H	⑥	⑦	0–⅛
	290 Horsepower	.035	⑤	①	18436572②	14°	Damper	.012H	.018H	⑥	⑦	0–⅛
1960–61	230 Horsepower	.035	④	30	18436572②	4°	Damper	1 Turn③		+2	Zero	⑧
	245 Horsepower	.035	④	30	18436572②	12°	Damper	1 Turn③		+2	Zero	⑧
	270 Horsepower	.035	⑥	①	18436572②	12°	Damper	.012H	.018H	+2	Zero	⑧

Continued

Year	Engine or Car Model	Spark Plug Gap	Distributor Point Gap	Distributor Dwell Angle	Firing Order	Ignition Timing BTDC or Mark	Ignition Timing Mark Location	Valve Lash Intake	Valve Lash Exhaust	Wheel Alignment Caster Degrees	Wheel Alignment Camber Degrees	Wheel Alignment Toe-In Inch
CORVETTE—Continued												
1960-61	275 Horsepower	.035	⑤	①	18436572②	8°	Damper	.012H	.018H	+2	Zero	⑧
	315 Horsepower	.035	⑤	①	18436572②	18°	Damper	.012H	.018H	+2	Zero	⑧
1962	250 Horsepower	.035	④	30	18436572②	4°	Damper	1 Turn③		+2	Zero	¼
	300 Horsepower	.035	④	30	18436572②	8°	Damper	1 Turn③		+2	Zero	¼
	340 Horsepower	.035	⑤	①	18436572②	10°	Damper	.008H	.018H	+2	Zero	¼
	360 Horsepower	.035	⑤	①	18436572②	10°	Damper	.008H	.018H	+2	Zero	¼
1963	250 Horsepower	.035	⑤	30	18436572②	4°	Damper	1 Turn③		+½	+2½	¼
	300 Horsepower	.035	⑤	30	18436572②	8°	Damper	1 Turn③		+½	+2½	¼
	340 Horsepower	.035	⑤	30	18436572②	10°	Damper	.008H	.018H	+½	+2½	¼
	360 Horsepower	.035	⑤	30	18436572②	10°	Damper	.008H	.018H	+½	+2½	¼
1964	250 Horsepower	.035	⑤	30	18436572②	4°	Damper	1 Turn③		+½	+2½	³⁄₁₆-⁵⁄₁₆
	300 Horsepower	.035	⑤	30	18436572②	8°	Damper	1 Turn③		+½	+2½	³⁄₁₆-⁵⁄₁₆
	365 Horsepower	.035	⑤	30	18436572②	10°	Damper	.030H	.030H	+½	+2½	³⁄₁₆-⁵⁄₁₆
	375 Horsepower	.035	⑤	30	18436572②	10°	Damper	.030H	.030H	+½	+2½	³⁄₁₆-⁵⁄₁₆
1965	250 Horsepower	.035	⑤	30	18436572②	4°	Damper	1 Turn③		+1½	+¾	⁷⁄₃₂-¹¹⁄₃₂
	300 Horsepower	.035	⑤	30	18436572②	8°	Damper	1 Turn③		+1½	+¾	⁷⁄₃₂-¹¹⁄₃₂
	350 Horsepower	.035	⑤	30	18436572②	8°	Damper	1 Turn③		+1½	+¾	⁷⁄₃₂-¹¹⁄₃₂
	365 Horsepower	.035	⑥	30	18436572②	12°	Damper	.030H	.030H	+1½	+¾	⁷⁄₃₂-¹¹⁄₃₂
	375 Horsepower	.035	⑤	30	18436572②	12°	Damper	.030H	.030H	+1½	+¾	⁷⁄₃₂-¹¹⁄₃₂
	425 Horsepower	.035	⑥	30	18436572②	10°	Damper	.020H	.024H	+1½	+¾	⁷⁄₃₂-¹¹⁄₃₂

①—Each set of points 28–30°, total dwell both sets 33–35°.
②—Engine numbering (front to rear): Left bank 1-3-5-7, right bank 2-4-6-8.
③—Turn rocker arm adjusting screw clockwise until all lash is eliminated, then turn screw the additional number of turns specified.
④—New points .018", used .015".
⑤—New points .019", used .016".
⑥—1958 +2¼°, 1959 +2°.
⑦—1958 +½°, 1959 Zero.
⑧—1960 0—⅛, 1961 ⅛ + ⅜°.

CROSLEY

Year	Engine or Car Model	Spark Plug Gap	Distributor Point Gap	Distributor Dwell Angle	Firing Order	Ignition Timing BTDC or Mark	Ignition Timing Mark Location	Valve Lash Intake	Valve Lash Exhaust	Wheel Alignment Caster Degrees	Wheel Alignment Camber Degrees	Wheel Alignment Toe-In Inch
1946-52	All Models	.025	.020	46	1-3-4-2	12°	Flywheel	.005C	.007C	10°	2°	³⁄₆₄-¹⁄₁₆

DE SOTO

Year	Engine or Car Model	Spark Plug Gap	Distributor Point Gap	Distributor Dwell Angle	Firing Order	Ignition Timing BTDC or Mark	Ignition Timing Mark Location	Valve Lash Intake	Valve Lash Exhaust	Wheel Alignment Caster Degrees	Wheel Alignment Camber Degrees	Wheel Alignment Toe-In Inch
1946-48	All Models	.030	.020	35–38	153624	"O"	Damper	.008H	.010H	Zero	+⅜	¹⁄₃₂
1949-50	All Models	.035	.020	35–38	153624	①	Damper	.008H	.010H	−2	+⅜	¹⁄₃₂
1951	All Models	.035	.020	35–38	153624	①	Damper	.008H	.010H	−2	Zero	Zero
1952-53	Six	.035	.020	35–38	153624	①	Damper	.008H	.010H	−2	Zero	Zero
	V8	.035	.018	②	18436572③	④	Damper	Zero	Zero	−2	Zero	Zero
1954	Six	.035	.020	39	153624	⑤	Damper	.008H	.010H	−2	Zero	Zero
	V8	.035	.018	②	18436572③	④	Damper	Zero	Zero	−2	Zero	Zero
1955	2 Bar. Carb.	.035	.017	②	18436572③	4°	Damper	Zero	Zero	⑥	⑦	0–¹⁄₁₆
	4 Bar. Carb.	.035	.017	34	18436572③	10°	Damper	Zero	Zero	⑥	⑦	0–¹⁄₁₆
1956	V8-330 2 Bar. Carb.	.035	.017	27–32	18436572③	8°	Damper	Zero	Zero	⑥	⑦	³⁄₃₂-⁵⁄₃₂
	V8-330 4 Bar. Carb.	.035	.017	27–32	18436572③	4°	Damper	Zero	Zero	⑥	⑦	³⁄₃₂-⁵⁄₃₂
	V8-341	.035	.017	27–32	18436572③	6°	Damper	Zero	Zero	⑥	⑦	³⁄₃₂-⁵⁄₃₂
1957	V8-325	.035	.017	27–32	18436572③	6°	Damper	Zero	Zero	⑧	⑨	³⁄₃₂-⁵⁄₃₂
	V8-341	.035	.017	27–32	18436572③	6°	Damper	Zero	Zero	⑧	⑨	³⁄₃₂-⁵⁄₃₂
1958	V8-350, 361 1 Carb.	.035	.017	27–32	18436572③	6°	Damper	.060–.210⑪		⑫	⑨	³⁄₃₂-⁵⁄₃₂
	V8-361 2 Carbs.	.035	.017	⑩	18436572③	8°	Damper	.060–.210⑪		⑫	⑨	³⁄₃₂-⁵⁄₃₂
1959	V8-361, 383 1 Carb.	.035	.017	27–32	18436572③	10°	Damper	.060–.210⑪		⑧	⑨	⅛
	V8-383 Two Carbs.	.035	.017	⑬	18436572③	10°	Damper	.060–.210⑪		⑧	⑨	⅛
1960	V8-361, 383	.035	.017	27–32	18436572③	10°	Damper	.060–.210⑪		⑧	⑦	⅛
1961	V8-361	.035	.017	27–32	18436572③	10°	Damper	.060–.210⑪		⑭	⑮	⅛

①—Third line after "O" mark.
②—Each set of points 26–28°, total dwell both sets 32–36°.
③—Cylinder numbering (front to rear): Left bank 1-3-5-7, right bank 2-4-6-8.
④—Fourth line after "O" mark.
⑤—Second line after "O" mark.
⑥—Manual steering −2°, power steering 0°.
⑦—Left side +⅜°, right side +⅛°.
⑧—Manual steering −¾°, power steering +¾°.
⑨—Left side +⅜°, right side 0°.
⑩—Each set of points 29–32°; total dwell both sets 36–39°.
⑪—With lifter collapsed.
⑫—Manual steering −¾°, power steering 0°.
⑬—Each set of points 27–32°; total dwell both sets 34–40°.
⑭—Manual steering −½°, power steering +¾°.
⑮—Left side +½°, right side +¼°.

DODGE

Year	Engine or Car Model	Spark Plug Gap	Distributor Point Gap	Distributor Dwell Angle	Firing Order	Ignition Timing BTDC or Mark	Ignition Timing Mark Location	Valve Lash Intake	Valve Lash Exhaust	Wheel Alignment Caster Degrees	Wheel Alignment Camber Degrees	Wheel Alignment Toe-In Inch
1946-48	All Models	.025	.020	35-38	153624	(1)	Damper	.008H	.010H	Zero	+3/8	1/16
1949	All Models	.025	.020	35-38	153624	(1)	Damper	.008H	.010H	Zero	+3/8	1/32
1950	All Models	.035	.020	35-38	153624	(1)	Damper	.008H	.010H	Zero	+3/8	1/32
1951-52	All Models	.035	.020	35-38	153624	(1)	Damper	.008H	.010H	Zero	Zero	Zero
1953-54	Six	.035	.020	36-42	153624	(1)	Damper	.010H	.010H	Zero	Zero	Zero
	V8	.035	.017	(2)	18436572(3)	4°	Pulley	Zero	Zero	Zero	Zero	Zero
1955	Six	.035	.020	39	153624	2°	Damper	.010H	.010H	(5)	(6)	0-1/16
	V8	.035	.017	(2)	18436572(3)	4°	Damper	Zero	Zero	(5)	(6)	0-1/16
1956	Six	.035	.020	39	153624	2°	Damper	.010H	.010H	(5)	(6)	3/32-5/32
	V8-270	.035	.017	29-32	18436572(3)	4°	Damper	Zero	Zero	(5)	(6)	3/32-5/32
	V8-315 2 Bar. Carb.	.035	.017	29-32	18436572(3)	6°	Damper	Zero	Zero	(5)	(6)	3/32-5/32
	V8-315 4 Bar. Carb.	.035	.017	29-32	18436572(3)	6°	Damper	.012H	.022H	(5)	(6)	3/32-5/32
1957	Six	.035	.020	39	153624	0°	Damper	.010H	.010H	(7)	(8)	3/32-5/32
	V8-325	.035	.017	29-32	18436572(3)	6°	Damper	Zero	Zero	(7)	(8)	3/32-5/32
	V8-354 One Carb.	.035	.017	29-32	18436572(3)	6°	Damper	Zero	Zero	(7)	(8)	3/32-5/32
	V8-354 Two Carbs.	.035	.017	(4)	18436572(3)	2°	Damper	.015H	.024H	(7)	(8)	3/32-5/32
1958	Six	.035	.020	39	153624	2°	Damper	.010H	.010H	(10)	(8)	3/32-5/32
	V8's	.035	.017	29-32	18436572(3)	6°	Damper	.060-.210(9)		(10)	(8)	3/32-5/32
1959	Six	.035	.020	39	153624	2½°	Damper	.010H	.010H	(7)	(8)	1/8
	V8	.035	.017	29-32	18436572(3)	10°	Damper	.060-.210(9)		(7)	(8)	1/8
1960	Six	.035	.020	36-42	153624	5°	Pulley	.010H	.020H	(7)	(11)	1/8
	V8	.035	.017	27-32	18436572(3)	(12)	Damper	(13)	(14)	(7)	(11)	1/8
1961	6-170, 225	.035	.020	40-45	153624	2½°	Pulley	.010H	.020H	(15)	(16)	1/8
	6-225 4 Bar. Carb.	.028	.020	40-45	153624	10°	Pulley	.010H	.020H	(15)	(16)	1/8
	V8-318 Std. Tr.	.035	.017	27-32	18436572(3)	5°	Damper	.010H	.018H	(15)	(16)	1/8
	V8-318 Auto. Tr.	.035	.017	27-32	18436572(3)	10°	Damper	.010H	.018H	(15)	(16)	1/8
	V8-361 2 Bar. Carb.	.035	.017	27-32	18436572(3)	10°	Damper	.060-.210(9)		(15)	(16)	1/8
	V8-361 4 Bar. Carb.	.035	.017	27-32	18436572(3)	10°	Damper	.016C	.028C	(15)	(16)	1/8
	V8-383	.035	.017	(17)	18436572(3)	7½°	Damper	.016C	.028C	(15)	(16)	1/8
1962	6 Cyl.	.035	.020	40-45	153624	2½°	Pulley	.010H	.020H	(15)	(16)	1/8
	8-318 Std. Tr.	.035	.017	27-32	18436572(3)	5°	Damper	.013H	.021H	(15)	(16)	1/8
	8-318 Auto. Tr.	.035	.017	27-32	18436572(3)	10°	Damper	.013H	.021H	(15)	(16)	1/8
	8-361 "880"	.035	.017	27-32	18436572(3)	10°	Damper	.060-.210(9)		(15)	(16)	1/8
	8-361 Dart, Polara	.035	.017	27-32	18436572(3)	10°	Damper	.060-.210(9)		(15)	(16)	1/8
	8-361 Hi-Perf.	.035	.017	(17)	18436572(3)	10°	Damper	.060-.210(9)		(15)	(16)	1/8
	8-383, 413 Hi-Perf.	.035	.017	(17)	18436572(3)	10°	Damper	.060-.210(9)		(15)	(16)	1/8
	8-413 Ram, Man.	.035	.017	(17)	18436572(3)	10°	Damper	.060-.210(9)		(15)	(16)	1/8
1963	6 Cyl.	.035	.020	40-45	153624	2½°	Damper	.010H	.020H	(15)	(16)	1/8
	8-318 Std. Trans.	.035	.017	28-33	18436572(3)	5°	Damper	.013H	.021H	(15)	(16)	1/8
	8-318 Auto. Trans.	.035	.017	28-33	18436572(3)	10°	Damper	.013H	.021H	(15)	(16)	1/8
	8-361, 383 2 B. Carb.	.035	.017	28-33	18436572(3)	10°	Damper	.060-.210(9)		(15)	(16)	1/8
	8-383 4 B. Carb.	.035	.017	(17)	18436572(3)	10°	Damper	.060-.210(9)		(15)	(16)	1/8
	8-426	.035	.017	(17)	18436572(3)	10°	Damper	.028C	.032C	(15)	(16)	1/8
1964	6 Cyl.	.035	.020	40-45	153624	2½°	Damper	.010H	.020H	(15)	(16)	1/8
	8-273 Std. Trans.	.035	.017	28-33	18436572(3)	5°	Damper	.013H	.021H	(15)	(16)	1/8
	8-273 Auto. Trans.	.035	.017	28-33	18436572(3)	10°	Damper	.013H	.021H	(15)	(16)	1/8
	8-318 Std. Trans.	.035	.017	28-33	18436572(3)	5°	Damper	.013H	.021H	(15)	(16)	1/8
	8-318 Auto. Trans.	.035	.017	28-33	18436572(3)	10°	Damper	.013H	.021H	(15)	(16)	1/8
	8-361, 383 2 B. Carb.	.035	.017	28-33	18436572(3)	10°	Damper	.060-.210(9)		(15)	(16)	1/8
	8-413	.035	.017	28-33	18436572(3)	10°	Damper	.060-.210(9)		(15)	(16)	1/8
	8-383, 426 4 B. Carb.	.035	.017	(17)	18436572(3)	10°	Damper	.060-.210(9)		(15)	(16)	1/8
	8-426 Hemi Charg.	.020	.017	(17)	18436572(3)	(19)	Damper	.028C	.032C	(15)	(16)	1/8
1965	6 Cyl.	.035	.020	40-45	153624	2½°	Damper	.010H	.020H	(15)	(16)	1/8
	8-273 Std. Trans.	.035	.017	28-33	18436572(3)	5°	Damper	.013H	.021H	(15)	(16)	1/8
	8-273 Auto. Trans.	.035	.017	28-33	18436572(3)	10°	Damper	.013H	.021H	(15)	(16)	1/8
	8-273 4 Bar. Carb.	.035	.017	28-33	18436572(3)	10°	Damper	.013H	.021H	(15)	(16)	1/8
	8-318 Std. Trans.	.035	.017	28-33	18436572(3)	5°	Damper	.013H	.021H	(15)	(16)	1/8

Continued

Year	Engine or Car Model	Spark Plug Gap	Distributor		Firing Order	Ignition Timing		Valve Lash		Wheel Alignment		
			Point Gap	Dwell Angle		BTDC or Mark	Mark Location	Intake	Exhaust	Caster Degrees	Camber Degrees	Toe-In Inch

DODGE—Continued

Year	Engine or Car Model	Spark Plug Gap	Point Gap	Dwell Angle	Firing Order	BTDC or Mark	Mark Location	Intake	Exhaust	Caster Degrees	Camber Degrees	Toe-In Inch
1965	8-318 Auto. Trans.	.035	.017	28–33	18436572③	10°	Damper	.013H	.021H	⑮	⑯	⅛
	8-361, 383 2 Bar. Carb.	.035	.017	28–32	18436572③	10°	Damper	.060–.210⑨		⑮	⑯	⅛
	8-383 4 Bar. Carb.	.035	.017	⑳	18436572③	10°	Damper	.060–.210⑨		⑮	⑯	⅛
	8-413	.035	.017	⑳	18436572③	12½°	Damper	.060–.210⑨		⑮	⑯	⅛
	8-426	.035	.017	⑳	18436572③	10°	Damper	.060–.210⑨		⑮	⑯	⅛

①—With Fluid Drive "O", others 2°.
②—Each set of points 26–28°, total dwell both sets 32–36°.
③—Cylinder numbering (front to rear): Left bank 1-3-5-7, right bank 2-4-6-8.
④—Each set of points 29–32°, total dwell both sets 36–39°.
⑤—Manual steering −2°, power steering 0°.
⑥—Left side +½°, right side 0°.
⑦—Manual steering −¾°, power steering +¾°.
⑧—Left side +⅜°, right side 0°.
⑨—With lifters collapsed.
⑩—Manual steering +¼, power steering +¾.
⑪—Left side +⅜°, right side +⅛°.
⑫—V8-383 Ram manifold 7½°, others 10°.
⑬—V8-318 .010H, V8-361, 383 .060–.210 w/lifters collapsed, V8-361, 383 Ram .016C.
⑭—V8-318 .018H, V8-361, 383 .060–.210 w/lifters collapsed, V8-361, 383 Ram .018C.
⑮—Manual steering −½, power steering +¾.
⑯—Left side +½°, right side +¼°.
⑰—Each set of points 27–32°. Total dwell both sets 34–40°.
⑱—Each set 27–31°, total dwell both sets 34–38°.
⑲—With N61Y plugs, 31° at 3000 R.P.M.; with N58R plugs, 34° at 3000 R.P.M.
⑳—Each set of points 27–31°; total dwell both sets 36–40°.

EDSEL

Year	Engine or Car Model	Spark Plug Gap	Point Gap	Dwell Angle	Firing Order	BTDC or Mark	Mark Location	Intake	Exhaust	Caster Degrees	Camber Degrees	Toe-In Inch
1958	Std. Trans.	.034	.015	26–28	15426378①	3°	Damper	Hydraulic		+1②	+1③	⅛
	Auto. Trans.	.034	.015	26–28	15426378①	6°	Damper	Hydraulic		+1②	+1③	⅛
1959–60	6 Cyl. Std. Tr.	.034	.025	35–38	153624	4°	Damper	.019H	.019H	+½	+1¼	⅛
	6 Cyl. Auto. Tr.	.034	.025	35–38	153624	6°	Damper	.019H	.019H	+½	+1¼	⅛
	V8-292 Std. Tr.	.034	.015	26–28	15486372①	3°	Damper	.019H	.019H	+½	+1¼	⅛
	V8-292 Auto. Tr.	.034	.015	26–28	15486372①	6°	Damper	.019H	.019H	+½	+1¼	⅛
	Other V8s Std. Tr.	.034	.015	26–28	15426378①	3°	Damper	Hydraulic		+½	+1¼	⅛
	Other V8s Auto. Tr.	.034	.015	26–28	15426378①	6°	Damper	Hydraulic		+½	+1¼	⅛

①—Cylinder numbering (front to rear): Right bank 1-2-3-4, left bank 5-6-7-8.
②—Corsair and Citation −¾°.
③—Corsair and Citation +⅜°.

FAIRLANE

Year	Engine or Car Model	Spark Plug Gap	Point Gap	Dwell Angle	Firing Order	BTDC or Mark	Mark Location	Intake	Exhaust	Caster Degrees	Camber Degrees	Toe-In Inch
1962	6 Cyl. Std. Trans.	.034	.025	37–42	153624	4°	Damper	.016H	.016H	Zero	+½	⅛
	6 Cyl. Auto. Trans.	.034	.025	37–42	153624	10°	Damper	.016H	.016H	Zero	+½	⅛
	V8 Std. Trans.	.034	.017	26–31	15426378①	4°	Damper	¾ Turn②		Zero	+½	⅛
	V8 Auto. Trans.	.034	.017	26–31	15426378①	12°	Damper	¾ Turn②		Zero	+½	⅛
1963	6 Cyl. Std. Trans.	.034	.025	37–42	153624	6°	Damper	.066–.216③		Zero	Zero	¼
	6 Cyl. Auto. Trans.	.034	.025	37–42	153624	12°	Damper	.066–.216③		Zero	Zero	¼
	V8 Std. Trans.	.034	.017	26–31	15426378①	6°	Damper	¾ Turn②		Zero	Zero	¼
	V8 Auto. Trans.	.034	.017	26–31	15426378①	10°	Damper	¾ Turn②		Zero	Zero	¼
1964	6 Cyl. Std. Trans.	.034	.025	37–42	153624	6°	Damper	.066–.216③		+½	+½	3/16–5/16
	6 Cyl. Auto. Trans.	.034	.025	37–42	153624	12°	Damper	.066–.216③		+½	+½	3/16–5/16
	V8-260 Std. Trans.	.034	.017	26–31	15426378①	6°	Damper	¾ Turn②		+½	+½	3/16–5/16
	V8-260 Auto. Trans.	.034	.017	26–31	15426378①	10°	Damper	¾ Turn②		+½	+½	3/16–5/16
	V8-289 Std. Trans.	.034	.017	26–31	15426378①	6°	Damper	¾ Turn②		+½	+½	3/16–5/16
	V8-289 Auto. Trans.	.034	.017	26–31	15426378①	10°	Damper	¾ Turn②		+½	+½	3/16–5/16
	V8-289 Hi Perf.	.034	.020	33–36	15426378①	10°	Damper	.020H	.020H	+½	+½	3/16–5/16
1965	6-170 Std. Trans.	.034	.025	37–42	153624	6°	Damper	.066–.216③		Zero	+¼	7/32
	6-170 Auto. Trans.	.034	.025	37–42	153624	12°	Damper	.066–.216③		Zero	+¼	7/32
	6-200 Std. Trans.	.034	.025	37–42	153624	6°	Damper	.066–.216③④		Zero	+¼	7/32
	6-200 Auto. Trans.	.034	.025	37–42	153624	12°	Damper	.066–.216③④		Zero	+¼	7/32
	V8-289	.034	.017	26–31	15426378①	6°	Damper	¾ Turn②		Zero	+¼	7/32
	V8-289 Hi Perf.	.030	.020	30–33	15426378①	12°	Damper	.018H	.018H	Zero	+¼	7/32

①—Cylinder numbering (front to rear): right bank 1-2-3-4, left bank 5-6-7-8.
②—Tighten rocker arm adjusting screw to eliminate all push rod end clearance, then tighten screw the number of turns listed.
③—Clearance is obtained at valve stem tip with hydraulic lifter collapsed. If clearance is less than the minimum install an undersize push rod; if greater than the maximum install an oversize push rod.
④—Engines built after 3-29-65 clearance should be .067–.200″.

Year	Engine or Car Model	Spark Plug Gap	Distributor Point Gap	Distributor Dwell Angle	Firing Order	Ignition Timing BTDC or Mark	Ignition Timing Mark Location	Valve Lash Intake	Valve Lash Exhaust	Caster Degrees	Camber Degrees	Toe-In Inch

FALCON

Year	Engine or Car Model	Spark Plug Gap	Point Gap	Dwell Angle	Firing Order	BTDC or Mark	Mark Location	Intake	Exhaust	Caster Degrees	Camber Degrees	Toe-In Inch
1960-62	6 Cyl. Std. Trans.	.034	.025	37–42	153624	4°	Pulley	.016H	.016H	+½	+½	¼-5/16
	6 Cyl. Auto. Trans.	.034	.025	37–42	153624	10°	Pulley	.016H	.016H	+½	+½	¼-5/16
1963	6-144 Std. Trans.	.034	.025	37–42	153624	8°	Damper	.066–.216②		+½	+⅜	¼-5/16
	6-144 Auto. Trans.	.034	.025	37–42	153624	12°	Damper	.066–.216②		+½	+⅜	¼-5/16
	6-170 Std. Trans.	.034	.025	37–42	153624	6°	Damper	.066–.216②		+½	+⅜	¼-5/16
	6-170 Auto. Trans.	.034	.025	37–42	153624	12°	Damper	.066–.216②		+½	+⅜	¼-5/16
	V8 Std. Trans.	.034	.017	26–31	15426378①	6°	Damper	¾ Turn③		+½	+⅜	¼-5/16
	V8 Auto. Trans.	.034	.017	26–31	15426378①	10°	Damper	¾ Turn③		+½	+⅜	¼-5/16
1964	6-144 Std. Trans.	.034	.025	37–42	153624	8°	Damper	.066–.216②		+½	+½	¼-5/16
	6-144 Auto. Trans.	.034	.025	37–42	153624	12°	Damper	.066–.216②		+½	+½	¼-5/16
	6-170 Std. Trans.	.034	.025	37–42	153624	6°	Damper	.066–.216②		+½	+½	¼-5/16
	6-170 Auto. Trans.	.034	.025	37–42	153624	12°	Damper	.066–.216②		+½	+½	¼-5/16
	6-200 Std. Trans.	.034	.025	37–42	153624	6°	Damper	.066–.216②		+½	+½	¼-5/16
	6-200 Auto. Trans.	.034	.025	37–42	153624	12°	Damper	.066–.216②		+½	+½	¼-5/16
	V8 Std. Trans.	.034	.017	26–31	15426378①	6°	Damper	¾ Turn③		+½	+½	¼-5/16
	V8 Auto. Trans.	.034	.017	26–31	15426378①	10°	Damper	¾ Turn③		+½	+½	¼-5/16
1965	6-170 Std. Trans.	.034	.025	37–42	153624	6°	Damper	.066–.216②		+¾	+½	9/32
	6-170 Auto. Trans.	.034	.025	37–42	153624	12°	Damper	.066–.216②		+¾	+½	9/32
	6-200 Std. Trans.	.034	.025	37–42	153624	6°	Damper	.066–.216②④		+¾	+½	9/32
	6-200 Auto. Trans.	.034	.025	37–42	153624	12°	Damper	.066–.216②④		+¾	+½	9/32
	V8-289	.034	.017	26–31	15426378①	6°	Damper	¾ Turn③		−¼	+½	9/32

①—Cylinder numbering (front to rear): right bank 1-2-3-4, left bank 5-6-7-8.
②—Clearance is obtained at valve stem tip with hydraulic lifter collapsed. If clearance is less than the minimum install an undersize push rod; if greater than the maximum install an oversize push rod.
③—Tighten rocker arm adjusting screw to eliminate all push rod end clearance, then tighten screw the number of turns listed.
④—Engines built after 3-29-65 clearance should be .067–.200".

FORD

Year	Engine or Car Model	Spark Plug Gap	Point Gap	Dwell Angle	Firing Order	BTDC or Mark	Mark Location	Intake	Exhaust	Caster Degrees	Camber Degrees	Toe-In Inch
1946	Six	.030	.015	36	153624	①	①	.014C	.014C	+6¾	+⅝	1/16
	V8	.030	.015	36②	15486372③	①	①	.012C	.014C	+6¾	+⅝	1/16
1947	Six	.030	.015	36	153624	①	①	.014C	.014C	+6¾	+⅝	1/16
	V8	.030	.015	36②	15486372③	①	①	.012C	.014C	+6¾	+⅝	1/16
1948	Six	.030	.025	35	153624	Groove	Pulley	.014C	.014C	+6¾	+⅝	1/16
	V8	.030	.015	36②	15486372③	①	①	.012C	.014C	+6¾	+⅝	1/16
1949	Six	.030	.025	36	153624	Groove	Pulley	.010C	.014C	−¼	+½	⅛
	V8	.030	.015	38	15486372③	Groove	Pulley	④	④	−¼	+½	⅛
1950-51	Six	.0300	.025	36	153624	Groove	Pulley	.010C	.014C	−¼	+½	3/16
	V8	.030	.015	28	15486372③	Groove	Pulley	.014C	.018C	−¼	+½	3/16
1952-53	Six	.035	.025	36	153624	Groove	Damper	.015H	.015H	−½	+½	3/32
	V8	.030	.015	28	15486372③	Groove	Pulley	.014C	.018C	−½	+½	3/32
1954	Six	.035	.025	36	153624	3°	Damper	.015H	.015H	+½	+¾	3/32
	V8 Std. Trans.	.035	.015	28	15486372③	3°	Pulley	.019H	.019H	+½	+¾	3/32
	V8 Fordomatic	.035	.015	28	15486372③	6°	Pulley	.019H	.019H	+½	+¾	3/32
1955	Six	.034	.025	35–38	153624	3°	Damper	.015H	.019H	+1	+¾	1/16-⅛
	V8 Std. Trans.	.034	.015	26–28	15486372③	3°	Damper	.019H	.019H	+1	+¾	1/16-⅛
	V8 Fordomatic	.034	.015	26–28	15486372③	6°	Damper	.019H	.019H	+1	+¾	1/16-⅛
1956	Six Std. Trans.	.034	.025	35–38	153624	4°	Damper	.019H	.019H	+1	+¾	1/16-⅛
	Six Fordomatic	.034	.025	35–38	153624	6°	Damper	.019H	.019H	+1	+¾	1/16-⅛
	V8 Std. Trans.	.034	.015	26–28	15486372③	3°	Damper	.019H	.019H	+1	+¾	1/16-⅛
	V8 Fordomatic	.034	.015	26–28	15486372③	6°	Damper	.019H	.019H	+1	+¾	1/16-⅛
1957	Six Std. Trans.	.034	.025	35–38	153624	4°	Damper	.019H	.019H	+1	+1	1/16-⅛
	Six Fordomatic	.034	.025	35–38	153624	6°	Damper	.019H	.019H	+1	+1	1/16-⅛
	V8 Std. Trans.	.034	.015	26–28	15486372③	3°	Damper	.019H	.019H	+1	+1	1/16-⅛
	V8 Fordomatic	.034	.015	26–28	15486372③	6°	Damper	.019H	.019H	+1	+1	1/16-⅛
1958	6-223 Std. Trans.	.034	.025	35–38	153624	4°	Damper	.019H	.019H	+½	+1	1/16-⅛
	6-223 Auto. Trans.	.034	.025	35–38	153624	6°	Damper	.019H	.019H	+½	+1	1/16-⅛
	V8-292 Std. Trans.	.034	.015	26–28	15486372③	3°	Damper	.019H	.019H	+½	+1	1/16-⅛
	V8-292 Auto. Trans.	.034	.015	26–28	15486372③	6°	Damper	.019H	.019H	+½	+1	1/16-⅛
	V8-332 Std. Trans.	.034	.015	26–28	15426378③	3°	Damper	.026H	.026H	+½	+1	1/16-⅛
	V8-332 Auto. Trans.	.034	.015	26–28	15426378③	6°	Damper	.026H	.026H	+½	+1	1/16-⅛

FORD—Continued

Year	Engine or Car Model	Spark Plug Gap	Distributor: Point Gap	Distributor: Dwell Angle	Firing Order	Ignition Timing: BTDC or Mark	Ignition Timing: Mark Location	Valve Lash: Intake	Valve Lash: Exhaust	Wheel Alignment: Caster Degrees	Wheel Alignment: Camber Degrees	Wheel Alignment: Toe-In Inch
1959	6-223 Std. Trans.	.034	.025	37–42	153624	6°	Damper	.019H	.019H	+½	+1	1/32–⅛
	6-223 Auto. Trans.	.034	.025	37–42	153624	12°	Damper	.019H	.019H	+½	+1	1/32–⅛
	V8-292 Std. Trans.	.034	.017	26–31	15486372③	5°	Damper	.019H	.019H	+½	+1	1/32–⅛
	V8-292 Auto. Trans.	.034	.017	26–31	15486372③	12°	Damper	.019H	.019H	+½	+1	1/32–⅛
	V8-332 Std. Trans.	.034	.017	26–31	15426378③	5°	Damper	.062–.1875⑤		+½	+1	1/32–⅛
	V8-332 Auto. Trans.	.034	.017	26–31	15426378③	8°	Damper	.062–.1875⑤		+½	+1	1/32–⅛
	V8-352 Std. Trans.	.034	.017	26–31	15426378③	5°	Damper	.062–.1875⑤		+½	+1	1/32–⅛
	V8-352 Auto. Trans.	.034	.017	26–31	15426378③	8°	Damper	.062–.1875⑤		+½	+1	1/32–⅛
1960	6-223 Std. Trans.	.034	.025	37–42	153624	6°	Damper	.019H	.019H	+⅝	+¾	⅛–¼
	6-223 Auto. Trans.	.034	.025	37–42	153624	10°	Damper	.019H	.019H	+⅝	+¾	⅛–¼
	V8-292 Std. Trans.	.034	.017	26–31	15486372③	5°	Damper	.019H	.019H	+⅝	+¾	⅛–¼
	V8-292 Auto. Trans.	.034	.017	26–31	15486372③	12°	Damper	.019H	.019H	+⅝	+¾	⅛–¼
	V8-352 Std. Trans.	.034	.017	26–31	15426378③	5°	Damper	.078–.218⑤		+⅝	+¾	⅛–¼
	V8-352 Auto. Trans.	.034	.017	26–31	15426378③	8°	Damper	.078–.218⑤		+⅝	+¾	⅛–¼
1961	6-223 Std. Trans.	.034	.025	37–42	153624	6°	Damper	.019H	.019H	Zero	+⅜	⅛–¼
	6-223 Auto. Trans.	.034	.025	37–42	153624	12°	Damper	.019H	.019H	Zero	+⅜	⅛–¼
	V8-292 Std. Trans.	.034	.017	26–31	15486372③	5°	Damper	.019H	.019H	Zero	+⅜	⅛–¼
	V8-292 Auto. Trans.	.034	.017	26–31	15486372③	12°	Damper	.019H	.019H	Zero	+⅜	⅛–¼
	V8-352, 390 Std. Tr.	.034	.017	26–31	15426378③	5°	Damper	.078–.218⑤		Zero	+⅜	⅛–¼
	V8-352, 390 Auto. Tr.	.034	.017	26–31	15426378③	8°	Damper	.078–.218⑤		Zero	+⅜	⅛–¼
	V8-390, 375 H.P.	.034	.020	26–31	15426378③	14°	Damper	.020H	.020H	Zero	+⅜	⅛–¼
	V8-390, 401 H.P.	.034	.020	26–31	15426378③	14°	Damper	.020H	.020H	Zero	+⅜	⅛–¼
1962	6-223 Std. Tr.	.034	.025	37–42	153624	6°	Damper	.025H	.025H	Zero	+⅜	⅛–¼
	6-223 Auto. Tr.	.034	.025	37–42	153624	12°	Damper	.025H	.025H	Zero	+⅜	⅛–¼
	V8-292 Std. Tr.	.034	.017	26–31	15486372③	5°	Damper	.019H	.019H	Zero	+⅜	⅛–¼
	V8-292 Auto. Tr.	.034	.017	26–31	15486372③	12°	Damper	.019H	.019H	Zero	+⅜	⅛–¼
	V8-352, 390 Std. Tr.	.034	.017	26–31	15426378③	5°	Damper	.078–.218⑤		Zero	+⅜	⅛–¼
	V8-352, 390 Auto. Tr.	.034	.017	26–31	15426378③	8°	Damper	.078–.218⑤		Zero	+⅜	⅛–¼
	V8-390, 375 H.P.	.034	.020	26–31	15426378③	5°	Damper	.025H	.025H	Zero	+⅜	⅛–¼
	V8-390, 401 H.P.	.034	.020	26–31	15426378③	5°	Damper	.025H	.025H	Zero	+⅜	⅛–¼
	V8-406, 385 H.P.	.034	.020	26–31	15426378③	8°	Damper	.025H	.025H	Zero	+⅜	⅛–¼
	V8-406, 405 H.P.	.034	.020	26–31	15426378③	8°	Damper	.025H	.025H	Zero	+⅜	⅛–¼
1963	6-223 Std. Trans.	.034	.025	37–42	153624	4°	Damper	.025H⑧	.025H⑧	Zero	+⅜	⅛–¼
	6-223 Auto. Trans.	.034	.025	37–42	153624	10°	Damper	.025H⑧	.025H⑧	Zero	+⅜	⅛–¼
	V8-260 Std. Trans.	.034	.017	26–31	15426378③	6°	Damper	¾ Turn⑨		Zero	+⅜	⅛–¼
	V8-260 Auto. Trans.	.034	.017	26–31	15426378③	10°	Damper	¾ Turn⑨		Zero	+⅜	⅛–¼
	V8-289 Std. Trans.	.034	.017	26–31	15426378③	6°	Damper	¾ Turn⑨		Zero	+⅜	⅛–¼
	V8-289 Auto. Trans.	.034	.017	26–31	15426378③	10°	Damper	¾ Turn⑨		Zero	+⅜	⅛–¼
	V8-352 Std. Trans.	.034	.017	26–31	15426378③	5°	Damper	.083–.183⑩		Zero	+⅜	⅛–¼
	V8-352 Auto. Trans.	.034	.017	26–31	15426378③	8°	Damper	.083–.183⑩		Zero	+⅜	⅛–¼
	V8-390 Std. Trans.⑥	.034	.017	26–31	15426378③	5°	Damper	.083–.183⑩		Zero	+⅜	⅛–¼
	V8-390 Auto. Trans.⑥	.034	.017	26–31	15426378③	8°	Damper	.083–.183⑩		Zero	+⅜	⅛–¼
	V8-390⑦	.034	.017	26–31	15426378③	6°	Damper	.083–.183⑩		Zero	+⅜	⅛–¼
	V8-390, 330 H.P.	.034	.017	26–31	15426378③	10°	Damper	.025H	.025H	Zero	+⅜	⅛–¼
	V8-406, 427	.035	.017	26–31	15426378③	5°	Damper	.025H	.025H	Zero	+⅜	⅛–¼
	V8-406, 427 2 Carbs.	.034	.017	26–31	15426378③	8°	Damper	.025H	.025H	Zero	+⅜	⅛–¼
1964	6-223 Std. Trans.	.034	.025	37–42	153624	4°	Damper	.025H⑧	.025H⑧	Zero	+⅝	⅛–¼
	6-223 Auto. Trans.	.034	.025	37–42	153624	10°	Damper	.025H⑧	.025H⑧	Zero	+⅝	⅛–¼
	V8-289 Std. Trans.	.034	.017	26–31	15426378③	6°	Damper	¾ Turn⑨		Zero	+⅝	⅛–¼
	V8-289 Auto. Trans.	.034	.017	26–31	15426378③	10°	Damper	¾ Turn⑨		Zero	+⅝	⅛–¼
	V8-352 Std. Trans.	.034	.017	26–31	15426378③	6°	Damper	⑪		Zero	+⅝	⅛–¼
	V8-352 Auto. Trans.	.034	.017	26–31	15426378③	10°	Damper	⑪		Zero	+⅝	⅛–¼
	V8-390 Std. Trans.	.034	.017	26–31	15426378③	4°	Damper	⑪		Zero	+⅝	⅛–¼
	V8-390 Auto. Trans.	.034	.017	26–31	15426378③	6°	Damper	⑪		Zero	+⅝	⅛–¼
	V8-390 H.P. Std. Tr.	.034	.017	26–31	15426378③	4°	Damper	.025H	.025H	Zero	+⅝	⅛–¼
	V8-390 H.P. Auto. Tr.	.034	.017	26–31	15426378③	6°	Damper	.025H	.025H	Zero	+⅝	⅛–¼
	V8-427	.034	.017	26–31	15426378③	8°	Damper	.025H	.025H	Zero	+⅝	⅛–¼

Continued

Year	Engine or Car Model	Spark Plug Gap	Distributor		Firing Order	Ignition Timing		Valve Lash		Wheel Alignment		
			Point Gap	Dwell Angle		BTDC or Mark	Mark Location	Intake	Exhaust	Caster Degrees	Camber Degrees	Toe-In Inch

FORD—Continued

Year	Engine or Car Model	Spark Plug Gap	Point Gap	Dwell Angle	Firing Order	BTDC or Mark	Mark Location	Intake	Exhaust	Caster Degrees	Camber Degrees	Toe-In Inch
1965	6-240 Std. Trans.	.034	.025	37–42	153624	6°	Damper	¾ Turn⑨		+1	+½	5/32
	6-240 Auto. Trans.	.034	.025	37–42	153624	8°	Damper	¾ Turn⑨		+1	+½	5/32
	V8-289	.034	.017	26–31	15426378③	6°	Damper	¾ Turn⑨		+1	+½	5/32
	V8-352	.034	.017	26–31	15426378③	6°	Damper	.050–.150⑩		+1	+½	5/32
	V8-390 Std. Trans.	.034	.017	26–31	15426378③	4°	Damper	.050–.150⑩⑫		+1	+½	5/32
	V8-390 Auto. Trans.	.034	.017	26–31	15426378③	6°	Damper	.050–.150⑩⑫		+1	+½	5/32
	V8-427	.030	.020	⑬	15426378③	8°	Damper	.025H	.025H	+1	+½	5/32

①—There are no timing marks. Spark can be advanced or retarded by adjusting the vacuum brake set screw on distributor housing.
②—Total dwell for both breakers.
③—Cylinder numbering (front to rear): Right bank 1-2-3-4, left bank 5-6-7-8.
④—Up to Serial No. 8BA-622468: intake .012C, exhaust .014C. Later cars, intake .014C, exhaust .018C.

⑤—Clearance specified is obtainable at valve stem tip with lifter collapsed.
⑥—Four barrel carburetor.
⑦—Two barrel carburetor.
⑧—"Silent Lash"—Clearance specified is obtained at valve stem tip with eccentric spring compressed.
⑨—Tighten rocker arm adjusting screw to eliminate all push rod end clearance, then tighten screw the number of turns listed.

⑩—Clearance specified is obtained at valve stem tip with hydraulic lifter collapsed.
⑪—Before 11-18-63 .083–.183", from 11-18-63 .050–.150" (see note ⑩).
⑫—Hi Performance engine with mechanical lifters clearance is .025H, intake and exhaust.
⑬—Conventional ignition 30–33°, transistor ignition 22–24°.

HENRY J

Year	Engine or Car Model	Spark Plug Gap	Point Gap	Dwell Angle	Firing Order	BTDC or Mark	Mark Location	Intake	Exhaust	Caster Degrees	Camber Degrees	Toe-In Inch
1951–54	Four Cyl.	.030	.020	44–47	1342	5°	Flywheel	.014C	.014C	Zero	+½	¼
	Six Cyl.	.030	.020	35–38	153624	TDC	Damper	.014C	.014C	Zero	+½	¼

HUDSON

Year	Engine or Car Model	Spark Plug Gap	Point Gap	Dwell Angle	Firing Order	BTDC or Mark	Mark Location	Intake	Exhaust	Caster Degrees	Camber Degrees	Toe-In Inch
1946–47	Six Cyl.	.032	.020	35–38	153624	①	Flywheel	.010H	.012H	+1	+1	1/32
	Eight Cyl.	.032	.017	27–30	16258374	TDC	Flywheel	.006H	.008H	+1	+1	1/32
1948–49	Six Cyl.	.032	.020	35–38	153624	UDC 1-6	Flywheel	.010H	.012H	+1	+1	1/32
	Eight Cyl.	.032	.017	27–30	16258374	UDC 1-8	Flywheel	.006H	.008H	+1	+1	1/32
1950–52	Six Cyl.	.032	.020	35–38	153624	UDC 1-6	Flywheel	.008H	.010H	+1	+1	1/32
	Eight Cyl.	.032	.017	27–30	16258374	UDC 1-8	Flywheel	.008H	.010H	+1	+1	1/32
1953–54	Jets	.032	.020	39	153624	②	Damper	.010H	.012H	+1	+¾	1/32
	Wasps, Hornet	.032	.020	39	153624	UDC 1-6	Flywheel	.008H	.010H	+1	+¾	1/32
1955	Wasp	.032	.020	39	153624	Line	Damper	.010C	.014C	⑤	Zero	1/16–3/16
	Hornet 6	.032	.020	39	153624	UDC 1-6	Flywheel	.010C	.014C	⑤	Zero	1/16–3/16
	Hornet V8	.035	.017	38	18436572④	5°	Damper	Zero	Zero	⑤	Zero	1/16–3/16
1956	Wasp	.032	.020	39	153624	Line	Damper	.010C	.014C	⑤	Zero	1/16–3/16
	Hornet 6	.030	.020	39	153624	UDC 1-6	Flywheel	Zero	Zero	⑤	Zero	1/16–3/16
	Hornet V8	.035	.017	⑥	18436572④	5°	Damper	Zero	Zero	⑤	Zero	1/16–3/16
	Special	.035	.016	26–33	18436572④	5°	Damper	Zero	Zero	⑤	Zero	1/16–3/16
1957	All Models	.035	.016	28–32	18436572④	5°	Damper	Zero	Zero	⑤	Zero	1/16–3/16

①—½" before DC mark.
②—Long line before "1 UDC" mark.
③—Cylinder numbering (front to rear): Left bank 1-3-5-7, right bank 2-4-6-8.

⑤—Manual steering +½°, power steering +1°.
⑥—Dual breaker units 38°, single breaker 31°.

IMPERIAL

Year	Engine or Car Model	Spark Plug Gap	Point Gap	Dwell Angle	Firing Order	BTDC or Mark	Mark Location	Intake	Exhaust	Caster Degrees	Camber Degrees	Toe-In Inch
1946–48	All Models	.025	.017	27–30	16258374	2°	Damper	.008H	.010H	Zero	+⅜	1/32
1949–50	All Models	.035	.017	27–30	16258374	"0"	Damper	.008H③	.010H③	−2	+⅜	1/32
1951–54	All Models	.035	.017	①	18436572②	"0"	Damper	Zero	Zero	−2	Zero	Zero
1955	All Models	.035	.017	①	18436572②	6°	Damper	Zero	Zero	⑥	⑦	0–1/16
1956	All Models	.035	.017	⑤	18436572②	4°	Damper	Zero	Zero	⑥	⑦	1/8
1957	All Models	.035	.017	⑤	18436572②	6°	Damper	Zero	Zero	⑧	⑨	3/32–5/32
1958	All Models	.035	.017	⑤	18436572②	6°	Damper	.060–.210⑩		⑪	⑨	3/32–5/32
1959	All Models	.035	.017	⑫	18436572②	10°	Damper	.060–.210⑩		−¾	⑨	1/8

Continued

IMPERIAL—Continued

Year	Engine or Car Model	Spark Plug Gap	Distributor Point Gap	Distributor Dwell Angle	Firing Order	Ignition Timing BTDC or Mark	Ignition Timing Mark Location	Valve Lash Intake	Valve Lash Exhaust	Wheel Alignment Caster Degrees	Wheel Alignment Camber Degrees	Wheel Alignment Toe-In Inch
1960	All Models	.035	.017	27–32	18436572②	10°	Damper	.060–.210⑩		⑧	⑦	⅛
1961–63	All Models	.035	.017	27–32	18436572②	10°⑮	Damper	.060–.210⑩		⑬	⑭	⅛
1964	All Models	.035	.017	28–33	18436572②	10°⑮	Damper	.060–.210⑩		⑬	⑭	⅛
1965	All Models	.035	.017	28–32	18436572②	10°⑮	Damper	.060–.210⑩		⑬	⑭	⅛

①—Each set of points 26–28°, total dwell both sets 32–36°.
②—Cylinder numbering (front to rear): Left bank 1-3-5-7, right bank 2-4-6-8.
③—Zero lash with hydraulic valve lifters.
④—Each set of points 29–32°, total dwell both sets 32–36°.
⑤—Each set of points 29–32°, total dwell both sets 36–39°.
⑥—Manual steering −2°, power steering 0°.
⑦—Left side +⅜°, right side +⅛°.
⑧—Manual steering −¾°, power steering +¾°.
⑨—Left side +⅜°, right side 0°.
⑩—With lifter collapsed.
⑪—Manual steering −¾°, power steering 0°.
⑫—Each set of points 27–32°. Total dwell both sets 34–40°.
⑬—Manual steering −½°, power steering +¾°.
⑭—Left side +½°, right side +¼°.
⑮—Whenever idle speed or ignition timing is adjusted, vacuum line to brake release mechanism must be disconnected and plugged to prevent parking brake from releasing when selector lever is moved to Drive. Set idle speed with A/C compressor operating.

KAISER-FRAZER

Year	Engine or Car Model	Spark Plug Gap	Distributor Point Gap	Distributor Dwell Angle	Firing Order	Ignition Timing BTDC or Mark	Ignition Timing Mark Location	Valve Lash Intake	Valve Lash Exhaust	Wheel Alignment Caster Degrees	Wheel Alignment Camber Degrees	Wheel Alignment Toe-In Inch
1947–48	All Models	.032	.020	35–38	153624	"O"①	Damper①	.014C②	.014C	Zero	+⅜	1/16
1949–50	All Models	.032	.020	35–38	153624	4°	Damper	.014C	.014C	Zero	+⅜	1/16
1951–53	All Models	.032	.020	35–38	153624	4°	Damper	.014C	.014C	Zero	+½	⅛
1954	All Models	.030	.016	38–45	153624	4°	Damper	.014C	.014C	Zero	+½	⅛

①—Early models TDC mark on flywheel.
②—Up to Eng. No. 10769, .010H.

LINCOLN

Year	Engine or Car Model	Spark Plug Gap	Distributor Point Gap	Distributor Dwell Angle	Firing Order	Ignition Timing BTDC or Mark	Ignition Timing Mark Location	Valve Lash Intake	Valve Lash Exhaust	Wheel Alignment Caster Degrees	Wheel Alignment Camber Degrees	Wheel Alignment Toe-In Inch
1946–48	All Models	.028	.015	36	①	③	③	Zero	Zero	+4	+⅞	3/32
1949–51	All Models	.030	.015	28	15486372②	Mark	Damper	Zero	Zero	Zero	+⅜	⅛
1952–54	All Models	.030	.015	28	15486372②	3°	Damper	Zero	Zero	−¾	+⅜	⅛
1955	All Models	.034	.015	26–28	15486372②	5°	Damper	Zero	Zero	−¾	+⅜	3/32–5/32
1956–57	All Models	.034	.015	26–28	15486372②	5°	Damper	Zero	Zero	−¾	+⅜	⅛–3/16
1958	All Models	.034	.015	26–28	15426378②	6°	Damper	.078–.218④		−¾	+⅜	⅛–3/16
1959–62	All Models	.034	.017	26–31	15426378②	⑤	Damper	.078–.218④		−¾	+⅜	⑥
1963	All Models	.034	.017	26–31	15426378②	8°	Damper	.078–.178④		−1½	+½	⅛–¼
1964	All Models	⑦	⑧	⑨	15426378②	8°	Damper	.078–.178④		−1½	+½	⅛–¼
1965	All Models	⑦	⑧	⑨	15426378②	6°⑩	Damper	.050–.150④		−1½	+¾	1/32–9/32

①—Cylinder numbering (front to rear): Left bank 1-3-5-7-9-11, right bank 2-4-6-8-10-12. Firing order 1-4-9-8-5-2-11-10-3-6-7-12.
②—Cylinder numbering (front to rear): Right bank 1-2-3-4, left bank 5-6-7-8.
③—There are no timing marks. Spark may be advanced or retarded by adjusting vacuum brake set screw on distributor housing.
④—With rocker arm rotated to collapse lifter, the clearance listed should exist between end of valve stem and rocker arm.
⑤—1959 6°, 1960–62 8°.
⑥—1959–60 ⅛–3/16, 1961–62 1/16–3/16.
⑦—Conventional ignition .034″, Transistor ignition .030″.
⑧—Conventional ignition .017″, Transistor ignition .020″.
⑨—Conventional ignition 26–31°, Transistor ignition 22–24°.
⑩—Whenever idle speed or ignition timing is adjusted, vacuum line to brake release mechanism must be disconnected and plugged to prevent parking brake from releasing when selector is moved to Drive.

MERCURY

Year	Engine or Car Model	Spark Plug Gap	Distributor Point Gap	Distributor Dwell Angle	Firing Order	Ignition Timing BTDC or Mark	Ignition Timing Mark Location	Valve Lash Intake	Valve Lash Exhaust	Wheel Alignment Caster Degrees	Wheel Alignment Camber Degrees	Wheel Alignment Toe-In Inch
1946–48	All Models	.030	.015	36	15486372①	②	②	.012C	.014C	+6¾	+⅝	1/16
1949–50	All Models	.030	.015	28	15486372①	Groove	Pulley	.012C	.014C	Zero	+⅜	⅛
1951	All Models	.030	.015	28	15486372①	Groove	Pulley	.014C	.018C	Zero	+⅜	⅛
1952–53	All Models	.030	.015	28	15486372①	Groove	Pulley	.014C	.018C	−¾	+⅜	⅛
1954	All Models	.030	.015	28	15486372①	3°	Pulley	.018C	.018C	−¾	+⅜	⅛
1955–56	All Models	.034	.015	26–28	15486372①	③	Damper	.019H	.019H	−¾	+⅜	3/32–5/32
1957	V8-312	.034	.015	26–28	15486372①	6°	Damper	.019H	.019H	−¾	+⅜	3/16–5/16
	V8-368	.034	.015	26–28	15486372①	8°	Damper	Zero	Zero	−¾	+⅜	3/16–5/16
1958	V8-312	.034	.015	26–28	15486372①	③	Pulley	.019H	.019H	−¾	+⅜	3/16–5/16
	V8-383, 430	.034	.015	26–28	15426378①	④	Damper	.078–.218⑤		−¾	+⅜	3/16–5/16
1959–60	V8-312	.034	.017	26–31	15486372①	③	Pulley	.019H	.019H	−¾	+⅜	1/16–3/16
	V8-383, 430	.034	.017	26–31	15426378①	8°	Damper	.078–.218⑤		−¾	+⅜	1/16–3/16
1961	Six	.034	.025	37–42	153624	⑥	Damper	.019H	.019H	Zero	+⅜	⅛–¼
	V8-292	.034	.017	26–31	15486372①	⑦	Pulley	.019H	.019H	Zero	+⅜	⅛–¼

Continued

Year	Engine or Car Model	Spark Plug Gap	Distributor Point Gap	Distributor Dwell Angle	Firing Order	Ignition Timing BTDC or Mark	Ignition Timing Mark Location	Valve Lash Intake	Valve Lash Exhaust	Caster Degrees	Camber Degrees	Toe-In Inch
MERCURY—Continued												
1961	V8-352, 390	.034	.017	26–31	15426378①	⑧	Pulley	.078–.218③		Zero	+⅜	⅛–¼
	V8-390, 375 H.P.	.034	.020	26–31	15426378①	14°	Damper	.020H	.020H	Zero	+⅜	⅛–¼
1962	6-223 Std. Tr.	.034	.025	37–42	153624	6°	Damper	.025H	.025H	Zero	+⅜	⅛–¼
	6-223 Auto. Tr.	.034	.025	37–42	153624	12°	Damper	.025H	.025H	Zero	+⅜	⅛–¼
	V8-292 Std. Tr.	.034	.017	26–31	15486372①	5°	Pulley	.019H	.019H	Zero	+⅜	⅛–¼
	V8-292 Auto. Tr.	.034	.017	26–31	15486372①	12°	Pulley	.019H	.019H	Zero	+⅜	⅛–¼
	V8-352, 390 Std. Tr.	.034	.017	26–31	15426378①	5°	Pulley	.078–.218⑤		Zero	+⅜	⅛–¼
	V8-352, 390 Auto. Tr.	.034	.017	26–31	15426378①	8°	Pulley	.078–.218⑤		Zero	+⅜	⅛–¼
	V8-390, 375 H.P.	.034	.020	26–31	15426378①	5°	Damper	.025H	.025H	Zero	+⅜	⅛–¼
1963	V8-390 Std. Trans.⑨	.034	.017	26–31	15426378①	5°	Damper	.083–.183⑤		Zero	+⅜	⅛–¼
	V8-390 Auto. Trans.⑨	.034	.017	26–31	15426378①	8°	Damper	.083–.183⑤		Zero	+⅜	⅛–¼
	V8-390⑩	.034	.017	26–31	15426378①	6°	Damper	.083–.183⑤		Zero	+⅜	⅛–¼
	V8-390 330 H.P.	.034	.017	26–31	15426378①	10°	Damper	.025H	.025H	Zero	+⅜	⅛–¼
	V8-406	.035	.017	26–31	15426378①	5°	Damper	.025H	.025H	Zero	+⅜	⅛–¼
	V8-406 Two Carbs.	.034	.017	26–31	15426378①	8°	Damper	.025H	.025H	Zero	+⅜	⅛–¼
1964	V8-390⑩	.034	.017	26–31	15426378①	6°	Damper	⑪		Zero	+⅝	⅛–¼
	V8-390 Std. Tr.⑨	.034	.017	26–31	15426378①	4°	Damper	⑪		Zero	+⅝	⅛–¼
	V8-390 Auto. Tr.⑨	.034	.017	26–31	15426378①	6°	Damper	⑪		Zero	+⅝	⅛–¼
	V8-390 H.P. Std. Tr.	.034	.017	26–31	15426378①	4°	Damper	.025H	.025H	Zero	+⅝	⅛–¼
	V8-390 H.P. Auto Tr.	.034	.017	26–31	15426378①	6°	Damper	.025H	.025H	Zero	+⅝	⅛–¼
1965	V8-390⑩	.034	.017	26–31	15426378①	6°⑬	Damper	.050–.150⑤		+1	+½	3/16
	V8-390 Std. Tr.⑨	.034	.017	26–31	15426378①	4°	Damper	.050–.150⑤		+1	+½	3/16
	V8-390 Auto. Tr.⑨	.034	.017	26–31	15426378①	6°⑬	Damper	.050–.150⑤		+1	+½	3/16
	V8-427	.034	.020	⑫	15426378①	8°	Damper	.025H	.025H	+1	+½	3/16

①—Cylinder numbering (front to rear): Right bank 1-2-3-4, left bank 5-6-7-8.
②—There are no timing marks. Spark may be advanced or retarded by adjusting the vacuum brake set screw on distributor housing.
③—Standard transmission 3°, Mercomatic 6°.
④—V8-383 4°, V8-430 7°.
⑤—Clearance specified is obtainable at valve stem tip with lifter collapsed.
⑥—Standard transmission 6°, auto. transmission 12°.
⑦—Standard transmission 5°, auto. transmission 12°.
⑧—Standard transmission 5°, auto. transmission 8°.
⑨—Four barrel carburetor.
⑩—Two barrel carburetor.
⑪—Before 11-18-63 .083–.183″, from 11-18-63 .050–.150″ (see note ⑤).
⑫—Conventional ignition 30–33°, transistor ignition 22–24°.
⑬—Whenever idle speed or ignition timing is adjusted, vacuum line to brake release mechanism must be disconnected and plugged to prevent parking brake from releasing when selector is moved to Drive.

METEOR

Year	Engine or Car Model	Spark Plug Gap	Distributor Point Gap	Distributor Dwell Angle	Firing Order	Ignition Timing BTDC or Mark	Ignition Timing Mark Location	Valve Lash Intake	Valve Lash Exhaust	Caster Degrees	Camber Degrees	Toe-In Inch
1962	6 Cyl. Std. Tr.	.034	.025	37–42	153624	4°	Pulley	.016H	.016H	Zero	+½	⅛
	6 Cyl. Auto. Tr.	.034	.025	37–42	153624	10°	Pulley	.016H	.016H	Zero	+½	⅛
	V8 Std. Tr.	.034	.017	26–31	15426378①	4°	Damper	¾ Turn②		Zero	+½	⅛
	V8 Auto Tr.	.034	.017	26–31	15426378①	12°	Damper	¾ Turn②		Zero	+½	⅛
1963	6 Cyl. Std. Tr.	.034	.025	37–42	153624	6°	Pulley	.066–.216③		Zero	+½	⅛
	6 Cyl. Auto. Tr.	.034	.025	37–42	153624	12°	Pulley	.066–.216③		Zero	+½	⅛
	V8 Std. Tr.	.034	.017	26–31	15426378①	6°	Damper	¾ Turn②		Zero	+½	⅛
	V8 Auto. Tr.	.034	.017	26–31	15426378①	10°	Damper	¾ Turn②		Zero	+½	⅛

①—Cylinder numbering (front to rear): Right bank 1-2-3-4, left bank 5-6-7-8.
②—Tighten rocker arm adjusting screw to eliminate all push rod end clearance, then tighten screw the number of turns listed.
③—Clearance is obtained at valve stem tip with hydraulic lifter collapsed. If clearance is less than the minimum install an undersize push rod; if greater than the maximum install an oversize push rod.

NASH

Year	Engine or Car Model	Spark Plug Gap	Distributor Point Gap	Distributor Dwell Angle	Firing Order	Ignition Timing BTDC or Mark	Ignition Timing Mark Location	Valve Lash Intake	Valve Lash Exhaust	Caster Degrees	Camber Degrees	Toe-In Inch
1946-48	"600" 6	.025	.020	35–38	153624	IGN	Damper	.015H	.015H	+½	+½	5/32
	Ambassador	.025	.020	35–38	153624	IGN	Damper	.015H	.015H	−¼	+½	1/16
1949	"600" 6	.030	.022	31–37	153624	IGN	Damper	.015H	.015H	+¼	Zero	⅛
	Ambassador	.025	.022	31–37	153624	IGN	Damper	.015H	.015H	+¼	Zero	⅛
1950	Rambler	.030	.022	31–37	153624	TDC	Damper	.016C	.018C	+1	+½	¼
	Statesman	.030	.022	31–37	153624	TDC	Damper	.016C	.018C	+¼	Zero	⅛
	Ambassador	.030	.022	31–37	153624	TDC	Damper	.012H	.016H	+¼	Zero	⅛

Continued

Year	Engine or Car Model	Spark Plug Gap	Distributor		Firing Order	Ignition Timing		Valve Lash		Wheel Alignment		
			Point Gap	Dwell Angle		BTDC or Mark	Mark Location	Intake	Exhaust	Caster Degrees	Camber Degrees	Toe-In Inch

NASH—Continued

Year	Engine or Car Model	Spark Plug Gap	Point Gap	Dwell Angle	Firing Order	BTDC or Mark	Mark Location	Intake	Exhaust	Caster Degrees	Camber Degrees	Toe-In Inch
1951	Rambler	.030	.022	31–37	153624	TDC	Damper	.016C	.018C	+1	+½	¼
	Statesman	.030	.022	31–37	153624	TDC	Damper	.016C	.018C	Zero	Zero	⅛
	Ambassador	.030	.022	31–37	153624	TDC	Damper	.012H	.016H	Zero	Zero	⅛
1952-54	Rambler	.030	.022	31–37	153624	4°③	Damper	.016C	.018C	+1	+½	¼
	Statesman	.030	.022	31–37	153624	4°③	Damper	.016C	.018C	+¼	Zero	⅛
	Ambassador	.030	.022	31–37	153624	TDC	Damper	.012H	.016H	+¼	Zero	⅛
1955	Statesman	.030	.022	31	153624	4°③	Damper	.016C	.018C	+½②	Zero	1/16–3/16
	Ambassador 6	.030	.016	38–45	153624	4°③	Damper	.012H	.016H	+½②	Zero	1/16–3/16
	Ambassador V8	.035	.017	38	18436572①	5°	Damper	Zero	Zero	+½②	Zero	1/16–3/16
1956	Statesman 6	.030	.016	28–35	153624	4°③	Damper	.012H	.016H	+½②	Zero	1/16–3/16
	Amb. Spec. V8	.035	.016	26–33	18436572①	5°	Damper	Zero	Zero	+½②	Zero	1/16–3/16
	Ambassador 6	.030	.020	39	153624	4°③	Damper	.012H	.016H	+½②	Zero	1/16–3/16
	Ambassador V8	.035	.017	31	18436572①	5°	Damper	.Zero	Zero	+½②	Zero	1/16–3/16
1957	Ambassador V8	.035	.016	30	18436572①	5°	Damper	Zero	Zero	+½②	Zero	1/16–3/16

①—Cylinder numbering (front to rear): Left bank 1-3-5-7, right bank 2-4-6-8. ②—With power steering +¾°. ③—After top dead center.

OLDSMOBILE & F-85

Year	Engine or Car Model	Spark Plug Gap	Point Gap	Dwell Angle	Firing Order	BTDC or Mark	Mark Location	Intake	Exhaust	Caster Degrees	Camber Degrees	Toe-In Inch
1946-48	Six Cyl.	.040	.022	31–37	153624	TDC	Flywheel	.008H	.011H	−⅜	+¼	3/32
	Eight Cyl.	.030	.016	21–30	16258374	Ball	Flywheel	.008H	.011H	−⅜	+¼	3/32
1949-50	Six Cyl.	.040	.022	31–37	153624	TDC	Flywheel	.008H	.011H	−⅜	Zero	3/32
	V8	.030	.016	26–33	18736542①	②	Pulley	Zero	Zero	−⅜	Zero	3/32
1951	All Models	.030	.016	26–33	18736542①	Slot	Pulley	Zero	Zero	−⅜	Zero	3/32
1952-54	All Models	.030	.016	26–33	18736542①	Slot	Pulley	Zero	Zero	−⅜	+¼	3/32
1955-56	All Models	.030	.016	26–33	18736542①	④	Damper	Zero	Zero	−⅜	Zero	1/16–⅛
1957	All Models	.030	③	30	18736542①	④	Damper	Zero	Zero	+⅜	Zero	1/16–⅛
1958	All Models	.030	③	30	18736542①	5°	Damper	Zero	Zero	−½	+⅛	0–⅛
1959	V8-371, 394	.030	③	30	18736542①	5°	Damper	Zero	Zero	−½	+⅛	0–⅛
1960	With 2 Bar. Carb.	.030	③	30	18736542①	5°	Damper	Zero	Zero	−½	+⅛	0–⅛
	With 4 Bar. Carb.	.030	③	30	18736542①	5°	Damper	Zero	Zero	−½	+⅛	0–⅛
1961	F85 Std. Tr.-155 H.P.	.040	③	30	18436572①	5°	Damper	Zero	Zero	−1	+⅜	0–⅛
	F85 Auto. Tr.-155 H.P.	.040	③	30	18436572①	7½°	Damper	Zero	Zero	−1	+⅜	0–⅛
	F85 Std. Tr.-185 H.P.	.040	③	30	18436572①	5°	Damper	Zero	Zero	−1	+⅜	0–⅛
	F85 Auto. Tr.-185 H.P.	.040	③	30	18436572①	7½°	Damper	Zero	Zero	−1	+⅜	0–⅛
	F85-215 H.P.	.025	③	30	18436572①	10°	Damper	Zero	Zero	−1	+⅜	0–⅛
	Olds. with 2 Bar. Carb.	.030	③	30	18736542①	5°	Damper	Zero	Zero	−½	+⅛	0–⅛
	Olds. with 4 Bar. Carb.	.030	③	30	18736542①	5°	Damper	Zero	Zero	−½	+⅛	0–⅛
1962	F85, 155 H.P. Std. Tr.	.030	③	30	18436572①	5°	Damper	Zero	Zero	−1¼	Zero	0–⅛
	F85, 155 H.P. Auto. Tr.	.030	③	30	18436572①	7½°	Damper	Zero	Zero	−1¼	Zero	0–⅛
	F85, 185 H.P. Std. Tr.	.030	③	30	18436572①	5°	Damper	Zero	Zero	−1¼	Zero	0–⅛
	F85, 185 H.P. Auto. Tr.	.030	③	30	18436572①	7½°	Damper	Zero	Zero	−1¼	Zero	0–⅛
	F85, 215 H.P.	.025	③	30	18436572①	10°	Damper	Zero	Zero	−1¼	Zero	0–⅛
	Olds 260 H.P.	.030	③	30	18736542①	2½°	Damper	Zero	Zero	−½	+⅛	0–⅛
	Olds All Others	.030	③	30	18736542①	5°	Damper	Zero	Zero	−½	+⅛	0–⅛
1963	F85, 155 H.P. Std. Tr.	.030	③	30	18436572①	5°	Damper	Zero	Zero	−1¼	Zero	0–⅛
	F85, 155 H.P. Auto. Tr.	.030	③	30	18436572①	7½°	Damper	Zero	Zero	−1¼	Zero	0–⅛
	F85, 185 H.P.	.025	③	30	18436572①	7½°	Damper	Zero	Zero	−1¼	Zero	0–⅛
	F85, 195 H.P.	.030	③	30	18436572①	7½°	Damper	Zero	Zero	−1¼	Zero	0–⅛
	F85, 215 H.P.	.025	③	30	18436572①	10°	Damper	Zero	Zero	−1¼	Zero	0–⅛
	Olds-260 H.P.	.030	③	30	18736542①	2½°	Damper	Zero	Zero	−½	+¼	0–⅛
	Olds-All Others	.030	③	30	18736542①	5°	Damper	Zero	Zero	−½	+¼	0–⅛
1964	F85, V6-225	.030	③	30	165432⑤	5°	Damper	Zero	Zero	−1	+⅛	1/16–⅛
	F85, V8-330	.030	③	30	18436572①	7½°	Damper	Zero	Zero	−1	+⅛	1/16–⅛
	Olds, V8-330	.030	③	30	18436572①	7½°	Damper	Zero	Zero	−½	+⅛	0–1/16
	V8-394 Std. Tr.	.030	③	30	18736542①	2½°	Damper	Zero	Zero	−½	+⅛	0–1/16
	V8-394 Auto. Tr.	.030	③	30	18736542①	5°	Damper	Zero	Zero	−½	+⅛	0–1/16

Continued

Year	Engine or Car Model	Spark Plug Gap	Distributor		Firing Order	Ignition Timing		Valve Lash		Wheel Alignment		
			Point Gap	Dwell Angle		BTDC or Mark	Mark Location	Intake	Exhaust	Caster Degrees	Camber Degrees	Toe-In Inch

OLDSMOBILE & F-85—Continued

Year	Engine or Car Model	Spark Plug Gap	Point Gap	Dwell Angle	Firing Order	BTDC or Mark	Mark Location	Intake	Exhaust	Caster	Camber	Toe-In
1965	V6-225	.030	③	30	165432⑤	5°	Damper	Zero	Zero	−1¼	+⅛	⅛-³⁄₁₆
	V8-330	.030	③	30	18436572①	7½°	Damper	Zero	Zero	⑥	+⅛	⅛-³⁄₁₆
	V8-400	.030	③	30	18436572①	7½°	Damper	Zero	Zero	⑥	+⅛	⅛-³⁄₁₆
	V8-425, 2 Bar. Carb.	.030	③	30	18436572①	⑦	Damper	Zero	Zero	−1	+⅛	⅛-³⁄₁₆
	V8-425, 4 Bar. Carb.	.030	③	30	18436572①	5°	Damper	Zero	Zero	−1	+⅛	⅛-³⁄₁₆

①—Cylinder numbering (front to rear): Left bank 1-3-5-7, right bank 2-4-6-8.
②—Between two steel balls.
③—Turn adjusting screw in (clockwise) until engine begins to misfire, then back off screw ½ turn.
④—Cars with one notch, set at leading edge of notch. Cars with three notches, set at center one.
⑤—Cylinder numbering (front to rear): Left bank 1-3-5, right bank 2-4-6.
⑥—F-85 set at −1¼; Full size car set at −1.
⑦—Low compression engine set at 7½°; high compression engine set at 5°.

PACKARD

Year	Engine or Car Model	Spark Plug Gap	Point Gap	Dwell Angle	Firing Order	BTDC or Mark	Mark Location	Intake	Exhaust	Caster	Camber	Toe-In
1946	Six Cyl.	.030	.020	35	153624	4°	Damper	.007H	.010H	−1	Zero	1/32
	Eight Cyl.	.030	.017	27-30	16258374	5°	Damper	.007H	.010H	−1	Zero	1/32
	Super Eight	.030	.017	27-30	16258374	4°	Damper	Zero	Zero	−2	Zero	1/32
1947	Six Cyl.	.030	.020	35	153624	6°	Damper	.007H	.010H	−1	Zero	1/32
	Eight Cyl.	.030	.017	27-30	16258374	7°	Damper	.007H	.010H	−1	Zero	1/32
	Super Eight	.030	.017	27-30	16258374	6°	Damper	Zero	Zero	−2	Zero	1/32
1948-50	Eight	.030	.017	27-30	16258374	6°	Damper	.007H	.010H	−1	Zero	1/32
	Super Eight	.030	.017	27-30	16258374	6°	Damper	.007H	.010H	−1	Zero	1/32
	Custom Eight	.030	.017	27-30	16258374	6°	Damper	Zero	Zero	−2	Zero	1/32
1951-53	200	.030	.017	27-30	16258374	6°	Damper	.007H	.010H	−1	Zero	1/32
	Others	.028	.017	26-33	16258374	6°	Damper	Zero	Zero	−1	Zero	1/32
1954	5400-1-2-11	.025	.017	27-30	16258374	6°	Damper	.007H	.010H	−1	Zero	1/32
	Others	.025	.016	26-33	16258374	TDC	Damper	Zero	Zero	−1	Zero	1/32

PLYMOUTH

Year	Engine or Car Model	Spark Plug Gap	Point Gap	Dwell Angle	Firing Order	BTDC or Mark	Mark Location	Intake	Exhaust	Caster	Camber	Toe-In
1946-50	All Models	.025	.020	35-38	153624	DC	Damper	.010H	.010H	0	+⅜	1/32
1951-53	All Models	.035	.020	35-38	153624	DC	Damper	.010H	.010H	0	0	0
1954	All Models	.035	.020	36-42	153624	2°	Pulley	.010H	.010H	0	0	0
1955	Six Cyl.	.035	.020	39	153624	2°	Damper	.010H	.010H	−1	④	⅛
	V8	.035	.017	①	18436572②	4°	Pulley	Zero	Zero	−1	④	⅛
1956	Six Cyl.	.035	.020	39	153624	2°	Damper	.010H	.012H	−1	④	⅛
	V8-270	.035	.017	31	18436572②	4°	Pulley	Zero	Zero	−1	④	⅛
	V8-277	.035	.017	31	18436572②	4°③	Damper	.012H	.020H	−1	④	⅛
	V8-318	.035	.017	31	18436572②	4°	Damper	.010H	.018H	−1	④	⅛
1957	Six Cyl.	.035	.020	39	153624	2°	Damper	.010H	.010H	⑧	⑨	1/6
	V8-277	.035	.017	29	18436572②	⑥	Pulley	.008H	.018H	⑧	⑨	⅛
	V8-301	.035	.017	29	18436572②	⑦	Pulley	.008H	.018H	⑧	⑨	⅛
	V8-318	.035	.017	⑤	18436572②	8°	Damper	.008H	.018H	⑧	⑨	⅛
1958	6-230	.035	.020	39	153624	2°	Damper	.010H	.010H	⑧	⑨	3/32-5/32
	V8-318 D't IBP-4003F	.035	.017	27-32	18436572②	10°	Damper	.010H	.018H	⑧	⑨	3/32-5/32
	V8-318 D't IBP-4003D	.035	.017	27-32	18436572②	10°	Damper	.010H	.018H	⑧	⑨	3/32-5/32
	V8-318 D't IBS-4003	.035	.017	⑤	18436572②	8°	Damper	.010H	.018H	⑧	⑨	3/32-5/32
	V8-350	.035	.017	⑤	18436572②	8°	Damper	.060-.210⑩		⑧	⑨	3/32-5/32
1959	6-230	.035	.020	39	153624	2½°	Damper	.010H	.010H	⑧	⑨	⅛
	8-318	.035	.017	27-32	18436572②	10°	Damper	.010H	.018H	⑧	⑨	⅛
	8-361	.035	.017	⑪	18436572②	7½°	Damper	.060-.210⑩		⑧	⑨	⅛
1960	6-170, 225 Valiant	.035	.020	40-45	153624	2½°	Pulley	.010H	.020H	⑬	⑭	⅛
	6-Cyl. 4 Bar. Carb.	.028	.020	40-45	153624	10°	Pulley	.010H	.020H	⑬	⑭	⅛
	6-225 Std. Tr. Ply.	.035	.020	36-42	153624	2½°	Pulley	.010H	.020H	⑬	⑭	⅛
	6-225 Auto. Tr. Ply.	.035	.020	36-42	153624	5°	Pulley	.010H	.020H	⑬	⑭	⅛
	8-318 Std. Trans.	.035	.017	27-32	18436572②	5°	Damper	.010H	.018	⑬	⑭	⅛
	8-318 Auto. Trans.	.035	.017	27-32	18436572②	10°	Damper	.010H	.018	⑬	⑭	⅛
	8-361, 383	.035	.017	27-32	18436572②	10°	Damper	.060-.210⑩		⑬	⑭	⅛
	8-383 Ram Manifold	.035	.017	27-32	18436572②	7½°	Damper	.016C	.028C	⑬	⑭	⅛

Continued

Year	Engine or Car Model	Spark Plug Gap	Distributor Point Gap	Distributor Dwell Angle	Firing Order	Ignition Timing BTDC or Mark	Ignition Timing Mark Location	Valve Lash Intake	Valve Lash Exhaust	Wheel Alignment Caster Degrees	Wheel Alignment Camber Degrees	Wheel Alignment Toe-In Inch

PLYMOUTH—Continued

Year	Engine or Car Model	Plug Gap	Point Gap	Dwell Angle	Firing Order	BTDC/Mark	Mark Location	Intake	Exhaust	Caster	Camber	Toe-In
1961	6-170, 225	.035	.020	36-42	153624	2½°	Pulley	.010H	.020H	[13]	[16]	⅛
	8-318 Std. Trans.	.035	.017	27-32	18436572[2]	5°	Damper	.010H	.018H	[13]	[16]	⅛
	8-318 Auto. Trans.	.035	.017	27-32	18436572[2]	10°	Damper	.010H	.018H	[13]	[15]	⅛
	8-361	.035	.017	[11]	18436572[2]	10°	Damper	[12]	[2]	[13]	[15]	⅛
	8-383	.035	.017	[11]	18436572[2]	7½°	Damper	.016C	.028C	[13]	[15]	⅛
1962	6-170, 225	.035	.020	40-45	153624	2½°	Pulley	.010H	.020H	[13]	[15]	⅛
	8-318 Std. Tr.	.035	.017	27-32	18436572[2]	5°	Damper	.013H	.021H	[13]	[15]	⅛
	8-318 Auto. Tr.	.035	.017	27-32	18436572[2]	10°	Damper	.013H	.021H	[13]	[15]	⅛
	8-361	.035	.017	[11]	18436572[2]	10°	Damper	.060-.210[10]		[13]	[15]	⅛
1963	6-170, 225	.035	.020	40-45	153624	2½°	Pulley	.010H	.020H	[13]	[16]	⅛
	8-318 Std. Tr.	.035	.017	28-33	18436572[2]	5°	Damper	.013H	.021H	[13]	[15]	⅛
	8-318 Auto. Tr.	.035	.017	28-33	18436572[2]	10°	Damper	.013H	.021H	[13]	[15]	⅛
	8-361, 383	.035	.017	28-33	18436572[2]	10°	Damper	.060-.210[10]		[13]	[15]	⅛
	8-383, 426 Hi-Perf.	.035	.017	[11]	18436572[2]	10°	Damper	.060-.210[10]		[13]	[15]	⅛
1964	6-170, 225	.035	.020	40-45	153624	2½°	Damper	.010H	.020H	[13]	[16]	⅛
	8-273 Std. Tr.	.035	.017	28-33	18436572[2]	5°	Damper	.013H	.021H	[13]	[16]	⅛
	8-273 Auto. Tr.	.035	.017	28-33	18436572[2]	10°	Damper	.013H	.021H	[13]	[16]	⅛
	8-318 Std. Tr.	.035	.017	28-33	18436572[2]	5°	Damper	.013H	.021H	[13]	[16]	⅛
	8-318 Auto. Tr.	.035	.017	28-33	18436572[2]	10°	Damper	.013H	.021H	[13]	[16]	⅛
	8-361	.035	.017	28-33	18436572[2]	10°	Damper	.060-.210[10]		[13]	[15]	⅛
	8-383, 426	.035	.017	[11]	18436572[2]	10°	Damper	.060-.210[10]		[13]	[15]	⅛
	8-426 Hemi-Charg.	.020	.017	[16]	18436572[2]	[17]	Damper	.028C	.032C	[13]	[13]	⅛
1965	6-170, 225	.035	.020	40-45	153624	2½°	Damper	.010H	.020H	[13]	[15]	⅛
	8-273 Std. Tr.	.035	.017	28-33	18436572[2]	5°	Damper	.013H	.021H	[13]	[16]	⅛
	8-273 Auto. Tr.	.035	.017	28-33	18436572[2]	10°	Damper	.013H	.021H	[13]	[15]	⅛
	8-273 4 Bar. Carb.	.035	.017	[18]	18436572[2]	10°	Damper	.013H	.021H	[13]	[16]	⅛
	8-318 Std. Tr.	.035	.017	28-33	18436572[2]	5°	Damper	.013H	.021H	[13]	[16]	⅛
	8-318 Auto. Tr.	.035	.017	28-33	18436572[2]	10°	Damper	.013H	.021H	[13]	[16]	⅛
	8-361, 383	.035	.017	28-32	18436572[2]	10°	Damper	.060-.210[10]		[13]	[15]	⅛
	8-426	.035	.017	[18]	18436572[2]	10°	Damper	.060-.210[10]		[13]	[15]	⅛

[1]—Each set of points 26-28°. Total dwell both sets 32-36°.
[2]—Cylinder numbering (front to rear): Left bank 1-3-5-7, right bank 2-4-6-8.
[3]—TDC on V8-277 engine with four barrel carburetor.
[4]—Left side +½°, right side 0°.
[5]—Each set of points 29-32°. Total dwell both sets 36-39°.
[6]—With IBJ distributor TDC, with IBP distributor 4°.
[7]—With IBP-4003A distributor 4°, with IBP-4003 10°.
[8]—With manual steering −¾°, power steering +¾°.
[9]—Left side +⅜°, right side 0°.
[10]—With lifter collapsed.
[11]—Each set of points 27-32°; total dwell both sets 34-40°.
[12]—W/2 Bar. Carb. .060-.210 w/lifter collapsed. W-4 Bar. Carb. Intake .016C Exhaust .028C.
[13]—Manual steering −½°, power steering +¾°.
[14]—Left side +⅜°, right side +⅛°.
[15]—Left side +½°, right side +¼°.
[16]—Each set 27-31°. Total dwell both sets 34-38°.
[17]—With N61Y plugs, 31° at 3000 R.P.M. (with N58R plugs, 34° at 3000 R.P.M.).
[18]—Each set of points 27-31°; total dwell both sets 36-40°.

PONTIAC & TEMPEST

Year	Engine or Car Model	Plug Gap	Point Gap	Dwell Angle	Firing Order	BTDC/Mark	Mark Location	Intake	Exhaust	Caster	Camber	Toe-In
1946-48	Six Cyl.	.025	.022	31-37	153624	IGN	Flywheel	.012H	.012H	−¾	Zero	1/32
	Eight Cyl.	.025	.016	21-30	16258374	IGN	Flywheel	.012H	.012H	−¾	Zero	1/32
1949-52	Six Cyl.	.025	.022	31-37	153624	[1]	Damper	.012H	.012H	−¾	Zero	1/32
	Eight Cyl.	.025	.016	21-30	16258374	[1]	Damper	.012H	.012H	−¾	Zero	1/32
1953	Six Cyl.	.025	.016	31-37	153624	[2]	Damper	.012H	.012H	Zero	+½	1/32
	Eight Cyl.	.025	.016	21-30	16258374	[1]	Damper	.012H	.012H	Zero	+½	1/32
1954	Six Cyl.	.025	.016	38-45	153624	[3]	Damper	.012H	.012H	Zero	+½	1/32
	Eight Cyl.	.025	.016	21-30	16258374	[1]	Damper	.012H	.012H	Zero	+½	1/32
1955	All Models	.035	.016	26-33	18436572[4]	[5]	Damper	Zero	Zero	−1	+½	0-1/16
1956	V8 One Carb.	.035	.016	26-33	18436572[4]	[5]	Damper	Zero	Zero	−1	+½	0-1/16
	V8 Two Carbs.	.035	.016	26-33	18436572[4]	10°	Damper	Zero	Zero	−1	+½	0-1/16
1957	All Models	.035	[3]	30	18436572[4]	[6]	Damper	Zero	Zero	−1	+½	0-1/16
1958	All Models	.035	[3]	30	18436572[4]	6°	Damper	Zero	Zero	−½	+½	0-1/16
1959-60	All Models	.035	[3]	30	18436572[4]	6°	Damper	Hydraulic		−1½	+¼	0-1/16

Continued

Year	Engine or Car Model	Spark Plug Gap	Distributor		Firing Order	Ignition Timing		Valve Lash		Wheel Alignment		
			Point Gap	Dwell Angle		BTDC or Mark	Mark Location	Intake	Exhaust	Caster Degrees	Camber Degrees	Toe-In Inch

PONTIAC & TEMPEST—Continued

Year	Engine or Car Model	Spark Plug Gap	Point Gap	Dwell Angle	Firing Order	BTDC or Mark	Mark Location	Intake	Exhaust	Caster Degrees	Camber Degrees	Toe-In Inch
1961	4-195	.035	.016	74-76	1342	6°	Damper	Hydraulic		−1⅔	+0° 8'	0-⅛
	V8-215	.032	.016	28-32	18436572④	5°	Damper	Hydraulic		−1⅔	+0° 8'	0-⅛
	V8-389	.035	③	30	18436572④	6°	Damper	Hydraulic		−1⅔	+¼	0-⅛
1962	4-195 Dist. 1110282	.035	.016	74-76	1342	6°	Damper	Zero	Zero	−1⅔	+0° 8'	0-⅛
	4-195 Dist. 1110283	.035	.016	74-76	1342	6°	Damper	Zero	Zero	−1⅔	+0° 8'	0-⅛
	4-195 Dist. 1110284	.035	.016	31-34	1342	6°	Damper	Zero	Zero	−1⅔	+0° 8'	0-⅛
	4-195 Dist. 1110285	.035	.016	31-34	1342	6°	Damper	Zero	Zero	−1⅔	+0° 8'	0-⅛
	V8-215	.032	.016	28-32	18436572④	5°	Damper	Zero	Zero	−1⅔	+0° 8'	0-⅛
	V8-389	.035	③	30	18436572④	6°	Damper	Zero	Zero	−1⅔	+0° 8'	0-⅛
1963	4-195	.035	.016	31-34	1342	6°	Damper	Zero	Zero	−1½	+¼	0-⅛
	V8-326	.035	③	30	18436572④	6°	Damper	Zero	Zero	−1⅔	+0° 8'	0-⅛
	V8-389 One Carb.	.035	③	30	18436572④	6°	Damper	Zero	Zero	−1⅔	+0° 8'	0-⅛
	V8-389 Tri-Carb.	.035	③	30	18436572④	6°	Damper	Zero	Zero	−1½	+¼	0-⅛
	V8-421 Tri-Carb.	.035	③	30	18436572④	6°	Damper	Zero	Zero	−1½	+¼	0-⅛
1964-65	6-215	.035	.016	31-34	153624	4°	Damper	1 Turn⑥		⑦	+¼	0-⅛
	V8-326	.035	③	30	18436572④	6°	Damper	Zero	Zero	⑦	+¼	0-⅛
	V8-389, 421	.035	③	30	18436572④	6°	Damper	Zero	Zero	⑦	+¼	0-⅛

①—Early 1949, "IGN" mark. Late 1949 and 1950-54, first line to come under pointer is for standard heads, second line for high compression heads, and third line is TDC.
②—Center of three lines.
③—Turn adjusting screw in (clockwise) until engine misfires, then back off screw ½ turn.
④—Cylinder numbering (front to rear): Left bank 1-3-5-7, right bank 2-4-6-8.
⑤—First line to come under pointer while cranking engine.
⑥—With valve fully closed, turn rocker arm nut down until all play in push rod is eliminated, then tighten nut additional turns specified.
⑦—Tempest wagons —2, all other cars —1½.

RAMBLER

Year	Engine or Car Model	Spark Plug Gap	Point Gap	Dwell Angle	Firing Order	BTDC or Mark	Mark Location	Intake	Exhaust	Caster Degrees	Camber Degrees	Toe-In Inch
1958	Six L-Head	.035	.016	28-35	153624	3°	Damper	.016H	.018C	Zero	+¼	1/16-3/16
	Six O-Head	.035	.016	28-33	153624	5°	Damper	.012H	.016H	Zero	+¼	1/16-3/16
	V8-250	.035	.016	28-32	18436572①	5°	Damper	.012H	.016H	Zero	+¼	1/16-3/16
	V8-327	.035	.016	28-32	18436572①	5°	Damper	.012H	.014H	+½④	Zero	1/16-3/16
1959	Flat Head Six	.035	.016	28-35	153624	3°	Damper	Zero	Zero	+½④	Zero	1/16-3/16
	OHV Six	.035	.016	28-35	153624	5°	Damper	.016C	.018C	+¼④	Zero	1/16-3/16
	V8-250	.035	.016	28-32	18436572①	TDC	Damper	.012H	.016H	+¼④	Zero	1/16-3/16
	V8-327	.035	.016	28-32	18436572①	5°	Damper	.012H	.014H	+½②	Zero	1/16-3/16
1960	American⑤	.035	.020	37-41	153624	3°	Damper	Zero	Zero	+½②	Zero	1/16-3/16
	American Custom⑥	.035	.016	28-35	153624	8°	Damper	.016C	.018C	+¼⑧	Zero	1/16-3/16
	American Custom⑦	.035	.016	28-35	153624	10°	Damper	.012H	.016H	+¼⑧	Zero	1/16-3/16
	Rambler 6	.035	.016	28-35	153624	5°	Damper	.012H	.016H	+¼⑧	Zero	1/16-3/16
	V8-250	.035	.016	28-32	18436572①	TDC	Damper	.012H	.016H	+¼④	Zero	1/16-3/16
	V8-327-250 H.P.	.035	.016	28-32	18436572①	TDC	Damper	.012H	.014H	+½②	Zero	1/16-3/16
	V8-327-270 H.P.	.035	.016	28-32	18436572①	5°	Damper	Zero	Zero	+½②	Zero	1/16-3/16
1961	American⑤	.035	.020	37-41	153624	3°	Damper	Zero	Zero	+½②	Zero	1/16-3/16
	American Custom⑥	.035	.016	28-35	153624	8°	Damper	.016C	.018C	+½⑧	Zero	1/16-3/16
	American Custom⑦	.035	.016	28-35	153624	10°	Damper	.012H	.016H	+½⑧	Zero	1/16-3/16
	Rambler 6	.035	.016	28-35	153624	8°	Damper	.012H	.016H	+½⑧	Zero	1/16-3/16
	V8-250 Std. Trans.	.035	.016	28-32	18436572①	TDC	Damper	.012H	.016H	+½④	Zero	1/16-3/16
	V8-250 Auto. Trans.	.035	.016	28-32	18436572①	5°	Damper	.012H	.014H	+½④	Zero	1/16-3/16
	V8-327	.035	.016	28-32	18436572①	5°	Damper	.012H	.014H	+½④	Zero	1/16-3/16
1962	American L-Head 6	.035	.020	36-42	153624	3°	Damper	Zero	Zero	+½④	Zero	1/16-3/16
	American OHV-6⑤	.035	.016	28-35	153624	8°	Damper	.016C	.018C	Zero⑦	⑩	⅛
	American OHV-6⑥	.035	.016	28-35	153624	10°	Damper	.012H⑧	.016H⑧	Zero⑦	⑩	⅛
	Rambler 6	.035	.016	28-35	153624	5°	Damper	Zero⑨	Zero⑨	Zero⑦	⑩	⅛
	V8-327 Std. Tr.	.035	.020	28-32	18436572①	5°	Damper	.012H	.016H	Zero③	⑩	⅛
	V8-327 Auto. Tr.	.035	.020	28-32	18436572①	3°	Damper	Zero	Zero	Zero③	⑩	⅛
1963	American L-Head 6	.035	.016	31-34	153624	3°	Damper	.016C	.018C	Zero③	⑩	⅛
	American OHV-6⑤	.035	.016	31-34	153624	8°	Damper	.012H⑫	.016H⑫	Zero⑦	⑩	⅛
	American OHV-6⑥	.035	.016	31-34	153624	10°	Damper	.012H⑫	.016H⑫	Zero⑦	⑩	⅛
	Rambler 6	.035	.016	31-34	153624	⑪	Damper	.012H⑫	.016H⑫	Zero③	⑩	⅛

Year	Engine or Car Model	Spark Plug Gap	Distributor		Firing Order	Ignition Timing		Valve Lash		Wheel Alignment		
			Point Gap	Dwell Angle		BTDC or Mark	Mark Location	Intake	Exhaust	Caster Degrees	Camber Degrees	Toe-In Inch

RAMBLER—Continued

Year	Engine or Car Model	Spark Plug Gap	Point Gap	Dwell Angle	Firing Order	BTDC or Mark	Mark Location	Intake	Exhaust	Caster Degrees	Camber Degrees	Toe-In Inch
1963	6-232	.035	.016	31–34	153624	5°	Damper	Zero	Zero	Zero③	⑩	⅛
	V8 Std. Trans.	.035	.016	28–32	18436572①	TDC	Damper	Zero	Zero	Zero③	⑩	⅛
	V8 Auto. Trans.	.035	.016	28–32	18436572①	5°	Damper	Zero	Zero	Zero③	⑩	⅛
1964	American L-Head 6	.035	.016	31–34	153624	3°	Damper	.016C	.018C	+¼⑬	Zero	1/16–3/16
	American OHV-6⑤	.035	.016	31–34	153624	8°	Damper	.012H⑫	.016H⑫	+¼⑬	Zero	1/16–3/16
	American OHV-6⑥	.035	.016	31–34	153624	10°	Damper	.012H⑫	.016H⑫	+¼⑬	Zero	1/16–3/16
	Rambler 6	.035	.016	31–34	153624	5°	Damper	.012H	.016H	+¼⑬	Zero	1/16–3/16
	6-232	.035	.016	31–34	153624	5°	Damper	Zero	Zero	+¼⑬	Zero	1/16–3/16
	V8-Std. Trans.	.035	.016	28–32	18436572①	TDC	Damper	Zero	Zero	+¼⑬	Zero	1/16–3/16
	V8-Auto. Trans.	.035	.016	28–32	18436572①	5°	Damper	Zero	Zero	+¼⑬	Zero	1/16–3/16
1965	American L-Head 6	.035	.016	31–34	153624	3°	Damper	.016C	.018C	+¼⑬	Zero	1/16–3/16
	American OHV-6⑤	.035	.016	31–34	153624	8°	Damper	.012H	.016H	+¼⑬	Zero	1/16–3/16
	American OHV-6⑥	.035	.016	31–34	153624	10°	Damper	.012H	.016H	+¼⑬	Zero	1/16–3/16
	6-199, 232	.035	.016	31–34	153624	5°	Damper	Zero	Zero	+¼⑬	Zero	1/16–3/16
	V8-287, 327	.035	.016	28–32	18436572①	5°	Damper	Zero	Zero	+¼⑬	Zero	1/16–3/16

①—Cylinder numbering (front to rear): Left bank 1-3-5-7, right bank 2-4-6-8.
②—With power steering +¾°.
③—With power steering +1°.
④—Deluxe and Super.
⑤—Standard transmission.
⑥—Automatic transmission.
⑦—Power steering +2.°
⑧—Cast iron block.
⑨—Aluminum block.
⑩—Left +¼°, right 0.
⑪—Early 5°, late 8°.
⑫—With aluminum block hydraulic lifters are used and clearance is "Zero".
⑬—With power steering +1½.

STUDEBAKER

Year	Engine or Car Model	Spark Plug Gap	Point Gap	Dwell Angle	Firing Order	BTDC or Mark	Mark Location	Intake	Exhaust	Caster Degrees	Camber Degrees	Toe-In Inch
1946	Champion	.025	.020	35–38	153624	IGN	Damper	.016C	.016C	+1½	+½	3/32
1947–48	Champion	.025	.020	35–38	153624	IGN	Damper	.016C	.016C	+½	+½	3/32
	Commander	.025	.020	35–38	153624	IGN	Damper	.016C	.016C	+½	+½	3/32
1949	Champion	.025	.020	35–38	153624	IGN	Damper	.016C	.016C	+1	+½	3/32
	Commander	.025	.020	35–38	153624	IGN	Damper	.016C	.016C	−2½	+½	3/32
1950	Champion	.025	.020	35–38	153624	IGN	Damper	.016C	.016C	−1½	+½	3/32
	Commander	.025	.022	31–37	153624	IGN	Damper	.016C	.016C	−2	+½	3/32
1951–52	Champion	.025	.020	35–38	153624	IGN	Damper	.016C	.016C	−1¾	+½	3/32
	Commander	.035	.016	21–30	18436572①	IGN	Damper	.015H	.015H	−1¾	+½	3/32
1953–54	Champion	.025	.020	38–40	153624	IGN	Damper	.016C	.016C	−1¾	+½	3/32
	Commander	.035	.016	28–34	18436572①	IGN	Damper	.022H	.022H	−1¾	+½	3/32
1955	Six Cyl.	.030	.020	39	153624	IGN	Damper	.016C	.016C	−1¾	+½	1/16–1/8
	V8	.035	.013	28–34	18436572①	IGN	Damper	.026C	.026C	−1¾	+½	1/16–1/8
1956	Six Cyl.	.030	.020	39	153624	IGN	Damper	.016C	.016C	−1¾	+½	1/16–1/8
	Studebaker V8	.035	.016	26–33	18436572①	IGN	Damper	.026C	.026C	−1¾	+½	1/16–1/8
	Packard V8	.035	.017	31	18436572①	IGN	Damper	Zero	Zero	−1¾	+½	1/16–1/8
1957	Six Cyl.	.030	.020	39	153624	IGN	Damper	.016C	.016C	−1¾	+½	1/16–1/8
	V8	.035	.016	26–33	18436572①	IGN	Damper	.026C	.026C	−1¾	+½	1/16–1/8
	Golden Hawk	.035	.016	26–33	18436572①	IGN	Damper	.026C	.026C	−1¾	+½	1/16–1/8
1958	6-186	.030	.020	38–40	153624	2°	Damper	.016C	.016C	−1¾②	+½③	1/16–1/8
	V8-259, 289	.035	.016	28–34	18436572①	4°	Damper	.026C	.026C	−1¾②	+½③	1/16–1/8
1959	Six Cyl.	.030	.020	38–40	153624	2°	Damper	.018C④	.018C④	−2¼②	+½③	1/16–1/8
	V8	.035	.016	28–34	18436572①	4°	Damper	.026C	.026C	−2¼②	+½③	1/16–1/8
1960	Six Cyl.	.030	.020	38–40	153624	2°	Damper	.018C	.018C	−2¼②	+½③	1/16–1/8
	V8	.035	.016	28–34	18436572①	4°	Damper	.026C	.026C	−2¼②	+½③	1/16–1/8
1961–62	Six Cyl.	.035	.020	37–41	153624	2°	Damper	.026C	.026C	−½②	+½③	¼④
	V8	.035	.016	28–32	18436572①	4°	Damper	.026C	.026C	−½②	+½③	¼④
1963–64	Six Cyl.	.035	.020	37–41	153624	2°	Damper	.026C	.026C	−½②	+½③	¼④
	V8 Std. Engine	.035	.017	27–31	18436572①	4°	Damper	.026C	.026C	−½②	+½③	¼④

①—Cylinder numbering (front to rear): Left bank 1-3-5-7, right bank 2-4-6-8.
②—Not more than ½° variation between wheels.
③—−½ more favored on drivers side.
④—With Power Steering ⅛".

Continued

Year	Engine or Car Model	Spark Plug Gap	Distributor		Firing Order	Ignition Timing		Valve Lash		Wheel Alignment		
			Point Gap	Dwell Angle		BTDC or Mark	Mark Location	Intake	Exhaust	Caster Degrees	Camber Degrees	Toe-In Inch
THUNDERBIRD												
1955–56	All Models	.034	.015	26–28	15486372①	②	Damper	.019H	.019H	+1	+¾	¹⁄₁₆–⅛
1957	All Models	.034	.015	26–28	15486372①	②	Damper	.019H	.019H	+1	+1	¹⁄₁₆–⅛
1958	All Models	.034	.015	26–28	15426378①	②	Damper	.062–.1875③		+1	+1	¹⁄₁₆–⅛
1959	All Models	.034	.017	26–31	15426378①	④	Damper	⑤		+1	+1	¹⁄₁₆–⅛
1960	All Models	.034	.017	26–31	15426378①	④	Damper	.078–.218③		+1	+1	¹⁄₁₆–⅛
1961	All Models	.034	.017	26–31	15426378①	8°	Damper	.078–.218③		+½	+½	¹⁄₁₆–⅛
1962	V8-390	.034	.017	26–31	15426378①	6°	Damper	.100–.200③		−½	+½	¹⁄₁₆–⅛
	V8-429	.035	.017	26–31	15426378①	6°	Damper	.075–.175③		−½	+½	¹⁄₁₆–⅛
1963	V8-390	.034	.017	26–31	15426378①	6°	Damper	.083–.183③		−1½	+⅜	⅛–¼
1964	V8-390	.034	.017⑥	26–31⑦	15426378①	6°	Damper	⑧		−1½	+⅜	⅛–¼
1965	V8-390	.034	.017⑥	26–31⑦	15426378①	6°⑨	Damper	.050–.150③		−1½	+½	¹⁄₃₂–⁵⁄₃₂

①—Cylinder numbering (front to rear): Right bank 1-2-3-4, left bank 5-6-7-8.
②—Standard transmission 3°, Fordomatic 6°.
③—Clearance specified is obtained at valve stem with lifter collapsed.
④—Standard transmission 5°, automatic transmission 8°.

⑤—V8-352 (.078–.218③), V8-430 (.126–.226③).
⑥—With transistor ignition .020″.
⑦—With transistor ignition 22–24°.
⑧—Engines built prior to Nov. 18, 1963 .083–.183″③; engines built from Nov. 18, 1963 .050–.150″③.

⑨—Whenever idle speed or ignition timing is adjusted, vacuum line to brake release mechanism must be disconnected and plugged to prevent parking brake from releasing when selector is moved to Drive.

TIRE WEAR CHART

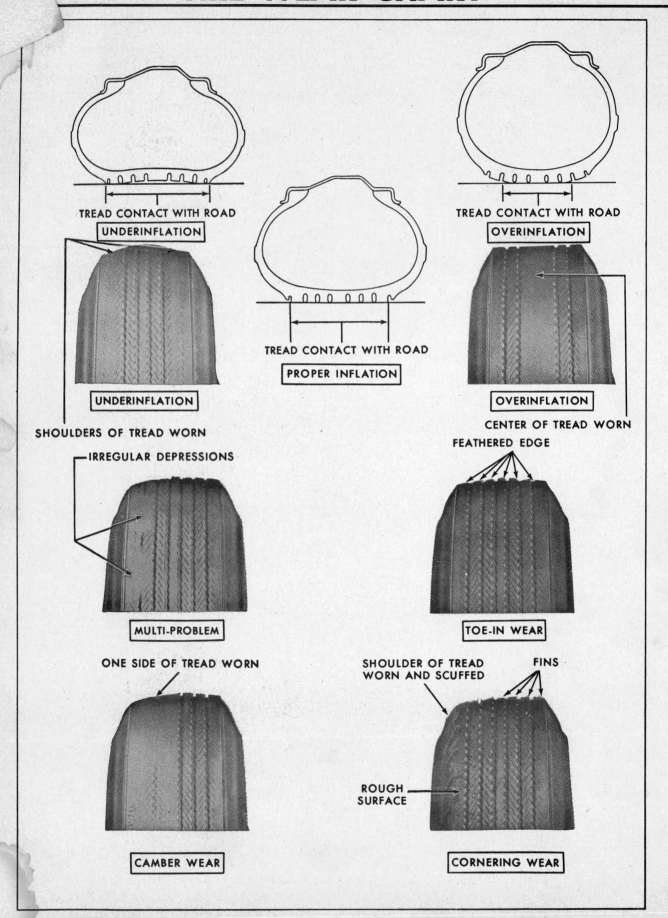

TREAD CONTACT WITH ROAD

UNDERINFLATION

TREAD CONTACT WITH ROAD

PROPER INFLATION

TREAD CONTACT WITH ROAD

OVERINFLATION

UNDERINFLATION

SHOULDERS OF TREAD WORN

OVERINFLATION

CENTER OF TREAD WORN

IRREGULAR DEPRESSIONS

MULTI-PROBLEM

FEATHERED EDGE

TOE-IN WEAR

ONE SIDE OF TREAD WORN

CAMBER WEAR

SHOULDER OF TREAD WORN AND SCUFFED

FINS

ROUGH SURFACE

CORNERING WEAR

SPARK PLUG CONDITION CHART

CARBON FOULED

IDENTIFIED BY BLACK, DRY FLUFFY CARBON DEPOSITS ON INSULATOR TIPS, EXPOSED SHELL SURFACES AND ELECTRODES.

CAUSED BY TOO COLD A PLUG, WEAK IGNITION, DIRTY AIR CLEANER, DEFECTIVE FUEL PUMP, TOO RICH A FUEL MIXTURE, IMPROPERLY OPERATING HEAT RISER OR EXCESSIVE IDLING. CAN BE CLEANED.

OIL FOULED

IDENTIFIED BY WET BLACK DEPOSITS ON THE INSULATOR SHELL BORE ELECTRODES CAUSED BY EXCESSIVE OIL ENTERING COMBUSTION CHAMBER THROUGH WORN RINGS AND PISTONS, EXCESSIVE CLEARANCE BETWEEN VALVE GUIDES AND STEMS, OR WORN OR LOOSE BEARINGS. CAN BE CLEANED IF ENGINE IS NOT REPAIRED, USE A HOTTER PLUG.

GAP BRIDGED

IDENTIFIED BY DEPOSIT BUILD-UP CLOSING GAP BETWEEN ELECTRODES.

CAUSED BY OIL OR CARBON FOULING. IF DEPOSITS ARE NOT EXCESSIVE, THE PLUG CAN BE CLEANED.

LEAD FOULED

IDENTIFIED BY DARK GRAY, BLACK' YELLOW OR TAN DEPOSITS OR A FUSED GLAZED COATING ON THE INSULATOR TIP CAUSED BY HIGHLY LEADED GASOLINE. CAN BE CLEANED.

NORMAL

IDENTIFIED BY LIGHT TAN OR GRAY DEPOSITS ON THE FIRING TIP CAN BE CLEANED.

WORN

IDENTIFIED BY SEVERELY ERODED OR WORN ELECTRODES. CAUSED BY NORMAL WEAR. SHOULD BE REPLACED.

FUSED SPOT DEPOSIT

IDENTIFIED BY MELTED OR SPOTTY DEPOSITS RESEMBLING BUBBLES OR BLISTERS.

CAUSED BY SUDDEN ACCELERATION CAN BE CLEANED.

OVERHEATING

IDENTIFIED BY A WHITE OR LIGHT GRAY INSULATOR WITH SMALL BLACK OR GRAY BROWN SPOTS AND WITH BLUISH-BURNT APPEARANCE OF ELECTRODES, CAUSED BY ENGINE OVERHEATING. WRONG TYPE OF FUEL, LOOSE SPARK PLUGS, TOO HOT A PLUG, LOW FUEL PUMP PRESSURE OR INCORRECT IGNITION TIMING. REPLACE THE PLUG.

PRE-IGNITION

IDENTIFIED BY MELTED ELECTRODES AND POSSIBLY BLISTERED INSULATOR. METALLIC DEPOSITS ON INSULATOR INDICATE ENGINE DAMAGE.

CAUSED BY WRONG TYPE OF FUEL, INCORRECT IGNITION TIMING OR ADVANCE, TOO HOT A PLUG, BURNT VALVES OR ENGINE OVERHEATING. REPLACE THE PLUG.

NOTES

NOTES

NOTES

Flasher Locations

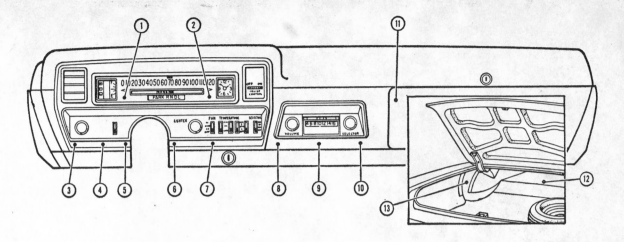

CAR	1966	1967 TSF	1967 HWF	1968 TSF	1968 HWF	1969 TSF	1969 HWF	1970 TSF	1970 HWF	1971 TSF	1971 HWF	1972 TSF	1972 HWF
Buick & Special	3	3	3	3	3	3	3	3	3	3	3	3	3
Cadillac & Eldorado	5	3	6	5	3	5	5	6	8	⑮	3	⑮	3
Camaro	—	8	3	8	3	8	3	8	3	8	3	8	3
Chevelle	8	8	3	8	3	8	3	1	3	7	3	7	3
Chevrolet	8	8	3	8	3	8	3	10	3	7	3	7	3
Chevy II & Nova	8	8	3	8	3	8	3	10	3	7	3	7	3
Chevrolet Vega	—	—	—	—	—	—	—	—	—	5	3	5	3
Chrysler	8	8	4	8	4	5	4	5	4	5	4	5	5
Comet & Montego	1	1	6	6	5	6	5	6	5	5	5	5	5
Corvair	8	7	3	7	3	7	3	—	—	—	—	—	—
Corvette	7	7	3	11	3	⑧	3	⑧	3	⑧	3	⑧	3
Cougar	—	13	13	13	13	8	10	8	10	11	6	8	10
Dart & Challenger	8	8	5	8	5	8	5	8	⑨	8	⑨	10	6
Dodge	8	8	①	8	①	⑤	①	5	6	①	—	①	5
Fairlane & Torino	1	1	6	6	5	6	5	6	5	5	5	5	5
Falcon & Maverick	1	1	6	6	5	6	⑩	6	⑩	5	5	5	5
Ford	2	1	2	1	2	6	5	11	3	8	3	8	3
Ford Pinto	—	—	—	—	—	—	—	—	—	10	10	10	10
Imperial	8	8	4	8	4	13	13	5	4	5	4	5	5
Lincoln	9	11	11	11	11	11	11	3⑫	3⑬	6	6	3	3
Mercury	5	3	6	4	6	4	6	11	3	8	3	8	3
Mustang	3	2	3	1	4	1	4	10	8	11	6	8	10
Oldsmobile	6	1	3	1	3	3	3	1	3	4	3	4	3
Oldsmobile F-85	1	1	3	3	3	3	3	3	3	4	3	4	3
Oldsmobile Toronado	3	3	3	3	3	3	3	4	3	4	3	4	3
Plymouth	8	8	②	8	②	⑦	⑥	⑦	6	②	—	②	5
Pontiac Ventura II	3	5	3	3	3	3	3	3	3	3	3	3	3
Pontiac Firebird	—	7	3	7	3	3	3	3	3	3	3	3	3
Pontiac Tempest, Le Mans	3	3	3	3	3	3	3	3	3	3	3	3	3
Rambler	③	2	3	2	3	2	3	2⑭	3	2⑯	3	3	3
Thunderbird	12	12	12	13	13	13	13	⑪	11	11	6	3	3
Valiant & Barracuda	8	8	5	8	5	8	5	8	6	8	6	10	6

TSF: Turn Signal Flasher   HWF: Hazard Warning Flasher.

①—Location 10 on Coronet & Charger. Location 5 on Polara & Monaco.
②—Location 10 on Belvedere & Satellite. Location 5 on Fury & VIP.
③—Location 1 on Marlin & Ambassador. Location 2 on American & Classic.
④—Location 1 on American & Ambassador. Location 7 on Classic.
⑤—Location 4 on Coronet & Charger. Location 8 on Polara & Monaco.
⑥—Location 6 on Belvedere & Satellite. Location 4 on Fury & VIP.
⑦—Location 4 on Belvedere & Satellite. Location 8 on Fury & VIP.
⑧—Extreme lower right corner of instrument panel.
⑨—Location 6 on Challenger. Location 10 on Dart.
⑩—Location 5 on Falcon. Behind ash tray on Maverick.
⑪—To right of glove box.
⑫—Mark III to right of glove box.
⑬—Mark III to left of glove box.
⑭—Location 3 on Hornet and Gremlin.
⑮—On the underside of steering column lower cover.
⑯—Location 3 on Hornet, Gremlin and Javelin.

DECIMAL & MILLIMETER EQUIVALENTS

INCH	INCH	MM
1/64	.015625	.397
1/32	.03125	.794
3/64	.046875	1.191
1/16	.0625	1.587
5/64	.078125	1.984
3/32	.09375	2.381
7/64	.109375	2.778
1/8	.125	3.175
9/64	.140625	3.572
5/32	.15625	3.969
11/64	.171875	4.366
3/16	.1875	4.762
13/64	.203125	5.159
7/32	.21875	5.556
15/64	.234375	5.953
1/4	.25	6.350
17/64	.265625	6.747
9/32	.28125	7.144
19/64	.296875	7.541
5/16	.3125	7.937
21/64	.328125	8.334
11/32	.34375	8.731

INCH	INCH	MM
23/64	.359375	9.128
3/8	.375	9.525
25/64	.390625	9.922
13/32	.40625	10.319
27/64	.421875	10.716
7/16	.4375	11.113
29/64	.453125	11.509
15/32	.46875	11.906
31/64	.484375	12.303
1/2	.5	12.700
33/64	.515625	13.097
17/32	.53125	13.494
35/64	.546875	13.890
9/16	.5625	14.287
37/64	.578125	14.684
19/32	.59375	15.081
39/64	.609375	15.478
5/8	.625	15.875
41/64	.640625	16.272
21/32	.65625	16.669
43/64	.671875	17.065

INCH	INCH	MM
11/16	.6875	17.462
45/64	.703125	17.859
23/32	.71875	18.265
47/64	.734375	18.653
3/4	.75	19.050
49/64	.765625	19.447
25/32	.78125	19.884
51/64	.796875	20.240
13/16	.8125	20.637
53/64	.828125	21.034
27/32	.84375	21.431
55/64	.859375	21.828
7/8	.875	22.225
57/64	.890625	22.622
29/32	.90625	23.019
59/64	.921875	23.415
15/16	.9375	23.812
61/64	.953125	24.209
31/32	.96875	24.606
63/64	.984375	25.003
1		25.400

DRILL SIZES

LETTER OR WIRE GAUGE	DRILL DIAMETER INCH
Z	0.413
Y	0.404
X	0.397
W	0.386
V	0.377
U	0.368
T	0.358
S	0.348
R	0.339
Q	0.332
P	0.323
O	0.316
N	0.302
M	0.295
L	0.290
K	0.281
J	0.277
I	0.272
H	0.266
G	0.261
F	0.257
E	0.250
D	0.246
C	0.242
B	0.238
A	0.234

LETTER OR WIRE GAUGE	DRILL DIAMETER INCH
1	0.2280
2	0.2210
3	0.2130
4	0.2090
5	0.2055
6	0.2040
7	0.2010
8	0.1990
9	0.1960
10	0.1935
11	0.1910
12	0.1890
13	0.1850
14	0.1820
15	0.1800
16	0.1770
17	0.1730
18	0.1695
19	0.1660
20	0.1610
21	0.1590
22	0.1570
23	0.1540
24	0.1520
25	0.1495
26	0.1470
27	0.1440

LETTER OR WIRE GAUGE	DRILL DIAMETER INCH
28	0.1405
29	0.1360
30	0.1285
31	0.1200
32	0.1160
33	0.1130
34	0.1110
35	0.1100
36	0.1065
37	0.1040
38	0.1015
39	0.0995
40	0.0980
41	0.0960
42	0.0935
43	0.0890
44	0.0860
45	0.0820
46	0.0810
47	0.0785
48	0.0760
49	0.0730
50	0.0700
51	0.0670
52	0.0635
53	0.0595

LETTER OR WIRE GAUGE	DRILL DIAMETER INCH
54	0.0550
55	0.0520
56	0.0465
57	0.0430
58	0.0420
59	0.0410
60	0.0400
61	0.0390
62	0.0380
63	0.0370
64	0.0360
65	0.0350
66	0.0330
67	0.0320
68	0.0310
69	0.0292
70	0.0280
71	0.0260
72	0.0250
73	0.0240
74	0.0225
75	0.0210
76	0.0200
77	0.0180
78	0.0160
79	0.0145
80	0.0135